Y0-CCL-790

OFFICIAL
Arrow

U.S. POSTAL
ZIP CODE
DIRECTORY

COVERING ALL FIFTY STATES

- Detailed ZIP Code maps of principal cities

- Special Mail Services

- Alphabetical list of all Cities & Towns

- Latest Postal Rates — Domestic & Foreign

- Detailed street listings for

  Atlanta, Chicago, Detroit, New York City, and Metropolitan Boston

International Standard Book Number: 0-913450-21-9
Copyright © 1974 by Pathfinder Publications, Inc.
All rights reserved

Published by Pathmark Books
Pathfinder Publications, Inc.
108 Massachusetts Avenue
Boston, Massachusetts 02115
(Not affiliated with U.S. Postal Service)

First Edition © Arrow Street Guides, Inc., 1972
Second Edition © Pathfinder Publications, Inc., 1974
Printed in the United States of America

CONTENTS

ZIP Code Map List vii

Introduction ix

Index to State Lists and
   City Appendices xi

Postal Rates xiii

Proposed Postal Rates xiv

Atlanta Street List 104

Chicago Street List 161

Boston Street List 259

Detroit Street List 351

New York Street List 465

Two-Letter State Abbreviations

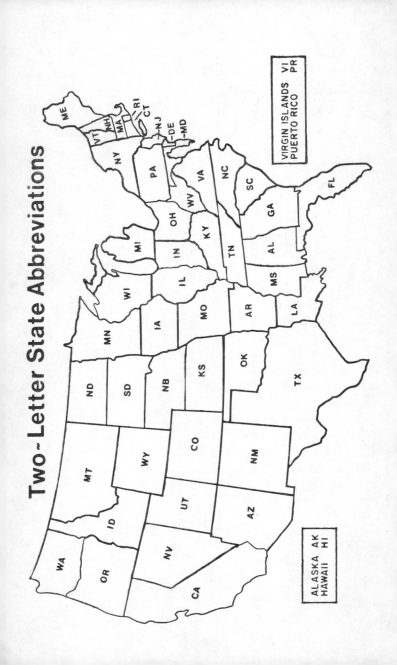

ZIP CODE MAP LIST

CITY	PAGE
Albuquerque, NM	436
Atlanta, GA	101
Baltimore, MD	248
Boston, MA	270
Boston Abbreviations	257
Bronx, NY	451
Brooklyn, NY	452
Charleston, SC	567
Chicago, IL	156
Cincinnati, OH	503
Dallas, TX	597
Des Moines, IA	210
Detroit, MI	350
Hartford, CT	67
Honolulu, HI	144
Indianapolis, IN	200
Kansas City, MO	400
Little Rock, AR	15
Los Angeles, CA	58
Manhattan, NY	461
Miami, FL	89
Milwaukee, WI	653
Minneapolis, MN	386
New Orleans, LA	234
Newark, NJ	428
Philadelphia, PA	543
Portland, ME	241
Portland, OR	523
Providence, RI	561
St. Louis, MO	404
San Francisco, CA	58
Tucson, AZ	15
Washington, D.C.	72

INTRODUCTION

WHAT IS ZIP CODE?

ZIP Code is a five-digit geographic code that identifies areas within the United States and its possessions for purposes of simplifying the distribution of mail by the U.S. Post Office Department.

In devising the ZIP Code, the United States and its possessions were divided into 10 large geographic areas. Each area consists of three or more States or possessions and is given a number between 0 and 9.

ZIP CODE NATIONAL AREAS

Because of favorable transportation facilities, key post offices in each area are designated as Sectional Centers. Each Sectional Center post office receives and transmits mail moving between post offices within its section. It also receives and transmits all mail moving into or out of the section.

WHAT YOUR ZIP CODE MEANS

- Together, the first three digits of any ZIP Code number stand for either a particular Sectional Center or a metropolitan city.
- The last two digits of a Sectional Center ZIP Code number stand for one of the associated post offices served by the Sectional Center.
- The last two digits of a metropolitan city ZIP Code stand for one of the delivery areas served by the city post office, its branches and stations.

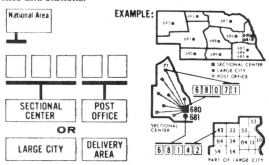

FINDING THE ZIP CODE IN THIS BOOK

Each State contains two parts, a STATE LIST containing all post offices in that State and all named stations and branches, and an APPENDIX, breaking down major cities that are multi-coded. The appendix section immediately follows the regular state listing, is in alphabetical order, and includes, if applicable, the following: Post Office Boxes, Rural Routes, Stations, Branches, and Units, Principal buildings, Hospitals, Colleges, and Universities. In the appendix section and street lists, the zip code is determined by copying the three digits at the top of the first column followed by the two digits beside the entry.

For Atlanta, Boston, Chicago, Detroit, and New York City, there are complete street listings. In these lists, where no house number is shown, the entire street is within the area of the ZIP Code indicated. When the word "out" appears after a number, it signifies that particular house number and any higher number on that street is within the ZIP Code area indicated. For example:

Walnut	06
Valley	
1-1399	09
1400 — out	03

Thus, any address on Walnut Street is 06. The address 138 Valley Street is 09, but 1650 Valley Street is 03. Duplicate street names in the same city are distinguished by the abbreviation of the branch or area designation in parenthesis, thus:

Velvet	10
Velvet (T)	11

(The listing of postal facilities at the beginning of that city's appendix will give the full name of the branch.)

NOTE: The notation "(1st)" is used to identify First Class Post Offices as an assistance to Parcel Post mailers. The class of a particular post office determines the size and weight of parcels that may be mailed from it.

In addition, the following abbreviations are used:

Alley—Aly	Causeway--Cswy	Drive--Dr
Arcade- Arc	Center--Ctr	Expressway Expy
Avenue Ave	Circle -Cir	Extended- Ext
Boulevard Blvd	Court--Ct	Extension- Ext
Branch Br	Courts--Cts	Freeway--Fwy
Bypass--Byp	Crescent Cres	Gardens- -Gdns
Grove- -Grv	Place- -Pl	Street—St
Heights Hts	Plaza- Plz	Terrace- -Ter
Highway Hwy	Point--Pt	Trail Trl
Lane--Ln	Road—Rd	Turnpike- -Tpke
Manor- Mnr	Rural--R	Viaduct—Via
Parkway--Pky	Square--Sq	Vista—Vis

The ZIP Code should appear on the last line of all postal addresses, following the city and State. The gap between the State and ZIP Code should not exceed six-tenths of an inch. Example:

> Mr. Eric Allen
> 3850 Clark
> Boston, MA 02109

INDEX to STATE LISTS and CITY APPENDICES

	Page
ALABAMA	1
Birmingham	5
Gadsden	6
Huntsville	6
Mobile	6
Montgomery	7
ALASKA	9
Anchorage	10
ARIZONA	11
Glendale	13
Mesa	13
Phoenix	13
Scottsdale	14
Tempe	14
Tucson	14
ARKANSAS	16
Little Rock	20
North Little Rock	20
CALIFORNIA	21
Alhambra	32
Anaheim	32
Bakersfield	33
Berkeley	33
Beverly Hills	34
Buena Park	34
Burbank	34
Canoga Park	34
Chula Vista	34
Compton	34
Concord	34
Costa Mesa	34
Daly City	34
Downey	35
El Cajon	35
El Monte	35
Escondido	35
Fremont	35
Fresno	35
Fullerton	36
Gardena	36
Garden Grove	37
Glendale	37
Hayward	37
Huntington Beach	38
Inglewood	38
Laguna Beach	38
Lakewood	38
La Puente	38
Long Beach	38
Los Angeles	39
Modesto	44
Mountain View	44
Newport Beach	44
North Hollywood	44
Oakland	45
Ontario	46
Orange	46
Palo Alto	46
Pasadena	46
Pomona	47
Redondo Beach	47
Redwood City	47
Richmond	47
Riverside	48
Sacramento	49
San Bernardino	50
San Diego	50
San Fernando	51
San Francisco	52
San Gabriel	53
San Jose	53
San Leandro	53
San Mateo	54
San Pedro	54
San Rafael	54
Santa Ana	54
Santa Barbara	55
Santa Clara	55
Santa Monica	55

	Page
Santa Rosa	55
Stockton	56
Sunnyvale	56
Thousand Oaks	56
Torrance	56
Van Nuys	56
Ventura	57
Walnut Creek	57
West Covina	57
Whittier	57
Wilmington	57
COLORADO	59
Arvada	62
Boulder	62
Colorado Springs	62
Denver	62
Littleton	64
Pueblo	64
CONNECTICUT	65
Bridgeport	68
Hartford	68
New Britain	68
New Haven	69
Norwalk	69
Stamford	69
Waterbury	70
DELAWARE	71
Wilmington	71
DISTRICT OF COLUMBIA	73
Washington	73
FLORIDA	79
Bradenton	85
Clearwater	85
Daytona Beach	85
Fort Lauderdale	85
Fort Myers	86
Hialeah	86
Hollywood	86
Jacksonville	87
Lakeland	88
Melbourne	88
Miami	90
Orlando	91
Pensacola	92
Pompano Beach	92
St. Petersburg	93
Sarasota	93
Tallahassee	94
Tampa	94
West Palm Beach	95
GEORGIA	96
Albany	102
Atlanta	102
Augusta	138
Columbus	139
Decatur	140
Macon	141
Savannah	142
HAWAII	143
Honolulu	145
IDAHO	146
Boise	148
ILLINOIS	149
Arlington Heights	157
Aurora	157
Belleville	157
Chicago	157
Decatur	190
Des Plaines	190
East Saint Louis	190
Evanston	190
Joliet	191
Melrose Park	191
Oak Lawn	191
Oak Park	191

	Page
Peoria	191
Rockford	192
Springfield	192
INDIANA	193
Anderson	198
Evansville	198
Fort Wayne	199
Gary	199
Hammond	201
Indianapolis	201
Lafayette	202
Muncie	202
South Bend	202
Terre Haute	203
IOWA	204
Cedar Rapids	209
Davenport	209
Des Moines	211
Sioux City	212
Waterloo	213
KANSAS	214
Kansas City	218
Shawnee Mission	218
Topeka	218
Wichita	219
KENTUCKY	220
Covington	227
Lexington	227
Louisville	228
Newport	229
LOUISIANA	230
Baton Rouge	233
Metairie	235
New Orleans	235
Shreveport	237
MAINE	238
Portland	242
MARYLAND	243
Annapolis	246
Baltimore	247
Ellicott City	251
Hyattsville	252
Rockville	252
Silver Spring	252
MASSACHUSETTS	253
Ayer	255
Boston	255
Brockton	340
Chicopee	340
Fall River	340
Falmouth	340
Lawrence	341
Lowell	341
Lynn	341
New Bedford	341
North Attleboro	341
Plymouth	341
Springfield	341
Worcester	342
MICHIGAN	342
Ann Arbor	348
Battle Creek	348
Birmingham	349
Dearborn	349
Detroit	349
Flint	376
Grand Rapids	377
Jackson	378
Kalamazoo	378
Lansing	378
Livonia	378
Muskegon	379
Pontiac	379
Royal Oak	379

(Continued)

INDEX to STATE LISTS and CITY APPENDICES – Cont

MICHIGAN
(Continued)

Page
Saginaw 379
Southfield 379
St. Clair Shores ...379
Sterling Heights ...380
Warren 380
Wyandotte 380
MINNESOTA 380
Duluth 385
Minneapolis 387
St. Paul 388
MISSISSIPPI 389
Biloxi 393
Jackson 393
MISSOURI 394
Florissant 401
Hazlewood 401
Independence 401
Kansas City 401
Saint Joseph 403
Saint Louis 405
Springfield 408
MONTANA 409
Billings 411
Great Falls 411
NEBRASKA 412
Lincoln 415
Omaha 415
NEVADA 417
Las Vegas 417
Reno 418
NEW HAMPSHIRE ..418
Manchester 420
NEW JERSEY 420
Atlantic City 424
Camden 425
Cherry Hill 425
Clifton 426
East Orange 426
Elizabeth 426
Englewood 427
Hackensack 427
Jersey City 427
Montclair 429
Newark 429
New Brunswick ...430
Orange 430
Passaic 430
Paterson 430
Perth Amboy 430
Plainfield 431
Rahway 431
Ridgewood 431
Rutherford 431
Trenton 431
Westfield 432
NEW MEXICO 432
Albuquerque 435
NEW YORK 437
Albany 448
Babylon 449
Binghamton 449
Bronx 449
Brooklyn 450
Buffalo 454
Elmira 456
Far Rockaway 456
Floral Park 457
Flushing 457
Great Neck 458
Hempstead 458
Hicksville 458
Jamaica 459
Long Island City ..459

Page
Mount Vernon 460
New Rochelle 460
New York 460
Niagara Falls 471
Poughkeepsie 471
Rochester 472
Rockville Centre ..473
Schenectady 473
Staten Island 474
Syracuse 475
Troy 476
Utica 476
Valley Stream 476
White Plains 477
Yonkers 477
NORTH CAROLINA ..478
Asheville 483
Charlotte 484
Durham 485
Fayettteville 486
Greensboro 487
High Point 488
Raleigh 488
Winston-Salem ...489
NORTH DAKOTA ...491
OHIO 494
Akron 501
Canton 501
Cincinnati 502
Cleveland 505
Columbus 507
Cuyahoga Falls ...509
Dayton 509
Elyria 509
Hamilton 509
Lima 510
Lorain 510
Mansfield 510
Springfield 510
Toledo 511
Warren 511
Youngstown 512
OKLAHOMA 513
Oklahoma City ...517
Tulsa 518
OREGON 519
Eugene 522
Portland 522
Salem 524
PENNSYLVANIA 525
Allentown 538
Altoona 538
Bethlehem 538
Chester 538
Erie 538
Harrisburg 539
Johnstown 540
Lancaster 540
Levittown 541
McKeesport 541
Media 541
New Castle 541
Norristown 542
Philadelphia 542
Pittsburgh 546
Pittston 552
Reading 552
Scranton 552
Upper Darby 553
Wilkes-Barre 553
York 554
PUERTO RICO 555
San Juan 557
RHODE ISLAND 559
Pawtucket 560
Providence 560

Page
Wakefield 560
Warwick 562
SOUTH CAROLINA ..563
Charleston 566
Columbia 568
Greenville 569
Spartanburg 570
SOUTH DAKOTA ...571
Sioux Falls 573
TENNESSEE 574
Chattanooga 578
Kingsport 579
Knoxville 579
Memphis 579
Nashville 581
TEXAS 583
Abilene 593
Amarillo 593
Arlington 594
Austin 594
Beaumont 595
Corpus Christi 595
Dallas 596
El Paso 598
Fort Worth 600
Garland 601
Houston 601
Irving 603
Lubbock 603
Pasadena 604
San Antonio 604
Waco 606
Wichita Falls 606
UTAH 608
Ogden 610
Salt Lake City 610
VERMONT 612
VIRGINIA 614
Alexandria 621
Arlington 621
Charlottesville 622
Chesapeake 622
Falls Church 622
Hampton 623
Lynchburg 623
Newport News ...623
Norfolk 624
Portsmouth 625
Richmond 625
Roanoke 627
Springfield 627
Virginia Beach ...627
WASHINGTON 628
Bellevue 632
Everett 632
Olympia 633
Seattle 633
Spokane 634
Tacoma 635
Vancouver 636
Yakima 636
WEST VIRGINIA ...638
Charleston 644
Huntington 644
WISCONSIN 646
Green Bay 651
Madison 651
Milwaukee 652
Racine 654
WYOMING 655

PACIFIC ISLANDS—
VIRGIN ISLANDS ..657

POSTAL RATES

INTERNATIONAL RATES		
CLASSIFICATION	SURFACE RATE	AIR MAIL RATE
LETTER MAIL: Central and South America* All other countries	15¢ per oz. 15¢ per oz.	17¢ per 1/2 oz. 21¢ per 1/2 oz.
POSTCARDS	10¢	15¢
AEROGRAMMES		15¢

*and the Caribbean Islands, Bahamas, Bermuda, St. Pierre, and Miquelon.

DOMESTIC RATES (ALSO INCLUDES CANADA AND MEXICO)		
CLASSIFICATION	SURFACE RATE	AIR MAIL RATE
LETTER MAIL (First Class) POST CARDS	8¢ per oz. 6¢ per oz.	11¢ per oz. 9¢ per oz.

NOTE: For Second Class (newspapers, periodicals, etc.), Third Class (bulk rate and nonprofit rates), and Fourth Class (educational or library materials), see your Postmaster for rates. Third Class includes small packages, and the rate is 8¢ for the first 2 ounces, and 2¢ for each additional ounce.

SPECIAL DELIVERY
(Rates listed apply to Continental U.S.)

CLASS OF MAIL	WEIGHT		
	Not more than 2 pounds	More than 2 pounds but not more than 10 pounds	More than 10 pounds
First class, airmail & Priority mail	60¢	75¢	90¢
All other classes	80¢	90¢	$1.05

REGISTERED MAIL

VALUE	FEES (In addition to postage)	
	For articles not covered by commercial or other insurance	For articles also covered by commercial or other insurance
$0.00 to 100. $100.01 to 200. $200.01 to 400. $400.01 to 600. $600.01 to 800. $800.01 to 1,000.	$0.95 1.25 1.55 1.85 2.15 2.45	$0.95 1.25 1.55 1.85 2.15 2.45
$1,000.01 to 2,000. $2,000.01 to 3,000. $3,000.01 to 4,000. $4,000.01 to 5,000. $5,000.01 to 6,000. $6,000.01 to 7,000. $7,000.01 to 8,000. $8,000.01 to 9,000. $9,000.01 to 10,000.	2.75 3.05 3.35 3.65 3.95 4.25 4.55 4.85 5.15	$2.45 plus handling charge of 20 cents per $1,000 or fraction over first $1,000.
$10,000 to $1,000,000	$5.15 plus handling charge of 20 cents per $1,000 or fraction over first $10,000.	
$1,000,000.01 to $15,000,000	$203.15 plus handling charge of 13 cents per $1,000 or fraction over first $1,000,000.	$202.25 plus handling charge of 13 cents per $1,000 or fraction over first $1,000,000.
Over $15,000,000	Additional charges may be based on considerations of weight, space and value.	

PROPOSED POSTAL RATES

NOTE: The U. S. Postal Service is considering the following rate increases, which are scheduled to become effective on March 2, 1974.

INTERNATIONAL RATES

CLASSIFICATION	SURFACE RATE	AIR MAIL RATES	
LETTER MAIL	1 ounce $ .18 2 ounces .31 4 ounces .41 8 ounces .92 16 ounces 1.74 32 ounces 2.89 64 ounces 4.62 Each add'l 32 ounces .58	Central America, South America, Caribbean Islands, Bahamas, Bermuda, St. Pierre, Mique- lon Other countries	Up to 2 oz. - 21¢ per ½ oz.; 17¢ each add'l ½ oz. Up to 2 oz. - 26¢ per ½ oz.;. 21¢ each add'l ½ oz.
POST CARDS	12¢	18¢	
AEROGRAMMES		18¢	

DOMESTIC RATES

CLASSIFICATION	SURFACE RATE	AIR MAIL RATE
LETTER MAIL	10¢ per oz.	13¢ per oz.
POST CARDS	8¢	.11¢
TRANSIENT SECOND CLASS RATE	8¢ first 2 oz.; 2¢ each add'l oz.	
CONTROLLED CIRCULATION	16¢ per lb.; 4.6¢ min. per piece	
THIRD CLASS Single Piece Rate Bulk Rate	8¢ each 2 oz.; 10¢ min. per piece Books - 28¢ per lb. Other matter - 32¢ per lb.	
FOURTH CLASS (BOOKS & FILM)	18¢ first lb.; 8¢ each add'l lb.	
LIBRARY RATE	6¢ first lb.; 3¢ each add'l lb.	

ALABAMA
(Abbreviation: AL)

Abbeville.................................36310
Abernant................................35440
Acmar.....................................35004
Adamsville.............................35005
Addison..................................35540
Adger......................................35006
Akron.....................................35441
Alabama City, Sta. Gadsden..35904
Alabaster (1st).......................35007
Alberta...................................36720
Albertville (1st)......................35950
Alden......................................35008
Alexander City (1st)...............35010
Alexandria..............................36250
Aliceville................................35442
Allen.......................................36419
Allgood...................................35013
Alma.......................................36501
Alpine.....................................35014
Alton......................................35015
Altoona...................................35952
Andalusia (1st).......................36420
Anderson................................35610
Annemanie.............................36721
Anniston (1st).........................36201
Ansley.....................................36001
Arab (1st)...............................35016
Ardmore Highway, Sta.
  Huntsville..........................35805
Ariton....................................36311
Arkadelphia, R. Br. Bremen..35033
Arley......................................35541
Arlington................................36722
Armstrong..............................36002
Ashford..................................36312
Ashland..................................36251
Asheville................................35953
  Whitney, R. Sta.................35991
Athens (1st)...........................35611
Atmore (1st)..........................36502
  Canoe, R. Br......................36514
Attalla (1st)...........................35954
Auburn (1st)..........................36830
Autaugaville...........................36003
Avondale, Sta. Birmingham...35222
Axis..36505
Baileyton................................35019
Baker Hill...............................36004
Banks.....................................36005
Bankston................................35542
Barlow Bend...........................36506
Barton....................................35614
Bates Field, R. Br. Mobile......36608
Bay Minette (1st)...................36507
Bayou La Batre.......................36509
Bear Creek.............................35543
Beatrice..................................36425
Beaverton...............................35544
Bel Air, Sta. Mobile................36606
Belk.......................................35545
Bellamy..................................36901
Belle Mina.............................35615
Bellwood................................36313
Benton, R. Br. Tyler...............36785
Berry......................................35546
Bessemer (1st).......................35020
Bexar......................................35547
Bigbee....................................36510
Billingsley...............................36006

BIRMINGHAM (1st) (see
  appendix)
Black......................................36314
Bladon Springs.......................36902
Blountsville............................35031
Blue Mountain, Br. Anniston..36201
Blue Spring, Sta. Huntsville
  (see appendix)
Bluff Park, Br. Birmingham....35226
Boaz (1st)..............................35957
Boligee...................................35443
Bolinger..................................36903
Bolling....................................36007
Bon Air..................................35032
Bon Secour.............................36511
Booth......................................36008
Borden Springs.......................36252
Boykin....................................36723
Boyleston, Br. Montgomery....36110
Boys Ranch, R. Br. Minter......36761
Brantley..................................36009
Bremen...................................35033
Brent......................................35034
Brewton (1st).........................36426
Bridgeport...............................35740
Brierfield................................35035
Brighton, Br. Bessemer...........35020
Brilliant..................................35548
Brooklyn.................................36429
Brookside...............................35036
Brookwood.............................35444
Browns...................................36724
Brownsboro............................35741
Brownville, R. Br. Northport...35445
Brundidge...............................36010
Bryant....................................35958
Bucks.....................................36512
Buena Vista............................36430
Buhl.......................................35446
Burkville.................................36725
Burnt Corn.............................36431
Burnwell.................................35038
Butler (1st).............................36904
  Choctaw, R. Br.................36905
Bynum....................................36253
Cahaba Heights, Br.
  Birmingham......................35243
Calcis, R. Br. Vincent.............35039
Calera.....................................35040
Calhoun..................................36012
Calvert....................................36513
Camden (1st)..........................36726
Camp Hill...............................36850
Campbell.................................36727
Canoe, R. Br. Atmore.............36514
Capitol Heights, Sta.
  Montgomery......................36107
Capps.....................................36315
Capshaw.................................35742
Carbon Hill............................35549
Cardiff....................................35041
Carlton, R. Br. Jackson..........36515
Caroline Avenue, Sta.
  Mobile...............................36604
Carolyn, Sta. Montgomery.....36106
Carrollton...............................35447
Castleberry.............................36432
Catherine................................36728
  Flatwood, R. Br.................36739
Cecil.......................................36013
Cedar Bluff.............................35959
Center Point, Br.
  Birmingham (see appendix)

Central....................................36014
Centre....................................35960
Centreville..............................35042
Chance....................................36729
Chancellor..............................36316
Chapman.................................36015
Chase.....................................35743
Chatom...................................36518
Chelsea...................................35043
Cherokee................................35616
Chickasaw, Br. Mobile...........36611
Childersburg...........................35044
Choccolocco...........................36254
Choctaw, R. Br. Butler...........36905
Chrysler..................................36520
Chunchula..............................36521
Citronelle................................36522
  Seaboard, R. Br.................36573
Claiborne, R. Br. Frisco City..36434
Clanton (1st)..........................35045
Clay..35048
Clayton...................................36016
Cleveland................................35049
Clinton....................................35448
Clio..36017
Clopton...................................36317
Cloverdale..............................35617
Cloverland, Sta.
  Montgomery......................36105
Coalburg.................................35050
Coaling...................................35449
Coatopa..................................35450
Coden.....................................36523
Coffee Springs........................36318
Coffeeville..............................36524
Coker......................................35452
Collinsville.............................35961
Columbia................................36319
Columbiana............................35051
Comer.....................................36018
Cooks Springs........................35052
Coosa Pines, Br.
  Childersburg.....................35044
Coosada..................................36020
Cordova..................................35550
Cottage Grove, R. Br.
  Kellyton............................35088
Cottage Hill, Sta. Mobile
  (see appendix)
Cottondale..............................35453
Cottonton...............................36851
Cottonwood............................36320
  Madrid, R. Br....................36348
Courtland................................35618
Cowarts..................................36321
Coy..36435
Cragford.................................36255
Craig A F B, Br. Selma...........36701
Crane Hill...............................35053
Creola.....................................36525
Crestline Heights, Br.
  Birmingham......................35213
Crichton, Sta. Mobile.............36607
Cromwell................................36906
Cropwell.................................35054
Crossville................................35962
Cuba.......................................36907
Cullman (1st).........................35055
Cullomburg, R. Br. Silas........36920
Cusseta...................................36852
Cypress...................................35454
Dadeville................................36853
Daleville (1st).........................36322

Danville	35619
Daphne	35626
Spanish Fort, R. Br.	36527
Garlington	36730
Dauphin Island	36528
Daviston	36256
Dawson	35963
Dayton	36731
De Armanville	36257
Deatsville	36022
Decatur (1st)	35601
Deer Park	36529
Delmar	35551
Delta	36258
Demopolis (1st)	36732
Detroit	35552
Dickinson	36436
Dixiana	35059
Dixons Mills	36736
Docena	35060
Dolomite	35061
Dora	35062
Dothan (1st)	36301
Double Springs	35553
Douglas	35964
Downtown, Sta. Tuscaloosa	35401
Dozier	36028
Drewry	36438
Duke	36259
Duncanville	35456
Dutton	35744
East Brewton, Br. Brewton	36426
East Gadsden, Sta.
Gadsden	35903
East Lake, Sta. Birmingham	35206
East Side, Sta. Tuscaloosa	35401
East Tallassee	36023
Eastaboga	36260
Eastbrook, Sta. Montgomery	36109
Eastern Valley, Br.
Bessemer	35020
Echola	35457
Eclectic	36024
Edwardsville	36261
Eight Mile, Br. Mobile	36613
Elba (1st)	36323
Elberta	36530
Eldridge	35554
Elkmont	35620
Elliotsville, R. Br. Siluria	35144
Elmore	36025
Elrod	35458
Elting, Sta. Florence	35630
Emelle	35459
Empire	35063
Ensley, Sta. Birmingham	35218
Enterprise (1st)	36330
Eoline, R. Br. Centreville	35042
Epes	35460
Equality	36026
Estillfork	35745
Ethelsville	35461
Eufaula (1st)	36027
Eutaw	35462
Eva	35621
Evergreen (1st)	36401
Excel	36439
Fabius	35965
Fackler	35746
Fairfax	36854
Fairfield (1st)	35064
Fairford, R. Br. Mc Intosh	36531
Fairhope (1st)	36532

Fairview, Sta. Birmingham	35208
Falkville	35622
Farley, Sta. Huntsville (see appendix)
Farmersville	36737
Faunsdale	36738
Fayette (1st)	35555
Fernbank	35558
Finchburg	36440
Fitzpatrick	36029
Five Points	36855
Flat Rock	35966
Flatwood, R. Br. Catherine	36739
Flomaton	36441
Florala	36442
Florence (1st)	35630
Foley (1st)	36535
Forest Home	36030
Forestdale, Br. Birmingham	35214
Forkland	36740
Fort Davis	36031
Fort Deposit	36032
Fort Mc Clellan, Br.
Anniston	36201
Fort Mitchell	36856
Fort Payne (1st)	35967
Fort Rucker, Br. Ozark	36360
Fosters	35463
Fountain	36443
Franklin	36444
Frankville	36538
Frisco City	36445
Claiborne, R. Br.	36434
Fruitdale	36539
Fruithurst	36262
Fulton	36446
Fulton Road, Sta. Mobile	36605
Fultondale	35068
Furman	36741
Fyffe	35971
GADSDEN (1st) (see appendix)
Gainestown	36540
Gainesville	35464
Gallant	35972
Gallion	36742
Gantt	36038
Gantts Quarry	35069
Garden City	35070
Gardendale	35071
Garland	36448
Gastonburg	36743
Gaylesville	35973
Geneva (1st)	36340
Georgiana	36033
Geraldine	35974
Gilbertown	36908
Glen Allen	35559
Glencoe, Br. Gadsden	35905
Glendean, Sta. Auburn	36830
Glenwood	36034
Golden Springs, Sta.
Anniston	36201
Goodsprings	35560
Goodwater	35072
Goodway	36449
Gordo	35466
Gordon	36343
Goshen	36035
Gosport, R. Br. Whatley	36450
Grady	36036
Graham	36263
Grand Bay	36541

Grant	35747
Grayson	35562
Graysville	35073
Green Lantern, Sta.
Montgomery	36111
Green Pond	35074
Greensboro	36744
Greenville (1st)	36037
Grove Hill	36451
Groveoak	35975
Guin	35563
Gulf Shores	36542
Gunter A F B, Br.
Montgomery (see appendix)
Guntersville (1st)	35976
Gurley	35748
Hackleburg	35564
Haleyville (1st)	35565
Halsell	36909
Hamilton (1st)	35570
Hanceville	35077
Hardaway	36039
Harpersville	35078
Hartford	36344
Hartselle (1st)	35640
Harvest	35749
Hatchechubbee	36858
Havana	35467
Hayden	35079
Hayneville	36040
Hazel Green	35750
Headland	36345
Heflin	36264
Helena	35080
Henagar	35978
Higdon	35979
Highland Home	36041
Hillsboro	35643
Hissop	35081
Hodges	35571
Hokes Bluff, R. Br. Gadsden	35903
Hollins	35082
Holly Pond	35083
Hollytree	35751
Hollywood	35752
Holt, Br. Tuscaloosa	35401
Holy Trinity	36859
Homewood, Br. Birmingham	35209
Honoraville	36042
Hoover, Br. Birmingham	35226
Hope Hull	36043
Horton	35980
Houston	35572
Hueytown, Br. Bessemer	35020
HUNTSVILLE (1st) (see appendix)
Hurtsboro	36860
Huxford	36543
Hybart	36452
Hytop	35753
Ider	35981
Irondale, Br. Birmingham	35210
Irvington	36544
Jachin	36910
Jack	36346
Jackson (1st)	36545
Carlton, R. Br.	36515
Jacksons Gap	36861
Jacksonville (1st)	36265
Jamestown	35982
Jasper (1st)	35501
Jefferson	36745

Jemison................................35085
Joe Wheeler Dam................35644
Johns...................................35086
Jones...................................36749
Jonesboro, Sta. Bessemer....35020
Joppa...................................35087
Kansas.................................35573
Kellerman............................35468
Kellyton...............................35089
   Cottage Grove, R. Br. 35088
Kennedy..............................35574
Kent....................................36045
Killen..................................35645
Kimberly..............................35091
Kimbrough, R. Br. Pine Hill...36746
Kinston................................36453
Knoxville.............................35469
Laceys Spring......................35754
Lafayette.............................36862
Lamison...............................36747
Lanett..................................36863
Langdale..............................36864
Langston..............................35755
Lapine.................................36046
Lavaca.................................36911
Lawley.................................36793
Leeds (1st)..........................35094
Leesburg.............................35983
Leighton..............................35646
Lenlock, Br. Anniston...........36201
Lenox..................................36454
Leroy...................................36548
Lester..................................35647
Letohatchee.........................36047
Lexington.............................35648
Lillian..................................36549
Lincoln................................35096
Linden.................................36748
Lineville...............................36266
Lipscomb, R. Br. Bessemer....35020
Lisman.................................36912
   Pushmataha, R. Br. 36917
Little River...........................36550
Littleville, R. Br. Russellville..35654
Livingston............................35470
Loachapoka..........................36865
Lockhart...............................36455
Locust Fork..........................35097
Logan..................................35098
Loop, Sta. Mobile.................36606
Louisville.............................36048
Lower Peach Tree.................36751
Lowndesboro.......................36752
Loxley.................................36551
Luverne (1st).......................36049
Lynn....................................35575
Madison...............................35758
Madrid, R. Br. Cottonwood....36348
Magazine.............................36554
Magnolia..............................36754
Magnolia Springs..................36555
Magnolia Terminal................36755
Malcolm...............................36556
Malvern...............................36349
Mantua................................35472
Maplesville...........................36750
Marbury...............................36051
Margaret..............................35112
Marion (1st).........................36756
Marion Junction....................36759
Marshall Space Flight
   Center, Br. Huntsville......35812
Marvel.................................35113

Mathews..............................36052
Maxwell A F B, Sta.
   Montgomery (see
   appendix)
Maylene...............................35114
Mc Calla..............................35111
Mc Cullough.........................36552
Mc Farland, Sta. Tuscaloosa..35401
Mc Intosh............................36553
   Fairford, R. Br. 36531
Mc Kenzie............................36456
Mc Shan...............................35471
Mc Williams.........................36753
Megargel..............................36457
Melvin.................................36913
Mentone..............................35984
Meridianville.........................35759
Mexia..................................36458
Midfield, Br. Birmingham
   (see appendix)
Midland City.........................36350
Midway................................36053
Miles, Sta. Fairfield..............35064
Millbrook.............................36054
Millers Ferry.........................36760
Millerville............................36267
Millport................................35576
Millry..................................36558
Minter..................................36761
MOBILE (1st) (see appendix)
Monroeville (1st)..................36460
Montevallo (1st)...................35115
   Underwood, R. Br. 35174
MONTGOMERY (1st) (see
   appendix)
Montrose..............................36559
Mooresville...........................35649
Morgan City, R. Br. Laceys
   Spring............................35754
Morris..................................35116
Morvin.................................36762
Moulton (1st)........................35650
Moundville...........................35474
Mount Hope.........................35651
Mount Meigs........................36057
Mount Olive.........................35117
Mount Vernon.......................36560
Mountain Brook, Br.
   Birmingham (see
   appendix)
Mountain Creek.....................36056
Mulga..................................35118
Munford...............................36268
Muscadine............................36269
Muscle Shoals, Br. Sheffield...35660
Myrtlewood..........................36763
Nanafalia.............................36764
Napier Field, R. Br. Dothan...36301
Natural Bridge......................35577
Nauvoo................................35578
Needham..............................36915
New Brockton.......................36351
New Castle............................35119
New Dora, R. Sta. Dora........35062
New Hope.............................35760
New Market...........................35761
New Site, R. Br. Alexander
   City...............................35010
Newbern..............................36765
Newell..................................36270
Newton................................36352
Newville...............................36353
Nixburg................................36058

Normal.................................35762
North Birmingham, Sta.
   Birmingham.....................35207
North Florence, Sta.
   Florence.........................35630
Northport (1st).....................35476
   Brownville, R. Br. 35445
Northside, Sta. Dothan..........36301
Notasulga.............................36866
Oak Grove, R. Br. Adger........35006
Oakhill.................................36766
Oakman................................35579
Oakwood College, R. Br.
   Huntsville.......................35806
Odenville..............................35120
Ohatchee.............................36271
Oneonta (1st).......................35121
Opelika (1st)........................36801
Opp (1st).............................36467
Orange Beach.......................36561
Orrville................................36767
Owassa................................36468
Owens Cross Roads..............35763
Oxford, Br. Anniston.............36201
Ozark (1st)...........................36360
Paint Rock............................35764
Palmerdale...........................35123
Panola..................................35477
Pansey.................................36370
Parkland, Sta. Jasper............35501
Parrish.................................35580
Paul.....................................36469
Pelham.................................35124
Pell City (1st).......................35125
Pennington...........................36916
Pepperell, Sta. Opelika.........36801
Perdido.................................36562
Perdido Beach, R. Br.
   Elberta...........................36530
Perdue Hill...........................36470
Perote..................................36061
Peterman..............................36471
Peterson..............................35478
Petrey..................................36062
Phenix City (1st)...................36867
Phil Campbell........................35581
Piedmont..............................36272
Pigeon Creek........................36063
Pike Road.............................36064
Pinckard...............................36371
Pine Apple............................36768
Pine Hill...............................36769
   Kimbrough, R. Br. 36746
   Pope, R. Br. 36770
   Yellow Bluff, R. Br. 36789
Pine Level............................36065
Pinson.................................35126
Pisgah..................................35765
Pittsview..............................36871
Plantersville.........................36758
Plateau, Br. Mobile...............36610
Pleasant Grove......................3512*
Point Clear...........................36564
Pope, R. Br. Pine Hill............36770
Powderly, Sta. Birmingham....35221
Powhatan.............................35128
Praco...................................35129
Prairie..................................36771
Pratt City, Sta. Birmingham....35214
Prattville (1st)......................36067
Prestwick.............................36566
Prichard, Br. Mobile..............36610
Princeton.............................35766

Pushmataha, R. Br. Lisman ...36917
Putnam....................................36772
Quinton....................................35130
Ragland....................................35131
Rainbow City, Br. Gadsden....35901
Rainsville.................................35986
Ralph.......................................35480
Ramer......................................36069
Ranburne.................................36273
Randolph..................................36792
Range.......................................36473
Red Bay...................................35582
Red Level.................................36474
Redstone Arsenal, Br.
  Huntsville (see appendix)
Reform.....................................35481
Remlap....................................35133
Repton.....................................36475
Riderwood................................36918
River Falls................................36476
River View................................36872
Riverside..................................35135
Roanoke (1st)...........................36274
Roba..36070
Robertsdale..............................36567
  Seminole, R. Br......................36574
Robinwood, R. Br.
  Birmingham............................35217
Rock Mills, R. Br. Roanoke 36274
Rockford...................................35136
Rogersville...............................35652
Roosevelt, R. Sta. Bessemer....35020
Russellville (1st).......................35653
  Littleville, R. Br....................35654
Rutledge..................................36071
Rutledge, Br. Birmingham 35228
Ryland.....................................35767
Safford....................................36773
Saginaw...................................35137
Saint Bernard............................35138
Saint Clair................................36774
Saint Elmo...............................36568
Saint Stephens..........................36569
Salem......................................36874
Salitpa....................................36570
Samantha.................................35482
Samford University, Br.
  Birmingham............................35209
Samson....................................36477
Saraland..................................36571
Sardis......................................36775
Satsuma...................................36572
Sawyerville...............................36776
Sayre.......................................35139
Scottsboro (1st).........................35768
Seaboard, R. Br. Citronelle....36573
Seale.......................................36875
Searles.....................................35483
Section.....................................35771
Sellers......................................36072
Selma (1st)...............................36701
Seminole, R. Br.
  Robertsdale............................36574
Semmes....................................36575
Shady Grove..............................36074
Shannon...................................35142
Shawmut..................................36876
Sheffield (1st)...........................35660
Shelby......................................35143
Shorter.....................................36075
Shorterville...............................36373
Silas..36919
  Cullomburg, R. Br................36920

Siluria......................................35144
Silverhill..................................36576
Sims Chapel..............................36577
Sipsey......................................35584
Skipperville...............................36374
Slocomb....................................36375
Smiths......................................36877
Snead, R. Br. Altoona 35952
Snow Hill..................................36778
Somerville.................................35670
South Guntersville, Sta.
  Guntersville............................35976
South Highlands, Sta.
  Birmingham............................35205
Southside, R. Br. Gadsden.....35901
Spanish Fort, R. Br. Daphne..36527
Sprague....................................36076
Spring Garden............................36275
Spring Hill, Sta. Mobile (see
  appendix)
Springville................................35146
Sprott......................................36779
Spruce Pine..............................35585
Standing Rock............................36878
Stanton....................................36790
Stapleton..................................36578
Steele.......................................35987
Sterrett....................................35147
Stevenson.................................35772
Stewart....................................35484
Stockton...................................36579
Sulligent..................................35586
Sumiton....................................35148
Summerdale..............................36580
Sumterville...............................35485
Sunflower.................................36581
Sunny South..............................36780
Suttle......................................36781
Sweet Water.............................36782
Sycamore..................................35149
Sylacauga (1st).........................35150
Sylvania...................................35988
Talladega (1st)..........................35160
Talladega Springs, R. Br.
  Sylacauga..............................35150
Tallassee..................................36078
Tanner.....................................35671
Tarrant, Br. Birmingham.......35217
Theodore..................................36582
Thomaston................................36783
Thomasville (1st).......................36784
Thorsby....................................35171
Three Notch...............................36079
Tibbie......................................36583
Tillmans Corner, Br. Mobile ...36619
Titus..36080
Toney......................................35773
Town Creek...............................35672
Townley....................................35587
Toxey......................................36921
Trafford....................................35172
Trenton....................................35774
Trinity......................................35673
Troy (1st).................................36081
Trussville (1st)..........................35173
Tunnel Springs...........................36479
Tuscaloosa (1st)........................35401
Tuscumbia (1st).........................35674
Tuskegee (1st)...........................36083
Tuskegee Institute (1st)............36088
Tyler..36785
Underwood, R. Br.
  Montevallo.............................35174

Union Grove..............................35175
Union Springs (1st)....................36089
Uniontown.................................36786
University (1st).........................35486
Uptown, Sta. Bessemer............35020
Uriah.......................................36480
Valhermoso Springs....................35775
Valley Head...............................35989
Vance.......................................35490
Vandiver...................................35176
Verbena....................................36091
Vernon.....................................35592
Vestavia Hills, Br.
  Birmingham (see
  appendix)
Veterans Administration Fac,
  Br. Tuskegee...........................36083
Veterans Hospital, R. Sta.
  Tuscaloosa.............................35401
Village Springs...........................35177
Vina...35593
Vincent.....................................35178
  Calcis, R. Br..........................35039
Vinegar Bend.............................36584
Vinemont..................................35179
Vredenburgh..............................36481
Wadley.....................................36276
Wagarville................................36585
Walker Springs...........................36586
Walnut Grove.............................35990
Ward.......................................36922
Warrior.....................................35180
Waterloo...................................35677
Watson.....................................35181
Wattsville.................................35182
Waverly....................................36879
Weaver.....................................36277
Webb.......................................36376
Wedowee...................................36278
Wellington.................................36279
Weogufka..................................35183
West, Sta. Huntsville (see
  appendix)
West Blocton..............................35184
West End, Sta. Birmingham ...35211
West Greene...............................35491
West Side, Sta. Montgomery...36108
Westover...................................35185
Wetumpka (1st).........................36092
Whatley....................................36482
  Gosport, R. Br........................36450
Whistler, Br. Mobile............36612
Whitfield...................................36923
Whitney, R. Sta. Ashville.....35991
Wilmer......................................36587
Wilsonville.................................35186
Wilton......................................35187
Winfield....................................35594
Wing..36483
Woodland...................................36280
Woodlawn, Sta. Birmingham...35212
Woodstock.................................35188
Woodville..................................35776
Woodward.................................35189
Wylam, Sta. Birmingham 35224
Yantley....................................36924
Yellow Bluff, R. Br. Pine
  Hill.......................................36789
Yellow Pine................................36588
York...36925

BIRMINGHAM 352

POST OFFICE BOXES

Box Nos.

1-116	Powderly Sta	21
1-2514	Main Office	01
2521-2799	Main Office	02
2801-2999	Woodlawn Sta ..	12
3201-3499	South Highlands Sta..	05
3501-3799	West End Sta	11
3801-3999	Fairview Sta......	08
4001-4699	East Lake Sta	06
5001-5199	Pratt City Sta ..	14
5201-5599	North Birmingham Sta.............	07
5701-6194	Homewood Br....	09
6201-6599	Tarrant Br........	17
6601-6899	Irondale Br.......	10
7001-7299	Wylam Sta........	24
7301-7699	Mountain Brook Br	23
7701-7937	Midfield	28
8001-8374	Ensley Sta	18
8901-9274	Crestline Heights Br	13
9501-9999	Center Point Br	15
10001-11112	Main Office......	02
20001-20260	Vestavia Hills Br.............	16
26001-26499	Bluff Park Br....	26
2801A-2899A	Woodlawn Sta ..	12
30001-31399	Avondale Sta.....	22
3201A-3499A	South Highland Sta..............	05
39001-39076	Fairview Sta	08
43001-43499	Cahaba Heights Br.....	43
57001-58099	Homewood Br.....	09
7301A-7572A	Mountain Brook Br	23
DRAWER A-F	Fairview Sta	08
DRAWER A-F	Pratt City Sta...	14
DRAWER A-H	Ensley Sta........	18
DRAWER A H	Midfield Br.......	28

RURAL ROUTES

1	11
2	17
3	14
4	10
5	15
6	17
7	15
8	24
10	28
11	10
12	15
13	43
14,15,16	24
17	11

STATIONS, BRANCHES AND UNITS

Avondale Sta.............................	22
Bluff Park Br.............................	26
Cahaba Heights Br.....................	43
Crestline Heights Br..................	13
East Lake Sta.............................	06

Birmingham (Con.)	352
Ensley Sta.............................	18
Fairview Sta.............................	08
Forestdale Br.............................	14
Homewood Br.............................	09
Hoover Br.............................	26
Irondale Br.............................	10
Midfield Br.............................	28
Mountain Brook Br.....................	23
North Birmingham Sta...............	07
Powderly Sta.............................	21
Pratt City Sta.............................	14
Robinwood Rural Br..................	17
Rutledge Br.............................	28
Samford University Br...............	09
South Highlands Sta..................	05
Tarrant Br.............................	17
West End Sta.............................	11
Woodlawn Sta.............................	12
Wylam Sta.............................	24
General Delivery........................	03
Postmaster.............................	03

APARTMENTS, HOTELS, MOTELS

A G Gaston Motel, 1510 5th Ave N.............................	02
Airport Motel, Municipal Airport.............................	06
Altamont Apts, 2831 Highland Ave....................	05
Bankhead, 2300 5th Ave N........	01
City Center Motel, 424 No 23rd.............................	03
Colony Motor Hotel, 2840 Highland Ave....................	05
Binkler, 2005 5th Ave..............	01
Downtowner Mtr Inn, 2224 5th Ave N.............................	01
Essex House Apts, 605 No 21st.............................	03
Guest House Mtr Inn, 951 18th S.............................	05
Holiday Inn, 1313 No 3rd Ave.............................	03
Molton, 507 N 20th..................	01
Parliament House, 420 20th S.............................	01
Redmont, 2101 5th Ave N.........	01
Ridgely Apts, 608 No 21st......	03
Sheraton Motor Inns, 2040 Highland Ave....................	05
Thomas Jefferson, 1631 2nd Ave N.............................	02
Town House Apts, 2008 8th Ave So.............................	33
Tutwiler, 2005 5th Ave	01

BUILDINGS

Alabama Power, 600 N 18th..	02
American Life, 2308 4th Ave N.............................	03
Bank For Savings, 1919 Morris Ave.............................	03
Brown Marx, 2000 1st Ave N..	03
Chamber Commerce, 1914 6th Ave No.............................	03
City Federal, 2026 2nd Ave N.............................	03
City Hall, 710 No 20th..............	03
City National Bank, 1928 1st Ave N.............................	03

Birmingham (Con.)	352
County Court House, 716 No 21st.............................	03
Farley, 1929 3rd Ave No..........	03
Federal Reserve Bank.............	02
Federal, 1800 5th Ave N...........	03
First National, 17 N 20th........	03
Frank Nelson, 205 N 20th	03
Jackson, 215 N 21st..................	03
Liberty Building, 301 So 20th.............................	02
Massey, 2025 3rd Ave N........	03
Municipal Auditorium, 1926 8th Ave No.............................	03
Protective Life, 2027 1st Ave N.............................	03
Seventeen Ten, 1710 1st Ave N.............................	03
Stallings, 1829 1st Ave N	03
Title, 2030 3rd Ave No.............	03
United States Post Office 351 North 24th Street......	03
Watts, 2008 3rd Ave N.............	03
Woodward, 1927 1st Ave N.....	03
2121 Building, 2121 8th Ave N.............................	03

HOSPITALS

Babtist Medical Center, 800 Montclair Rd......................	13
Birmingham Baptist, 701 Princeton Ave S. W............	11
Carraway Methodist, 2506 16th Ave N....................	34
Childrens, 1601 6th Ave S.......	33
Crippled Childrens Clinic, 620 19th S..........................	33
East End Memorial, 7916 2nd Ave S..........................	06
Saint Vincents, 2701 9th Ct S..............................	01
Salvation Army, 6001 Crestwood Blvd..................	12
South Highlands Infirmary, 1127 S 12th..........................	05
University, 619 S 19th..............	33
Veterans Administration, 720 S 19th..............................	33

UNIVERSITIES AND COLLEGES

Alverson-Draughn Business College 2110 1st Ave N	01
B'Ham Babtist.............................	11
B'Ham School Of Law................	03
B'Ham Southern, 800 8th Ave W.............................	04
Booker T Washington Business College, 1527 5th Ave N..........................	02
Massey, 2024 1/2 3rd Ave No.............................	03
Medical College Of Ala, 1919 7th Ave So......................	33
Miles College, Vinesville.........	08
Samford University, 800 Lakeshore Dr......................	09
Southern Business College, Clark Bldg.............................	03
University Of Ala (B'Ham Center), 720 So 20th..........	33

GADSDEN 359

POST OFFICE BOXES

Box Nos.

A-R	Alabama City Sta	04
1-539	Glencoe Br	05
1-1920	Gadsden	02
2001-2596	East Gadsden Sta	03
4001-4410	Alabama City	04

RURAL ROUTES

1	01
2	03
3	01
4	04
5	03
6	01
7	03
8	04
9	05
10	01

STATIONS, BRANCHES AND UNITS

Alabama City Sta	04
East Gadsden Sta	03
Glencoe Br	05
Hokes Bluff Rural Br	03
Rainbow City Br	01
Southside Rural Br	01
General Delivery	01
Postmaster	01

BUILDINGS

Medical Arts Building, 303 Bay St	01

HUNTSVILLE 358

POST OFFICE BOXES

Box Nos.

1-999	Main Office	04
1000-1999	West Sta	07
2000-2999	Main Office	04
3000-3999	Blue Spring Sta	10
4000-49..	Farley Sta.	02
5000-5999	Ardmore Highway Sta	05
6000-6999	Contract Station 04	06

RURAL ROUTES

1	10
2	11
3	06
4	03
5	11

STATIONS, BRANCHES AND UNITS

Ardmore Highway Sta	05
Blue Spring Sta	10
Farley Sta	02
Marshall Space Flight Center Br	12

Huntsville (Con.) 358

Oakwood College Rural Br	06
Redstone Arsenal, Br	08
West Sta	05
General Delivery	04
Postmaster	04

APARTMENTS, HOTELS, MOTELS

Russell Erskine, 125 Clinton Ave W	04

BUILDINGS

Boeing Company, 220 Wynn Dr, N W	07
Brown Engineering Company, 300 Sparkman Dr NW	07
Chrysler Corp, 102 Wynn Dr, N W	07
Clinton Bldg, 2109 Clinton Ave, W	05
Dunnavants Mall Shopping Center	01
Five Points Shopping Center, 5 Points E	01
Haysland Square Shopping Center	02
Heart Of Huntsville Shopping Center, S Memorial Pkwy	01
Holiday Office Center, 3322 S Memorial Pkwy	01
Holiday Plaza Shopping Center, Patton Rd-Bob Wallace	05
Huntsville West Shopping Center 4700 University Dr NW	05
International Business Machines Corporation	07
Jetport, Highway 20 West	06
National Aeronautics & Space Agency	12
North Memorial Plaza Shopping Center	10
Northside Plaza Shopping Center, 3300 Memorial Pkwy NW	10
Parkway City Shopping Center, S Memorial Pkwy NE	01
Pearsall Shopping Center, 2400 Memorial Pkwy NW	10
Sahara Office Center, 3313 Memorial Pkwy SW	01
South Memorial Plaza Shopping Center	02
State National Bank Bldg., East Side Square	01
Terry-Hutchens, 102 Clinton Ave W	01
Times, 226 Holmes Ave E	01

GOVERNMENT OFFICES

City Hall, Gallatin & Fountain Rw	01
Court House, Square	01
United States Court House, 101 Holmes Ave E	04
United States Post Office, 101 Holmes Ave E	04

Huntsville (Con.) 358

HOSPITALS

Crestwood Hospital, Mc Callister Dr SW	05
Fifth Ave Hospital, 107 Governors Dr SW	01
Huntsville Clinic, Lowell Dr	01
Huntsville Hospital, 910 Madison S	01
Medical Center Hospital Inc., 911 Big Cove Rd SE	01

MILITARY INSTALLATIONS

Marshall Space Flt Ctr Br	12
Redstone Arsenal, Redstone Arsenal, Al	09

UNIVERSITIES AND COLLEGES

Oakwood College, Oakwood Rd NW	06
University Of Alabama Huntsville C, 4701 University Dr NW	07

MOBILE 366

POST OFFICE BOXES

Box Nos.

A-K	Mobile	01
1-2748	Mobile	01
4000-4999	Caroline Avenue Sta	04
5000-5599	Fulton Road Sta	05
6000-6999	Loop Sta	06
7000-7999	Crichton Sta	07
8000-8599	Spring Hill Sta	08
8901-8949	Bates Field R Br	08
9000-9999	Cottage Hill Sta	09
10000-10699	Prichard Br	10
10800-10900	Plateau	10
11000-11428	Chickasaw	11
12000-12250	Whistler	12
13000-13599	Eight Mile	13
16000-16999	Bel Air	16

RURAL ROUTES

1	05
2	09
3	08
4	09
5	08
6	13
7,8	08
9	13
10	09

STATIONS, BRANCHES AND UNITS

Bates Field Rural Br	08
Bel Air Sta	06
Caroline Avenue Sta	04
Chickasaw Br	11

Mobile (Con.)	366
Crichton Sta	07
Eight Mile Br	13
Fulton Road Sta	05
Loop Sta	06
Plateau Br	10
Prichard Br	10
Tillmans Corner Br	19
Whistler Br	12
American National Bank	29
G M & O Railroad	24
G M A C General Motors Accep	31
Gayfer S Bel-Air	26
General Delivery	01
Hammels	23
Merchants National Bank	22
Mobile Press Register	30
Morrison S Cafeteria	25
Postmaster	01
U S Engineers	28

APARTMENTS, HOTELS, MOTELS

Admiral Semmes	01
Admiral Semmes Motor	01
Battle House	01
Downtown Hotel Courts	04
Mobile Travelodge	01
Roadway Inn 1500 Government St	04
Saint Francis Motor Courts, 2501 Government Blvd	06
Town House Motor, 1061 Government St	04

BUILDINGS

American National Bank, 130 St Joseph	02
E A Roberts Bldg 61 St Joseph	02
Federal, 109 St Joseph	02
First Federal Towers, Bel-Air	06
First Federal, 100 St Joseph	02
First National Bank, 31 N Royal St	02
Government Street Office, 951 Government	04
Merchants Bank, 58 St Joseph	02
Milner, 118 N Royal	02
Mobile Public Library, 701 Government	02
Office Park Bldg, 273 Azalea Rd	09
Van Antwerp, 103 Dauphin	02

GOVERNMENT OFFICES

City Auditorium, 401 Auditorium Dr	02
County Court House, 109 Government	02
Police Station, 51 Government	02

HOSPITALS

Doctors Hospital	01
Mobile General, 2451 Fillingim	17

Mobile (Con.)	366
Mobile Infirmary	07
Providence Hospital, 1504 Springhill Ave	04
Sixth District Tuberculosis, 800 St Anthony	03

UNIVERSITIES AND COLLEGES

Carver State Technical School	07
Catholic Schools Office	01
Mobile College, Kali-Oka Rd	13
Mobile Public Schools Office	01
Mobile State Jr College 351 N Broad	03
Southwest State Technical Institute	05
Spring Hill College, 4307 Old Shell Rd	08
University Of South Alabama 307 Gaillard Dr	88

MONTGOMERY   361

POST OFFICE BOXES

Box Nos.		
A-Q	Cloverland Sta	05
1-711	Main Office	01
721-1671	Main Office	02
1681-2271	Main Office	03
2501-2830	Cloverland Sta	05
3001-3417	Eastbrook Sta	09
4001-4327	Main Office	04
6001-6250	Carolyn Sta	06
7001-7504	Capitol Heights Sta	07
8001-8296	Boylston Br	10
9001-9432	West Side Sta	08
11001-11432	Green Lantern	11

RURAL ROUTES

1	05
2	08
3	10
4	11
5	09
6	08
7	09
8	08
9	09
10	11

STATIONS, BRANCHES AND UNITS

Boyleston Br	10
Capitol Heights Sta	07
Carolyn Sta	06
Cloverland Sta	05
Eastbrook Sta	09
Green Lantern Sta	11
West Side Sta	08
General Delivery	04
Postmaster	04

APARTMENTS, HOTELS, MOTELS

Camelot Mcgehee Rd	11
Capitol Towers 7 Clayton	04

Montgomery (Con.)	361
Carriage Hills 5605 Calmar Dr	11
Exchange, 5 Commerce	01
Holiday Inn East, Eastern Blvd	09
Holiday Inn Midtown, 924 Madison Ave	04
Holiday Inn So. West, 4231 Mobile Hwy	08
Howard Johnson Motor Lodge, 1108 Eastern Bypass	09
Howard Johnson Motor Lodge, 995 W. South Blvd.	05
Jefferson Davis, 348 Montgomery	01
Red Lion Narrow Lane Rd	11
Richardson Terrace 1301 Adams Ave	04
Richlieu 555 So Mcdonough	04
Sheraton Motor Inn, 1100 W. South Blvd.	05
Spanish Gardens 4017 Beth Manor Dr	09
Spanish Quarters 5700 Calmar Dr	11
Travelodge Motel, 1550 Federal Dr	09
Vieux Carre 3551 Carter Hill Rd	11
Whitley, 231 Montgomery	01
Woodley Square East, South, Boulevard	11

BUILDINGS

Alabama National Bank, 32 Commerce	01
Aronov, 474 So. Court	04
Associations, 660 Adams	04
Bartlett, 48 Clayton	04
Bell, 207 Montgomery	04
Burkhart, 137 South Court	04
City Hall, 127 N Perry	02
County Court House, 142 Washington	02
Davis, 136 Catoma	04
Executive Building	04
First National Bank, 8 Commerce	01
Government Office, 474 S Court	04
Hill, 73 Washington	04
Leu, 79 Commerce	04
Moore, 217 South Court	04
Reese, 145 Molton	04
State Capitol	04
Town House, 238 S Decatur	04
Tyson, 41 South Lawrence	04
Union Bank & Trust, 100 Commerce	03
Washington, 125 Washington	04
10 High, 10 High St	04

GOVERNMENT OFFICES

Aronov, 474 So. Court	04
City Hall, 127 North Perry	02
County Court House, 142 Washington	02
State Capitol	04
United States Post Office, 15 Lee	04

Montgomery (Con.)   361

HOSPITALS

Baptist, S Boulevard 11
Edgefield Gables, 100 Perry
    Hill Rd................................ 09
Engle Side, 1837 Upper
    Wetumpka Rd 07
Jackson, 1235 Forest Ave 06
Meadhaven, 2007 E So Blvd .. 11
Montgomery Tuberculosis
    Sanitorium, 2140 Upper
    Wetumpka 07
Pineview Manor, 510
    Dalraida Rd 09
Professional Center, 219
    Church 04

Montgomery (Con.)   361
Saint Jude Catholic, 2018
    West Fairview Ave............. 08
Saint Margarets, 834 Adams
    Ave 01
South Haven Manor, 1300 E
    So Blvd 11
Tyson Manor, N Country Club
    Dr..................................... 06
Veterans United States Perry,
    Perry Hill Rd 09
Woodley Manor, 3312
    Woodley Rd 11

MILITARY INSTALLATIONS

Gunter Air Force Base, Boxes
    And Military Branch............ 14

Montgomery (Con.)   361
Gunter Air Force Base,
    Quarters Branch 15
Maxwell Air Force Base,
    Boxes And Military Station. 12
Maxwell Air Force Base,
    Quarters Station 13

UNIVERSITIES AND COLLEGES

Alabama Christian, Atlanta
    Hwy.................................. 09
Alabama State, 915 So
    Jackson 01
Auburn University At
    Montgomery Atlanta Hwy.... 09
Huntingdon, 1500 East
    Fairview............................. 06

ALASKA
(Abbreviation: AK)

Akhiok, R. Br. Kodiak....99615
Akiachak....99551
Akiak....99552
Akutan....99553
Alakanuk....99554
Aleknagik....99555
Alitak, R. Br. Kodiak....99615
Allakaket....99720
Ambler....99786
Amchitka, R. Br. Anchorage....99541
Anaktuvuk Pass....99721
Anchor Point....99556
ANCHORAGE (1st) (see appendix)
Angoon....99820
Aniak....99557
Annette....99920
Anvik....99558
Arctic Village....99722
Auke Bay....99821
Baranof....99822
Barrow....99723
Beaver....99724
Bethel....99559
  Kongiganak, R. Br.....99559
  Napaskiak, R. Br.....99559
  Newtok, R. Br.....99559
  Nightmute, R. Br.....99690
  Toksook Bay, R. Br.....99637
  Tuluksak, R. Br.....99679
  Tuntutuliak, R. Br.....99680
Bettles Field....99726
Border, R. Br. Tok....99780
Brevig Mission....99785
Buckland....99727
Cantwell....99729
Cape Yakataga....99560
Central....99730
Chalkyitsik, R. Br. Fort Yukon....99788
Chatanika....99731
Chefornak....99561
Chevak....99563
Chicken....99732
Chignik....99564
Chignik Lagoon....99565
Chignik Lake, R. Br. Anchorage....99502
Chitina....99566
Chugiak....99567
Circle....99733
Clam Gulch....99568
Clarks Point....99569
Clear, MOU. Fairbanks....99704
Cohoe....99570
Cold Bay....99571
College, Br. Fairbanks....99701
College Village, Br. Anchorage....99504
Cooper Landing....99572
Copper Center....99573
Cordova....99574
Craig....99921
Crooked Creek....99575
Deering....99736
Delta Junction....99737
Dillingham....99576
Dot Lake, R. Br. Delta Junction....99737

Douglas....99824
Eagle....99738
Eagle River....99577
Eastchester, Sta. Anchorage (see appendix)
Eek....99578
Egegik....99579
Eielson A F B, Br. Fairbanks....99702
Ekwok....99580
Elfin Cove....99825
Elim....99739
Elmendorf A F B, Br. Anchorage....99506
Emmonak....99581
Ester....99725
Fairbanks (1st)....99701
  Clear, MOU....99704
  College, Br....99701
  Eielson A'' Br....99702
  Federal, Sta....99707
  Fort Wainwright, Br.....99703
  Hogatza, R. Br....99744
  Mckinley Park, R. Br....99755
  North Pole, R. Br.....99705
  University, Br.....99701
False Pass....99583
Federal, Sta. Fairbanks....99707
Federal, Sta. Anchorage....99501
Flat....99584
Fort Richardson, Br. Anchorage....99505
Fort Wainwright, Br. Fairbanks....99703
Fort Yukon....99740
  Chalkyitsik, R. Br.....99788
Fortuna Ledge....99585
Gakona....99586
Galena....99741
Gambell....99742
Girdwood....99587
Glennallen....99588
Golovin, R. Br. Nome....99762
Goodnews Bay....99589
Grayling....99590
Gustavus....99826
Haines....99827
Halibut Cove, R. Br. Homer....99603
Healy....99743
  Usibelli, R. Br.....99787
Hogatza, R. Br. Fairbanks....99744
Holy Cross....99602
Homer....99603
Hoonah....99829
Hooper Bay....99604
Hope....99605
Hughes....99745
Huslia....99746
Hydaburg....99922
Hyder....99923
Iguigig, R. Br. King Salmon....99613
Iliamna....99606
  Kokhanok, R. Br.....99606
  Pedro Bay, R. Br.....99647
Indian, R. Br. Anchorage....99540
Ivanof Bay, R. Br. Anchorage....99502
Juneau (1st)....99801
Kake....99830
Kaktovik....99747
Kalskag....99607
Kaltag....99748
Karluk....99608
Kasaan....99924

Kasigluk....99609
Kasilof....99610
Kenai (1st)....99611
Ketchikan (1st)....99901
  Meyers Chuck, R. Br.....99903
Kiana....99749
King Cove....99612
King Salmon....99613
Kipnuk....99614
Kivalina....99750
Klatt Road, R. Br. Anchorage....99501
Klawock....99925
Kobuk....99751
Kodiak (1st)....99615
  Akhiok, R. Br.....99615
  Alitak, R. Br.....99615
Kokhanok, R. Br. Iliamna....99606
Koliganek, R. Br. Dillingham....99576
Kongiganak, R. Br. Bethel....99559
Kotlik....99620
Kotzebue....99752
Koyuk....99753
Koyukuk....99754
Kwethluk....99621
Kwigillingok....99622
Lake Minchumina....99623
Larsen Bay....99624
Levelock....99625
Little Diomede, R. Br. Nome....99762
Lower Kalskag....99626
Manley Hot Springs....99756
Manokotak....99628
Mc Grath....99627
  Nikolai, R. Br.....99691
Mckinley Park, R. Br. Fairbanks....99755
Medfra....99629
Mekoryuk....99630
Metlakatla....99926
Meyers Chuck, R. Br. Ketchikan....99903
Miller House, R. Br. Central....99730
Minto....99758
Moose Pass....99631
Mount Edgecumbe, Br. Sitka....99835
Mountain View, Sta. Anchorage....99504
Mountain Village....99632
Naknek....99633
Napakiak....99634
Napaskiak, R. Br. Bethel....99559
Nenana....99760
New Stuyahok....99636
Newtok, R. Br. Bethel....99559
Nightmute, R. Br. Bethel....99690
Nikolai, R. Br. Mc Grath....99691
Nikolski....99638
Ninilchik....99639
Noatak....99761
Nome....99762
Nondalton....99640
Noorvik....99763
North Kenai, R. Br. Kenai....99611
North Pole, R. Br. Fairbanks....99705
Northway....99764
Nulato....99765
Nunaka Valley, Br. Anchorage....99504
Nunapitchuk....99641
Old Harbor....99643
Ouzinkie....99644

9

Palmer (1st)	99645	
Pauloff Harbor	99646	
Paxson, R. Br. Delta Junction	99737	
Pedro Bay, R. Br. Iliamna	99647	
Pelican	99832	
Perryville	99648	
Petersburg	99833	
Pilot Point	99649	
Pilot Station	99650	
Pitka's Point, R. Br. Saint Marys	99658	
Platinum	99651	
Point Baker	99927	
Point Hope	99766	
Port Alsworth	99653	
Port Ashton	99654	
Port Lions	99550	
Portage Creek, R. Br. Dillingham	99576	
Quinhagak	99655	
Rampart	99767	
Red Devil	99656	
Ruby	99768	
Russian Mission	99657	
Saint Marys	99658	
Saint Michael	99659	
Saint Paul Island	99660	
Sand Point	99661	

Savoonga	99769
Scammon Bay	99662
Selawik	99770
Seldovia	99663
Seward	99664
Shageluk	99665
Shaktoolik	99771
Sheldon Point, R. Br. Emmonak	99666
Shishmaref	99772
Shungnak	99773
Sitka (1st)	99835
Skagway	99840
Skwentna	99667
Sleetmute	99668
Soldotna (1st)	99669
South Naknek	99670
Spenard, Sta. Anchorage	99503
Stebbins	99671
Sterling	99672
Stevens Village	99774
Sutton	99674
Takotna	99675
Talkeetna	99676
Tanacross, R. Br. Tok	99776
Tanana	99777
Tatitlek	99677
Teller	99778

Tenakee Springs	99841
Tetlin, R. Br. Tok	99779
Togiak	99678
Tok	99780
Border, R. Br.	99780
Tanacross, R. Br.	99776
Tetlin, R. Br.	99779
Toksook Bay, R. Br. Bethel	99637
Tuluksak, R. Br. Bethel	99679
Tuntutuliak, R. Br. Bethel	99680
Tununak	99681
Tyonek	99682
Ugashik	99683
Unalakleet	99684
Unalaska	99685
University, Br. Fairbanks	99701
Usibelli, R. Br. Healy	99787
Valdez	99686
Venetie	99781
Wainwright	99782
Wales	99783
Ward Cove	99928
Wasilla	99687
White Mountain	99784
Whittier, R. Br. Anchorage	99501
Willow	99688
Wrangell	99929
Yakutat	99689

ANCHORAGE		995
POST OFFICE BOXES		
Box Nos.		
1-2999	Federal	10
4A-4ZZZ	Spenard Sta	09
8A-8AF	Mountain View Sta	08
3600-3999	Eastchester Sta	01
6000-6999	Main Office Br.	02

7000-7999	Federal Sta	01
8000-8999	Mountain View Sta	08
10000-10999	Klatt Road Br	02
4-001-4-2200	Spenard Sta	09

STATIONS, BRANCHES AND UNITS

Amchitka Rural Br	41
Chignik Lake Rural Br	02
College Village Br	04

Eastchester Sta	01
Elmendorf A F B Br	06
Federal Sta	01
Fort Richardson Br	05
Indian Rural Br	40
Ivanof Bay Rural Br	02
Klatt Road Rural Br	01
Mountain View Sta	04
Nunaka Valley Br	04
Spenard Sta	03
Whittier Rural Br	01
General Delivery	01
Postmaster	02

ARIZONA

(Abbreviation: AZ)

Agua Fria, R. Br. Prescott......86301
Aguila 85320
Ajo 85321
Alpine 85920
Amado, R. Br. Tumacacori......85640
Apache Junction (1st)............85220
  Florence Junction, R. Br......85233
  Queen Valley, R. Br. 85220
Arcadia, Sta. Phoenix...........85018
Arivaca 85601
Arizona City, R. Br. Casa
  Grande 85223
Arlington 85322
Ash Fork 86320
Avondale 85323
Bagdad 86321
Bapchule 85221
Bellemont, R. Br. Flagstaff......86001
Benson 85602
Benson Highway, Br. Tucson....85706
Bisbee (1st)........................85603
Black Canyon City.................85324
Blue 85922
Bouse 85325
Bowie 85605
Boys Ranch, R. Br.
  Chandler 85224
Buckeye (1st)......................85326
Buckhorn, R. Br. Mesa...........85201
Bullhead City (1st)................86430
  Mohave Valley, R. Br...........86440
  Riviera, R. Br. 86442
Bumble Bee 85327
Bylas 85530
Cameron 86020
Camp Verde 86322
Capitol, Sta. Phoenix (see
  appendix)
Carefree, R. Br. Cave Creek....85331
Casa Grande (1st) 85222
  Arizona City, R. Br.............85223
  Eleven Mile Corner, R.
    Br. 85222
Casas Adobes, R. Br.
  Tucson..........................85704
Cashion 85329
Cave Creek 85331
Central 85531
Chambers 86502
Chandler (1st)......................85224
Chandler Heights 85227
Chinle 86503
Chino Valley 86323
Chloride 86431
Cibecue, R. Br. Show Low......85901
Clarkdale 86324
Clay Springs 85923
Claypool............................85532
Clifton 85533
Cochise 85606
College, Sta. Tucson..............85719
Colorado City 86021
Commerce, Sta. Phoenix.........85030
Concho 85924
Congress............................85332
Coolidge (1st)......................85228
Copper Queen, Sta. Bisbee....85603
Cornville 86325

Coronado, Sta. Tucson 85711
Cortaro.............................85230
Cottonwood 86326
Crown King, R. Br. Mayer......86333
Dateland 85333
Davis Monthan A F B, Br.
  Tucson (see appendix)
Desert Sage, Br. Mesa...........85201
Dewey 86327
Dinosaur City, R. Br. Peach
  Springs..........................86434
Dolan Springs, R. Br.
  Kingman.........................86441
Douglas (1st)......................85607
Downtown, Sta. Phoenix (see
  appendix)
Downtown, Sta. Tempe...........85281
Dragoon 85609
Duncan 85534
Eagar 85925
East Fork, R. Br. Whiteriver......85941
Eden 85535
Ehrenberg 85334
El Mirage 85335
Eleven Mile Corner, R. Br.
  Casa Grande 85222
Elfrida 85610
Elgin 85611
Eloy 85231
Emery Park, Sta. Tucson
  (see appendix)
Fairbank 85612
Flagstaff (1st).......................86001
  Bellemont, R. Br...............86001
  Gray Mountain, R. Br..........86001
  Happy Jack, R. Br. 86024
  Mormon Lake, R. Br...........86038
  Mountainaire, R. Br............86001
  Munds Park, R. Br.............86001
  N A U, Sta. 86001
  Parks, R. Br. 86001
  Two Gun Town, R. Br..........86001
Florence 85232
Florence Junction, R. Br.
  Apache Junction................85233
Fort Apache 85926
Fort Defiance 86504
Fort Grant, R. Br. Willcox......85643
Fort Huachuca (1st)...............85613
Fort Thomas 85536
Franklin, R. Br. Duncan..........85534
Fredonia 86022
Gadsden 85336
Ganado 86505
Gila Bend 85337
Gilbert..............................85234

GLENDALE (1st) (see appendix)

Globe (1st).........................85501
Goodyear...........................85338
Grand Canyon (1st)...............86023
Gray Mountain, R. Br.
  Flagstaff........................86001
Greasewood, R. Br. Ganado....86505
Green Valley 85614
Greenway, Sta. Tucson..........85713
Greer 85927
Guadalupe, R. Br. Tempe........85281
Hackberry, R. Br. Kingman......86401
Happy Jack, R. Br. Flagstaff....86024
Hawley Lake, R. Br. Mc
  Nary..............................85930
Hayden..............................85235

Heber 85928
Hereford 85615
Higley...............................85236
Holbrook (1st)......................86025
  Indian Wells, R. Br.............86031
  Petrified Forest National
    Pk, R. Br. 86025
  Sun Valley, R. Br. 86025
Hotevilla 86030
Houck 86506
  Lupton, R. Br. 86508
Huachuca City......................85616
Hualapai, R. Br. Kingman......86401
Humboldt...........................86329
Indian School, Sta. Phoenix
  (see appendix)
Indian Wells, R. Br.
  Holbrook 86031
Inspiration 85537
Iron Springs, R. Br. Prescott......86330
Jacob Lake, R. Br. Fredonia......86022
Jerome 86331
Joseph City 86032
Kaibito, R. Br. Tonalea..........86044
Kayenta.............................86033
Keams Canyon 86034
Kearny..............................85237
Kingman (1st)......................86401
  Dolan Springs, R. Br...........86441
  Hackberry, R. Br...............86401
  Hualapai, R. Br. 86401
  Temple Bar Marina, R.
    Br. 86443
Kino, Sta. Tucson.................85705
Kirkland 86332
Klondyke, R. Br. Willcox........85643
Kofa, R. Br. Yuma................85364
Kohls Ranch, R. Br. Payson....85538
Lake Havasu City (1st) 86403
Lake Montezuma, R. Br.
  Sedona..........................86336
Lakeside 85929
Laveen 85339
Leupp 86035
Litchfield Park 85340
Littlefield 86432
Lowell, Sta. Bisbee................85603
Lukachukai 86507
Luke A F B, Br. Glendale........85301
Lukeville 85341
Lupton, R. Br. Houck............86508
Mammoth 85618
Many Farms, R. Br. Chinle 86503
Marana 85238
Marble Canyon, R. Br. Page....86036
Maricopa............................85239
Marine Corps Air Station, Br.
  Yuma............................85364
Martinez Lake, R. Br. Yuma....85364
Maryvale, Sta. Phoenix (see
  appendix)
Mayer...............................86333
Mc Dowell, Sta. Phoenix (see
  appendix)
Mc Nary 85930
Mc Neal 85617

MESA (1st) (see appendix)

Miami 85539
Miller Valley, R. Sta.
  Prescott.........................86301
Miracle Valley, R. Br. Sierra
  Vista.............................85645

11

Mohave Valley, R. Br.	
Bullhead City	86440
Morenci	85540
Mormon Lake, R. Br.	
Flagstaff	86038
Morristown	85342
Mount Lemmon	85619
Mountainaire, R. Br.	
Flagstaff	86001
Munds Park, R. Br.	
Flagstaff	86001
N A U, Sta. Flagstaff	86001
Naco	85620
Navajo	86509
Nogales (1st)	85621
North Rim, R. Br. Fredonia	86022
Northeast, Sta. Phoenix	85016
Northwest, Sta. Phoenix (see appendix)	
Nutrioso	85932
Oatman	86433
Oracle	85623
Oraibi	86039
Overgaard	85933
Page	86040
Marble Canyon, R. Br.	86036
Palo Verde	85343
Papago, Sta. Scottsdale	85257
Paradise Valley, Br.	
Scottsdale	85253
Parker (1st)	85344
Poston, R. Br.	85371
Parks, R. Br. Flagstaff	86001
Patagonia	85624
Paulden	86334
Payson	85541
Kohls Ranch, R. Br.	85538
Peach Springs	86434
Pearce	85625
Peoria	85345
Peridot	85542
Petrified Forest National Pk,	
R. Br. Holbrook	86025
PHOENIX (1st) (see appendix)	
Picacho	85241
Pima	85543
Pine	85544
Pinedale	85934
Pinetop	85935
Pinon	86510
Pirtleville	85626
Pisinemo, R. Br. Sells	85634
Polacca	86042
Pomerene	85627
Portal, R. Br. San Simon	85632
Poston, R. Br. Parker	85371
Prescott (1st)	86301
Agua Fria, R. Br.	86301
Iron Springs, R. Br.	86330

Miller Valley, R. Sta.	86301
Whipple, Sta.	86301
Quartzsite	85346
Queen Creek	85242
Queen Valley, R. Br. Apache	
Junction	85220
Randolph	85243
Red Rock	85245
Rillito	85246
Rimrock	86335
Rincon, Sta. Tucson (see appendix)	
Riverside Stage Stop, R. Br.	
Kearny	85237
Riviera, R. Br. Bullhead City	86442
Roll	85347
Roosevelt	85545
Sacaton	85247
Safford (1st)	85546
Sahuarita	85629
Saint David	85630
Saint Johns	85936
Saint Michaels	86511
Salome	85348
San Carlos	85550
San Luis	85349
San Manuel	85631
San Simon	85632
Sanders	86512
Sasabe	85633
Sawmill, R. Br. Fort	
Defiance	86504
SCOTTSDALE (1st) (see appendix)	
Second Mesa	86043
Sedona (1st)	86336
Seligman	86337
Sells	85634
Sherwood, Sta. Mesa	85201
Shonto, R. Br. Tonalea	86044
Show Low	85901
Sierra Vista (1st)	85635
Miracle Valley, R. Br.	85645
Silver Bell	85270
Skull Valley	86338
Snowflake	85937
Solomon	85551
Somerton	85350
Sonoita	85637
South Central, Sta. Phoenix (see appendix)	
South Tucson, Br. Tucson	85713
Speedway, Sta. Tucson	85716
Springerville	85938
Stanfield	85272
Student Union, Sta. Tucson	85720
Sun City (1st)	85351
Sun Valley, R. Br. Holbrook	86025
Sunnyslope, Sta. Phoenix (see appendix)	

Supai	86435
Superior	85273
Surprise, R. Br. Peoria	85345
Tacna	85352
Taylor	85939
Teec Nos Pos	86514
TEMPE (1st) (see appendix)	
Temple Bar Marina, R. Br.	
Kingman	86443
Thatcher	85552
Tolleson	85353
Tombstone	85638
Tonalea	86044
Tonopah	85354
Tonto Basin	85553
Topawa	85639
Topock	86436
Tortilla Flat	85290
Tuba City	86045
Tubac, R. Br. Tumacacori	85640
TUCSON (1st) (see appendix)	
Tumacacori	85640
Two Gun Town, R. Br.	
Flagstaff	86001
University, Sta. Tucson (see appendix)	
Vail	85641
Valentine	86437
Valley Farms	85291
Vernon	85940
Waddell	85355
Warren, Sta. Bisbee	85603
Wellton	85356
Wenden	85357
West Sedona, R. Br. Sedona	86340
Whipple, Sta. Prescott	86301
White Mountain Lake, R. Br.	
Show Low	85901
Whiteriver	85941
Why, R. Br. Ajo	85321
Wickenburg (1st)	85358
Wide Ruins, R. Br.	
Chambers	86502
Wikieup	85360
Willcox (1st)	85643
Williams	86046
Williams A F B, Br.	
Chandler	85224
Window Rock	86515
Winkelman	85292
Winslow (1st)	86047
Wittmann	85361
Woodruff	85942
Yarnell	85362
Young	85554
Youngtown (1st)	85363
Yucca	86438
Yuma (1st)	85364
Yuma Proving Ground, Br.	
Yuma	85364

GLENDALE 853

POST OFFICE BOXES

Box Nos.
1-1762 Main Office 11

RURAL ROUTES

1,2,3 01

STATIONS, BRANCHES AND UNITS

Luke A F B Br 01
General Delivery 01
Main Office 01
Postmaster 01

GOVERNMENT OFFICES

County Offices 7115 N 57 Dr. 01
Municipal 7022 N 58 Dr........ 01

MILITARY INSTALLATIONS

Luke A F B 09

UNIVERSITIES AND COLLEGES

Thunderbird Graduate School
Of International
Management 06

MESA 852

POST OFFICE BOXES

Box Nos.
A-R Main Office 01
1-1999 Main Office 01
2000-2699 Sherwood Sta ... 04
3900-3999 Desert Sage
 Sta................ 07
4000-4999 Main Office 01

STATIONS, BRANCHES AND UNITS

Buckhorn Rural Br 01
Desert Sage Br.......................... 01
Sherwood Sta 01
General Delivery 01
Postmaster 01

BUILDINGS

Valley National Bank, 66 W
Main................................... 01

HOSPITALS

Mesa General. 515 N Mesa
Dr...................................... 01
Mesa Lutheran, 501 W 10th
Pl....................................... 01
Southside, 21 S Hibbert........... 02

PHOENIX 850

POST OFFICE BOXES

Box Nos.
1-2199 Downtown........ 01
2200-2699 Downtown........ 02
2900-2999 Main Office 36
2900-2999 Main Office 62
5000-5999 Mc Dowell Sta.. 10
6000-6999 Capital Sta........ 05
7000-7999 Indian School
 Sta.................. 11
8000-8999 South Central
 Sta 40
9000-9999 Sunnyslope
 Sta.................. 68
10000-10999 Northeast Sta.. 16
11000-11999 Northwest Sta.. 61
13000-13999 Downtown........ 02
14000-14999 Maryvale Sta.... 31
15000-15999 Arcadia............ 60
16000-16999 Indian School
 Sta.................. 11
19000-19999 Capitol Sta....... 09
20000-21999 Main Office 36
22000-22999 Sta 24 28

RURAL ROUTES

1 40
3 09
4 31
5 09

STATIONS, BRANCHES AND UNITS

Arcadia Sta................................. 18
Capitol Sta.................................. 05
Commerce Sta............................ 30
Downtown Sta............................ 04
Indian School Sta....................... 31
Maryvale Sta.............................. 31
Northeast Sta............................. 16
Northwest Sta............................ 16
South Central Sta....................... 40
Sunnyslope Sta.......................... 20
Black Canyon Star Route........... 20
Cave Creek Star Route.............. 20
General Delivery 26
Postmaster 26

BUILDINGS

Arizona Bank, 34 W Monroe.... 03
Arizona Title Annex, 135 N
2nd Ave............................. 03
Arizona Title, 111 W Monroe.... 03
Central Towers, 2727 N
Central Ave 04
Del Webb, 3800 N Central
Ave 12
Del Webb'S Townhouse, 100
- W Clarendon Ave 13
Executive Towers, 207 W
Clarendon Ave 13
Financial Center, 3443 N
Central Ave 12
First Federal Savings, 3003
N Central Ave 12
First National Bank Plaza
100 W Washington 03
Ford Law, 11 N 2nd Ave......... 03

Phoenix (Con.) 850

Goodrich, 14 N Central Ave.... 04
Greater Arizona Savings, 112
N Central Ave 04
Greyhound Towers 111 W
Clarendon Ave 13
Luhrs Central, 132 S Central
Ave 04
Luhrs Tower, 45 W Jefferson.. 03
Luhrs, 11 W Jefferson.............. 03
Mayer Central, 3033 N
Central Ave 12
Park Central, 550 W Thomas
Rd 13
Phoenix Public Library, 12 E
Mcdowell Rd 04
Phoenix Towers, 2201 N
Central Ave 04
Professional, 15 E Monroe 04
Rosenzweigs Center, 3814 N
Central Ave 12
Security Center, 222 N
Central Ave 04
Security, 234 N Central Ave.... 04
State Highway, 1739 W
Jackson 07
Terminal, 218 S 4th................. 04
Transamerica Title, 114 W.
Adams................................ 03
United Bank Of Arizona,
3550 N Central Ave........... 12
Oarizona Public Service 411
N Central Ave 04

GOVERNMENT OFFICES

Arizona State Capitol, 1700
W Washington 07
Arizona State Office, 1632 W
Adams 07
County Court House, 125 W
Washington 03
County Office, 101 W
Jefferson 03
Federal, 230 N 1st Ave............ 25
Municipal, 251 W
Washington 03

HOSPITALS

Arizona State Hospital, 2500
E Van Buren 08
Baptist Hospital Of Phoenix,
6025 N 20th Ave................ 15
Camelback Hospital, 5055 N
34th 18
Crippled Childrens 1825 E
Garfield.............................. 06
Doctor'S, 1947 E Thomas Rd.. 16
Franklin, 367 N 21st Ave........ 09
Good Samaritan, 1033 E Mc
Dowell Rd.......................... 06
Lincoln John C, 9111 2nd....... 20
Maricopa County 2601 E
Roosevelt........................... 08
Maryvale Community, 5102 W
Campbell Ave.................... 31
Memorial, 1200 S 5th Ave...... 03
North Mountain, 48 E Foothill
Dr 20
Phoenix General, 1950 W
Indian School Rd............... 15

13

Phoenix (Con.)	850
Phoenix Phs Indian 4212 N 16th	16
Saint Josephs Hospital, 350 W Thomas Rd	13
Saint Lukes Hospital, 1820 E Polk	06
Veterans Administration, 650 E Indian School Rd	12

UNIVERSITIES AND COLLEGES

City School Administration, 125 E Lincoln	04
Grand Canyon College, 3300 W Camelback Rd	17
Phoenix Union High Sch System 2225 N 16th 2526 W Osborn Rd	17

SCOTTSDALE 852

POST OFFICE BOXES

Box Nos.
A-Z	Main Office	52
1-2999	Main Office	52
3001-3599	Papago Sta	57

RURAL ROUTES

1	56

STATIONS, BRANCHES AND UNITS

Papago Sta	57
Paradise Valley Br	53
General Delivery	51
Postmaster	51

TEMPE 852

POST OFFICE BOXES

Box Nos.
A-Z	Downtown Sta	81
1-3189	Downtown Sta	81
AA-UF	Downtown Sta	81
2A-2U	Main Office	82
26001-28999	Main Office	82

RURAL ROUTES

1,2	82

STATIONS, BRANCHES AND UNITS

Downtown Sta	81
Guadalupe Rural Br	81
General Delivery	82
Postmaster	82

UNIVERSITIES AND COLLEGES

Arizona State University	81

TUCSON 857

POST OFFICE BOXES

Box Nos.
1-3069	Main Office	02
3301-3744	College Sta	22
3901-4999	University Sta	17
5001-5987	Kino Sta	03
6001-6809	Speedway Sta	16
7001-7897	South Tucson Br	25
8001-8416	Greenway Sta	23
9001-10999	Student Union Sta	20
11001-11727	Emery Park Sta	06
12001-13499	Coronado Sta	11
15001-15177	Davis Monthan A F B	08
17001-17960	Rincon Br	10
20001-21110	Student Union	20
49001-49337	University Sta	17
50001-50895	Kino Sta	03
80001-83958	Davis Monthan A F B Military	07

RURAL ROUTES

1	04
2	15
3	06
4	04
5	18
6	04
7	14
8	10
9	05
10	18
11	06
12	15
13	05
14	04
15	15
16	06

STATIONS, BRANCHES AND UNITS

Benson Highway Br	06
Casas Adobes Rural Br	04
College Sta	19
Coronado Sta	11
Emery Park Sta	06
Greenway Sta	13
Kino Sta	05
Rincon Sta	10
South Tucson Br	13
Speedway Sta	16
Student Union Sta	20
General Delivery	02

Tuscon (Con.)	857
Postmaster	26

APARTMENTS, HOTELS, MOTELS

Arizona Inn, 2200 East Elm	19
Arizona, 35 North 6th Ave	01
Congress, 311 East Congress	01
El Presidio, 245 East Broadway	01
Pioneer, 80 North Stone Ave	01
Roskruge, 57 South Scott	01
Santa Rita, 109 South Scott	01
Westerner, 63 South Stone Ave	01

BUILDINGS

Arizona Bank, Alameda & Stone	01
Garden Plaza, 201 North Stone	01
Lawyers Title, 199 North Stone	01
Pima Plaza, 2030 East Broadway	19
Pima, 151 North Stone	01
Transamerica Title, 177 North Church	01
Tucson Federal Savings Tower, 32 North Stone	01
Tucson Title, 45 West Pennington	01
Valley National Bank, 2 East Congress	01

HOSPITALS

Carl Hayden Memorial, 402 West Congress	01
Pima County, 2900 South 6th Ave	13
Saint Josephs, 350 North Wilmot Rd	11
Saint Marys, 1700 West St. Marys Rd	05
Tucson General, 3838 North Campbell Ave	19
Tuscon Medical Center E Grant And Beverly Blvd	16
Veterans Adm., 3601 South 6th Ave	23

MILITARY INSTALLATIONS

Davis Monthan AFB	07

UNIVERSITIES AND COLLEGES

Arizona Medical Center	24
Pima College	09
University Of Arizona	21

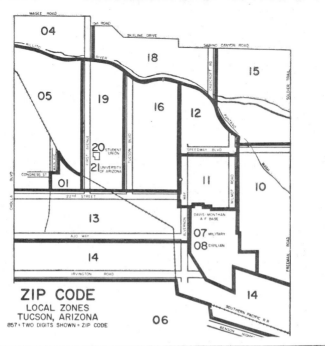

ZIP CODE
LOCAL ZONES
TUCSON, ARIZONA
857 + TWO DIGITS SHOWN = ZIP CODE

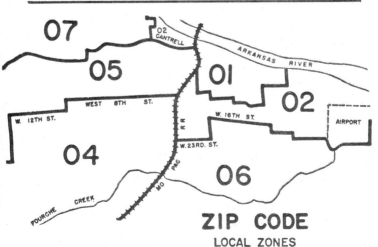

ZIP CODE
LOCAL ZONES
LITTLE ROCK, ARK.
722 + TWO DIGITS SHOWN = ZIP CODE

ARKANSAS
(Abbreviation: AR)

Abbott	72920
Adona	72001
Agnos	72510
Air Base, Sta. Jacksonville	72076
Albert Pike, Sta. Hot Springs National Park	71901
Alco	72610
Alexander	72002
Alicia	72410
Alix	72820
Alleene	71826
Allison, R. Br. Mountain View	72511
Alma	72921
Almyra	72003
Alpena	72611
Alpine	71920
Altheimer	72004
Altus	72821
Amagon	72005
Amity	71921
Antoine	71922
Appleton, R. Br. Atkins	72822
Arkadelphia (1st)	71923
Arkansas City	71630
Arkinda	71821
Armorel	72310
Ash Flat	72513
Ashdown (1st)	71822
Asher, Sta. Little Rock	72204
Athens, R. Br. Glenwood	71927
Atkins	72823
Appleton, R. Br.	72822
Aubrey	72311
Augusta	72006
Austin	72007
Auvergne, R. Br. Newport	72008
Avoca	72711
Balch	72009
Bald Knob	72010
Banks	71631
Barber	72922
Barling	72923
Barton	72312
Bass	72612
Bassett	72313
Bates	72924
Batesville (1st)	72501
Bauxite	72011
Bay	72411
Bearden	71720
Beaver	72613
Bee Branch	72013
Beebe	72012
Beech Grove	72412
Beedeville	72014
Beirne	71721
Bella Vista, R. Br. Bentonville	72712
Belleville	72824
Ben Hur	72825
Ben Lomond	71823
Benton (1st)	72015
Bentonville (1st)	72712
Bergman	72615
Berryville (1st)	72616
Bexar	72515
Bigelow	72016

Bigflat, R. Br. Marshall	72617
Biggers	72413
Birdeye	72314
Biscoe	72017
Bismarck	71929
Black Fork	72925
Black Oak	72414
Black Rock	72415
Black Springs	71930
Blackwell	72019
Blakely	71931
Blevins	71825
Blue Mountain	72826
Bluff City	71722
Bluffton	72827
Blytheville (1st)	72315
Blytheville A F B, Br. Blytheville	72315
Board Camp	71932
Boles	72926
Bonnerdale	71933
Bono	72416
Booneville (1st)	72927
Boston	72715
Boswell	72516
Boydell	71632
Bradford	72020
Bradley	71826
Brady Sta. Little Rock	72205
Branch	72928
Brickeys	72320
Briggsville	72828
Brinkley (1st)	72021
Brockwell	72517
Brookland	72417
Bruno	72618
Bryant	72022
Buckner	71827
Buckville	71934
Bull Shoals	72619
Burdette	72321
Busch	72620
Byron	72518
Cabot	72023
Caddo Gap	71935
Calamine, R. Br. Strawberry	72418
Caldwell	72322
Cale	71828
Calico Rock	72519
Calion	71724
Camden (1st)	71701
Camp	72520
Canehill	72717
Canfield, R. Br. Lewisville	71829
Caraway	72419
Carlisle	72024
Carthage	71725
Princeton, R. Br.	71761
Casa	72025
Cash	72421
Casscoe	72026
Cauthron	72929
Cave City	72521
Cave Springs	72718
Cavecreek	72621
Cecil	72930
Cedar Creek	72931
Cedarville	72932
Center Hill, R. Br. Paragould	72450
Center Ridge	72027
Centerton	72719
Centerville	72829

Central Baptist College, ... Conway	72032
Central City, Br. Hot Springs National Park	71901
Charleston	72933
Charlotte	72522
Chatfield	72323
Cherokee Village, R. Br. Hardy	72542
Cherry Valley	72324
Chester	72934
Chidester	71726
Chimes	72622
Choctaw	72028
Clarendon	72029
Clarkedale	72325
Clarkridge	72623
Clarksville (1st)	72830
Cleveland	72030
Clifty	72720
Clinton	72031
Coal Hill	72832
College City, Br. Walnut Ridge	72476
College Heights, Br. Monticello	71655
Collins	71634
Colt	72326
Columbus	71831
Combs	72721
Compton	72624
Concord	72523
Conway (1st)	72032
Cord	72524
Corning (1st)	72422
Cotter	72626
Cotton Plant	72036
Cove	71937
Coy	72037
Cozahome	72627
Crawfordsville	72327
Crocketts Bluff	72038
Crossett (1st)	71635
Crumrod	72328
Crystal Springs, R. Br. Royal	71938
Cullendale, Sta. Camden	71701
Curtis	71728
Cushman	72526
Daisy, R. Br. Glenwood	71939
Dalton	72423
Damascus	72039
Danville	72833
Dardanelle	72834
Datto	72424
De Queen (1st)	71832
De Valls Bluff	72041
De Witt (1st)	72042
Decatur	72722
Deer	72628
Delaney, R. Br. Elkins	72723
Delaplaine	72425
Delaware	72835
Delight	71940
Dell	72426
Dennard	72629
Denver	72630
Dermott	71638
Des Arc	72040
Desha	72527
Diamond City, R. Br. Lead Hill	72644
Diaz	72543

Dierks	71833
Doddridge	71834
Dogpatch	72648
Dollarway, Br. Pine Bluff	71601
Dolph	72528
Donaldson	71941
Dover	72837
Dowdy	72529
Drasco	72530
Driver	72329
Dumas (1st)	71639
Dutton	72726
Dyer	72935
Dyess	72330
Eagle Mills	71729
Earle	72331
East Camden, Br. Camden	71701
Edgemont	72044
Edmondson	72332
Egypt	72427
El Dorado (1st)	71730
El Paso	72045
Elaine	72333
Elizabeth	72531
Elkins	72727
Delaney, R. Br.	72723
Elm Springs	72728
Emerson	71740
Emmet	71835
England	72046
Enola	72047
Ethel	72048
Etowah	72428
Eudora (1st)	71640
Eureka Springs	72632
Evansville	72729
Evening Shade	72532
Everton	72633
Fair Oaks, R. Br. Wynne	72397
Fairfield Bay, R. Br. Shirley	72153
Fargo	72049
Farmington	72730
Fayetteville (1st)	72701
Ferndale, R. Br. Little Rock	72208
Fiftysix, R. Br. Mountain View	72533
Fisher	72429
Flippin	72634
Floral	72534
Fordyce (1st)	71742
Foreman	71836
Forest Park, Sta. Little Rock	72207
Forrest City (1st)	72335
Fort Smith (1st)	72901
Forty Four	72535
Forum	72731
Fouke	71837
Fountain Hill	71642
Fox	72051
Franklin	72536
Frenchmans Bayou	72338
Friendship	71942
Fulton	71838
Gamaliel	72537
Garfield	72732
Garland	71839
Garner	72052
Gassville (1st)	72635
Gateway	72733
Genevia	72053
Genoa	71840
Gentry	72734
Georgetown, R. Br. Searcy	72054
Gepp	72538
Gilbert	72636
Gillett	72055
Gillham	71841
Gilmore	72339
Glencoe	72539
Glenwood	71943
Athens, R. Br.	71927
Daisy, R. Br.	71939
Goodwin	72340
Goshen	72735
Gould	71643
Grady	71644
Grand Glaise	72056
Grandview	72637
Grannis	71944
Grapevine	72057
Gravel Ridge, R. Br. Jacksonville	72076
Gravelly	72838
Gravette	72736
Green Forest	72638
Greenbrier	72058
Greenland	72737
Greenway	72430
Greenwood	72936
Gregory	72059
Griffithville	72060
Grubbs	72431
Guion	72540
Gurdon	71743
Guy	72061
Hackett	72937
Hagarville	72839
Hamburg	71646
Hampton	71744
Hanover	72541
Hardy (1st)	72542
Harrell	71745
Harriet	72639
Harrisburg	72432
Harrison (1st)	72601
Hartford	72938
Hartman	72840
Harvey	72841
Haskell	72062
Hasty	72640
Hatfield	71945
Hattieville	72063
Hatton	71946
Havana	72842
Haynes	72341
Hazen	72064
Heber Springs	72543
Hector	72843
Helena (1st)	72342
Henderson	72544
Henderson College, Sta. Arkadelphia	71923
Hendrix College, Sta. Conway	72032
Hensley	72065
Hermitage	71647
Ingalls, R. Br.	71648
Heth	72346
Hickory Plains	72066
Hickory Ridge	72347
Higden	72067
Higginson	72068
Hillcrest, Sta. Little Rock	72205
Hindsville	72738
Hiwasse	72739
Holly Grove	72069
Holly Springs, R. Br. Sparkman	71746
Hon	72939
Hope (1st)	71801
Horatio	71842
Horseshoe Bend, R. Br. Franklin	72536
Hot Springs National Park (1st)	71901
Houston	72070
Howell	72071
Hoxie	72433
Huff	72545
Hughes	72348
Hulbert, Sta. West Memphis	72301
Humnoke	72072
Humphrey	72073
Hunt	72844
Hunter	72074
Huntington	72940
Huntsville	72740
Huttig	71747
Ida	72546
Imboden	72434
Industrial, Sta. Little Rock	72209
Ingalls, R. Br. Hermitage	71648
Ivan	71748
Jacksonport	72075
Jacksonville (1st)	72076
Jamestown	72547
Jasper	72641
Jefferson	72079
Jennie	71649
Jerome	71650
Jersey	71651
Jerusalem	72080
Jessieville	71949
Johnson	72741
Joiner	72350
Jones Mill, R. Br. Malvern	72105
Jonesboro (1st)	72401
Jordan	72548
Judsonia	72081
Junction City	71749
Keiser	72351
Kensett	72082
Keo	72083
Kingsland	71652
Kingston	72742
Kirby	71950
Knobel	72435
Knoxville	72845
La Crosse	72549
La Grange	72352
Lafe, R. Br. Marmaduke	72436
Lake Catherine, R. Br. Hot Springs National Park	71901
Lake City	72437
Lake Hamilton	71951
Lake Village	71653
Lakeview	72642
Lamar	72846
Lambert, R. Br. Bismarck	71929
Lambrook	72353
Landis	72643
Laneburg	71844
Langley	71952
Larue	72743
Lavaca	72941
Lawson	71750
Leachville (1st)	72438
Lead Hill	72644
Leola	72084

Lepanto	72354	
Leslie	72645	
Letona	72085	
Lewisville	71845	
Canfield, R. Br.	71829	
Lexa	72355	
Light, R. Br. Paragould	72439	
Limestone	72646	
Lincoln	72744	
LITTLE ROCK (1st) (see appendix)		
Lockesburg	71846	
Locust Grove	72550	
London	72847	
Lonoke	72086	
Lonsdale	72087	
Louann	71751	
Lowell	72745	
Luber	72551	
Luxora	72358	
Lynn	72440	
Mabelvale	72103	
Macks, R. Br. Newport	72113	
Madison	72359	
Magazine	72943	
Magness	72553	
Magnolia (1st)	71753	
Main Street, Sta. North Little Rock	72119	
Malvern (1st)	72104	
Jones Mill, R. Br.	72105	
Mammoth Spring	72554	
Manila	72442	
Manning	71757	
Mansfield	72944	
Marble	72746	
Marcella	72555	
Marianna (1st)	72360	
Marion	72364	
Marked Tree	72365	
Marmaduke	72443	
Lafe, R. Br.	72436	
Marsena	72649	
Marshall	72650	
Bigflat, R. Br.	72617	
Snowball, R. Br.	72676	
Marvell	72366	
Mayflower	72106	
Maynard	72444	
Maysville	72747	
Mc Caskill	71847	
Mc Crory	72101	
Mc Dougal	72441	
Mc Gehee (1st)	71654	
Mc Hue	72552	
Mc Nab	71849	
Mc Neil	71752	
Mc Rae	72102	
Melbourne	72556	
Mellwood	72367	
Mena (1st)	71953	
Menifee	72107	
Midland	72945	
Midway	72651	
Mineral Springs	71851	
Minturn	72445	
Moko	72557	
Monette	72447	
Monroe	72108	
Monticello (1st)	71655	
Montrose	71658	
Moreland	72849	
Morganton	72109	
Moro	72368	
Morrilton (1st)	72110	
Morriston, R. Br. Salem	72559	
Morrow	72749	
Moscow	71659	
Mossville	72652	
Mount Holly	71758	
Mount Ida	71957	
Mount Judea	72655	
Mount Pleasant	72561	
Mount Vernon	72111	
Mountain Home (1st)	72653	
Mountain Pine	71956	
Mountain Top	72850	
Mountain View	72560	
Allison, R. Br.	72511	
Fiftysix, R. Br.	72533	
Newnata, R. Br.	72657	
Saint James, R. Br.	72574	
Mountainburg	72946	
Mulberry	72947	
Murfreesboro	71958	
Nail	72656	
Nashville (1st)	71852	
Natural Dam	72948	
Nettleton, Sta. Jonesboro	72401	
New Blaine	72851	
New Edinburg	71660	
Newark	72562	
Newburg	72563	
Newhope	71959	
Newnata, R. Br. Mountain View	72657	
Newport (1st)	72112	
Auvergne, R. Br.	72008	
Macks, R. Br.	72113	
Shoffner, R. Br.	72154	
Weldon, R. Br.	72177	
Nimmons	72448	
Norfork	72658	
Old Joe, R. Br.	72659	
Norman	71960	
Norphlet	71759	
North Cedar, Sta. Pine Bluff	71601	
NORTH LITTLE ROCK (1st) (see appendix)		
North Rural Branch, R. Br. Crossett	71635	
O'Kean	72449	
Oakgrove	72660	
Oakland	72661	
Oark	72852	
Oden	71961	
Ogden	71853	
Oil Trough	72564	
Okay	71854	
Okolona	71962	
Ola	72853	
Old Joe, R. Br. Norfork	72659	
Olmstead, R. Br. North Little Rock	72116	
Olyphant, R. Br. Bradford	72020	
Omaha	72662	
Oneida	72369	
Onia	72663	
Opal	71963	
Osage	72664	
Osceola (1st)	72370	
Ouachita College, Sta. Arkadelphia	71923	
Oxford	72565	
Ozan	71855	
Ozark (1st)	72949	
Ozone	72854	
Palestine	72372	
Pangburn	72121	
Paragould (1st)	72450	
Center Hill, R. Br.	72450	
Light, R. Br.	72439	
Paris	72855	
Park Hill, Sta. North Little Rock	72116	
Parkdale	71661	
Parkin	72373	
Parks	72950	
Paron	72122	
Parthenon	72666	
Patmos	71856	
Patrick	72750	
Patterson	72123	
Payneway, R. Br. Trumann	72472	
Pea Ridge	72751	
Peach Orchard	72453	
Pearcy	71964	
Peel	72668	
Pelsor	72856	
Pencil Bluff	71965	
Perla	72124	
Perry	72125	
Perrytown, R. Br. Hope	71801	
Perryville	72126	
Pettigrew	72752	
Philander Smith College, Sta. Little Rock	72203	
Pickens	71662	
Piggott	72454	
Pindall	72669	
Pine Bluff (1st)	71601	
Pine Ridge	71966	
Pinecrest, Br. Pine Bluff	71601	
Pineville	72566	
Plainview	72857	
Pleasant Grove	72567	
Pleasant Plains	72568	
Plumerville	72127	
Pocahontas (1st)	72455	
Warm Springs, R. Br.	72478	
Pollard	72456	
Ponca	72670	
Poplar Grove	72374	
Portia	72457	
Portland	71663	
Postelle	72375	
Pottsville	72858	
Poughkeepsie	72569	
Powhatan	72458	
Poyen	72128	
Prairie Grove	72753	
Prairie View, R. Br. Scranton	72859	
Prattsville	72129	
Prescott (1st)	71857	
Prim	72130	
Princeton, R. Br. Carthage	71761	
Proctor	72376	
Pruitt	72671	
Pyatt	72672	
Quitman	72131	
Ratcliff	72951	
Ravenden	72459	
Ravenden Springs	72460	
Reader, R. Br. Chidester	71726	
Readland	71664	
Rector	72461	
Redfield	72132	
Reed, R. Br. Tillar	71670	

Reydell	72133
Reyno	72462
Rison	71665
Rivervale	72377
Rockwell, R. Br. Hot Springs National Park	71901
Rodney	72570
Roe	72134
Rogers (1st)	72756
Rohwer	71666
Roland	72135
Rolla	71967
Romance	72136
Rose Bud	72137
Rose City, Sta. North Little Rock	72117
Roseland	72463
Rosie	72571
Rosston	71858
Round Pond	72378
Rover	72860
Royal	71968
Crystal Springs, R. Br.	71938
Rudy	72952
Rule	72673
Russell	72139
Russellville (1st)	72801
Saffell	72572
Sage	72573
Saint Charles	72140
Saint Francis	72464
Saint James, R. Br. Mountain View	72574
Saint Joe	72675
Saint Paul	72760
Salado	72575
Salem	72576
Morriston, R. Br.	72559
Salus	72861
Saratoga	71859
Scotland	72141
Scott	72142
Scottsville	72862
Scranton	72863
Prairie View, R. Br.	72859
Searcy (1st)	72143
Sedgwick	72465
Sheridan (1st)	72150
Sherrill	72152
Sherwood, Br. North Little Rock	72116
Shirley (1st)	72153
Shoffner, R. Br. Newport	72154
Sidney	72577
Sidon	72155
Siloam Springs (1st)	72761
Sims	71969
Smackover	71762
Smithville	72466
Snow Lake	72379
Snowball, R. Br. Marshall	72676
Solgohachia	72156
South Fort Smith, Sta. Fort Smith	72901
South Side, Sta. Little Rock	72206
Southern State College, Sta. Magnolia	71753

Sparkman	71763
Holly Springs, R. Br.	71746
Springdale (1st)	72764
Springfield	72157
Springtown	72767
Stamps	71860
Star City (1st)	71667
State Capitol, Sta. Little Rock	72201
State College Of Arkansas, Sta. Conway	72032
State Hospital	72158
State University	72467
Stephens	71764
Steprock	72159
Steve	72864
Stonewall	72468
Story	71970
Strawberry	72469
Calamine, R. Br.	72418
Strong	71765
Sturkie	72578
Stuttgart (1st)	72160
Subiaco	72865
Success	72470
Sulphur Rock	72579
Sulphur Springs	72768
Summers	72769
Summit	72677
Sweet Home	72164
Swifton	72471
Tamo, R. Br. Grady	71644
Taylor	71861
Tech, Br. Russellville	72801
Texarkana (1st)	75501
Thida	72165
Thornton	71766
Tichnor	72166
Tillar	71670
Tilly	72679
Tilton	72380
Timbo	72680
Tinsman	71767
Tomato	72381
Tontitown	72770
Traskwood	72167
Trumann (1st)	72472
Tucker	72168
Tuckerman	72473
Tull, R. Br. Benton	72015
Tulot	72483
Tumbling Shoals	72581
Tupelo	72169
Turner	72383
Turrell	72384
Twist	72385
Tyronza	72386
Ulm	72170
Umpire	71971
Union	72582
Uniontown	72955
Urbana	71768
Urbanette	72681
Valley Springs	72682
Van	72172
Van Buren (1st)	72956
Vandervoort	71972

Vanndale	72387
Vendor	72683
Veterans Administration Fac, Br. North Little Rock	72114
Victoria	72388
Village	71769
Vilonia	72173
Viola	72583
Violet Hill	72584
Wabash	72389
Wabbaseka	72175
Walcott	72474
Waldenburg	72475
Waldo	71770
Waldron	72958
Walnut Ridge (1st)	72476
Ward	72176
Warm Springs, R. Br. Pocahontas	72478
Warren (1st)	71671
Washington	71862
Watson	71674
Waveland	72867
Wayton	72684
Weathers	72772
Weiner	72479
Weldon, R. Br. Newport	72177
Wesley	72773
West Fork	72774
West Helena (1st)	72390
West Memphis (1st)	72301
West Point	72178
West Ridge	72391
Western Grove	72685
Wheatley	72392
Wheeler	72775
Whelen Springs	71772
White Hall, Br. Pine Bluff	71601
Wickes	71973
Wideman	72585
Widener	72394
Wilburn	72179
Williford	72482
Willisville	71864
Wilmar	71675
Wilmot	71676
Wilson	72395
Wilton	71865
Winchester	71677
Wing	72868
Winslow	72959
Winthrop	71866
Wiseman	72587
Witter	72776
Witts Springs	72686
Wolf Bayou	72588
Woodson	72180
Wooster	72181
Wright	72182
Wrightsville	72183
Wynne (1st)	72396
Fair Oaks, R. Br.	72397
Yellville	72687
Yorktown	71678
Zinc	72688
Zion	72589

LITTLE ROCK   722

POST OFFICE BOXES

Box Nos.

1-3864	Main Office	03
4001-4584	Asher Sta	04
5001-5199	Hillcrest Station	05
5200-5999	Brady Station	05
6001-6319	South Side Sta.	06
7201-7594	Forest Park Sta.	07
9001-9999	Industrial Sta.	09

RURAL ROUTES

1	04
2	06
3	05
4	06
5	07

STATIONS, BRANCHES AND UNITS

Asher Sta	04
Brady Sta	05
Ferndale Rural Br	08
Forest Park Sta	07
Hillcrest Sta	05
Industrial Sta	09
Philander Smith College Sta.	03
South Side Sta	06
State Capitol Sta	01
General Delivery	01
Postmaster	01

BUILDINGS

Adkins, 115 E Capitol	0
Albert Pike Memorial Temple, 700 Scott	01
Arkansas Education Association, 1500 W 4th	01
Baptist Medical Arts, 1120 Marshall	02
Baptist, 525 W. Capitol	01
Boyle, 103 W Capitol	01
Commercial National Bank, 200 Main	01
Commercial Warehouse, 1800 E 26th	06

Little Rock (Con.)   722

Cotton Exchange, 202 E 2nd	01
Doctors, 500 So University St	05
Donaghey, 103 E 7th	01
Dyke, 309 Center	01
Elrock, 1015 Louisiana St	02
Exchange, 106 E Capitol	01
Farm Bureau, 7th & High	02
Fausett, Markham & University	05
First Federal Savings, 312 Louisiana	01
Gazette, 118 W 3rd	01
Hall, 209 W Capitol	01
Justice, Capitol Grounds	01
Little Rock Public Library, 7th & Louisiana	01
Mart, Cantrell & Cedar Hill	02
National Investors Life, 2nd & Broadway	01
National Old Line, Capitol & Woodlone	01
Pulaski Federal Savings, 410 W 3rd	01
Pyramid, 221 W 2nd	01
Rector, 409 W 3rd	01
Reed, 112 E 7th	01
Southern Equitable, 3rd & Center	01
State Capitol, 5th & Woodlane	01
Stephens, 114 E Capitol	01
Terminal Warehouse, 500 E Markham	01
Tower, 4th & Center	01
Union Life, 212 Center	01
Union National Bank, 124 W. Capitol	01
Union Station, Markham & Victory St	01
University Tower, 1200 So University St	04
Waldon, 110 E 7th	01
Wallace, 105 S Main	01
Worthen Bank, 200 W. Capitol	01
Worthern Motor Bank, 4th & Scott	01

GOVERNMENT OFFICES

City Hall, Markham & Broadway	01

Little Rock (Con.)   722

County Court House, 405 W. Markham	01
Federal Offices Building, 700 W. Capitol	01
Police Department, 700 W Markham	01
U.s. Post Office & Court House Building, 600 W. Capitol	01

NORTH LITTLE ROCK   721

POST OFFICE BOXES

Box Nos.

1-277	Levy Sta	18
1-1189	North Little Rock	15
3001-3114	Rose City Sta	17
4001-4220	Park Hill Sta	16
5001-5851	Main St Sta	19
6001-6115	Sherwood	16

RURAL ROUTES

1	17
2	18
3	16
4	17
6	18

STATIONS, BRANCHES AND UNITS

Main Street Sta	19
Olmstead Rural Br	16
Park Hill Sta	16
Rose City Sta	17
Sherwood Br	16
Veterans Administration Fac Br	14
General Delivery	14
Postmaster	14

APARTMENTS, HOTELS, MOTELS

Campus Towers	14
East Gate Ter	14
Heritage House	14
Lakewood House	16
Shorter College Gardens	14
Willow House, 2500 Willow	14

CALIFORNIA
(Abbreviation: CA)

Acampo...95220
Acton..93510
Adelanto...92301
Adin..96006
Agnew, Sta. Santa Clara......95054
Agoura..91301
Agua Caliente Springs, R.
  Br. Julian...................................92036
Agua Dulce, R. Br. Saugus.....91350
Aguanga...92302
Ahwahnee.......................................93601
Airport, Sta. Ontario..................91761
Airport, Br. San Francisco......94128
Airport, Sta. Oakland..............94614
Al Tahoe, Sta. South Lake
  Tahoe.......................................95705
Alameda (1st)...............................94501
Alamo (1st)....................................94507
Albany, Br. Berkeley (see
  appendix)
Albion...95410
Alderpoint......................................95411
ALHAMBRA (1st) (see
  appendix)
Alisal, Sta. Salinas.................93901
All American, Sta. Cupertino..95014
Alleghany.......................................95910
Almanor, R. Br. Greenville....95911
Alondra, Br. Gardena..............90249
Alpaugh..93201
Alpine...92001
Alta...95701
Alta Loma.......................................91701
Altadena (1st)................................91001
Altaville...95221
Alturas (1st)...................................96101
Alvarado, Sta. Union City......94587
Alviso...95002
Amador City....................................95601
Ambassador, Sta. Los
  Angeles....................................90070
Amboy...92304
American Canyon, Br.
  Vallejo.....................................94590
Amphibious Base, Br. San
  Diego.......................................92155
ANAHEIM (1st) (see
  appendix)
Anderson (1st)...............................96007
Andrew Jackson, Sta. San
  Diego.......................................92115
Angels Camp...................................95222
Angelus Oaks.................................92305
Angwin (1st)...................................94508
  Deer Park, Br........................94576
Annapolis..95412
Antelope...95602
Antioch (1st)..................................94509
Anza..92306
Apple Valley (1st)...........................92307
Applegate.......................................95703
Aptos (1st).....................................95003
Arbuckle...95912
Arcade, Sta. Los Angeles......90052
Arcadia (1st)..................................91006
Arcata (1st)....................................95521
Arden, Br. Sacramento............95825
Argus, Br. Trona............................93562
Arlanza Village, Sta.
  Riverside..................................92505

Arleta, Sta. Pacoima...............91331
Arlington, Sta. Riverside......92503
Armona..93202
Army Terminal, Sta.
  Oakland...................................94626
Arnold...95223
  Bear Valley, R. Br..............95223
  Camp Connell, R. Br...........95223
  Lake Alpine, R. Br..............95235
Aromas..95004
Arroyo, Sta. Walnut Creek....94598
Arroyo Grande (1st)........................93420
Artesia (1st)...................................90701
Artois..95913
Arvin (1st)......................................93203
Ashlan Park, Sta. Fresno......93726
Asti...95413
Atascadero (1st)............................93422
Atherton, Br. Menlo Park......94025
Atwater (1st)..................................95301
Atwood..92601
Auberry...93602
Auburn (1st)...................................95603
Avalon...90704
Avenal...93204
Avery..95224
Avila Beach....................................93424
Azusa (1st).....................................91702
Baden, Sta. South San
  Francisco.................................94080
Badger, R. Br. Miramonte......93603
Bailey, Sta. Whittier (see
  appendix)
Baker..92309
BAKERSFIELD (1st) (see
  appendix)
Balboa, Sta. Newport Beach...92661
Balboa Island, Sta. Newport
  Beach.......................................92662
Baldwin Park (1st)...........................91706
Ballico..95303
Ballroad, Sta. Cypress...........90630
Bangor...95914
Banning (1st)..................................92220
Banta, Br. Tracy.............................95304
Bard..92222
Barrington, Sta. Los
  Angeles....................................90049
Barstow (1st)..................................92311
Barton, Sta. Fresno.....................93702
Base Line, Sta. San
  Bernardino................................92410
Bass Lake.......................................93604
Bassett, Br. La Puente...........91746
Baxter...95704
Bay, Sta. Big Bear Lake..........92315
Bay View, Sta. San
  Francisco.................................94124
Bay-Osos, Br. San Luis
  Obispo......................................93401
Bayliss, R. Br. Glenn...............95943
Bayside...95524
Beach Center, Sta.
  Huntington Beach...................92648
Beale A F B, Br. Marysville....95903
Bear River Lake, R. Br.
  Pioneer....................................95666
Bear Valley, R. Br. Arnold......95223
Beaumont (1st)...............................92223
Beckwourth, R. Br. Portola......96129
Belden..95915
Bell (1st)..90201
Bell, Sta. Merced.........................95340

Bell Gardens, Br. Bell...........90201
Bella Vista.....................................96008
Bellflower (1st)..............................90706
Belmont (1st).................................94002
Belvedere-Tiburon (1st)..............94920
Ben Lomond....................................95005
Bendix, Sta. North
  Hollywood................................91605
Benicia (1st)..................................94510
Benton..93512
BERKELEY (1st) (see
  appendix)
Bermuda Dunes, R. Br.
  Indio...92201
Bernal, Sta. San Francisco....94110
Berry Creek....................................95916
Berwick, Br. Carmel.................93921
Bethel Island................................94511
BEVERLY HILLS (1st) (see
  appendix)
Bieber...96009
Big Bar..96010
Big Basin, R. Br. Boulder
  Creek.......................................95006
Big Bear City..................................92314
  Sugarloaf, R. Br...................92386
Big Bear Lake (1st)........................92315
Big Bend...96011
Big Creek..93605
  Cedar Crest, R. Br................93605
  Huntington Lake, R. Br.......93629
Big Oak Flat...................................95305
Big Pine..93513
Big Sur..93920
Biggs..95917
Biola...93606
Birds Landing................................94512
Bishop (1st)....................................93514
Bixby, Sta. Long Beach............90807
Blairsden..96103
  Cromberg, R. Br...................96103
  Graeagle, R. Br....................96103
  Sloat, R. Br..........................96127
Blocksburg.....................................95414
Bloomington (1st)...........................92316
Blossom Hill, Sta. San Jose...95123
Blossom Valley, Sta.
  Mountain View.......................94040
Blue Jay..92317
Blue Lake..95525
Blythe (1st)....................................92225
Bodega..94922
Bodega Bay.....................................94923
Bodfish...93205
Bolinas..94924
Bolsa, Sta. Westminster........92683
Bonita...92002
Bonsall...92003
Boonville...95415
Boron..93516
Borrego Springs............................92004
Bostonia, Sta. El Cajon..........92021
Boulder Creek................................95006
Boulevard.......................................92005
Bowman, Br. Auburn................95603
Boyes Hot Springs........................95416
Boyle, Sta. Los Angeles.........90033
Boys Republic, R. Br. Chino...91710
Bradbury, Br. Duarte...............91010
Bradford, Sta. Hayward..........94541
Bradley...93426
Brandeis, R. Br. Simi Valley...93064
Branscomb......................................95417

Brawley (1st) 92227
　Glamis, R. Br. 92248
Brea (1st) 92621
Brentwood (1st) 94513
Bridgeport 93517
Bridgeville 95526
Briggs, Sta. Los Angeles 90048
Brisbane (1st) 94005
Bristol, Sta. Santa Ana 92703
Broadway, Sta. Sacramento ...95818
Broadway Manchester, Sta.
　Los Angeles 90003
Broderick 95605
Brookdale 95007
Brookhurst Center, Sta.
　Anaheim 92804
Brooks 95606
Browns Valley 95918
Brownsville 95919
Bryant, Sta. Long Beach 90815
Bryn Mawr 92318
Bryte, Br. Broderick 95605
Buellton 93427
BUENA PARK (1st) (see
　appendix)
BURBANK (1st) (see
　appendix)
Burlingame (1st) 94010
Burney 96013
Burnt Ranch 95527
　Denny, R. Br. 95535
Burrel 93607
Burson 95225
Butte City 95920
Butte Meadows, R. Br.
　Chico 95921
Buttonwillow 93206
Byron 94514
Cabazon 92230
Cabrillo, Sta. Long Beach 90810
Cachuma, R. Br. Santa
　Barbara 93101
Cadiz 92319
Calabasas (1st) 91302
Calabasas Park, Br.
　Calabasas 91302
Calexico (1st) 92231
Caliente 93518
California City, Br. Mojave 93501
California Hot Springs 93207
California Valley, R. Br.
　Santa Margarita 93453
Calimesa (1st) 92320
Calipatria 92233
Calistoga 94515
Callahan 96014
Calpella, Br. Ukiah 95418
Calpine, R. Sta. Sattley 96124
Calwa, Br. Fresno (see
　appendix)
Camarillo (1st) 93010
Cambria 93428
Cambrian Park, Br. San Jose
　(see appendix)
Camellia Station. Sta.
　Sacramento 95819
Camino 95709
Camp Connell, R. Br. Arnold ..95223
Camp Kaweah, Br. Sequoia
　National Park 93262
Camp Meeker 95419
Camp Nelson, R. Br.
　Springville 93208

Camp Pendleton, Br.
　Oceanside 92055
Camp Richardson, R. Br.
　South Lake Tahoe 95705
Campbell (1st) 95008
Campo 92006
Campo Seco, R. Br. Valley
　Springs 95226
Camptonville 95922
Canby 96015
Canoga Annex, Sta. Canoga
　Park 91304
CANOGA PARK (1st) (see
　appendix)
Cantil 93519
Cantua Creek 93608
Canyon 94516
Canyon Country, Br. Saugus ...91350
Canyon Crest, Sta.
　Riverside 92507
Canyondam 95923
Capay 95607
Capistrano Beach, Br. San
　Clemente 92624
Capitola (1st) 95010
Cardiff By The Sea 92007
Cardwell, Sta. Fresno (see
　appendix)
Caribou, R. Br. Belden 95915
Carlotta 95528
Carlsbad (1st) 92008
Carmel (1st) 93921
Carmel Rancho, Br. Carmel 93921
Carmel Valley 93924
Carmichael (1st) 95608
Carnelian Bay 95711
Carpinteria 93013
Carson, Br. Wilmington 90746
Carson, Br. Wilmington 90745
Cartago 93520
Caruthers 93609
Carwood, Sta. Lakewood 90713
Casa Blanca, Sta. Riverside 92504
Casa Correo, Sta. Concord 94521
Casmalia 93429
Caspar, R. Br. Fort Bragg 95420
Cassel 96016
Castaic 91310
Castella 96017
Castle A F B, Br. Merced 95342
Castro Valley, Br. Hayward 94546
Castroville 95012
Catalina, Sta. Pasadena 91106
Cathedral City (1st) 92234
Catheys Valley 95306
Cayucos 93430
Cazadero 95421
Cecilville 96018
Cedar, Sta. Lancaster 93534
Cedar Crest, R. Br. Big
　Creek 93605
Cedar Glen 92321
Cedar Ridge 95924
Cedarpines Park 92322
Cedarville 96104
Central District, Sta.
　Pomona (see appendix)
Central Valley 96019
Centre, Sta. Sacramento 95860
Century City, Sta. Los
　Angeles (see appendix)
Ceres (1st) 95307
Cerritos, Br. Artesia 90701

Challenge 95925
Charter Oak, Br. Covina 91722
Chatsworth (1st) 91311
Cherry Valley, R. Br.
　Beaumont 92223
Chester 96020
Chicago Park 95712
Chico (1st) 95926
　Butte Meadows, R. Br. 95921
　Midtown, Sta. 95926
　Richardson Springs, R.
　　Br. 95973
Chilcoot 96105
Childrens Fairyland, Sta.
　Oakland 94622
China, Sta. San Francisco 94108
China Lake, Br. Ridgecrest 93555
Chinese Camp 95309
Chino (1st) 91710
Chiriaco Summit, R. Br.
　Indio 92201
Cholame 93431
Chowchilla (1st) 93610
Chualar 93925
CHULA VISTA (1st) (see
　appendix)
Cima 92323
Cimarron, Sta. Los Angeles 90018
Citrus Heights (1st) 95610
City Hall, Sta. San
　Francisco 94102
City Of Commerce, Sta. Los
　Angeles (see appendix)
City Of Industry, Br. La
　Puente 91744
City Terrace, Sta. Los
　Angeles (see appendix)
Civic Center, Br. San Rafael ..94903
Civic Center, Sta. Oakland 94604
Claremont (1st) 91711
Clarksburg 95612
Clayton 94517
Clearlake Highlands 95422
Clearlake Oaks 95423
Clearlake Park 95424
Clements 95227
Clinter, Sta. Fresno 93703
Clio 96106
Clipper Mills 95930
Cloverdale (1st) 95425
Clovis (1st) 93612
Coarfella (1st) 92236
Coalinga (1st) 93210
Coarsegold 93614
Cobb 95426
　Hobergs, R. Br. 95496
　Loch Lomond, R. Br. 95426
Coddingtown, Sta. Santa
　Rosa 95406
Cole, Br. Los Angeles 90046
Coleville 96107
Colfax 95713
College Center, Br.
　Bakersfield 93306
College City 95931
College Grove Center, Sta.
　San Diego 92115
Collier, Sta. Canoga Park 91304
Colma, Sta. Daly City 94014
Coloma 95613
Colonial, Sta. Sacramento
　(see appendix)

Colton (1st) 92324
Columbia 95310
Colusa (1st) 95932
Commonwealth, Sta.
  Fullerton 92632
Comptche 95427
COMPTON (1st) (see
  appendix)
CONCORD (1st) (see
  appendix)
Cool 95614
Copperopolis 95228
Corcoran (1st) 93212
Cornell, R. Sta. Agoura 91301
Corning (1st) 96021
  Flournoy, R. Br. 96029
Corona (1st) 91720
Corona Del Mar (1st) 92625
Coronado, Br. San Diego 92118
Corralitos, Br. Watsonville ..95076
Corte Madera (1st) 94925
COSTA MESA (1st) (see
  appendix)
Cotati (1st) 94928
Cottonwood 96022
  Manzanita Lake, R. Br. ..96060
Coulterville 95311
Court, Sta. Martinez 94553
Courtland 95615
Covelo 95428
Covina (1st) 91722
Coyote 95013
Crenshaw, Sta. Los Angeles
  (see appendix)
Crenshaw Imperial, Sta.
  Inglewood (see appendix)
Crescent City (1st) 95531
Crescent Mills 95934
Cressey 95312
Crest Park 92326
Cresta Blanca, R. Br.
  Livermore 94550
Crestline 92325
Creston 93432
Crockett (1st) 94525
Cromberg, R. Br. Blairsden ..96103
Crows Landing 95313
Cucamonga (1st) 91730
Cudahy, Br. Bell 90201
Culver City (1st) 90230
Cummings, R. Br. Willits 95477
Cupertino (1st) 95014
Curry Village, Br. Yosemite
  National Park 95389
Cutler 93615
Cutten 95534
Cuyama 93214
Cypress (1st) 90630
Daggett 92327
Dairy Farm, R. Br. Vallejo 94590
DALY CITY (1st) (see
  appendix)
Dana Point (1st) 92629
Danville (1st) 94526
Dardanelle, R. Br. Pinecrest ..95314
Darwin 93522
Davenport 95017
Davis (1st) 95616
  El Macero, R. Br. 95618
  U C D, Br. 95616
Davis Creek 96108
Death Valley 92328
Death Valley Junction, R. Br.

Death Valley 92328
Deer Park, Br. Angwin 94576
Del Mar (1st) 92014
Del Mar Heights, R Sta.
  Morro Bay 93442
Del Monte Park, Br. Pacific
  Grove 93950
Del Paso Heights, Sta.
  Sacramento 95838
Del Rey 93616
Del Rey Oaks, Br. Monterey ..93940
Del Rosa, Br. San
  Bernardino 92404
Del Valle, Sta. Los Angeles ..90015
Delano (1st) 93215
Delevan, R Br. Willows 95988
Delhi 95315
Delkern, R. Br. Bakersfield ..93309
Delta, Sta Stockton (see
  appendix)
Denair 95316
Denny, R. Br. Burnt Ranch ..95535
Descanso 92016
Desert Center 92239
Desert Hot Springs (1st) 92240
Di Giorgio 93217
Diablo 94528
Diamond, Sta. Santa Ana 92704
Diamond Bar, Br. Pomona 91765
Diamond Heights, Sta San
  Francisco 94131
Diamond Springs 95619
Dillon Beach 94929
Dimond, Sta. Oakland 94602
Dinkey Creek, R. Br. Shaver
  Lake 93617
Dinuba (1st) 93618
Dixon (1st) 95620
Dobbins 95935
Dockweiler, Sta. Los
  Angeles 90007
Dollar Ranch, Sta. Walnut
  Creek 94595
Domingues Hills, Br.
  Gardena 90247
Dorris 96023
Dos Palos (1st) 93620
Dos Rios, R Br. Willits 95429
Douglas, Sta. Santa Monica ..90405
Douglas City 96024
Douglas Flat. R. Br. Vallecito ..95229
DOWNEY (1st) (see
  appendix)
Downieville 95936
Downtown, Sta. Burbank 91503
Downtown, Sta. San
  Bernardino 92403
Downtown, Sta. Redwood
  City 94063
Downtown, Sta. Manhattan
  Beach 90266
Doyle 96109
Drytown, R. Br. Sutter Creek ..95699
Duarte (1st) 91010
Dublin, Br. Pleasanton 94566
Ducor 93218
Dulzura 92017
Duncans Mills 95430
Dunlap 93621
Dunnigan 95937
Dunsmuir 96025
Durham 95938
Dutch Flat 95714

Dutch Village, Sta.
  Lakewood 90713
Eagle Mountain 92241
Eagle Rock, Sta. Los
  Angeles (see appendix)
Eagleville 96110
Earlimart 93219
Earp 92242
East Compton, Sta.
  Compton 90220
East Fresno, Br. Fresno 93727
East Highlands 92329
East Irvine 92650
East Long Beach, Sta. Long
  Beach 90804
East Los Angeles. Br. Los
  Angeles (see appendix)
East Lynwood, Sta. Lynwood ..90262
East Nicolaus 95622
East Palo Alto, Sta. Palo
  Alto (see appendix)
East Pasadena, Sta.
  Pasadena 91107
East San Diego, Sta. San
  Diego 92105
East Santa Cruz, Sta. Santa
  Cruz 95060
East Stockton, Sta. Stockton ..95205
East Ventura, Sta. Ventura ..93003
Eastgate, Sta. Fresno 93702
Eastmont, Sta. Oakland 94605
Easton, R. Br. Fresno 93706
Eastside, Sta San
  Bernardino 92410
Echo Lake, R. Br. Little
  Norway 95721
Edendale, Sta. Los Angeles
  (see appendix)
Edgemont, Br. Riverside 92508
Edgewood, R. Br. Weed 96094
Edison 93220
Edwards (1st) 93523
Edwards Air Force Base,
  Sta. Edwards 93523
EL CAJON (1st) (see
  appendix)
El Camino College. Br.
  Torrance 90506
El Centro (1st) 92243
  Plaster City. R. Br. 92269
El Cerrito (1st) 94530
El Dorado 95623
El Dorado Hills, R. Br.
  Folsom 95630
El Granada 94018
El Macero, R. Br. Davis 95618
El Modena, Sta. Orange 92667
EL MONTE (1st) (see
  appendix)
El Nido 95317
El Portal 95318
El Segundo (1st) 90245
El Sereno, Sta. Los Angeles
  (see appendix)
El Sobrante, Br. Richmond ..94803
El Toro (1st) 92630
El Toro Marine Corp Air Sta,
  Br. Santa Ana 92709
El Verano 95433
El Viejo Sta. Modesto (see
  appendix)
Eldridge 95431

Elk	95432
Elk Creek	95939
Elk Grove (1st)	95624
Elmhurst, Sta. Oakland	94603
Elmira	95625
Elmwood, Sta. Berkeley (see appendix)	
Elsinore (1st)	92330
Elverta	95626
Emeryville, Br. Oakland	94608
Emigrant Gap	95715
Empire	95319
Encanto, Sta. San Diego (see appendix)	
Encinal, Sta. Sunnyvale	94087
Encinitas (1st)	92024
Encino, Br. Van Nuys	91316
Enterprise, Br. Redding	96001
Escalon (1st)	95320
ESCONDIDO (1st) (see appendix)	
Esparto	95627
Essex	92332
Estudillo, Sta. San Leandro	94577
Etiwanda	91739
Etna	96027
Eureka (1st)	95501
A., Sta.	95501
Henderson, Sta.	95501
Myrtletowne, Br.	95501
Evergreen, Br. Santa Maria	93454
Exeter (1st)	93221
Fair Oaks (1st)	95628
Fairfax (1st)	94930
Fairfield (1st)	94533
Travis A F B, Sta	94535
Fairmount, Sta. El Cerrito	94530
Fairview, Br. Goleta	93017
Fall River Mills	96028
Glenburn, R. Br.	96036
Fallbrook (1st)	92028
Fallen Leaf, R. Br. South Lake Tahoe	95716
Fallon, R. Br. Tomales	94932
Fancher, Br. Fresno	93702
Farmers Market, Sta. Los Angeles	90036
Farmersville	93223
Farmington	95230
Fawnskin	92333
Feather Falls	95940
Federal, Sta. Covina	91722
Federal, Sta. Anaheim	92805
Federal Annex, Sta. Oxnard	93030
Federal Terrace, Br. Vallejo	94590
Fellows	93224
Felton (1st)	95018
Fenner	92334
Fernbridge, R. Br. Fortuna	95540
Ferndale	95536
Fiddletown	95629
Fields Landing	95537
Fig Garden Village, Br. Fresno	93704
Figueroa, Sta. Altadena	91001
Fillmore (1st)	93015
Finley	95435
Firebaugh	93622
Firestone, Sta. South Gate	90280
First Street, Sta. Oceanside	92054
Fish Camp	93623
Fisk, Sta. San Francisco	94122

Fitchburg, Sta. Oakland	94621
Five Points	93624
Fleet, Sta. San Diego	92132
Fleetwood Annex, Br. Covina	91722
Fletcher Hills, Sta. El Cajon	92020
Florence, Br. Los Angeles (see appendix)	
Florin, Br. Sacramento (see appendix)	
Floriston	96111
Flournoy, R. Br. Corning	96029
Folsom (1st)	95630
Fontana (1st)	92335
Foothill Center, Sta. Azusa	91702
Foothill Farms, Br. Sacramento (see appendix)	
Forbestown	95941
Forest Falls	92339
Forest Glen, R. Br. Hayfork	96030
Forest Knolls	94933
Forest Ranch	95942
Foresthill	95631
Forestville	95436
Forks Of Salmon	96031
Fort Baker, Br. Sausalito	94965
Fort Bidwell	96112
Fort Bragg (1st)	95437
Caspar, R. Br.	95420
Fort Dick	95538
Fort Irwin, Br. Barstow	92311
Fort Jones	96032
Fort Mac Arthur, Sta. San Pedro	90731
Fort Ord, Br. Monterey	93941
Fort Seward	95438
Fort Sutter, Sta. Sacramento	95816
Fortuna (1st)	95540
Foster City, Br. San Mateo	94404
Fountain Valley, Br. Santa Ana	92708
Fowler	93625
Foy, Sta. Los Angeles	90017
Franklin, Sta. Napa	94558
Frazier Park	93225
Freedom (1st)	95019
Freestone, R. Br. Sebastopol	95472
FREMONT (1st) (see appendix)	
French Camp	95231
French Gulch	96033
FRESNO (1st) (see appendix)	
Friant	93626
Frontera, R. Br. Corona	91720
Fruitvale, Sta. Oakland	94601
FULLERTON (1st) (see appendix)	
Fulton	95439
Gabilan, Sta. Salinas	93901
Galt (1st)	95632
Garberville	95440
GARDENA (1st) (see appendix)	
GARDEN GROVE (1st) (see appendix)	
Garden Valley	95633
Gasquet	95543
Gateway, Sta. Culver City	90230
Gaviota, R. Br. Goleta	93017
Gazelle	96034
Geary, Sta. San Francisco	94108

George A F B, Br. Victorville	92392
George Washington, Sta. San Diego	92102
Georgetown	95634
Gerber	96035
Geyserville	95441
Giant Forest, R. Sta. Sequoia National Park	93262
Gilman Hot Springs	92340
Gilroy (1st)	95020
Glamis, R. Br. Brawley	92248
Glassell, Sta. Los Angeles	90065
Glen Ellen	95442
Glenburn, R. Br. Fall River Mills	96036
Glencoe	95232
GLENDALE (1st) (see appendix)	
Glendora (1st)	91740
Glenhaven	95443
Glenn	95943
Glennville	93226
Gleneaks, Sta Burbank (see appendix)	
Gold Run	95717
Goleta (1st)	93017
Gonzales	93926
Goodyears Bar	95944
Gorman, R. Br. Lancaster	93534
Goshen	93227
Graeagle, R. Br. Blairsden	96103
Granada Hills, Br. San Fernando	91344
Grand Avenue, Sta. Elsinore	92330
Grand Central, Sta. Glendale	91201
Grand Lake, Sta. Oakland	94610
Grand Terrace, Br. Colton	92324
Grantville, Sta. San Diego (see appendix)	
Grass Valley (1st)	95945
Penn Valley, R. Br.	95946
Graton	95444
Green, Sta. Los Angeles	90037
Green Valley, R. Br. Saugus	91350
Green Valley Lake	92341
Greenacres, R. Br. Bakersfield	93308
Greenbrae, Br. San Rafael	94904
Greenfield	93927
Greenmead, Sta. Los Angeles	90059
Greenview	96037
Greenville	95947
Almanor, R. Br.	95911
Greenwood	95635
Grenada	96038
Gridley (1st)	95948
Griffith, Sta. Los Angeles	90039
Grimes	95950
Grizzly Flats	95636
Groveland	95321
Mather, R. Br.	95339
Grover City	93433
Guadalupe	93434
Gualala	95445
Guasti	91743
Guatay	92031
Guerneville	95446
Guernewood Park, R. Br.	95446
Rio Nido, R. Br.	95471
Guernewood Park, R. Br. Guerneville	95446

Guinda.............................95637
Gustine............................95322
Hacienda Heights, Br. La
  Puente.........................91745
Halcyon, Br. Arroyo Grande....93420
Half Moon Bay....................94019
Hamilton Air Force Base
  (1st)............................94934
Hamilton (1st)....................95951
Hancock, Sta. Los Angeles......90044
Hanford (1st).....................93230
Happy Camp........................96039
Harbor City (1st)................90710
Harder Annex, Sta. Hayward
  (see appendix)
Hardman Center, Sta.
  Riverside......................92504
Harmony...........................93435
Harris.............................95447
Hat Creek..........................96040
Hathaway Pines....................95233
Havasu Lake, R. Br.
  Needles........................92363
Hawaiian Gardens, Br.
  Lakewood (see appendix)
Hawthorne (1st)...................90250
Hayfork
  Forest Glen, R. Br...........96030
HAYWARD (1st) (see
  appendix)
Hazard, Br. Los Angeles.........90063
Healdsburg (1st)..................95448
Heber.............................92249
Helena, R. Br. Weaverville......96042
Helendale.........................92342
Helm..............................93627
Hemet (1st).......................92343
Henderson, Sta. Eureka...........95501
Herald............................95638
Hercules..........................94547
Herlong...........................96113
Hermosa Beach, Br.
  Redondo Beach..................90254
Herndon, R. Br. Fresno...........93721
Hesperia (1st)....................92345
Heyer, Br. Hayward................94541
Hickman...........................95323
Highgrove, Br. Riverside.........92507
Highland (1st)....................92346
Highland Park, Sta. Los
  Angeles (see appendix)
Highway City, Br. Fresno.........93705
Hillcrest, Sta. San Diego........92103
Hillcrest Center, Br.
  Bakersfield...................93306
Hillsborough, Br.
  Burlingame....................94010
Hillsdale, Sta. San Mateo........94403
Hilmar............................95324
Hilt..............................96043
Hinkley...........................92347
Hobergs, R. Br. Cobb.............95496
Hollister (1st)...................95023
Hollydale, Sta. South Gate.......90280
Hollywood, Sta. Los Angeles
  (see appendix)
Holt..............................95234
Holtville.........................92250
Holy City.........................95026
Homeland..........................92348
Homestead, Sta. Stockton.........95206
Homewood..........................95718
Honeydew..........................95545

Hood..............................95639
Hoopa.............................95546
Hope Valley, R. Br.
  Markleeville..................96139
Hopland...........................95449
Hornbrook.........................96044
Hornitos..........................95325
Horse Creek.......................96045
Hub City, Sta. Compton...........90220
Hudson, Sta. Modesto..............95354
Hughson...........................95326
Hume, R. Br. Miramonte............93628
Hunter Liggett, MOU. Jolon.......93928
Hunters Point, Sta. San
  Francisco.....................94135
HUNTINGTON BEACH (1st)
  (see appendix)
Huntington Lake, R. Br. Big
  Creek.........................93629
Huntington Park (1st).............90255
Huron.............................93234
Hyampom...........................96046
Hydesville........................95547
Idria.............................95027
Idyllwild.........................92349
Ignacio, Br. Novato...............94947
Igo...............................96047
Imola, Br. Napa...................94558
Imperial (1st)....................92251
Imperial Beach (1st)..............92032
Independence......................93526
Indian Wells, Br. Palm
  Desert........................92260
Indio (1st).......................92201
Industrial, Sta. Santa Ana.......92705
INGLEWOOD (1st) (see
  appendix)
Institute, Sta. Riverside........92503
Inverness.........................94937
Inyokern..........................93527
Ione..............................95640
Iowa Hill, R. Br. Colfax.........95713
Irvine, Br. Newport Beach.........92664
Irvington, Sta. Fremont..........94538
Irwindale, Br. Baldwin Park......91706
Isla Vista, Br. Goleta...........93017
Island Mountain, R. Br.
  Willits.......................95478
Isleton...........................95641
Italian Swiss Colony, R. Br.
  Madera........................93638
Ivanhoe...........................93235
Jackson (1st).....................95642
Jacumba...........................92034
Jamestown.........................95327
Jamul.............................92035
Janesville........................96114
  Wendel, R. Br................96136
Jenner............................95450
Johannesburg......................93528
John Adams, Sta. San Diego.......92116
Johnsondale.......................93236
Jolon.............................93928
Joshua Tree.......................92252
Julian............................92036
Junction City.....................96048
June Lake.........................93529
Kaiser Center, Sta. Oakland......94612
Kaweah............................93237
Kearny, Sta. Los Angeles.........90011
Keddie, R. Br. Quincy.............95952
Keeler............................93530

Keene.............................93531
Kelsey............................95643
Kelseyville.......................95451
Kelso.............................92351
Kensington, Br. Berkeley
  (see appendix)
Kentfield, Br. San Rafael........94904
Kenwood...........................95452
Kerman (1st)......................93630
Kern City, R. Br. Bakersfield....93309
Kernville.........................93238
Kester, Sta. Van Nuys (see
  appendix)
Kettleman City....................93239
Keyes.............................95328
King, Sta. Santa Ana.............92706
King City (1st)...................93930
Kings Beach.......................95719
Kings Canyon National Park,
  R. Br. Miramonte..............93633
Kingsburg (1st)...................93631
Kit Carson, R. Br. Pine
  Grove.........................95644
Klamath...........................95548
Klamath River.....................96050
Kneeland..........................95549
Knights Ferry, R. Br.
  Oakdale.......................95361
Knights Landing...................95645
Knightsen.........................94548
Korbel............................95550
Kyburz............................95720
La Canada (1st)...................91011
  Mount Wilson, R. Br..........91023
La Costa, Sta Malibu..............90265
La Crescenta, Sta. Glendale......91214
La Grange.........................95329
La Habra (1st)....................90631
La Honda..........................94020
La Jolla (1st)....................92037
La Mesa (1st).....................92041
La Mirada (1st)...................90638
La Palma, Br. Buena Park.........90620
La Porte, R. Br. Strawberry
  Valley........................95981
LA PUENTE (1st) (see
  appendix)
La Quinta.........................92253
La Selva Beach, R. Br.
  Watsonville...................95076
La Sierra, Sta. Riverside........92505
La Tijera, Sta. Los Angeles......90043
La Verne (1st)....................91750
La Vina, Sta. Altadena...........91001
Ladera, Br. Menlo Park...........94025
Ladera Heights, Sta. Los
  Angeles.......................90045
Lafayette (1st)...................94549
LAGUNA BEACH (1st) (see
  appendix)
Laguna Hills, Br. Laguna
  Beach.........................92653
Laguna Niguel, Br. Laguna
  Beach.........................92677
Lagunitas.........................94938
Lake Alpine, R. Br. Arnold.......95235
Lake Arrowhead....................92352
Lake City.........................96115
Lake Hughes.......................93532
Lake Isabella.....................93240
Lake Kirkwood, R. Br.
  Pioneer.......................95646

Lake San Marcos, Br. San
Marcos 92069
Lake View Terrace, Br. San
Fernando 91342
Lakehead 96051
O'Brien, R. Br. 96070
Lakeport (1st) 95453
Lakeshore 93634
Mono Hot Springs, R. Br. 93642
Lakeside (1st) 92040
Lakeview 92353
LAKEWOOD (1st) (see
appendix)
Lamont (1st) 93241
Lancaster (1st) 93534
Land Park, Sta. Sacramento
(see appendix)
Landers, R. Br. Yucca
Valley 92284
Landscape, Sta. Berkeley
(see appendix)
Larkfield, Br. Santa Rosa 95401
Larkspur 94939
Lathrop (1st) 95330
Laton 93242
Laurel, Sta. Oakland 94619
Lawndale (1st) 90260
Laytonville 95454
Le Grand 95333
Lebec 93243
Lee Vining 93541
Leggett 95455
Lemon Grove (1st) 92045
Lemoncove 93244
Lemoore (1st) 93245
Lennox, Br. Inglewood 90304
Lenwood, R. Br. Barstow 92311
Leona Valley, R. Br.
Palmdale 93550
Letterman, Sta. San
Francisco 94129
Leucadia, Br. Encinitas 92024
Lewiston 96052
Liberty Farms 95647
Likely 96116
Lincoln 95648
Lincoln Acres, Br. National
City 92047
Lincoln Heights, Sta. Los
Angeles (see appendix)
Lincoln Village, Br. Stockton...95207
Linda Vista, Sta. San Diego
(see appendix)
Linden 95236
Linden Avenue, Sta. South
San Francisco 94080
Lindsay (1st) 93247
Linnell, R. Br. Visalia 93277
Litchfield 96117
Little Lake 93542
Little Norway 95721
Little Valley, R. Br. Mc
Arthur 96053
Littleriver 95456
Littlerock 93543
Live Oak 95953
Livermore (1st) 94550
Livingston 95334
Llano 93544
Loch Lomond, R. Br. Cobb.....95426
Lockeford 95237

Lockheed S C T B, R. Br.
Santa Cruz 95060
Lockwood 93932
Lodi (1st) 95240
Loleta 95551
Loma, Sta. Long Beach (see
appendix)
Loma Linda (1st) 92354
Loma Mar 94021
Lomita (1st) 90717
Lompoc (1st) 93436
Vandenberg A F B, Br. 93437
London, R. Br. Dinuba 93618
Lone Pine 93545
Long Barn 95335
LONG BEACH (1st) (see
appendix)
Lookout 96054
Loomis 95650
Loop, Sta. South Gate 90280
Los Alamitos (1st) 90720
Los Alamos 93440
Los Altos (1st) 94022
Los Altos Hills, Br. Los
Altos 94022
Los Amigos, Sta. Downey 90240
LOS ANGELES (1st) (see
appendix)
Los Banos (1st) 93635
Los Feliz, Sta. Los Angeles 90027
Los Gatos (1st) 95030
Los Molinos 96055
Los Nietos, Br. Whittier 90606
Los Olivos 93441
Los Serranos, R. Br. Chino 91710
Lost Hills 93249
Lost Lake, R. Br. Blythe 92225
Lotus 95651
Lower Lake 95457
Loyalton 96118
Lucerne 95458
Lucerne Valley 92356
Ludlow 92357
Lugo, Sta. Los Angeles 90023
Lynwood (1st) 90262
Lytle Creek 92358
Macdoel 96058
Maclay, Sta. San Fernando 91340
Mad River 95552
Madeline 96119
Madera (1st) 93637
Italian Swiss Colony, R.
Br. 93638
Madison 95653
Magalia 95954
Magnolia Center, Sta.
Riverside 92506
Magnolia Park, Sta.
Burbank 91505
Malaga, Br. Fresno 93725
Malibu (1st) 90265
Mammoth Lakes 93546
Manchester 95459
Manhattan Beach (1st) 90266
Manteca (1st) 95336
Manton 96059
Manzanita Lake, R. Br.
Cottonwood 96060
Mar Corps Rct Dep, Sta.
San Diego 92140
Mar Vista, Sta. Los Angeles
, (see appendix)
Marcelina, Sta. Torrance 90501

March A F B, Br. Riverside 92508
Mare Island, Sta. Vallejo 94592
Maricopa 93252
Marin City, Br. Sausalito 94965
Marina, Sta. San Francisco 94123
Marina (1st) 93933
Marina Del Rey, Br. Venice 90291
Marine Corps Base, Br.
Twentynine Palms 92278
Marine Corps Supply Center,
Br. Barstow 92311
Mariposa 95338
Market, Sta. Los Angeles 90021
Markleeville 96120
Hope Valley, R. Br. 96139
Woodfords, R. Br. 96120
Marshall 94940
Martell 95654
Martinez (1st) 94553
Marysville (1st) 95901
Beale A F B, Br. 95903
Mather, R. Br. Groveland 95339
Mather A F B, Br.
Sacramento 95655
Maxwell 95955
Maywood (1st) 90270
Mc Arthur 96056
Little Valley, R. Br. 96053
Mc Clellan A F B, Br.
Sacramento 95652
Mc Cloud 96057
Mc Farland 93250
Mc Henry Village, Sta.
Modesto 95350
Mc Kinleyville, Br. Arcata 95521
Mc Kittrick 93251
Mc Laren, Sta. San
Francisco 94134
Mead Valley, R. Br. Perris 92370
Meadow Valley 95956
Meadow Vista 95722
Mecca 92254
Meeks Bay, R. Br. Tahoe
City 95723
Meiners Oaks, R. Br. Ojai 93023
Mendocino 95460
Mendota 93640
Menlo Park (1st) 94025
Mentone 92359
Merced (1st) 95340
Bell, Sta. 95340
Castle A F B, Sta. 95342
Red Top, R. Br. 95340
Meridian 95957
Merrill, Br. Fontana 92335
Mesa Center, Sta. Costa
Mesa 92627
Metro Main, Sta.
Sacramento 95801
Metropolitan, Sta. Los
Angeles (see appendix)
Mi-Wuk Village 95346
Mid City, Sta. Stockton 95202
Middlefield Road, Br.
Redwood City 94061
Middletown 95461
Midpines 95345
Midtown, Sta. Chico 95926
Midway City (1st) 92655
Milford 96121
Mill Creek 96061
Mill Valley (1st) 94941
Millbrae (1st) 94030

Mills, Sta. San Francisco......94104
Mills College, Sta. Oakland...94613
Millsdale, Sta. Burlingame....94010
Millville......................................96052
Milpas, Sta. Santa Barbara....93103
Milpitas (1st)..........................95035
Mineral.....................................96063
Mineralking, R. Br. Three
  Rivers...................................93253
Mira Loma...............................91752
Mira Vista, Sta. Richmond....94805
Miracle Hot Springs, R. Br.
  Bakersfield...........................93301
Miraleste, Br. San Pedro.....90732
Miramar, Br. San Diego......92145
Miramonte...............................93641
  Badger, R. Br.......................93603
  Hume, R. Br.........................93628
  Kings Canyon National
    Park, R. Br........................93633
Miranda...................................95553
Missile View, Br. Santa
  Maria...................................93454
Mission, Sta. Santa Clara......95051
Mission Hills, Br. San
  Fernando (see appendix)
Mission Rafael, Sta. San
  Rafael..................................94901
Mission San Jose, Sta.
  Fremont................................94538
Mission Viejo, Br. San Juan
  Capistrano............................92675
Moccasin.................................95347
MODESTO (1st) (see
  appendix)
Moffett Field (1st)..................94035
Mojave (1st)............................93501
Mokelumne Hill.......................95245
Mono Hot Springs, R. Br.
  Lakeshore.............................93642
Monolith..................................93548
Monrovia (1st).........................91016
Monta Vista, Br. Cupertino....95014
Montague.................................96064
Montalvo, Br. Ventura...........93003
Montara...................................94037
Montclair (1st).........................91763
Monte Rio................................95462
Monte Sereno, Br. Los Gatos..95030
Montebello (1st)......................90640
Montecito, Br. Santa
  Barbara.................................93103
Monterey (1st).........................93940
  Del Rey Oaks, Br................93940
  Fort Ord, Br........................93940
  Presidio Of Monterey,
    Sta....................................93940
  U S N Postgraduate
    School, Sta........................93940
Monterey Bay Academy, R.
  Br. Watsonville.....................95076
Monterey Park (1st).................91754
Montgomery Creek..................96055
Montgomery Village, Sta.
  Santa Rosa...........................95405
Montrose (1st).........................91020
Mooney, Sta. Visalia..............93277
Moorpark.................................93021
Mora Villa, Sta. Santa
  Barbara.................................93104
Moraga (1st)............................94556
Moreno....................................92360
Morgan Hill (1st).....................95037

Morningside Park, Sta.
  Inglewood.............................90305
Morongo Valley.......................92256
Morro Bay (1st).......................93442
Moss Beach..............................94038
Moss Landing...........................95039
Mount Baldy............................91759
Mount Eden (1st).....................94557
Mount Hamilton, R. Br. San
  Jose......................................95140
Mount Hebron..........................96066
Mount Hermon.........................95041
Mount Laguna..........................92048
Mount Shasta (1st)..................96067
Mount Wilson, R. Br. La
  Canada.................................91023
Mountain Center.......................92361
Mountain Mesa, R. Br. Lake
  Isabella................................93240
Mountain Pass, R. Br.
  Nipton...................................92366
Mountain Ranch........................95246
Mountain View (1st)................94040
Mt. Aukum...............................95066
Murphys...................................95247
Murrieta...................................92362
Muscoy, Br. San Bernardino...92405
Myers Flat................................95554
Myrtletowne, Br. Eureka.........95501
Napa (1st)...............................94558
National City (1st)...................92050
  Lincoln Acres, Br................92047
Naval, Sta. San Diego...........92136
Naval, Sta. Port Hueneme......93043
Naval Air Station, Br. San
  Diego....................................92135
Naval Air Station, Br.
  Alameda...............................94501
Naval Air Station, Br.
  Lemoore................................93245
Naval Hospital, Sta. San
  Diego....................................92134
Naval Hospital, Sta.
  Oakland................................94627
Naval Supply Center, Sta.
  Oakland................................94625
Naval Training Center, Sta.
  San Diego.............................92133
Navarro, R. Br. Philo............95463
Needles (1st)...........................92363
Nelson......................................95958
Nestor.....................................92053
Nevada City (1st)....................95959
New Almaden............................95042
New Cuyama.............................93254
Newark (1st)............................94560
Newberry Springs....................92365
Newbury Park, Br. Thousand
  Oaks.....................................91320
Newcastle................................95658
Newhall (1st)...........................91321
Newman....................................95360
NEWPORT BEACH (1st) (see
  appendix)
Nicasio....................................94946
Nice..95464
Nicolaus..................................95659
Niland.....................................92257
Niles, Sta. Fremont.................94536
Nipomo.....................................93444
Nipton.....................................92364
Noe Valley, Sta. San
  Francisco..............................94114

Norco (1st)..............................91760
Norden.....................................95724
North Annex, Br. San
  Fernando..............................91342
North Beach, Sta. San
  Francisco..............................94133
North Berkeley, Sta.
  Berkeley...............................94709
North Downey, Sta. Downey...90240
North Edwards, R. Sta.
  Edwards...............................93523
North Fork...............................93643
North Gardena, Br. Gardena...90247
North Glendale, Sta.
  Glendale (see appendix)
North Highlands (1st).............95660
North Hills, Br. San
  Fernando..............................91344
NORTH HOLLYWOOD (1st)
  (see appendix)
North Inglewood, Sta.
  Inglewood (see appendix)
North Long Beach, Sta. Long
  Beach...................................90805
North Palm Springs.................92258
North Park, Sta. San Diego....92104
North Redondo Beach, Sta.
  Redondo Beach......................90278
North San Juan.......................95960
North Seal Beach, Sta.
  Seaside.................................90740
North Shore, R. Br. Mecca.....92254
North Torrance, Sta.
  Torrance...............................90504
Northridge (1st)......................91324
Norton A F B, Sta. San
  Bernardino...........................92409
Norwalk (1st)..........................90650
Norwalk Manor, Br. Norwalk..90650
Norwood Center, Br. San
  Fernando..............................91343
Novato (1st)............................94947
Nubieber..................................96068
Nuevo......................................92367
Number Fifty Seven, Sta.
  San Francisco.................94101
Number Forty, Sta. San
  Francisco..............................94101
Number Forty Four, Sta. San
  Francisco..............................94101
Number Twenty Three, Sta.
  San Francisco......................94101
Nut Tree, R. Sta. Vacaville...95688
O'Brien, R. Br. Lakehead.....96070
O'Neals....................................93645
Oak Knoll, Sta. Redwood
  City......................................94061
Oak Park, Sta. Sacramento....95817
Oak Run...................................96069
Oak Valley, Br. Agoura........91301
Oak View.................................93022
Oakdale (1st)...........................95361
Oakhurst..................................93644
OAKLAND (1st) (see
  appendix)
Oakley.....................................94561
Oaks, Sta. Arroyo Grande....93420
Oakville...................................94562
Oakwood, Sta. Los Angeles...90004
Occidental................................95465
Ocean Beach, Sta. San
  Diego....................................92107

27

Ocean Park, Sta. Santa
Monica 90405
Oceano 93445
Oceanside (1st) 92054
  Camp Pendleton, Br. 92055
  First Street, Sta. 92054
Ocotillo 92259
Oildale, Br. Bakersfield 93308
Ojai (1st) 93023
Olancha 93549
Old San Diego, Sta. San
Diego 92110
Old Station 96071
Olema 94950
Olinda, R. Br. Anderson 96007
Olive, Sta. Orange 92665
Olive View, Br. San
Fernando 91330
Olivehurst 95961
Olivenhain, R. Br. Encinitas ...92024
Olympic, Sta. Beverly Hills 90212
Olympic Valley, Br. Tahoe
City 95730
Omo Ranch 95661
Ono, R. Br. Redding 96072
ONTARIO (1st) (see
appendix)
Onyx 93255
Opal Cliffs, Sta. Santa Cruz ...95060
ORANGE (1st) (see
appendix)
Orange Cove 93646
Orangehurst, Sta. Fullerton 92632
Orangevale (1st) 95664
Orcutt, Br. Santa Maria 93453
Ordbend, R. Br. Glenn 95942
Oregon House 95962
Orick 95555
Orinda (1st) 94563
Orland (1st) 95963
Orleans 95556
Oro Grande 92368
Orosi 93647
Oroville (1st) 95965
  Pulga, R. Br. 95965
  Storrie, R. Br. 95980
Osbourne, Sta. Los Angeles 90028
Oval, Sta. Visalia 93277
Oxnard (1st) 93030
Pacheco, Br. Martinez 94553
Pacific, Sta. Long Beach 90806
Pacific Beach, Sta. San
Diego 92109
Pacific Grove (1st) ....939:)
Pacific House 95725
Pacific Palisades (1st) 90272
Pacifica (1st) 94044
Pacoima (1st) ....9133?
Paicines ....9504¿
Pala 92059
Palermo 95968
Palm City, Br. Palm Desert 92260
Palm Desert (1st) 92260
Palm Springs (1st) 92262
Palmdale (1st) 93550
Palms, Sta. Los Angeles
  (see appendix)
PALO ALTO (1st) (see
appendix)
Palo Cedro 96073
Palo Verde 92266
Palomar Mountain 92060
Palos Verdes Estates, Br.

Palos Verdes Peninsula 90274
Palos Verdes Peninsula
  (1st) 90274
Panorama City, Sta. Van
Nuys (see appendix)
Paradise (1st) 95969
Paramount (1st) 90723
Parcel Post, Sta. Berkeley 94710
Park, Sta. Berkeley 94702
Parker Dam 92267
Parkside, Sta. San
Francisco 94116
Parkway, Br. Sacramento
  (see appendix)
Parlier 93648
PASADENA (1st) (see
appendix)
Paskenta 96074
Paso Robles (1st) 93446
Patterson (1st) 95363
Patton (1st) 92369
Pauma Valley 92061
Paynes Creek 96075
Pearblossom 93553
Pebble Beach (1st) 93953
Pedley, Br. Riverside 92509
Peninsula Village, R. Br.
Westwood 96137
Penn Valley, R. Br. Grass
Valley 95946
Penngrove 94951
Penryn 95663
Perkins, Br. Sacramento (see
appendix)
Permanente, R. Br.
Cupertino 95014
Perris (1st) 92370
Perry, Sta. Whittier (see
appendix)
Pescadero 94060
Petaluma (1st) 94952
Petrolia 95558
Phelan 92371
Phillipsville 95559
Philo 95466
  Navarro, R. Br. 95463
Pico, Sta. Pico Rivera 90660
Pico Heights, Sta. Los
Angeles (see appendix)
Pico Rivera (1st) 90660
Piedmont, Sta. Oakland (see
appendix)
Piedra 93649
Piercy 95467
Pilot Hill 95664
Pine Grove 95665
  Kit Carson, R. Br. 95644
Pine Valley 92062
Pinecrest 95364
  Dardanelle, R. Br. 95314
  Strawberry, R. Br. 95375
Pinedale 93650
Pinole (1st) 94564
Pinon Hills 92372
Pioneer 95666
  Bear River Lake, R. Br. 95666
  Lake Kirkwood, R. Br. 95646
Pioneertown 92268
Piru 93040
Pismo Beach (1st) 93449
Pittsburg (1st) 94565
Pixley 93256
Placentia (1st) 92670

Placerville (1st) 95667
Plainview, R. Br. Strathmore ...93267
Planada 95365
Plaster City, R. Br. El
Centro 92269
Platina 96076
Playa Del Rey, Sta. Venice 90291
Plaza, Sta. Orange 92666
Plaza Center, Sta. Ontario 91762
Pleasant Grove 95668
Pleasant Hill, Br. Concord 94523
Pleasanton (1st) 94566
Plymouth 95669
Point Arena 95468
Point Loma, Sta. San Diego 92106
Point Mugu, Br. Port
Hueneme 93042
Point Reyes Station 94956
Point Richmond, Sta.
Richmond 94807
Points, Sta. El Monte 91732
Pollock Pines 95726
POMONA (1st) (see
appendix)
Pond, R. Br. Wasco **93280**
Pondosa 9607/
Pope Valley 9456/
Poplar, R. Br. Porterville 93257
Port Costa 94569
Port Hueneme (1st) 93041
Porterville (1st) 93257
Portola 96122
  Beckwourth, R. Br. 96129
Portola Valley, Br. Menlo
Park 94025
Portuguese Bend, R. Br.
Palos Verdes Peninsula 90274
Posey 93260
Potrero 92063
Potter Valley 95469
Poway (1st) 92064
Prather 93651
Presidio, Sta. San Francisco ...94129
Presidio Of Monterey, Sta.
Monterey 93940
Preuss, Sta. Los Angeles
  (see appendix)
Princeton 95970
Proberta 96078
Project City 96079
Prunedale, R. Br. Salinas 93901
Pulga, R. Br. Oroville 95965
Pumpkin Center, R. Br.
Bakersfield 93309
Quail Valley, R. Br. Sun City ..92380
Quartz Hill, R. Br. Lancaster ..93534
Quincy (1st) 95971
  Keddie, R. Br. 95952
  Spring Garden, R. Br. 95971
Rackerby 95972
Rail Road Flat 95248
Rainbow Valley, R. Br.
Fallbrook 92028
Raisin 93652
Ramirez, Sta. Los Angeles 90037
Ramona (1st) 92065
Ranchita 92066
Rancho California, R. Br.
Temecula 92390
Rancho Cordova (1st) 95670
Rancho Del Rey, Br. Chula
Vista ....920¦1

Rancho La Costa, R. Br.
  Carlsbad 92008
Rancho Mirage (1st)............92270
Rancho Park, Sta. Los
  Angeles (see appendix)
Rancho Santa Fe (1st)............92067
Randsburg............93554
  Red Mountain, R. Br............93558
Ravendale............96123
Raymond............93653
Red Bluff (1st)............96080
Red Mountain, R. Br.
  Randsburg............93558
Red Top, R. Br. Merced............95340
Redcrest............95569
Redding (1st)............96001
  Enterprise, Br............96001
  Ono, R. Br............96072
  Wildwood, R. Br............96001
Redlands (1st)............92373
REDONDO BEACH (1st) (see
  appendix)
Reds Meadow, R. Br.
  Mammoth Lakes............93546
Redway............95560
REDWOOD CITY (1st) (see
  appendix)
Redwood Estates............95044
Redwood Valley............95470
Reedley (1st)............93654
Refugio Beach, R. Br
  Goleta............93017
Rescue............95672
Reseda (1st)............91335
Rheem Valley............94570
Rialto (1st)............92376
Richardson Grove, R. Br
  Garberville............95440
Richardson Springs R. Br.
  Chico............95973
Richgrove............93261
RICHMOND (1st) (see
  appendix)
Richvale............95974
Ridgecrest (1st)............93555
Rimforest............92378
Rimpau, Sta. Los Angeles
  (see appendix)
Rincon Annex, Sta. San
  Francisco (see appendix)
Rio Dell............95562
Rio Linda (1st)............95673
Rio Nido, R. Br. Guerneville...95471
Rio Oso............95574
Rio Vista (1st)............94571
Ripley............92272
Ripon (1st)............95366
River Pines............95675
Riverbank (1st)............95367
Riverdale............93656
RIVERSIDE (1st) (see
  appendix)
Robbins............95676
Rocket Test Site, Br.
  Edwards............93523
Rocklin............95677
Ruckridge, Sta. Oakland............94618
Rodeo............94572
Rohnert Park, Br. Cotati............94928
Rohnerville, Br. Fortuna............95540
Rolling Hill Estates, R. Br.
  Palos Verdes Peninsula............90274
Rolling Hills, R. Br. Palos

Verdes Peninsula............90274
Romie Lane, Sta. Salinas............93901
Romoland, Br. Sun City............92380
Roosevelt, Sta. Modesto............95350
Roosevelt Corner, R. Br.
  Lancaster............93534
Rosamond............93560
Rose Bowl, Sta. Pasadena......91103
Roseland, Br. Santa Rosa............95401
Rosemead (1st)............91770
Roseville (1st)............95678
Ross............94957
Rossmoor, Br. Los Alamitos......90720
Rough and Ready............95975
Round Mountain............96084
Rowland Heights, Br. La
  Puente............91745
Rubidoux, Br. Riverside............92509
Ruby Valley, R. Br. Redway......95560
Rumsey............95679
Running Springs............92382
Ruth, R. Br. Bridgeville............95526
Rutherford............94573
Ryde............95680
SACRAMENTO (1st) (see
  appendix)
Saint Helena (1st)............94574
Saint James Park, Sta. San
  Jose............95113
Saint Matthew, Sta. San
  Mateo............94401
Salida............95368
Salinas (1st)............93901
Salton City, R. Br. Thermal......92274
Salyer............95563
Samoa............95564
San Andreas (1st)............95249
  Sheephorn, R. Br............95250
San Anselmo (1st)............94960
San Ardo............93450
SAN BERNARDINO (1st) (see
  appendix)
San Bruno (1st)............94066
San Carlos (1st)............94070
San Clemente (1st)............92672
SAN DIEGO (1st) (see
  appendix)
San Dimas (1st)............91773
SAN FERNANDO (1st) (see
  appendix)
SAN FRANCISCO (1st) (see
  appendix)
San Gabriel (1st)............91776
San Geronimo............94963
San Gregorio............94074
San Jacinto (1st)............92383
San Joaquin............93660
SAN JOSE (1st) (see
  appendix)
San Juan Bautista............95045
San Juan Capistrano (1st)......92675
SAN LEANDRO (1st) (see
  appendix)
San Lorenzo (1st)............94580
San Lucas............93954
San Luis Obispo (1st)............93401
San Luis Rey............92068
San Luis Rey Downs, Br.
  San Luis Rey............92068
San Marcos (1st)............92069
San Marino, Br. Pasadena......91108
San Martin............95046
SAN MATEO (1st) (see

appendix)
San Miguel............93451
San Pablo, Br. Richmond......94806
SAN PEDRO (1st) (see
  appendix)
San Quentin............94964
SAN RAFAEL (1st) (see
  appendix)
San Ramon............94583
San Roque, Sta. Santa
  Barbara............93105
San Simeon............93452
San Tomas, Br. Campbell......95008
San Ysidro (1st)............92073
Sand City, Br. Seaside............93955
Sanford, Sta. Los Angeles......90005
Sanger (1st)............93657
SANTA ANA (1st) (see
  appendix)
SANTA BARBARA (1st) (see
  appendix)
SANTA CLARA (1st) (see
  appendix)
Santa Cruz (1st)............95060
Santa Fe Springs (1st)............90670
Santa Margarita............93453
Santa Maria (1st)............93454
SANTA MONICA (1st) (see
  appendix)
Santa Nella, R. Br. Gustine......95322
Santa Paula (1st)............93060
Santa Rita Park............93661
SANTA ROSA (1st) (see
  appendix)
Santa Susana, Sta. Simi
  Valley............93063
Santa Western, Sta. Los
  Angeles............90072
Santa Ynez............93460
Santa Ysabel............92070
Santee............92071
Saratoga (1st)............95070
Sather Gate, Sta. Berkeley......94704
Saticoy, Br. Ventura............93003
Sattley............96124
Saugus (1st)............91350
  Agua Dulce, R. Br............91350
  Canyon Country, Br............91350
  Green Valley, R. Br............91350
  Val Verde Park, R. Br............91350
  Valencia, R. Br............91355
Sausalito (1st)............94965
Saviers Annex, Sta. Oxnard......93030
Sawyers Bar, R. Br. Etna............96027
Scenic Center, Br. Modesto......95350
Scotia............95565
Scott Bar............96085
Scotts Valley, R. Br. Santa
  Cruz............95060
Seabright, Sta. Santa Cruz......95060
Seal Beach (1st)............90740
Seaside (1st)............93955
Sebastopol (1st)............95472
Seeley............92273
Seiad Valley............96086
Selma (1st)............93662
Sepulveda, Br. San
  Fernando............91343
Sequoia National Park............93262
Serra Mesa, Sta. San Diego
  (see appendix)
Shafter (1st)............93263
Shandon............93461

Shasta............................96087
Shaver Lake.....................93664
  Dinkey Creek, R. Br..........93617
Sheepranch, R. Br. San
  Andreas........................95250
Shell Beach, Sta. Pismo
  Beach...........................93449
Sheridan.........................95681
Sherman Oaks, Sta. Van
  Nuys (see appendix)
Shingle Springs.................95682

Shingletown.....................96088
Shore Acres, Br. Pittsburg.....94565
Shoshone.........................92384
Sierra, Sta. Fresno.............93703
Sierra City......................96125
Sierra Madre (1st)..............91024
Sierraville......................96126
Signal Hill, Br. Long Beach.....90806
Silver Lake, R. Br. Jackson.....95642
Silverado........................92676
Simi Valley (1st)...............93065
Skyforest........................92385
Sloat, R. Br. Blairsden........96127
Sloughhouse......................95683
Smartville.......................95977
Smith River......................95567
Smithflat........................95727
Smoke Tree, Sta. Palm
  Springs........................92262
Snelling.........................95369
Soda Springs.....................95728
Solana Beach (1st)..............92075
Soledad (1st)....................93960
Solvang (1st)....................93463
Somerset.........................95684
Somesbar.........................95568
Somis............................93066
Sonoma (1st).....................95476
Sonora (1st).....................95370
Soquel (1st).....................95073
Soto, Sta. Huntington Park......90255
Soulsbyville.....................95372
South, Sta. Van Nuys............91404
South, Sta. Los Angeles.........90061
South Alhambra, Sta.
  Alhambra.......................91803
South Berkeley, Sta. Berkeley
  (see appendix)
South Dos Palos.................93665
South Downey, Sta. Downey.......90242
South El Monte, Br. El
  Monte..........................91733
South Gardena, Sta.
  Gardena........................90247
South Gate (1st)................90280
South Laguna, Br. Laguna
  Beach..........................92677
South Lake Tahoe (1st)..........95705
  Al Tahoe, Sta..................95705
  Camp Richardson, R. Br........95705
  Fallen Leaf, R. Br............95716
  Stateline, Sta................95705
  Tahoe Paradise, R. Br.........95705
  Tahoe Valley, Sta.............95705
South Main, Sta. Santa Ana......92707
South Modesto, Br. Modesto......95350
South Pasadena (1st)............91030
South San Francisco (1st).......94080
South San Gabriel, Sta.
  Rosemead.......................91770
South San Leandro, Sta. San
  Leandro........................94578

South Shore, Sta. Alameda.......94501
South Whittier, Br. Whittier....90605
Southeastern, Sta. San
  Diego..........................92113
Southland, Sta. Hayward.........94545
Spanish Flat, R. Br. Napa.......94558
Spreckels........................93962
Spring Garden, R. Br.
  Quincy.........................95971
Spring Valley (1st).............92077
Springstowne, Sta. Vallejo......94590
Springville......................93265
  Camp Nelson, R. Br............93208
Spurgeon, Sta. Santa Ana........92702
Spyrock, R. Br. Willits........95479
Squaw Valley, R. Br. Orange
  Cove...........................93646
Standard.........................95373
Standish.........................96128
Stanford, Br. Palo Alto........94305
Stanton (1st)....................90680
State Capitol, Sta.
  Sacramento.....................95814
State Street, Sta. Huntington
  Park...........................90255
Stateline, Sta. South Lake
  Tahoe..........................95705
Station A, Sta. Walnut
  Creek..........................94596
Steele Park, R. Br. Napa........94558
Stevinson........................95374
Stewarts Point...................95480
Stinson Beach....................94970
Stirling City....................95978
STOCKTON (1st) (see
  appendix)
Stonestown, Sta. San
  Francisco......................94132
Stonyford........................95979
Storrie, R. Br. Oroville........95980
Stratford........................93266
Strathmore.......................93267
Strawberry, R. Br. Pinecrest....95375
Strawberry Valley................95981
Studio City, Sta. North
  Hollywood......................91604
Subway, Sta. Los Angeles........90052
Sugarloaf, R. Br. Big Bear
  City...........................92386
Suisun City (1st)...............94585
Sultana..........................93666
Summerland.......................93067
Summit...........................92387
Summit City......................96089
Sun City (1st)...................92381
  Quail Valley, R. Br...........92380
  Romoland, Br...................92380
Sun Valley (1st)................91352
Sunkist, Sta. Anaheim...........92806
Sunland (1st)....................91040
Sunny Hills, Sta. Fullerton.....92632
Sunnymead (1st)..................92388
Sunnyside........................92079
SUNNYVALE (1st) (see
  appendix)
Sunol............................94586
Sunset, Sta. San Francisco......94122
Sunset Beach.....................90742
Sunset Whitney Ranch, R.
  Sta. Rocklin...................95677
Surfside.........................90743
Susana Knolls, R. Br. Simi
  Valley.........................93063

Susanville (1st)................96130
Sutter...........................95982
Sutter Creek.....................95685
  Drytown, R. Br................95699
Sylmar, Br. San Fernando........91342
Taft (1st).......................93268
Tahoe City (1st)................95730
  Meeks Bay, R. Br..............95723
  Olympic Valley, Br............95730
Tahoe Paradise, R. Br. South
  Lake Tahoe.....................95705
Tahoe Valley, Sta. South
  Lake Tahoe.....................95705
Tahoe Vista......................95732
Tahoma...........................95733
Talmage..........................95481
Tamal, Sta. San Quentin.........94964
Tarzana (1st)....................91356
Taylorsville.....................95983
Tecate...........................92080
Tecopa...........................92389
Tehachapi (1st).................93561
Tehama...........................96090
Temecula.........................92390
Temescal, Sta. Oakland..........94609
Temple City (1st)...............91780
Templeton........................93465
Terminal Annex, Sta. Los
  Angeles........................90054
Terminal Island, Sta. San
  Pedro..........................90731
Termo............................96132
Terra Bella......................93270
Terra Linda, Sta. San
  Rafael.........................94901
Textile, Sta. Los Angeles.......90015
The Sea Ranch, R. Br.
  Gualala........................95497
Thermal (1st)....................92274
Thornton.........................95686
THOUSAND OAKS (1st) (see
  appendix)
Thousand Palms...................92276
Three Rivers.....................93271
  Mineralking, R. Br............93253
Tipton...........................93272
Todos Santos, Sta. Concord......94522
Tollhouse........................93667
Toluca Lake, Sta. North
  Hollywood......................91602
Tomales..........................94971
  Fallon, R. Br.................94932
Toms Place, R. Br. Bishop.......93514
Topanga..........................90290
Topaz............................96133
TORRANCE (1st) (see
  appendix)
Tower, Sta. Fresno (see
  appendix)
Town And Country Village,
  Br. Sacramento.................95821
Trabuco Canyon...................92678
Tracy (1st)......................95376
Tranquillity.....................93668
Traver...........................93673
Travis A F B, Sta. Fairfield....94535
Treasure Island, Sta. San
  Francisco......................94130
Tres Pinos.......................95075
Trinidad.........................95570
Trinity Center...................96091
Trona............................93562

Tropico, Sta. Glendale (see appendix)
Trowbridge.................................95687
Truckee......................................95734
Tujunga (1st)..............................91042
Tulare (1st)................................93274
Tulelake.....................................96134
Tuolumne...................................95379
Tuolumne Meadows, Sta. Yosemite National Park....95389
Tupman......................................93276
Turlock (1st)..............................95380
Tustin (1st)................................92680
Tuxedo Park, Sta. Stockton...95204
Twain...95984
Twain Harte...............................95383
Twentynine Palms (1st).........92277
    Marine Corps Base, Br......92278
Twin Bridges.............................95735
Twin Peaks................................92391
U C D, Br. Davis.......................95616
U S N Postgraduate School, Sta. Monterey....................93940
U S Naval Hospital, Br. Long Beach........................90801
Ukiah (1st).................................95482
Union City (1st).........................94587
Univ Of Santa Clara, Sta. Santa Clara...................95053
Universal City, Br. North Hollywood....................91608
University, Br. Santa Barbara.......................93107
University City, Sta. San Diego..........................92122
University Park, Sta. Los Angeles........................90007
Upland (1st)...............................91786
Upper Lake................................95485
Uptown, Sta. San Bernardino (see appendix)
Vacaville (1st)...........................95688
Val Verde Park, R. Br. Saugus........................91350
Valencia, R. Br. Saugus........91355
Valinda, Br. La Puente...........91744
Vallecito....................................95251
    Douglasflat, R. Br..............95229
Vallejo (1st)...............................94590
    A, Sta..................................94590
    American Canyon, Br.........94590
    Dairy Farm, R. Br..............94590
    Federal Terrace, Br............94590
    Mare Island, Sta................94592
    Springstowne, Sta..............94590
Valley Center.............................92082
Valley Fair, Sta. San Jose....95128
Valley Ford................................94972
Valley Home..............................95384
Valley Plaza, Sta. North Hollywood....................91606
Valley Springs...........................95252
    Campo Seco, R. Br............95226
Valley Village, Sta. North Hollywood....................91607
Valleydale, Br. Azusa.............91702
Valyermo...................................93563
Van Duzen, R. Br. Bridgeville......................95526
VAN NUYS (1st) (see appendix)
Vandenberg A F B, Br. Lompoc.........................93437

Vanowen, Sta. Van Nuys......91407
Venice (1st)...............................90291
VENTURA (1st) (see appendix)
Verdugo City (1st)...................91046
Vermont Avenue, Sta. Los Angeles.........................90029
Vernalis.....................................95385
Vernon, Br. Los Angeles (see appendix)
Veterans Administration, Br. Los Angeles...................90073
Veterans Administration Hosp, Br. Long Beach....90801
Veterans Bureau Hospital, Sta. Palo Alto...............94304
Veterans Home, Sta. Yountville..........................94599
Victor...95253
Victorville (1st)..........................92392
Victory Center Annex, Sta. North Hollywood (see appendix)
Vidal..92280
Viking, Sta. Long Beach........90808
Villa Grande..............................95486
Villa Park, R. Br. Orange.......92667
Village, Sta. Los Angeles......90024
Vina...96092
Vineburg....................................95487
Vinton..96135
Visalia (1st)...............................93277
Visitacion, Sta. San Francisco.......................94134
Vista (1st)..................................92083
Vista Grande, Sta. Daly City...94016
Vista Park, Br. Bakersfield.....93307
Volcano......................................95689
Wagner, Sta. Los Angeles.....90047
Waite, Sta. Los Angeles........90018
Wallace......................................95254
Walnut (1st)...............................91789
WALNUT CREEK (1st) (see appendix)
Walnut Grove.............................95690
Walteria, Sta. Torrance..........90505
Warm Springs, Sta. Fremont...94538
Warner Springs.........................92086
Wasco (1st)...............................93280
Washington................................95986
Washington Manor, Sta. San Leandro.........................94579
Waterford...................................95386
Waterman, Br. San Bernardino...................92408
Watsonville (1st)......................95076
Watts, Sta. Los Angeles (see appendix)
Waukena....................................93282
Wawona, Sta. Yosemite National Park...............95389
Weaverville................................96093
    Helena, R. Br.....................96042
Webster Street, Sta. Alameda.........................94501
Weed..96094
Weimar.......................................95736
Weldon.......................................93283
Wendel, R. Br. Janesville.......96136
Weott..95571
West, Br. Los Angeles...........90069
West Adams, Sta. Los Angeles (see appendix)

West Arcadia, Sta. Arcadia....91006
WEST COVINA (1st) (see appendix)
West Garden Grove, Sta. Garden Grove.................92641
West Los Angeles, Sta. Los Angeles (see appendix)
West Menlo Park, Br. Menlo Park............................94025
West Orange, Sta. Orange.....92668
West Pittsburg, Br. Pittsburg.........................94565
West Point..................................95255
West Portal, Sta. San Francisco.......................94127
West Sacramento (1st).........95691
Westchester, Sta. Los Angeles (see appendix)
Westend.....................................93564
Western Avenue, Br. San Pedro............................90732
Westgate, Sta. San Jose.......95129
Westhaven, R. Br. Trinidad...95570
Westlake, Sta. Daly City.......94015
Westlake Village, Br. Thousand Oaks...............91360
Westley......................................95387
Westminster (1st).....................92683
Westmorland..............................92281
Westport....................................95488
Westside, Sta. Modesto.........95351
Westvern, Sta. Los Angeles...90062
Westwood...................................96137
Wheatland..................................95692
Wheeler Ridge...........................93284
Whiskeytown..............................96095
Whispering Pines, R. Br. Middletown......................95461
White Pines................................95256
White Water................................92282
Whitethorn.................................95489
Whitmore....................................96096
WHITTIER (1st) (see appendix)
Wilcox, Sta. Los Angeles.......90038
Wildomar....................................92395
Wildwood, R. Br. Redding......96001
Will Rogers, Sta. Santa Monica..........................90401
William Howard Taft, Sta. San Diego (see appendix)
Williams.....................................95987
Willits (1st)................................95490
    Cummings, R. Br................95477
    Dos Rios, R. Br..................95429
    Island Mountain, R. Br.......95478
    Spyrock, R. Br...................95479
Willow Brook, Br. Compton....90222
Willow Creek..............................95573
Willow Ranch.............................96138
Willows (1st).............................95988
Wilmington (1st).......................90744
Wilseyville.................................95257
Wilshire-La Brea, Sta. Los Angeles.........................90036
Wilton...95693
Winchester.................................92396
Windsor......................................95492
Winnetka, Sta. Canoga Park...91306
Winterhaven...............................92283
Winters......................................95694
Winton..95388
Wishon.......................................93669

31

Witter Springs	95493	Worldway Postal Center, Sta.		Yosemite Lodge, Br.	
Wofford Heights	93285	Los Angeles (see appendix)		Yosemite National Park	95389
Wondacre	94973	Wrightwood	92397	Yosemite National Park	
Woodbridge	95258	Yermo	92398	(1st)	95389
Woodfords, R. Br.		Yermo Annex, Br. Barstow	92311	Yountville	94599
Markleeville	96120	Yettem	93670	Yreka (1st)	96097
Woodlake	93286	Yolo	95697	Yuba City (1st)	95991
Woodland (1st)	95695	Yorba, Sta. Pomona	91767	Yucaipa (1st)	92399
Woodland Hills (1st)	91364	Yorba Linda (1st)	92686	Yucca Valley (1st)	92284
Woodside, Br. Redwood City	94062	York, Sta. Los Angeles	90050	Zamora	95698
Woodville, R. Br. Porterville	93257	Yorkville	95494	Zenia	95495
Woody	93287				

ALHAMBRA   918

POST OFFICE BOXES

Box Nos.		
1-1311	Alhambra	02
2001-2344	South Alhambra Sta.	03

STATIONS, BRANCHES AND UNITS

South Alhambra Sta.	03
General Delivery	02
Postmaster	02

ANAHEIM   928

POST OFFICE BOXES

Box Nos.		
1-999	Federal Sta.	05
2001-2999	Brookhurst Center Sta.	04
3001-4709	Main Office	03
5000-5215	Brookhurst Center Sta.	04
6000-6579	Sunkist Sta.	06

RURAL ROUTES

1	06

STATIONS, BRANCHES AND UNITS

Brookhurst Center Sta.	04
Federal Sta.	05
Sunkist Sta.	06
General Delivery	03
Postmaster	03

APARTMENTS, HOTELS, MOTELS

Broadway Village, 801 N Loara	01
Charterhouse, 1700 S Harbor Blvd	02
City Center, 610 N Anaheim Blvd	05
Commons, 425 N Magnolia	01
Desert Inn, 1600 S Harbor Blvd	02
Disneyland Hotel, 1441 S West	02
Dunes, 1326 S West	02
El Coco Palms, 1919 E Center	05
French Quarter, 2001 S Haster	02
Frontier, 933 S Harbor Blvd	05
Grand Hotel, 7 Freedman Way	02
Jolly Roger Inn, 640 W Katella	02
Kettle, 1760 W Lincoln	01
Lincoln Arms, 145 S Westchester Dr	04
Mauna Loa Apartments, 1541 E La Palma	05
Musketeer, 733 W Katella Ave	02
Palm Gardens, 629 W Vermont	05
Peter Pan Motor Lodge, 2029 S Harbor Blvd	02
Pickwick, 225 S Anaheim Blvd	05
Pleasant, 306 W Lincoln	05
Rose Marie Apartments, 309 W Lincoln	05
Saga Motor, 1650 S Harbor Blvd	02
Sandman, 1248 E Lincoln	05
Shellstone Apartments, 613 W Lincoln	05
Tops, 909 S Harbor Blvd	05
Twilight, 1050 W Katella	02
Valencia, 182 W Lincoln	05
Wanderlust, 1701 S West	02
Water Wheel Lodge, 1144 N Euclid	01

BUILDINGS

Anaheim Bulletin, 232 S Lemon	05
Anaheim Stadium, 2000 S State College	06
Autonetics, 3370 Miraloma	06
Broadway, 444 N Euclid	01
California Federal Savings, 1695 W Crescent	01
Convention Center, 800 W Katella	02
Disneyland, 1313 S Harbor	02
Kraemer Bldg, 106 N Claudina	05
Medical Arts, 1120 W La Palma	01
Pacific Telephone, 217 N Lemon	05
Palomar, 800 S Brookhurst	04
Robinsons, 530 N Euclid Ave.	01
Wilshire Towers, 280 N Wilshire	01

GOVERNMENT OFFICES

Anaheim City Hall, 204 E Lincoln	05
Anaheim Fire Dept, 500 E Broadway	05
Anaheim Police Department, 425 S Harbor Blvd	05
Municipal Court, 1170 N Anaheim Blvd	01

HOSPITALS

Anaheim General Hospital, 3350 W Ball Rd	04
Anaheim Memorial Hospital, 1111 W La Palma	01
Broadway Clinic Hospital, 1660 W Broadway	02
Buena Vista Hospital, 1682 W Buena Vista	02

Anaheim (Con.)   928
Garden Park General
    Hospital, 9922 Gilbert......   04
Hillhaven Convalescent
    Hospital, 1130 W La
    Palma................................   01
Lutheran Home Convalescent
    Hospital, 1303 W Ball Rd..   02
Martin Luther Hospital, 1825
    W Romneya Dr.................   01
Parkview Convalescent
    Hospital, 1514 E Lincoln..   05
West Anaheim Community,
    3033 W Orange.................   04

BAKERSFIELD   933

POST OFFICE BOXES

Box Nos.
1-149   Del Kern R.
                Sta................   07
1-288   Pumpkin
                Center R. Sta.   07
1-926   Miracle Hot
                Springs R.
                Sta................   01
1-1799   Main Office......   02
1800-2999   Main Office......   03
3000-3499   Station A.........   05
4001-4288   Station B.........   07
5001-5749   Oildale Br.......   08
6001-6446   Hillcrest Center
                Br................   06
9000-9458   Kern City R.
                Sta................   09

RURAL ROUTES

1..   08
2,3,4,5,6,7,8.......................   07

STATIONS, BRANCHES AND UNITS

College Center Br...................   06
Delkern Rural Br....................   09
Greenacres Rural Br..............   08
Hillcrest Center Br...............   06
Kern City Rural Br.................   09
Miracle Hot Springs Rural Br.   01
Oildale Br.............................   08
Pumpkin Center Rural Br......   09
Vista Park Br.........................   07
General Delivery.....................   02
Postmaster.............................   02

BUILDINGS

Bakersfield Savings, 1730
    Chester..............................   01
Civic Center, 1601 H.............   01
Great Western Savings 1730
    Chester..............................   01
Haberfeld, 1706 Chester.......   01
Hay, 1612 19th.......................   01
Moronet, 1522 18th...............   01
Sill, 1508 18th.......................   01

GOVERNMENT OFFICES

City Hall 1501 Truxtun......   01

Federal Offices, 800 Truxtun..   01
Kern County Courts &
    Adminisrative, 1415
    Truxtun.............................   01
Social Security Admin (H E
    W) 2619f............................   01

HOSPITALS

Bakersfield Memorial, 420
    34th..................................   01
Kern County General, 1830
    Flower...............................   05
Mercy, 2215 Truxtun..............   01
Physicians, 901 Olive Dr.......   08
San Joaquin, 2628 I St..........   01

UNIVERSITIES AND COLLEGES

Bakersfield Junior, 1801
    Panorama...........................   05
Calif. State College, 9001
    Stockdale Highway.......   09

BERKELEY   947

POST OFFICE BOXES

Box Nos.
1-1999   Main Office......   01
2000-2999   A Sta..............   02
3000-3999   South Berkeley
                Sta................   03
4000-4999   Sather Gate
                Sta................   04
5000-5999   Elmwood Sta....   05
6000-6999   Albany Br.........   06
7000-7999   Landscape Sta.   07
9000-9999   North Berkeley..   09

STATIONS, BRANCHES AND UNITS

Albany Br..............................   06
Elmwood Sta..........................   05
Kensington Br.........................   07
Landscape Sta.........................   07
North Berkeley Sta.................   09
Parcel Post Sta.......................   10
Park Sta.................................   02
Sather Gate Sta.......................   04
General Delivery......................   01
Postmaster.............................   04

APARTMENTS, HOTELS, MOTELS

Amherst, 2231 Shattuck Ave..   04
Bel Air Motel, 1330
    University Ave......................   02
Berkeley Hotel, 2039
    Shattuck Ave.......................   04
Berkeley House, 920
    University Ave......................   10
Berkeley Inn, 2501 Haste......   04
Berkeley Motel, 2001
    Bancroft Way.......................   04
Bonanza Motel, 1720 San
    Pablo Ave............................   02
Cal Hotel, 2008 Shattuck
    Ave....................................   04
California Motel, 1461
    University Ave......................   02
Campanile Hotel, 2070
    University Ave......................   04

Campus Motel, 1619
    University Ave......................   03
Capri Motel, 1512 University
    Ave....................................   03
Carlton, 2338 Telegraph Ave..   04
Claremont, Ashby &
    Claremont...........................   05
Durant, 2600 Durant Ave.......   04
Flamingo Motel, 1761
    University Ave......................   03
Golden Bear Motel, 1620 San
    Pablo Ave............................   02
Marina Lodge, 975 University
    Ave....................................   10
Marriott Inn 200 Marina
    Blvd....................................   10
Nash House, 2045 University
    Ave....................................   04
Oxford Hall, 2140 Oxford.......   04
Plaza Motel, 1175 University
    Ave....................................   02
Stark, 2024 University Ave.....   04
Travelodge Motel, 1820
    University Ave......................   03
U C Hotel, 1040 University
    Ave....................................   10
University Hotel 2057
    University Ave......................   04
Villa Motel, 1155 San Pablo
    Ave....................................   06
Ymca, 2001 Allston Way.........   04

BUILDINGS

Acheson, 2131 University
    Ave....................................   04
Berkeley Center Bldg., 2000
    Center................................   04
Berkeley Professional, 2975
    Sacramento.........................   02
Cal-Farm Bureau, 2855
    Telegraph Ave......................   05
Central Berkeley Medical,
    3031 Telegraph Ave.............   05
Farm Credit Administration,
    2180 Milvia..........................   04
Great Western Savings Bldg.,
    2150 Shattuck Ave...............   04
Koerber, 2054 University Ave..   04
Medical-Dental, 2490
    Channing Way......................   04
Milvia Center, 2118 Milvia.....   04
Physicians, 2131 University
    Ave....................................   04
Shattuck, 2171 Shattuck Ave.   04
Stead, 1960 Addison...............   04
Tioga, 2020 Milvia.................   04
Wells Fargo Bldg., 2140
    Shattuck Ave.......................   04
Woolsey, 2168 Shattuck Ave..   04
Wright, 2161 Shattuck Ave.....   04

GOVERNMENT OFFICES

City Hall, Allston & Grove......   04
State Department Of Public
    Health, 2151 Berkely Way..   04
Western Regional Laboratory,
    800 Buchanan......................   10

33

Berkeley (Con.)   947

HOSPITALS

Albany Hospital, 1247 Marin
Ave. 06
Alta Bates Community
Hospital, 3000 Regent. 05
Cowell Memorial Hospital,
Univ Of California............... 20
Herrick Memorial Hospital,
2001 Dwight Way 04

UNIVERSITIES AND COLLEGES

American Baptist Seminary
Of The West, 2606 Dwight
Way 04
Armstrong College, 2222
Harold Way........................... 04
Berkeley Baptist Divinity
School, 2606 Dwight Way.... 04
Blind School Of California,
3001 Derby 05
California School Of Deaf,
2601 Warring....................... 04
Church Divinity School Of
The Pacific, 2451 Ridge
Road.. 09
Franciscan School Of
Theology, 1712 Euclid
Ave... 09
Graduate Theological Union,
2465 Le Conte Ave............... 09
Jesuit School Of Theology,
1735 Le Roy Ave.................. 09
Pacific Lutheran Theological
Seminary, 2770 Marin Ave. .. 08
Pacific School Of Religion,
1798 Scenic Ave.................. 09
University Of California........... 20
Williams College 1960 San
Antonio Ave.......................... 07

BEVERLY HILLS   902

POST OFFICE BOXES

Box Nos.		
A-Z	Main Office	13
1-2090	Main Office	13
AA-AH	Main Office	13
AA-HH	Main Office	13
3001-3799	Olympic Sta.....	12
5001-5399	Maple Annex.....	10

STATIONS, BRANCHES AND UNITS

Olympic Sta................................ 12
General Delivery 13
Postmaster 13

BUENA PARK   906

POST OFFICE BOXES

Box Nos.		
6441-6570	Main Office	22

STATIONS, BRANCHES AND UNITS

La Palma Br............................... 20
Postmaster 22

HOSPITALS

Beach Community Hospital
5742 Beach Blvd................ 21

BURBANK   915

POST OFFICE BOXES

Box Nos.		
1-911	Downtown Sta..	03
1000-1714	Magnolia Park Sta.................	05
3001-3399	Glenoaks Sta.....	05
4000-4440	Downtown Sta..	03
6001-7277	Main Office	05

STATIONS, BRANCHES AND UNITS

Downtown Sta........................... 03
Glenoaks Sta.............................. 04
Magnolia Park Sta..................... 05
General Delivery 05
Postmaster................................. 05

CANOGA PARK   913

POST OFFICE BOXES

Box Nos.		
1-632	Main Office	05
1000-1599	Canoga Park Annex Sta.........	04
2000-2399	Winnetka Sta.....	06

STATIONS, BRANCHES AND UNITS

Canoga Annex Sta..................... 04
Collier Sta 04
Winnetka Sta.............................. 06
General Delivery 03
Postmaster 03

CHULA VISTA   920

POST OFFICE BOXES

Box Nos.		
1-1749	Main Office	12
3001-3866	Rancho Del Rey Br............	11

STATIONS, BRANCHES AND UNITS

Rancho Del Rey Br.................... 11
General Delivery 10
Postmaster 10

COMPTON   902

POST OFFICE BOXES

Box Nos.		
1-1199	Hub City Sta	23
2000-2999	East Compton Sta.................	23
3000-3999	Willowbrook Br .	23
4000-5999	Compton...........	24

STATIONS, BRANCHES AND UNITS

East Compton Sta...................... 20
Hub City Sta.............................. 20
Willow Brook Br....................... 22
General Delivery 20
Postmaster................................. 20

CONCORD   945

POST OFFICE BOXES

Box Nos.		
1-1134	Todos Santos Station............	22
2101-21419	Casa Correo	21
2301-23666	Pleasant Hill Br	23
5001-6094	Main Office	24
20-300-		
1-0203108	Station A...........	20

STATIONS, BRANCHES AND UNITS

Casa Correo Sta......................... 21
Pleasant Hill Br.......................... 23
Todos Santos Sta........................ 22
General Delivery 20
Postmaster................................. 20

COSTA MESA   926

POST OFFICE BOXES

Box Nos.		
1-1049	Mesa Center Sta...................	27
1101-2299	Main Office	26

STATIONS, BRANCHES AND UNITS

Mesa Center Sta......................... 27
General Delivery 26
Postmaster................................. 26

DALY CITY   940

POST OFFICE BOXES

Box Nos.		
A-M	Main Office	17
1-0000360	Vista Grande Sta...................	16
301-1799	Colma Sta	14
501-979	Main Office	17
3001-3645	Westlake Sta	15

STATIONS, BRANCHES AND UNITS

Colma Sta 14
Vista Grande Sta........................ 16
Westlake Sta 15
General Delivery 15
Postmaster... 17

34

Daly City (Con.)   940

HOSPITALS

Junipero Serra Emergency Center	14
Marys Help	15
Skyline Convalescent	15
Villa Sanitarium	14

DOWNEY   902

POST OFFICE BOXES

Box Nos.		
A-Z	Main Office	41
1-999	Main Office	41
1001-1999	North Downey Sta	40
2001-2999	South Downey Sta	42
3001-3999	Los Amigos Sta	42
4000-4999	Main Office	41

STATIONS, BRANCHES AND UNITS

Los Amigos Sta	40
North Downey Sta	40
South Downey Sta	42
General Delivery	41
Postmaster	41

GOVERNMENT OFFICES

California St Bd Of Equalization, 11229 Woodruff	41
California St Dept Of Agriculture, 8635 Firestone Blvd	41
Los Angeles Municipal Court, 8206 3rd	41
United States Revenue Service, 8524 Firestone Blvd	41

HOSPITALS

Downey Community, 11500 Brookshire Ave	41
Rancho Los Amigos, 7601 Imperial Hwy	42
Rio Hondo Memorial, 8300 Telegraph Rd	40

EL CAJON   920

POST OFFICE BOXES

Box Nos.		
1-1494	Main Office	22
2001-2596	Bostonia Sta	21
3001-3244	Fletcher Hills	20

STATIONS, BRANCHES AND UNITS

Bostonia Sta	21
Fletcher Hills Sta	20

General Delivery	20
Postmaster	20

EL MONTE   917

POST OFFICE BOXES

Box Nos.		
1-1999	Main Office	34
2000-2999	Points Sta	32
3000-3999	South El Monte Br	33

STATIONS, BRANCHES AND UNITS

Points Sta	32
South El Monte Br	33
General Delivery	34
Postmaster	31

ESCONDIDO   920

	25
	26
	27

FREMONT   945

POST OFFICE BOXES

Box Nos.		
A-T	Main Office	37
1-999	Main Office	37
M-1-M-50	Main Office	37
1000-1999	Irvington Sta	38
2000-2999	Niles Sta	36
3000-3999	Mission San Jose Sta	38
4000-4999	Warm Springs Sta	38

STATIONS, BRANCHES AND UNITS

Irvington Sta	38
Mission San Jose Sta	38
Niles Sta	36
Warm Springs Sta	38
General Delivery	36
Postmaster	36

FRESNO   937

POST OFFICE BOXES

Box Nos.		
A-K	Cardwell	55
1-192	Main Office	07
201-432	Main Office	08
441-672	Main Office	09
681-872	Main Office	12
881-1112	Main Office	14
1121-1352	Main Office	15
1361-1592	Main Office	16
1601-1832	Main Office	17
1841-2072	Main Office	18
2081-2194	Main Office	19
2201-2314	Main Office	20
2321-2499	Main Office	23
2501-2999	Calwa Br	45
3001-3499	G Street Sta	66
4001-4757	Tower Sta	44
5001-5999	Cardwell	55
6001-6999	Clinter	03
7701-8999	E Fresno Br	27
10001-10187	Calwa Br	45

RURAL ROUTES

2	27
3,4,5	25
6,7,8	06
9,10,11	05
12	06

STATIONS, BRANCHES AND UNITS

Ashlan Park Sta	26
Barton Sta	02
Calwa Br	25
Cardwell Sta	04
Clinter Sta	03
East Fresno Br	27
Eastgate Sta	02
Easton Br	06
Fancher Br	02
Fig Garden Village Br	04
Herndon Rural Br	21
Highway City Br	05
Malaga Br	25
Sierra Sta	03
Tower Sta	44
General Delivery	21
Postmaster	21
Star Route	21

APARTMENTS, HOTELS, MOTELS

Airport Marina Hotel, 5155 Mckinley Ave. E	27
Alhambra Trailer Lodges, 1898 E Gettysburg Ave	26
Americana 205 N Blackstone Ave	01
Ashcroft, 4415 N Clark	26
Avalon Motel, 3621 N U S Hwy 99	05
Ayres Motel, 2710 S. Orange Ave	25
Balmoral, 1741 W Clinton	05
Bel Air Motel, 740 W Olive Ave	28
Blackstone Motel 5577 N Blackstone Ave	10
Brix, 2311 Fresno	21
Broadway Motel, 1840 Broadway	21
Brooks Manor, 1558 N Brooks Ave	28
Calaveras Gardens, 150 N Calaveras	01
Californian, Van Ness & Kern	21
Carousel Motel 1444 W White	28
City Motel, 2309 S G	21
Del Mar Motel, 1849 N Motel Dr	28
Del Webb Towne House, 2220 Tulare St	21
Desert Inn 2445 W Whites Bridge Rd	06

El Capitan Motel, 4850 N
Blackstone Ave 26
El Grande Motel, 1425 N
Motel Dr 28
El Rancho Motel 1265 N
Motel Dr 28
Fresno Mill Motel, 2835 E.
Church Ave 21
Fresno Motor Lodge Motel,
1587 N Motel Dr 28
Fresno, 1257 Broadway 21
Golden Key Motel, 2425
Merced 21
Hacienda Motel, 2515 N Hwy
99 05
Hillcrest Arms, 2964 E
Mckenzie 01
Holiday Motel, 1409 N Motel
Dr 28
Imperial 400 Motel, 2127
Inyo 21
Kings Canyon Motel 4770 E
Kings Canyon Rd 02
London Motel, 797 N Pkwy
Dr 28
Manchester Manor, 2147 E
Shields 26
Manchester Motel 3844 N
Blackstone Ave 26
Millbrook Garden, 3384 N
Millbrook 26
Motel Fresno, 1325 N Motel
Dr 28
Motel 6, 4245 N Blackstone
Ave 26
Motel 6, 949 N Parkway Dr ... 28
Nordic Inn, 949 N Pkwy Dr ... 28
Normandie Apartments, ... 28
Osage 635 E Belmont Ave 01
Palm Motel, 1515 N Motel
Dr 28
Palms, 104 N Calaveras 01
Park Cedar, 522 S Cedar 02
Park Motel, 327 W Belmont
Ave 28
Park Terrace, 1040 S 21
Parkview Mobile Lodge, 1719
W Olive Ave 28
Parkway Motel, 6239 N
Blackstone Ave 10
Plaza Motel, 1940 Broadway .. 21
Ramada Inn 324 E Shaw
Ave 10
Ranch-O-Tel Motel, 1487 N
Motel Dr 28
Ritz Motor, 1557 N Motel Dr .. 28
Sahara Motel, 530 N Weber
Ave 28
Sands Motel, 1441 N Motel
Dr 28
Sequoia Motel, 4707 E Kings
Canyon Rd 02
Talsness Terrace, 2039 E
Simpson 03
Tower Motel, 3353 N U S
Hwy 99 05
Town House Motor, 1383 N
Motel Dr 28
Towne & Country Lodge,
3093 N Hwy 99 05
Travelodge Motel, 888
Broadway 21
Tropicana Lodge, 4061 N

Blackstone 26
Valeria Arms, 248 Valeria 01
Villa Motel, 817 N Pkwy Dr 28
Virginia 2125 Kern 21

BUILDINGS

Bank Of America, 1015
Fulton 21
Brix, 1221 Fulton 21
Caplan-Lowe, 1715 Fulton 21
Crocker Citizens, 2135
Fresno 21
Del Webb, 2220 Tulare St. 21
Fresno Guarantee Savings,
1171 Fulton 21
Helm, 1111 Fulton 21
Mason, 1044 Fulton 21
New Bank Of America Bldg,
1011 Van Ness, ... 21
Pacific Gas & Electric, 1401
Fulton 21
Patterson, 2014 Tulare 21
Rowell, 2100 Tulare 21
Security Bank, 1060 Fulton 21
United California Bank Bldg,
1177 Van Ness 21

GOVERNMENT OFFICES

Federal Bldg, 1130 O. 21
Fresno City Hall, 2326
Fresno 21
Fresno County Courthouse,
1100 Van Ness Ave. 21
Fresno County Hall Of
Records 2281 Tulare 21
Fresno I R S Center, 5045
Butler Ave. E. 30
Law Enforcement Admin.
Bldg., 2200 Fresno 21
State Building, 2550
Mariposa 21

HOSPITALS

Fresno Community, 2823
Fresno 21
Fresno County Tuberculois,
435 S Cedar Ave 02
Saint Agnes, 530 W
Floradora 28
Sierra, 2025 E Dakota Ave 26
U.s. Government Veterans
Admin., 2615 Clinton Ave
E. 03
Valley Childrens Hospital &
Guidance Clinic 03
Valley Medical Center 445
So. Cedar Ave 02

UNIVERSITIES AND COLLEGES

California Christian College,
4481 E. University Ave. 03
Central California
Commercial, 1921
Tuolumne 21
Fresno City, 1101 E
University 04

Fresno State University 5241
N. Maple Ave 10

FULLERTON   926

POST OFFICE BOXES

Box Nos.
1-672   Commonwealth
                Sta 32
800-899   Contest Mail. 38
20AA-20JK   Orangehurst
                Sta 33
2001-2849   Orangehurst
                Sta 33
3001-4372   Main Office 34
5001-5534   Sunny Hills
                Sta 35

STATIONS, BRANCHES AND UNITS

Commonwealth Sta 32
Orangehurst Sta 33
Sunny Hills Sta 32
General Delivery 31
Postmaster 31

APARTMENTS, HOTELS, MOTELS

Fullerton Continental, 400 N
Acacia 31
Holiday Inn, 1500 S
Raymond 31
Hyatt Lodge, 1009 S Harbor
Blvd. 32
International Hotel, 1830 W
Commonwealth 33
Meredith Manor, 1500 S
Pomona 32
Orange Gardens, 400 N
Orangethorpe 32
Othrys Hall, 601 & 651 N
Titan 31

HOSPITALS

Fullerton Community, 100 E
Valley View Dr 35
St Jude, 101 E Valencia
Mesa Dr 34

UNIVERSITIES AND COLLEGES

Cal State Fullerton, 800 N
State College 34
Fullerton Junior College, 321
E Chapman 34

GARDENA   902

POST OFFICE BOXES

Box Nos.
A-F   Main Office 47
1-472   South Gardena
                Sta 47

Gardena (Con.)   902

1001-1647	Alondra Br......	49
2001-2550	Main Office......	47

STATIONS, BRANCHES AND UNITS

Alondra Br........................	49
Domingues Hills Br...............	47
North Gardena Br.................	47
South Gardena Sta................	47
General Delivery.................	47
Postmaster.......................	47

BUILDINGS

California Highway Patrol, 18220 S Broadway............	47
Gardena Ciy Hall, 1700 W 162 Nd St......................	47
Gardena Fire Dept, 1650 W 162 Nd St......................	47
Gardena Y M C A, 1700 Redondo Bch Blvd..............	47
Los Angeles County Public Library, 1731 Gardena Blvd.............................	47
Masonic Temple, 1250 W 155 Th St........................	47
U S Selective Service, 14911 Crenshaw Blvd...............	49

HOSPITALS

Community Hospital, 1246 W 155 Th St...................	47
Gardena Medical Center, 2315 Compton Blvd............	49
Memorial Hospital Of Gardena, 1145 W Redondo Bch Blvd......................	47

GARDEN GROVE   926

POST OFFICE BOXES

Box Nos.		
1-1647	Main Office......	42
AA-FR	Main Office......	42
5000-5600	West Garden Grove Station..	45

STATIONS, BRANCHES AND UNITS

West Garden Grove Sta...........	41
General Delivery.................	40
Postmaster.......................	40

GLENDALE   912

POST OFFICE BOXES

Box Nos.		
1-2074	Main Office......	09
4001- -0004689	North Glendale Sta...............	02
5001-5245	Grand Central Sta...............	01

0003001- -0003985	Grand Central Sta...............	01
0006001- -6999	Tropico Sta......	05
0008001- -8694	La Crescenta....	14
0010001- -0010880	Main Office......	09

STATIONS, BRANCHES AND UNITS

Grand Central Sta................	01
La Crescenta Sta.................	14
North Glendale Sta...............	02
Tropico Sta......................	04
General Delivery.................	09
Postmaster.......................	09

APARTMENTS, HOTELS, MOTELS

Bell Motor, 1126 E Colorado...	05
English Garden, 1227 S Central Ave...................	04
Gainsborough, 1003 S Central Ave...................	04
Gene Louise, 140 N Jackson...	06
Glendale, 701 E Broadway......	05
Golden Key, 123 W Colorado...	04
Golden State, 214 E Chestnut......................	05
Jackson, 115 N Jackson..........	06
Mackenzie, 339 N Brand Blvd.............................	03
Maryland, 202 E Wilson Ave...	06
Orange Grove, 700 Orange Grove Ave.....................	05
Park Lane, 309 W Colorado.....	04
Regalodge, 200 W Colorado...	04
Regent Annex, 315 W Lomita Ave.............................	04
Regent, 445 S Central Ave.....	04
Ritz, 721 N Brand Blvd..........	03
Vagabond, Motor Hotel, 120 W Colorado...................	04
Woodlands, 1756 N Verdugo Rd.............................	08

BUILDINGS

Bank Of America, 110 W Broadway......................	04
Central, 111 E Broadway.......	05
Federal, 313 E Broadway.......	05
Fidelity Federal, 225 E Broadway......................	05
Forest Lawn Memorial Park, 1712 S Glendale...............	05
Glendale Federal Savings, 401 N Brand Blvd............	03
Glendale News-Press, 111 N Isabel........................	06
Grandview Memorial Park, 1341 Glenwood Rd............	01
Hahn, 103 N Brand Blvd........	03
Jensen, 203 E Broadway........	05
Library, 319 E Harvard..........	05
Professional, 229 N Central Ave.............................	03
Public Service, 119 N Glendale Ave.................	06
Salvation Army, 320 W Windsor Rd....................	04

Security, 102 N Brand Blvd...	03

GOVERNMENT OFFICES

Chamber Of Commerce, 200 S Louise........................	05
City Hall Annex, 111 Howard..	05
City Hall, 613 E Broadway......	05
Police, 600 E Wilson Ave........	06

HOSPITALS

Behrens Memorial, 446 Piedmont......................	06
Broadway Medical, 660 W Broadway......................	04
Glendale Adventist Hospital, 1509 E Wilson Ave...........	06
Glendale Community, 800 S Adams.........................	05
Memorial, 1420 S Central Ave.............................	04
North Glendale, 1401 W Glenoaks Blvd.................	01
Pacific Glen, 712 S Pacific Ave.............................	04

UNIVERSITIES AND COLLEGES

Board Of Education, 411 E Wilson.........................	06
Glendale Business, 120 S Glendale Ave.................	05
Glendale, 1500 N Verdugo Rd.............................	08
Los Angeles Chiropractic, 920 E Broadway...............	05

HAYWARD   945

POST OFFICE BOXES

Box Nos.		
1-1999	Bradford Sta.....	43
2000-2999	Castro Valley Br..................	46
3000-5999	Main Office......	40
6000-6999	Southland Sta..	45

RURAL ROUTES

1.................................	46

STATIONS, BRANCHES AND UNITS

Bradford Sta.....................	41
Castro Valley Br.................	46
Harder Annex Sta................	44
Heyer Br.........................	41
Southland Sta....................	45
General Delivery.................	41
Postmaster.......................	44

UNIVERSITIES AND COLLEGES

California State College, 25800 Hillary................	42
Chabot College, 25555 Hesperian Blvd...............	45

HUNTINGTON BEACH 926

POST OFFICE BOXES

Box Nos.		
A-Q	Beach Center Sta	48
1-899	Beach Center Sta	48
1001-2557	Main Office	47

STATIONS, BRANCHES AND UNITS

Beach Center Sta	48
General Delivery	47
Postmaster	47

BUILDINGS

Huntington Center 7777 Edinger Ave	47
Mc Donnell Douglas Corp. 5301 Bolsa Ave	47

HOSPITALS

Huntington Intercommunity Hospital, 17772 Beach Blvd	47

UNIVERSITIES AND COLLEGES

Goldenwest College	47

INGLEWOOD 903

POST OFFICE BOXES

Box Nos.		
1-459	Main Office	06
ANY	Main Office	06
461-999	Main Office	07
1000-1999	Main Office	08
2000-2999	Morningside Park Sta	05
3000-3999	Lennox Br	04
4000-4999	North Inglewood Sta	09
5000-5999	Crenshaw Sta	10

STATIONS, BRANCHES AND UNITS

Crenshaw Imperial Sta	03
Lennox Br	04
Morningside Park Sta	05
North Inglewood Sta	01
General Delivery	06
Postmaster	06

GOVERNMENT OFFICES

Department Of Veterans Affairs, 830 N La Brea Ave	09
Social Security Administration, 608 E Manchester	06
State Board Of Equalization, 630 N La Brea Ave	09
State Department Of	

Employment, 4546 W Century Blvd		04
State Department Of Motor Vehicles, 150 W Florence		01

HOSPITALS

Brierwood Territory Convalescent, 301 Centinela	02
Centinela Valley Community, P O Box 720	07
Daniel Freeman Memorial, P O Box 100	06
Imperial, 11222 Inglewood	04
Inglewood Bassinette, 9619 S Inglewood	01
Inglewood Convalarium, 100 S Hillcrest Blvd	01
Inglewood Hospital, 426 E 99th	01
Kaiser Foundation Extended Care, 3425 W. Manchester	05
Manchester, 401 W Manchester	01

UNIVERSITIES AND COLLEGES

Northrop Institute Of Technology, P O Box 260	06

LAGUNA BEACH 926

POST OFFICE BOXES

Box Nos.		
A-D	Laguna Hills Br	53
1-758	South Laguna	77
1-1649	Finance Station A	52
2001-2367	Laguna Hills	53

STATIONS, BRANCHES AND UNITS

Laguna Hills Br	53
Laguna Niguel Br	77
South Laguna Br	77
General Delivery	52
Postmaster	51

LAKEWOOD 907

POST OFFICE BOXES

Box Nos.		
A-P	Main Office	14
1-719	Main Office	14
1301-1896	Hawaiian Gardens Br	16

STATIONS, BRANCHES AND UNITS

Carwood Sta	13
Dutch Village Sta	13
Hawaiian Gardens Br	16
General Delivery	14
Postmaster	14

LA PUENTE 917

POST OFFICE BOXES

Box Nos.		
A-Z	Main Office	47
1-1099	Main Office	47
2001-2488	Bassett Br	46
3000-3746	City Of Industry Br	44

STATIONS, BRANCHES AND UNITS

Bassett Br	46
City Of Industry Br	44
Hacienda Heights Br	45
Rowland Heights Br	45
Valinda Br	44
General Delivery	47
Postmaster	47

LONG BEACH 908

POST OFFICE BOXES

Box Nos.		
1-2919	Main Office	01
3001-3999	Sta B	03
4000-4535	East Long Beach Sta	04
5001-5736	North Long Beach Sta	25
6001-6448	Pacific Sta	06
6501-6796	Bryant Sta	15
7000-7996	Bixby Sta	07
8000-8659	Viking Sta	08
9001-9355	Cabrillo Sta	10
14351-14799	Loma Sta	14
15001-15505	Bryant Sta	15
16001-16184	Pacific Sta	06
17001-17148	Bixby Sta	07
20001-20900	Main Office	01

STATIONS, BRANCHES AND UNITS

Bixby Sta	07
Bryant Sta	15
Cabrillo Sta	10
East Long Beach Sta	04
North Long Beach Sta	05
Pacific Sta	06
Signal Hill Br	06
U S Naval Hospital Br	01
Veterans Administration HospBr	01
Viking Sta	08
General Delivery	01
Postmaster	01

APARTMENTS, HOTELS, MOTELS

Bixby Knolls Towers, 3737 Atlantic Ave	07
Blackstone, 330 W Ocean Blvd	02
Brethren Manor, 3333 N Pacific Place	06
Buffum, 210 E 3rd	12
Edgewater Inn Marina Hotel, 6400 E Pacific Coast Hwy	03
Golden Sails Inn, 6285 E Pacific Coast Hwy	03

38

Huntington Vista, 1290 E Ocean Blvd	02
International Tower, 666 E Ocean Blvd	02
Lafayette, 140 Linden Ave	02
New Robinson Hotel & Apts, 334 E Ocean Blvd	02
Pacific Holiday Apartments	02
Portofino Marina Apts, 5400 E The Toledo	03
Schuyler, 117 W Ocean Blvd .	02
Six Hundred Ocean Bldg, 600 E Ocean Blvd	02
The Breakers, 210 E Ocean Blvd	02
The Galaxy Condominium, 2999 E Ocean Blvd	03

BUILDINGS

Andrus, 215 N Long Beach Blvd	02
Armed Services Ymca, 151 Queens Way	02
Bank Of California, 444 W Ocean Blvd	02
Edison, 100 N Long Beach Blvd	02
F & M, 320 Pine Ave	12
Fidelity Federal Plaza, 525 E Ocean Blvd	02
Harbor Administrative, 925 S Hacbor Plaza	02
Heartwell, 19 Pine Ave	02
Insurance Exchange, 205 E Broadway	02
Jergins Trust, 100 E Ocean Blvd	02
Kennebec, 141 W Ocean Blvd	02
Kress, 122 W 5th	12
Labor Temple, 1231 Locust Ave	13
Municipal Auditorium, 270 E Seaside Way	02
Municipal Utilities, 215 W Broadway	02
Ocean Center, 110 W Ocean Blvd	02
One-Fifteen Pine Avenue, 115 Pine Ave	02
Press-Telegram, 604 Pine Ave	01
Professional Annex, 812 Pine Ave	13
Professional Center, 125 E 8th	13
Professional, 117 E 8th	13
Security, 110 Pine Ave	02
Veterans Memorial, 245 W Broadway	02
Ymca, 600 N Long Beach Blvd	12
Ywca, 550 Pacific Ave	12

GOVERNMENT OFFICES

City Hall, 205 W. Broadway	02
County Court, 415 W Ocean Blvd	02
Federal, 300 N Long Beach Blvd	01

Public Safety, 400 W Broadway	02

HOSPITALS

Community, 1720 Termino Ave	01
Long Beach El Cerrito, 1401 Chestnut Ave	13
Long Beach General, 2597 Redondo Ave	06
Los Altos, 3340 Los Coyotes Diagl	08
Magnolia, 2101 Magnolia Ave	06
Memorial Hospital Of Long Beach, 2801 Atlantic Ave..	01
Pacific Hospital Of Long Beach, 2776 Pacific Ave	01
Saint Marys, 509 E 10th	01
US Naval, 7500 E Carson	01
Veterans Administration, 5901 E 7th	01
Woodruff Community, 3800 Woodruff Ave	08

UNIVERSITIES AND COLLEGES

California State, 6101 E 7th..	01

LOS ANGELES   **900**

POST OFFICE BOXES

Box Nos.		
A-L	Ambassador Sta	70
1-210	Ambassador Sta	70
1-3431	Main Office	53
1-4164	Terminal Annex Box Sta	51
1-4220	Hollywood Sta..	28
5001-6647	Metropolitan Sta	55
6651-7327	East Los Angeles Br	22
8051-8999	Crenshaw Sta	08
11001-11599	Kearny Sta	11
15001-15944	Del Valle Sta	15
17001-17899	Foy Sta	17
18000-18994	Cimarron Sta	18
19391-19999	Rimpau Sta	19
20501-20999	Pico Heights Sta	06
21001-21999	Market Sta	21
22001-22300	East Los Angeles Br	22
23001-23646	Lugo Sta	23
24001-24999	Village Sta	24
25001-25999	West Los Angeles Sta	25
26001-26600	Edendale Sta	26
27001-27999	Los Feliz Sta	27
29001-29920	Vermont Avenue Sta	29
30001-30099	Terminal Annex Sta	30
31001-31999	Lincoln Heights Sta	31
32001-32999	El Sereno Sta	32
33101-33549	Boyle Sta	33

34001-34877 Palms Sta	34
35001-35999 Preuss Sta	35
36001-36694 Wilshire La Brea Sta	36
37001-37999 Green Sta	37
38001-38999 Wilcox Sta	38
39601-39999 Griffith Sta	39
41001-41999 Eagle Rock Sta	41
42001-42499 Highland Park Sta	42
42501-42999 York Sta	50
43001-43546 La Tijera Sta	43
44531-44914 Hancock Sta	44
45000-45999 Westchester Sta	45
46001-46714 Cole Br	46
47601-47999 Wagner Sta	47
48301-48999 Briggs Sta	48
49001-49999 Barrington Sta	49
54001-54999 Terminal Annex Sta	54
55001-55999 Metropolitan - Sta	55
57001-57999 Flint Sta	57
58001-58767 Vernon Br	58
59001-59999 Greenmead Sta	59
60001-60999 Terminal Annex Sta	60
61001-61999 South Sta	61
62001-62999 Westvern Sta	62
63001-63999 Hazard Br	63
64151-64799 Rancho Park Sta	64
65551-65978 Glassell Sta	65
66001-66578 Mar Vista Sta	66
67001-67572 Century City Sta	67
69581-69995 West Br	69
71401-71998 Florence Br	01
72001-72419 Watts Sta	02
73101-73644 Broadway- Manchester Sta	03
74151-74999 Oakwood Sta	04
75001-75999 Sanford Sta	75
76000-76999 Sanford Sta	76
77001-77999 Dockweiler Sta	07
78001-78598 West Adams Sta	16
80000-81000 World Way Sta..	80
84001-84599 Veterans Ad- ministration Br	73
85001-85449 Santa Western Sta	72
90001-95999 World Way Sta	09

STATIONS, BRANCHES AND UNITS

Ambassador Sta	70
Arcade Sta	52
Barrington Sta	49
Boyle Sta	33
Briggs Sta	48
Broadway Manchester Sta	03
Central City Sta	67
Cimarron Sta	18
City of Commerce Sta	22
City Terrace Sta	63

Los Angeles (Con.)   900
Cole Br. 46
Crenshaw Sta. 08
Del Valle Sta. 15
Dockweiler Sta. 07
Eagle Rock Sta. 41
East Los Angeles Sta. 22
Edendale Sta. 26
El Sereno Sta. 32
Farmers Market Sta. 36
Florence Sta. 01
Foy Sta. 17
Glassell Sta. 65
Green Sta. 37
Greenmead Sta. 59
Griffith Sta. 39
Hancock Sta. 44
Hazard Br. 63
Highland Park Sta. 42
Hollywood Sta. 28
Kearny Sta. 11
La Tijera Sta. 43
Ladera Heights Sta. 45
Lincoln Heights Sta. 31
Los Feliz Sta. 27
Lugo Sta. 23
Market Sta. 21
Mar Vista Sta. 66
Metropolitan Sta. 14
Oakwood Sta. 04
Osbourne Sta. 28
Palms Sta. 34
Pico Heights Sta. 06
Preuss Sta. 35
Ramirez Sta. 37
Rancho Park Sta. 64
Rimpau Sta. 19
Sanford Sta. 05
Santa Western Sta. 72
South Sta. 61
Subway Sta. 52
Terminal Annex Sta. 54
Textile Sta. 15
University Park Sta. 07
Vermont Avenue Sta. 29
Vernon Br. 58
Veterans Administration Br. .. 73
Village Sta. 24
Wagner Sta. 47
Waite Sta. 18
Watts Sta. 02
West Br. 69
West Adams Sta. 16
Westchester Sta. 45
West Los Angeles Sta. 25
Westvern Sta. 62
Wilcox Sta. 38
Wilshire-La Brea Sta. 36
Worldway Postal Center Sta. . 09
York Sta. 50
General Delivery 53
Postmaster 52

APARTMENTS, HOTELS, MOTELS

Admiral, 840 S Serrano Ave .. 05
Alexandria, 210 W 5th 13
Alvarado, 847 S Alvarado 57
Ambassador, 3400 Wilshire
    Blvd. 10

Ancelle, 701 S Gramercy Pl 05
Ansonia, 2505 W 6th 57
Ardmore, 1850 Whitley Ave 28
Asbury Apartment, 2505 W
    6th 57
Ashley Arms, 10490 Wilshire
    Blvd. 24
Bel Air Sands, 11461 Sunset
    Blvd. 49
Bel Air, 701 Stone Canyon
    Rd 24
Beverly Comstock, 10300
    Wilshire Blvd. 24
Biltmore, 515 S Olive 13
Blair House, 445 N Rossmore
    Ave 04
Bresner Towers, 8440 Sunset
    Blvd. 69
Bryson Apartment, 2701
    Wilshire Blvd. 57
Bunker Hill Towers, 222 S
    Figueroa 12
Bunker Hill Towers, 234 S
    Figueroa 12
Bunker Hill Towers, 800 W
    1st 12
Canterbury, 1746 N
    Cherokee 28
Cavalier, 10724 Wilshire
    Blvd. 24
Cecil, 640 S Main 14
Chalfonte, 720 S Normandie .. 05
Chancellor, 1842 N Cherokee . 28
Chancellor, 3191 W 7th 05
Chapman Park, 615 S
    Alexandria Ave 05
Chateau Marmont, 8221
    Sunset Blvd 46
Churchill Towers, 10450
    Wilshire Blvd. 24
Clark International, 426 S
    Hill 13
Coliseum, 457 W Santa
    Barbara Av. 37
Commodore, 1203 W 7th 17
Cordingly, 10401 Wilshire
    Blvd. 24
Crescent Heights, 6301
    Orange 48
Del Capri, 10587 Wilshire
    Blvd. 24
Doheny Towers, 838 N
    Doheny Dr 69
Dracker, 10824 Lindbrook Dr .. 24
Du Barry, 458 S Catalina 05
El Royale, 450 N Rossmore
    Ave 04
Elaine, 1245 N Vine 38
Embassy, 851 S Grand Ave 17
Fifield Wilshire, 2619
    Wilshire Blvd 57
Figueroa, 939 S Figueroa 15
Fireside Manor, 7070
    Franklin Ave 28
Garden Court, 7021
    Hollywood Blvd 28
Gates, 830 W 6th 17
Gaylord, 3355 Wilshire Blvd ... 10
Gene Autrys Continental,
    8401 Sunset Blvd 69
Harvey, 5640 Santa Monica

Blvd. 38
Hastings, 6162 Hollywood
    Blvd 28
Hayward, 206 W 6th 14
Hermoyne, 569 N Rossmore
    Ave 04
Hollywood Astoria, 7100
    Hillside Ave 46
Hollywood Biltmore, 1745 N
    Orange Dr 28
Hollywood Inn, 6724
    Hollywood Blvd. 28
Hollywood Landmark, 7055
    Franklin Ave 28
Hollywood Plaza, 1637 Vine ... 28
Hollywood Roosevelt, 7000
    Hollywood Blvd. 28
Hollywood Tower, 6200
    Franklin Ave 28
Hyatt House, 5547 W Century
    Blvd. 45
Langham, 715 S Normandie
    Ave 05
Lankershim, 230 W 7th 14
Leighton, 2127 W 6th 57
Lido, 6500 Yucca 28
Los Altos, 4121 Wilshire
    Blvd. 05
Los Angeles Hilton, 930
    Wilshire Blvd. 17
Marie Antoinette Towers,
    10787 Wilshire Blvd 24
Marie Antoinette, 10795
    Wilshire Blvd. 24
Mayan, 3049 W 8th 05
Mayfair, 1256 W 7th 17
Mayflower, 535 S Grand Ave .. 17
Miramar, 2000 Miramar 57
Montecito, 6650 Franklin Ave . 28
Oliver Cromwell, 418 S
    Normandie Ave 20
Olympian, 1903 W Olympic
    Blvd. 06
Padre, 1961 N Cahuenga
    Blvd. 28
Palms Wilshire, 626 S
    Alvarado 57
Park La Brea Towers, 6200 W
    3rd 36
Park Sunset, 8462 Sunset
    Blvd. 69
Park Westwood Towers, 969
    Hilgard Ave 24
Park Wilshire Apartment,
    2424 Wilshire Blvd 57
Ravenswood, 570 N
    Rossmore Ave 04
Rex Arms, 945 Wilshire Blvd .. 17
Rosslyn, 111 W 5th 13
Saint Paul, 1021 W 6th 17
San Carlos, 527 W 5th 13
Sands Of Hollywood, 7220
    Hollywood Blvd 46
Sands Sunset, 8775 Sunset
    Blvd. 69
Savoy Plaza, 601 W 6th 17
Sheraton-West, 2961 Wilshire
    Blvd. 10
Sheraton-West, 639 S
    Commonwealth Ave 05
Sir Francis Drake, 841 S
    Serrano 05

Los Angeles (Con.)   900

Sunset Terrace, 11783
 Sunset Blvd 49
Sunset Towers West, 8400
 Sunset Blvd 69
Talmadge, 3276 Wilshire
 Blvd 05
Teris, 1254 W 6th 17
Thunderbird Inn, 8300
 Sunset Blvd 69
Tiverton Terrace, 1052
 Tiverton Ave 24
Towers, 10941 Strathmore
 Dr 24
Twilight Doric, 4300
 Wilshire Blvd 10
Versailles, 614 S St Andrews
 Pl 05
Westchester, 1275
 Westchester Pl 19
Westwood Manor, 10527
 Wilshire Blvd 24
Westwood Sovereign, 10776
 Wilshire Blvd 24
Westwood Towers, 10717
 Wilshire Blvd 24
William Penn, 2208 W 8th ... 57
Wilshire Ardmore, 1129
 Westwood Blvd 24
Wilshire Carlton, Blvd & 875
 Comstock Av 24
Wilshire Carlton, 10635
 Wilshire Blvd 24
Wilshire Holmby, 10437
 . Wilshire Blvd 24
Wilshire Manor, 620 S St
 Andrews Pl 05
Wilshire Terrace, 10375
 Wilshire Blvd 24
Wilshire Terrace, 850 S
 Beverly Glen Bd 24
Wilshire Westwood, 10530
 Whilshire Blvd 24
Wilshire, 10620 Wilshire
 Blvd 24
Windsor, 3198 W 7th 05

BUILDINGS

A G Bartlett, 215 W 7th 14
A P Giannini, 649 S Olive....... 14
Adams Plaza, 1541 Wilshire
 Blvd 17
American Cement, 2404
 Wilshire Blvd 57
Apparel Mart, 112 W 9th....... 15
Atlantic Richfield Plaza 505
 S Flower 71
Atlantic Richfield Plaza 525
 S Flower 71
Atlantic Richfield Plaza 555
 S Flower 71
Bank Of America, 650 S
 Spring 14
Bank Of California, 550 S
 Flower 17
Bankers Life, 6400 Wilshire
 Blvd 48
Bankers, 629 S Hill 14
Banks Huntley, 634 S Spring ... 14
Barrington Plaza, 11700
 Wilshire Blvd 25
Bendix, 1206 Maple Ave 15

Brack Shops, Broadway
 Arcade, 542 S Broadway.... 13
Brack Shops, 527 W 7th 14
Broadway-Hill, 233 S
 Broadway 12
Broadway-Third, 306 W 3rd 13
Brockman, 520 W 7th 14
Buckeye, 9225 Sunset Blvd... 69
Builders Exchange, 656 S
 Los Angeles 14
Cahuenga Sunset, 6430 W
 Sunset Blvd 28
Cairns, 108 W 6th 14
California Federal Plaza,
 5670 Wilshire Blvd 36
California Highway, 120 S
 Spring 12
California State Office, 107 S
 Broadway 12
California State, 217 W 1st... 12
Canadian, 432 S Main 13
Capitol Tower, 1750 N Vine... 28
Casualty National 600 S
 Commonwealth Ave 05
Century City, 1801 Ave Of
 The Stars 67
Chapman, 756 S Broadway 14
Chester Williams, 215 W 5th.. 13
Citizens National Bank, 453
 S Spring 13
City Health, 111 E 1st................ 12
City National Bank, 9229
 Sunset Blvd 69
Civic Center, 205 S
 Broadway 12
Coast Federal, 315 W 9th....... 15
Commercial Exchange, 416 W
 8th 14
Consolidated, 607 S Hill 14
Continental Bank, 8730
 Sunset Blvd 69
Continental, 408 S Spring....... 13
Cooper, 860 S Los Angeles ... 14
Corporation, 724 S Spring....... 14
Cotton Exchange, 106 W 3rd.. 13
Crocker Citizens Plaza, 611
 W 6th 17
Douglas Oil, 530 W 6th 14
Douglas, 257 S Spring 12
Edison, 601 W 5th 17
Equitable Life, 411 W 9th 13
Equitable, 6253 Hollywood
 Blvd 28
F P Fay, 326 W 3rd................ 13
Faiabrino Giannini, 3400 W
 6th 20
Farmers And Merchants
 Bank, 124 W 4th 13
Farmers And Merchants
 Bank, 401 S Main 13
Fashion Design Center, 117
 W 9th 14
Federal, 11000 Wilshire Blvd.. 24
Federal, 300 N Los Angeles.... 12
Financial Center, 704 S
 Spring 14
First Federal, 1717 N
 Highland Ave 28
First Western Bank, 548 S
 Spring 13
Folb, Stanley, 6464 W Sunset
 Blvd 28
Foreman, 707 S Hill................ 14

Franklin Life, 3780 Wilshire
 Blvd 05
Garfield, 403 W 8th 14
Garland, 740 S Broadway 14
Guaranty, 6331 Hollywood
 Blvd 28
H W Hellman, 354 S Spring ... 13
Halliburton, 1709 W 8th 17
Harris Newmark, 127 E 9th.... 15
Hass, 219 W 7th................ 14
Havenstrite Oil, 811 W 7th..... 17
Hollywood Center, 1655 N
 Cherokee Ave 28
Hollywood First National,
 6777 Hollywood Blvd 28
Hollywood Pantages, 6233
 Hollywood Blvd 28
Hollywood Security, 6381
 Hollywood Blvd 28
Hollywood Western, 5504
 Hollywood Blvd 28
Hollywood, 6404 Hollywood
 Blvd 28
Holmby, 921 Westwood Blvd... 24
Home Furnishings Mart, 1933
 S Broadway 07
Home Savings, 307 W 8th...... 14
James Oviatt, 617 S Olive...... 14
Jewelry Trades, 220 W 5th.... 13
Jewish Community, 590 N
 Vermont Ave 04
Judson C Rives, 424 S
 Broadway 13
Kirkeby Center, 10889
 Wilshire Blvd 24
Knickerbocker, 643 S Olive.... 14
Lane Mortgage, 208 W 8th.... 14
Latin American, 430 S
 Broadway 13
Laughlin Homer, 315 S
 Broadway 13
Lee Tower, 5455 Wilshire
 Blvd 26
Liberty Mutual, 6006 Wilshire
 Blvd 36
Lissner, 524 S Spring 13
Los Angeles Home Furnishing
 Mart, 1933 S Broadway..... 07
M B Scott, 8721 Sunset
 Blvd 69
M J Connell, 746 S Los
 Angeles 14
Maxfield, 819 Santee 14
Mc Comas, 120 E 8th............ 14
Mc Kinley, 3757 Wilshire
 Blvd 10
Mercantile Center, 122 E 7th. 14
Merchandise Mart, 712 S
 Olive................................ 14
Merchants Exchange, 719 S
 Los Angeles 14
Metropolitan, 315 W 5th........ 13
Mid Wilshire Medical, 6317
 Wilshire Blvd 48
Mirror, 145 S Spring 12
Mobil, 612 S Flower................ 17
Mortgage Guarantee, 626 S
 Spring 14
Mutual Of Omaha, 5225
 Wilshire Blvd 36
National Oil, 609 S Grand
 Ave 17

41

Los Angeles (Con.)   900

National Title, 3540 Wilshire
Blvd.... 05
New Orpheum, 846 S
Broadway 14
Ninth And Broadway, 850 S
Broadway 14
Occidental Center, 1150 S
Olive 15
Occidental Life, 1151 S
Broadway 15
One Park Plaza 3250 Wilshire
Blvd. 10
Pacific Electric, 610 S Main... 14
Pacific Employers Group,
4050 Wilshire Blvd 10
Pacific Finance, 621 S Hope.. 17
Pacific Indemnity, 3200
Wilshire Blvd 05
Pacific Mutual, 523 W 6th 14
Pacific Southwest, 215 W
6th 14
Park Central, 412 W 6th 14
Park Wilshire Professional,
2412 W 7th 57
Patroitic Hall, 1816 S
Figueroa 15
Pershing Square, 448 S Hill... 13
Petroleum, 714 W Olympic
Blvd 15
Pioneer Savings & Loan,
4243 Wilshire Blvd 05
Professional, 1052 W 6th 17
Quinby, 650 S Grand Ave 17
Radio Center, 1509 Vine 28
Roosevelt, 727 W 7th 17
Rowan, 458 S Spring 13
San Fernando, 108 E 4th 13
San Fernando, 406 S Main 13
Santa Fe, 121 E 6th 14
Sassony, 356 S Broadway 13
Security, 510 S Spring 13
Shell Oil, 1008 W 6th 17
Signal Oil & Gas, 1010
Wilshire Blvd 17
Spreckels, 714 S Hill 14
Spring Arcade, 541 S Spring.. 13
Spring Street, 621 S Spring... 13
Standard Oil, 615 W Olympic
Blvd 15
Statler Center, 675 S
Figueroa 17
Statler Center, 900 Wilshire
Blvd 17
Stauffer Chemical, 500 S
Virgil Ave 05
Stock Exchange, 618 S
Spring 14
Sunset Doheny West, 9255
Sunset Blvd 69
Taft, 1680 Vine 28
Taul, 312 E 1st 12
Texaco, 3350 Wilshire Blvd.... 10
Third And Broadway, 306 W
3rd 13
Tidewater, 4201 Wilshireblvd.. 05
Time Oil, 5150 Wilshire Blvd.. 36
Times Mirror, 202 W 1st 12
Tishman, 3400 Wilshire Bd.... 10
Title Insurance, 433 S
Spring 13
Transport Indemnity, 3670

Wilshire Blvd 05
Travelers Insurance, 3600
Wilshire Blvd 10
Union Bank Center, 3810
Wilshire Blvd 05
Union Bank, 325 W 8th 14
Union Bank, 742 S Hill 14
Union Federal, 426 S Spring.. 13
Union Oil Center, 461 S
Boylston 17
United California Bank, 600
S Spring 14
United Of America, 4055
Wilshire Blvd 10
United States Borax, 3075
Wilshire Blvd 05
United States Courthouse,
Temple & Spring 12
United, 707 S Broadway 14
Van Nuys I N, 210 N 7th 14
Walter P Story, 610 S
Broadway 14
Western Federal, 606 S Hill
St 14
Western Pacific, 1031 S
Broadway 15
Westlake Park, 2024 W 6th... 57
Westrade, 420 S San Pedro.... 13
Wilcox, 206 S Spring 12
Wilflower, 515 S Flower 17
William Fox, 608 S Hill 14
Wilshire Center Company,
5371 Wilshire Blvd 36
Wilshire Center, 3055
Wilshire Blvd 10
Wilshire Central, 3723
Wilshire Blvd 05
Wilshire Grand, 611 Wilshire
Blvd 17
Wilshire Professional, 3875
Wilshire Blvd 10
Wilshire Tower, 5514 Wilshire
Blvd 36
Wilshire West, 10880 Wilshire
Blvd 24
Wilshire Westlake, 2007
Wilshire Blvd 57
Wilson, 132 W 1st 12
Wright And Callender, 405 S
Hill 13
Yellow Pages, 3636 Beverly
Blvd 04
Yucca Vine, 6305 Yucca 28

GOVERNMENT OFFICES

California State Office, 107 S
Broadway 12
California State, 217 W 1st... 12
City Hall, 200 N Spring 12
City Health, 111 E 1st 12
Civic Center, 205 S
Broadway 12
County Court House, 110 N
Grand Ave 12
County Engineering, 108 W
2nd 12
Hall Of Administration, 500
Temple 12
Hall Of Justice, 211 Temple... 12
Hall Of Record New, 320
Temple 12
Hall Of Record Old, 220 N

Broadway 12
Los Angeles City Police
Administration, 150 N Los
Angeles 12
United States Courthouse,
Temple & Spring 12
United States Post Office,
300 N Los Angeles 12

HOSPITALS

Baldwin Hills, 5525 W
Slauson Ave 56
Bel Air Chateau, 2311
Roscomare Rd 24
Bella Vista, 5425 E Pomona
Blvd 22
Belvedere, 127 S Utah 33
Beverly Glen, 10361 W Pico
Blvd 64
Beverly Hills Doctors, 10390
Santa Monica Bd 25
Beverly Sunset Medical, 9201
Sunset Blvd 69
Brentwood Veterans
Administration Facility 25
California Babies &
Childrens, 1415 S Grand
Ave 15
California Lutheran, 1414 S
Hope 15
California Medical, 1401 S
Hope 15
Childrens, 4614 W Sunset
Blvd 27
City Of Hope Administration
Office, 208 W 8th 14
City View, 3711 Baldwin 31
Community Of Los Angeles,
4081 E Olympic Blvd 23
Crenshaw Center, 3831
Stocker 08
Crenshaw Medical Arts
Center, 3756 Santa
Rosalta Dr 08
Crenshaw Medical Center,
3701 Stocker 08
Crippled Childrens, 3160
Geneva 05
Doctors, 325 W Jefferson
Blvd 07
Eastside General, 4056
Whittier Blvd 23
Edgemont, 4841 Hollywood
Blvd 27
Eye & Ear, 1314 N Vermont
Ave 27
French, 531 W College 12
Gateway, 1891 Effie 26
General Hospital, 1200 N
State 33
Good Samaritan, 1212
Shattoo 17
Hollywood Community, 6245
Delongpre Ave 28
Hollywood Med' il Center,
6755 Hollywood Blvd 28
Hollywood West, 1233 N La
Brea Ave 38
Japanese, 101 S Fickett 33
John Wesley, 2826 S Hope 07

Los Angeles (Con.)　　　　900

Kaiser Foundation, 4867
　Sunset Blvd 27
Lincoln, 443 S Soto 33
Linde Medical, 10921
　Wilshire Blvd 24
Medical Office, 1136 W 6th.... 17
Medico Dental, 947 W 8th 17
Monte Sano, 2834 Glendale
　Blvd 39
Morningside, 8711 S Harvard
　Blvd 47
Mount Sinai General, 8720
　Beverly Blvd 48
Oak Park Community, 369 W
　Manchester Ave 03
Olmsted Memorial, 1322 N
　Vermont Ave 27
Optical, 314 W 6th 14
Park View, 1021 N Hoover 29
Queen Of Angels, 2301
　Bellevue Ave 26
Rose, 3858 W 54th 43
Saint Annes, 155 N
　Occidental Ave 26
Saint Vincents, 2131 W 3rd ... 57
San Vincente, 6000 San
　Vincente Blvd 36
Santa Fe, 610 S St Louis 23
Santa Marta, 328 N
　Humpreys Ave 22
Shriners 20
South Hoover, 5700 S Hoover ... 37
Southern California, 3261
　Overland Ave 34
Stephan A Seymour, 3324
　Sunset Blvd 26
Sunset Boulevard, 4670
　Sunset Blvd 27
Sunset Medical, 6642 W
　Sunset Blvd 28
U C L A Medical Center,
　10833 Le Conte Ave 24
University, 3787 S Vermont
　Ave 07
View Park, 5035 Coliseum 16
Wadsworth General Veterans
　Administration Facility 25
Washington, 12101 W
　Washington Bd 66
West Wilshire Medical Center,
　11600 Wilshire Blvd 25
Westlake Medical, 1913
　Wilshire Blvd 57
Westlake, 644 S Alvarado 57
Weyburn Medical, 10911
　Weyburn Blvd 24
White Memorial, 1720
　Brooklyn Ave 33
Wilshire Carthay Medical,
　6333 Wilshire Blvd 48
Wilshire La Jolla Medical,
　6360 Wilshire Blvd 48
Wilshire Medical Arts, 6221
　Wilshire Blvd 48
Wilshire Medical, 1930
　Wilshire Blvd 57

UNIVERSITIES AND COLLEGES

East Los Angeles, 5357
　Brooklyn Ave 22
George Pepperdine, 8035 S

Vermont Ave 44
Immaculate Heart, 2021 N
　Western Ave 27
Loma Linda University, 1720
　Brooklyn Ave 33
Los Angeles City, 855 N
　Vermont Ave 29
Los Angeles College Of
　Optometry, 950 W
　Jefferson Blvd 07
Los Angeles Pacific, 625
　Coleman Ave 42
Los Angeles Trade-Technical,
　400 W Washington Blvd 15
Loyola University School Of
　Law, 1137 S Grand Ave 15
Loyola University, 7101 W
　80th 45
Marymount, 10643 Sunset
　Blvd 24
Metropolitan College Of
　Business, 1601 S Olive 15
Mount Saint Marys, 12001
　Chalon Rd 49
Occidental, 1600 Campus
　Rd 41
Pacific States University,
　1516 S Western Ave 06
Southwestern University,
　1121 S Hill 15
State College At Los Angeles,
　5151 State College Dr 32
U C L A Extension Division,
　813 S Hill 14
U C L A Medical Center,
　10833 Le Conte Ave 24
U S C School Of Medicine,
　2025 Zonal Ave 33
U S C School Of Public
　Administration, 145 S
　Spring 12
U S C University College,
　3551 University Ave 07
U S C University Park, 3551
　University Ave 07
University Of California At
　Los Angeles, 405 Hilgard
　Ave 24
Van Norman University, 1001
　N Vermont Ave 29
West Coast University, 3006
　W 7th 05
Wilshire Medical Arts, 6221
　Wilshire Blvd 48
Woodbury, 1017 Wilshire
　Blvd 17

GOVERNMENT OFFICES

California State Office, 107 S
　Broadway 12
California State, 217 W 1st 12
City Hall, 200 N Spring 12
City Health, 111 E 1st 12
Civic Center, 205 S
　Broadway 12
County Court House, 110 N
　Grand Ave 12
County Engineering, 108 W
　2nd 12
Hall Of Administration, 500
　Temple 12
Hall Of Justice, 211 Temple ... 12

Hall Of Record New, 320
　Temple 12
Hall Of Record Old, 220 N
　Broadway 12
Los Angeles City Police
　Administration, 150 N Los
　Angeles 12
United States Courthouse,
　Temple & Spring 12
United States Post Office,
　300 N Los Angeles 12

HOSPITALS

Baldwin Hills, 5525 W
　Slauson Ave 56
Bel Air Chateau, 2311
　Roscomare Rd 24
Bella Vista, 5425 E Pomona
　Blvd 22
Belvedere, 127 S Utah 33
Beverly Glen, 10361 W Pico
　Blvd 64
Beverly Hills Doctors, 10390
　Santa Monica Bd 25
Beverly Sunset Medical, 9201
　Sunset Blvd 69
Brentwood Veterans
　Administration Facility 25
California Babies &
　Childrens, 1415 S Grand
　Ave 15
California Lutheran, 1414 S
　Hope 15
California Medical, 1401 S
　Hope 15
Childrens, 4614 W Sunset
　Blvd 27
City Of Hope Administration
　Office, 208 W 8th 14
City View, 3711 Baldwin 31
Community Of Los Angeles,
　4081 E Olympic Blvd 23
Crenshaw Center, 3831
　Stocker 08
Crenshaw Medical Arts
　Center, 3756 Santa
　Rosalta Dr 08
Crenshaw Medical Center,
　3701 Stocker 08
Crippled Childrens, 3160
　Geneva 05
Doctors, 325 W Jefferson
　Blvd 07
Eastside General, 4056
　Whittier Blvd 23
Edgemont, 4841 Hollywood
　Blvd 27
Eye & Ear, 1314 N Vermont
　Ave 27
French, 531 W College 12
Gateway, 1891 Effie 26
General Hospital, 1200 N
　State 33
Good Samaritan, 1212
　Shattoo 17
Hollywood Community, 6245
　Delongpre Ave 28
Hollywood Medical Center,
　6755 Hollywood Blvd 28

43

Los Angeles (Con.)	900
Hollywood West, 1233 N La Brea Ave	38
Japanese, 101 S Fickett	33
John Wesley, 2826 S Hope	07
Kaiser Foundation, 4867 Sunset Blvd	27
Lincoln, 443 S Soto	33
Linde Medical, 10921 Wilshire Blvd	24
Medical Office, 1136 W 6th	17
Medico Dental, 947 W 8th	17
Monte Sano, 2834 Glendale Blvd	39
Morningside, 8711 S Harvard Blvd	47
Mount Sinai General, 8720 Beverly Blvd	48
Oak Park Community, 369 W Manchester Ave	03
Olmsted Memorial, 1322 N Vermont Ave	27
Optical, 314 W 6th	14
Park View, 1021 N Hoover	29
Queen Of Angels, 2301 Bellevue Ave	26
Rose, 3858 W 54th	43
Saint Annes, 155 N Occidental Blvd	26
Saint Vincents, 2131 W 3rd	57
San Vincente, 6000 San Vincente Blvd	36
Santa Fe, 610 S St Louis	23
Santa Marta, 328 N Humpreys Ave	22
Shriners	20
South Hoover, 5700 S Hoover	57
Southern California, 3261 Overland Ave	34
Stephan A Seymour, 3324 Sunset Blvd	26
Sunset Boulevard, 4670 Sunset Blvd	27
Sunset Medical, 6642 W Sunset Blvd	28
U C L A Medical Center, 10833 Le Conte Ave	24
University, 3787 S Vermont Ave	07
View Park, 5035 Coliseum	16
Wadsworth General Veterans Administration Facility	25
Washington, 12101 W Washington Bd	66
West Wilshire Medical Center, 11600 Wilshire Blvd	25
Westlake Medical, 1913 Wilshire Blvd	57
Westlake, 644 S Alvarado	57
Weyburn Medical, 10911 Weyburn Ave	24
White Memorial, 1720 Brooklyn Ave	33
Wilshire Carthay Medical, 6333 Wilshire Blvd	48
Wilshire La Jolla Medical, 6360 Wilshire Blvd	48
Wilshire Medical Arts, 6221 Wilshire Blvd	48
Wilshire Medical, 1930 Wilshire Blvd	57

UNIVERSITIES AND COLLEGES

East Los Angeles, 5357 Brooklyn Ave	22
George Pepperdine, 8035 S Vermont Ave	44
Immaculate Heart, 2021 N Western Ave	27
Loma Linda University, 1720 Brooklyn Ave	33
Los Angeles City, 855 N Vermont Ave	29
Los Angeles College Of Optometry, 950 W Jefferson Blvd	07
Los Angeles Pacific, 625 Coleman Ave	42
Los Angeles Trade-Technical, 400 W Washington Blvd	15
Loyola University School Of Law, 1137 S Grand Ave	15
Loyola University, 7101 W 80th	45
Marymount, 10643 Sunset Blvd	24
Metropolitan College Of Business, 1601 S Olive	15
Mount Saint Marys, 12001 Chalon Rd	49
Occidental, 1600 Campus Rd	41
Pacific States University, 1516 S Western Ave	06
Southwestern University, 1121 S Hill	15
State College At Los Angeles, 5151 State College Dr	32
U C L A Extension Division, 813 S Hill	14
U C L A Medical Center, 10833 Le Conte Ave	24
U S C School Of Medicine, 2025 Zonal Ave	33
U S C School Of Public Administration, 145 S Spring	12
U S C University College, 3551 University Ave	07
U S C University Park, 3551 University Ave	07
University Of California At Los Angeles, 405 Hilgard Ave	24
Van Norman University, 1001 N Vermont Ave	29
West Coast University, 3006 W 7th	05
Wilshire Medical Arts, 6221 Wilshire Blvd	48
Woodbury, 1017 Wilshire Blvd	17

MODESTO   953

POST OFFICE BOXES

Box Nos.		
1-1532	El Viejo Sta	53
1601-2145	Hudson Sta	54
2201-2546	Westside Sta	51
3001-3489	El Viejo Sta	53
3501-4445	Main Office	52

RURAL ROUTES

1	55
2	50
3,4,5	51
6	50
7,8,9	51
10	50

STATIONS, BRANCHES AND UNITS

Hudson Sta	54
Mc Henry Village Sta	50
Roosevelt Sta	50
Scenic Center Br	50
South Modesto Br	50
Westside Sta	51
General Delivery	53
Postmaster	50

MT VIEW   940

STATIONS, BRANCHES AND UNITS

Blossom Valley Sta	40

NEWPORT BEACH   926

POST OFFICE BOXES

Box Nos.		
1-537	Balboa Island Sta	62
501-999	Balboa Sta	61
1001-2346	Main Office	63
4001-5050	Irvine	64

STATIONS, BRANCHES AND UNITS

Balboa Sta	61
Balboa Island Sta	62
Irvine Br	64
General Delivery	60
Postmaster	60

NORTH HOLLYWOOD   916

POST OFFICE BOXES

Box Nos.		
1-999	Main Office	03
1000-1778	Studio City Sta	04
2001-2540	Toluca Lake Sta	02
3000-3297	Victory Center Annex Sta	09
4001-4917	Valley Village Sta	07
5001-5099	Bendix Sta	05
6000-6099	Main Office	03
8001-8699	Universal City Br	08
9151-9747	Victory Center Annex	09

STATIONS, BRANCHES AND UNITS

Bendix Sta	05
Studio City Sta	04

North Hollywood (Con.)   916
Toluca Lake Sta 02
Universal City Br 06
Valley Plaza Sta 06
Valley Village Sta 07
Victory Center Annex Sta........... 05
General Delivery 03
Postmaster 03

APARTMENTS, HOTELS, MOTELS

Aloha Garden, 6227 Craner
  Ave 06
Aqua Vista, 11022 Aqua
  Vista 02
Biltmore Palms, 5017
  Bakman Ave 01
Chandler Pines, 12541
  Chandler Blvd 07
Coral Gables, 3874
  Willowcrest Ave 04
Denny Plaza, 6737 Denny
  Ave 06
Diplomat, 12360 Riverside
  Dr 07
Fulton Plaza, 7144 Fulton
  Ave 05
Glenn Valley, 12933 Ventura
  Blvd 04
Lankershim Gardens, 5110
  Bakman Ave 01
Mayers Apartments, 10920
  Ventura Blvd 04
New Frontier, 7130 Ethel Ave. 05
North Hollywood, 6724
  Tujunga Ave 06
Oxnard Dunes, 12524
  Oxnard 06
Park Village, 11563 Magnolia
  Blvd 01
Parkmoor Gardens, 11308
  Moorpark 02
Sans Souci, 6045 Whitsett
  Ave 06
Sheraton Universal Hotel, 30
  Universal City Plz 08
Sherman, 11439 Sherman
  Way 05
Sportsmen's Lodge Hotel,
  12825 Ventura Blvd 04
Tahitienne, 4616 Cahuenga
  Ave 02
Toluca Isle, 4604 Cahuenga
  Ave 02
Toluca Lake, 4258 Cahuenga
  Ave 02
Toluca Lanai, 4130
  Cahuenga Ave 02
Toluca Tropics, 10250
  Camarillo 02
Twin Palms, 11458 Burbank
  Blvd 01
Valley Heart Terrace, 12958
  Valleyheart Dr 04
Valley Terrace, 6706 Laurel
  Grove Ave 06
Valli Sahara, 4020 Arch Dr 04
Victory Plaza, 11601 Victory
  Blvd 06
Villa Nova, 7125 Fulton Ave 05
Villi Sands, 4040 Arch Dr 04

Whipple Pine, 10869
  Whipple 02
Wilson, 4918 Cahuenga Ave... 01

HOSPITALS

Colonial Convalescent, 10830
  Oxnard 06
Community, 6421 Coldwater
  Canyon Ave 06
Toluca Lake, 10425 Magnolia
  Blvd 01
Valley Doctors, 12629
  Riverside Dr 07

OAKLAND   946

POST OFFICE BOXES

Box Nos.
1-2099   Civic Center
                 Station........... 04
2101-2299   Fitchburg Sta... 21
2301-2699   Airport Sta.... 14
2701-2799   Dimond Sta 02
2801-2999   Rockridge Sta.. 18
3001-3999   Temescal Sta .. 09
5001-5999   Eastmont Sta... 05
6001-6999   Elmhurst Sta... 03
7001-7999   Fruitvale Sta ... 01
8001-8999   Emeryville Br... 62
9001-9999   Mills College
                 Sta............. 13
10001-10999   Grand Lake...... 10
11001-11999   Piedmont Sta ... 11
12001-12999   Civic Center
                 Station........... 04
13001-13999   Station E........ 11
19001-19999   Laurel Station .. 19
23001-24999   Main Office 23

STATIONS, BRANCHES AND UNITS

Airport Sta............................... 14
Army Terminal Sta 26
Childrens Fairyland Sta 22
Civic Center Sta...................... 04
Dimond Sta 02
Eastmont Sta 05
Elmhurst Sta 03
Emeryville Br.......................... 08
Fitchburg Sta 21
Fruitvale Sta........................... 01
Grand Lake Sta 10
Kaiser Center Sta.................... 12
Laurel Sta............................... 19
Mills College Sta..................... 13
Naval Hospital Sta.................. 27
Naval Supply Center Sta......... 25
Piedmont Sta........................... 11
Rockridge Sta......................... 18
Temescal Sta 09
General Delivery 17
Postmaster 15

APARTMENTS, HOTELS, MOTELS

Claremont, Po Box 2807 18
Coit-Ramsey, 1445 Harrison ... 12
Harrison, 1415 Harrison 12
Hill Castle Apartments, 1431
  Jackson 12

Lake Merritt, 1800 Madison. ... 12
Leamington, 1814 Franklin..... 12
Menlo, 344 13th...................... 12
Saint Mark, 394 12th.............. 07
San Pablo, 1955 San Pablo
  Ave 12
Touraine, 559 16th 12

BUILDINGS

Bank Of America, 1212
  Broadway 12
Bermuda, 2150 Franklin......... 12
Broadway, 1419 Broadway..... 12
California, 1736 Franklin........ 12
Cathedral, 1615 Broadway 12
Central, 436 14th................... 12
Chamber Of Commerce, 1320
  Webster 12
El Dorado, 360 22nd.............. 12
Financial Center, 405 14th..... 12
First Savings, 1706
  Broadway 12
Fox Oakland, 1815 Telegraph
  Ave 12
Franklin, 1624 Franklin.......... 12
Fruitvale Professional, 3124
  East 14th.............................. 01
Insurance, 1404 Franklin........ 12
Jules, 364 14th....................... 12
Kaiser Center, 300 Lakeside
  Dr 12
Labor Temple, 2315 Valdez 12
Latham Square, 508 16th 12
Ludar, 2030 Franklin 12
Mc Mullen, 1305 Franklin....... 12
Medical, 1904 Franklin 12
Morgan, 512 16th................... 12
Ordway, 2150 Valdez 12
Pacific, 610 16th..................... 12
Plaza, 506 15th...................... 12
Popper Bernheim, 414 13th.... 12
Press, 408 12th 07
Tribune Tower, 409 13th......... 12
Union Bank, 1540 San Pablo . 12
Union Trust, 428 13th 12
United California Bank, 1330
  Broadway 12
Wakefield, 426 17th................ 12
Webster, 1956 Webster 12
1440 Broadway, 1440
  Broadway 12
1916 Broadway, 1916
  Broadway 12
1924 Broadway, 1924
  Broadway 12

GOVERNMENT OFFICES

City Hall, 14th &
  Washington........................... 12
County Administration, 1221
  Oak...................................... 12
County Of Alameda Health
  Department, 499 5th........... 07
Court House. 1225 Fallon....... 12
Federal, 201 13th 12
Main Post Office, 1675 7th 07
Oakland Hall Of Justice, 600
  Washington........................... 07
State, 1111 Jackson................ 07

45

Oakland (Con.)   946

HOSPITALS

Booth Memorial, 2794 Garden	01
Childrens Of East Bay, 5105 Dover	09
Civic Center, 390 40th	09
Highland-Alameda County, 2701 14th Ave	06
Kaiser Foundation, 280 West Macarthur Bd	11
Merritt, 3321 Webster	09
Oakland, 2648 East 14th	01
Peralta, 450 30th	09
Providence, 3012 Summit	09

UNIVERSITIES AND COLLEGES

California College Of Arts & Crafts, 5212 Broadway	18
College Of The Holy Names, 3500 Mountain Blvd	19
Grove Street College 5714 Grove	09
Laney College 900 Fallon	07
Merritt College 12500 Campus Dr	19
Mills College, Seminary Av & Macarthur	13

ONTARIO   917

POST OFFICE BOXES

Box Nos.		
1-999	Main Office	61
1001-1999	Plaza Center Sta	62

RURAL ROUTES

1		61

STATIONS, BRANCHES AND UNITS

Airport Sta	61
Plaza Center Sta	62
General Delivery	61
Postmaster	61

ORANGE   926

POST OFFICE BOXES

Box Nos.		
1-999	Plaza Sta	66
1000-1999	West Orange Sta	68
2000-2999	El Modeno Sta	69
3000-3999	Olive Sta	65
5000-6999	Main Office	67

STATIONS, BRANCHES AND UNITS

El Modena Sta	67
Olive Sta	65
Plaza Sta	66
Villa Park Rural Br	67
West Orange Sta	68
General Delivery	67

Postmaster	67
Star Route	67

BUILDINGS

Orange Mall	65
The City	68
Town And Country	68
Union Bank Square	68

HOSPITALS

Chapman General Hosp 2601 E Chapman	69
Childrens Hosp.,1109 W.la Veta	68
Orange Co. Med. Center.,101 S. Manchester	68
St. Joseph Hosp., 1100 W. Stewart	68

UNIVERSITIES AND COLLEGES

Champman College., 333 N. Glassell	66

PALO ALTO   943

POST OFFICE BOXES

Box Nos.		
1-1505	Main Office	02
V-1-V-30	Veterans Hosp Br	04
2001-9680	Stanford Br	05
10000-10999	East Palo Alto Sta	04
11001-11806	A Sta	06

STATIONS, BRANCHES AND UNITS

East Palo Alto Sta	0.
Stanford Br	05
Veterans Bureau Hospital Sta	04
General Delivery	02.
Postmaster	02

APARTMENTS, HOTELS, MOTELS

Alma Terrace, 3039 Alma	06
Amarillo Apartments, 2570 W Bayshore	03
Cabana, 4290 El Camino	06
Casa Real, 360 Forest	01
Channing House, 850 Webster	01
Craig, 164 Hamilton	01
Escondido Village, Stanford University	05
Everett House Community, 360 Everett	01
Forest Towers, 501 Forest	01
Galantine Apartments, 724 Arastradero Rd	06
Laning Chateaux, 345 Forest..	01
Midtown Gardens, 2727 Midtown Ct	03
Oak Creek Apartments, 1600 Willow	04
Palo Alto Apartment, 101 Alma	01

Palo Alto Town House Apartments, 2721 Midtown Ct	03
President, 488 University	01
Rickeys Studio Inn, 4219 El Camino	06
Stanford Villa, 3351 Alma	06
Tan Plaza Continental, 580 Arastradero	06
Tan Plaza International, 565 Arastradero	06
Tan Village, 1094 Tanland Dr	03
Villa Capri, 3085 Middlefield..	06
Villa Capri, 750 University Ave	01
Willow Creek, 1850 Willow	04

BUILDINGS

Palo Alto Office Center, 525 University Ave	01
Palo Alto Square 3000 El Camino	04
Stanford Shopping Center, 150 El Camino	04
Town & Country Village, 855 El Camino	01

HOSPITALS

Stanford Medical Center, 300 Pasteur	04
Veterans Admin Hosp, 3801 Miranda	04

UNIVERSITIES AND COLLEGES

Stanford University	05

PASADENA   911

POST OFFICE BOXES

Box Nos.		
A-Z	Main Office	09
1-60	Arroyo Annex	09
1-200	C Sta	04
1-1199	Main Office	02
1200-1999	Main Office	09
2000-2999	D Sta	05
3000-3999	Rose Bowl	03
4000-4999	Catalina Sta	06
5000-5999	East Pasadena Sta	07
8001-8384	San Marino Br..	08

STATIONS, BRANCHES AND UNITS

Catalina Sta	06
East Pasade na Sta	07
Rose Bowl Sta	03
San Marino Br	08
General Delivery	09
Postmaster	09

APARTMENTS, HOTELS, MOTELS

Green, 50 E Green	05
Huntington Sheraton, 1401 S Oak Knoll	09

Pasadena (Con.) 911

Pasadena Hilton 150 South Los Robles Avenue		01
Sage Motor Lodge, 1633 E Colorado		06

BUILDINGS

Citizens Bank	01
First Western	01
Mutual	01
Oak Knoll Bank	01
Professional	01
Security	01
Union Bank	01

GOVERNMENT OFFICES

City Hall	09

HOSPITALS

California Emergency, 536 S Arroyo Pkwy	05
City Of Pasadena Emergency Hospital, 142 N Arroyo Pkwy	03
Huntington Memorial, 100 Congress	05
Las Encinas, 2900 Del Mar Blvd	07
Pasadena Community, 1845 N Fair Oaks	03
St.luke, 2632 E Washington Blvd	07

UNIVERSITIES AND COLLEGES

Ambassador College, Box 1250	09
Cal Tech, 1201 E Calif Blvd	09
Fuller Theological Seminary, 135 N Oakland	01
Highland College, 450 Ave 64	05
Pasadena City College, 1570 E Colorado Blvd	06
Pasadena College, 1539 E Howard	04

POMONA 917

POST OFFICE BOXES

Box Nos.		
A-J	Pomona	66
1-1372	Central District Sta	69
2001-2815	Pomona	66
4001-4146	Diamond Bar Br	65

STATIONS, BRANCHES

Central District Sta	66
Diamond Bar Br	65
Yorba Sta	67
General Delivery	66
Postmaster	66

HOSPITALS

Pacific State Hospital, 3530 Pomona Blvd		68
Pomona Valley Community Hospital, 1798 N Garey Ave		67

UNIVERSITIES AND COLLEGES

Calif State Polytechnic College, 3801 W Temple Ave		68

REDONDO BEACH 902

POST OFFICE BOXES

Box Nos.		
1-513	Main Office	77
1-746	Hermosa Beach Br	54
1000-1389	North Redondo Beach Sta	78

STATIONS, BRANCHES AND UNITS

Hermosa Beach Br	54
North Redondo Beach Sta	78
General Delivery Hermosa Bea	54
General Delivery Redondo Bea	77
Postmaster	77

APARTMENTS, HOTELS, MOTELS

Plush Horse Inn, 1700 S. Pacific Coast Hwy		77
Portofino Inn, 260 Portofino Way		77

BUILDINGS

T R W, Inc., 1 Space Park		78

HOSPITALS

South Bay Hospital, 514 N. Prospect Ave		77

REDWOOD CITY 940

POST OFFICE BOXES

Box Nos.		
1-2180	Downtown Finance Section	64
5001-5598	Main Office	63

STATIONS, BRANCHES AND UNITS

Downtown Sta	63
Middlefield Road Br	61
Oak Knoll Sta	61
Woodside Br	62
General Delivery	63
Postmaster	64

RICHMOND 948

POST OFFICE BOXES

Box Nos.		
1-476	Point Richmond Sta	07
1-807	San Pablo Br	06
150-647	A Sta	08
691-988	El Sobrante Br	03
1001-1872	Main Office	02

STATIONS, BRANCHES AND UNITS

El Sobrante Br	03
Mira Vista Sta	05
Point Richmond Sta	07
San Pablo Br	06
General Delivery	02
Postmaster	02

APARTMENTS, HOTELS, MOTELS

Aztec Apartments, 2677 Rollingwood Dr		06
Bond, 334 2nd St		01
Brookside Apartments, 1230 Brookside Dr		06
Casa Del Sol Apartments, 5017 San Pablo Dm Rd		03
Chancelor Apartments, 225 16th		01
De Anza Sands Apartments, 4670 San Pablo Dm Rd		03
Denver, 621 Mac Donald Ave		01
Don, 10th & Nevin Ave		01
Frazier, 56 Gertrude Ave		01
John L Davis, 430 Mac Donald Ave		01
Johnson, 1514 Mac Donald Ave		01
Leo, 275 16th St		01
Mac, 50 Washington Ave		01
Metropolitan, 208 23rd St		04
Monson Apartments, 4017 Garvin Ave		05
Montoya Garden Apartments, 5005 Montoya Ave		05
Nichol Court Apartments, 226 28th		04
Richmond Hacienda, 1300 Roosevelt		01
Richmond, 1214 Mac Donald Ave		01
Ricks, 335 1st St		01
Sun Garden Apartments, 4231 San Pablo Dm Rd		03
Travelers, 521 Mac Donald Ave		01
Travelodge, 425 24th St		04

BUILDINGS

American Trust, 1001 Mac Donald Ave		01
Standard Oil, Po Box 1272		02

GOVERNMENT OFFICES

County Building, 100 37th		05

47

Richmond (Con.) 948

Richmond City Hall, Civic
Center & Mac Donald........ 04

HOSPITALS

Convalescent Church Lane
Branch, Dover & Church
Lane................................. 06
Greenvale Convalescent,
2140 Vale Rd................... 06
Kaiser, S 14th & Cutting
Blvd................................. 04
Richmond Convalescent, 955
23rd St............................ 04
Richmond, 23rd & Gaynor 04
Shields & Terrell
Convalescent, 1919
Cutting Blvd.................... 04
Ventura Sanitarium, 1520
Ventura............................ 06
Walkers Convalescent, 955
23rd St............................ 04

MILITARY INSTALLATIONS

Pt. Molate Naval Fuel Depot... 04

UNIVERSITIES AND COLLEGES

Contra Costa.......................... 06

RIVERSIDE 925

POST OFFICE BOXES

Box Nos.
1-1799   Main Office 02
2000-2999 Magnolia
           Center Sta...... 06
3000-3999 Rubidoux Br 09
4000-4999 Hardman
           Center Sta...... 04
5000-5999 Canyon Crest
           Sta................ 07
7000-7999 Arlington Sta..... 03
8000-8999 La Sierra Br 05

RURAL ROUTES

1... 03
3... 04
5... 09

STATIONS, BRANCHES AND UNITS

Arlanza Village Sta................ 05
Arlington Sta........................ 03
Canyon Crest Sta.................. 07
Casa Blanca Sta.................... 04
Edgemont Br......................... 08
Hardman Center Sta.............. 04
Highgrove Br........................ 07
Institute Sta......................... 03
La Sierra Sta........................ 05
Magnolia Center Sta............. 06
March A F B Br...................... 08
Pedley Br............................. 09
Rubidoux Br.......................... 09
General Delivery.................... 02
Postmaster........................... 02

APARTMENTS, HOTELS, MOTELS

Ace, 3593 Wallace 09
Aloha, 905 La Cadena Dr........ 01
Alvord Heights Trailer Village,
12149 Indiana Ave............ 03
Ambler, 10900 Magnolia Ave.. 05
Arcadia Acres, 3720
Crestmore Rd.................... 09
Arlington, 11011 Magnolia
Ave................................... 05
Aurea Vista, 3480 8th............ 01
Avalon Trailer Village, 3319
Avalon.............................. 09
Bahia, 7450 Mt Vernon........... 04
Bel-Air Mobile Estates, 6154
Mission Blvd..................... 09
Box Springs Canyon, Bos
Springs Grade.................... 07
Braemar Co-Op, 4600
Braemar Pl........................ 01
California Mobile Estates,
3695 Avalon....................... 09
Caravan Inn, 1860 8th............ 07
Colonial, 4221 Brockton Ave.... 01
Cottonwood, 5171 Mission
Blvd................................. 09
Country Club, 2005 Linden...... 07
Crescent, 3474 8th................. 01
Dale, 11848 Revena Ave......... 05
De Anza Motel & Apartments,
3425 Market...................... 01
De Luxe Madison, 7490
Magnolia Ave.................... 04
Edgemont, 13810 Highway
395................................... 08
El Camino, 1616 8th............... 07
Elm, 5741 Mission Blvd.......... 09
Farm House, 1393 8th............. 07
Franklin Square, 4160
Ottawa Ave....................... 07
Glen Avon Mobile Estates,
9861 Mission Blvd............. 09
Harmony Motel And Trailer
Park, 6045 Mission Blvd ... 09
Hi-Ho, 2055 8th..................... 07
Highgrove Trailer Court, 220
La Cadena Dr.................... 01
Holiday House, 13931
Ellsworth Ave................... 08
Imperial 400, 3225 Main........ 01
Imperial, 2045 Linden............ 07
Iowa Motel, 3735 Iowa Ave..... 07
Jefferson Arms, 3742
Jefferson.......................... 04
La Cadena, 219 La Cadena
Dr..................................... 01
La Casa Contenta, 1435 8th.... 07
Las Palmas, 5943 Palm Ave .. 06
Magnolia Palms, 6979 Palm
Ave................................... 06
Magnolia, 6555 Brockton
Ave................................... 06
Major House, 2032 Linden...... 07
Mark Allison, 4575 Jurupa
Ave................................... 06
Market House Motel &
Apartments, 1077 La
Cadena Dr........................ 01
Mission Inn Garden, 3649
7th................................... 01
Mission, 5687 Mission Blvd.... 09

Mount Vernon Manor, 7432
Mt Vernon........................ 04
Mountain View Trailer Court,
5479 34th......................... 09
Mowrys Motel & Apartments,
9646 Magnolia.................. 03
Orange Tract, 6353 Mission
Blvd................................. 09
Palm Rose Garden, 6684
Palm Ave.......................... 06
Palm View, 6038 Mission
Blvd................................. 09
Palms, 9245 Mission Blvd...... 09
Paradise Manor, 4206 Tyler
Ave................................... 03
Park Terrace, 9452 California
Ave................................... 03
Plaza Lane, 4572 Plaza Lane. 09
Plaza, 3824 8th..................... 01
Poolside, 9442 Hayes............ 03
Riverside Motor Inn, 5115
Mission Blvd..................... 09
Riverside Town House, 3412
5th................................... 01
Riverside Travelodge, 1911
8th................................... 07
Riverside, 3401 8th............... 01
Roosevelt, 3772 Roosevelt..... 03
Ross, 983 La Cadena Dr........ 01
Rubidoux Trailer Village,
3661 Pacific Ave............... 09
Rubidoux, 4296 8th............... 01
Sage And Sand, 1971 8th...... 07
Shady Grove Trailer Terrace,
5803 Mission Blvd............. 09
Shady Rest, 7721 Mission
Blvd................................. 09
Shady Terrace, 4146 Melrose
Dr..................................... 04
Sierras, 3766 8th................... 01
Sixty-Nine Palms Motel, 5887
Mission Blvd..................... 09
Skylark, 2140 E 8th............... 07
Spring Garden, 1175 Spring.... 07
Stagecoach, 6050 Mission
Blvd................................. 09
Swiss Inn, 3210 Main............. 01
Thunderbird Lodge, 2711 8th.. 07
Town And Country, 1910 8th... 07
Town Lodge, 4045 8th............ 01
Twin Palms, Box Springs
Grade............................... 07
Wagon Wheel, 10299
Magnolia Ave.................... 03
Walnut Grove Mobile Estates,
5925 Mission Blvd............. 09
Western Village, 10513
Magnolia Ave.................... 05

BUILDINGS

Bonnett, 3820 Orange............ 01
Central, 3859 Main................ 01
Health And Finance Bldg,
4080 Lemon...................... 01
Law, 3972 Main..................... 01
Lerner, 3631 10th.................. 01
Loring, 3691 Main.................. 01
Magnolia Professional, 5896
Magnolia Ave.................... 06
Masonic Temple, 3650 11th.... 01
Mile Square, 3500 13th.......... 01
Mission Inn Rotunda, 8616
Main................................. 01

Riverside (Con.) 925

Pritchard, 3514 9th 01
Security Bank Rooms In 200-
300 Series, 6363 De Anza
Ave 06
Security Bank Rooms In 400
Series, 3800 Main 01
Security Title Insurance,
3610 8th 01
Shacker 01

GOVERNMENT OFFICES

Court House Annex, 3998
Orange 01
Court House, 4050 Main 01
Federal, 3890 Orange 01

HOSPITALS

Community, 4445 Magnolia
Ave 01
General 9851 Magnolia Ave.... 03
Hillhaven Convalescent, 8487
Magnolia Ave 04
Knollwood, 5900 Brockton
Ave 06
Medical Square, 4033
Brockton Ave 01
Medico Dental, 4177
Brockton Ave 01
Permanente Medical Group,
3951 Van Buren 03
Riverside Convalescent, 4768
Palm Ave 01
Riverside Medical Clinic,
3660 Arlington Ave 06

MILITARY INSTALLATIONS

March AFB Calif 08

UNIVERSITIES AND COLLEGES

California Baptist College,
8432 Magnolia 04
La Sierra, Pierce And Sierra
Vsta 05
Loma Linda University-La
Sierra Campus 05
University Of California 02

SACRAMENTO 958

POST OFFICE BOXES

Box Nos.
A-Z   Main Office 13
1-231   Metro Main
                 Sta 01
241-471   Metro Main
                 Sta 02
481-711   Metro Main
                 Sta 03
721-959   Metro Main
                 Sta 04
961-1139   Metro Main
                 Sta 05
1141-1379   Metro Main
                 Sta 06
1381-1619   Metro Main
                 Sta 07
1621-1799   Metro Main
                 Sta 08
1801-2038   Metro Main
                 Sta 0n
2041-2271   Metro Main
                 Sta 10
2281-2511   Metro Main
                 Sta 11
2521-3027   Metro Main
                 Sta 12
4401-4999   Arden Br 25
5001-5599   Oak Park Sta..... 17
6001-6499   Centre Br 60
7001-7499   Perkins Br 26
9001-9499   Fort Sutter Sta. 16
9501-9999   Parkway Br 23
13001-13999   Main Office 13
15001-15999   Main Office 13
16001-16999   Fort Sutter Sta . 16
18001-18499   Broadway Sta..... 18
19001-19999   Camellia Sta 19
20001-20999   Colonial Sta 20
22001-22999   Land Park Sta.... 22
26001-26999   Perkins Br 26
28001-28999   Florin Br 28
38001-38999   Del Paso
                 Heights Sta 38
41001-41999   Foot Hill Farms
                 Br 41
214001-
215099   Town &
                 Country Br...... 21

RURAL ROUTES

2 26
3 15
8 23

STATIONS, BRANCHES AND UNITS

Arden Br 25
Broadway Sta 18
Camellia Station Sta 19
Centre Br 60
Colonial Sta 20
Del Paso Heights Sta 38
Florin Br 28
Foothill Farms Br 41
Fort Sutter Sta 16
Land Park Sta 22
Mather AFB Br 55
McClellan AFB Br 52
Metro Main Sta 01
Oak Park Sta 17
Parkway Br 23
Perkins Br 26
State Capitol Sta 14
Town and Country Village Br...... 21
General Delivery 14
Postmaster 13

APARTMENTS, HOTELS, MOTELS

Aloha Manor, 2421 Marconi.... 21
Arden Fair, 2229 Royale Rd.... 15
Berry, 725 L 14
Bohemian Gardens, 2900
Calderwood Ln 21
California, 800 I St 14
Capitol Towers, 530 N 14
Carriage House Apts, 2724
Elvyra Way 21
Castle Hill, 2725 Elvyra Way.. 21
Charlotte Manor, 5488
Carlson Dr 19
Club, 3401 Balmoral Dr 21
Clunie, 805 K 14
Coralaire, 2545 Fulton Ave 21
Cosmopolitan El Mirador,
1230 N 14
Country Club Town House,
2833 El Camino Ave 21
Crisler, 2425 I 16
Cypress Arms, 2909 Marconi
Ave 21
Del Mar, 3821 Annandale
Lane 21
Edison Estates, 2501 Edison
Ave 21
Fountain Garden, 2227 N 16
Freeport Manor, 5942
Freeport Blvd 22
Holiday Inn North, 1900
Canterbury Rd 15
Holiday Inn South, 4390 47th
Ave 24
Imperial 400 Motel, 1319
30th 16
Jamaica Plaza, 2251 Watt
Ave 25
Lake Crest Manor, 5949 Lake
Crest Wy 22
Lewis, 1100 N 14
Mansion Inn, 728 16th 14
Morris, 2900 Marconi Ave....... 21
Palm, 3909 Watt Ave 21
Park Hills Place, 6050 South
Land Park Dr 22
Park Vista, 1326 N 14
Park, 1121 9th 14
Parkfair Garden, 431 Parkfair
Dr 25
Ramona, 1007 6th 14
Rigsby Arms, 1100 39th.......... 16
Rosemont Gardens, 9216
Kiefer Blvd 26
Sacramento Inn, 1501 Arden
Way 15
Sacramento Manor, 7300
24th St By-Pass 22
Senator, 12th & L 14
Sequoia, 911 K 14
Sunset Garden, 3836 Auburn
Blvd 21
Thayer, 1228 N 14
The Royal Villa, 4900 Royal
Villa Dr 41
Town & Country Garden,
2927 Marconi Ave 21
Travelodge, 1101 H 14
Vanguard Village, 1055
Fairlake Ave 25
Village Oaks, 2839 Marconi
Ave 21
Whitney Arms, 3525 Whitney
Ave 21
Woodlake Inn, 500 Leisure
Lane 15

BUILDINGS

Anglo Bank, 1007 7th.............. 14
Arcade Square, 3333 Watt
Ave 21
Bank Of America, 900 8th...... 14

49

Sacramento (Con.).   958

California Fruit, 1006 4th.....	14	
Eleventh & L, 1127 11th......	14	
Forum, 1107 9th................	14	
I B M Office Bldg, 520 Capitol Mall..............	14	
Medical Arts, 2720 Capitol Ave.......................	16	
Nine Twenty Six Jay, 926 J.....	14	
St. Lukes Medical, 2600 Capitol Ave...........	16	
Wright, 1209 8th................	14	

GOVERNMENT OFFICES

Chamber Of Commerce, 919 7th........................	14
City Hall, 915 I St...............	14
City School Administration, 1619 N.......................	14
County Administration, 827 7th........................	14
County Courthouse, 720 9th St.........................	14
Federal & Crthse Bldg, 650 Capitol Mall..............	14
Federal Bldg, 2800 Cottage Wy.........................	25
Federal Bldg, 805 I St.........	14
Motor Vehicle, 2570 24th	18
Post Office, 2000 Royal Oaks Dr.........................	15
Resources Bldg, 1416-9th.....	14
State Agricultural, 1220 N.....	14
State Board Of Education, 721 Capitol Mall..........	14
State Capitol, 10th At L & N..	14
State Department Of Public Works, 1120 N..............	14
State Dept. Of Employment, 800 Capitol Mall..........	14
State Office 01, 915 Capital Mall.......................	14
State Office Bldg No 8, 714 P...........................	14
State Office Bldg No 9, 744 P...........................	14
State Personnel Bd, 801 Capitol Mall.............	14
State Prof. & Vocational Stds., 1020 N.............	14

HOSPITALS

Community Memorial, 2251 Hawthorne................	15
Kaiser Foundation, 2025 Morse Ave..............	25
Mercy General, 40th & Jay.....	19
Sacramento Medical Center, 2325 Stockton Blvd	17
Sutter General, 2820 L St.....	16
Sutter Memorial, 52nd & F.....	19
Woodside Community, 3201 Del Paso Blvd...........	15

UNIVERSITIES AND COLLEGES

American River College E, 4700 College Oak Dr..........	41
Cosumnes River College, 8400 Center Pky..........	23

Sacramento City, 3835 Freeport Blvd.............	22	
Sacramento Nursing, 2325 Stockton Blvd............	17	
Sacramento State, 6000 J.....	19	

SAN BERNARDINO   924

POST OFFICE BOXES

Box Nos.		
1-1318	Downtown Sta..	02
2001-2968	Uptown Sta	06
3001-3689	Del Rosa Br.....	04
4001-4569	Norton Air Force Base Sta...............	09
5001-6472	Main Office	12

STATIONS, BRANCHES AND UNITS

Base Line Sta.................	10
Del Rosa Br....................	04
Downtown Sta.................	03
Eastside Sta..................	10
Muscoy Br.....................	05
Norton A F B Sta.............	09
Uptown Sta....................	05
Waterman Br..................	08
General Delivery.............	03
Postmaster....................	03

BUILDINGS

Anderson, 320 N E St.........	01
Arrowhead, 515 Arrowhead Ave.......................	01
Blackstone, 362 N Arrowhead Ave.....................	01
Katz, 315 N E..................	01
Law, 560 Arrowhead Ave.......	01
Platt, 491 5th.................	01
Professional, 481 W Church ...	01
State Office, 303 Third..........	01

GOVERNMENT OFFICES

City Hall, 426 W 3rd Street.....	01
Civic Center, 157 W 5th........	01
County Court House, 351 No Arrowhead Ave.............	01
Federal Bldg., 390 W 5th	01
Hall Of Justice, 453 No Arrowhead Ave.............	01
Hall Of Records, 172 W 3rd...	01

HOSPITALS

Community, 1500 17th..........	05
County, 780 E Gilbert..........	04
Saint Bernardine'S, 2101 Waterman Ave.............	04

UNIVERSITIES AND COLLEGES

Cajon High, 1200 Hill Dr.......	07
City Schools Administration, 799 N F...................	10
San Bernardino State College, 5500 State College Pky.............	07
San Bernardino Valley College, 701 S Mt Vernon ..	10

SAN DIEGO   921

POST OFFICE BOXES

Box No.		
1-578	Coronado Br.....	18
1-2999	Main Office	12
01-0199	College Grove Center Sta	15
3001-3994	Hillcrest Sta	03
4001-4519	North Park Sta .	04
5001-5727	East San Diego Sta................	05
6001-6599	Point Loma Sta................	06
7001-7539	Ocean Beach Sta................	07
8001-8447	George Washington Sta................	02
9001-9999	Pacific Beach Sta................	09
10001-10775	Old San Diego Sta................	10
11011-11299	Linda Vista Sta................	11
12001-12389	Main Office	12
13001-13294	Southeastern Sta................	13
14001-14294	Encanto Sta	14
15001-15594	Andrew Jackson Sta...	15
16001-16118	John Adams Sta................	16
17001-17446	William H Taft Sta................	17
19001-19147	Navajo Sta.....	19
20001-20866	Grantville Sta..	20
22001-22230	University City Station...........	22
23001-23448	Serra Mesa.....	23
45001-45089	Miramar Sta.....	45
80000-82999	Main Office	38
99001-99240	Pacific Beach Sta................	09

STATIONS, BRANCHES AND UNITS

Amphibious Base Br............	55
Andrew Jackson Sta............	15
College Grove Center Sta.......	15
Coronado Br....................	18
East San Diego Sta............	05
Encanto Sta....................	14
Fleet Sta......................	32
George Washington Sta.........	02
Grantville Sta..................	20
Hillcrest Sta...................	03
John Adams Sta................	16
Linda Vista Sta................	11
Mar Corps Rct Dep Sta........	40
Miramar Br....................	45
Naval Sta......................	36
Naval Air Station Br............	35
Naval Hospital Sta.............	34
Naval Training Center Sta......	33
North Park Sta................	04
Ocean Beach Sta..............	07
Old San Diego Sta.............	10
Pacific Beach Sta..............	09
Point Loma Sta................	06

San Diego (Con.)	921
Serra Mesa Sta.	23
Southeastern Sta.	13
University City Sta.	22
William Howard Taft Sta.	17
General Delivery	01
Postmaster	10

APARTMENTS, HOTELS, MOTELS

Bahia Motor, 998 Ventura Blvd	09
Catamaran Motor, 3999 Mission Blvd	09
Churchill, 827 C	01
El Cortez, 702 Ash	12
Embassy, 3645 Park Blvd	03
Golden West, 720 4th	01
Grant, 326 Broadway	12
Half Moon Inn, 1180 Yacht Harbor Dr	06
Hanalei, 2270 West Hotel Circle	08
Islandia, 1441 Quivira Rd	09
Kings Inn, 1333 West Hotel Circle	08
Maryland, 630 F	12
Master Hosts Inn, 950 Hotel Circle	08
Mission Valley Inn, 875 West Hotel Circle	08
Mission Valley Travelodge, 1201 West Hotel Circle	08
New Palace, 480 Elm	01
New Plaza, 1037 4th Ave	01
New Saint James, 830 6th Ave	12
Pickwick, 132 W Broadway	01
Point Loma Inn, 2930 Fenelon	06
San Diego, 339 West Broadway	01
Sands, 5550 Kearny Mesa Road	11
Shelter Island Inn, 950 Yacht Harbor Dr	06
Town And Country, 500 Hotel Circle	08
Travolator Motor, 719 Ash	01
Villa Fontana Hotel, 2101 South Hotel Circle	08
Westgate Plaza Hotel, 1055 2nd Avenue	01

BUILDINGS

Armed Services Ymca, 500 West Broadway	01
Bank Of America, 625 Broadway	01
California State, 1350 Front	01
California Theatre, 1122 4th Ave	01
Central Federal Savings And Loan, 640 C	01
Chamber Of Commerce, 233 A	01
Chamberlain, 1551 4th Ave	01
Channel 8 Tv, 1405 5th Ave	01
Charter Oil, 110 West C	01
Cosgrove, 411 Broadway	01
Crabtree, 303 A	01

Driver Insurance, 400 Cedar	01
Fifth Avenue Financial Center, 2550 5th Ave	03
First National Bank, 1201 5th Avenue	01
Fox, 770 B	01
Frank Hope, 1475 6th Avenue	01
Granger, 964 5th Avenue	01
Home Tower, 707 Broadway	01
Imperial Corporation, 1010 2nd Ave	01
Lawyers Professional, 1140 Union	01
Pacific Center, 1017 1st Avenue	01
Park Plaza, 333 Plaza	01
Robinson, 520 E	01
San Diego Gas & Electric, 101 Ash	01
San Diego Trust & Savings Ba, 530 Broadway	01
Scripps, 525 C	01
Security First National Bank, 233 A	01
Spreckels, 121 Broadway	01
Telephone Company, 1188-6th Ave	01
Time Savings, 1023 2nd Avenue	01
Travelator, 1430 7th Avenue	01
Union Tribune, 940 3rd Avenue	01
United States National Bank, 1010 2nd Ave	01
Ymca, 1115 8th Ave	01
Ywca, 1012 C	01

GOVERNMENT OFFICES

City Concourse	01
County Administration Center, 1600 Pacific Hwy	01
County Court House, 210 West Broadway	01
US Customs, 1415 6th Ave	01

HOSPITALS

Childrens Hospital, 8001 Frost	23
Clairemont General, 5255 Mt Etna Dr	17
College Park, 6666 Montezuma Rd	15
County University, 225 W Dickenson	03
Doctors, 3475 Kenyon	10
Hillside, 1940 El Cajon Blvd	04
Mercy, 4099 Hillcrest Dr	03
Mesa Vista, 7850 Vista Hill	23
Naval Hospital	34
Sharp Memorial, 7901 Frost	23
Veterans Hospital 3350 La Jolla Village Dr	61
Villa View, 4095 55th	15

MILITARY INSTALLATIONS

Anti-Submarine Warfare School	47
Coast Guard Air Station, 2710 Harbor Dr	01

Commander Training Pacific	47
Fleet Anti-Air Warfare Training Center	47
Fleet Anti-Submarine Warfare School	47
Fleet Station	32
Fleet Training Group	47
Fort Rosecrans	06
Marine Corps Recruit Depot	40
Miramar Naval Air Station	45
Naval Air Station	35
Naval Amphibious Base	55
Naval Electronics Laboratory	52
Naval Hospital	34
Naval Radio Station, Chollas Heights	15
Naval Receiving Station	36
Naval Station	36
Naval Supply Depot	32
Naval Training Center	33
Naval Underseas Warfare Center	32
Naval Undersea Research And Development Center	32
Submarine Development Group 1 and 3	32
United States Quarantine Station, Point Loma	06
11th Naval District, Foot Of Broadway	32

UNIVERSITIES AND COLLEGES

California Western University, 3902 Lomaland Dr	06
San Diego City College, 1425 Russ Blvd	01
San Diego Mesa College, 7250 Artillery Dr	11
San Diego State College, 5402 College Avenue	15
U S. International Unversity 8655 E. Pomerado Rd	24
University Of San Diego, Alcala Park	10

SAN FERNANDO 913

POST OFFICE BOXES

Box Nos.		
1-1272	Main Office	41
2001-2864	Sepulveda Br	43
3001-3524	Granada Hills Br	44
4001-4588	North Annex Sta	42
5001-5591	Mission Hills Br	40

STATIONS, BRANCHES AND UNITS

Granada Hills Br	44
Lake View Terrace Br	42
Maclay Sta	40
Mission Hills Br	40
North Annex Br	42
North Hills Br	44
Norwood Center Br	43
Olive View Br	30
Sepulveda Br	43
Sylmar Br	42

San Fernando (Con.)	913
General Delivery	40
Postmaster	40

BUILDINGS

Bendix Corporation	42
Farmers Insurance Group	42
General Telephone Co Of California	42
I T & T	42
Metropolitan Life Insurance	40
Spectrolab	42
Warwick Electronics, Inc	43

HOSPITALS

Holy Cross Hospital	40
Pacoima Lutheran Hospital	42
San Fernando Hospital	40
Sepulveda Veterans Hospital	43

SAN FRANCISCO   941

POST OFFICE BOXES

Box Nos.		
1-1899	Main Office	01
2001-2999	B Sta	26
3000-3999	Rincon Sta	19
4001-6200	Main Office	01
7000-7999	Rincon Sta	20
8000-8099	Airport Sta	28
9000-9099	Presidio Sta	29
12000-12296	F Sta	12
14000-14287	G Sta	14
15000-15446	A Sta	15
16000-16099	Parkside Sta	16
18000-18099	M Sta	18
22000-22099	Sunset Sta	22
24000-24539	Bayview Station	24
26000-26499	B Sta	26
27000-27428	West Portal	27
31000-31099	Diamond Heights Sta	31
34000-34499	Visitacion Sta	34
36000-36099	Federal Building Sta	02
37000-37999	Rincon Sta	37
38000-38999	Rincon Sta	38
39000-39999	Rincon Sta	39
40000-40999	C Sta	40
42000-42999	Main Office	42
44000-44999	Rincon Sta	44
45000-45999	Rincon Sta	45
77000-77099	E Sta	09
99001-99580	O Sta	09

STATIONS, BRANCHES AND UNITS

Airport Br	28
Bay View Sta	24
Bernal Sta	10
China Sta	08
City Hall Sta	02
Diamond Heights Sta	31
Fisk Sta	22
Geary Sta	08
Hunters Point Sta	35
Letterman Sta	29
Marina Sta	23

Mc Laren Sta	34
Mills Sta	04
Noe Valley Sta	14
North Beach Sta	33
Number Fifty Seven Sta	01
Number Forty Sta	01
Number Forty Four Sta	01
Number Twenty Three Sta	01
Parkside Sta	16
Presidio Sta	29
Rincon Sta	19
Stonestown Sta	32
Sunset Sta	22
Treasure Island Sta	30
Visitacion Sta	34
West Portal Sta	27
General Delivery	01
Postmaster	01

APARTMENTS, HOTELS, MOTELS

Bellevue, 505 Geary	01
Californian, 405 Taylor	01
Cartwright, 524 Sutter	01
Chancellor, 433 Powell	01
Clift, 495 Geary	01
Del Webb'S Towne House, 1185 Market	01
Drake-Wiltshire, 340 Stockton	06
Fairmont, 950 Mason	06
Fielding, 386 Geary	01
Golden State, 114 Powell	01
Jack Tar, 1101 Van Ness Ave	01
Manx, 225 Powell	01
Mark Hopkins, 999 California	06
Olympic, 230 Eddy	01
Oxford, 16 Turk	01
Plaza, 310 Post	06
Saint Francis, 335 Powell	19
San Franciscan, 1231 Market	19
San Francisco Hilton Inn	28
San Francisco Hilton, 333 O'Farrell	01
Sheraton Palace, 637 Market	19
Sir Francis Drake, 450 Powell	01
Stewart, 351 Geary	01

BUILDINGS

Adam Grant, 114 Sansome	04
Aetna Life And Casualty Bldg. Crocker Plaza 1 Post	04
Alaska Commercial, 310 Sansome	04
Alcoa, 1 Maritime Plz	11
Alexander, 155 Montgomery	04
American International, 206 Sansome	04
American Savings, 690 Market	04
Anglo Bank, 830 Market	02
Appraisers, 630 Sansome	11
Balboa, 593 Market	05
Bank Of America Plaza, 555 California	04
Bank Of America, 300 Montgomery	04

Bankers Investment, 742 Market	02
Bechtel, 50 Beale	05
Board Of Trade, 444 Market	11
Brooks Hall, 99 Grove	02
California Commercial Union, 315 Montgomery	04
California Pacific, 105 Montgomery	04
Call, 74 New Montgomery	05
Central Tower, 703 Market	03
Chronicle, 905 Mission	03
Columbus Towers, 916 Kearny	33
Commercial, 833 Market	03
Crocker Plaza, 1 Post	04
Crocker-Anglo National Bank, 1 Montgomery	04
Crown Zellerbach, 1 Bush	04
Custom House, 555 Battery	11
Equitable Life, 120 Montgomery	04
Exchange Block, 369 Pine	04
Executive Towers, 503 Market	05
Federal Office, 50 Fulton	02
Federal Reserve Bank, 400 Sansome	20
Federal, 45 Golden Gate Ave	02
Ferry, Foot Of Market	11
First Savings, 401 California	04
Fitzhugh, 384 Post	08
Flood, 870 Market	02
Foremost, 111 Pine	11
Fox Plaza, 1390 Market	02
Fox Warfield, 988 Market	02
Fremont, 344 Market	05
Golden Gate, 25 Taylor	02
Grant, 1095 Market	03
Hall Of Justice, 850 Bryant	03
Hartford, 650 California	08
Hearst, 5 3rd	03
Hobart, 582 Market	04
Holbrook, 58 Sutter	04
Hong Kong Bank, 160 Sansome	04
Humboldt Bank, 785 Market	03
Industrial Indemnity, 255 California	11
Insurance Center, 450 Sansome	11
Insurance Exchange, 433 California	04
Insurance Securities, 100 California	11
International, 601 California	08
J. Harold Dollar, 351 California	04
Kohl, 400 Montgomery	04
Matsen, 100 Mission	04
Medico-Dental, 490 Post	02
Merchants Exchange, 465 California	04
Mills Tower, 220 Bush	04
Mills, 220 Montgomery	04
Monadnock, 681 Market	05
Mutual Benefit Life, 1 California	11
Pacific Mutual, 600 - 610 California	08
Pacific, 821 Market	03
Phelan, 760 Market	02

San Francisco (Con.)	941
Rialto, 116 New Montgomery..	05
Robert Dollar, 311 California..	04
Royal Insurance, 201 Sansome	04
Russ, 235 Montogomery	04
S F Civic Auditorium, 99 Grove	02
Sheldon, 9 1st	05
Shell Oil, 100 Bush	04
Southern Pacific, 1 Market	05
Standard Oil, 225 Bush	04
Standard Oil, 555 Market	20
State Annex, 455 Golden Gate Ave	02
State, 350 Mcallister	02
Tidewater, 55 New Montgomery	05
Transport, Foot Of Mission..	05
Underwood, 525 Market	05
United California Bank, 405 Montgomery	04
Van Ness Post Center, 1255 Post	09
Wells Fargo, 44 Montgomery..	04
West Coast Life, 605 Market..	05
Western Merchandise Mart, 1355 Market	03
World Trade Center, Foot Of Market	11

GOVERNMENT OFFICES

Main Post Office, 99 7th	03
Rincon Annex Post Office, 99 Mission	19
San Francisco City Hall, 400 Van Ness Ave	02
United States Mint, 133 Herman	02
Veterans Administration, 49 4th	03

HOSPITALS

Callison Memorial, 1055 Pine	09
Children&s, 3700 California ..	18
Chinese, 835 Jackson	33
Elizabeth'S	18
Franklin, 2 Noe	14
French, 4131 Geary Blvd	19
Garden, 2750 Geary Blvd	18
Golden Gate, 1065 Sutter	09
Hahnemann, 3698 California..	18
Harkness Memorial, 1400 Fell	17
Joseph'S	17
Kaiser Foundation, 2425 Geary Blvd	15
Laguna Honda, 375 Laguna Honda Blvd	16
Langley Porter Clinic, Parnassus Ave & Arguello Blvd	22
Letterman General, Presidio Of San Francisco	29
Luke'S	10
Mary'S	17
Mount Zion, 1600 Divisadero..	19
Notre Dame, 1590 Broadway..	09
Presbyterian Medical Center,	

2351 Clay	15
Saint Francis Memorial, 900 Hyde	09
San Francisco Eye & Ear, 1801 Bush	09
San Francisco General, 1001 Potrero Ave	10
Shriners Hospital For Crippled Children, 1651 19th Ave	22
United States Public Health, 2 14th Ave	18
University Of Calif Medical Center, 551 Parnassus Ave	22
Veterans Administration, 4150 Clement	21

UNIVERSITIES AND COLLEGES

City College Of San Francisco, 50 Phelan Ave..	12
Golden Gate College, 536 Mission	05
Hastings College Of Law, 198 Mcallister	02
Lone Mountain College	18
San Francisco State, 1600 Holloway Ave	32
University Of California Extension Center, 55 Laguna	02
University Of California Medical Center, 551 Parnassus Av	22
University Of San Francisco, 2130 Fulton	17
University Of The Pacific, 2155 Webster	15

SAN GABRIEL 917

POST OFFICE BOXES

Box Nos.		
A-P	Main Office	78
1-0001195	Main Office	78

STATIONS, BRANCHES AND UNITS

General Delivery	76
Postmaster	76

SAN JOSE 951

POST OFFICE BOXES

Box Nos.		
1-511	Saint James Park Sta	03
521-910	Saint James Park Sta	06
911-1300	Saint James Park Sta	08
1301-1799	Saint James Park Sta	09
3001-3999	D Sta	16
4001-4999	C Sta	26
5001-7999	Main Office	50

8001-8999	B Sta	25
9001-9999	Westgate Sta	29
21001-21999	Hillview Sta	51
23001-23999	Blossom Hill Sta	53
24001-24999	Cambrian Park Sta	54

RURAL ROUTES

2	31
3	21

STATIONS, BRANCHES AND UNITS

Blossom Hill Sta	23
Cambrian Park Br	24
Mount Hamilton Rural Br	40
Saint James Park Sta	13
Valley Fair Sta	28
Westgate Sta	29
General Delivery	13
Postmaster	25

GOVERNMENT OFFICES

City Hall, 801 N 1 St St	10
Court House, 139 N 1st	13
Post Office, 105 N 1st	13
Santa Clara County Offices, 70 W Hedding St	10

HOSPITALS

Agnew State, Mauvais Ln	14
Alexan Bros, 225 N Jackson Ave	16
Alum Rock Sanitarium, Crothrs RdOpo Box 71)..	03
Doctors, 976 Lenzen Avenue...	26
Good Samaritan, 15825 Samaritan Dr	24
O'Connor, 2105 Forest Ave	14
San Jose 14th And Santa Clara St	12
Santa Clara Valley Medical Center, 751 S Bascom Ave	28

UNIVERSITIES AND COLLEGES

Heald Business, 10 Notre Dame Ave	13
San Jose City, 2060 Kingman Ave	14
San Jose State, Washington Square	14

SAN LEANDRO 945

POST OFFICE BOXES

Box Nos.		
1-999	Estudilto Sta	77
1500-2999	Main Office	77
3000-3499	South San Leandro Sta	78
5000-5599	Main Office	77

53

San Leandro (Con.) 945

STATIONS, BRANCHES AND UNITS

Estudillo Sta.	77
South San Leandro Sta.	78
Washington Manor Sta.	79
General Delivery	77
Postmaster	77

SAN MATEO 944

POST OFFICE BOXES

Box Nos.		
1-812	Saint Matthews Sta.	01
901-1198	A Sta.	03
1201-2091	Saint Matthews Sta.	01
3001-3355	Hillsdale Sta.	03
4001-4299	Foster City	04
5001-5550	San Mateo	02
6001-6299	A Sta.	03

STATIONS, BRANCHES AND UNITS

Foster City Br.	04
Hillsdale Sta.	03
Saint Matthew Sta.	01
General Delivery	02
Postal Data Center	49
Postmaster	02

BUILDINGS

City Hall, 330 W 20th Ave.	03

HOSPITALS

Mills Memorial Hospital, 100 S San Mateo Dr.	01
Mills Square Extended Care Hospital, 101 S San Mateo Dr.	01
Rehabilitation Center, 35 Tower Rd.	02
San Mateo County General Hospital, 222 W 39th Ave.	03

UNIVERSITIES AND COLLEGES

College Of San Mateo, 1700 W Hillsdale Blvd	02

SAN PEDRO 907

POST OFFICE BOXES

Box Nos.		
1-1999	Main Office	33
2601-2728	Fort Mac Arthur Sta.	31
3001-3432	Terminal Island Sta.	31

STATIONS, BRANCHES AND UNITS

Fort Mac Arthur Sta.	31
Miraleste Br.	32

Terminal Island Sta.	31
Western Avenue Br.	32
General Delivery	31
Postmaster	31

BUILDINGS

Consolidated Marine Terminal	31
Fidelity Federal Savings & Loan	32
Harbor	31
Los Angeles County Court House	31
Pacific Trade Center	31
San Pedro City Hall	31

GOVERNMENT OFFICES

Federal Bldg.	31
Federal Correctional Institution, Box 7, Term Is, Ca	31
U S Customs House	31
U. S. Immigration And Naturalization Service	31

HOSPITALS

Los Palos Convalescent	32
San Pedro Community	32
Seacrest Convalescent	32

MILITARY INSTALLATIONS

Fort Macarthur	31
U. S. Coast Guard Base	31

SAN RAFAEL 949

POST OFFICE BOXES

Box Nos.		
1-689	Kentfield Br.	04
1-1380	Mission Rafael Sta.	02
2000-3799	Main Office	02
4001-4430	Civic Center Br.	03
6000-6399	Terra Linda Sta.	03

STATIONS, BRANCHES AND UNITS

Civic Center Br.	03
Greenbrae Br.	04
Kentfield Br.	04
Mission Rafael Sta.	01
Terra Linda Sta.	01
General Delivery	02
Postmaster	01

HOSPITALS

Marin General Hospital, 250 Bon Air Rd.	02

UNIVERSITIES AND COLLEGES

College Of Marin, Kentfield	04
Dominican College & Convent, 1520 Grand Ave.	01

SANTA ANA 927

POST OFFICE BOXES

Box Nos.		
1-1999	Spurgeon Sta.	02
2000-2999	South Main Sta.	07
4000-4999	Spurgeon Sta.	02
5000-5999	Diamond Sta.	04
8000-8999	Fountain Valley Br.	08
10000-11999	Main Office	11
15000-15399	Industrial Sta.	05
0006000- -0006999	King Sta.	06

RURAL ROUTES

2	05

STATIONS, BRANCHES AND UNITS

Bristol Sta.	03
Diamond Sta.	04
El Toro Marine Corp Air Sta Br.	09
Fountain Valley Br.	08
Industrial Sta.	05
King Sta.	06
South Main Sta.	07
Spurgeon Sta.	02
General Delivery	11
Postmaster	11

APARTMENTS, HOTELS, MOTELS

Bali Hi, 432 S Harbor	04
Bit O'Home, 5002 W Mc Fadden	04
California, 2901 W 1st	03
Caravana, 306 S Sullivan	04
Contempo Mobilehome Park, 4080 W 1st	03
Continental, 2804 W 1st	03
Country Club Mobile Manor, 518 S Sullivan	04
Fairview, 206 S Sullivan	04
Gardners, 2424 W 1st	03
Kellogg, 2613 Arnett	06
Kona Kai, 4117 W Mcfadden	04
Liberty, 329 S Harbor	04
New Holiday Mobile Estates, 3424 W Washington	03
Quiet Village, 3126 W Bolsa	03
Rainbow, 12062 Edinger	04
Royal Coach, 215 So Sullivan	04
Sahara, 1517 N Newhope	03
Sandlewood Mobil Homes, 507 S Euclid	04
Santa Ana Trailer Park, 1669 E 1st	01
Standard Avenue Mobile Homes, 1527 S Standard	07
Taggin Wagon, 2767 W 1st	03
The Meadows, 14851 Jeffrey Rd	05
Town & Country, 3928 W 5th.	03

Santa Ana (Con.) 927

BUILDINGS

Arcade, 515 N Main	01
Bank Of America, 801 N Main	01
Commercial, 514 Main	01
Community Center, 1104 W 8th	01
Duncan, 1905 E 17th	01
First Western Bank, 102 W 4th	01
Grand Central, 116 N Sycamore	01
Great American Of Dallas, 1525 E 17th	01
Hall Of Records, 212 W 8th	01
Library, 502 W 8th	01
Marsile, 1833 E 17th	01
Muckenthaler, 325 N Broadway	01
New Arcade, 1740 S Main	07
Otis, 408 N Main	01
Pacific, 225 W Broadway	01
Pan American Medical, 1206 E 17th	01
Ramona, 118 W 5th	01
Santa Ana Medical Arts Center, 1125 E 17th	01
Santiago, 206 N Main	01
Second & Broadway, 207 N Broadway	01
Segerstrom Center, 1010 N Main	01
Social Welfare, 601 N Ross	01
Spurgeon, 206 W 4th	01

GOVERNMENT OFFICES

City Hall, 217 N Main	01
County Jail, 550 N Flower	03
Court House, 700 W 8th	01
Police, 511 W 6th	01

HOSPITALS

Community, 600 E Washington	01
Doctors, 1901 College	06
Riverview, 1901 Berrydale	06

MILITARY INSTALLATIONS

Marine Corps Air Station	09
Station (H)	10

UNIVERSITIES AND COLLEGES

Santa Ana Junior College, 1530 W 17th	06

SANTA BARBARA 931

POST OFFICE BOXES

Box Nos.		
A-Z	Santa Barbara	02
1-1999	Santa Barbara	02
3000-39999	San Roque Sta.	05
4000-4999	Milpas Sta	03
5000-5999	Montecito Br	08
9000-9999	Cachuma Rural Sta	05
11101-15260	University Of California Br	07
0006000- -0006999	Magnolia Branch	11

STATIONS, BRANCHES AND UNITS

Cachuma Rural Br	01
Milpas Sta	03
Montecito Br	03
Mora Villa Sta	04
San Roque Sta	05
University Br	07
General Delivery	02
Postmaster	02

APARTMENTS, HOTELS, MOTELS

Biltmore	02
California, 35 State	01
Carrillo, 31 W Carrillo	01
El Encanto	02
Miramar, 1555 S Jameson Ln	02
San Ysidro Ranch, 900 San Ysidro Lane	08

BUILDINGS

Balboa, 735 State St	01
El Paseo, 813 Anacapa St	01
Federal, 836 Anacapa St	01
Granada, 1216 State St	01
Howard Canfield, 831 State St	01
La Arcada, 1114 State St	01
La Rinconada, 205 E Carillo St	01
State, 411 E Canon Perido St	01

GOVERNMENT OFFICES

City Hall, De La Guerra Plaza	01
Court House, 1120 Anacapa St	01

HOSPITALS

Cottage Hospital	02
County General Hospital	05
Goleta Valley Community Hospital, 351 S Patterson Ave	11
Saint Francis Hospital, 601 E Micheltorena St	02
Sansum Medical Clinic	02
Santa Barbara Medical Clinic, 215 Pesetas L(	02

UNIVERSITIES AND COLLEGES

Santa Barbara City, 721 Cliff Dr	09
University Of California, Santa Barbara Cal	06

Westmont College, 955 La Paz Rd	08

SANTA CLARA 950

POST OFFICE BOXES

Box Nos.		
1-629	Agnew Station	54
1-805	Main Office	52
2001-2854	Mission Station	51

STATIONS, BRANCHES AND UNITS

Agnew Sta	54
Mission Sta	51
Univ Of Santa Clara Sta	53

SANTA MONICA 904

POST OFFICE BOXES

Box Nos.		
1-1999	Main Office	06
3001-3999	Will Rogers Sta	03
5001-5999	Ocean Park Sta	05

STATIONS, BRANCHES AND UNITS

Douglas Sta	05
Ocean Park Sta	05
Will Rogers Sta	01
General Delivery	06
Postmaster	06

SANTA ROSA 954

POST OFFICE BOXES

Box Nos.		
A-Z	Santa Rosa	02
1-1199	Santa Rosa	02
AA-ZZ	Santa Rosa	03
1201-1999	Santa Rosa	03
2001-2999	Montgomery Village Sta	05
3001-3400	Santa Rosa Sta	03
6001-6999	Coddingtown Sta	06
7001-7999	Roseland Sta	01
9000-9999	Montgomery Village Sta	05
11000-11999	Coddingtown Sta	06

RURAL ROUTES

3,4	04

STATIONS, BRANCHES AND UNITS

Coddingtown Sta	06
Larkfield Br	01
Montgomery Village Sta	05
Roseland Br	01
General Delivery	02
Postmaster	02

Santa Rosa (Con.)   954

HOSPITALS

Santa Rosa General, 7 & A....   01
Santa Rosa Memorial, 1165
   Montgomery Dr..............   02
Sonoma County Community,
   3325 Chanate Rd..........   02
Warrack, 2457 Summerfield
   Rd.............................   05

UNIVERSITIES AND COLLEGES

Los Guilocos School For Girls,
   7501 Sonoma Hwy..........   05
Santa Rosa Junior College,
   1501 Mendocino Ave........   02
Ursuline School, Angela Ave...   01

STOCKTON   952

POST OFFICE BOXES

Box Nos.
A-Z   Delta Sta............   01
1-2169   Delta Sta............   01
4001-4698   Tuxedo Park
                Sta.................   04
5001-5294   East Stockton
                Sta.................   05
6000-6700   Homestead
                Sta.................   06
7001-7358   Lincoln Village
                Br..................   07
8000-9200   Main Office......   04

STATIONS, BRANCHES AND UNITS

Delta Sta..........................   02
East Stockton Sta...............   05
Homestead Sta...................   06
Lincoln Village Br...............   07
Mid City Sta.....................   02
Tuxedo Park Sta................   04
General Delivery.................   02
Postmaster.......................   04

BUILDINGS

Bank Of America, 343 East
   Main............................   02
Bank Of Stockton, 311 East
   Main............................   02
Belding, 110 North San
   Joaquin........................   02
California, 11 South San
   Joaquin........................   02
Center, 7 West Acacia..........   02
City Hall, 425 North El
   Dorado.........................   02
Eden Square Medical Center,
   127 East Acacia..............   02
Elks, 42 North Sutter..........   02
Exchange, 142 North
   California......................   02
Federal, 401 North San
   Joaquin........................   02
Five Forty, 540 North
   California......................   02

Hunter, 607 North San
   Joaquin........................   02
Medico Dental, 242 North
   Sutter..........................   02
San Joaquin County Court
   House, 222 East Weber......   02
San Joaquin Farm Bureau,
   145 South American.........   02
State, 31 East Channel.........   02
Wells Fargo, 305 North El
   Dorado.........................   02

GOVERNMENT OFFICES

City Hall, 425 North El
   Dorado.........................   02
Federal, 401 North San
   Joaquin........................   02
San Joaquin County
   Courthouse, 222 E Weber...   02
State Building, 31 East
   Channel........................   02

HOSPITALS

Dameron, 525 W. Acacia......   03
Oak Park Community, 2510 N
   California......................   04
Saint Josephs, 1800 North
   California......................   04
San Joaquin General, Box
   1020............................   01
Stockton State, 510 East
   Magnolia.......................   02

MILITARY INSTALLATIONS

Nav. Com. Sta...................   03

UNIVERSITIES AND COLLEGES

Humphreys, 6650 Inglewood
   Ave.............................   07
San Joaquin Delta, 3301
   Kensington Way...............   04
University Of The Pacific,
   3601 Pacific Ave..............   04

SUNNYVALE   940

POST OFFICE BOXES

Box Nos.
A-J   Encinal Sta......   87
1-1536   Main Office......   88
2001-2417   Encinal Sta......   87

STATIONS, BRANCHES AND UNITS

Encinal Sta.......................   87
General Delivery.................   88
Postmaster.......................   86

THOUSAND OAKS   913

POST OFFICE BOXES

Box Nos.
1-800   Station A.........   60

1000-1999   Main Office......   60

RURAL ROUTES

1...................................   60

STATIONS, BRANCHES AND UNITS

Newbury Park Br................   20
Westlake Village Br.............   60
Gen Delivery.....................   60
Postmaster.......................   60

BUILDINGS

California Luthern College,
   Olsen Rd.......................   60
Capitol Records, 1050
   Rancho Conejo Blvd..........   60

TORRANCE   905

POST OFFICE BOXES

Box Nos.
A-X   Marcelina Sta..   07
1-328   Marcelina Sta..   07
AA-VV   Marcelina Sta..   08
331-629   Marcelina Sta..   08
1001-1466   Walteria Sta....   05
2900-2999   Main Office......   09
3001-4299   Main Office......   10
6001-6509   North Torrance
                Sta.................   04

STATIONS, BRANCHES AND UNITS

El Camino College Br...........   06
Marcelina Sta....................   01
North Torrance Sta..............   04
Walteria Sta......................   05
General Delivery.................   03
Postmaster.......................   10

HOSPITALS

Harbor General...................   09
Little Company Of Mary,
   4101 Torrance Blvd...........   03
Riviera Community Hospital,
   4026 W 226th.................   05
Torrance Memorial Hospital
   3330 Lomita Blvd.............   09

UNIVERSITIES AND COLLEGES

El Camino College, 16007
   Crenshaw Blvd.................   06

VAN NUYS   914

POST OFFICE BOXES

Box Nos.
1-599   Main Office......   08
1-787   Encino Br.........   16
1681-1797   Encino Br.........   16
2000-2999   South Sta........   04
3001-3594   Van Owen Sta...   07
4001-4999   Panorama City
                Sta.................   12

56

Van Nuys (Con.) 914

5001-5999	Sherman Oaks Sta	13
7000-7999	Valley Annex Sta	09
44000-44999	Panorama City Sta	12
55001-55999	Sherman Oaks	13

STATIONS, BRANCHES AND UNITS

Encino Br	16
Kester Sta	05
Panorama City Sta	02
Sherman Oaks Sta	03
South Sta	04
Vanowen Sta	07
General Delivery	08
Postmaster	08

APARTMENTS, HOTELS, MOTELS

A Kingston, 5401 Sepulveda Blvd	01
Ace, 16008 Arminta	06
Birmingham, 7740 Balboa Blvd	06
C Horace Heidt, 14155 Magnolia Blvd	03
C Magnolia Biltmore, 15101 Magnolia Blvd	03
Central Valley, 16741 Saticoy	06
Homestead, 8009 Haskell Ave	06
Metropolitan, 16823 Saticoy	06
Park Royale, 7650 Balboa Blvd	06
Shady Grove, 16811 Saticoy	06
Strathern, 15927 Strathern	06
Valencia, 7800 Balboa Blvd	06
Van Nuys V M T, 7625 Hayvenhurst Ave	06
Youngs, 15460 Erwin	01
Youngs, 7647 Hayvenhurst Ave	06

BUILDINGS

County, 14401 Delano	01
Panorama Towers, 8155 Van Nuys Blvd	02
Titus, 14547 Titus	02
Union Bank, 14530 Roscoe Blvd	02

GOVERNMENT OFFICES

City Hall, 14410 Sylvan	01

HOSPITALS

Balowen Convalescent, 16955 Van Owen	06
Kaiser Foundation, 13652 Cantara	02
Mid Valley Community, 7533 Van Nuys Blvd	05
Presbyterian, 15107 Van Owen	05
Sher Wood 13524 Sherman Way	05
Sherman Oaks Community 4929 Van Nuys Blvd	03
Valley, 14500 Sherman Cir	05
Van Nuys Golden Cross, 7447 Sepulveda Blvd	05

UNIVERSITIES AND COLLEGES

Valley, 5800 Fulton Ave	01

VENTURA 930

POST OFFICE BOXES

Box Nos.		
A-Z	Main Office	01
1-2117	Main Office	01
AA-DG	Main Office	01
3001-3564	East Ventura Sta	03
4001-4299	Saticoy Br	03
5001-5312	Montalvo Br	03

STATIONS, BRANCHES AND UNITS

East Ventura Sta	03
Montalvo Br	03
Saticoy Br	03
General Delivery	01
Postmaster	01

WALNUT CREEK 945

POST OFFICE BOXES

Box Nos.		
236-359	Station A	97
2001-2200	Dollar Ranch Station	95
4000-5999	Main Office	96

STATIONS, BRANCHES AND UNITS

Arroyo Sta	98
Dollar Ranch Sta	95
Station A Sta	96
General Delivery	96
Postmaster	96

WEST COVINA 917

POST OFFICE BOXES

Box Nos.		
A-M	Main Office	90
1-999	Main Office	93

STATIONS, BRANCHES AND UNITS

General Delivery	90
Postmaster	90

WHITTIER 906

POST OFFICE BOXES

Box Nos.		
1-999	Bailey Sta	08
1000-1999	Perry Sta	09
2000-2999	Los Nietos Br	06
3000-3999	South Whittier Br	05
4000-4999	Whittier	07

STATIONS, BRANCHES AND UNITS

Bailey Sta	01
Los Nietos Br	06
Perry Sta	03
South Whittier Br	05
General Delivery	07
Postmaster	05

WILMINGTON 907

STATIONS, BRANCHES AND UNITS

Carson Br	45
Carson Br	46

COLORADO
(Abbreviation: CO)

Alameda, Br. Denver..............80226
Alamosa (1st)..........................81101
Alcott, Sta. Denver...............80212
Allenspark..............................80510
Alma.......................................80420
Almont....................................81210
Altura, Br. Aurora..................80010
Amherst..................................80721
Anton......................................80801
Antonito.................................81120
Arapahoe................................80802
Arboles..................................81121
Arlington...............................81021
Arriba....................................80804
Arvada (1st) see appendix
Aspen (1st).............................81611
Aspen Gerbaz, R. Br. Aspen...81611
Association Camp, R. Br.
   Estes Park..........................80511
Atwood...................................80722
Ault..80610
Aurora (1st)............................80010
Austin....................................81410
Avon.......................................81620
Avondale................................81022
Bailey....................................80421
Basalt....................................81621
Bayfield.................................81122
Bedrock.................................81411
Bellvue..................................80512
Belmar, Br. Denver (see
   appendix)
Belmont, Sta. Pueblo.............81001
Bennett..................................80102
Berthoud................................80513
Bethune..................................80805
Beulah....................................81023
Black Forest, R. Br. Colorado
   Springs...............................80908
Black Hawk.............................80422
Blanca....................................81123
Boncarbo...............................81024
Bond.......................................80423
Boone.....................................81025
BOULDER (1st) (see
   appendix)
Boyero....................................80806
Brandon, R. Br. Eads.............81026
Branson..................................81027
Breckenridge..........................80424
Briggsdale.............................80611
Brighton (1st).........................80601
Bristol...................................81028
Broadmoor, Br. Colorado
   Springs (see appendix)
Brookridge, Sta. Englewood....80110
Broomfield (1st).....................80020
Brush (1st).............................80723
Buena Vista............................81211
   Granite, R. Br...................81228
Buffalo Creek, R. Br. Pine....80425
Burlington (1st)......................80807
Burns......................................80426
Byers......................................80103
Cadet, Sta. U S A F
   Academy.............................80840
Cahone...................................81320
Calhan....................................80808

Campo....................................81029
Canon City (1st).....................81212
   Royal Gorge, R. Br............81246
Capitol Hill, Sta. Denver.......80218
Capulin..................................81124
Carbondale.............................81623
Carr.......................................80612
Cascade.................................80809
   Chipita Park, R. Br...........80811
Castle Rock............................80104
Cedaredge..............................81413
Centennial, Sta. Englewood...80110
Center....................................81125
Central City...........................80427
Chama....................................81126
Cheraw..................................81030
Cherry Creek, Sta. Denver......80206
Cheyenne Wells......................80810
Chimney Rock, R. Br.
   Pagosa Springs..................81127
Chipita Park, R. Br.
   Cascade.............................80811
Chivington.............................81031
Chromo..................................81128
Cimarron................................81220
Clark......................................80428
Clifton...................................81520
Climax....................................80429
Coal Creek.............................81221
Coaldale................................81222
Coalmont...............................80430
Cokedale................................81032
Collbran.................................81624
College, Sta. Greeley.............80631
College Heights, Sta.
   Durango.............................81301
Colorado City, R. Br. Pueblo...81004
COLORADO SPRINGS (1st)
   (see appendix)
Commerce City (1st)...............80022
Como, R. Br. Fairplay.............80432
Conejos..................................81129
Conifer...................................80433
Cope......................................80812
Cortez (1st)............................81321
Cory.......................................81414
Cotopaxi................................81223
Cowdrey.................................80434
Craig (1st)..............................81625
   Elk Springs, R. Br............81633
   Lay, R. Br..........................81625
Crawford.................................81415
Creede....................................81130
Crescent, R. Br. Golden..........80401
Crested Butte.........................81224
Crestone.................................81131
Cripple Creek.........................80813
Crook.....................................80726
Crowley..................................81033
Cuchara, R. Br. La Veta..........81055
Dacono...................................80514
Dayton, Sta. Aurora................80010
De Beque................................81630
Deer Trail...............................80105
Del Norte...............................81132
Delhi.....................................81034
Delta (1st)..............................81416
DENVER (1st) (see appendix)
Deora.....................................81035
Dillon....................................80435
Dinosaur................................81610
Divide....................................80814
Dolores..................................81323

Dove Creek.............................81324
Downtown, Sta. Englewood....80110
Drake.....................................80515
Dumont..................................80436
Dupont...................................80024
Durango (1st)..........................81301
   Brandon, R. Br..................81026
Eagle.....................................81631
Eads.......................................81036
Eastlake.................................80614
Eaton.....................................80615
Eckert....................................81418
Eckley....................................80727
Edgemont, Br. Golden............80401
Edgewater, Br. Denver...........80214
Edwards.................................81632
Egnar.....................................81325
El Rancho, R. Br. Golden........80401
Elbert....................................80106
Eldora, R. Br. Nederland........80437
Eldorado Springs...................80025
Elizabeth...............................80107
Elk Springs, R. Br. Craig.......81633
Empire...................................80438
Englewood (1st)......................80110
Ent A F B, MOU. Colorado
   Springs...............................80912
Erie..80516
Estes Park (1st)......................80517
   Association Camp, R. Br....80511
Evans.....................................80620
Evergreen (1st).......................80439
Fairplay.................................80440
   Como, R. Br.......................80432
   South Park City, Sta.........80440
Farisita.................................81037
Federal Heights, Br. Denver...80221
Firestone...............................80520
Fitzsimons, Br. Denver...........80240
Flagler...................................80815
Fleming..................................80728
Florence.................................81226
Florissant..............................80816
Fort Carson, Br. Colorado
   Springs...............................80913
Fort Collins (1st)....................80521
Fort Garland...........................81133
Fort Logan, Br. Denver...........80236
Fort Lupton............................80621
Fort Lyon...............................81038
Fort Morgan (1st)....................80701
Fountain.................................80817
Fountain Valley School, R.
   Br. Colorado Springs.........80911
Fowler....................................81039
Foxton....................................80441
Franktown..............................80116
Fraser.....................................80442
Frederick................................80530
Frisco....................................80443
Fruita.....................................81521
Galeton..................................80622
Garcia, R. Br. San Luis..........81134
Gardner..................................81040
Garfield, R. Br. Salida...........81227
Gateway.................................81522
Genoa....................................80818
Georgetown............................80444
Gilcrest.................................80623
Gill..80624
Gilman...................................81634
Gilsonite, R. Br. Fruita..........81521
Glade Park..............................81523

59

Glen Haven	80532	
Glendale, Br. Denver (see appendix)		
Glendevey, R. Br. Walden	80485	
Glenwood Springs (1st)	81601	
Golden (1st)	80401	
Goodrich	80625	
Gould	80445	
Granada	81041	
Granby	80446	
Grand Junction (1st)	81501	
Grand Lake	80447	
Grand Valley	81635	
Granite, R. Br. Buena Vista	81228	
Grant	80448	
Greeley (1st)	80631	
Green Mountain, Br. Denver (see appendix)		
Green Mountain Falls	80819	
Greystone	81636	
Grover	80729	
Guffey	80820	
Gulnare	81042	
Gunnison (1st)	81230	
Sapinero, R. Br.	81247	
Gypsum	81637	
Hale	80730	
Hamilton	81638	
Hartman	81043	
Hartsel	80449	
Hasty	81044	
Haswell	81045	
Haxtun	80731	
Hayden	81639	
Heeney, R. Br. Kremmling	80459	
Henderson	80640	
Hereford	80732	
Hesperus	81326	
Hideaway Park	80450	
High Mar, Sta. Boulder	80303	
Highlands, Sta. Denver	80211	
Hillrose	80733	
Hillside, R. Br. Salida	81232	
Hoehne	81046	
Hoffman Heights, Sta. Aurora	80010	
Holly	81047	
Holyoke	80734	
Homelake, R. Br. Monte Vista	81135	
Hooper	81136	
Hot Sulphur Springs	80451	
Hotchkiss	81419	
Howard	81233	
Hoyt	80641	
Hudson	80642	
Hugo	80821	
Hygiene	80533	
Idaho Springs	80452	
Idalia	80735	
Idledale	80453	
Ignacio	81137	
Iliff	80736	
Indian Hills	80454	
Jamestown	80455	
Jansen	81048	
Jaroso	81138	
Jefferson	80456	
Joes	80822	
Johnstown	80534	
Julesburg	80737	
Karval	80823	
Keenesburg	80643	
Keota	80738	
Kersey	80644	
Kim	81049	
Kiowa	80117	
Kirk	80824	
Kit Carson	80825	
Kittredge	80457	
Knob Hill, Sta. Colorado Springs (see appendix)		
Kremmling	80459	
Heeney, R. Br.	80459	
Radium, R. Br.	80472	
La Garita	81139	
La Jara	81140	
La Junta (1st)	81050	
La Salle	80645	
La Veta	81055	
Lafayette	80026	
Laird	80739	
Lake City	81235	
Lake George	80827	
Lakeside, Br. Denver (see appendix)		
Lakewood, Br. Denver (see appendix)		
Lamar (1st)	81052	
Laporte	80535	
Virginia Dale, R. Br.	80548	
Larkspur	80118	
Las Animas	81054	
Lay, R. Br. Craig	81625	
Lazear	81420	
Leadville (1st)	80461	
Lewis	81327	
Limon	80828	
Lindon	80740	
LITTLETON (1st) (see appendix)		
Livermore	80536	
Loma	81524	
Longmont (1st)	80501	
Loretto, Sta. Denver (see appendix)		
Louisville	80027	
Louviers	80131	
Loveland (1st)	80537	
Lowry A F B, Sta. Denver	80230	
Lucerne	80646	
Lycan	81056	
Lyons	80540	
Mack	81525	
Maher	81421	
Manassa	81141	
Mancos	81328	
Manitou Springs	80829	
Manzanola	81058	
Marvel	81329	
Masonville	80541	
Matheson	80830	
Maybell	81640	
Mc Clave	81057	
Mc Coy	80463	
Mead	80542	
Meadowlark, Br. Denver (see appendix)		
Meeker	81641	
Meredith	81642	
Merino	80741	
Mesa, Sta. Pueblo	81005	
Mesa	81643	
Mesa Verde National Park	81330	
Mesita	81142	
Milliken	80543	
Milner, R. Br. Steamboat Springs	80477	
Minturn	81645	
Model	81059	
Moffat	81143	
Molina	81646	
Montclair, Sta. Denver	80220	
Monte Vista (1st)	81144	
Homelake, R. Br.	81135	
Montezuma	80464	
Montrose (1st)	81401	
Monument	80132	
Morrison	80465	
Mosca	81146	
Mountain Park, R. Br. Golden	80401	
Nathrop	81236	
Naturita	81422	
Nederland	80466	
Eldora, R. Br.	80433	
New Castle	81647	
New Raymer	80742	
Niwot	80544	
North Avondale, R. Br. Pueblo	81061	
North End, Sta. Colorado Springs (see appendix)		
North Pecos, Br. Denver	80221	
North Pole, R. Br. Colorado Springs	80901	
Northglenn, Br. Denver (see appendix)		
Norwood	81423	
Nucla	81424	
Number Five, Sta. Denver	80202	
Number One, Sta. Denver	80202	
Nunn	80648	
Oak Creek	80467	
Ohio	81237	
Olathe	81425	
Olney Springs	81062	
Ophir	81426	
Orchard	80649	
Orchard Plaza, Br. Littleton	80121	
Ordway	81063	
Otis	80743	
Ouray	81427	
Ovid	80744	
Padroni	80745	
Pagosa Springs	81147	
Chimney Rock, R. Br.	81127	
Palisade	81526	
Palmer Lake	80133	
Paoli	80746	
Paonia	81428	
Paradox	81429	
Park Hill, Sta. Denver (see appendix)		
Parker	80134	
Parlin	81239	
Parshall	80468	
Peetz	80747	
Penrose (1st)	81240	
Peoples, Sta. Aurora	80010	
Peterson Field, Br. Colorado Springs	80914	
Peyton	80831	
Phippsburg	80469	
Pierce	80650	
Pine	80470	
Buffalo Creek, R. Br.	80425	
Pinecliffe	80471	
Pitkin	81241	

Placerville	81430	
Platteville	80651	
Pleasant View	81331	
Poncha Springs	81242	
Powderhorn	81243	
Pritchett	81064	
Pryor	81065	
PUEBLO (1st) (see appendix)		
Pueblo West, R. Br. Pueblo	81007	
Radium, R. Br. Kremmling	80472	
Ramah	80832	
Rand	80473	
Rangely	81648	
Red Feather Lakes	80545	
Red Wing, R. Br.		
Walsenburg	81066	
Redcliff	81649	
Redvale	81431	
Rico	81332	
Ridgway	81432	
Rifle	81650	
Rio Blanco, R. Br.	81651	
Rio Blanco, R. Br. Rifle	81651	
Rockvale	81244	
Rocky Ford (1st)	81067	
Roggen	80652	
Rollinsville	80474	
Romeo	81148	
Royal Gorge, R. Br. Canon		
City	81246	
Rush	80833	
Rye	81069	
Saguache	81149	
Salida (1st)	81201	
Garfield, R. Br.	81227	
Hillside, R. Br.	81232	
San Acacio	81150	
San Luis	81152	
Garcia, R. Br.	81134	
San Pablo	81153	
Sanford	81151	
Santa Fe Drive, Sta. Denver	80204	
Sapinero, R. Br. Gunnison	81247	
Sargents	81248	
Security, Br. Colorado		
Springs	80911	
Sedalia	80135	
Sedgwick	80749	
Segundo	81070	
Seibert	80834	
Severance	80546	
Shawnee	80475	
Sheridan Lake	81071	
Silt	81652	

Silver Cliff	81249	
Silver Plume	80476	
Silverthorne, R. Br. Dillon	80435	
Silverton	81433	
Simla	80835	
Slater	81653	
Slick Rock	81333	
Snowmass	81654	
Snyder	80750	
Somerset	81434	
South Denver, Sta. Denver		
(see appendix)		
South Fork	81154	
South Park City, Sta.		
Fairplay	80440	
Spivak, Br. Sta. Denver	80214	
Springfield	81073	
Starkville	81074	
Steamboat Springs (1st)	80477	
Sterling (1st)	80751	
Stockyards, Sta. Denver	80216	
Stoneham	80754	
Stonington	81075	
Strasburg	80136	
Stratton	80836	
Sugar City	81076	
Swink	81077	
Tabernash	80478	
Telluride	81435	
Terminal Annex, Sta. Denver	80217	
Texas Creek	81250	
Thatcher	81078	
Thornton, Br. Denver (see		
appendix)		
Timnath	80547	
Toponas	80479	
Towaoc	81334	
Towner	81080	
Trinchera	81081	
Trinidad (1st)	81082	
Twin Lakes	81251	
Two Buttes	81084	
U S A F Academy (1st)	80840	
University Park, Sta. Denver	80210	
Uravan	81436	
Utleyville	81086	
Vail	81657	

Vernon	80755	
Victor	80860	
Vilas	81087	
Villa Grove	81155	
Villegreen	81088	
Virginia Dale, R. Br. Laporte	80548	
Vona	80861	
Walden	80480	
Glendevey, R. Br.	80485	
Walsenburg	81089	
Red Wing, R. Br.	81066	
Walsh	81090	
Ward	80481	
Watkins	80137	
Weldona	80653	
Wellington	80549	
Wellshire, Sta. Denver (see		
appendix)		
West End, Sta. Colorado		
Springs	80904	
West Village, Br. Aspen	81611	
Westcliffe	81252	
Westminster (1st)	80030	
Weston	81091	
Westwood, Sta. Denver (see		
appendix)		
Wetmore	81253	
Wheat Ridge (1st)	80033	
Whitewater	81527	
Wiggins	80654	
Wild Horse	80862	
Wiley	81092	
Windsor	80550	
Windsor Gardens, Sta.		
Denver	80222	
Winter Park	80482	
Wolcott	81655	
Woodland Park	80863	
Woodrow	80757	
Woody Creek	81656	
Wray	80758	
Yampa	80483	
Yellow Jacket	81335	
Yoder	80864	
Yuma	80759	

61

ARVADA 800

STATIONS, BRANCHES AND UNITS

General Delivery	01
Postmaster	01

GOVERNMENT OFFICES

City Of Arvada	02

BOULDER 803

POST OFFICE BOXES

Box Nos.
A-Z	Main Office	02
1-2999	Main Office	02
3000-3999	High-Mar Sta	03

RURAL ROUTES

1	03
2	01
3	03

STATIONS, BRANCHES AND UNITS

High Mar Sta	03
Flagstaff Star Route	02
General Delivery	02
Jamestown Star Route	02
Nederland Star Route	02
Postmaster	02
Salina Star Route	02
Sugarloaf Star Route	02

APARTMENTS, HOTELS, MOTELS

Williams Village	02

GOVERNMENT OFFICES

Environmental Science Services Administration	02
National Bureau Of Standards	02
National Center For Atmospheric Research	02

HOSPITALS

Boulder Memorial Hospital, 250 Maxwell Ave	02
Community Hospital, 1100 Balsam Ave	02

UNIVERSITIES AND COLLEGES

University Of Colorado	02

COLORADO SPRINGS 809

POST OFFICE BOXES

Box Nos.
1-2999	Main Office	01
4000-4999	Knob Hill Sta	09

5000-5999	Security Br	31
6001-6999	West End Sta	04
7000-7999	North End Sta	33
9000-9999	Station A	32
14000-14999	Peterson Field Br	14

RURAL ROUTES

1	07
2	09
3,4	08
5	07
6	09
7,8	07
10	16
12	07

STATIONS, BRANCHES AND UNITS

Black Forest Br	08
Broadmoor Br	06
Fort Carson	13
Fountain Valley School Br	11
Knob Hill Sta	09
North End Sta	07
North Pole Br	01
Peterson Field Br	14
Security Br	11
West End Sta	04
General Delivery	01
Postmaster	01

APARTMENTS, HOTELS, MOTELS

Acacia, 104 E Platte Ave	02
Albany, 228 N Tejon	02
Antlers Plaza, 130 Chase Stone Ctr	02
Broadmoor, Broadmoor	06
Holiday Inn, 8th & Cimarron	05
Mayfair, 120 E Platte Ave	02

BUILDINGS

Burns, 23 E Pikes Peak Ave	02
Colorado Commercial Bank, 104 S Tejon	02
Colorado Springs National Bank, 31 N Tejon	02
El Paso County Office, 27 E. Vermijo	03
Exchange National Bank, 6 S Tejon	02
First National Bank, 6 N Tejon	02
Holly Sugar, 100 Chase Stone Center	02
Independence, 121 E Pikes Peak Ave	02
Mining Exchange, 8 S Nevada Ave	02

GOVERNMENT OFFICES

City Hall, 107 N Nevada Ave	02
Courthouse, 215 S Tejon	02

HOSPITALS

Emory John Brady, 401 Southgate Rd	06

Mamie Doud Eisenhower Osteopathic, 33 Barnes Ave	09
Memorial, 1400 E. Boulder	09
Penrose, 2215 N Cascade Ave	07
Saint Francis, 800 E Pikes Peak Ave	03

MILITARY INSTALLATIONS

Ent Afb, 1500 E Boulder	12
Federal Aviation Agency, Peterson Field	14
Fort Carson, South Of Colorado Sprg	13
Headquarters Air Defense Command, 1500 E Boulder	12
Headquarters Commander Naval Forces Norad	12
Headquarters United States Army Air Defense Command	12
North American Air Defense Command, 1500 E Boulder	12
Peterson Field Administrative Offices	16
Peterson Field Air Terminal Of Colorado Springs	16
Peterson Field, E Of Colorado Springs - Military	14
United States Naval Reserve Training Center, Lake & Logan	10

UNIVERSITIES AND COLLEGES

Blair Business College, 10 N Farragut	09
Colorado College	03
University Of Colorado Extension, Cragmor Rd	07

DENVER 802

POST OFFICE BOXES

Box Nos.
1-388	Ft Logan Brch	36
1-3199	Main Office Sta	01
4001-4999	Santa Fe Dr Sta	04
5001-5999	Terminal Annex Sta	17
6001-6418	Fitzsimons Br	40
6001-6999	Cherry Creek Sta	06
7001-7999	Park Hill Sta	07
9001-9999	South Denver Sta	09
10001-10999	University Park Sta	10
11001-11999	Highlands Sta	11
12001-12999	Alcott Sta	12
14001-14999	Edgewater Br	14
15001-15999	Lakewood Br	15
16001-16999	Stockyards Sta	16

Denver (Con.)   802

17001-17999 Terminal Annex Sta	17
18001-18999 Capitol Hill Sta	18
19001-19999 Westwood Sta	19
20001-20999 Montclair Sta	20
21001-21999 North Pecos Br	21
22001-22999 Wellshire Sta	22
26001-26999 Belmar Br	26
29001-29999 Thornton Br	29
30001-30999 Lowry Air Force Base	30

RURAL ROUTES

1	29
2	22

STATIONS, BRANCHES AND UNITS

Alameda Br	26
Alcott Sta	12
Belmar Br	26
Capitol Hill Sta	18
Cherry Creek Sta	06
Edgewater Br	14
Fitzsimons Br	40
Fort Logan Br	36
Glendale Br	22
Green Mountain Br	28
Highlands Sta	11
Lakeside Br	12
Lakewood Br	15
Loretto Sta	36
Lowry AFB Sta	30
Meadowlark Br	15
Montclair Sta	20
Northglenn Br	33
North Pecos Br	21
Number One Sta	02
Number Five Sta	02
Park Hill Sta	07
Santa Fe Drive Sta	04
South Denver Sta	09
Spivak Br	14
Stockyards Sta	16
Terminal Annex Sta	17
Thornton Br	29
University Park Sta	10
Wellshire Sta	22
Westwood Sta	19
Windsor Gardens Sta	22
General Delivery	01
Postmaster	02

APARTMENTS, HOTELS, MOTELS

Albany, 1720 Stout	02
Ambassador, 130 Pearl	03
Americana, 1121 Albion	20
Argonaut, 233 E Colfax Ave	03
Avondale Village, 3295 W Avondale Dr	04
Bahama, 1180 Sherman	03
Bermuda, 1080 Logan	03
Brown Palace, 321 17th	02
Buchtel Grove, 2105 Buchtel Blvd	10
Cheesman Towers, 1201 Williams	18

Cherry Creek Towers, 3100
Cherry Creek S Dr	09
Colburn Apts, 350 Grant St	03
Colburn Hotel, 980 Grant St	03
Cosmopolitan, 1780 Broadway	02
Country Club Gardens, 1100 E Ellsworth Ave	09
Denver Downtowner Mtr Inn, 303 W Colfax Ave	04
Denver-Hilton, 1550 Court Pl	01
Eight-Eighty-Eight Logan, 888 Logan	03
Eleven Hundred Cheesman Pk, 1111 Race	06
Grosvenor Arms, 333 E 16th Ave	03
Holiday Central, 1975 Bryant St	04
Holiday So Colo, 1475 So Colo Blvd	22
La Fontana, 4570 E Yale Ave	22
Lanai, 800 Washington	03
Lido, 790 Washington	03
Lion Gate, 90 Corona	18
Mayflower Motel, 1710 Grant	03
Olin Hotel & Apts, 1420 Logan St	03
Park Lane Towers, 480 S. Marion St Pky	09
Penn Vii, 700 Pennsylvania	03
Polo Club, 3131 E Alameda Ave	09
Radisson-Denver, 1790 Grant	03
Ramada Inn, 455 S Colo Blvd	22
Regency Roadway Inn, 3900 Elati	16
Roger Williams Manor, 101 Grant	03
Rossonian, 2642 Welton	05
Sherman Plaza, 901 Sherman	03
Skyline, 1801 Arapahoe	02
Skyways Motor, 3855 Quebec	07
Travelodge North, 200 W Warner Pl	16
Twelve-Hundred Vine, 1200 Vine	06
Versailles, 789 Clarkson	18
Wellshire Arms, 2499 S Colo Blvd	22
Windsor Gardens, 600 S Clinton	31
Writers Manor, 1730 S Colo Blvd	02
Ymca, 25 E 16 Th Ave	02
Ywca Colorado Hotel, 406 17th	02

BUILDINGS

American National Bank, 818
17th	02
Boston, 828 17th	02
Brooks Tower, 1020 15th St	02
C A Johnson, 509 17th	02
Capitol Life Center, 225 E 16th Ave	03
Central Bank, 1108 15th	02
Colorado Bldg, 1615 California St	02

Colorado State Bank, 1600 Broadway	02
Continental Oil 1755 Glenarm Pl	02
Denham Bldg, 1812 California	02
Denver Center 1776 Lincoln	03
Denver Club Bldg, 518 17 Th St	02
Denver Merchandise Mart, 451 E. 58th Ave	16
Empire, 430 16th	02
Equitable, 730 17th	02
Executive Club	10
First National Bank, 621 17th	02
Guaranty Bank, 817 17th	02
Hilton Office, 1515 Cleveland Pl	02
Ideal Cement, 821 17 Th St	02
Insurance Exchange, 910 15th	02
Insurance, 831 14 Th St	02
Kittredge, 511 16th	02
Lincoln Tower Office, 1860 Lincoln	03
Livestock Exchange, 4701 Marion	16
Majestic, 209 16th	02
Metropolitan, 1612 Court Pl	02
Midland Savings, 444 17th	02
One-O-One University, 101 University Blvd	06
Park Central, 1515 Arapahoe	02
Patterson, 555 17th	02
Petroleum, 110-16th	02
Prudential Plaza, 1050 17th	02
Republic, 1612 Tremont Pl	02
Security Life, 1616 Glenarm Pl	02
Security, 650 17th	02
Symes, 820 16th	02
Three-Thirty-Three, 333 W Colfax Ave	04
Title, 909 17 Th St	02
Tower, 1700 Broadway	02
United Bank Of Denver, 1740 Broadway	02
University, 910 16th	02
Western Federal Savings, 718 17th	02

GOVERNMENT OFFICES

City & County, 1437 Bannock	02
Denver Chamber Of Commerce, 1301 Welton	04
Denver Convention Complex, 1323 Champa	04
Denver Federal Center	25
Federal Office Building, 1961 Stout	02
Hall Of Justice, 1929 Stout	02
Post Office, 1823 Stout	02
State Capitol Annex, 1375 Sherman	03
State Capitol, 200 E. Colfax Ave	03
State Museum, 200 E. 14th Ave	03
State Office, 201 E Colfax Ave	03
State Service, 1525 Sherman	03

Denver (Con.)   802

State Social Services, 1575
  Sherman................................. 03
United States Customs
  House, 721 19th.................... 02

HOSPITALS

American Medical Center, (J
  C R S) 6401 W Colfax
  Ave.. 14
Beth Israel, 1601 Lowell
  Blvd... 04
Childrens Asthma ,3401 W
  19th Ave.................................. 04
Childrens Hospital
  Association, 1056 E 19th
  Ave.. 18
Colorado General, 4200 E 9th
  Ave.. 20
Denver General, 301 W 7th
  Ave.. 04
Fitzsimons General, 12101 E
  Colfax Ave................................ 40
Fort Logan Mental Health,
  3520 W Oxford Ave.................. 36
General Rose Memorial, 1050
  Clermont.................................. 20
Life Center, 5775 E 8th Ave... 20
Mercy, 1619 Milwaukee.......... 06
National Jewish Hospital In
  Denver, 3800 E Colfax
  Ave.. 06
Porter Memorial Hospital,
  2525 S Downing....................... 10
Presbyterian Medical Center,
  1719 E 19th Ave....................... 18
Rocky Mountain Osteopathic
  4701 E 9th Ave........................ 20
Saint Anthonys, 4231 W 16th
  Ave.. 04
Saint Josephs, 1835 Franklin.. 18
Saint Lukes, 601 E 19th Ave.. 03
Spears Chiropractic
  Santarium & Hospital, 927
  Jersey...................................... 20
Valley View, 8451 Pearl.......... 29
Veterans Administration,
  1055 Clermont......................... 20

MILITARY INSTALLATIONS

Air Force Acct & Finance
  Center, 3800 York St.............. 05
Lowry AFB................................. 30
Martin Company........................ 01
Rocky Mountain Arsenal........... 40
Stapleton International Airp..... 07

UNIVERSITIES AND COLLEGES

Barnes School O₂ Commerce,
  1410 Glenarm Pl...................... 02
Central Business, 1177
  Grant....................................... 03

Community College Of
  Denver, 1001 E. 62nd
  Ave.. 16
Iliff School Of Theology, 2201
  S University Blvd..................... 10
Loretto, 3001 S Federal Blvd.. 36
Metro State, 250 W 14th Ave. 04
Regis, 3539 W 50th Ave.......... 21
Temple-Buell, 1800 Pontiac
  St... 20
University Of Colorado School
  Of Medicine, 4200 E 9th
  Ave.. 20
University Of Colorado,denver
  Center, 1100 14 Th St........... 02
University Of Denver, 2115 S
  University Blvd........................ 10

LITTLETON   801

POST OFFICE BOXES

Box Nos.
1-1999   Main Office 20
1-1999   Main Office 20

RURAL ROUTES

1,2,3,3 20

STATIONS, BRANCHES AND UNITS

Orchard Plaza Br...................... 21

PUEBLO   810

POST OFFICE BOXES

Box Nos.
1-1999   Pueblo 02
2000-2999   A Sta 04
3000-3999   Mesa Sta......... 05
4000-4999   Parel Post
                 Annex............. 03
11000-11999 Belmont Sta....... 01

RURAL ROUTES

1,2,3,4 04

STATIONS, BRANCHES AND UNITS

Belmont Sta 01
Colorado City Rural Br............. 04
Mesa Sta 05
North Avondale Rural Br.......... 61
Pueblo West Rural Br.............. 07
General Delivery 02
Postmaster 03

APARTMENTS, HOTELS, MOTELS

B T C Tower House, 1111
  Bonforte Blvd.......................... 01
Chilton Inn, 800 Highway 50
  W... 08
Continental, 1021 Ruppel........ 01
Presbyterian Towers, 220 W
  15th... 03
Ramada Inn, E Hwy 50
  Bypass & N Hudson Ave 01
Town House Moter Hotel, 8th
  & Santa Fe.............................. 08

BUILDINGS

Bon Durant Bldg, 5th &
  Court St................................... 03
City Hall, 100 N Union............. 03
Colorado Bldg, 407 N Main...... 03
Federal Building 5th & Main.... 03
Judicial 10th & Grand.............. 03
Pueblo Clinic, 702 N Main........ 03
Pueblo County Court House,
  10th & N Grand....................... 03
St Mary-Corwin Medical Arts,
  1925 E Orman Ave................. 04
Thatcher Bldg, 5th & Main
  St... 03

GOVERNMENT OFFICES

Government Printing Office,
  Pueblo Industrial Park........ 09

HOSPITALS

Colorado State Hospital,
  1600 W 24th............................ 03
Parkview Episcopal, 400 W
  16th... 03
St Mary Corwin, 1008
  Minnequa 04

MILITARY INSTALLATIONS

Pueblo Army Depot................... 01
Pueblo Memorial Airport.......... 04
US High Speed Ground Test
  Center 01

UNIVERSITIES AND COLLEGES

Belmont Campus, 2200
  Bonforte Blvd.......................... 01
Southern Colorado State
  College, 900 W Orman
  Ave.. 05

CONNECTICUT
(Abbreviation: CT)

Abington 06230
Amity, Sta. New Haven 06525
Amston 06231
Andover 06232
Ansonia (1st) 06401
Avon (1st) 06001
Ballouville 06233
Baltic 06330
Bantam 06750
Barnum, Sta. Bridgeport 06605
Barry Square, Sta. Hartford 06114
Beacon Falls 06403
Beardsley, Sta. Bridgeport 06606
Belden, Sta. Norwalk 06850
Berlin, Br. Kensington 06037
Bethel (1st) 06801
Bethlehem 06751
Bishops Corner, Br. Hartford 06117
Bissell, Sta. South Windsor 06074
Bloomfield (1st) 06002
Blue Hills, Sta. Hartford 06112
Bolton, Br. Manchester 06040
Borough, Sta. Groton 06340
Botsford 06404
Branford (1st) 06405
BRIDGEPORT (1st) (see
     appendix)
Bridgewater 06752
Bristol (1st) 06010
Broad Brook 06016
Brookfield (1st) 06804
Brookfield Center 06805
Brooklyn 06234
Buckland, Sta. Manchester 06040
Burlington, R. Br. Unionville 06085
Byram, Br. Port Chester, N
     Y...10573
Canaan (1st) 06018
Candlewood Isle, Br.
     Danbury.....................................06810
Canterbury...06331
Canton 06019
Canton Center 06020
Center, Br. Bridgeport 06611
Centerbrook 06409
Centerville-Mount Carmel,
     Br. New Haven (see
     appendix)
Central, Sta. Hartford 06103
Central Village 06332
Chaplin 06235
Cheshire (1st) 06410
Chester (1st) 06412
Clinton (1st) 06413
Cobalt 06414
Colchester (1st) 06415
Colebrook 06021
Collinsville 06022
Columbia 06237
Corbins Corner, Br. Hartford 06110
Cornwall 06753
Cornwall Bridge 06754
Cos Cob (1st) 06807
Coventry (1st) 06238
Cromwell (1st) 06416
Danbury (1st) 06810
Danielson (1st) 06239
Darien (1st) 06820
Dayville 06241
Deep River (1st) 06417
Derby (1st) 06418

Devon, Sta. Milford 06460
Durham...06422
East Berlin 06023
East Canaan 06024
East Derby, Sta. Derby 06418
East End, Sta. Waterbury......06705
East Glastonbury 06025
East Granby 06026
East Haddam 06423
East Hampton (1st) 06424
East Hartford, Br. Hartford
     (see appendix)
East Hartland 06027
East Haven, Br. New Haven......06512
East Killingly 06243
East Lyme 06333
East Windsor Hill 06028
East Woodstock 06244
Eastford 06242
Easton 06425
Ellington 06029
Elmwood, Br. Hartford............06110
Enfield (1st) 06082
Essex (1st) 06426
Fabyan 06245
Fair Haven, Sta. New Haven......06513
Fairfield (1st) 06430
Falls Village 06031
Farmington (1st) 06032
Fitchville 06334
Forestville, Sta. Bristol............06010
Gales Ferry (1st) 06335
     Ledyard, Sta.............................06339
Garden, Br. Bridgeport............06611
Gaylordsville 06755
Georgetown (1st) 06829
Gilman 06336
Glasgo 06337
Glastonbury (1st) 06033
Glenbrook, Sta. Stamford 06906
Glenville, Sta. Greenwich 06830
Goshen 06756
Granby 06035
Grand Street, Sta.
     Waterbury...................................06701
Greens Farms 06436
Greenwich (1st) 06830
Grosvenor Dale 06246
Groton (1st) 06340
Groton Long Point, Sta.
     Groton...06340
Guilford (1st) 06437
Haddam 06438
Hadlyme 06439
Hamden, Br. New Haven
     (see appendix)
Hampton...06247
Hanover 06350
HARTFORD (1st) (see
     appendix)
Harwinton, Br. Torrington......06790
Hawleyville 06440
Hazardville, Sta. Enfield 06082
Hebron 06248
Higganum 06441
Hillside, Br. Bridgeport............06610
Hotchkiss School, Sta.
     Lakeville.....................................06039
Huntington, Sta. Shelton......06484
Ivoryton 06442
Jewett City (1st) 06351
Kensington (1st) 06037
Kent 06757
Kilby, Sta. New Haven............06519

Lakeside 06758
Lakeville (1st) 06039
Lebanon 06249
Ledyard, Sta. Gales Ferry......06339
Lisbon, R. Br. Jewett City......06351
Litchfield (1st) 06759
Madison (1st) 06443
Manchester (1st) 06040
Mansfield Center 06250
Mansfield Depot 06251
Maple Hill, Br. Hartford 06111
Marble Dale 06761
Marion 06444
Mechanicsville 06252
Melrose 06049
Meriden (1st) 06450
Merrow 06253
Middle Haddam 06456
Middlebury (1st) 06762
Middlefield (1st) 06455
Middletown (1st) 06457
Milford (1st) 06460
Milldale 06467
Monroe (1st) 06468
Montville 06353
Moodus 06469
Moosup 06354
Morris 06763
Mystic (1st) 06355
Naugatuck (1st) 06770
NEW BRITAIN (1st) (see
     appendix)
New Canaan (1st) 06840
New Fairfield, Br. Danbury......06810
New Hartford (1st) 06057
NEW HAVEN (1st) (see
     appendix)
New London (1st) 06320
New Milford (1st) 06776
New Preston 06777
Newfield, Sta. Bridgeport......06607
Newington, Br. Hartford......06111
Newtown (1st) 06470
Niantic (1st) 06357
Noank, Sta. Groton 06340
Noble, Sta. Bridgeport............06608
Norfolk 06058
Noroton, Sta. Darien............06820
Noroton Heights, Sta.
     Darien...06820
North Branford (1st) 06471
North Canton 06059
North End, Sta. Waterbury......06704
North Franklin 06254
North Granby 06060
North Grosvenordale 06255
North Haven (1st) 06473
North Stonington 06359
North Westchester 06474
North Windham 06256
North Woodstock 06257
Northfield 06778
Northford 06472
NORWALK (1st) (see
     appendix)
Norwich (1st) 06360
Oakdale 06370
Oakville (1st) 06779
Old Greenwich (1st) 06870
Old Lyme (1st) 06371
Old Mystic 06372
Old Saybrook (1st) 06475
Oneco 06373
Orange (1st) 06477

Oxford, R. Br. Seymour...........06483
Parcel Post, Sta.
  Manchester 06040
Parcel Post, Sta. Milford. 06460
Parcel Post Annex, Sta.
  Waterbury.........................06704
Pawcatuck, Br. Westerly, R I..02891
Pequabuck 06781
Pine Meadow 06061
Pine Rock Park, R. Sta.
  Shelton.............................06484
Plainfield 06374
Plainville (1st).......................06062
Plantsville (1st)....................06479
Pleasant Valley......................06063
Plymouth................................06782
Pomfret...................................06258
Pomfret Center.......................06259
Poquonock 06064
Portland (1st).........................06480
Prospect, Br. Waterbury.........06712
Putnam (1st)...........................06260
Quaker Hill 06375
Quinebaug 06262
Redding...................................06875
Redding Ridge........................06876
Ridgefield (1st).......................06877
Ridgeway, Sta. Stamford........06905
Riverside (1st).........................06878
Riverton 06065
Rockfall 06481
Rocky Hill (1st).......................06067
Rogers 06263
Rowayton, Sta. Norwalk.........06853
Roxbury...................................06783
Salisbury.................................06068
Samp Mortar, Sta. Fairfield....06430
Sandy Hook.............................06482
Saugatuck, Sta. Westport.......06880
Scotland..................................06264
Seymour (1st).........................06483
Sharon.....................................06069
Shelton (1st) 06484
Sherman...................................06784
Short Beach, Sta. Branford.....06405
Simsbury (1st).........................06070
Somers.....................................06071
Somersville 06072
South Britain...........................06487

South Glastonbury..................06073
South Kent...............................06785
South Lyme..............................06376
South Meriden, Sta. Meriden ..06450
South Willington......................06265
South Windham........................06266
South Windsor (1st)................06074
South Woodstock.....................06267
Southbury (1st)........................06488
Southington (1st).....................06489
Southport (1st).........................06490
Springdale, Sta. Stamford......06907
Stafford 06075
Stafford Springs (1st).............06076
Staffordville............................06077
STAMFORD (1st) (see
  appendix)
Sterling...................................06377
Stevenson................................06491
Stonington (1st).......................06378
Stony Creek, Sta. Branford.....06405
Storrs (1st)..............................06268
Submarine Base, Sta.
  Groton..............................06340
Suffield (1st)....... 06078
Taconic...................................06079
Taftville (1st)..........................06380
Tariffville................................06081
Terminal, Sta. New Haven 06511
Terryville (1st).........................06786
Thomaston (1st)......................06787
Thompson.................................06277
Tolland (1st)............................06084
Torrington (1st)........................06790
  Harwinton, Br.....................06790
Trumbull, Br. Bridgeport........06611
Uncasville (1st).......................06382
Union City, Sta. Naugatuck.....06770
Unionville (1st)....... 06085
Vernon (1st).............................06086
Versailles................................06383
Voluntown..............................06384
Wallingford (1st).....................06492
Warehouse Point (1st).............06088
Warren, R. Br. Cornwall
  Bridge 06754
Warrenville.......... 06278
Washington..............................06793
Washington Depot 06794

WATERBURY (1st) (see
  appendix)
Waterford (1st).......................06385
Watertown (1st).......................06795
Waterville, Sta. Waterbury......06714
Wauregan.................................06387
Weatogue.................................06089
Wesleyan, Sta. Middletown 06457
West Cornwall..........................06796
West Granby.............................06090
West Hartford, Br. Hartford
  (see appendix)
West Hartland..........................06091
West Haven, Br. New Haven.....06516
West Mystic.............................06388
West Putnam Avenue, Sta.
  Greenwich.........................06830
West Redding............................06896
West Simsbury..........................06092
West Suffield............................06093
West Willington........................06279
Westbrook (1st)........................06498
Weston, Br. Westport...............06880
Westport (1st)...........................06880
Westville, Sta. New Haven.......06515
Wethersfield, Br. Hartford 06109
Whitneyville, Br. New Haven
  (see appendix)
Wildemere Beach, Sta.
  Milford.............................06460
Willimantic (1st) 06226
Wilson, Sta. Windsor...............06095
Wilton (1st) 06897
Winchester Center, R. Sta.
  Winsted............................06094
Windham..................................06280
Windsor (1st)...........................06095
Windsor Locks (1st)................06096
Windsorville.............................06097
Winsted (1st)...........................06098
  Winchester Center, R.
  Sta.................................06094
Wolcott, Br. Waterbury............06716
Woodbury (1st)........................06798
Woodmont, Sta. Milford..........06460
Woodstock................................06281
Woodstock Valley.....................06282
Yale, Sta. New Haven..............06520
Yalesville, Sta. Wallingford.....06492
Yantic......................................06389

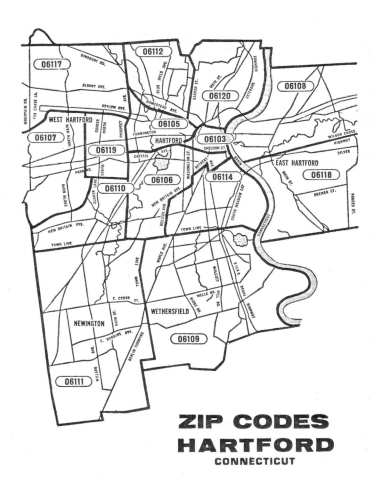

ZIP CODES

HARTFORD

CONNECTICUT

BRIDGEPORT   066

POST OFFICE BOXES

Box Nos.

1-400	Trumbull Br......	11
1-1999	Main Office	01
2001-2999	Noble Sta.......	08
3000-3999	Barnum Sta......	05
4000-4999	Newfield Sta.....	07
5000-5999	Hillside Sta	10
6000-6999	Beardsley Sta....	06
9000-9200	Main Office	01

STATIONS, BRANCHES AND UNITS

Barnum Sta.............................	05
Beardsley Sta........................	06
Center Br...............................	11
Garden Br...............................	11
Hillside Sta............................	10
Newfield Sta...........................	07
Noble Sta...............................	08
Trumbull Br............................	11
General Delivery	01
Postmaster	02

APARTMENTS, HOTELS, MOTELS

Barnum, 140 Fairfield Ave......	03
Beardsley Terrace, Trumbull Ave...........................	06
Canaan Village........................	10
Charles F Greene, Highland Ave................................	04
Father Panik Village................	08
Harbor View Towers, 376 E Washington Ave	08
Marina Village........................	04
P T Barnum, Taylor Dr...........	05
Pequonnock, Broad & Allen	04
Stratfield Motor Inn, 1241 Main................................	03
Success Park, Granfield & Success Av............................	10

BUILDINGS

City Savings Bank, 948 Main................................	03
Conn National Bank 886 Main................................	03
Jayson, 181 Middle	03
Mechanics & Farmers Bldg., 114 State St....................	03
Medical Center, 2660 Main	06
Medical, 144 Golden Hill	03
Newfield, 1188 Main..............	03
Peoples Saving Bank, 855 Main................................	03
Professional, 881 Lafayette Blvd................................	03
Raffel, 240 Fairfield Ave........	03
Security, 1115 Main...............	03
Underwood-Commerce, 527 Broad	04
Warner, 83 Fairfield Ave	03

GOVERNMENT OFFICES

State Court House, 172 Golden Hill........................	04

US Court House & Federal Office Building 915 Lafayette Blvd.................... 03

HOSPITALS

Bridgeport, 267 Grant.............	02
Emergency, 835 Washington Ave................................	04
Hillside Hospital, 540 Bond....	10
Park City, 695 Park Ave..........	04
Saint Vincents, 2820 Main......	06

UNIVERSITIES AND COLLEGES

Sacred Heart University, 5229 Park Ave	04
University Of Bridgeport, 285 Park Ave........................	02

HARTFORD   061

POST OFFICE BOXES

Box Nos.

1-2580	Main Office	01
3001-3999	Central Sta........	03
6001-6999	Station A.........	06
7001-7999	West Hartford Br..........	07
8001-8999	East Hartford Br..........	08
9001-9999	Wethersfield Br................	09
10001-10999	Elmwood Br......	10
11001-11999	Newington Br ...	11
12001-12999	Blue Hills Sta....	12
14001-14999	Barry Square Sta...............	14
17001-17999	Bishops Corners Br.......	17

STATIONS, BRANCHES AND UNITS

Barry Square Sta...................	14
Bishops Corner Br..................	17
Blue Hills Sta........................	12
Central Sta............................	03
Corbins Corner Br..................	10
East Hartford Br....................	08
Elmwood Br...........................	10
Maple Hill Br.........................	11
Newington Br........................	11
West Hartford Br...................	07
Wethersfield Br.....................	09
General Delivery	01
Postmaster	01

APARTMENTS, HOTELS, MOTELS

Ambassador, 206 Farmington Ave................................	05
Briarcliff, 7 May.....................	05
Hampshire House, 887 Farmington Av	19
Kingswood Court, 877 Farmington Ave...............	19
Packard, 745 Farmington Av ..	19
Shoreham, 440 Asylum...........	03
Sonesta, Constitution Plz........	03
Statler-Hilton, 10 Ford............	01

Westgate, 1248 Farmington....	07
Wickham Gardens, 1267-1299 Burnside Ave	08
Willoughby, 330 Laurel	05
Woodland House, 31 Woodland........................	05

BUILDINGS

American Industrial, 983 Main................................	03
Capitol, 410 Asylum...............	03
Medical, 85 Jefferson	06
Municipal, 550 Main...............	03
Woodland Medical Center, 140 Woodland..................	05
100 Constitution Plaza	03

GOVERNMENT OFFICES

Federal Office, 450 Main........	03
State Capitol, 210 Capitol Ave................................	15
State Office, 165 Capitol Ave................................	15
United States Post Office, 135 High.........................	01

HOSPITALS

Hartford Hospital, 80 Seymour............................	15
Institute of Living, 200 Retreat Ave.....................	02
Mt Sinai, 500 Blue Hills Ave...	12
Newington Childrens'S Hospital............................	11
St Francis, 114 Woodland St..	05
University Of Connecticut Hospital - Mccook Div......	12
Veterans, 555 Willard Ave......	11

UNIVERSITIES AND COLLEGES

Hartford Seminary Foundation, 55 Elizabeth....	05
Saint Josephs College, 1687 Asylum Ave......................	17
Trinity College, Summit...........	06
University Of Connecticut, 1280 Asylum Ave..............	05
University Of Hartford, 200 Bloomfield Ave..................	17

NEW BRITAIN   060

POST OFFICE BOXES

Box Nos.

1-1328	Main Office	50

STATIONS, BRANCHES AND UNITS

General Delivery	50
Postmaster	50

HOSPITALS

New Britain General, 100 Grand St.........................	50

New Britain (Con.) 060

New Britain Memorial, 2150
Corbin Ave 50

UNIVERSITIES AND COLLEGES

Central Connecticut State
College, 1615 Stanley St.... 50

NEW HAVEN 065

POST OFFICE BOXES

Box Nos.		
1-210	Main Office	01
1-320	East Haven Br..	12
1-325	Fair Haven Sta.	13
1-392	West Haven Br.	16
1-3440	Yale Sta	20
211-506	Main Office	02
511-806	Main Office	03
811-1106	Main Office	04
1111-1406	Main Office	05
1411-1630	Main Office	06
1631-1810	Main Office	07
1811-1900	Main Office	08
1901-1970	Main Office	09
2901-3131	Westville Sta	15
3601-3994	Amity Br	25
4001-4380	Hamden Br.......	14
5001-5548	Mount Carmel Br.............	18
6001-6206	Whitneyville Br.	17
7001-7447	Kilby Sta..........	19

RURAL ROUTES

1,2,3,4,5,6,7 25

STATIONS, BRANCHES AND UNITS

Amity Sta..............................	25
East Haven Br.......................	12
Fair Haven Sta	13
Kilby Sta...............................	19
Terminal Sta	11
West Haven Br	16
Westville Sta	15
Yale Sta................................	20
General Delivery	10
Postmaster	10

APARTMENTS, HOTELS, MOTELS

Crown Towers, 123 York	11
Duncan, 1151 Chapel..............	11
Holiday Inn 0 1, 1605 Whalley Ave..................	15
Holiday Inn 0 2, 30 Whalley Ave...............................	11
Madison Towers, 111 Park......	11
Midtown Moter Inn, 1157 Chapel...............................	11
Park Plaza, 155 Temple..........	10
Taft Hotel, 265 College	10

University Towers, 100 York.....	11
Ymca, 52 Howe......................	11
Ywca, 42 Howe......................	11

BUILDINGS

Chapel Square, 900 Chapel....	10
Community Services Bldg, 1 State...............................	11
Knights Of Columbus Supr Hdg, Church....................	07
Malley, 2 Church....................	10
Medical Bldg, 2 Church So.....	19
Penn. Central R.r. New Haven Dist.	06
Southern New England Telephone Co, 300 George..	06
US Post Office & Federal Bldg, 141 Church...............	10

HOSPITALS

Hospital Of Saint Raphael, 1450 Chapel.....................	10
Physician & Surgeons, 198 Sherman Ave....................	11
U. S. Veterans Hospital, West Spring.........................	16
Yale-New Haven Community Hospital, 789 Howard Ave...	04

UNIVERSITIES AND COLLEGES

Albertus Magnus, 700 Prospect..........................	11
Quinnipiac College, Mt. Carmel Avenue.................	18
Southern Conn State College, 501 Crescent	15
Stone, 54 Wall........................	07
University Of New Haven	05

NORWALK 068

POST OFFICE BOXES

Box Nos.		
A-J	Rowayton Sta ...	53
1-192	Rowayton Sta ...	53
1-761	Norwalk Main Office................	56
1-940	Belden Sta	52

RURAL ROUTES

1..	51
2,3	50

STATIONS, BRANCHES AND UNITS

Belden Sta..............................	50
Rowayton Sta	53
General Delivery	56
Postmaster	56

APARTMENTS, HOTELS, MOTELS

Admiral Motel, 377 Main Ave.	51
Carlton Court, Monterey Pl......	54

Carver Apts, 43 Butler St.......	50
Clarmore, 1 Clarmore Dr.......	50
Dreamy Hollow, 41 Wolfpit Ave................................	51
Elmcrest, 8 Elmcrest Tr........	50
Flax Hill, 208 Flax Hill Rd	54
General Putman Inn, 1 Park St...................................	51
Kingsley Garden, 11 Bedford Ave...............................	50
Meadow Garden, Meadow St..	54
Nor-West, 80 County St..........	51
Norwalk Motor Inn, 99 East Ave...............................	51
Overlook Terrace, 45 Maple St...................................	50
Park Towers, 9-11 Park..........	51
Town House, 25 Monroe........	54
Trinity, 17 Fairfield Ave	54

BUILDINGS

Executive House Bldg, 83 East Ave............................	51
Frost Bldg, 520 West Ave.......	50
W N L K Building, 64 Wall St...................................	50
50 Washington St Bldg...........	54

GOVERNMENT OFFICES

Dept Of Internal Revenue, 83 East Ave............................	52

HOSPITALS

Norwalk Hospital, 24 Stevens St...................................	56

UNIVERSITIES AND COLLEGES

Norwalk Community College, Highland Ave	56

STAMFORD 069

POST OFFICE BOXES

Box Nos.		
1-1999	Main Office	04
2000-2999	Glenbrook Sta...	06
3000-3999	Ridgeway Sta ...	05
4000-4999	Springdale Sta.	07

STATIONS, BRANCHES AND UNITS

Glenbrook Sta........................	06
Ridgeway Sta	05
Springdale Sta	07
General Delivery	04
Postmaster	04

APARTMENTS, HOTELS, MOTELS

Mayflower Gardens, Summer..	05
Morgan Manor, 83 Morgan St...................................	05
Roger Smith, 65 River...........	01

Stamford (Con.)   069

St John'S Towers, South &
  Willow................................... 01
Stamford Motor, Main St &
  Seaside Ave 02
Woodside Village, Bridge St.... 05

BUILDINGS

Gurley, 322 Main...................... 01
State National Bank Of
  Connecticut, 1 Atlantic...... 01
Union Trust Co, 300 Main 01
Washington Plaza 65
  Washington Ave 02

GOVERNMENT OFFICES

Municipal Offices, 429
  Atlantic St 01
Town Hall, Atlantic Square..... 01

HOSPITALS

Saint Josephs, 128
  Strawberry Hill Ave............. 04
Stamford Hospital, 190 W
  Broad 02

UNIVERSITIES AND COLLEGES

Saint Basils, 14 Peveril Rd 02
University Of Connecticut,
  Scofieldtown Rd.................. 03

WATERBURY   067

POST OFFICE BOXES

Box Nos.
1-2600   Main Office 20
3000-3999   East End Sta.... 05
4000-4999   Waterville Sta.. 14
5000-5999   North End Sta... 04
6000-6999   Wolcott Br 16
7000-7200   Prospect Br 12

RURAL ROUTES

1.. 12

STATIONS, BRANCHES AND UNITS

East End Sta........................... 05
Grand Street Sta..................... 01
North End Sta.......................... 04
Parcel Post Annex Sta............. 04
Prospect Br.............................. 12
Waterville Sta.......................... 14
Wolcott Br............................... 16
General Delivery...................... 20
Postmaster 01

APARTMENTS, HOTELS, MOTELS

Alma, 32 Willow...................... 10
Bernard, 174 Willow................ 10
Cables, 43 Prospect................ 02
Carroll, 44 Willow.................... 10
Carrollton, 80 Willow............... 10
Glen Ridge, 7 Glenridge.......... 10
Gloria, 261 Grove.................... 10
Grove Hall, 38 Grove............... 10
Grove Manor, 145 Grove......... 10
Hitchcock, 164 W Main........... 02
Holiday Inn 82 South Elm
  Street 02
Howard Johnson'S Motor
  Lodge 2640 South Main
  Street 06
Kingsbury Incorporated, 44
  Center 02
Northrop, 182 W Main............. 02
Palace, 94 E Main................... 20
Plaza, 365 Willow.................... 10
Quality Motel Schraffts Drive... 05
Ridgewood, 51 Ridgewood...... 10
Saint Regis, 330 E Main.......... 02
Trinity, 41 Prospect................. 02
Waterbury Motor Inn Scott
  Road 05
Waterbury, 364 W Main........... 02
Watorian, 144 Grove............... 10

BUILDINGS

Apothecaries Hall, 63 Bank..... 02
Bergins Block, 246 E Main...... 02
Boys Club................................ 05
Brown, 1 S Main...................... 02
Brown, 20 E Main.................... 02
Camps Block, 33 Center......... 02
Cassidy Patrick, 33
  Leavenworth....................... 02
Castle Memorial, 30 Central
  Ave 02

Chipman, 49 Center................. 02
Cowell-Guifoile, 186 Grand 02
Cowell-Guifoile, 65
  Leavenworth....................... 02
Farrington, 131 W Main........... 02
Fox-Poli, 84 E Main................. 02
G L D, 95 N Main.................... 02
Garden, 162 E Main................. 02
Hampson, 91 W Main.............. 02
Howland-Hughes Company,
  110 Bank............................ 20
Jefferson Sq., 1 Jefferson Sq... 06
Johnson Block, 111 Bank........ 02
Jones-Morgan, 96 Bank.......... 02
Lilley, 103 W Main................... 02
Lincoln House, 35 Field 02
Masonic Temple, 156 W
  Main 02
Palomba, 100 Grand................ 02
Platt Irving, 1 E Main............... 02
Prichard, 187 Bank.................. 02
Professional, 43 Central Ave .. 02
Russell, 73 & 230 Bank........... 02
Steele, 51 W Main................... 02
Telephone, 348 Grand.............. 20
Telephone, 65 State................. 20
Waterbury National Bank,
  193 Grand........................... 02
Waterbury Trust Company,
  132 Grand........................... 02
Ymca, 136 W Main 02
Ywca, 80 Prospect 02

GOVERNMENT OFFICES

Court House, 7 Kendrick Ave.. 02
Federal Building 14 Cottage
  Pl....................................... 02
Post Office, 135 Grand............ 01

HOSPITALS

Saint Marys, 56 Franklin 02
Waterbury, 64 Robbins............ 20

UNIVERSITIES AND COLLEGES

Mattatuck Community
  College, 236 Grand.............. 02
Mattatuck Community
  College, 411 Highland
  Ave 08
Post College, 800 Country
  Club Rd............................... 08
University Of Connecticut, 32
  Hillside Ave......................... 10

DELAWARE
(Abbreviation: DE)

Bear	19701
Bellefonte, Br. Wilmington	19809
Bethany Beach	19930
Bethel	19931
Bridgeville	19933
Brookside, Br. Newark	19711
Camden-Wyoming (1st)	19934
Cannon	19935
Cheswold	19936
Christiana	19702
Clarksville	19937
Claymont (1st)	19703
Clayton (1st)	19938
Crossroads, Br. New Castle	19720
Dagsboro	19939
Delaware City	19706
Delmar	19940
Dewey Beach, R. Br. Rehoboth Beach	19971
Dover (1st)	19901
Dover A.F.B, Br. Dover	19901
Ellendale	19941
Farmington	19942
Federal, Sta. Newark	19711
Felton	19943
Fenwick Island, R. Br. Selbyville	19944

Frankford	19945
Frederica	19946
Georgetown (1st)	19947
Greenville, Br. Wilmington	19807
Greenwood	19950
Hamilton Park, Br. New Castle	19720
Harbeson	19951
Harrington (1st)	19952
Hartly	19953
Hockessin	19707
Houston	19954
Kenton	19955
Kirkwood	19708
Laurel (1st)	19956
Lewes (1st)	19958
Lincoln	19960
Little Creek	19961
Magnolia	19962
Manor, Br. New Castle	19720
Marshallton, Br. Wilmington	19808
Meadowood, Br. Newark	19711
Middletown	19709
Milford (1st)	19963
Millsboro (1st)	19966
Millville	19967
Milton	19968
Montchanin	19710
Nassau	19969
New Castle (1st)	19720

Newark (1st)	19711
Newport, Br. Wilmington	19804
Ocean View	19970
Odessa	19730
Ogletown, Br. Newark	19711
Polly Drummond, Br. Newark	19711
Port Penn	19731
Rambleton Acres, Br. New Castle	19720
Rehoboth Beach (1st)	19971
Rockland	19732
Rodney Village, Br. Dover	19901
Saint Georges	19733
Seaford (1st)	19973
Selbyville (1st)	19975
Fenwick Island, R. Br.	19944
Smyrna (1st)	19977
Stanton, Br. Wilmington	19804
Talleyville, Br. Wilmington	19803
Townsend	19734
Union Street, Sta. Wilmington	19805
Viola	19979
WILMINGTON (1st) (see appendix)	
Winterthur, R. Br. Wilmington	19735
Woodside	19980
Yorklyn	19736

WILMINGTON 198

POST OFFICE BOXES

Box Nos.
1-2499	Main Office	99
2501-2999	Union Street Sta.	05
3001-3499	Newport Br.	04
3501-4499	Greenville Br.	07
5001-5499	Marshallton Br.	08
6001-6499	Stanton Br.	04
7001-7499	Talleyville Br.	03

STATIONS, BRANCHES AND UNITS

Bellefonte Br.	09
Greenville Br.	07
Marshallton Br.	08
Newport Br.	04
Stanton Br.	04
Talleyville Br.	03
Union Street Sta.	05
Winterthur Rural Br.	19735
General Delivery	99
Postmaster	99

APARTMENTS, HOTELS, MOTELS

Brandywine Hundred Apts.	03
Cedar Tree Apts	10
Clifton Park	02
Darling Court	06
Denbigh Hall	06
Devon	06
Dorset	06
Du Pont	99
Electra Arms	02
Foster Park	05
Fourteen-O-One	06
Kynlyn	09
Lancaster Court	05
Lord De La Warr	99
Mayfair	06
Monroe Park	07
Parklyn	05
Plaza	06
Rockford Park	06
Rockford Tower	06
Rodney Court	06
Stratford Apts	10
Towne House	06
Woodland	05

BUILDINGS

Bank Of Delaware	01
Continental American	01
Delaware Trust	01
Di Sabatino	01
Du Pont	01
E I Du Pont De Nemours & Company Incorporated	98
Farmers Bank	01
Federal	01
Market Twr	01
Municipal	01
Nemours	01
Wilmington Trust	01
Wimington Twr	01

HOSPITALS

A I Du Pont Institute	99
Delaware	99
Emily P Bissell	08
Eugene Du Pont Memorial	07
Memorial	99
Riverside	99
Saint Francis	05
Veterans Administration	05
Wilmington General	99

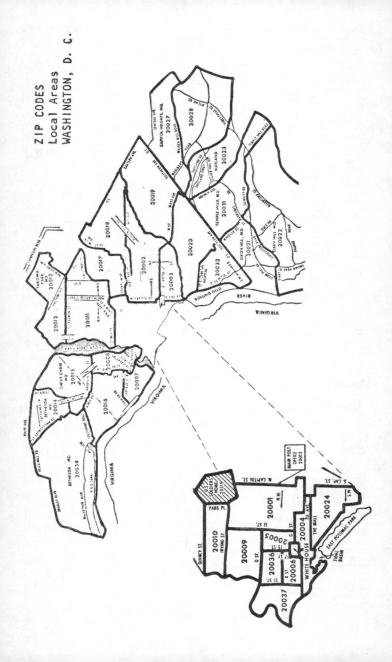

ZIP CODES
Local Areas
WASHINGTON, D. C.

DISTRICT OF COLUMBIA
(Abbreviation: DC)

Anacostia, Sta. Washington....20020
Benjamin Franklin, Sta.
   Washington 20044
Benning, Sta. Washington 20019
Bolling A F B, Sta.
   Washington 20332
Brightwood, Sta.
   Washington 20011
Brookland, Sta. Washington...20017
Calvert, Sta. Washington........20007
Cardinal, Sta. Washington.......20017
Central, Sta. Washington.......20005
Cleveland Park, Sta.
   Washington 20008
Columbia Heights, Sta.
   Washington (see
   appendix)
Congress Heights, Sta.
   Washington 20032
Customs House, Sta.
   Washington 20018

Eagle, Sta. Washington...........20016
F Street, Sta. Washington.......20004
Fort Davis, Sta. Washington...20020
Fort Mc Nair, Sta.
   Washington 20315
Friendship, Sta. Washington...20016
Georgetown, Sta.
   Washington 20007
Hoya, Sta. Washington............20007
Kalorama, Sta. Washington 20009
Kendall Green, Sta.
   Washington 20002
Mid City, Sta. Washington 20005
National Airport, Sta.
   Washington 20001
Naval Research Laboratory,
   Sta. Washington 20390
Naval Station, Sta.
   Washington 20390
Northeast, Sta. Washington.....20002
Northwest, Sta. Washington....20015
Palisades, Sta. Washington.....20016
Park View, Sta. Washington....20010

Petworth, Sta. Washington......20011
Randle, Sta. Washington 20020
Southeast, Sta. Washington.....20003
Southwest, Sta. Washington....20024
State Department, Sta.
   Washington 20520
T Street, Sta. Washington.......20009
Temple Heights, Sta.
   Washington 20009
Treasury, Sta. Washington 20220
Truxton Circle, Sta.
   Washington 20002
Twentieth Street, Sta.
   Washington (see
   appendix)
Walter Reed, Sta.
   Washington 20012
WASHINGTON (1st) (see
   appendix)
Watergate, Sta. Washington ...20037
West End, Sta. Washington 20037
Woodley Road, Sta.
   Washington 20008
Woodridge, Sta. Washington...20018

Appendix   Washington

WASHINGTON   200

POST OFFICE BOXES

Box Nos.		
1-999	Benjamin Franklin Sta ..	44
1000-2999	Main Office	13
3000-3499	Columbia Heights Sta	10
3500-3999	Georgetown Sta.......	07
4000-4199	Chevy Chase Br	15
4200-4399	Takoma Park Br	12
4400-4599	Brookland Sta ..	17
4600-4799	Anacostia Sta ..	20
4800-4999	Cleveland Park Sta	08
5000-5199	Benning Sta	19
5200-5499	Seat Pleasant Br	27
5500-5699	Friendship Sta..	16
5700-5999	Bethesda Br	14
6000-6099	Mid City Sta	05
6100-6199	Benjamin Franklin Sta ..	44
6200-6399	Northwest Sta..	15
6400-6699	T Street Sta......	09
6700-6899	Fort Davis Sta ..	20
6900-7099	Congress Heights Sta ..	32
7100-7999	Benjamin Franklin Sta ..	44
8000-8299	Southwest Sta..	24
8300-8599	Capitol Heights Br ......, ...	27

8600-8799	Brightwood Sta................	11
8801-9099	Southeast Sta ..	03
9100-9299	Suitland Br......	23
9300-9399	Mid City Sta	05
9401-9599	Calvert Sta.......	07
9600-9799	Friendship Sta..	16
9800-9999	Chevy Chase Br................	15
10000-10299	Woodridge Sta..	18
10301-10499	Oxon Hill Br.....	21
11001-11999	Cleveland Park Sta................	08
12001-12999	Mid City Sta.....	05
13001-13999	T Street Sta.....	09
14001-14999	Benjamin Franklin Sta ...	44
16001-16999	Suitland Br.......	23
17001-17999	Dulles International Airportbr.........	41
18001-18999	Oxon Hill Br.....	21
19001-19999	Twentieth Street Sta ...	36
21001-21999	Kalorama Sta....	09
22001-22999	Northeast Sta...	02
26001-26999	Truxton Circle Sta................	02
28001-28999	Central Sta.......	05
29001-29052	Brookland Sta ..	17
30001-30399	Bethesda Br	14
31001-31252	Temple Hills Br	31
33001-33499	District Heights Br	28
34001-34999	West Bethesda Br	34
38001-38999	Anacostia Sta...	20

39001-39999 Friendship Sta..	16
40001-40999 Palisades Sta...	16

STATIONS, BRANCHES AND UNITS

Anacostia Sta............................	20
Andrews A F B Br 20331	
Andrews Air Force Hospital	
Br...............................20331	
Benjamin Franklin Sta............	44
Benning Sta	19
Bethesda Br..............................	14
Bolling A F B Sta................20332	
Brightwood Sta........................	11
Brookland Sta	17
Calvert Sta...............................	07
Camp Springs Br	31
Capitol Heights Br	27
Cardinal Sta.............................	17
Central Sta...............................	05
Chevy Chase Br.......................	15
Cleveland Park Sta	08
Columbia Heights Sta..............	09
Congress Heights Sta	32
Customs House Sta..................	18
District Heights Br...................	28
Dulles International AirportBr..	41
Eagle Sta..................................	16
F Street Sta..............................	04
Fort Davis Sta	20
Fort Mc Nair Sta 20315	
Friendship Sta..........................	16
Georgetown Sta........................	07
Hoya Sta...................................	07
Kalorama Sta............................	09
Kendall Green Sta....................	02
Marlow Heights Br	31
Mid City Sta	05
National Airport Sta.................	01

Washington, D.C. (Con.)   200

National Naval Med Center
  Br... 14
Naval Air Facility Br.............20390
Naval Research Laboratory
  Sta..20390
Naval Station Sta...................20390
Navy Annex Br.....................20370
Northeast Sta........................... 02
Northwest Sta.......................... 15
Oxon Hill Br............................ 21
Palisades Sta........................... 16
Park View Sta.......................... 10
Pentagon Br 20301
Petworth Sta............................ 11
Randle Sta............................... 20
Seat Pleasant Br...................... 27
Southeast Sta........................... 03
Southwest Sta.......................... 24
State Department Sta 20520
Suitland Br.............................. 23
T Street Sta............................. 09
Takoma Park Br 12
Temple Heights Sta.................. 09
Temple Hills Br 31
Treasury Sta.........................20220
Truxton Circle Sta.................... 02
Twentieth Street Sta................. 06
U S Naval Communications
  CtrBr...................................20390
Walter Reed Sta....................... 12
Watergate Sta.......................... 37
West Bethesda Br 34
West End Sta........................... 37
Woodley Road Sta.................... 08
Woodridge Sta......................... 18
General Delivery....................... 13
Postmaster.............................. 13

APARTMENTS, HOTELS, MOTELS

Aberdeen Hall, Mclean
  Gardens, 3415 38th N. W.. 16
Alban Towers, 3700
  Massachusetts Ave NW 16
Albermarle House, 4501
  Connecticut Ave NW 08
Albert Pick Motor Inn, 1201
  K, NW.................................. 05
Ambassador, 1412 K NW........ 05
Annapolis, 1111 H, NW........... 05
Army Navy Club, 1627 I, NW.. 06
Bay State, 1701
  Massachusetts Ave NW 36
Bellevue, 15 E NW 01
Benning Hall, Mclean
  Gardens, 3445 38th N. W. 16
Berkshire, 4201
  Massachusetts Ave NW 16
Boston House, 1711
  Massachusetts Ave N. W.... 36
Brandywine, 4545
  Connecticut Ave NW 08
Brighton, 2123 California
  NW...................................... 08
Brittany, 5432 Connecticut
  Ave NW................................ 15
Broadmoor, 3601 Connecticut
  Ave NW................................ 08
Brunswick House, 1414 17th
  NW...................................... 36

Burlington, 1120 Vermont
  Ave NW................................ 05
Cairo, 1615 Q NW.................... 09
Calvert Woodley, 2601
  Woodley Place NW................ 08
Cambridge, 921 19th NW.......... 06
Capitol Park, 800 4th SW........ 24
Carillon, 2500 Wisconsin Ave
  NW...................................... 07
Carlyn, 2500 Q NW.................. 07
Cathedral Mansions,................. 08
Cavalier, 3500 14th NW........... 10
Chalfonte, 1601 Argonne Pl
  NW...................................... 09
Chancery, 3130 Wisconsin
  Ave NW................................ 16
Chanute Hall, Mclean
  Gardens, 3800 Porter N W. 16
Chase Plaza, 5406
  Connecticut Ave NW 15
Chastleton, 1701 16th NW 09
Chesapeake, 4607
  Connecticut Ave NW 08
Chesterfield, 3315 Wisconsin
  Ave NW................................ 16
Chillum Manor, 5320 Rock
  Creek Church Rd NE............. 11
Clifton Terrace, 1300-1350
  Clifton NW............................ 09
Commodore, 520-530 North
  Capitol................................. 01
Conard, 1228 I NW.................. 05
Congressional, 300 New
  Jersey Ave SE....................... 03
Connecticut House, 4500
  Connecticut Av NW............... 08
Coronet, 200 C SE 03
Cosmos Club, 2121
  Massachusetts Ave NW 08
Crestwood, 3900 16th NW........ 11
Croydon, 1815 17th NW.......... 09
Davenport Terrace, 3511
  Davenport NW....................... 08
Davenport Terrace, 4817
  36th NW............................... 08
Delano, 2745 29th NW............. 08
Devans Hall, Mclean
  Gardens, 20 Plattsburg Ct
  NW...................................... 16
Devonshire Courts,
  4105&4115 Wisconsin Ave
  NW...................................... 16
Diplomat, 2420 16th NW.......... 09
Dodge, 20 E NW...................... 01
Dorchester House, 2480 16th
  NW...................................... 09
Drake, 2119 H NW................... 37
Dresden, 2126 Connecticut
  NW...................................... 08
Dunbar, 2105 15th NW............. 09
Dupont Plaza, 1500 New
  Hampshire Ave NW............... 36
Ebbitt, 10 & H NW................... 01
Elise, 825 New Hampshire
  Ave NW................................ 37
Embassy, 1613 Harvard N W.. 09
Empire, 2000 F NW.................. 06
Envoy Towers, 2400 16th NW.. 09
Envoy, 2144 California NW...... 08
Essex, 4740 Connecticut Ave
  NW...................................... 08

Eustis Hall, Mclean Gardens,
  3831 Porter NW.................... 16
Evangeline, 1330 L NW........... 05
Everglades, 2223 H NW........... 37
Executive House, 1515 Rhode
  Island Ave NW...................... 05
Fairfax, 2100 Massachusetts
  Ave NW................................ 08
Frankford Hall, Mclean
  Gardens, 40 Plattsburg Ct
  N W..................................... 16
Frontenac, 4550 Connecticut
  Ave NW................................ 08
Gadsden Hall, Mclean
  Gardens, 30 Plattsburg Ct
  NW...................................... 16
Garfield, 5410 Connecticut
  Ave NW................................ 15
Gelmarc Towers, 1930
  Columbia Rd NW................... 09
General Scott, 1 Scott Cir
  NW...................................... 36
Governor Shepherd, 2121
  Virginia Ave NW................... 37
Gramercy Inn, 1616 Rhode
  Island Ave NW...................... 36
Granite State, 1731 New
  Hampshire Ave NW............... 09
Greenbrier, 4301
  Massachusetts Ave NW 16
Greystone, 815 18th NW.......... 06
Guthridge, 2115 F NW............. 37
Gwenwood, 1020 19th NW........ 36
Hamilton, 1001 14th NW.......... 05
Hampshire Gardens, 4900
  New Hampshire Ave NW..... 11
Hampton Court, 2013 New
  Hampshire Ave NW............... 09
Hancock Hall, Mclean
  Gardens, 3665 38th N W... 16
Harrington, 11th & E NW........ 04
Hartnett Hall, 1426 21st NW.. 36
Harvard Hall, 1650 Harvard
  NW...................................... 09
Hay Adams House, 800 16th
  NW...................................... 06
Hotel Sonesta, 10 Thomas
  Cir NW................................. 05
Huntington, 5225
  Connecticut Ave NW 15
Idaho Terrace, 3040 Idaho
  Ave NW................................ 16
Jefferson Hall, Mclean
  Gardens, 3685 38th N W... 16
Jefferson, 1200 16th NW......... 36
John Paul Jones, 1717 G NW.. 06
Kenesaw, 3060 16th NW.......... 09
Kenmore, 5415 Connecticut
  Ave NW................................ 15
Kennedy-Warren, 3133
  Connecticut Ave NW 08
Kenwood House, 5100 Dorset
  Ave (Md)............................. 15
Kew Gardens, 2700 Q NW....... 07
La Reine, 5425 Connecticut
  Ave NW................................ 15
La Salle, 1028 Connecticut
  Ave NW................................ 36
Le Bourget, 2127 California
  N W..................................... 08
Lenschire House, 3140
  Wisconsin Ave NW............... 16

Washington, D.C. (Con.)   200

Lombardy, 2019 I NW 06
Madison, 1177 15th NW 05
Majestic, 3200 16th NW 10
Marcheta, 1121 New
  Hampshire NW 37
Marlyn, 3000 39th NW............ 16
Marriott Key Bridge Motor
  Hotel, Key Bridge............. 07
Marriott Motor Hotel, Twin
  Bridges On US 1................ 01
Maryland Courts, 518 9th
  NE 02
Maryland Courts, 816 E NE.... 02
Mayflower, 1127 Connecticut
  Ave NW 36
Mclean Gardens, 3811 Porter
  N W 16
Melwood, 1803 Biltmore NW... 09
Meridian Hill, 2601 16th NW.. 09
Metropolitan Club, 1700 H
  NW 06
Metropolitan, 200 Rhode
  Island Ave NE 02
Milton Hall, 2222 I NW 37
Miramar, 1301 15th NW......... 05
New Amsterdam, 2701 14th
  NW 09
Normandie, 6817 Georgia Ave
  NW 12
North Brook Courts, 3426
  16th NW 10
Ogden Gardens, 1445 Ogden
  NW 10
Ontario, 2853 Ontario Rd
  NW 09
Pall Mall, 1112 16th NW....... 36
Park Central, 705 18th NW.... 06
Park Lane, 2025 I NW 06
Park Plaza, 1629 Columbia
  Rd NW 09
Pennsylvania Hotel, 20 F NW.. 01
Pick-Lee House, 15th & L
  NW 05
Potomac Plaza, 2475 Virginia
  Ave NW 37
President, 2101 I NW.............. 37
Presidential Apts, 1026 16th
  NW 36
Presidential Hotel, 900 19th
  NW 06
Quebec House North, 2801
  Quebec NW 08
Quebec House South, 2800
  Quebec NW 08
Rhode Island Plaza, 2705
  13th NE........................... 18
Rittenhouse, 6101 16th NW.... 11
Roger Smith, 18th &
  Pennsylvania Ave NW 06
Roosevelt, 2101 16th NW 09
Saxony, 1801 Clydesdale Pl
  NW 09
Schenley, 2121 H NW............. 37
Schuyler Arms, 1954
  Columbia Rd NW 09
Sedgewick Gardens, 3726
  Connecticut Ave NW 08
Sheraton Carlton, 923 16th
  NW 06

Sheraton Park, 2660 Woodley
  Rd NW 08
Shoreham, 2500 Calvert NW... 08
South Brook Courts, 3420
  16th NW 10
State House, 2122
  Massachusetts Ave NW 08
Statler Hilton, 16th & K NW... 36
Stratford, 25 E NW................ 01
Tilden Gardens, 3900
  Connecticut Ave NW 08
Touraine, 1630 R NW............. 09
Town House, 601 19th NW 06
Trinity Towers, 3023 14th
  NW 09
University Club, 1135 16th
  NW 36
Valley Vista, 2032 Belmont
  NW 09
Wakefield Hall, 2101 New
  Hampshire Ave NW 09
Washington Circle, 2430
  Pennsylvania Ave NW 37
Washington Hilton, 1919
  Connecticut Ave NW 09
Washington Hotel, 15th &
  Pennsylvania Ave NW 04
Washington House, 2120
  16th NW 09
Watergate East, 2500
  Virginia Ave., N.w............. 37
Watergate Hotel, 2650
  Virginia Ave., N.w............. 37
Watergate South, 700 New
  Hampshire Ave., N.w. 37
Watergate West, 2700
  Virginia Ave., N.w............. 37
Westchester, 3900 & 4000
  Cathedral Ave NW............. 16
Willard, 14th & Pennsylvania
  Ave NW 04
Wiltshire Crescent, 3801
  Connecticut Ave NW 08
Wiltshire Parkway, 3701
  Connecticut Ave NW 08
Windemere, 1825 New
  Hampshire Ave NW 09
Windsor Park, 2300
  Connecticut Ave NW 08
Winthrop House, 1727
  Massachusetts Ave NW 36
Woodley Park Towers, 2737
  Devonshire Pl NW 08
Woodner, 3636 16th NW........ 10
Wyoming, 2022 Columbia Rd
  NW 09
York, 532 20th NW................ 06
Young Men'S Christian
  Association, 1726-1736 G
  NW 06

BUILDINGS

A F Of L-C I O, 16th NW........ 06
Acacia Life Insurance, 51
  Louisiana Ave NW............-... 01
Adams, 1333 F NW................ 04
Air Rights, 7315 Wisconsin
  Ave (Md)......................... 14
Ajax, 1107 19th NW............... 36
Albee, 1426 G NW................. 05

Altimont, 4929 Bethesda Ave
  (Md) 14
American Council On
  Education, 1785
  Massachusetts Ave NW 36
American Security, 730 15th
  NW 05
American, 1317 F NW............. 04
Andrew Jackson, 806
  Connecticut Ave NW 06
Appeals, 426 5th NW.............. 01
Associations, 1145 19th NW.... 36
Atlas, 527 9th NW.................. 04
Baker, 1320 F NW.................. 04
Barlow, 5454 Wisconsin Ave
  (Md) 15
Barnabas, 4400 Stamp Rd
  SE (Md)........................... 31
Barr, 910 17th NW................. 06
Barrister, 635 F NW............... 04
Becker, 1314 F NW................ 04
Bender, 1120 Connecticut
  Ave NW 36
Bethesda (The), 4725
  Bethesda Ave (Md) 14
Bethesda Bank, 7500
  Wisconsin Ave (Md)........... 14
Bethesda Bradley, 6900
  Wisconsin Ave (Md) ....: 15
Bond, 1404 New York Ave
  NW 05
Boss & Phelps, 1417 K NW..... 05
Bowen, 815 15th NW.............. 05
Bragg, 705 12th NW.............. 05
Brawner, 888 17th NW 06
Brookings, 1775
  Massachusetts Ave NW 36
Cafritz, 1625 I NW................. 06
Carpenters, 1003 K NW.......... 01
Carry, 927 15th NW............... 05
Central National Bank, 631
  Pennsylvania Ave NW 04
Central, 805 G NW................. 01
Century, 412 5th NW.............. 01
Chamber Of Commerce, U. S.
  1615 H N W 06
Chandler, 1427 I NW.............. 05
City Bank, 1612 K NW............ 06
City Post Office, N Capital &
  Mass Ave 13
Coal, 1130 17th NW 36
Colonial, 923 15th NW........... 05
Colorado, 1341 G NW............ 05
Columbia Medical, 1835 I
  NW 06
Columbian, 416 5th NW 01
Commerce, 1700 K NW 06
Commonwealth, 1625 K NW.... 06
Communications, 710 14th
  NW 05
Continental, 1012 14th NW 05
Daily News, 1013 13th NW..... 05
De Moll, 700 12th NW............ 05
De Sales, 1741 De Sales NW... 36
Denrike, 1010 Vermont Ave
  NW 05
District National Bank, 1406
  G NW 05
District Of Columbia National
  Bank, 1812 K NW 06
District, 14th & Pennsylvania
  NW 04

Dupont Circle, 1344-1346
Connecticut Ave NW 36
Duryea, 1101 Connecticut
Ave NW 36
Editors, 1729 H NW 06
Edmonds, 917 15th NW 05
Electrical Workers, 1200 15th
NW 05
Engineers, 921 17th NW 06
Enterprise, 1718 I NW 06
Equitable Life Insurance,
3900 Wisconsin Ave NW 16
Evans, 1420 New York Ave
NW 05
Executive, 1030 15th NW 05
Farragut, 900 17th NW 05
Federal, 1522 K NW 05
Federation, 817 14th NW 05
Fleming, 800 17th NW 06
Folger, 725 15th NW 05
Franklin Square North, 1325
K NW 05
Franklin, 1327 F NW 04
Georgetown, 2233 Wisconsin
Ave NW 07
Glover & Flather, 1508 H NW ... 05
Headquarters, 2002 P NW 36
Heurich, 1627 K NW 06
Hibbs, 723 15th NW 05
Hill, 839 17th NW 06
Homer, 601 13th NW 05
Hyde, 7979 Old Georgetown
Rd (Md) 14
Indiana, 633 Indiana Ave
NW 04
International Telephone &
Telegraph, 1707 L NW 36
International, 1319 F NW 04
Investment, 1511 K NW 05
Jefferson, 1225 19th NW 36
Jordan, 1301 G NW 05
Judiciary, 601 Indiana Ave
NW 04
Le Droit, 802 F NW 04
Lenox, 1523 L NW 05
Lewis, 2001 11th NW 01
Lincoln, 514 10th NW 04
Machinist, 1300 Connecticut
Ave NW 36
Madison, 1155 15th NW 05
Marlo - Edgemoor, 4801
Montgomery Ln (Md) 14
Marsh, 1832 M NW 36
Mather, 916 G NW 01
Mc Gill, 910 G NW 01
Mc Kim, 1311 G NW 05
Mc Lachlen, 666 11th NW 01
Medical Science, 1029
Vermont Ave NW 05
Mercury, 1925 K NW 06
Methodist, 100 Maryland Ave
NE 02
Metropolis, 201 Pennsylvania
Ave SE 03
Metropolitan Bank, 613 15th
NW 05
Mills, 1700 Pennsylvania Ave
N W 06
Montgomery, 4720
Montgomery Ln (Md) 14
Municipal, 300 Indiana Ave
NW 01
Munsey, 1329 E NW 04

Mutual, 1309 L NW 05
N A D A, 2000 K NW 06
National Assoc Of Letter
Carriers, 100 Indiana Ave
NW 01
National Bank, 6917
Arlington Rd (Md) 14
National Grange, 1616 H NW 06
National Press, 529 14th NW 04
National Savings & Trust,
719 15th NW 05
National Union, 918 F NW 04
Naval Lodge Hall, 328
Pennsylvania Ave SE 03
New Medical, 1726 I NW 06
Northwestern, 1800 G NW 05
Occidental, 1411
Pennsylvania Ave NW 04
Ocean Sciences, 4905 Del
Ray Ave (Md) 14
Octagon, 1741 New York Ave
NW 06
Operations Engineers, 1125
17th NW 36
Oriental, 600 F NW 04
Otis, 810 18th NW 06
Parkwood Medical, 1746 K
NW 06
Pennsylvania, 425 13th NW 04
Peoples Life Insurance, 601
New Hampshire Ave NW 37
Perpetual, 1111 E NW 04
Philips, 4915 Saint Elmo Ave
(Md) 14
Premier, 1725 I NW 06
Professional Arts, 1722 I NW 05
Prudential Bank, 1334 G NW 05
Public Employee Union, 815
Mount Vernon Pl NW 01
Public National Bank, 1430 K
NW 05
R C A, 1725 K NW 06
Realty, 1424 K NW 05
Richards (The), 6935
Arlington Rd (Md) 14
Riddell, 1730 K NW 06
Riggs National Bank, 1503
Pennsylvania Ave NW 05
Ring, 1200 18th NW 36
Rust, 1001 15th NW 05
Saint Albans, 1419 H NW 05
Saul, 925 15th NW 05
Securities, 729 15th NW 05
Semmes Riggs, Dupont Cir
NW 36
Sheraton, 711 14th NW 05
Shoreham, 806 15th NW 05
Solar, 1000 16th NW 36
Southern Railroad, 920 15th
NW 05
Southern, 1425 H NW 05
Taft, 1603 K NW 06
Tivoli, 3313 14th NW 10
Tower, 1403 K NW 05
Trades Unionist, 720 5th NW 01
Trailways, 1200 I NW 05
Trans-Lux, 724 14th NW 05
Trans-World Airline, 1026
17th NW 36
Transporation, 815 17th NW 06
Union Trust, 740 15th NW 05
United Assn, 901
Massachusetts Ave NW 01

Universal, North, 1875
Connecticut Ave NW 09
Universal, 1825 Connecticut
Ave NW 09
Vanguard, 1111 20th NW 36
Vermont, 1100 Vermont Ave
NW 05
Victor, 724 9th NW 01
Walker, 734 15th NW 05
Warner, 501 13th NW 04
Washington Evening Star,
225 Virginia Avenue SE....... 03
Washington Gas Light, 740
11th NW 01
Washington Loan & Trust,
9th & F NW 04
Washington Medical, 1801 I
NW 06
Washington Post, 1150 15th
N.w. 05
Washington, 15th & New
York Ave NW 05
Wender, 2026 I NW 06
Western Union, 1405 G NW 05
Westory, 605 14th NW 05
Whitfield Professional,
Branch Ave & Colebrook
Dr SE (Md) 31
Whitford, 424 5th NW 01
Willco, 7824 Eastern Ave NW ... 12
Wire, 1000 Vermont Ave NW ... 05
Wiscon, 7550 Wisconsin Ave
(Md) 14
Woodward, 733 15th NW 05
World Center, 918 16th NW 05
Wyatt, 777 14th NW 05

GOVERNMENT OFFICES

Administrative Office, U S
Courts 20544
Advisory Commission On
Intergovermental
Relations 20575
Agency For International
Development (A I D) 20523
Agriculture, Dept Of (Offices
At Headquarters) 20250
Agriculture, Dept Of (Other
Offices) 20251
Air Force, Dept Of (Offices At
Headquarters-Pentagon) 20330
Air Force, Dept Of (Offices In
Forrestal Bldg) 20314
Air Force, Dept Of (Other
Offices) 20333
American Revolution
Bicentennial Commission ... 06
Architect Of The Capitol 20515
Arlington Annex, Marines
Headquarters 20380
Arlington Annex, Navy 20370
Arms Control And
Disarmament Agency, U S
(Field Oper Off) 20451
Army-Air Force Recruiting
Station 04
Army, Dept Of (Offices At
Headquarters-Pentagon) 20310
Army, Dept Of (Offices In
Forrestal Bldg) 20314
Army, Dept Of (Other
Offices) 20315

Washington, D.C. (Con.) 200

Atomic Energy Commission,
U S 20545
Board Of Governors Of The
Federal Reserve System 20551
Bureau Of Employees
Compensation (Labor) 20211
Bureau Of Standards,
National 20234
Capitol Building, Architect 20515
Capitol Building, House Of
Representatives 20515
Capitol Building, United
States Senate 20510
Census Bureau 20233
Central Intelligence Agency
(C I A) 20505
Civil Aeronautics Board 20428
Civil Service Commission, U
S 20415
Coast Guard, U S 20591
Commerce, Dept Of (Offices
At Headquarters) 20230
Commerce, Dept Of (Other
Offices) 20235
Commerce, Dept Of, Bureau
Of Census 20233
Commerce, Dept Of, National
Bureau Of Standards 20234
Commerce, Dept Of, Patent
Office 20231
Commission On Civil Rights 20425
Court Of Customs And Patent
Appeals, U S 20439
Court Of Military Appeals, U
S 20442
Defense, Dept Of (Offices At
Headquarters-Pentagon) 20301
Defense, Dept Of (Other
Offices) 20305
Environmental Protection
Agency 20460
Equal Employment
Opportunity Commission 20506
Exec Offices Of The President
C I A 20505
Exec Offices Of The
President, (Other
Organizations) 20506
Exec Offices Of The
President, Mgmt, Budget
Off 20503
Exec Offices Of The
President, N. A. S. C. 20502
Exec Offices Of The
President, Office Of Emerg
Prep'Dness 20504
Exec Offices Of The
President, The White
House Office 20500
Export Import Bank Of
Washington 20571
Farm Credit Administration 20578
Federal Aviation
Administration 20590
Federal Bureau Of
Investigation (F B I) 20535
Federal Communications
Commission 20554
Federal Deposit Insurance
Corporation 20429

Federal Home Loan Bank
Board 20552
Federal Housing
Administration,
Comptroller (H U D) 20412
Federal Housing
Administration, Main, (H U
D) 20411
Federal Maritime
Commission, U S 20573
Federal Mediation And
Conciliation Service 20427
Federal Metal And Non-
Metallic Safety Board Of
Review 09
Federal National Mortgage
Association (H U D) 05
Federal Power Commission 20426
Federal Records Center (G S
A) 20409
Federal Reserve System,
Board Of Governors 20551
Federal Trade Commission 20580
Food And Agriculture
Organization Of The
United Nations 20437
Food And Drug
Administration (H E W) 20204
Foreign Claims Settlement
Commission, U S 20579
Foreign Service Posts And
Mail Room (State Dept) 20521
General Accounting Office 20548
General Services
Administration (G S A
Headquarters) 20405
General Services
Administration, Crystal
Mall Bldg. 4 20406
General Services
Administration, Federal
Records Ctr 20409
General Services
Administration, National
Archives 20408
General Services
Administration, Region 3 20407
Government Printing Office 20401
Government Printing Office,
Field Service Division 20403
Government Printing Office,
Superintendent Of
Documents 20402
H E W, Food And Drug
Administration 20204
H E W, National Institutes Of
Health 14
H E W, Office Of Education 20202
Harry Diamond Laboratories .. 20438
Health, Education And
Welfare, Dept Of
(Headquarters) 20201
Health, Education And
Welfare, Dept Of (Other
Offices) 20203
House Of Representatives
And Office Buildings 20515
Housing And Urban
Development, Dept Of
(Headquarters) 20410
Housing Assistance
Administration (H U D) 20413
Immigration And
Naturalization Service 20536

Inter American Defense
Board 20441
Inter American Development
Bank 20577
Interior, Dept Of
(Headquarters) 20240
Interior, Dept Of (Other
Offices) 20242
Internal Revenue Service
(Int'L) Treasury Dept. 20225
Internal Revenue Service,
Treasury Dept. 20224
International Bank For
Reconstruction And
Development 20433
International Joint
Commission - U S And
Canada 20440
International Monetary Fund .. 20431
Interstate Commerce
Commission 20423
J F Kennedy Center For
Performing Arts 20566
Justice, Dept Of
(Headquarters) 20530
Justice, Dept Of (Other
Offices) 20537
Justice, Dept Of Immigration
And Naturalization Service . 20536
Justice, Dept Of, Federal
Bureau Of Investigation 20535
Labor, Dept Of
(Headquarters) 20210
Labor, Dept Of (Other
Offices) 20212
Labor, Dept Of, Bureau Of
Employees Compensation ... 20211
Lib Of Congress, Div Of
Blind 20542
Library Of Congress 20540
Library Of Congress, Card
Division 20541
Marine Corps Headquarters,
Arlington Annex 20380
National Academy Of
Sciences And Research
Council 20418
National Aeronautics And
Space Administration (N A
S A) 20546
National Aeronautics And
Space Council 20502
National Archives And
Records Service (G S A) 20408
National Bureau Of
Standards 20234
National Capitol Housing
Authority 20430
National Capitol Planning
Commission 05
National Credit Union
Administration 20456
National Gallery Of Art 20565
National Institutes Of Health .. 14
National Labor Relations
Board 20570
National Library Of Medicine .. 14
National Mediation Board 20572
National Naval Medical
Center 14
National Science Foundation .. 20550
Naval Hospital 14

Washington, D.C. (Con.) 200

Navy Dept Of Offices At Crystal City Complex 20360
Navy Ship Research And Development Center 34
Navy-Marine Recruiting Station 04
Navy, Dept Of (Arlington Annex) 20370
Navy, Dept Of (Other Offices Located Out Of H Q) 20390
Navy, Dept Of, (Offices At H Q-Pentagon) 20350
Navy, Dept Of, Main Navy Building 20360
Navy, Dept Of, Marine Headquarters, Arlington Annex 20380
Office Of Economic Opportunity 20506
Office Of Education (H E W) ..20202
Office Of Emergency Preparedness 20504
Office Of Management, Budget 20503
Oversea'S Private Investment Corp 20527
Passport Office, State Dept ..20524
Patent Office 20231
Pay Board And Price Commission 20508
Pentagon, Dept Of Air Force..20330
Pentagon, Dept Of Army 20310
Pentagon, Dept Of Defense...20301
Pentagon, Dept Of Navy......20350
Postal Rate Commission, U S 20268
Postal Service U S (Headquarters) 20260
Postal Service U S Regional Office 20269
President Of The United States 20500
President'S Committee Equal Opportunity Armed Forces ..20453
President'S Committee On Status Of Women 20210
Renegotiation Board 20446
Renegotiation Board, Eastern Region 20447
Securities And Exchange Commission 20549
Selective Service System, U S 20435
Senate, U S And Office Buildings 20510
Small Business Administration 20416
Smithsonian Institution......20560
Soldiers Home, U. S......20315
State, Dept Of (Headquarters) 20520
State, Dept Of (Other Offices) 20525
State, Dept Of, Agency For International Development..2υ523
State, Dept Of, Foreign Service Posts And Mail Room 20521

State, Dept Of, Passport Office 20524
Subversive Activities Control Board 37
Superintendent Of Documents, Government Printing Office 20402
Supreme Court Of The U S ..20543
Tariff Commission, U S........20436
Tax Court Of The U S......... 44
Tennessee Valley Authority...20444
Transportation, Dept Of (Headquarters) 20590
Transportation, Dept Of (Other Offices) 20591
Treasury, Dept Of (Headquarters) 20220
Treasury, Dept Of Internal Revenue, International......20225
Treasury, Dept Of, (Other Offices Located Out Of H Q) 20226
Treasury, Dept Of, Internal Revenue (Main) 20224
United States Coast Guard....20591
United States House Of Representatives 20515
United States Information Agency (U S I A) 20547
United States Postal Service Hq 20260
United States Senate 20510
United States Supreme Court..20543
United States Tariff Commission 20436
Veterans Administration, (Central) 20420
Veterans Administration, Benefits Office 20421
Veterans Administration, New Veterans Hospital 20422
Vice President Of The U S ..20501
Vice President Of The U S At U S Senate 20510
Walter Reed Army Medical Center (Hospital) 12
White House, The 20500

HOSPITALS

Cafritz Memorial, 1310 Southern Ave 32
Childrens, 2125 13th NW 09
Columbia, 2425 L NW 37
D C General, 19th & C SE..... 03
Doctors, 1815 I NW 06
Freedmans, 6th & Bryant NW 01
George Washington University, 901 23rd NW 37
Georgetown, 3800 Reservoir Rd NW 07
Hadley Memorial, 4601 Nichols Ave SW 32
Metropolitan, 1143 New Hampshire Ave., N.w. 37
Providence, 1150 Varnum NE . 17
Rogers Memorial, 708 Massachusetts Ave, NE 02

Saint Elizabeth, 2690-2698 Ave SE M.I. King Jr. 32
Sibley, 5255 Loughboro Rd NW 16
Suburban, 8600 Old Georgetown Rd (Md) 14
United States Naval, Bethesda Md. 14
Upshur Street, 14th & Upshur NW 11
Veterans Hospital, 50 Irving NW 20422
Walter Reed Army Medical Cen, 6825 16th NW 12
Washington Hospital Center, 110 Irving NW 10
Washington Sanitarium, Takoma Park Md. 12

MILITARY INSTALLATIONS

Andrews AFB 20331
Bolling AFB......20332

UNIVERSITIES AND COLLEGES

American University, Massachusetts & Nebraska Ave NW 16
Benjamin Franklin University, 1100 16th NW...... 36
Catholic University, 620 Michigan Ave NE 17
Columbus University, 620 Michigan Ave N. E. 17
D C Teachers, Wilson Bldg., 11th & Harvard NW 09
Dunbarton, 2935 Upton Street NW 08
Federal City College, 425 2nd NW 01
Gallaudet, Florida Avenue At 7th NE 02
George Washington University Medical School, 1335 H NW 05
George Washington University, 2029 G NW 06
Georgetown University Law School, 506 E St NW 01
Georgetown University, 37th & O NW 07
Howard University, 2401 6th NW 01
Marjorie Webster Junior, 7775 17th N W 12
Montgomery Junior, Takoma Park, M D 12
Mount Vernon Seminary, 2100 Foxhall Rd NW 07
Potomac University, 6830 Laurel NW 12
Southeastern University, 1736 G NW 06
Strayers Business, 601 13th NW 05
Trinity, Michigan Av & Franklin NE 17
Washington Missionary, Takoma Park, Md. 12

FLORIDA
(Abbreviation: FL)

Air Mail Facility, Br. Miami....33159
Airgate, Br. Sarasota 33578
Airport, Br. Saint Petersburg .33732
Alachua 32615
   Sante Fe, R. Br.................32616
Alford 32420
Allandale, Br. Daytona
   Beach 32023
Allapattah, Sta. Miami...........33142
Altamonte Springs..................32701
Altha.....................................32421
Altoona 32702
Alturas..................................33820
Alva 33920
Anna Maria............................33501
Anthony.................................32617
Apalachicola...........................32320
Apollo Beach, R. Br. Ruskin ..33570
Apopka (1st)...........................32703
Arcadia (1st)...........................33821
Archer 32618
Argyle....................................32422
Aripeka 33502
Arlington, Sta. Jacksonville
   (see"appendix)
Astatula.................................32705
Astor.....................................32002
Astronaut Trail, Sta.
   Titusville...........................32780
Atlantic Beach, Br.
   Jacksonville.......................32233
Auburndale (1st).....................33823
Audubon, Br. Merritt Island...32952
Auxiliary Field Nine, Br.
   Eglin A F B.......................32544
Avon Park (1st).......................33825
Azalea Park, Br. Orlando........32807
Babson Park...........................33827
Bagdad..................................32530
Bahia Mar, Sta. Fort
   Lauderdale........................33316
Baker.....................................32531
Bal Harbour, Br. Miami..........33154
Baldwin, Br. Jacksonville.......32234
Balm......................................33503
Barberville.............................32005
Barry College, Br. Miami........33161
Barth.....................................32532
Bartow (1st)............................33830
Bascom..................................32423
Basinger.................................33428
Bay Pines..............................33504
Bay Vista, Sta. Saint
   Petersburg........................33705
Bayard, R. Sta. Jacksonville ..32224
Bayshore Gardens, Br.
   Bradenton..........................33505
Beach, Sta. Vero Beach.........32960
Beacon Light, Br. Pompano
   Beach 33064
Bean City...............................33429
Bee Ridge, Br. Sarasota 33578
Bell 32619
Belle Glade (1st).....................33430
Belleair Bluffs, Br. Largo.......33540
Belleview................................32620
Benbow, R. Br. Clewiston......33440
Bens Lake, Sta. Eglin A F B..32542
Betty Lane, Sta. Clearwater....33515

Big Bayou, Sta. Saint
   Petersburg........................33739
Big Bend Farm, R. Br.
   Tallahassee........................32311
Big Pine Key, Br.
   Summerland Key.................33043
Biscayne Annex, Sta. Miami ..33152
Blind Pass, Br. Saint
   Petersburg........................33706
Blountstown...........................32424
Boca Grande...........................33921
Boca Raton (1st)......................33432
Bokeelia.................................33922
Bonifay..................................32425
Bonita Springs 33923
Bostwick................................32007
Boulevard, Sta. Clearwater....33515
Bowling Green 33834
Boynton Beach (1st) 33435
Braden Castle, R. Sta.
   Bradenton..........................33505
Bradenton (1st)........................33505
Bradenton Beach (1st).............33510
   Holmes Beach, R. Br.........33509
Bradfordville, R. Br.
   Tallahassee........................32301
Bradley 33835
Brandon (1st)..........................33511
Branford 32008
Brent, Br. Pensacola..............32505
Bright, Sta. Hialeah 33013
Bristol....................................32321
Bronson 32621
Brooker 32622
Brooks Plaza, Sta. Fort
   Walton Beach.....................32548
Brooksville (1st).......................33512
Brookview, Sta. Jacksonville ..32211
Bruce, R. Br. Ponce De Leon ..32455
Bryant, R. Br. Canal Point.....33439
Bryceville...............................32009
Buena Vista, Sta. Miami
   (see appendix)
Bunnell..................................32010
Bushnell.................................33513
Callahan.................................32011
Calloway, R. Br. Panama
   City...................................32401
Campbellton 32426
Canal Point.............................33438
   Bryant, R. Br....................33439
   Pelican Lake, R. Br...........33491
Candler 32624
Cantonment............................32533
Cape Canaveral (1st)...............32920
Cape Coral, Br. Fort Myers 33904
Captiva..................................33924
Carl Fisher, Br. Miami...........33139
Carlton, Br. Clearwater 33515
Carrabelle..............................32322
   Lanark Village, R. Br........32323
Carver, Sta. Jacksonville.......32209
Caryville.................................32427
Cassadaga 32706
Casselberry.............................32707
Cecil Field, MOU.
   Jacksonville.......................32215
Cedar Key 32625
Center Hill 33514
Century..................................32535
Charlotte Harbor, Br. Punta
   Gorda 33950
Chattahoochee (1st)................32324

Chiefland...............................32626
Chipley (1st)............................32428
Chipola, R. Br. Marianna.......32450
Chokoloskee...........................33925
Christmas...............................32709
Chuluota, R. Br. Oviedo.........32766
Citra......................................32627
Citrus Tower, Sta. Clermont...32711
Clair Mel City, Br. Tampa......33619
Clarcona.................................32710
Clarksville..............................32430
Clearview, Br. Saint
   Petersburg........................33714
CLEARWATER (1st) (see
   appendix)
Clearwater Beach, Sta.
   Clearwater.........................33515
Clermont (1st)..........................32711
Cleveland Street, Sta.
   Clearwater.........................33517
Clewiston (1st).........................33440
Cocoa (1st)..............................32922
   Five Points, Sta. 32922
   Patrick A F B, Br. 32925
Cocoa Beach (1st)....................32931
Coconut Grove, Sta. Miami 33133
Colee, Sta. Fort Lauderdale 33303
Coleman.................................33521
College Park, Sta. Orlando.....32804
Colonialtown, Sta. Orlando 32803
Compass Lake, R. Br.
   Marianna...........................32448
Congress Avenue, Br. Lake
   Worth.................................33460
Cooper City, Br. Fort
   Lauderdale........................33314
Copeland................................33926
Coral Gables, Br. Miami (see
   appendix)
Coral Ridge, Sta. Fort
   Lauderdale........................33306
Coral Springs, R. Br.
   Pompano Beach.................33060
Cornwell, R. Br. Lorida.........33836
Coronado, Sta. New Smyrna
   Beach 32069
Cortez....................................33522
Cortez Plaza, Br. Bradenton...33505
Cottage Hill, R. Br.
   Cantonment 32533
Cottondale..............................32431
Country Club, R. Br. Fort
   Pierce................................33450
Country Club Estates, Br.
   Lakeland............................33801
Cove, Sta. Panama City........32401
Coytown, Sta. Orlando...........32803
Crawfordville 32327
Crescent Beach, Br.
   Sarasota............................33578
Crescent City..........................32012
Crestview (1st).........................32536
   Lakewood, R. Br. 32566
   Milligan, R. Br. 32537
   Paxton, R. Br. 32538
Cross City..............................32628
Crossroads, Sta. Saint
   Petersburg........................33710
Crystal Beach..........................33523
Crystal Lake, R. Br. Wausau..32463
Crystal River...........................32629
Crystal Springs.......................33524
Cutler Ridge, Br. Miami.........33157

Cypress............................32432
Cypress Gardens, R. Br.
   Winter Haven.................33880
Dade City (1st)...................33525
Dania (1st).........................33004
Davenport...........................33837
Davie, Br. Fort Lauderdale......33314
Day....................................32013
DAYTONA BEACH (1st) (see
   appendix)
Daytona Beach Shores, Br.
   Daytona Beach...............32016
De Bary..............................32713
De Funiak Springs (1st).......32433
   Mossy Head, R. Br..........32434
De Land (1st).....................32720
   Glenwood, R. Br.............32722
De Leon Springs..................32028
Deerfield Beach (1st)...........33441
Delray Beach (1st)..............33444
Deltona, R. Br. Orange City.....32763
Destin................................32541
Dinsmore, R. Sta.
   Jacksonville...................32219
Disston Plaza, Sta. Saint
   Petersburg.....................33710
Dixie Village, Sta. Orlando.....32806
Dixieland, Sta. Lakeland.......33803
Doctors Inlet.......................32030
Dona Vista, R. Br. Umatilla.....32784
Dover.................................33527
Dover Shores, Sta. Orlando.....32806
Dowling Park, R. Br. Live
   Oak..............................32060
Downtown, Sta. Orlando.......32802
Downtown, Sta. Tampa........33602
Driftwood, Sta. Hollywood.....33024
Dundee...............................33838
Dunedin (1st)......................33528
Dunlawton, Br. Daytona
   Beach...........................32019
Dunn Avenue, Sta.
   Jacksonville...................32218
Dunnellon...........................32630
Durant................................33530
Eagle Lake..........................33839
Earleton..............................32631
East Avenue, Sta. Sarasota.....33578
East Hill, Sta. Pensacola
   (see appendix)
East Palatka........................32031
Eastgate, Sta. Winter Park.....32789
Eastlake Weir.......................32632
Eastpoint............................32328
Eaton Park...........................33840
Eatonville, R. Br. Maitland.....32751
Eau Gallie, Sta. Melbourne.....32935
Ebro...................................32437
Edgar, R. Br. Interlachen.......32049
Edgewater...........................32032
Edgewater Gulf Beach, R.
   Br. Panama City.............32401
Edison Center, Sta. Miami.....33151
Eglin A F B (1st)..................32542
   Auxiliary Field Nine, Br......32544
   Bens Lake, Sta................32542
   U S A F Hospital, Sta.......32542
El Jobean, R. Br. Punta
   Gorda...........................33927
Elfers.................................33531
Elkton................................32033
Ellenton..............................33532

Ellinor Village, Sta. Ormond
   Beach...........................32074
Ellyson Field, Br. Pensacola.....32509
Eloise, Br. Winter Haven.......33880
Englewood (1st)..................33533
Ensley, Br. Pensacola...........32504
Enterprise, R. Br. Orange
   City..............................32763
Estero................................33928
Esto, R. Br. Bonifay............32425
Euclid, Sta. Saint Petersburg
   (see appendix)
Eustis (1st).........................32726
Everglades City....................33929
Evinston..............................32633
Fairfield..............................32634
Fairvilla, Br. Orlando...........32804
Fedhaven, R. Br. Lake
   Wales............................33854
Felda.................................33930
Fellsmere............................32948
Fern Park (1st)....................32730
Fernandina Beach (1st).......32034
Ferndale..............................32729
Five Points, Sta. Cocoa........32922
Flagler, Sta. Key West..........33040
Flagler Beach.......................32036
Flamingo, R. Br. Homestead.....33030
Florahome...........................32635
Floral City...........................32636
Florence Villa, Sta. Winter
   Haven...........................33880
Florida City, Br. Homestead.....33030
Florida Southern College,
   Sta. Lakeland.................33802
Forest City, R. Br. Maitland.....32751
Forest Hills, Sta. Tampa
   (see appendix)
Forest Ridge, Br. Hollywood.....33023
Fort George Island, R. Sta.
   Jacksonville...................32226
Fort Green, R. Br. Bowling
   Green............................33834
FORT LAUDERDALE (1st)
   (see appendix)
Fort Mc Coy........................32637
Fort Meade..........................33841
FORT MYERS (1st) (see
   appendix)
Fort Myers Beach (1st).........33931
Fort Ogden..........................33842
Fort Pierce (1st)..................33450
Fort Pierce Beach, Br. Fort
   Pierce...........................33450
Fort Walton Beach (1st).......32548
Fort White...........................32038
Forty Ninth Street, Br. Saint
   Petersburg.....................33707
Fountain.............................32438
Four Points, Br. West Palm
   Beach...........................33406
Freeport..............................32439
Frostproof...........................33843
Fruitland Park......................32731
Fruitville, Br. Sarasota..........33578
Gainesville (1st)..................32601
Garden City, R. Sta.
   Jacksonville...................32218
Gateway Mall, Sta. Saint
   Petersburg.....................33702
Geneva...............................32732
Georgetown.........................32039

Gibson Plaza, Sta. Fort
   Walton Beach.................32548
Gibsonton...........................33534
Gifford, Br. Vero Beach.........32960
Glen Saint Mary...................32040
Glenwood, R. Br. De Land.....32722
Golden Beach, Br. Miami.......33160
Golden Gate, R. Br. Naples.....33940
Golden Glades, Br. Opa
   Locka...........................33054
Goldenrod...........................32733
Gonzalez.............................32560
Goodland.............................33933
Gotha.................................32734
Goulds................................33170
Graceville............................32440
Graham...............................32042
Grand Crossing, Sta.
   Jacksonville...................32205
Grand Island........................32735
Grand Ridge.........................32442
Grandin...............................32638
Grant.................................32949
Gratigny, Br. Miami (see
   appendix)
Green Cove Springs (1st).......32043
Greenacres City, Br. Lake
   Worth............................33460
Greensboro..........................32330
Greenville...........................32331
Greenwood..........................32443
Gretna................................32332
Grove City, R. Br.
   Englewood.....................33533
Grove Park, Sta. Lakeland.....33803
Groveland............................32736
Gulf Breeze (1st)..................32561
Gulf Hammock......................32639
Gulfport, Br. Saint
   Petersburg (see appendix)
Haines City (1st)..................33844
Hallandale (1st)..................33009
Hamilton, Sta. Pompano
   Beach...........................33062
Hampton.............................32044
Harbour Heights, R. Br.
   Punta Gorda...................33950
Harlem, R. Br. Clewiston.......33440
Harlem Heights, R. Sta.
   Winter Garden.................32787
Harold................................32563
Hastings..............................32045
Havana...............................32333
Hawthorne...........................32640
Hernando............................32642
Herndon, Sta. Orlando.........32814
HIALEAH (1st) (see
   appendix)
Hialeah Lakes, Sta. Hialeah
   (see appendix)
High Springs........................32643
Highland Beach, R. Br.
   Delray Beach.................33444
Highland City.......................33846
Highland Terrace, Sta.
   Pensacola.....................32503
Hiland Park, Br. Panama
   City..............................32401
Hilldale, Sta. Tampa (see
   appendix)
Hilliard...............................32046
Hobe Sound.........................33455
Holder................................32645

Holiday, Br. Tarpon Springs......33589
Holiday Plaza, Br. Panama
   City..................................32401
Holley, R. Br. Gulf Breeze......32561
Hollister..................................32047
Holly Hill, Br. Daytona
   Beach..............................32017
HOLLYWOOD (1st) (see
   appendix)
Hollywood Hills, Sta.
   Hollywood........................33021
Holmes Beach, R. Br.
   Bradenton Beach..............33509
Holt..32564
Homeland................................33847
Homestead (1st)......................33030
Homestead A F B, Br.
   Homestead........................33030
Homosassa..............................32646
Homosassa Springs..................32647
Horseshoe Beach......................32648
Hosford....................................32334
   Sumatra, R. Br.................32335
Howey In The Hills..................32737
Hudson, R. Br. Port Richey......33568
Immokalee................................33934
Indialantic, Br Melbourne......32903
Indian Harbor Beach, Br.
   Melbourne........................32937
Indian Lake Estates, R. Br.
   Lake Wales......................33855
Indian River City, Sta.
   Titusville........................32780
Indian Rocks Beach (1st)......33535
Indiantown..............................33456
Indrio-Saint Lucie, Br. Fort
   Pierce..............................33450
Inglis......................................32649
Interbay, Sta. Tampa..............33611
Intercession City......................33848
Interlachen..............................32048
   Edgar, R. Br.....................32049
International Airport, Br.
   Miami..............................33148
Inverness (1st)........................32650
Inwood, Br. Winter Haven......33880
Irvine......................................32653
Islamorada..............................33036
Island Grove............................32654
Istachatta................................33536
JACKSONVILLE (1st) (see
   appendix)
Jacksonville A M F, Sta.
   Jacksonville......................32229
Jacksonville Beach, Br.
   Jacksonville......................32250
Jacksonville Nas. Sta.
   Jacksonville......................32212
Jacksonville University, Sta.
   Jacksonville......................32211
Jasper....................................32052
Jay..32565
Jennings..................................32053
Jensen Beach (1st)..................33457
Johns Pass, Br. Saint
   Petersburg........................33708
Jupiter (1st)............................33458
Kathleen..................................33849
Kenansville..............................32739
Kendall, Br. Miami..................33156
Kennedy Space Center, Br.
   Orlando (see appendix)

Kenneth City, Br. Saint
   Petersburg........................33709
Key Biscayne, Br. Miami........33149
Key Colony Beach, R. Br.
   Marathon..........................33051
Key Largo................................33037
   Upper Key Largo, R. Br.....33038
Key West (1st)........................33040
Keystone Heights......................32656
Keysville, R. Br. Lithia..........33547
Killarney..................................32740
Kinard, R. Br. Marianna..........32449
Kissimmee (1st)......................32741
La Belle..................................33935
La Crosse................................32658
Lacoochee................................33537
Lady Lake................................32659
Lafayette, R. Br.
   Tallahassee......................32308
Laguna Beach, R. Br.
   Panama City......................32401
Lake Alfred..............................33850
Lake Butler..............................32054
Lake City (1st)........................32055
Lake Como..............................32057
Lake Forest, Sta.
   Jacksonville (see
   appendix)
Lake Geneva............................32660
Lake Hamilton..........................33851
Lake Harbor............................33459
Lake Helen..............................32744
Lake Jem, R. Br. Mount
   Dora................................32745
Lake Lucina, Sta.
   Jacksonville......................32211
Lake Mary................................32746
Lake Monroe............................32747
Lake Panasoffkee......................33538
Lake Park, Br. West Palm
   Beach..............................33403
Lake Placid (1st)......................33852
Lake Shore, Sta. Jacksonville
   (see appendix)
Lake Tarpon, Br. Palm
   Harbor..............................33563
Lake Wales (1st)......................33853
   Fedhaven, R. Br................33854
   Indian Lake Estates, R.
   Br...................................33855
   Nalcrest, R. Br.................33856
Lake Worth (1st)......................33460
LAKELAND (1st) (see
   appendix)
Lakewood, R. Br. Crestview......32566
Lamont....................................32336
Lanark Village, R. Br.
   Carrabelle........................32323
Land O'Lakes..........................33539
Lantana, Br. Lake Worth..........33460
Largo (1st)..............................33540
Lauderdale-by-the-Sea, Br.
   Fort Lauderdale................33308
Lauderhill, Br. Fort
   Lauderdale........................33313
Laurel....................................33545
Laurel Hill..............................32567
Lawtey....................................32058
Lecanto..................................32661
Lee..32059
Leesburg (1st)........................32748
Lehigh Acres (1st)............ 33936

Leisure City, Br. Homestead......33030
Lelyland, R. Br. Naples............33940
Lemon City, Sta. Miami............33137
Leon, Sta. Tallahassee............32303
Leonia, R. Br. Westville............32464
Lighthouse Point, Br.
   Pompano Beach..................33064
Lincoln, Br. Miami..................33139
Lithia......................................33547
Little River, Sta. Miami (see
   appendix)
Live Oak (1st)........................32060
Lloyd......................................32337
Lochloosa................................32662
Lockhart, Br. Orlando..............32810
Lockwood Ridge, Sta.
   Sarasota..........................33578
Long Key..................................33001
Longboat Key............................33548
Longwood................................32750
Lorida......................................33857
   Cornwell, R. Br.................33836
Loughman................................33858
Loveridge Heights, Sta.
   Melbourne........................32935
Lowell......................................32663
Loxahatchee..............................33470
Ludlam, Br. Miami..................33155
Lulu..32061
Lutz..33549
Lynn Haven..............................32444
Mac Dill A F B, Br. Tampa......33608
Macclenny................................32063
Madeira Beach, Br. Saint
   Petersburg (see appendix)
Madison (1st)..........................32340
Mainland, Sta. Ormond
   Beach..............................32074
Maitland (1st)..........................32751
Malabar....................................32950
Malone....................................32445
Manatee, Sta. Bradenton..........33505
Mandarin, Sta. Jacksonville......32217
Mango......................................33550
Marathon (1st)........................33050
   Key Colony Beach, R. Br....33051
   Marathon Shores, R. Br......33052
Marathon Shores, Br.
   Marathon..........................33052
Marco......................................33937
Margate, Br. Pompano
   Beach..............................33063
Marianna (1st)........................32446
   Chipola, R. Br..................32450
   Compass Lake, R. Br........32448
   Kinard, R. Br....................32449
   Round Lake, R. Br............32447
   West End, Sta...................32446
Mary Esther..............................32569
Masaryktown, R. Br.
   Brooksville........................33512
Mascotte..................................32753
Matlacha, R. Br. Fort Myers......33901
Maxville, R. Br.
   Jacksonville......................32265
Mayo......................................32066
Mayport, Sta. Jacksonville......32267
Mayport Naval Station, Sta.
   Jacksonville (see
   appendix)
Mc Alpin..................................32062
Mc Coy A F B, MOU.
   Orlando............................32812

Mc David 32568
Mc Intosh 22664
Melbourne (1st) 32901
Melbourne Beach, Br.
  Melbourne 32951
Melrose 32666
Merritt Island (1st) 32952
Mexico Beach, R. Br.
  Panama City 32410
MIAMI (1st) (see appendix)
Miami Beach, Br. Miami
  (see appendix)
Miami Gardens, Br. Opa
  Locka 33054
Miami Shores, Br. Miami 33153
Miami Springs, Br. Miami
  (see appendix) -
Micanopy 32667
Miccosukee, R. Br.
  Tallahassee 32309
Middleburg 32068
Midway 32343
Milligan, R. Br. Crestview...32537
Milton (1st) 32570
Mims 32754
Minneola 32755
Mintons Corner, Br.
  Melbourne 32901
Miracle Mile, Sta. Fort
  Myers 33901
Miramar, Br. Hollywood..........33023
Miramar Beach, R. Br.
  Destin 32541
Mobile Home Park, Sta.
  Sarasota 33578
Mobile Manor, R. Br.
  Longwood 32750
Molino 32577
Monticello (1st) 32344
Montverde 32756
Moore Haven 33471
Morriston 32668
Mossy Head, R. Br. De
  Funiak Springs 32434
Motel Row, Br. Miami 33160
Mount Dora (1st)................32757
  Lake Jem, R. Br. 32745
  Triangle, Sta. 32757
Mount Pleasant, R. Br.
  Quincy 32352
Mulberry (1st) 33860
Murdock 33938
Murray Hill, Sta. Jacksonville
  (see appendix)
Myakka City 33551
Myrtle Grove, Br. Pensacola...32506
Nalcrest, R. Br. Lake Wales...33856
Naples (1st) 33940
Naranja, Br. Homestead......33030
Naval, Sta. Key West...........33040
Naval Comm Training
  Center, Br. Pensacola...32511
Naval Hospital, Sta.
  Jacksonville 32214
Naval Station, Sta.
  Pensacola......................32508
Naval Training Center, Sta.
  Orlando 32813
Neptune Beach, Br.
  Jacksonville 32233
New Port Richey (1st)........33552
New Smyrna Beach (1st).....32069
Newberry 32669

Newport, R. Br. Saint Marks...32355
Newtown Heights, Sta.
  Sarasota 33578
Niceville 32578
Nichols 33863
Nobles, Sta. Pensacola 32504
Nobleton 33554
Nocatee 33864
Nokomis (1st).....................33555
Noma 32452
Norland, Br. Miami..............33169
Normandy, Br. Miami 33141
North Babcock, Sta.
  Melbourne 32901
North Bay Village, Br.
  Miami 33141
North Fort Myers, Br. Fort
  Myers 33903
North Miami, Br. Miami 33161
North Miami Beach, Br.
  Miami (see appendix)
North Palm Beach, Br. West
  Palm Beach 33403
North Port Charlotte, R. Br.
  Venice 33595
Northeast Park, Sta. Saint
  Petersburg.....................33704
Northside, Sta. Sarasota 33578
Northside Center, Br. Miami...33147
Northwest, Br. Miami 33147
Northwood, Sta. West Palm
  Beach 33407
Nova Road, Br. Ormond
  Beach 32074
O'Brien 32071
Oak Hill 32759
Oakland 32760
Oakland Park, Br. Fort
  Lauderdale (see
  appendix)
Ocala (1st) 32670
Ocean Ridge, R. Br. Delray
  Beach 33444
Ocean View, Br. Miami 33140
Oceanway, Sta. Jacksonville
  (see appendix)
Ochopee 33943
Ocoee 32761
Odessa 33556
Ojus, Br. Miami...................33163
Okahumpka 32762
Okeechobee (1st)...............33472
Okeelanta, R. Br. South Bay...33493
Oklawaha 32679
Old Town 32680
Oldsmar 33557
Olustee, R. Br. Sanderson......32072
Olympia Heights, Br. Miami...33165
Ona 33865
One Hundred Sixty Third St,
  Br. Miami......................33162
Oneco (1st)........................33558
Opa Locka (1st) 33054
Open Air, Sta. Saint
  Petersburg (see appendix)
Orange Blossom, Sta.
  Orlando 32805
Orange City (1st) 32763
Orange Lake........................32681
Orange Park (1st) 32073
Orange Springs 32682
ORLANDO (1st) (see
  appendix)

Orlando Naval Hospital, Sta.
  Orlando 32813
Orlovista, Br. Orlando 32811
Ormond Beach (1st)............32074
Ormond By The Sea, Br.
  Ormond Beach 32074
Ortega, Sta. Jacksonville......32210
Osprey 33559
Osteen 32764
Otter Creek 32683
Overstreet 32453
Oviedo 32765
  Chuluota, R. Br. 32766
Oxford 32684
Ozona 33560
Pace, Br. Milton 32570
Pahokee (1st) 33476
Paisley 32767
Palatka (1st) 32077
Palm Bay, Br. Melbourne......32905
Palm Beach (1st) 33480
Palm City 33490
Palm Harbor 33563
Palm River, Br. Tampa 33619
Palm Shores, R. Br.
  Melbourne 32935
Palm Springs, Br. Lake
  Worth 33460
Palm Village, Sta. Hialeah...33012
Palma Ceia, Sta. Tampa......33609
Palma Sola, R. Br.
  Bradenton 33505
Palmdale 33944
Palmetto (1st) 33561
Panacea 32346
Panama City (1st)...............32401
  Calloway, R. Br..............32401
  Cove, Sta. 32401
  Edgewater Gulf Beach, R.
    Br. 32401
  Hiland Park, Br. 32401
  Holiday Plaza, Br. 32401
  Laguna Beach, R. Br.......32401
  Mexico Beach, R. Br.......32410
  Panama City Beach, Br....32401
  Parker, Br. 32401
  Saint Andrews, Sta.........32401
  Southport, R. Br.............32409
  Springfield, Br. 32401
  Tyndall A F B, Br. 32401
  U S Navy Mine Defense
    Lab, Br. 32401
  West Panama City Beach,
    Br. 32401
  Westbay, R. Br. 32401
Panama City Beach, Br.
  Panama City 32401
Parker, Br. Panama City......32401
Parrish 33564
Pass-a-Grill Beach, Br. Saint
  Petersburg.....................33741
Patrick A F B, Br. Cocoa......32925
Paxon, Sta. Jacksonville......32205
Paxton, R. Br. Crestview......32538
Pelican Lake, R. Br. Canal
  Point 33491
Pembroke 33866
Pembroke Pines, Br.
  Hollywood 33023
Peninsula, Sta. Daytona
  Beach 32018
Peninsula, Sta. Tampa.........33609
Penney Farms 32079

PENSACOLA (1st) (see appendix)
Pensacola Beach, Br. Gulf Breeze 32561
Perrine, Br. Miami (see appendix)
Perry (1st) 32347
Pierce 33867
Pierson 32080
Pine Castle, Br. Orlando 32809
Pine Hills, Br. Orlando 32808
Pinecraft, Br. Sarasota 33578
Pineland 33945
Pinellas Park (1st) 33565
Pinetta 32350
Placida 33946
Plant City (1st) 33566
Plantation, Br. Fort Lauderdale (see appendix)
Plaza, Sta. Ocala 32670
Plymouth 32768
Point Washington 32454
Polk City 33868
Pomona Park 32081
POMPANO BEACH (1st) (see appendix)
Pompano Isles, Sta. Pompano Beach 33062
Ponce, Br. Miami 33134
Ponce De Leon 32455
Ponte Vedra Beach 32082
Port Charlotte, Br. Punta Gorda 33950
Port Everglades, Sta. Fort Lauderdale 33316
Port Orange, Br. Daytona Beach 32019
Port Richey (1st) 33568
Port Saint Joe (1st) 32456
Port Saint Lucie, Br. Fort Pierce 33450
Port Salerno 33492
Port Tampa City, Sta. Tampa (see appendix)
Pottsburg, Sta. Jacksonville (see appendix)
Princeton 33171
Produce, Sta. Tampa (see appendix)
Punta Gorda (1st) 33950
   Charlotte Harbor, Br. 33950
   El Jobean, R. Br. 33927
   Harbour Heights, R. Br. 33950
   Port Charlotte, Br. 33950
   Tropic Heights, R. Br. 33950
Putnam Hall 32685
Quincy (1st) 32351
   Mount Pleasant, R. Br. 32352
Raiford 32083
Rainbow Lakes, R. Br. Dunnellon 32630
Redbay, R. Br. Ponce De Leon 32455
Reddick 32686
Redington Beach, Br. Saint Petersburg 33708
Ridge Manor, R. Br. Dade City 33525
Ritta, R. Br. Clewiston 33440
River Junction, Sta. Chattahoochee 32324

Riverside, Sta. Miami (see appendix)
Riverview 33569
Riviera Beach, Br. West Palm Beach 33404
Rockledge (1st) 32955
Roseland 32957
Rotonda West, R. Br. Placida 33946
Round Lake, R. Br. Marianna 32447
Rubonia, R. Br. Palmetto 33561
Ruskin (1st) 33570
Safety Harbor 33572
Saint Andrews, Sta. Panama City 32401
Saint Armands, Sta. Sarasota 33578
Saint Augustine (1st) 32084
Saint Augustine Beach, Br. Saint Augustine 32084
Saint Catherine 33573
Saint Cloud (1st) 32769
Saint James City 33956
Saint Leo 33574
Saint Marks 32355
SAINT PETERSBURG (1st) (see appendix)
Saint Petersburg Beach, Br. Saint Petersburg (see appendix)
Salem 32356
Samoset, Br. Bradenton 33505
San Antonio 33576
San Mateo 32088
Sanderson 32087
   Olustee, R. Br. 32072
Sanford (1st) 32771
Sanibel 33957
Santa Rosa Beach 32459
Sante Fe, R. Br. Alachua 32616
SARASOTA (1st) (see appendix)
Sarno Plaza, Sta. Melbourne ... 32935
Satellite Beach, Br. Melbourne 32937
Satsuma 32089
Saufley Field, Br. Pensacola ... 32510
Scottsmoor 32775
Seabreeze, Sta. Daytona Beach 32020
Searstown, Sta. Lakeland 33801
Sebastian 32958
Sebring (1st) 33870
Sebring Southgate, Sta. Sebring 33870
Seffner 33584
Seminole, Br. Largo 33540
Seminole Annex, Sta. Fort Lauderdale (see appendix)
Seminole Heights, Sta. Tampa 33603
Seville 32090
Shackleford, Sta. Pensacola 32503
Shady Grove 32357
Shalimar 32579
Sharpes 32959
Shell Land, Br. Clearwater 33516
Shenandoah, Sta. Miami (see appendix)
Siesta, Br. Sarasota 33578

Silver Springs 32688
Singer Island, Br. West Palm Beach 33404
Sipes, R. Br. Sanford 32771
Skycrest, Sta. Clearwater 33515
Sneads 32460
Sopchoppy 32358
Sorrento 32776
Soutel, Sta. Jacksonville 32208
South Andrews, Sta. Fort Lauderdale (see appendix)
South Bay 33493
South Daytona, Br. Daytona Beach 32021
South Fort Myers, Sta. Fort Myers 33901
South Jacksonville, Sta. Jacksonville 32207
South Miami, Br. Miami 33143
South Pasadena, Br. Saint Petersburg 33707
South Patrick, Br. Melbourne 32937
South Trail, Br. Sarasota 33578
South Venice, Br. Venice 33595
Southboro, Sta. West Palm Beach 33405
Southeast, Sta. Winter Haven 33880
Southgate, Sta. Sarasota 33579
Southport, R. Br. Panama City 32409
Southshore, R. Br. Clewiston 33440
Southside, Sta. Sarasota 33578
Sparr 32690
Spring Hill, Br. Brooksville 33512
Spring Park, Sta. Jacksonville 32207
Springfield, Br. Panama City 32401
Starke (1st) 32091
Steinhatchee 32359
Stuart (1st) 33494
Sugar Loaf Shores, R. Br. Summerland Key 33044
Sulphur Springs, Sta. Tampa 33604
Sumatra, R. Br. Hosford 32335
Summerfield 32691
Summerland Key 33042
   Big Pine Key, Br. 33043
   Sugar Loaf Shores, R. Br. .. 33044
Sumterville 33585
Sun City 33586
Sun City Center, Br. Ruskin 33570
Sunny Isles, Br. Miami 33160
Sunnyside 32461
Sunrise, Sta. Fort Lauderdale (see appendix)
Sunrise Golf Village, Br. Fort Lauderdale 33313
Sunshine, Br. Tampa 33615
Surfside, Br. Miami 33154
Suwannee 32692
Sydney 33587
T B Hospital, Sta. Tampa 33614
Taft, R. Br. Orlando 32809
TALLAHASSEE (1st) (see appendix)

83

Tallevast..............................33588
Tamarac, Br. Fort
  Lauderdale........................33313
Tamiami, Sta. Miami (see
  appendix)
TAMPA (1st) (see appendix)
Tangerine............................32777
Tarpon Springs (1st)............33589
Tavares (1st).......................32778
Tavernier.............................33070
  Vacation Village, ⅋ Br.......33071
Telogia...............................32360
Temple Terrace, Br. Tampa..33617
Tequesta, Br. Jupiter...........33458
Terra Ceia...........................33591
The Village, R. Br. Odessa..33556
Thonotosasse.......................33592
Tice, Br. Fort Myers............33905
Tierra Verde, R. Br. Saint
  Petersburg.........................33715
Tildenville, R. Br. Winter
  Garden.............................32787
Titusville (1st)....................32780
Towers, Sta. Winter Park......32789
Town And Country Plaza, Br.
  Pensacola..........................32505
Trailer City, R. Br.
  Tallahassee.......................32301
Trailer Estates, Br.
  Bradenton..........................33505
Trailer Haven, Sta.
  Melbourne.........................32901
Treasure Island, Br. Saint
  Petersburg.........................33740
Trenton...............................32693
Triangle, Sta. Mount Dora....32757
Trilby................................33593
Tropic Heights, R. Br. Punta
  Gorda...............................33950
Twin Lake, Br. Tampa...........33604
Tyndall A F B, Br. Panama
  City.................................32401
U S A F Hospital, Sta. Eglin
  A F B...............................32542
U S Navy Mine Defense Lab,
  Br. Panama City...................32401
Uleta, Br. Miami...................33164
Umatilla.............................32784
Union Park, R. Br. Orlando....32807
University, Sta. Gainesville...32601

University Of Miami, Br.
  Miami...............................33124
University Of Tampa, Sta.
  Tampa...............................33606
University Of West Florida,
  R. Br. Pensacola..................32504
Upper Key Largo, R. Br. Key
  Largo...............................33038
Vacation Village, R. Br.
  Tavernier..........................33071
Valparaiso (1st)...................32580
Valrico..............................33594
Venice (1st)........................33595
Venus................................33960
Vernon...............................32462
Vero Beach (1st)...................32960
Village Green, Sta.
  Rockledge..........................32955
Wabasso..............................32970
Wacissa..............................32361
Wahneta, Br. Winter Haven.....33880
Wakulla Springs, R. Br.
  Tallahassee.......................32305
Waldo................................32694
Walnut Hill, R. Br. Mc
  David...............................32568
Warm Mineral Springs, R.
  Br. Venice.........................33595
Warrington, Br. Pensacola.....32507
Wauchula (1st).....................33873
Wausau...............................32463
Waverly..............................33877
Webbs City, Sta. Saint
  Petersburg.........................33701
Webster..............................33597
Weeki Wachee, R. Br.
  Brooksville........................33512
Weirsdale............................32695
Welaka...............................32093
Wellborn.............................32094
Wesconnett, Sta.
  Jacksonville.......................32210
Wesley Manor, R. Br.
  Jacksonville.......................32223
West Bay Annex, Sta.
  Jacksonville.......................32203
West Central, Sta. Saint
  Petersburg.........................33707
West Eau Gallie, Br.
  Melbourne.........................32935

West End, Sta. Marianna.......32446
West Hollywood, Br.
  Hollywood (see appendix)
West Lantana, Br. Lake
  Worth...............................33460
WEST PALM BEACH (1st)
  (see appendix)
West Palmetto Park, Sta.
  Boca Raton.........................33432
West Panama City Beach,
  Br. Panama City...................32401
West Pensacola, Br.
  Pensacola..........................32505
West Tampa, Sta. Tampa........33607
Westbay, R. Br. Panama
  City.................................32401
Westgate, Br. Bradenton.......33505
Westville............................32464
Westwood, Br. Hollywood......33024
Wewahitchka..........................32465
Whispering Palms, Sta. Lake
  Worth...............................33460
White Springs........................32096
Whitehouse, R. Sta.
  Jacksonville.......................32220
Wildwood.............................32785
Williston............................32696
Wilton Manors, Br. Fort
  Lauderdale.........................33305
Wimauma..............................33598
Windermere...........................32786
Winter Beach.........................32971
Winter Garden (1st)..............32787
Winter Haven (1st)................33880
Winter Park (1st)..................32789
Woodville............................32362
Woodward Avenue, Sta.
  Tallahassee.......................32304
Worthington Springs..............32697
Wright, Br. Fort Walton
  Beach...............................32548
Yalaha...............................32797
Yankeetown...........................32698
Ybor City, Sta. Tampa (see
  appendix)
Youngstown...........................32466
Yukon, Sta. Jacksonville.......32230
Yulee................................32097
Zellwood.............................32798
Zephyrhills (1st)..................33599
Zolfo Springs.......................33890

BRADENTON 335

POST OFFICE BOXES

Box Nos.
1 143	Braden Castle Rural Sta.	05
1-2480	Main Office	06
P33-P78	Palma Sola Rural Sta.	05
	Manatee Sta.	05
2001-3147	Cortez Plaza Br	07
4001-4199		
5001-6999	Trailer Estates Br	07
7001-7599	Samoset Br	05
8000-8999	Bayshore Gardens Br	07

RURAL ROUTES

1,2,3 05

STATIONS, BRANCHES AND UNITS

Bayshore Gardens Br	05
Braden Castle Rural Sta.	05
Cortez Plaza Br	05
Manatee Sta.	05
Palma Sola Rural Br	05
Samoset Br	05
Trailer Estates Br	05
Westgate Br	05
General Delivery	06
Myakka Star Route	05
Postmaster	06

CLEARWATER 335

POST OFFICE BOXES

Box Nos.
A-Q	Main Office	18
1-1880	Cleveland St Sta.	17
3001-3477	Clearwater Beach Sta	15
4001-5309	Main Office	18

RURAL ROUTES

1	16
2	15

STATIONS, BRANCHES AND UNITS

Betty Lane Sta	15
Boulevard Sta.	15
Carlton Br.	15
Clearwater Beach Sta	15
Cleveland Street Sta	17
Shell Land Br	16
Skycrest Sta	15
General Delivery	15
Postmaster	15

APARTMENTS, HOTELS, MOTELS

Ambassador, 432 Bay Ave.	16
Bayview Gardens, 2855 Gulf To Bay Blvd.	15

Belleview Biltmore P O Box 1430	17
Belvedere, 300 N. Osceola Ave.	15
Betty Drew, 200 N. Betty Lane	15
Clearwater Point Apts, 825 Gulfview Dr	15
Continental Towers, 668 S Gulfview Blvd.	15
Dearborn Towers, 223 Island Way	15
Fleetwood, 1200 S Greenwood Ave.	16
Golfview, 1280 E. Druid Road	16
Gray Moss Inn, P O Box 1328	17
Greenwood, N Greeewood Ave ½ Palmetto St	15
Horizon House, 31 Island Way	15
Imperial Court, 1425 S Blecher Road	16
Imperial Cove, 1433 U S Hwy 19 S	16
Imperial Gardens, 2100 Nursery Road	16
Jack Tar Harrison, P O Box 1049	17
Kalmia, 1227 S Highland Ave.	16
Lindru, 711 S. Lincoln Ave.	16
Mandalay Shores, 880 Mandalay Ave.	15
Seville, 999 US Hwy 19 S	16
Spanish Villas, State Route 60	15
Yacht Basin, 501 Mandalay Ave.	15

BUILDINGS

City Building, 112 S Osceola Ave.	16
Pinellas County Court House, 315 Haven	16
Professional Building, 301 Pierce	16

HOSPITALS

Clearwater Community	16
Morton F Plant, P O Box 210	17

DAYTONA BEACH 320

POST OFFICE BOXES

Box Nos.
1-792	Holly Hill Br.	17
1-1287	Port Orange Br.	19
1-0002767	Main Office	15
3001-3999	Peninsula Sta.	18
4001-4655	South Daytona Br	21
5001-5897	Seabreeze Sta.	20
6001-6369	A Sta.	22
7001-7527	Datona Beach Shores Br	16

8001-8999	Allandale Br	23

RURAL ROUTES

1	14
2,3	19

STATIONS, BRANCHES AND UNITS

Allandale Br	23
Daytona Beach Shores Br	16
Dunlawton Br	19
Holly Hill Br	17
Peninsula Sta	18
Port Orange Br	19
Seabreeze Sta	20
South Daytona Br	21
General Delivery	15

PORT LAUDERDALE 333

POST OFFICE BOXES

Box Nos.
A-Z	South Andrews	15
1-1782	Fort Lauderdale	02
2000-2999	Colee Sta.	03
3000-3999	Bahia-Mar Sta.	16
4000-4999	Sunrise Sta	04
6500-6999	Station 9	16
7000-7999	Sunrise Sta	04
8000-9999	Seminole Annex Sta.	10
10000-10999	Wilton Manors Br	05
11000-11999	Coral Ridge Sta.	06
12000-12999	Plantation Br.	14
13000-13999	Port Everglades Sta.	16
22000-22999	South Andrews Sta.	15
23000-24500	Oakland Park Br	07

RURAL ROUTES

1 14

STATIONS, BRANCHES AND UNITS

Bahia Mar Sta.	16
Colee Sta.	03
Cooper City Br.	14
Coral Ridge Sta.	06
Davie Br.	14
Lauderdale-by-the-Sea Br.	08
Lauderhill Br.	13
Oakland Park Br.	08
Plantation Br.	14
Port Everglades Sta.	16
Seminole Annex Sta.	10
South Andrews Sta.	15
Sunrise Sta.	04
Sunrise Golf Village Br.	13
Tamarac Br.	13
Wilton Manors Br.	05
General Delivery	10
Postmaster	10

Fort Lauderdale (Con.)   333

APARTMENTS, HOTELS, MOTELS

Atlantic Towers, 1920 S Ocean Dr	16
Birch River, 3003 Terramar	04
Breakwater Towers, 1900 S Ocean Dr	16
Broward, 304 S Andrews Ave.	01
Caribe, 4050 N Ocean Dr	08
Casa Glamoretta, 435 N Bayshore Dr	04
Coral Ridge Towers, 3233 NE 34th	08
Coral Sands, 1224 E Las Olas Blvd	01
Doctor Kennedy Homes, 1004 W Broward Blvd	12
Dorset House, 2881 NE 32nd	06
Edgewater Arms, 3600 Galt Ocean Dr	08
Escape, 2900 Riomar	04
Everglades House, 2000 S Ocean Dr	16
Fountain Head, 3900 N Ocean Dr	08
Galt Ocean Mile, 3200 Galt Ocean Dr	08
Holiday, 1250 Mayan Dr	16
Karen Club, 1943 Karen Dr	04
Lago Mar, 1700 S Ocean Dr	16
Lauderdale Beach, 101 S Atlantic Blvd	16
Marie Anntoinette, 2222 N Atlantic	05
Maybury Mansions, 5200 NE 24 Ter	08
Ocean Manor, 4040 Galt Ocean Dr	08
Ocean Summit, 4010 N Ocean Dr	08
Park View, 907 NE 15th Ave	04
Pier 66, 2301 SE 17th	16
Riverside, 620 E Las Olas Blvd	01
Riverview Gardens, 1000 SE 4th	01
Royal Admiral, 3800 Galt Ocean Dr	08
Sea Tower, 2840 N Ocean Blvd	08
Sheraton, 303 N Atlantic Blvd	04
Sky Harbor East, 2100 S Ocean Dr	16
Springtide, 345 N Atlantic Blvd	04
Sunrise Tower, 888 Intracostal	04
Trade Winds, 1 N Atlantic Blvd	04
Versailles, 215 N Birch Rd	04
Yankee Clipper Beachside, 1136 Holiday Dr	16
Yankee Clipper, 1140 Seabreeze Blvd	16

BUILDINGS

Anaconda, 1766 E Sunrise Blvd	04

Atlantic Federal, 1750 E Sunrise Blvd	04
Bayview, 1040 Bayview Dr	04
Blount, 25 E Las Olas Blvd	01
Broward Bank, 25 S Andrews Ave	01
Coral Center, 30 108	06
Coral Ridge, 3350 N Federal Hwy	06
Court House Square, 200 SE 6th	01
First Federal, 301 E Las Olas Blvd	01
First National Bank, 1 Financial Plaza	94
Gateway, 1800 E Sunrise Blvd	04
Grandway, 3901 W Broward Blvd	12
Kenann, 3101 N Federal Hwy	06
Las Olas, 305 S Sndrews Ave	01
Plaza, 3900 W Broward Blvd	12
Professional, 915 Middle River Dr	04
Romark, 3521 W Broward Blvd	12
Sunrise Plaza, 2501 E Sunrise Blvd	01
Sweet, 305 S Andrews Ave	01
Times Square Professional, 3042 N Federal Hwy	06
Tropical Arcade, 224 S Andrews Ave	01

GOVERNMENT OFFICES

Broward County Courthouse, 221 SE 6th	01
City Hall, 100 N. Andrews Ave	01
Internal Revenue, 2309 N Federal Hwy	05
Social Security, 308 NE 3rd Ave	01

HOSPITALS

Beach, 125 N Birch Rd	04
Broward General, 1600 S Andrews Ave	16
Doctors General, 6701 W Sunrise Blvd	13
Holy Cross, 4701 N Federal Hwy	08
Las Olas, 1516 E Las Olas Blvd	01
Plantation General, 401 NW 42nd Ave	13

UNIVERSITIES AND COLLEGES

Broward Community College, 3600 SW 70th Ave	14
Drake, 1401 E Broward Blvd	01
Nova, College Ave	14

FORT MYERS   339

POST OFFICE BOXES

Box Nos.		
A-Z	Cape Coral	04

A-Z	Main Office	02
1-697	Matlacha R. Sta	01
1-898	Tice Br	05
1-1379	Cape Coral Br	04
1-2415	Main Office	02
AA-ZZ	Cape Coral	04
AA-ZZ	Main Office	02
AB-AZ	Cape Coral	04
BA-BP	Cape Coral	04
CE-CP	Cape Coral	04
AAA-BBB	Main Office	02
3001-3317	North Fort Myers Br	03
5001-5148	South Fort Myers Sta	01
6001-7192	Miracle Mile Br	01

RURAL ROUTES

1	05
2	03
3	01
4	05
5	01
6	03
7	05
8	01
9	04

STATIONS, BRANCHES AND UNITS

Cape Coral Br	04
Matlacha Rural Br	01
Miracle Mile Sta	01
North Fort Myers Br	03
South Fort Myers Sta	01
Tice Br	05
General Delivery	02
Postmaster	02

HIALEAH   330

POST OFFICE BOXES

Box Nos.		
1-1999	Main Office	11
2000-2999	Palm Village Sta	12
3000-3999	Bright Sta	13
4000-4999	Hialeah-Lakes Sta	14

RURAL ROUTES

1	10

STATIONS, BRANCHES AND UNITS

Bright Sta	13
Hialeah Lakes Sta	14
Palm Village Sta	12
General Delivery	10
Postmaster	10

HOLLYWOOD   330

POST OFFICE BOXES

Box Nos.		
A-HHH	Main Office	22

Hollywood (Con.)   330

1-2454	Main Office	22
3551-4455	West Hollywood	
	Br	23
5000-5294	Driftwood Br	24
6001-7075	Hollywood Hills	
	Sta	21

STATIONS, BRANCHES AND UNITS

Driftwood Sta	24
Forest Ridge Br	23
Hollywood Hills Sta	21
Miramar Br	23
Pembroke Pines Br	23
West Hollywood Br	23
Westwood Br	24
General Delivery	22
Postmaster	22

JACKSONVILLE   322

POST OFFICE BOXES

Box Nos.

A-Z	West Bay	
	Annex Sta	03
1-38	Ft George	
	Island Sta	26
1-88	Grand Crossing	
	Sta	05
1-108	Maxville Rural	
	Sta	65
1-114	Ortega Sta	10
1-148	Bayard Rural	
	Sta	24
1-225	Neptune Beach	
	Sta	33
1-298	Whitehouse R	
	Sta	20
1-313	Dinsmore R	
	Sta	19
1-360	Mayport Sta	67
1-467	Oceanway Sta	18
1-746	Baldwin Br	34
1-1148	Atlantic Beach	
	Br	33
1-1999	Main Office	01
138-276	Ft George	
	Island Sta	26
2000-2999	West Bay	
	Annex Sta	03
3000-3999	Station F	06
4000-4999	Main Office	01
5000-5999	South	
	Jacksonville	
	Sta	07
6000-6999	Murray Hill	
	Sta	05
7000-7999	Lake Shore	
	Sta	10
8000-8999	Arlington Sta	11
9000-9999	Lake Forest	
	Sta	08
10000-10999	South	
	Jacksonville	
	Sta	07
11000-11999	Arlington Sta	11
12000-12999	Carver Sta	09
13000-13999	Station F	06

14000-14999	Lake Shore	
	Sta	10
16000-17999	Pottsburg Sta	16
18000-18999	Air Mail	
	Facility Sta	29
26000-26999	Oceanway Sta	18
27000-27999	Station 19	05
30000-31999	Yukon Sta	30
35000-35999	Main Office	02
36000-36999	Garden City R	
	Sta	18
37000-37999	Murray Hill	
	Sta	05
38000-38999	Station G	06
50000-51999	Jacksonville	
	Beach Br	50

RURAL ROUTES

1	11
2,3	18
4	10
5	05
6	17
7	05
8	16
9	08
SR	29
10	05
11	17
12	18
13	05
14	08
15	34
16	08
17	17
18	16
19	18

STATIONS, BRANCHES AND UNITS

Arlington Sta	11
Atlantic Beach Br	33
Baldwin Br	34
Bayard Sta	24
Brookview Sta	11
Carver Sta	09
Cecil Field MOU	15
Dinsmore Sta	19
Dunn Avenue Sta	18
Fort George Island Sta	26
Garden City Rural Sta	18
Grand Crossing Sta	05
Jacksonville AMF Sta	29
Jacksonville Beach Br	50
Jacksonville NAS Sta	12
Jacksonville University Sta	11
Lake Forest Sta	08
Lake Lucina Sta	11
Lake Shore Sta	10
Maxville Rural Sta	65
Mayport Sta	67
Mayport Naval Station Sta	28
Mandarin Sta	17
Murray Hill Sta	05
Naval Hospital Sta	14
Neptune Beach Br	33
Oceanway Sta	18
Ortega Sta	10
Paxon Sta	05
Pottsburg Sta	16
Soutel Sta	08
South Jacksonville Sta	07
Spring Park Sta	07

Wesconnett Sta	10
Wesley Manor Rural Br	*23
West Bay Annex Sta	03
Whitehouse Rural Sta	20
Yukon Sta	30
General Delivery	01
Postmaster	01

APARTMENTS, HOTELS, MOTELS

Adrian, 118 Clay	02
Amelia, 1308 Willowbranch	
Ave	05
Aragon	01
Commander, 3946 St Johns	
Ave	05
Durkeeville Project, 1601 N	
Myrtle Ave	09
Floridan	01
Hilton, 565 S Main	07
Johnson Terrace, 33 E	
Monroe	02
Joseph H Blodgett Homes,	
1207 Davis	09
Martha Washington, 1636	
King	04
Mayflower	01
Park Lane, 1846 Margaret	04
Pickwick, 521 N Main	02
Place By The Sea, 901 Ocean	
Blvd	33
Ramada Inn Airport, 1351	
Airport Rd	18
Ramada Inn Downtown, 510	
Lane Ave S	05
Riverton Towers, 5353	
Mathews Expy	11
Robert Meyer	01
Rollins, 312 W Forsyth	02
Tahitian Village, 1100	
Seagate	33
Talleyrand, 720 Talleyrand	
Ave	02
Thunderbird Motor Hotel,	
5865 Mathews Expy	11

BUILDINGS

American Heritage Life, 13 E	
Forsyth	02
American National Bank Of	
Jacksonville, 2031	
Hendricks	07
Atlantic Bank, 121 W	
Forsyth	02
Barnett, 112 W Adams	02
Baymar, 233 E Bay	02
Bugbee, 1143 Mary	07
Carpenters, 920 N Main	02
Clara White Mission, 613 W	
Ashley	02
Coffey, 404 W Monroe	02
Daniel, 325 N Main	02
Exchange, 218 W Adams	02
Federal, 400 W Bay	02
Fidelity Federal, 16 N Laura	02
First Bank & Trust Company,	
231 E Forsyth	02
First Federal Savings, 306 W	
Adams	02
Florida Bank, 223 W Adams	02
Florida Baptist, 1230	
Hendricks Ave	07
Florida State Office, 300 E	
Monroe	02

Jacksonville (Con.)   322

Florida Title, 108 W Forsyth....   02
Graham Title, 108 W Forsyth..   02
Greenleaf Annex, 111 W
    Adams.........................   02
Greenleaf, 208 N Laura   02
Guaranty Life, 137 E Forsyth..   02
Hamby, 325 W Forsyth..........   02
Hemming Park, 46 W Duval....   02
Hildebrandt, 306 W Adams.....   02
Independent Life, 233 W
    Duval.........................   02
J C Lanier, 107 N Market   02
Jacksonville National Bank
    Annex, 117 Laura   02
Jacksonville National Bank,
    45 W Forsyth..................   02
Law Exchange, 238 E
    Forsyth   02
Nasrallah, 2720 Park..........   05
Oreilly, 237 W Forsyth..........   02
Professional, 127 W Adams....   02
Prudential 841 Prudential Dr..   07
Saint James, 117 W Duval   02
Schultz, 118 W Adams..........   02
Seminole, 122 W Forsyth   02
Stappey, 317 W Forsyth   02
Smith, 211 E Forsyth...........   02
Suwannee, 424 W Forsyth.....   02
Title & Trust, 200 E Forsyth...   02
Trout, 28 E Bay................   02
Union Terminal Warehouse,
    700 E Union...................   06
Universal-Marion, 21 W
    Church   02
Williams, 7 W Forsyth..........   02

GOVERNMENT OFFICES

City Hall, 220 E Bay............   02
City Utilities, 34 S Laura........   02
County Court House, 330 E
    Bay............................   02
Criminal Court, 330 E Bay   02
United States Court House,
    311 W Monroe.................   02
United States Federal Bldg,
    400 W Bay.....................   02

HOSPITALS

Baptist, 800 Prudential Dr   07
Doctor Millers Sanitarium,
    2460 Atlantic Blvd   07
Doctors, 2821 Riverside Ave...   05
Duval Medical Center, 2000
    Jefferson......................   06
Five Points Medical Center,
    800 Lomax.....................   04
Hope Haven Association,
    5721 Atlantic Blvd   07
Jacksonville Convalescnet,
    131 E 7th......................   06
Medical Dental, 225 W
    Ashley.........................   02
Memorial Hospital, 3625
    University Blvd, S   16
Methodist, 1640 Jefferson......   09
Riverside Hospital, 2033
    Riverside Ave..................   04
Saint Lukes, 1900 Boulevard..   06
Saint Vincents, Foot Of
    Barrs..........................   04

University Hospital, 655 W
    8th   09

UNIVERSITIES AND COLLEGES

Edward Waters College,
    Kings Rd   09
Jacksonville University,
    University Blvd N..............   11

LAKELAND   338

POST OFFICE BOXES

Box Nos.
A-BW   Main Office   02
1-1999   Main Office   02
2001-2736   Dixieland Sta......   03
3000-3520   Main Office   02

RURAL ROUTES

1..............................   03
2,3............................   01
4..............................   03
5,6,7..........................   01
8..............................   03
9,10,11........................   01

STATIONS, BRANCHES AND UNITS

Country Club Estates Br   01
Dixieland Sta..................   03
Florida Southern College Sta..   02
Grove Park Sta................   03
Searstown Sta................   01
General Delivery   02
Postmaster   02

MELBOURNE   329

POST OFFICE BOXES

Box Nos.
1-837   Palm Bay Br.....   05
1-957   Melbourne
            Beach Br.......   51
1-1560   Eau Gallie Sta..   35
1-2316   Main Office   01
2001-2875   Satellite Beach
            Br   37
3001-3599   Indialantic Br...   03

RURAL ROUTES

1..............................   35
2..............................   01
3..............................   51
STAR..........................   01

STATIONS, BRANCHES AND UNITS

Eau Gallie Sta................   35
Indialantic Br................   03
Indian Harbor Beach Br........   37
Loveridge Heights Sta.........   35
Melbourne Beach Br............   51
Mintons Corner Br.............   01
North Babcock Sta.............   01

Palm Bay Br...................   05
Palm Shores Rural Br..........   35
Sarno Plaza Sta...............   35
Satellite Beach Br.............   37
South Patrick Br..............   37
Trailer Haven Sta.............   01
West Eau Gallie Br............   35

APARTMENTS, HOTELS, MOTELS

Apollo Apartments 650 Palm
    Dr.............................   37
Eau Gallie Imperial Hotel
    1477 Pineapple Ave..........   35
Holiday Inn Of Melbourne
    440 So Harbor City Blvd ...   01
Holiday Inn West, 10900
    West New Haven Ave..........   01
Host Of America 420 So
    Harbor City Blvd   01
Hotel Melbourne 1960 So
    Harbor City Blvd   01
Howard Johnson Motor Lodge
    1515 So Harbor City Blvd..   01
Ocean View Apartments 2642
    A-1-A Hwy.....................   37
Orange Court Apartments
    2100 So Melbourne Court...   01
Parkway Palms Apartments
    201 Harbor City Parkway..   37
Pentagon Apartments 21 E
    Strawbridge Ave..............   01
Pines Motel 1894 So Patrick
    Drive..........................   37
Royal Motor Lodge 1423 So
    Harbor City Blvd   01
Sandpiper Towers 205 A-1-A
    Hwy............................   37
Shore View Apartments 50
    Berkeley St....................   37
Southgate Blvd Apartments
    50 E Southgate Blvd..........   01
Trinity Towers Apartments
    East 700 E Strawbridge
    Ave.............................   01
Trinity Towers Apartments
    West 632 E Strawbridge
    Ave.............................   01
Wickham Oaks Apartments
    1432 Parkway Drive..........   35

GOVERNMENT OFFICES

Chamber Of Commerce 657
    Eau Gallie Blvd................   35
County Court House South
    Brevard Branch 55 So
    Neiman Ave....................   01

HOSPITALS

Brevard Crippled Childrens
    Clinic 450 E Sheridan Rd..   01
Brevard Hospital 1350 S
    Hickory St.....................   01
Carnegie Gardens Nursing
    Home 1415 S Hickory St...   01
Florida Convalescent Home
    Of Melbourne 516 E
    Sheridan Rd...................   01
Medic Home Health Center
    1420 S Oak St.................   01

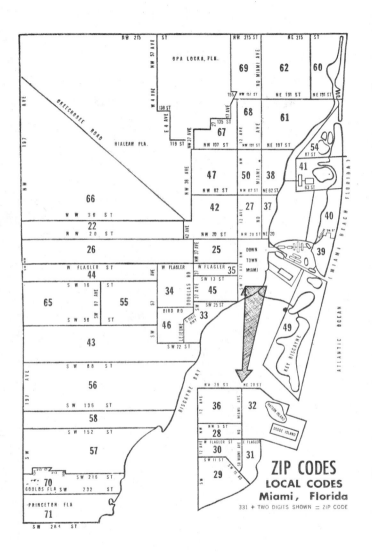

ZIP CODES
LOCAL CODES
Miami, Florida
331 + TWO DIGITS SHOWN = ZIP CODE

Melbourne (Con.)   329

MILITARY INSTALLATIONS

Armed Forces Reserve Center
1889 Stewart Rd 35
Naval Reserve Training
Facility 1889 Stewart Rd.... 35

UNIVERSITIES AND COLLEGES

Florida Institute Of
Technology 7901 S
Country Club Rd 01

MIAMI   331

POST OFFICE BOXES

Box Nos.
A-G	Allapattah Sta..	42
A-M	Northwest Br	47
A-T	Perrine	57
A-Y	Kendall Br	56
A-Y	Little River Sta................	38
A-Y	Miami Beach Br	39
A-Y	Uleta Br............	64
1-379	Uleta Br............	64
1-444	Edison Center Sta................	51
1-444	Olympia Heights Br.....	65
1-597	Gratigny Br......	68
1-697	Allapattah Sta..	42
1-729	North Miami Beach Br........	60
1-734	Miami Shores Br................	53
1-759	Shenandoah Sta................	45
1-829	Tamiami Sta	44
1-846	Miami Springs Br	66
1-894	Ojus Br............	63
1-897	Coconut Grove Sta................	33
1-912	Biscayne Annex Sta................	52
1-975	Riverside Sta....	35
1-1014	Kendall Br........	56
1-1110	Perrine Br........	57
1-1112	Buena Vista Sta................	37
1-1115	Northwest Br....	47
1-1405	North Miami Br................	61
1-1444	International Airport Br	48
1-1546	South Miami Br	43
1-1782	Little River Sta................	38
1-1800	Miami Beach Br	39
1-1918	Coral Gables Br	34
161-5222	Main Office	01
2001-2617	Airport Mail Facility Br....	59

2001-2899	Ocean View Br..	40
3001-3742	Norland Br.......	69
4001-4890	Normandy Br....	41
6001-6447	B Sta................	23
6001-6787	Surfside Br.......	54
7001-7597	Ludlam Br........	55
8001-9194	University Of Miami Br........	24

RURAL ROUTES

1..	44
2..	57
4..	56

STATIONS, BRANCHES AND UNITS

Air Mail Facility Br..................	59
Allapattah Sta......................	42
Bal Harbour Br	54
Barry College Br....................	61
Biscayne Annex Sta................	52
Buena Vista Sta......................	27
Carl Fisher Br........................	39
Coral Gables Br......................	34
Coconut Grove Sta................	33
Cutler Ridge Br......................	57
Edison Center Sta.................	51
Golden Beach Br....................	60
Gratigny Br............................	67
International Airport Br...........	48
Kendall Br..............................	56
Key Biscayne Br.....................	49
Lemon City Sta......................	37
Lincoln Br..............................	39
Little River Sta.......................	38
Ludlam Br..............................	55
Miami Beach Br......................	39
Miami Shores Br.....................	53
Miami Springs Br....................	66
Motel Row Br.........................	60
Norland Br.............................	69
Normady Br............................	41
North Bay Village Br...............	41
North Miami Br.......................	61
North Miami Beach Br.............	60
Northside Center Br...............	47
Northwest Br.........................	47
Ocean View Br.......................	40
Ojus Br..................................	63
Olympia Heights Br................	65
One Hundred Sixty Third St Br	62
Perrine Br..............................	57
Ponce Br................................	34
Riverside Sta.........................	35
Shenandoah..........................	29
South Miami Br......................	43
Sunny Sunny Isles Br.............	60
Surfside Br.............................	54
Tamiami Sta...........................	26
Uleta Br.................................	64
University of Miami Br............	24
General Delivery....................	01
Postmaster............................	01

APARTMENTS, HOTELS, MOTELS

Alcazar, 500 Biscayne Blvd......	32
Algiers, 2555 Collins Ave........	40
Alhambra, 119 SE 2nd St........	31
Americana, 9701 Collins Ave...	54
Balmoral, 9801 Collins Ave.....	54
Beau Rivage, 9955 Collins Ave	54

Biltmore Way, 713 Biltmore Way	34
Biscayne Terrace, 340 Biscayne Blvd.....................	32
Cadillac, 3925 Collins Ave	40
Caribbean, 3737 Collins Ave..	40
Carillon, 6801 Collins Ave......	41
Casablanca, 6345 Collins Ave....................................	41
Castaways, 16375 Collins Ave....................................	60
Columbus, 312 NE 1st............	32
Cortez, 241 NE 1st Ave...........	32
Dallas Park, 111 SE 3rd...........	31
Deauville, 6701 Collins Ave.....	41
Delano, 1685 Collins Ave........	39
Desert Inn, 17201 Collins Ave....................................	60
Di Lido, 155 Lincoln Rd...........	39
Doral Beach, 4833 Collins Ave....................................	40
Du Pont Plaza, 300 Biscayne Blvd Way......................	31
Dunes Motel, 17001 Collins Ave....................................	60
Eden Roc, 4525 Collins Ave	40
Everglades, 244 Biscayne Blvd....................................	32
Fontainebleau, 4441 Collins Ave....................................	40
Gateway, 656 East Dr............	66
Golden Gate, 19400 Collins Ave....................................	60
Kenilworth, 10201 Collins Ave....................................	54
Key Biscayne & Villas, 300 Ocean Dr..........................	49
Leamington, 307 NE 1st.........	32
Lucerne, 4101 Collins Ave	40
Mc Allister, 10 Biscayne Blvd..................................	32
Miami Colonial, 146 Biscayne Blvd..................................	32
Miami Gateway, 656 East Dr..	66
Monte Carlo, 6551 Collins Ave....................................	41
Patricia, 312 SE 2nd Ave.......	31
Roney Plaza, 2301 Collins Ave....................................	39
Royalton, 131 SE 1st..............	31
San Souci, 3101 Collins Ave....	40
Saxony, 3201 Collins Ave........	40
Sea Isle, 3001 Collins Ave.......	40
Sea View, 9909 Collins Ave.....	54
Seville, 2901 Collins Ave........	40
Sherry Frontenac, 6565 Collins Ave.........................	41
Thunderbird Motel, 18401 Collins Ave.........................	60
Towers, 332 SE 2nd Ave.........	31
Urmey, 34 SE 2nd Ave............	31
Versailles, 3425 Collins Ave....	40
Whispering Palms, 18901 Collins Ave.........................	60

BUILDINGS

Aladdin, 1213 Lincoln Rd	39
American Bankers Insurance Company, 600 Brickell Ave	31
American Title, 901 N E 2nd Ave	32

Miami (Con.)   331

Biscayne Towers, 100
  Biscayne Blvd 32
Calumet, 10 NE 3rd Ave 32
Capital Bank, 117 NE 1 Ave .. 32
Chamber Of Commerce, 141
  NE 3 Ave 32
Congress, 111 N E 2nd Ave ... 32
Coral Gables First National
  Bank, 100 Coral Way 34
Dade Commonwealth, 139 NE
  1st 32
Dinner Key Exposition, 3360
  Dinner Key Dr 33
Du Pont-Plaza, 300 Biscayne
  Blvd Way 31
Fashion Mart, 127 NW 2nd ... 28
Federal Office 51 SW 1 Ave ... 30
First Federal, 100 NE 1st
  Ave 32
First National Bank Miami,
  100 Biscayne Blvd S 31
First National Bank Miami,
  350 SE 1st 31
First National Bank Miami,
  351 SE 2nd St 31
First National Bank-Miami
  Beach- 39
Five-Fifty, 550 Brickell Ave 39
Flagler 31
Flagler Federal Savings &
  Loan 111 NE 1st St 32
Florida National Bank Coral,
  159 Miracle Mile 34
Huntington Medical, 168 SE
  1 St 31
Ingraham, 25 SE 2nd Ave 31
Insurance Exchange, 901 NE
  2nd Ave 32
Langford, 121 SE 1st 31
Lincoln Medical, 541 Lincoln
  Rd 39
Lincoln, 350 Lincoln Rd 39
Mercantile Natl Bank, 420
  Lincoln Rd 39
Meridian Medical Center,
  1680 Meridian Ave 39
Merrick, 5300 University Dr 46
Miami Beach Federal, 407
  Lincoln Rd 39
Municipal, 1700 Washington
  Ave 39
Northeast Airlines, 150 SE
  2ave 31
Number One Miami, 300
  Biscayne Blvd Way 31
Olympia, 174 Flagler St 31
One Lincoln Road, 169
  Lincoln Road 39
Pan American Bank, 150 SE
  3rd Ave 31
Plaza, 245 SE 1st 31
Professional, 216 NE 2nd
  Ave 32
Roper, 20 SE 3rd Ave 31
Seybold, 36 NE 1st 32
Shoreland, 119 E Flagler St ... 31
Six-Hundred-Five Lincoln
  Road, 605 Lincoln Road 39
Sterling, 927 Lincoln Rd 39

Three Thirty, 330 Biscayne
  Blvd 32
Three-Fifty Lincoln Road,
  1643 Washington Ave 39
Two-Twenty, 220 Miracle
  Mile 34
Y M C A, 40 NE 3 Ave 32

GOVERNMENT OFFICES

Chamber Of Commerce, 141
  NE 3rd Ave 32

HOSPITALS

Baptist, 8900 N Kendall Dr 56
Cedars of Lebanon, 1321 NW
  14 St 25
Christian, 4700 NW 32 Ave ... 42
Dade County, Hospital Rd 56
Doctors, 5000 University Dr ... 46
Jackson Memorial, 1000 NW
  17 St 36
Mercy, 3663 So Miami Ave 33
Miami Heart Institute 4701
  N. Meridian Ave 40
Mt Sinai, 4300 Alton Rd 40
National Childrens Cardiac,
  1475 NW 12 Ave 36
North Dade General, 16951
  NW 2 Ave 69
North Miami General, 1701
  NE 127 St 61
North Shore, 9200 NW 11
  Ave 50
Northwest, 1060 NW 79 50
Osteopathic Genl, 1750 N E
  167 62
Pan American, 5959 NW 7
  St 26
Saint Francis, 250 W 63 St 41
South Coral Gables, 3100
  Douglas Rd 34
South Miami, 7400 SW 62
  Ave 43
South Shore Hospital &
  Medical Center 39
United States Veterans, 1201
  NW 16 St 25
Variety Childrens, 6125 SW
  31 St 55
Victoria, 930 NW 4 St 28
Westchester Genl, 2500 S W
  75 Ave 55

UNIVERSITIES AND COLLEGES

Barry, 11300 NE 2nd Ave 61
Dade Junior North Campus
  11380 NW 27th Ave 67
Dade Junior South Campus
  11011 SW 104th St 56
Florida International 11200
  SW 8th St. 44
University Of Miami, Cgab 24

ORLANDO   328

POST OFFICE BOXES

Box Nos.
1-3833   Downtown Sta .. 02
M-1-M-2099 Mc Coy A F B
               Sta 12

5000-5999   Orange
               Blossom Sta ... 05
6000-6999   Colonialtown
               Sta 03
7000-7999   College Park
               Sta 04
8000-8999   Dixie Village
               Sta 06
9000-9999   Union Park
               Rural Br 07
10000-10999 Taft Rural Br ... 09
11000-11999 Coytown Sta 03
13000-13999 Pinecastle Br ... 09
14000-14999 Azalea Park Br . 07
15000-15999 Pine Hills Br 08
16000-16999 Orlovista Br 11
17000-17999 Lockhart Br 10
20000-20999 Herndon Sta 14
21000-21999 Kennedy Space
               Center Br 15
22000-24999 Lake Buena
               Vista Br 30
25000-26999 Fla Tech
               University 16

RURAL ROUTES

1 09
2 10
3 11
4,5,6 07
7 05

STATIONS, BRANCHES AND UNITS

Azalea Park Br 07
College Park Sta 04
Colonialtown Sta 03
Coytown Sta 03
Dixie Village Sta. 06
Dover Shores Sta 06
Downtown Sta 02
Fairvilla Br 04
Herndon Sta 14
Kennedy Space Ctr Br 15
Lockhart Br 10
Mc Coy A F B MOU 12
Naval Training Center Sta 13
Orange Blossom Sta 05
Orlando Naval Hospital Sta 13
Orlovista Br 11
Pine Castle Br 09
Pine Hills Br 08
Taft Rural Br 09
Union Park Rural Br. 07
General Delivery 02
Postmaster 02

APARTMENTS, HOTELS, MOTELS

Angebilt, 37 Orange Ave N 02
Baptist Terrace, 414 Pine E ... 01
Central Towers, 350 E
  Jackson 01
Downtowner, 264 Orange Ave
  S 02
Executive House, 1200
  Holden Ave 09
Georgetown Apts, 5500 Silver
  Star Rd 08
Gurtler Lake Ivanhoe, 1701
  Gurtler Ct 04
Kinneret 515 Delaney Ave 01

Orlando (Con.)   328

Lake Fairview Apts, 4328
Edgewater Dr 04
Lake Lucerne Plaza, 545
Delaney Ave S 01
Lake Mann Homes, Bethune
Dr 05
Lucerne Towers, 20 Lucerne
Cir W 01
Magnolia Towers, 100
Anderson E 01
Orlando Reeves Terrace,
1607 South E 01
Park Plaza, 431 Central Blvd
E 02
Robert Meyer Inn, 151
Washington E 02
San Juan, 32 Orange Ave N ... 01

BUILDINGS

Bradshaw 14 Washington E ... 01
Citizens National Bank, 240
Orange Ave N 01
Cna, 255 Orange Ave S 01
Columbia Professional, 61
Columbia W 06
Executive, 2520 Orange Ave
N 04
Federal 46 Robinson E 01
First Federal, 109 Church E ... 01
First National Bank, 200-228
Orange Ave S 01
Hartford 200 Robinson E 01
Metcalf, 102 Orange Ave S 01
One North Orange, 1-7
Orange Ave N 01
Rosalind, 160 Washington E .. 01
Summerlin Center, 618 South
E 01

GOVERNMENT OFFICES

Chamber Of Commerce
Building, 75 Ivanhoe Blvd
E 04
County Court House & Annex,
65 Central Blvd E 01
Orlando City Hall 400 Orange
Ave S 01

HOSPITALS

Florida Hospital, 601 Rollins
E 02
Holiday, 92 Miller W 06
Mercy Medical Center, 1800
Mercy Dr 08
Orange Memorial, 1416
Orange Ave S 02
Orlando General, 7727 Lake
Underhill Rd 07
Sunland Training Center,
Hiawassa Rd 02

MILITARY INSTALLATIONS

Finance Unit 1 Recruit Trng
Command 13
Kennedy Space Center 15
Mc Coy A F B 12
N A S A 99
Naval Training Ctr 13

Naval Training Device Ctr 13
Navy Research Lab
Underwater Sound
Reference Div 06

UNIVERSITIES AND COLLEGES

Fla Tech Univ, Alafaya Trail ... 16
Mid Florida Technical
Institute, 2908 Oak Ridge
Rd W 09
Valencia Jr College, 2908
Oak Ridge Rd W 09

PENSACOLA   325

POST OFFICE BOXES

Box Nos.
1-1999   Main Office 02
2000-2999   East Hill Sta ... 03
3000-3999   Myrtle Grove
Br 06
4000-4999   Warrington Br... 07
5000-5999   West Pensacola
Br 05
6000-6999   Brent Br 03
7000-7999   Ensley Br 04
8000-8999   Town &
Country Plaza
Br 05
10000-10999   Nobles Sta 04
11000-11999   Naval Hospital
Br 12
12000-12999   Main Office 02
14000-14999   Naval Communications
Training Ctr
Br 11
19000-19999   Shackleford
Sta 03
31000-31999   University Of
West Florida
Br 04

RURAL ROUTES

1 07
2 06
3,4 03
6 07
7,8 06
9 03
10 06
11 03

STATIONS, BRANCHES AND UNITS

Brent Br 05
East Hill Sta 03
Ellyson Field Br 09
Ensley Br 04
Highland Terrace Sta 03
Myrtle Grove Br 06
Naval Comm Training Center
Br 11
Naval Station Br 08
Nobles Sta 04
Saufley Field Br 10
Shackleford Sta 03

Town And Country Plaza Br 05
University Of West Florida
Rural Br 04
Warrington Br 07
West Pensacola Br 05
General Delivery 02
Postmaster 02

MILITARY INSTALLATIONS

Fort Barrancas National
Cemetary 08
Naval Air Station 08
Naval Air Station Ellyson
Field 09
Naval Air Station Saufley
Field 10
Naval Communications
Training Ctr 11
Naval Hospital 12

UNIVERSITIES AND COLLEGES

Pensacola Junior College 04
University Of West Florida 04

POMPANO BEACH   330

POST OFFICE BOXES

Box Nos.
A-X   Main Office 61
1-2499   Main Office 61
2501-3288   Hamilton Sta ... 62
4000-4999   Margate Br 63
5000-6034   Light House
Point Br 64
6000-6999   1 Sta 60
7000-7499   2 Sta 60
8000-
-0009244   Coral Springs
Rural Br 65
10001-10059   Main Office 61

RURAL ROUTES

1,2 60

STATIONS, BRANCHES AND UNITS

Beacon Light Br 64
Coral Springs Rural Br 60
Hamilton Sta 62
Lighthouse Point Br 64
Margate Br 63
Pompano Isles Sta 62
General Delivery 60
Postmaster 60

HOSPITALS

Cypress Community Hospital
600 SW 3rd 60
Margate General Hospital
5850 Margate Blvd 63
North District Hospital, 201 E
Sample Rd 64
Pompano Beach Hospital &
Clinic, 155 E Atlantic
Blvd 60

SAINT PETERSBURG 337

POST OFFICE BOXES

Box Nos.
A-Z	Open Air Sta	31
1-4192	Open Air Sta	31
5001-5236	Gulfport Br	37
6001-6999	Saint Petersburg Beach Br	36
7000-7999	Euclid Sta	34
8001-8999	Madeira Sta	38
9000-9999	Treasure Island Br	40
10000-14999	Saint Petersburg	33
20000-20999	Gateway Mall Sta	42
46341-46999	Pass-A-Grille Beach	41
54691-54749	Big Bayou	39

STATIONS, BRANCHES AND UNITS

Airport Br	32
Bay Vista Sta	05
Big Bayou Sta	39
Blind Pass Br	06
Clearview Br	14
Crossroads Sta	10
Disston Plaza Sta	10
Euclid Sta	02
Forty Ninth Street Br	07
Gateway Mall Sta	02
Gulfport Br	37
Johns Pass Br	08
Kenneth City Br	09
Madeira Beach Sta	08
Northeast Park Sta	04
Open Air Sta	01
Pass-A-Grill Beach Br	41
Redington Beach Br	08
Saint Petersburg Beach Br	06
South Pasadena Br	07
Tierra Verde Rural Br	15
Treasure Island Br	40
Webbs City Sta	01
West Central Sta	07
General Delivery	33
Postmaster	30

APARTMENTS, HOTELS, MOTELS

Albemarle, 115 3rd Ave NE	31
Carleve, 357 2nd N	31
Central, 119 2nd N	31
Colonial, 126 2nd Ave NE	31
Concord, 100 2nd N	31
Cordova, 253 2nd Ave N	31
Dennis, 326 1st Ave N	31
Detroit, 215 Central Ave	31
Edge Park, 256 1st No	31
Edward James, 11750 Gulf Blvd	06
Hilton 333 1 S	31
Hollander, 421 4th Ave N	31
Martha Washington, 234 3rd Ave N	31
Moulton, 342 3rd Ave N	31
Park House, 335 2nd Ave N	31
Pennflora, 443 2nd Ave N	31
Pennsylvania, 300 4th N	31

Poinsettia, 460 Central Ave	31
Ponce De Leon, 95 Central Ave	31
Priness Martha, 401 1st Ave N	31
Randolph, 200 4th N	31
Soreno, 100 Beach Dr NE	31
Suwannee, 501 1st Ave N	31
Ten Eyck, 132 Mirror Lake Dr.	31
The Madison, 424 Central Ave	31
Toffenetti, 25 2nd N	31
Vinoy Park, 325 5th Ave NE	31

BUILDINGS

First Federal, 11 4th N	01
First National Bank, 9 4th S..	01
Florida National Bank, 700 Central Ave	01
Florida Office, 472 Central Ave	01
Florida, 2201 4th No	04
Hall, 4 4th S	01
Legal, 447 3rd Ave N	01
Medical Square, 666 6 Th S..	01
Saint Peterburg Medical Clinic, 501 11 Th N	05
Suncoast Medical Clinic, 500 7 Th S	01
300, 300 31st N	13

GOVERNMENT OFFICES

County, 150 5 Th N	01
Federal, 144 1st Ave S	01

HOSPITALS

All Childrens Hospital, 801 6th S	01
Apollo 400 30th Ave S	05
Bayfront Medical Center, 701 6st St S	31
Doctors, 401 15 Th N	05
Palms Of Pasadena, 1501 Pasadena Ave So	36
Saint Anthony, 601 12th No	33
Saint Petersburg General, 6500 38 Ave N	33

UNIVERSITIES AND COLLEGES

Eckerd College 5401 34th So.	33
Saint Petersburg Junior, 6605 5th Ave N	33
Stetson University College Of Law, 1401 61st S	07
University South Florida, 830 1 St S	01

SARASOTA 335

POST OFFICE BOXES

Box Nos.
1-4322	Main Office	78
5001-5717	Southgate Sta	79
6001-6284	Saint Armands Sta	78
7001-7799	Pinecraft Br	78

8001-8724	Mobile Home Park Sta	78
9001-9337	Newtown Sta	78
10121-10237	Fruitville Br	78
11601-11895	Bee Ridge Br	78
12001-12291	East Avenue Sta	78
13001-13095	Airgate Br	78
15001-15452	Southgate Sta	79

RURAL ROUTES

1,2	77
3	80
4	77

STATIONS, BRANCHES AND UNITS

Airgate Br	78
Bee Ridge Br	78
Crescent Beach Br	78
East Avenue Sta	78
Fruitville Br	78
Lockwood Ridge Sta	78
Mobile Home Park Sta	78
Newtown Heights Sta	78
Northside Sta	78
Pinecraft Br	78
Saint Armands Sta	78
Siesta Sta	78
South Trail Br	78
Southgate Sta	79
Southside Sta	78
General Delivery	78
Postmaster	78

BUILDINGS

Azar 3800 So. Tamiami Trail..	79
Doctors Garden 1880 Arlington	79
Marina Mar, 2 Marina Mar Drive	77
Medical Arts 1950 Arlington	79
Palmer Bank 1405 Main	77
Sarasota Bank 1605 Main	77
1900 Bldg. 1900 Main	77

GOVERNMENT OFFICES

City Hall 1565 1st	77
County Court House 2000 Main	77
Federal Building 111 So. Orange Ave.	77

HOSPITALS

Doctors 2750 Bahia Vista	79
East Manor 1524 East Ave., So	79
Extendicare 1650 Osprey Ave, So	79
Geri-Care 3250 12th	80
Hill Haven 1625 Qsprey Ave., So	79
Memorial 1901 Arlington	79
Sunnyside Haven, 5201 Bahia Vista	80

Sarasota (Con.)   335

UNIVERSITIES AND COLLEGES

New College Administrative Po Box 1898	78
New College Students Po Box 1958	78

TALLAHASSEE   323

POST OFFICE BOXES

Box Nos.		
1-1999	Main Office	02
2001-2999	Woodward Avenue Sta	04
3001-3999	Leon Sta	03

RURAL ROUTES

1	03
2	01
3	03
4,5,6	01
7	03
8	01
9	03
10	04
11	03

STATIONS, BRANCHES AND UNITS

Big Bend Farm Rural Br	11
Bradfordville Rural Br	01
Lafayette Rural Br	08
Leon Sta	03
Miccosukee Rural Br	09
Trailer City Rural Br	01
Wakulla Springs Rural Br	05
Woodward Avenue Sta	04
General Delivery	02
Postmaster	02
Star Routes	04

APARTMENTS, HOTELS, MOTELS

Berkshire Manor, Continental Ave & Ocala Rd	04
Chateau Deville, 2020 Continental Ave	04
Colony Inn, 2191 Tennessee W	04
Floridan, Monroe & Call	02
Holiday Inn Downtown	01
Holiday Inn, 1302 Apalachee Pky	01
Howard Johnson, Brevard W & Tennessee	04
Howard Johnson, 722 Apalachee Pky	01
Osceola Hall, 500 Chapel Dr	04
Southernaire, Brevard W & Tennessee	04
Town & Campus, 940 Brevard W	04
Travelodge, 691 Tennessee W	04
W. T. Cash Hall, 700 Woodward Ave N	04

BUILDINGS

Bloxham	04
Bryant	04
Burns	04
Caldwell	04
Capitol	04
Carlton	04
City Hall	04
Collins	04
County Courthouse	01
Holland	04
Johns	04
Knott	04
Larson	04
Mayo	04
Midyette-Moor	01
Supreme Court	04
Tallahassee	03
Tallahassee Bank & Trust	01
Whitfield	04

HOSPITALS

Sunland	04
Tallahassee Convalescent	03
Tallahassee Memorial	04

UNIVERSITIES AND COLLEGES

Florida A & M University	07
Florida State University	06
Tallahassee Jr. College	04

TAMPA   336

POST OFFICE BOXES

Box Nos.		
1-3500	Downtown	01
4000-4708	West Tampa Sta	07
5000-5999	Ybor City Sta	05
6000-6999	Macdill Air Force Base Br	08
7001-7299	Seminole Heights Sta	03
8000-9999	Sulphur Springs Sta	04
10001-10999	Peninsula Sta	09
11001-11844	Produce Sta	10
13000-13999	Interbay Sta	11
14000-14999	Palma Ceia Sta	09
15000-15999	Hilldale Sta	14
16001-16200	Temple Terrace Br	17
17000-17999	Forest Hills Sta	12
18000-18999	Peninsula Sta	09
19000-19999	Port Tampa City Sta	16
0022000-0023999	Main Office	22

RURAL ROUTES

1	12
2	10
3	19
4	15
5	14
6	17

STATIONS, BRANCHES AND UNITS

Clair Mel City Br	19
Downtown Sta	02
Forest Hills Sta	12
Hilldale Sta	14
Interbay Sta	11
Mac Dill A F B Br	08
Palm River Br	19
Palma Ceia Sta	09
Peninsula Sta	09
Port Tampa City Sta	16
Produce Sta	10
Seminole Heights Sta	03
Sulphur Springs Sta	04
Sunshine Br	15
T B Hospital Sta	14
Temple Terrace Br	17
Twin Lake Br	04
University of Tampa Sta	06
West Tampa Sta	07
Ybor Sta	05
General Delivery	02
Postmaster	02

APARTMENTS, HOTELS, MOTELS

Bay View 208 Jackson	02
Bayshore Royal 2109 Bayshore Blvd	06
Bayshore Towers 4015 Bayshore Blvd	11
Davis Island Towers 84 Davis Blvd	06
Florida Motor Hotel 905 Florida Ave	02
Harbor House 2401 Bayshore Blvd	09
Hyde Park Towers 406 Azeele	06
Manager Motor Inn 200 Ashley Dr	02
Morrison Court 2311 Morrison Ave	09
Sheraton Tampa Motor 515 E. Cass	02
University Apartments 4314 E. Fletcher	12

BUILDINGS

Citizens 706 N. Franklin	02
Exchange National Bank - 610 N. Florida Ave	02
First National Bank 215 E. Madison	02
Legal Center 725 J F Kennedy Blvd E	02
Marine Bank 315 E. Madison	02
Medical 1 Davis Blvd	06
Ross 112 E Cass	02
Stovall Professional 305 N Morgan	02
Tampa Theatre 709 N Franklin	02
Wallace S 608 Tampa	02
Western Union 501 Twiggs	02

Tampa (Con.)   336

GOVERNMENT OFFICES

City Hall 315 J F Kennedy
  Blvd E.. 02
County Court House 401
  Pierce.. 02
Federal 500 Zack........................ 02
State Office 800 Twiggs........ 02

HOSPITALS

Centro Asturiano 21st Ave
  13th.. 05
Centro Espanol 4801 N
  Howard Ave.............................. 03
Edwards W T Tuberculosis
  4001 Tampa Bay Blvd.......... 14
Saint Joseph0s 3001 W
  Buffalo Ave.............................. 03
Tampa General Davis Island.. 06
University Community 13505
  N 31st.. 12

UNIVERSITIES AND COLLEGES

Florida College N Glen Arven
  Ave.. 17
University Of South Florida -
  4202 E Fowler Ave.............. 20
University Of Tampa 401 J F
  Kennedy Blvd W.................... 06

WEST PALM BEACH   334

POST OFFICE BOXES

Box Nos.
1-3451   Main Office...... 02
6001-6894   Southboro Sta.. 05
8001-8428   Northwood Sta.. 07
9001-10729   Riviera Beach
             Br.................. 04
12001-12687 Lake Park Br.... 03
14001-14577 North Palm
             Beach............ 08
15001-16144 Four Points...... 06

RURAL ROUTES

1 06

STATIONS, BRANCHES AND UNITS

Four Points Br................................ 06
Lake Park Br.................................... 03
North Palm Beach Br................ 03
Northwood Sta................................ 07
Riviera Beach Br.......................... 04
Singer Island Br............................ 04
Southboro Sta.................................. 05
General Delivery............................ 01
Postmaster.. 01

APARTMENTS, HOTELS, MOTELS

Alma, 534 Datura St.................. 01
Andover Century Village.......... 01
Augusta Bldg Royal Palm
  Beach.. 06
Barclay, 120 Celestial Way.... 08
Bedford Century Village.......... 01
Berkshire, Century Village...... 01
C Royal Palm Beach.................. 06
Cambridge, Century Village.... 01
Camden, Century Village.......... 01
Canterbury, Century Village.... 01
Colonnades, 101 Ocean Ave.... 04
Coventry, Century Village........ 01
Doolin, Doolin Ct.......................... 08
Dorchester, Century Village.... 01
Easthampton, Century
  Village.. 01
Elcid, 315 Almeria Rd.............. 05
Firestone Bldg Royal Palm
  Beach.. 06
Flagler Manor, 3705 S
  Flagler Dr.................................. 05
Flagler Towers, 1401 S
  Flagler Dr.................................. 01
Flagler, 214 Trinity Pl............ 02
Garden Lane, 1809 N Flagler
  Dr.. 07
Golf'S Edge, Century Village... 01
Granada, 500 N Congress
  Ave.. 01
Greenbrier, Century Village.... 01
Greenbrier, 50 Celestial Way.. 08
Harbor Point, 5000 Ocean Dr.. 04
Hastings, Century Village 01
Hibiscus Garden, 619
  Hibiscus St................................ 02
Holiday Inn Town House, 100
  Datura St.................................... 01
Kingswood, Century Village.... 01
La Fontana, 2800 N Flagler
  Dr.. 07
Lake Hotel, 201 Flagler Dr.... 01
Lincoln Plaza, 564 15th St.... 01
Marine Harbor, 100 Le Hane
  Ter.. 08
Monterey, 635 Clematis St 01
Norton Park Towers, 1501 S
  Flagler Dr.................................. 01
Norwich, Century Village........ 01
Old Westbury Bldg Royal
  Palm Beach................................ 06
Oxford Century Village.......... 01
Palm Beach Cooperative, 33
  Ocean Ave.................................. 04
Parklane, 1701 N Flagler Dr.... 07
Patio, 323 Almeria Rd 05
Pebble Beach Bldg Royal
  Palm Beach................................ 06
Plymouth Century Village...... 01
Portofino South, 3800
  Washington Rd 05
Portofino, 2600 N Flagler Dr.... 07
Ramada Inn, 1800 P. B.
  Lakes Blvd.................................. 01
Rapallo, 1701 S Flagler Dr..... 01
Regence Club, 4500 N Dixie... 07

Salisbury, Century Village...... 01
Sandpiper, 120 Le Hane Ter... 08
Sea Spray, 123 Ocean Ave...... 04
Seminole, 40 Celestial Way... 08
Sheffield Century Village 01
Shore, Shore Ct............................ 08
South Bridge, 3915 S Flagler
  Dr.. 05
Spanish Courts, 1124
  Broadway.................................... 04
St Andrews Bldg Royal Palm
  Beach.. 06
St Andrews Residence 208
  Fern St.. 01
Stratford, Century Village 01
The Pennsylvania 208
  Evernia.. 01
Villas, 3600 Ocean St................ 04
Waltham, Century Village 01
Warrington Bldg Royal Palm
  Beach.. 06
Wellington Century Village...... 01
Windsor, Century Village........ 01
Woodhaven Villa, 4000 Forest
  Hill Blvd.................................... 06
Yacht Harbor Landing, 37
  Yacht Club Dr.......................... 08

BUILDINGS

Citizens, 105 S Narcissus
  Ave.. 01
Comeau, 319 Clematis St........ 01
Commerce, 324 Datura St...... 01
Court House, 300 N Dixie
  Hwy.. 01
Datura, 205 Datura St.............. 01
Flagler Court, 601 Flagler
  Drive Ct...................................... 01
Guaranty, 120 S Olive Ave...... 01
Harvey, 224 Datura St............ 01
Lakeview, 515 U S Highway
  1.. 08
Pan-A, 307 N Dixie Hwy.......... 01
Professional, 531 U S
  Highway 1.................................. 08

GOVERNMENT OFFICES

Internal Revenue, 421 Iris...... 01
Social Security, 715 S Dixie
  Hwy.. 02

HOSPITALS

Good Samaritan, 1300 N
  Dixie Hwy.................................. 02
P B County, 1200 45th.......... 07
St Marys, 900 49th.................. 07

UNIVERSITIES AND COLLEGES

Palm Beach Atlantic College,
  1101 S Olive Ave.................. 01
Rosarian Academy, 807 N
  Flagler Dr.................................. 01
University Of Palm Beach,
  660 Fern.................................... 02

GEORGIA
(Abbreviation: GA)

Abac, R. Sta. Tifton	31794
Abbeville	31001
Acworth (1st)	30101
Adairsville	30103
Adel (1st)	31620
Adrian	31002
Agnes Scott College, Sta. Decatur	30030
Ailey	30410
Airport Mail Facility, Br. Atlanta	30320
Alamo	30411
Alapaha	31622
ALBANY (1st) (see appendix)	
Alexander, R. Br. Waynesboro	30801
Allenhurst	31301
Allentown	31003
Alma (1st)	31510
Alpharetta	30201
Alps Road, Sta. Athens	30604
Alston	30412
Alto	30510
Alvaton	30202
Ambrose	31512
Americus (1st)	31709
Amsterdam, R. Br. Climax	31734
Andersonville	31711
Appling	30802
Arabi	31712
Aragon	30104
Arco, Br. Brunswick	31520
Argyle	31623
Arlington	31713
Armuchee	30105
Arnoldsville	30619
Arrowhead, Br. Jonesboro	30236
Ash Mor, Sta. Forest Park	30050
Ashburn	31714
Athens (1st)	30601
Alps Road, Sta.	30604
Campus, Sta.	30601
Gaines Community, Br.	30601
Georgia University, Sta.	30601
Navy Supply Corps School, Sta.	30601
Timothy, Br.	30601
ATLANTA (1st) (see appendix)	
Attapulgus	31715
Auburn	30203
AUGUSTA (1st) (see appendix)	
Austell (1st)	30001
Avera	30803
Avondale Estates (1st)	30002
Axson	31624
Bacon Park, Sta. Savannah	31406
Baconton	31716
Bainbridge (1st)	31717
Baker Village, Sta. Columbus	31903
Baldwin	30511
Ball Ground	30107
Barnesville (1st)	30204
Barnett	30804
Barney	31625
Bartow	30413
Barwick	31720

Battey State Hospital, Br. Rome	30161
Baxley (1st)	31513
Beallwood, Sta. Columbus	31904
Bellville, R. Br. Claxton	30414
Belvedere Plaza, Br. Decatur	30032
Bemiss, R. Br. Valdosta	31601
Ben Hill, Sta. Atlanta	30331
Benevolence	31721
Berlin	31722
Berryton, R. Br. Summerville	30748
Bethlehem	30620
Bibb City, Pr. Columbus	31904
Bishop	30621
Blackshear	31516
Blair Village, Sta. Atlanta	30354
Blairsville	30512
Blakely (1st)	31723
Bloomfield, Sta. Macon	31206
Bloomingdale	31302
Blue Ridge	30513
Hemp, R. Br.	30515
Bluffton	31724
Blythe	30805
Bogart	30622
Bolingbroke	31004
Bolton, Sta. Atlanta	30318
Bonaire	31005
Boneville	30806
Boston	31626
Bostwick	30623
Bowdon	30108
Bowdon Junction	30109
Bowersville	30516
Bowman	30624
Box Springs	31801
Boys Estate, R. Br. Brunswick	31520
Bradley, R. Br. Gray	31032
Braselton	30517
Bremen (1st)	30110
Briarcliff, Br. Atlanta	30329
Briarwood, Br. Atlanta	30344
Bridgeboro, R. Br. Albany	31701
Brinson	31725
Bristol	31518
Bronwood	31726
Brookfield	31727
Brooklet	30415
Brooks	30205
Broxton	31519
Brunswick (1st)	31520
Arco, Br.	31520
Boys Estate, R. Br.	31520
Glynco, Br.	31520
Jekyll Island, Br.	31520
Lanier Plaza, Sta.	31520
Saint Simons Island, Br.	31522
Sterling, R. Br.	31520
Buchanan	30113
Buckhead	30625
Buena Vista	31803
Buford (1st)	30518
Butler	31006
Byromville	31007
Byron	31008
Cadwell	31009
Cairo (1st)	31728
Calhoun (1st)	30701
Calvary	31729
Camak	30807

Camilla (1st)	31730
Campton, R. Br. Monroe	30626
Campus, Sta. Athens	30601
Canon	30520
Canoochee	30416
Canton (1st)	30114
Canton Plaza, Br. Marietta	30060
Capitol Hill, Sta. Atlanta	30334
Carl, R. Br. Auburn	30203
Carlton	30627
Carnesville	30521
Carrollton (1st)	30117
Carters	30704
Cartersville (1st)	30120
Cascade Heights, Sta. Atlanta	30311
Cassville	30123
Castle Park, Sta. Valdosta	31601
Cataula	31804
Cave Spring	30124
Cecil	31627
Cedar Springs	31732
Cedartown (1st)	30125
Centerville, R. Br. Warner Robins	31093
Chamblee, Br. Atlanta	30341
Charing	31010
Chatillon, Br. Rome	30161
Chatsworth (1st)	30705
Chattahoochee, Sta. Atlanta	30321
Chauncey	31011
Cherrylog	30522
Chester	31012
Chestnut Mountain, R. Br. Gainesville	30502
Chickamauga	30707
Chicopee, Br. Gainesville	30501
Chula	31733
Cisco	30708
Civic Center, Sta. Atlanta	30308
Clarkdale	30020
Clarkesville (1st)	30523
Clarkston	30021
Claxton (1st)	30417
Bellville, R. Br.	30414
Clayton (1st)	30525
Clem	30128
Clermont	30527
Cleveland	30528
Climax	31734
Clinchfield	31013
Cloudland	30709
Clyattville, R. Br. Valdosta	31604
Clyo	31303
Cobb	31735
Cobb County Center, Sta. Smyrna	30080
Cobbtown	30420
Cochran (1st)	31014
Empire, R. Br.	31026
Cogdell	31628
Cohutta	30710
Colbert	30628
Coleman	31736
College, Sta. Fort Valley	31030
College Heights, Sta. Columbus	31907
College Park, Br. Atlanta	30337
Collins	30421
Colquitt	31737
COLUMBUS (1st) (see appendix)	

Comer	30629
Commerce (1st)	30529
Concord	30206
Conley	30027
Conyers (1st)	30207
Coolidge	31738
Coosa	30129
Cordele (1st)	31015
Cornelia (1st)	30531
Cotton	31739
Court Square, Sta. Dublin	31021
Covena	30422
Covington (1st)	30209
Crandall	30711
Crawford	30630
Crawfordville	30631
Crescent	31304
Cross Keys, Sta. Macon	31201
Culloden	31016
Cumming (1st)	30130
Cusseta	31805
Custer Terrace, Br.	
Columbus	31905
Cuthbert	31740
Dacula	30211
Dahlonega	30533
Daisy	30423
Dallas	30132
Dalton (1st)	30720
Damascus	31741
Danburg	30632
Danielsville	30633
Danville	31017
Darien	31305
Dasher, R. Br. Valdosta	31601
Davisboro	31018
Dawson (1st)	31742
Dawsonville	30534
De Kalb Airport, Br. Atlanta	30341
De Lowe, Br. Atlanta	30344
De Soto	31743
Dearing	30808
DECATUR (1st) (see appendix)	
Deepstep, R. Br.	
Sandersville	31082
Demorest	30535
Habersham, R. Br.	30544
Denton	31532
Devereux, R. Br. Sparta	31087
Dewy Rose	30634
Dexter	31019
Dillard	30537
Dixie	31629
Dobbins A F B, Br. Marietta	30060
Doerun	31744
Donalsonville (1st)	31745
Doraville, Br. Atlanta	30340
Douglas (1st)	31533
Douglasville (1st)	30134
Dover	30424
Dry Branch	31020
Du Pont	31630
Dublin (1st)	31021
Court Square, Sta.	31021
East Dublin, Br.	31021
Lovett, R. Br.	31053
Scott, R. Br.	31095
Dudley	31022
Duluth	30136
Dunaire, Br. Decatur	30032
Dunwoody, Br. Atlanta	30338

East Atlanta, Sta. Atlanta	30316
East Dublin, Br. Dublin	31021
East Ellijay	30539
East Point, Br. Atlanta	30344
East Side, Sta. Dalton	30720
East Stone Mountain, R. Br.	
Stone Mountain	30083
Eastanollee	30538
Eastman (1st)	31023
Eastwood, Sta. Atlanta	30317
Eatonton (1st)	31024
Eden	31307
Edgewood, Sta. Columbus	31907
Edison	31746
Elberton (1st)	30635
Eldorendo, R. Br.	
Bainbridge	31717
Elizabeth, Br. Marietta	30060
Elko	31025
Ellabell	31308
Ellaville	31806
Ellenton	31747
Ellenwood	30049
Ellerslie	31807
Ellijay (1st)	30540
Elmodel, R. Br. Newton	31748
Embry Hills, Br. Atlanta	30341
Emerson	30137
Emory University, Br. Atlanta (see appendix)	
Empire, R. Br. Cochran	31026
Enigma	31749
Epworth	30541
Esom Hill	30138
Eton	30724
Evans	30809
Everett	31536
Experiment	30212
Fair Oaks, Br. Marietta	30060
Fairburn	30213
Fairmount	30139
Fargo	31631
Farmington	30638
Farrar	31027
Fayetteville (1st)	30214
Inman, R. Br.	30232
Peachtree City, Br.	30269
Federal Annex, Sta. Atlanta (see appendix)	
Federal Reserve, Sta.	
Atlanta	30303
Felton	30140
Fender, R. Br. Tifton	31794
Fitzgerald (1st)	31750
Fleming	31309
Flintstone	30725
Flippen, R. Br. Mc Donough	30215
Flovilla	30216
Flowery Branch	30542
Folkston	31537
Forest Park (1st)	30050
Forsyth (1st)	31029
Fort Benning, Br. Columbus	31905
Fort Gaines	31751
Fort Gordon, Br. Augusta	30905
Fort Mc Pherson, Sta.	
Atlanta	30330
Fort Oglethorpe, Br.	
Rossville	30741
Fort Screven, R. Sta.	
Savannah Beach	31311
Fort Stewart, Br. Hinesville	31313
Fort Valley (1st)	31030

Fortson	31808
Four Points, Br. Albany	31705
Fowlstown	31752
Franklin	30217
Franklin Springs	30639
Fry, R. Br. Copperhill, T N	37317
Funston	31753
Gabbettville	31809
Gaines Community, Br.	
Athens	30601
Gainesville (1st)	30501
Chestnut Mountain, R.	
Br.	30502
Chicopee, Br.	30501
New Holland, Br.	30501
Park Hill, Sta.	30501
Westside, Br.	30501
Garden City, Br. Savannah	31408
Garfield	30425
Gate City, Sta. Atlanta	30312
Gay	30218
Geneva	31810
Georgetown	31754
Georgia Southern, Sta.	
Statesboro	30458
Georgia Southwestern	
College, R. Sta. Americus	31709
Georgia University, Sta.	
Athens	30601
Gibson	30810
Gillsville	30543
Girard	30426
Glenn	30219
Glennville	30427
Glenwood	30428
Glynco, Br. Brunswick	31520
Godfrey, R. Br. Madison	30650
Good Hope	30641
Gordon	31031
Gordon Road, Sta. Atlanta	30310
Gough, R. Br. Keysville	30811
Gracewood	30812
Grantville	30220
Graves	31755
Gray	31032
Grayson	30221
Graysville	30726
Greenbriar, Sta. Atlanta	30331
Greensboro	30642
Greenville	30222
Gresham, Br. Atlanta	30316
Griffin (1st)	30223
Grovetown	30813
Guyton	31312
Habersham, R. Br.	
Demorest	30544
Haddock	31033
Hagan	30429
Hahira	31632
Hamilton	31811
Hampton	30228
Hapeville, Br. Atlanta	30354
Haralson	30229
Hardwick	31034
Harlem	30814
Harrison	31035
Hartsfield	31756
Hartwell (1st)	30643
Hawkinsville (1st)	31036
Hazlehurst (1st)	31539
Helen	30545
Helena	31037
Hemp, R. Br. Blue Ridge	30515

Hephzibah	30815	
Herndon	30430	
Hi Way Eighty, Br.		
Savannah	31408	
Hiawassee	30546	
Higgston, R. Br. Ailey	30410	
High Shoals	30645	
Hill City, R. Br. Resaca	30735	
Hillsboro	31038	
Round Oak, R. Br.	31080	
Hilltonia, R. Br. Sylvania	30467	
Hilton	31758	
Hinesville (1st)	31313	
Hinsonton, R. Br. Pelham	31779	
Hiram	30141	
Hoboken	31542	
Hogansville	30230	
Holly Springs	30142	
Hollywood, R. Br.		
Clarkesville	30523	
Homer	30547	
Homerville	31634	
Hortense	31543	
Hoschton	30548	
Howard	31039	
Huber	31040	
Hull	30646	
Hunter Army Airfield, Br.		
Savannah	31409	
Hurst, R. Br. Morganton	30561	
Ideal	31041	
Ila	30647	
Indian Springs	30231	
Industrial, Br. Atlanta	30336	
Inman, R. Br. Fayetteville	30232	
International Office Park, Br.		
Atlanta	30354	
Iron City	31759	
Irwinton	31042	
Irwinville	31760	
Isle Of Hope, Br. Savannah	31406	
Jackson (1st)	30233	
Jacksonville	31544	
Jakin	31761	
Jasper	30143	
Jefferson (1st)	30549	
Jeffersonville	31044	
Jekyll Island, Br. Brunswick	31520	
Jenkinsburg	30234	
Jersey	30235	
Jesup (1st)	31545	
Jewell	31045	
Jonesboro (1st)	30236	
Juliette	31046	
Junction City	31812	
Juniper	31813	
Juno	30551	
Kathleen	31047	
Kelly	31048	
Kennesaw	30144	
Kensington, R. Br. La		
Fayette	30727	
Keysville	30816	
Gough, R. Br.	30811	
Kibbee	30431	
Kingsland	31548	
Kingston	30145	
Kite	31049	
Knoxville	31050	
La Fayette (1st)	30728	
Kensington, R. Br.	30727	
La Grange (1st)	30240	
La Vista, Br. Atlanta	30329	

Lake Park	31636	
Lakeland	31635	
Lakemont	30552	
Lakeview Estates, R. Br.		
Conyers	30207	
Lakewood, Sta. Atlanta	30315	
Lanier Plaza, Sta.		
Brunswick	31520	
Lavonia	30553	
Lawrenceville (1st)	30245	
Leary	31762	
Lebanon	30146	
Leesburg	31763	
Lenox	31637	
Lenox Square, Sta. Atlanta	30326	
Leslie	31764	
Lexington	30648	
Lexsy, R. Br. Swainsboro	30432	
Lilburn	30247	
Lilly	31051	
Lincolnton	30817	
Lindale	30147	
Lindsay Creek, Sta.		
Columbus	31907	
Lithia Springs	30057	
Lithonia (1st)	30058	
Lizella	31052	
Locust Grove	30248	
Loganville	30249	
Lollie	30433	
Louisville (1st)	30434	
Louvale	31814	
Lovejoy	30250	
Lovett, R. Br. Dublin	31053	
Ludowici	31316	
Lula	30554	
Lumber City	31549	
Lumpkin	31815	
Luthersville	30251	
Luxomni	30252	
Lyerly	30730	
Lyons	30436	
Mableton (1st)	30059	
MACON (1st) (see appendix)		
Madison (1st)	30650	
Madras	30254	
Manassas	30438	
Manchester (1st)	31816	
Manor	31550	
Mansfield	30255	
Marblehill	30148	
Marietta (1st)	30060	
Marshallville	31057	
Martech, Sta. Atlanta	30318	
Martin	30557	
Martinez, Br. Augusta	30907	
Matthews	30818	
Mauk	31058	
Maxeys, R. Br. Union Point	30671	
Mayfield	31059	
Maysville	30558	
Mc Caysville	30555	
Mc Donough (1st)	30253	
Flippen, R. Br.	30215	
Mc Intosh	31317	
Mc Intyre	31054	
Mc Rae (1st)	31055	
Meansville	30256	
Meigs	31765	
Meldrim	31318	
Menlo	30731	
Meridian	31319	
Mershon	31551	

Mesena	30819	
Metter (1st)	30439	
Midland	31820	
Midville	30441	
Midway	31320	
Milan	31060	
Milledgeville (1st)	31061	
Millen (1st)	30442	
Millwood	31552	
Milner	30257	
Milstead, Br. Conyers	30207	
Mineral Bluff	30559	
Mitchell	30820	
Molena	30258	
Monroe (1st)	30655	
Campton, R. Br.	30626	
Montezuma (1st)	31063	
Monticello	31064	
Montrose	31065	
Moody A F B, MOU.		
Valdosta	31601	
Moreland	30259	
Morgan	31766	
Morganton	30550	
Hurst, R. Br.	30561	
Morris	31767	
Morris Brown, Sta. Atlanta	30314	
Morrow (1st)	30260	
Morven	31638	
Moultrie (1st)	31768	
Mount Airy	30563	
Mount Berry	30149	
Mount Vernon	30445	
Mount Zion	30150	
Mountain City	30562	
Mountain View	30070	
Mountville	30261	
Mulberry Street, Sta. Macon		
(see appendix)		
Murrayville	30564	
Musella	31066	
Mystic	31769	
Nahunta	31553	
Nashville (1st)	31639	
Navy Supply Corps School,		
Sta. Athens	30601	
Naylor	31641	
Nelson	30151	
New Holland, Br. Gainesville	30501	
Newborn	30262	
Newington	30446	
Newnan (1st)	30263	
Newton	31770	
Elmodel, R. Br.	31748	
Nicholls	31554	
Nicholson	30565	
Norcross (1st)	30071	
Norman Park	31771	
Norristown	30447	
North Atlanta, Br. Atlanta	30319	
North Decatur, Br. Decatur	30033	
North Druid Hills, Br.		
Decatur	30033	
North Side, Sta. Atlanta (see		
appendix)		
Northeast Plaza, Br. Atlanta	30329	
Northwoods, Br. Atlanta	30340	
Norwood	30821	
Nunez	30448	
Oak Park, R. Br. Swainsboro	30401	
Oakdale, Br. Smyrna	30080	
Oakfield	31772	
Oakland Park, Sta.		
Columbus	31903	

Oakman	30732
Oakwood	30566
Ochlocknee	31773
Ocilla	31774
Oconee	31067
Odum	31555
Offerman	31556
Ogeechee Road, Br. Savannah	31405
Oglethorpe, Br. Savannah	31406
Oglethorpe	31068
Okefenokee, R. Br. Waycross	31501
Oliver	30449
Omaha	31821
Omega	31775
Orchard Hill	30266
Oxford	30267
Palmetto	30268
Park Hill, Sta. Gainesville	30501
Parrott	31777
Patterson	31557
Pavo	31778
Peach Orchard, Br. Augusta	30906
Peachtree Center, Sta. Atlanta	30343
Peachtree City, Br. Fayetteville	30269
Pearson	31642
Pelham	31779
Pembroke	31321
Pendergrass	30567
Penfield	30658
Perkins	30822
Perry (1st)	31069
Perry Homes, Sta. Atlanta	30318
Philomath	30659
Pine Lake	30072
Pine Log	30152
Pine Mountain	31822
Pine Mountain Valley	31823
Pinehurst	31070
Pineview	31071
Pio Nono, Sta. Macon (see appendix)	
Pitts	31072
Plainfield	31073
Plains	31780
Plainville	30733
Plaza, Sta. Forest Park	30050
Pooler	31322
Port Wentworth, Br. Savannah	31407
Portal	30450
Porterdale	30270
Poulan	31781
Powder Springs	30073
Powersville	31074
Preston	31824
Pulaski	30451
Putney	31782
Quitman (1st)	31643
Rabun Gap	30568
Ranger	30734
Ray City	31645
Rayle	30660
Raymond	30271
Rebecca	31783
Red Oak	30272
Redan	30074
Register	30452
Reidsville	30453
Remerton, R. Br. Valdosta	31601
Rentz	31075

Resaca	30735
Rex	30273
Reynolds	31076
Rhine	31077
Riceboro	31323
Richland	31825
Richmond Hill	31324
Ridgeville, R. Br. Townsend	31325
Rincon	31326
Ringgold (1st)	30736
Rising Fawn	30738
Riverdale	30274
Riverside, Sta. Macon	31204
Roberta	31078
Robins A F B, Br. Warner Robins	31093
Robinson	30661
Rochelle	31079
Rock Spring	30739
Rockledge	30454
Rockmart (1st)	30153
Rocky Face	30740
Rocky Ford	30455
Rome (1st)	30161
Roopville	30170
Rose Hill, Sta. Columbus	31904
Rosemont, Sta. Columbus	31904
Rossville (1st)	30741
Roswell (1st)	30075
Round Oak, R. R. Br. Hillsboro	31080
Royston	30662
Rupert	31081
Rutledge	30663
Rydal	30171
Saint George	31646
Saint Marys	31558
Saint Simons Island, Br. Brunswick	31522
Sale City	31784
Sand Town, Br. Marietta	30060
Sandersville (1st)	31082
Sandy Springs, Br. Atlanta	30328
Sapelo Island	31327
Sardis	30456
Sargent	30275
Sasser	31785
Sautee-Nacoochee	30571
SAVANNAH (1st) (see appendix)	
Savannah Beach	31328
Fort Screven, R. Sta.	31311
Scotland	31083
Scott, R. Br. Dublin	31095
Scottdale	30079
Screven	31560
Sea Island	31561
Senoia	30276
Seville	31084
Shady Dale	31085
Shannon	30172
Sharon	30664
Sharpsburg	30277
Shellman	31786
Shiloh	31826
Shurlington, Sta. Macon	31201
Siloam	30665
Silver Creek	30173
Silvertown, Br. Thomaston	30286
Six Flags Over Georgia, R. Br. Atlanta	30336
Skyland, Br. Atlanta	30319
Smarr	31086
Smithville	31787

Smyrna (1st)	30080
Snellville	30278
Social Circle	30279
Soperton	30457
South Base, Br. Warner Robins	31093
South Cobb, Br. Austell	30001
South De Kalb, Br. Decatur	30034
South Decatur, Br. Decatur (see appendix)	
South Macon, Sta. Macon (see appendix)	
Southern Tech, Sta. Marietta	30060
Sparks	31647
Sparta	31087
Spring Place, R. Br. Chatsworth	30705
Springfield	31329
Springvale	31788
Stapleton	30823
Starrsville	30280
State College, Br. Savannah	31404
Statenville	31648
Statesboro (1st)	30458
Statham	30666
Stephens	30667
Sterling, R. Br. Brunswick	31520
Stevens Pottery	31088
Stillmore	30464
Stillwell	31330
Stilson, R. Br. Brooklet	30415
Stockbridge	30281
Stockton	31649
Stone Mountain (1st)	30083
Stonewall	30282
Stovall	30283
Suches	30572
Sugar Hill, Br. Buford	30518
Sugar Valley	30746
Summertown, R. Br. Swainsboro	30466
Summerville (1st)	30747
Berryton, R. Br.	30748
Sumner	31789
Sunny Side	30284
Surrency	31563
Suwanee	30174
Swainsboro (1st)	30401
Lexsy, R. Br.	30432
Oak Park, R. Br.	30401
Summertown, R. Br.	30466
Sycamore	31790
Sylvania (1st)	30467
Sylvester (1st)	31791
Talbotton	31827
Talking Rock	30175
Tallapoosa	30176
Tallulah Falls	30573
Talmo	30575
Tarrytown	30470
Tate	30177
Taylorsville	30178
Tazewell	31828
Temple	30179
Tennga	30751
Tennille	31089
The Hill, Sta. Augusta	30904
The Rock	30285
Thomaston (1st)	30286
Thomasville (1st)	31792
Thomson (1st)	30824
Thunderbolt, Br. Savannah	31404

Tifton (1st) 31794
Tiger 30576
Tignall 30668
Timothy, Br. Athens 30601
Toccoa (1st) 30577
Toccoa Falls, R. Br. Toccoa 30577
Toco Hills, Br. Atlanta 30329
Toomsboro 31090
Town And Country, Sta.
  Marietta 30060
Townsend 31331
  Ridgeville, R. Br. 31325
Trenton 30752
Trion 30753
Tucker (1st) 30084
Tunnel Hill 30755
Turin 30289
Turnerville 30580
Twin City 30471
Twin Lakes, R. Br. Valdosta ...31605
Ty Ty 31795
Tyrone 30290
U S M C Supply Center, Br.
  Albany 31704
U S Naval Air Station, Br.
  Albany 31703
Unadilla 31091
Union City 30291
Union Point 30669
  Maxeys, R. Br. 30671
  Woodville, R. Br. 30670
University, Sta. Macon 31207
Upatoi 31829
Uvalda 30473
Vada, R. Br. Climax 31734
Valdosta (1st) 31601
  Bemiss, R. Br. 31601
  Castle Park, Sta. 31601
  Clyattville, R. Br. 31604

Dasher, R. Br. 31601
Moody A F B, MOU 31601
Remerton, R. Br. 31601
Twin Lakes, R. Br. 31605
Valona 31332
Vanna 30672
Varnell 30756
Veterans Hospital, Sta.
  Augusta 30904
Vidalia (1st) 30474
Vienna 31092
Villa Rica 30180
Vinings, R. Br. Smyrna 30080
Vista Grove, Br. Decatur 30033
Waco 30182
Wadley 30477
Waleska 30183
Walnutgrove, R. Br.
  Covington 30209
Walthourville 31333
Waresboro 31564
Warm Springs 31830
Warner Robins (1st) 31093
Warrenton 30828
Warthen 30829
Warwick 31796
Washington (1st) 30673
Watkinsville 30677
Waverly 31565
Waverly Hall 31831
Waycross (1st) 31501
Waynesboro (1st) 30830
  Alexander, R. Br. 30801
Waynesville 31566
Wayside, R. Br. Gray 31032
Wesleyan, Sta. Macon 31201
West Bainbridge, Sta.
  Bainbridge 31717
West End, Sta. Rome 30161

West Green 31567
West Point (1st) 31833
Westgate, Sta. Macon 31206
Weston 31832
Westside, Br. Gainesville 30501
Whigham 31797
White 30184
White Oak 31568
White Plains 30678
Whitesburg 30185
Whitestone 30186
Wildwood 30757
Wiley 30581
Willacoochee 31650
Williamson 30292
Wilmington Island, R. Br.
  Savannah 31404
Wilson Airport, R. Br. Macon ...31201
Winder (1st) 30680
Windsor Forest, Br.
  Savannah 31406
Windsor Park, Br. Columbus ...31904
Winston 30187
Winterville 30683
Woodbine 31569
Woodbury 30293
Woodland 31836
Woodstock 30188
Woodville, R. Br. Union
  Point 30670
Woolsey 30294
Wray 31798
Wrens 30833
Wright Square, Sta.
  Savannah 31402
Wrightsville 31096
Wynnton, Sta. Columbus 31906
Yatesville 31097
Young Harris 30582
Zebulon 30295

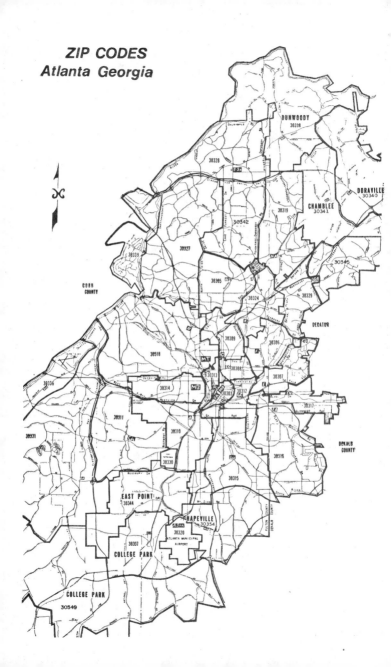

ALBANY   317

POST OFFICE BOXES

Box Nos.
1-2054	Main Office	02

RURAL ROUTES

1,2,3,4,5,6,7	01

STATIONS, BRANCHES AND UNITS

Bridgeboro Rural Br	01
Four Points Br	05
U S M C Supply Center Br	04
U S Naval Air Station Br	03

ATLANTA   303

POST OFFICE BOXES

Box Nos.
1-2214	Main Office	01
2301-3100	Martech Sta	18
3101-5200	Federal Annex Sta	02
5201-6000	Sta E	07
6001-6500	Civic Center Sta	08
6501-7000	Lakewood Sta	15
7001-8000	Sta C	09
8001-9000	Sta F	06
9001-9300	Morris Brown Sta	14
9301-9600	Ben Hill Sta	31
9601-10490	North Atlanta Br	19
10491-11500	Sta A	10
11501-12500	Northside Sta	05
12501-13000	Lakewood Sta	15
13001-15000	Sta K	24
15001-17000	Emory University Br	33
17001-17500	Chattahoochee Sta	21
17501-18500	East Atlanta Sta	16
18501-19500	Lenox Square Sta	26
19501-20500	Sta N	25
20501-21000	Airport Sta	20
21001-26000	Emory University Mail Room Sta	22
26001-27000	Grady Hospital Sta	03
27001-27500	Eastwood Sta	17
27501-28000	Sta No 7	27
28001-29000	Sandy Springs Br	28
29001-30000	Briarcliff Sta	29
30001-38000	Georgia Tech Sta	32
38001-38500	Capitol Hill Sta	34
39001-39500	Bolton Sta	18
41001-42000	Ben Hill	31
42001-43000	Cascade Heights Sta	11

43001-45000	Industrial	36
45001-47000	Airport	20
47001-49000	Doraville Br	40
49001-50000	Briarcliff Br	29
50001-52000	Federal Annex	02
52001-54000	Northside	05
54001-56000	Civic Center Sta	08
56001-58000	Peachtree Center Sta	43
58001-59000	Station 18	18
73001-74000	Federal Annex	50
77001-0078000	Sta C	09
80001-82000	Chamblee Br	41
82001-84000	Hapeville Br	54
84001-86000	Int Office Park Br	54
87001-88000	College Park Br	37
88001-89000	Dunwoody Br	38
89001-90000	Gate City	12
90001-92000	East Point Br	44
92001-93000	Morris Brown Sta	14
93001-95000	Martech Sta	18
100001-105000	Federal Annex	48
720001-721000	Perimeter Center Station	46

RURAL ROUTES

1	31
2,3	40
4,5,6,7	37
8,9	38
10	27
13	45

STATIONS, BRANCHES AND UNITS

Airport Mail Facility Br	20
Ben Hill Sta	31
Blair Village Sta	54
Bolton Sta	18
Briarcliff Br	29
Briarwood Br	44
Capitol Hill Sta	34
Cascade Heights Sta	11
Chamblee Br	41
Chattahoochee Sta	21
Civic Center Sta	08
College Park Br	37
De Kalb Airport Sta	41
De Lowe Br	44
Doraville Br	40
Dunwoody Br	38
East Atlanta Sta	16
East Point Br	44
Eastwood Br	17
Embry Hills Br	41
Emory Univ Br	22
Federal Annex Br	02
Federal Reserve Sta	03
Fort Mc Pherson Sta	30
Gate City Br	12
Gordon Road Sta	10
Greenbriar Sta	31
Gresham Br	16
Hapeville Br	54
Industrial Br	36
International Office Park Br	54

La Vista Br	29
Lakewood Sta	15
Lenox Square Sta	26
Martech Sta	18
Morris Brown Sta	14
North Atlanta Br	19
Northeast Plaza Br	29
North Side Sta	05
Northwoods Br	40
Peachtree Center Sta	43
Perry Homes Sta	18
Sandy Springs Br	28
Six Flags Over Georgia Rural Br	36
Skyland Br	19
Toco Hills Br	29
General Delivery	01
Postmaster	04

APARTMENTS, HOTELS, MOTELS

Air Way, Carrol Rd NW	36
Alamo Plaza Courts, 2370 Stewart Ave SW	15
Argonne, 339 Luckie NW	13
Arlington, 126 Ellis NE	03
Atlanta Americana Motor, 160 Spring NW	03
Atlanta Cabana Motor, 870 Peachtree NE	83
Atlanta Towers, 1270 W Peachtree NW	09
Atlanta Travelodge, 1541 Peachtree NW	09
Atlantan, 11 Luckie NW	03
Avon, 5 Houston NE	03
Barbizon Plaza Of New York, 1000 Peachtree NE	09
Bentley, 72 Pryor SW	03
Briarcliff, 1050 Ponce De Ln Ave NE	83
Capitol, 73 Pryor NE	03
Capri, 1152 Spring NW	09
Carlton House, 2030 Peachtree Rd NW	09
Cherokee Motor Inn, 310 Ponce De Ln Ave NE	83
Cherokee Rose Court, 1387 Northside Dr NW	18
Chestatee Inn, 580 Ponce De Ln Ave NE	08
Clermont, 789 Ponce De Ln Ave NE	83
Colonial Homes, 214 Colonial Hms Dr NW	09
Colonial Motor Lodge, 2720 Stewart Ave SW	15
Colonial Terrace, 2140 Peachtree Rd NW	09
Cotillion, 2200 Reynolds Dr SW	15
Cox Carlton, 683 Peachtree NE	83
Danzig, 345 Chappell Rd NW	18
Darlington, 2025 Peachtree Rd NW	09
Dinkler Mtr, 98 Forsyth, N W	03
Dixie, 72 Baker NW	08
Downtown, 330 W Peachtree NW	08
Duke, 420 Piedmont Ave NE	08
Emory, 17 Baker NW	08
Five Acre Auto Court, 2056 Buford Hwy NE	24

Atlanta (Con.)   303

Flamingo Courts, 2766
Stewart Ave SW 15
Frances, 1865 Buford Hwy
NE 24
Garys, 2275 Stewart Ave SW .. 15
Georgia, 114 Luckie NW 03
Georgian Terrace, 659
Peachtree NE 83
Georgian, 4300 Buford Hwy
NE 29
Gordon, 211 Mitchell SW 03
Greenwood, 2160 Stewart Ave
SW 15
Hampton, 35 Houston NE 03
Heart Of Atlanta, 225
Courtland NE 03
Henry Grady, 210 Peachtree
NW 03
Holiday Inn, 175 Piedmont
Ave NE 03
Holiday Inn, 1810 Howell Mill
Rd NW 18
Holiday Inn, 1944 Piedmont
Cir, N E 24
Hopkins, 2865 Old Hapevl Rd
SW 54
Howard Johnsons Motor
Lodge, 1701 Northside Dr
NW 18
Howard Johnsons Motor
Lodge, 2090 N Druid Hills
Rd NE 29
Howard Johnsons Motor
Lodge, 745 Washington
SW 15
Howel House, 710 Peachtree
NE 08
Imperial, 355 Peachtree NE 83
Ivy, 195 Ivy NE 03
Jefferson, 87 Pryor SW 03
Lenox, 4 Porter Pl NE 08
Luckie, 180 Luckie NW 03
Mark Inn, 1848 Howell Mill
Rd NW 18
Mark Inn, 2750 Forrest Hill
Dr SW 15
Mark Inn, 277 Moreland Ave
SE 16
Marriott Motor Hotel, 165
Cain St NE 03
Miller, 155 Ivy NE 03
Oaks Motor Court, 1650
Stewart Ave SW 10
Old South, 331 Cleveland
Ave SW 15
Paces Ferry Tower, 374 E
Paces Ferry Rd NE 05
Park, 70 Cain NE 03
Parliment House Motor Inn,
70 Houston St NE 03
Paschal Mot. Hotel, 830
Hunter, N W 14
Pavilion, 14 17th NE 09
Peachtree Manor, 826
Peachtree NE 83
Peachtree North Ave, 620
Peachtree NE 08
Peachtree Towers, 300 W
Peachtree NW 08
Pershing, 1428 Peachtree NE . 83

Ponce De Leon, 551 Ponce
De Ln Ave NE 83
Ponce De Leon, 75 Ponce De
Leon Av NE 83
Regency Hyatt House, 265
Peachtree NE 03
Ritz, 103 Luckie NW 03
Riviera Of Atlanta, 1630
Peachtree NW 09
Rodeway Inn, 144 14th NW 18
Royal, 214 Auburn Ave NE 03
Savoy, 239 Auburn Ave NE 03
Scoville, 225 Mitchell SW 03
Shelton, 304 W Peachtree
NW 08
Sheraton Biltmore, 817 W
Peachtree NW 83
Sidney, 87 Harris NW 03
Skyline, 1375 Northside Dr
NW 18
Southland, 825 Ponce De Ln
Ave NE 83
Stafford, 2640 Stewart Ave
SW 15
Starlight, 1450 Memorial Dr
SE 17
Sylvan, 233 Mitchell SW 03
Tech, 120 North Ave NW 13
Three Thirty Peachtree, 330
Peachtree NE 08
Tower, 374 E Paces Ferry Rd
NE 05
Town & Country Courts, 2380
Stewart Ave SW 15
Travelers, 139 Luckie NW 03
University, 55 Northside Dr
NW 14
Vesta, 265 Williams NW 03
Waluhaje, 239 W Lake Ave
NW 14

BUILDINGS

Agriculture Laboratory, 19
Hunter SW 34
American Savings Bank, 140
Peachtree NW 03
Archetects & Engineers
Institute, 230 Spring NW 03
Atlanta Federal Savings, 22
Marietta NW 03
Atlanta Joint Terminal, 104
Central Ave SW 03
Atlanta Merchandise Market,
240 Peachtree NW 03
Atlanta National, 50
Whitehall SW 03
Atlanta Public Library, 126
Carnegie Way NW 03
Auditorium, 30 Courtland SE .. 03
Bankers Fidelity, 2045
Peachtree Rd NW 09
Baptist Professional, 340
Boulevard NE 12
Baptist, 291 Peachtree NE 03
Belle Isle, 105 Pryor NE 03
Bolling Jones, 20 Ivy SE 03
Bona Allen, 133 Luckie NW 03
Candler, 127 Peachtree NE ... 03
Carnegie, 133 Carnegie Way
NW 03
Citizens & Southern National
Bank, 35 Broad NW 03

Communicable Disease
Center, 1600 Clifton Rd N
E 33
Continental Insurance, 165
Peachtree St NE 03
Crumley, 70 Fairlie NW 03
Cyrus R Strickler, 1293
Peachtree NE 09
Electric, 270 Peachtree NW ... 03
Exchange Pl, 41 Exchange Pl
SE 03
Federal Annex, 77 Forsyth
SW 03
Federal Office, 275 Peachtree
NE 03
First Federal, 40 Marietta
NW 03
First National Bank, 2
Peachtree NW 03
First National Bank, 615
Peachtree NE 08
Five Points Center, 15
Peachtree NE 03
Forsyth, 86 Forsyth NW 03
Fulton Federal, 11 Pryor SW .. 03
Fulton National Bank, 55
Marietta NW 03
Gas Light Tower, 235
Peachtree St N E 03
Georgia Life Health Insurance
Company, 66 Luckie NW 03
Georgia Power, 15 Forsyth
SW 03
Georgia Savings Bank, 84
Peachtree NW 03
Glenn, 120 Marietta NW 03
Haas Howell, 77 Poplar NW ... 03
Hartford, 100 Edgewood Ave
SE 03
Healey, 57 Forsyth NW 03
Henry Grady, 26 Cain NW 03
Herndon, 239 Auburn Ave NE . 03
Hickey, 81 Walton NW 03
Highway, 2 Capitol Sq SW 34
Home Savings, 75 Forsyth
NW 03
Hurt, 45 Edgewood Ave SE 03
John Hancock, 230 Houston
NE 03
Journal, 10 Forsyth NW 03
Labor, 254 Washington SW 34
Lenox Towers, 3390
Peachtree Rd NE 26
Life Of Georgia, 600 W
Peachtree St NW 08
Lullwater, 441 Peachtree NE .. 08
Mark, 98 Alabama SW 03
Methodist, 155 Forrest Ave
NE 03
National Bank Of Ga, 34
Peachtree NW 03
New Title, 30 Pryor SW 03
Palmer, 41 Maritta NW 03
Peachtree Ctr, 230 Peachtree
NW 03
Peachtree Medical, 401
Peachtree NE 08
Peachtree Palisades, 1819
Peachtree St NE 09
Peachtree Seventh, 50
Seventh St NE 23
Plaza, 5 Plaza Way SW 03

Atlanta (Con.)   303

Red Rock, 187 Spring NW	03
Rhodes Haverty, 134 Peachtree St NW	03
Richardson, 160 Peachtree NW	03
Sheffield Memorial, 1938 Peachtree NW	09
Southern Bell Telephone, 51 Ivy NE	03
Standard Federal Savings, 44 Broad NW	03
Standard, 95 Fairlie NW	03
State Capitol, Capitol Sq SW	34
State Office, 12 Capitol Sq SW	34
Toco Hills Shopping Center	29
Trust Company Of Georgia, 36 Edgewood Ave NE	03
Walton, 87 Walton NW	03
Western Union, 56 Marietta NW	03
William Oliver, 32 Peachtree NW	03
Y W C A, 72 Edgewood Ave NE	03

GOVERNMENT OFFICES

Civil Criminal Court, 160 Pryor SW	03
Court House, 130 Pryor SW	03
Fulton County Adminstration, 165 Central Ave SW	03
Fulton County Health, 99 Butler, S E	03
Fulton County Juvenile Court, 445 Capitol Ave SW	15
Post Office Main, 56 Forsyth NW	03
Union Station, 2 Forsyth NW	03

HOSPITALS

Atlanta Sanitorium, 774 W Peachtree NW	08
Battle Hill Haven, 1821 Anderson Ave W SW	14
Doctors Memorial Hospital, 573 West Peachtree St., N.w.	08
Doctors North Annex, 490 Peachtree NE	08
Doctors, 478 Peachtree NE	08
Elks Aidmore, 600 Aidmore Dr NE	07
Emory University, 1364 Clifton Rd NE	22
Frank K Medical Boland, 101 3rd NE	08
Fulton, 907 Edgewood Ave NE	07
Georgia Baptist, 300 Boulevard NE	12
Georgian Clinic, 1260 Briarcliff Rd NE	06
Grady Memorial, 80 Butler SE	03
Happy Haven, 1821 Anderson Ave W SW	14

Henderson, 567 Courtland NE	08
High View Nursing Home, 2800 Springdale Rd SW	15
Holy Family, Sewell & Fairburn SW	31
Jesse Parker Williams, 542 Peachtree NE	08
Mc Lendon, 1370 Sharon NW	14
Medical Arts, 384 Peachtree NE	08
Our Lady Of Perpetual Care, 760 Washington SW	15
Peachtree Medical, 401 Peachtree NE	08
Piedmont, 1968 Peachtree Rd NW	09
Ponce De Leon Infirmary, 144 Ponce De Leon Ave	08
Saint Joseph Infirmary, 265 Ivy NE	03
Sky Ranch Rest Home, 3700 Cascad-Palmto SW	11
Spalding Hughes Pavilion, 35 Butler SE	03
United States Veterans, 1670 Clairmont Rd N E	29

UNIVERSITIES AND COLLEGES

Atlanta Christian, 2775 Ben Hill Rd SW	11
Atlanta Law School, 134 Peachtree NW	03
Atlanta University, 223 Chestnut SW	14
Clark, 240 Chestnut SW	14
Emory University School Of Dentistry, 106 Forrest Ave NE	03
Emory University School Of Medicine, 1364 Clifton Rd NE	22
Emory University, 1364 Clifton Rd NE	22
Gammon Theological Seminary, 9 Mcdonough Blvd SE	15
Georgia Institute Of Technology, 225 North Ave, NW	32
Greenleaf School Of Business, 193 Peachtree NE	03
John Marshall Law School, 105 Forrest Ave NE	03
Marist, 3790 Ashford-Dunwdy NE	19
Marsh Business, 322 Ivy NE	03
Massey Business, Henry Grady Square	03
Mercer University School Of Pharmacy, 223 Walton St NW	03
Morehouse, 223 Chestnut SW	14
Morris Brown, 643 Hunter NW	14
Oglethorpe University, 4484 Peachtree Rd NE	19
Sacred Heart, 335 Ivy NE	03

Southern Business University, 417 Peachtree NE	08
Southern College Of Pharmacy, 223 Walton NW	03
Spelman, 350 Leonard SW	14
State University, 33 Gilmer SE	03
The Westminster Schools, 1424 W Pace Ferry Rd NW.	27

NAMED STREETS

Aaron NW	14
Abbey NW	14
Abbey Rd (EP)	44
Abbott (CP)	37
Abbott SW	
1-250	14
251-OUT	10
Abby Ct (DOR)	40
Abby Ln NE	45
Abeberdeen Dr NW	18
Aberdeen NE	07
Aberdeen Dr & Ln NE	28
Abernathy Rd NE & NW	28
Abington Dr NE	28
Abner Ct, Pl & Ter NW	18
Academy Ct NE	45
Acadia (EP)	44
Acapulco Way (EP)	44
Acl Terminal NW	13
Acorn Ave NE	05
Acres Mill Rd NW, NW	39
Acuba Ln NE	45
Ada Ave NW	18
Adair SW	14
Adair Ave NE	06
Adair Ave SE	15
Adams (CP)	37
Adams Dr NW	18
Adams Dr SW	11
Adams St & Ave SW	15
Adams St & Rd (CHA)	41
Adamson SW	15
Adamson Ave (HAP)	54
Adamsville Dr SW	31
Addie NW	18
Addington SW	10
Addison Dr (DOR)	40
Addison Pl NW	18
Adele Ave SW	14
Adelia Pl NE	29
Adeline Ave NW	14
Adelle SE	15
Adena Ln E & W (CP)	49
Adowholdt Ferry Rd SW	31
Adina Dr NE	24
Adkins Rd NW	31
Admiral Dr & Way (CHA)	41
Adolphus Ave NE	07
Adrian Pl NW	27
Aero Ct (EP)	44
Afond Ct (CHA)	41
Afton Ln NE	29
Aidmore Dr NE	07
Aiken Dr NE	19
Aikens SW	15
Aircond Way SE	16
Airfine Pl SE	12
Airline St NE & SE	12
Ajax Dr NW	18
Akers Mill Rd NW	39

Atlanta (Con.)　　　　　　　303

Albert NW 18
Alberta Dr & Ter NE 05
Albion Ave NE 07
Alco NE 24
Alcoa Ct (CHA) 41
Alcott Pl (CP) 37
Alden Ave NW 09
Alden Green Trl (EP) 44
Alder Ct SE 17
Alder Ln SW 11
Alderbrook Ct NE 45
Alderbrook Rd NE
　1597-OUT 45
Aldredge Blvd SW 36
Aldredge Rd SW 31
Ale Cir (EP) 44
Alexa SE 17
Alexander NE 08
Alexander NW
　1-100 08
　101-OUT 13
Alexander Dr (CP) 37
Alexander Dr NE 05
Alexandria Way (CP) 37
Alfred Rd NW 31
Alice SW 12
Alice Ln (CP) 49
Aline Dr NW 18
Alison Ct SW 11
Allaire Ln NE 45
Allegheny SW 10
Allegro Dr NW 18
Allen Ct NE 28
Allen Dr (CP) 37
Allen Dr (DOR) 40
Allen Ln SE 54
Allen Rd NE
　1-300 28
　301-OUT 24
Allen Way NE
　1-300 28
　301-OUT 24
Allen Temple Ct NW 11
Allendale Dr SE 17
Allene Ave SW 10
Allison Dr (DOR) 40
Allison Dr NE 42
Ansted Ln (CP) 49
Alloway Pl SE 16
Alma NW 18
Alma SW 11
Almetta Ave NE 07
Almond Dr (CP) 37
Almond Rd SE 16
Almont Dr SW 10
Alpine Rd NE 05
Alston Dr SE
　1-2964 17
Alta Ave NE 07
Alta Pl NW 18
Alta Vis Dr NE 19
Altadena Pl SW 11
Altaview Dr SE 54
Alton Rd (CHA) 41
Alton Rd NW 05
Altoona Pl SW
　1-280 14
　281-OUT 10
Alva NE 07
Alvarado Ter NW 10
Alverstone Dr (HAP) 54
Alvin Dr NW 18

Amal Dr SW 15
Amanda NE 07
Amber Pl & Rd NW 31
Amberglades Ln NW 28
Amberly Ct N & S (DOR) 40
Amberly Ct, Dr & Way (DOR) 40
Amberridge Trl NW 28
Amberwood Dr & Way NE 45
American Dr (CHA) 41
American Ind Blvd & Way
　(CHA) 41
Amherst Ct NE 28
Amherst Pl NW 27
Amhurst Dr NW 18
Ami SE
　1-650 12
　651-OUT 15
Amsterdam Ave NE 06
Amwiler Rd (DOR) 40
Amy Ct (CP) 37
Anchor Ter SW 11
Andalusia Ter (DOR) 40
Anderson Ave NW & SW 14
Andover Ct & Dr (DOR) 40
Andover Dr NW 27
Andrews NW 14
Andrews Cir NE 07
Andrews Dr NW 05
Angelo Ct & Dr NE 19
Angier Ave NE
　1-420 12
　421-OUT 08
Angier Pl NE 08
Angier Springs Rd NE 06
Angus Trl NE & NW 28
Anita Pl NE 06
Aniwaka Ave SW 11
Anjaco Rd NW 09
Ann St & Ct (CHA) 41
Annapolis Ct NE 45
Anne NW 18
Anne Ave SE 15
Annelaine Dr SW 11
Annie NW 18
Anniston Ave SE 17
Ansley Ct & Ln NE 24
Ansley Dr NE 09
Ansley Forest Dr NE 24
Anthony NW 18
Antioch Dr NE 19
Antone NW 18
Antwerp Dr SE 15
Apache Trl SE 16
Apache Trl SW 31
Appalachee Dr NE 19
Apple Orchard Dr (CHA) 41
Apple Valley Rd NE 19
Applewood Ct NE 45
Appling Cir, Ct, Dr & Way
　(CHA) 41
Aragon Ave NE 19
Arbor Ave SE 17
Arbor Vis Dr NE 29
Arc Way NW 05
Arcadia Cir NW 14
Archcrest Dr (HAP) 54
Archer SW 14
Archer Way NW 14
Archway Dr (CHA) 41
Archwood Dr (DOR) 40
Ard Pl NW 31
Arden Ave SW 10

Arden Rd NW
　1-2924 27
　2925-OUT 05
Arden Way NE 42
Arden At Argonne NW 05
Ardley Rd SW 11
Ardmore Cir & Rd NW 09
Argo Dr (HAP) 54
Argonne Ave NE
　1-870 08
　871-OUT 09
Argonne Dr NW 05
Argonne Way NE 24
Argus Cir NE 31
Argyle Dr NW 18
Arizona Ave NE 07
Arkose Dr SE 16
Arkwright Pl SE 17
Arlene Rd (CP) 37
Arlene Way NE 05
Arlington Ave SW 10
Arlington Ave & Pky NE 24
Arlington Cir NW 18
Arlington Dr (DUN) 38
Arlington Dr NW 11
Arlington Pl NE 06
Arlington Rd (EP) 44
Armand Ct & Rd NE 24
Armour Cir, Dr & Pl NE 24
Armstrong SE 03
Arnand Ct (DUN) 38
Arno Ct & Dr NW 18
Arnold (HAP) 54
Arnold NE 08
Arnold Ave NE 24
Arrow Cir (CHA) 41
Arrow Creek Dr (CHA) 41
Arrowhead Trl NE 45
Arrowwood Dr SW
　1-3000 44
　3001-OUT 31
Arthur SW 10
Artwood Rd NE 07
Aruba Cir NE 28
Arundel Dr NW 27
Arundel Rd (CP) 37
Asbury Ln SW 31
Ascent NE 19
Ascot Ct (CHA) 41
Ascot Dr NE 19
Ash (DOR) 40
Ashburn Ln (CHA) 41
Ashburton Ave SE 17
Ashby NW
　1-560 14
　561-OUT 18
Ashby SW
　1-300 14
　301-OUT 10
Ashby Cir & Ter NW 14
Ashby Grv & Pl SW 14
Ashentree Ct & Dr (CHA) 41
Ashford Rd NE 19
Ashford Dunwoody Rd NE
　1-4150 19
　4151-4665 46
　4666-OUT 38
Ashland Ave & Dr NE 07
Ashley Ave NE 12
Ashley Oaks Ct & Dr NE 45
Ashmont Ct (DUN) 38
Ashton Woods Dr NE 19
Ashwood Ave SW 15

Atlanta (Con.)	303
Ashwoody Ct & Trl NE	19
Aspen Dr NE	
1-1955	45
Astor Ave SW	10
Athens Ave SW	10
Atkins (HAP)	54
Atkinson Dr SE	54
Atlanta (CP)	37
Atlanta (EP)	44
Atlanta Ave (HAP)	54
Atlanta Ave N (CP)	37
Atlanta Ave SE	
1-600	15
601-OUT	12
Atlanta Ave SW	15
Atlantic Dr NW	18
Atlantis Ave NE	07
Atwood SW	10
Atwood Rd NE	05
Auburn Ave NE	
1-338	03
339-OUT	12
Auditorium Dr (CP)	37
Audrey Pl NW	18
Audubon Cir SW	11
Audubon Dr NE	29
Augusta Ave & Pl SE	15
Aurora Ave NW	14
Austell Way NW	05
Austin Ave NE	07
Austin Dr (CP)	49
Austin Rd SW	31
Autumn Dr (DOR)	40
Autumn Ln SW	10
Avalon Pl NE	06
Avebury Dr (EP)	44
Avenida SW	10
Avenue Of Redwoods (CP)	49
Avery Dr NE	09
Avery Rd SW	15
Avon Ave SW	
1-1480	10
1481-OUT	11
Avondale Ave SE	12
Avonwood Cir SW	11
Ayrshire Cir NW	18
Azalia SW	10
Azlee Pl NW	18
Aztec Rd (DOR)	40
Bachelor (EP)	44
Bader Ave SW	10
Bagley Dr (CHA)	41
Bagwell Dr SW	15
Bailey SW	14
Bailey Dr SE	16
Baker (DOR)	40
Baker NE	
1-100	03
101-OUT	12
Baker NW	
1-100	08
101-OUT	13
Baker Cir, Rd & Ter NW	18
Baker Dr SW	54
Baker Ridge Dr NW	18
Bakers Ferry Rd SW	
1-4675	31
4676-5650	36
5651-OUT	31
Baldwin St & Pl SW	10

Ball Mill Ct & Rd (DUN)	38
Balmoral Dr (CHA)	41
Balmoral Rd NE	19
Baltimore Pl NW	08
Banberry Dr SE	15
Bankhead Ave NW	
1-3200	18
3201-OUT	31
Bankhead Ct NW, NW	31
Bankhead Hwy NW	
1-3200	18
3201-OUT	31
Banks SW	15
Banks Cir (CP)	37
Banks Pl NE	03
Banner Rd (CP)	49
Barbara Ln NW	27
Barcelona Ct (CP)	49
Barclay Pl NE	06
Barfield Ave SW	10
Barfield Rd NE	28
Barge Rd SW	31
Barksdale Cir (EP)	44
Barksdale Dr NE	09
Barkside Ct (CHA)	41
Barkston Ct (CHA)	41
Barnes NW	18
Barnesdale Way NE	09
Barnett St & Cir (HAP)	54
Barnett St & Pl NE	06
Barret Dr NW	18
Barret Rd NW	31
Barrett Ave & Way (EP)	44
Barron Ct NW	27
Barrow Pl SW	31
Barryln Dr (DOR)	40
Barton Dr (HAP)	54
Barton Woods Rd NE	07
Bartow SW	15
Bass SE	15
Bass SW	
1-330	15
331-OUT	10
Bassetthall Pl NW	18
Batavia (EP)	44
Bates Ave NE & SE	17
Bates Ct NE	19
Battery Pl NE	07
Battery Way (EP)	44
Battle Dr NE	45
Battle Overlook NW	27
Battlefield Ave SE	17
Battleford Ct (CHA)	41
Battleview Dr NW	27
Baxter Rd SW	15
Bayard St & Cir (EP)	44
Bayberry Dr SW	11
Baylor NW	18
Baywood Dr SE	15
Beach Way SW	10
Beachland Dr NE	42
Beacon Dr (DOR)	40
Beacon Dr (CP)	49
Beacon Hill Blvd NE	29
Beard SW	12
Beatie Ave SW	10
Beauprie SW	15
Beauregard Ave SE	16
Beaver Rd SW	45
Beaverbrook Dr NW	18
Beck NW	18
Becket Dr NE	19
Beckwith St & Ct SW	14

Bedford NW	18
Bedford Pl NE	
1-490	12
491-OUT	08
Beech Dr (EP)	44
Beech Hill Dr (DOR)	40
Beech Valley Rd & Way NE	06
Beechcliffe Dr NE	29
Beecher SW	
1-1990	10
1991-OUT	11
Beecher Cir & Ct SW	11
Beecher Rd SW	
1-1990	10
1991-OUT	11
Beechhaven Rd NE	24
Beechview Dr SE	16
Beechwood Ave (DOR)	40
Beechwood Ave SW	10
Beechwood Blvd SW	11
Beechwood Dr NW	27
Beeler Dr SW	15
Belaire Cir (DOR)	40
Belfast SW	10
Belfort Rd SE	54
Belgarde Pl SE	54
Belgrade Ave NE	06
Belhaven Ln SE	15
Belingham Dr NE	45
Bell (EP)	44
Bell (CP)	37
Bell NE	03
Bell SE	
1-100	03
101-OUT	12
Bellaire Dr NE	19
Bellburn Rd (CP)	49
Belle Isle Cir NE	29
Belleau Ln SE	16
Bellemeade Ave NW	18
Bellevue Dr NE	06
Bellingrath NW	18
Bellview NW	18
Belmont Ave SW	10
Belvedere Ave SW	11
Belvedere Dr NW	18
Ben Hill Ave & Rd (EP)	44
Ben Hill Rd (CP)	49
Ben Hill Rd SW	
2013-OUT (EP)	44
2201-2400	11
Bencal Dr SE	16
Bench Mark Dr (CP)	49
Bend Creek Ct, Rd & Way (DUN)	38
Bender SW	10
Bennett NW	09
Benning Pl NE	07
Bent Brook Ct & Dr (DOR)	40
Bent Creek Way SW	11
Benteen Ave SE	
1-1200	12
1201-OUT	15
Benteen St & Way SE	15
Benton Pl NW	27
Benton Woods Dr NE	42
Benwell Dr (DUN)	38
Berean Ave SE	
1-300	16
301-OUT	12
Berkford Cir & Ct NE	19
Berkle SW	10
Berkley Ave NW	18

Atlanta (Con.)   303

Berkley Ln NE	29
Berkley Ridge Dr (DUN)	38
Berkley Tarn (DUN)	38
Berkshire Rd NE	
1-1000	24
1001-OUT	06
Bernadette Ln NE	29
Bernard NW	14
Bernard Rd NW	18
Berne SE	
1-770	16
771-OUT	12
Bernice SW	10
Bernina Ave NE	07
Berwick Ave NE	06
Berwick Dr NE	28
Beryl SW	10
Best Rd (CP)	37
Best Friend Rd (DOR)	40
Besto Dr NW	18
Bethel Dr NW	14
Bethesda Ct & Trl (CHA)	41
Betsy Ave SW	10
Beutell NW	14
Beverly Dr (CHA)	41
Beverly Ln NE	42
Beverly Rd NE	09
Beverly Hills Dr (CHA)	41
Beverly Woods Ct (CHA)	41
Beya Way (DOR)	40
Bicknell Dr SW	15
Biggers SE	12
Biglin SW	10
Bill Cook Rd (CP)	49
Billings Ave SE	15
Billups SW	10
Biltmore Dr NE	29
Biltmore Pl NW	08
Binder Pl NE	07
Binford Pl SW	31
Binghamton Ct & Dr (DOR)	40
Birch (HAP)	54
Birch NW	10
Birchwood Dr NE	05
Bisbee Ave SE	15
Biscayne Dr NW	09
Bishop Aly NE	08
Bishop St & Pl NW	18
Bishop Hollow Ct (CHA)	41
Bishop Hollow Run (CHA)	41
Bismark Rd NE	24
Bixby St & Ter SE	17
Black Forrest Tr SW	31
Black Fox Dr NE	45
Black Fox Trl (EP)	44
Black Oak Dr SE	16
Blackberry Ln (CHA)	41
Blackburn Way (CHA)	41
Blackland Dr & Rd NW	42
Blackwater Trl, SW	28
Blackwater Cove NW	28
Blair Cir SW	19
Blair Villa Dr (HAP)	54
Blake Ave SE	16
Blakely Dr NE	24
Blalock (HAP)	54
Blanche NW	18
Blanton Ave SW	31
Blanton Rd NW	42
Blashfield SE	15
Blayton Cir NW	14

Blossom SW	10
Blossom Ln (EP)	44
Blount St & Pl (EP)	44
Blue Ridge Ave & Ct NE	06
Bluefield Dr SW	10
Bluestone Rd NE	28
Bluff NW	10
Blyss Ave NW	18
Boat Rock Blvd SW, SW	36
Boat Rock Rd SW	31
Bob White Dr SW	11
Bobolink Cir SW	11
Bocage Walk NW	05
Bohler Ct NW	27
Bohler Rd NW	
1-2200	18
2201-OUT	27
Boland Dr NE	19
Bolero Dr (CHA)	41
Bolfair Dr NW	31
Bolissa Dr (DOR)	40
Bolling Rd & Way NE	05
Bolling Brook Dr SW	11
Bolton Dr NW	18
Bolton Pl NW	31
Bolton Rd NW	
1-1600	31
1601-OUT	18
Bon Echo Dr (CP)	49
Bonair SW	14
Bonaventure Ave NE	06
Bond Dr SW	15
Bonn SE	15
Bonner Rd (EP)	44
Bonneville Ter NW	31
Bonnevit Ct NE	45
Bonnie Ave (DOR)	40
Bonnie Ln NE & NW	28
Bonnie Ln SE	54
Bonnie Brae Ave SW	10
Bonnington Ct (CHA)	41
Bonniview SW	10
Bonnybrook Dr & Way SW	11
Bonnybrook Way (EP)	44
Bonview Ln NE	24
Booker NW	
1-100	14
101-500	15
501-OUT	10
Booker SW	
1-100	14
101-500	15
501-OUT	10
Booker Ave NW	
1-100	14
101-500	15
501-OUT	10
Booker Ave SW	
1-100	14
101-500	15
501-OUT	10
Booker Washington Dr NW	14
Booth NW	18
Bordeau Ct (DUN)	38
Boston Dr (CP)	37
Boulder Rd SE	16
Boulder Way (EP)	44
Boulder Park Dr Dr SW	
1-3300	11
3301-OUT	31
Bouldercliff Ct & Way SE	16
Bouldercrest Dr SE	
1-2846	16

Boulderview Dr SE	16
Boulderwoods Dr SE	16
Boulevard NE	
1-380	12
381-OUT	08
Boulevard SE	
1-1250	12
1251-OUT	15
Boulevard Dr NE	
1001-2930	17
Boulevard Dr SE	
1001-2930	17
Boulevard Pl NE	08
Boulevard Granada SW	11
Boulevard Lorraine SW	11
Bowen NW	18
Bowen Ave SE	15
Bowen Cir SW	15
Bowers SW	31
Bowling Green Way (DOR)	40
Box NE	08
Boxwood Ct & Dr NE	45
Boyce Ct & Dr SE	16
Boyd Ave NW	18
Boykin St SW	15
Boyleston Dr NE	28
Boynton Ave SE	15
Bradbury SW	13
Bradcliff Ct & Dr NE	45
Braddock SW	10
Bradley SE	
1-500	12
501-OUT	16
Bradley St & Aly NE	12
Brady Ave NW	14
Braeburn Cir & Dr SE	16
Braemer Ave SW	11
Bragg (CHA)	41
Braithwood Ct & Dr NE	45
Bramble Rd NE	29
Bramblewood Dr NE	29
Branch Ave NW	05
Branch Dr SW	31
Branchwood (EP)	44
Brandon Rd (CP)	37
Brandon Mill Rd NW	28
Brandon Ridge Dr NE	28
Brandy Tuck Way (DOR)	40
Brandywine SW	10
Branham NE	17
Brannen Rd SE	16
Brantley NE	07
Brantley NW	18
Brantley Pl NW	14
Brantley Rd (DUN)	38
Bratton NW	09
Brawley Cir, Dr & Way NE	19
Breckenridge Ct, Dr & Way	
NE	45
Breezy Ln NE	29
Brendon Dr (DUN)	38
Breninghame Dr (CP)	37
Brenmar Way (DOR)	40
Brennan Ln SW	10
Brenton Ct (DUN)	38
Brenton Dr & Way NE	19
Brentwood Dr & Ter NE	05
Brentwood Rd (CP)	49
Breton Cir & Ct NE	19
Brevard Ave SW	15
Brewer Blvd SW	10
Brewster SW	10
Briar Ct (EP)	44

Atlanta (Con.)   303

Briar Glade Way (DOR)	40
Briar Park Ct Ct NE	06
Briar Ridge Cir (DOR)	40
Briar Wood Ind Ct NE	29
Briarcliff Ct, Pl & Ter NE	06
Briarcliff Ln, Trl & Way NE	45
Briarcliff Rd NE	
1-1799	06
1800-3250	29
Briarcliff Rd NE, NE	
3251-4850	45
Briarcrest Trl NE	45
Briardale Ln NE	06
Briarhills Dr NE	06
Briarlake Rd NE	
1-2900	45
Briarlake Woods Way NE	45
Briarlyn Ct NE	45
Briarmill Rd NE	29
Briarmoor Rd NE	45
Briarvista Ter NE	24
Briarwillow Dr NE	45
Briarwood Blvd (EP)	44
Briarwood Dr NE	29
Briarwood Dr NE	06
Briarwood Rd NE	
1-1700	19
1701-OUT	29
Briarwood Way NE	19
Briarwood Hills Dr NE	19
Briarwood Ind Ct NE	29
Brick Plant Rd NW	18
Bridgeport Dr NE	29
Bridgeport Dr NW	18
Bridges Ave SW	10
Bridges Creek Trl NE	28
Bridgewater SW	10
Bridgewater Dr NW	28
Bridgewood Valley Rd NW	28
Brier Glen Ct & Dr (DOR)	40
Brier Green Ct (DOR)	40
Brighton NW	18
Brighton Rd NE & NW	09
Brinkley Ln NE	42
Bristol Dr NE	29
Brittain Dr NW	13
Brittamy Trl (CP)	49
Brittley Ter (CP)	49
Brixham Ct NE	28
Broad (CHA)	41
Broad Ave (EP)	44
Broad St NW & SW	03
Broadland Ct NW	42
Broadland Rd NW	
1-520	42
521-OUT	27
Broadview Plz NE	24
Broadwell SW	10
Bromack Rd SE & SW	15
Brompton Ct (DUN)	38
Bronx NW	14
Brook Dr NE	28
Brook Way SW	31
Brook Forrest Dr NE	24
Brook Hollow Dr NW	27
Brook Park Way (DOR)	40
Brook Valley Ln NE	24
Brookcliff Way NE	45
Brookdale Dr (EP)	44
Brookdale Dr NE	
1-2529	45

2530-ONLY	05
2531-2535	45
2536-OUT	05
Brookdale Dr NW	
1-2529	29
2530-ONLY	05
2531-2535	29
2536-OUT	05
Brookdale Dr SW	15
Brookfield Dr NE	42
Brookgreen Rd NE	28
Brookhaven Dr NE	19
Brookhurst Dr (CHA)	41
Brooklawn Ct & Rd NE	19
Brookline SW	10
Brookline Cir & Ct (DUN)	38
Brooklyn Ave NW	06
Brookridge Dr NE	06
Brooks Ave NE	07
Brooks Ave NW	18
Brooks Ave SW	10
Brookshire Ln NE	19
Brookview Dr NW	
1-3000	18
3000-OUT	39
Brookwood Dr NE	
1-1000	09
1001-OUT	05
Brookwood Dr NW	
1-1000	09
1001-OUT	05
Broughton Ct (DUN)	38
Brown NW	18
Brown Ave SE	15
Brown Dr (HAP)	54
Brown Pl SE	16
Brown Pl & Rd (CP)	37
Browning NW	17
Browning SW	14
Brownlee Pl & Ter SW	31
Brownlee Rd SW	
1-293	31
294-ONLY	11
Brownlee Rd, SW	
295-320	31
321-OUT	11
Browns Mill Rd SE	
1-2430	15
2431-OUT	54
Brownsville Rd NW	18
Browntown Rd NW	18
Brownwood Ave SE	16
Broyles SE	12
Bruce (DOR)	40
Bruce Cir SE	16
Bruce Pl SW	31
Bruce Rd NE	29
Brunswick Ave SE	17
Bry-Mar Dr NE	45
Bryan SE	12
Bryan Ave & Cir (EP)	44
Bryant (HAP)	54
Bryant Dr (EP)	44
Brynmawr Cir & Ln NW	27
Bubbling Creek Rd NE	19
Buchanan NE	08
Buchanan NW	18
Buchanan Ln SE	15
Buckeye SW	10
Buckeye Rd (CHA)	41
Buckhead Ave & Way NE	05
Buckhorn (DUN)	38
Buckhorn E (DUN)	38

Buckingham Cir NW	27
Buckley Ct (CHA)	41
Buckline Cir & Ct (DUN)	38
Bucknell Dr SW	36
Bucktrout Pl (CHA)	41
Buena Vista Ave (DOR)	40
Buena Vista Ave Ave SW	15
Buff Dr NE	42
Buffington Rd (CP)	49
Buford Dr (CHA)	41
Buford Hwy NE	
1-2800	24
2801-3920	29
3921-4310	45
4311-5054	41
Buford Hwy NE, NE	
5055-6106	40
Buford Rd NE	
1-2800	24
2801-3920	29
3921-4310	45
4311-5054	41
Buford Rd NE, NE	
5055-6106	40
Buford Hwy	
4141-5791 (GC)	40
Bullock SW	15
Bunker Hill Dr SW	31
Burbank Dr NW & SW	14
Burch Cir NE	19
Burchitt SW	10
Burden NW	18
Burdett Dr NW	28
Burdett Rd (CP)	37
Burdett Rd NE	27
Buris Ct	49
Burke Dr (CHA)	41
Burke Rd NE	05
Burlingame Dr (DOR)	40
Burlington Pl & Rd NE	07
Burnham Ct (DOR)	40
Burns SE	16
Burns Dr SW	10
Burnt Hickory Dr SW	11
Burroughs St & Ave SE	15
Burton Dr NE	29
Burton Rd NW	11
Burton Plaza Ln NE	19
Burton Plaza Way Way NE	19
Burtz NW	18
Bush NW	14
Bussey NW	18
Butler NE	
1-200	03
201-400	12
401-OUT	08
Butler SE	03
Butler Way NW	18
Butner Rd SW	
1-3600	31
3601-OUT	49
Button Rd NE	24
Button Gwinnett Dr (DOR)	40
Bynum Rd NE	19
Byrd SE	15
Byrere Ter SW	10
Byron Dr SW	10
Byway NE	06
Bywood Ln SW	10
Cadillac Dr NE	45
Cadiz Ln N & W (CP)	49
Cahaba Dr SW	11
Cahoon SW	10

Atlanta (Con.) 303

Cain NE
  1-300 03
  301-OUT 12
Cain NW 03
Cains Hill Pl NW 05
Cairo NE 14
Caladium Dr NE 45
Caldwell Rd NE 19
Calhoun NW 18
Calhoun Ave (EP) 44
Calhoun Ter SW 14
Callahan NW 18
Callan Cir NE 07
Calloway Dr NW 14
Calmer Cir (EP) 44
Calvert Ln NE 19
Calvin Ave (EP) 44
Cambria NW 18
Cambridge Ave (EP) 44
Cambridge Ave (CP) 37
Cambridge Dr (DUN) 38
Cambridge Dr SW 31
Camden Rd NE & NW 09
Cameron SE 12
Cameron Ct NE 06
Camfield Ct SW 10
Camilla SW 14
Camille Dr NE 19
Camp Creek Pkwy
  1-3000 (CP) 37
  3001-OUT (EP) 44
Camp Creek Pky SW 31
Camp Ground Rd SW 31
Campbell SE 17
Campbell Cir (HAP) 54
Campbell Rd (CP) 49
Campbellton Cir SW 31
Campbellton Pl SW 10
Campbellton Rd SW
  1-1400 10
  1401-3400 11
  3401-OUT 31
Camrose Way NW 31
Canaan Ct & Dr SE 16
Candace Dr & Ln SE 16
Candlelight Ln SW 31
Candler NE 07
Candler Rd NE
  1-100 17
Candler Rd SE
  1-375 17
Candler Lake Cir & Ct NE 19
Candler Park Dr Dr NE 07
Candlewood Dr (EP) 44
Canfield Dr (CHA) 41
Canmont Rd NE 19
Canna Ridge Cir NE 45
Cannon St & Ct (CP) 37
Cannon Farm Hills Rd NE 29
Cannon Farm Meadows Rd
  NE 29
Canoochee Dr NE 19
Canova SW 11
Canter Rd NE 24
Canterbury Rd NE 24
Cantey Pl NW 27
Cantrell Rd NE 19
Canyon Creek Trl NE 42
Capehart Cir & Pl NE 45
Capitol Ave SE
  1-400 34

401-650 12
651-OUT 15
Capitol Ave SW
  1-400 34
  401-650 12
  651-OUT 15
Capitol Pl & Sq SW 34
Capitol View Ave NW 18
Capri Ct & Ter (EP) 44
Captain Dr (CHA) 41
Cardera Ct (CP) 49
Cardigan Cir NE 28
Cardinal Way SW 11
Cardine Pl NW 05
Cardo Dr NW 18
Cardova Dr NE 24
Carey Dr SE 15
Careygate NW 05
Caribea Trl SE 16
Carlile Ct NE 28
Carlington Ct NE 45
Carlisle NW 18
Carlo Ct & Ter SW 31
Carlo Woods Dr SW 31
Carlton Dr (CHA) 41
Carlton Dr NE 42
Carlton Pl NE 19
Carmain Dr NE 42
Carmel Ave NE 07
Carmel Dr (EP) 44
Carmel Dr & Rd (CHA) 41
Carmel Ln (CP) 37
Carnaby Ct (DUN) 38
Carnegie Ave (EP) 44
Carnegie Way NW 03
Carol Ct (EP) 44
Carol Ln NE 06
Carol Ln & Way NW 27
Carole Dr (DOR) 40
Caroline NE 07
Carolwood Ln NE 42
Carolyn NW 18
Carolyn SW 31
Carolyn Dr NE 29
Caron Cir NW 18
Carpenter Dr NE 28
Carr NW 18
Carriage Ct, Ln & Way (CP) 49
Carriage Dr NE 28
Carriage Way (EP) 44
Carriage Way NW 27
Carriage House Ct (EP) 44
Carrol Ave & Cir (CHA) 41
Carroll SE 12
Carroll Ave SW 31
Carroll Rd NW
  1-1350 36
  1351-OUT 31
Carroll St, Ave & Dr NW 18
Carson Pass SW 31
Cartecay Dr NE 19
Carter NW 14
Carter Ave SE
  1-260 17
Carter Cir (EP) 44
Carter Dr NE 19
Carter Rd SE
  1-260 17
Carver Cir (DOR) 40
Carver Cir & Dr NW 14
Carver Hill Dr (DOR) 40
Cascade Ave SW
  1-822 10

823-3500 11
3501-OUT 31
Cascade Cir & Ter SW 11
Cascade Pl SW 10
Cascade Rd SW
  1-822 10
  823-3350 11
  3351-OUT 31
Cascade Palmetto Hwy SW 31
Cascade Springs Rd SW 36
Casplan SW
  1-650 15
  651-OUT 10
Casplan Ct SW 10
Cassanova SE 15
Casson NE 07
Castaway Ct & Ln (CHA) 41
Castle Falls Dr NE 29
Castleberry NW 03
Castlegate Dr NW 27
Castleridge Dr NE 42
Castleton Dr NW 28
Castleway Dr & Ln NE 45
Castlewood (EP) 44
Castlewood Dr NW 27
Catalina Cir (EP) 44
Catalina Dr (CHA) 41
Cates Ave NE 19
Catherine SW 10
Cativo Dr SW 11
Cato NW 18
Cavanaugh Ave SE 16
Cave Rd NW 27
Cecelia Dr SE 16
Cecil St NE 17
Cecile Ave SE 16
Cedar (DOR) 40
Cedar Ave (EP) 44
Cedar Ave NW 18
Cedar Brook Ct SE 16
Cedar Canyon Ct & Dr NE 45
Cedar Island Dr SW 11
Cedarhurst Ct, Trl & Way
  (CP) 49
Cedarhurst Dr (DUN) 38
Cedarwood Ct, Dr & Trl (CP) 49
Celeste Dr (HAP) 54
Center NW 18
Center Ave (EP) 44
Center Hill Ave NW 18
Centra Villa Dr SW 11
Central Ave (EP) 44
Central Ave (HAP) 54
Central Ave (DOR) 40
Central Ave SW
  1-350 03
  351-650 12
  651-OUT 15
Central Dr NW 14
Century Blvd & Pky NE 45
Century Ct (DOR) 40
Cerro SW 14
Cerro Vista Dr Dr SE 16
Chadwell Ct & Ln (DUN) 38
Chaise Rd (CHA) 41
Chalet Ct (DOR) 40
Chalmers Dr NW 18
Chalmette Dr NE 06
Chamberlin SE 12
Chambers Ave (EP) 44
Chambiee Dunwoody Rd
  1-4920 (CHA) 41

Entry	Page
Atlanta (Con.)	303
Chamblee Tucker Rd	
1-3792 (CHA)	41
3793-4317 (DOR)	40
Chambord Way NE	19
Champa Ave NW	18
Chancery Ln (CHA)	41
Channing Dr & Pl NW	18
Chantilly Dr NE	24
Chantilly Ter (CP)	49
Chaparral Dr & Pl (DUN)	38
Chapel SW	13
Chapman Ave (EP)	44
Chapman Springs Rd (CP)	37
Chappel Cir & Ln (DOR)	40
Chappell Rd NW	
1-300	14
301-OUT	18
Chappell Rd SW	14
Charity Dr SE	16
Charles Ct SE	17
Charles Dr (EP)	44
Charles Pl NW	18
Charles Allen Dr NE	
1-920	08
921-OUT	09
Charleston Ave SE	15
Charlestown Dr (CP)	37
Charline Dr NE	06
Charlotte Pl NW	18
Charmant Pl (DOR)	40
Charter Oak Dr SW	31
Chase Rd (CHA)	41
Chaseland Rd NE	28
Chastain SE	12
Chateau Blvd (EP)	44
Chateau Ct & Dr NW	05
Chateaugay Ln NE	42
Chatham Ave SW	11
Chatham Dr (DOR)	40
Chatham Rd NW	05
Chatham Way NW	14
Chattahoochee Ave & Cir NW	18
Chattahoochee Dr SW	31
Chattahoochee Pl (EP)	44
Chatterton Rd (CP)	49
Chatworth Ct NE	42
Chaucer Dr SW	11
Chaucer Ln NE	19
Chaumont Sq NW	27
Cheateau Ct & Dr (CHA)	41
Chelsea Cir NE	
301-OUT	07
Chelsea Cres NE	19
Cheminde Vie NW	42
Chenault Pl NW	14
Cheney (EP)	44
Cherie Ct & Ln (CP)	49
Cherokee (DUN)	38
Cherokee Ave SE	
1-650	12
651-OUT	15
Cherokee Cir (CP)	49
Cherokee Ct & Rd (DOR)	40
Cherokee Pl SE	12
Cherokee Rd NW	05
Cherokee Trl SW	31
Cherring Dr & Ln (CHA)	41
Cherry (EP)	44
Cherry NW	
1-800	13
801-OUT	18
Cherry SE	15
Cherry Blossom Dr SW	31
Cherry Blossom Ln (EP)	44
Cherry Hill (DOR)	40
Cherry Laurel Ln (CP)	44
Cherry Laurel Ln SW	11
Cherry Tree Ln NE	28
Cherry Valley Cir & Dr SE	16
Cherrywood Ct NE	45
Cherrywood Ln NE	42
Cheryl Dr (EP)	44
Cheryl Lynne Ln (CP)	49
Chesapeake Pt NW	28
Chesapeake Way (EP)	44
Cheshire Way NE	19
Cheshire Bridge Rd NE	24
Chesson Ct NE	19
Chester Ave SE	16
Chesterfield Ct (CP)	49
Chesterfield Dr NE	45
Chestnut (HAP)	54
Chestnut NW	
1-430	14
431-OUT	18
Chestnut SW	14
Chestnut Aly, Ave & Way NE	12
Chestnut Dr (EP)	44
Chestnut Dr (DOR)	40
Chestnut Pl NW	14
Chestnut Forest Ct & Ln (DOR)	40
Chestnut Hall Dr NW	27
Chestnut Oak Ct NW	27
Chevelle Ln SE	
1001-2930	17
Cheviot Glen (EP)	44
Chevron Dr & Way (DUN)	38
Chicago Ave NW	14
Chicamauga Ave & Pl SW	14
Chicopee Dr (DOR)	40
Childerlee Ln NE	24
Childers Rd NE	24
Childress Dr SW	11
Childs Dr NW	14
Chilton Dr NW	18
Chinaberry Way SW	11
Chipley Ne	07
Chippewa Pl NE	19
Chivers NW	18
Chowning Way (CHA)	41
Christian City (CP)	49
Christman SW	10
Christmas Ln NE	29
Christopher Ct (DOR)	40
Christophers Walk NW	27
Chrysler Dr & Ter NE	45
Church (EP)	44
Church (DOR)	40
Church NW	18
Churchill Downs Dr NE	19
Circle NW	18
Circle 85 (CP)	49
Circlewood Rd NE	45
Citadel Dr NE	24
Clair Dr (HAP)	54
Claire Dr NE	
1-300	15
301-OUT	07
Claire Dr SE	
1-300	15
301-OUT	07
Claire Dr SW	
1-100	15
101-OUT	10
Clairmont Ct, Ln, Pl & Way NE	29
Clairmont Rd NE	
2201-3390	29
3391-3620	19
3621-OUT	41
Clairmont Ter NE	45
Clairview Dr (CHA)	41
Clairwood Ter (CHA)	41
Claremont NW	18
Clarendale Dr NW	27
Claridge Ct (DOR)	40
Clarissa Dr NW	18
Clark NW	18
Clark Dr (EP)	44
Clark Howell Hwy (CP)	49
Clark Howell Hwy (HAP)	54
Clark Howell Pl NW	13
Clarke SE	12
Claude NW	18
Clay Dr (DOR)	40
Clay Dr (DUN)	38
Clay St NE & SE	17
Clayton Ct SE	17
Clearbrook Dr SW	11
Clearview Ave, Dr, Pky & Pl (DOR)	40
Clearview Dr NE	19
Clearvue Ter SW	11
Clearwater Dr (CP)	49
Clearwater Rd SW	31
Cleburne Ave NE	07
Cleburne Ter NE	
1-600	07
601-OUT	06
Clement Dr & Way SW	31
Clementstone Dr NE	42
Clemont Dr NE	06
Clemson Dr (CHA)	41
Cleremont Ave & Ct (EP)	44
Cleveland Ave (EP)	44
Cleveland Ave SE	16
Cleveland Ave SE	
1-130	15
131-OUT (HAP)	54
Cleveland Ave SW	
1-1000	15
1001-OUT	44
Cleveland Cir SW	15
Cliff Valley Way NE	
1-1500	19
1501-OUT	29
Clifford Ave NE	17
Cliffway Dr (CHA)	41
Clifton NE	
1-100	17
101-1350	07
1351-1363	33
1364-1364	22
1365-1404	33
1405-1405	22
1406-1450	33
1451-1461	29
1462-ONLY	33
1463-1599	29
1600-1600	33
1601-OUT	29
Clifton SE	
1-350	17
351-OUT	16
Clifton Ct NE	29

Atlanta (Con.)   303

Clifton Ct Cir NE...................... 29
Clifton Pl NE.......................... 12
Clifton Rd NE
  1-100.............................. 17
  101-1350........................... 07
  1351-1450.......................... 22
  1451-1461.......................... 29
  1462-ONLY.......................... 33
  1463-1599.......................... 29
  1600-ONLY.......................... 33
  1601-OUT........................... 29
Clifton Rd SE
  1-350.............................. 17
  351-OUT............................ 16
Clifton Ter NE........................ 07
Clifton Way NE
  1-1000............................. 29
  1001-OUT........................... 16
Clifton Way SE
  1-1000............................. 29
  1001-OUT........................... 16
Clifton Church Rd SE.................. 16
Cliftondale Pl (CP)................... 49
Cliftwood Dr NE....................... 28
Climax SE............................. 15
Climax Pl SW.......................... 15
Clipper Trl NW........................ 28
Cloudland Dr NW....................... 27
Clover SW............................. 10
Clover Ln NE.......................... 08
Cloverdale Dr SE...................... 16
Cloverhurst Cir & Dr (EP)............. 44
Cloverleaf Dr SE...................... 16
Clovis Ct NW.......................... 31
Club Cir, Dr, Ln & Ter NE............. 19
Club Pl SE............................ 17
Club Valley Dr NE..................... 19
Clyde Dr (CHA)........................ 41
Cobble Ln (CHA)....................... 41
Coca Cola Pl SE....................... 03
Cochise Dr NW......................... 39
Cochran Dr NW......................... 27
Cochran Rd (CP)....................... 49
Cochran Rd SW......................... 31
Cofield Dr (HAP)...................... 54
Coggins Dr SE......................... 12
Cohen SW.............................. 10
Coldsprings Ln (CHA).................. 41
Coldstream Ct NW...................... 28
Coldstream Dr (DOR)................... 40
Colebridge Rd NW...................... 28
Colebrook Ct NW....................... 27
Colegate Dr SW........................ 36
Coleman (HAP)......................... 54
Coleman NW............................ 10
Colewood Ct & Way NW.................. 28
Colina Ct (CP)........................ 49
Colland Dr NW......................... 18
College (HAP)......................... 54
College (CP).......................... 37
College Ave NE........................ 17
College Ave & Pl SW................... 15
College Park Rd (HAP)................. 54
College Park Rd (CP).................. 49
Collier Ct NW......................... 31
Collier Dr NW
  1-3300............................. 18
  3301-OUT........................... 31
Collier Pl NW......................... 18
Collier Rd NW
  1-460.............................. 09

461-OUT............................... 18
Collier St NW & SW.................... 14
Collier Ridge Dr NW................... 18
Collingswood Ter (CP)................. 49
Collins SE............................ 03
Collins Dr (EP)....................... 44
Collins Dr & Rd NW.................... 18
Collum NW............................. 14
Colmer SE............................. 17
Cologne Dr SE......................... 54
Colonial Dr (CP)...................... 37
Colonial Dr NE........................ 19
Colonial Way (CHA).................... 41
Colonial Homes Dr NW.................. 09
Colony Sq NE.......................... 09
Colorado Ave (HAP).................... 54
Colorado Pl & Trl SW.................. 31
Colquitt Ave NE....................... 07
Colquitt Dr (DUN)..................... 38
Colquitt Dr (DOR)..................... 40
Colt Dr (CHA)......................... 41
Colton Dr NE.......................... 42
Columbia Ave (CP)..................... 37
Columbia Ave E & W (CP)............... 37
Columbia Ave NE....................... 09
Colville Ave (HAP).................... 54
Commander Dr (CHA).................... 41
Commerce Cir SW....................... 36
Commerce Dr NW
  1-2000............................. 18
  2001-OUT........................... 36
Commerce Dr SW
  1-2000............................. 18
  2001-OUT........................... 36
Commerce Way (HAP).................... 54
Commercial Ave NW..................... 18
Commodore Ct, Dr & Ln
  (CHA).............................. 41
Commodore Dr NW....................... 18
Commodore Way NE...................... 45
Compton Dr SE......................... 15
Concord Ct (EP)....................... 44
Cone NW............................... 03
Confederate Ave SE
  1-990.............................. 12
  991-OUT............................ 16
Confederate Ct SE..................... 12
Congress Cir & Ct (CHA)............... 41
Conifer Cir NE........................ 42
Conley (CP)........................... 37
Conley S
  100-299 (CP)....................... 37
Conley Cir (HAP)...................... 54
Conley Rd SE.......................... 54
Conley Old N
  100-590 (CP)....................... 37
Connally (CP)......................... 37
Connally SE
  1-650.............................. 12
  651-OUT............................ 15
Connally Ave SW....................... 10
Connally Ct (EP)...................... 44
Connally Dr SW
  1-2700............................. 44
  2701-OUT........................... 11
Connally Pl SE........................ 12
Connecticut Ave NE.................... 07
Connell Ave SW........................ 15
Connell Rd (CP)....................... 49
Conover Dr (DUN)...................... 38
Conrad SE............................. 15
Constance (EP)........................ 44

Constitution Rd SE
  1-1200............................. 15
  1201-OUT........................... 16
Continental Dr NE..................... 45
Continental Colony Pky SW............. 31
Converse Dr NE........................ 24
Convoy Dr (HAP)....................... 54
Conway NW
  1-1250............................. 27
  1551-OUT........................... 27
Conway Dr NW, E
  1-1200............................. 27
  1551-OUT........................... 27
Conway Dr NW, W
  1-1200............................. 27
  1551-OUT........................... 27
Conway Pl NW.......................... 18
Conway Pl SE.......................... 12
Conway Rd NW, E
  1-1250............................. 27
  1551-OUT........................... 27
Conway Rd NW, W
  1-1250............................. 27
  1551-OUT........................... 27
Conway Forrest Dr NW.................. 27
Conway Valley Ct & Rd NW.............. 27
Cook NW............................... 18
Cook Rd (CP).......................... 49
Cooks Aly SE.......................... 12
Cooledge Ave NE....................... 06
Coolridge Cir (CHA)................... 41
Cooper SW
  1-650.............................. 12
  651-OUT............................ 15
Coosawalte Dr NE...................... 19
Copeland SW........................... 10
Copeland Rd NE........................ 42
Copenhill Ave NE...................... 07
Coral Dr SE........................... 16
Coral Pl NW........................... 18
Coral Way (CHA)....................... 41
Corando Way (CHA)..................... 41
Corbally Pl SW........................ 12
Cordell Dr (CP)....................... 49
Cordoba Sq NW......................... 05
Cordova SW............................ 10
Corley SE............................. 12
Cornelia SE........................... 12
Cornell Blvd SW....................... 31
Cornell Rd NE......................... 06
Coronado Dr NW........................ 27
Coronation Ct & Dr NE................. 28
Coronet Way NW........................ 18
Corporate Sq NE....................... 29
Corporate Sq Blvd NE.................. 29
Corporate Sq Mall Sq Mall
  NE................................. 29
Corral Dr SE.......................... 16
Cortez Ln & Way NE.................... 19
Corvair Dr SE......................... 54
Cosmos Ct & Dr NE..................... 45
Cotillion Dr (CHA).................... 41
Cotswold Dr NE........................ 19
Cottage Grv Ave SE.................... 17
Cottage Ln NW......................... 18
Cottonwood Dr SE...................... 16
Council Bluff Ct & Dr NE.............. 45
Country Ln NE......................... 24
Country Club Dr & Ln SW............... 11
County Line Rd SW..................... 31
Courtenay Dr NE....................... 06
Courtland NE
  1-400.............................. 03

Atlanta (Con.)	303
Courtland SE	03
Courtleigh Dr (DUN)	38
Cove Cir NE	19
Cowley Ave SW	14
Cox Ave SW	
1-500	11
501-OUT	10
Cox Dr SW	
1-500	11
501-OUT	10
Craggy Point NW	39
Crane Rd NE	24
Cranton Ct NE	19
Cravenridge Dr NE	19
Cravey Dr NE	45
Creek Valley Ct SW	31
Creek View Cir (CP)	49
Creel Cir (CP)	37
Creel Rd (CP)	49
Creighton Rd SW	31
Crescendo Dr NW	18
Crescent Ave NE	09
Crest Ave NE	24
Crest Valley Dr NW	27
Crestdale Cir NE	16
Cresthill Ave NE	06
Crestline Ct & Dr NE	45
Crestline Rd NE	28
Crestline Valley Cir NE	28
Crestmont Ln SW	11
Crestridge Dr NE	06
Crestwood Cir (CP)	49
Crestwood Dr (CP)	37
Crestwood Dr SE	16
Crestwood Ln NW	39
Crew SW	
1-650	12
651-OUT	15
Crocus Ave, NW	14
Croft Pl NW	31
Crogman SE	15
Cromwell Rd NE	28
Crosby Dr NW	31
Cross NW	18
Cross Rd SE	54
Cross Creek Pky NW	27
Cross Gate Ct NW	27
Cross Keys Dr NE	19
Crown Rd	54
Crumley Pl SW	12
Crumley Row SW	10
Crventry St SE & SW	12
Crystal Ln (CP)	49
Crystal Lake Rd (CP)	49
Culberson SW	10
Culpepper NW	18
Cumberland Cir & Rd NE	06
Cumberland Dr & Rd (CHA)	41
Cumberland Pky NW	39
Cumberland Rd (EP)	44
Cumberland Club Cir & Dr NW	39
Cumming Dr SW	11
Cummings SE	16
Cunningham Pl SW	10
Curran NW	18
Currier NE	
1-300	08
301-OUT	12
Currier Pl NE	12

Curtis Dr NE	19
Cushman Cir SW	11
Custer (HAP)	54
Custer Ave SE	
1-800	15
801-OUT	16
Cynthia Dr NE	19
Cypress NE	
1-870	08
871-OUT	09
Dabney Ter (EP)	44
Dahlgreen SE	15
Dahlia Ave NW	14
Dale Dr NE	05
Dale Dr SE	15
Dale Ln SW	
1-3400	11
3401-OUT	31
Dale Creek Dr NW	18
Daleview Dr SE	15
Dalewood Dr NE	29
Dallas NE	08
Dalmer Rd NE	42
Dalney NW	18
Dalon Rd NE	06
Dalrymple Rd NE	28
Dalton SE	15
Dalvigney NW	18
Dameron Cir SW	31
Damon Ct & Pl (DUN)	38
Dan Ln NE	24
Dan Johnson Rd NE	07
Danbury Ln NW	27
Danby Ct (DOR)	40
Danbyshire Ct NE	45
Danforth Rd SW	31
Daniel SE	12
Daniel Ave NE & SE	17
Daniel Rd SW	31
Danner SE	16
Danny Rd SW	31
Dantzler St, Ct & Dr NE	29
Danube Rd NE	42
Dargan Pl SW	10
Darlington Cir & Rd NE	05
Darlington Oak Dr (DOR)	40
Darrah Dr SW	31
Dartford Dr (DUN)	38
Dartmoor Cir NE	28
Dartmouth Dr SW	31
Datona Dr SW	31
Dauphine (EP)	44
Davage SW	15
Daventry Ct & Dr (DUN)	38
David Rd (CHA)	41
Davidson Ave NE	19
Davis (HAP)	54
Davis NW	
1-380	14
381-OUT	18
Davis SW	13
Davis Ave (EP)	44
Davis Cir & Pl NW	18
Davis Ct & Rd (CP)	37
Davis Dr NW	27
Dawn View Ln NW	27
Daws Ave SE	17
Day SW	10
Dayton Pl NE	08
De Clair Dr NE	29
De Foor Ave, Cir & Pl NW	18
De Foor Ferry Rd NW	18

De Foor Hills Rd NW	18
De Gress Ave NE	07
De Kalb Ave NE	07
De Lowe Dr SW	
1-2010	11
2011-OUT (EP)	44
De Lowe Pl SW	11
Deacon Ave (HAP)	54
Deacon Ln (CHA)	41
Dean Dr NW	18
Dearborn SE	17
Dearborn Plz (HAP)	54
Dearwood Dr SW	15
Deauville Ct NW	18
Deborah Dr (DOR)	40
Deborah Dr NE	45
Decatur SE	
1-310	03
311-OUT	12
Deckner Ave SW	10
Deer Park Rd NE	45
Deer Run Trl (CP)	49
Deere Dr (CHA)	41
Deerfield Ct & Ln (CP)	49
Deerfield Tr (CP)	49
Deering Rd NW	09
Dejarnette Dr (EP)	44
Del Mar Ln NW	
1-3250	11
3251-OUT	31
Delano Dr NE	17
Delaware Ave NE	07
Delaware Ave SE	16
Delbridge NW	14
Delevan SW	
1-314	15
315-OUT	10
Dellwood Dr NW	
1-2150	09
2151-OUT	05
Delmar Ave SE	
1-800	12
801-OUT	16
Delmar Ct SE	16
Delmar Ln NW	
1-3250	11
3251-OUT	31
Delmont Dr NE	05
Delmoor Ct & Dr NW	11
Delray Dr NW	18
Delta Dr (EP)	44
Delta Pl NE	07
Delverton Dr (DUN)	38
Demooney Rd (CP)	49
Demorest Ave NE	05
Denise Dr (CP)	37
Denny Dr (CP)	49
Depauw Dr SW	36
Derby Dr SW	11
Deren Way NE	45
Dering Cir & Ct NE	45
Derrick Rd (CP)	49
Derrick Jones Rd (CP)	49
Derry Ave SW	10
Desert Dr (EP)	44
Desoto NW	14
Desoto Ave SW	10
Detroit Ave & Ct NW	14
Devereaux Ct (DUN)	38
Devilla Trce (CP)	49
Devin Cir NE	19
Devinney Cir NE	19

Atlanta (Con.)   303

Devonshire Ct, Rd & Way
(DUN) 38
Devonwood Dr NE 28
Dewberry Ln SW 44
Dewey SW 10
Dewey Ave (EP) 44
Diamond Ave SE 16
Diana Dr SW 15
Diane Ct SE 16
Diane Dr (DOR) 40
Dickson NE 19
Dickson Pl NE 09
Dilbeck Pl NW 42
Dill Ave SW 10
Dillon NE 18
Dimmock SW 10
Division NW 14
Division Pl NW 10
Dixie SE 17
Dixie Ave NE 07
Dixie Hills Cir NW 14
Dixon NE 19
Doane SW 15
Dobbs Cir NW 27
Dobbs Dr SE 16
Dobbs Way (EP) 44
Dodd Ave SW 15
Dodge NE 12
Dodson (HAP) 54
Dodson Dr SW
  1-2100 11
  2101-OUT 44
Dodson Ter (EP) 44
Dodson Ter SW 11
Dodson Connector Dr (EP) 44
Dodson Lee Dr (EP) 44
Dogwood (CP) 37
Dogwood Dr (EP) 44
Dogwood Ln (CP) 49
Dogwood Ln NE 45
Dogwood Ter NE 19
Dogwood Valley Dr NE 42
Dollar Mill Ct, Rd & Way SW 31
Dolphin Dr SW 11
Don Juan Cir (CHA) 41
Donaldson Dr NE 19
Donaldson Dr NE
  1-3750 19
  3751-OUT 41
Doncaster Dr NE 09
Donnalee SE 16
Donnebrook Ln SE 54
Donnelly Ave SW 10
Donzi Ln SE 16
Dora SW 14
Doral Cir, Ct & Dr (DOR) 40
Dorchester Ave NW 18
Doreen Ct NE 45
Doroco Ct, Dr & Way (DOR) 40
Dorothy SE 15
Dorsey SW 10
Dorsey Ave (EP) 44
Dorsey Rd (HAP) 54
Dot Rd (CP) 49
Douglas SE 17
Douglas SW 14
Douglas Dr (EP) 44
Douglas Rd NE 42
Dove Dr SW 31
Dover Blvd & Ct SW 31
Dover Rd NW 27

Doverhill Pl NE 45
Dovers Aly SW 10
Dowdell Dr (CHA) 41
Dower SW 10
Downey Dr (CP) 49
Downs Dr SW 11
Downwood Cir NW 27
Doyle SE 17
Drake Dr SW 36
Draper Dr (CP) 37
Dresden Ct & Way (CHA) 41
Dresden Dr NE
  1-1960 19
  1961-OUT 41
Dresden Trl (EP) 44
Drew Dr & Pl NW 19
Drew Valley Rd NE 19
Drewry NE 06
Drexel Ln (EP) 44
Druid Cir & Pl NE 07
Druid Valley Dr & Rd NE 29
Drummond NE 14
Drury Ct (DOR) 40
Duberry Ct NE 19
Dublin Dr SW 31
Dudley Ct & Ln NW 27
Duffield Dr NE 18
Duke Rd (CHA) 41
Duke Of Gloucester (EP) 44
Duke Of Windsor (EP) 44
Dumbarton Ct & Rd NW 27
Dummereland Ct & Ter (CP)... 49
Dunbar SW 10
Dunbritton (CP) 49
Duncan (CP) 49
Duncan Dr (CHA) 41
Duncannon Ct (CHA) 41
Duncourtney Dr NE 28
Dundee Ave NE 07
Dunedin Dr, SW 31
Dunex Hill Ln NE 24
Dunhaven Ct, Dr & Rd (CHA). 41
Dunhill Ct NE 28
Dunhill Ter NE 28
Dunkerrin Ln (DOR) 40
Dunlap Ave (EP) 44
Dunn SW 10
Dunning SE 15
Dunnington Cir (CHA) 41
Dunover Ct (DOR) 40
Dunridge Ct (DUN) 38
Dunseath Ave NW 18
Dunwoody NE 17
Dunwoody Ln NE 19
Dunwoody Park (CHA) 41
Dunwoody Pl & Rd (DUN) 38
Dunwoody Pl & Trl NE 24
Dunwoody Rd NE 28
Dunwoody Club Dr
  1-2700 (DUN) 38
  2701-3100 (DOR) 40
  3101-4000 (DUN) 38
  4001-OUT (DOR) 40
Dunwoody Village Rd (DUN) 38
Dupont Ave NW 18
Dupont Ave SE 17
Dupree Ave NW 18
Dupree Dr NW 27
Durand Dr NE 07
Durango Rd SW 31
Durant Pl NE
  1-870 08
  871-OUT 09

Durden Dr NE 19
Dutch Valley Pl & Rd NE 24
Dyer Cir (CHA) 41
Dykes Dr NW 42
Dyson Dr NE
  1-1770 07
Eaglerock Dr (DOR) 40
Earle NW
  1-2000 13
  2001-OUT 18
Earlhurst Ln (CP) 49
Earlston Dr NE 28
Early NW 05
Eason NW 14
East Ave NE 12
East Ave NW 18
East Dr NE 05
East Park Ln NE 09
East Andrews Dr NW 05
East Anthony NW 18
East Beechwood Dr NW 27
East Belle Isle Rd NE 42
East Brookhaven Dr NE 19
East Cedar Ln SW 11
East Clifton Rd NE 07
East Club Dr & Ln NE 19
East Confederate Ave SE
  1-800 12
  801-OUT 16
East Conway Dr NW
  1-1250 27
  1551-OUT 27
East Conway Rd NW
  1-1250 27
  1551-OUT 27
East Deckner Ave SW 10
East Hampton Ct (CP) 49
East Handy Dr NW 18
East Kildare Ave NW 18
East Lake Blvd, Dr, Rd & Ter
  SE 17
East Lake Dr (DOR) 40
East Lake Dr NE
  1-100 17
  1101-2291 07
East Lake Rd NE
  1-100 17
  1101-2291 07
East Lindmont Ct NE 24
East Nancy Creek Dr NE
  1-1675 19
  1676-OUT 41
East Northbrook Ct (DOR) 40
East Ontario Ave SW 10
East Osborne Rd NE 19
East Paces Ferry Rd, NE
  1-800 05
  801-OUT 26
East Park Ln NE 09
East Pine Valley Rd NW 05
East Point (EP) 44
East Side Ave SE 16
East Simon Ter NW 18
East Sussex Rd NE 06
East Tupelo SE 17
East Wesley Ave NE
  1-600 05
  601-OUT 24
East Wesley Rd NE
  1-600 05
  601-OUT 24
East Wesley Ter NE 24

Atlanta (Con.)   303

East Wood Valley Rd NW 27
Eastbrook Ct (DOR)................ 40
Eastland Rd SE....................... 16
Easton Dr SW 31
Eastport Ter SE...................... 17
Eastridge Rd SW 11
Eastwood Ave SE.................... 16
Eaton Pl (CHA) 41
Eberhart Dr (HAP) 54
Echo NW 18
Echo Dr & Trl NE 45
Echo Hills Cir NE 45
Echo W NW............................ 18
Echocliff Ct NE 45
Echoto Dr NW........................ 18
Ector Ct NE 45
Eddie Ave SE......................... 12
Eden Ave SE 16
Eden Roc Ln NW 42
Edenton Ct NE 19
Edgefield Dr SW 10
Edgehill Ave NW 18
Edgemore Dr SE..................... 16
Edgewater Ct, Dr & Trl NW 28
Edgewater Dr SW 11
Edgewood Ave NE
  1-300.............................. 03
  301-670........................... 12
  671-OUT.......................... 07
Edgewood Ave SE
  1-300.............................. 03
  301-670........................... 12
  671-OUT.......................... 07
Edinboro Dr & Rd NW 27
Edinburg Ter NE..................... 07
Edison Ave NE 05
Edison Dr (CP)....................... 37
Edison Rd (DOR).................... 40
Edith NE................................ 08
Edwards (DOR)....................... 40
Edwards NW 14
Edwards Dr NW 18
Edwin St & Pl NW.................. 18
Edwina Ln SW 31
Egleston SW 10
Eisenhower Cir, Ct & Rd SE.... 54
El Paso Rd SW 31
Elaine Ave NW 18
Elbert SW.............................. 10
Elbridge Dr NW...................... 18
Elden Dr NE........................... 42
Eldorado Dr NE...................... 45
Eleanor SE............................. 17
Eleanor Ct & Ter NW.............. 18
Electric Ave NW..................... 14
Elinor Pl NW 18
Elinwood Ct & Dr (EP) 44
Elixir Ave SW 14
Elizabeth NE.......................... 07
Elizabeth Ave SW 10
Elizabeth Ln (EP)................... 44
Elizabeth Pl NW..................... 18
Elizabeth Ann Ln NE 24
Elkins (HAP).......................... 54
Elkmont Dr NE....................... 06
Elks Dr SW 31
Elleby Rd SE.......................... 15
Ellen NW............................... 18
Ellendale Ln NW 18
Ellery Dr (HAP) 54
Ellijay Dr NE.......................... 19

Ellington SE........................... 17
Elliott NW
  1-200.............................. 13
  201-1000......................... 14
  1001-OUT........................ 18
Elliott SW.............................. 13
Elliott Cir (CHA) 41
Elliott Cir NE 05
Ellis St NE & NW.................... 03
Ellisbury Dr (CHA) 41
Ellsworth Dr NW 18
Ellsworth Industrial Dr NW 18
Ellwood Dr NE........................ 05
Ellwyn Dr (CHA)..................... 41
Elm (EP)................................ 44
Elm (HAP).............................. 54
Elm (CP)................................ 37
Elm NW
  1-416.............................. 14
  417-OUT.......................... 18
Elm SW................................. 14
Elm St Ct SW 14
Elmco Rd SW 31
Elmhurst Cir SE...................... 16
Elmira Pl NE 07
Elmtree Dr SW 11
Elmwood Dr NE 06
Elmwood Rd NW 18
Eloise St & Ct SE 12
Elrod (DOR)........................... 40
Elsinor (EP)........................... 44
Elva Dr SW 31
Elvira SE 15
Elysian Way NW..................... 27
Embry Cir N (CHA) 41
Embry Cir & Ct (CHA)............. 41
Embry Hills Dr (CHA).............. 41
Emerald Ave SE...................... 16
Emerald Ave SW..................... 10
Emerson Ave SE 16
Emery NW 18
Emery Pl NE 17
Emily Pl NW 18
Emily Way (CP)...................... 49
Emma Ln NE 42
Emmanual Dr SW 36
Emmett NW 18
Emory Cir, Ct & Dr NE............ 07
Emory Rd NE 06
Emory Court Annex NE............ 07
Empire Blvd & Way SW........... 54
Engle Rd NW 18
Englewood SE......................... 15
Englewood Dr (EP) 44
English Cir & Dr SW 31
English Ln (CP)...................... 37
English St & Ave NW 18
English Oak Dr (DOR)............. 40
Ennis Aly NW 14
Enoch Dr (CP) 37
Enon Rd (CP) 49
Enon Rd SW 31
Enota Pl SW 10
Ensign Ct & Dr (CHA)............. 41
Enterprise Blvd SW 36
Epping Forest Dr NE 19
Eppington Dr NW.................... 27
Epworth SW........................... 10
Eric SE.................................. 15
Ericson SE............................. 17
Erin Ave SW 10
Erin Rd SW 31

Ernest NW............................. 18
Essex Ave SW 11
Essie SE 16
Estelle (HAP) 54
Esten SE................................ 16
Estes (CP)............................. 49
Estes Dr SW 10
Estoria SE.............................. 16
Ethan Allen Ct & Dr (CP) 49
Ethel NW............................... 18
Etheridge St & Dr NW............ 18
Eton Ct NE 19
Etowah (DUN)........................ 38
Etowah Dr NE 19
Eubanks Ave (EP)................... 44
Euclid Ave & Ter NE 07
Eugenia SW 12
Eugenia Pl NW 18
Euharlee SW 14
Eula Cir (DOR) 40
Eulalia Rd NE 19
Eureka Dr NE.......................... 05
Eustace SE............................. 15
Eva Dr NW 18
Evans (HAP)........................... 54
Evans Dr (CP) 37
Evans Ln SE 17
Evans Rd
  1-3550 (CHA) 41
  3551-OUT (DOR).............. 40
Evans St & Dr SW 10
Evans Dale Cir & Dr (DOR) 40
Evans Wood Dr (DOR)............ 40
Evelyn Pl & Way NW 18
Evelyn St NE.......................... 06
Everett Pl SW 10
Evergreen Dr NE 19
Evergreen Ln NW.................... 18
Everhart SW........................... 10
Ewing SW.............................. 31
Ewing Dr NE 19
Ewing Pl SW 10
Exchange Pl SE....................... 03
Executive Park NE, E............... 29
Executive Park NE, S............... 29
Executive Park NE, W............. 29
Executive Park Dr NE 29
Exeter Close NW 27
Ezra Church Dr NW 14
Ezzard SE 12
Fabin NW............................... 18
Fair SW
  1-370.............................. 03
  371-510........................... 13
  511-OUT.......................... 14
Fair Dr SW 15
Fair Oaks Mnr NW.................. 27
Fairbanks SW 10
Fairburn Ave & Rd SW............ 31
Fairburn Cir, Pl & Rd NW 31
Fairfax Ave (EP) 44
Fairfield Pl NW 14
Fairfield Rd NW...................... 27
Fairhaven Cir NE 05
Fairhill Ln NE 19
Fairlane Cir, Ct & Dr NW 31
Fairlane Dr (DOR)................... 40
Fairlane Dr SE........................ 54
Fairlie NW 03
Fairlock Ln NW 31
Fairmont NW 18
Fairview Rd NE....................... 06
Fairway Cir NE 19

Fairway Cir SW	31
Fairway Dr (CP)	49
Fairway Hill Dr SE	17
Fairwood Ln NE	45
Faith Ave SE	16
Fala Pl NE	19
Falcon Dr SW	11
Falkirk Pl NE	45
Fallview Ter (EP)	44
Fama Dr NE	29
Fargo Pl SE	16
Farley Ave SW	31
Farley St & Ct (EP)	44
Farmington Ct, Dr & Ter NW	39
Farmington Ln NE	19
Faronview Dr (DOR)	40
Farrington Ave & Pl SE	15
Farris Ave (EP)	44
Faulkner Rd SE	24
Faunsworth Dr NE	28
Fay SE	16
Fayetteville Ct SE	16
Fayetteville Rd NE	
1-500	17
501-OUT	16
Fayetteville Rd SE	
1-500	17
501-OUT	16
Fayetteville Rd W	
4525-5008 (CP)	37
5096-OUT (CP)	49
Feagin Dr NE	19
Fearn Cir NE	19
Federal Ter SE	15
Fedora Way NW	31
Fellwood Pl & Rd (CP)	49
Felton Dr (EP)	44
Felton Dr NE	
1-500	12
501-OUT	08
Felton Way NE	08
Fenwood SW	14
Ferguson NE	07
Fermi Dr SW	36
Fern Ave SE	15
Fern Creek Ln NE	29
Fern Valley Cir & Rd SW	31
Fern Valley Ct & Dr (EP)	44
Fernbank Dr NE	31
Ferncliff Pl & Rd NE	24
Fernleaf Cir & Ct NW	18
Ferno Dr NW	18
Fernwood Cir NE	19
Fernwood Dr (EP)	44
Fernwood Rd NW	18
Ferris SW	10
Ferry Dr NE	28
Ferry Landing NW	28
Field SE	16
Field Rd NW	18
Fielder NW	18
Fielding Ct & Ln SW	11
Finch Dr SE	15
Finchley Ct NW	28
Finistere Ct NE	19
Finley NE	07
Finley Ave NW	18
Firth Ln (DOR)	40
Fisher SE	
1-1600	16
1601-OUT	15
Fisher Ave NW	18

Fisher Rd SE	
1-1600	16
1601-OUT	15
Fisher Trl NE	45
Fisk Dr, SW	36
Fitzgerald SE	12
Flagler Ave NE	09
Flagstone Ct & Dr SW	31
Flagstone Dr SE	16
Flair Knoll Ct & Dr NE	45
Flamingo Dr (EP)	44
Flamingo Dr SW	11
Flat Rock Rd	
1-1300 (CP)	49
Flat Shoals Ave SE	
1-2373	16
Flat Shoals Rd	
1-4630 (CP)	49
Flat Shoals Rd SE	
1-2373	16
Flat Shoals Way SE	16
Fleet SW	10
Fleetwood Cir & Ct SW	11
Fleetwood Dr SE	16
Flemington Rd NE	45
Flemish Ct (EP)	49
Fletcher SW	
1-312	15
313-OUT	10
Fleur De Lis Ct, Pl & Way	
(DOR)	40
Flindt Ct (CHA)	41
Flintlock Rd NW	27
Flintshire Ct (CHA)	41
Flintwood Dr SE	16
Flora Ave NE	07
Florence NE	12
Florence Pl NW	18
Florida Ave (DOR)	40
Florida Ave SE	16
Florida Ave SW	10
Flowerland Dr NE	19
Flowers Dr (CP)	49
Flowers Dr, S.	41
Flowers Pl NW	14
Flowers Rd (CHA)	41
Flowers Rd (DOR)	40
Flynn NW	18
Flynn Rd SE	54
Folkstone Rd NE	29
Fontainbleau Ct & Dr (DOR)	40
Fontaine Ave SW	11
Fontainebleau SW	31
Foote St & Row NE	07
Ford NW	18
Ford Pl NE	06
Ford St & Pl SE	16
Fordham Ct NE	06
Forest Ave (HAP)	54
Forest Trl (EP)	44
Forest Hills Dr (HAP)	54
Forest Park Rd SE	
1-2790	15
2791-OUT	54
Forest Valley Ct & Rd NE	42
Forest Valley Dr SE	54
Foresta Ct (CHA)	41
Forestdale Dr NE	42
Forestwood Ln NE	28
Formwalt SW	
1-650	12
651-OUT	15
Forrest Ave (FP)	44

Forrest Ave NE	
1-160	03
161-OUT	12
Forrest Cir, Dr & Ter SE	54
Forrest Ct (CHA)	41
Forrest Rd CHA	
1-800	12
801-OUT	06
Forrest St, Ave, Pl & Trl NW	18
Forrest Way NE	
1-1000	08
1001-OUT	05
Forrest Green Dr NE	29
Forrest Hills Dr NE	
1-1000	42
1001-OUT	15
Forrest Hills Dr SW	
1-1000	42
1001-OUT	15
Forrest Lake Dr NW	27
Forrest Ridge Dr NW	18
Forrestal Dr (CHA)	41
Forsyth St NW & SW	03
Fort NE	12
Fort Valley Dr (EP)	44
Fort Valley Dr NW	11
Fortingale Dr (CHA)	41
Fortner (EP)	44
Fortress Ave SW	15
Fortune St & Pl NE	12
Foster St & Pl NW	18
Foster Ridge Ct & Rd NE	45
Foundry NW	
1-260	03
261-470	13
471-OUT	14
Fountain Dr SW	14
Fowler NE	17
Fowler NW	
1-850	13
851-OUT	18
Fox NW	18
Fox Creek Ct (DOR)	40
Fox Glen Ct NE	19
Fox Hollow Ct (DOR)	40
Fox Hunt Ln (EP)	44
Foxcroft Rd NW	27
Foxford Ct & Dr (DOR)	40
Foxhall Ln (CP)	49
Foxhall Ln SE	16
Foxlair Dr & Ln (CP)	49
Foxwood Ct (DOR)	40
Fradon Ct (CP)	49
Framons Ct (DUN)	38
Frances Ave SE	12
Francis NE	19
Francis St, Ave & Pl NW	18
Francona Dr SW	36
Frank SW	14
Franklin Cir NE	24
Franklin Rd NE	42
Fraser SE	
1-650	12
651-OUT	15
Fredell Cir (EP)	44
Frederica NE	06
Frederick Ct & Dr SW	36
Fredicksburg Dr (CP)	37
Freeman Ct (CP)	37
Fremont SE	15
Friair Tuck Way (DOR)	40
Friar Tuck Rd NE	09
Frisco NW	18

Atlanta (Con.)   303

Front Royal Ct (CHA)............... 41
Frontac Way NW...................... 05
Frontage Rd (CP)..................... 49
Frontenac Ct NE...................... 19
Frontier Ct & Trl (CHA)........... 41
Fulford Dr (HAP)..................... 54
Fuller Rd NE........................... 19
Fulton Ave
   1-3000 (EP)........................ 44
   3001-OUT (HAP).................. 54
Fulton St SE & SW.................. 12
Fulton Ter SE......................... 16
Fulton Industrial Blvd SW
   1-5400.............................. 36
   5400-OUT........................... 31
Fulton Industrial Blvd NW,
   NW
   1-1350.............................. 36
   1351-OUT........................... 31
Funston Ave SE....................... 15
Gail Dr SE.............................. 19
Gainer Rd SW......................... 15
Gainsborough Dr (CHA)........... 41
Gaither Cir NE........................ 24
Galahad Dr NE........................ 45
Galengale Way (DOR).............. 40
Gammon Ave SE...................... 15
Garber Dr NE.......................... 28
Garden Ln NW........................ 09
Gardenia St & Dr NW.............. 14
Gardenside Ct NE.................... 19
Gardner SW............................ 10
Garfield Way SE (HAP)............ 54
Garibaldi SW
   1-660................................ 12
   661-OUT............................ 15
Garland SW............................ 15
Garmon Rd NW....................... 27
Garnett SW............................ 03
Garrett Cir (DOR)................... 40
Garrison Dr SW...................... 31
Garroux Rd NW...................... 27
Garson Dr NE......................... 24
Gartrell St & Pl SE................. 12
Gary Ave, Ct & Rd NW............ 18
Gaskill SE.............................. 16
Gaspero NE............................ 12
Gaston SW............................. 10
Gatewood Dr NW.................... 27
Gatewood Rd NE..................... 29
Gault SE................................. 15
Geary Dr NW.......................... 09
General Truman NW................. 18
Geneva (HAP)......................... 54
Gentilly Pl (DOR).................... 40
George NW............................. 18
George SE.............................. 12
George Wythe Pl NW.............. 18
Georgetown Ct & Way (CHA)... 41
Georgia Ave (DOR)................. 40
Georgia Ave (EP).................... 44
Georgia Ave (HAP).................. 54
Georgia Ave SE & SW............. 12
Georgia Ave, Cir & Dr (CP)..... 37
Georgian Dr E & W (CHA)....... 41
Georgian Ter (CHA)................ 41
Georgiana Dr NE.................... 29
Geraldine Ct (DOR)................ 40
Gerry Ln NE........................... 28
Gertrude Pl NW...................... 18
Giben Rd SW.......................... 15

Gibson SE.............................. 16
Gideons Dr SW....................... 14
Gift Ave SE............................ 16
Gilbert SE.............................. 16
Gilbert Rd SE......................... 54
Gilbert Way (HAP).................. 54
Gillem Dr (EP)....................... 44
Gillette Ave SW...................... 10
Gilmer SE.............................. 03
Givens NW............................. 18
Glace Rd (CP)........................ 49
Glade Springs Ct NE............... 45
Gladney Dr
   1-3850 (CHA)..................... 41
   3851-OUT (DOR)................. 40
Gladstone Rd NW.................... 18
Glass NW............................... 18
Glaze Dr (DOR)...................... 40
Glen Arden Dr & Pl NW........... 05
Glen Arden Way NE................. 06
Glen Bonnie Ct & Dr (DOR)..... 40
Glen Castle Dr NW.................. 27
Glen Devon Dr NW.................. 27
Glen Echo Dr SW.................... 11
Glen Errol Rd NW................... 27
Glen Forrest Rd NE................. 28
Glen Iris Dr NE
   1-370................................ 12
   371-OUT............................ 08
Glen Lake Dr NW.................... 27
Glen View Cir, Dr & Ter SW..... 31
Glenairy Ct & Dr NE................ 28
Glenald Way NW..................... 27
Glenbriar Dr NW..................... 45
Glenbrook Dr NW.................... 18
Glencourtney Dr NE................. 28
Glencove Ave SE..................... 17
Glenda Dr (CP)....................... 37
Glenda Way (DOR).................. 40
Glendale Ave NE..................... 07
Glendale Ct & Dr (EP)............. 44
Glendale Ter NE
   1-880................................ 08
   881-OUT............................ 09
Glendalough Pl SW.................. 10
Glengary Dr NE...................... 42
Glenn SE............................... 12
Glenn SW
   1-620................................ 12
   621-OUT............................ 10
Glenn Ave NW........................ 18
Glenrich Ct & Dr (DUN).......... 38
Glenridge Dr NE
   1-5700.............................. 42
   5701-OUT........................... 28
Glenrock Dr NW...................... 18
Glenrose Cir & Ct SW.............. 54
Glenway Dr (EP)..................... 44
Glenwood Ave SE
   1-750................................ 12
   751-2330........................... 16
   2331-2944.......................... 17
Glenwood Dr NE..................... 05
Glenwood Pl SE...................... 16
Glenwood Rd SE
   1-750................................ 12
   751-2330........................... 16
   2331-2944.......................... 17
Glidden NW............................ 18
Glynn Dr SE........................... 16
Godby Pl & Rd (CP)................. 49
Goddard SE............................ 15
Godfrey Dr NW....................... 18

Golden Dr (EP)....................... 44
Golden Dawn Dr SW................ 11
Golden Gate Dr NW................. 09
Goldsboro Rd NE..................... 07
Golf Cir NE............................ 09
Golf View Dr & Rd NW............ 09
Goodson Rd (CP)..................... 49
Goodwin Rd NE....................... 24
Gordon SW
   1-2320.............................. 10
   2321-3300.......................... 11
   3301-3815.......................... 31
   3816-OUT........................... 36
Gordon Ave NE....................... 07
Gordon Cir N & S (HAP).......... 54
Gordon Pl SW......................... 10
Gordon Rd
   1-2320.............................. 10
   2321-3300.......................... 11
   3307-3815.......................... 36
Gordon Rd SW
   3816-OUT........................... 36
Gordon Ter SW....................... 14
Gotham Way NE...................... 24
Gould SE............................... 15
Grace SE............................... 16
Grace Dr (HAP)...................... 54
Gracewood Ave SE.................. 16
Grady Pl (HAP)....................... 54
Grady Pl SW........................... 10
Graham SW............................ 10
Graham Cir SE........................ 16
Granada Pl (EP)...................... 44
Grand Ave NW
   1-2000.............................. 18
   2001-OUT........................... 15
Grand Ave SW
   1-2000.............................. 18
   2001-OUT........................... 15
Grand De Ct (CP).................... 49
Grand Prix Ct & Dr NE............ 45
Grandview Ave NE
   1-2500.............................. 18
   2501-OUT........................... 05
Grandview Ave NW
   1-2500.............................. 18
   2501-OUT........................... 05
Grandview Cir SE.................... 16
Grange Ct & Dr SE.................. 15
Granger Ct & Dr (CHA)........... 41
Grant SE............................... 18
Grant SE
   1-660................................ 12
   661-OUT............................ 15
Grant Cir SE.......................... 15
Grant Dr NE........................... 19
Grant Dr & Rd SW.................. 31
Grant Pl SE............................ 08
Grant St & Ave SW................. 15
Grant Park Pl Pl SE................ 15
Grant Valley Rd NE................. 05
Grape NE............................... 12
Grape SE............................... 15
Grass Valley Rd SW................ 11
Graves NW............................ 14
Gray NW
   1-380................................ 14
   381-OUT............................ 18
Graymont Dr SW..................... 10
Graywall St & Ct (EP)............. 44
Great Southwest Pky SW......... 36
Green NW.............................. 18
Green Hill Pl & Rd NE............. 42
Green Ind Way (CHA).............. 41
Green Meadows Ln NE............. 19

Atlanta (Con.)   303

Green Mountain Trl (CP)	49
Green Oak Cir NE	45
Green Oak Ct NW	27
Green Oak Dr (DOR)	40
Green Pines Dr NE	42
Green Rock Ct & Trl (DOR)	40
Green Trail Dr (CP)	49
Green Tree Ln (CP)	49
Green Valley (EP)	44
Green Valley Dr (CP)	37
Greenbriar Pky & Trl SW	31
Greenbriar Rd NE	28
Greenbrook Trl & Way NE	45
Greenbush Pl NE	45
Greencove Ave NE	06
Greencove Ln SE	16
Greencrest Dr NE	45
Greendale Dr NW	27
Greendale Dr SE	15
Greenfield NW	18
Greenfield Ave SE	15
Greenglade Rd NE	45
Greenhill Dr (CHA)	41
Greenland Dr NE	06
Greenland Rd NE	42
Greenleaf Cir SW	31
Greenleaf Rd SE	16
Greensboro Dr SW	36
Greensferry Ave SW	
1-770	14
771-OUT	10
Greensprings Rd (CP)	37
Greensward Dr NE	45
Greentree Trl (CP)	49
Greenview Ave NE	05
Greenway (DUN)	38
Greenwich (DUN)	10
Greenwillow Dr NE	45
Greenwood Ave NE	
1-600	08
601-OUT	06
Greenwood Cir (EP)	44
Gregg SW	12
Grenoble Ct (DOR)	40
Grenock Cir NE	28
Gresham Ave & Rd SE	16
Gress Ave SE	12
Greystone Rd NW	18
Griffin NW	
1-410	14
411-OUT	18
Griggs NW	14
Grossmont Dr SW	36
Grove Ave (EP)	44
Grove Cir (HAP)	54
Grove St & Dr NE	19
Grove Park Pl Pl NW	18
Groveland Ave NW	09
Guilford Ln (CP)	49
Gun Club Rd NW	18
Gunby SE	12
Gwendolyn Dr (CP)	49
Haas Ave SE	16
Habersham Rd NE & NW	05
Habersham Way NW	05
Haddon Hall Rd NW	27
Hadlock SW	11
Halcyon Dr (CP)	49
Haldane Rd SW	11
Hale NE	07
Hall SW	10

Hall Ave SE	16
Hall St & Pl NW	18
Hallcrest Dr NE	19
Hallie Ln (CP)	49
Hallie Mill Ln (CP)	49
Hallman NE	17
Hallman Ave NW	18
Hallmark Ct SE	16
Ham Dr (CHA)	41
Hambrick Dr (CP)	49
Hamilton (HAP)	54
Hamilton Ave (EP)	44
Hamilton Ave SE	12
Hamilton Blvd SW	54
Hamlin Cir & Rd (CHA)	24
Hammarskjold Dr (EP)	44
Hammock Pl SE	12
Hammond SW	10
Hammond Dr NE	28
Hampton NW	18
Hampton Ter NE	07
Hampton Way NE	24
Hampton Hall Dr & Way NE	19
Hancock Dr NE	06
Handley Ave SW	10
Handy Dr NW	18
Hanford Dr SW	15
Hannah SE	15
Hannah Rd (CP)	49
Hanover SE	16
Hanover West Ct, Dr, Ln & Ter NW	27
Hansell SE	12
Hapeville Rd SW	
1-2700	15
2701-OUT	54
Happy Hollow Ct (CP)	49
Happy Hollow Rd (DOR)	40
Happy Valley Cir SW	31
Happy Valley Tr Trl SE	16
Heralson Ave NE	07
Harber Valley (DOR)	40
Harbin Rd SW	11
Hardee NE	
1-1490	07
1491-OUT	17
Hardee Ave (CHA)	41
Hardee Ave SW	10
Hardee Ave W (CHA)	41
Hardee Cir NE	17
Hardeman Rd NE	42
Harden SE	12
Harden Dr NW	31
Harden Rd NW	15
Hardendorf Ave NE	07
Hardin Ave (CP)	49
Hardin Ave (EP)	44
Harding Ave (HAP)	54
Hardman Pl NE	05
Hardwick SE	15
Hergis SE	15
Harlan Dr (EP)	44
Harlan Rd SW	11
Harleston Rd NE	28
Harmony Way (EP)	44
Harold Ave NE	
1-700	07
701-OUT	16
Harold Ave SE	
1-700	07
701-OUT	16
Harper NW	18
Harper Rd SE	15

Harper Valley Dr (CP)	49
Harriett SE	15
Harrington Pl, SW	11
Harris NE	
1-100	03
101-OUT	12
Harris NW	
1-100	03
101-166	13
167-OUT	03
Harris Cir (DUN)	38
Harris Dr (CP)	37
Harris St & Dr (EP)	44
Harris Manor Dr SW	11
Harris Tr NW	27
Harris Valley Rd NW	27
Harrison Ct & Rd (CP)	37
Harrison Pl SW	14
Harrison Pl Ct SW	14
Harrison Rd (EP)	44
Harrogate Dr NW	27
Harrogate Ln NE	28
Harrow Dr (CHA)	41
Harte Dr NE	10
Hartford Ave & Pl SW	10
Harts Mill Ct (CHA)	41
Harts Mill Rd NE	
1-1700	19
1701-OUT	41
Harts Mills Ln NE	19
Harvard Ave (CP)	37
Harvard Rd NE	06
Harvel Dr NW	18
Harvest Ln SE	17
Harvester Rd (EP)	44
Harwell NW	14
Harwell Pl NW	18
Harwell Rd NW	
1-100	11
101-470	31
471-OUT	18
Harwood Dr (EP)	44
Hascall Rd NW	09
Hasty Ct NE	19
Hasty Pl NW	18
Hatcher Ave SW	15
Hatfield Cir SE	16
Hathaway Ct (CHA)	41
Hathburn Ct (DUN)	38
Hathcock Rd (CP)	37
Havalyn Ln (DOR)	40
Haven SE	15
Haven Ridge Dr NW	05
Maverhil Dr NE	42
Havermill Way NE	45
Haverstraw Ct & Dr (CHA)	41
Havilen NE	11
Hawick Dr NW	27
Hawkins NW	14
Hawthorne NE	07
Hawthorne Ave (CP)	37
Hawthorne Ave NW	09
Hawthorne Dr NE	45
Hawthorne Way (EP)	44
Hawthorwe Pl NE	45
Hayden NW	13
Hayden Dr (EP)	44
Haygood Ave SE & SW	15
Haygood Dr NE	07
Haynes NW	
1-180	13
181-OUT	14
Haynes SW	13

Atlanta (Con.)   303

Hazel Dr SE	16
Hazelrig Dr SE	15
Hazelwood Ct & Dr NE	45
Hazelwood Dr SW	11
Head Rd SW	11
Headland Dr SW	
1826-2900	44
2901-OUT	11
Headland Ter (EP)	44
Heard Pl SW	10
Heards Dr NW	
1-800	27
801-OUT	28
Heards Creek Trl NW	28
Heards Ferry Rd NW	28
Hearst Cir & Dr NE	19
Heartwood Ln (DOR)	40
Heather Ct SW	31
Heather Dr (EP)	44
Heather Ln (CP)	49
Heatherdale Ln (DOR)	40
Heatherland Dr SW	31
Heatherly Dr (CP)	49
Heatherwood Dr SW	31
Heathfield Dr NW	28
Heaton Dr (EP)	44
Heaton Park Dr NE	
1-195	07
Hedden Rd NE	42
Hedgewood Dr & Ln NW	11
Helen Dr NE	06
Helen Ln SW	31
Helena SE	15
Helena Ave NW	
1-50	10
51-OUT	14
Helmsdale Dr NE	45
Hemlock Cir SE	16
Hemperley Rd (CP)	49
Hemphill (CP)	37
Hemphill Ave NW	18
Hemphill Rd NW	31
Hemphill School Rd NW	31
Henderson Creek Rd (CHA)	41
Henderson Mill Ct NE	45
Henderson Mill Rd NE	
1-2610	45
2611-OUT	41
Hendon Rd SE	54
Hendrix Ave (EP)	44
Hendrix Ave SW	15
Henry Ave SW	10
Henry Thomas Dr SE	15
Hensley Dr (DUN)	38
Heritage Ct NW	27
Heritage Dr NE	45
Heritage Way NE	28
Heritage Valley Rd SW	31
Hermance Dr NE	19
Hermer Cir NW	11
Herndon NW	18
Herring Rd SW	11
Herrington Dr NE	42
Herschel Pl (CP)	49
Herschel Rd (CP)	37
Hewlett Dr (DUN)	38
Hiawassee Dr SW	11
Hickman Dr NW	11
Hickory Ln (DOR)	40
Hickory Rd (CHA)	41
Hickory Wood Ln (DOR)	40

Hidden Ct (CP)	49
Hidden Acres Dr (DOR)	40
Hidden Branches Ct, Dr & Way (DUN)	38
Hidden Branches Close (DUN)	38
Hidden Brook Ct, Dr & Trl (CP)	49
Hidden Forest Ct SE	16
Hidden Valley Ct & Dr (CP)	49
Higgins SW	10
High Court Rd NW	27
High Haven Ct NE	29
High Point Dr & Pl NE	06
High Point Ln & Rd NE	42
High Point Trl, SW	31
High Tarn (DUN)	38
Highbrook Dr NE	42
Highbury Trl SW	54
Highland Ave NE	05
Highland Dr NE	05
Highland Ter NE	06
Highland View NE	06
Hightower Ct & Pl NW	18
Hightower Rd NW	
1-100	11
101-OUT	18
Hightower Trl (DUN)	38
Highview Rd SW	31
Highway 85 (CP)	49
Highwood Dr SW	31
Hilderbrand Dr NE	28
Hildon Cir & Rd (CHA)	41
Hill NW	18
Hill SE	
1-660	12
661-OUT	15
Hill Acres Rd SW	31
Hillandale Dr (CP)	49
Hillburn Dr SE	16
Hillcrest Ave NE & SE	17
Hillcrest Dr (EP)	44
Hillcrest Dr SE	16
Hilliard St NE & SE	12
Hillpine Dr NE	06
Hills Ave SW	13
Hills Ave & Pl NW	18
Hillsdale Dr SE	15
Hillside Ave SE	15
Hillside Dr (DOR)	40
Hillside Dr NW	42
Hillside Dr SW	10
Hillstone Ct NE	19
Hillswick Ct NE	28
Hilltop Cir NW	14
Hilltop Dr (CHA)	41
Hilltop Dr (CP)	37
Hilltop Dr, Pl & Way SW	15
Hilltop Rd SW	31
Hillview Ave NE	19
Hillwood Ct SE	16
Hillwood Ter NE	19
Hipp SW	15
Hirsch NW	18
Hitching Post Trl NE	42
Hobart Ave SE	12
Hobart Dr NW	18
Hobson St & Cir SW	10
Hogan Rd SW	
1-3000	44
3001-OUT	31
Hogue NE	12
Hoke NW	18

Holcomb St & Ct (EP)	44
Holderness SW	
1-270	14
271-OUT	10
Holiday Ave NE	07
Holiday Pl (DOR)	40
Holley NW	18
Holley Rd NW	
1-300	14
301-OUT	18
Hollis Ter NW	11
Holliston Ct & Rd (DOR)	40
Holly NW	18
Holly Ct (EP)	44
Holly Dr SE	54
Holly Ln NE	29
Holly Bank Cir (DUN)	38
Holly Oaks Dr (DUN)	38
Hollydale Ct NW	42
Hollydale Dr SW	11
Hollywood Ct, Dr & Rd NW	18
Holmes NW	18
Holtzclaw SE	16
Home Ave SE	12
Home Park Ave Ave NW	18
Homeland Dr (DOR)	40
Homestead Ave NE	06
Honeysuckle Ln (DOR)	40
Honeysuckle Ln (CP)	49
Honeysuckle Ln SW	11
Honour Ave & Cir NW	05
Hood SW	12
Hood Ave (CHA)	41
Hood Ave NW	18
Hoods Dr SW	10
Hooper NE	
1-100	18
101-500	17
501-1800	07
2001-OUT	18
Hooper NW	
1-100	18
101-500	17
501-1800	07
2001-OUT	18
Hooper SE	
1-500	17
501-OUT	07
Hooper Ave NE	
1-100	18
101-500	17
501-1800	07
2001-OUT	18
Hooper Ave NW	
1-100	18
101-500	17
501-1800	07
2001-OUT	18
Hooper Ave SE	
1-100	18
101-500	17
501-1800	07
2001-OUT	18
Hope (HAP)	54
Hope Rd (DUN)	38
Hope St & Dr SW	10
Hopewell Rd (CP)	37
Hopkins SE	15
Hopkins SW	
1-300	14
301-OUT	10
Hopkins Ter NE	24
Hornady NW	18

Atlanta (Con.) 303

Horseshoe Dr SE 16
Hortense St, Pl & Way NW 18
Horton Dr (CP) 37
Hospital Ave W (CHA) 41
Houghton Ct (DUN) 38
Houghton Ct N (DUN) 38
Houston NE
  1-300 03
  301-OUT 12
Houston Mill Rd NE 29
Hovey Ct (CP) 49
Howard NW 14
Howard Cir NE 07
Howard Dr (CP) 37
Howard St NE & SE 17
Howell Dr SE 16
Howell Dr & Ter SW 31
Howell Pl SW 10
Howell St NE & SE 12
Howell Mill Rd NW
  1-2570 18
  2571-OUT 27
Howland Ct (DUN) 38
Hubbard SW 10
Huber NW 18
Hudgens Rd (CP) 49
Hudgins Aly SW 12
Hudson Dr NE 06
Huff Rd NW 18
Hugh SW 10
Hughes NW 31
Hugo SW 15
Hull NW 13
Humility Dr & Ln NE 19
Humming Bird Ln NE 07
Humphries (EP) 44
Humphries SW
  1-660 12
  661-OUT 10
Humphries Dr SE 54
Humphries Way (DOR) 40
Hunnerkoff NW 18
Hunnicutt NW
  1-100 08
  101-OUT 13
Hunt NE 08
Hunt Ct (CP) 37
Huntcliff St & Pt (DUN) 38
Huntcliff Lake Ct (DUN) 38
Huntcliff Trace (DUN) 38
Hunter NW
  1-20 34
  21-300 03
  301-470 13
  471-OUT 14
Hunter SE
  1-3 34
  4-ONLY 03
  5-12 34
  13-OUT 12
Hunter SW
  1-20 34
  21-300 03
  301-470 13
  471-OUT 14
Hunter Pl NW 14
Hunter Rd (CP) 49
Hunters Pt NE 28
Hunters Branch St, Clse, Dr
  & Ln NE 28

Hunters Glen Ct NE 28
Hunters Trace Cir NE 28
Hunting Creek Rd NE 28
Huntington Cir (CHA) 41
Huntington Rd NE & NW 09
Huntington Trl (DUN) 38
Huntley Dr NE 42
Hurst Dr NE 05
Hurt NE 07
Hutchens Rd SE 54
Hutchinson NE 07
Hutton Pl NW 18
Hyacinth Ave NW 14
Hyde Mnr Dr NW 27
Idlewood Ct & Trl NE 19
Idlewood Dr (EP) 44
Idlewood Oaks Ct NE 19
Illinois Ave NW 14
Impala Dr NE 45
Imperial Dr NE 45
Indale Pl SW 10
Independence Pl NW 18
Indian Ln (DOR) 40
Indian Trl NW 27
Indian Rock Rd SW 31
Indian Valley Trl (CHA) 41
Indiana Ave NE 07
Indigo Ln NW 18
Industrial Blvd SW
  1-5400 36
  5401-OUT 31
Industrial Cir SW 36
Ingersoll Rand Dr (CHA) 41
Ingledale Dr SW 31
Inman SW 10
Inman Ave NE 08
Inman Cir NE 09
Inman Dr NE 19
Innsbruck Dr (DUN) 38
Innwood Rd NE 29
Interchange Dr SW 36
Interlochen Dr NE 42
International Blvd (HAP) 54
Interstate Pky NW 39
Interstate Pl NW, NW 39
Interstate North NW 39
Inverness Ave NE 06
Inwood Cir NE & NW 09
Iona Dr SE 16
Ira SW
  1-660 12
  661-OUT 10
Irby Ave NW 05
Ireland Pl NW 18
Iron Bound Pl NW 18
Iroquois Path NE 19
Irvindale Dr (CHA) 41
Irwin NE 12
Isa Dr SE 15
Island Ferry Rd (DUN) 38
Ison Rd (DUN) 38
Iswald SE 16
Ivan Hill Cir & Dr SW 11
Ivanhoe Dr NW 27
Iverson NE 07
Ivy Ln, Pky, Rd, Sq & Trl NE .. 42
Ivy Pl NE 07
Ivy St NE & SE 03
Ivy Gates NE 42
Ivy Ridge NE 42
Ivydale (EP) 44
Ivydale Dr SW 11
Ivywood Dr SW 31

Jackson (CP) 37
Jackson (HAP) 54
Jackson Dr (EP) 44
Jackson Pl SW 11
Jackson St NE & SE 12
Jacolyn Pl NE 29
Jailette Rd (CP) 49
Jamaica Rd NW 18
James Dr NW 18
James Jackson Pky NW 18
Jan Dr (CP) 37
Jan Hill Ln NE 29
Jane Rd (DOR) 40
Janellen Dr NE 45
Janes Ln NE 24
Janice Cir & Ct (CHA) 41
Janice Dr (EP) 44
Janice Dr (CP) 37
Jasmine Ct NE 45
Jasper SW 14
Jay Pl SE 15
Jefferson (CP) 37
Jefferson (CHA) 41
Jefferson NW 18
Jefferson Ave SW
  1-850 15
  851-OUT 44
Jefferson Ter (EP) 44
Jeffrey Dr (CP) 49
Jenkins SW 15
Jenny Wren Ln SW 11
Jeptha SW 14
Jernigan Dr & Pl SE 15
Jerome Rd (CP) 49
Jersey Rd (EP) 44
Jesup (EP) 44
Jetal Pl NW 18
Jett NW
  1-870 18
  871-OUT 14
Jett Dr (DOR) 40
Jett Rd NW 27
Jett Ferry Ct & Rd (DUN) 38
Jettridge Rd NW 27
Jewell (EP) 44
Joan Of Arc Pl (CP) 49
Jobeth SE 16
Jody Ln NE 29
Joe Louis Dr NW 14
Joel Ct, Ln & Pl (DOR) 40
John NW
  1-390 14
  391-OUT 18
John Calvin Ave (CP) 37
John Freeman Way (EP) 44
John Glen Dr (CHA) 41
John Hope Ct & Dr SW 14
John Wesley Ave (CP) 37
Johnny's Ln (DOR) 40
Johns Way NE 08
Johns NW 14
Johnson Ave NE 12
Johnson Cir E & W (CHA) 41
Johnson Dr (DOR) 40
Johnson Rd NE
  1-1910 06
  1911-OUT 45
Johnson Rd NW 18
Johnson Ferry Rd NE
  1-800 28
  801-1100 42
  1101-2320 19
  2321-2600 41

Atlanta (Con.)   303

Johnson Ferry Rd NW 28
Jolly Rd (CP).......................... 49
Jolyn Pl NE 42
Jonathon Ln NE 19
Jones Aly SW ....
Jones Ave (EP)........................ 44
Jones Ave NW
  1-1000................................ 14
  1001-OUT............................. 18
Jones Cir & Rd (CP).................. 49
Jones Rd NW 18
Jones Ferry Dr (CP).................. 40
Jones Mill Rd (DOR).................. 40
Jonesboro Rd (CP).................... 49
Jonesboro Rd SE
  1-2600................................ 15
  2601-3900............................ 54
Jordan SE 15
Jordan Ter NE 45
Josephine (CP)........................ 49
Josephine SE 16
Josephine Ave SE 16
Josephine Ave (DOR)................. 40
Journal Way NW....................... 03
Joyce SW 14
Joylan Pl SW 15
Joyland Ave SW 15
Judith Way NE 24
Judson (EP)............................ 44
Judy Ln SW 15
Judy Lynn (CP)........................ 49
Julian NW 18
Juniper NE
  1-870.................................. 08
  871-OUT.............................. 09
Kadleston Way NE 19
Kalb SE 12
Kammeyer Ln (CHA).................. 41
Karen Rd (CP)......................... 37
Karland Dr NW........................ 05
Katherwood Dr SW.................... 10
Kathryn Cir SW........................ 31
Kathryn Ct (EP)....................... 44
Katomarick Dr SE 54
Kay Ln NE.............................. 06
Kayron Dr NE
  1-5620................................ 42
  5621-OUT............................. 28
Keats Dr SW 11
Keenan Ct, Ln & Rd (CP) 49
Keiths Cir NE.......................... 05
Kelden Cir & Ct (CP)................. 49
Kelley St & Pl SE 12
Kellog Cir (DUN)...................... 38
Kellog Springs Dr (DUN)............ 38
Kelso Dr NW 11
Kemper Way NE....................... 42
Kenbrook Dr & Way NW............. 27
Kendall NE............................. 12
Kendall Ct NE......................... 42
Kendrick Ave SE 15
Kendrick Rd NE 19
Kenelworth Dr (EP)................... 44
Kenilworth Dr SW..................... 10
Kenlock Pl NE......................... 05
Kenmore SE 11
Kennedy St & Ct NW................. 18
Kennesaw Ave NE..................... 08
Kennesaw Dr NW..................... 18
Kennett SE............................. 15
Kenney Ct (EP)........................ 44

Kenneys Aly SW....................... 03
Kennington Ct NE..................... 19
Kenny Rd SW.......................... 31
Kenolia Dr SW 10
Kenora Dr SW 31
Kensington NE......................... 07
Kent SE 12
Kent Rd (CP).......................... 37
Kenton Pl SE 16
Kentucky Ave NE...................... 06
Kentucky Ct (EP)...................... 44
Kenway Dr (HAP)..................... 54
Kenwood Ave NW..................... 09
Kenwood Dr (HAP)................... 54
Kenyon SE.............................. 16
Kerry Cir NW, NW.................... 18
Kerry Dr & Pl NW 18
Keswick Ct & Dr (CHA).............. 41
Kevin Ct (CP).......................... 37
Kevin Ct NW........................... 11
Key Rd SE.............................. 16
Keystone Dr (HAP).................... 54
Kilburn Dr NE 24
Kilby Pl NW 27
Kildare Ave NW........................ 18
Kilgore SE.............................. 18
Kilgore Rd (CP)....................... 49
Killian SE
  1-800.................................. 12
  801-OUT.............................. 16
Kilt Ct (DOR).......................... 40
Kim Ct (DOR).......................... 40
Kimball Rd SW 31
Kimball Way NE....................... 03
Kimberly Ct (DOR).................... 40
Kimberly Ct SW, SW.................. 11
Kimberly Ln NE 06
Kimberly Rd SW....................... 31
Kimberly St & Cir (CP).............. 49
Kimberly Mill Ln & Rd (CP)....... 49
Kimblewick Cove (DUN).............. 38
Kimmeridge Dr (EP).................. 44
Kimsey Dr (CP)........................ 37
King (DOR)............................. 40
King SE 12
King Rd (HAP)......................... 54
King Rd NW 42
King Alfred Dr SW.................... 31
King Arnold (HAP).................... 54
King Arthur Cir & Ct NE............ 45
King Arthur Rd SW................... 31
King Charles Rd SW.................. 31
King Edward Trl SW.................. 31
King George Ln SW................... 31
King Henry Rd SW.................... 31
King James Dr SW.................... 31
King Richard Dr SW.................. 31
King Smith Rd SE..................... 54
Kings Cir NE........................... 05
Kings Ct NE............................ 06
Kings Walk NE......................... 07
Kings Way NW 27
Kings Down Cir, Ct, Rd &
  Way (DUN).......................... 38
Kings Grant Dr NW................... 18
Kings Point Cir E (CHA)............. 41
Kings Point Cir, Ct & Dr
  (CHA)................................ 41
Kingsboro Rd NE
  1-3500................................ 26
  3501-OUT............................. 19
Kingscliff Dr & Way NE.............. 45
Kingsdale Dr SW 11

Kingsfield Ct (CHA)................... 41
Kingsgate Ct & Dr (CHA)........... 41
Kingsglenn Ct & Dr (DOR).......... 40
Kingslake Ct NE....................... 45
Kingsland Ct & Dr (DOR)........... 40
Kingsley Cir NE 24
Kingstavern Pl NW 18
Kingston Ct & Dr NE................. 42
Kingston Rd NW 18
Kingston Ter (EP)..................... 44
Kingswood Cir (CP)................... 49
Kingswood Ln NW.................... 05
Kinlock NW 27
Kinnard (DOR)........................ 40
Kinsey Ct NE.......................... 05
Kipling Dr NW 18
Kipling St & Cir SE................... 15
Kirkland Dr NE 45
Kirkwood Ave SE...................... 16
Kirkwood Rd NE...................... 17
Kittredge Ct & Dr NE................ 29
Kittredge Park Rd NE................ 29
Kittrell Dr SW 31
Kitty Hawk Dr & Pl NE.............. 42
Knight Ct SE 16
Knighton Cir & Dr (CP)............. 49
Knob Hill Ct & Dr NE................ 29
Knob Hill Dr NW 39
Knollwood Dr NW 05
Knollwood Trl (EP)................... 44
Knott SE................................ 16
Knotts Ave (EP)....................... 44
Knox NE 17
Knox Ave (CHA)....................... 41
Knox Dr SE 15
Kodiak Cir & Dr NE.................. 45
Kowetta Rd & Trl (CP)............... 49
Krog NE 07
La Chona Ct NE....................... 18
La Dawn Ln NW....................... 18
La Fayette Dr NE...................... 09
La Fayette Rd & Way NW........... 27
La France NE........................... 07
La Rue Pl NW 27
La Salle Way SW 31
La Verne Dr NW...................... 18
La Vista Rd
  1-1500................................ 24
La Vista Rd NE
  1501-2460............................ 29
Lacey Cir (HAP)....................... 54
Ladd St & Pl SW 10
Ladovia Ln NE......................... 45
Lady Marion Ln NE................... 09
Lafayette Ave NW..................... 27
Lafayette Ln (CP)..................... 37
Lagrange Blvd SW..................... 36
Lajean Dr (CP)........................ 49
Lake Ave NE........................... 07
Lake Ave SW........................... 11
Lake Ave & Dr (HAP)................ 54
Lake Cir & Dr SE 15
Lake Dr (CP)........................... 37
Lake Dr (DOR)........................ 40
Lake Ter (EP).......................... 44
Lake Allen Ln NE 28
Lake Brook Ct (DOR)................ 40
Lake Flair Cir & Ct NE.............. 45
Lake Forrest Ct & Ln NE............ 42
Lake Forrest Dr NE
  1-5750................................ 42
  5751-OUT............................. 28

Atlanta (Con.)   303

Lake Forrest Dr NW
1-5750...................................... 42
5751-OUT.................................. 28
Lake Hearn Ct, Dr & Pl NE.... 19
Lake Island Dr NW.................. 27
Lake Mirror Rd (CP)................ 49
Lake Placid Dr NE.................... 42
Lake Valley Rd NW.................. 31
Lakehaven Dr NE...................... 19
Lakeland Dr NE & NW............ 05
Lakemont Dr
1-4000 (EP)............................ 44
4001-OUT (CP)........................ 37
Lakemoore Dr NE.................... 42
Lakeridge Cir SW...................... 31
Lakeshore Cir NE...................... 24
Lakeshore Dr (CP).................... 37
Lakeshore Dr NE
1-200...................................... 24
201-OUT.................................. 07
Lakeshore Dr At Crystal Lake
(CP)...................................... 49
Lakeside Dr (DOR).................. 40
Lakeside Dr NE........................ 26
Lakeview Ave NE
1-500...................................... 05
501-OUT.................................. 08
Lakeview Dr (CP)...................... 37
Lakeview Dr NE & SE.............. 17
Lakeview Ln (DOR).................. 40
Lakewood Ave (EP).................. 44
Lakewood Ave SW, SE
1-2930.................................... 15
2931-OUT................................ 10
Lakewood Ter SE...................... 15
Lakewood Way SW.................. 15
Lamar SE.................................. 15
Lamar Ave SW
1-50.. 10
51-OUT.................................... 14
Lambert Dr NE.......................... 24
Lambeth Cir & Ln (DOR)........ 40
Lamon Ave SW.......................... 16
Lampkin NE.............................. 12
Lamsden Ln NW........................ 27
Lanark Dr SW............................ 31
Lancaster Dr (EP)...................... 44
Lancaster Loop NE.................... 28
Land Olakes Ct & Dr NE........ 42
Landmark Dr NE........................ 42
Landrum Dr SW........................ 11
Landsdowne Dr NW.................. 28
Lanes Ln NE.............................. 17
Lang Ave (HAP)........................ 54
Lang Dr SW................................ 15
Langford Ln NW........................ 27
Langhorn SW.............................. 10
Langland Ct NE.......................... 45
Langston Ave SW...................... 10
Langston Dr SW........................ 15
Lanier NW.................................. 18
Lanier Blvd & Pl NE................ 06
Lanier Dr NE.............................. 19
Lanier Dr SW............................ 10
Lannon Ave NE.......................... 17
Lansbury Dr NE........................ 42
Lansbury Village Dr (CHA).... 41
Lansing SE................................ 15
Lansol Rd (DOR)...................... 40
Lantern Ln (CP)........................ 49

Lanvale Dr SW.......................... 10
Laquita Dr SE............................ 15
Laramie Dr NW........................ 39
Larchmont Cir, Ct & Dr NW.... 18
Larchwood SW.......................... 10
Laren Ln SW.............................. 11
Largo Ln SW.............................. 31
Larkfield Dr NE........................ 28
Larkin SW
1-530...................................... 13
531-OUT.................................. 14
Larkin Ct SW
1-530...................................... 13
531-OUT.................................. 14
Larkin Pl SW............................ 13
Larkspur Dr SE.......................... 16
Larosa Ter SW.......................... 10
Larose (EP)................................ 44
Latham SW................................ 10
Lathrop SE................................ 15
Latimer NW.............................. 13
Latona Dr SW............................ 54
Lauderdale Dr NE...................... 45
Laurel Ave NW........................ 18
Laurel Ave SW
1-280...................................... 14
281-OUT.................................. 10
Laurel Dr NE.............................. 42
Laurel Ln (EP).......................... 44
Laurel Forrest Cir NE.............. 42
Laurel Oak Ct (DOR).............. 40
Laurelmont Dr SW.................... 11
Laurelwood Dr SW.................... 11
Laurelwood Rd (DOR).............. 40
Laurens Cir, Dr & Way SW...... 11
Lavender Dr NW........................ 14
Laventure Dr & Rd (CHA)...... 41
Lavista Cir & Dr (HAP).......... 54
Law NW...................................... 18
Lawn SW.................................... 10
Lawrence NW............................ 31
Lawrence St & Ave (EP).......... 44
Lawshe NE................................ 14
Lawshe St Ct SW...................... 14
Lawson Way (CHA).................. 41
Lawton SW
1-270...................................... 14
271-OUT.................................. 10
Lawton Ave & Pl SW................ 10
Layton Ave NW........................ 18
Le Baron Dr NE........................ 45
Le Brun Rd NE.......................... 10
Le Conte Ave NE...................... 19
Le Conte Hwy SW.................... 31
Leach NW.................................. 14
Leathers Cir NW...................... 14
Leavens (EP).............................. 44
Lebanon Dr NE.......................... 24
Ledgewood Dr (CHA)................ 41
Lee (EP)...................................... 44
Lee (CP)...................................... 37
Lee Cir NE................................ 24
Lee St & Pl SW.......................... 10
Lee Andrews Ave SE................ 15
Leeds Ct & Way (DUN).......... 38
Lees Mill Rd (CP).................... 49
Leesburg Ct SW........................ 31
Legion Way (EP)........................ 44
Leila Ln SE................................ 15
Leisure Ct, Dr & Ln (DOR)...... 40
Leisure Ln (CP).......................... 49
Leisure Lake Dr (DOR)............ 40
Leith (EP).................................. 44

Leland Pl SW............................ 31
Leland Ter NE............................ 17
Lena NW.................................... 14
Lenox Cir NE............................ 06
Lenox Pl & Way NE.................. 24
Lenox Rd NE
1-2020.................................... 06
2021-3290.............................. 24
3291-OUT................................ 26
Lenox Sq Shopping Center...... 26
Leonard SW
381-OUT.................................. 13
Leonardo Ave NE...................... 07
Leonardo Dr SW........................ 31
Lesley Dr (CP).......................... 37
Leslie NE.................................... 07
Leslie SE.................................... 17
Leslie Ave (HAP)...................... 54
Leslie Ct, Dr & Ln NE............ 45
Lester (EP)................................ 44
Lester NW.................................. 14
Lester Rd (CP).......................... 49
Lethea SE.................................. 15
Level Ridge Rd SE.................... 54
Lewfield Cir SE........................ 16
Lewis Cir (CP).......................... 37
Lewis Rd SE.............................. 15
Lexington Ave (EP).................. 44
Lexington Ave SW.................... 10
Liawen Ct NE............................ 29
Liberty (CP).............................. 37
Liberty Ave NE.......................... 17
Liddell Dr NE............................ 24
Light House Pt NW.................. 28
Lilla Cir & Dr SW.................... 10
Lillian SW.................................. 10
Limerick Dr SW........................ 31
Limey Dr NW............................ 18
Linam Ave SE............................ 15
Lincoln Ave SE.......................... 17
Lincoln Ct & Dr NW................ 18
Lincoln St, Ave, Dr & Pl SW.... 15
Linda Ln SE.............................. 15
Linda Way SW.......................... 10
Lindberg Way NE...................... 24
Lindbergh Cir NE...................... 24
Lindbergh Dr NE
1-450...................................... 05
451-OUT.................................. 24
Linden Ave NE & NW.............. 08
Linden Ln (DOR)...................... 40
Linden Garden Dr (CP)............ 49
Lindenwood Ln NE.................. 19
Lindmont Cir & Ct NE............ 24
Lindridge Dr & Way NE.......... 24
Lindsay NW
1-560...................................... 14
561-OUT.................................. 18
Lindsay Pl NW.......................... 14
Lindsey Dr SE............................ 15
Line Rd SW................................ 31
Lingo Way SW.......................... 12
Linkwood Pl NW...................... 18
Linkwood Rd NW
1-160...................................... 11
161-OUT.................................. 18
Linwood Ave (EP).................... 44
Linwood Ave NE...................... 06
Lisa Ct & Dr SW...................... 11
Lisa Ln (DUN).......................... 38
Lisbon Dr SW............................ 10
Little St SE & SW.................... 15
Little John Trl NE.................... 09

Atlanta (Con.)   303

Little John Way (DOR)	40
Live Oak Dr (DOR)	40
Lively Trl NE	45
Lively Ridge Rd NE	29
Livermore SE	15
Livesy Ct (DOR)	40
Loch Lomond Tr Trl SW	31
Lochland Rd SE	16
Locke Dr SE	16
Lockhaven Cir SW	11
Locklear Ct & Way (DOR)	40
Lockridge Dr (DOR)	40
Lockwood Dr SW	11
Locust SE	17
Locust Ln SE	15
Lofton Rd NW	09
Logan SE	12
Logan Cir NE	
1-1500	18
1501-OUT	19
Logan Cir NW	
1-1500	18
1501-OUT	19
Logan Pl (HAP)	54
Loghaven Dr NW	18
Lois Ln SE	15
Lois Pl NW	18
Loma Linda SW	10
Lombardy Way NE	09
Lomita Rd SE	16
London Dr NW	27
London Rd (CHA)	41
Londonberry Rd NW	27
Lone Oak Ave SW	54
Lone Star Trl (DOR)	40
Lonetia SE	12
Long (EP)	44
Long Acres Dr NW	28
Long Branch Ct NE	19
Long Island Ct NE & NW	28
Long Island Dr NE	
1-4900	42
4901-5800	27
5801-OUT	28
Long Island Dr NW	
1-4900	42
4901-5800	27
5801-OUT	28
Long Island Pl NE & NW	28
Long Island Rd & Way NW	27
Long Island Ter NE	42
Long Leaf Dr NE	42
Longchamps Rd NE	19
Longley Ave NW	18
Longmeadow Ln (CP)	49
Longmire Way (DOR)	40
Longview (EP)	44
Longview Ave NE	12
Longview Dr & Way (CHA)	41
Longwood Dr NW	05
Lookout Ave NW	18
Lookout Pl NE	05
Loomis Ave SE	12
Loraine Dr NE	19
Lorell Ter NE	28
Lorenzo Dr SW	10
Lori Ln (DOR)	40
Loridan Cir & Dr NE	42
Loring SE	16
Loring Dr NW	09
Los Angeles Ave NE	06
Los Olas Dr (CP)	49
Lost Mine Trl (DOR)	40
Lottie Pl (CP)	37
Lotus Ave NW	18
Louden Dr NE	45
Louis Xiv Ln (CP)	49
Louise (HAP)	54
Louise Aly NW	13
Louise Pl NW	18
Love St SE & SW	13
Lovejoy NE	13
Loveless Ave NW	18
Lovridge Dr SW	31
Lowe (CP)	37
Lowe NW	18
Lowergate Dr NE	07
Lowes Aly SW	13
Lowndes (CP)	37
Lowndes (EP)	44
Lowndes Ave SW	10
Lowry NE	07
Loyd SW	03
Loyola Dr SW	36
Lu-Jan Dr (CHA)	41
Lucile Ln (EP)	44
Lucille Ave SW	10
Luckie NW	
1-234	03
235-OUT	13
Luckie Ln NE	29
Lucy SE	12
Lullwater Pky, Pl & Rd NE	07
Lumpkin (EP)	44
Luray Ct & Dr (CHA)	41
Luther SE	15
Luther Cir & Dr (EP)	44
Lydia Dr SE	15
Lyle Ave	
1-1500 (EP)	44
1501-OUT (CP)	37
Lyle Pl NW	18
Lyle Rd & Ter (CP)	37
Lynch Ave NW	18
Lyndale Dr SE	16
Lynfield Ct & Dr (CP)	49
Lynfield Dr SW	11
Lynford Dr SW	11
Lynhaven Dr SW	10
Lynhurst Cir & Dr SW	11
Lynmoor Dr NE	19
Lynn Cir & Dr SW	11
Lynn Dr (CP)	37
Lynn Valley Rd SW	11
Lynnray Dr (DOR)	40
Lynrix Ln & Pl (DOR)	40
Lynway Ln SW	11
Lynwood SE	12
Lynwood Ave (CP)	37
Lynwood Dr NE	19
Lynwyn Ln SE	16
Lyons Ave NE	12
Lyric Ct & Ln (HAP)	54
Lyric Way NW	18
Lytle Ave SE	16
Mabry Ln NE	19
Mabry Rd NE	
1-1000	28
1001-OUT	19
Mac Dougall Dr SW	36
Macaw NW	18
Macedonia Rd SE	54
Mack Dr NW	18
Macklone NE	07
Maco NW	18
Macon Dr SE	
1-2700	15
2701-OUT	54
Macon Dr SW	
1-2700	15
2701-OUT	54
Macon Pl SE	54
Macon Ter SW	15
Maddox Aly SE	12
Maddox Dr NE	09
Maderia Ave NE	07
Madison (CP)	37
Madison Ave NE	19
Madronah NW	18
Magic Pac Way SW	54
Magna Carta Dr NW	18
Magnolia (EP)	44
Magnolia NW	
1-470	13
471-OUT	14
Magnolia Pl NW	13
Mailing Ave SE	15
Main (HAP)	54
Main (EP)	44
Main (CP)	37
Main NW	18
Main St E & S (EP)	44
Main At Crystal Lake (CP)	49
Maison Pl NW	27
Malabar Dr NE	45
Maldo Dr NW	18
Mallard NW	18
Mallory Rd (CP)	49
Malone Dr (CHA)	41
Manchester Rd NE	24
Maney Ln	10
Manford Rd SW	
1-300	15
301-OUT	10
Manget Ct & Way (DUN)	38
Mango Cir NW	18
Mangum NW	
1-180	13
181-OUT	14
Mangum SW	13
Mangum Ln SW	11
Manhasset Dr (DUN)	38
Manhasset Cove (DUN)	38
Manigault SE	16
Manning (DOR)	40
Manor (EP)	44
Manor Pl SW	10
Manor Ridge Dr NW	05
Mansfield Ave NE	07
Manson Ave SW	10
Mantissa NW	18
Manville Dr (CHA)	41
Maple (EP)	44
Maple (HAP)	54
Maple Dr NE	05
Maple St, Aly & Pl NW	14
Mapledale Ln (CP)	49
Marann Dr NE	45
Marbury Cir NW	27
Marbut Ave SE	16
Marcell Ave SW	11
Marchman Dr NW	42
Marco Dr NW	18
Marcus SE	16
Marcy SE	15
Margaret (HAP)	54
Margaret SE	15

Atlanta (Con.)   303

Margaret Cir (CP)..................... 49
Margaret Pl NW....................... 18
Margaret Mitchell Ct & Dr
  NW....................................... 27
Margavera Ter (CHA)................ 41
Marian Rd NE.......................... 24
Maribeau Sq NW...................... 27
Marie Ave NW.......................... 14
Marie Head Ter (EP)................ 44
Marietta NW
  1-245................................... 03
  246-666............................... 13
  667-OUT............................... 18
Marietta Blvd, Pl & Rd NW...... 18
Marina (HAP)........................... 54
Marion SE
  1-1060................................. 12
  1001-OUT............................. 15
Marion Ave SE
  1-1000................................. 12
  1001-OUT............................. 15
Marion St, Ave & Pl NE........... 07
Marjan St, Ct & Dr (DOR)....... 31
Mark Pl NW............................. 31
Mark Two NW........................... 14
Markan Ct & Dr NE.................. 06
Market Dr (HAP)...................... 54
Market Sq Pl NW...................... 18
Markham SW............................ 13
Markone NW............................. 18
Marktray NW............................ 18
Marlborough Cir (CP)............... 49
Marlbrook Dr NE...................... 07
Marlin Cir, Dr & Way (CHA)..... 41
Marne Dr NW........................... 05
Marona NE............................... 07
Marray Dr (CHA)...................... 41
Marstevan Dr NE...................... 06
Martell Dr (EP)......................... 44
Martha Ave NE......................... 17
Martin (EP).............................. 44
Martin SE
  1-650................................... 12
  651-OUT............................... 15
Martin Ave SE.......................... 15
Martina Dr (DUN).................... 38
Martina Dr NE.......................... 05
Marvin NW............................... 18
Marvin Ln SW........................... 11
Marvin Miller Dr SW................. 36
Mary SW.................................. 10
Mary Briggs Ct (DOR)............. 40
Mary Dell Dr SE........................ 16
Mary George Ave NW............... 18
Mary Lou Ln SE........................ 16
Maryeanna Dr NE..................... 42
Maryland (EP).......................... 44
Maryland Ave NE...................... 06
Maryland Dr (DOR).................. 40
Mason Rd (CP)......................... 49
Mason Mill Rd NE
  1-1730................................. 29
Mason Woods Dr NE................. 29
Massachusetts Blvd (CHA)....... 37
Matador Ct (EP)....................... 44
Mathews NE............................. 19
Mathews SW............................ 10
Mathews Ave NE...................... 07
Mathewson Pl SW
  1-280................................... 14
  281-OUT............................... 10

Mathieson Dr, Pl & Rd NE...... 05
Matilda Pl NW.......................... 18
Mauldin NW............................. 18
Mauldin SE.............................. 16
Maxwell Dr SW......................... 11
May Ave NE............................. 19
May Ave SE.............................. 16
Mayes NW................................ 14
Mayfair Dr NE.......................... 24
Mayflower Ave SW................... 11
Mayflower Rd (CP)................... 37
Mayland Ave & Cir SW............. 10
Maynard Ct & Rd NW............... 31
Maynard Ter SE........................ 16
Mayo Pl SW............................. 11
Mayson NE............................... 24
Mayson Ave NE
  1-70..................................... 17
  71-OUT................................. 07
Mayson Turner Ave & Rd NW.. 14
Maywood Pl NW....................... 18
Mc Afee NW............................. 13
Mc Alister SW.......................... 10
Mc Callie Blvd NW................... 18
Mc Clatchey Cir NE.................. 42
Mc Clure Ave NW..................... 14
Mc Cully Ct & Dr NE................ 45
Mc Daniel SW
  1-400................................... 13
  401-660............................... 12
  661-OUT............................... 10
Mc Donald SE........................... 12
Mc Donough Blvd SE................ 15
Mc Dougall Dr SW.................... 36
Mc Griff NW............................. 18
Mc Gruder NE.......................... 12
Mc Jenkins Dr NE..................... 45
Mc Kay Dr SE........................... 15
Mc Kenzie Dr NE...................... 12
Mc Kinley Rd NW..................... 18
Mc Lain NE.............................. 07
Mc Lendon Ave NE................... 07
Mc Lendon Cir NW................... 18
Mc Lynn Ave NE....................... 06
Mc Millan NW.......................... 18
Mc Murray Dr SW..................... 11
Mc Pherson Ave & Pl SE.......... 16
Mc Veigh Ln SW....................... 10
Mc Williams Ave SE................. 16
Mc Williams Rd SE................... 15
Mcalpine Ter (EP).................... 44
Mcarthur Blvd NW.................... 18
Mcbaine Ln (DOR)................... 40
Mccall Dr & Pl (DOR).............. 40
Mcclaren Cir (DOR).................. 40
Mcclave (DOR)......................... 40
Mcclelland Ave (EP)................. 44
Mcconnell Dr (DOR)................. 40
Mccree Dr (EP)......................... 37
Mcdaniel (CHA)........................ 41
Mcdonald (CP)......................... 37
Mcdonald Dr SE........................ 15
Mcdonald Trl (CP).................... 49
Mcelroy (CP)............................ 49
Mcelroy Rd (DOR).................... 40
Mcgaw Dr (CHA)...................... 41
Mcghee Way (EP)..................... 44
Mckenzie Ct SW....................... 11
Mckenzie Dr (EP)..................... 44
Mcmullin Ter (EP).................... 44
Mcpherson Dr (EP)................... 44
Mead SE
  1-580................................... 15

581-OUT................................. 12
Meador Ave & Way SE............. 15
Meadow Rd (HAP).................... 54
Meadow Lane Rd (DUN)........... 38
Meadow Park Dr & Ln SW........ 15

Meadow Valley Dr NE............... 42
Meadowbrook Dr NE................. 42
Meadowcliff Dr NE................... 45
Meadowdale Ave NE................. 06
Meadowlake Dr SE.................... 17
Meadowlake Dr & Ln (DUN)..... 38
Meadowlane Dr SW................... 11
Meadowlane Pl SW
  1-3400................................. 11
  3401-OUT............................. 31
Meadowlark Dr & Ln (EP)......... 44
Meadowood Ln (CHA).............. 41
Meadowridge Dr SW................. 31
Meadowvale Dr NE................... 45
Meadowview Dr & Ln SE........... 16
Means NW............................... 18
Mecaslin NW
  1-1400................................. 18
  1401-OUT............................. 09
Mechanic NW........................... 13
Mechanicsville Rd (DOR)......... 40
Medfield Tr NE......................... 45
Medinah Ct (CHA).................... 41
Meeting Rd NE......................... 19
Melanie Ln (CP)....................... 49
Melante Dr NE......................... 24
Melbenan Dr SW...................... 11
Meldon Ave SE & SW............... 15
Meldrum NW............................ 18
Melinda Ct & Dr NE.................. 45
Mell Ave NE............................. 07
Mellrich Ave NE....................... 17
Mellview Ave SW...................... 10
Mellwood Ave SW..................... 31
Melrose Dr SE.......................... 16
Melrose Dr SW......................... 10
Melvin Dr SW........................... 31
Memorial Dr SE
  1-670................................... 12
  671-1272............................. 16
  1273-3150........................... 17
Memorial Dr SW....................... 03
Memorial Ter SE....................... 16
Mendell Cir NE......................... 19
Mendell Ct & Dr SW................. 36
Mendenhall Dr (CHA).............. 41
Menlo Dr NW
  1-3400................................. 18
  3401-4050 (DOR)................. 40
Menlo Way (DOR)..................... 40
Mentelle Dr NE........................ 08
Mercedes Ct & Dr NE............... 45
Mercer (EP).............................. 44
Mercer SE
  1-850................................... 12
  851-OUT............................... 16
Mercer Ave (CP)....................... 37
Merck Rd SW............................ 31
Mercury Dr NW......................... 31
Meredith Dr NW....................... 18
Meridian SE............................. 17
Merlendale Ct & Dr NW........... 27
Merlin Ave SE........................... 17
Merrick Dr NE.......................... 24
Merrill Ave SW......................... 10
Merrimac Ct NE........................ 29
Merriman Ln NE....................... 24
Merritts Ave NE........................ 08

Atlanta (Con.)   303

Merritts Ave NW 13
Merry Ln NE 29
Merton Rd NE 06
Mesa Dr SE 16
Metal Rd NE 24
Metropolitan Ave & Pl SE 16
Miami Cir NE 24
Michael NE 29
Michael Dr (CP) 49
Michael Pl 10
Michelle Cir NW 42
Michigan Ave NW 14
Middle SW 10
Middle Plantation Rd NW 18
Middleburg Dr (CP) 49
Middlebury Ln NW 27
Middlesex Ave NE 06
Middleton SW 15
Middleton Dr & Rd NW 11
Midvale Dr NE 42
Midvale Rd NE
   1-3400 45
Midway SE 15
Mifflin Pl NE 24
Milam Ave SW 15
Milan Dr (CP) 49
Mildred SW 14
Mildred Pl NW 18
Miles Cir (EP) 44
Miles Rd (CP) 49
Mill Ct (DOR) 40
Mill Acres Dr SW 11
Mill Brook Dr (DUN) 38
Mill Creek Rd NE 19
Mill Gate Dr (DUN) 38
Mill Glen Ct & Dr (DUN) 38
Mill Race Ct (DUN) 38
Mill Shire Ln (DUN) 38
Mill Stream Dr (DUN) 38
Mill Trace Ct & Dr (DUN) 38
Mill Vale Ct (DOR) 40
Mill Valley Rd SW 31
Millboro Ln (CP) 49
Millbrook Dr NW 27
Milledge Ave SE
   1-1000 12
   1001-OUT (EP) 44
Milledge Ct SE 12
Milledge Pl NE 29
Millege Ave 44
Miller Ave NE 07
Miller Cir & Dr SW 10
Miller Ct (DOR) 40
Miller Dr (CHA) 41
Miller Rd (CP) 49
Miller Reed Ave SE 15
Millirons Dr SW 15
Mills NW
   1-100 08
   101-OUT 13
Mills Pl SW 36
Milmar Dr NW 27
Milowyn Pl NE 19
Milton SW 14
Milton Ave & Ter SE 15
Milton Pl SE 16
Mims SW 14
Mirror Ln SE 17
Mission Ridge Cir, Ct, Ln & Rd NW 39

Mitchell SW
   1-250 03
   251-470 13
   471-OUT 14
Mitchell Rd NW 28
Mobile NW 14
Mobile Ave NE 05
Mobile Ave SW 15
Mobley Ct & Dr SE 15
Mocking Bird Ln NW 11
Mollie SE 16
Monarch Rd SE 16
Monica Ct SW 11
Monroe Cir NE 08
Monroe Dr (CP) 37
Monroe Dr NE
   1-1000 08
   1001-1320 06
   1321-OUT 24
Monroe Pl NE 24
Montana Rd NW 27
Montclair Dr NW 09
Monte Sq NW 27
Monte Carlo Dr NW 27
Montecello Ct & Dr (DUN) 38
Monteel Dr NW 18
Montego Bay Dr (CP) 49
Monterey Dr NW 18
Montevallo Dr NE 42
Montevista NW 10
Montford Dr (CHA) 41
Montgomery NE 09
Montgomery SE 17
Montgomery Ferry Dr NE
   1-450 09
   451-OUT 24
Montgomery Ferry Rd NE
   1-450 09
   451-OUT 24
Monticello Way (CP) 37
Montilly Cir & Pl (CP) 49
Montreat Ave SW
   1-1500 10
   1501-OUT 11
Montreat Pl SW 11
Montrose Ave SW 11
Montrose Dr (EP) 44
Montvallo Ter SE 16
Montview Dr NW 05
Monument Ave SE 16
Moody Dr SW 15
Moore NW 18
Moore SE
   1-200 03
   201-OUT 12
Moore Dr (CHA) 41
Moores Mill Rd NW
   1-600 05
   601-1700 27
   1701-OUT 18
Moray SW 11
Morehouse Dr NW 14
Moreland Ave NE
   1-660 07
   661-OUT 06
Moreland Ave SE
   1-2070 16
   2071-2910 15
Moreland Dr SE 16
Moreland Pl SE 16
Moreland Way (HAP) 54
Morgan NE 08
Morgan Pl SE 17

Morgan Rd (DOR) 40
Morgan Falls Rd (DUN) 38
Morley Ave SE 12
Morning Trl (CP) 49
Morning Creek Cir & Dr (CP) .. 49
Morningside Dr NE
   1-850 24
   851-OUT 06
Mornington Dr NW 27
Morosgo Ct, Dr, Pl & Way NE . 24
Morris (HAP) 54
Morris NW
   1-4000 18
Morris NW, NW
   4001-OUT 42
Morris Ave (EP) 44
Morris Ave NE
   1-4000 18
Morris Ave NE, NE
   4001-OUT 42
Morris Rd NW
   1-4000 18
Morris Rd NW, NW
   4001-OUT 42
Morris Brown Ave NW 14
Morris Brown Dr SW 14
Morris Landers Dr NE 45
Mortimer St & Pl SE 17
Morton Ave SW 15
Mosey Vale Way NW 28
Moss Oak Dr (DOR) 40
Motors Ind Way (DOR) 40
Moughorn NW 14
Mount Airy Dr SW 11
Mount Brian Rd NE 29
Mount Gilead Pl SW 11
Mount Gilead Rd SW
   1-3000 31
   3001-3350 11
   3351-OUT 31
Mount Mariah Pl & Rd NE 29
Mount Paran Pky & Rd NW 27
Mount Paran Rd NE 42
Mount Royal Dr NE 29
Mount Vernon Hwy NE
   1-1000 28
   1001-2380 38
   2381-2900 (EVEN) 38
   2381-2900 (ODD) 40
   2901-OUT 40
Mount Vernon Hwy NW
   1-400 28
   401-OUT 27
Mount Vernon Pky NW 27
Mount Vernon Rd NW
   1-400 28
   401-OUT 27
Mount Zion Rd SE 54
Mount Zion Rd SW
   1-280 54
Mountain Dr & Way NE 42
Mountain Brook Ln & Way NW 28
Mountain Creek Rd NE 28
Mountain Creek Trl NW 28
Moury SE 15
Moury Ave SW 15
Mozley Dr & Pl SW 14
Mt Olive Rd (EP) 44
Mt Vernon Dr (EP) 44
Mt Vernon Pl & Way (DUN) 38
Mt Vernon Way (CP) 37

Atlanta (Con.)　　　　　　303

Mt Vernon Forest Ct (DUN) 38
Mulberry St & Ct (EP) 44
Mundy Dr (CHA) 41
Mural Dr (CHA) 41
Muriel Ave NE 07
Murphy Ave & Cir SW 10
Murphy Candler Ct NE 19
Murray SE 15
Murray Hill Ave NE 17
Muscogee Ave NW 05
Muse SW 10
Musket Ridge NW 27
Myrtle (HAP) 54
Myrtle NE
　1-870 08
　871-OUT 09
Myrtle Dr SW 11
Myrtle St & Ln (CP) 37
Mystic Dr & Pl NE 42
N Powers Ferry Rd NW 27
N Stratford Rd NE 42
Nabel (EP) 44
Nacoochee Dr NW 05
Nancy Ln NE 45
Nancy Creek Rd NW 27
Nancy Creek Way NE 19
Nancy Creek Bluffs NW 27
Nandina Ln (DUN) 38
Nantahalla Ct NE 29
Napier SE 16
Napoleon (NEWCP) 37
Napoleon (OLDCP) 37
Napoleon Dr SW 14
Narmore Dr NE 19
Narron Ct SW, SW 31
Narron Dr SW, SW 31
Narrow Ave SE 12
Nash Ave SE 16
Nash Rd NW 31
Nassau NW 03
Natham Dr SE 15
Nathan Rd SW 31
Navaho Trl (CP) 49
Navajo Pl & Trl NE 19
Navajo Trl SW 31
Nawench Dr NW 27
Neal NW
　1-860 18
　861-OUT 14
Neal Pl NW 14
Neely Ave (EP) 44
Nekoma NW 18
Nelms Ave NE 07
Nelms Dr SW 15
Nelson SW
　1-300 03
　301-OUT 13
Neola Ln (CP) 49
Neptune Pl NW 31
Nerene Cir (DUN) 38
Nesbit Dr NE 19
Nesbit Ferry Rd (DOR) 40
Neveis Rd (CP) 49
New (EP) 44
New NE 07
New Hope Rd SW 31
New Jersey Ave NW 14
New London Trace NW 27
New Macon Hwy SE
　1-2910 15

New Paces Ferry Rd NW 39
New Peachtree Rd
　1-5715 (CHA) 41
　5716-OUT (DOR) 40
New South Pryor Rd SW 15
New York Ave NE 07
Newborn Dr (CP) 49
Newcastle SW 14
Newman Cir & Pl NW 18
Newnan Ave (EP) 44
Newport NW
　1-430 14
　431-OUT 18
Newport Pl NW 18
Newton Ave NW 14
Newton Ave SE 16
Newton Dr (DOR) 40
Newton Dr SW 31
Niles Ave NW 18
Niskey Lake Cir, Rd & Trl
　SW 31
Noble Dr NE 06
Noel Ave NW 18
Noel Dr NE 19
Noland SE 15
Norcross SW 10
Norfleet Rd NW 05
Norfolk NE 14
Norman Blvd & Dr (CP) 49
Norman Berry Blvd (EP) 44
Normandy Dr NE
　1-2000 06
　2001-OUT 05
Normandy Dr NW
　1-2000 06
　2001-OUT 05
North (EP) 44
North Ave NE
　1-700 08
　701-1070 06
　1071-1462 07
North Ave NW
　1-100 08
　101-400 13
　225-225 32
　401-OUT 18
North Dr SW 31
North St & Ave (HAP) 54
North Akin Dr NE 45
North Amanda Cir NE 29
North Angier Ave NE 08
North Blackland Rd NW 27
North Boundary Pl NW 18
North Broadland Rd NW 42
North Camp Creek Pky SW,
　SW 31
North Circle Dr NW 18
North Cliff Valley Way NE
　1-1500 19
　1501-OUT 29
North Close SW 31
North Colonial Homes Cir
　NW 09
North Decatur Rd NE
　1-1500 06
　1501-2049 07
North Dekalb Dr (DOR) 40
North Druid Hills Rd NE
　1-2000 19
　2001-3050 29
North East Expressway (CHA) .. 41
North East Expressway
　Access (CHA) 41

North Ellington SE 17
North Emory Pl NE 06
North Fulton Dr NE 05
North Garden Ln NW 09
North Gatewood Rd NE 29
North Green Dr & Rd NW 28
North Hampton Dr NE 28
North Harbor Ct & Dr NW 28
North Haven Ln (DOR) 40
North Highland Ave NE
　1-610 07
　611-OUT 06
North Hills Dr NE 05
North Holly Ln NE 29
North Howard NE 17
North Island Dr & Ter NW 27
North Island Ferry Rd (DUN) ... 38
North Ivy Rd NE 42
North Kimberly Dr (DOR) 40
North Lake Dr, Trl & Way
　(DOR) 40
North Mill Ct & Rd NW 28
North Muscogee Ave NW 05
North Paces Ferry Rd NW 39
North Peachtree Rd
　1-4825 (CHA) 41
　4826-5050 (DOR) 40
　5051-OUT (DUN) 38
North Peachtree Way (DUN) ... 38
North Pelham Rd NE 24
North Pharr Ct NW 05
North Piper Cir SE 16
North Ponce De Leon Ave NE .. 07
North Powers Ferry Rd NW 27
North Rhodes Center NW 09
North Ridgeway Rd NE 45
North River Dr (DUN) 38
North Shore Dr SW 11
North Spring Ct NW 28
North Springs Dr (DUN) 38
North Star Trl SW 31
North Stratford Rd NE 42
North Thompson Rd NE 19
North Umberland Dr (DOR) 40
North Virginia Ave NE 06
North Warren NE 17
North Wood Valley Rd NW 27
North Woodland Cir & Dr
　(DOR) 40
North Woods Pl (HAP) 54
Northbrook Ct (DOR) 40
Northbrook Dr
　1-3050 (DOR) 40
　3051-3255 (CHA) 41
　3256-OUT (DOR) 40
Northchester Ct (DUN) 38
Northcliffe Dr NW 18
Northcrest Rd (DOR) 40
Northeast Fwy NE
　1-1900 29
　1901-2850 45
　2851-3500 41
Northeast Fwy, NE
　3501-OUT 40
Northeast Plz NE 29
Northeast Shopping Center
　NE 29
Northern Ave SE 16
Northfield Blvd & Ct (CP) 49
Northland Ct & Dr NE 42
Northridge Dr (DUN) 38
Northrope Dr NE 24
Northside Cir NW 09

Atlanta (Con.)   **303**

Northside Dr (HAP)	54
Northside Dr NW	
1-340	14
341-2020	18
2021-3850	05
3851-4240	42
4241-5500	27
5501-OUT	28
Northside Dr SW	
1-450	13
451-500	03
501-600	10
Northside Pky NW	27
Northside 75 NW	18
Northview Ave NE	06
Northway Dr & Ln NE	42
Northwest (HAP)	54
Northwest Dr (CP)	37
Northwest Dr NW	
1-1514	18
1515-ONLY	31
1516-1550	18
1551-OUT	31
Northwood Ave NE & NW	09
Norwalk Ct (CHA)	41
Norwich Cir NE	24
Norwood Ave NE	17
Norwood Rd SE	15
Nottaway Ct (CHA)	41
Nottingham Way NE	09
Nutting NE	08
Oak (EP)	44
Oak (CP)	37
Oak NW	18
Oak SW	10
Oak Dr SE & SW	54
Oak Ln NE	29
Oak Rd (DOR)	40
Oak St & Dr (HAP)	54
Oak Forest Dr (HAP)	54
Oak Forrest Ct & Dr NE	19
Oak Grove Ave SE	16
Oak Grove Rd NE	
1806-OUT	45
Oak Knoll Cir & Ter SE	15
Oak Ridge Ave (HAP)	54
Oak Ridge Ln (EP)	44
Oak Tree Ct (EP)	44
Oak Valley Rd NE	26
Oakawana Dr NE	45
Oakcliff Ct NW	31
Oakcliff Rd (DOR)	40
Oakcliff Rd NW	
1-3200	11
3201-OUT	31
Oakcliff Ind Ct (DOR)	40
Oakcliff Industrial (DOR)	40
Oakcrest Dr SW	11
Oakdale NW	18
Oakdale Rd (HAP)	54
Oakdale Rd NE	07
Oakfield Dr SE	16
Oakhill Ave SW	10
Oakhill Dr (CP)	37
Oakland Ave SE	
1-650	12
651-OUT	15
Oakland Dr, Ln & Ter SW	10
Oaklawn Ave NE	19
Oakleigh Dr (EP)	44
Oakley Rd (CP)	49

Oakmont Ave (DOR)	40
Oakmont Dr NW	14
Oakridge Ave NE & SE	17
Oakside Dr SW	31
Oakview Rd NE & SE	17
Oana NW	10
Ocala Ave SW	11
Ocean Valley Dr (CP)	49
Oconee Pass NE	19
Octavia SE	15
Octavia Pl (DOR)	40
Odd Fellows Pl SE	12
Ogden SW	14
Ogilvie Dr NE	24
Oglethorpe Ave (CP)	37
Oglethorpe Ave NE	19
Oglethorpe Ave SW	10
Ohara Pl SE	15
Ohenry SW	15
Ohoopee Dr NE	19
Old Alabama SW	03
Old Bolton Rd NW	27
Old Briarcliff Rd NE	06
Old Cabin Rd NW	28
Old Cambellton Rd SW	31
Old Chamblee Tucker Rd (DOR)	40
Old Chattahoochee Ave NW	18
Old College Way NE	28
Old Colony (EP)	44
Old Conley Rd SE	54
Old Creek Rd NE	42
Old Creek Trl NW	28
Old Decatur Rd NE	05
Old Dixie Rd (HAP)	54
Old Dominion (DUN)	38
Old Fairburn Rd (CP)	49
Old Fairburn Rd SW	
1-4100	31
4101-OUT	49
Old Fairburn Close SW	31
Old Farm Rd (CP)	49
Old Field Rd (CP)	49
Old Flat Shoals Rd SE	12
Old Gordon Rd NW	
1-3815	31
3816-OUT	36
Old Hapeville Rd SW	
1-2700	15
2701-OUT	54
Old Harbor Dr NW	28
Old Hickory Pt NW	28
Old Highway 41 (HAP)	54
Old House Trl NE	42
Old Ivy Ln & Rd NE	42
Old Johnson Ferry Rd NE	19
Old Jonesboro Rd SW	
1-3073	15
3074-OUT	54
Old Lawrenceville Rd	
1-2700 (DUN)	38
2701-OUT (DOR)	40
Old Maine Pl NE	28
Old Marietta Rd NW	18
Old Mcdonough Rd SE	15
Old National Hwy	
1-4990 (CP)	37
4991-OUT (CP)	49
Old Orchard Ct (CHA)	41
Old Peachtree Rd (DOR)	40
Old Planatation Rd NW	27
Old Post Rd NW	28
Old Powers Ferry Rd NW	27

Old Pryor SW	03
Old Rough & Ready Rd SE	54
Old Settlement Rd NW	27
Old Spanish Trl (CP)	49
Old Spring House Ct & Ln (CHA)	41
Old Village Run (CHA)	41
Old Wheat NE	12
Old Winters Chapel Rd (DOR)	40
Old Woodbine Rd NE	19
Old 10th NE	09
Olde Village Ct & Ln (CHA)	41
Oldfield Ct (CP)	49
Oldfield Rd NW	27
Oldknow Dr NW	18
Oleander NW	14
Olive SE	15
Olive SW	10
Oliver NW	
1-560	14
561-OUT	18
Oliver Dr & Rd SW	31
Ollie St & Cir NW	14
Ollinger Way NE	08
Olympian Cir, Dr & Way SW	10
Omaha Rd SW	31
Ontario Ave SW	10
Oostanaula Dr NE	19
Ora Ave SW	16
Orange Dr SW	31
Orange Blossom Trl SE	16
Orchard (HAP)	54
Orchard Ln SE	54
Orchard Rd (CP)	49
Orchard Knob Dr & Rd NW	39
Orchard Lake Rd NW	39
Oriole Dr SW	11
Orkney Ln SW	31
Orlando St & Pl SW	11
Orleans SE	12
Orleans Ct, Dr & Way (CHA)	41
Orly Ter (CP)	49
Orme Dr NE	06
Ormewood Ave SE	
1-830	12
831-OUT	16
Ormewood Ter SE	16
Ormond St SE & SW	15
Orr NW	14
Orr Dr (EP)	44
Ortega Way (CHA)	41
Osborne NW	10
Osborne Rd NE	19
Osner Dr NE	42
Ottley Dr NE	24
Overbrook Dr NW	18
Overhill Ct NW	28
Overland Ter SE	17
Overlook Dr (EP)	44
Overlook Dr & Way NE	45
Overton NW	18
Ovidia Cir SW	11
Owens SE	15
Oxford Ave (CP)	37
Oxford Cres NE	19
Oxford Pl NE	07
Oxford Rd NE	
1-1310	06
1311-OUT	07
Ozark Trl SW	31
Ozburn Rd NW	18
Ozone SW	14

Atlanta (Con.)	303
Pace Setter Dr NW	18
Paces Pl NW	27
Paces Ferry Dr NW	39
Paces Ferry Pl NW	05
Paces Ferry Rd NW	
1-4150	27
4151-OUT	39
Paces Forest Dr & Rd NW	27
Paces Green Rd NW, NW	05
Paces Lake Ct & Dr NW	39
Paces Park Rd NW, NW	05
Paces Valley Rd NW	27
Pacific Dr SW	31
Page Ave NW	07
Paine Ave NW	
1-420	14
421-OUT	18
Palace Green Pl NW	18
Palatine Ave SE	16
Palatka SE	17
Palifox Dr NE	
1-1900	24
1901-OUT	07
Palisades Rd NE & NW	09
Palm Dr (EP)	44
Palm Springs Ct & Dr (EP)	44
Palmetto SW	
1-2000	14
2001-OUT	31
Palmetto Ave SW	
1-2000	14
2001-OUT	31
Palmour Dr NE	05
Pamela Dr NE	19
Pamela Ln SW	31
Pamlico Dr SW	11
Pamona Way (EP)	44
Pansy NW	14
Panther Trl SW	11
Paoli Ave SE	16
Paper Mill Pl NW	18
Paran Pl NW	27
Paran Glen Rd NW	27
Paran Pines Dr NW	27
Paran Valley NW	27
Parian Ridge Rd NW	27
Park (EP)	44
Park SW	10
Park Ave SE	
1-200	15
201-800	12
801-OUT	15
Park Ave NE, NE	42
Park Ave & Rd (DOR)	40
Park Ave & Way SW	15
Park Cir NE	05
Park Dr NE	06
Park Ln (CHA)	41
Park Ln NE	09
Park Pl NE	17
Park Rd SE	15
Park Ter (CP)	37
Park Way NE	42
Park Valley Dr NW	18
Parkcrest Dr NE	19
Parkdale Pl NE	
1-1000	09
1001-OUT	05
Parkdale Pl NW	
1-1000	09
1001-OUT	05

Parkdale Way NE	
1-1000	09
1001-OUT	05
Parkdale Way NW	
1-1000	09
1001-OUT	05
Parker NW	
1-100	08
101-OUT	13
Parker Ave SE	17
Parker Ranch Rd SE	16
Parklake Dr NE	45
Parkridge Cres (CHA)	41
Parkridge Dr NE	19
Parks Rd SE	15
Parkside Dr NE	
1-2000	19
2001-OUT	05
Parkside Ter (EP)	44
Parkview Cir & Dr (CP)	37
Parkview Dr NE	45
Parkview Plz (EP)	17
Parkway Dr (HAP)	54
Parkway Dr NE	
1-410	12
411-OUT	08
Parkwood Ln NW	27
Parliament Dr & Way (DUN)	38
Parrott Ave NW	18
Parson Dr (CHA)	41
Parsons SE	15
Parsons St Ct SW	14
Parsons St & Pl SW	14
Pasadena Ave NE	06
Pasco Ln SE	16
Pasley Ave SE	16
Patrick Ct SE	17
Patrick Dr SW	36
Patrick Pl NE	28
Patterson Ave SE	16
Patton Dr SW	
1-1000	36
1001-3000	44
3001-OUT	36
Paul Ave NW	18
Paul West Dr (CP)	37
Pauley Pl NE	28
Pavillion SE	15
Paxon Ave SE	17
Payton Rd NE	45
Peace Valley Ct & Dr (CP)	49
Peachford Rd (CHA)	41
Peachtree NE	
1-291	03
292-354	08
355-355	83
356-658	08
659-659	83
660-682	08
683-683	83
684-825	08
826-826	83
827-869	08
870-870	83
871-1427	09
1428-1428	83
1429-2320	09
2321-3300	05
3301-3630	26
3631-4790	19
4791-5800	41
5801-OUT (ODD)	40
5802-OUT (EVEN)	41

Peachtree NW	
1-291	03
292-354	08
355-355	83
356-658	08
659-659	83
660-682	08
683-683	83
684-825	08
826-826	83
827-869	08
870-870	83
871-1427	09
1428-1428	83
1429-2320	09
2321-3300	05
3301-3630	26
3631-4790	19
4791-5800	41
5801-OUT (ODD)	40
5802-OUT (EVEN)	41
Peachtree Ave, Dr & Way NE	05
Peachtree Cir & Pl NE	09
Peachtree Ct N (CHA)	41
Peachtree Park Dr NE	09
Peachtree Park Dr NW	09
Peachtree Pl NW	
1-100	09
101-OUT	18
Peachtree Rd NE	
1-291	03
292-354	08
355-355	83
356-658	08
659-659	83
660-682	08
683-683	83
684-825	08
826-826	83
827-869	08
870-870	83
871-1427	09
1428-1428	83
1429-2320	09
2321-3300	05
3301-3630	26
3631-4790	19
4791-5800	41
5801-OUT (ODD)	40
5802-OUT (EVEN)	41
Peachtree Rd NW	
1-291	03
292-354	08
355-355	83
356-658	08
659-659	83
660-682	08
683-683	83
684-825	08
826-826	83
827-869	08
870-870	83
871-1427	09
1428-1428	83
1429-2320	09
2321-3300	05
3301-3630	26
3631-4790	19
4791-5800	41
5801-OUT (ODD)	40
5802-OUT (EVEN)	41
Peachtree Battle Ave NW	
1-580	05

Atlanta (Con.)   303

Peachtree Battle Cir NW	27
Peachtree Dunwoody Cir NE	42
Peachtree Dunwoody Ct NE	28
Peachtree Dunwoody Rd NE	
1-5850	42
5851-OUT	28
Peachtree Hills Ave NE	05
Peachtree Ind Blvd	
1-6000 (CHA)	41
6001-OUT (DOR)	40
Peachtree Ind Ct (CHA)	41
Peachtree Memorial Dr NW	09
Peachtree North Ct (DOR)	40
Peachtree Shopping Center NE	29
Peachtree Valley Rd NE & NW	09
Peachtree View NE	19
Peachtree Village Plaza NE	29
Peachwood Cir NE	45
Pear SE	15
Pearce SW	10
Pearl (EP)	44
Pearl SE	16
Pearl Ln (CHA)	41
Pearl Ln (DOR)	40
Pearl Lane Ct (CHA)	41
Pebble Dr (EP)	44
Pebble Beach Dr (EP)	49
Pecan Dr SW	15
Peeks Rd NW	18
Peeler Rd	
1-2500 (CHA)	41
2501-OUT (DOR)	40
Peeler Mill Ct & Rd (CHA)	41
Peeples SW	10
Pegg Rd SW	15
Pegg Rd & Ter (EP)	44
Pelham NW	18
Pelham Rd NE	24
Pelot Dr (EP)	44
Pelton Pl NW	18
Pemberton Rd SW	31
Pembroke Pl NE	
1-2000	09
2001-OUT	24
Pembroke Pl NE	
1-2000	09
2001-OUT	24
Pendleton SE	16
Pendley (DOR)	40
Penelope St, Dr, Pl & Rd NW	14
Penfield Cir (HAP)	54
Penn Ave NE	
1-870	08
871-OUT	09
Penn Ct SE	15
Pennington Cir SW	54
Pennington Pl SE	16
Pennsylvania (EP)	44
Penny Ln (EP)	44
Penrose Dr (EP)	44
Perdue NW	18
Perimeter Ctr NE, E.	46
Perimeter Ctr NE, W.	46
Perimeter Park S (EP)	44
Perimeter Parkway (CHA)	41
Perkerson Rd SW	
1-2100	10
2101-OUT	15

Perkins (HAP)	54
Perkins Aly NE	12
Perkins Dr (CP)	37
Permalume Pl NW	18
Pernoshall Ct (CHA)	41
Perry Blvd NW	18
Pershing Ave & Pl SE	12
Pete NW	18
Peters SW	13
Peyton Ave & Rd NW	18
Peyton Pl & Rd SW	11
Peyton Woods Trl SW	11
Pharr Rd NE	
1-1000	05
1001-OUT	17
Pharr Rd NW	05
Philadelphia Ave SW	11
Philadelphia Pl (EP)	44
Phillips Ave & Ct (EP)	44
Phillips Dr & Pl SE	15
Phillips-Lee Rd SW	36
Phipps Plz NE	26
Phoenix Blvd, Ctr & Pky (CP)	49
Pickens SE	16
Pickett SE	16
Pickfair Ave SW	15
Piedmont Ave NE	
1-200	03
201-350	12
351-870	08
871-1500	09
1501-2680	24
2681-OUT	05
Piedmont Ave SE	03
Piedmont Cir & Way NE	24
Piedmont Rd NE	
1-200	03
201-350	12
351-870	08
871-1500	09
1501-2680	24
2681-OUT	05
Pierce (CP)	37
Pierce NW	18
Pierce Dr NE	
1-3000	07
3001-OUT	41
Pierce Rd (CP)	49
Pike Ave NW	14
Pin Oak Cir & Way (DOR)	40
Pine (HAP)	54
Pine NW	
1-100	08
101-500	13
501-1500	09
1501-OUT	18
Pine Ave (EP)	44
Pine Cir NE	05
Pine Dr (CP)	49
Pine Grv Ave NE	19
Pine Grv Dr NW	18
Pine Grv Ter NE	19
Pine Mnr Ct SE	16
Pine St & Pl NE	08
Pine St & Rd (DOR)	40
Pine Trl SE	16
Pine Bark Cir, Clse, Ct & Ln (DUN)	38
Pine Branches Clse (DUN)	38
Pine Castle Dr & Way (DUN)	38
Pine Cone Dr SW	31
Pine Cone Ln NE	19

Pine Forest Dr SE	54
Pine Forest Rd NE	
1-1000	42
1001-OUT	45
Pine Forrest Dr NE	
1-1000	42
1001-OUT	45
Pine Haven Ln NE	42
Pine Knoll Ave SW	31
Pine Lake Dr NW	27
Pine Meadow Rd NW	27
Pine Mill Ln NE	28
Pine Needle Ct, Dr & Ter (EP)	44
Pine Oak Dr SW	10
Pine Ridge Dr & Rd NE	24
Pine Tree Cir NE	29
Pine Tree Dr NE	
1-1000	05
1001-OUT	24
Pine Tree Rd NE	
1-1000	05
1001-OUT	24
Pine Valley Dr (CP)	37
Pine Valley Ln (EP)	44
Pine Valley Rd NW	05
Pinebrook Rd NE	28
Pinecliff Dr NE	45
Pinecrest Dr (CP)	37
Pinecrest Rd NE	42
Pinedale Dr NW	14
Pinehill Pl NW	42
Pinehurst Dr (EP)	44
Pinehurst Dr (HAP)	54
Pinehurst Dr SW	11
Pinehurst Ter SW	10
Pineland Ave (DOR)	40
Pineland Rd NW	42
Pinella Dr SW	31
Pineside Dr (CP)	49
Pinestream Rd NW	27
Pinevalley Cir & Ct (EP)	44
Pineview Dr (CP)	49
Pineview Ter SW	11
Pineway Dr NE	29
Piney Fork Ln (CP)	49
Piney Wood Dr, Ln & Ter (EP)	44
Pioneer Ct (CHA)	41
Piper Cir SE	16
Pitman Rd (CP)	49
Pittman NW	18
Pitts Rd (DUN)	38
Plainville Dr SW	31
Plant (EP)	44
Plantation Dr (EP)	44
Plantation Ln (CHA)	41
Plasamour Dr NE	24
Plaster Ave NE	
1-2200	24
2201-OUT	05
Plaster Rd NE	45
Plaster Bridge Rd NE	
1-2200	24
2201-OUT	05
Play Lane NW	14
Plaza Ave SW	10
Plaza Ln SW	11
Plaza Way (CHA)	41
Plaza Way SW	03
Pleasant Hill Rd (CP)	49
Pleasant Valley Rd & Trl (DOR)	40

Atlanta (Con.)	303
Pleasantdale Rd (DOR)	40
Plum NW	
1-660	13
661-OUT	18
Pluma Dr SE	16
Plymouth Ave & Rd NW	18
Plymouth Rd NE	06
Plymstock Ln NW	27
Pointer Ct & Rd (CP)	49
Pointview Dr (EP)	44
Polar Rock Ave, Dr, Pl, Rd & Ter SW	15
Pollard Dr (EP)	44
Pollard Dr SW	11
Polo Dr NE	09
Pomona Cir SW	15
Pompey Dr SW	31
Ponce De Leon Ave NE	
1-74	08
75-75	83
76-319	08
320-320	83
321-550	08
551-551	83
552-700	08
701-788	06
789-789	83
790-824	06
825-825	83
826-1049	06
1050-1050	83
1051-1400	06
1401-2177	07
Ponce De Leon Cir (DOR)	44
Ponce De Leon Ct NE	08
Ponce De Leon Mnr NE	07
Ponce De Leon Pl & Ter NE	06
Pond NW	14
Ponder Aly SW	03
Ponders Aly NE	08
Ponders Ave NW	18
Ponders Way (EP)	44
Pontiac Cir (DOR)	40
Pontiac Pl SE	
1-1500	16
1501-OUT	15
Poole Dr & Rd SW	11
Poole Pl SW	10
Poole Creek Rd (HAP)	54
Pope SW	15
Poplar (EP)	44
Poplar NW	03
Poplar Cir NE	07
Poplar Grv Dr NE	06
Poplar St, Dr & Rd (DOR)	40
Poplar Springs Dr	19
Poplarcrest Cir SE	16
Porter Dr NW	14
Porter Pl NE	08
Porter Glade Ct (DOR)	40
Portland Ave SE	16
Postell NW	14
Potomac Ave NE	05
Potomac Ct, Dr & Ter (EP)	44
Potomac Way (DOR)	38
Powderhorn Rd NE	42
Powell St & Ct SE	16
Powers Ferry Rd NW	
1-4300	42
4301-6590	27
6591-OUT	39

Prado NE	09
Prairie View Dr & Pl SW	11
Prescott NE	08
Prescott Walk NE	07
Presley Way NE	17
Prestwood Ct (DUN)	38
Primrose SE	
1-650	12
651-OUT	15
Primrose Cir SE	15
Prince George (EP)	44
Princess Ave SW	10
Princess Cir NE	45
Princeton Ave E & W (CP)	37
Princeton Ave & Dr (CP)	37
Princeton Pl SW	31
Princeton Trce NE	28
Princeton Way NE	07
Pritchard Way NE	26
Proctor (HAP)	54
Proctor NW	14
Produce Pl & Row SW	03
Prospect Ave SE	16
Prospect Pl NE	12
Pryor SW	
1-350	03
351-660	12
661-OUT	15
Pryor Rd SW	
1-350	03
351-660	12
661-OUT	15
Pryor St & Pl NE	03
Pueblo Dr SW	31
Pullen Ln (CP)	49
Pulliam SW	
1-650	12
651-OUT	15
Putnam Cir NE	42
Putnam Dr NW	42
Pylant NE	06
Pyrenees Ct (DOR)	40
Pyrite Cir SW	31
Quaker SW	15
Queen NW	18
Queen SW	10
Queen Anne Pl NW	18
Queen Elizabeth (EP)	44
Queens Way (CHA)	41
Queensborough Dr NE	28
Queensbury Ln NW	05
Quillian SE	17
Rabun Dr SW	11
Rachael SE	15
Racine SW	14
Radar Dr (HAP)	54
Radar Rd NE	45
Radcliffe Dr NW	18
Ragley Hall Rd NE	19
Railroad Ave NE	26
Rainbow Ridge NW	28
Rainey Ave (HAP)	54
Rainier Falls Dr NE	29
Rains Ct NE	19
Raintree Ct & Dr NE	45
Raintree Ln NW	27
Ralph Rd NE	24
Ramsgate St & Ct NW	05
Ramundo Dr (DOR)	40
Ranchwood Dr NE	45
Randall (EP)	44
Randall Rd NW	39
Randall Farm Rd NW	39

Randall Hall NW	27
Randall Mill Rd NW	27
Randall Ridge Rd NW	27
Randee NW	18
Rando Ln NW	18
Randolph NE	12
Randolph Ct & Rd NE	45
Rangewood Ct & Dr NE	45
Ranier Dr NW	27
Ranier Pl NE	06
Rankin St & Pl NE	08
Ranlo Dr (DOR)	40
Rantin Dr (EP)	44
Raspberry Aly NE	03
Raven Ave SW	18
Raven Hill Dr NE	19
Ravencliff Ln (CP)	49
Ravenwood Dr (CP)	49
Ravenwood Dr & Way NE	29
Rawlins SE	15
Rawson St SE & SW	12
Raymond Dr (DOR)	40
Raymond St NW & SW	14
Read Ln NE	28
Rebecca Dr SW	11
Rebel Trl NW	27
Rebel Forest Dr SE	15
Rector Dr SW	11
Red Oak Dr (DOR)	40
Red Oak Rd (CP)	49
Red Valley Rd NW	05
Redbud Ln SW	11
Redcliff Ct & Way (DUN)	38
Redding Rd & Way NE	19
Redford Dr SE	15
Redland Rd NW	09
Redwine (CP)	37
Redwine Ct & Rd (EP)	44
Redwine Rd (CP)	49
Redwine Rd SW	31
Redwood (DOR)	40
Reed (CP)	37
Reed SE	
1-646	12
647-OUT	15
Reed Ave (EP)	44
Reeder Cir NE	06
Reeves (CHA)	41
Reeves Cir NW	11
Regalwoods Dr (DOR)	40
Regency Rd NW	27
Regent SW	10
Regina Dr NW	18
Regis Rd SE	15
Reid Ln NW	27
Reindeer Dr NE	29
Reinhardt SE	12
Rembrandt Rd NW	27
Remington (EP)	44
Remington Rd (CHA)	41
Rena Cir SW	11
Renault Ln NE	45
Renault Rd SE	54
Renfrew Ct SW	31
Renfro Dr NW	18
Renfroe St & Aly SE	16
Rennes Ct & Dr NE	19
Reservoir Dr NW	18
Revere Ct (EP)	44
Revere Dr NW	18
Revere Rd SW	31
Reville Cir SE	16
Rex Ave SW	31

Atlanta (Con.)   303

Rey NW	18
Reynolds Ave NW	18
Reynolds Dr SW	
1-1980	31
1981-OUT	15
Reynolds Rd SW	
1-1980	31
1981-OUT	15
Rhinehill Rd SE	15
Rhineland Ct NE	45
Rhodenhaven Dr NW	27
Rhodes (CP)	37
Rhodes NW	
1-470	13
471-OUT	14
Rhodes Ctr NW	09
Rhodesia Ave SE	15
Rhomboid NW	18
Rhondo Rd (HAP)	54
Riada Dr NW	05
Rice NW	18
Richards NW	18
Richardson Rd NW	14
Richardson St SE & SW	12
Richland Rd SW	
1-1500	10
1501-OUT	11
Richmond SE	12
Richmond Ave & Cir SE	15
Richwood Dr NE	19
Rickehbacker Dr NE	42
Rickenbacker Way NE	42
Ridge Ave NW	18
Ridge Ave SW	15
Ridge Mill Ln NE	18
Ridge Tarn (DUN)	38
Ridge Valley Ct & Rd NW	27
Ridgecrest Ct & Rd NE	07
Ridgecrest Ln (EP)	44
Ridgedale Rd NE	17
Ridgeland Way NE	05
Ridgelock Ct (DOR)	40
Ridgemont Rd (DUN)	38
Ridgemore Dr (DOR)	40
Ridgemore Pl & Rd NW	18
Ridgeside Ct (CHA)	41
Ridgeview Rd (DUN)	38
Ridgeview Trl NE	28
Ridgeway Ave NW	18
Ridgeway Dr (DOR)	40
Ridgeway Dr (CP)	37
Ridgewood Ave NE	
1-2320	07
2321-2600	18
2601-OUT	27
Ridgewood Ave NW	
1-2320	07
2321-2600	18
2601-OUT	27
Ridgewood Cir NW	27
Ridgewood Dr NE	
1-2320	07
2321-2600	18
2601-OUT	27
Ridgewood Dr NW	
1-2320	07
2321-2600	18
2601-OUT	27
Ridgewood Ln SW	11
Ridgewood Rd NE	
1-2320	07

2321-2600	18
2601-OUT	27
Ridgewood Rd NW	
1-2320	07
2321-2600	18
2601-OUT	27
Ridgewood Ter NW	18
Rigdon Pl NW	14
Riggs Dr (EP)	44
Rilman Dr & Rd NW	27
Rimell Ln (CP)	49
Ringle Rd (CHA)	41
Ringsmith Rd NE	45
Rio Grande Rd SW	31
Ripplewater Dr SE	16
River Clse (DUN)	38
River Pky E, N & W (DUN)	38
River Court Pky NW	28
River Crest Ct NW	28
River Forest Rd NW	27
River Gate Dr (DUN)	38
River Hill Dr NW	28
River North Cir, Ct, Dr, Pky & Run NW	28
River North Walk NW, NW	28
River Overlook Ct & Dr NW	28
River Park Dr NE	28
River Ridge Dr SE	54
River Ridge Rd (DUN)	38
River Run (DUN)	38
River Shore Ct & Pky NW	28
River Springs Ct, Ln & Rd NW	28
River Valley Rd NW	28
Riverchase Cir & Pt NW	28
Riverchase Ridge NW	28
Rivercliff Dr NW	28
Riverdale Rd	
1-5100 (CP)	37
5101-OUT (CP)	49
Riveredge Dr & Ln NW	28
Riverglen Cir (CHA)	41
Riverglen Trce NW	28
Riverly Rd NW	27
Rivermeade Dr, Ln & Way NW	28
Rivers Rd NW	05
Riverside Dr NW	
1-5900	27
5901-OUT	28
Riverside Dr SW	31
Riverside Pky, Trce & Way NW	28
Riverview Rd NW	27
Riverwood Dr NW	28
Roach SW	14
Roanoke Ave NE	05
Robert NW	18
Roberta Dr NW	27
Roberts (HAP)	54
Roberts Dr SE	
1-1500	15
1501-OUT	38
Roberts Way NE	19
Robin Ln (CP)	49
Robin Ln NE	06
Robin Pl (CP)	37
Robin Hood Rd NE	09
Robinson Ave (HAP)	54
Robinson Ave SE	
1-580	15
581-OUT	12
Robson Pl NE	17

Rochelle Ct & Dr (CHA)	41
Rochelle Dr SW	10
Rochelle Way (CP)	49
Rock NW	14
Rock Hill Dr	49
Rock Hill Rd (CP)	37
Rock Springs Cir, Ct & Ter NE	06
Rock Springs Rd NE	
1-850	24
851-1600	06
1601-OUT	24
Rockbridge Rd (DOR)	40
Rockcliff Pl & Rd SE	16
Rockhaven Cir NE	24
Rockingham Dr NW	27
Rockland Dr SE	16
Rockledge Rd NE	24
Rockmart Dr NW & SW	14
Rockmont Dr NE	24
Rockport Pl SW	31
Rockridge Trl NW	39
Rockwell SW	
1-300	54
301-OUT	10
Rockwood NW	18
Rockwood Rd (EP)	44
Rockyford Rd NE & SE	17
Rodeo Ct SE	16
Rodney Dr SW	11
Rogerette Dr NE	29
Rogers Ave SW	10
Rogers St NE & SE	17
Rolling Brook Trl (EP)	44
Rolling Green Ridge SW	31
Rolling Hill Rd SW	31
Rollingwood Ct, Dr & Ln SE	16
Romain Way (EP)	44
Rome Dr NW	14
Romelie Dr (DOR)	40
Roosevelt (CP)	37
Roosevelt Dr SE	54
Roosevelt Hwy	
1941-3040 (CP)	37
3041-4900 (CP)	49
Rosaire Pl NW	27
Rosalia SE	12
Rosalind Dr NE	29
Rose Cir SW	10
Rose Ter (HAP)	54
Roseclair Dr SE	17
Rosedale Ave SE	12
Rosedale Dr & Rd NE	06
Rosehaven Ter SW	10
Rosemary Ave SW	11
Rosemary Dr NW	18
Rosemont Dr SE	17
Roses Of Picardy (CP)	49
Rosewood Dr NE	06
Ross (CP)	37
Ross SW	
1-1000	15
1001-OUT	54
Ross Dr (EP)	44
Ross Rd (DOR)	40
Rosser SW	14
Roswell SW	31
Roswell Ct NE	05
Roswell Rd NE	
1-3652	05
3653-5750	42
5751-7450	28
7451-OUT	38

Atlanta (Con.) 303

Roswell Rd NW
1-3652................................ 05
3653-5750.......................... 42
5751-7450.......................... 28
7451-OUT........................... 38
Rou Royal Ave SW................ 31
Roxboro Cir NE.................... 26
Roxboro Dr NE.................... 24
Roxboro Rd NE
1-3400................................ 24
3401-OUT........................... 26
Roy SW............................... 10
Royal Ct (CHA).................... 41
Royervista Dr NE.................. 42
Rufus Pl (DOR).................... 40
Rugby Ave
1-1600 (EP)........................ 44
1601-2440 (CP)................... 37
2441-OUT (EP).................... 37
Rugby Cir, Ln & Ter (CP)....... 37
Rumson Rd & Way NE........... 05
Runnemede NW.................... 27
Runnymeade Ln (EP)............. 44
Runnymeade Rd NE............... 19
Rupley Dr NE....................... 06
Rushton NE......................... 07
Russell (HAP)...................... 54
Russell NE........................... 17
Russian River Dr (CP)........... 49
Rustic Ridge Dr NE............... 19
Rustlewood Ln (DOR)........... 40
Rutgers Dr SW..................... 31
Ruth NW............................. 18
Rutherford NW.................... 18
Rux Rd SW.......................... 31
Ruzelle Dr SE & SW.............. 54
Ryan SW............................. 10
Rycroft Way NW.................. 05
Ryefield Ct & Dr (DUN)........ 38
Ryland Trl SW...................... 31
Ryne NW............................ 18
Saffron Ct, Dr & Way (DUN).. 38
Sagamore Dr NE
1-2000................................ 45
2001-OUT........................... 05
Sagamore Dr NW
1-2000................................ 45
2001-OUT........................... 05
Sage (DOR)......................... 40
Sage Ln SE.......................... 16
Sahara Dr SE....................... 16
Sahara Dr SW...................... 31
Saint Andrews Ct NE............. 45
Saint Andrews Dr SW............ 31
Saint Augustine Pl NE........... 06
Saint Charles Ave NE
1-600................................. 08
601-OUT............................. 06
Saint Charles Pl NE............... 06
Saint Charles Way NE............ 08
Saint Clair Ct NE.................. 19
Saint George Ave NE............. 12
Saint James Dr & Pl NW........ 18
Saint Johns Ave & Cir SW...... 15
Saint Joseph Ave NW............ 18
Saint Louis Pl NE.................. 06
Saint Patrick SE................... 17
Saint Paul Ave NW............... 18
Saint Paul Ave SE................. 12
Saint Peters Ave NW............. 18
Salmon Ave SE..................... 17

Sam NW.............................. 18
Sample Way (EP).................. 44
Sampson NE......................... 12
San Antonio Dr NE............... 06
San Marino Ct (CP).............. 49
Sancroft Ct (DUN)............... 38
Sandell Ct (DUN)................. 38
Sanders Ave SE.................... 16
Sanderson NE....................... 07
Sandgate Rd (CP)................. 49
Sandlewood Ln (CHA)........... 41
Sandpiper Cir SW................. 11
Sandringham Dr SW.............. 11
Sandtown Rd SW
1-1000................................ 31
1001-OUT........................... 11
Sandy Creek Dr NW
1-3500................................ 31
3501-OUT........................... 36
Sandy Creek Rd NW
1-3500................................ 31
3501-OUT........................... 36
Sandy Springs Cir, Dr & Pl
NE..................................... 28
Santa Barbara Dr NW........... 18
Santa Fe Trl (DOR).............. 40
Santa Fe Trl SW................... 31
Santa Lucia Ter NW.............. 18
Santa Monica Dr NW............ 18
Santa Rosa Dr SW................ 31
Saramac (HAP)..................... 54
Sargent Ave SE.................... 16
Sargent Dr & Pl SE............... 15
Sarnia Ln SW....................... 31
Saturn Dr NW...................... 31
Saunders NE........................ 17
Savannah SE......................... 16
Savoy Dr (CHA).................... 41
Sawtell Ave SE..................... 15
Saxon Pl NE......................... 19
Saybrook Dr NE................... 19
Scarborough Rd (CP)............. 49
Scarlett Oak Ct & Dr (DOR)... 40
Scenic Cir & Dr (EP)............. 44
Schell Rd SE........................ 15
Schoen SE........................... 15
School NE............................ 08
School Dr (CHA).................. 41
School Dr
1-3000 (DOR)...................... 40
3001-OUT (CHA).................. 41
School Dr NW...................... 27
School Dr SE........................ 54
Schooner Cir NW.................. 28
Schuyler Ave SE................... 12
Sciple Ter NW...................... 14
Scofield Rd (CP).................. 49
Scott NW
1-500................................. 14
501-OUT............................. 18
Scott SW
1-100................................. 15
101-1000............................. 11
1001-3000........................... 15
3001-OUT........................... 11
Scott Valley Rd NW.............. 28
Scottland Pl NW................... 18
Scottridge Dr NW................ 18
Scout (HAP)........................ 54
Screven NE.......................... 07
Sea Marsh Ct NW................. 28
Seaboard Ave NE.................. 07
Seaboard Ave & Pl NW.......... 18

Seaboard Industrial Blvd NW.. 18
Seaborn Pl (CP).................... 49
Seaborn Rd NW.................... 18
Seal Pl NE........................... 08
Seaman Cir & Way (CHA)...... 41
Seaton Dr (DUN)................. 38
Second Ave (CP).................. 37
Selig Dr SW......................... 36
Selkirk Dr NE...................... 28
Sells Ave SW....................... 10
Selman SE........................... 16
Selwin SW........................... 10
Seminole Ave NE.................. 07
Semmes (EP)....................... 44
Sentinel Post Rd NW............. 27
Sentinel View NW................. 27
Sentry Hill Trl NE................. 28
Sequoia Dr NE
1-2840................................ 19
2841-OUT........................... 27
Sequoia Rd NE
1-2840................................ 19
2841-OUT........................... 27
Sequoyah Dr NW
1-2840................................ 19
2841-OUT........................... 27
Sequoyah Rd NW
1-2840................................ 19
2841-OUT........................... 27
Serpentine Dr NE................. 45
Service Rd (CP).................... 49
Settle Cir SE........................ 16
Seven Oaks Ln (EP).............. 44
Seville Ln (EP)..................... 44
Sewanee Ave NW.................. 14
Sewell Rd SW
1-3400................................ 11
3401-OUT........................... 31
Sexton Woods Dr (CHA)........ 41
Shadecrest Dr NE.................. 19
Shadow Ln NE...................... 19
Shadowlawn Ave E & W......... 05
Shadowlawn Plain NE............ 05
Shadowood Pky NW.............. 39
Shadowridge Dr SE............... 16
Shadromat Way (CHA).......... 41
Shady Oak Ct & Dr (DOR)..... 40
Shady Valley Dr NE............... 24
Shadydale Ave SE................. 15
Shalimar Dr NE.................... 45
Shallowford Rd N (CHA)........ 41
Shallowford Rd NE
1-2650................................ 45
2651-3372.......................... 41
3373-3600 (ODD)................. 40
3374-3600 (EVEN)................ 41
3601-OUT........................... 40
Shallowford Ter (CHA).......... 41
Shancey Ln (CP)................... 49
Shannon Dr SW.................... 10
Shannon Mill Rd NE.............. 19
Shannonlore Dr (CP)............. 49
Shanter Trl SW..................... 11
Sharon NW.......................... 14
Sharon Valley Ct
1-4625 (CHA)...................... 41
4626-OUT (DOR).................. 40
Sharondale Cir, Ct & Dr NE.... 05
Shasta Way NE..................... 45
Shaw SW............................. 15
Shawnee Ln NE.................... 19
Sheffield Dr NE.................... 29
Sheffield Dr SW.................... 11

Atlanta (Con.)   303

Sheffield Pl & Rd (CP)...... 49
Shelborne Dr (CHA)...... 41
Shelby Pl SE...... 16
Sheldon Dr NE...... 42
Shell Rd SE...... 15
Shelly Dr SW...... 11
Shelton Ave SW...... 10
Shenandoah Ave NE...... 05
Shenandoah Valley Rd NE...... 05
Shepherd Cir SW...... 11
Shepherd Ln NE...... 24
Sheppard Pl NE...... 07
Sherbrook Ct & Dr (CP)...... 49
Sherbrooke Ct & Dr NE...... 45
Sherbrooke Way SW...... 31
Sheridan Dr NE...... 05
Sheridan Rd NE...... 24
Sheriff Rd (CP)...... 49
Sherman Rd (HAP)...... 54
Sherrell Dr NE...... 42
Sherwood Cir & Dr (CP)...... 37
Sherwood Rd NE...... 24
Sheryl Pl NW...... 09
Shirley SW
    1-1900...... 10
    1901-OUT...... 11
Shirley Dr SW...... 36
Shirley Pl NW...... 14
Shoppers Ln (CP)...... 49
Shore Dr SW...... 31
Shoreham Ct (CP)...... 37
Shoreham Dr (CP)...... 49
Shoreland Dr SW...... 31
Short (EP)...... 44
Short SE...... 16
Shorter Dr NE...... 18
Shoshonee Dr (CP)...... 49
Shurfine Dr (CP)...... 37
Sidis Ct (DOR)...... 40
Silvapine Trl NE...... 45
Silvastone Dr NE
    1976-OUT...... 45
Silver Ln NE...... 28
Silver Lake Dr NE...... 19
Silver Springs Cir SW...... 10
Silverdale Rd (CP)...... 49
Silverwood Rd NE...... 42
Simca SE...... 14
Simmons NW...... 18
Simmons Ave (CP)...... 37
Simmons Cir (DOR)...... 40
Simon SE...... 54
Simon Ter NW...... 18
Simpson NW
    1-100...... 08
    101-330...... 13
    331-OUT...... 14
Simpson Cir NE...... 19
Simpson Ter NW...... 14
Sims (HAP)...... 54
Sims SW...... 10
Sims Ave NW...... 18
Sims Cir SW...... 05
Sims Ct (CP)...... 37
Sinclair Ave NE...... 07
Sir Henry (EP)...... 44
Sirron Dr (DUN)...... 38
Sisk NW...... 18
Sisson Ave NE...... 17
Sizemore Ave NW...... 18

Skipper Dr, Ln & Pl NW...... 18
Sky Haven Rd SE...... 16
Skyland Dr NE
    1-2780...... 19
    2781-4300...... 41
    4301-OUT...... 42
Skyland Plz, Rd, Ter, Trl &
    Way NE...... 19
Skyland Shopping Center NE.. 19
Skyline Dr (CP)...... 37
Skyview Dr SW...... 31
Slaton Dr NW...... 05
Sloan (CP)...... 37
Sloan Ave...... 10
Sloan Cir SE...... 16
Sloop Way (CP)...... 49
Smith NW...... 18
Smith SE...... 16
Smith SW
    1-660...... 12
    661-OUT...... 10
Smoketree Ct & Rd NE...... 45
Snow Rd SW...... 11
Snyder NW...... 18
Solomon SE...... 12
Sombrero Way SE...... 16
Somerled Trl (CP)...... 49
Somerset Cir & Trl SW...... 31
Somerset Dr NW...... 27
Somerset Ter NE...... 06
Sommers Pl NW...... 08
Sorrento Cir SW...... 31
South (HAP)...... 54
South (CP)...... 49
South Ave SE...... 15
South Akin Dr NE...... 45
South Alvarado Ter SW...... 11
South Bamby Ln NE...... 19
South Bend Ave SE...... 15
South Colonial Homes Cir
    NW...... 09
South Expressway (HAP)...... 54
South Gordon SW...... 10
South Hampton Rd (CP)...... 49
South Howard SE...... 17
South Johnson Ferry Rd NE.. 19
South Olympian Way SW...... 10
South Peachtree Rd
    1-5715 (CHA)...... 41
    5716-OUT (DOR)...... 40
South Perimeter Hwy (CP)..... 49
South Pharr Ct NW...... 05
South Piper Cir SE...... 16
South Prado NE...... 09
South Pryor Cir SW...... 15
South Rhodes Center NW...... 09
South River Industrial Blvd
    SE...... 15
South Warren SE...... 17
South Woodland Dr (DOR)..... 40
Southerland Ter NE...... 07
Southern NW...... 18
Southland Cir NW...... 18
Southland Ct (EP)...... 44
Southland Vis Ct NE...... 29
Southwest (HAP)...... 54
Southwick Ct (CP)...... 49
Spad Ave NW...... 18
Spain Dr (EP)...... 44
Spain Pl NW...... 18
Spalding Cir, Ct & Ln NE...... 28
Spalding Dr NE

1-1300...... 28
1301-3670...... 38
3671-3900...... 40
3901-4038...... 28
4039-4045...... 40
4046-4050...... 28
4051-OUT...... 40
Spanish Oak Dr (DOR)...... 40
Spanish Tr (EP)...... 44
Sparks SW...... 10
Spellman NW...... 14
Spelman Ln SW...... 14
Spence Ave NE & SE...... 17
Spencer NW...... 14
Spencer Ave (EP)...... 44
Spinks NW...... 18
Spinks Aly NW...... 13
Spinning House Pl NW...... 18
Spreading Oak Dr SW...... 11
Spring (EP)...... 44
Spring (CHA)...... 41
Spring (HAP)...... 54
Spring (CP)...... 49
Spring NW
    1-282...... 03
    283-920...... 08
    921-2000...... 09
    2001-OUT...... 18
Spring SW...... 03
Spring Ave, Cir & Rd NW..... 18
Spring Dr (DOR)...... 40
Spring Grv Ave NW...... 18
Spring Ln Dr NW...... 14
Spring Garden Dr & Ln SW..... 15
Spring Green Pl NW...... 18
Spring Lake Dr NW...... 05
Spring Lake Rd (CP)...... 49
Spring Mill Cove (DOR)...... 40
Spring Mill Ct & Ln NE...... 19
Spring Valley Blvd, Cir, Ct,
    Pky, Rd & Way (CP)...... 49
Spring Valley Ln NE...... 06
Spring Valley Rd NE...... 06
Spring Valley Trace (CP)...... 49
Springdale Cir & Pl SW...... 15
Springdale Cir & Rd (EP)...... 44
Springdale Dr NE...... 05
Springdale Rd NE...... 06
Springdale Rd SW
    1-3000...... 15
    3001-OUT...... 54
Springer NW...... 18
Springfield Ct (CP)...... 49
Springfield Ct & Dr (DUN)..... 38
Springhaven (HAP)...... 54
Springside Dr (CP)...... 49
Springside Dr SE & SW...... 54
Springside Pl SE...... 54
Springside Ter SW...... 54
Springview Rd NW...... 14
Spruce NE...... 07
Spruce Point Rd (CP)...... 49
Spruill Springs Rd NE...... 42
Spurgeon Rd (CP)...... 49
Squire Pl, NE...... 24
St Francis (EP)...... 44
St Joseph (EP)...... 44
St Lo Ln (CP)...... 49
St Michael (EP)...... 44
St Tropez Way (DUN)...... 38
St. Johns Dr (EP)...... 44
Stacks Rd (CP)...... 49
Stafford Pl (DOR)...... 40

Atlanta (Con.)   303

Stafford St NW & SW.............. 14
Stallings Ave SE.............. 16
Stamford Rd SW.............. 31
Stancil Rd (CP).............. 49
Standard Dr NE.............. 19
Standish Ave NW.............. 09
Stanhope Cir NW.............. 14
Stanley Way SE.............. 16
Stanton Cir & Ct (EP)..... 44
Stanton Rd SW
  1-1799.............. 11
  1800-OUT.............. 44
Stantondale Dr (CHA).............. 41
Stanwood Ave SE.............. 17
Star Dr NE.............. 19
Star Mist Dr SW.............. 11
Starcross Ct (DUN).............. 38
Starfire Dr NE.............. 45
Stark Ln (CHA).............. 41
Starlight Cir, Ct, Dr & Ln NE. 42
State NW
  1-778.............. 13
  779-OUT.............. 18
Statewood Rd NE.............. 42
Steele Ave SW.............. 15
Steele Dr NW.............. 09
Stella Dr NW.............. 27
Stephanie Dr SW.............. 31
Stephen Long Ave & Dr NE.. 05
Stephens SW.............. 10
Stephens Dr NE.............. 29
Sterling NE.............. 07
Sterling SE.............. 15
Stetson Pl NW.............. 18
Steve Dr (DOR).............. 40
Steve Dr SW.............. 15
Stevens NW.............. 18
Stewart Ave SW
  1-1655.............. 10
  1656-3000.............. 15
  3001-OUT.............. 54
Stewart Dr NE.............. 42
Stewart Rd (DOR).............. 40
Stiff NW.............. 18
Stillman SE.............. 15
Stillwood Dr (HAP).............. 54
Stillwood Dr NE.............. 06
Stirrup Ln SE.............. 16
Stockbridge Dr SE.............. 16
Stokes Ave SW.............. 10
Stokeswood Ave SE.............. 16
Stoland Dr NE.............. 19
Stone Rd SW
  1-3150.............. 44
  3151-OUT.............. 31
Stone Hogan Rd Connector SW.............. 31
Stone Mill Trl NE.............. 28
Stonecrest Ct (CHA).............. 41
Stonegate Ct, Dr, Trl & Way (DOR).............. 40
Stoneham Ct (CP).............. 49
Stonehill Dr SW.............. 36
Stonehurst Pl NW.............. 11
Stoneview Ter (EP)....... 44
Stonewall SW
  1-500.............. 13
  501-OUT.............. 14
Stonewall Dr SE.............. 15
Stonewall Tell Rd (CP).............. 49

Stonewall Tell Rd SW.............. 31
Stonington Cir & Rd (CHA).... 41
Stonington Dr NW.............. 28
Stonybrook Dr SE.............. 16
Stovall SE.............. 16
Stovall Blvd NE
  1-900.............. 42
  901-OUT.............. 18
Stovall Ter NE.............. 42
Strait (DOR).............. 41
Strasburg Ct (CHA).............. 41
Stratfield Cir & Dr NE.............. 19
Stratford Dr NW.............. 11
Stratford Rd NE.............. 42
Stratford Arms Dr (CHA).............. 41
Stratham Dr (DUN).............. 38
Strathmore Dr NE.............. 24
Street De Ville NE.............. 45
Strong NW.............. 18
Stubbs Rd (CP).............. 49
Sturbridge Way (CP).............. 49
Suber Rd SW.............. 31
Sudbury Ct E & W (DOR).............. 40
Sudbury Rd
  1-1000 (DOR).............. 28
Sudbury Rd NE
  1-1000.............. 28
  1001-OUT (DOR).............. 40
  1001-OUT (DOR).............. 45
Sugar Creek Pl SE.............. 16
Sugarplum Ct & Rd NE.............. 45
Sulene Dr (CP).............. 49
Sullivan Rd
  1-1015 (CP).............. 49
  1016-OUT (CP).............. 37
Sumac Dr (DOR).............. 40
Sumlin Ave NW.............. 18
Summerford Ct & Dr (DUN).... 28
Summit NE.............. 42
Summit Ave NW.............. 18
Summitridge Dr (DOR).............. 40
Sumter NE.............. 18
Sun Valley Blvd (EP).............. 44
Sunbury Pl NW.............. 18
Suncrest Ln NE.............. 45
Sunderland Cir, Ct & Way NE.............. 19
Sundown Dr NE.............. 45
Sunland Dr NE.............. 19
Sunny Hill Dr SE.............. 16
Sunnybrook Dr (DUN).............. 38
Sunnybrook Ln & Pl NE.............. 18
Sunridge Ave SE.............. 15
Sunrise Ct & Trl (CP).............. 49
Sunrise Dr NE.............. 45
Sunset Ave NW
  1-410.............. 14
  411-OUT.............. 18
Sunset Dr (HAP).............. 54
Sunset Dr NE.............. 45
Sunset Dr SW.............. 31
Sunset Ln (EP).............. 44
Sunset Ridge NE.............. 19
Sunshine Dr SW.............. 54
Surrey Cir & Ln (CHA).............. 41
Surrey Ln (CP).............. 37
Surrey Trl (CP).............. 49
Surry County Pl NW.............. 18
Susaleen Ct NE.............. 45
Susan Ln (DOR).............. 40
Susan Ln SW.............. 31
Sussex Rd NE.............. 06
Susy Griffin Rd SE.............. 54

Sutton SE.............. 17
Suzanne Way (CP).............. 37
Swallow Cir SE.............. 15
Swann Dr SE.............. 15
Swansea Ct (CP).............. 49
Swathmore Dr NW.............. 27
Sweat Rd NW.............. 18
Swims Valley Dr NW.............. 27
Sydney SE.............. 12
Sylvan Cir NE.............. 19
Sylvan Cir, Pl & Way SW....... 10
Sylvan Rd SW
  1-2100.............. 10
  2101-3000.............. 44
  3001-OUT.............. 54
Sylvan Ter (CP).............. 44
Sylvan Ramble Rd NE.............. 45
Sylvan Ridge Dr SW.............. 10
Sylvester Cir SE.............. 16
Symphony Ln NW.............. 18
Tacoma Dr NW.............. 18
Taft Ave NE.............. 09
Taft St & Pl SW.............. 15
Tahoe Dr (CP).............. 49
Taliaferro NW.............. 14
Talisman Ct NE.............. 45
Tall Oaks Dr NE.............. 42
Tall Pines Ct & Dr NW.............. 27
Tall Tree Dr NE.............. 24
Talley Dr (CHA).............. 41
Tallulah NW.............. 18
Tallulah Dr NE.............. 19
Tally Ho Dr SE.............. 16
Tamassee Ct (DOR).............. 40
Tamerlane NW.............. 27
Tampa Trl SW.............. 31
Tamworth Dr NE.............. 28
Tanacrest Cir, Ct & Dr NW.... 28
Tanbark Ct NE.............. 19
Tanglewood Cir NE.............. 45
Tanglewood Ct & Trl NW.............. 27
Tanglewood Dr NW.............. 39
Tanglewood Trl (EP).............. 44
Tanner SE.............. 12
Tanner Rd (CP).............. 37
Tara Cir SE.............. 54
Tara Trl NW.............. 27
Tartan Ln SW.............. 31
Tarver Ter (CP).............. 49
Tate Rd (CP).............. 49
Tatnall SW
  1-470.............. 13
  471-OUT.............. 14
Taylor NW.............. 18
Taylor Ave (EP).............. 44
Tazor NW.............. 14
Teal Rd (CHA).............. 41
Techwood Dr NW
  1-100.............. 03
  101-900.............. 13
  901-OUT.............. 18
Tee Rd SW.............. 11
Tejas Trl SW.............. 31
Telfair Ln SW.............. 11
Telford Dr NE.............. 19
Telhurst SW.............. 10
Tell Rd SW.............. 31
Temple NW.............. 14
Temple Ave (CP).............. 37
Templewood Dr NE.............. 19
Tennelle SE.............. 12
Tennessee Ave SW.............. 15
Tennyson Dr NW.............. 18

Atlanta (Con.) 303

Terian Pl (EP)	44
Terminal NW	13
Terrace Ave NE	07
Terrace Dr NE	05
Terrace Way SE	15
Terrell NW	18
Terrell Dr (CHA)	41
Terrell Mill Rd (CP)	49
Terry SE	
1-650	12
651-OUT	15
Terry Mill Rd SE	16
Teton Ave SE	12
Teton Dr NW	39
Thackery Pl SW	11
Thames Rd (CP)	49
Thaxton Dr & Pl SE	15
Thaxton Rd SW	
1-4000	31
4001-OUT	49
Thayer Ave SE	15
The Ascent NE	19
The Byway NE	06
The Cottage (CHA)	41
The Falls Ct NE	07
The Fountainebleau SW	31
The Meadow's Way (CP)	49
The Prado NE	09
The Savoy (CP)	49
The 16th Fairway (DUN)	38
The 5th Green (DUN)	38
Thirkield Ave SE & SW	15
Thomas Rd NW	18
Thomasville Ct & Dr SE	15
Thompson Ave (EP)	44
Thompson Dr NW	31
Thompson Rd (CP)	49
Thompson Rd NE	19
Thoms Dr NW	18
Thorn Briar Dr (DOR)	40
Thornberry Ln SW	31
Thornburg Way (CP)	49
Thorncliff Dr NE	45
Thorne Ave SW	10
Thornhill Ct (DUN)	38
Thornhill Ln NE	28
Thornridge Dr & Way (DOR)	40
Thornton Dr (CP)	49
Thornton St & Pl SW	15
Thornwell Dr NE	19
Thornwood (DOR)	40
Thornwood Dr NE	28
Thurgood SW	14
Thurman Rd (CP)	49
Thurmond SW	
1-300	13
301-OUT	14
Tichnor Ct (DUN)	38
Tift St & Ave SW	10
Tiger Flowers Cir & Dr NW	14
Tilden NW	18
Tilly Mill Rd (DOR)	40
Tilson Dr SE	17
Tilton Ln (DOR)	40
Timber Ln Ter NE	28
Timber Trl NE	42
Timber Oak Dr (DOR)	40
Timber Valley Rd NE	42
Timberland Dr NE	
1-1000	42
1001-OUT	45

Timberland Rd NE	
1-1000	42
1001-OUT	45
Timms Cir SE	16
Timms Valley Rd NE	05
Timothy Dr NE	29
Timothy Dr SW	11
Tobey Rd (CHA)	41
Tocoma Trl (CP)	49
Todd SE	12
Todd Rd NE	06
Toll House Ln SW	31
Tolleson Ct (DUN)	38
Tonawanda Dr SE	15
Toni Pl SE	15
Topaz Ln SW	31
Torrence NW	14
Towanda Cir & Dr (CP)	49
Tower Hill Rd NW	18
Towerview Dr NE	24
Town Country Dr SE	16
Townly Cir & Ct (DOR)	40
Toxaway Ct (CHA)	41
Trabert NW	
1-600	09
601-OUT	18
Trabert Ave NW	
1-600	09
601-OUT	18
Trafalgar Way (CHA)	41
Trafalger Ct NW	27
Trail Ridge Ln (DUN)	38
Trammell Dr (HAP)	54
Trapnall Ct & Dr (DUN)	38
Travis NW	18
Treadwell Cir SW	31
Tree Haven Dr NE	42
Tremont Dr NW	14
Trenholm SW	13
Trenton SE	16
Trentwood Pl NE	19
Tribble Dr NW	18
Tribble Ln NW	11
Trilby SE	16
Trimble Rd NE	42
Trinity Ave SW	
1-70	34
71-OUT	03
Tripple Creek Ct NE	19
Tristan Cir & Way NE	45
Triumph Cir SE	54
Trotti NE	17
Troup SW	15
Trowbridge Dr (DUN)	38
Troy NW	14
Troy SE	15
Truitt SW	10
Trumbull Ct & Dr (DUN)	38
Trusco Way SW	10
Tryon Pl & Rd NE	10
Tuckawanna Dr SW	11
Tucker St, Ave & Pl SW	10
Tucson Trl SW	31
Tudor SW	15
Tugaloo Dr NE	19
Tula NW	09
Tulane Dr SW	36
Tully Cir & Rd NE	29
Tumlin NW	18
Tupelo SE	17
Turman Ave SE	15
Turner (CP)	49
Turner (EP)	44

Turner Dr (DOR)	40
Turner Rd SE	15
Turpin Ave SE	12
Tuskegee SE	
1-1000	15
1001-OUT	54
Tuskegee Ave SE	
1-1000	15
1001-OUT	54
Tuxedo Ave NE	07
Tuxedo Pky NW	05
Tuxedo Rd NW	
1-3830	05
Tuxedo Rd NW, NW	
3831-OUT	42
Tuxedo Ter NW	42
Twiggs SW	15
Twilley Dr NW	18
Twin Branch Ct, Ln & Rd NE	28
Twin Branches Way (DUN)	38
Twin Branches Close (DUN)	38
Twin Brooks Rd NE	19
Twin Springs Rd NW	27
Tycoon Sq (CHA)	41
Tye SE	16
Tyewood Ln (EP)	44
Tyler NW	14
Tyndall Ct (DUN)	38
Tynecastle Dr & Way (DUN)	38
Umberland Dr (DOR)	40
Underground Atlanta SW	03
Underwood Ave SE	16
Underwood Dr NW	28
Union Ave (HAP)	54
Union Rd SW	
1-3500	31
3501-OUT	49
University Ave SW	
1-270	15
271-OUT	10
University Dr NE	06
University Pl NW	14
University Plz SE	03
Upshaw SE	15
Upton Rd NW	18
Utoy Cir & Ct SW	31
Utoy Springs Rd SW	31
Valante Ter (EP)	44
Valcouri Sq NW	05
Valeland Ave SW	31
Valiant Dr NE	45
Valley Cir & Rd NW	05
Valley Dr (EP)	44
Valley Ln NE	28
Valley Trl Dr NW	39
Valley Bend Dr (CP)	49
Valley Bluff Dr (DOR)	40
Valley Brook Dr NE	42
Valley Creek Dr NW	39
Valley Green Dr NE	42
Valley Hall Dr (DUN)	38
Valley Heart Dr NW	18
Valley Lake Rd & Ter (CP)	49
Valley Ridge Dr & Ter SW	31
Valley Stream Dr (DOR)	40
Valley Tarn (DUN)	38
Valley View Ct & Rd (DUN)	38
Valley View Dr (EP)	44
Valley View Rd SE	15
Valleydale Dr SW	11
Vallo Vis Ct NE	42
Valmar Dr (DOR)	40
Valvedere Dr NE	19

Atlanta (Con.)   303

Van Buren SW 10
Van Epps Ave SE 16
Van Fleet Cir (DOR) 40
Van Heusen Blvd NW 18
Van Vleck Ave SE 14
Vance SW 16
Vance Ave NE 06
Vance Dr (EP) 44
Vance Dr NE 45
Vanderbilt Ct & Ln NW 18
Vanderlyn Dr (DUN) 38
Vandiver Rd SW
    1-4000 10
    4001-OUT 31
Vanet Rd (CHA) 41
Vanetta Pl NW 18
Vanira SE 15
Vannoy SE 17
Vanse Dr (EP) 44
Varner Dr NE 45
Vassar SW 15
Vassar Ave (CP) 37
Vaud Ave NE 07
Vaughn SE 17
Vedado Way NE 08
Velma SE 15
Veltre Cir & Pl SW 11
Venable NW 13
Venetian Dr SW 11
Venice Dr SE 17
Venus Pl NW 31
Vera SE 16
Verbena NW 14
Verdon Ct & Dr (DUN) 38
Verdun Dr NW 05
Verlaine Pl NW 27
Vermack Rd (DUN) 38
Vermont Rd NE 19
Verner NW 18
Vernon N (DUN) 38
Vernon Ave SE 16
Vernon Pl NE 12
Vernon Rd NW 05
Vernon Lake Dr (DUN) 38
Vernon Oaks Dr (DUN) 38
Vernon Ridge Ct & Dr (DUN) .. 38
Vernon Springs Ct, Dr & Trl
    NW 27
Vernon Springs Dr (DUN) 38
Vernon Way Ct (DUN) 38
Vernon Woods Dr NE 28
Vesta Ave (CP) 37
Vesta Ave NW 14
Vesta Ave & Ter (EP) 44
Veterans (EP) 44
Vicar Rd (DOR) 40
Vickers SE 16
Vickers Dr NE 07
Vicki Ln SE 16
Victor Cir NW 14
Victor Rd NE 24
Victoria (CP) 37
Victoria NE 19
Victoria NW 14
Victoria Dr (EP) 44
Victoria Dr (HAP) 54
Victoria St N & S (CP) 37
Victoria Falls Dr NE 29
Victory Cir (DOR) 40
Victory Dr SW 10
Vienah Ln NE 07

Villa Cir (HAP) 54
Villa Dr NE 06
Villa Esta Dr (CHA) 41
Village Dr SW 31
Village Creek Ct & Dr (CHA).. 41
Village Green Dr (CP) 49
Village Mill Ct & Rd (CHA) 41
Villanova Dr SW 36
Ville SE 15
Vine NW
    1-416 14
    417-OUT 18
Vine SW 14
Vinson Dr SE 17
Vinson Pl SW 15
Vintage Ln (CHA) 41
Violet Ave NW 18
Violet Ave SE 15
Violet Ave SW 10
Virgil NE 07
Virginia Ave (DOR) 40
Virginia Ave (CP) 37
Virginia Ave NE 44
Virginia Ave & Cir NE 06
Virginia Ave & Pl (HAP) 54
Virginia Pl NE 05
Vista Sq NW 27
Vista Trl NE 24
Vista Valley Dr NE 29
Vivian Ln NE 05
Volberg NW 18
Wabash Ave NE 12
Waddell NE 07
Waddeston Way NE 19
Wade NE 07
Wade Ave NE 17
Wadley NW 14
Wadley Ave (EP) 44
Wadsworth Dr NW 18
Wainwright Dr SE 16
Waits Ave SW 31
Wake Robin Trl (CHA) 41
Wakefield Dr NE & NW 09
Walden NW 18
Waldo SE 12
Wales Ave NW 18
Waleska Way (EP) 44
Walker (HAP) 54
Walker SW 13
Walker Ave (EP) 44
Walker Ave (CP) 37
Walker Ave SE 16
Walker Rd (CP) 49
Walker Ter NE 09
Walker View Ct SE 16
Wall St E & W 03
Wall Plain SW 03
Wallace Ave & Rd SW 31
Wallace Cir NW 39
Wallace Dr (CHA) 41
Wallace Dr SW 54
Walnut (HAP) 54
Walnut NW
    1-400 14
    401-OUT 18
Walnut SW 14
Walnut Hill Pl NW 18
Walthall NE 07
Walthall SE
    1-50 17
    51-OUT 16
Walthall Ct & Dr NW 18
Waltham Pl SE 16

Walton NW 03
Walton Ln SE 17
Wanda Cir SW 15
Wandawood Rd (DOR) 40
Ward Dr SE & SW 54
Ward St & Cir (EP) 44
Ware Ave (EP) 44
Warfield NW 18
Warfield Ct (CP) 49
Warlick Pl NE 17
Warner SW 10
Warren Ct & Rd NW 18
Warren Pl SE 03
Warren St NE & SE 17
Warren Way (EP) 44
Warrenhall Ln NE 19
Warrington Pl (CP) 49
Warwick SE 16
Warwick Cir NE 45
Wascanna Rd (HAP) 54
Washington (CP) 37
Washington NW 18
Washington SW
    1-230 03
    231-270 34
    271-300 03
    301-650 12
    651-OUT 15
Washington Ave
    900-4485 (EP) 44
    4486-OUT (CP) 49
Washington Cir (EP) 44
Washington Hts Ter NW 14
Washington Pl SW 14
Washington Rd
    900-4485 (EP) 44
    4486-OUT (CP) 49
Washita Ave NE 07
Water Front Dr & Rd SW............ 36
Water Oak Way (DOR) 40
Waterbury Dr SW 14
Waterford Rd NW 18
Waters Dr SW 10
Waters Rd SW 54
Waterton Ct (DUN) 38
Watkins Pl NE 19
Watkins St & Dr NW 18
Watson NE 07
Watson Cir SE 17
Watson Dr (DOR) 40
Watts Rd NW 18
Waverly Way NE 07
Wawona Dr & Ter NE 19
Wayland Cir NE 19
Wayne Ave NE 06
Wayne Pl SW 10
Wayside Dr NE 19
Weatherby SE 16
Weatherly Dr & Ln NW 28
Weaver Way (DOR) 40
Webster SW 14
Wedgeway (DUN) 38
Wedgewood Dr NW 18
Wee Kirk Rd SE 16
Weems Dr (CP) 49
Weigelia Rd NE 45
Welborn Ct (CP) 49
Welch SE 15
Welch SW 10
Welcome All Rd SW
    1-3850 31
    3851-OUT 49
Welcome All Ter (CP) 49
Weldon Pl NE 12

Atlanta (Con.)   303

Weldstone Ct & Ter NE	28
Welland Ave SE	16
Wellborn SW	10
Wellbourne Dr NE	24
Wellesley Dr NW	05
Wellington SW	
1-280	14
281-OUT	10
Wellona Pl NE	45
Wells SW	
1-620	12
621-OUT	10
Wells Ave (CP)	37
Wells Ct SW	12
Wells Dr SW	11
Wellswood Dr SE	15
Wendell Dr NW & SW	36
Wendell Dr SE	15
Wendland Dr NE	19
Wendover Dr NE	45
Wenlock Ave NW	14
Wentworth Dr NE	45
Wesco Way NW	18
Wesley Ave NE	07
Wesley Dr NW	05
Wesley Pky NW	27
Wesley Oaks Rd NW	28
Wesleyan Dr SW	36
Wessyngton Rd NE	06
West Ave NE	18
West Ave SW	18
West Mnr Ct NW	11
West Mnr Ln SW	11
West Rd NE	24
West Anderson Ave SW	14
West Andrews Dr NW	05
West Anthony NW	07
West Ashland Ave NE	08
West Belle Isle Rd NE	42
West Brookhaven Dr NE	19
West Candler Lake Ct NE	19
West Caribea Trl SE	16
West Cedar Ln SW	11
West Chester Blvd NW	14
West Club Dr & Ln NE	19
West Conway Dr NW	
1-1250	27
1551-OUT	27
West Conway Rd NW	
1-1250	27
1551-OUT	27
West Druid Hills Dr NE	29
West Echo NW	18
West End Ave & Pl SW	10
West Fontainbleau Ct & Dr (DOR)	40
West Garmon Rd NW	27
West Handy Dr NW	18
West Kildare Ave NW	18
West Kimberly Rd SW	31
West Kingston Ct & Dr NE	19
West Lake Ave NW	
1-300	14
301-OUT	18
West Lake Ave NW	14
West Lake Ct & Dr NW	14
West Lane Dr NW	18
West LeeOs Mill Rd (CP)	49
West Lindmont Ct NE	24
West Main NW	18
West Marietta NW	18

West Moreland Cir NW	18
West Muscogee Ave NW	05
West Nancy Creek Ct NE	19
West Nancy Creek Dr NE	
1-1750	19
1751-OUT	41
West Northbrook Ct (DOR)	40
West Ontario Ave SW	10
West Paces Ferry Rd NW	
1-600	05
601-OUT	27
West Peachtree NW	
1-816	08
817-817	83
818-870	08
871-OUT	09
West Peachtree Pl NW	
1-100	08
101-OUT	13
West Pine Valley Rd NW	05
West Point Ave & Rd (CP)	37
West Roxboro Rd NE	24
West Simon Ter NW	18
West Sussex Rd NE	06
West Wesley Rd NW	
1-600	05
601-OUT	27
West Whitehall SW	10
West Wieuca Rd NE & NW	42
Westboro Dr	10
Westchester Dr (EP)	44
Westerhall Ct NE	28
Western Ave NW	14
Westfalia Ct NE	42
Westfield Dr NE	42
Westfield Trl (CP)	49
Westford Cir & Ct (CP)	49
Westhaven Dr SW	11
Westhill Cir (CP)	49
Westland Blvd NW	11
Westmart Ln (DOR)	40
Westmeath Dr SW	10
Westminster Cir NW	27
Westminster Dr NE	
1-500	09
501-OUT	24
Westminster Way NE	07
Westmont Dr (DOR)	40
Westmont Rd SW	11
Westmoor Dr NW	14
Westover Dr (EP)	44
Westover Dr NW	05
Westover Plantation Rd NW	18
Westridge Rd NW	11
Westshire Pl NW	18
Westview Dr SW	10
Westview Pl SW	14
Westwood Ave (EP)	44
Westwood Ave SW	10
Westwood Dr (DOR)	40
Wetzel Dr SW	10
Wexford Dr & Rd (CP)	49
Weyman Ave SW	15
Weyman Ct NW	27
Wharton Dr SW	36
Whatley SE	15
Wheaton Dr SW	36
Wheeler (HAP)	54
Wheeler NW	18
Wheeler Dr (DOR)	40
Wheeler Dr SW	10
Whipple Ave (HAP)	54
Whipple Ave (EP)	44

Whispering Ln, Trl & Way NE	28
Whispering Hills Ct & Dr (CHA)	41
Whisperwood Trl (EP)	44
Whitaker NW	18
Whitaker Cir NW	14
Whitam Dr (DUN)	38
Whitby Dr (DOR)	40
White (CP)	37
White NW	18
White SW	10
White City Rd (CP)	37
White Oak Ave NW	18
White Oak Ave SW	10
White Oak Hollow NE	24
White Water Creek Rd NW	27
Whiteford Ave NE	07
Whiteford Ave SE	17
Whitehall SW	
1-620	03
621-OUT	10
Whitehall Ter SW	
1-430	03
431-OUT	12
Whitehouse Dr SW	14
Whiteleigh Ct & Dr NE	45
Whites Aly & Pl SW	10
Whiteway (EP)	44
Whitewood Ct (DUN)	38
Whitfield Dr (DUN)	38
Whiting NW	18
Whitmore Dr NW	05
Whitner Dr NW	27
Whitney Ave (HAP)	54
Whittier Ave NW	18
Whittington Ct & Dr NE	42
Whitworth Dr SW	31
Wichita Dr SW	11
Wickcliff Ct (CHA)	41
Wickersham Dr (CP)	37
Wickersham Dr NW	27
Wickford Way (DUN)	38
Wieuca Rd & Ter NE	42
Wilbur Ave SE	16
Wilcox St NW	15
Wild Creek Trl NE	24
Wilder Ct (DUN)	38
Wildwood Pl NE	
1-930	24
931-1800	06
1801-OUT	24
Wildwood Rd NE	
1-930	24
931-1800	06
1801-OUT	24
Wildwood Lake Dr SW	31
Wilford Dr NE	19
Wilkerson Dr SE	17
Wilkes Cir NW	18
Will Lee Pl & Rd (CP)	49
Will Rogers Pl SE	16
Will Ross Ct (CHA)	41
Willard Ave SW	10
Williams NW	
1-284	03
285-500	08
501-700	13
701-900	08
901-OUT	09
Williams Ave (EP)	44
Williams Pl NW	18
Williams Mill Rd NE	06
Williamsburg Dr (CP)	37

Atlanta (Con.)   303

Willingham Dr
  1-1565 (EP) 44
  1566-OUT (CP) 37
Willis NW 14
Willis Mill Rd SW 11
Willoughby Way NE 12
Willow NE 08
Willow Ave NE 05
Willow Pl SE 16
Willow Trl SW 11
Willow Bend Dr NE 28
Willow Cove Dr NE 31
Willow Creek Dr NE 28
Willow Heights Dr NE 28
Willow Lake Dr NE 29
Willow Oak Way (DOR) 40
Willowbrook Dr SW 11
Willowdale Cir SE 16
Willowwood Cir SE 17
Willowwood Ct NE 45
Wilmer NE 08
Wilmington SW 10
Wilmont Dr NE 29
Wilmont Ln SW 10
Wilson Ave NW
  1-100 10
  101-OUT 14
Wilson Dr SW 11
Wilson Rd (CP) 49
Wilson Rd NW
  1-3000 18
  3001-OUT 54
Wilson Rd SE
  1-3000 18
  3001-OUT 54
Wilson James Rd SW 31
Wilson Mill Rd SW 31
Wilton Ave (DOR) 40
Wimberly Rd NE 19
Wimbledon Rd NE 24
Winall Down Rd NE 19
Winburn Dr & Ter (EP) 44
Winchester Trl (CHA) 41
Windemere Dr NE 24
Windhaven Trl SW, SW 31
Winding Ln NE 19
Winding Branch Cir, Ct, Dr &
  Ln (DUN) 38
Winding Creek Ct & Trl NW ... 28
Winding Ridge Ct (DUN) 38
Winding River Dr (DUN) 38
Windsor SW
  1-660 12
  661-760 10
  761-870 15
  871-OUT 10
Windsor Dr SW 11
Windsor Pky NE
  1-250 19
  251-1000 42
  1001-OUT 19
Windsor Forest Dr (CHA) 41
Windsor Oak Dr (DOR) 40
Windwood Ct, Dr & Ln (DOR) . 40
Windy Ridge Dr NE 42
Windy Rush Dr (EP) 44
Winfield Ave SE
  1-1500 16
  1501-OUT 17
Winfred Ter (EP) 44
Wing (DUN) 38

Wingate SW 10
Wingate Dr & Rd (CHA) 41
Wingedfoot Dr (DUN) 38
Winslow Dr NE 05
Winstead Ct (CP) 49
Winter Ave NE 17
Winter Crest Ct (DOR) 40
Winters Chapel Rd (DOR) ... 40
Winterthur Dr & Ln NW 28
Winterthur Ridge NW 28
Winthrop Dr SE 16
Winthrop Rd (CP) 37
Winton Ter NE 08
Wise Way NE 19
Wisteria Ln SW 31
Wisteria Way (EP) 44
Wisteria Way NE 17
Withers Pl SW 15
Withrow St & Dr (DOR) 40
Wolf Creek Cir & Dr SW 31
Wolfe Ave NE 26
Womack Ave (EP) 44
Womack Ct & Dr (DOR) 40
Womack Rd
  1-2800 (DUN) 38
  2801-OUT (DOR) 40
Wood St & Ave NW 18
Wood Acres Rd NE 45
Wood Hollow Dr (DOR) 40
Wood Valley Ct NE 19
Wood Valley Rd NW 27
Woodall Way (DOR) 40
Woodall Ferry (DOR) 40
Woodberry St & Dr NE 11
Woodbine Ave NE & SE 17
Woodbine Cir SE 17
Woodbine Ter NE 29
Woodbourne Dr SW 10
Woodbury Ave (EP) 44
Woodbury St & Dr SW 11
Woodcastle Ln SE 16
Woodcliffe Dr NE 29
Woodcliffe Ter NE 24
Woodcrest Ave NE & NW ... 09
Wooddale Dr NE 26
Woodgreen Dr (CHA) 41
Woodham Way NE 16
Woodhaven Cir (EP) 44
Woodhaven Dr NE 19
Woodhaven Rd NW 05
Woodhill Cir & Ln (EP) 44
Woodlake Dr NE 29
Woodland Ave (CP) 37
Woodland Ave NE 24
Woodland Ave SE
  1-1650 16
  1651-OUT 15
Woodland Cir (EP) 44
Woodland Cir SE 16
Woodland Ct & Way (DOR) ... 40
Woodland Dr (HAP) 54
Woodland Park Dr NE 45
Woodland Ter SW 11
Woodland Brook Dr NE 39
Woodland Hills Ave NW 18
Woodland Hills Dr NE 24
Woodlawn Ave NW 18
Woodley Dr NW 18
Woodlynne Way (DOR) 40
Woodmere Dr NW 18
Woodmere Sq NW 27
Woodmont Ln NW 18
Woodrow NW 18

Woodrow SW 10
Woodrow Ave (HAP) 54
Woodrow Way NE 19
Woods Cir NE 24
Woods Dr NE
  1-1500 18
  1501-OUT 19
Woods Dr NW
  1-1500 18
  1501-OUT 19
Woods Rd NE
  1-1500 18
  1501-OUT 19
Woods Rd NW
  1-1500 18
  1501-OUT 19
Woods St & Ave NW 18
Woodsdale Rd NE 24
Woodsey Way SE 15
Woodside Way (CHA) 41
Woodson SE 15
Woodsong Ct, Dr & Trl (DUN) . 38
Woodstock Dr SW 31
Woodstock Rd SE 16
Woodstream Cir NE 19
Woodvale Dr NW 27
Woodvalley Dr (EP) 44
Woodward Ave SE 12
Woodward Dr (CP) 49
Woodward Way NW
  1-600 05
  601-800 27
  801-OUT 05
Woodwardia Rd NE 45
Woodwin Ct & Rd (DOR) 40
Woody Trl NE 19
Worchester Dr NE 06
Worth Dr NW 27
Wortham Ave SW 11
Wrenwood Dr & Pl NE 07
Wright NE
  1-1000 26
  1001-OUT 24
Wright Ave NE
  1-1000 26
  1001-OUT 24
Wright Cir & Rd NE 28
Wright Dr SW 11
Wyatt (HAP) 54
Wycherly Ct NE 19
Wycliff Rd NW 09
Wycombe Rd NE 28
Wye Ln (CHA) 41
Wyland Dr SW 10
Wylie SE
  1-1195 16
  1196-OUT 17
Wyman St NE & SE 17
Wyncourtney Dr & Ln NE ... 28
Wyndale Ct (CHA) 41
Wyndham Dr NW 28
Wyngate NW 05
Wynhill Dr NE 28
Wynnton Dr NE 19
Wynwood Dr SW 10
Xavier Dr SW 36
Yale Ave (CP) 37
Yale Pl SW 15
Yarmouth Ct (DUN) 38
Yates Dr NW 18
Yates Rd (CP) 37
Yonah Dr NE 09
Yonge St NE & SE 12

Atlanta (Con.)   303

Yonkers Ave NW 14
York Ave SW 10
York Rd (CP) 37
Yorkshire Rd NE 06
Young SE 16
Young Dr (CP) 37
Young Dr (EP) 44
Young Rd (CHA) 41
Yukon Ct SE 16
Zachery SW 10
Zane Grey Dr SE 16
Zelda Dr NE 45
Zimmer Dr NE 06
Zip Industrial Blvd SE 54
Zone Ave SW 31
Zonolite Pl & Rd NE 06

NUMBERED STREETS

1st NE
   1-1000 14
   1001-1500 18
   1501-2400 07
   2401-2500 18
1st NW
   1-1000 14
   1001-1500 18
   1501-2400 07
   2401-2500 18
1st SW
   1-1000 14
   1001-1500 18
   1501-2400 07
   2401-2500 18
1st Ave (CP) 37
1st Ave NE & SE 17
1st Ave NW 18
1st Ave SW 15
1st thru 6th St (EP) 44
2nd Ave (DOR) 40
2nd Ave NE & SE 17
2nd St & Ave NW 18
3rd (DOR) 40
3rd NW
   1-6 18
   7-100 08
   101-400 13
   401-OUT 18
3rd Ave NE & SE 17
3rd St & Ave SW 15
3rd thru 6th St NE 08
4th NW
   1-100 08
   101-300 13
   301-1000 32
   1001-OUT 18
4th Ave NE & SE 17
4th thru 5th St SW 15
4th thru 6th St (CHA) 41

5th (HAP) 54
5th (DOR) 40
5th NW
   1-100 08
   101-200 13
   201-OUT 18
5th Ave NE 17
6th NW
   1-200 13
   201-OUT 18
7th NE
   1-49 08
   50-50 23
   51-OUT 08
7th thru 8th St SW 15
7th thru 9th St NW 18
8th (EP) 44
8th NE
   1-450 09
   451-OUT 08
8th thru 9th St (CHA) 41
9th thru 12th St NE 09
10th NW
   1-150 09
   151-OUT 18
11th NW
   1-300 09
   301-OUT 18
12th NW 09
13th St NE & NW 09
14th NW
   1-130 09
   131-OUT 18
14th St & Pl NE 09
15th NW 18
15th thru 17th St NE 09
16th NW
   1-100 09
   101-OUT 18
18th NW 09
25th thru 26th St NW 09
28th NW 09

AUGUSTA   309

POST OFFICE BOXES

Box Nos.
1-1999   Main Office 03
2701-3999   The Hill Sta 04
4001-4999   Martinez Br 07
5001-5999   Peach Orchard
         Br 06
7001-7999   Fort Gordon Br . 05

RURAL ROUTES

1 06
2 04
3 08
4,5 07
6 06

STATIONS, BRANCHES AND UNITS

Fort Gordon Br 05
Martinez Br 07
Peach Orchard Br 06
The Hill Sta 04
Veterans Hospital Sta 04
General Delivery 03
Postmaster 01

APARTMENTS, HOTELS, MOTELS

Alamo Plaza, Gordon Hwy 01
Augusta Homes, 100 Telfair
   Extension 01
Aumond Villa, W Lake Forrest
   Dr 04
Bon Air, Walton Way 04
Broadway, 335 Broad 01
Calcutta 1011 River Ridge
   Rd 04
Charlestowne South, 2119
   Lumpkin Rd 06
Colonial Court, 2549 Walton
   Way 04
Continental Airport, Bush
   Field 06
Country Club, Milledge Rd 04
East Gate, Gwinnett 01
Fairway Village, 2910
   Richmond Hill Rd 06
Forest Hills, 2801 Walton
   Way 04
Gateway, 110 3rd 01
George Walton, 2068 Walton
   Way 04
Georgetown Court, Walton
   Way 04

Augusta (Con.)   309

Georgian Arms, 2440
  Damascus Rd 04
Gilbert Manor, 1300 Railroad
  Ave 01
Golf Park, 156 Damascus Rd . 04
Heritage, Wrightsboro &
  Jackson Rd 04
Hickman Arms, Hickman Rd ... 04
Holiday Inn, 1602 Gordon
  Hwy 06
Hornes Motor Lodge, 1520
  Gordon Hwy 06
Howard Johnson Motor Lodge,
  1238 Gordon Hwy 01
James, Po Sq 02
Keystone, 1927 Central Ave ... 04
Magnolia Villa, Walton Way ... 04
Mcdonald, Wrightsboro Rd &
  Baker 04
Medical Terrace, 1105 15 Th
  St 01
Miles, 2077 Old Savannah
  Rd 01
Monte Sano, 801 Monte Sano
  Ave 04
Peachtree Gardens,
  Wrightsboro Rd 04
Pine Hill, Henry 04
Ramada Inn 1365 Gordon
  Highway 01
Richmond 744 Broad 02
Royal Palms, 2904 Peach
  Orchard Rd 06
Town Towers, 444 Broad St ... 02
University, 1410 Gwinnett 02
Valley Park, 3100
  Wrightsboro Rd 04
Warrick, 441 Broad 02
Waverly Villa, 500 Norwich
  Rd 04
Williamsburg South 04

BUILDINGS

Augusta Aviation 04
Augusta Medical Park, 1021
  15 Th St 01
Bush Field 06
Campbell, 102 8th 02
Commerce, 666 Broad St 02
Daniel Village, Wrightsboro
  Rd 04
First Federal, 958 Broad 02
First National, 801 Broad St .. 02
Georgia Railroad Bank, 699
  Broad St 02
Johnson, 208 8th 02
Marion, 739 Broad 02
Medical Arts, 1467 Harper
  St 02
Mid South, 360 Bay St 01
National Hills, 2701
  Washington Rd 04
News, 725 Broad 02
Peach Orchard Plz 06
Seaboard Coast Line, 120
  Gwinnett 01
Southern Finance, 753 Broad . 02
Southgate Plaza, Gordon
  Hwy 06

The 500, 501 Greene St 02
Union Savings Bank, 142
  8th 02

GOVERNMENT OFFICES

City-County Municipal, 530
  Greene St 02

HOSPITALS

Andress Nursing Home, 2121
  Scott Rd 06
Bayvale Rest Home, 3212
  Milledgeville Rd 04
Beverly Manor 1600 Anthony
  Rd 04
Blair Nursing Home, 2541
  Milledgeville Rd 04
Georgia War Veterans
  Nursing Home, 1101 15th .. 01
Leisure Homes, 3235 Deans
  Bridge Rd 04
Marioni Convalescent Home,
  409 Pleasant Home Rd 07
Medical College Of Georgia,
  1459 Gwinnett St 02
Medicenter, 1355 Nelson 01
Myers Rest Home, 2622
  Milledgeville Rd 04
Saint Josephs Hospital, 1600
  Winter 04
Talmadge Memorial Hospital,
  1120 15th 02
University Hospital, University
  Pl 02
Vetrans Administration
  Hospital, Forest Hills 04
Virginias Convalescent Home,
  717 Bohler Ave 04

UNIVERSITIES AND COLLEGES

Augusta College, 2500
  Walton Way 04
Medical College Of Georgia,
  1459 Gwinnett St 02
Paine College, 1235 15th 01

COLUMBUS   319

POST OFFICE BOXES

Box Nos.		
1-2872	Main Office	02
1400-2386	Fort Benning Br	05
3000-3277	Baker Village Sta	03
4000-4246	Beallwood Sta ..	04
5000-5399	Wynnton Sta	06
6001-6592	Lindsey Creek...	07

RURAL ROUTES

1 04
2 07

STATIONS, BRANCHES AND UNITS

Baker Village Sta 03
Beallwood Sta 04
Bibb City Br 04
College Heights Sta 07
Custer Terrace Br 05
Edgewood Sta 07
Fort Benning Br 05
Lindsay Creek Sta 07
Oakland Park Sta 03
Rose Hill Sta 04
Rosemont Sta 04
Windsor Park Br 04
Wynnton Sta 06
General Delivery 02
Postmaster 02

APARTMENTS, HOTELS, MOTELS

Baker Village 03
Baker Village Annex 03
Booker T Washington 01
Buena Vista Estates 06
Camelia Motel Apts 03
Cardinal Hotel 01
Central Court 01
Chase 01
Cherokee 06
Coronado 03
Cusseta Place 03
Delmar 06
Diane 06
Eliz F Canty 03
Elliot 03
Gateway 03
Glendale Arms 01
Grady 04
Haralson 01
Highland Court 06
Hilton Arms 04
Illeges Road Apartments 06
Impalla Apartments 06
Ladelle 06
Lincoln Court 06
Luther C Wilson 04
Manor Arms 01
Mirada 06
Peabody 04
Pine Terrace 03
Prince 01
Ralston 02
Rankin 02
Stripling Terrace 04
Victory 03
Warren Williams 06
Waverly 01

BUILDINGS

Biggers 01
Bush 01
Columbus Bank & Trust
  Company 01
Commerce 01
Edge 01
Empire 01
First National Bank 01
Flowers 01
Fourth National Bank 01
Hill 01
Interstate 01

Columbus (Con.) 319

Martin	01
Professional	01
Swift Kyle	01
416	01

HOSPITALS

Martin Army Hospital, Ft Benning	05
Medical Center, 710 Center St	02
Saint Francis, Expressway	04

UNIVERSITIES AND COLLEGES

Columbus College, Algonquin Dr	07
Meadows Business College	02
Phillips College	02

DECATUR 300

POST OFFICE BOXES

Box Nos.
A-H	South Decatur	32
1-1875	Main Office	31
32001-32499	South Decatur	32
33001-33299	North Decatur	33

RURAL ROUTES

1,2	34

STATIONS, BRANCHES AND UNITS

Agnes Scott College Sta	30
Belvedere Plaza Br	32
Dunaire Br	32
North Decatur Br	33
North Druid Hills Br	33
South Decatur Br	32
South De Kalb Br	34
Vista Grove Br	33
General Delivery	30
Postmaster	30

APARTMENTS, HOTELS, MOTELS

Adair Oaks, 222 Adair Ct	30
Alexandria Fairington Pky	34
Alpine, 2571 Candler Rd	32
Ambridge Arms, 1031 Scott Blvd	30
Belvedere Medical Center, 3300 Memorial Dr	32
Belvedere Motel, 3480 Memorial Dr	32
Belvedere Park, 1593 1/2 1592 Line Cir	32
Belvedere Park, 1642 1/2 1584 Line	32
Brittany, 3320 Covington Dr	32
Camellia Ct, 4082 1/2 4108 Glenwood Rd	32
Candler East, 2423 & 2425 Candler Rd	32
Candler Hotel, 150 E. Ponce De Leon	30

Casa Rio, 3850 Memorial Dr	32
Catalina, 4371 Glenwood Rd	32
Cedar Brook Village, Cedar Brook Dr	33
Cedar Creek Village Cedar Creek Pky	33
Charter Square, Town Houses, 1-24 Charter Square	30
Chateau-Belvedere, 1668 Welika Dr	32
Christian Towers, 1438 Church	30
Cindy Ct 4120 Glenwood Rd	32
Columbia Heights, 1221 Forest Blvd	30
Country Estates, 2505 Columbia Dr	34
Crescent Court, 1021 Scott Blvd	30
Decatur Inn, 921 Church	30
Decatur Townhouses 317 Adair St	30
Dekalb Towers 02, 1501 Clairmont Road	33
Dekalb Towers, Farnell Ct	33
Dekalb-Cambridge, 3661 N. Decatur Rd	33
Eagle 212 Adair St	30
East Lake, 746 East Lake Dr	30
Eastwyck Village, Candler Rd	32
Emory Gardens, 1111 Clairmont Ave	30
Emory Woods, North Decatur Rd	33
Fairington, Fairington Ct, Dr, Pky	34
Fontain, Rue Fontaine	34
Four Forty 1/2 nine, 449 Clairmont Ave	30
Gateway Manor, 421 W. Trinity Pl	30
Glen Hollow, Glen Hollow Cir	34
Glen Hollow, Glen Hollow Dr	34
Glen Hollow, Glen Hollow Ln	34
Glen Point, Highcourt Pl	32
Glenshire Townhouses, Glen Acres Ct	32
Glenwood Springs, 3481 1/2 3513 Glenwood Rd	32
Gray Manor, 2825-2853 Belvedere Ln	32
Green Acres, 3937 Glenwood Rd	32
Gresham Park, 2520 - 2548 Flat Shoals Rd	32
Grovenor House, 2517 Columbia Dr	34
Habitat, Habitat Cir	34
Habitat, Habitat Ct	34
Habitat, Habitat Pl	34
Habitat, Habitat Way	34
Harbour Oaks, 2503 Lawrenceville Hwy	33
Heart Of Decatur Motel, 245 E Trinity Pl	30
Hearthstone, Ember Dr	34
Hillcrest, 351 Hillcrest St	30
Hillyer Square, Hillyer Sq	30
Kandy Court, 3975 Covington Hwy	32

Kenco-Decatur, 1175 & 1225 Church St	30
Kenco-Memorial, 3754 - 3766 Memorial Dr	32
Lin-Del, 1575 Line St	32
Medical Surgical Plaza, 365 Winn Way	30
Medlock Pines, 773 1/2 813 Scottdale Rd	33
Midway Manor, 3626 Midway Rd	32
Misty Waters Misty Waters Dr	32
Montclair, 1272 - 1378 Clairmont Rd	33
Montville, 1760 Clairmont Rd	33
Mountain Trace, 3360 Mountain Dr	30
North Decatur Gardens, 1384 Lawrenceville Hwy	33
North Decatur Manor, 3757 - 3805 North Decatur Rd	33
North Decatur Office Center, 3796 N Decatur Rd	33
North Dekalb, 2326 1/2 2340 Lawrenceville Hwy	33
Old South Gardens, 135 East Hill St	30
One West Court Square, W Court Sq	30
Phillips Towers, 218 E Trinity Pl	30
Pinewood, Treeview Ct	34
Pinewood, Treeview Dr	34
Pinewood, Treeview Ln	34
Plantation Oaks, 1043 Holcomb Rd	32
President Park, 1231 Clairmont Ave	30
Province-East, 3800 Flat Shoals Rd	34
Rainbow Forest, Rainbow Forest Cir	34
Robin Hood Villa, 2427 Lawrenceville Hwy	33
Rodeway Inn, 1706 Clairmont Rd	33
Scott Pines, 927 Scott Blvd	30
Scott-Landover, 1020 Scott Blvd	30
Sharwell, 1111 1/2 1219 & 1301 1/2 1321 Oakview Rd	30
Snapfingerwoods, Snapfinger Woods Dr	32
Spanish Trace, 2929 Panthersville Rd	34
Susan Court, 3961 Covington Hwy	32
Sycamore Square, Town Houses, 1-26 Sycamore Sq	30
Tower Gardens, 4015 Covington Hwy	32
Tregoney, Tregoney Dr	34
Twin Oaks, Twin Oaks Dr	30
University, Williams Ln., Shoupe Ct., & O'Neal Pl	33
Venetian Club, 510 Coventry Rn	30

Decatur (Con.) 300

Villa, 2812 - 2870 Villa Cir.... 30
Wellington Wellington Ct........ 34
Westchester Square,
　Westchester Sq 30
Whispering Pines, 2784 1/2
　2800 Kelly Lake Rd 32
Williamsburg Medical Center,
　Mcconnell Dr.................... 33
Williamsburg, Blackshear &
　North Jamestown 33
Willowick, Willowick Ct.......... 34
Willowick, Willowick Dr.......... 34
Winston Manor, 2420 Candler
　Rd 32
Woodlake, Clubhouse,
　Gatehouse, Whitepine........ 32

BUILDINGS

Court House, Court Sq 30
Decatur Federal, 250 E Ponce
　De Leon 30
Decatur Professional North,
　755 Columbia 30
Dekalb Administration, 556 N
　Mcdonough........................ 30
Dekalb County Federal, 116
　Clairmont Ave.................... 30
Dekalb Professional, 2754 N
　Decatur Rd........................ 33
Dekalb, 430 N Mc Donough.... 30
Executive Square, 4277-79
　Memorial Dr 32
Executive, 125 Trinity Pl........ 30
Federal, 141 Trinity Pl.......... 30
First National Bank, 315 W
　Ponce De Leon 30
Hooper, 525 Marshall............ 30
Law, 103 Beaumont Pl.......... 30
Masonic Temple, 108 E
　Ponce De Leon 30
Professional, 235 E Ponce De
　Leon 30
Trinity, 118 Trinity Pl.............. 30
Trust, 545 N Mc Donough...... 30
Watkins, 112 E Ponce De
　Leon 30
Weeks, 140 Sycamore 30

HOSPITALS

Dekalb General, 2701 N
　Decatur Rd........................ 33
Georgia Regional Hospital,
　3073 Panthersville Rd........ 34
V A, 1660 & 1670 Clairmont
　Rd 33

UNIVERSITIES AND COLLEGES

Agnes Scott, E College Ave..... 30
Columbia Seminary, 701
　Columbia Dr...................... 30

MACON 312

POST OFFICE BOXES

Box Nos.
A-U　　　　Mulberry Street
　　　　　　　Sta................ 02
1-999　　　Mulberry Street
　　　　　　　Sta................ 02
1-1539　　　University Sta.... 07
101-942　　Wesleyan Sta.... 01
2001-2999　Pio Nono Sta 03
3001-3999　South Macon
　　　　　　　Sta................ 05
4001-6999　Macon............ 08
7001-7354　Riverside Sta.... 04

RURAL ROUTES

1,2 04
3.. 06
4,5,6.................................... 01
7,8.. 06
9.. 01
10.. 06

STATIONS, BRANCHES AND UNITS

Bloomfield Sta...................... 06
Cross Keys Sta...................... 01
Mulberry Street Sta.............. 01
Pionono Sta.......................... 03
Riverside Sta........................ 04
South Macon Sta.................. 05
Shurlington Sta...................... 01
University Sta........................ 07
Wesleyan Sta........................ 01
Westgate Sta........................ 01
Wilson Airport Rural Br.......... 01
General Delivery.................... 01
Postmaster............................ 01

APARTMENTS, HOTELS, MOTELS

Alpine Lodge, 1900 Riverside
　Dr...................................... 02
Ambassador Motel, 2772
　Riverside Dr...................... 04
Azalea Motel, 5797 Houston
　Rd...................................... 06
Belmont, 625 Walnut.............. 01
Biltmore, 811 Poplar.............. 01
Bowden Homes, 2250 Cedar... 06
Brooks, 165 5th...................... 01
Brookwood, 3111 Brookwood
　Dr...................................... 04
Brown House Motor, 589
　Broadway 01
Buckingham Court, 111
　Buckingham Pl 04
Capitol, 580 Plum.................. 01
Central, 310 Broadway.......... 02
College Hill, 464 College 01
Colonial, 544 Orange............ 01
Courtesy Court Incorporated,
　2240 Gray Hwy.................. 01
Dempsey Motor, 387 3rd........ 02
Douglas, 373 Broadway........ 01
Drills Motel, 1232
　Jeffersonville Rd................ 01
Ellisonian, 478 College.......... 01
Felton Homes, 2035 Felton
　Ave.................................... 01
Fireproof Courts, 4168
　Broadway 06

Franklin, 1131 Broadway........ 01
Fredonia, 1007 Bond.............. 01
Georgian Terrace, 1061
　Georgia Ave...................... 01
Georgian, 683 Mulberry.......... 02
Georgian, 819 Poplar............ 01
Gilman, Smith, 2281
　Vineville Ave 04
Glenwood Terrace, Ricemill
　Road.................................. 06
Grace, 233 Corbin Ave.......... 04
Grady, 301 Cherry................ 02
Heart Of Georgia, 561
　Broadway 01
Heritage Motel, 2690
　Riverside Dr...................... 04
Holiday Inn Of America, 1044
　Riverside Dr...................... 08
Inglewood, 2484 Ingleside
　Ave.................................... 04
J & J, 1112 Broadway............ 01
J Clay Murphy Homes, 2499
　B Street.............................. 06
Jacksons Motor Court, 4670
　Houston Rd........................ 06
Katherine Court, 855
　Mulberry............................ 01
Knox, 333 Cherry.................. 02
Lafayette, 233 College.......... 01
Lake Terrace Apartments........ 04
Lake Terrace Court................ 04
Laurine, 635 Orange.............. 01
Leonard Court, 575 Virgin...... 01
Macon Homes, 2850 Cherry
　Ave.................................... 04
Macon Motor Court, 4057
　Houston Ave...................... 06
Macon Plaza Motel, 759
　Orange Ter 01
Macon, 389 Mulberry............ 01
Magnolia Court & Grill, 4739
　Houston Rd........................ 06
Married Students & Faculty
　Apartments, Stadium Dr..... 01
Massee, 347 College.............. 01
Middle Street, 425 Middle...... 01
Miller, 601 3rd........................ 01
Monroe, 633 Monroe.............. 01
Nevarro, 551 Orange............ 01
New Street Apartments, 363
　New 01
Normandy, 2416 Vineville
　Ave.................................... 04
North Garden, 833 North Ave... 01
North Napier Apartment,
　Napier Ave 04
Oglethorpe Homes, 1130
　Oglethorpe........................ 01
Old South, 1034 Georgia Ave.... 01
Palisades, 643 Orange.......... 01
Park, 506 Poplar.................... 01
Peach State Motel, 5417
　Houston Rd........................ 06
Pendleton Homes, 3401
　Houston Ave...................... 06
Pinebrook Inn & Courts, 4420
　Forsyth Rd.......................... 04
Plaza, 518 Mulberry.............. 01
Pursley, 455 Pursley.............. 01
Rembert, 1605 Rembert Ave.... 01
Riverdale, 1080 Nottingham
　Dr...................................... 01

Macon (Con.)	312

Rushin, 397 College	01
Siesels, 619 College	01
Simmons, 578 College	01
Skyline Grill & Court, Clinton Rd	01
South Winds Motel, 3010 Riggins Mill Rd	01
Terrace, 876 Mulberry	01
Tindall Heights Homes, 985 Plant	01
Town House Apartments, Rogers Ave	04
Town Pavilion, 205 Broadway	01
Twin Pine, 1585 Hawthorne Rd	01
Vineville Court, 1975 Vineville Ave	01
Vineville Gardens, 2020 Vineville Ave	04
Walnut, 931 Walnut	01
Welchs Lounge, 361 Mulberry	01
Williamson Terrace, Williamson Road	06
Winship Gardens, 2140 Ingleside Ave	04

BUILDINGS

Chandler, 154 Broadway	01
Cochran Field	01
Colonnade, 1073 Georgia Ave	01
Federal, 475 Mulberry	01
First National Bank, 425 2nd	01
Georgia Power, 595 Mulberr	01
Hardeman, 305 Cotton Ave	01
Hart, 348 Cotton Ave	01
Mc Cowen Plaza, 2110 Ingleside Ave	04
One Sixty Five First	01
One Sixty Two First	01
Persons, 544 Mulberry	01
Robert E Lee, 830 Mulberry	01
Schwartz, 653 2nd	01
Seven Forty Hemlock	01
Southern Trust, 682 Cherry	01
Southern United, 407 Cherry	01
United States Post Office, 451 College	01
Walker & Meadows, 828 Riverside Dr	01
Walton, 591 Cotton Ave	01
Washington Block, 590 Mulberry	01
Westgate Shopping Center, 2525 Pio Nono Ave	06

GOVERNMENT OFFICES

Bibb County Courthouse, 275 2nd	01
City Hall, 718 Poplar	01
Macon Municipal Airport	01
United States Federal Building & Courthouse, 475 Mulberry	01
United States Federal, 451 College	01

HOSPITALS

Coliseum Hospital, 350 Hospital Dr	01
College Street Hospital 685 College	01
Doctors, 700 Spring	01
Macon Hospital, 777 Hemlock	08
Medical Center Office, 724 Hemlock	01
Middle Georgia Hospital, 746 Spring	01
Parkview Private Hospital, 1429 Oglethorpe	01
Physicians & Surgeons, 729 Pine	01
Riverside Clinic, 577 Walnut	01
Saint Luke Hospital, 853 Tatnall	08

UNIVERSITIES AND COLLEGES

Business Training Institute, Box 144	02
Crandall Business College, 555 Mulberry	01
G A B School Of Commerce, 556 First	01
Georgia Beauty Academy, 524 Mulberry	01
Macon Junior College, 5357	06
Macon University Of Cosmetology, 1248 Oglethorpe	01
Mercer University, 1400 Coleman Ave	07
Wesleyan College, 4760 Forsyth Rd	01

SAVANNAH	314

POST OFFICE BOXES

Box Nos.		
1-399	Thunderbolt Br.	04
1-2792	Main Office	02
3000-3499	A Sta	03
3500-3999	B Sta	04
4000-4999	Port Wentworth Br	07
5001-5194	A Sta	03
6000-6999	C Sta	05
7000-7399	Garden City Br.	08
8001-10999	Wright Square Sta	02
13001-13607	Oglethorpe Br	06
20001-20840	Savannah State College	04

RURAL ROUTES

1	01
2	04
3	06
4	05
5	01
6,7	04
8	05

STATIONS, BRANCHES AND UNITS

Bacon Park Sta	06
Garden City Br	08
Hi Way Eighty Br	08
Hunter Army Airfield Br	09
Isle Of Hope Br	06
Ogeechee Road Br	05
Oglethorpe Br	06
Port Wentworth Br	07
State College Br	04
Thunderbolt Br	04
Wilmington Island Rural Br	04
Windsor Forest Br	06
Wright Square Sta	02
General Delivery	02
Postmaster	01

APARTMENTS, HOTELS, MOTELS

Alamo Plaza, 1600 W Bay	01
Chatham City, 4309 Augusta Rd	08
Chatham, 609 Abercorn	01
Chelsea, 11-B Chelsea Dr	04
Clark Terrace, Cedar Ave & Metts Dr	04
Continental Inn, 412 W. Bay	01
Court, 1712 Abercorn	01
De Renne, 24 E Liberty	01
Desoto, 15 E Liberty	01
Drayton Arms, 102 E Liberty	01
Forsyth, 106 W Gwinnett	01
Fort Wayne, 36 E Broad	01
Franklin, 1800 E 38th	04
Graham, 210 E State	01
Heart Of Savannah, 300 W Bay	01
Holiday Inn, 121 W Boundary	01
John Wesley, 29 Abercorn	01
Lamara, De Renne Ave & Habershm	05
Nelson, De Renne Ave & Reynolds	05
Savannah Club, 1800 E 38th	04
Savannah Inn & Country Club 612, Wilmington Island Rd	04

BUILDINGS

A C L, 601 E Liberty	01
American Bldg, 7 Drayton St	01
Arcade, 105 E Bay	01
Board Of Education, 208 Bull	01
Central Of Georgia, 233 W Broad	01
Citizens And Southern Bank Bldg, 300, Bull St	01
Georgia State Bank, 136 Bull	01
Industrial Bank, 35 Bull	01
Liberty National Bank, 41 Bull	01
Morel, 5 Bull	01
Realty, 24 Drayton	01
Savannah Bank, 2 E Bryan	01
Western Union, 15 Drayton	01

Savannah (Con.) 314

GOVERNMENT OFFICES

Chatham County Court, 130 Bull	01
U S Post Office Bldg	01
United States Custom, 1 E Bay	01

HOSPITALS

Candler General, 601 Abercorn	01
Candler-Central, 3025 Bull	05
Candler, 17 E Park Ave.	01
Georgia Infirmary, 1900 Abercorn	01
Georgia Regional Hospital 1915 Eisenhower Drive	06
Memorial Medical Center, 4700 Waters Ave	04

Saint Josephs 11705 Mercy Blvd	06
United States Public Health Service, 115 E York	01

UNIVERSITIES AND COLLEGES

Armstrong State College, 11935 Abercorn	06
Savannah State College, Georgia	04

State List of Post Offices

HAWAII

HAWAII
(Abbreviation: HI)

Aiea (1st)	96701
Aina Haina, Sta. Honolulu (see appendix)	
Airport, Sta. Honolulu	96820
Ala Moana, Sta. Honolulu	96814
Anahola	96703
C C H, Sta. Laie	96762
Captain Cook	96704
Chinatown, Sta. Honolulu	96817
Eleele	96705
Ewa, Sta. Ewa Beach	96706
Ewa Beach (1st)	96706
Ford Island, Sta. Honolulu	96818
Fort Shafter, Sta. Honolulu	96823
Haiku	96708
Haina	96709
Hakalau	96710
Halaula, Br. Kapaau	96711
Haleiwa	96712
Haliimaile, Br. Makawao	96787
Hana	96713
Hanalei	96714
Hanamaulu	96715
Hanapepe	96716
Hauula	96717
Hawaii National Park	96718
Hawaiian Village, Sta. Honolulu	96813
Hawi	96719
Hickam A F B, Sta. Honolulu	96824
Hilo (1st)	96720
Holualoa	96725
Honaunau	96726
Honokaa	96727
HONOLULU (1st) (see appendix)	
Honomu	96728
Hoolehua	96729
Kaaawa	96730
Kahuku	96731
Kahului (1st)	96732

Kailua (1st)	96734
Kailua Kona (1st)	96740
Kaimuki, Sta. Honolulu	96816
Kalaheo	96741
Kalaupapa	96742
Kalihi, Sta. Honolulu	96817
Kamuela (1st)	96743
Kaneohe	96744
Kaneohe M C A S, Br. Kailua	96734
Kapaa	96746
Kapaau	96755
Kaumakani	96747
Kaunakakai	96748
Kawaihae, R. Sta. Kamuela	96743
Keaau	96749
Kealakekua	96750
Kealia	96751
Kekaha	96752
Kihei	96753
Kilauea	96754
Koloa	96756
Kualapuu	96757
Kukuihaele	96758
Kula	96790
Kunia	96759
Kurtistown	96760
Lahaina (1st)	96761
Laie	96762
Lanai City	96763
Laupahoehoe	96764
Lawai	96765
Lihue (1st)	96766
Makaha Valley, Br. Waianae	96792
Makakilo, Br. Ewa Beach	96706
Makawao	96768
Haliimaile, Br.	96787
Pukalani, R. Br.	96788
Makaweli	96769
Maunaloa	96770
Mililani Town Area, Sta. Wahiawa	96789
Moiliili, Sta. Honolulu	96814
Mountainview	96771
Naalehu	96772
Nanakuli, Br. Waianae	96792

Napili, R. Br. Lahaina	96761
Naval Air Station, Sta. Ewa Beach	96706
Naval Communication Station, Sta. Wahiawa	96786
Navy Cantonment, Sta. Honolulu	96818
Navy Terminal, Sta. Honolulu	96818
Ninole	96773
Ookala	96774
Paauhau	96775
Paauilo	96776
Pahala	96777
Pahoa	96778
Paia	96779
Papaaloa	96780
Papaikou	96781
Pawaa, Sta. Honolulu (see appendix)	
Pearl City (1st)	96782
Pepeekeo	96783
Puhi, R. Br. Lihue	96766
Pukalani, R. Br. Makawao	96788
Puunene	96784
Schofield Barracks, Sta. Wahiawa	96786
Submarine Base, Sta. Honolulu	96818
Tripler Army Hospital, Sta. Honolulu	96819
Ulupalakua, R. Br. Kula	96790
University, Sta. Honolulu	96825
Volcano	96785
Wahiawa (1st)	96786
Mililani Town Area, Sta.	96789
Naval Communication Station, Sta.	96786
Schofield Barracks, Sta.	96786
Waialae-Kahala, Sta. Honolulu	96816
Waialua	96791
Waianae (1st)	96792
Waikiki, Sta. Honolulu	96815
Wailuku (1st)	96793
Waimanalo	96795
Waimea	96796
Waipahu (1st)	96797

143

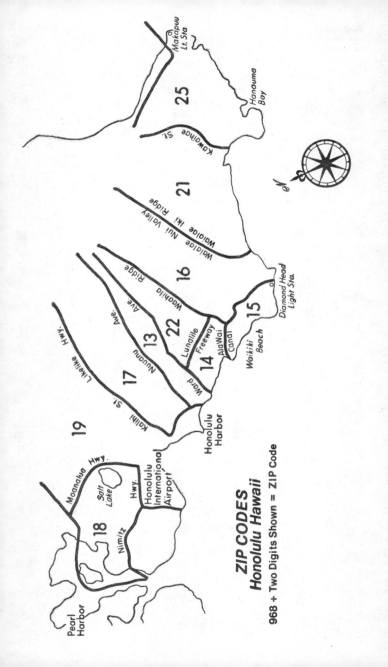

ZIP CODES
Honolulu Hawaii

968 + Two Digits Shown = ZIP Code

HONOLULU   968
POST OFFICE BOXES

Box Nos.		
A-Z	Waikiki Sta	15
A-CD	Waikiki Sta	15
A-AAB	Waikiki	15
1-230	Main Office	10
10A-10Q	Waialae-Kahala	16
231-701	Main Office	09
711-1101	Main Office	08
1111-1410	Main Office	07
1411-1801	Main Office	06
1811-2201	Main Office	05
2211-2561	Main Office	04
2571-2870	Main Office	03
2871-3170	Main Office	02
3171-3470	Main Office	01
3473-3710	Main Office	11
3713-3950	Main Office	12
3953-4545	Main Office	13
5000-5999	Pawaa Sta	14
6000-6999	Navy Cantonment Sta	18
7000-7499	Aina Haina Sta	21
7500-7999	Hawaii Kai Sta	25
8000-8999	Waikiki Sta	15
9000-9999	Airport Sta	20
10000-10999	Waialae-Kahala	16
11000-11999	Moiliili Sta	14
17001-17934	Kapalama Sta	17
88001-88149	Waikiki Sta	15

STATIONS, BRANCHES AND UNITS

Airport Sta	20
Aina Haina Sta	16
Ala Moana Sta	14
Chinatown Sta	17
Ford Island Sta	18
Fort Shafter Sta	23
Hawaiian Village Sta	13
Hickam A F B Sta	24
Kaimuki Sta	16
Kalihi Sta	17
Moiliili Sta	14
Navy Cantonment Sta	18
Navy Terminal Sta	18
Pawaa Sta	14
Submarine Base Sta	18
Tripler Army Hospital Sta	19
University Sta	25
Waialae-Kahala Sta	16
Waikiki Sta	15
General Delivery	13
Postmaster	13

APARTMENTS, HOTELS, MOTELS

Ainahau Apartments, 334 Seaside Ave	15
Ala Wai Terrace, 1547 Ala Wai Blvd	15
Alexander Young, 1077 Bishop	13
Atkinson Towers, 419 A Atkinson Dr	14
Breakers, 250 Beach Walk	15
Colony Surf, 2895 Kalakaua Ave	15
Diamond Head Ambassador, 2957 Kalakaua Ave	15
Diamond Head Apartments, 2969 Kalakaua Ave	15
Edgewater, 2168 Kalia Rd	15
Foster Tower, 2500 Kalakaua Ave	15
Halekulani, 2199 Kalia Rd	15
Hawaiiana, 260 Beach Walk	15
Hilton Hawaiian Village, 2005 Kalia Rd	15
Islander, 351 Seaside Ave	15
Kalia, 425 Ena Rd	15
Moana, 2365 Kalakaua Ave	15
Oahuan Tower, 1710 Makiki	22
Park Terrace, 509 University Ave	14
Polynesian, 314 Beach Walk	15
Princess Kaiulani, 120 Kaiulani Ave	15
Reef Tower, 227 Lewers	15
Reef, 2169 Kalia Rd	15
Rosalei Apartments, 445 Kaiolu	15
Royal Hawaiian, 2259 Kalakaua Ave	15
Sans Souci, 2877 Kalakaua Ave	15
Seaside Towers, 435 Seaside Ave	15
Surfrider, 2365 Kalakaua Ave	15
Town House, 1415 Victoria	22
Tradewinds Apartments, 1720 Ala Moana Blvd	15
Waikiki Biltmore, 2424 Kalakaua Ave	15
Waikiki Cadillac, 411 Kuamoo	15
Waikiki Shores, 2161 Kalia Rd	15
Waikikian, 1811 Ala Moana Blvd	15

BUILDINGS

Aina Haina Shopping Center, 820 Hind Dr	21
Ala Moana Shopping Center, 1450 Ala Moana Blvd	14
Ala Moana, 1441 Kapiolani Blvd	14
Alexander & Baldwin, 141 Merchant	13
Alexander Young, 1015 Bishop	13
Ahiolani Hale, 417 S King	13
Boston 1037 Fort St Mall	13
Capital Investment, 850 Richard	13
Continental, 1521 S King	14
Damon, 919 Bishop	13
Dillingham Transportation, 735 Bishop	13
Federal, 335 Merchant	13
Finance Factor, 195 S King	13
Financial Plaza Of The Pacific 111 S King	13
First Hawaiian Bank, 161 S King St	13
Gasco, 1060 Bishop	13
Hawaiian Life, 1311 Kapiolani Blvd	14
Honolulu Merchandise Mart, 198 S Hotel	13
Kahala Mall, 4211 Waialae	16
Kalihi Shopping Center, 2295 N King	19
Kamamalu, 250 S King St	13
King Center, 1451 S King	14
Marine Finance, 1109 Bethel	13
Moanalua Shopping Center	18
Professional Center, 1481 S King	14
Queen Street Corporation, 235 S Queen	13

HOSPITALS

Childrens, 226 N Kuakini	17
Convalescent Nursing, 5113 Maunalani Cir	16
Emergency, 1027 Hala Dr	17
Kaiser Foundation Medical Center, 1697 Ala Moana Blvd	15
Kapiolani Maternity, 1611 Bingham	14
Kuakini, 347 N Kuakini	17
Leahi, 3675 Kilauea Ave	16
Maluhia, 1027 Hala Dr	17
Queens Medical Center, 1301 Punchbowl	13
Saint Francis, 2260 Liliha	17
Shriners, 1310 Punahou	14

UNIVERSITIES AND COLLEGES

Chaminade, 3140 Waialae Ave	16
Hawaii Pacific College, 1149 Bethel	13
Honolulu Christian, 829 Pensacola	14
University Of Hawaii, 1801 University Ave	22

145

IDAHO
(Abbreviation: ID)

Aberdeen	83210
Acequia	83310
Ahsahka	83520
Air Base, MOU. Mountain Home	83648
Alameda, Sta. Pocatello	83201
Albion	83311
Almo	83312
American Falls	83211
Arbon	83212
Arco	83213
Arimo	83214
Ashton	83420
Athol	83801
Atlanta	83601
Atomic City	83215
Avery	83802
Baker	83461
Bancroft	83217
Banida, R. Br. Preston	83264
Banks	83602
Bannock, Sta. Pocatello	83201
Basalt	83218
Bayview	83803
Bear, R. Br. Council	83603
Bellevue	83313
Bennington, R. Br. Montpelier	83219
Bern	83220
Blackfoot (1st)	83221
Springfield, R. Br.	83277
Blanchard	83804
Bliss	83314
Bloomington	83223
BOISE (1st) (see appendix)	
Bonners Ferry	83805
Borah, Sta. Boise (see appendix)	
Bovill	83806
Bridge, R. Br. Malta	83315
Bruneau	83604
Buhl (1st)	83316
Burke, R. Br. Wallace	83807
Burley (1st)	83318
Calder	83808
Caldwell (1st)	83605
Cambridge	83610
Carey	83320
Careywood, R. Br. Sandpoint	83809
Carmen	83462
Cascade	83611
Warm Lake, R. Br.	83611
West Mountain, R. Br.	83611
Castleford	83321
Cataldo	83810
Challis	83226
Chester	83421
Chubbuck, R. Br. Pocatello	83201
Clark Fork	83811
Clarkia	83812
Clayton	83227
Clearwater	83521
Clifton	83228
Cobalt	83229
Cocolalla	83813
Coeur D' alene (1st)	83814
Colburn, R. Br. Sandpoint	83865
Collister, Sta. Boise	83703
Conda	83230

Coolin	83821
Copeland	83822
Corral, R. Br. Fairfield	83322
Cottonwood	83522
Keuterville, R. Br.	83538
Council	83612
Bear, R. Br.	83603
Craigmont	83523
Culdesac	83524
Darlington	83231
Dayton	83232
Deary	83823
Declo	83323
Denton, Br. Boise	83704
Desmet	83824
Dietrich	83324
Dingle	83233
Dixie, R. Br. Elk City	83525
Donnelly	83615
Dover	83825
Downey	83234
Driggs	83422
Dubois	83423
Eagle	83616
Eagle Rock, Sta. Idaho Falls	83401
Eastport	83826
Eden	83325
Elba	83326
Elk City	83525
Elk River	83827
Ellis	83235
Emida, R. Br. Saint Maries	83828
Emmett (1st)	83617
Enaville	83829
Fairfield	83327
Corral, R. Br.	83322
Farragut, Br. Bayview	83803
Felt	83424
Fenn, R. Br. Grangeville	83531
Ferdinand	83526
Fernwood	83830
Filer	83328
Firth	83236
Fish Haven, R. Br. Paris	83261
Fort Hall, R. Br. Pocatello	83203
Franklin	83237
Fruitland	83619
Fruitvale	83620
Garden City, Br. Boise	83704
Garden Valley	83622
Gardena	83621
Genesee	83832
Geneva	83238
Georgetown	83239
Gibbonsville	83463
Glenns Ferry	83623
Gooding (1st)	83330
Grace	83241
Thatcher, R. Br.	83283
Grand View	83624
Grangeville (1st)	83530
Fenn, R. Br.	83531
Grasmere	83625
Greencreek	83533
Greenleaf	83626
Grouse	83242
Hagerman	83332
Tuttle, R. Br.	83354
Hailey	83333
Hamer	83425
Hammett	83627
Hansen	83334
Harrison	83833

Medimont, R. Br.	83842
Harvard	83834
Hayden Lake	83835
Hazelton	83335
Headquarters	83534
Heyburn	83336
Hill City	83337
Hillview, Br. Idaho Falls	83401
Holbrook	83243
Homedale	83628
Hope	83836
Horseshoe Bend	83629
Sweet, R. Br.	83670
Howe	83244
Huston	83630
Idaho City	83631
Placerville, R. Br.	83666
Idaho Falls (1st)	83401
Indian Valley	83632
Inkom	83245
Iona	83427
Irwin	83428
Island Park	83429
Jerome (1st)	83338
Juliaetta	83535
Kamiah	83536
Kellogg (1st)	83837
Kendrick	83537
Ketchum	83340
Keuterville, R. Br. Cottonwood	83538
Kimberly	83341
King Hill	83633
Kingston	83839
Kooskia	83539
Kootenai, R. Br. Sandpoint	83840
Kuna	83634
Laclede	83841
Lake Fork	83635
Lamont	83430
Lapwai	83540
Lava Hot Springs	83246
Leadore	83464
Lemhi	83465
Lenore	83541
Leslie	83249
Letha	83636
Lewiston (1st)	83501
Lewisville	83431
Lorenzo	83432
Lowman, R. Br. Boise	83637
Lucile	83542
Mackay	83251
Macks Inn	83433
Malad City	83252
Malta	83342
Marsing	83639
May	83253
Mc Call	83638
Mc Cammon	83250
Meadows, R. Br. New Meadows	83640
Medimont, R. Br. Harrison	83842
Melba	83641
Menan	83434
Meridian (1st)	83642
Mesa	83643
Middleton	83644
Midvale	83645
Minidoka	83343
Monteview	83435
Montour	83646
Montpelier	83254
Bennington, R. Br.	83219

Moore	83255
Moreland	83256
Moscow (1st)	83843
Mountain Home (1st)	83647
Air Base, MOU.	83648
Mountain Home A F B,	
Br.	83648
Mountain Home A F B, Br.	
Mountain Home	83648
Mountain View, Sta. Boise	83704
Moyie Springs	83845
Mullan	83846
Murphy	83650
Murray, R. Br. Wallace	83874
Murtaugh	83344
Naf, R. Br. Malta	83345
Nampa (1st)	83651
Naples	83847
New Meadows	83654
Meadows, R. Br.	83640
New Plymouth	83655
Newdale	83436
Nezperce	83543
Nordman	83848
North Fork	83466
Shoup, R. Br.	83469
Notus	83656
Oakley	83346
Obsidian	83259
Ola	83657
Oreana	83659
Orofino (1st)	83544
Osburn	83849
Ovid	83260
Page, R. Br. Pinehurst	83850
Palisades	83437
Paris	83261
Parker	83438
Parma	83660
Paul	83347
Payette (1st)	83661
Peck	83545
Picabo	83348
Pierce	83546
Pinehurst	83850
Pingree	83262
Placerville, R. Br. Idaho City	83666
Plummer	83851
Pocatello (1st)	83201
Alameda, Sta.	83201
Bannock, Sta.	83201

Chubbuck, R. Br.	83201
Fort Hall, R. Br.	83203
Pollock	83547
Ponderay	83852
Porthill	83853
Post Falls	83854
Potlatch	83855
Preston	83263
Banida, R. Br.	83264
Priest Lake, R. Br. Priest	
River	83856
Priest River	83856
Princeton	83857
Rathdrum	83858
Reubens	83548
Rexburg (1st)	83440
Thornton, R. Br.	83453
Richfield	83349
Rigby	83442
Riggins	83549
Ririe	83443
Roberts	83444
Rockland	83271
Rogerson, R. Br. Twin Falls	83302
Rupert (1st)	83350
Sagle	83860
Saint Anthony	83445
Saint Charles	83272
Saint Maries	83861
Emida, R. Br.	83828
Salmon (1st)	83467
Samaria, R. Br. Malad City	83252
Samuels	83862
Sanders	83863
Sandpoint (1st)	83864
Careywood, R. Br.	83809
Colburn, R. Br.	83865
Kootenai, R. Br.	83840
Santa	83866
Shelley	83274
Shoshone	83352
Shoup, R. Br. North Fork	83469
Silverton	83867
Skyline, Sta. Idaho Falls	83401
Smelterville	83868
Soda Springs	83276
South Gate Plaza, Br.	
Lewiston	83501
Southside, Sta. Boise	83706
Southwick	83550
Spalding	83551

Spencer	83446
Spirit Lake	83869
Springfield, R. Br. Blackfoot	83277
Squirrel	83447
Stanley	83278
Star	83669
Sterling	83279
Stites	83552
Stone	83280
Sugar City	83448
Sun Valley	83353
Swan Valley	83449
Swanlake	83281
Sweet, R. Br. Horseshoe	
Bend	83670
Tendoy	83468
Tensed	83870
Terreton	83450
Teton	83451
Tetonia	83452
Thain Road, R. Br. Lewiston	83501
Thatcher, R. Br. Grace	83283
Thornton, R. Br. Rexburg	83453
Troy	83871
Tuttle, R. Br. Hagerman	83354
Twin Falls (1st)	83301
Rogerson, R. Br.	83302
Ucon	83454
University, Sta. Moscow	83843
Ustick, R. Br. Boise	83702
Victor	83455
Viola	83872
Wallace (1st)	83873
Burke, R. Br.	83807
Murray, R. Br.	83874
Wardner	83875
Warm Lake, R. Br. Cascade	83611
Warren	83671
Wayan	83285
Weippe	83553
Weiser (1st)	83672
Wendell	83355
West Mountain, R. Br.	
Cascade	83611
Weston	83286
White Bird	83554
Whitney, Sta. Boise	83705
Wilder	83676
Winchester	83555
Worley	83876
Yellow Pine	83677

BOISE 837

POST OFFICE BOXES

Box Nos.
1-80	Main Office	07
81-2999	Borah Sta	01
3000-3999	Collister Sta	03
5000-5899	Whitney Sta	05
7000-8599	Main Office	07

RURAL ROUTES

1,2	02
3	05
4	02
5	05

STATIONS, BRANCHES AND UNITS

Borah Sta	02
Collister Sta	03
Denton Br	04
Garden City Br	04
Lowman Rural Br	83637
Mountain View Sta	04
Southside Sta	06
Ustick Rural Sta	02
Whitney Sta	05
General Delivery	01
Postmaster	07

APARTMENTS, HOTELS, MOTELS

Baxter, 303 N 2nd	02
Belgravia, 100 S 5th	02
Belgravia, 415 Main	02
Boise Courtel, 3525 Chinden Blvd	04
Boise, 800 Bannock	01
Boisean, 1300 S Capitol Blvd	06
Boulevard, 1121 S Capitol Blvd	06
Cabana, 1618 Main	06
Cambridge Square, 303 S Straughn	02
Capital, 1009 S 9th	06
Capri, 2600 Fairview Ave	06
Chalet, 1300 S Capitol Blvd	06
Cole, 112 E Idaho	02
Colorado, 999 Federal Way	05
Columbia, 1006 1/2 Main	02

Crescent Rim, 3011 Crescent Rim Dr	04
Desert Skies, 3636 Chinden Blvd	04
Dorchester Apts, 300 S Straughn	02
Downtowner, 1901 Main	07
East Side, 2519 Federal Way	05
Evergreen Motor Court, 1315 S Capitol Blvd	06
Garden City, 4509 Chinden Blvd	04
Grandview, 1315 Federal Way	05
Green Gables, 6608 Fairview Ave	04
Hiway 30 Motel, 7121 Fairview Ave	04
Holiday Inn, 3300 Vista	05
Holiday, 5416 Fairview Ave	04
Home, 105 N 11th	02
Idan-Ha, 928 Main	01
Imperial Plaza Apts., 200 N 3rd	02
Jim Dandy, 6727 Fairview Ave	04
Lakeside, 6911 State	03
Magnolia, 702 Hays	02
Magnolia, 708 Hays	02
Manitou	02
Mitchell, 235 S 10th	06
Olympic, 1009 1/2 Main	02
Overland, 213 S 9th	01
Owyhee Motor Inn, 1109 Main	07
Park View Apts, 3110 Crescent Rim Dr	04
Plaza Inn, 1025 S Capitol Blvd	06
Ralfroy, 2223 Federal Way	05
Rim Crest Apts, 3701 Crescent Rim Dr	04
Riverview, 1070 Leadville Ave	06
Rose Hill, 2709 Rose Hill	05
Sands, 1111 State	02
Seek Rest, 3349 Federal Way	05
Seven K, 3633 Chinden Blvd	04
Skyline, 3209 Federal Way	05
Sunliner, 3433 Chinden Blvd	04
Sunset Cottages, 6713 Fairview Ave	04

Town And Ranch, 4902 Fairview Ave	04
Travelers, 5620 Fairview Ave	04
Travelodge, 1314 Grove	06
University Village, 538 Hale	06
Valencia, 612 Idaho	02
Vista Courts, 415 Vista	05
Wellman, 500 Franklin	02
White Savage, 1307 Washington	02
White Savage, 521 N 13th	02
Whitney, 402 Vista	05

BUILDINGS

Bank Of Idaho	02
Broadbent	02
Continental Life	06
Eastman	02
Equitable Life, 501 N 5th	02
Fidelity	02
First National Bank	02
First Security Bank	02
Gem	02
Idaho	02
Jefferson	02
Owyhee Plaza	02
Provident S & L Bldg	02
Simplot	02
Sonna	02
Sun	02

GOVERNMENT OFFICES

City Hall	02
County Courthouse	02
Federal Bldg Borah Sta	02
Federal Bldg U S Court House	02

HOSPITALS

Booth Memorial, 1617 N24	07
Elks Rehabilitation Center, 204 Fort	02
Saint Alphonsus, 506 N 5th	02
Saint Lukes, 130 E Bannock	02
Veterans	07

UNIVERSITIES AND COLLEGES

Boise State College	07

ILLINOIS
(Abbreviation: IL)

Abbott Park, Br. North
  Chicago.............................60064
Abingdon.............................61410
Adair.................................61411
Addieville............................62214
Addison (1st).........................60101
Adrian................................62310
Akin..................................62805
Albany................................61230
Albers................................62215
Albion................................62806
Alden, R. Br. Harvard.................60001
Aledo (1st)...........................61231
Alexander.............................62601
Alexis................................61412
Algonquin (1st).......................60102
Alhambra..............................62001
Allendale.............................62410
Allenville, R. Br. Sullivan...........61901
Allerton..............................61810
Alma..................................62807
Alpha.................................61413
Alsey.................................62610
Alsip, R. Br. Chicago (see
  appendix)
Alta, R. Br. Peoria...................61608
Altamont..............................62411
Alto Pass.............................62905
Alton (1st)...........................62002
Altona................................61414
Alvin.................................61811
Amboy.................................61310
Anchor................................61720
Ancona, R. Br. Streator...............61311
Andalusia.............................61232
Andover...............................61233
Anna (1st)............................62906
Annapolis.............................62413
Annawan...............................61234
Antioch (1st).........................60002
Apple River...........................61001
Arcola................................61910
Arenzville............................62611
Argenta...............................62501
Argo (1st)............................60501
Argonne, Br. Lemont...................60439
Arlington.............................61312
ARLINGTON HEIGHTS (1st)
  (see appendix)
Armington.............................61721
Armstrong.............................61812
Aroma Park............................60910
Arrowsmith............................61722
Arthur................................61911
Ashburn, Sta. Chicago.................60652
Ashkum................................60911
Ashland...............................62612
Ashley................................62808
Ashmore...............................61912
Ashton................................61006
Assumption............................62510
Astoria...............................61501
  Summum, R. Br......................61566
Athens................................62613
Atkinson..............................61235
Atlanta...............................61723
Atwater...............................62511
Atwood................................61913
Auburn................................62615

Auburn Park, Sta. Chicago.....60620
Augusta...............................62311
AURORA (1st) (see
  . appendix)
Austin, Sta. Chicago..................60644
Ava...................................62907
Aviston...............................62216
Avon..................................61415
Baileyville...........................61007
Baldwin...............................62217
Bardolph..............................61416
Barnhill..............................62809
Barrington (1st)......................60010
Barry.................................62312
Barstow...............................61236
Bartelso..............................62218
Bartlett (1st)........................60103
Bartonville, Br. Peoria...............61607
Basco.................................62313
Batavia (1st).........................60510
Batchtown.............................62006
Bath..................................62617
Baylis................................62314
Beardstown (1st)......................62618
Beason................................62512
Beaverville...........................60912
Beckemeyer............................62219
Beecher...............................60401
Beecher City..........................62414
Belknap...............................62908
Belle Rive............................62810
Belleview.............................62008
BELLEVILLE (1st) (see
  appendix)
Bellflower............................61724
Bellmont..............................62811
Bellwood (1st)........................60104
Belmont Road, Sta. Downers
  Grove...............................60515
Belvidere (1st).......................61008
Bement................................61813
Benld.................................62009
Bensenville (1st).....................60106
Benson................................61516
Bentley...............................62315
Benton (1st)..........................62812
Berwick...............................61417
Berwyn (1st)..........................60402
Bethalto..............................62010
Bethany...............................61914
Bible Grove...........................62813
Big Rock..............................60511
Biggsville............................61418
Bingham...............................62011
Birds.................................62435
Bishop Hill...........................61419
Bismarck..............................61814
Blackstone............................61313
Blandinsville.........................61420
Bloomingdale..........................60108
Bloomington (1st).....................61701
Blue Island (1st).....................60406
Blue Mound............................62513
Bluff Springs.........................62622
Bluffs................................62621
Bluford...............................62814
Bogota................................62416
Boles.................................62909
Bolingbrook, R. Br. Lemont...........60439
Bondville.............................61815
Bone Gap..............................62815
Bonfield..............................60913

Bonnie................................62816
Boody.................................62514
Boulder Hill, Br.
  Montgomery.........................60538
Bourbonnais (1st).....................60914
Bowen.................................62316
Braceville............................60407
Bradford..............................61421
Bradley (1st).........................60915
Braidwood.............................60408
Breese................................62230
Brettwood, Sta. Decatur...............62526
Bridgeport............................62417
Bridgeview, Br. Oak Lawn..............60455
Brighton..............................62012
Brimfield.............................61517
  Oak Hill, R. Br....................61518
Bristol...............................60512
Broadlands............................61816
Broadview, Br. Maywood................60153
Broadway, Sta. Rockford...............61106
Broadwell.............................62623
Brocton...............................61917
Brookfield (1st)......................60513
Brookport.............................62910
Broughton.............................62817
Brownfield............................62911
Browning..............................62624
Browns................................62818
Brownstown............................62418
Brussels..............................62013
Bryant................................61519
Buckingham............................60917
Buckley...............................60918
Buckner...............................62819
Buda..................................61314
Buffalo...............................62515
Buffalo Grove, Br. Wheeling..........60090
Buffalo Prairie.......................61237
Bulpitt...............................62517
Buncombe..............................62912
Bunker Hill...........................62014
Burbank, Br. Oak Lawn.................60459
Bureau................................61315
Burlington............................60109
Burnside..............................62318
Burnt Prairie.........................62820
Bushnell..............................61422
Butler................................62015
Byron.................................61010
Cabery................................60919
Cache.................................62913
Cahokia, Br. East Saint
  Louis..............................62206
Cairo (1st)...........................62914
Caledonia.............................61011
Calhoun...............................62419
Calumet City (1st)....................60409
Calumet Park, Br. Chicago
  (see appendix)
Camargo...............................61919
Cambria...............................62915
Cambridge.............................61238
Camden................................62319
Cameron...............................61423
Camp Grove............................61424
Camp Point............................62320
Campbell Hill.........................62916
Campus................................60920
Canton (1st)..........................61520
Cantrall..............................62625
Capitol, Sta. Springfield.............62706
Capron................................61012

Carbon Cliff	61239	
Carbondale (1st)	62901	
Carlinville (1st)	62626	
Carlock	61725	
Carlyle (1st)	62231	
Carman	61425	
Carmi (1st)	62821	
Carpentersville (1st)	60110	
Carriers Mills	62917	
Carrollton	62016	
Carterville	62918	
Carthage (1st)	62321	
Fountain Green, R. Br.	62337	
Cary (1st)	60013	
Casey	62420	
Caseyville (1st)	62232	
Castleton	61426	
Catherine Avenue, Br. La Grange	60525	
Catlin	61817	
Cave In Rock	62919	
Cazenovia	61522	
Cedar Point	61316	
Cedarville	61013	
Centralia (1st)	62801	
Centreville, Br. East Saint Louis	62206	
Cerro Gordo	61818	
Chadwick	61014	
Chambersburg	62323	
Champaign (1st)	61820	
Chana	61015	
Chandlerville	62627	
Channahon	60410	
Chanute A F B, Sta. Rantoul	61868	
Chapin	62628	
Charleston (1st)	61920	
Chatham	62629	
Chatsworth	60921	
Chebanse	60922	
Chenoa	61726	
Cherry	61317	
Cherry Valley	61016	
Chester (1st)	62233	
Chesterfield	62630	
Chesterville	61923	
Chestnut	62518	
Chestnut Street, Sta. Chicago	60610	
CHICAGO (1st) (see appendix)		
Chicago Heights (1st)	60411	
Chicago Lawn, Sta. Chicago	60629	
Chicago Ridge (1st)	60415	
Chillicothe (1st)	61523	
Chrisman	61924	
Christopher	62822	
Cicero, Br. Chicago	60650	
Cisco	61830	
Cisne	62823	
Cissna Park	60924	
Clare	60111	
Claremont	62421	
Clarence	60925	
Clarendon Hills (1st)	60514	
Clay City	62824	
Clayton	62324	
Claytonville	60926	
Clearing, Sta. Chicago	60638	
Clifton	60927	
Clinton (1st)	61727	
Coal City	60416	

Coal Valley	61240	
Coatsburg	62325	
Cobden	62920	
Coello	62825	
Coffeen	62017	
Colchester	62326	
Coleta, R. Br. Sterling	61017	
Colfax	61728	
Collinsville (1st)	62234	
Collison	61831	
Colmar	62327	
Colona	61241	
Colp	62921	
Columbia (1st)	62236	
Columbus, R. Br. Quincy	62328	
Colusa	62329	
Compton	61318	
Concord	62631	
Congerville	61729	
Congress Park, Sta. Brookfield	60513	
Cooksville	61730	
Cordova	61242	
Cornell	61319	
Cornland	62519	
Cortland	60112	
Cottage Hills	62018	
Coulterville	62237	
Country Club Hills Br. Tinley Park	60477	
Country Fair, Sta. Champaign	61820	
Cowden	62422	
Cragin, Sta. Chicago	60639	
Creal Springs	62922	
Crescent City	60928	
Crest Hill, Br. Joliet	60435	
Creston	60113	
Crete (1st)	60417	
Creve Coeur, Br. Peoria	61611	
Cropsey	61731	
Crossville	62827	
Crystal Lake (1st)	60014	
Cuba	61427	
Cullom	60929	
Curran, R. Br. New Berlin	62632	
Custer Park	60418	
Cutler	62238	
Cypress	62923	
Dahinda	61428	
Dahlgren	62828	
Dakota	61018	
Dale	62829	
Dallas City	62330	
Dalton City	61925	
Dalzell	61320	
Dana	61321	
Danforth	60930	
Danvers	61732	
Danville (1st)	61832	
Darien, Br. Westmont	60559	
Davis	61019	
Davis Junction	61020	
Dawson	62520	
De Kalb (1st)	60115	
De Land	61839	
De Soto	62924	
DECATUR (1st) (see appendix)		
Deer Creek	61733	
Deer Grove	61243	
Deerfield (1st)	60015	
Delavan	61734	

Dennison	62423	
Denver	62331	
Depue	61322	
DES PLAINES (1st) (see appendix)		
Detroit	62332	
Dewey	61840	
Dewitt	61735	
Dieterich	62424	
Divernon	62530	
Division Street, Sta. Chicago	60651	
Dix	62830	
Dixon (1st)	61021	
Dolton (1st)	60419	
Dongola	62926	
Donnellson	62019	
Donovan	60931	
Dorchester, R. Br. Gillespie	62020	
Dorsey	62021	
Dover	61323	
Dow	62022	
Dowell	62927	
Downers Grove (1st)	60515	
Downey, Br. North Chicago	60064	
Downs	61736	
Downtown, Sta. Springfield (see appendix)		
Du Quoin (1st)	62832	
Dubois	62831	
Dundas	62425	
Dundee (1st)	60118	
Dunfermline	61524	
Dunlap	61525	
Dunning, Sta. Chicago	60634	
Dupo	62239	
Durand	61024	
Dwight (1st)	60420	
Eagarville	62023	
Earlville	60518	
East Alton (1st)	62024	
East Carondelet	62240	
East Dubuque	61025	
East Galesburg	61430	
East Lynn	60932	
East Moline (1st)	61244	
East Peoria, Br. Peoria	61611	
East Rockford, Sta. Rockford (see appendix)		
EAST SAINT LOUIS (1st) (see appendix)		
Easton	62633	
Eddyville	62928	
Edelstein	61526	
Eden, R. Br. Hanna City	61527	
Edgebrook, Sta. Chicago	60646	
Edgemont, Sta. East Saint Louis	62203	
Edgewood	62426	
Edinburg	62531	
Edison Square, Sta. Waukegan	60085	
Edwards	61528	
Edwardsville (1st)	62025	
Effingham (1st)	62401	
Egan	61026	
El Dara	62333	
El Paso	61738	
El Vista, Sta. Peoria	61604	
Elburn	60119	
Elco	62929	
Eldena	61324	
Eldorado (1st)	62930	

Eldred	62027
Eleroy	61027
Elgin (1st)	60120
Elizabeth	61028
Elizabethtown	62931
Elk Grove Village, Br.	
Arlington Heights	60007
Elkhart	62634
Elkville	62932
Ellery	62833
Elliott	60933
Ellisgrove	62241
Ellisville	61431
Ellsworth	61737
Elmhurst (1st)	60126
Elmwood	61529
Elmwood Park, Br. Chicago	
(see appendix)	
Elsah	62028
Elsdon, Sta. Chicago	60632
Elvaston	62334
Elwin	62532
Elwood	60421
Emden	62635
Emington	60934
Emma	62834
Energy	62933
Enfield	62835
Englewood, Sta. Chicago	60621
Eola	60519
Equality	62934
Erie	61250
Esmond	60129
Essex	60935
Eureka (1st)	61530
EVANSTON (1st) (see	
appendix)	
Evansville	62242
Evergreen Park, Br. Chicago	
(see appendix)	
Ewing	62836
Fairbury (1st)	61739
Fairfield (1st)	62837
Fairmount	61841
Fairview	61432
Fairview Heights, Br.	
Caseyville	62232
Fairview Heights, Br. East	
Saint Louis	62208
Fancy Prairie	62637
Farina	62838
Farmer City	61842
Farmersville	62533
Farmington	61531
Middlegrove, R. Br.	61549
Fenton	61251
Ferris	62336
Fiatt	61433
Fidelity	62030
Fieldon	62031
Fillmore	62032
Filson	61926
Findlay	62534
Fireworks, Br. East Saint	
Louis	62207
Fisher	61843
Fithian	61844
Flanagan	61740
Flat Rock	62427
Flora (1st)	62839
Flossmoor (1st)	60422
Foosland	61845
Forest City	61532
Forest Park (1st)	60130
Forrest	61741
Forreston	61030
Forsyth	62535
Fort Dearborn, Sta. Chicago	60611
Fort Sheridan, Br. Highland	
Park	60037
Fountain Green, R. Br.	
Carthage	62337
Fowler	62338
Fox Lake (1st)	60020
Fox River Grove	60021
Frankfort	60423
Frankfort Heights	62840
Franklin	62638
Franklin Grove	61031
Franklin Park (1st)	60131
Schiller Park, Br.	60176
Frederick	62639
Freeburg	62243
Freeman Spur	62841
Freeport (1st)	61032
Scioto Mills, R. Br.	61076
Fulton (1st)	61252
Fults	62244
Gages Lake, Br. Grayslake	60030
Galatia	62935
Gale	62936
Galena (1st)	61036
Galesburg (1st)	61401
Galt	61037
Galva	61434
Garden Prairie	61038
Gardner	60424
Garfield Park, Sta. Chicago	60624
Garrett	61927
Gays	61928
Geff	62842
Geneseo (1st)	61254
Geneva (1st)	60134
Genoa (1st)	60135
Georgetown	61846
Gerlaw	61435
German Valley	61039
Germantown	62245
Gibson City (1st)	60936
Gifford	61847
Gilberts	60136
Gillespie	62033
Dorchester, R. Br.	62020
Gilman	60938
Gilson	61436
Girard	62640
Gladstone	61437
Glasford	61533
Glen Carbon	62034
Glen Ellyn (1st)	60137
Glenarm	62536
Glencoe (1st)	60022
Glendale	62937
Glenview (1st)	60025
Naval Air Station, Br.	60026
Glenwood (1st)	60425
Godfrey (1st)	62035
Golconda	62938
Golden	62339
Golden Eagle	62036
Goldengate	62843
Golf	60029
Golf Mill, Br. Chicago	60648
Good Hope	61438
Goodfield	61742
Goodwine	60939
Goreville	62939
Gorham	62940
Grafton	62037
Grand Chain	62941
Grand Crossing, Sta.	
Chicago	60619
Grand Ridge	61325
Grand Tower	62942
Granite City (1st)	62040
Grant Park	60940
Grantsburg	62943
Granville	61326
Graymont	61743
Grayslake (1st)	60030
Grayville	62844
Great Lakes, Br. Waukegan	60088
Green Valley	61534
Greenfield	62044
Greenup (1st)	62428
Hazel Dell, R. Br.	62430
Greenview	62642
Greenville (1st)	62246
Gridley	61744
Griggsville	62340
Groveland	61535
Gurnee (1st)	60031
Hagarstown	62247
Hamburg	62045
Hamel	62046
Hamilton (1st)	62341
Hamletsburg	62944
Hammond	61929
Hampshire	60140
Hampton	61256
Hanna City	61536
Eden, R. Br.	61527
Hanover	61041
Hanover Park-Ontarioville,	
Br. Bartlett	60103
Hardin	62047
Harmon	61042
Harrisburg (1st)	62946
Harristown	62537
Hartford	62048
Hartsburg	62643
Harvard (1st)	60033
Alden, R. Br.	60001
Harvel	62538
Harvey (1st)	60426
Harwood Heights, Br.	
Chicago (see appendix)	
Havana (1st)	62644
Hawthorne, Sta. Chicago	60623
Haymarket, Sta. Chicago	60606
Hazel Crest (1st)	60429
Hazel Dell, R. Br. Greenup	62430
Hebron (1st)	60034
Hecker	62248
Hegewisch, Sta. Chicago	60633
Henderson	61439
Hennepin	61327
Henning	61848
Henry	61537
Herald	62845
Herod	62947
Herrick	62431
Herrin (1st)	62948
Herscher	60941
Hersman, R. Br. Mount	
Sterling	62342
Hettick	62649
Heyworth	61745
Hickory Hills, Br. Oak Lawn	60457

Hidalgo	62432
Highland (1st)	62249
Highland Park (1st)	60035
Fort Sheridan, Br.	60037
Ravinia, Sta.	60035
Highwood (1st)	60040
Hillcrest, Sta. East Moline	61244
Hillsboro (1st)	62049
Hillsdale	61257
Hillside-Berkeley, Br. Melrose Park (see appendix)	
Hillview	62050
Hinckley	60520
Hindsboro	61930
Hines (1st)	60141
Hinsdale (1st)	60521
Hodgkins, Br. La Grange	60525
Hoffman	62250
Hoffman Estates, Br. Roselle	60172
Holcomb	61043
Holder	61746
Homer	61849
Hometown, Br. Oak Lawn	60456
Homewood (1st)	60430
Hoopeston (1st)	60942
Hoopole	61258
Hopedale	61747
Hopkins Park	60944
Hoyleton	62803
Hubbard Woods, Sta. Winnetka	60093
Hudson	61748
Huey	62252
Hull	62343
Humboldt	61931
Hume	61932
Huntley (1st)	60142
Huntsville	62344
Hurst	62949
Hutsonville	62433
Hyde Park, Sta. Chicago (see appendix)	
Illinois City	61259
Illiopolis	62539
Ina	62846
Indianola	61850
Industry	61440
Ingleside	60041
Ingraham	62434
Iola	62847
Ipava	61441
Iroquois	60945
Irving	62051
Irving Park, Sta. Chicago	60641
Irvington	62848
Island Lake	60042
Itasca (1st)	60143
Iuka	62849
Ivesdale	61851
Jackson Park, Sta. Chicago	60637
Jacksonville (1st)	62650
Jacob	62950
Janesville	62435
Jefferson, Sta. Chicago	60630
Jerseyville (1st)	62052
Jewett	62436
Johnsonville	62850
Johnston City	62951
JOLIET (1st) (see appendix)	
Jonesboro	62952
Joppa	62953
Joy	61260

Junction	62954
Junction City, Sta. Peoria	61614
Kampsville	62053
Kane	62054
Kaneville	60144
Kankakee (1st)	60901
Kansas	61933
Karbers Ridge	62955
Karnak	62956
Kasbeer	61328
Kedzie Grace, Sta. Chicago	60618
Keenes	62851
Keensburg	62852
Keithsburg	61442
Kell	62853
Kemper	62055
Kempton	60946
Kenilworth (1st)	60043
Kenney	61749
Kent	61044
Kewanee (1st)	61443
Keyesport	62253
Kilbourne	62655
Kincaid	62540
Kinderhook	62345
Kings, R. Br. Rochelle	61045
Kingston	60145
Kingston Mines	61539
Kinmundy	62854
Kinsman	60437
Kirkland	60146
Kirkwood	61447
Kishwaukee, Br. Rockford	61109
Knoxville	61448
La Clede	62437
La Fayette	61449
La Grange (1st)	60525
La Grange Highlands, Br. La Grange	60525
La Grange Park, Br. La Grange	60525
La Harpe	61450
La Hogue	60947
La Moille	61330
La Place	61936
La Prairie	62346
La Rose	61541
La Salle (1st)	61301
Lacon	61540
Ladd	61329
Lafox	60147
Lake Bluff (1st)	60044
Lake City	61935
Lake Forest (1st)	60045
Lake Fork	62541
Lake Villa (1st)	60046
Lake Zurich (1st)	60047
Lakeview, Sta. Chicago	60613
Lakewood	62438
Lanark	61046
Lancaster	62855
Lane	61750
Langleyville	62542
Lansdowne, Sta. East Saint Louis	62204
Lansing (1st)	60438
Latham	62543
Laura	61451
Lawndale	61751
Lawrenceville (1st)	62439
Le Roy	61752
Leaf River	61047
Lebanon	62254

Lee	60530
Lee Center	61331
Leland	60531
Lemont (1st)	60439
Lena	61048
Lenzburg	62255
Leonore	61332
Lerna	62440
Lewistown	61542
Lexington	61753
Liberty	62347
Libertyville (1st)	60048
Lima	62348
Limestone, Br. Peoria	61607
Lincoln (1st)	62656
Lincoln Park, Sta. Chicago	60614
Lincolns New Salem	62659
Lincolnwood, Br. Chicago (see appendix)	
Lindenhurst, Br. Lake Villa	60046
Lindenwood	61049
Lisle (1st)	60532
Litchfield (1st)	62056
Literberry	62660
Little York	61453
Littleton	61452
Liverpool	61543
Livingston	62058
Loami	62661
Lockport (1st)	60441
Loda	60948
Logan	62856
Logan Square, Sta. Chicago	60647
Lomax	61454
Lombard (1st)	60148
London Mills	61544
Long Grove, R. Br. Lake Zurich	60047
Long Point	61333
Longview	61852
Loogootee	62857
Loraine	62349
Lostant	61334
Louisville	62858
Lovejoy	62059
Loves Park, Br. Rockford	61111
Lovington	61937
Lowder	62662
Lowpoint	61545
Ludlow	60949
Lyndon	61261
Lynn Center	61262
Lyons (1st)	60534
Macedonia	62860
Mackinaw	61755
Macomb (1st)	61455
Macon	62544
Madison (1st)	62060
Madison Park, Br. Peoria	61604
Maeystown	62256
Magnolia	61336
Mahomet	61853
Main Post Office, Sta. Chicago	60680
Makanda	62958
Malden	61337
Malta	60150
Manchester	62663
Manhattan	60442
Manito	61546
Manlius	61338
Mansfield	61854
Manteno	60950

Manville	61339
Maple Park	60151
Virgil, R. Br.	60182
Mapleton	61547
Maquon	61458
Marblehead	62350
Marengo (1st)	60152
Marietta	61459
Marine	62061
Marion (1st)	62959
Marissa	62257
Mark	61340
Markham, Br. Harvey	60426
Maroa	61756
Marseilles	61341
Marshall (1st)	62441
Martinsville	62442
Martinton	60951
Maryville	62062
Mascoutah (1st)	62258
Mason	62443
Mason City	62664
Matherville	61263
Matteson (1st)	60443
Mattoon (1st)	61938
Maunie	62861
Maywood (1st)	60153
Mazon	60444
Mc Clure	62957
Mc Connell	61050
Mc Cook, Br. La Grange	60525
Mc Gaw Park, Br. Waukegan	60085
Mc Henry (1st)	60050
Mc Lean	61754
Mc Leansboro	62859
Mc Nabb	61335
Meadow Mart, Br. Rockford	61111
Meadows Avenue, Br. Peoria	61611
Mechanicsburg	62545
Media	61460
Medinah	60157
Medora	62063
MELROSE PARK (1st) (see appendix)	
Melvin	60952
Menard	62259
Mendon	62351
Mendota (1st)	61342
Meppen	62064
Merchandise Mart, Sta. Chicago	60654
Merchants, Sta. Alton	62002
Meredosia	62665
Merna	61758
Metamora	61548
Metcalf	61940
Metropolis (1st)	62960
Michael	62065
Mid-West, Sta. Chicago	60612
Middlegrove, R. Br. Farmington	61549
Middletown	62666
Midlothian (1st)	60445
Milan (1st)	61264
Milford	60953
Mill Shoals	62862
Millbrook	60536
Millcreek	62961
Milledgeville	61051
Miller City	62962
Millington	60537
Millstadt	62260

Milmine	61855
Milton	62352
Mineral	61344
Minier	61759
Minonk	61760
Minooka	60447
Mitchell, Br. Granite City	62040
Mode	62444
Modesto	62667
Modoc, R. Br. Prairie Du Rocher	62261
Mokena	60448
Moline (1st)	61265
Momence (1st)	60954
Monee	60449
Monica, R. Br. Princeville	61559
Monmouth (1st)	61462
Monroe Center	61052
Montgomery (1st)	60538
Monticello (1st)	61856
Montrose	62445
Mooseheart (1st)	60539
Morgan Park, Sta. Chicago	60643
Moro	62067
Morris (1st)	60450
Morrison (1st)	61270
Morrisonville	62546
Morton (1st)	61550
Morton Grove (1st)	60053
Mossville	61552
Mound City	62963
Mounds	62964
Mount Auburn	62547
Mount Carmel (1st)	62863
Mount Carroll	61053
Mount Clare	62068
Mount Erie	62446
Mount Greenwood, Sta. Chicago	60655
Mount Morris (1st)	61054
Mount Olive	62069
Mount Prospect (1st)	60056
Mount Pulaski	62548
Mount Sterling	62353
Hersman, R. Br.	62342
Mount Vernon (1st)	62864
Mount Zion	62549
Moweaqua	62550
Mozier	62070
Muddy	62965
Mulberry Grove	62262
Mulkeytown	62865
Muncie	61857
Mundelein (1st)	60060
Murdock	61941
Murphysboro (1st)	62966
Murrayville	62668
Nachusa	61057
Nameoki, Sta. Granite City	62040
Naperville (1st)	60540
Naples	62669
Nashville	62263
Nason	62866
National Stock Yards (1st)	62071
Nauvoo	62354
Naval Air Station, Br. Glenview	60026
Nebo	62355
Nelson, R. Br. Rock Falls	61058
Neoga	62447
Neponset	61345
New Athens	62264
New Baden	62265

New Bedford	61346
New Berlin	62670
Curran, R. Br.	62632
New Boston	61272
New Burnside	62967
New Canton	62356
New Douglas	62074
New Haven	62867
New Holland	62671
New Lenox (1st)	60451
New Liberty	62968
New Memphis	62266
New Minden	62804
New Salem	62357
New Windsor	61465
Newark	60541
Newman	61942
Newton (1st)	62448
Rose Hill, R. Br.	62457
Niantic	62551
Niles, Br. Chicago (see appendix)	
Nilwood	62672
Nineteenth Avenue, Sta. Melrose Park	60160
Niota	62358
Noble	62868
Nokomis	62075
Nora	61059
Normal (1st)	61761
Normandy	61347
Norris	61553
Norris City	62869
North, Sta. Evanston	60201
North Aurora (1st)	60542
North Chicago (1st)	60064
North Henderson	61466
North Riverside, Br. Riverside	60546
North Town, Sta. Chicago	60645
Northbrook (1st)	60062
Northfield, Br. Winnetka	60093
Northlake, Br. Melrose Park	60164
Norwood Park, Sta. Chicago	60631
O Hare Airport, Sta. Chicago	60666
O'Fallon (1st)	62269
Oak Brook, Br. Hinsdale	60521
Oak Forest (1st)	60452
Oak Hill, R. Br. Brimfield	61518
OAK LAWN (1st) (see appendix)	
OAK PARK (1st) (see appendix)	
Oak Street, Sta. Danville	61832
Oakdale	62268
Oakford	62673
Oaklgen, Sta. Lansing	60438
Oakland	61943
Oakley	62552
Oakton, Sta. Des Plaines	60018
Oakwood	61858
Oblong	62449
Oconee	62553
Odell	60460
Odin	62870
Ogden	61859
Ogden Park, Sta. Chicago	60636
Oglesby	61348
Ohio	61349
Ohlman	62076
Okawville	62271
Venedy, R. Br.	62296

Old Orchard, Sta. Skokie	60076
Old Post Office, Sta. Chicago (see appendix)	
Olive Branch	62969
Olivet	61860
Olmsted	62970
Olney (1st)	62450
Olympia Fields	60461
Omaha	62871
Onarga	60955
Oneida	61467
Opdyke	62872
Opheim	61468
Oquawka	61469
Orangeville	61060
Oraville	62971
Orchardville	62873
Oreana	62554
Oregon (1st)	61061
Orient	62874
Orion	61273
Orland Park (1st)	60462
Osco	61274
Oswego	60543
Ottawa (1st)	61350
Owaneco	62555
Ozark	62972
Palatine (1st)	60067
Palestine	62451
Palmer	62556
Palmyra	62674
Paloma	62359
Palos Heights (1st)	60463
Palos Hills, R. Br. Palos Park	60465
Palos Park (1st)	60464
Palos Hills, R. Br.	60465
Pana (1st)	62557
Panama	62077
Papineau	60956
Parcel Post, Sta. East Saint Louis	62205
Paris (1st)	61944
Park Forest (1st)	60466
Park Ridge (1st)	60068
Parkersburg	62452
Patoka	62875
Patterson	62078
Pawnee	62558
Pawpaw	61353
Paxton (1st)	60957
Payson	62360
Pearl	62361
Pearl City	61062
Pecatonica	61063
Pekin (1st)	61554
Penfield	61862
PEORIA (1st) (see appendix)	
Peoria Heights, Br. Peoria	61614
Peotone	60468
Percy	62272
Perks	62973
Perry	62362
Peru (1st)	61354
Pesotum	61863
Petersburg (1st)	62675
Philo	61864
Piasa	62079
Pierron	62273
Pierson Station	61947
Pilsen, Sta. Chicago	60608
Pinckneyville (1st)	62274
Pinkstaff	62453
Piper City	60959
Pittsburg	62974
Pittsfield (1st)	62363
Plainfield (1st)	60544
Plainview	62676
Plainville	62365
Plano (1st)	60545
Plato Center	60170
Plaza, Sta. Belleville	62223
Plaza, Sta. Chicago	60607
Pleasant Hill	62366
Pleasant Plains	62677
Plymouth	62367
Pocahontas	62275
Polo	61064
Pomona	62975
Pontiac (1st)	61764
Pontoosuc	62368
Poplar Grove	61065
Port Byron	61275
Posen	60469
Potomac	61865
Prairie City	61470
Prairie Du Rocher	62277
Modoc, R. Br.	62261
Prairie View	60069
Preemption	61276
Princeton (1st)	61356
Princeville	61559
Prophetstown	61277
Prospect Heights (1st)	60070
Prudential Plaza, Sta. Chicago	60601
Pulaski	62976
Putnam	61560
Quad City Airport, R. Br. Moline	61265
Quincy (1st)	62301
Columbus, R. Br.	62328
Quinsippi, R. Sta.	62301
Soldiers Home, Sta.	62301
Quinsippi, R. Sta. Quincy	62301
Radom	62876
Raleigh	62977
Ramsey	62080
Rankin	60960
Ransom	60470
Rantoul (1st)	61866
Rapids City	61278
Rardin	61948
Raritan	61471
Ravenswood, Sta. Chicago	60625
Ravinia, Sta. Highland Park	60035
Raymond	62560
Red Bud	62278
Red Oak	61066
Reddick	60961
Redmon	61949
Renault	62279
Reynolds	61279
Richmond (1st)	60071
Richton Park	60471
Richview	62877
Ridge Farm	61870
Ridgway	62979
Ridott	61067
Riggston	62680
Rinard	62878
Ringwood	60072
Rio	61472
River Forest, Br. Oak Park	60305
River Grove (1st)	60171
Riverdale, Br. Chicago (see appendix)	
Riverside (1st)	60546
Riverton	62561
Roanoke	61561
Robbins	60472
Robbs	62980
Roberts	60962
Robinson (1st)	62454
Rochelle (1st)	61068
Kings, R. Br.	61045
Rochester	62563
Rock City	61070
Rock Falls (1st)	61071
Nelson, R. Br.	61058
Rock Island (1st)	61201
Rockbridge	62081
Rockdale, Br. Joliet	60436
ROCKFORD (1st) (see appendix)	
Rockport	62370
Rockton (1st)	61072
Rockwood	62280
Rogers Park, Sta. Chicago	60626
Rolling Acres, Sta. Peoria	61614
Rolling Meadows, Br. Arlington Heights	60008
Rome	61562
Roodhouse	62082
Rosamond	62083
Roscoe	61073
Rose Hill, R. Br. Newton	62457
Rosebud	62981
Roseland, Sta. Chicago	60628
Roselle (1st)	60172
Rosemont, Br. Des Plaines	60018
Roseville	61473
Rosewood, Br. East Alton	62024
Rosiclare	62982
Rossville	60963
Round Grove	61280
Round Lake (1st)	60073
Roxana	62084
Royal	61871
Royalton	62983
Rushville	62681
Russell	60075
Rutland	61358
S I U, Br. Edwardsville	62025
Sadorus	61872
Sailor Springs	62879
Saint Anne	60964
Wichert, R. Br.	60965
Saint Augustine	61474
Saint Charles (1st)	60174
Saint David	61563
Saint Elmo	62458
Saint Francisville	62460
Saint Jacob	62281
Saint Joseph	61873
Saint Libory	62282
Saint Peter	62880
Sainte Marie	62459
Salem (1st)	62881
San Jose	62682
Sandoval	62882
Sandwich (1st)	60548
Sauget, Br. East Saint Louis	62201
Sauk Village, Br. Chicago Heights	60411
Saunemin	61769

Savanna (1st)	61074	
Savoy	61874	
Sawyerville	62085	
Saybrook	61770	
Scales Mound	61075	
Schaumburg, Br. Roselle	60172	
Scheller	62883	
Schiller Park, Br. Franklin Park	60176	
Sciota	61475	
Scioto Mills, R. Br. Freeport	61076	
Scott A F B, Br. Belleville	62225	
Scottville	62683	
Seaton	61476	
Seatonville	61359	
Secor	61771	
Seneca	61360	
Serena	60549	
Sesser	62884	
Seward	61077	
Seymour	61875	
Shabbona	60550	
Shannon	61078	
Shattuc	62283	
Shawneetown	62984	
Sheffield	61361	
Shelbyville (1st)	62565	
Sheldon	60966	
Sheridan	60551	
Sheridan Village, Sta. Peoria	61614	
Sherman	62684	
Sherrard	61281	
Shipman	62685	
Shirland	61079	
Shirley	61772	
Shobonier	62885	
Shorewood, R. Br. Joliet	60436	
Shumway	62461	
Sibley	61773	
Sidell	61876	
Sidney	61877	
Sigel	62462	
Silvis (1st)	61282	
Simpson	62985	
Sims	62886	
Skokie (1st)	60076	
Smithboro	62284	
Smithfield	61477	
Smithshire	61478	
Smithton	62285	
Soldiers Home, Sta. Quincy	62301	
Solon Mills	60080	
Somonauk	60552	
Sorento	62086	
South, Sta. Evanston	60202	
South Beloit (1st)	61080	
South Bridgeview, Br. Oak Lawn	60455	
South Central, Sta. Chicago	60605	
South Chicago, Sta. Chicago	60617	
South Chicago Heights, Br. Chicago Heights	60411	
South Elgin	60177	
South Holland (1st)	60473	
South Jacksonville, Br. Jacksonville	62650	
South Oak Park, Sta. Oak Park	60304	
South Pekin	61564	
South Roxana	62087	
South Shore, Sta. Chicago	60649	
South Standard	62686	
South Stickney, Br. Oak Lawn	60459	
South Wilmington	60474	
Sparland	61565	
Sparta (1st)	62286	
Speer	61479	
Spring Grove	60081	
Spring Valley (1st)	61362	
Springerton	62887	
SPRINGFIELD (1st) (see appendix)		
Standard	61363	
Stanford	61774	
Staunton	62088	
Steeleville	62288	
Steger (1st)	60475	
Sterling (1st)	61081	
Coleta, R. Br.	61017	
Steward	60553	
Stewardson	62463	
Stickney, Br. Berwyn	60402	
Stillman Valley	61084	
Stock Yards, Sta. Chicago	60609	
Stockland	60967	
Stockton	61085	
Stone Park, Br. Melrose Park	60165	
Stonefort	62987	
Stonington	62567	
Stoy	62464	
Strasburg	62465	
Strawn	61775	
Streamwood, Br. Bartlett	60103	
Streator (1st)	61364	
Ancona, R. Br.	61311	
Stronghurst	61480	
Sublette	61367	
Sugar Grove	60554	
Sullivan (1st)	61951	
Allenville, R. Br.	61901	
Summer Hill	62372	
Summerfield	62289	
Summit, Sta. Argo	60501	
Summum, R. Br. Astoria	61566	
Sumner	62466	
Sunnyland, Br. Washington	61571	
Sutter	62373	
Swansea, Br. Belleville	62221	
Swanwick	62290	
Sweet Water	62687	
Sycamore (1st)	60178	
Table Grove	61482	
Taft, Br. Melrose Park	60163	
Tallula	62688	
Tamaroa	62888	
Tamms	62988	
Unity, R. Br.	62993	
Tampico	61283	
Taylor Ridge	61284	
Taylor Springs	62089	
Taylorville (1st)	62568	
Techny (1st)	60082	
Temple Hill	62989	
Tennessee	62374	
Teutopolis	62467	
Texico	62889	
Thawville	60968	
Thayer	62689	
Thebes	62990	
Thomasboro	61878	
Thompsonville	62890	
Thomson	61285	
Thornton	60476	
Tilden	62292	
Timewell	62375	
Tinley Park (1st)	60477	
Tioga, R. Br. Mendon	62351	
Tiskilwa	61368	
Toledo	62468	
Tolono	61880	
Toluca	61369	
Tonica	61370	
Topeka	61567	
Toulon	61483	
Tovey	62570	
Towanda	61776	
Tower Hill	62571	
Tremont	61568	
Trenton	62293	
Trilla	62469	
Triumph	61371	
Trivoli	61569	
Troy	62294	
Troy Grove	61372	
Tunnel Hill	62991	
Tuscola (1st)	61953	
Twenty Second Street, Sta. Chicago	60616	
Ullin	62992	
Union	60180	
Union Hill	60969	
Unity, R. Br. Tamms	62993	
University, Sta. Urbana	61801	
Upper Alton, Sta. Alton	62002	
Uptown, Sta. Chicago	60640	
Urbana (1st)	61801	
Ursa	62376	
Utica	61373	
Valier	62891	
Valmeyer	62295	
Van Orin	61374	
Vandalia (1st)	62471	
Varna	61375	
Venedy, R. Br. Okawville	62296	
Venice	62090	
Vergennes	62994	
Vermilion	61955	
Vermont	61484	
Vernon	62892	
Verona	60479	
Versailles	62378	
Victoria	61485	
Vienna	62995	
Villa Grove	61956	
Villa Park (1st)	60181	
Villa Ridge	62996	
Viola	61486	
Virden	62690	
Virgil, R. Br. Maple Park	60182	
Virginia	62691	
Waddams Grove, R. Br. Lena	61048	
Wadsworth	60083	
Waggoner	62572	
Walnut	61376	
Walnut Grove	61487	
Walnut Hill	62893	
Walsh	62297	
Walshville	62091	
Waltonville	62894	
Wapella	61777	
Warren	61087	
Warrensburg	62573	
Warrenville	60555	
Warsaw	62379	

155

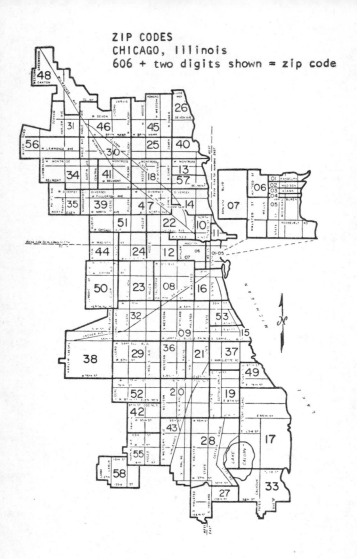

ZIP CODES
CHICAGO, Illinois
606 + two digits shown = zip code

Wasco	60183
Washburn	61570
Washington (1st)	61571
Washington Park, Br. East	
Saint Louis	62204
Wataga	61488
Waterloo (1st)	62298
Waterman	60556
Watseka (1st)	60970
Watson	62473
Wauconda	60084
Waukegan (1st)	60085
Edison Square, Sta.	60085
Great Lakes, Br.	60088
Mc Gaw Park, Br.	60085
Waverly	62692
Wayne	60184
Wayne City	62895
Waynesville	61778
Wedron	60557
Weldon	61882
Weige	62299
Wellington	60973
Wenona	61377
Wentworth Woods, Sta.	
Calumet City	60409
West Brooklyn	61378
West Chicago (1st)	60185
West Frankfort (1st)	62896
West Gate, Sta. Joliet (see	

appendix)	
West Glen, Sta. Peoria	61614
West Liberty	62475
West Point	62380
West Salem	62476
West Union	62477
West York	62478
Westchester, Br. Maywood	60153
Western Springs (1st)	60558
Westervelt	62574
Westfield	62474
Westmont (1st)	60559
Westville	61883
Wheaton (1st)	60187
Wheeler	62479
Wheeling (1st)	60090
White Hall	62092
White Heath	61884
Whittington	62897
Wichert, R. Br. Saint Anne	60965
Wicker Park, Sta. Chicago	60622
Wildwood, Br. Grayslake	60030
Williamsfield	61489
Williamsville	62693
Willisville	62997
Willow Hill	62480
Willow Springs (1st)	60480
Wilmette (1st)	60091
Wilmington (1st)	60481
Wilsonville	62093

Winchester	62694
Windsor	61957
Windsor Square, Sta. Peoria	61614
Winfield (1st)	60190
Winnebago	61088
Winnetka (1st)	60093
Winslow	61089
Winthrop Harbor	60096
Witt	62094
Wolf Lake	62998
Wonder Lake	60097
Wood Dale (1st)	60191
Wood River (1st)	62095
Woodhull	61490
Woodland	60974
Woodlawn	62898
Woodridge, Br. Downers	
Grove	60515
Woodson	62695
Woodstock (1st)	60098
Woosung	61091
Worden	62097
Worth (1st)	60482
Wrights	62098
Wyanet	61379
Wyoming	61491
Xenia	62899
Yale	62481
Yates City	61572
Yorkville	60560

Appendix

Arlington Heights — Aurora
Belleville — Chicago ILLINOIS

ARLINGTON HEIGHTS 600

POST OFFICE BOXES

Box Nos.		
ANY	Arlington Heights	06

STATIONS, BRANCHES AND UNITS

Elk Grove Village Br.	07
Rolling Meadows Br.	08
General Delivery	04
Postmaster	04

AURORA   **605**

POST OFFICE BOXES

Box Nos.		
1-1612	Main Office	07

RURAL ROUTES

1,2,3	04

STATIONS, BRANCHES AND UNITS

General Delivery	07
Postmaster	07

BELLEVILLE   **622**

POST OFFICE BOXES

Box Nos.		
A-Z	Main Office	22
1-690	Main Office	22
1-790	Scott Air Force Base Sta.	25
800-999	Plaza Sta.	23

RURAL ROUTES

1,2,3	21

STATIONS, BRANCHES AND UNITS

Plaza Sta.	23
Scott A F B Br.	25
Swansea Br.	21
General Delivery	20
Postmaster	20

CHICAGO   **606**

POST OFFICE BOXES

Box Nos.		
A-Z	Downtown Sta.	90
1-2000	Downtown Sta.	90
AA-ZZ	Downtown Sta.	90

2000-2999	Downtown Sta.	90
3000-4230	Merchandise Mart	54
4301-8687	Chicago	80
9000-9999	Downtown Sta.	90
09000-09199	Stock Yards	09
11000-11999	Fort Dearborn Street Station	11
16000-16999	Twenty Second Sta.	16
17001-17599	South Chicago	17
24001-24999	Garfield Park	24
27001-27179	Riverdale	27
35001-35270	Elmwood Park	35
42601-42999	Evergreen Park	42
45001-45375	Northtown	59
48001-48329	Niles	48
50001-50397	Cicero	50
56001-56239	Harwood Heights	56
66001-66518	O Hare International Airport	66
91000-97899	Bank Boxes	90

RURAL ROUTES

1	58

STATIONS, BRANCHES AND UNITS

Aslip Br.	58
Ashburn Sta.	52
Auburn Park Sta.	20

Chicago (Con.)　　　　606

Austin Sta.	44
Calumet Park Br.	43
Chestnut Street Sta.	10
Chicago Lawn Sta.	29
Cicero Br.	50
Clearing Br.	38
Cragin Sta.	39
Division Street Sta.	51
Dunning Sta.	34
Edgebrook Sta.	46
Elmwood Park Br.	35
Englewood Sta.	21
Evergreen Park Br.	42
Fort Dearborn Sta.	11
Garfield Park Sta.	24
Golf Mill Br.	48
Grand Crossing Sta.	19
Harwood Heights Br.	56
Hawthorne Sta.	23
Haymarket Sta.	06
Hegewisch Sta.	33
Hillside-Berkley Br.	62
Hyde Park Sta.	15
Irving Park Sta.	41
Jackson Park Sta.	37
Jefferson Sta.	30
Kedzie Grace Sta.	18
Lakeveiw Sta.	13
Lincoln Park Sta.	14
Logan Square Sta.	47
Main Post Office Sta.	80
Merchandise Mart Sta.	54
Mid-West Sta.	54
Mid-West Sta.	12
Morgan Park Sta.	43
Mount Greenwood Sta.	55
Niles Sta.	48
Nineteenth Avenue Sta.	60
North Town Sta.	45
Norwood Park Sta.	31
O Hare Airport Sta.	66
Ogden Park Sta.	36
Old Post Office.	02
Pilsen Sta.	08
Plaza Sta.	07
Prudential Plaza Sta.	01
Ravenswood Sta.	25
Riverdale Br.	27
Rogers Park Sta.	26
Roseland Sta.	28
South Central Sta.	05
South Chicago Sta.	17
South Shore Sta.	49
Stock Yards Sta.	09
Twenty Second Street Sta.	16
Uptown Sta.	40
Wicker Park Sta.	22
General Delivery.	07
Postmaster.	07

APARTMENTS, HOTELS, MOTELS

Allerton, 701 N Michigan.	11
Ambassador West, 1300 N State.	10
Ambassor East, 1301 N State St.	10
Belden Stratford, 2300 N Lincoln Park W.	14
Belmont, 3156 N Sheridan.	57
Berkshire, 15 E Ohio.	11
Bismarck, 171 W Randolph.	01
Cass, 640 N Wabash.	11
Civic Center, 167 W Washington.	02
Congress, 520 S Michigan.	05
Conrad Hilton, 720 S Michigan.	05
Continental, 909 N Michigan.	11
Croydon, 616 N Rush.	11
Del Prado, 5307 S Hyde Park.	15
Devonshire, 19 E Ohio.	11
Drake, 140 E Walton.	11
East End Park, 5240 S Hyde Park.	15
Eastgate, 162 E Ontario.	11
Executive House, 71 E Wacker Dr.	01
Flamingo, 5520 S South Shore.	37
Fort Dearborn, 117 W Van Buren.	05
Harrison, 65 E Harrison.	05
Knickerbocker, 163 E Walton.	11
La Salle, 12 N La Salle.	02
Lake Shore Drive, 181 Lake Shore.	11
Maryland, 900 N Rush.	11
Midland, 172 W Adams.	03
New Lawrence, 1020 W Lawrence.	40
Oxford House, 225 N Wabash.	01
Palmer House, 17 E Monroe.	90
Parkway, 2100 N Lincoln Park W.	14
Pearson, 190 E Pearson.	11
Planters, 19 N Clark.	02
Plaza, 1555 N Clark.	10
Saint Clair, 162 E Ohio St.	11
Seneca, 200 E Chestnut.	11
Sheraton Blackstone, 636 S Michigan.	05
Sheraton-Chicago, 505 North Michigan Ave.	11
Sherman, 112 W Randolph.	01
Sherry, 1725 E 53rd.	15
Shoreland, 5454 S South Shore.	15
Somerset, 5009 N Sheridan.	40
Southmoor, 6646 S Stony Island.	37
Sovereign, 6200 N Kenmore.	26
Water Tower Inn, 800 N Michigan.	11
Webster, 2150 N Lincoln Park W.	14
Windermere, 1642 E 56th.	37
Y M C A, 826 S Wabash St.	05

BUILDINGS

Adams & Franklin, 222 W Adams.	06
Adams & Wabash, 207 S Wabash.	04
American Dental Assoc, 211 E Chicago St.	11
American National Bank, 33 N La Salle.	02
Apollo Savings, 430 N Michigan Ave.	11
Art Institute, S Michigan & E Adams.	03
Association, 19 S La Salle.	03
Bankers, 105 W Adams.	03
Barrister Hall, 29 S La Salle St.	03
Bay State, 140 N State.	02
Bell Savings, 79 W Monroe.	03
Bell Telephone, 208 W Washington.	06
Bentley-Murray, 511 S Plymouth Ct.	05
Blum, 624 S Michigan.	05
Board Of Trade, 141 W Jackson.	04
Borg-Warner, 200 S Michigan.	04
Borland Manufacturing, 636 S Federal.	05
Borland, 105 S La Salle.	03
Boyce, 510 N Dearborn.	10
Brooks, 223 W Jackson.	06
Brunswick, 623 S Wabash.	05
Brunswick, 69 W Washington.	02
Builders, 228 N La Salle.	01
Butler, 162 N State.	01
Canterbury, 173 W Madison.	02
Carbide & Carbon, 230 N Michigan.	01
Central Station, 135 E. 11th Pl.	05
Champlain, 37 S Wabash.	03
Chicago Burlington & Quincy, 547 W Jackson.	06
Chicago Daily Defender, 2400 Michigan.	16
Chicago Federal Savings, 108 N State.	02
Chicago Garment Center, 337 S Franklin.	06
Chicago Mercantile Exchange, 308 W Washington.	06
Chicago Motor Club, 66 E South Water St.	01
Chicago Northwestern, 500 W Madison.	06
Chicago Park District Burnham Park, 425 E. Mcfetridge Dr.	05
Chicago Real Estate Board, 105 W Madison.	02
Chicago Stadium, 1800 W Madison St.	12
Chicago Temple, 77 W Washington.	02
Chicago Title & Trust, 111 W Washington.	02
Chicago Today, 445 N. Michigan Ave.	11
Chicago Tribune, 435 N Michigan.	11
Chicago-Clark, 800 N Clark.	10
Chicago, 7 W Madison.	02
Civic Center, 50 W Washington.	02
Congress Bank, 506 S Wabash.	05
Consumers Company, 220 S State.	04

Chicago (Con.)   606

Continental Illinois Bank, 231 S La Salle St 04
Continental Illinois Bank, 231 S. La. Salle St 93
Converse, 618 W Jackson 06
Corn Products, 201 N Wells 06
Coronet, 65 E South Water 01
County, 118 N Clark 02
Crane, 836 S Michigan 05
Cuneo, 151 N Michigan 01
Daily News, 401 N Wabash 11
Daily Sun Times, 401 N Wabash 11
Dearborn Station, 47 W Polk St 05
Delaware, 36 W Randolph 01
Distributors, 236 N Clark 01
Donohue, 711 S Dearborn 05
Douglas, 20 E Jackson 04
Dwight, 626 S Clark 05
Edison, 72 W Adams 03
Eiger, 1255 S Wabash 05
Electrical, 625 W Jackson 06
Engineering, 205 W Wacker Dr 06
Enterprise, 311 N Desplaines .. -06
Equitable, 401 N Michigan St 11
Esquire, 65 E South Water 01
Everett Mckinley Dirksen, 219 S. Dearborn 04
Exchange, Union Stock Yards . 09
Exhibitors, 325 N Wells 10
Fairbanks-Morse, 600 S Michigan 05
Farwell, 664 N Michigan 11
Fashion Trades, 318 W Adams 06
Federal Reserve Bank, 230 S La Salle 04
Federal, 536 S. Clark 05
Federation, 175 W Madison 02
Finchley, 23 E Jackson 04
Findlay, 320 S Michigan 04
Fine Arts, 410 S Michigan 05
First Federal, 7 S Dearborn 03
First National Bank, One First National Plaza 70
Fisher, 343 S Dearborn 04
Flomor, 1018 S Wabash 05
Frank J Lewis, 25 E Jackson ... 04
Franklin, 525 S Dearborn 05
Fulton Market Cold Storage, 1000 W Fulton 07
Furniture Mart, 666 N Lake Shore Dr 11
Garland, 111 N Wabash 02
Goddard, 27 E Monroe 03
Great Lakes, 180 N Wacker Dr 06
Greyhound, 71 W Lake St 01
Harris Bank, 111 W Monroe.... 03
Harrison-Clark, 85 W Harrison 05
Hearst, 326 W Madison 06
Hertz, 218 S Wabash St 04
Heyworth, 29 E Madison 02
Hull House, 800 S Halsted St 07

I.b.m. Plaza, 1 E. I.b.m. Plaza 11
Illinois Central Station, 135 E 11 Th Pl 05
Industry, 117 N Wells St 06
Inland Steel, 30 W Monroe 03
Insurance Center, 330 S Wells 06
Insurance Exchange Annex, 166 W Van Buren 04
Insurance Exchange, 175 W Jackson 04
International Harvester, 180 N Michigan 01
Isabella, 21 E Van Buren 05
Jackson-Franklin, 309 W Jackson 06
Jewelers, 19 S Wabash 03
Joel Hunter, 123 W Madison .. 02
John Crerar Library, 35 W 33rd St 16
John Hancock, 875 N. Michigan 11
Kemper Insurance, 20 N Wacker Dr 06
Kiwanis International, 101 E Erie 11
L B Knight, 549 W Randolph.. 06
La Salle Bank, 135 S Lasalle 03
La Salle Station, 139 W Van Buren St 05
La Salle-Wacker, 221 N La Salle 01
Lake View, 116 S Michigan St 03
Lawyers, 166 W Washington... 02
Le Moyne, 180 N Wabash 01
Lees, 19 S Wells 06
Lincoln Towers, 75 E Wacker Dr 01
Lions, 209 N Michigan........... 01
Loop End, 177 N State 01
Lundington, 1104 S Wabash .. 05
Lyon & Healy, 64 E Jackson ... 04
Lytton, 14 E Jackson 04
Machinery Hall, 549 W Washington 06
Machinery Sales, 565 W Washington 06
Madison Terminal, 9 S Clinton 06
Magill Weinsheimer, 1332 S Wabash 05
Majestic, 22 W Monroe 03
Mallers, 5 S Wabash 05
Manhattan, 431 S Dearborn ... 05
Maremont, 168 N Michigan 01
Marina City, 300 N State St.... 10
Market Exchange, 1440 S Racine 08
Marlennan Plaza, 222 S. Riverside Plaza 06
Marquette, 140 S Dearborn 03
Marshall Field Annex, 25 E Washington 02
Marycrest, 120 S State 03
Masonite, 29 N Wacker Dr...... 06
Mc Cormick Place Chicago Exposit, 23 Rd & S Lake Shore Dr 16
Mc Cormick, 332 S Michigan 04

Mc Graw Hill, 520 N Michigan St 11
Mc Kinlock, 209 W Jackson 06
Memorial Hall, 85 E Randolph 01
Mentor, 6 E Monroe.............. 03
Merchandise Mart, 222 Merchandise Mart Plaza .. 54
Metropolitan, 134 N La Salle.. 02
Michigan Boulevard, 30 N Michigan 02
Michigan Square, 540 N Michigan 11
Midland, 176 W Adams 03
Midway Airport Terminal, 5700 S Cicero St 38
Millinery Mart, 323 S Franklin 06
Monadnock Block, 53 W Jackson 04
Monroe, 104 S Michigan........ 03
Morton Salt, 110 N Wacker Dr 06
Moser, 621 S Plymouth Ct...... 05
Moses, 234 S Wells.............. 06
Mossner, 108 W Lake.............. 01
National Cash Register, 223 N Michigan 01
National Republic, 134 S La Salle 03
North American Life, 35 E Wacker St 01
North American, 36 S State.... 03
Northern Trust Company, 50 S La Salle 03
Northwestern, 500 W Madison 06
Oakes, 650 S Clark 05
Occidental, 109 N Wacker Dr 06
Ogden, 192 N Clark 01
Ohio, 509 S Wabash 05
Old Colony, 407 S Dearborn .. 05
Old Republic, 307 N Michigan 01
One La Salle Street, 1 N La Salle 02
One-Sixty-Two, 162 N State St 01
Orchestra Hall, 220 S Michigan 04
Otis Elevator, 600 W Jackson 06
Otis, 10 S La Salle 03
Outer Drive East, 400 E Randolph St 01
Patten, 161 W Harrison 05
Pelouze, 230 E Ohio.............. 11
Peoples Gas, 122 S Michigan 03
Peterson, 523 S Plymouth Ct. 05
Pittsfield, 55 E Washington.... 02
Playboy Club 919 Michigan Ave. N. 11
Plymouth-Polk, 731 S Plymouth Ct 05
Pontiac, 542 S Dearborn........ 05
Pope, 633 S Plymouth Ct....... 05
Printers, 732 S Sherman 05
Prudential, 130 E Randolph .. 01
Railway Exchange, 80 E Jackson St 04
Randolph Towers, 188 W Randolph 01
Randolph-Wells, 130 N Wells.. 06

Chicago (Con.)   606

Riverside Plaza, 2 N
  Riverside Plaza.................... 06
Roanoke, 11 S La Salle.......... 03
Rookery, 209 S La Salle......... 04
Roosevelt, 179 W
  Washington...................... 02
Science Research, 259 E
  Erie............................. 11
Security, 189 W Madison........ 02
Shops, 17 N Wabash............. 02
Silversmiths, 10 S Wabash
  St............................... 03
Socony Vacuum, 59 E Van
  Buren........................... 05
Standard Oil, 910 S
  Michigan........................ 05
Stark, 234 S.Wabash............ 04
State & Lake, 190 N State...... 01
State & Randolph, 6 W
  Randolph........................ 01
State-Madison, 22 W
  Madison......................... 02
Steger, 28 E Jackson............ 04
Stevens, 17 N State............. 02
Stone Container, 360 N
  Michigan........................ 01
Sun-Times Sun-Times Daily
  News Plaza, 401 N
  Wabash.......................... 11
Telephone, 230 W
  Washington...................... 05
Terminals, 537 S Dearborn...... 06
The Canterbury, 173 W
  Madison......................... 02
Thirty Five East Wacker......... 01
Thirty North La Salle........... 02
Thirty Three East Congress
  Parkway, 33e. Congress
  Pkwy............................ 05
Transportation, 608 S
  Dearborn........................ 05
Tribune Tower, 435 N
  Michigan........................ 11
Tuttle, 6 E Lake................. 01
Union Station, 516 W
  Jackson St...................... 06
Union Tank, 111 Jackson
  Blvd............................ 04
United Insurance, 1 E
  Wacker.......................... 01
United States Gypsum, 101 S
  Wacker.......................... 06
Utilities, 327 S La Salle........ 04
Van Buren, 210 W Van
  Buren........................... 07
Wall Street Journal, 711 W.
  Monroe.......................... 90
Western Union, 427 S La
  Salle........................... 05
Westminster, 110 S
  Dearborn........................ 03
Williams, 59 E Monroe........... 03
Williamson, 605 W
  Washington...................... 06
Willoughby, 8 S Michigan........ 03
Woods, 54 W Randolph........... 01
Wrigley Annex, 410 N
  Michigan........................ 11
Wrigley, 400 N Michigan......... 11

GOVERNMENT OFFICES
Chicago Police Dept, 1111 S
  State Street.................... 05
Chicago Public Library, 78 E
  Washington St................... 02
City Hall, 121 N La Salle St.... 02
Main Post Office, 433 W Van
  Buren........................... 07
State Of Illinois Office, 160
  N La Salle...................... 01
United States Courthouse,
  219 S Dearborn.................. 04

HOSPITALS
Alexian Brothers, 1200 W
  Belden.......................... 14
American, 850 W Irving Park..... 13
Augustana, 409 W Dickens........ 14
Belmont, 4058 W Melrose......... 41
Bethany Home & Hospital Of
  The Methodist, 5015 N
  Paulina......................... 40
Bethany, 3420 W Van Buren....... 24
Bethesda, 2451 W Howard......... 45
Billings, 950 E 59 Th St........ 37
Bobs Roberts, 920 E 59th........ 37
Central Community, 5701 S
  Wood............................ 36
Chicago Eye Ear Nose &
  Throat, 231 W
  Washington...................... 06
Chicago Lying-In, 5845 S
  Maryland........................ 37
Chicago Osteopathic, 5200 S
  Ellis........................... 15
Chicago State, 6500 W Irving
  Park Rd......................... 34
Children Department Michael
  Reese, 29th & Ellis............. 16
Childrens Memorial, 2300
  Children'S Plaza................ 14
Columbus, 2520 N Lakeview....... 14
Contagious Disease, 3026 S
  California...................... 08
Cook County, 1835 W
  Harrison........................ 12
Covenant, 5145 N California..... 25
Cuneo Frank, 750 W
  Montrose St..................... 13
Doctors General, 6970 N
  Clark........................... 26
Dunning, 6500 W Irving Park
  Rd.............................. 34
Edgewater, 5700 N Ashland....... 60
Englewood, 6001 S Green......... 21
Evangelical, 5421 S Morgan...... 09
Forkesh, 2544 W Montrose........ 18
Franklin Boulevard
  Community, 3240 W
  Franklin Blvd................... 24
Friend Pavillion, 3001 S Ellis.. 16
Garfield Park, 3821 W
  Washington...................... 24
Grant, 551 W Grant.............. 14
Henrotin, 939 N La Salle........ 10
Holy Cross, 2700 W 69th......... 29
Ida Mae Scott, 5027 S
  Prairie......................... 15
Illinois Central, 5800 S Stony
  Island.......................... 37
Illinois Eye & Ear Infirmary
  904 W Adams..................... 07

Illinois Masonic, 834 W
  Welhngton....................... 57
Illinois State Pediatric, 1640
  W Roosevelt Road................ 08
Illinois State Psychiatric
  Institute, 1601 W Taylor........ 12
Jackson Park, 7531 S Stony
  Island.......................... 49
La Rabida, 6501 So
  Promontory Dr................... 49
Little Company Of Mary,
  2800 W 95th..................... 42
Loretto, 625 S Central.......... 44
Louis A Weiss Memorial,
  4646 N Marine Drive............. 40
Louise Burg, 225 W Cermak
  Rd.............................. 16
Lutheran Deaconess, 1138 N.
  Leavitt......................... 22
Martha Washington, 2318 W
  Irving Park..................... 18
Mary Thompson, 140 N
  Ashland......................... 07
Mercy Hospital, 2510 S King
  Dr.............................. 16
Michael Reese, E 29th &
  Ellis........................... 16
Misericordia, 2916 W 47th....... 32
Mount Sinai, 2750 W 15th
  Pl.............................. 08
Municipal Tuberculosis
  Sanitarium, 5601 N
  Pulaski Rd...................... 46
North Avenue, 1625 W North
  St.............................. 22
Northwest, 5645 W Addison....... 34
Norweigian American, 1044 N
  Francisco....................... 22
Passavant Memorial, 303 E
  Superior........................ 11
Presbyterian Saint Lukes........ 12
Provident, 426 E 51st........... 15
Ravenswood, 1917 W Wilson....... 40
Resurrection, 7435 W Talcott.... 31
Roosevelt Memorial, 426 W
  Wisconsin....................... 14
Roseland Community, 45 W
  111th........................... 28
Saint Annes, 4950 W
  Thomas.......................... 51
Saint Anthony De Padua,
  2875 W 19th..................... 23
Saint Bernards, 6337 S
  Harvard......................... 21
Saint Elizabeths, 1435 N
  Claremont....................... 22
Saint Francis X Cabrini, 811
  S Lytle St...................... 07
Saint Georges, 449 W
  Winneconna...................... 20
Saint Josephs, 2900 N
  Lakeshore Dr.................... 57
Saint Marys Of Nazareth,
  1120 N Leavitt.................. 22
Saint Vincents Infant, 721 N
  La Salle........................ 10
Sarah Morris, 29th & Ellis...... 16
Shriners, 2211 N Oak Park
  Ave............................. 35
South Chicago Community,
  2320 E 93rd..................... 17
South Shore, 8015 S Luella...... 17

Chicago (Con.)   606

Swedish Covenant, 5145 N
  California 25
University Of Illinois General,
  840 S Wood 12
University Of Illinois
  Neuropsychiatric, 912
  Wood St. 12
Veterans Administration
  Research, 333 E Huron 11
Veterans Administration, 820
  S Damen 12
Walther Memorial, 1116 N
  Kedzie 51
Wesley Memorial, 250 E
  Superior............................ 11
Woodlawn, 6060 S Drexel 37

UNIVERSITIES AND COLLEGES

Chicago Kent College Of Law,
  10 N Franklin 06
De Paul University, 2322 N
  Kenmore 14
Illinois Institute Of
  Technology, 3300 S
  Federal 16
John Marshall Law, 315 S
  Plymouth Ct 04
Lewis Towers, 820 N
  Michigan 11
Loyola University, 6525 N
  Sheridan Rd 26
Mundelein, 6363 N Sheridan .. 26
North Park, 5125 N
  Spaulding 25
Northwestern University
  Chicago Camp Us, 301 E
  Chicago Av........................ 11
Roosevelt University 430
  Michigan Ave. S................. 05
Saint Xavier, 103rd &
  Central Park...................... 55
University Of Chicago,
  Downtown Center, 65 E.
  South Water....................... 01
University Of Chicago, 5801
  S Ellis 37
University Of Ill Cir Campus... 80
University Of Illinois Medic,
  1853 W Polk 12

NAMED STREETS

Abbott Ave S 20
Aberdeen N
  1-399................................. 07
  400-OUT 22
Aberdeen S
  1-1199............................... 07
  1200-3499.......................... 08
  4700-5499.......................... 09
  5500-7499.......................... 21
  7500-9499.......................... 20
  9500-13199........................ 43
Achsah Bond Dr...................... 05
Acme Ave W 27
Ada N
  1-399................................. 07
  400-OUT 22
Ada S
  600-999............................. 07
  1600-1799.......................... 08
  4700-5499.......................... 09

  5500-7499.......................... 36
  7500-9499.......................... 20
  9500-13199........................ 43
Adams E................................. 03
Adams W
  1-199................................. 03
  200-799............................. 06
  800-1599............................ 07
  1600-3199.......................... 12
  3200-4599.......................... 24
  4600-5999.......................... 44
Addison W
  500-1999............................ 13
  2000-3999.......................... 18
  4000-5599.......................... 41
  5600-8399.......................... 34
Agatite Ave W
  800-999............................. 40
  2100-3999.......................... 25
  4000-6399.......................... 30
  6400-8799.......................... 56
Ainslie W
  800-1999............................ 40
  2000-3999.......................... 25
  4000-6399.......................... 30
  7200-8799.......................... 56
Albany Ave N
  1-799................................. 12
  800-1599............................ 22
  1600-2799.......................... 47
  2800-4399.......................... 18
  4400-5599.......................... 25
  5600-6399.......................... 59
  6400-7599.......................... 45
Albany Ave S
  1-1199............................... 12
  1200-3499.......................... 23
  3500-5499.......................... 32
  5500-7499.......................... 29
  7500-8699.......................... 52
  8700-10299........................ 42
  10300-11499....................... 55
Albany Dr S
  11500-11899....................... 55
Albion Ave W
  1000-1999.......................... 26
  2000-3999.......................... 45
  4000-5199.......................... 46
  6500-7299.......................... 31
Aldine Ave W 57
Alexander W............................ 16
Algonquin Ave N...................... 46
Allen Ave N 18
Allport S 08
Almond S 12
Alpine Dr S............................. 58
Alta Vis Ter N......................... 13
Altgeld W
  800-1999............................ 14
  2000-3999.......................... 47
  4000-6399.......................... 39
  6400-7999.......................... 35
Amelia Dr W 48
Ancona W 22
Anthony Ave S
  6800-7099.......................... 37
  7100-7999.......................... 19
  8000-OUT 17
Arcade Pl W
  100-199............................. 03
  500-799............................. 06
  800-1599............................ 07
  1600-OUT 12

Arch S.................................... 08
Archer Ave S
  1900-2499.......................... 16
  2500-3499.......................... 08
  3500-3699.......................... .09
  3700-5399.......................... 32
  5400-7199.......................... 38
Ardmore Ave W
  900-1999............................ 60
  2000-3999.......................... 59
  4000-6399.......................... 46
  6400-7899.......................... 31
Argyle W
  800-1999............................ 40
  2000-3999.......................... 25
  4000-6399.......................... 30
  6400-8799.......................... 56
Arlington Pl W 14
Armitage Ave W
  200-1499............................ 14
  1500-1999.......................... 22
  2000-3999.......................... 47
  4000-6399.......................... 39
  6400-7999.......................... 35
Armour N 22
Armstrong E 11
Armstrong Ave W
  5200-5599.......................... 46
Artesian Ave N
  200-799............................. 12
  800-1599............................ 22
  1600-2799.......................... 47
  2800-4399.......................... 18
  4400-5599.......................... 25
  5600-6399.......................... 59
  6400-7599.......................... 45
Artesian Ave S
  300-399............................. 12
  2500-3499.......................... 08
  3500-5499.......................... 32
  5500-7499.......................... 29
  7500-8699.......................... 52
  8700-10299........................ 42
  10300-11899....................... 55
Arthington W
  400-1599............................ 07
  1600-3199.......................... 12
  3200-4599.......................... 24
  4600-5999.......................... 44
Arthur Ave W
  1100-1999.......................... 26
  2000-3999.......................... 45
  4000-4799.......................... 46
  7100-7199.......................... 31
Ashland Ave N
  1-399................................. 07
  400-1999............................ 22
  2000-2799.......................... 14
  2800-3599.......................... 57
  3600-4399.......................... 13
  4400-5599.......................... 40
  5600-6399.......................... 60
  6400-7799.......................... 26
  8800-9599.......................... 48
Ashland Ave S
  1-1199............................... 07
  1200-3499.......................... 08
  3500-5499.......................... 09
  5500-7499.......................... 36
  7500-9499.......................... 20
  9500-12925........................ 43
  12927-13199 (ODD)............. 43
Astor N 10

Chicago (Con.) 606

Atlantic Ave S	27
Attrill W	47
Augusta Blvd W	
1200-3199	22
3200-5999	51
Austin Ave N	
1-799 (ODD)	44
801-1599 (ODD)	51
1600-2799	39
2800-4399	34
4400-5599	30
5600-6399	46
Austin Ave S	
1-1199 (ODD)	44
1200-3899	50
4700-7499	38
Avalon Ave S	
7600-9499	19
9500-OUT	28
Avenue A S	17
Avenue B S	
10200-12199	17
Avenue C S	
10100-12199	17
Avenue D S	
10100-12199	17
Avenue E S	17
Avenue F S	
10200-12199	17
12200-13799	33
Avenue G S	17
Avenue H S	17
Avenue J S	17
Avenue K S	33
Avenue L S	
9500-12199	17
12200-13799	33
Avenue M S	
9500-12199	17
12200-13599	33
Avenue N S	
9500-12199	17
12200-13599	33
Avenue O S	
8500-12199	17
12200-14399	33
Avers Ave N	
200-799	24
800-1599	51
1600-2799	47
2800-4399	18
4400-5599	25
5600-6399	59
6400-7399	45
Avers Ave S	
1200-3499	23
3500-5499	32
5500-7499	29
7500-8699	52
8700-10299	42
10300-11899	55
11900-13299	58
Avondale Ave N	
2900-3899	18
3900-4399	41
4400-5599	30
5600-5699	46
5700-OUT	31
Badger Dr W	58
Baker Ave S	17

Balbo Ave E	05
Ballard Rd W	48
Balmoral Ave W	
900-1999	40
2000-3999	25
4000-6399	30
6400-8399	56
Baltimore Ave S	
8300-12199	17
12200-13599	33
Banks E	10
Barber W	07
Barry Ave W	
300-1999	57
2000-3999	18
4000-5599	41
5600-7199	34
7200-7499	35
Bauwans N	22
Beach Ave W	
1600-1799	22
3200-5999	51
Beacon N	40
Belden Ave W	
300-1999	14
2000-3999	47
4000-6399	39
6400-7999	35
Bell Ave N	
1-799	12
800-1599	22
1600-2799	47
2800-4399	18
4400-5599	25
5600-6399	59
6400-7599	45
Bell Ave S	
1-1199	12
1200-3499	08
3500-5499	09
5500-7499	36
7500-9499	20
9500-11899	43
Belle Plaine Ave W	
800-1999	13
2000-3999	18
4000-5599	41
5600-8399	34
Bellefort N	48
Bellevue Pl E	11
Belmont Ave W	
300-1999	57
2000-3999	18
4000-5599	41
5600-7599	34
7600-7998 (EVEN)	34
7601-7999 (ODD)	35
8000-8398 (EVEN)	34
Belt Circle Dr S	38
Benck Dr W	58
Bennett Ave S	
6700-7899	49
7900-12199	17
Bensley Ave S	
9400-12199	17
12200-14599	33
Benson S	08
Berenice Ave W	
1800-1999	13
2000-3999	18
4000-5599	41
5600-7999	34

Berkeley Ave S	
4100-4699	53
4700-OUT	15
Bernard N	
1600-2799	47
2800-4399	18
4400-5599	25
5600-6399	59
6400-7199	45
Berry Dr S	16
Berteau Ave W	
1400-1999	13
2000-3999	18
4000-5599	41
5600-8399	34
Berwyn Ave W	
1000-1999	40
2000-3999	25
4000-6399	30
6400-8799	56
Besly Ct N	22
Betty Ter W	48
Beverly Ave S	
8700-9499	20
9500-OUT	43
Beverly Glen Pky W	43
Bingham N	47
Birchdale Ave W	35
Birchwood Ave W	
1300-1999	26
2000-3199	45
6800-7799	48
Birkhoff Ave S	20
Bishop N	
1-99	07
400-OUT	22
Bishop S	
800-999	07
1800-1899	08
4600-5499	09
5500-7499	36
7500-9499	20
9500-13199	43
Bissell N	14
Bittersweet Pl W	13
Blackhawk W	
400-799	10
800-OUT	22
Blackstone Ave S	
4800-5499	15
5500-7099	37
7100-9499	19
9500-OUT	28
Blake S	09
Blanchard Ct S	16
Bliss W	22
Bloomingdale Ave W	
1500-1999	22
2000-3999	47
4000-6399	39
6400-7999	35
Blue Island Ave S	
600-1199	07
1200-OUT	08
Bonaparte S	08
Bond Ave S	17
Bonfield S	08
Bosworth Ave N	
1200-1999	22
2300-2799	14
2800-3599	57
3600-4399	13
6400-7799	26

Chicago (Con.)	606
Boulevard Way S	23
Bowen Ave E	53
Bowler W	12
Bowmanville Ave N	25
Bradley Pl W	
800-1999	13
2000-OUT	18
Brainard Ave S	33
Brandon Ave S	
7900-12199	17
12200-13699	33
Brayton St E & W	28
Breen Ave W	48
Brennan Ave S	17
Brewery Ave S	16
Briar Pl W	57
Brighton Pl S	32
Broad S	08
Broadway N	
2800-3599	57
3600-4399	13
4400-5599	40
5600-6399	60
Brodman Ave W	56
Brompton Ave W	57
Bross Ave W	08
Browning Ave E	53
Bruce Dr W	48
Bryn Mawr Ave W	
900-1999	60
2000-3999	59
4000-6399	46
6400-8799	31
Buckingham Pl W	57
Buena Ave W	13
Buffalo Ave S	
7900-12199	17
13000-13699	33
Burley Ave S	
7900-12199	17
12200-13599	33
Burling N	
1200-1599	10
1600-2699	14
2800-2999	57
Burnham Ave S	
7600-7899	49
7900-12199	17
12200-14399	33
Burr Oak Ave W	
1600-1799	43
1800-1948 (EVEN)	43
Burton Pl E & W	10
Busse Ave N	56
Butler Dr E	33
Byron W	
1000-1999	13
2000-3999	18
4000-5599	41
5600-8399	34
Cable Pl E	37
Cabrini N	07
Cal-Sag Rd S	58
Caldwell Ave N	
5600-7199	46
7200-8399	48
Calhoun Ave S	
9400-12199	17
12200-14599	33

California Ave N	
1-799	12
800-1599	22
1600-2799	47
2800-4399	18
4400-5599	25
5600-6399	59
6400-7599	45
California Ave S	
1-1199	12
1200-3499	08
3500-5499	32
5500-7499	29
7500-8699	52
8700-10299	42
10300-11499	55
Callero Dr N	48
Calumet Ave S	
1800-3499	16
3500-4699	53
4700-5499	15
5500-7099	37
7100-9499	19
9500-12999	28
13000-13799	27
Calumet River S	
8900-12199	17
12200-OUT	33
Cambridge Ave N	
800-1199	10
2300-2399	14
2800-3199	57
Campbell Ave N	
1-799	12
800-1599	22
1600-2799	47
2800-4399	18
4400-5599	25
5600-6399	59
6400-7599	45
Campbell Ave S	
1-1199	12
1200-3499	08
3500-5499	32
5500-7499	29
7500-8699	52
8700-10299	42
10300-11899	55
Campbell Park W	12
Canal N	06
Canal S	
1-399	06
400-1599	07
1600-3499	16
3500-OUT	09
Canalport Ave S	
1700-2057	16
2058-OUT	08
Canfield Ave N	
4400-5599	56
5600-6399	31
Capitol Dr N	45
Carmen Ave W	
800-1999	40
2000-3999	25
4000-6399	30
6400-8799	56
Carol Ave W	48
Carolyn Ln S	58
Carondolet Ave S	
10600-12199	17
12200-13499	33

Carpenter N	
1-399	07
400-OUT	22
Carpenter S	
400-1099	07
1600-3499	08
5000-5499	09
5500-7499	21
7500-9499	20
9500-13199	43
Carroll Ave W	
1-399	10
400-799	06
800-1599	07
1600-3199	12
3200-4599	24
4600-OUT	44
Carver Plz E	53
Castlewood Ter W	40
Catalpa Ave W	
900-1999	40
2000-3999	25
4000-6399	30
6400-8799	56
Cathedral Sq N	11
Catherine Ave W	56
Catino Ter W	48
Caton W	47
Cedar E	11
Cedar Ln W	48
Central Ave N	
1-799	44
800-1599	51
1600-2799	39
2800-4399	34
4400-5599	30
5600-6799	46
6800-7198 (EVEN)	46
7200-7599	48
Central Ave S	
1-1199	44
1200-3899	50
4700-7499	38
12525-12699 (ODD)	58
Central Park Ave N	
200-799	24
800-1599	51
1600-2799	47
2800-4399	18
4400-5599	25
5600-6399	59
6400-7199	45
Central Park Ave S	
1-1199	24
1200-3499	23
3500-5499	32
5500-7499	29
7500-8699	52
8700-10299	42
10300-11899	55
11900-13299	58
Cermak Rd E	16
Cermak Rd W	
1-799	16
800-2799	08
2800-4599	23
4600-6199	50
Chalmers Pl W	14
Champlain Ave S	
4200-4699	53
4700-5099	15
6000-7099	37
7100-9499	19

Chicago (Con.) 606

9500-12699	28
13000-13799	27
Chanay W	47
Chappel Ave S	
6700-7899	49
7900-OUT	17
12200-13799	33
Charles S	
9400-9499	20
9500-OUT	43
Charleston W	47
Charmaine Rd W	56
Chase Ave W	
1200-1999	26
2000-3999	45
4000-4899	46
7100-7799	48
Chelsea Pl W	43
Cheltenham Pl E	49
Cherry Ave N	
900-OUT	22
Cherry Ave W	
6800-6899	48
Cherry Ln N	
6400-7399	45
Chester Ave N	
4400-5599	56
8100-9199	48
Chestnut E	11
Chestnut W	
1-799	10
800-OUT	22
Chicago Ave E	11
Chicago Ave W	
1-799	10
800-3199	22
3200-5999	51
Chicago Beach Dr S	15
Chicora Ave N	46
Childrens Plz W	14
Chippewa Ave S	
11600-12199	17
13800-13999	33
Christiana Ave N	
400-799	24
800-1199	51
2800-4399	18
4400-5599	25
5600-6399	59
6400-7199	45
Christiana Ave S	
300-399	24
1200-3499	23
4300-5499	32
5500-7499	29
7500-8699	52
10300-11499	55
Church S	43
Church St & Ter W	48
Churchill W	47
Churchill Ave W	
8000-8099	48
Churchill Cir N	
9000-9099	48
Cicero Ave N	
1-799	44
800-1599	51
1600-2799	39
2800-4399	41
4400-5599	30
5600-7399	46

Cicero Ave S	
1-1199	44
1200-4199	50
4200-5498 (EVEN)	38
4201-5499 (ODD)	32
5500-7099	38
7100-7499	29
7500-8299	52
8301-8699 (ODD)	52
11100-12899	58
Clara Dr W	48
Claremont Ave N	
300-799	12
800-1599	22
1600-2799	47
2800-4399	18
4400-5599	25
5600-6399	59
6400-7599	45
Claremont Ave S	
400-1199	12
1300-3499	08
3500-5499	09
5500-7499	36
7500-9499	20
9500-OUT	43
Clarence Ave W	31
Clarendon Ave N	
3900-4399	13
4400-OUT	40
Clark N	
1-149	02
150-299	01
300-1599	10
1600-2799	14
2800-3599	57
3600-4399	13
4400-5599	40
5600-6399	60
6400-7599	26
Clark S	
1-199	03
200-399	04
400-1599	05
1600-2199	16
13000-14599	27
Clark Dr W	42
Cleaver N	22
Cleveland W	
6800-7599	48
Cleveland Ave N	
800-1599	10
1600-OUT	14
Clifford Ave N	46
Clifton N	
4800-5199	56
8100-9199	48
Clifton Ave N	
1600-2799	14
2800-3599	57
3600-4399	13
4400-OUT	40
Clifton Park Ave S	42
Clinton N	06
Clinton S	
1-399	06
400-1599	07
1600-OUT	16
Clybourn Ave N	
1200-1565	10
1566-1599	22
1600-2799	14
2800-OUT	18

Clyde Ave S	
6700-7899	49
7900-12199	17
12200-13799	33
Coast Guard Dr S	49
Coles Ave S	
7100-7899	49
7900-OUT	17
Colfax Ave S	
7400-7899	49
7900-OUT	17
Columbia Ave W	
1000-1999	26
2000-3999	45
4000-4799	46
7600-7799	31
Columbus Ave W	
2400-2599	29
2600-4022	52
Columbus Dr S	
200-ONLY	03
201-399	04
400-OUT	05
Commercial Ave S	
7900-10399	17
12200-13499	33
Commons Dr N	56
Commonwealth Ave N	
2300-2399	14
2800-2999	57
Concord Ln N	48
Concord Pl W	
300-1199	14
1200-1999	22
2000-3999	47
4000-6399	39
Congress Pky E	05
Congress Pky W	
1-199	05
200-1599	07
1600-3199	12
3200-4599	24
4600-5999	44
Conrad W	48
Constance Ave S	
6700-7899	49
7900-12199	17
Coral Dr W	56
Corbett S	08
Corcoran Dr W	
(ODD)	44
Corliss Ave S	
10300-12699	28
13000-13799	27
Cornelia Ave W	
500-1999	57
2000-3999	18
4000-5599	41
5600-8399	34
Cornell Ave S	
4800-5499	15
5500-5599	37
6700-7899	49
7900-12199	17
Cortez W	
1200-3199	22
3200-5999	51
Cortland W	
1200-1429	14
1430-1999	22
2000-3999	47
4000-6399	39
6400-7799	35

Chicago (Con.)	606
Cortland Pky W	35
Cottage Grv Ave S	
2200-3499	16
3500-4699	53
4700-5499	15
5500-7099	37
7100-9499	19
9500-12999	28
13000-13799	27
Cottage Pl W	07
Couch Pl W	06
Coulter W	08
Country Club Dr S	42
Court Pl W	06
Courtland Ave N	
4400-5599	56
5600-5699	31
9000-9599	48
Courtland Ave W	
7900-8199	56
Coyle Ave W	
2400-3999	45
4000-4899	46
7200-7399	31
Crain W	48
Crandon Ave S	
6700-7899	49
7900-12199	17
12200-13799	33
Crawford Ave N	
6400-7399	46
Crawford Ave S	
8701-10299 (ODD)	42
10301-11099 (ODD)	55
11100-11499	55
11500-13299	58
Cregier Ave S	
6700-7899	49
7900-12199	17
Crescent Ave N	
4800-5599	56
5600-5699	31
Cressett Dr W	35
Crestline W	52
Crilly Ct N	14
Croissant Dr S	33
Croname Rd N	48
Crosby S	10
Crowell S	08
Crystal W	
1300-3199	22
3200-5999	51
Cullerton E	16
Cullerton W	
1-799	16
800-2799	08
2800-4599	23
Cullom Ave W	
900-1999	13
2000-3999	18
4000-5599	41
5600-8399	34
Cumberland Ave N	
4400-5299	56
5600-5999	31
8000-9199	48
Cuyler Ave W	
800-1999	13
2000-3999	18
4000-5599	41
5600-7199	34

Cyril Ct S	49
Czagany Ave N	56
Bakin W	
800-1999	13
2000-3999	18
4000-5599	41
5600-7999	34
Damen Ave N	
1-399	12
400-1599	22
1600-2799	47
2800-4399	18
4400-5599	25
5600-6399	59
6400-7599	45
Damen Ave S	
1-1199	12
1200-3499	08
3500-5499	09
5500-7499	36
7500-9499	20
9500-10099	43
Daniel Ave, S	
13000-13199	27
Dante Ave S	
6300-7099	37
7100-OUT	19
Dauphin Ave S	
8700-9299	19
10000-OUT	28
Davis W	48
Davlin Ct N	18
Davol S	43
Dawson Ave N	18
Days Ter N	48
Dayton N	
1400-1599	22
1600-2799	14
2800-3599	57
3600-4399	13
De Koven W	07
De Saible W	09
Dean N	22
Dearborn N	
1-149	02
150-299	01
300-OUT	10
Dearborn S	
1-199	03
200-399	04
400-799	05
1200-1599	05
1600-3499	16
3500-5499	09
13800-14599	27
Dearborn Pky N	10
Delaware Pl E	11
Delaware Pl W	10
Delphia Ave N	
4400-5599	56
8100-8399	48
Deming Pl W	
400-699	14
4000-6399	39
Dempster W	
7001-7999 (ODD)	48
7700-7998 (EVEN)	48
8000-8599	48
Denal N	56
Denvir Ave S	12
Desplaines N	
1-399	06
400-OUT	10

Desplaines S	
1-399	06
400-1199	07
1600-OUT	16
Devon Ave W	
1000-1999	60
2000-3999	59
4000-6399	46
6400-7799	31
Dewitt Pl N	11
Dexter Park Ave S	09
Dickens Ave W	
300-1999	14
2000-3999	47
4000-6399	39
6400-7999	35
Dickinson Ave N	41
District Blvd W	32
Diversey Ave W	
300-399	57
400-1999	14
2000-3999	47
4000-6399	39
6400-7999	35
Diversey Blvd W	
300-399	57
400-1999	14
2000-3999	47
4000-6399	39
6400-7999	35
Diversey Pky W	
300-399	57
400-1999	14
2000-3999	47
4000-6399	39
6400-7999	35
Division E	10
Division W	
1-799	10
800-3199	22
3200-5999	51
Dobson W	
6800-7599	48
Dobson Ave S	
7100-9499	19
9500-9899	28
13000-13799	27
Dominick N	14
Dorchester Ave S	
4700-5499	15
5500-7099	37
7100-9499	19
9500-OUT	28
Doty Ave S	
9500-10299	17
10300-12199	28
12200-12998 (EVEN)	28
12201-12999 (ODD)	33
Douglas Blvd W	23
Dover N	40
Dowagiac Ave N	46
Drake Ave N	
400-799	24
800-1199	51
1600-2799	47
2800-4399	18
4400-5599	25
5600-6399	59
6400-7199	45
Drake Ave S	
1400-3499	23
4300-5499	32

Chicago (Con.) 606

5500-7499	29
7500-8699	52
10300-11699	55
11900-13299	58
Draper W	14
Drew S	43
Drexel Ave S	
3900-4699	53
4700-5499	15
5500-7099	37
7100-9499	19
9500-9899	28
12700-12999	28
13000-13799	27
Drexel Blvd S	
3900-4699	53
4700-5499	15
5500-7099	37
7100-9499	19
9500-9899	28
13000-13799	27
Drexel Sq E	15
Drummond Pl W	
500-1499	14
2000-3999	47
4000-6399	39
Dunbar Ave S	19
Early Ave W	60
East Cir Ave N	31
East Brook Rd N	35
East End Ave S	
4800-5099	15
6700-7899	49
7900-12199	17
East Prairie Rd N	45
East River Rd N	
4800-5599	56
5600-5999	31
East View Park S	15
Eastlake Ter N	26
Eastman W	22
Eastwood Ave W	
800-1999	40
2000-3999	25
4000-6399	30
7000-8799	56
Eberhart Ave S	
3900-3999	53
6000-7099	37
7100-9499	19
9500-12699	28
13000-13399	27
Ebinger Br W	48
Edbrooke Ave S	
9900-12699	28
13000-14599	27
Eddy W	
1000-1999	57
2000-3999	18
4000-5599	41
5600-7999	34
Edens Pky N	30
Edgebrook Ter N	46
Edgewater Ave W	60
Edmaire W	43
Edmunds W	30
Edward Ct N	14
Eggleston Ave S	
5900-7499	21

7500-9499	20
9500-12999	28
13400-14599	27
Elaine Pl N	57
Elbridge Ave N	18
Eleanor N	08
Elias Ct S	08
Elizabeth N	
1-399	07
400-899	22
Elizabeth S	
4700-5499	09
5500-7499	36
7500-9499	20
10000-13199	43
Elizabeth W	
8000-8399	48
Elk Grv N	22
Ellen W	22
Elliot Ave S	17
Ellis Ave S	
2800-3299	16
3500-4699	53
4700-5499	15
5500-7099	37
7100-9499	19*
9500-12999	28
13000-13799	27
Ellis Park S	53
Elm E	11
Elm W	10
Elm Dr W	56
Elmdale Ave W	60
Elmgrove Dr W	35
Elmore N	48
Elmwood Pky	35
Elston Ave N	
800-1999	22
2000-2399	14
2400-2799	47
2800-4299	18
4300-4399	41
4400-5599	30
5600-6399	46
Emerald Ave S	
2400-3499	16
3500-5499	09
5500-7499	21
7500-9499	20
9500-13099	28
13800-14599	27
Emmett N	47
Engle Rd S	
4800-5099	58
12700-12799	58
Englewood Ave W	21
Entre Ave S	33
Erie E	11
Erie W	
1-799	10
800-1999	22
2000-3199	12
3200-4599	24
4600-5999	44
Ernst Ct N	11
Escanaba Ave S	
7800-7899	49
7900-12199	17
12200-13299	33
Esmond S	43
Essex Ave S	
7500-7899	49

7900-12199	17
Estes Ave W	
1300-1999	26
2000-3999	45
4000-6399	46
7200-7799	31
Euclid Ave S	
6700-7899	49
7900-12199	17
Euclid Pky S	49
Eugenie W	14
Evans Ave S	
4200-4699	53
4700-5099	15
6000-7099	37
7100-9499	19
10300-10799	28
13000-13799	27
Evelyn Ln W	56
Everell Ave W	31
Everett Ave S	
5400-5499	15
5500-OUT	37
Evergreen Ave W	
200-799	10
800-3199	22
3200-OUT	51
Evergreen Park Arc S	42
Evergreen Park Plz S	42
Ewing Ave S	17
Exchange Ave S	
7100-7899	49
7900-12199	17
12200-13399	33
Exchange Ave W	09
Executive Ct W	56
Fair Pl W	10
Fairbanks Ct N	11
Fairfield Ave N	
200-799	12
800-1599	22
1600-2799	47
2800-3199	18
4400-5599	25
5600-6399	59
6400-7599	45
Fairfield Ave S	
900-1199	12
1200-2199	08
4100-5499	32
5500-7499	29
7500-8699	52
8700-10299	42
10300-11499	55
Fairview Ave N	
5500-5599	56
5600-5899	31
Fargo Ave W	
1300-1999	26
2000-3199	45
6800-7799	48
Farnsworth Dr N	48
Farragut Ave W	
1400-1999	40
2000-3999	25
4000-6399	30
6400-8399	56
Farrell S	08
Farwell Ave W	
1100-1999	26
2000-3999	45
4000-4899	46
7200-7399	31

Chicago (Con.)　　　　　　606

Federal S
　300-399............................04
　400-1599..........................05
　1600-3499........................16
　3500-5499........................09
Felton Ct N..........................10
Ferdinand W
　1400-1999........................22
　2000-2399........................12
　3600-4599........................24
　4600-OUT.........................44
Fern Ct N.............................14
Fey Ln S..............................58
Field Dr N............................48
Fielding Ave S.....................20
Fillmore W
　1300-1599........................07
　1600-3199........................12
　3200-4599........................24
　4600-5999........................44
First National Plz S...............70
Fitch Ave W
　2000-3999........................45
　4000-4899........................46
　5800-6399........................46
　7200-7999........................31
Fletcher W
　700-1999..........................57
　2000-3999........................18
　4000-5599........................41
　5600-7199........................34
　7200-7999........................35
Flournoy W
　1200-1599........................07
　1600-3199........................12
　3200-4599........................24
　4600-5999........................44
Ford Ave S...........................16
Ford City Dr W.....................52
Forest Ave S
　9100-9499........................19
　9500-11499......................28
　13000-13799....................27
Forest Glen Ave N
　5300-5599........................30
　5600-6399........................46
Forest Preserve Ave W
　6400-6699........................56
　6700-8399........................34
Forest View Dr W.................48
Forestview Ave N.................56
Forrestville Ave S
　4300-4699........................53
　4700-5099........................15
　11100-11499....................28
　13000-13499....................27
Foster Ave W
　900-1999..........................40
　2000-3999........................25
　4000-6399........................30
　6400-9399........................56
　9400-9998 (EVEN).............56
Foster Ln W
　8000-8199........................48
Foster Pl & Ter W.................56
Francis Pl W........................47
Francisco Ave N
　1-799..............................12
　800-1599..........................22
　1600-2799........................47

2800-4399...........................18
4400-5599...........................25
5600-6399...........................59
6400-7599...........................45
Francisco Ave S
　1-1199............................12
　2400-3499........................23
　3500-5499........................32
　5500-7499........................29
　7500-8699........................52
　8700-10299......................42
Frank Pky N..........................56
Franklin N
　1-299..............................06
　300-OUT...........................10
Franklin S
　1-399..............................06
　400-OUT...........................07
Franklin Blvd W
　3000-3199........................12
　3200-OUT.........................24
Franks Ave N.......................48
Fremont N
　1400-1599........................22
　1600-2299........................14
　3200-3599........................57
　3600-3999........................13
Front Ave S..........................28
Frontier Ave N
　1200-1599........................10
　3900-OUT.........................13
Fry W...................................22
Fuller W...............................08
Fullerton Ave W
　300-1999..........................14
　2000-3999.........................47
　4000-6399........................39
　6400-7999........................35
Fulton W
　400-799............................06
　800-1599..........................07
　1600-3199........................12
　3200-4599........................24
　4600-5999........................44
Fulton Market W
　600-799............................06
　800-OUT...........................07
Gale W.................................30
Gale Ter N............................48
Garfield Blvd E
　1-399 (ODD).....................37
　2-398 (EVEN)....................15
Garfield Blvd W
　1-1199 (ODD)...................21
　2-2398 (EVEN)..................09
　1201-2399 (ODD)..............36
Garibaldi Pl S.......................07
Garvey Ct N.........................01
Gaslight Sq W
　3700-3899........................58
Geneva Ter N.......................14
Genoa Ave S
　8700-9499........................20
　9500-OUT.........................43
George W
　800-1999..........................57
　2000-3999........................18
　4000-5599........................41
　5600-7199........................34
　7200-7799........................35
Georgia Dr W.......................48
Germania Pl W.....................10

Gettysburg W.......................30
Giddings W
　2000-3999........................25
　4000-6399........................30
　7700-8799........................56
Gilbert Ct S..........................20
Giles Ave S
　3100-3499........................16
　3500-OUT.........................53
Givins Ct S...........................20
Gladys Ave W
　700-799............................06
　800-1399..........................07
　2100-2799........................12
　3300-4599........................24
　4600-OUT.........................44
Glen Ln W............................27
Glendale Ln N......................48
Glenlake Ave W
　900-1999..........................60
　2000-3999........................59
　4000-6399........................46
　7700-7899........................31
Glenroy Ave S......................43
Glenwood Ave N
　4900-5599........................40
　5600-6399........................60
　6400-7799........................26
Goethe St E & W...................10
Golf Rd W
　8001-8499 (ODD)..............48
　8500-8599........................48
Goodman W.........................30
Gordon Ter W.......................13
Grace W
　600-1999..........................13
　2000-3999........................18
　4000-5599........................41
　5600-8399........................34
Grace Ave N........................48
Grady Ct S............................08
Graham Ct N........................10
Grand N
　8800-8999........................48
Grand Ave E.........................11
Grand Ave W
　1-799..............................10
　800-1999..........................22
　2000-2899........................12
　2900-3199........................22
　3200-4341........................51
　4342-6399........................39
　6400-7999........................35
Grand Ct N
　8100-8199........................48
Grant Pl W............................14
Granville Ave W
　900-1999..........................60
　2000-3999........................59
　4000-6399........................46
Gratten Ave S.......................08
Green N
　1-399..............................07
　400-OUT...........................22
Green S
　1-599..............................07
　2400-3299........................08
　4700-5499........................09
　5500-7499........................21
　7500-9499........................20
　9500-13199......................43

Chicago (Con.) 606

Green Bay Ave S
| 8100-12199 | 17 |
| 12200-14499 | 33 |

Greendale Ave W 48

Greenleaf Ave W
1000-1999	26
2000-3999	45
4000-6399	46
7000-8399	48
7200-7499	31

Greenview Ave N
800-1699	22
2200-2799	14
2800-3599	57
3600-4399	13
4400-5599	40
5600-6399	60
6400-7799	26

Greenwood Ave N
4800-5199	56
8100-8599	48
8601-9799 (ODD)	48

Greenwood Ave S
4200-4699	53
4700-5499	15
5500-7099	37
7100-9499	19
9500-9899	28
13000-13799	27

Gregory W
1400-1999	40
2000-3999	25
4000-6399	30
6400-8799	56

Grennan Pl W 48

Grenshaw W
300-1599	07
1600-3199	12
3200-OUT	24

Gresham Ave N 18
Gross Point Rd W 48
Grove S 16
Groveland Park E 16
Grover W 30

Gunnison W
800-1299	40
2400-3099	25
4400-6399	30
6400-8399	56

Haddon Ave W
| 1300-3199 | 22 |
| 3200-5999 | 51 |

Haft W 46

Haines W
| 700-799 | 10 |
| 800-OUT | 22 |

Hale Ave S 43

Halsted N
1-399	06
400-1599	22
1600-2799	14
2800-3599	57
3600-OUT	13

Halsted S
1-399	06
400-1599	07
1600-3499	08
3500-5499	09
5500-7499	21
7500-9499	20

9500-12299	28
12300-12698 (EVEN)	43
12301-12699 (ODD)	28
12700-12999	28
13000-14599	27

Hamlin Ave N
| 5600-6399 | 59 |

Hamilton Ave N
2200-2799	47
2800-4399	18
4400-4999	25
5600-6399	59
6400-7599	45

Hamilton Ave S
1-1199	12
1700-3499	08
3500-4299	09
5500-7499	36
7500-9499	20
9500-10699	43

Hamilton Dr W 48
Hamlet Ave S 43

Hamlin Ave N
1-799	24
800-1599	51
1600-2799	47
2800-4399	18
4400-5599	25
5600-6399	59
6400-7199	45
7227-7227	45

Hamlin Ave S
1-599	24
1400-3499	23
3500-5499	32
5500-7499	29
7500-8699	52
8700-10299	42
10300-11899	55
11900-13299	58

Hamlin Ct S 58
Hampden Ct N 14
Harbor Ave S 17

Harding Ave N
1-799	24
800-1599	51
1600-2799	47
2800-4399	18
4400-5599	25
5600-6399	59
6400-7399	45

Harding Ave S
1200-3499	23
3500-5499	32
5500-7499	29
7500-8699	52
8700-10299	42
10300-11899	55
11900-13299	58

Harlem Ave N
1600-2999	35
3000-4399	34
4400-5599	56
5600-7199	31
7200-8799	48

Harlem Ave S
| 5101-7499 (ODD) | 38 |

Harper Ave S
5000-5499	15
5500-7099	37
7100-9499	19
9500-9899	28

Harrison E 05

Harrison W
1-199	05
200-1599	07
1600-3199	12
3200-4599	24
4600-5999	44

Harrison, W, W
| 8201-8399 (ODD) | 48 |

Hart N 22
Hartland Ct N 22
Harts Rd W 48
Hartwell Ave S 37
Harvard W 48

Harvard Ave S
6300-7499	21
7500-9499	20
9500-13099	28

Haskins Ave N 26
Hastings W 08
Haussen Ct N 18
Hawthorne Pl W 57
Hayes Ave W 31
Hayes Dr S 49
Hayford W 52
Haynes Ct S 08

Hazel N
| 4200-4399 | 13 |
| 4400-OUT | 40 |

Heath Ave S 08

Henderson W
1200-1999	57
2700-3999	18
4000-5599	41
5600-7199	34

Henry Ct W 47
Hermione W 46

Hermitage Ave N
1-399	12
400-1999	22
2000-2799	14
2800-3599	57
3600-4399	13
4400-5599	40
5600-6399	60
6400-7799	26

Hermitage Ave S
1-1199	12
3400-3499	08
3500-5499	09
5500-7499	36
7500-9499	20

Hermosa Ave S 43
Hiawatha Ave N 46
Hickory Ave N 22

Higgins Ave W
5400-6399	30
6400-7499	56
7500-8399	31
8401-8999 (ODD)	31

Highland Ave W
1400-1999	60
2000-3999	59
4000-6399	46
6400-7399	31

Highlawn Ave S 27
Hill W 10
Hillock Ave S 08
Hirsch W
| 2200-3199 | 22 |
| 3200-5999 | 51 |

Hobart Ave W 31
Hobbie W 10

Chicago (Con.)   606

Hobson Ave N................................ 14
Hoey S... 08
Holbrook W.................................... 46
Holden Ct S
  400-1599.................................... 05
  1600-OUT................................... 16
Holland Rd S................................. 20
Holly Ave N
  2000-2099.................................. 14
  2600-OUT................................... 47
Hollywood Ave W
  900-1999.................................... 60
  2000-3999.................................. 59
  4000-6399.................................. 46
Homan Ave N
  1-799... 24
  800-OUT..................................... 51
Homan Ave S
  1-1199....................................... 24
  1200-3499.................................. 23
  3500-5499.................................. 32
  5500-7499.................................. 29
  7500-8699.................................. 52
  8700-10299................................ 42
  10300-11899.............................. 55
  11900-12699.............................. 58
Homer W
  1500-1699.................................. 22
  2000-3999.................................. 47
  4000-6399.................................. 39
Homewood Ave S........................... 43
Honore N
  900-1999.................................... 22
  2000-2799.................................. 24
  2800-3599.................................. 57
  3600-4399.................................. 13
  5200-5299.................................. 40
  6700-7599.................................. 26
Honore S
  1-599... 12
  1500-1599.................................. 08
  3500-5499.................................. 09
  5500-7499.................................. 36
  7500-9499.................................. 20
  11800-12699.............................. 43
Hood Ave W
  1200-1999.................................. 60
  2000-3999.................................. 59
  7100-7799.................................. 31
Hooker N....................................... 22
Hopkins Pl W................................. 20
Hortense Ave W............................. 31
Houston Ave S
  8000-12199................................ 17
  12200-13499.............................. 33
Howard W
  1300-1999.................................. 26
  2001-3207 (ODD)........................ 45
  5601-5999 (ODD)........................ 48
  6000-7599.................................. 48
  7601-7799 (ODD)........................ 48
Howdy Ln W.................................. 58
Howe N
  1100-1299.................................. 10
  1800-OUT................................... 14
Howland Ave W............................. 20
Hoxie Ave S
  9400-12199................................ 17
  12200-14599.............................. 33
Hoyne Ave N
  1-799... 12

800-1599.................................... 22
1600-2799.................................. 47
2800-4399.................................. 18
4400-5599.................................. 25
5600-6399.................................. 59
6400-7599.................................. 45
Hoyne Ave S
  1-1199....................................... 12
  1200-3499.................................. 08
  3500-5499.................................. 09
  5500-7499.................................. 36
  7500-9499.................................. 20
  9500-11199................................ 43
Hoyt Ave S.................................... 08
Hubbard E..................................... 11
Hubbard W
  1-799... 10
  800-1999.................................... 22
  2000-3199.................................. 12
  4600-OUT................................... 44
Huber Ln N.................................... 48
Hudson Ave N
  600-1599.................................... 10
  1600-2199.................................. 14
  3100-3199.................................. 57
Huguelet Pl N................................ 11
Humboldt Blvd N........................... 47
Hunt Ave W................................... 20
Huntington W................................ 46
Hurlbut W...................................... 31
Huron E... 11
Huron W
  1-799... 10
  800-1999.................................... 22
  2000-3199.................................. 12
  3200-4599.................................. 24
  4600-5999.................................. 44
Hutchinson W
  600-1499.................................... 13
  2000-3999.................................. 18
  4000-OUT................................... 41
Hyacinth W.................................... 46
Hyde Park Blvd
  700-1799.................................... 15
  5000-5499.................................. 15
  5500-OUT................................... 37
Ibm Plz E...................................... 11
Ibsen W.. 31
Iglehart Ct S.................................. 16
Illinois E....................................... 11
Illinois S
  13700-14599.............................. 27
Illinois W....................................... 10
Imlay W... 31
Independence Blvd S
  500-1199.................................... 24
  1200-OUT................................... 23
Indian Rd N................................... 46
Indiana Ave S
  1200-1599.................................. 05
  1600-3499.................................. 16
  3500-4699.................................. 53
  4700-5499.................................. 15
  5500-7099.................................. 37
  7100-9499.................................. 19
  9500-12999................................ 28
  13000-14599.............................. 27
Indianapolis Ave S........................ 17
Ingleside Ave S
  4700-5499.................................. 15
  5500-7099.................................. 37
  7100-9499.................................. 19
  9500-12999................................ 28

13000-13799.............................. 27
Institute Pl W................................ 10
Ionia Ave N................................... 46
Iowa W
  500-799...................................... 10
  1800-3199.................................. 22
  3200-5999.................................. 51
Irene Ave N................................... 18
Iron S
  3200-3499.................................. 08
  3500-OUT................................... 09
Irving Park Rd W
  600-1999.................................... 13
  2000-3999.................................. 18
  4000-5599.................................. 41
  5600-8399.................................. 34
Isham Ave W................................. 31
Ivanhoe Dr E................................. 27
Ivanhoe Ter.................................. 27
Jackson E...................................... 04
Jackson W
  1-199... 04
  200-799...................................... 06
  800-1599.................................... 07
  1600-3199.................................. 12
  3200-4599.................................. 24
  4600-5999.................................. 44
James W.. 09
Janssen Ave N
  2200-2799.................................. 14
  2800-3599.................................. 57
  3600-4399.................................. 13
  4900-4999.................................. 40
Jarlath W
  2000-3999.................................. 45
  4000-4899.................................. 46
  7200-7799.................................. 48
Jarvis Ave W
  1200-1999.................................. 26
  2000-3399.................................. 45
  3801-3999 (ODD)........................ 45
  4001-4899 (ODD)........................ 46
  5600-7799.................................. 48
Jasper Pl S.................................... 09
Jean W.. 58
Jean Ave N.................................... 46
Jefferson N
  1-399... 06
  400-OUT..................................... 10
Jefferson S
  1-399... 06
  400-1599.................................... 07
  1600-OUT................................... 16
Jeffery Ave S
  6700-7899.................................. 49
  7900-12199................................ 17
  12200-13799.............................. 33
Jerome W
  2000-3199.................................. 45
  7200-7799.................................. 48
Jersey Ave N
  5600-6399.................................. 59
Jessie Ct N.................................... 12
Joalyce Ct S
  11801-11827 (ODD)..................... 58
Joalyce Dr S.................................. 58
Jobev Ln S.................................... 58
Joey Dr N...................................... 48
Johanna Dr W............................... 48
Jones N... 47
Jonquil Ter W
  1400-1799.................................. 26
  6800-7599.................................. 48

Chicago (Con.) 606

Jourdan Ct S	08
Julia Ct W	47
Julian W	22
Juneway Ter W	
1400-1899	26
Junior Ter W	13
Justine N	07
Justine S	
3300-3499	08
3500-5499	09
5500-7499	36
7500-9499	20
11500-13199	43
Kamerling Ave W	51
Karlov Ave N	
1-799	24
800-1599	51
1600-2799	39
2800-4399	41
4400-5599	30
5600-7399	46
Karlov Ave S	
1-1199	24
1200-3499	23
3900-5499	32
5500-7499	29
7500-8699	52
11500-13299	58
Kasson Ave N	30
Kay W	48
Kearsarge Ave N	41
Keating Ave N	
1200-1599	51
1600-2799	39
2800-4399	41
4400-5599	30
5600-7399	46
Keating Ave S	
3900-5499	32
5500-7499	29
7500-8699	52
Kedvale Ave N	
1-799	24
800-1599	51
1600-2799	39
2800-4399	41
4400-5599	30
5600-7399	46
Kedvale Ave S	
600-899	24
1200-3499	23
3900-5499	32
5500-7499	29
7500-8699	52
11500-13299	58
Kedzie Ave	
7000-8599	48
Kedzie Ave N	
1-799	12
800-1599	51
1600-2799	47
2800-4399	18
4400-5599	25
5600-6399	59
6400-7599	45
Kedzie Ave S	
1-1199	12
1200-3499	23
3500-5499	32
5500-7499	29
7500-8699	52

8700-10299	42
10300-11899	55
Keefe Ave S	37
Keeler Ave N	
1-799	24
800-1599	51
1600-2799	39
2800-4399	41
4400-5599	30
5600-7399	46
Keeler Ave S	
1-1199	24
1200-3499	23
3900-5499	32
5500-7499	29
7500-8699	52
11500-13299	58
Keeley S	08
Keene Ave N	46
Keeney W	48
Kelso Ave N	30
Kemper Pl W	14
Kendall W	12
Kenmore Ave N	
1800-2799	14
2800-3599	57
3600-4399	13
4400-5599	40
5600-6399	60
Kenneth Ave N	
200-299	24
1600-2799	39
2800-4399	41
4400-5599	30
5600-7399	46
Kenneth Ave S	
600-899	24
1200-3499	23
4000-5499	32
5500-7499	29
7500-8699	52
11500-11699	58
Kennicott Ave N	30
Kennison Ave N	30
Kenosha Ave N	41
Kensington Ave E	28
Kenton Ave N	
1-799	44
1600-2799	39
2800-4399	41
4400-5599	30
5600-7399	46
Kenton Ave S	
1-1199	44
1200-3499	23
3900-5499	32
5500-7499	29
7500-8699	52
11500-11699	58
Kentucky Ave N	30
Kenwood Ave S	
4700-5499	15
5500-7099	37
7100-9499	19
9500-OUT	28
Keokuk Ave N	30
Keota Ave N	46
Kerbs N	46
Kercheval Ave N	46
Kerfoot Ave S	20
Kewanee Ave N	30
Keystone Ave N	
1-799	24

800-1599	51
1600-2799	39
2800-4399	41
4400-5599	30
5600-7399	46
Kilbourn Ave N	
1-799	24
800-1599	51
1600-2799	39
2800-4399	41
4400-5599	30
5600-7399	46
Kilbourn Ave S	
1-1199	24
1200-3499	23
4100-5499	32
5500-7499	29
7500-8699	52
11500-11699	58
Kildare Ave N	
1-799	24
800-1599	51
1600-2799	39
2800-4399	41
4400-5599	30
5600-7399	46
Kildare Ave S	
1-1199	24
1200-3499	23
3900-5499	32
5500-7499	29
7500-8699	52
11500-13299	58
Kilpatrick Ave N	
1-799	44
800-1599	51
1600-2799	39
2800-4399	41
4400-5599	30
5600-7399	46
Kilpatrick Ave S	
1-1199	44
3900-5499	32
5500-7499	29
7500-8699	52
Kimball Ave N	
1600-2799	47
2800-4399	18
4400-5599	25
5600-6399	59
6400-7199	45
Kimbark Ave S	
4700-5499	15
5500-7099	37
7100-9499	19
9500-OUT	28
Kimberly Ave N	30
King (Martin Luther Jr) Dr, S	
1200-1599	05
1600-3499	16
3500-4699	53
4700-5499	15
5500-7099	37
7100-9499	19
9500-12999	28
13000-13799	27
Kingsbury N	
300-1199	10
1200-1599	22
1600-OUT	14
Kingsdale Ave N	46
Kingston Ave S	
7300-7899	49

Chicago (Con.) 606

Kinzie E	11
Kinzie W	
1-799	10
800-1999	22
2000-3199	12
3200-4599	24
4600-OUT	44
Kinzua Ave N	46
Kiona Ave N	30
Kirby Ave N	46
Kirk W	48
Kirkland Ave S	
2200-2499	23
7900-8699	52
Kirkwood Ave N	46
Knight Ave N	
4800-5199	56
8200-8399	48
Knox Ave N	
1600-2799	39
2800-4399	41
4400-5599	30
5600-7399	46
Knox Ave S	
3900-5499	32
5500-7499	29
7500-8699	52
11500-11699	58
Kolin Ave N	
1-799	24
800-OUT	51
Kolin Ave S	
1200-3499	23
4000-5499	32
5500-7499	29
7500-8699	52
11500-13299	58
Kolmar Ave N	
200-799	24
800-1599	51
1600-2799	39
2800-4399	41
4400-5599	30
5600-7399	46
Kolmar Ave S	
1-1199	24
1200-3499	23
4100-5499	32
5500-7499	29
7500-8699	52
11500-11699	58
Komensky Ave S	
1200-3499	23
3900-5499	32
5500-7499	29
7500-8699	52
11500-13299	58
Kostner Ave N	
1-799	24
800-1599	51
1600-2799	39
2800-4399	41
4400-5599	30
5600-7399	46
Kostner Ave S	
1-1199	24
1200-3499	23
3500-5499	32
5500-7499	29
7500-8699	52
11500-13299	58

Kroll Dr S	58
Kruger Ave N	30
La Crosse Ave N	
100-299	44
1600-2799	39
2800-4399	41
4400-5599	30
5600-6399	46
La Crosse Ave S	
4300-7499	38
11500-12999	58
La Salle N	
1-149	02
150-299	01
300-1599	10
1600-OUT	14
La Salle S	
1-199	03
200-399	04
400-999	05
1600-3499	16
3500-5499	09
5500-7499	21
7500-9499	20
9500-12899	28
13700-14599	27
Lacey Ave N	46
Lafayette Ave S	
5500-7499	21
7500-9499	20
9500-12799	28
Laflin N	07
Laflin S	
1-1199	07
1200-3499	08
3500-5499	09
5500-7499	36
7500-9499	20
11000-13199	43
Laflin Pl S	09
Lake E	01
Lake W	
1-199	01
200-799	06
800-1599	07
1600-3199	12
3200-4599	24
4600-5999	44
8000-8199	48
Lake Park Ave S	
2300-3499	16
3500-4699	53
4700-5499	15
5500-5699	37
Lake Park Ave S	
7100-OUT	49
Lake Shore Dr N	
100-1199	11
1200-1599	10
2800-3599	57
3600-4399	13
4400-5599	40
Lake Shore Dr S	
1200-1599	05
1600-OUT	16
Lake Shore Plz N	11
Lakeside Pl W	40
Lakeview Ave N	14
Lakewood Ave N	
2000-2799	14
2800-3599	57
3600-3999	13
5200-5599	40

5600-6399	60
6400-6999	26
Lamon Ave N	
1-799	44
800-1599	51
1600-2799	39
2800-4399	41
4400-5599	30
5601-7399 (ODD)	46
Lamon Ave S	
4300-7499	38
11500-12999	58
Landers Ave N	46
Langley Ave S	
3700-4699	53
4700-4999	15
6000-7099	37
7100-9499	19
9500-12999	28
13000-13799	27
Lansing Ave N	46
Laporte Ave N	
1-799	44
1600-2799	39
2800-4399	41
4400-5599	30
5600-6799	46
Laporte Ave S	
4300-7499	38
11900-12999	58
Laramie Ave N	
1-799	44
800-1599	51
1600-2799	39
2800-4399	41
4400-OUT	30
Laramie Ave S	
1-1199	44
1200-3899	50
4300-7499	38
11900-12799	58
Larchmont Ave W	13
Larcom Ave W	46
Larned Ave N	30
Larrabee N	
600-1599	10
1600-OUT	14
Las Casas Ave N	46
Latham Ave N	30
Latrobe Ave N	
1-799	44
800-1599	51
1600-2799	39
2800-4399	41
4400-OUT	30
Latrobe Ave S	
4700-7499	38
Lauren Ln N	48
Lavergne Ave N	
1-799	44
800-1599	51
1600-2799	39
2800-4399	41
4400-OUT	30
Lavergne Ave S	
1-1199	44
4300-7499	38
11900-12999	58
Lawler W	
7400-7599	48
Lawler Ave N	
400-799	44
800-1599	51

Street	
Chicago (Con.)	606
1600-2799	39
2800-4399	41
4400-OUT	30
Lawler Ave S	
4300-7499	38
11900-12999	58
Lawndale Ave N	
400-799	24
800-1599	51
1600-2799	47
2800-4399	18
4400-5599	25
5600-6399	59
6400-7199	45
Lawndale Ave S	
1-1199	24
1200-3499	23
3500-5499	32
5500-7499	29
7500-8699	52
8700-10299	42
10300-11899	55
11900-13299	58
Lawrence Ave W	
700-1999	40
2000-3999	25
4000-6399	30
6400-8799	56
Le Mai Ave N	46
Le Moyne W	
1200-3199	22
3200-5999	51
Leader Ave N	46
Leamington Ave N	
1-799	44
800-1599	51
1600-2799	39
2800-4399	41
4400-OUT	30
Leamington Ave S	
1-1199	44
4300-7499	38
11900-12799	58
Leavenworth Ave N	30
Leavitt N	
1-799	12
800-1599	22
1600-2799	47
2800-4399	18
4400-5599	25
5600-6399	59
6400-7599	45
Leavitt S	
1-1199	12
1200-3499	08
3500-5499	09
5500-7499	36
7500-9499	20
9500-OUT	43
Leclaire Ave N	
1-799	44
800-1599	51
1600-2799	39
2800-4399	41
4400-OUT	30
Leclaire Ave S	
4300-7499	38
11900-12799	58
Lee W	
7100-8399	48
Lee Pl W	12
Lee Rd S	
11500-11699	58
Legett Ave N	46
Lehigh Ave N	
6100-7199	46
7200-7999	48
Lehmann Ct N	14
Leland Ave W	
700-1999	40
2000-3999	25
4000-6399	30
6800-8799	56
Lemont Ave N	46
Lenox Ave N	46
Leona Ave N	46
Leonard Ave N	
5400-5599	30
5600-5999	46
Leonard Dr Dr N	56
Leonora Ave N	35
Leoti Ave N	46
Leroy Ave N	46
Lessing N	22
Lester Ave N	30
Levee N	08
Lexington W	
500-1599	07
2000-3199	12
3200-4599	24
4600-5999	44
Lexington Ln N	48
Leyden Ave S	27
Liano Ave N	30
Liberty W	
500-799	07
1000-OUT	08
Lieb Ave N	30
Lightfoot Ave N	46
Lill W	
7100-7399	48
Lill Ave W	
800-1499	14
Lill Ct W	
7800-7899	48
Lincoln S	
12300-12699	43
Lincoln Ave N	
1800-2799	14
2800-3599	57
3600-3999	13
4000-4399	18
4400-5599	25
5600-6399	59
6400-6749	45
6750-7399	46
Lincoln Ln N	48
Lincoln Park West N	14
Lincolnwood Dr N	46
Lind Ave N	30
Linden Ave N	
5400-5599	56
Linden Pl N	
1600-2599	47
Linder Ave N	
1200-1599	51
1600-2799	39
2800-4399	41
4400-5599	30
5600-6399	46
Linder Ave S	
4700-7499	38
Linecrest Dr W	58
Linn White Dr S	05
Lipps Ave N	30
Lister Ave N	14
Lituanica Ave S	
3100-3499	08
3500-OUT	09
Livermore Ave N	46
Lloyd Ave S	08
Lock S	08
Lockwood Ave N	
1-799	44
800-1599	51
1600-2799	39
2800-4399	41
4400-5599	30
5600-6799	46
Lockwood Ave S	
1-1199	44
4700-7499	38
Locust W	10
Logan Blvd W	47
Loleta Ave N	46
Lomax Pl W	07
Lombard Ave S	
1201-3899 (ODD)	50
Lombard Ln S	58
London Ave N	30
Long Ave N	
1-799	44
800-1599	51
1600-2799	39
2800-4399	41
4400-OUT	30
Long Ave S	
4700-7499	38
Longmeadow Ave N	46
Longwood Ave S	
8700-9499	20
9500-11899	43
Longwood Blvd	
8700-9499	20
9500-11899	43
Longwood Dr	
8700-9499	20
9500-11899	43
Loomis N	07
Loomis Blvd S	
7500-9499	20
Loomis Blvd S,	
1-1199	07
1200-3499	08
3500-5499	09
5500-7499	36
7500-13199	43
Loomis Pl S	09
Loras Ln N	48
Lorel Ave N	
1-799	44
800-1599	51
1600-2799	39
2800-OUT	41
Lorel Ave S	
4700-7499	38
Loring Ave N	30
Loron Ave N	46
Lothair Ave S	43
Lotus Ave N	
1-799	44
800-1599	51
1600-2799	39
2800-4399	41
4400-OUT	30

Chicago (Con.) 606

Lotus Ave S
 1-1199........................ 44
 4700-7499.................. -38
Louise Ave N.................. 46
Lovejoy Ave N............... 30
Loveland S.................... 58
Lowe Ave S
 2400-3499................... 16
 3500-5499................... 09
 5500-7499................... 21
 7500-9499................... 20
 9500-13099................. 28
 13100-14599............... 27
Lowell Ave N
 1600-2799................... 39
 2800-4399................... 41
 4400-5599................... 30
 5600-7399................... 46
Loyola Ave W
 1000-1999................... 26
 2000-3999................... 45
Lucerne Ave N............... 46
Ludlam Ave N................ 30
Luella Ave S
 7100-7899................... 49
 7900-12199................. 17
 12200-13799............... 33
Lumber S
 1200-1599................... 07
 1600-2399................... 16
 2400-OUT.................... 08
Luna Ave N
 1200-1599................... 51
 1600-2799................... 39
 2800-4399................... 41
 4400-5599................... 30
 5600-6399................... 46
Luna Ave S
 4700-7499................... 38
Lundy Ave N.................. 46
Lunt Ave W
 1100-1999................... 26
 2000-3999................... 45
 4000-4899................... 46
 5400-5599................... 46
 7200-7799................... 31
Luther W....................... 08
Lutz Pl W...................... 10
Lyman S........................ 08
Lynch Ave N.................. 30
Lyndale W
 2000-3999................... 47
 4000-6399................... 39
Lyon Ave S.................... 19
Lyons W........................ 48
Lytle S.......................... 07
Mackinaw Ave S
 7900-12199................. 17
 13000-14399............... 33
Madison E
 1-50........................... 02
 51-69 (ODD)................ 03
 52-68 (EVEN)............... 02
 70-OUT....................... 02
Madison W
 1-199......................... 02
 200-799...................... 06
 800-1599.................... 07
 1600-3199.................. 12
 3200-4599.................. 24
 4600-5999.................. 44

 6800-8799.................. 48
Madison Ct W................ 48
Madison Park E.............. 15
Magnet Ave N................ 30
Magnolia Ave N
 1400-1699................... 22
 1900-2799................... 14
 3600-4399................... 13
 4400-5599................... 40
 5600-6399................... 60
 6400-6599................... 26
Main W......................... 48
Major Ave N
 1600-2799................... 39
 2800-4399................... 34
 4400-5599................... 30
 5600-6399................... 46
Major Ave S
 4900-7499................... 38
Malden N....................... 40
Malta S......................... 43
Mandell Ave N............... 46
Mango Ave N
 1600-2799................... 39
 2800-4399................... 34
 4400-5599................... 30
 5600-6399................... 46
Manila Ave N................. 30
Manistee Ave S
 7900-12199................. 17
 12200-14599............... 33
Mankato Ave N.............. 46
Manor Ave N.................. 25
Manor Ln N
 5400-5599................... 56
 5600-5699................... 31
Manton Ave N................ 46
Maple W
 1-199......................... 10
 3200-3599.................. 42
Maple Ave W
 8100-8399.................. 56
Maplewood Ave N
 200-799...................... 12
 800-1599.................... 22
 1600-2799.................. 47
 2800-4299.................. 18
 4400-5599.................. 25
 5600-6399.................. 59
 6400-7599.................. 45
Maplewood Ave S
 300-799...................... 12
 3200-3499.................. 08
 3500-5499.................. 32
 5500-7499.................. 29
 7500-8699.................. 52
 8700-10299................ 42
 10300-11899.............. 55
Marble Pl W.................. 06
Marcey N....................... 14
Margate Ter W............... 40
Marine Dr N
 3900-4399.................. 13
 4400-OUT................... 40
Marion Ct N................... 22
Markham Ave N............. 46
Marmora Ave N
 1600-2799.................. 39
 2800-4399.................. 34
 4400-5599.................. 30
 5600-6399.................. 46
Marquette Ave S
 7500-7899.................. 49

 7900-12199................. 17
 12200-14599............... 33
Marquette Rd E & S........ 37
Marquette Rd W
 1-1199....................... 21
 1200-2399.................. 36
 2400-4799.................. 29
 4800-6399.................. 38
Marshall Blvd S.............. 23
Marshfield Ave N
 400-1999.................... 22
 2000-2799.................. 14
 2800-3599.................. 57
 3600-4399.................. 13
 7500-7799.................. 26
Marshfield Ave S
 1-1199....................... 12
 3400-3499.................. 08
 3500-5499.................. 09
 5500-7499.................. 36
 7500-9499.................. 20
 11900-12999.............. 43
Marshfield Ave S,
 11100-11199.............. 43
Marwood Ave W............. 35
Mary S.......................... 08
Maryland N
 8800-9599.................. 48
Maryland Ave S
 4900-5499.................. 15
 5500-7099.................. 37
 7100-9499.................. 19
 9500-10599................ 28
 13000-13799.............. 27
Mason Ave N
 1-799......................... 44
 800-1599.................... 51
 1600-2799.................. 39
 2800-4399.................. 34
 4400-5599.................. 30
 5600-7199.................. 46
Mason Ave S
 1-1199....................... 44
 4900-7499.................. 38
Massasoit Ave N
 800-OUT..................... 51
Massasoit Ave S
 5100-7499.................. 38
Matson Ave W................ 46
Maud Ave N................... 14
Mautene Ct N................ 22
Maxwell W
 500-799...................... 07
 800-OUT..................... 08
May N
 1-399......................... 07
 400-OUT..................... 22
May S
 600-1199.................... 07
 1200-3499.................. 08
 3500-5499.................. 09
 5500-7499.................. 21
 7500-9499.................. 20
 9500-13199................ 43
Mayfield Ave N
 1-799......................... 44
 800-1599.................... 5
 1600-OUT................... 39
Mayfield Ave S
 1-3199....................... 44
 5100-7499.................. 38
Maynard Dr N................ 48
Maynard Rd W............... 48

Chicago (Con.) 606

Maypole Ave W
1600-3199 ... 12
3200-4599 ... 24
4600-OUT ... 44
Mc Alpin Ave N ... 46
Mc Clellan Ave N ... 46
Mc Clurg Ct N ... 11
Mc Cook Ave N ... 46
Mc Cormick Blvd N
5600-6399 ... 59
6400-7299 ... 45
Mc Daniel S ... 58
Mc Dermott S ... 08
Mc Dowell Ave S ... 09
Mc Lean Ave W
1400-1999 ... 14
2000-3999 ... 47
4000-6399 ... 39
6400-7999 ... 35
Mc Leod Ave N ... 46
Mc Vicker Ave N
1600-2799 ... 39
2800-4399 ... 34
4400-5599 ... 30
5600-6399 ... 46
7200-7399 ... 48
Mc Vicker Ave S
5100-7499 ... 38
Mccarthy Dr S ... 16
Mcfetridge Dr E ... 05
Meacham Ct N ... 48
Meade Ave N
1600-2799 ... 39
2800-4399 ... 34
4400-5599 ... 30
5600-6399 ... 46
7200-7399 ... 48
Meade Ave S
5100-7499 ... 38
Meadow Ln Dr S
11500-11899 ... 55
Meadow Ln Dr W ... 55
Medford Ave N ... 46
Medill Ave W
1200-1799 ... 14
2000-3999 ... 47
4000-6399 ... 39
6400-7999 ... 35
Medina Ave N ... 46
Melrose W
400-1999 ... 57
2000-3999 ... 18
4000-5599 ... 41
5600-7999 ... 34
Melvina Ave N
1600-2799 ... 39
2800-4399 ... 34
4400-5599 ... 30
5600-7199 ... 46
7200-7499 ... 48
Melvina Ave S
5100-7499 ... 38
Memory Ln W ... 56
Menard Ave N
1-799 ... 44
800-1599 ... 51
1600-2799 ... 39
2800-4399 ... 34
4400-5599 ... 30
5600-6399 ... 46
7500-7599 ... 48

Menard Ave S
1-1199 ... 44
4900-7499 ... 38
Mendell N
1900-1999 ... 22
2000-OUT ... 14
Mendota Ave N ... 46
Menomonee W ... 14
Merchandise Mart Plz ... 54
Meredith Ave N ... 46
Merrill N
8000-8999 ... 48
Merrill Ave S
6700-7899 ... 49
7900-12199 ... 17
12200-13799 ... 33
Merrimac Ave N
1600-2799 ... 39
2800-4399 ... 34
4400-5599 ... 30
5600-7199 ... 46
7600-7899 ... 48
Merrimac Ave S
4800-7499 ... 38
Merrion Ave S ... 17
Metron Dr S ... 33
Metropole W, W ... 35
Meyer Ct N ... 14
Miami Ave W ... 46
Michigan N
5200-5299 ... 56
Michigan Ave N
1-149 ... 02
150-399 ... 01
400-OUT ... 11
Michigan Ave S
1-199 ... 03
200-399 ... 04
400-1599 ... 05
1600-3499 ... 16
3500-4699 ... 53
4700-5499 ... 15
5500-7099 ... 37
7100-9499 ... 19
9500-12699 ... 28
13000-14599 ... 27
Michigan Blvd N
1-149 ... 02
150-399 ... 01
400-OUT ... 11
Michigan Blvd S
1-199 ... 03
200-399 ... 04
400-1599 ... 05
1600-3499 ... 16
3500-4699 ... 53
4700-5499 ... 15
5500-7099 ... 37
7100-9499 ... 19
9500-12699 ... 28
13000-14599 ... 27
Midway Park W ... 44
Mildred Ave N
2600-2799 ... 14
2800-2999 ... 57
Millard Ave S
500-599 ... 24
1200-3499 ... 23
3500-5499 ... 32
5500-7499 ... 29
7500-8699 ... 52
8700-10299 ... 42
10300-11899 ... 55

Miller S
600-1199 ... 07
1200-OUT ... 08
Miltimore Ave N ... 46
Milwaukee Ave N
200-399 ... 06
400-499 ... 10
500-1599 ... 22
1600-2799 ... 47
2800-3299 ... 18
3300-4399 ... 41
4400-5599 ... 30
5600-6399 ... 46
6400-6599 ... 31
6600-9799 ... 48
Minerva Ave S ... 37
Minnehaha Ave N ... 46
Minnetonka Ave N ... 46
Mission Dr N ... 56
Mobile Ave N
1600-2799 ... 39
2800-4399 ... 34
4400-5599 ... 30
5600-7199 ... 46
Mobile Ave S
5100-7499 ... 38
Moffat W
2000-3999 ... 47
4000-6399 ... 39
Mohawk N
800-1599 ... 10
1600-OUT ... 14
Monitor Ave N
1000-1599 ... 51
1600-2799 ... 39
2800-4399 ... 34
4400-5599 ... 30
5600-6399 ... 46
Monitor Ave S
1-1199 ... 44
4900-7499 ... 38
Monon Ave N ... 46
Monroe E ... 03
Monroe W
1-199 ... 03
200-799 ... 06
800-1599 ... 07
1600-3199 ... 12
3200-4599 ... 24
4600-5999 ... 44
7000-8399 ... 48
Monroe Ct W
6900-7099 ... 48
Mont Clare Ave N
2300-2799 ... 35
2800-2999 ... 34
4400-5599 ... 56
Montana W
900-1699 ... 14
2000-2399 ... 47
4000-6399 ... 39
Monterey Ave N ... 56
Monterey Ave W
1600-1999 ... 43
Montgomery Ave S
2600-4199 ... 32
Monticello N
6400-7199 ... 45
Monticello Ave N
400-799 ... 24
800-1599 ... 51
1600-2799 ... 47
2800-4399 ... 18

Chicago (Con.)   606

4400-5599	25
5600-6399	59
6400-7199	45
Montrose Ave W	
600-1999	13
2000-3999	18
4000-5599	41
5600-8399	38
Montvale Ave W	43
Moody Ave N	
1600-2799	39
2800-4399	34
4400-5599	30
5600-7199	46
Moody Ave S	
5100-7499	38
Moore N	10
Moorman N	22
Moreland Ave N	56
Morgan N	
1-399	07
400-OUT	22
Morgan S	
1-1199	07
1200-3499	08
3500-5499	09
5500-7499	21
7500-9499	20
9500-13199	43
Morse Ave W	
1100-1999	26
2000-3999	45
4000-OUT	46
Moselle Ave N	46
Mozart N	
100-299	12
800-1599	22
1600-2799	47
2800-4399	18
4400-5599	25
5600-6399	59
6400-7599	45
Mozart S	
300-1199	12
3500-5499	32
5500-7499	29
7500-8699	52
8700-10299	42
Mulford W	48
Mulligan Ave N	
1600-2799	39
2800-4399	34
4400-5599	30
5600-6399	46
Mulligan Ave S	
5100-7499	38
Museum Dr E	37
Muskegon Ave S	
7700-7899	49
7900-12199	17
12200-13299	33
Myrick W	52
Myrtle Ave W	31
Nagle Ave N	
1600-2799	35
2800-4399	34
4400-4599	56
4600-5599	30
5600-7199	46
Nagle Ave S	
5100-7499	38

Naper Ave N	31
Naples Ave N	31
Napoleon Ave N	31
Narragansett Ave N	
1600-2799	39
2800-4399	34
4400-5599	30
Narragansett Ave S	
5100-7499	38
Nashotah Ave N	31
Nashville Ave N	
1600-2799	35
2800-4399	34
4400-5599	56
5600-6599	31
Nashville Ave S	
5100-7499	38
Nassau Ave N	31
Natchez Ave N	
1600-2799	35
2800-4399	34
4400-5599	56
7400-7599	48
Natchez Ave S	
5100-7499	38
National N	48
Natoma Ave N	
1600-2799	35
2800-4399	34
4400-5599	56
5600-6599	31
Natoma Ave S	
5100-7499	38
Navajo Ave N	46
Navarre Ave N	31
Navy Pier E	11
Neenah Ave N	
2800-4399	34
4400-5599	56
5600-6399	31
Neenah Ave S	
5100-7499	38
Nelson W	
800-1999	57
2000-2999	18
4000-5599	41
5600-7199	34
Neola Ave N	31
Nettleton Ave N	31
Neva Ave N	
1600-2799	35
2800-4399	34
4400-5599	56
5600-6599	31
7200-8399	48
Neva Ave S	
5100-7499	38
New England Ave N	
1600-2799	35
2800-4399	34
4400-5599	56
6400-6499	31
7200-8399	48
New England Ave S	
5100-7499	38
New Hampshire Ave N	31
Newark Ave N	
5600-6499	31
6500-7199	48
Newberry Ave S	
1000-1199	07
1200-OUT	08
Newburg Ave N	31

Newcastle Ave N	
1600-2799	35
2800-4399	34
4400-5599	56
5600-6699	31
8000-8299	48
Newcastle Ave S	
5100-7499	38
Newgard Ave N	26
Newland Ave N	
1600-2799	35
2800-4399	34
4400-5599	56
6400-6599	31
8000-8399	48
Newland Ave S	
5100-7499	38
Newport Ave W	
800-1999	57
2000-3999	18
4000-5599	41
5600-7999	34
Niagara Ave N	31
Nickerson Ave N	31
Nicolet Ave N	31
Niles Ave & Ter W	48
Nina Ave N	31
Nixon Ave N	31
Noble N	22
Nokomis Ave N	46
Nora Ave N	
2800-4399	34
7200-8099	48
Nordica Ave N	
1600-2799	35
2800-4399	34
4400-5599	56
5600-6699	31
7400-7999	48
Nordica Ave S	
5100-7499	38
Norma Ct N	48
Normal Ave S	
1600-3499	16
3500-5499	09
5500-7499	21
7500-9499	20
9500-12999	28
13000-14599	27
Normal Ave W	
8400-8799	48
Normal Blvd S	
1600-3499	16
3500-5499	09
5500-7499	21
7500-9499	20
9500-12999	28
13000-14599	27
Normal Pky W	21
Normandy Ave N	
1600-2799	35
2800-4399	34
4400-5599	56
6200-6699	31
7200-7599	48
Normandy Ave S	
5100-7499	38
Norridge W	56
North Ave W	
100-799	10
800-1999	22
2000-3999	47
4000-5999	39

Chicago (Con.) 606

North Blvd E	10
North Blvd W	
1-99	10
North Park Ave N	
1300-1599	10
1600-OUT	14
North Ter W	
8400-8799	48
North Branch N	22
North Shore Ave W	
1000-1999	26
2000-3999	45
4000-5399	46
7200-7799	31
North Water E	11
Northcott Ave N	31
Northwest Hwy N	
4800-5599	30
5600-5729	46
5730-OUT	31
Norton S	07
Norwood W	
1200-1999	60
2000-3999	59
6000-6399	46
7600-7899	31
Norwood Ct W	56
Nottingham Ave N	
2800-4399	34
4400-5599	56
5600-7199	31
7200-7799	48
Nottingham Ave S	
5100-7499	38
Nursery N	14
Oak E	11
Oak N	
4500-4599	56
Oak W	10
Oak Ave W	
8000-8599	48
Oak Ln W	48
Oak Park Ave N	
1600-2799	35
2800-4399	34
4400-5599	56
5600-6699	31
7200-7599	48
Oak Park Ave S	
5100-7499	38
Oak View N	56
Oakdale Ave W	
300-1999	57
2000-3999	18
4000-5599	41
5600-7299	34
Oakenwald Ave S	53
Oakland Cres S	53
Oakleaf Ave W	35
Oakley Ave N	
1-799	12
800-1599	22
1600-2799	47
2800-4399	18
4400-5599	25
5600-6399	59
6400-7599	45
Oakley Ave S	
1-1199	12
1200-3499	08
3500-5499	09

5500-7499	36
7500-9499	20
9500-11899	43
Oakley Blvd N	
1-799	12
800-1599	22
1600-2799	47
2800-4399	18
4400-5599	25
5600-6399	59
6400-7599	45
Oakley Blvd S	
1-1199	12
1200-3499	08
3500-5499	09
5500-7499	36
7500-9499	20
9500-11899	43
Oakton W	
6700-7999	48
8000-8398 (EVEN)	48
Oakton Ct W	
6700-7199	48
Oakwood Ave E	53
Oakwood Blvd	53
Obrien W	07
Oconto Ave N	
3000-3199	35
3200-4399	34
4400-5599	56
5600-7199	31
7200-8399	48
Octavia Ave N	
3000-3199	35
3200-4399	34
4400-5599	56
5600-7199	31
7200-8399	48
Odell Ave N	
3000-3199	35
3200-4399	34
4400-5599	56
5600-7199	31
7200-8399	48
Ogallah Ave N	31
Ogden Ave N	
1-399	07
400-1199	22
1200-1599	10
1600-OUT	14
Ogden Ave W	
1567-1599	07
1600-2299	12
2300-2799	08
2800-4599	23
4600-6199	50
Ogden Blvd W	
1567-1599	07
1600-2299	12
2300-2799	08
2800-4599	23
4600-6199	50
Oglesby Ave S	
6700-7899	49
7900-12199	17
12200-13799	33
Ohio E	11
Ohio W	
1-799	10
800-1999	22
2000-3199	12
3200-4599	24
4600-5999	44

Oketo Ave N	
3000-3199	35
3200-4399	34
4400-5599	56
5600-7199	31
7200-8799	48
Olcott Ave N	
3000-3199	35
3200-4399	34
4400-5599	56
5600-7199	31
7200-8799	48
Oleander Ave N	
3000-3199	35
3200-4399	34
4400-5599	56
5600-7199	31
7200-8799	48
Oliphant Ave N	31
Olive Ave W	
1400-1999	60
2000-3999	59
7200-7899	31
Olmsted Ave N	31
Olympia Ave N	
5000-5199	56
6000-6799	31
Onarga Ave N	31
Oneida Ave N	
5000-5199	56
6400-6799	31
Ontario E	11
Ontario W	
1-599	10
1600-1699	22
3900-OUT	24
Opal Ave N	
3200-4399	34
4400-5199	56
Orange Ave N	
3200-4399	34
4400-4999	56
5700-5799	31
Orchard N	
1200-1599	10
1600-2799	14
2800-3199	57
Orchard S	
11900-12799	58
Oriole Ave N	
3000-3199	35
3200-4399	34
4400-5599	56
5600-7199	31
7200-8799	48
Orleans N	
300-398 (EVEN)	10
301-399 (ODD)	54
400-1599	10
1700-2099	14
Osage Ave N	
3200-4399	34
4400-4799	56
5600-5799	31
Osceola Ave N	
3000-3199	35
3200-4399	34
4400-5599	56
5600-7199	31
7200-8399	48
Oshkosh Ave N	31
Oswego N	22
Otsego Ave N	31

Chicago (Con.)   **606**

Ottawa Ave N
3200-4399.......................... 34
4400-5599.......................... 56
5600-7199.......................... 31
7200-8799.......................... 48
Otto Ave N............................ 56
Overhill Ave N
3200-4399.......................... 34
4400-5599.......................... 56
5600-7199.......................... 31
7200-8799.......................... 48
Owen Ave N........................... 31
Oxford Ave N......................... 31
Ozanam Ave N
3200-4399.......................... 34
4400-5599.......................... 56
5600-7199.......................... 31
8000-8999.......................... 48
Ozark Ave N
3200-4399.......................... 34
4400-5599.......................... 56
5600-7199.......................... 31
7400-8799.......................... 48
Pacesetter Pky W.................... 27
Pacific Ave N......................... 34
Packers Ave S........................ 09
Page S
11900-12999........................ 43
Page Ave N
3200-3999.......................... 34
Palatine Ave N....................... 31
Palisades Dr W....................... 55
Palmer W
2000-3999.......................... 47
4000-6399.......................... 39
6400-7999.......................... 35
Panama Ave N
3200-3999.......................... 34
5400-5599.......................... 56
Paris Ave N
3200-3999.......................... 34
4400-5599.......................... 56
Park Ave W
5600-6199.......................... 50
7800-8599.......................... 48
Park Ln W............................ 48
Park Pl E............................. 37
Park Lane W.......................... 58
Parker Ave W
3000-3999.......................... 47
4000-6399.......................... 39
Parkside Ave N
1-799................................ 44
800-1599............................ 51
1600-2799.......................... 39
2800-4399.......................... 34
4400-5599.......................... 30
5600-6399.......................... 46
Parkside Ave S
1-1199.............................. 44
5100-7499.......................... 38
Parnell Ave S
2900-3499.......................... 16
3500-5499.......................... 09
5500-7499.......................... 21
7500-9499.......................... 20
9500-13099........................ 28
13100-14599....................... 27
Patterson Ave W
600-1999............................ 13

4000-5599.......................... 41
5600-7999.......................... 34
Paulina N
1-399................................ 12
400-1999............................ 22
2000-2799.......................... 14
2800-3599.......................... 57
3600-4399.......................... 13
4400-5599.......................... 40
5600-6399.......................... 60
6400-7799.......................... 26
Paulina S
1-1199.............................. 12
1200-3499.......................... 08
3500-5499.......................... 09
5500-7499.......................... 36
7500-9499.......................... 20
11600-12999....................... 43
Paxton Ave S
6700-7899.......................... 49
7900-12199........................ 17
12200-13799....................... 33
Pearl Ct N............................ 14
Pearson E............................ 11
Pearson W
1-799................................ 10
1500-OUT........................... 22
Pensacola Ave W
900-1999............................ 13
2000-3999.......................... 18
4000-5599.......................... 41
5600-8399.......................... 34
Peoria N
1-399................................ 07
400-OUT............................ 22
Peoria S
1-1199.............................. 07
1200-2699.......................... 08
3900-5499.......................... 09
5500-7499.......................... 21
7500-9499.......................... 20
9500-13199........................ 43
Perry Ave S
5500-7499.......................... 21
7500-9499.......................... 20
9500-12999........................ 28
13000-13699....................... 27
Pershing Pl W........................ 09
Pershing Rd E........................ 53
Pershing Rd W
1-2399.............................. 09
2400-4599.......................... 32
4600-6299.......................... 50
Peshtigo Ct N........................ 11
Peter Ter W.......................... 48
Peterson Ave W
1600-1999.......................... 60
2000-3999.......................... 59
4000-6399.......................... 46
6400-7899.......................... 31
Phillips Ave S
7200-7899.......................... 49
7900-12199........................ 17
Pierce Ave W
1600-3199.......................... 22
3200-OUT........................... 51
Pine Ave N
1-799................................ 44
800-OUT............................ 51
Pine Grv Ave N
2700-2799.......................... 14
2800-3599.......................... 57
3600-3999.......................... 13

Pioneer Ave N
3200-4199.......................... 34
4800-5599.......................... 56
Pippin W............................. 52
Pitney Ct S........................... 08
Pittsburgh Ave N
3200-4399.......................... 34
4800-5599.......................... 56
Plainfield Ave N
3200-4399.......................... 34
4400-5399.......................... 56
Pleasant Ave S....................... 20
Plymouth Ct S
300-399............................. 04
400-OUT............................ 05
Poe N................................. 14
Point N............................... 47
Polk W
1-199................................ 05
200-1599............................ 07
1600-3199.......................... 12
3200-4599.......................... 24
4600-5999.......................... 44
Ponchartrain Blvd N................. 46
Pontiac Ave N
3200-4399.......................... 34
4400-5299.......................... 56
Poplar Ave S......................... 08
Portland Ave S....................... 09
Potawatami N........................ 56
Potomac Ave W
1300-3199.......................... 22
3200-5999.......................... 51
Prairie Ave S
1600-3499.......................... 16
3500-4699.......................... 53
4700-5499.......................... 15
5500-7099.......................... 37
7100-9499.......................... 19
9500-12999........................ 28
13000-13799....................... 27
Pratt Ave W
1000-1999.......................... 26
2000-3999.......................... 45
4000-4899.......................... 46
4901-5599 (ODD)................... 46
7200-7799.......................... 31
Pratt Blvd W
1000-1999.......................... 26
2000-3999.......................... 45
4000-4899.......................... 46
4901-5599 (ODD)................... 46
7200-7799.......................... 31
Prescott Ave N....................... 46
Princeton Ave S
2200-3499.......................... 16
3500-5499.......................... 09
5500-7499.......................... 21
7500-9499.......................... 20
9500-12699........................ 28
Prindiville W......................... 47
Proesel Ave N........................ 45
Promontory Dr S..................... 49
Prospect Ave N
4800-5599.......................... 56
5600-5799.......................... 31
8000-9599.......................... 48
Prospect Ave S
9500-11099........................ 43
Prospect Ct W........................ 48
Prospect Sq S........................ 20
Prudential Plz E...................... 01
Pryor Ave W.......................... 43

Chicago (Con.)   606

Pueblo Ave N
3200-4399	34
4400-5599	56
5300-5399	56

Pulaski Rd N
1-799	24
800-1599	51
1600-2799	39
2800-4399	41
4400-5599	30
5600-6399	46

Pulaski Rd S
1-1199	24
1200-3899	23
3900-5499	32
5500-7499	29
7500-8699	52
8701-10299 (ODD)	42
10301-11099 (ODD)	55
11100-11499	55

Purple S | 16 |

Quincy W
1-199	04
200-799	06
800-1599	07
1700-1799	12
4800-5599	44

Quinn S | 08 |

Race Ave W
1200-1999	22
2000-2299	12
4600-5999	44

Racine Ave N
1-399	07
400-999	22
1900-2799	14
2800-3599	57
3600-4399	13
4400-OUT	40

Racine Ave S
1-1199	07
1200-3499	08
3500-5499	09
5500-7499	36
7500-9499	20
9500-13199	43

Railroad Ave S | 17 |

Ramona N | 46 |

Rance Ter W
2000-3999	45

Randolph E | 01 |

Randolph W
1-199	01
200-799	06
800-1599	07
3100-OUT	12

Rascher Ave W
1400-1999	40
2000-3999	25
4000-6399	30
6400-8799	56

Raven W
6200-6399	46
6400-6899	31

Ravenswood Ave N
2800-3599	57
3600-4399	13
4400-5599	40
5600-6399	60
6400-7799	26

Rays Ct S | 09 |

Redwood Dr N
4400-5599	56
5600-5799	31

Reilly Ter S | 52 |

Reserve Ave N | 56 |

Reta Ave N | 57 |

Rexford S | 58 |

Rhodes Ave S
3100-3499	16
3500-3999	53
6000-7099	37
7100-9499	19
9500-10899	28
13000-13399	27

Rice W
1800-3199	22
3200-5999	51

Richmond N
800-1599	22
1600-2799	47
2800-4399	18
4400-5599	25
5600-6399	59
6400-7599	45

Richmond S
300-399	12
1100-1199	12
3500-5499	32
5500-7499	29
7500-8699	52
8700-10299	42

Ridge Ave N
5600-6399	60
6400-6799	26
6800-7599	45

Ridge Blvd N
5600-6399	60
6400-6799	26
6800-7599	45

Ridge Rd N
5600-6399	60
6400-6799	26
6800-7599	45

Ridgeland Ave S
6700-7899	49
7900-12199	17

Ridgeway Ave N
400-799	24
800-1599	51
1600-2799	47
2800-4399	18
4400-5599	25
5600-6399	59
6400-7199	45

Ridgeway Ave S
1400-3499	23
3500-5499	32
5500-7499	29
7500-8699	52
8700-10299	42
10300-11899	55
11900-13299	58

Ridgewood Ave N
4800-5099	56

Ridgewood Ct S | 15 |

Ritchie Ct N | 10 |

River Rd N | 56 |

Riverdale Ave S | 27 |

Riverside Dr N
7100-7199	48

Riverside Plz N | 06 |

Riverside Plz S
1-99	06

Riverview Rd N | 48 |

Robbins Ter W | 13 |

Robin Rd N | 48 |

Robinson S | 08 |

Rochdale Pl E | 15 |

Rockwell N
200-799	12
800-1599	22
1600-2799	47
2800-4399	18
4400-5599	25
5600-6399	59
6400-7599	45

Rockwell S
1-1199	12
1200-3499	08
3500-5499	32
5500-7499	29
7500-8699	52
8700-10299	42
10301-11899	55

Rogers Ave N
5200-5599	30
5600-6099	46
6100-6399	59
6400-7299	45
7300-7699	26

Ronald N | 56 |

Roosevelt Rd E | 05 |

Roosevelt Rd W
1-299	05
300-799	07
800-2799	08
2800-3199	12
3200-4599	24
4600-5999	50
6001-6199 (ODD)	50

Root W | 09 |

Root St & Ct N | 48 |

Roscoe W
400-1999	57
2000-3999	18
4000-5599	41
5600-8399	34

Rose N | 56 |

Rosedale Ave W
1200-1399	60
4000-6399	46
7400-7899	31

Rosehill Dr W | 60 |

Rosemary Ln N | 48 |

Rosemary Ln S
11700-11899	58

Rosemont Ave W
900-1999	60
2000-3999	59
4000-6399	46

Roseview Dr W | 48 |

Roslyn Pl W | 14 |

Ross Ave S | 21 |

Ruble S | 16 |

Rumsey Ave W | 52 |

Rundell Pl W | 07 |

Rush N
400-1099	11
1100-OUT	10

Rutherford Ave N
1600-2799	35
2800-4399	34
4400-5599	56

Rutherford Ave S
5100-7499	38

Chicago (Con.)   606

Sacramento Ave N
  1-799 12
  800-1199 22
  1600-2799 47
  2800-4399 18
  4400-5599 25
  5600-6399 59
  6400-7599 45
Sacramento Ave S
  1-1199 12
  2200-3499 23
  3500-5499 32
  5500-7499 29
  7500-8699 52
  8700-10299 42
  10300-11499 55
Sacramento Dr S
  11500-11899 55
Sacramento Sq W 12
Saginaw Ave S
  7500-7899 49
  7900-12199 17
  12200-14599 33
Saint Clair N 11
Saint Georges Ct W 47
Saint Helen Ct W 47
Saint James Pl W 14
Saint Joseph Ave W 56
Saint Lawrence Ave S
  3200-3299 16
  3700-4699 53
  4700-5099 15
  6000-7099 37
  7100-9499 19
  9500-12999 28
  13000-13799 27
Saint Louis Ave N
  200-799 24
  800-1599 51
  1600-2799 47
  2800-4399 18
  4400-5599 25
  5600-6399 59
  6400-7199 45
Saint Louis Ave S
  1-1199 24
  1200-3499 23
  3500-5499 32
  5500-7499 29
  7500-8699 52
  8700-10299 42
  10300-11699 55
Saint Marys St & Ct W 47
Saint Michaels Ct N 14
Saint Paul Ave W
  200-299 14
  2000-3999 47
  4000-6399 39
Sandburg Ter N 10
Sangamon N
  1-399 07
  400-OUT 22
Sangamon S
  1-1199 07
  1200-2399 08
  3500-5499 09
  5500-7499 21
  7500-9499 20
  9500-13199 43
Sauganash Ave N 46

Sawyer Ave N
  400-799 24
  1600-2799 47
  2800-4399 18
  4400-5599 25
  5600-6399 59
Sawyer Ave S
  1200-3499 23
  3500-5499 32
  5500-7499 29
  7500-8699 52
  8700-10299 42
  10300-11499 55
Sayre Ave N
  1600-2799 35
  2800-4399 34
  4400-5599 56
  5600-6599 31
Sayre Ave S
  5100-7499 38
Schick Pl N 10
Schiller E 10
Schiller W
  1-799 10
  1900-OUT 22
School N
  7200-7499 48
School W
  900-1999 57
  2000-3999 18
  4000-5599 41
  5600-8399 34
School Ave S
  13400-14599 27
Schorsch W 34
Schreiber Ave W
  1400-1999 26
  2000-3999 45
  6600-7199 31
Schubert Ave W
  600-1799 14
  2300-3999 47
  4000-6399 39
  6400-7999 35
Scott Dr W
  3600-3699 58
Scott St E & W 10
Scottsdale Ave S 52
Sedgwick N
  600-1599 10
  1600-OUT 14
Seeley Ave N
  400-499 12
  2200-2799 47
  2800-4399 18
  4400-5599 25
  5600-6399 59
  6400-7599 45
Seeley Ave S
  1-1099 12
  2300-2399 08
  3200-3499 08
  3500-5499 09
  5500-7499 36
  7500-9499 20
  9500-10899 43
Seipp W 52
Seminary Ave N
  1900-2799 14
  2800-3599 57
  3600-4399 13

Seminole W
  5200-6399 46
  7400-8299 31
Seneca N 11
Senior Pl W 34
Senour Ave S 08
Seward W 48
Shakespeare Ave W
  600-1499 14
  2000-3999 47
  4000-6399 39
  6400-7999 35
Sheffield Ave N
  1500-1599 22
  1600-2799 14
  2800-3599 57
  3600-3899 13
Shelby Ct S 08
Sheridan Rd N
  2800-3599 57
  3600-4399 13
  4400-5599 40
  5600-6399 60
  6400-7799 26
Sheridan Rd W
  600-999 13
  1000-1199 60
Sherman S
  300-399 04
  400-OUT 05
Shermer Rd N 48
Sherwin Ave W
  1200-1999 26
  2000-3399 45
  3800-3999 45
  4000-4899 46
  6000-7799 48
Shields Ave S
  2600-3499 16
  3500-5499 09
  5500-OUT 21
Shirley Ln W 58
Short S 08
Silverton Way S 16
Sioux Ave N 46
Somerset Ave W 31
South Chicago Ave S
  6700-7099 37
  7100-7899 19
  7900-OUT 17
South Park Ln Dr W 55
South Shore Blvd
  2400-2599 49
  4700-5499 15
  5500-5599 37
  6700-7899 49
  7900-OUT 17
South Water E 01
South Water Market District 08
Southport Ave N
  1900-2799 14
  2800-3599 57
  3600-4199 13
Spaulding Ave N
  400-799 24
  800-1599 51
  1600-2799 47
  2800-4399 18
  4400-5599 25
  5600-6399 59
  6400-7199 45

Chicago (Con.) 606

Spaulding Ave S
1-1199 ... 24
1200-3499 ... 23
3500-5499 ... 32
5500-7499 ... 29
7500-8699 ... 52
8700-10299 ... 42
10300-11499 ... 55
Spencer S ... 58
Spokane Ave N ... 46
Springfield Ave N
400-799 ... 24
800-1599 ... 51
1600-2799 ... 47
2800-4399 ... 18
4400-5599 ... 25
5600-6399 ... 59
6400-7399 ... 45
Springfield Ave S
1-1199 ... 24
1200-3499 ... 23
3500-5499 ... 32
5500-7499 ... 29
7500-8699 ... 52
8700-10299 ... 42
10300-11899 ... 55
11900-13299 ... 58
Stark S ... 08
State E
2400-2998 (EVEN) ... 33
State N
1-149 ... 02
150-299 ... 01
300-OUT ... 10
State S
1-199 ... 03
200-399 ... 04
400-1599 ... 05
1600-3499 ... 16
3500-5499 ... 09
5500-6299 ... 21
6300-7099 ... 37
7100-9499 ... 19
9500-12799 ... 28
12800-14599 ... 27
State Pky N ... 10
State Line Rd S ... 17
Stave N ... 47
Stetson Ave N ... 01
Steuben W ... 43
Stewart Ave S
1600-3499 ... 16
3500-5499 ... 09
5500-7499 ... 21
7500-9499 ... 20
9500-13099 ... 28
13100-14599 ... 27
Stockton Dr N ... 14
Stolting Rd W ... 48
Stone N ... 10
Stony Island Ave S
5500-6699 ... 37
6700-7899 ... 49
7900-12199 ... 17
12200-13799 ... 33
Stratford Pl W ... 57
Streeter Dr N ... 11
Strong W
3900-3999 ... 25
4800-6399 ... 30
6400-8399 ... 56

Sullivan W ... 10
Summerdale Ave W
1400-1999 ... 40
2000-3999 ... 25
6900-8799 ... 56
Summit Ave S ... 20
Sunnyside Ave W
800-1999 ... 40
2000-3999 ... 25
4000-6399 ... 30
6400-8699 ... 56
Sunrise Ln N ... 56
Sunset Dr W
7600-7999 ... 35
Sunset Rd W
8600-8799 ... 48
Superior E ... 11
Superior W
1-799 ... 10
800-1999 ... 22
2000-3199 ... 12
4600-5999 ... 44
Surf W ... 57
Surrey Ct N ... 14
Susan Ct N ... 48
Swann W ... 09
Tahoma Ave N ... 46
Talcott Ave W
6900-7798 ... 31
Talcott Ave W, W
6700-6899 ... 56
Talcott Rd W, W
6700-6899 ... 56
6900-7798 ... 31
Talman Ave N
1-799 ... 12
800-1599 ... 22
1600-2799 ... 47
2800-4399 ... 18
4700-5599 ... 25
5600-6399 ... 59
6400-7599 ... 45
Talman Ave S
400-1199 ... 12
1200-1499 ... 08
3900-5499 ... 32
5500-7499 ... 29
7500-8699 ... 52
8700-10299 ... 42
10300-11499 ... 55
Taylor W
1-199 ... 05
200-1599 ... 07
1600-3199 ... 12
3200-4599 ... 24
4600-5999 ... 44
Terra Cotta Pl W ... 14
Thatcher Ave N
1600-1999 ... 35
4400-4799 ... 56
Thomas W
1300-3199 ... 22
3200-5999 ... 51
Thome Ave W
1400-1999 ... 60
2000-3999 ... 59
4400-OUT ... 46
Thorndale Ave W
900-1999 ... 60
2000-3999 ... 59
4000-6399 ... 46
6400-7899 ... 31
Throop N
1-99 ... 07

700-OUT ... 22
Throop S
1-1199 ... 07
1200-3299 ... 08
4700-5499 ... 09
5500-7499 ... 36
7500-9499 ... 20
9500-13199 ... 43
Tilden W
700-1599 ... 07
1600-OUT ... 12
Todd S ... 16
Tonty Ave N ... 46
Tooker Pl W ... 10
Torrence Ave S
9400-12199 ... 17
12200-14599 ... 33
Touhy Ave W
1200-1999 ... 26
2000-3999 ... 45
4000-4899 ... 46
5600-7799 ... 48
Tower Cir Dr E ... 46
Tower Cir Dr N ... 46
Tower Cir Dr S ... 46
Tower Cir Dr W ... 46
Tracy Ave S ... 27
Transit Ave W ... 09
Tremont W ... 21
Tripp Ave N
800-1599 ... 51
1600-2799 ... 39
2800-4399 ... 41
4400-5599 ... 30
5600-7399 ... 46
Tripp Ave S
600-899 ... 24
1200-3499 ... 23
3900-5499 ... 32
5500-7499 ... 29
7500-8699 ... 52
11500-13299 ... 58
Trowbridge Pl W ... 32
Troy N
400-799 ... 12
800-1599 ... 22
1600-2799 ... 47
2800-4399 ... 18
4400-5599 ... 25
5600-6399 ... 59
6400-7599 ... 45
Troy S
100-1199 ... 12
1200-3399 ... 23
4300-5499 ... 32
5500-7499 ... 29
7500-8699 ... 52
8700-10299 ... 42
10300-11499 ... 55
Troy Dr S
11500-11899 ... 55
Trumbull Ave N
400-799 ... 24
800-1199 ... 51
5600-7199 ... 45
Trumbull Ave S
300-599 ... 24
1400-3499 ... 23
4300-5499 ... 32
5500-7499 ... 29
7500-8699 ... 52
8700-10299 ... 42
10300-11699 ... 55
11900-13299 ... 58

Chicago (Con.)   606

Turner Ave S	42
Union Ave N	
1-399	06
400-OUT	10
Union Ave S	
1200-1599	07
1600-3499	16
3500-5499	09
5500-7499	21
7500-9499	20
9500-13099	28
13800-14599	27
University Ave S	
4400-4699	53
4700-5499	15
5500-7099	37
7100-9499	19
9500-OUT	28
Urban Ave S	19
Utica Ave S	42
Van Buren E	05
Van Buren W	
1-165	05
166-166	04
167-199	05
200-1599	07
1600-3199	12
3200-4599	24
4600-5999	44
Van Vlissingen Rd S	17
Vanderpool Ave S	
9200-9499	20
9500-OUT	43
Vermont Ave W	
500-799	28
800-1599	43
3400-4799	58
Vernon Ave S	
2800-3499	16
3500-4399	53
6000-7099	37
7100-9499	19
9500-12999	28
13000-13799	27
Vernon Park Pl W	07
Victoria W	
1200-1999	60
2400-3999	59
4000-4299	46
7600-7899	31
Vincennes Ave S	
3500-4699	53
4700-5099	15
6700-7499	21
7500-9499	20
9500-11899	43
Vine N	
1200-1599	10
1600-OUT	14
4800-5599	56
5600-5699	31
Vintage S	08
Virginia Ave N	
4500-5599	25
5600-6399	59
Wabansia Ave W	
1300-1999	22
2000-3999	47
4000-6399	39
6400-7999	35

Wabash Ave N	
1-149	02
150-329	01
330-OUT	11
Wabash Ave S	
1-199	03
200-399	04
400-1599	05
1600-3499	16
3500-4699	53
4700-5499	15
5500-7099	37
7100-9499	19
9500-12799	28
12800-14599	27
Wacker Dr E	01
Wacker Dr N	
1-199	06
Wacker Dr S	
1-399	06
400-OUT	07
Wacker Dr W	
1-199	01
200-399	06
Walden Pky S	43
Wallace S	
2300-3499	16
3500-5499	09
5500-7499	21
7500-9499	20
9500-13099	28
13100-14599	27
Wallen Ave W	
1600-1799	26
3700-3999	45
Waller Ave N	
1-799	44
800-OUT	51
Waller Ave S	
1-1199	44
Walnut W	
600-799	06
1600-3199	12
3200-OUT	24
Walter Ln W	58
Walton E	11
Walton W	
1-799	10
1300-3199	22
3200-5999	51
Warner Ave W	
1400-1999	13
2000-3999	18
4000-OUT	41
Warren Ave W	
600-799	06
1500-1599	07
1600-3199	12
3200-OUT	24
Warren Blvd W	
600-799	06
1500-1599	07
1600-3199	12
3200-OUT	24
Warren Rd N	48
Warwick Ave W	
4000-5599	41
5600-6399	34
Waseca Pl W	43
Washburne Ave W	08
Washington E	02
Washington N	
5300-5599	56

8000-8999	48
9000-9598 (EVEN)	48
Washington W	
1-199	02
200-799	06
800-1599	07
1600-3199	12
3200-4599	24
4600-5999	44
Washington Park Ct S	15
Washtenaw Ave N	
1-799	12
800-1599	22
1600-2799	47
2800-3399	18
4700-5599	25
5600-6399	59
6400-7599	45
Washtenaw Ave S	
1-1199	12
1200-3499	08
3500-5499	32
5500-7499	29
7500-8699	52
8700-10299	42
10300-11499	55
Waterloo Ct N	57
Watkins Ave S	43
Waukegan Rd N	48
Waukesha Ave N	46
Waveland Ave W	
600-1999	13
2000-3999	18
4000-5599	41
5600-8399	34
Wayman W	
600-799	06
800-999	07
4600-OUT	44
Wayne Ave N	
2100-2799	14
2800-3599	57
3600-3999	13
5200-5599	40
5600-6399	60
6400-6999	26
Webster N	
2400-2499	35
Webster Ave W	
300-1999	14
2000-OUT	47
Weed W	
600-799	10
800-OUT	22
Wellington Ave W	
300-1999	57
2000-3999	18
4000-5599	41
5600-7199	34
7200-7999	35
Wells N	
1-299	06
300-398 (EVEN)	54
301-399 (ODD)	10
400-1599	10
1600-OUT	14
Wells S	
1-199	06
200-398 (EVEN)	06
201-399 (ODD)	04
400-1199	07
2600-3499	16
3500-5499	09

Chicago (Con.)   606

Wendell W	10
Wendy Way N	48
Wentworth Ave S	
1600-3499	16
3500-5499	09
5500-7499	21
7500-9499	20
9500-12899	28
12900-14599	27
Wesley Ter N	56
West Cir Ave N	31
West District Blvd	32
West End Ave W	
3800-4599	24
4600-5999	44
Westbrook Rd N	35
Western Ave N	
1-799	12
800-1599	22
1600-2799	47
2800-4399	18
4400-5599	25
5600-6399	59
6400-7599	45
8200-8399	48
Western Ave S	
1-1199	12
1200-3499	08
3500-5499	09
5500-7499	36
7500-9499	20
9500-9798 (EVEN)	42
9501-9799 (ODD)	43
Western Ave, S	
9800-11899	43
Westgate Ter W	07
Weston Pl W	
9501-9799 (ODD)	20
Westwood Dr W	35
Whipple N	
300-799	12
800-1599	22
1600-2799	47
2800-4399	18
4400-5599	25
5600-6399	59
6400-7599	45
Whipple S	
1-1199	12
2200-3299	23
4200-5499	32
5500-7499	29
7500-8699	52
8700-10299	42
10300-11499	55
Whipple Dr W	
3100-3199	55
Wicker Park Ave N	22
Wieland N	10
Wilcox W	
2300-2999	12
3800-OUT	24
Wildwood Ave N	46
Willard Ct N	
100-199	07
700-OUT	22
Willets Ct N	47
Williams Ave S	19
Willow W	
200-1099	14
1400-1499	22

Willow Ln N	48
Wilmot Ave N	47
Wilson Ave W	
700-1999	40
2000-3999	25
4000-6399	30
6400-8799	56
Wilton Ave N	
2000-2799	14
3000-3599	57
3600-3899	13
Winchester Ave N	
400-1999	22
2000-2799	14
2800-3599	57
3600-4399	13
4400-5599	40
5600-6399	60
6400-7599	26
Winchester Ave S	
1-1199	12
1200-3499	08
3500-5499	09
5500-7499	36
7500-9499	20
9500-12299	43
12301-12699 (ODD)	43
Windsor Ave W	
800-999	40
2100-3999	25
4000-6399	30
6400-8599	56
Winnebago Ave N	47
Winneconna Pky W	20
Winnemac Ave W	
1200-1999	40
2000-3999	25
4000-6399	30
7200-8599	56
Winona W	
800-1999	40
2000-3999	25
4000-6399	30
6400-8599	56
Winston Ave S	43
Winthrop Ave N	
4600-5599	40
5600-6399	60
6400-6699	26
Wisconsin W	14
Wisner N	
8000-8999	48
Wisner Ave N	
2900-2999	18
Wolcott Ave N	
1-399	12
400-1999	22
2000-3599	14
2800-3599	57
3600-4399	13
4400-5599	40
5600-6399	60
6400-7599	26
Wolcott Ave S	
1-1199	12
1200-3499	08
3500-5499	09
5500-7499	36
7500-9499	20
11800-12699	43
Wolfram W	
800-1999	57

2300-3999	18
4000-5599	41
5600-7199	34
Wood N	
1-399	12
400-1999	22
2000-OUT	14
Wood S	
1-1199	12
1200-3499	08
3500-5499	09
5500-7499	36
7500-9499	20
9500-12699	43
Woodard N	18
Woodland Dr N	48
Woodland Park E	16
Woodlawn Ave S	
4400-4699	53
4700-5499	15
5500-7099	37
7100-9499	19
9500-10399	28
13000-13799	27
Wright Ter W	48
Wrightwood Ave W	
400-1999	14
3200-3999	47
4000-6399	39
6400-7599	35
Yale Ave S	
6300-7499	21
7500-9499	20
9500-12999	28
Yates Ave S	
7100-7899	49
7900-12199	17
12200-14599	33

NUMBERED STREETS

5th Ave W	
2800-3199	12
3200-4399	24
4600-5999	44
8th thru 14th St E	05
11th W	07
12th Pl W	
300-799	07
2600-2799	08
3400-3599	23
4600-4799	50
13th W	
1-299	05
300-799	07
800-2799	08
2800-4599	23
4600-6199	50
13th Pl W	
1-299	05
300-799	07
800-2799	08
2800-4599	23
4600-6199	50
14th W	
1-299	05
300-799	07
800-2799	08
2800-4599	23
4600-6199	50
14th Pl W	
1-299	05

Chicago (Con.)   606

300-799	07
800-2799	08
2800-4599	23
4600-6199	50
15th W	
1-299	05
300-799	07
800-2799	08
2800-4599	23
4600-6199	50
15th Pl W	
1-299	05
300-799	07
800-2799	08
2800-4599	23
4600-6199	50
16th W	
1-799	16
800-2799	08
2800-4599	23
4600-6199	50
16th Pl W	
1-799	16
800-2799	08
2800-4599	23
4600-6199	50
16th thru 35th St E	16
17th W	
1-799	16
800-2799	08
2800-4599	23
4600-6199	50
17th Pl W	
1-799	16
800-2799	08
2800-4599	23
4600-6199	50
18th W	
1-799	16
800-2799	08
2800-4599	23
4600-6199	50
18th Pl W	
1-799	16
800-2799	08
2800-4599	23
4600-6199	50
19th W	
1-799	16
800-2799	08
2800-4599	23
4600-6199	50
19th Pl W	
1-799	16
800-2799	08
2800-4599	23
4600-6199	50
20th W	
1-799	16
800-2799	08
2800-4599	23
4600-6199	50
20th Pl W	
1-799	16
800-2799	08
2800-4599	23
4600-6199	50
21st W	
1-799	16
800-2799	08
2800-4599	23
4600-6199	50
21st Pl W	
1-799	16
800-2799	08
2800-4599	23
4600-6199	50
22nd W	
1-799	16
800-2799	08
2800-4599	23
4600-6199	50
22nd Pl W	
1-799	16
800-2799	08
2800-4599	23
4600-6199	50
23rd W	
1-799	16
800-2799	08
2800-4599	23
4600-6199	50
23rd Pl W	
1-799	16
800-2799	08
2800-4599	23
4600-6199	50
24th W	
1-799	16
800-2799	08
2800-4599	23
4600-6199	50
24th Blvd W	
2800-2999	23
24th Pl W	
1-799	16
800-2799	08
2800-4599	23
4600-6199	50
25th W	
1-799	16
800-2799	08
2800-4599	23
4600-6199	50
25th Pl W	
1-799	16
800-2799	08
2800-4599	23
4600-6199	50
26th W	
1-799	16
800-2799	08
2800-4599	23
4600-6199	50
26th Pl W	
1-799	16
800-2799	08
2800-4599	23
4600-6199	50
27th W	
1-799	16
800-2799	08
2800-4599	23
4600-6199	50
27th Pl W	
1-799	16
800-2799	08
2800-4599	23
4600-6199	50
28th W	
1-799	16
800-2799	08
2800-4599	23
4600-6199	50
28th Pl W	
1-799	16
800-2799	08
2800-4599	23
4600-6199	50
29th W	
1-799	16
800-2799	08
2800-4599	23
4600-6199	50
29th Pl W	
1-799	16
800-2799	08
2800-4599	23
4600-6199	50
30th W	
1-799	16
800-2799	08
2800-4599	23
4600-6199	50
30th Pl W	
1-799	16
800-2799	08
2800-4599	23
4600-6199	50
31st W	
1-799	16
800-2799	08
2800-4599	23
4600-6199	50
31st Blvd W	
31st Pl W	
1-799	16
800-2799	08
2800-4599	23
4600-6199	50
32nd W	
1-799	16
800-2799	08
2800-4599	23
4600-6199	50
32nd Pl W	
1-799	16
800-2799	08
2800-4599	23
4600-6199	50
33rd W	
1-799	16
800-2799	08
2800-4599	23
4600-6199	50
33rd Pl W	
1-799	16
800-2799	08
2800-4599	23
4600-6199	50
34th W	
1-799	16
800-2799	08
2800-4599	23
4600-6199	50
34th Pl W	
1-799	16
800-2799	08
2800-4599	23
4600-6199	50
35th W	
1-799	16
800-2399	09
2400-2799	32
2800-4599	23

Chicago (Con.)   **606**

35th Pl W	
1-2399	09
2400-4599	32
4600-6199	50
36th, W	
1-2399	09
2400-3999	32
4600-6199	50
36th Pl W	
1-2399	09
2400-4599	32
4600-6199	50
36th thru 47th St E	53
37th, W	
1-2399	09
2400-3999	32
4600-6199	50
37th Pl W	
1-2399	09
2400-4599	32
4600-6199	50
38th, W	
1-2399	09
2400-3999	32
4600-6199	50
38th Pl W	
1-2399	09
2400-4599	32
4600-6199	50
39th Pl W	
1-2399	09
2400-4799	32
40th W	
1-2399	09
2400-4799	32
4800-5999	50
40th Pl W	
300-599	09
2600-4799	32
41st W	
1-2399	09
2400-4799	32
4800-5999	50
41st Pl W	
4600-4799	32
42nd W	
1-2399	09
2400-4799	32
42nd Pl W	
1-2399	09
2400-4799	32
43rd W	
1-2399	09
2400-4799	32
4800-5199	38
43rd Pl W	
1-2399	09
2400-4799	32
4800-5199	38
44th W	
1-2399	09
2400-4799	32
4800-5199	38
44th Ave & Pl, S	58
44th Ct S	58
44th Pl W	
1-2399	09
2400-4799	32
4800-5199	38
45th W	
1-2399	09

2400-4799	32
4800-5599	38
45th Ave S	58
45th Pl W	
1-2399	09
2400-4799	32
4800-5599	38
46th W	
1-2399	09
2400-4799	32
4800-5999	38
46th Ave S	
1200-3899	50
46th Ct S	
1200-3899	50
46th Pl W	
1-2399	09
2400-4799	32
4800-5999	38
47th W	
1-2399	09
2400-4799	32
4800-5999	38
47th Ave S	
1200-3899	50
47th Ct S	
1200-3899	50
47th Pl E	15
47th Pl W	
1-2399	09
2400-4799	32
4800-5999	38
48th W	
1-2399	09
2400-4799	32
4800-6299	38
48th Ave S	
1200-3899	50
48th Ct S	
1200-3899	50
48th Pl W	
1-2399	09
2400-4799	32
4800-6299	38
48th St & Pl E	15
49th W	
1-2399	09
2400-4799	32
4800-6299	38
49th Ave S	
1200-3899	50
49th Ct S	
1200-3899	50
49th Pl W	
1-2399	09
2400-4799	32
4800-6299	38
49th thru 50th St E	15
50th W	
1-2399	09
2400-4799	32
4800-6699	38
50th Ave S	
1200-4199	50
50th Ct S	
1200-3899	50
50th Pl W	
1-2399	09
2400-4799	32
4800-6699	38
50th thru 51st Pl E	15
51st W	
1-2399	09

2400-4799	32
4800-7199	38
51st, E	15
51st Ave S	
1200-3899	50
51st Ct S	
1200-3899	50
51st Pl W	
1-2399	09
2400-4799	32
4800-7199	38
52nd W	
1-2399	09
2400-4799	32
4800-7199	38
52nd Ave S	
1200-3899	50
52nd Ct S	
1200-3899	50
52nd Pl W	
1-2399	09
2400-4799	32
4800-7199	38
52nd thru 54th St E	15
53rd W	
1-2399	09
2400-4799	32
4800-7199	38
53rd Ave S	
1200-3899	50
53rd Ct S	
1200-3899	50
53rd Pl W	
1-2399	09
2400-4799	32
4800-7199	38
54th W	
1-2399	09
2400-4799	32
4800-7199	38
54th Ave S	
1200-3899	50
54th Ct S	
1200-3899	50
54th Pl E	15
54th Pl W	
1-2399	09
2400-4799	32
4800-7199	38
55th E	
1-399 (ODD)	37
2-398 (EVEN)	15
800-1899	15
55th W	
1-1199 (ODD)	21
2-2398 (EVEN)	09
1201-2399 (ODD)	36
2400-4799	32
4800-7199	38
55th Ave S	
1200-3899	50
55th Ct S	
1200-3899	50
55th Pl E	37
55th Pl W	
1-1199	21
1200-2399	36
2400-4799	29
4800-7199	38
56th W	
1-1199	21
1200-2399	36
2400-4799	29

Chicago (Con.)	606
800-2399	43
2400-3999	55
4000-4899	58
118th Pl E	
1-1599	28
1600-OUT	17
118th Pl W	
1-799	28
800-2399	43
2400-3999	55
4000-4899	58
119th E	
1-1599	28
1600-OUT	17
119th W	
1-799	28
800-1899	43
1900-2398 (EVEN)	43
2400-3598 (EVEN)	55
3600-5599	58
119th Pl E	
1-1599	28
1600-OUT	17
119th Pl W, W	
4000-4435	58
120th E	
1-1599	28
1600-OUT	17
120th W	
1-799	28
800-1799	43
120th Pl E	
1-1599	28
1600-OUT	17
120th Pl W	
1-799	28
800-1799	43
3400-5599	58
121st E	
1-1599	28
1600-OUT	17
121st W	
1-799	28
800-1799	43
3400-5599	58
121st Pl E	
1-1599	28
1600-OUT	17
121st Pl W	
1-799	28
800-1799	43
3400-5599	58
122nd E	
1-899	28
900-OUT	33
122nd W	
1-799	28
800-1799	43
3400-5599	58
122nd Pl E	28
122nd Pl W	
1-799	28
800-1799	43
3400-5599	58
123rd W	
1-799	28
800-1949	43
3400-5599	58
123rd E, E	
1-999	28
1000-OUT	38

123rd Pl-W	
3400-5599	58
124th E	
1-999	28
1000-OUT	33
124th W	
1-799	28
800-1949	43
3400-5599	58
124th Pl E	
1-999	28
124th W	
1-799	28
800-1949	43
3400-5599	58
125th E	
1-1099	28
1100-OUT	33
125th W	
1-799	28
800-1949	43
3400-5599	58
125th Pl E	28
125th Pl W	
1-799	28
800-1949	43
3400-5599	58
126th E	
1-1199	28
1200-OUT	33
126th W	
1-799	28
800-1949	43
3400-5599	58
126th Pl W	
1-799	28
800-1949	43
3400-5599	58
126th Pl, E	
1200-OUT	33
126th Pl E, E	
1-1199	28
127th E	
1-1199	28
1200-OUT	33
127th W	
1-799	28
800-1799	43
1800-1948 (EVEN)	43
5400-5598 (EVEN)	58
127th W, W	
3400-5399	58
127th Pl W	
1-799	28
800-1799	43
3400-4999	58
128th E	
200-1299	28
1300-OUT	33
128th Pl W	
1-799	28
800-1799	43
3400-4999	58
129th E	
200-1399	28
1400-OUT	33
129th Pl W	
1-799	28
800-1799	43
130th W	
1-199	27
200-498 (EVEN)	28
201-499 (ODD)	27

500-1399	28
1400-OUT	33
130th W	
1-799	28
800-1599	43
3400-4799	58
130th Pl E	
1-1599	27
1600-OUT	33
131st E	
1-1599	27
1600-OUT	33
131st W	
3400-4799	58
131st Pl E	
1-1599	27
1600-OUT	33
132nd E	
1-1599	27
1600-OUT	33
132nd W	
3400-4799	58
132nd Pl E	
1-1599	27
1600-OUT	33
133rd E	
1-1599	27
1600-OUT	33
133rd W	
3400-4799	58
133rd Pl E	
1-1599	27
1600-OUT	33
134th E	
1-1599	27
1600-OUT	33
134th W	
1-1599	27
134th Pl E	
1-1599	27
1600-OUT	33
135th E	
1-1599	27
1600-OUT	33
135th W	
1-799	27
135th Pl E	
1-1599	27
1600-OUT	33
136th E	
1-1599	27
1600-OUT	33
136th W	
1-799	27
136th Pl E	
1-1599	27
1600-OUT	33
137th E	
1-1599	27
1600-OUT	33
137th W	
1-799	27
137th Pl E	
1-1599	27
1600-OUT	33
137th Pl W W	
1-799	27
138th E	
1-1599	27
1600-OUT	33
138th W	
1-799	27

Chicago (Con.) 606

138th Pl E	
2800-OUT	33
139th E	
1-199	27
2400-OUT	33
139th W	
1-799	27
140th E	
1-199	27
2400-OUT	33
140th W	
1-799	27
140th Ct E & W	27
141st E	
1-199	27
2400-OUT	33
141st W	
1-799	27
142nd E	
1-199	27
2400-OUT	33
142nd W	
1-799	27
143rd E	
1-199	27
2400-OUT	33
143rd W	
1-799	27
144th E	
1-199	27
2400-OUT	33
144th W	
1-799	27
145th E	
1-199	27
2400-OUT	33
145th W	
1-799	27
145th Pl W	27
146th E	
1-199	27
2400-2998 (EVEN)	33
146th W	
1-799	27

DECATUR 625

POST OFFICE BOXES

Box Nos.		
1-1999	Main Office	25
2000-2999	Brettwood Sta ..	26

RURAL ROUTES

1	26
2	21
3	26
4,6,7	21
8	22

STATIONS, BRANCHES AND UNITS

Brettwood Sta	26
General Delivery	21
Postmaster	21

DES PLAINES 600

POST OFFICE BOXES

Box Nos.		
1-281	Main Office	17
300-499	Oakton Sta	18
500-799	Rosemont	18

STATIONS, BRANCHES AND UNITS

Oakton Sta	18
Rosemont Br	18
General Delivery	16
Postmaster	16

EAST SAINT LOUIS 622

POST OFFICE BOXES

Box Nos.		
1-799	Main Office	02
800-999	Edgemont Sta ..	03
1000-1199	Lansdowne Sta	04
1200-1399	Fireworks Br	07
1400-1599	Parcel Post Sta	05
1600-1799	Cahokia Br	06

STATIONS, BRANCHES AND UNITS

Cahokia Br	06
Centreville Br	06
Edgemont Br	03
Fairview Heights Br	08
Fireworks Br	07
Lansdowne Sta	04
Parcel Post Sta	05
Sauget Br	01
Washington Park Br	04
General Delivery	01
Postmaster	01

APARTMENTS, HOTELS, MOTELS

Brenton Bldg, 2901 Waverly	04
John Deshields, 1235 Mc Casland	01
John Robinson, 12th & Market	01
Orr, 1300 Missouri	01
Roosevelt, 1300 N 44th	04
Ruggeri, 2901 Waverly	04
Rukavina, 2901 Waverly	04
Samuel Gompers, 6th & Ohio	01
Starnes, 2901 Waverly	04
Villa Griffin, 26th & Lincoln	04

BUILDINGS

Arcade, 112-116 Collinsville Ave	01
City Hall, 7 Collinsville	01
Coldman, 338 Missouri Ave	01
First Federal, 435 Missouri Ave	01
First National Bank, 325 Missouri Ave	01
Illinois, 417 Missouri Ave	01
Murphy, 234 Collinsville Ave ..	01
New Federal, 650 Missouri Ave	01
Shop City Medical, 4601 State St	05

GOVERNMENT OFFICES

U S Attorney, 750 Missouri Ave	02
U S Clerk Of The Court, 750 Missouri Ave	02
U S Internal Revenue Service, 650 Missouri Ave	01
U S Judge Of Federal Courts, 750 Missouri Ave	02
U S Marshall, 750 Missouri Ave	02
U S Railroad Retirement Board, 650 Missouri Ave	01
U S Referee In Bankruptcy, 750 Missouri Ave	02
U S Social Security Admin, 650 Missouri Ave	02

HOSPITALS

Centreville Township, 5900 Bond Ave	07
Christian Welfare, 1509 Illinois Ave	01
Saint Mary'S, 129 N 8th	01

UNIVERSITIES AND COLLEGES

Park College Of Aero Tech, Falling Springs Rd	01

EVANSTON 602

POST OFFICE BOXES

Box Nos.		
1-1670	Main Office	04

STATIONS, BRANCHES AND UNITS

North Sta	01
South Sta	02
General Delivery	04
Postmaster	04

APARTMENTS, HOTELS, MOTELS

Evanshire, 860 Hinman Ave	02
Evanston Inn, 840 Forest Ave	02
Homestead, 1625 Hinman Ave	01
Library Plaza, 1637 Orrington Ave	01
North Shore, 1611 Chicago Ave	01
Orrington, 1710 Orrington Ave	01
Ridgeview, 901 Maple Ave	02

Evanston (Con.) 602

BUILDINGS

State National Bank Plaza,
1603 Orrington Ave 01

HOSPITALS

Community Hospital, 2040
Brown Ave........................ 01
Evanston Hospital, 2650
Ridge Ave........................ 01
Saint Francis Hospital, 355
Ridge Ave........................ 02

UNIVERSITIES AND COLLEGES

Garrett Theological Seminary,
2121 Sheridan Rd 01
Kendall College, 2408
Orrington Ave.................. 04
National College Of
Education, 2840 Sheridan
Rd 01
Northwestern University, 633
Clark 01
Seabury Western Theological
Seminary, 2122 Sheridan
Rd 01

JOLIET 604

POST OFFICE BOXES

Box Nos.
1-948   Main Office 34

RURAL ROUTES

1,2,3,4,5 31

STATIONS, BRANCHES AND UNITS

Crest Hill Br........................ 35
Rockdale Br........................ 36
Shorewood Rural Br. 36
West Gate Sta..................... 35
General Delivery 31
Postmaster 31

MELROSE PARK 601

POST OFFICE BOXES

Box Nos.
1-499   19th Ave Sta.... 60
600-799   Hillside-
           Berkeley Br..... 62
1000-1199 Main Office 61
2001-2299 Northlake....... 64

STATIONS, BRANCHES AND UNITS

Hillside-Berkeley Br.............. 62
Nineteenth Avenue Sta........... 60
Northlake Br........................ 64
Stone Park Br...................... 65
Taft Br.............................. 63
General Delivery 60
Postmaster 60

OAK LAWN 604

POST OFFICE BOXES

Box Nos.
ANY   Main Office 54

RURAL ROUTES

1,2,3,4,5,6 53

STATIONS, BRANCHES AND UNITS

Bridgeview Br....................... 55
Burbank Br........................... 59
Hickory Hills Br.................... 57
Hometown Br........................ 56
South Bridgeview Br 55
South Stickney Br................. 59
General Delivery 54
Postmaster 54

OAK PARK 603

POST OFFICE BOXES

Box Nos.
1-314   River Forest Br. 05
1-997   Oak Park 03
1001-1179   South Oak Park
            Sta. 04
2001-2117   Oak Park 03

STATIONS, BRANCHES AND UNITS

River Forest Br 05
South Oak Park Sta 04
General Delivery 03
Postmaster 01

APARTMENTS, HOTELS, MOTELS

Carleton & Motor Inn, 1110
Pleasant........................... 02
Oak Manor, 211 N Oak Park
Ave 02
Oak Park Arms, 408 S Oak
Park Ave........................... 02
Oak Park Chateau, 330 N
Austin Blvd 02
Oak, 855 Lake...................... 01
Oakshire Apartment, 12
Washington Blvd................. 02
Plaza, 123 S Marion 02
Ymca, 255 S Marion 02

BUILDINGS

Avenue State Bank, 104 N
Oak Park Ave 01
Oak Park Federal Savings &
Loan Association, 1001
Lake................................ 01
Oak Park National Bank, 11
Madison 02
Oak Park Trust & Savings
Bank, 1048 Lake 01
River Forest State Bank &
Trust Company, 7727 W
Lake 05

Suburban Trust & Savings

Bank, 840 S Oak Park
Ave 04
Tri City Savings & Loan
Association, 6020
Roosevelt.......................... 04
Village Hall, 655 Lake St....... 01
Village Savings & Loan
Association, 810 S Oak
Park Ave........................... 04

HOSPITALS

Oak Park Hosp., 520 S Maple
Ave 04
West Suburban Hospital, 518
N Austin Blvd 02

PEORIA 616

POST OFFICE BOXES

Box Nos.
1-99   Alta R. Sta 08
1-99   Creve Coeur
            Sta................ 11
1-99   Limestone Br...... 07
1-99   Peoria Heights
            Br................. 14
1-2000   Main Office 01
2001-2999   East Peoria Br.. 11
3001-3999   West Glen Sta.... 14
4001-4999   Bartonville Br... 07

RURAL ROUTES

1 11
2 14
3 07
4 14
5,6,8 11

STATIONS, BRANCHES AND UNITS

Alta Rural Br 08
Bartonville Br 07
Creve Coeur Br 11
East Peoria Br.................... 11
El Vista Sta 04
Junction City Sta................. 14
Limestone 07
Madison Park Br 04
Meadows Avenue Br.............. 11
Peoria Heights Br................ 14
Rolling Acres Sta 14
Sheridan Village Sta 14
West Glen Sta 14
Windsor Square Sta 14
General Delivery 01
Postmaster 01

APARTMENTS, HOTELS, MOTELS

Clayton House, 5712 N
Knoxville.......................... 14
Downtown Motel, 705
Hamilton 03

Peoria (Con.)   616

Four Winds Motel, 3527
  Harmon Hwy............................ 04
Holiday Inn, 401 N Main E
  Peoria.................................... 11
Howard Johnson Motel, 225 N
  E Adams................................ 02
Imperial 400 Hotel, 202 N E
  Washington........................... 02
Lee, 225 E State........................ 02
Manias Manor Motel, 1501
  Knoxville............................... 03
Pere Marquette, 501 Main...... 02
Ramada Inn, 415 Saint
  Marks Ct............................... 03
Sands Motel, 220 NE Adams.... 02
Vonachen'S Hyatt Lodge,
  5901 N Prospect..................... 14
Voyager Inn, 504 Hamilton..... 02

BUILDINGS

Board Of Trade, 300 S
  Washington........................... 02·
Caterpillar Administration,
  100 N E Adams..................... 02
Central, 101 S W Adams.......... 02
Citizens, 225 Main.................. 02
Commercial Nat'L. Bank
  Bldg,.................................... 02
First Nat'L. Bank Bldg............. 02
Insurance, 3100 N Knoxville.... 03
Jefferson, 331 Fulton............... 02
Junction City............................ 14
Lafayette, 410 Fayette............ 02
Lehman, 405 Main................... 06
Madison Park........................... 04
Savings Center Tower, 411
  Hamilton............................... 02
Savings, 111 NE Jefferson...... 02
Security Savings, 200 N E
  Adams................................... 02
Sheridan Village....................... 14
Stockyards, Ft Of South St...... 02
Town Hall, Junction City......... 14

GOVERNMENT OFFICES

City Hall, 419 Fulton............... 02
County Courthouse, 300
  Main..................................... 02
No Reg Research Lab, 1815
  N University.......................... 04
U S Post Office, 100 N E
  Monroe................................. 01
2628 N Knoxville...................... 01

HOSPITALS

Methodist, 221 NE Glen Oak... 03
Peoria State, 7101 S Adams.... 07
Proctor, 5409 Knoxville........... 14
St. Francis, 530 N.e. Glen
  Oak...................................... 03
Zeller Zone Clinic, 5407 N
  University............................. 14

UNIVERSITIES AND COLLEGES

Bradley University, 1502 W
  Bradley................................. 06
Illinois Central College, 2129
  Highview Rd E Peroia II...... 11·

ROCKFORD   611

POST OFFICE BOXES

Box Nos.
1-1199   Main Office   05
1500-1999   East Rockford
               Sta........... 10
2000-2999   Loves Park Br... 11
3000-3999   Broadway Sta... 06
4000-4999   East Rockford
               Sta........... 10

RURAL ROUTES

1...................................... 09
2...................................... 02
3...................................... 03
4...................................... 11
5...................................... 08
6...................................... 03
7...................................... 08
8...................................... 03
9...................................... 09
10.................................... 11

STATIONS, BRANCHES AND UNITS

Broadway Sta.......................... 06
East Rockford Sta.................... 07
Kishwaukee Br......................... 09
Loves Park Br........................... 11
Meadow Mart Br...................... 11
General Delivery....................... 01
Postmaster............................... 01

BUILDINGS

American National Bank, 501
  7th...................................... 04
Atwood Center, 2500 N Main.. 01
Camelot Tower,1415 E. State
  Street................................... 08
City National Bank, 1100
  Broadway.............................. 04
Empire, 206 S Main................. 01
First National Bank, 401 E
  State.................................... 04
Gas & Electric, 303 N Main.... 01
Illinois National Bank, 226 S
  Main..................................... 01
Labor Temple, 212 S 1st.......... 04
Loves Park City Hall, 540
  Loves Park Drive.................. 11
Nu Arcade, 125 N Church........ 01
Nu State, 119 N Church.......... 01
Rock River Savings & Loan,
  401 W State........................... 01
Rockford Commercial
  Building, 101 Chestnut......... 01
Rockford Life, 526 W State..... 01
Rockford Professional, 1221
  E State.................................. 08
Rockford Trust, 206 W State... 01
Talcott,321 W State................. 01

GOVERNMENT OFFICES

City Hall, 425 E State.............. 04
Courthouse.............................. 01

HOSPITALS

Children'S Medical, 1429
  Myott Ave............................. 01
Family Medical, 2623
  Edgemont.............................. 03
Rockford Memorial, 2400 N
  Rockton................................. 01
Saint Anthony, 5666 E State
  St... 01
Singer Zone Center, 4402 N.
  Main..................................... 05
Swedish American, 1316
  Charles................................. 01

UNIVERSITIES AND COLLEGES

Rock Valley College, 3301 N
  Mulford................................ 01
Rockford College, 5050 E
  State.................................... 01

SPRINGFIELD   627

POST OFFICE BOXES

Box Nos.
1-2385   Downtown Sta.. 05
2501-4500   Main Office 08

RURAL ROUTES

1,2,3,4,5,6,7,8....................... 07

STATIONS, BRANCHES AND UNITS

Capitol Sta.............................. 06
Downtown Sta.......................... 01
General Delivery....................... 08
Postmaster............................... 08

APARTMENTS, MOTELS, MOTELS

A Lincoln, 2927 S 6th.............. 03
Bel-Aire Manor, 2636 S 6th.... 03
Down Towner, 400 N 9th......... 02
Governor, 418 E Jefferson....... 01
Highway, 1305 Wabash Ave ... 04
Holiday Inn, 625 E Saint
  Joseph................................. 03
Howard Johnson Motor Lodge,
  1025 S 5th............................ 05
Lamp Liter, U S Route 66 S.... 07
Leland, 527 E Capitol.............. 05
Mansion View, 529 S 4th........ 01
Ramada Inn, 3751 S 6th.......... 03
Saint Nicholas.......................... 01
Sheraton Motor Inn, 3090
  Stevenson Dr........................ 03
State House Inn, 101 E
  Adams................................... 01
Travelodge, 500 S 9th.............. 01

BUILDINGS

Abraham Lincoln Building 01

Springfield (Con.)	627
Ferguson, 522 E Monroe	01
Illinois, 601 E Adams	01
Jefferson West	02
Myers, 101 S 5th	01
Reisch, 117 S 5th	01
Ridgely, 504 E Monroe	01
Security, 516 E Monroe	01
Thrifty, 425 E Monroe	01
Washington, 531 E	

Washington	01
1st National Bank, 201 S 5th	01

GOVERNMENT OFFICES

Centennial, State Capitol Complex	06
Federal, 600 E. Monroe	01
Municipal, 300 S 7th	01

Sangamon County Courthouse	01
State Office, State Capitol Complex	06

HOSPITALS

Memorial	05
Saint Johns	01

State List of Post Offices

INDIANA

INDIANA
(Abbreviation: IN)

Acton, Br. Indianapolis	46259
Adams, R. Br. Greensburg	47240
Advance	46102
Air Mail Field, Sta. Indianapolis	46241
Akron	46910
Alamo	47916
Albany	47320
Albion	46701
Alexandria (1st)	46001
Ambia	47917
Amboy	46911
Amo	46103
ANDERSON (1st) (see appendix)	
Andrews	46702
Angola (1st)	46703
Arcadia	46030
Arcola	46704
Argos	46501
Arlington	46104
Ashley	46705
Athens	46912
Atlanta	46031
Attica (1st)	47918
Atwood	46502
Auburn (1st)	46706
Aurora (1st)	47001
Austin	47102
Avilla	46710
Avoca	47420
Avon, Br. Plainfield	46168
Bainbridge	46105
Bargersville	46106
Batesville (1st)	47006
Bath	47010
Battle Ground	47920
Bedford (1st)	47421
Beech Grove (1st)	46107
Bellmore	47830
Bennington	47011
Bentonville	47322
Berne (1st)	46711
Bethlehem	47104
Beverly Shores	46301
Bicknell	47512
Bippus	46713
Birdseye	47513
Blanford	47831

Biocher, R. Br. Scottsburg	47170
Bloomfield (1st)	47424
Bloomingdale	47832
Bloomington (1st)	47401
Bluffton (1st)	46714
Boggstown	46110
Boone Grove	46302
Boonville (1st)	47601
Borden	47106
Boston	47324
Boswell	47921
Bourbon	46504
Bowling Green	47833
Bradford	47107
Branchville	47514
Brazil (1st)	47834
Bremen (1st)	46506
Bridgeport, Br. Indianapolis	46231
Bridgeton	47836
Brightwood, Sta. Indianapolis	46218
Brimfield	46720
Bringhurst	46913
Bristol	46507
Bristow	47515
Broad Ripple, Sta. Indianapolis	46220
Brook	47922
Brooklyn	46111
Brookston	47923
Brookville (1st)	47012
Brownsburg (1st)	46112
Brownstown (1st)	47220
Brownsville	47325
Bruceville	47516
Brunswick, Sta. Gary	46406
Bryant	47326
Buck Creek	47924
Buckskin	47647
Buffalo	47925
Buffaloville	47518
Buffington, Sta. Gary	46406
Bunker Hill	46914
Burket	46508
Burlington	46915
Burnettsville	47926
Burney	47222
Burns City, R. Br. Loogootee	47553
Burr Oak	46509
Burrows	46916
Butler	46721
Butlerville	47223

Cambridge City (1st)	47327
Camby	46113
Camden	46917
Campbellsburg	47108
Canaan	47224
Cannelburg	47519
Cannelton	47520
Carbon	47837
Carlisle	47838
Carlos	47329
Carmel (1st)	46032
Cartersburg	46114
Carthage	46115
Castleton, Br. Indianapolis (see appendix)	
Cates	47927
Cayuga	47928
Cedar Grove	47016
Cedar Lake (1st)	46303
Celestine	47521
Center	46918
Centerpoint	47840
Centerton, R. Br. Martinsville	46116
Centerville	47330
Central	47110
Chalmers	47929
Chandler	47610
Charlestown (1st)	47111
Charlottesville	46117
Chesterfield, Br. Anderson	46017
Chesterton (1st)	46304
Chicago Avenue, Sta. East Chicago	46312
Chili, R. Br. Denver	46926
Chrisney	47611
Churubusco (1st)	46723
Cicero	46034
Clarks Hill	47930
Clarksburg	47225
Clarksville, Br. Jeffersonville	47130
Clay City	47841
Claypool	46510
Clayton	46118
Clear Creek	47426
Clermont	46119
Clifford	47226
Clinton (1st)	47842
Cloverdale	46120
Coal City	47427
Coalmont	47845
Coatesville	46121

Coesse, R. Br. Columbia
  City..................................46724
Colburn..................................47931
Colfax....................................46035
Collegeville, Br. Rensselaer....47978
Columbia City (1st)................46725
  Coesse, R. Br.....................46724
Columbus (1st)......................47201
Commiskey.............................47227
Connersville (1st)...................47331
Converse................................46919
Cortland.................................47228
Corunna.................................46730
Cory......................................47846
Corydon (1st).........................47112
Covington...............................47932
Craigville...............................46731
Crandall.................................47114
Crane....................................47522
Crawfordsville (1st)................47933
Cromwell...............................46732
Cross Plains...........................47017
Crothersville..........................47229
Crown Point (1st)...................46307
Culver (1st)............................46511
Culver Military Academy, Br.
  Culver..............................46511
Cumberland, Br.
  Indianapolis.......................46229
Cutler...................................46920
Cynthiana..............................47612
Dale......................................47523
Daleville................................47334
Dana.....................................47847
Danville (1st).........................46122
Darlington..............................47940
Dayton..................................47941
Decatur (1st).........................46733
Decker...................................47524
Deedsville..............................46921
Delong...................................46922
Delphi (1st)...........................46923
Demotte................................46310
Denham................................46925
Denver..................................46926
Depauw.................................47115
Deputy..................................47230
Derby....................................47525
Desoto, R. Br. Muncie..........47302
Diflsboro...............................47018
Diplomat Plaza, Sta. Fort
  Wayne (see appendix)
Donaldson..............................46513
Downtown, Sta. Muncie........47305
Dublin...................................47335
Dubois...................................47527
Dugger..................................47848
Dunkirk (1st).........................47336
Dunreith...............................47337
Dupont..................................47231
Dyer.....................................46311
Earl Park...............................47942
  Raub, R. Br.......................47976
Earlham, Sta. Richmond........47374
East Cedar Lake, R. Br.
  Cedar Lake........................46303
East Chicago (1st)................46312
East Enterprise......................47019
East Gary, Br. Gary..............46405
Eaton....................................47338
Eckerty.................................47116
Economy...............................47339
Edinburg (1st).......................46124

Edwardsport..........................47528
Elberfeld...............................47613
Elizabeth...............................47117
Elizabethtown........................47232
Elkhart (1st).........................46514
Ellettsville............................47429
Elnora...................................47529
Elwood (1st).........................46036
Eminence..............................46125
Emison..................................47530
English..................................47118
English Lake, R. Br. North
  Judson..............................46366
Etna Green...........................46524
Evanston...............................47531
EVANSVILLE (1st) (see
  appendix)
Fair Oaks...............................47943
Fairbanks...............................47849
Fairfield, Sta. Fort Wayne....46807
Fairland................................46126
Fairmount..............................46928
Falmouth...............................46127
Farmersburg..........................47850
Farmland...............................47340
Ferdinand...............................47532
Fillmore.................................46128
Finly......................................46129
Fishers...................................46038
Flat Rock...............................47234
Flora......................................46929
Florence.................................47020
Floyds Knobs..........................47119
Folsomville.............................47614
Fontanet................................47851
Foraker, R. Br. Goshen.........46525
Forest....................................46039
Fort Benjamin Harrison, Br.
  Indianapolis.......................46216
Fort Branch............................47648
Fort Ritner.............................47430
FORT WAYNE (1st) (see
  appendix)
Fortville.................................46040
Fountain City.........................47341
Fountaintown.........................46130
Fowler (1st)...........................47944
  Templeton, R. Br..............47986
Fowlerton..............................46930
Francesville...........................47946
Francisco...............................47649
Frankfort (1st).......................46041
  Scircleville, R. Br.............46066
Franklin (1st).........................46131
Frankton...............................46044
Fredericksburg.......................47120
Freedom................................47431
Freelandville..........................47535
Freetown...............................47235
Fremont................................46737
French Lick...........................47432
Friends, Sta. Richmond.........47374
Friendship.............................47021
Fulda....................................47536
Fulton...................................46931
Galveston..............................46932
Garfield, Sta. Indianapolis....46203
Garrett (1st)..........................46738
GARY (1st) (see appendix)
Gas City (1st)........................46933
Gaston..................................47342
Geneva..................................46740
Gentryville............................47537

Georgetown............................47122
Glen Park, Sta. Gary (see
  appendix)
Glendale, Sta. Indianapolis....46220
Glenwood..............................46133
Goldsmith..............................46045
Goodland...............................47948
Goshen (1st)..........................46526
  Foraker, R. Br..................46525
  West Side, Br...................46526
Gosport.................................47433
Grabill..................................46741
Grammer...............................47236
Grandview.............................47615
Granger.................................46530
Grantsburg............................47123
Grass Creek, R. Br.
  Kewanna...........................46935
Graysville..............................47852
Greencastle (1st)...................46135
Greenfield (1st)......................46140
Greens Fork...........................47345
Greensboro............................47344
Greensburg (1st)....................47240
Greentown.............................46936
Greenville.............................47124
Greenwood (1st)....................46142
Griffin...................................47616
Griffith (1st)..........................46319
Grissom A F B, Br. Peru........46970
Grovertown............................46531
Guilford.................................47022
Gwynneville...........................46144
Hagerstown (1st)....................47346
Hall, R. Br. Monrovia.............46145
Hamilton................................46742
Hamlet..................................46532
HAMMOND (1st) (see
  appendix)
Hanna...................................46340
Hanover.................................47243
Harbor, Sta. East Chicago.....46312
Hardinsburg...........................47125
Harlan...................................46743
Harmony................................47853
Harrodsburg...........................47434
Hartford City (1st).................47348
Hartsville..............................47244
Hatfield.................................47617
Haubstadt.............................47639
Hayden..................................47245
Haysville, R. Br. Jasper........47546
Hazelton................................47640
Hazelwood, Sta. Fort Wayne..46805
Hebron..................................46341
Helmer..................................4674
Helmsburg.............................47435
Heltonville.............................47436
Hemlock................................46937
Henryville..............................47126
Hessville, Sta. Hammond......46323
Highland, Br. Hammond........46322
Hillisburg...............................46046
Hillsboro................................47949
Hillsdale................................47854
Hoagland...............................46745
Hobart (1st)...........................46342
Hobbs...................................46047
Holland..................................47541
Holton...................................47023
Homer...................................46146
Honey Creek..........................47350
Hope....................................47246

Howe................................46746
Howell, Sta. Evansville..........47712
Hudson............................46747
Hudson Lake, R. Br. New
  Carlisle..........................46552
Huntertown.......................46748
Huntingburg (1st)...............47542
Huntington (1st).................46750
Huron..............................47437
Hymera............................47855
Idaho, Sta. Terre Haute.........47802
Idaville (1st).....................47950
Illinois Street, Sta.
  Indianapolis....................46225
Independence Hill, Br. Crown
  Point............................46307
Indian Springs....................47544
INDIANAPOLIS (1st) (see
  appendix)
Ingalls............................46048
Inglefield.........................47618
Inwood, R. Br. Plymouth........46533
Ireland............................47545
Irvington, Sta. Indianapolis....46219
Jamestown........................46147
Jasonville.........................47438
Jasper (1st).......................47546
Jeffersonville (1st)...............47130
Jonesboro.........................46938
Jonesville.........................47247
Judson............................47856
Kempton...........................46049
Kendallville (1st).................46755
Kennard...........................47351
Kentland..........................47951
Kewanna...........................46939
  Grass Creek, R. Br..........46935
Keystone...........................46759
Kimmell............................46760
Kingman...........................47952
Kingsbury.........................46345
Kingsford Heights................46346
Kirklin............................46050
Knightstown (1st)................46148
Knightsville.......................47857
Knox (1st).........................46534
Kokomo (1st)......................46901
Koleen.............................47439
Kouts.............................46347
Kramer............................47953
Kurtz..............................47249
Kyana.............................47549
La Crosse.........................46348
La Fontaine.......................46940
La Porte (1st).....................46350
  Otis R. Br....................46367
  Parcel Post Annex, Sta......46350
  Stillwell, R. Br...............46351
Laconia...........................47135
Ladoga............................47954
LAFAYETTE (1st) (see
  appendix)
Lagrange (1st)....................46761
Lagro..............................46941
Lake Cicott.......................46942
Lake Village.......................46349
Laketon...........................46943
Lakeville..........................46536
Lamar.............................47550
Landess...........................46944
Lanesville.........................47136
Laotto.............................46763
Lapaz..............................46537

Larwill............................46764
Laurel.............................47024
Lawndale, Sta. Evansville.......47715
Lawrence, Br. Indianapolis......46226
Lawrenceburg (1st)...............47025
Leavenworth......................47137
Lebanon (1st).....................46052
Leesburg..........................46538
Leipsic............................47440
Leiters Ford.......................46945
Leo................................46765
Leopold............................47551
Leroy..............................46355
Lewis..............................47858
Lewisville.........................47352
Lexington.........................47138
Liberty............................47353
Liberty Center....................46766
Liberty Mills......................46946
Ligonier (1st).....................46767
Lincoln City.......................47552
Linden.............................47955
Linn Grove........................46769
Linton (1st).......................47441
Linwood, Sta. Indianapolis......46201
Little York........................47139
Lizton.............................46149
Logansport (1st)..................46947
Loogootee (1st)...................47553
Losantville........................47354
Lowell (1st).......................46356
Lucerne............................46950
Lynn...............................47355
Lynnville..........................47619
Lyons..............................47443
Mackey............................47654
Macy..............................46951
Madison (1st).....................47250
Magnet............................47555
Manilla............................46150
Mapleton, Sta. Indianapolis.....46208
Maplewood Plaza, Br. Fort
  Wayne..........................46805
Marengo...........................47140
Mariah Hill........................47556
Marion (1st).......................46952
Markle.............................46770
Markleville........................46056
Marshall...........................47859
Marshfield.........................47956
Martinsville (1st).................46151
  Centerton, R. Br.............46116
Marysville.........................47141
Matthews..........................46957
Mauckport.........................47142
Maxwell...........................46154
Mays..............................46155
Mc Cordsville.....................46055
Meadows, Sta. Terre Haute......47803
Mecca.............................47860
Medaryville.......................47957
Medora.............................47260
Mellott............................47958
Memphis..........................47143
Mentone...........................46539
Merom.............................47861
Merrillville, Br. Gary............46410
Metamora.........................47030
Methodist Memorial Home,
  R. Br. Warren................46792
Mexico............................46958
Miami.............................46959
Michigan City (1st)..............46360

Michigantown.....................46057
Middlebury (1st)..................46540
Middletown........................47356
Midland...........................47445
Milan..............................47031
Milford............................46542
Mill Creek.........................46365
Miller, Sta. Gary..................46403
Millersburg........................46543
Millhousen........................47261
Milltown...........................47145
Milroy.............................46156
Milton.............................47357
Mishawaka (1st)..................46544
Mitchell (1st).....................47446
Modoc.............................47358
Mongo.............................46771
Monon.............................47959
Monroe............................46772
Monroe City.......................47557
Monroeville.......................46773
Monrovia..........................46157
  Hall, R. Br...................46145
Monterey..........................46960
Montezuma........................47862
Montgomery.......................47558
Monticello (1st)...................47960
Montmorenci......................47962
Montpelier.........................47359
Mooreland.........................47360
Moores Hill.......................47032
Mooresville (1st)..................46158
Morgantown.......................46160
Morocco...........................47963
Morris.............................47033
Morristown........................46161
Mount Ayr.........................47964
Mount Pleasant...................47559
Mount Saint Francis.............47146
Mount Summit.....................47361
Mount Vernon (1st)..............47620
Mulberry..........................46058
MUNCIE (1st) (see appendix)
Munster, Br. Hammond..........46321
Nabb..............................47147
Napoleon..........................47034
Nappanee (1st)...................46550
Nashville..........................47448
Nebraska..........................47262
Needham..........................46162
New Albany (1st)..................47150
New Augusta, Br.
  Indianapolis (see
  appendix)
New Carlisle.......................46552
New Castle (1st)..................47362
New Goshen.......................47863
New Harmony......................47631
New Haven (1st)...................46774
New Lebanon, R. Br.
  Sullivan.......................47864
New Lisbon........................47366
New Market........................47965
New Middletown..................47160
New Palestine......................46163
New Paris..........................46553
New Point..........................47263
New Richmond.....................47967
New Ross..........................47968
New Salisbury.....................47161
New Trenton.......................47035
New Washington...................47162

New Waverly	46961	
New Whiteland, Br. Whiteland	46184	
Newberry	47449	
Newburgh	47630	
Newport	47966	
Newton Stewart	47450	
Newtonville	47632	
Newtown	47969	
Nineveh	46164	
Noblesville (1st)	46060	
Nora, Br. Indianapolis (see appendix)		
Norman	47264	
North Judson	46366	
North Liberty	46554	
North Madison, Sta. Madison	47250	
North Manchester (1st)	46962	
North Park, Sta. Evansville	47710	
North Salem	46165	
North Terre Haute, Br. Terre Haute	47805	
North Vernon (1st)	47265	
North Webster	46555	
Notre Dame (1st)	46556	
Oakford	46965	
Oakland City	47660	
Oaklandon, Br. Indianapolis	46236	
Oaktown	47561	
Oakville	47367	
Ober	46560	
Ockley	46966	
Odon	47562	
Oldenburg	47036	
Olive Street, Sta. South Bend	46619	
Onward	46967	
Oolitic	47451	
Ora	46968	
Orestes	46063	
Orland	46776	
Orleans	47452	
Osceola	46561	
Osgood	47037	
Ossian	46777	
Tocsin, R. Br.	46790	
Otis, R. Br. La Porte	46367	
Otisco	47163	
Otterbein	47970	
Otwell	47564	
Owensburg	47453	
Owensville	47665	
Oxford	47971	
Palmyra	47164	
Paoli (1st)	47454	
Paragon	46166	
Parcel Post, Sta. Richmond	47374	
Parcel Post Annex, Sta. Fort Wayne	46802	
Parcel Post Annex, Sta. Lafayette	47905	
Parcel Post Annex, Sta. La Porte	46350	
Parcel Post Annex, Sta. Michigan City	46360	
Paris Crossing	47270	
Park Fletcher, Br. Indianapolis	46241	
Parker	47368	
Parkmor, Sta. Elkhart	46514	
Patoka	47666	
Patricksburg	47455	
Patriot	47038	
Paxton	47865	
Pekin	47165	
Pence	47973	
Pendleton (1st)	46064	
Pennville	47369	
Perrysville	47974	
Pershing	47370	
Peru (1st)	46970	
Petersburg (1st)	47567	
Petroleum	46778	
Pierceton	46562	
Pierceville	47039	
Pierre Moran, Sta. Elkhart	46514	
Pimento	47866	
Pine Village	47975	
Pittsboro	46167	
Plainfield (1st)	46168	
Plainville	47568	
Pleasant Lake	46779	
Pleasant Mills	46780	
Plymouth (1st)	46563	
Inwood, R. Br.	46533	
Poland	47868	
Poneto	46781	
Portage (1st)	46368	
Porter, Br. Chesterton	46304	
Portland (1st)	47371	
Poseyville	47633	
Prairie Creek	47869	
Prairieton	47870	
Preble	46782	
Princeton (1st)	47670	
Putnamville	46170	
Quincy	47456	
Radnor	46981	
Ragsdale	47573	
Rainbow, Sta. Indianapolis	46222	
Ramsey	47166	
Raub, R. Br. Earl Park	47976	
Ravenswood, Br. Indianapolis	46240	
Ray, R. Br. Fremont	46737	
Real Silk Hosiery Mills, Sta. Indianapolis	46202	
Redkey	47373	
Reelsville	46171	
Remington	47977	
Rensselaer (1st)	47978	
Reynolds	47980	
Richland	47634	
Richmond (1st)	47374	
Richvalley	46973	
Ridgeville	47380	
Riley	47871	
Rising Sun	47040	
River Park, Sta. South Bend (see appendix)		
Roachdale	46172	
Roann	46974	
Roanoke	46783	
Roby, Sta. Hammond	46326	
Rochester (1st)	46975	
Rockfield	46977	
Rockport	47635	
Rockville (1st)	47872	
Rolling Prairie	46371	
Rome	47574	
Rome City	46784	
Romney	47981	
Rosedale	47874	
Roselawn	46372	
Rossville	46065	
Royal Center	46978	
Rushville (1st)	46173	
Russellville	46175	
Russiaville	46979	
Saint Anthony	47575	
Saint Bernice	47875	
Saint Croix	47576	
Saint Joe	46785	
Saint John	46373	
Saint Louis Crossing	47271	
Saint Mary-of-the-Woods	47876	
Saint Marys, Br. Notre Dame	46556	
Saint Meinrad (1st)	47577	
Saint Paul	47272	
Salamonia	47381	
Salem (1st)	47167	
San Pierre	46374	
Sandborn	47578	
Sandford	47877	
Santa Claus (1st)	47579	
Saratoga	47382	
Schererville	46375	
Schneider	46376	
Schnellville	47580	
Scipio	47273	
Scircleville, R. Br. Frankfort	46066	
Scotland	47457	
Scottsburg (1st)	47170	
Blocher, R. Br.	47170	
Underwood, R. Br.	47177	
Sedalia	46067	
Seelyville	47878	
Sellersburg (1st)	47712	
Selma	47383	
Servia	46980	
Seventeenth Avenue, Sta. Gary	46407	
Seymour (1st)	47274	
Sharpsville	46068	
Shelburn	47879	
Shelby	46377	
Shelbyville (1st)	46176	
Shepardsville	47880	
Sheridan	46069	
Shipshewana	46565	
Shirley	47384	
Shoals	47581	
Siberia	47582	
Sidney	46566	
Silver Lake	46982	
Sims	46983	
Smithville	47458	
Soldiers Home, Br. Lafayette	47901	
Solsberry	47459	
Somerset	46984	
Somerville	47683	
SOUTH BEND (1st) (see appendix)		
South Calumet Avenue, Sta. Hammond	46324	
South Kokomo, Sta. Kokomo	46901	
South Marion, Sta. Marion	46952	
South Milford	46786	
South Whitley (1st)	46787	
Southport, Br. Indianapolis (see appendix)		
Speed, R. Br. Sellersburg	47172	
Speedway, Br. Indianapolis (see appendix)		
Spencer (1st)	47460	
Spencerville	46788	

Spiceland	47385
Springport	47386
Springville	47462
Spurgeon	47584
Stanford	47463
Star City	46985
State Line	47982
State Office Building, Sta. Indianapolis	46204
Staunton	47881
Stendal	47585
Stewartsville	47636
Stilesville	46180
Stillwell, R. Br. La Porte	46351
Stinesville	47464
Stockwell	47983
Straughn	47387
Stroh	46789
Sullivan (1st)	47882
New Lebanon, R. Br.	47864
Sulphur	47174
Sulphur Springs	47388
Sumava Resorts	46379
Summitville	46070
Sunman	47041
Swayzee	46986
Sweetser	46987
Switz City	47465
Syracuse (1st)	46567
Talbot	47984
Tangier	47985
Taswell	47175
Taylorsville	47280
Tefft	46380
Tell City (1st)	47586
Templeton, R. Br. Fowler	47986
Tennyson	47637
TERRE HAUTE (1st) (see appendix)	
Thayer	46381
Thorntown	46071
Times Corner, Br. Fort Wayne	46804
Tippecanoe	46570
Tipton (1st)	46072
Tobinsport	47587
Tocsin, R. Br. Ossian	46790
Tolleston, Sta. Gary	46404
Topeka	46571
Trafalgar	46181
Troy	47588
Tunnelton	47467
Twelve Mile	46988
Twelve Points, Sta. Terre Haute	47804
Tyner	46572
Underwood, R. Br. Scottsburg	47177
Union City (1st)	47390
Union Mills	46382
Uniondale	46791
Uniontown	47589
Unionville	47468
Universal	47884
Upland	46989
Uptown, Sta. Indianapolis	46205
Urbana	46990
Vallonia	47281
Valparaiso (1st)	46383
Van Buren	46991
Veedersburg	47987
Velpen	47590
Vernon	47282
Versailles	47042
Vevay	47043
Vincennes (1st)	47591
Wabash (1st)	46992
Wadesville	47638
Wakarusa	46573
Waldron	46182
Walkerton	46574
Wallace	47988
Walton	46994
Wanamaker, Br. Indianapolis	46239
Wanatah	46390
Warren	46792
Warsaw (1st)	46580
Washington (1st)	47501
Waterloo	46793
Waveland	47989
Wawaka	46794
Waynedale, Sta. Fort Wayne (see appendix)	
Waynetown	47990
Webster	47392
Weisburg	47044
West Baden Springs	47469
West Fork	47178
West Indianapolis, Sta. Indianapolis	46221
West Lafayette, Br. Lafayette	47906
West Lebanon	47991
West Middleton	46995
West Newton	46183
West Side, Br. Goshen	46526
West Terre Haute	47885
Westfield	46074
Westphalia	47596
Westpoint	47992
Westport	47283
Westville	46391
Wheatfield	46392
Wheatland	47597
Wheeler	46393
White Swan, Br. Fort Wayne (see appendix)	
Whiteland	46184
Whitestown	46075
Whiting (1st)	46394
Wilkinson	46186
Williams	47470
Williamsburg	47393
Williamsport	47993
Willow Branch	46187
Winamac (1st)	46996
Winchester (1st)	47394
Windfall	46076
Wingate	47994
Winona Lake (1st)	46590
Winslow	47598
Wolcott	47995
Wolcottville	46795
Wolflake	46796
Woodburn	46797
Worthington	47471
Wyatt	46595
Yeoman	47997
Yoder	46798
Yorktown	47396
Young America	46998
Youngs Creek	47472
Zanesville	46799
Zionsville (1st)	46077

ANDERSON   460

POST OFFICE BOXES

Box Nos.

1-209	Chesterfield Br	17
1-1200	B Sta	15
1691-1968	A Sta	14
2000-2727	Main Office	11

RURAL ROUTES

1,2,3,4,5,6,7,8,9		11

STATIONS, BRANCHES AND UNITS

Chesterfield Br	17
General Delivery	11
Postmaster	11

APARTMENTS, HOTELS, MOTELS

Abbott Apts, 1003 - 11 East 8th	12
Anderson College Apts, 1700 East 1st	12
Anderson Motor Inn, 912 Meridian	16
Beverly Terrace Apts, 1102 Central Ave	16
Bi-Nine Motel, 3114 St Rd 9 N	12
Boulevard Apts, 802 Harter Blvd	11
Brock Apts, 23 West 11th	16
Country Charm Motel, 5015 St Rd 9 N	12
Delaware Court Apts, 128 West 10th	16
Eberhart Apts, 1412 Meridian	16
Edgewood Plaza, 2725 West 16th & 1710 Brentwood Dr	11
Empire Apts, 2800 Crystal	12
Franklin Apts, 3606 - 24 Scatterfield Rd	13
Gaslight Apts, 814 - 910 West 53rd	13
Giant Oaks Apts, 1300 - 32 West 8th	11
Hilltop Apts, 4511 Columbus Ave	14
Holiday Inn Motel, 5920 Scatterfield Rd	13
Hoosier Motor Court, R 03	11
Johnsons Motel, 3711 St Rd 9 N	12
Kings Inn, 583 Broadway	12
Kingston Greene Apts, 2505 East 10th	12
Lincolnshire Apts, 330 West 12th	16
Madison Ridge Apts, 1627-31 Madison Ave N	12
Mainview Apts, 2459 Main	14
Mar Jon Motel, 1327 East 53rd	13
Mark Motor Inn, 2400 St Rd 109 S	13
New Leigh Apts, 1324 - 26 West 11th	11

Pine Tree Village, 2801 West 28th	11
Pricewood Ct, Pricewood Ct	14
Tower Apts, 1109 Jackson	16
Town Motel, 1002 Main	16
Travelers Rest, R 08	11
Vickers Apts, 2012 East 7th & 1808 East 8th	12

BUILDINGS

Anderson Bank, 931 Meridian	16
Anderson Federal Savings, 100 West 11th	16
Citizens Bank, 1106 Meridian	16
City Hall, 708 Main	11
Delco Administration, 2401 Columbus Ave	11
First Savings And Loan, 10th And Jackson	16
Guide Lamp Administration, 2915 Pendleton Ave	11
Madison Co Court House, 8th And Meridian	16
Medical Arts, 1931 Brown	14
Professional Office, 1415 Raible Ave	11
Warner Press Administration, 1200 East 5th	11

HOSPITALS

Anderson Emergency	11
Community	12
Saint Johns	11

UNIVERSITIES AND COLLEGES

Anderson	11
Indiana Business	11

EVANSVILLE   477

POST OFFICE BOXES

Box Nos.

1-159	Main Office	01
19-ONLY	Waterworks Dept	40
161-335	Main Office	02
341-515	Main Office	03
358-ONLY	Geo Koch And Sons	44
521-695	Main Office	04
569-ONLY	Sou Ind Gas And Elec Co	41
701-875	Main Office	05
778-ONLY	Citizens Natl Bank	39
881-999	Main Office	06
1000-1199	Station C	13
2001-2999	Station D	14
3001-3119	Main Office	30
3037-ONLY	District Manager Evv Postal District	99
3121-3277	Main Office	31
3281-3397	Main Office	32

3401-3477	Main Office	33
3481-3597	Main Office	34
3601-3735	Main Office	35
3741-3855	Main Office	36
4001-4999	Station A	11
5000-5999	Lawndale Sta	15
6001-6999	Station B	12
7000-7999	Howell Sta	12

RURAL ROUTES

1,2		12
3		11
4		12
5		11
7		12
8		11
13		12

STATIONS, BRANCHES AND UNITS

Howell Sta	12
Lawndale Sta	15
North Park Sta	10
General Delivery	08
Postmaster	08

APARTMENTS, HOTELS, MOTELS

Audubon	13
Beal	13
Becker	13
Bernardin	08
Buckingham	13
Cambridge Arms	13
Claremont	08
Colonial	13
Continental	15
Deakin	13
Donaldson Arms	13
Executive Inn, 600 Walnut	08
Fabian	13
Georgetown	15
Jackson House Motel, 20 Walnut	08
Jamestown	14
Maybelle	13
Mayflower	14
Mc Curdy, 101 SE 1st	08
Plaza	08
Riviera	13
Savannah	15
Shamrock	15
Sonntag, 614 Main	08
Stratford	13
Towne Motel, 15 NW Riverside Dr	08
Washington Court	13
Wedgewood	14
Williamson	13

BUILDINGS

Citizens National Bank, 19 NW 4th St	08
Commercial, 16 SE 2nd	08
Grein, 19 NW 2nd	08
Hulman, 24 NW 4th	08
Indiana Bell Telephone Company, 133 NW 5th	08
Kinkle	08
Lawndale Shopping Center	15

Evansville (Con.)   477

Metropolitan, 9 NW 4th.......... 08
National City Bank, 227
     Main................................. 01
Old National Bank, 416
     Main................................. 08
Southern Securities, 329
     Main................................. 08
Third & Main, 11 NW 3rd....... 08
Washington Square Mall......... 15
Werner 12
Wright, 109 SE 3 Rd St......... 08
312, 312 NW 7th.................. 08
320 08

GOVERNMENT OFFICES

City Hall 08
City Health Dept.................. 08
Civic Center Complex............ 08
Court, 123 NW 4th St........... 08
Courts Bldg........................ 08
Federal Bldg....................... 08
Main Post Office, 800
     Sycamore........................ 08

HOSPITALS

Clearview Sanitarium,
     Kratzville Rd 01
Evansville State, Outer
     Lincoln Ave 01
Protestant Deaconness, 600
     Mary............................... 10
Saint Marys, 3700
     Washington Ave................ 15
Welborn Baptist Memorial,
     412 SE 4th 13

MILITARY INSTALLATIONS

Army Reserve Center.............. 14
United States Naval Armory.... 12

UNIVERSITIES AND COLLEGES

Bramswell Business 3rd And
     Main Bldg 08
Evansville Univ, 1800 Lincoln
     Ave................................. 01
Ind State Univ Highway 62
     W................................... 12
Lockyears Business, 209 NW
     5th 01

FORT WAYNE   468

POST OFFICE BOXES

Box Nos.
1-1400   Main Office 01
2600-2799   D Sta............... 08
5000-6000   Hazlewood Sta.. 05
6001-6999   Diplomat Plaza
         Sta................. 06
7001-7999   Fairfield Sta 07
9000-9999   Waynedale Sta . 09

RURAL ROUTES

1,2 25
3 08
4 19
5 18
6 04
7 16
8 09
9 15
13 08

STATIONS, BRANCHES AND UNITS

Fairfield Sta 07
Hazelwood Sta.................... 05
Maplewood Plaza Br............. 05
Parcel Post Annex Sta........... 02
Times Corner Br 04
General Delivery 02
Postmaster.......................... 02

APARTMENTS, HOTELS, MOTELS

Keenan, 1006 S Harrison....... 02
Key Largo Motor Inn,
     Highways 30 & 33, W........ 08
Lincoldale Trailer Court,
     2922 Coliseum Blvd W...... 08
Rose Marie, 119 W Columbia. 02
Sheraton Inn, 330 E
     Washington Blvd............... 02
Van Orman Northcrest, 505
     Coliseum Blvd E 05

BUILDINGS

Anthony Wayne Bank, 203 E
     Berry.............................. 02
Central, 203 W Wayne 02
Commerce Building 127 W
     Berry Street..................... 02
Federal, 1302 S Harrison....... 02
Ft Wayne National Bank, 110
     W Berry.......................... 02
Gettle, 801-03 S Calhoun...... 02
Indiana Bank, 915 S Clinton.. 02
Kover, 124 W Wayne 02
Library, 900 Webster............ 02
Lincoln Tower, 114 E Berry.... 02
National Management, 104 W
     Main............................... 02
Peoples Trust, 913 S
     Calhoun.......................... 02
School Administration, 1230
     S Clinton 02
Standard, 217 E Berry........... 02
Strauss, 809 S Calhoun......... 02
Utility, 116 E Wayne 02

GOVERNMENT OFFICES

City-County Bldg, One Main.... 02
Courthouse, Allen County....... 02

HOSPITALS

Irene Byron Sanitorium,
     12515 Lima Rd................. 08
Lutheran Hospital, 3024
     Fairfield Ave.................... 07
Parkview Hospital, 2200
     Randalia Dr 05

Saint Joseph Hospital, 700
     Broadway........................ 02
State School, 801 E State 05
United States Veterans, 1600
     Randalia Dr 05

UNIVERSITIES AND COLLEGES

Concordia College, 6600 N
     Clinton 25
Fort Wayne Bible College,
     800 W Rudisill Blvd 07
Indiana Institute Of
     Technology, 1600 E
     Washington...................... 03
Indiana Univ. & Purdue Univ.
     2101 Coliseum Blvd E........ 05
Saint Francis College, 2701
     Spring 08

GARY   464

POST OFFICE BOXES

Box Nos.
1-899   Gary................... 01
1100-1699   17th Avenue
         Sta................... 07
1700-2199   Glen Park West
         Sta................... 08
2400-2699   Miller Sta 03
4000-4999   Tolleston Sta 04
5000-5999   East Gary Br 05
6000-6999   Brunswick Sta.... 06
7000-8170   Merrillville 10
9000-9267   Gary................. 01

STATIONS, BRANCHES AND UNITS

Brunswick Sta 06
Buffington Sta...................... 06
Diplomat Plaza Sta............... 06
East Gary Br........................ 05
Glen Park Sta....................... 08
Merrillville Br...................... 10
Miller Sta 03
Seventeenth Avenue Sta........... 07
Tolleston Sta........................ 04
Waynedale Sta 09
White Swan Br...................... 08
General Delivery................... 01
Postmaster.......................... 01

APARTMENTS, HOTELS, MOTELS

Ambassador Apartment
     Building, 574 Monroe........ 02
Beverly Furnished
     Apartments, 411 W 8th
     Ave................................. 02
Boulevard, 764 Washington.... 02
City, 127 W 4th Ave.............. 02
Courtview, 428 Washington.... 02
Dalton Apartments, 131 E
     5th Ave 02
Dobbies, 1838 Virginia......... 07
Dolly Madison, 529 Madison... 02
Gary Travel Lodge, 6230
     Melton Rd 03
Gary, 578 Broadway.............. 02
Gateway Apartments, 406
     Washington...................... 02

199

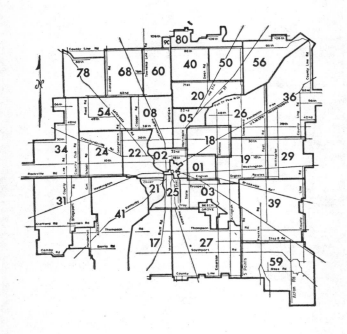

ZIP CODES
INDIANAPOLIS, Ind.
462 + two digits shown = zip code

Gary (Con.) 464

Gotham, 1235 Madison.......... 07
Holiday Inn Of America, 3030
E 8th Ave............................ 02
Holiday Inn Of America, 465
Broadway............................ 02
Holiday Inn Of America, 800
E 81st Ave.......................... 10
Knight Of Columbus Club,
331 W 5th Ave.................... 02
Lake, 734 Washington 02
Madison Square Apartments,
325 W 6th Ave.................... 02
Ramada Inn, 2075 Ripley....... 05
Roosevelt, 105 E 5th Ave 02
Seville Court Apartments,
1720 W 5th Ave.................. 04
Sheraton Diplomat, U S 20
Clay St............................... 03
Toledo, 2195 Adams 07
Victory Arms Apartments,
413 Connecticut 02
Westbrook Apartments, 2301
Waverly Dr.......................... 04

BUILDINGS

Federal, 610 Connecticut St ... 02
Gary National Bank, 504
Broadway............................ 02
Gibralter, 1649 Broadway....... 07
Hall, 607 Broadway................ 02
Herschbach, 1085 Broadway .. 02
Lake County Superior Court,
400 Broadway..................... 02
Lee, 673 Broadway................. 02
Marshall House, 31 E 5th
Ave..................................... 02
Medical Center, 2717
Wabash.............................. 04
Model, 738 Broadway............. 02
Veterans Administration, 610
Connecticut St 02

GOVERNMENT OFFICES

City Hall, 401 Broadway......... 02
County Building, 400
Broadway............................ 02

HOSPITALS

Methodist Hospital, 1600 W
6th Ave 02
Saint Mary Mercy Hospital,
540 Tyler............................ 02

UNIVERSITIES AND COLLEGES

Indiana University, Gary
Center, 3400 Broadway 08

HAMMOND 463

POST OFFICE BOXES

Box Nos.
1-1200   Hammond.......... 25
1000-1999   Highland Br...... 22
2000-2999   Hessville Sta 23
3000-3999   Munster Br 21

4000-4999   South Calumet
            Avenue Sta 24

STATIONS, BRANCHES AND UNITS

Hessville Sta 23
Highland Br............................. 22
Munster Br 21
Roby Sta 26
South Calumet Avenue Sta...... 24
General Delivery 20
Postmaster 20

INDIANAPOLIS 462

POST OFFICE BOXES

Box Nos.
1-2000   Indianapolis 06
11000-11999 Linwood Sta 01
16000-16999 Fort Benjamin
             Harrison Br.... 16
18000-18999 Brightwood
             Sta................ 18
19000-19999 Eastgate Sta.... 19
20000-20999 Broad Ripple
             Sta................ 20
21000-21999 West
             Indianapolis
             Sta................ 21
22000-22999 Rainbow Sta..... 22
24000-24999 Speedway Sta.... 24
26000-26999 Lawrence Br..... 26
27000-27999 Southport Br.... 27
29000-29999 Cumberland
             Br 29
31000-31999 Bridgeport Br .. 31
33000-33999 Garfield Sta..... 03
36000-36999 Oaklandon Br ... 36
39000-39999 Wanamaker Br . 39
40000-40999 Nora Br........... 40
41000-41499 Park Fletcher.... 41
41501-41599 Amf Sta 41
44001-44999 Federal Sta....... 04
50000-50999 Castleton Br..... 50
55000-55999 Uptown Sta 05
59000-59999 Acton Br 59
68000-68999 New Augusta
             Br 68
88000-88999 Mapleton Sta.... 08

RURAL ROUTES

1... 27
2... 31
3... 41
4... 27
5... 59
7... 41
8... 31
9,10... 39
11... 29
12,13....................................... 36
15... 59
16... 68
17,18....................................... 24

STATIONS, BRANCHES AND UNITS

Acton Br 59
Air Mail Field Sta..................... 41
Bridgeport Br 31

Brightwood Sta........................ 18
Broad Ripple Sta...................... 20
Castleton Br 50
Cumberland Br......................... 29
Fort Benjamin Harrison Br....... 16
Garfield Sta 03
Glendale Sta 20
Illinois Street Sta..................... 25
Irvington Sta 19
Lawrence Br 26
Linwood Sta 01
Mapleton Sta........................... 08
New Augusta Br....................... 68
Nora Br 40
Oaklandon Br 36
Park Fletcher Br....................... 41
Rainbow Sta 22
Ravenswood Br........................ 40
Real Silk Hosiery Mills Sta....... 02
Southport Br 17
Speedway Br 24
State Office Building Sta........... 04
Uptown Sta 05
Wanamaker Br 39
West Indianapolis Sta.............. 21
General Delivery....................... 04
Postmaster............................... 06

BUILDINGS

Architects & Builders, 333 N
Pennsylvania...................... 04
Bankers Trust, 39 East Ohio .. 04
Big Four, 105 S Meridian 25
Board Of Trade, 143 N
Meridian............................ 04
Century, 36 S Pennsylvania ... 04
Chamber Of Commerce, 320
N Meridian........................ 04
Circle Tower, 5 E Market 04
City-County, 200 E
Washington 04
Coliseum, State Fairgrounds... 05
Consolidated, 115 N
Pennsylvania...................... 04
Doctors Bldg, 224 N
Meridian............................ 04
Electric, 17 N Meridian........... 04
Empire Life, 2801 N
Meridian............................ 08
Employment Security Division
State Of Indian, 10 N
Senate............................... 04
English Foundation, 615 N
Alabama............................. 04
Farm Bureau Co-Op, 47 S
Pennsylvania...................... 04
Farm Bureau Insurance, 130
E Washington..................... 04
Federal, Meridian & Ohio....... 04
Fidelity, 111 Monument Cir 04
First Federal, 11 N
Pennsylvania...................... 04
Goodman, 40 W Washington... 04
Guaranty, 20 N Meridian........ 04
Hornblower, 129 East Market . 04
Hume Mansur, 23 E Ohio....... 04
I S T A Center, 150 W
Market............................... 04
Illinois, 17 W Market.............. 04
Indiana Lumbermans Mutual,
429 N Pennsylvania............ 04
Indiana, 120 E Market............ 04

Indianapolis (Con.) 462

Inland, 156 E Market..............	04
Jackson, 546 S Meridian..........	25
Jefferson National, 241 N	
Pennsylvania.......................	04
Kresge, 41 E Washington.........	04
Larosa, 107 N Pennsylvania....	04
Manufacturers, State	
Fairgrounds........................	05
Merchants Bank, 11 S	
Meridian............................	04
Morris Plan, 108 E	
Washington........................	04
Ober, 38 N Pennsylvania	04
Peoples Bank, 134 E Market..	04
Roosevelt, 9 N Illinois............	04
Star & News, 307 N Penn	06
State House, 200 W	
Washington........................	04
State Office, 100 N Senate	
Ave	04
Test, 54 Monument Cir..........	04
Underwriters, 445 N	
Pennsylvania.......................	04
Union Title, 155 E Market......	04
120 W Market.....................	04

GOVERNMENT OFFICES

Army Finance Center..............	49

HOSPITALS

Childrens, 1040 W Michigan ..	02
Community, 1500 N Ritter	
Ave	19
Indiana University, 1100 W	
Michigan...........................	02
Larue D Carter, 1315 W	
10th.................................	02
Marion County General, 960	
Locke...............................	02
Medical Center, 1100 W	
Michigan...........................	02
Methodist Hospital Of Ind,	
1640 N Capitol Ave............	02
Riley, 1040 W Michigan........	02
Robert W Long, 1100 W	
Michigan...........................	02
Saint Vincents, 120 W Fall	
Creek Pkwy........................	08
University Heights, 3350	
Carson Ave	27
Veterans Administration,	
1461 W 10th......................	02
William H Coleman, 1100 W	
Michigan...........................	02
Winona Memorial, 3202 N	
Meridian............................	08

UNIVERSITIES AND COLLEGES

Butler University, 4600	
Sunset Ave	08
Central Business, 802 N	
Meridian............................	06
Herron Art Institute, 110 E	
16th.................................	02
Indiana Business, 802 N	
Meridian............................	06
Indiana Central, 4001 S	
Otterbein	27

Indiana State School For The	
Blind, 7725 College Ave.....	40
Indiana State School For The	
Deaf, 1200 E 42nd............	05
Indiana U Grad School Of	
Scocial Science, 122 E	
Michigan...........................	04
Indiana University Extension,	
518 N Delaware..................	04
Indiana University School Of	
Dentistry, 1121 W	
Michigan...........................	02
Indiana University School Of	
Law, 102 W Michigan.........	04
Indiana University School Of	
Medicine, 1100 W	
Michigan...........................	02
Indiana University School Of	
Nursing, 1232 W	
Michigan...........................	02
Jordan College Of Music	
Branch, 3411 N	
Pennsylvania.......................	05
Jordan College Of Music Of	
Butler Univ, 4600 Sunset	
Ave	08
Ladywood School, 5375	
Millersville Rd....................	26
Lain Business, 601 N	
Delaware...........................	04
Lincoln Chiropractice College	
Incorporat, 3171 N	
Meridian............................	08
Marian, 3200 Cold Springs	
Rd	22
Normal College Of American	
Gymnastic Unio, 415 E	
Michigan...........................	04
Purdue University Extension,	
1201 E 38th......................	05

LAFAYETTE 479

POST OFFICE BOXES

Box Nos.		
1-1538	Lafayette	02
2001-2270	West Lafayette	
	Br	06
3000-3250	Sta 11	06

RURAL ROUTES

1,2...................................	06
3,4,5,6,7,8.........................	05
9,10..................................	06
11,12,13,14,15....................	05
16.....................................	06
17.....................................	05

STATIONS, BRANCHES AND UNITS

Parcel Post Annex Sta..........	05
Soldiers Home Br	01
West Lafayette Br.................	06
General Delivery	02
Postmaster	01

UNIVERSITIES AND COLLEGES

Purdue University	07

MUNCIE 473

POST OFFICE BOXES

Box Nos.		
1-1312	Downtown Sta..	05
D1-D126	Desoto R. Sta..	02
2001-2856	Main Office	02

RURAL ROUTES

1,2,3,4,5,6,7,8,9...................	02

STATIONS, BRANCHES AND UNITS

Desoto Rural Br....................	02
Downtown Sta......................	05
General Delivery	02
Postmaster	02

APARTMENTS, HOTELS, MOTELS

Anthony Apartments Bethel	04
Canopic 215 S Jefferson.........	05
Chateau 2001 N Walnut	03
Cohen 110 1/2 W Seymour....	05
Elliott 620 N Mckinley Ave.....	03
Grays Court 2000 Burlington	
Dr	02
Graystone 900 E Washington..	04
Greenbrier 720 W Centennial..	03
Imperial 1200 S Mulberry.......	02
Jackson-Vine 209 S Vine........	05
Kimberly Court 615 W	
Charles..............................	05
Linden House 510 Riverside..	03
Middletown Gardens 2301 S	
Manhattan.........................	02
Munsyana Homes 800 S	
Madison	02
Oakwood 326 Oakwood..........	04
Parkview Nursing Home.........	03
Rector 522 W Adams	05
Schiedler N Tillotson	04
Star 310 S Mulberry..............	05
Thomas 316 N Mulberry........	05
Westbriar 2904 Brook	04
400 Apartments 408	
Riverside...........................	03

UNIVERSITIES AND COLLEGES

Ball State Univ.....................	06

SOUTH BEND 466

POST OFFICE BOXES

Box Nos.		
1-1999	Main Office	24
2001-2499	River Park Sta..	15
2501-2999	Station A	13
3001-3999	Olive Street	
	Sta..................	19

RURAL ROUTES

1.......................................	14
2.......................................	19
4	28

South Bend (Con.)　　　　466

STATIONS, BRANCHES AND UNITS

Olive Street Sta	19
River Park Sta	15
General Delivery	24
Postmaster	24

APARTMENTS, HOTELS, MOTELS

Alou Motel, 52547 U S 31	37
Blackwood, 422 S 25th	15
Blue & Gold Motel, 204 Dixie Way S	37
Broadway, 104 E Broadway	18
Capitol Motel, 236 Dixie Way N	37
City Motel, 1631 Lincoln Way E	13
Drake Motel, 60971 US 31	14
Eddy Colfax, 132 N Eddy	17
Foust Motel, 23040 US 20	28
Garst Arms, 103 W Garst	18
Holiday Inn Motel, 515 Dixie Way N	37
Howard Johnson Motor Lodge, 52939 US 31	37
Ivanhoe, 1112 S 20th	15
Jefferson, 332 W Jefferson Blvd	01
Kenrose Motel, 25725 US 20	28
Kentre Motel, 25190 St Rd 2	19
Lasalle Motor Inn, 237 N Michigan	24
Lincolnwood Motel, 3300 Lincoln Way W	28
Mar Main Arms, 119-125 W Marion	01
Morningside, 413 W Colfax Ave	01
North Shore, 1405-21 North Side Blvd	15
Plaza, 628 W Western Ave	25
Ramada Inn, 52890 U S 31	37
Randalls Inn, 130 Dixie Way S	37
Riverside, 1587-1683 Riverside Dr	16
Rushton, 501 W Washington	01
Shirley Motel, 60855 US 31	14
South Bend Motel, 3420 S Michigan	14
Southern, 124 W Tutt	18
Sunnyside, 1009 E Jefferson Blvd	17
The Villa, 18644 Cleveland Rd	37
Town Tower Motel, 423 N Michigan	01*
Travelodge, 614 N Michigan	01
Washington Colfax, 618 W Colfax Ave	01
Westwood Motel, 25200 State Rd 2	19
Y W C A, 802 N Lafayette Blvd	01

BUILDINGS

American National Bank, 211 W Washington	01
Bendix Corporation, 401 N Bendix Dr	20
Building & Loan Tower, 216 W Washington	01
Burke, 115 N William	01
Christman, 211 N Main	01
Commerce, 105 W Wayne	01
First Bank, 205 W Jefferson Blvd	01
Hibberd, 321 S Main	01
I O O F, 104 S Main	01
J M S, 108 N Main	01
Jefferson Medical Arts, 919 E Jefferson Blvd	22
Kirk, 220 S William	25
La Salle West, 120 W La Salle Ave	01
Lafayette, 115 S Lafayette Blvd	01
Lincoln Life, 622 N Michigan	01
National Bank, 110 W Jefferson Blvd	01
Oliver Theatre, 114 N Main	01
Poledor, 102 E Colfax Ave	01
Saint Joseph Bank, 202 S Michigan	01
Sherland, 105 E Jefferson Blvd	01
South Bend Tribune, 223 W Colfax Ave	26
Tower, 216 W Washington	01
Whitcomb & Keller, 224 W Jefferson Blvd	01
Y M C A, 1201 North Side Blvd	15

GOVERNMENT OFFICES

Central Services, 701 W Sample	21
County-City, 227 W Jefferson Blvd	01
Court House 115 S Main	01
Federal, 204 S. Main	24

HOSPITALS

Healthwin, 20531 Darden Rd	37
Memorial, 615 N Michigan	01
Northern Indiana Childrens, 1234 N Notre Dame Ave	22
Saint Josephs, 811 E Madison	22
South Bend Osteopathic, 2515 E Jefferson Blvd	15

UNIVERSITIES AND COLLEGES

Indiana University Center, 1825 North Side Blvd	15

TERRE HAUTE　　　478

POST OFFICE BOXES

Box Nos.		
1-1699	Main Office	08
2000-2099	Idaho Sta	02
3000-3099	Meadows Sta	03
4000-4999	Twelve Points Sta	04
5000-5099	North Terre Haute Br	05

RURAL ROUTES

21,22,23,24,25	02
31,32	03
51,52	05

STATIONS, BRANCHES AND UNITS

Idaho Sta	02
Meadows Sta	03
North Terre Haute Br	05
Twelve Points Sta	04
General Delivery	08
Postmaster	08

APARTMENTS, HOTELS, MOTELS

Albert Pick Motel, U S Hwy 41 South	02
Greenbriar Village Apts, 4961 Dixie Bee Rd	02
Heritage Apts, 3600 Poplar	03
Holiday Inn Motel, U S Hwy 41 South	02
Imperial House, Motel, 2150 N 3rd	04
Ritz Plaza Motor Lodge, 6000 Wabash Ave	03

BUILDINGS

Honey Creek Square Shopping Center, U S 41 S	02
K-Mart Plaza, 2500 Wabash Ave	03
Meadows Shopping Center, 2600 Poplar	03
Merchants Bank Bldg, 17 S 7th	07
Sycamore Bldg, 19 S 6th	07

HOSPITALS

Saint Anthony Hospital, 1021 S 6th	07
Union Hospital, 1606 N 7th	04

UNIVERSITIES AND COLLEGES

Indiana State University, 217 N 6th	09
Rose Hulman Institute Of Technology 5500 Wabash Ave	03

IOWA
(Abbreviation: IA)

Ackley	50601	
Ackworth	50001	
Adair	50002	
Adel	50003	
Afton	50830	
Agency	52530	
Ainsworth	52201	
Akron	51001	
Albert City	50510	
Albia (1st)	52531	
Albion	50005	
Alburnett	52202	
Alden	50006	
Alexander	50420	
Algona (1st)	50511	
Irvington, R. Br.	50550	
Alleman	50007	
Allendorf	51330	
Allerton	50008	
Allison	50602	
Alpha	52130	
Alta	51002	
Alta Vista	50603	
Alton	51003	
Altoona	50009	
Alvord	51230	
Amana (1st)	52203	
Amber, R. Br. Anamosa	52204	
Ames (1st)	50010	
Anamosa (1st)	52205	
Amber, R. Br.	52204	
Andover	52701	
Andrew	52030	
Anita	50020	
Ankeny (1st)	50021	
Anthon	51004	
Aplington	50604	
Arcadia	51430	
Archer	51231	
Aredale	50605	
Argyle	52619	
Arion	51520	
Arispe	50831	
Arlington	50606	
Armstrong	50514	
Arnolds Park	51331	
Arthur	51431	
Ashton	51232	
Aspinwall, R. Br. Manning	51432	
Atalissa	52720	
Athelstan, R. Br. Blockton	50832	
Atkins	52206	
Atlantic (1st)	50022	
Attica, R. Br. Knoxville	50024	
Auburn	51433	
Audubon (1st)	50025	
Aurelia	51005	
Aurora	50607	
Austinville	50608	
Avoca	51521	
Ayrshire	50515	
Badger	50516	
Bagley	50026	
Baldwin	52207	
Bancroft	50517	
Barnes City	50027	
Barnum	50518	
Bartlett, R. Br. Thurman	51655	
Batavia	52533	
Battle Creek	51006	
Baxter	50028	
Bayard	50029	
Beacon	52534	
Beaconsfield	50030	
Beaman	50609	
Beaver	50031	
Beaverdale, Sta. Des Moines	50310	
Bedford	50833	
Conway, R. Br.	50834	
Belle Plaine (1st)	52208	
Bellevue	52031	
Belmond (1st)	50421	
Bennett	52721	
Benton	50835	
Bernard	52032	
Berwick	50032	
Bettendorf (1st)	52722	
Bevington	50033	
Big Rock	52725	
Birmingham	52535	
Blairsburg	50034	
Blairstown	52209	
Blakesburg	52536	
Blanchard	51630	
Blencoe	51523	
Blockton	50836	
Athelstan, R. Br.	50832	
Bloomfield (1st)	52537	
Troy, R. Br.	52537	
West Grove, R. Br.	52538	
Blue Grass	52726	
Bode	50519	
Bonaparte	52620	
Bondurant	50035	
Boone (1st)	50036	
Booneville	50038	
Boulevard, Sta. Sioux City	51109	
Bouton	50039	
Boxholm	50040	
Boyden	51234	
Braddyville	51631	
Bradford	50041	
Bradgate	50520	
Brandon	52210	
Brayton	50042	
Breda	51436	
Bremer	50610	
Bridgewater	50837	
Brighton	52540	
East Pleasant Plain, R. Br.	52541	
Bristow	50611	
Britt	50423	
Bronson	51007	
Brooklyn	52211	
Brooks, R. Br. Corning	50838	
Brunsville	51008	
Bryant	52727	
Buckeye	50043	
Buckingham	50612	
Buffalo	52728	
Buffalo Center	50424	
Burchinal	50425	
Burlington (1st)	52601	
Burnside	50521	
Burr Oak	52131	
Burt	50522	
Bussey	50044	
Calamus	52729	
Call Terminal, Sta. Sioux City	51101	
Callender	50523	
Calmar	52132	
Calumet	51009	
Camanche	52730	
Cambria, R. Br. Corydon	50045	
Cambridge	50046	
Cantril	52542	
Carbon	50839	
Carlisle	50047	
Carnarvon	51437	
Carpenter	50426	
Carroll (1st)	51401	
Carson	51525	
Cascade	52033	
Casey	50048	
Castalia	52133	
Castana	51010	
Cedar	52543	
Cedar Falls (1st)	50613	
Cedar Hills, Sta. Cedar Rapids	52405	
CEDAR RAPIDS (1st) (see appendix)		
Center Junction	52212	
Center Point	52213	
Centerville (1st)	52544	
Rathbun, R. Br.	52545	
Central, Sta. Davenport	52805	
Central City	52214	
Central College, Sta. Pella	50219	
Central Heights, R. Br. Mason City	50401	
Chapin	50427	
Chariton (1st)	50049	
Charles City (1st)	50616	
Colwell, R. Br.	50620	
Charlotte	52731	
Charter Oak	51439	
Chatsworth, R. Br. Hawarden	51011	
Chelsea	52215	
Cherokee (1st)	51012	
Chester	52134	
Chillicothe	52548	
Churdan	50050	
Cincinnati	52549	
Clare	50524	
Clarence	52216	
Clarinda (1st)	51632	
Clarion (1st)	50525	
Clarksville	50619	
Clear Lake (1st)	50428	
Clearfield	50840	
Cleghorn	51014	
Clemons	50051	
Clermont	52135	
Climbing Hill, R. Br. Hornick	51015	
Clinton (1st)	52732	
Lyons, Sta.	52732	
Teeds Grove, R. Br.	52771	
Clio	50052	
Clive, Br. Des Moines	50053	
Clutier	52217	
Coggon	52218	
Prairieburg, R. Br.	52219	
Coin	51636	
Colesburg	52035	
Colfax	50054	
College Springs	51637	
Collins	50055	
Colo	50056	
Columbia	50057	
Columbus City	52737	

Columbus Junction	52738
Colwell, R. Br. Charles City	50620
Conesville	52739
Conrad	50621
Conroy	52220
Conway, R. Br. Bedford	50834
Coon Rapids (1st)	50058
Cooper	50059
Coralville, Br. Iowa City	52240
Corning (1st)	50841
Brooks, R. Br.	50838
Correctionville	51016
Corwith	50430
Corydon	50060
Cambria, R. Br.	50045
Cotter	52221
Coulter	50431
Council Bluffs (1st)	51501
Craig, R. Br. Le Mars	51017
Cranston	52741
Crawfordsville	52621
Crescent	51526
Cresco (1st)	52136
Creston (1st)	50801
Cromwell	50842
Crystal Lake	50432
Cumberland	50843
Cumming	50061
Curlew	50527
Cushing	51018
Cylinder	50528
Dakota City	50529
Dallas	50062
Dallas Center	50063
Dana	50064
Danbury	51019
Danville	52623
DAVENPORT (1st) (see appendix)	
Davis City	50065
Pleasanton, R. Br.	50224
Dawson	50066
Dayton	50530
De Soto	50069
De Witt (1st)	52742
Decatur	50067
Decorah (1st)	52101
Dedham	51440
Deep River	52222
Defiance	51527
Delaware	52036
Delhi	52223
Delmar	52037
Deloit	51441
Delphos	50844
Delta	52550
Denison (1st)	51442
Denmark	52624
Denver	50622
Derby	50068
DES MOINES (1st) (see appendix)	
Dewar	50623
Dexter	50070
Diagonal	50845
Dickens	51333
Dike	50624
Dixon	52745
Dolliver	50531
Donahue	52746
Donnan	52139
Donnellson	52625
Doon	51235

Dorchester	52140
Douds	52551
Dougherty	50433
Dow City	51528
Dows	50071
Drakesville	52552
Dubuque (1st)	52001
Dumont	50625
Duncombe	50532
Dundee	52038
Dunkerton	50626
Dunlap	51529
Durango	52039
Durant	52747
Dyersville (1st)	52040
Dysart	52224
Eagle Grove (1st)	50533
Earlham	50072
Earling	51530
Earlville	52041
Early	50535
East Des Moines, Sta. Des Moines	50309
East Fourteenth Street, Sta. Des Moines (see appendix)	
East Pleasant Plain, R. Br. Brighton	52541
Eddyville	52553
Edgewood	52042
Elberon	52225
Eldon	52554
Eldora (1st)	50627
Eldorado, R. Br. West Union	52175
Eldridge	52748
Elgin	52141
Elk Horn	51531
Elkader (1st)	52043
Elkhart	50073
Elkport	52044
Elliott	51532
Ellston	50074
Ellsworth	50075
Elma	50628
Elwood	52226
Ely	52227
Emerson	51533
Emmetsburg (1st)	50536
Epworth	52045
Essex	51638
Estherville (1st)	51334
Evansdale, Br. Waterloo	50707
Everly	51338
Exira	50076
Exline	52555
Fairbank	50629
Fairfax	52228
Fairfield (1st)	52556
Farley	52046
Farlin	50077
Farmersburg	52047
Farmington	52626
Farnhamville	50538
Farragut	51639
Fayette	52142
Fenton	50539
Ferguson	50078
Fertile	50434
Festina	52143
First Street, Sta. Cedar Rapids	52407
Floris	52560
Floyd	50435

Fonda	50540
Knoke, R. Br.	50553
Fontanelle	50846
Forest City (1st)	50436
Fort Atkinson	52144
Fort Dodge (1st)	50501
Fort Madison (1st)	52627
Fostoria	51340
Fredericksburg	50630
Frederika	50631
Fremont	52561
Fruitland	52749
Galt	50101
Galva	51020
Garber	52048
Garden City	50102
Garden Grove	50103
Garnavillo	52049
Garner	50438
Hayfield, R. Br.	50445
Miller, R. Br.	50438
Garrison	52229
Garwin	50632
Geneva	50633
George	51237
Gibson	50104
Gifford, R. Br. Union	50259
Gilbert	50105
Gilbertville	50634
Gillett Grove	51341
Gilman	50106
Gilmore City	50541
Gladbrook	50635
Glenwood	51534
Glidden	51443
Goldfield	50542
Goodell	50439
Gooselake	52750
Gowrie	50543
Graettinger	51342
Grafton	50440
Grand, Sta. Des Moines	50309
Grand Junction	50107
Grand Mound	52751
Grand River	50108
Grandview	52752
Granger	50109
Grant	50847
Granville	51022
Gravity	50848
Gray	50110
Greeley	52050
Green Island	52051
Green Mountain	50637
Greene	50636
Greenfield	50849
Greenville, R. Br. Royal	51343
Grimes	50111
Grinnell (1st)	50112
Griswold	51535
Grundy Center (1st)	50638
Gruver	51344
Guernsey, R. Br. Montezuma	50172
Guthrie Center	50115
Guttenberg	52052
Halbur	51444
Hale	52230
Hamburg (1st)	51640
Hamilton	50116
Hamlin	50117
Hampton (1st)	50441
Hancock	51536
Hanlontown	50444

Hansell	50640
Harcourt	50544
Hardy	50545
Harlan (1st)	51537
Harper	52231
Harpers Ferry	52146
Harris	51345
Hartford	50118
Hartley	51346
Hartwick	52232
Harvey	50119
Hastings	51540
Havelock	50546
Haverhill	50120
Hawarden	51023
Chatsworth, R. Br.	51011
Hawkeye	52147
Hayesville	52562
Hayfield, R. Br. Garner	50445
Hazleton	50641
Hedrick	52563
Henderson	51541
Herndon, R. Br. Jamaica	50121
Hiawatha	52233
Hickman Road, Br. Des Moines	50322
Highland Center	52564
Highland Park, Sta. Des Moines	50333
Highlandville	52149
Hills	52235
Hillsboro	52630
Hinton	51024
Holland	50642
Holmes	50547
Holstein	51025
Holy Cross	52053
Homestead	52236
Honey Creek	51542
Hopkinton	52237
Hornick	51026
Climbing Hill, R. Br.	51015
Hospers	51238
Houghton	52631
Hubbard	50122
Hudson	50643
Hull	51239
Humboldt (1st)	50548
Humeston	50123
Huxley	50124
Ida Grove (1st)	51445
Imogene	51645
Independence (1st)	50644
Indianola (1st)	50125
Inwood	51240
Ionia	50645
Iowa City (1st)	52240
Iowa Falls (1st)	50126
Iowa State University, Sta. Ames	50010
Ira	50127
Ireton	51027
Irvington, R. Br. Algona	50550
Irwin	51446
Jackson Junction	52150
Jamaica	50128
Herndon, R. Br.	50121
Janesville	50647
Jefferson (1st)	50129
Jesup	50648
Jewell	50130
Johnston	50131
Joice	50446
Jolley	50551
Kalona	52247
Kamrar	50f32
Kanawha	50447
Kellerton	50133
Kelley	50134
Kellogg	50135
Kensett	50448
Kent	50850
Keokuk (1st)	52632
Keosauqua	52565
Keota	52248
Kesley	50649
Keswick	50136
Keystone	52249
Killduff	50137
Kimballton	51543
Kingsley	51028
Kinross	52250
Kirkman	51447
Kirkville	52566
Kiron	51448
Klemme	50449
Knierim	50552
Knoke, R. Br. Fonda	50553
Knoxville (1st)	50138
Attica, R. Br.	50024
La Motte	52054
La Porte City	50651
Lacona	52251
Ladora	52252
Lake City	51449
Lake Mills	50450
Lake Park	51347
Lake View	51450
Lakeside, R. Br. Storm Lake	50588
Lakota	50451
Lamoni	50140
Lamont	50650
Lanesboro	51451
Langworthy	52252
Lansing (1st)	52151
Lanyon, R. Br. Harcourt	50544
Larchwood	51241
Larrabee	51029
Latimer	50452
Laurel	50141
Laurens	50554
Lawler	52154
Lawton	51030
Le Claire (1st)	52753
Le Grand	50142
Le Mars (1st)	51031
Craig, R. Br.	51017
Struble, R. Br.	51057
Le Roy, R. Br. Humeston	50123
Ledyard	50556
Leeds, Sta. Sioux City	51108
Lehigh	50557
Leighton	50143
Leland	50453
Lenox	50851
Leon	50144
Lester	51242
Letts	52754
Lewis	51544
Liberty Center	50145
Libertyville	52567
Lidderdale	51452
Lime Springs	52155
Saratoga, R. Br.	52167
Lincoln	50652
Linden	50146
Lineville	50147
Linn Grove	51033
Lisbon	52253
Liscomb	50148
Little Cedar	50454
Little Rock	51243
Little Sioux	51545
Littleport	52055
Livermore	50558
Lockridge	52635
Logan (1st)	51546
Magnolia, R. Br.	51550
Lohrville	51453
Lone Rock	50559
Lone Tree	52755
Long Grove	52756
Lorimor	50149
Lost Nation	52254
Loveland	51547
Lovilia	50150
Low Moor	52757
Lowden	52255
Lu Verne	50560
Luana	52156
Lucas	50151
Luther	50152
Luxemburg	52056
Luzerne	52257
Lynnville	50153
Lyons, Sta. Clinton	52732
Lytton	50561
Macedonia	51549
Macksburg	50155
Madrid (1st)	50156
Magnolia, R. Br. Logan	51550
Malcom	50157
Mallard	50562
Maloy	50852
Malvern	51551
Manchester (1st)	52057
Manilla	51454
Manly	50456
Manning	51455
Aspinwall, R. Br.	51432
Manson	50563
Maple Hill	50564
Mapleton	51034
Maquoketa (1st)	52060
Marathon	50565
Marble Rock	50653
Marcus	51035
Marengo	52301
Marion (1st)	52302
Marne	51552
Marquette	52158
Marshalltown (1st)	50158
Martelle	52305
Martensdale	50160
Martinsburg	52568
Mason City (1st)	50401
Masonville	50654
Massena	50853
Matlock	51244
Maurice	51036
Maxwell	50161
May City, R. Br. Ocheyedan	51349
Maynard	50655
Mc Callsburg	50154
Mc Causland	52758
Mc Clelland	51548
Mc Gregor	52157
Mc Intire	50455
Mechanicsville	52306

Mediapolis	52637	New Providence	50206	Peterson	51047
Melbourne	50162	New Sharon	50207	Pierson	51048
Melcher	50163	New Vienna	52065	Pilot Grove	52648
Melrose	52569	New Virginia	50210	Pilot Mound	50223
Melvin	51350	Newell	50568	Pioneer	50572
Menlo	50164	Newhall	52315	Pisgah	51564
Meriden	51037	Newton (1st)	50208	Plainfield	50666
Merrill	51038	Nichols	52766	Plano	52581
Meservey	50457	Nodaway	50857	Pleasant Valley	52767
Middle	52307	Nora Springs	50458	Pleasanton, R. Br. Davis	
Middletown	52638	North Buena Vista	52066	City	50224
Miles	52064	North English	52316	Pleasantville	50225
Milford	51351	North Liberty	52317	Plover	50573
Miller, R. Br. Garner	50438	North Side, Sta. Sioux City	51104	Plymouth	50464
Millersburg	52308	North Washington, R. Br.		Pocahontas	50574
Millerton	50165	New Hampton	50661	Polk City	50226
Milo	50166	Northboro	51647	Pomeroy	50575
Milton	52570	Northwest, Sta. Davenport		Popejoy	50227
Minburn	50167	(see appendix)		Portsmouth	51565
Minden	51553	Northwood	50459	Postville	52162
Mineola	51554	Norwalk	50211	Prairie City	50228
Mingo	50168	Norway	52318	Prairieburg, R. Br. Coggon	52219
Missouri Valley	51555	Numa	52575	Prescott	50859
Mitchell, R. Br. Osage	50485	Oakdale	52319	Preston	52069
Mitchellville	50169	Oakland	51560	Primghar	51245
Modale	51556	Oakville	52646	Princeton	52768
Mondamin	51557	Ocheyedan	51354	Prole	50229
Moneta	51352	May City, R. Br.	51349	Promise City	52583
Monmouth	52309	Odebolt	51458	Protivin	52163
Monona	52159	Oelwein (1st)	50662	Pulaski	52584
Monroe	50170	Ogden	50212	Quasqueton	52326
Montezuma (1st)	50171	Okoboji	51355	Quimby	51049
Guernsey, R. Br.	50172	Olds	52647	Radcliffe	50230
Montgomery	51353	Olin	52320	Rake	50465
Monticello (1st)	52310	Ollie	52576	Ralston	51459
Montour	50173	Onawa	51040	Randalia	52164
Montpelier	52759	Onslow	52321	Randall	50231
Montrose	52639	Oran	50664	Randolph	51649
Moorhead	51558	Orange City (1st)	51041	Rathbun, R. Br. Centerville	52545
Moorland	50566	Orchard	50460	Raymond	50667
Moravia	52571	Orient	50858	Readlyn	50668
Morley	52312	Osage (1st)	50461	Reasnor	50232
Morning Sun	52640	Mitchell, R. Br.	50485	Red Oak (1st)	51566
Morningside, Sta. Sioux City		New Haven, R. Br.	50461	Redding	50860
(see appendix)		Osceola (1st)	50213	Redfield	50233
Morrison	50657	Oskaloosa (1st)	52577	Reinbeck	50669
Moscow	52760	Ossian	52161	Rembrandt	50576
Moulton	52572	Otho	50569	Remsen	51050
Mount Auburn	52313	Otley	50214	Renwick	50577
Mount Ayr	50854	Oto	51044	Rhodes	50234
Mount Etna	50855	Ottosen	50570	Riceville	50466
Mount Pleasant (1st)	52641	Ottumwa (1st)	52501	Richland	52585
Rome, R. Br.	52642	Oxford	52322	Richmond, R. Br. Kalona	52247
Mount Sterling	52573	Oxford Junction	52323	Ricketts	51460
Mount Union	52644	Oyens	51045	Ridgeway	52165
Mount Vernon (1st)	52314	Pacific Junction	51561	Rinard, R. Br. Somers	50587
Moville	51039	Packwood	52580	Ringsted	50578
Murray	50174	Palmer	50571	Rippey	50235
Muscatine (1st)	52761	Palo	52324	Riverside	52327
Mystic	52574	Panama	51562	Riverton	51650
Nashua	50658	Panora	50216	Robins	52328
Nemaha	50567	Parkersburg	50665	Rock Falls	50467
Neola	51559	Parnell	52325	Rock Rapids	51246
Nevada (1st)	50201	Paton	50217	Rock Valley	51247
Nevinville	50856	Patterson	50218	Rockford	50468
New Albin	52160	Paullina	51046	Rockwell	50469
New Hampton (1st)	50659	Pella (1st)	50219	Rockwell City	50579
North Washington, R. Br.	50661	Peosta	52068	Rodman	50580
New Hartford	50660	Percival	51648	Rodney	51051
New Haven, R. Br. Osage	50461	Perry (1st)	50220	Roland	50236
New Liberty	52765	Pershing	50221	Rolfe	50581
New London	52645	Persia	51563	Rome, R. Br. Mount	
New Market	51646	Peru	50222	Pleasant	52642

Rose Hill	52586	
Rossie	51356	
Rowan	50470	
Rowley	52329	
Royal	51357	
Greenville, R. Br.	51343	
Rubio	52587	
Rudd	50471	
Runnells	50237	
Russell	50238	
Ruthven	51358	
Rutland	50582	
Ryan	52330	
Sabula	52070	
Sac City (1st)	50583	
Saint Ansgar	50472	
Saint Anthony	50239	
Saint Charles	50240	
Saint Donatus	52071	
Saint Lucas	52166	
Saint Marys	50241	
Saint Olaf	52072	
Saint Paul, R. Br. West Point	52657	
Salem	52649	
Salix	51052	
Sanborn	51248	
Saratoga, R. Br. Lime Springs	52167	
Scarville	50473	
Schaller	51053	
Schleswig	51461	
Scotch Grove	52331	
Scranton	51462	
Searsboro	50242	
Selma	52588	
Sergeant Bluff	51054	
Sewal	52589	
Sexton	50474	
Seymour	52590	
Shambaugh	51651	
Shannon City	50861	
Sharpsburg	50862	
Sheffield	50475	
Shelby	51570	
Sheldahl	50243	
Sheldon (1st)	51201	
Shell Rock	50670	
Shellsburg	52332	
Shenandoah (1st)	51601	
Sherrill	52073	
Sibley (1st)	51249	
Sidney	51652	
Sigourney	52591	
Silver City	51571	
Sioux Center (1st)	51250	
SIOUX CITY (1st) (see appendix)		
Sioux Rapids	50585	
Slater	50244	
Sloan	51055	
Smithland	51056	
Soldier	51572	
Solon	52333	
Somers	50586	
Rinard, R. Br.	50587	
South Amana	52334	
South Des Moines, Sta. Des Moines (see appendix)		
South English	52335	
Spencer (1st)	51301	
Sperry	52650	
Spillville	52168	

Spirit Lake (1st)	51360	
Spragueville	52074	
Spring Hill	50245	
Springbrook	52075	
Springville	52336	
Stacyville	50476	
Stanhope	50246	
Stanley	50671	
Stanton	51573	
Stanwood	52337	
State Center	50247	
Steamboat Rock	50672	
Stock Yards, Sta. Sioux City	51107	
Stockport	52651	
Stockton	52769	
Storm Lake (1st)	50588	
Story City	50248	
Stout	50673	
Stratford	50249	
Strawberry Point	52076	
Struble, R. Br. Le Mars	51057	
Stuart	50250	
Sully	50251	
Sulphur Springs	50589	
Sumner	50674	
Sunbury	52770	
Superior	51363	
Sutherland	51058	
Swaledale	50477	
Swan	50252	
Swea City	50590	
Swedesburg	52652	
Swisher	52338	
Tabor	51653	
Taintor	50253	
Tama	52339	
Teeds Grove, R. Br. Clinton	52271	
Templeton	51463	
Tennant	51574	
Terril	51364	
Thayer	50254	
Thompson	50478	
Thor	50591	
Thornburg	50255	
Thornton	50479	
Thurman	51654	
Bartlett, R. Br.	51655	
Tiffin	52340	
Tingley	50863	
Tipton (1st)	52772	
Titonka	50480	
Toddville	52341	
Toeterville	50481	
Toledo	52342	
Toronto	52343	
Tracy	50256	
Traer	50675	
Treynor	51575	
Tripoli	50676	
Troy, R. Br. Bloomfield	52537	
Troy Mills	52344	
Truesdale	50592	
Truro	50257	
Turin	51059	
Udell	52593	
Ulmer	51464	
Underwood	51576	
Union	50258	
Gifford, R. Br.	50259	
Unionville	52594	
University Park	52595	
University Place, Sta. Des Moines	50311	
Urbana	52345	

Urbandale, Br. Des Moines (see appendix)		
Ute	51060	
Vail	51465	
Van Horne	52346	
Van Meter	50261	
Van Wert	50262	
Varina	50593	
Ventura	50482	
Victor	52347	
Villisca	50864	
Vincent	50594	
Vining	52348	
Vinton (1st)	52349	
Viola	52350	
Volga	52077	
Wadena	52169	
Walcott	52773	
Walford	52351	
Walker	52352	
Wall Lake	51466	
Wallingford	51365	
Walnut	51577	
Wapello	52653	
Washburn, Br. Waterloo	50706	
Washington (1st)	52353	
Washta	51061	
WATERLOO (1st) (see appendix)		
Waterville	52170	
Watkins	52354	
Waucoma	52171	
Waukee	50263	
Wauken (1st)	52172	
Waverly (1st)	50677	
Wayland	52654	
Webb	51366	
Webster	52355	
Webster City (1st)	50595	
Weldon	50264	
Wellman	52356	
Wellsburg	50680	
Welton	52774	
Wesley	50483	
West	52357	
West Bend	50597	
West Branch	52358	
West Burlington	52655	
West Chester	52359	
West Des Moines, Br. Des Moines	50265	
West Grove, R. Br. Bloomfield	52538	
West Liberty	52776	
West Point	52656	
Saint Paul, R. Br.	52657	
West Union (1st)	52175	
Westfield	51062	
Westgate	50681	
Westphalia	51578	
Westside	51467	
Wever	52658	
What Cheer	50268	
Wheatland	52777	
Whiting	51063	
Whittemore	50598	
Whitten	50269	
Whittier	52360	

William Penn College, Sta.
  Oskaloosa................52577
Williams...........................50271
Williamsburg 52361
Williamson......................50272
Wilton.............................52778
Windsor Heights, Br. Des
  Moines....................50311
Winfield...........................52659

Winterset (1st) 50273
Winthrop 50682
Wiota..............................50274
Woden............................50484
Woodbine 51579
Woodburn........................50275
Woodward.......................50276
Woolstock.......................50599
Worthington....................52078

Wright.............................52596
Wyoming.........................52362
Yale................................50277
Yarmouth........................52660
Yetter, R. Br. Auburn 51433
Yorktown.........................51656
Zearing...........................50278
Zwingle...........................52079

Appendix

Cedar Rapids — Davenport IOWA

CEDAR RAPIDS   524

POST OFFICE BOXES

Box Nos.
1-3999	Main Office	06
4001-5035	First Street Sta..............	07

RURAL ROUTES

1,2,3... 01

STATIONS, BRANCHES AND UNITS

Cedar Hills Sta......................	05
First Street Sta......................	07
General Delivery	01
Postmaster	01

APARTMENTS, HOTELS, MOTELS

Allison, 325 1st Ave E...........	01
Ausadie, 845 1st Ave SE.......	02
Blair House, 2222 1st Ave N E....................	02
Brandywyne	04
Brown, 1234 4th Ave SE........	03
Carleton, 1920 1st Ave E	02
Cedar Valley..........................	04
Cedarwood Trace, 2040 Glass Rd NE............................	02
College, 1261 1st Ave E.........	02
Commonwealth Apartment, 1400 2nd Ave SE..............	03
East Towne Place SE	03
Eleanor, 319 1st Ave E...........	01
Gateway Gardens	04
Holiday Inn	06
Iowa, 1263 1st Ave E	02
Magnus, 324 2nd Ave SE	07
Meth Wick Manor, 1224 13th St NW...................	05
Montrose, 223 3rd Ave SE......	01
North Towne Place NE............	02
Oakland Court, 1500 Oakland Rd NE............................	02
Oakland Gardens, 1300 Oakland Rd NE................	02
Park Towne Court NE..............	02
Park Towne Place NE..............	02

Roosevelt, 200 1st Ave E........	07
Taft, 403 2nd Ave SE	01
Town House Motor, 4747 1st Ave E............................	06
Windemere, 205 14th SE........	03

BUILDINGS

American, 101 2nd SE.............	01
Arco, 308 3rd SE....................	01
Dows, 210 2nd SE	01
Executive Plaza, 4403 1st Ave NE............................	02
First Avenue, 411 1st Ave E....	01
First Trust & Savings Bank, 1201 3rd SE	01
Granby, 224 2nd SE................	01
Green Engineering. 417 1st Ave E............................	01
Guaranty, 216 3rd SE	01
Higley, 118 3rd Ave SE...........	01
Insurance, 526 2nd Ave SE....	01
Iowa Theatre, 108 3rd SE.......	01
Memorial Coliseum, Mays Island..............................	01
Merchants National Bank, 115 3rd SE	01
Mount Vernon Professional, 3330 Mt Vernon Rd SE.....	03
Mullin, 219 2nd SE.................	01
Naibert, 117 3rd Ave SE.........	01
Namsho, 509 3rd Ave SE.......	01
Paramount, 305 2nd SE	01
S G A, 122 2nd SE	01
Security, 203 2nd SE..............	01
Town & Country, 136 36th Dr SE....................................	02
Twenty Seventh Street............	02

GOVERNMENT OFFICES

Chamber Of Commerce..........	01
City Hall, Mays Island.............	01
County Courthouse	01
Federal, 101 1st SE................	01

HOSPITALS

Americana Nursing Home, 1940 1st Ave NE..............	02
Hallmar, 835 6th Ave S E	03
Mercy, 835 6th Ave SE	03

Saint Lukes, 1026 A Ave NE...	02

UNIVERSITIES AND COLLEGES

Cedar Rapids Business College, 128 2nd Ave S W..	04
Coe College, 1220 1st Ave E..	02
Kirkwood Community College, 6301 Bowling SW.............	06
Mount Mercy, 1300 Elmhurst Dr NE............................	02

DAVENPORT   528

POST OFFICE BOXES

Box Nos.
1-1240	Central Sta......	05
2001-2250	Northwest Sta ..	04
3001-4549	Main Office	08

RURAL ROUTES

1,2,3,4... 04

STATIONS, BRANCHES AND UNITS

Central Sta............................	05
Northwest Sta	04
General Delivery	02
Postmaster	02

APARTMENTS, HOTELS, MOTELS

Anderson, 602 W 3rd............	01
Argyle, 730 Brady.................	03
Bakeris, 2935 Dubuque	03
Blackhawk, 309 Perry............	01
Bronze Lantern Motel, 1661 W Kimberly......................	06
Brown Motel, 4847 W Kimberly..........................	06
Capitol, 224 E 6th.................	03
Carroll, 628 Pershing Ave......	03
Century, 110 E 4th................	01
Chateau, 121 W 8th	03
Clayton House, East River & Le Claire..........................	01
Colonial, 839 Brady...............	03
Colonnades, 2016 Rockingham Rd	02

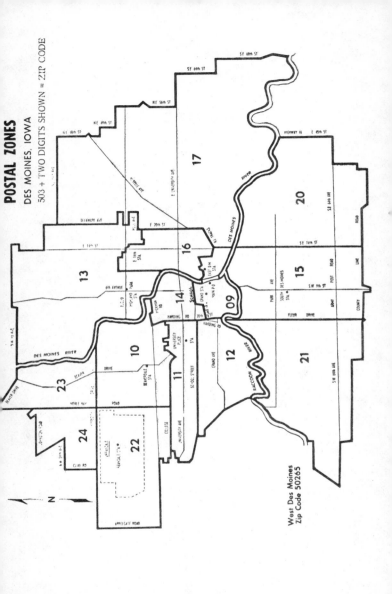

POSTAL ZONES
DES MOINES, IOWA
503 + TWO DIGITS SHOWN = ZIP CODE

West Des Moines
Zip Code 50265

Davenport (Con.)   528

Cora Lee Roy, 602 Brady 03
Courtland, 321 E 7th 03
Crest Motel, 3917 Brady 06
Crown, 805 W 2nd 02
Davenport Motel, 3202
   Harrison 03
Davenport, 324 Main 01
Dempsey, 408 Main 01
Ellis & Fish, 1324 Gaines...... 04
Ellis & Fish, 705 W 14th........ 04
Fejervary, 124 W 13th............ 03
Fisher Crest, 223 E 35th........ 06
Five Seasons 5112 N
   Fairmount...................... 06
Franklin, 316 Brady 01
Frey, 210 W 4th 01
Gadient, 1002 Ash 02
Geurinks, 1402 Harrison 03
Harrison Manor, 2502
   Harrison 03
Holiday Inn, 5202 Brady 06
Holiday Terrace, 1935 W
   40th 06
Iowa Motel, 4005 Brady........ 06
Janssen, 502 Perry................ 03
Kahl, 311 W 3rd.................... 01
Langwith, 320 W 4th 01
Lend-A-Hand, 105 S Main...... 01
Linden Flats, 219 Scott 01
Maple Lane Motel, 5001
   Brady 06
Mississippi, 106 E 3rd............ 01
Motel Six, 6111 N Brady........ 06
Pasadena, 1224 Main............ 03
Quality Motel Midtown, 226
   W 6th 02
Rose Garden Motel, 4108
   Hickory Grove Rd 06
Roslyn, 739 Perry.................. 03
Scharff, 105 W 2nd 01
Schick, 120 Harrison............ 01
Schricker, 401 W 4th............ 01
Security, 117 W 4th.............. 01
Shorey, 930 Perry 03
Standard, 712 W 2nd............ 02
Strahmeier, 1317 E Locust...... 03
Tall Corn Motor Inn, 427 W
   Kimberly........................ 06
Vale, 210 E 4th 01
Van Dresky, 1003 W Locust.... 04
Voyager Inn, 4002 Brady 06

BUILDINGS

Bayers, 230 W 3rd 01
Brenton, 1600 Brady St 03
Citizens Federal, 218 Brady.... 01
Davenport Bank, 220 Main.... 01
Davenport Municipal Art
   Gallery, 1737 W 12th 04
Davenport Public Museum,
   1717 W 12th.................... 04
Eastern Office, 2212 E 12th.... 03
First National, 201 W 2nd...... 01
Insurance Exchange, 220 E
   2nd.............................. 01
Kahl, 326 W 3rd.................... 01
Kresge, 210 Main.................. 01
Lee, 130 E 2nd 01

Midtown Plaza, 1726 Brady
   Street 03
Priester, 610 Brady 01
Professional Arts, 121 W
   Locust 03
Putnam, 215 Main 01
Union Arcade, 111 E 3rd........ 01
Whitaker, 230 Brady 01

GOVERNMENT OFFICES

City Hall, 226 W 4th.............. 01
Courthouse 01
Federal Building.................... 01

HOSPITALS

Davenport Osteopathic, 1111
   W Kimberly.................... 06
Mercy, 1326 W Lombard 04
Pine Knoll, 2504 Telegraph
   Rd................................ 04
Saint Lukes, 1227 E
   Rusholme 03

UNIVERSITIES AND COLLEGES

American Institute Of
   Commerce, 617 Brady........ 03
Marycrest, 1607 W 12th 04
Palmer College Of
   Chiropractic, 1000 Brady ... 03
Palmer Junior College, 1000
   Brady............................ 03
Saint Ambrose, 518 W
   Locust 03

DES MOINES   503

POST OFFICE BOXES

Box Nos.		
A-B	East 14th Street Sta......	16
A-F	So Des Moines Sta.......	15
C-D	East 14th Street Sta......	16
E-Z	University Place Sta.......	11
1-147	East Des Moines Sta....	09
1-300	General Post Office...........	01
AA-AJ	General Post Office...........	01
AK-AP	General Post Office...........	02
AQ-AZ	General Post Office...........	03
BA-BJ	General Post Office...........	04
BK-BS	General Post Office...........	05
BT-BZ	General Post Office...........	06
CA-CB	General Post Office...........	06
301-600	General Post Office...........	02
601-800	General Post Office...........	03
801-1000	General Post Office...........	04
1001-1184	University Place Sta.......	11
1200-1457	General Post Office...........	05
1461-2000	General Post Office...........	06
2001-2254	Beaverdale Sta...........	10
2501-2815	So Des Moines Sta...........	15
3001-3399	East 14th Street Sta.......	16
3501-3827	Urbandale Br......	22
4000-4199	Highland Park Sta..............	33
4501-5199	General Post Office...........	06

RURAL ROUTES

1 22
3 15
4 13
5 17

STATIONS, BRANCHES AND UNITS

Beaverdale Sta...................... 10
Clive Br 50053
East Des Moines Sta.............. 09
East Fourteenth Street Sta...... 13
Grand Sta 09
Hickman Road Br.................... 22
Highland Park Sta.................. 33
South Des Moines Sta.............. 15
University Place Sta................ 11
Urbandale Br.......................... 22
West Des Moines Br.............50265
Windsor Heights Br................ 11
General Delivery...................... 18
Postmaster.............................. 18

APARTMENTS, HOTELS, MOTELS

Americana Park, 2nd &
   University 14
Argonne, 1729 Grand Ave...... 09
Arlington, 1301 Locust............ 09
Brady, 650 16th 14
Chamberlain, 407 7th............ 09
Commodore, 3440 Grand Ave. 12
Eddy, 1120 Polk Blvd............ 11
Elliott, 219 4th...................... 09
Ewing, 917 Locust 07
Fort Des Moines, 10th &
   Walnut.......................... 03
Franklin Courts, 4925
   Franklin Ave.................... 10
Franklin, 5th & Locust............ 09
Frederick, 717 4th.................. 09
Grand Towers, 3663 Grand.... 12
Hamilton, 2825 Grand Ave 12
Hampton House, 4200 Grand
   Ave 12
Jefferson, 1519 Grand Ave...... 09
Kingston, 1200 Grand Ave...... 09
Kirkwood, 4th & Walnut.......... 03
Martin, 303 Locust................ 09
Milner, 6th & Cherry.............. 09
Northwestern, 321 E Walnut... 09

Des Moines (Con.)   503

Park Fleur, Fleur Dr & Park
Ave 21
Randolph, 4th & Ct Ave 09
Rogers, 118 6th Ave 09
Savery, 4th & Locust 03
Thirty Six Sixty, 3660 Grand
Ave 12
Tours, 206 11th 09
University Terrace, 3523
University Ave 11
Wakonda Village, 1800
Watrous Ave 15
Windsor Terrace, 3333 Grand
Ave 12

BUILDINGS

American, 2200 Grand 06
Bankers Trust, 406 6th Ave 09
Capital City Bank, 431 E
Locust 09
Central National, 317 6th
Ave 09
City Hall, East 1st & Locust... 07
City Library, 1st & Walnut..... 09
Des Moines, 405 6th Ave........ 09
Eastgate Shopping Center 16
Empire, 309 6th Ave 09
Equitable, 604 Locust 09
Farm Bureau, 507 10th 09
Federal Office, 210 Walnut..... 09
Fleming, 218 6th Ave 09
Hawley Welfare, 700 6th Ave.. 09
Historical, E 12th & Grand
Ave 19
Home Federal, 601 Grand
Ave 09
Hubbell, 904 Walnut 09
I N A, 1055 6th Ave................ 14
Insurance Exchange, 505 5th
Ave 09
Iowa Des Moines National
Bank, 518 Walnut.................. 09
James Grimes Bldg, E 14th
& Grand 19
Jewett, 914 Grand Ave 09
Key, 518 Grand Ave 09
Kresge, 307 7th 09
Liberty, 418 6th Ave 09
Mc Kinley Plaza 15
Merle Hay Plaza 10
National Travelers Life Bldg.,
820 Keo Way 09
Oliver Plaza 10
Paramount, 507 Grand Ave 09
Park Fair 13
Plymouth, 919 Walnut............ 09
Polk County Court House 09
Register & Tribune, 715
Locust 09
Robert Lucas Bldg, E 12th &
Walnut 19
Roosevelt 12
Royal Union Life, 706 Grand
Ave 09
Savings & Loan, 206 6th
Ave 09
Securities, 418 7th 09
Seneca Plaza 13
Sherwood Forest 22

Shoppers Fair 10
Shops, 806 Walnut.................. 09
State Capitol Complex, E. 6th
& Des Moines Street............. 19
State Capitol, E 10 & Grand
Ave 19
Stephens................................... 09
Telephone, 604 9th................. 09
Thompson Plaza 10
Travelers Insurance, 215 Keo.
Way 09
Wakonda 21

HOSPITALS

Blank Memorial, 1200
Pleasant 08
Broadlawns, 18th & Hickman
Rd 14
Des Moines General, 603 E
12th 16
Helen Powell Convalescent
Center, 1200 Pleasant.......... 08
Iowa Lutheran, 716 Parnell.... 16
Iowa Methodist Hospital,
1200 Pleasant 08
Mercy, 5th & Ascension......... 14
N W Hospital, 1818 48th........ 10
Veterans, 30th & Euclid Ave .. 09
Wilden Clinic, 717 Lyon......... 16
Younker Memorial
Rehabilitation Center,
1200 Pleasant 08

UNIVERSITIES AND COLLEGES

American Institute Of
Business, 10th & Grand
Ave 07
College Of Automation, 3001
Grand Ave 02
College Of Osteopathic
Medicine & Surgery, 722
6th Ave 09
Drake University, 25th &
University Ave 11
Grandview, E 13th &
Grandview Ave 16

SIOUX CITY   511

POST OFFICE BOXES

Box Nos.		
1-1918	Main Office	02
1L-158L	Leeds Sta	08
2001-2128	North Side Sta .	04
2301-2468	Stock Yards Sta .	07
2501-2788	Morningside Sta .	06
3001-3455	Main Office	02

RURAL ROUTES

1 08
2 06
3 03

STATIONS, BRANCHES AND UNITS

Boulevard Sta........................... 09
Call Terminal Sta.................... 01
Leeds Sta 08
Morningside Sta 06
North Side Sta.......................... 04
Stock Yards Sta 07
General Delivery 01
Postmaster 01

APARTMENTS, HOTELS, MOTELS

Alhambra, 801 8th St............. 05
Argonout, 1103 Nebraska. 05
Aventino Hotel 517-6th St...... 01
Bellevue, 2104 Summit............ 04
Biltmore Motel, 5900 Gordon
Dr 06
Bolstein, 1626 Jackson............ 05
Carroll, 1101 Jackson 05
Castle, 2119 Nebraska 04
Chicago House, 807 4th St 01
Clifton Apts, 55 W Clifton 04
Follis, 923 Douglas St 01
Holiday Inn, 1401 Gordon Dr
W 03
Ida, 1901 Pierce....................... 04
Imperial 400 Motel, 110 S
Nebraska 01
Martin Apartments, 4th &
Pierce ....:............... 02
Metz, 2001 Summit.................. 04
Morningside Country Estates,
1331 South Maple 06
Murray Apts, 823 Jackson...... 05
Palmer House Motel, 3440
Gordon Dr.............................. 06
Parkview, 104 24th St 04
Parkwood, 4351 Lincoln Way.. 06
Pierce Plaza West, 414-11th
St 05
River Heights Apts, 2201
Gibson 06
Roadway Inn, 2nd &
Nebraska 01
Sioux, 217 19th........................ 05
Smith, 1716 Nebraska 05
Stellart, 2117 Nebraska 04
Swanson, 1700 Jackson........... 05
Sydney, 1003 Pierce................. 05
Terrace, 1623 Nebraska 05
Valley Park, 3029 Park Ave 04
Vincent, 615 Jones................... 05
Wirick, 402 14th St.................. 05

BUILDINGS

Badgerow, 4th & Jacksen........ 01
Benson, 7th & Douglas............ 01
Brown Block, 602 1/2 4th 01
Call Terminal, 4th & Court..... 01
Commerce, 520 Nebraska........ 01
Davidson, 505 6th St............... 01
Federal, 6th & Douglas............ 01
Frances, 503 5th St.................. 01
Home Federal Saving And
Loan 701 Pierce.................... 01
Insurance Exchange, 7th &
Pierce 01
Livestock Exchange, 807
Cunningham Dr 07

Sioux City (Con.)   511

Municipal, 114 6th 03
Northwest National Bank 500
  Jackson 01
Orpheum Electric, 6th &
  Pierce 01
Security Bank, 6th & Pierce ... 01
Sioux City Federal Plaza On
  The Mall At Jackson 01
Wright, 413 Nebraska 01

GOVERNMENT OFFICES

City Hall, 401 6th St 01
County Courthouse, 620
  Douglas St 01
Federal, 6th & Douglas St 01

HOSPITALS

Gordon Memorial, 1816 West.. 03
Saint Joseph, 2101 Court 04
Saint Vincents, 624 Jones 05
St Lukes Medical Center
  (East), 2714 Pierce............. 04

UNIVERSITIES AND COLLEGES

Briar Cliff, 32nd & Rebecca... 04
Morningside, 1601
  Morningside Ave 06

WATERLOO   507

POST OFFICE BOXES

Box Nos.
1-320   Washburn Br 06
1-1177   Main Office 04
2001-2617   A Sta 05
3001-3447   Evansdale Br.... 07
4000-9000   Main Office 04

RURAL ROUTES

1,2,3,4,5................................. 01

STATIONS, BRANCHES AND UNITS

Evansdale Br............................ 07
Washburn Br 06
General Delivery 01
Postmaster 01

APARTMENTS, HOTELS, MOTELS

Armory, 209 E 6th.................. 03
Belmont Court, 400 1/2 438
  Belmont............................. 01
Brockwell Arms, 501
  Jefferson........................... 01
Brown, 420 Commercial.......... 01
Cedar 21 1/2 -27 1/2 E 5th... 03
Clayton House Motel, 300 W
  Mullan Ave........................ 01
Colonial Manor Apts 425
  Allen................................ 01
Colonial, 801 1/2 811 W 4th .. 02
Drake, 933 1/2 935 W 3rd...... 01
Ellis Hotel, 705 Sycamore....... 05
Friedel, 302 Commercial......... 01
Fullerton, 533 Lime................ 03
Grand Hotel 328 W 4th........... 01
Greystone, 1306 W 3rd 01
Hileman, 617 Mulberry........... 03
Hillcrest, 309 Allen 01
Hillcrest, 833 W 2nd.............. 01
Lo Dema, 222 Walnut............. 03
Martin Hotel 514 Sycamore 03
Mc Kinley, 1907 Franklin 03
Melrose, 618 1/2 620 W 3rd... 01
Mulberry 612 1/2 -614 1/2
  Mulberry........................... 03
Oak Lawn Terrace, 400 1/2
  434 Oak Lawn 01
Park View, 200 1/2 255 Park
  View Blvd......................... 02
Plaza, 1308 W 4th 02
Quality Motel, W 5th &
  Jefferson........................... 01
Ramada Inn W2-Washington.... 01
Rath-Donnell, 217 1/2 E 5th.. 03

Russell Lamson Apts, 209 W
  5th 04
Star Hotel, 617 1/2
  Sycamore.......................... 03
Stonewall, 614 Washington 01
Superior, 422 W 6th............... 01
Superior, 725 Washington....... 01
Walnut Court, 315 Walnut 03
Wellington, 505 1/2 507
  Wellington......................... 01
Wellington, 727 W Park Ave ... 01
Windsor, 225 W 5th................ 01

BUILDINGS

Black Hawk, 206 W 4th.......... 01
Black, 525 Sycamore 03
First National, 601 1/2 609
  Sycamore.......................... 03
K W W L, 500 E 4th............... 03
Lafayette, 609 Lafayette......... 03
Marsh Place, 627 Sycamore ... 03
Repass, 604 Mulberry............ 03
Waterloo, 531 1/2 535
  Commercial........................ 01

GOVERNMENT OFFICES

City Hall, 715 Mulberry.......... 05
Court House, 316 E 5th.......... 03

HOSPITALS

Allen Memorial, 1825 Logan
  Ave 03
Saint Francis, 3421 W 9th 02
Schoitz Memorial, 2101
  Kimball Ave....................... 02

UNIVERSITIES AND COLLEGES

Gates College, 209 W Park
  Ave 01
Hawkeye Institute Of
  Technology, P O Box 8015.. 04

KANSAS
(Abbreviation: KS)

Abbyville....67510
Abilene (1st)....67410
Ada....67414
Admire....66830
Agenda....66930
Agra....67621
Agricola....66831
Alamota....67830
Albert....67511
Alden....67512
Alexander....67513
Aliceville....66832
Allen....66833
Alma....66401
  Mc Farland, R. Br....66501
Almena....67622
Alta Vista....66834
Altamont....67330
Alton....67623
Altoona....66710
Americus....66835
Ames....66931
Andale....67001
Andover....67002
Angola, R. Br. Coffeyville....67331
Antelope....66836
Anthony (1st)....67003
Antonino....67624
Arcadia....66711
Argentine, Sta. Kansas City....66106
Argonia....67004
Arkansas City (1st)....67005
Arlington....67514
Arma....66712
Arnold....67515
Arrington....66001
Asherville....67415
Ashland....67831
Assaria....67416
Atchison (1st)....66002
Athol....66932
Atlanta....67008
Attica....67009
Atwood....67730
Auburn....66402
Augusta (1st)....67010
Aurora....67417
Axtell....66403
Baileyville....66404
Baldwin City....66006
Barnard....67418
Barnes....66933
Bartlett....67332
Basehor....66007
Bavaria....67419
Baxter Springs (1st)....66713
Bazaar....66837
Bazine....67516
Beattie....66406
Beaumont....67012
Beaver....67517
Beeler....67518
Bellaire....66934
Belle Plaine....67013
Belleville (1st)....66935
Belmont, R. Br. Kingman....67014
Beloit (1st)....67420
  Scottsville, R. Br....67477
Belpre....67519
Belvidere....67015

Belvue....66407
Bendena....66008
Benedict....66714
Bennington....67422
Bentley....67016
Benton....67017
Bern....66408
Berryton....66409
Bethel, Sta. Kansas City
  (see appendix)
Beverly....67423
Big Bow....67832
Bird City....67731
Bison....67520
Blaine....66410
Bloom....67833
Blue Mound....66010
Blue Rapids....66411
Bluff City....67018
Bogue....67625
Bonner Springs (1st)....66012
Bremen....66412
Brewster....67732
Bridgeport....67424
Bronson....66716
Brookville....67425
Brownell....67521
Bucklin....67834
Bucyrus....66013
Buffalo....66717
Buhler....67522
Bunker Hill....67626
Burden....67019
Burdett....67523
Burdick....66838
Burlingame....66413
Burlington....66839
Burns....66840
Burr Oak....66936
Burrton....67020
Bushong....66841
Bushton....67427
Byers....67021
Caldwell....67022
Cambridge....67023
Camp Funston, Br. Junction
  City....66442
Caney (1st)....67333
Canton....67428
Carbondale....66414
Carlton....67429
Carlyle....66718
Corona....66719
Cassoday....66842
Catharine....67627
Cawker City....67430
Cedar....67628
Cedar Point....66843
Cedar Vale....67024
Centerville....66014
Centralia....66615
Chanute (1st)....66720
  Earlton, R. Br....66731
Chapman....67431
Chase....67524
Chautauqua....67334
Cheney....67025
Cherokee....66724
Cherryvale....67335
Chetopa....67336
Chisholm, Sta. Wichita (see
  appendix)
Cimarron....67835

Circleville....66416
Civic Center, Sta. Kansas
  City (see appendix)
Claflin....67525
Clay Center (1st)....67432
Clayton....67629
Clearwater....67026
Clements....66844
Clifton....66937
Climax....67027
Clyde....66938
Coats....67028
Codell....67630
Coffeyville (1st)....67337
Colby (1st)....67701
Coldwater....67029
College, Sta. Pittsburg....66762
Collyer....67631
Colony....66015
Columbus (1st)....66725
Colwich....67030
Concordia (1st)....66901
Conway....67434
Conway Springs....67031
Coolidge....67836
Copeland....67837
Corbin....67032
Corning....66417
Cottonwood Falls....66845
Council Grove....66846
Courtland....66939
Coyville....66727
Crestline....66728
Crystal Springs, R. Br.
  Harper....67033
Cuba....66940
Culver....67435
Cummings....66016
Cunningham....67035
Damar....67632
Danville....67036
De Soto....66018
  Sunflower, R. Br....66019
Dearing....67340
Deerfield....67838
Delavan....66847
Delia....66418
Delphos....67436
Denison....66419
Dennis....67341
Densmore....67633
Denton....66017
Derby (1st)....67037
Devon....66730
Dexter....67038
Dighton....67839
Dodge City (1st)....67801
Dorrance....67634
Douglass....67039
Dover....66420
Downs....67437
Dresden....67635
Duluth....66421
Dunlap....66848
Duquoin....67040
Durham....67438
Dwight....66849
Earlton, R. Br. Chanute....66731
Easton....66020
Edgerton....66021
Edmond....67636
Edna....67342
Edson....67733

Edwardsville, Br. Kansas
City.................................66113
Effingham................................66023
El Dorado (1st).......................67042
Elbing.....................................67041
Elgin, R. Br. Sedan.................67361
Elk City..................................67344
Elk Falls.................................67345
Elkhart...................................67950
Ellinwood...............................67526
Ellis..67637
Ellsworth................................67439
Elmdale..................................66850
Elsmore..................................66732
Elwood...................................66024
Emmett...................................66422
Emporia (1st)..........................66801
Englewood..............................67840
Ensign....................................67841
Enterprise...............................67441
Erie..66733
Esbon.....................................66941
Eskridge.................................66423
Eudora....................................66025
Eureka (1st)............................67045
Everest...................................66424
Fairfax, Sta. Kansas City.......66115
Fairview..................................66425
Fall River...............................67047
Falun.....................................67442
Farlington...............................66734
Fellsburg................................67048
Florence.................................66851
Fontana..................................66026
Forbes A F B, Br. Topeka.......66620
Ford.......................................67842
Formoso.................................66942
Fort Dodge.............................67843
Fort Larned, R. Br. Larned....67550
Fort Leavenworth (1st)..........66027
Fort Riley, Br. Junction City...66442
Fort Scott (1st).......................66701
Fostoria..................................66426
Fowler....................................67844
Frankfort................................66427
Franklin..................................66735
Fredonia (1st).........................66736
Freeport..................................67049
Friend....................................67845
Frontenac, Br. Pittsburg.........66762
Fulton.....................................66738
Gage Center, Sta. Topeka......66604
Galatia, R. Br. Hoisington......67528
Galena....................................66739
Galesburg...............................66740
Galva.....................................67443
Garden City (1st)....................67846
Garden Plain...........................67050
Gardner (1st)...........................66030
Garfield...................................67529
Garland...................................66741
Garnett (1st)...........................66032
Gas...66742
Gaylord..................................67638
Gem..67734
Geneseo..................................67444
Geuda Springs........................67051
Girard (1st).............................66743
Glade......................................67639
Glasco....................................67445
Glen Elder..............................67446
Goddard..................................67052
Goessel..................................67053

Goff..66428
Goodland (1st)........................67735
Gorham...................................67640
Gove.......................................67736
Grainfield...............................67737
Grantville................................66429
Great Bend (1st).....................67530
Greeley...................................66033
Green......................................67447
Greenleaf................................66943
Greensburg.............................67054
Greenwich...............................67055
Grenola...................................67346
Gridley....................................66852
Grinnell...................................67738
Gypsum..................................67448
Haddam..................................66944
Hallowell................................66744
Halstead..................................67056
Hamilton.................................66853
Hamlin....................................66430
Hanover..................................66945
Hanston..................................67849
Hardtner..................................67057
Harlan.....................................67641
Harper.....................................67058
Hartford..................................66854
Harveyville..............................66431
Havana....................................67347
Haven......................................67543
Havensville..............................66432
Haviland..................................67059
Trousdale, R. Br.................67145
Hays (1st)................................67601
Schoenchen, R. Br............67667
Haysville (1st).........................67060
Hazelton..................................67061
Healy.......................................67850
Hepler.....................................66746
Herington................................67449
Herkimer.................................66433
Herndon..................................67739
Hesston (1st)...........................67062
Hewins, R. Br. Cedar Vale......67024
Hiattville.................................66747
Hiawatha (1st).........................66434
Willis, R. Br......................66435
Hicrest, Sta. Topeka (see
appendix)
Highland..................................66035
Hill City..................................67642
Hillsboro (1st).........................67063
Hillsdale..................................66036
Hoisington...............................67544
Galatia, R. Br....................67528
Holcomb..................................67851
Hollenberg...............................66946
Holliday, R. Br. Shawnee
Mission.............................66037
Holton (1st).............................66436
Holyrood.................................67450
Home......................................66438
Hope.......................................67451
Hopewell.................................67064
Horton....................................66439
Howard....................................67349
Hoxie......................................67740
Hoyt..66440
Hudson....................................67545
Hugoton..................................67951
Humboldt................................66748
Hunnewell, R. Br. South
Haven...............................67141

Hunter.....................................67452
Huron......................................66038
Hutchinson (1st)......................67501
Idana......................................67453
Independence (1st)..................67301
Ingalls.....................................67853
Inman......................................67546
Iola (1st).................................66749
Ionia.......................................66947
Isabel.....................................67065
Iuka..67066
Jamestown..............................66948
Jayhawk, Sta. Lawrence..........66044
Jennings..................................67643
Jetmore...................................67854
Jewell.....................................66949
Johnson...................................67855
Junction City (1st)..................66441
Camp Funston, Br.............66442
Fort Riley, Br....................66442
Kalvesta..................................67856
Kanopolis................................67454
Kanorado................................67741
KANSAS CITY (1st) (see
appendix)
Kechi......................................67067
Kelly.......................................66446
Kendall...................................67857
Kensington..............................66951
Kincaid....................................66039
Kingman (1st)..........................67068
Kingsdown...............................67858
Kinsley....................................67547
Kiowa......................................67070
Kirwin.....................................67644
Kismet.....................................67859
La Crosse................................67548
La Cygne.................................66040
La Harpe.................................66751
Labette....................................67350
Lafontaine...............................66750
Lake City.................................67071
Lake Of The Forest, R. Br.
Bonner Springs.................66012
Lakin.......................................67860
Lamont, R. Br. Madison..........66855
Lancaster.................................66041
Lane..66042
Langdon...................................67549
Lansing...................................66043
Larned (1st).............................67550
Latham....................................67072
Lawrence (1st).........................66044
Lawton....................................66752
Le Roy....................................66857
Leavenworth (1st)....................66048
Leawood, Br. Shawnee
Mission (see appendix)
Lebanon..................................66952
Lebo..66856
Lecompton...............................66050
Lehigh.....................................67073
Lenexa, Br. Shawnee Mission
(see appendix)
Lenora.....................................67645
Leon..67074
Leona......................................66448
Leonardville.............................66449
Leoti.......................................67861
Leoville, R. Br. Selden............67742
Levant.....................................67743
Lewis......................................67552
Liberal (1st).............................67901

Liberty	67351
Liebenthal	67553
Lincoln	67455
Lincolnville	66858
Lindsborg	67456
Linn	66953
Linwood	66052
Little River	67457
Logan	67646
Long Island	67647
Longford	67458
Longton	67352
Lorraine	67459
Lost Springs	66859
Louisburg	66053
Louisville	66450
Lovewell	66954
Lucas	67648
Ludell	67744
Luray	67649
Lyndon	66451
Lyons (1st)	67554
Macksville	67557
Madison	66860
Lamont, R. Br.	66855
Mahaska	66955
Maize	67101
Manchester	67463
Manhattan (1st)	66502
Mankato	66956
Manter	67862
Maple City	67102
Maple Hill	66507
Mapleton	66754
Marienthal	67863
Marion	66861
Marquette	67464
Marysville (1st)	66508
Matfield Green	66862
Mayetta	66509
Mayfield	67103
Mc Connell A F B, Br. Wichita	67221
Mc Cracken	67556
Mc Cune	66753
Mc Donald	67745
Mc Farland, R. Br. Alma	66501
Mc Louth	66054
Mc Pherson (1st)	67460
Meade	67864
Meadow Lake, Br. Shawnee Mission	66208
Medicine Lodge	67104
Medora	67558
Melvern	66510
Menlo	67746
Mentor	67465
Mercier	66511
Meriden	66512
Merriam, Br. Shawnee Mission	66203
Midland, Sta. Wichita (see appendix)	
Milan	67105
Mildred	66055
Milford	66514
Milton	67106
Miltonvale	67466
Minneapolis	67467
Minneola	67865
Mission, Br. Shawnee Mission	66222
Modoc	67866
Moline	67353
Montezuma	67867
Montrose	66957
Monument	67747
Moran	66755
Morganville	67468
Morland	67650
Morrill	66515
Morrowville	66958
Moscow	67952
Mound City	66056
Mound Valley	67354
Moundridge	67107
Mount Hope	67108
Mulberry	66756
Mullinville	67109
Mulvane	67110
Muncie, Sta. Kansas City	66111
Munden	66959
Munger, Sta. Wichita (see appendix)	
Murdock	67111
Muscotah	66058
Narka	66960
Nashville	67112
Natoma	67651
Navarre, R. Br. Enterprise	67469
Neal	66863
Nekoma	67559
Neodesha	66757
Neosho Falls	66758
Neosho Rapids	66864
Ness City	67560
Netawaka	66516
New Albany	66759
New Almelo	67652
New Cambria	67470
Newton (1st)	67114
Nickerson	67561
Niles	67471
Niotaze	67355
Norcatur	67653
North Newton	67117
North Topeka, Sta. Topeka	66608
North Wichita, Sta. Wichita (see appendix)	
Northbranch, R. Br. Burr Oak	66936
Northwest, Sta. Kansas City	66104
Norton (1st)	67654
Nortonville	66060
Norway	66961
Norwich	67118
Oakhill	67472
Oaklawn, Br. Wichita	67216
Oakley	67748
Oberlin	67749
Odin	67562
Offerle	67563
Ogallah	67656
Ogden	66517
Oketo	66518
Olathe (1st)	66061
Olivet, R. Br. Melvern	66519
Olmitz	67564
Olpe	66865
Olsburg	66520
Onaga	66521
Oneida	66522
Opolis	66760
Osage City	66523
Osawatomie (1st)	66064
Osborne	67473
Oskaloosa	66066
Oswego	67356
Otis	67565
Ottawa (1st)	66067
Overbrook	66524
Overland Park, Br. Shawnee Mission (see appendix)	
Oxford	67119
Ozawkie	66070
Packers, Sta. Kansas City (see appendix)	
Palco	67657
Palmer	66962
Paola (1st)	66071
Paradise	67658
Park	67751
Park City, Br. Wichita	67219
Parker	66072
Parsons (1st)	67357
Partridge	67566
Pauline, Br. Topeka	66619
Pawnee Rock	67567
Paxico	66526
Peabody	66866
Peck	67120
Penalosa	67121
Penokee	67659
Perry	66073
Peru	67360
Pfeifer	67660
Phillipsburg (1st)	67661
Piedmont	67122
Pierceville	67868
Piper, R. Br. Kansas City	66109
Piqua	66761
Pittsburg (1st)	66762
Plains	67869
Plainville	67663
Pleasanton	66075
Plevna	67568
Pomona	66076
Portis	67474
Potter	66077
Potwin	67123
Powhattan	66527
Prairie View	67664
Prairie Village, Br. Shawnee Mission (see appendix)	
Pratt (1st)	67124
Prescott	66767
Preston	67569
Pretty Prairie	67570
Princeton	66078
Protection	67127
Quenemo	66528
Quincy	66867
Quinter	67752
Radium	67571
Radley	66768
Rago	67128
Ramona	67475
Randall	66963
Randolph	66554
Ransom	67522
Rantoul	66079
Raymond	67573
Reading	66868
Redfield	66769
Republic	66964
Reserve	66529
Rexford	67753
Rice	66965

Richfield 67953
Richmond 66080
Riley....................................66531
Riverdale 67130
Riverton 66770
Robinson 66532
Rock....................................67131
Rolla...................................67954
Rosalia 67132
Rose Hill.............................67133
Rosedale, Sta. Kansas City....66103
Rossville.............................66533
Roxbury 67476
Rozel..................................67574
Rush Center 67575
Russell (1st)........................67665
Russell Springs....................67755
Sabetha...............................66534
Saffordville, R. Br. Strong
   City.................................66869
Saint Francis........................67756
Saint George........................66535
Saint John 67576
Saint Mary'S College, Sta.
   Leavenworth.....................66048
Saint Marys 66536
Saint Paul 66771
Salina (1st).........................67401
Satanta 67870
Savonburg 66772
Sawyer 67134
Scammon..............................66773
Scandia 66966
Schoenchen, R. Br. Hays........67667
Scott City (1st).....................67871
   Shallow Water, R. Br.........67872
Scottsville, R. Br. Beloit........67477
Scranton 66537
Sedan..................................67361
Sedgwick 67135
Selden.................................67757
   Leoville, R. Br................67742
Selkirk................................67873
Seneca................................66538
Severance 66081
Severy 67137
Seward 67577
Shallow Water, R. Br. Scott
   City.................................67872
Sharon 67138
Sharon Springs.....................67758
Shawnee, Br. Shawnee
   Mission (see appendix)
SHAWNEE MISSION (1st)
   (see appendix)
Shields................................67874
Silver Lake..........................66539
Silverdale, R. Br. Arkansas
   City.................................67005
Simpson...............................67478
Smith Center 66967

Smolan 67479
Soldier................................66540
Solomon...............................67480
South Haven..........................67140
   Hunnewell, R. Br.............67141
Southeast, Sta. Wichita (see
   appendix)
Spearville............................67876
Spivey 67142
Spring Hill............................66083
Stafford 67578
Stanley................................66084
Stark...................................66775
State Hospital, Br.
   Osawatomie 66064
State House, Sta. Topeka........66612
Sterling...............................67579
Stilwell................................67577
Stockton 67669
Strawn, R. Br. Burlington........66839
Strong City...........................66869
Studley................................67759
Stuttgart..............................67670
Sublette...............................67877
Summerfield..........................66541
Sun City...............................67143
Sunflower, R. Br. De Soto........66019
Susank.................................67580
Sycamore 67363
Sylvan Grove.........................67481
Sylvia.................................67581
Syracuse 67878
Talmage...............................67482
Tampa 67483
Tecumseh 66542
Tescott................................67484
Thayer.................................66776
Timken.................................67582
Tipton 67485
Tonganoxie...........................66086
TOPEKA (1st) (see appendix)
Toronto................................66777
Towanda 67144
Treece.................................66778
Tribune................................67879
Trousdale, R. Br. Haviland......67145
Troy 67087
Turner, Sta. Kansas City
   (see appendix)
Turon..................................67583
Tyro 67364
Udall...................................67146
Ulysses (1st) 67880
Uniontown.............................66779
University, Sta. Lawrence........66044
Utica...................................67584
V A Hospital, Sta. Topeka......66622
Valley Center........................67147
Valley Falls..........................66088
Vassar.................................66543
Vermillion 66544

Victoria 67671
Viola 67149
Virgil...................................66870
Vliets..................................66545
Wa Keeney...........................67672
Wakarusa.............................66546
Wakefield.............................67487
Waldo..................................67673
Waldron 67150
Walker.................................67674
Wallace...............................67761
Walnut.................................66780
Walton.................................67151
Wamego...............................66547
Washburn Univ, Sta. Topeka....66621
Washington...........................66968
Washington Street, Sta.
   Wichita...........................67211
Waterville.............................66548
Wathena 66090
Waverly 66871
Wayside...............................67366
Webber.................................66970
Weir....................................66781
Welda..................................66091
Wellington (1st).....................67152
Wells...................................67488
Wellsville.............................66092
Weskan................................67762
West Mineral 66782
Westfall, R. Br. Beverly..........67489
Westmoreland........................66549
Westphalia............................66093
Wetmore...............................66550
Wheaton...............................66551
Wheeler...............................67763
White City.............................66872
White Cloud...........................66094
Whitewater............................67154
Whiting.................................66552
WICHITA (1st) (see
   appendix)
Williamsburg.........................66095
Willis, R. Br. Hiawatha...........66435
Wilmore................................67155
Wilsey..................................66873
Wilson.................................67490
Winchester 66097
Windom................................67491
Winfield (1st).........................67156
Winifred...............................66553
Winona.................................67764
Woodbine 67492
Woodston..............................67675
Wright..................................67882
Yates Center 66783
Yoder..................................67585
Zenda..................................67159
Zenith..................................67586
Zurich..................................67676

217

KANSAS CITY   661

POST OFFICE BOXES

Box Nos.
1000-1999	Civic Center	17
2000-2999	Main Office	10
3000-3999	Rosedale	03
4000-4999	Northwest	04
5000-5999	Packers	19
6000-6999	Argentine	06
9000-9999	Bethel	09
11000-11999	Muncie	11
14000-14999	Piper Br	14
15000-15999	Fairfax	15
16000-16999	Turner	16

RURAL ROUTES

2	06
3	04
4,5,6	09
8,9	11

STATIONS, BRANCHES AND UNITS

Argentine Sta	06
Bethel Sta	09
Civic Center Sta	01
Edwardsville Br	13
Fairfax Sta	15
Muncie Sta	11
Northwest Sta	04
Packers Sta	05
Piper Rural Br	09
Rosedale Sta	03
Turner Sta	16
General Delivery	10
Postmaster	10

APARTMENTS, HOTELS, MOTELS

Bethany Park Plaza, 1036 Calvin	02
Beverly, 2030 West 39th Ave	03
Boulevard, 1919 Olathe Blvd	03
Casa Linda Gardens, 512 Splitlog	01
Colonial, 3930 Rainbow Blvd	02
Connelly Hall, 3101 Minn	02
Eighth & Ann, 717 North 8th	01
Fairfax Hills Gardens, 3176 W Parkwood	04
Hawthorne, 3061 Parkwood	04
Hillcrest, 938 North 34th	02
Hillview, 448 North 18th	02
Holiday Inn, 425 Minnesota	17
Karloma, 1920 Olathe Blvd	03
Phoenix Fountain Bleau, 2330 Central	02
Redwood Garden, 1000 N 71st	12
Roe Gardens, County Line & Roe Ln	03
Rosina, 851 Barnett	01
Saint Charles, 720 N 6th	01
Tally Ho	02
Terrace, 1601 Washington Ave	02
Town House	17
University, 3735 Booth	03
Watts, 904 Armstrong	01

Westheight Manor, 1201 N 18th		02
Wyandotte Towers, 915 Washington Blvd		01
Wyandotte, 2311 Tauromee Ave		02

BUILDINGS

Brotherhood, 754 Minnesota Ave	01
City Hall, 805 N 6th	01
Commercial Bank, 601 Minnesota Ave	01
Fairfax Airport Administration, 3101 Fairfax	15
Fidelity, 609 Minnesota	01
Gateway No. 1, State At 5th	01
Getty, 819 N 7th	01
Grossman, 640 Minnesota	01
Huron, 907 N 7th	01
Leinbach, 721 Minnesota	01
Library, 625 Minnesota	01
Medical, 155 S. 18th	02
New Brotherhood, 745 State	01
Public Levee Terminal, 1401 Fairfax Trfw	15
Security Bank, 915 N 7th	01
Siebers, 823 N 7th	01
Soldiers & Sailors Memorial, 600 N 7th	01
Terrace, 1645 Washington	02
Y M C A, 900 N. 8th	01
Y W C A, 1017 N. 6th	01

GOVERNMENT OFFICES

City Hall, 805 N 6th	01
Courthouse	01
Federal Building	01

HOSPITALS

Bell Memorial, 39th & Rainbow	03
Bethany, 12th & Reynolds	02
Douglass, 3700 N 27th	04
Eleanor Taylor, 311 Seminary	03
Providence, 18th & Barnett	02
Saint Margaret, 8th & Vermont	01
University Of Kansas Medical Center, 39th & Rainbow Blvd	03
Wesleyan Hospital, 4125 Rainbow Blvd	03

UNIVERSITIES AND COLLEGES

Donnelly College, 1236 Sundusky	02
Kansas City Kansas Junior College, 824 State Ave	01

SHAWNEE MISSION   662

POST OFFICE BOXES

Box Nos.
1-999	Main Office	01

1000-1999	Mission Br	22
2000-2999	Main Office Br	01
3000-3999	Shawnee Br	03
4000-4999	Overland Park Br	04
5000-5999	Lenexa Br	15
6000-6999	Leawood Br	06
8000-9999	Prairie Village Br	08

RURAL ROUTES

1	03
2	15

STATIONS, BRANCHES AND UNITS

Holliday Rural Br	66037
Leawood Br	06
Lenexa Br	15
Meadow Lake Br	08
Merriam Br	03
Mission Br	22
Overland Park Br	04
Prairie Village Br	08
Shawnee Br	03
General Delivery	02
Postmaster	02

HOSPITALS

Shawnee Mission Hospital, 74th & Grandview	04

UNIVERSITIES AND COLLEGES

Kansas City College & Bible School, 7401 Metcalf	04

TOPEKA   666

POST OFFICE BOXES

Box Nos.
1-1999	Main Office	01
4000-4999	Gage Center Sta	04
5000-5999	Hicrest Sta	05
8000-8999	North Topeka Sta	08
19000-19999	Pauline Branch	19

RURAL ROUTES

1	19
2,3	08
4	05
5,6	08
7,8,9	04

STATIONS, BRANCHES AND UNITS

Forbes A F B Br	20
Gage Center Sta	04
Hillcrest Sta	05
North Topeka Sta	08
Pauline Br	19
State House Sta	12
V A Hospital Sta	22
Washburn Univ Sta	21

Topeka (Con.)   666

General Delivery	01
Postmaster	03

APARTMENTS, HOTELS, MOTELS

Brewster Place, 1205 W 29th	11
Capper, 918 Tyler	12
Curtis, 914 Tyler	12
Holiday Inn North	01
Holiday Inn South	01
Howard Johnson'S Motor Lodge, 3839 Topeka Ave	09
Jayhawk	01
Kanasas Towers, 100 E 9th	12
Meadow Acres Motel	01
Methodist Home, 1135 College Ave	04
Mount Vernon Court, 2133 Potomac Dr	11
Presbyterian Manor, 4712 W 6th Ave	06
Ramada Inn	01
Senate, 900 Tyler	12
Town House, 635 Harrison	03
University Place, Washburn Ter	04

BUILDINGS

Capitol Federal, 700 Kansas Ave	03
Columbian, 112 W 6th Ave	03
First National Bank, 535 Kansas Ave	03
Garlinghouse, 820 Quincy	12
Insurance, 701 Jackson	03
Kansas Power & Light, 818 Kansas Ave	12
Medical Arts, 1001 Horne	04
Medical Plaza, 1001 Garfield	04
Merchants National Bank, 900 Jackson	12
Mills, 109 W 9th	12
New England, 501 Kansas Ave	03
Topeka Dental, 4301 Huntoon	04
Topeka Medical Center, 918 W 10th Ave	04
V F W, 214 W 6th Ave	03

GOVERNMENT OFFICES

City Hall, 215 E 7th	03
County Courthouse, 214 E 7th St	03
Federal, 424 Kansas Ave	03
Municipal, 215 E 7th	03
State House	12
State Office	12

HOSPITALS

At & Sf, 417 E 6th Ave	07
City County Clinic, 1615 W 8th Ave	06

Kansas Neuological Institute, 3107 W 21st	04
Menninger Foundation	01
Saint Francis, 1719 W 6th Ave	06
Stormont Vail, 845 Washburn Ave	06
Veterans, 2200 Gage Blvd	22

MILITARY INSTALLATIONS

Forbes A F B	20

UNIVERSITIES AND COLLEGES

Washburn Univ	21

WICHITA   672

POST OFFICE BOXES

Box Nos.		
2-2898	Main Office	01
4000-4999	North Wichita Sta	04
7000-7192	Main Office	01
8000-8999	Munger Sta	08
9001-9112	Delano Sta	12
11000-11999	Washington Sta	02
12001-12152	Delano Sta	12
13000-13999	West Wichita Sta	13
16000-16999	Midland Sta	16
17000-17999	Chisholm Sta	17
18000-18999	Southeast Sta	18

RURAL ROUTES

2	04
3,4	08
5	07
6	16
7	12
8	17
9	12

STATIONS, BRANCHES AND UNITS

Chisholm Sta	09
Mc Connell A F B Br	21
Midland Sta	16
Munger Sta	06
North Wichita Sta	04
Oaklawn Br	16
Park City Br	19
Southeast Sta	07
Washington Street Sta	11
West Wichita Sta	05
General Delivery	02
Postmaster	02

APARTMENTS, HOTELS, MOTELS

Allis, 200 S Broadway	02
Broadview, 101 N Waco	02
Commodore, 222 E Elm	14
Highland House, 1400 N Woodlawn	08
Hillcrest, 115 S Rutan	18
Mc Clellan, 229 E William	02
Parklane Towers, 5051 E Lincoln	18
Shirkmere, 256 N Topeka	02

BUILDINGS

Beacon	02
Bitting	02
Brown	02
Century Plaza	02
College	02
Colorado Derby	02
Commerce Plaza	02
County Court House	03
Derby	02
Farmers & Bankers	02
First National Bank	02
Fourth National Bank	02
Garvey	02
Holliday Inn Plaza	02
Insurance	02
Kaufman	02
One Twenty	02
Orpheum	02
Paige Court	02
Petroleum	02
Rule	02
Sutton Place	02
The Kiva	02
Union Center	02
Union National	02
Vickers K.s.b.&t	02

GOVERNMENT OFFICES

United States Post Office	02

HOSPITALS

County, 1001 N Minneapolis	14
Osteopathic, 2622 W Central	03
Saint Francis 929 N Saint Francis	14
Saint Joseph, 3400 Grand	18
Salvation Army, 2050 W 11th	03
Sedgwick County, 1001 Nminneapolis	14
Veterans, 5500 E Kellogg	18
Wesley, 550 N Hillside	14

UNIVERSITIES AND COLLEGES

Friends University, 2000 University	13
Sacred Heart, 3100 Mccormick	13
Wichita State University, 1845 Fairmont	08

KENTUCKY
(Abbreviation: KY)

Aaron 42601
Aberdeen 42201
Acorn 42510
Adairville 42202
Adams 41201
Adolphus 42120
Aflex 41510
Ages 40801
Airport, Br. Cincinnati, O H....45275
Albany 42602
Alcalde 42511
Aleorn 40401
Alexandria 41001
Allegre 42203
Allen 41601
Allensville 42204
Allock 41710
Almo 42020
Alpha 42603
Alpine 42512
Altro 41306
Alva 40802
Alvaton 42122
Amburgey 41801
Anchorage, Br. Louisville 40223
Anco 41711
Anneta, R. Br. Leitchfield 42710
Annville 40402
Appliance Park, Br.
  Louisville 40225
Argillite 41121
Argo 41511
Arjay 40902
Arlington 42021
Artemus 40903
Arvel 40303
Ary 41712
Ashcamp 41512
Asher 40803
Ashers Fork 40904
Ashland (1st) 41101
Athol 41307
Auburn 42206
Augusta 41002
Ault 41122
Austin 42123
Auxier 41602
Avawam 41713
Avondale, Sta. Paducah 42001
Axtel 40103
Bagdad 40003
Baileys Switch 40905
Bakerton 42711
Balkan 40804
Bandana 42022
Banner 41603
Baptist 41308
Barbourville (1st) 40906
  Baughman, R. Br. 40911
  Gausdale, R. Br. 40906
  Jarvis, R. Br. 40906
  Kayjay, R. Br. 40906
Bardstown (1st) 40004
Bardwell 42023
Bark Camp 40720
Barlow 42024
Barnetts Creek 41202
Barrier 42604
Barterville 40304
Baskett 42402

Battletown 40104
Baughman, R. Br.
  Barbourville 40911
Baxter 40806
Baxter Avenue, Sta.
  Louisville 40204
Bays 41310
Bear Branch 41714
Bearville 41715
Beattyville 41311
Beaumont 42124
Beauty 41203
Beaver 41604
Beaver Dam 42320
Bedford 40006
Bee Spring 42207
Beech Creek 42321
Beech Grove 42322
Beechmont 42323
Beechville 42125
Beechwood, R. Br. Owenton 40359
Beetle 41123
Belcher 41513
Belfry 41514
  Hatfield, R. Br. 41514
  Toler, R. Br. 41569
Belknap 41312
Bell Farm 42605
Bellevue, Br. Newport 41073
Belmont, R. Br. Lebanon
  Junction 40105
Belton 42324
Benham 40807
Benton (1st) 42025
Berea (1st) 40403
Bernstadt, R. Br. London 40741
Berry 41003
Berrys Lick 42208
Bethanna 41401
Bethany 41313
Bethel 40306
Bethelridge 42516
Bethlehem 40007
Betsey 42606
Betsy Layne 41605
Beulah Heights 42607
Beverly 40913
Bevinsville 41606
Big Clifty 42712
Big Creek 40914
Big Laurel 40808
Big Rock 41717
Big Spring 40106
Biggs 41515
Bighill 40405
Bimble 40915
Blackey 41804
Blackford 42403
Blaine 41124
Blair, R. Br. Cumberland 40809
Blairs Mills 41402
Blandville 42026
Blaze 41403
Bledsoe 40810
Bloomfield 40008
Blue Diamond 41718
Blue River 41607
Bluehole 40917
Boaz 42027
Bond 40407
Bondville 40308
Bonnieville 42713
Bonnyman 41719

Boone 40408
Booneville 41314
Boons Camp 41204
Boston 40107
Bow 42714
Bowen 40309
Bowling Green (1st) 42101
Bradfordsville 40009
Bradley 41404
Brandenburg 40108
Breeding 42715
Bremen 42325
Bridge Street, Sta. Paducah ...42001
Brightshade, R. Br.
  Manchester 40962
Brinkley 41805
Broad Bottom 41516
Brodhead 40409
Bronston 42518
Brooklyn 42209
Brooks 40109
Brookside 40811
Brooksville 41004
Browder 42326
Browns Fork 41720
Brownsville 42210
Bruin 41125
Brutus 40920
Bryants Store 40921
Bryantsville 40410
Buchanan, R. Br.
  Catlettsburg 41205
Buckhorn 41721
Buckingham 41611
Buckner 40010
Buechel, Br. Louisville (see
  appendix)
Buffalo 42716
Bulan 41722
Burdine 41517
Burgin 40310
Burke 41126
Burkesville 42717
Burkhart 41315
Burlington 41005
Burna 42028
Burning Fork 41405
Burning Springs, R. Br.
  Manchester 40922
Burnside 42519
Burnwell 41518
Bush 40724
Buskirk 41406
Busy 41723
Butler 41006
Butterfly 41724
Bybee 40412
Bypro 41612
Cadiz 42211
  Golden Pond, R. Br. 42231
Cains Store 42520
Calhoun 42327
California 41007
Callaway 40812
Calvert City (1st) 42029
Calvin 40813
Camp Dix 41127
Camp Taylor, Sta. Louisville ...40213
Campbellsburg 40011
Campbellsville (1st) 42718
Campton 41301
Canada 41519
Cane Valley 42720

Caney..........................41407
Caneyville...................42721
Canmer.......................42722
Cannel City.................41408
Cannon.......................40923
Canoe.........................41316
Canton........................42212
Carcassonne................41806
Carlisle.......................40311
Carpenter....................40726
Carr Creek...................41807
Carrie.........................41725
Carrollton (1st)............41008
Carrsville....................42030
Carter.........................41128
Carver.........................41409
Casey Creek................42723
Catlettsburg................41129
   Buchanan, R. Br........41205
Cave City....................42127
Cawood.......................40815
Cecilia........................42724
Center.........................42214
Centertown..................42328
Central, Sta. Louisville...40202
Central City (1st)..........42330
Cerulean......................42215
Chance........................42725
Chaplin.......................40012
Chappell......................40816
Charley........................41207
Chavies.......................41727
Chenoa........................40925
Cherokee, Sta. Louisville..41130
Cherokee, Sta. Louisville..40205
Chesnutburg................40926
Chevrolet.....................40817
Cinda...........................41728
Cisco..........................41410
Clarkson.....................42726
Clay............................42404
Clay City.....................40312
Clayhole......................41317
Clearfield....................40313
Cleaton.......................42332
Clementsville, R. Br. Liberty..42521
Clermont......................40110
Cliff............................41613
Clifford.......................41208
Clifty..........................42216
Climax.........................40413
Clinton (1st).................42031
Closplint......................40927
Clover Bottom..............40414
Cloverport....................40111
Co Operative................42610
Coal Run, R. Br. Pikeville..41501
Coalgood......................40818
Cobb...........................42405
Cobhill........................40415
Cody...........................41808
Cold Spring-Highland
   Heights, Br. Newport..41076
Coldiron......................40819
College, Sta. Berea........40403
College Campus, Sta.
   Murray......................42071
College Heights, Sta.
   Bowling Green...........42101
College Hill.................40416
Colson.........................41809
Columbia.....................42728
   Sparksville, R. Br.......42778

Columbus.....................42032
Combs.........................41729
Concord.......................41131
Confluence...................41730
Conkling......................41318
Conley........................41411
Conrard.......................42523
Constance....................41009
Constantine..................40114
Conway.......................40417
Cooper........................42609
Coopersville.................42611
Corbin (1st).................40701
Cordell........................41210
Corinth........................41010
Cornettsville................41731
Cornishville..................40314
Corydon.......................42406
Cottle..........................41412
Cottonburg...................40418
COVINGTON (1st) (see
   appendix)
Coxs Creek...................40013
Coxton, R. Br. Harlan.....40831
Crab Orchard...............40419
Crane Nest...................40928
Cranks........................40820
Cranston......................40315
Crayne........................42033
Craynor.......................41614
Creekville....................40929
Crescent Hill, Sta. Louisville..40206
Creston.......................42524
Crestwood...................40014
Crittenden....................41030
Crockett......................41413
Crofton........................42217
Cromona.....................41810
Cromwell.....................42333
Cropper.......................40015
Crown..........................41811
Crummies....................40821
Crutchfield...................42034
Crystal........................40420
Cub Run......................42729
Cubage........................40822
Culver.........................41211
Cumberland.................40823
   Blair, R. Br.................40809
Cumberland College, Sta.
   Williamsburg.............40769
Cundiff........................42730
Cunningham.................42035
Curdsville....................42334
Curt............................41319
Custer.........................40115
Cutshin.......................41732
Cutuno........................41414
Cynthiana (1st)............41031
Dabolt.........................40421
Daisy..........................41733
Dalton.........................42407
Dana..........................41615
Danville (1st)...............40422
Darfork, R. Br. Hazard....41701
Davella.......................41212
David..........................41616
Davisport.....................41213
Dawson Springs............42408
Day, R. Br. Whitesburg...41858
Dayhoit.......................40824
Daysboro.....................41320
Dayton, Br. Newport......41074

De Mossville................41033
Deane.........................41812
Deatsville....................40016
Debord........................41214
Decoy..........................41321
Defoe..........................40017
Delphia.......................41735
Delta...........................42613
Dema..........................41859
Democrat.....................41813
Denney.......................42614
Denniston....................40316
Denton........................41132
Denver........................41215
Depoy.........................42336
Dewitt........................40930
Dexter.........................42036
Dice............................41736
Dingus........................41417
Disputanta...................40425
Dixon..........................42409
Dizney........................40825
Donerail, R. Br. Lexington..40505
Dongola.......................41814
Dorton.........................41520
Dover..........................41034
Draffin........................41521
Drake..........................42128
Drakesboro...................42337
Dreyfus.......................40426
Drift............................41619
Drip Rock....................40427
Drum..........................42527
Dry Creek....................41860
Dry Ridge....................41035
Dryhill, R. Br. Hyden.....41749
Dubre..........................42731
Duco...........................41418
Duluth........................40428
Dunbar........................42219
Dundee.......................42338
Dunmor.......................42339
Dunnville....................42528
Dwale.........................41621
Dwarf..........................41739
Dycusburg....................42037
Dyer...........................40116
Earlington....................42410
East Bernstadt..............40729
East Mc Dowell............41623
East Point....................41216
Eastern........................41622
Eastview......................42732
Eastwood.....................40018
Eberle.........................40429
Echols........................42340
Eddyville.....................42038
Edmonton....................42129
Edna..........................41419
Egypt..........................40430
Eighty Eight.................42130
Ekron.........................40117
Elamton......................41420
Elias...........................40431
Elihu..........................42530
Elizabethtown (1st)........42701
Elizaville.....................41037
Elk Horn......................42733
Elkatawa.....................41322
Elkfork........................41421
Elkhorn City.................41522
Elkton.........................42220
Elliottville....................40317

Elhston 41038
Elmrock 41624
Elna 41217
Elsie 41422
Emerson 41135
Eminence 40019
Emlyn 40730
Emma 41625
Emmalena 41740
Endicott 41626
Engle 41741
Eolia 40826
Epson 41423
Eriline 40931
Erlanger, Br. Covington 41018
Ermine 41815
Essie 40827
Estill 41627
Etoile 42131
Etty 41523
Eubank 42567
Evanston 41628
Evarts 40828
   Verda, R. Br. 40872
Ever 41424
Ewing 41039
Ezel 41425
Fairdale 40118
Fairfield 40020
Fairplay 42735
Fairview 42221
Falcon 41426
Fall Rock 40932
Falls Of Rough 40119
Fallsburg 41218
Falmouth 41040
Fancy Farm 42039
Farler 41742
Farmers 40319
Farmington 42040
Faubush 42532
Fedscreek 41524
Felty 40933
Ferguson 42533
Fern Creek, Br. Louisville 40291
Field 40934
Fillmore 41323
Finchville 40022
Finley 42736
Firebrick 41137
Fisherville 40023
Fishtrap 41525
Fisty 41743
Fitch 41138
Flat 41325
Flat Fork 41427
Flat Lick 40935
Flatgap 41219
Flatwoods 41139
Fleming 41816
Flemingsburg 41041
Flippin, R. Br. Tompkinsville 42132
Florence (1st) 41042
Florress 41428
Fogertown 40936
Fonde 40937
Foraker 41429
Ford 40320
Fords Branch 41526
Fordsville 42343
Forest Hills 41527
Fort Campbell (1st) 42223
Fort Knox (1st) 40121

Fort Mitchell, Br. Covington 41017
Fort Thomas, Br. Newport 41075
Foster 41043
Fount 40938
Fountain Run 42133
Fourmile 40939
Foxtown 40432
Frakes 40940
   Pearl, R. Br. 40975
Frankfort (1st) 40601
Franklin (1st) 42134
Frazer 42618
Fredonia 42411
Fredville 41430
Freeburn 41528
Frenchburg 40322
Frew 41744
Fritz 41431
Frozen Creek 41326
Fuget 41220
Fulton (1st) 42041
Fultz 41140
Furnace 40433
Galveston 41629
Gamaliel 42140
Gapville 41433
Gardenside, Sta. Lexington 40504
Garfield 40140
Garlin 42739
Garner 41817
Garrard 40941
Garrett 41630
Garrison 41141
Gausdale, R. Br.
   Barbourville 40906
Gays Creek 41745
Georgetown (1st) 40324
Germantown 41044
Ghent 41045
Gibbs 40942
Gifford 41434
Gilbertsville 42044
Gilley 41818
Gillmore 41327
Girdler 40943
Glasgow (1st) 42141
Glen Dean 40141
Glencoe 41046
Glendale 42740
Glens Fork 42741
Glenview 40025
Golden Pond, R. Br. Cadiz 42231
Goody 41529
Gooserock 40944
Gordon 41819
Goshen 40026
Grace 40945
Gracey 42232
Gradyville 42742
Graham 42344
Grahn 41142
Grand Rivers 42045
Grant 41047
Grassy Creek 41435
Gratz 40327
Gravel Switch 40328
Gray 40734
Gray Hawk 40434
Grays Knob 40829
Grayson 41143
Green Hall 41328
Green Road 40946
Greenmount, R. Br. London 40741

Greensburg 42743
Greenup 41144
Greenville (1st) 42345
Greenwood 42620
Grethel 41631
Guage 41329
Guerrant 41330
Gulnare 41530
Gulston 40830
Gunlock 41632
Guston 40142
Guthrie 42234
Gypsy 41438
Haddix 41331
Hadley 42235
Hager 41439
Hagerhill 41222
Haldeman 40329
Halfway 42150
Hall 41820
Hallie 41821
Halo 41633
Hamlin 42046
Hammond 40947
Hampton 42047
Handshoe 41634
Hanson 42413
Happy 41746
Hardburly 41747
Hardin 42048
Hardinsburg 40143
Hardshell, R. Br. Lost Creek 41348
Hardy 41531
Hardyville 42746
Harlan (1st) 40831
   Coxton, R. Br. 40831
   Helton, R. Br. 40840
   Sunshine, Sta. 40831
Harned 40144
Harold 41635
Harper 41440
Harrods Creek 40027
Harrodsburg (1st) 40330
Hartford 42347
Hartley 41532
Hatfield, R. Br. Belfry 41514
Hatton 40332
Hawesville 42348
Hazard (1st) 41701
Hazel 42049
Hazel Green 41332
Hazel Patch 40735
Head Of Grassy 41145
Hebbardsville 42414
Hebron 41048
Hector 40948
Heidelberg 41333
Heidrick 40949
Helechawa 41334
Hellier 41534
Helton, R. Br. Harlan 40840
Henderson (1st) 42420
Hendricks 41441
Henry Clay, Sta. Lexington
   (see appendix)
Herd 40435
Herndon 42236
Hestand 42151
Hi Hat 41636
Hickman 42050
Hickory 42051
Hidalgo 42622
High Bridge 40334

Highsplint	40841	
Hikes Point, Sta. Louisville	40220	
Hill Top	42624	
Hillsboro	41049	
Hima	40951	
Himyar	40952	
Hindman	41822	
Hinkle	40953	
Hippo	41637	
Hisel	40436	
Hiseville	42152	
Hitchins	41146	
Hite	41638	
Hode	41223	
Hodgenville	42748	
Hogue	42535	
Holland	42153	
Hollybush	41823	
Hollyhill	42625	
Holmes Mill	40843	
Homer	42237	
Honaker	41639	
Honeybee	42626	
Hooker	40954	
Hope	40334	
Hopkinsville (1st)	42240	
Horse Branch	42349	
Horse Cave	42749	
Hoskinston	40844	
Houston	41336	
Howardstown	40028	
Huddy	41535	
Hudson	40145	
Hueysville	41640	
Huff	42250	
Hulen	40845	
Hunter	41641	
Huntsville	42251	
Hustonville	40437	
Hyden	41749	
Dryhill, R. Br.	41749	
Sizerock, R. Br.	41762	
Independence	41051	
Index	41442	
Inez	41224	
Ingle	42536	
Ingram	40955	
Insko	41443	
Iroquois, Sta. Louisville	40214	
Irvine	40336	
Irvington	40146	
Island	42350	
Island City	41338	
Isom	41824	
Isonville	41149	
Iuka	42052	
Ivel	41642	
Ivyton	41444	
Jabez	42628	
Jackhorn	41825	
Jackson	41339	
Juan, R. Br.	41339	
Wilstacy, R. Br.	41392	
Jacobs	41150	
Jamboree	41536	
Jamestown	42629	
Jarvis, R. Br. Barbourville	40906	
Jeff	41751	
Jeffersontown, Br. Louisville	40299	
Jeffersonville	40337	
Jenkins	41537	
Jenson	40957	
Jeremiah	41826	
Jeriel	41151	
Jetson	42252	
Jett	40338	
Jinks	40438	
Job	41225	
Johnetta	40439	
Johns Run	41152	
Jonancy	41538	
Jonesville	41052	
Juan, R. Br. Jackson	41339	
Julip	40736	
Junction City	40440	
Justell, R. Br. Betsy Layne	41605	
Kaliopi	41752	
Kayjay, R. Br. Barbourville	40906	
Keaton	41226	
Keavy	40737	
Keene	40339	
Keith	40846	
Kellacey, R. Br. West Liberty	41472	
Keltner	42750	
Kenton	41053	
Kenvir	40847	
Kerby Knob	40441	
Kettle	42752	
Kettle Island	40958	
Kevil	42053	
Kidder, R. Br. Bronston	42518	
Kimper	41539	
Kingbee	42538	
Kings Creek	41827	
Kings Mountain	40442	
Kirksey	42054	
Kirksville	40443	
Kite	41828	
Kitts	40848	
Knifley	42753	
Knob Lick	42154	
Kodak, R. Br. Vicco	41753	
Kona	41829	
Korea	40340	
Krypton	41754	
Kuttawa	42055	
La Center	42056	
La Fayette	42254	
La Grange	40031	
Lackey	41643	
Lamb	42155	
Lambric	41340	
Lamero	40341	
Lamont	41755	
Lancaster (1st)	40444	
Langley	41645	
Langnau	40738	
Larkslane	41830	
Latonia, Sta. Covington	41015	
Laura	41227	
Lawrenceburg (1st)	40342	
Lawton	41153	
Leander	41228	
Leatherwood	41756	
Lebanon (1st)	40033	
Lebanon Junction	40150	
Belmont, R. Br.	40105	
Leburn	41831	
Ledbetter	42058	
Lee City	41342	
Leeco	41343	
Leitchfield (1st)	42754	
Anneta, R. Br.	42710	
Lejunior	40849	
Lenox	41447	
Lerose	41344	
Letcher	41832	
Lewis Creek	40851	
Lewisburg	42256	
Lewisport	42351	
LEXINGTON (1st) (see appendix)		
Liberty	42539	
Clementsville, R. Br.	42521	
Lick Creek	41540	
Lickburg	41448	
Lida	40739	
Liggett	40852	
Ligon	41646	
Lily	40740	
Lincoln	40961	
Lincoln Ridge, R. Br. Simpsonville	40035	
Lindseyville	42257	
Linefork	41833	
Littcarr	41834	
Little	41346	
Little Sandy	41155	
Livermore	42352	
Livingston	40445	
Lloyd	41156	
Load	41229	
Lockport	40036	
Locust Hill	40151	
Lodiburg, R. Br. Irvington	40146	
Logansport, R. Br. Morgantown	42258	
Logville	41449	
Lola	42059	
London (1st)	40741	
Lone	41347	
Lone Oak, Br. Paducah	42001	
Lookout	41542	
Loretto	40037	
Lost Creek	41348	
Lothair, R. Br. Hazard	41701	
Louellen	40853	
Louisa	41230	
LOUISVILLE (1st) (see appendix)		
Lovelaceville	42060	
Lovely	41231	
Lowes	42061	
Lowmansville	41232	
Loyall	40854	
Lucas	42156	
Ludlow, Br. Covington	41016	
Lynch	40855	
Lyndon, Br. Louisville	40222	
Lynn, R. Br. Greenup	41144	
Lynn Grove	42062	
Lynnville	42063	
Lytten	41157	
Maceo	42355	
Mackville	40040	
Madisonville (1st)	42431	
Maggard	41450	
Magnolia	42757	
Main Street, Sta. Pikeville	41501	
Majestic	41547	
Mallie	41836	
Malone	41451	
Maloneton	41158	
Mammoth Cave	42259	
Manchester	40962	
Brightshade, R. Br.	40962	
Burning Springs, R. Br.	40922	
Mangum	42540	
Manila	41233	

223

Manitou	42436
Mannington	42260
Mannsville	42758
Manton	41648
Maple Mount	42356
Marcum	40963
Mariba	40345
Marion (1st)	42064
Marrowbone	42759
Marshallville	41452
Marshes Siding	42631
Martha	41159
Martin	41649
Martwick, R. Br. Central City	42330
Mary	41350
Mary Alice	40964
Marydell	40751
Mashfork	41453
Mason	41054
Masonic Home	40041
Matthew	41454
Maud	40042
Maulden	40449
Mayfield (1st)	42066
Mayking	41837
Mays Lick	41055
Maysville (1st)	41056
Maytown	41455
Mazie	41160
Mc Andrews	41543
Mc Carr	41544
Mc Combs	41545
Mc Daniels	40152
Mc Dowell	41647
Mc Henry	42354
Mc Kee	40447
Mc Kinney	40448
Mc Quady	40153
Mc Roberts	41835
Mc Veigh	41546
Mc Whorter	40750
Meally	41234
Means	40346
Melber	42069
Melbourne	41059
Melvin	41650
Mentor	41060
Meta, R. Br. Pikeville	41501
Middleburg	42541
Middlesboro (1st)	40965
Middletown, Br. Louisville	40243
Midway	40347
Milburn	42070
Milford	41061
Mill Springs	42632
Millard, R. Br. Pikeville	41501
Millersburg	40348
Mills	40970
Millstone	41838
Milltown	42761
Millwood	42762
Milo	41235
Milton	40045
Mima	41456
Minerva	41062
Minnie	41651
Mintonville	42542
Miracle	40856
Mistletoe	41351
Mitchellsburg	40452
Mize	41352
Monticello	42633

Montpelier	42763
Mooleyville	40154
Moon	41457
Moorefield	40350
Moores Creek	40453
Moorman	42357
Morehead (1st)	40351
Moreland	40454
Morganfield (1st)	42437
Morgantown	42261
Logansport, R. Br.	42258
Morning View	41063
Morrill	40455
Morris Fork	41353
Mortons Gap	42440
Mount Eden	40046
Mount Hermon	42157
Mount Olivet	41064
Mount Sherman	42764
Mount Sterling (1st)	40353
Mount Vernon	40456
Pine Hill, R. Br.	40364
Mount Washington	40047
Mountain Valley	41354
Mousie	41839
Mouthcard	41548
Mozelle	40858
Mud Lick	42158
Muldraugh	40155
Mummie	40457
Munfordville	42765
Murray (1st)	42071
Muses Mills	41065
Myers, R. Br. Carlisle	40311
Myra	41549
Nancy	42544
Napfor	41757
Napier	40859
Naples, R. Br. Ashland	41101
Narrows	42358
Nazareth	40048
Neafus	42766
Nebo	42441
Ned	41355
Nelse	41550
Neon	41840
Nerinx	40049
Netty	41458
Nevisdale	40754
New Castle	40050
New Concord	42076
New Haven	40051
New Hope	40052
New Liberty	40355
New Zion	40458
Newfoundland	41162
Newgarden, Sta. Fort Knox	40121
Newman	42359
NEWPORT (1st) (see appendix)	
Nicholasville (1st)	40356
Nippa	41236
Noble	41356
Noctor	41357
Noland, R. Br. Irvine	40336
North, Sta. Lexington (see appendix)	
North Middletown	40357
North Pleasureville, Sta. Pleasureville	40057
Nortonville	42442
Nuckols	42360
Oak Grove	42262

Oakland	42159
Oakton	42077
Oakville	42263
Offutt	41237
Ogle	40971
Oil Springs	41238
Okolona, Br. Louisville (see appendix)	
Olaton	42361
Old Allen, R. Sta. Allen	41601
Old Landing	41358
Oldtown	41163
Olive Hill	41164
Ollie	42264
Olmstead	42265
Olympia	40358
Omaha	41841
Oneida	40972
Onton	42443
Ophir	41459
Orkney	41652
Orlando	40460
Orville, R. Br. Pleasureville	40057
Oscaloosa	41842
Oven Fork	40861
Overlook, R. Br. Eddyville	42038
Owensboro (1st)	42301
Owenton	40359
Owingsville	40360
Owsley, R. Br. Pikeville	41501
Paducah (1st)	42001
Paint Lick	40461
Paintsville (1st)	41240
Paris (1st)	40361
Park City	42160
Parkers Lake	42634
Parksville	40464
Parrot	40465
Partridge	40862
Pathfork	40863
Patsey	40466
Paw Paw	41551
Payne Gap	41552
Payneville	40157
Peabody	40974
Pearl, R. Br. Frakes	40975
Pebworth	41359
Pellville	42364
Pembroke	42266
Pendleton	40055
Penrod	42365
Peoples	40467
Perry Park	40363
Perryville	40468
Petersburg	41080
Pewee Valley	40056
Peytonsburg	42768
Phelps	41553
Philpot	42366
Phyllis	41554
Pigeonroost	40976
Pike View	42770
Pikeville (1st)	41501
Pilgrim	41250
Pilot	40469
Pine Grove, R. Br. Winchester	40470
Pine Hill, R. Br. Mount Vernon	40364
Pine Knot	42635
Pine Mountain	40864
Pine Ridge	41360
Pine Top	41843

Pineville (1st)	40977
Pinsonfork	41555
Pippa Passes	41844
Raven, R. Br.	41861
Piso	41556
Pittsburg	40755
Plank	40978
Pleasant View, R. Br. Williamsburg	40769
Pleasure Ridge Park, Br. Louisville	40258
Pleasureville	40057
Plummers Landing	41081
Pointer	42547
Pomeroyton	40365
Poole	42444
Poplarville	42548
Port Royal	40058
Portsmouth	41361
Powderly	42367
Premium	41845
Preston	40366
Prestonsburg (1st)	41653
Price	41654
Primrose	41362
Princeton (1st)	42445
Printer	41655
Prospect	40059
Providence	42450
Provo	42267
Pryse	40471
Public	42637
Pueblo	42549
Pulaski	42550
Puncheon	41846
Putney	40865
Pyramid	41656
Quality	42268
Quicksand	41363
Quincy	41166
Raccoon	41557
Raceland, Br. Russell	41169
Radcliff (1st)	40160
Ransom	41558
Raven, R. Br. Pippa Passes	41861
Ravenna	40472
Raywick	40060
Ready	42771
Redbush	41251
Redfox	41847
Redwine	41462
Reed	42451
Regina	41559
Reidland, Br. Paducah	42001
Relief	41463
Renfro Valley	40473
Revelo	42638
Reynolds Station	42368
Rhodelia	40161
Rice Station	40474
Ricetown	41364
Riceville	41252
Richardson	41253
Richardsville	42270
Richelieu	42271
Richmond (1st)	40475
Rineyville	40162
Risner	41658
Ritchie	41758
Ritner	42639
River	41254
Riverside	42272
Roark	40979

Robards	42452
Robinson	41082
Robinson Creek	41560
Rochester	42273
Rockfield	42274
Rockholds	40759
Rockhouse	41561
Rockport	42369
Rocky Hill	42163
Rockybranch	42640
Rogers	41365
Rosine	42370
Rosslyn	40369
Roundhill	42275
Rouse, Sta. Covington	41014
Rousseau	41366
Rowdy	41367
Rowletts	42772
Roxana	41848
Royalton	41464
Rumsey	42371
Rush	41168
Russell	41169
Russell Springs	42642
Russellville (1st)	42276
Ruth	42552
Sacramento	42372
Sadieville	40370
Sadler	42773
Saint Catharine	40061
Saint Charles	42453
Saint Francis	40062
Saint Helens	41368
Saint Joseph	42373
Saint Mary	40063
Saint Matthews, Br. Louisville	40207
Saint Paul	41170
Saldee	41369
Salem	42078
Salt Gum	40980
Salt Lick	40371
Salvisa	40372
Salyersville	41465
Sample	40163
Samuels	40064
Sanders	41083
Sandgap	40481
Sandy Hook	41171
Sardis, R. Br. Maysville	41056
Sassafras	41759
Sasser	40760
Saul	40981
Sawyer	42643
Saxton, R. Br. Williamsburg	40769
Scalf	40982
Science Hill	42553
Scottsville (1st)	42164
Scranton	40373
Scuddy	41760
Se Ree	40164
Sebastians Branch	41370
Sebree	42455
Seco	41849
Sedalia	42079
Seitz	41466
Sergent	41850
Sextons Creek	40983
Sharon Grove	42280
Sharpsburg	40374
Shelbiana	41562
Shelby, Sta. Louisville (see appendix)	

Shelby Gap	41563
Shelbyville (1st)	40065
Shepherdsville (1st)	40165
Sheridan	42080
Shively, Br. Louisville	40216
Shoal	41761
Shopville	42554
Sibert	40984
Sidell	40985
Sidney	41564
Siler	40763
Silver Grove	41085
Silverhill	41467
Simpsonville	
Lincoln Ridge, R. Br.	40035
Sinai	40375
Sitka	41255
Sizerock, R. Br. Hyden	41762
Skyline	41851
Slade	40376
Slaughters	42456
Slavans	42645
Slemp	41763
Sloans Valley	42555
Smilax	41764
Smile	40377
Smith	40867
Smith Mills	42457
Smith Town	42646
Smithfield	40068
Smithland	42081
Smiths Creek	41172
Smiths Grove	42171
Smithsboro	41852
Soft Shell	41853
Soldier	41173
Somerset (1st)	42501
Sonora	42776
South	42777
South Carrollton	42374
South Irvine	40483
South Portsmouth	41174
South Shore	41175
South Union	42283
Southdown, R. Br. Ermine	41815
Southgate, Br. Newport	41071
Southland, Br. Lexington	40503
Sparksville, R. Br. Columbia	42778
Sparta	41086
Speight	41565
Spence, Sta. Newport	41071
Spottsville	42458
Spring Lick	42779
Spring Station	40378
Springfield	40069
Texas, R. Br.	40072
Sprule	40986
Spurlock	40987
Squib	42556
Stab	42557
Stacy Fork	41468
Staffordsville	41256
Stambaugh	41257
Stamping Ground	40379
Standiford, Sta. Louisville	40221
Stanford	40484
Stanley	42375
Stanton	40380
Stanville	41659
Stark	41176
Stay	41373
Stearns	42647
Steele	41566

Steff	42780	Tyner	40486	West Louisville	42377
Stella	41469	Typo	41771	West Paducah	42086
Stephens	41177	Ulvah	41856	West Point	40177
Stephensburg	42781	Ulysses	41264	West Prestonsburg	41668
Stephensport	40170	Union	41091	West Somerset, Sta.	
Steubenville	42648	Union City	40382	Somerset	42501
Stinnett	40868	Union Star	40171	West Van Lear	41268
Stone	41567	Uniontown	42461	Westbend	40388
Stoney Fork	40988	Unity, Sta. Ashland	41101	Westport	40077
Stopover	41568	University, Sta. Lexington	40506	Westview	40178
Straight Creek	40989	Upper Tygart	41178	Westwood, Br. Ashland	41101
Strunk	42649	Upton	42784	Wheatcroft	42463
Sturgis	42459	Urban	40765	Wheatley	40389
Sublett	41470	Utica	42376	Wheelersburg	41473
Subtle, R. Br. Edmonton	42129	Vada	41383	Wheelwright	41669
Sudith	40381	Valeria	41384	Whick	41390
Sullivan	42460	Valley Station, Br. Louisville	40272	White Mills	42788
Sulphur	40070	Van	41857	White Oak	41474
Sulphur Well, R. Br.		Van Lear	41265	White Plains	42464
Edmonton	42129	Vanceburg	41179	Whitehouse	41269
Summer Shade	42166	Vancleve	41385	Whitesburg	41858
Summersville	42782	Vanzant	40174	Whitesville	42378
Summit	42783	Varney	41571	Whitley City	42653
Sunfish	42284	Verda, R. Br. Evarts	40872	Wiborg	42654
Sunnybrook	42650	Verne	40766	Wickliffe	42087
Sunshine, Sta. Harlan	40831	Verona	41092	Widecreek	41391
Swamp Branch	41258	Versailles (1st)	40383	Wilbur	41270
Swampton	41471	Vertrees	42785	Wild Cat	40998
Sweeden	42285	Vest	41772	Wildie	40492
Symbol	40764	Vicco	41773	Willaila	40493
Symsonia	42082	Kodak, R. Br.	41753	Willard	41181
Talbert	41377	Victory	40767	Williamsburg (1st)	40769
Talcum	41765	Vincent	41386	Cumberland College, Sta.	40769
Tallega	41378	Vine Grove	40175	Pleasant View, R. Br.	40769
Tanksley	40990	Viper	41774	Saxton, R. Br.	40769
Tateville	42558	Virgie	41572	Wofford, R. Br.	40770
Taylorsville	40071	Volga	41266	Williamsport	41271
Teaberry	41660	Vortex	41387	Williamstown	41097
Tedders	40991	Waco	40385	Willis Creek	42789
Teges	40992	Waddy	40076	Willisburg	40078
Texas, R. Br. Springfield	40072	Walden	40768	Willow Shade	42169
Thealka	41259	Waldo	41664	Wilmore	40390
Thelma	41260	Wales	41573	Wilstacy, R. Br. Jackson	41392
Thornton	41855	Walker	40997	Win	41272
Thousandsticks	41766	Walkertown, Sta. Hazard	41701	Winchester (1st)	40391
Threeforks	41261	Wallingford	41093	Pine Grove, R. Br.	40470
Tiline	42083	Wallins Creek	40873	Wind Cave	40494
Tina	41768	Walnut Grove	42563	Windsor	42565
Tinsley	40993	Walton	41094	Windy	42655
Toler, R. Br. Belfry	41569	Waneta	40488	Wingo	42088
Tollesboro	41189	War Creek	41388	Winifred	41273
Tolu	42084	Warbranch	40874	Winston	40495
Tomahawk	41262	Warfield	41267	Wittensville	41274
Tompkinsville	42167	Warsaw	41095	Wofford, R. Br.	
Flippin, R. Br.	42132	Washington	41096	Williamsburg	40770
Topmost	41862	Water Valley	42085	Wolf	41182
Totz	40870	Watergap	41665	Wolf Coal	41393
Toulouse	41769	Waterview	42786	Wolverine	41394
Touristville	42651	Watts, R. Br. Lost Creek	41348	Wonnie	41475
Tram	41663	Waverly	42462	Woodbine	40771
Trammel, R. Br. Scottsville	42164	Wax	42787	Woodburn	42170
Trappist	40073	Wayland	41666	Woodbury	42288
Tremont	40871	Waynesburg	40489	Woodman	41574
Trenton	42286	Webbs Cross Roads	42652	Woodsbend	41476
Tribbey	41770	Webbville	41180	Woollum	40999
Trimble	42559	Webster	40176	Wooton	41776
Trinity	41190	Weeksbury	41667	Worthington	41183
Trosper	40995	Welchburg	40490	Worthville	41098
Turkey	41382	Welchs Creek	42287	Wrigley	41477
Turkey Creek	41570	Wellington	40387	Wurtland, R. Br. Greenup	41144
Turners Station	40075	Wendover	41775	Yeaddiss	41777
Tutor Key	41263	West Irvine	40491	Yeaman	42379
Tuttle	40996	West Liberty	41472		

COVINGTON   410

POST OFFICE BOXES

Box Nos.		
1-106	Rouse Sta	14
1-125	Fort Mitchell	
	Br	17
1-255	Erlanger Br	18
1-1108	Main Office	12
101-399	Ludlow Br	16
802-917	Latonia Sta	15

RURAL ROUTES

1,2		17
5		15

STATIONS, BRANCHES AND UNITS

Erlanger Br	18
Fort Mitchell Br	17
Latonia Sta	15
Ludlow Br	16
Rouse Sta	14
General Delivery	11
Postmaster	11

BUILDINGS

Coppin	11
Covington Trust & Banking Co	11
First Nat Banking & Trust Co	11
Internal Revenue Service	19

HOSPITALS

Booth Memorial	11
Saint Elizabeth	14

UNIVERSITIES AND COLLEGES

Community College	11
Thomas More College	17

LEXINGTON   405

POST OFFICE BOXES

Box Nos.		
1-2000	Lexington	01
4001-4250	Gardenside	04
4431-5089	University Sta	06
5001-5500	North	05
7001-7300	Henry Clay Sta	02
8001-8297	Southland Br	03

RURAL ROUTES

1		03
2		04
3,4		05
5		02
6		05
7		02
8		04
9		05

STATIONS, BRANCHES AND UNITS

Donerail Rural Br	05
Gardenside Sta	04
Henry Clay Sta	02
North Sta	05
Southland Br	03
University Sta	06
General Delivery	07
Postmaster	07

APARTMENTS, HOTELS, MOTELS

Beaumont Cabana Apts., 2044 Georgian Way	04
Connie R. Griffith Manor, 540 West 2nd	08
Continental Apts., 2121 Nicholasville Road	03
Cooperstown	08
Creekside Apts., 2223 Devonport Dr	04
Hanover Towers Apts., 101 S. Hanover Ave	02
Holly Tree Manor Apts, 1435 S. Limestone St	03
Jamestown Apts, 2200 Richmond Rd	02
Lansbrook Village Apts., 3400 Lansdowne Dr	02
Lexington Hills Apts, 2150 Richmond Rd	02
Locustwood Estates, Georgetown Rd	05
Phoenix Hotel, 120 E Main	07
Rolling Ridge Apts 3525 Tates Creek Rd	02
Shawneetown Apts	03
Todds Trace Apts, 151 Todds Road	09
Wellington Arms Apts., 508 East Main Street	08

BUILDINGS

American Mutual, 496 Southland Dr	03
Bakhaus, 1500 Leestown Road	05
Bank Of Commerce, 318 E. Main	07
Bank Of Lexington, 311 E Main	07
Cardinal Valley Shopping Center, 2000 Bl Versailles Rd	04
Central Bank, 163 W Short	07
Chevy Chase Shopping Center, E High & Euclid	02
Citizens Bank Square	07
Citizens Union National Bank, 201 W Short	07
Cross Roads Shopping Center, Nicholasville Rd	03
Dunn, 288 S Limestone	08
Eastland Shopping Center, Winchester Rd	05
Exchange, 147 N Upper	07
Fayette Mall, Nicholasville Rd	03
Federal, 101 Barr	07

First Federal Savings & Loan, 134 N Limestone	07
First Security National Bank & Trust Co, 167 W Main	07
Gardenside Shopping Center, 1800 Alexandria Dr	04
General Telephone Company, 2001 Harrodsburg Rd	07
Hi-Acres Shopping Center, 1800 Bl Bryan Station Rd	05
Idle Hour Shopping Center, 2000 Richmond Rd	02
Imperial Plaza Shopping Center, 300 Waller Ave	04
Internal Revenue, 1500 Leestown Rd	05
International Business Machines Corporation	07
Kentucky Central, 200 E Main	07
Kentucky Utilities Company, 120 S Limestone	07
Lafayette Shopping Center, 1900 Harrodsbrg Rd	03
Lansbrook Village Shopping Center, 3500 Lansdowne Dr	03
Lexington Mall, 2397 Richmond Rd	02
Meadowthrope Shopping Center, 1400 Leestown Rd	05
Northland Shopping Center, 1300 N Broadway	05
Nunn, 121 Walnut	07
Romany Road Shopping Center, 300 Romany Road	02
Second National Bank & Trust Co, 123 Cheapside	07
Security Trust, 271 W Short	07
Social Security, 1500 Leestown Rd	05
Southland Shopping Center, 300 Southland Dr	03
State Office, 300 S Upper	08
Turfland Mall, 2000 Bl Harrodsburg Rd	04
Vittetow, 269 W Main	07
Zandale Shopping Center, 2200 Nichlsvlle Rd	03

GOVERNMENT OFFICES

City Hall, 136 Walnut	07
Courthouse, 201 W Main	07
Lexington Fayette County Health Departmen, 330 Waller Ave	04

HOSPITALS

Cardinal Hill Convalescent Hospital, 2050 Versailles Rd	04
Central Baptist Hospital, 1740 S Limestone	03
Eastern State Hospital, 627 W 4th	08
Good Samaritan Hospital, 310 S Limestone	08
National Institute Of Mental Health, Leestown Road	07

Lexington (Con.) 405

Saint Joseph Hospital, 1400
Harrodsburg Rd 04
Shriners Hospital For
Crippled Children, 1900
Richmond Rd 02
University Hospital, 800 Rose
St 06
Veterans Administration
Hospital, Leestown Rd 07

MILITARY INSTALLATIONS

Lexington Blue Grass Army
Depot 07

UNIVERSITIES AND COLLEGES

Copperstown 08
Lexington Theological
Seminary, 631 S
Limestone 08
Transylvania College, 201 W
3rd 08
University Of Kentucky,
Limestone & Euclid 06

LOUISVILLE 402

POST OFFICE BOXES

Box Nos.
1-2159   Louisville   01
4001-4336   Baxter Avenue
              Sta   04
5001-5657   Cherokee Sta...   05
6001-6247   Crescent Hill
              Sta 06
7001-7564   Saint Matthews
              Br 07
8001-8434   E Sta 08
10001-10128   D Sta 10
11001-11086   H Sta 11
12001-12206   R Sta 12
13001-13321   Camp Taylor
              Sta 13
14001-14303   Iroquois Sta....... 14
16001-16374   Shively Sta....... 16
17001-17272   Shelby Sta....... 17
18001-18430   Buechel Br....... 18
19001-19307   Okolona Br 19
20001-20277   Hikes Point
              Sta 20
21001-21477   Standiford Sta.. 21
22001-22277   Lyndon Br....... 22
23001-23447   Anchorage Br... 23
43001-43298   Middletown Br... 43
58001-58416   Pleasure Ridge
              Park Br....... 58
72001-72386   Valley Station
              Br 72
91001-91250   Fern Creek Br... 91
99001-99398   Jeffersontown
              Br 99

RURAL ROUTES

1 22
2,3,4 99
5,6 91
7,8 72
10 18
11,12,13,14,15,16,17 23
18 99
19 91

STATIONS, BRANCHES AND UNITS

Anchorage Br 23
Appliance Park Br.................... 25
Baxter Avenue Sta.................... 04
Buechel Br.................... 18
Camp Taylor Sta.................... 13
Central Sta.................... 02
Cherokee Sta.................... 05
Crescent Hill Sta.................... 06
Fern Creek Br.................... 91
Hikes Point Sta.................... 20
Iroquois Sta.................... 14
Jeffersontown Br.................... 99
Lyndon Br.................... 22
Middletown Br.................... 43
Okolona Br.................... 19
Pleasure Ridge Park Br.......... 58
Saint Matthews Br.................... 07
Shelby Sta.................... 17
Shively Br.................... 16
Standiford Sta.................... 21
Valley Station Br.................... 72
General Delivery.................... 02
Postmaster.................... 01

APARTMENTS, HOTELS, MOTELS

Adams House, 512 W Ormsby
Ave 03
Admiral Benbow Inn, 3315
Bardstown Rd 18
Alamo Plaza Court, 5229
Dixie Hwy.................... 16
Albert Pick Motel, 1620
Arthur 17
Barkley Towers, 3201 Leith
Ln.................... 18
Berkeley, 664 S 4th 02
Browns, 3320 Bardstown Rd.. 18
Churchill Inn, 4444 Dixie
Hwy.................... 16
Commodore, 2140
Bonnycastle Ave.................... 05
Dartmouth Apartments, 1416
Willow Ave.................... 04
Executive Inn, Watterson Expy
At Fairgrounds.................... 13
Guthrie Coke, 411 W
Chestnut.................... 02
Hampton Hall, 209 York........ 03
Hillebrand House, 1235 S
3rd.................... 03
Holiday Inn, Central, 1921
Bishop Ln.................... 18
Holiday Inn, Downtown, 927
S 2nd.................... 03
Holiday Inn, Northeast, 4805
Brownsboro Rd.................... 07

Holiday Inn, South, 3317
Fern Valley Rd.................... 13
Holiday Inn, Southeast, 3255
Bardstown Rd.................... 05
Howard Johnsons Motor
Lodge, 100 E Jefferson.... 02
Howard Johnsons Motor
Lodge, 4621 Shelbyville
Rd.................... 07
Leslies Motel, 5215 Dixie
Hwy.................... 16
Louisville Manor Motor Court,
4600 Dixie Hwy.................... 16
Mayflower Apartments, 425
W Ormsby Ave.................... 03
Milner Highland, 231 W
Jefferson.................... 02
Motel 6, 3304 Bardstown Rd.. 18
Parks Motel, 4700 Dixie Hwy.. 16
Puritan Apartments, 1244 S
4th.................... 03
Quality Courts Motel, 735 S
2nd.................... 02
Ramada Inn, 9700 Bluegrass
Pky.................... 99
Roadway Inn, Airport, 1465
Gardiner Ln.................... 13
Roadway Inn, 101 E.
Jefferson.................... 02
Salem Square Apartments,
521 Zorn Ave.................... 06
Seelbach, 500 S 4th.................... 01
Sheraton Inn, Louisville East,
9608 Blairwood Rd.................... 22
Southland, 1315 S 3rd.................... 08
Standiford Motor Hotel,
Watterson Expy At Airport.... 21
Stouffers Inn, 120 W
Broadway.................... 02
Travelodge, 401 S 2nd.................... 02
Trinity Towers Apartments,
537 S 3rd.................... 02
Watterson, 415 W Walnut.................... 02
Willow Terrace Apartments,
1412 Willow Ave.................... 04
Y M C A, 231 W Broadway.................... 02
Y W C A, 604 S 3rd.................... 02
York Towers, 201 York.................... 03
800, 800 S 4th.................... 03

BUILDINGS

American Life, 431 W Main.... 02
Brown, 321 W Broadway........ 02
Center, 522 W Jefferson.................... 02
Commerce, 304 W Liberty.................... 02
Commonwealth, 674 S 4th.................... 02
Cosmopolitan, 981 S 3rd.................... 03
Doctors Office, 250 E Liberty.. 02
Fincastle, 305 W Broadway.... 02
Heyburn, 332 W Broadway.... 02
Hilliard, 419 W Jefferson 02
Hoffman, 139 S 4th.................... 02
Kentucky Home Life, 239 S
5th.................... 02
Kenyon, 112 S 5th.................... 02
Lincoln Federal, 600 S 4th.... 02
Lincoln Towers, 6100
Dutchmans Ln.................... 05
Louisville Trust, 208 S 5th.... 02
Marion E Taylor, 312 S 4th.... 02
Mc Dowell, 505 S 3rd.................... 02

Louisville (Con.)   402

Medical Arts, 1169 Eastern
Pky.. 17
Medical Towers, N, 233 E
Gray... 02
Medical Towers, S, 234 E
Gray... 02
Metropolitan, 151 S 5th........... 02
Portland Federal, 200 W
Broadway................................ 02
Republic, 429 W Walnut............ 02
Snead, 817 W Market............... 02
Speed, 333 Guthrie................... 02
Starks, 455 S 4th..................... 02
Theatre, 629 1/2 S 4th.............. 02
Tyler, 319 W Jefferson............. 02
Washington, 136 S 4th............. 02
Watterson City, 1941 Bishop
Ln.. 18
300, 300 W Main...................... 02

GOVERNMENT OFFICES

City Hall, 6th & Jefferson........ 02
Courthouse, 531 W Jefferson.. 02
Federal, 600 Federal Pl........... 02
Fiscal Courts, 527 Court Pl...... 02
Post Office, 601 W Broadway. 02
State Office, 600 Cedar.......... 03

HOSPITALS

Central State, Lakeland Rd 23
Childrens, 226 E Chestnut 02
City, 323 E Chestnut 02
General, 323 E Chestnut 02
Hazelwood Sanitarium, 1800
Bluegrass Ave 15

Jewish, 217 E Chestnut.......... 02
Kentucky Baptist, 810 Barret
Ave.. 04
Kosair Crippled Children, 982
Eastern Pkwy 17
Louisville Memorial, 2215
Portland Ave 12
Methodist Evangelical, 315 E
Broadway............................. 02
Norton Memorial Infirmary,
231 W Oak St 03
Our Lady Of Peace, 2020
Newburg Rd.......................... 05
Red Cross, 1436 S Shelby..... 01
Saint Anthony, 1313 St
Anthony Pl........................... 04
Saint Joseph Infirmary, 735
Eastern Pkwy 17
Saints Mary & Elizabeth,
4400 Churchman Ave........... 15
Veterans Administration,
Mellwood Ave & Zorn Av 02

UNIVERSITIES AND COLLEGES

Bellarmine, 2000 Norris Pl..... 05
Presbyterian Seminary, 1042
Alta Vista Rd........................ 05
Southern Baptist Theological
Seminary, 2825 Lexington
Rd.. 06
Spalding, 851 S 4th................. 03
U Of L School Of Dentistry,
129 E Broadway.................... 02
U Of L School Of Medicine,
101 W Chestnut.................... 02
U Of L School Of Music,
9001 Shelbyville Rd............. 22

University Of Louisville, 2301
S 3rd...................................... 08
Ursuline, 3105 Lexington Rd .. 06

NEWPORT   410

POST OFFICE BOXES

Box Nos.
1-56   Dayton Br.......... 74
1-147   Cold Spring-
Highland
Heights Br...... 76
1-274   Fort Thomas
Br 75
1-477   Main Office 72
1-539   Bellevue Br....... 73
1000-1199   Spence Sta........ 71

RURAL ROUTES

1 76

STATIONS, BRANCHES AND UNITS

Bellevue Br................................ 73
Cold Spring-Highland
Heights Br............................. 76
Dayton Br.................................. 74
Fort Thomas Br 75
Southgate Br............................. 71
Spence Sta................................ 71
General Delivery 71
Postmaster................................ 71

LOUISIANA
(Abbreviation: LA)

Abbeville (1st)...................70510
Abita Springs...................70420
Acadia Academy, R. Br.
  Eunice............................70535
Acme.................................71316
Addis.................................70710
Aimwell.............................71401
Akers.................................70421
Albany...............................70711
Alco...................................71402
Alexandria (1st).................71301
Alto, R. Br. Rayville...........71216
Ama..................................70031
Amelia...............................70340
Amite (1st).........................70422
Anacoco.............................71403
Angie.................................70426
Angola...............................70712
Arabi (1st)..........................70032
Arcadia..............................71001
Archibald............................71218
Arnaudville.........................70512
Ashland..............................71002
Athens................................71003
Atlanta...............................71404
Audubon, Sta. Baton Rouge...70806
Avery Island.......................70513
Avondale, Br. Westwego.......70094
Bains.................................70713
Baker (1st)..........................70714
Baldwin..............................70514
Ball....................................71405
Barataria............................70036
Barksdale A F B, Br.
  Shreveport........................71110
Basile.................................70515
Baskin................................71219
Bastrop (1st).......................71220
Batchelor............................70715
BATON ROUGE (1st) (see
  appendix)
Bayou Chicot, R. Br. Ville
  Platte..............................70586
Bayou Goula........................70716
Bayou Pigeon, R. Br.
  Plaquemine.......................70764
Bayou Sorrel, R. Br.
  Plaquemine.......................70764
Bayou Vista, R. Br. Morgan
  City..................................70380
Bel, R. Br. Reeves................70675
Belcher...............................71004
Bell City.............................70630
Belle Chasse (1st)................70037
Belle River, R. Br. Morgan
  City..................................70380
Belle Rose..........................70341
  Klotzville, R. Br................70370
Belmont..............................71406
Benson...............................71005
Bentley...............................71407
Benton................................71006
Bernice..............................71222
Berwick...............................70342
Bethany..............................71007
Bienville.............................71008
Big Bend.............................71318
Blanchard............................71009
Blanks................................70717
Bogalusa (1st).....................70427

Bonita................................71223
Boothville............................70038
Bordelonville.......................71320
Bossier City (1st).................71010
Bourg.................................70343
Boutte................................70039
Boyce.................................71409
Braithwaite..........................70040
Branch................................70516
Breaux Bridge (1st)..............70517
Bridge City, Br. Westwego......70094
Brittany...............................70718
Broadmoor, Sta. New
  Orleans.............................70125
Broadview, Sta. Baton
  Rouge (see appendix)
Broussard............................70518
Brownfields, Br. Baton
  Rouge...............................70807
Brusly................................70719
Bryceland............................71014
Buckeye..............................71321
Bueche................................70720
Bunkie (1st)........................71322
Buras (1st)..........................70041
Burnside, R. Br. Gonzales......70738
Bush...................................70431
Bywaters, Sta. New Orleans....70117
Cade...................................70519
Calcasieu, R. Br. Glenmora....71433
Calhoun..............................71225
Calvin................................71410
Cameron..............................70631
Campti................................71411
Capitol, Sta. Baton Rouge......70804
Carencro..............................70520
Carlisle...............................70042
Carrollton, Sta. New Orleans...70118
Carville...............................70721
Caspiana.............................71015
Castor.................................71016
Catahoula, R. Br. Saint
  Martinville.........................70582
Cecilia................................70521
Cedar Grove, Sta.
  Shreveport........................71106
Centenary, Sta. Shreveport....71104
Center Point.........................71323
Centerville...........................70522
Central City, Sta. Baton
  Rouge...............................70806
Chackbay, R. Br. Thibodaux....70301
Chalmette (1st)...................70043
Charenton............................70523
Chase.................................71324
Chataignier..........................70524
Chatham.............................71226
Chauvin..............................70344
Chef Menteur, Sta. New
  Orleans (see appendix)
Cheneyville..........................71325
Chestnut.............................71017
Chopin...............................71412
Choudrant...........................71227
Church Point........................70525
Clarence.............................71414
Clarks................................71415
Clay, R. Br. Ruston...............71228
Clayton...............................71326
Clinton...............................70722
Cloutierville.........................71416
Colfax.................................71417
College, Sta. Hammond.........70401

Collinston............................71229
Columbia.............................71418
Convent...............................70723
  Uncle Sam, R. Br..............70792
  Union, R. Br......................70723
Converse.............................71419
Cooper Road, Br. Shreveport...71101
Cotton Valley.......................71018
Cottonport...........................71327
Coushatta (1st)....................71019
Covington (1st)....................70433
Creole.................................70632
Creston...............................71020
Crowley (1st).......................70526
Crowville.............................71230
Cullen.................................71021
Custom House, Sta. New
  Orleans.............................70116
Cut Off...............................70345
Cypress...............................71420
Darnell, R. Br. Pioneer..........71231
Darrow................................70725
Davant................................70046
De Quincy...........................70633
De Ridder (1st)....................70634
Delcambre...........................70528
Delhi..................................71232
Delta..................................71233
Denham Springs (1st)...........70726
Derry..................................71421
Des Allemands.....................70030
Destrehan............................70047
Deville................................71328
Diamond..............................70048
Dixie..................................71022
Dodson...............................71422
Donaldsonville (1st).............70346
Donner................................70352
Downsville...........................71234
Downtown, Sta. Morgan City...70380
Downtown, Sta. Monroe.........71201
Doyline...............................71023
Drew, Sta. Lake Charles........70601
Dry Creek...........................70637
Dry Prong...........................71423
Dubach................................71235
Dubberly.............................71024
Dulac..................................70353
Dunn...................................71236
Duplessis.............................70728
Dupont................................71329
Duson................................70529
East Point............................71025
Easton................................70530
Echo...................................71330
Edgard................................70049
Effie...................................71331
Egan..................................70531
Elizabeth.............................70638
Elmer..................................71424
Elton..................................70532
Embarkation, Sta. New
  Orleans.............................70140
Empire................................70050
England A F B, Br.
  Alexandria.........................71301
Enterprise............................71425
Eola...................................71332
Epps...................................71237
Erath..................................70533
Eros...................................71238
Erwinville............................70729
Estherwood..........................70534

230

Ethel 70730
Eunice (1st) 70535
Evangeline 70537
Evans 70639
Evergreen 71333
Extension 71239
Fair Grounds, Sta.
  Shreveport 71109
Fairbanks 71240
Farmerville 71241
Felixville 70731
Fenton 70640
Ferriday (1st) 71334
Fields 70641
Fisher 71426
Flatwoods 71427
Flora 71428
Florien 71429
Fluker 70436
Folsom 70437
Forbing 71026
Fordoche 70732
Forest 71242
Forest Hill 71430
Forked Island, R. Br.
  Abbeville 70510
Fort Necessity 71243
Fort Polk, Br. Leesville 71459
Franklin (1st) 70538
Franklinton (1st) 70438
French Settlement 70733
Frierson 71027
Frisco, R. Br. Livonia 70755
Frogmore 71335
Fullerton 70642
Galliano 70354
Garden City 70540
Gardner 71431
Garyville 70051
Geismar 70734
Gentilly, Sta. New Orleans ... 70122
Georgetown 71432
Gheens 70355
Gibsland 71028
Gibson 70356
Gilbert 71336
Gilliam 71029
Girard 71244
Glenmora 71433
Gloster 71030
Glynn 70736
Golden Meadow 70357
  South Lafourche, R. Br. ... 70338
Goldonna 71031
Gonzales (1st) 70737
  Burnside, R. Br. 70738
Good Hope, Br. Norco 70079
Good Pine 71337
Gorum 71434
Goudeau 71338
Grambling 71245
Gramercy 70052
Grand Cane 71032
Grand Chenier 70643
Grand Coteau 70541
Grand Isle 70358
Grant 70644
Gray 70359
Grayson 71435
Greensburg 70441
Greenwell Springs 70739
Greenwood 71033
Gretna (1st) 70053

Grosse Tete 70740
Gueydan 70542
Hackberry 70645
Hahnville 70057
Haile, R. Br. Marion 71246
Hall Summit 71034
Hamburg 71339
Hammond (1st) 70401
Hanna 71035
Harahan, Br. New Orleans 70123
Hardwood 70742
Harmon 71036
Harrisonburg 71340
Harvey (1st) 70058
Haughton 71037
Hayes 70646
Haynesville 71038
Hebert 71436
Heflin 71039
Henderson, R. Br. Breaux
  Bridge 70517
Hessmer 71341
Hester 70743
Hicks 71437
Highland Road, Br. Baton
  Rouge 70808
Hineston 71438
Hodge 71247
Holden 70744
Holly Ridge 71248
Homer (1st) 71040
Hornbeck 71439
Hospital, Br. Alexandria 71301
Hosston 71043
Houma (1st) 70360
Husser 70442
Iberville 70746
Ida 71044
Independence 70443
Industrial, Sta. Shreveport ... 71107
Innis 70747
International Trade Mart,
  Sta. New Orleans 70130
Intracoastal City, R. Br.
  Abbeville 70510
Iota 70543
Iowa 70647
Istrouma, Sta. Baton Rouge
  (see appendix)
Jackson 70748
Jamestown 71045
Jarreau 70749
Jeanerette (1st) 70544
Jefferson, Br. New Orleans ... 70121
Jefferson Island 70545
Jena 71342
Jennings (1st) 70546
Jewella, Sta. Shreveport 71109
Jigger 71249
Jones 71250
Jonesboro (1st) 71251
Jonesville 71343
Joyce 71440
Junction City 71749
Kaplan (1st) 70548
Keatchie 71046
Keithville 71047
Kelly 71441
Kenner (1st) 70062
Kentwood 70444
Kilbourne 71253
Killona 70066
Kinder 70648

Klotzville, R. Br Belle Rose ... 70370
Kolin, R. Br. Alexandria 71301
Kraemer 70371
Krotz Springs 70750
Kurthwood 71443
La Place (1st) 70068
Labadieville 70372
Labarre 70751
Lacamp 71444
Lacassine 70650
Lacombe 70445
Lafayette (1st) 70501
Lafayette Square, Sta. New
  Orleans 70130
Lafitte 70067
Lake Arthur 70549
Lake Charles (1st) 70601
Lake Providence (1st) 71254
Lakeland 70752
Lakeshore, Sta. Shreveport ... 71109
Lakeside, Sta. Metairie 70002
Lakeview, Sta. New Orleans ... 70124
Larose 70373
Larto 71344
Lawtell 70550
Le Blanc 70651
Le Moyen 71347
Leander 71445
Lebeau 71345
Lecompte 71346
Leesville (1st) 71446
  Fort Polk, Br. 71459
  Post Trailer Park, Br. 71446
  South Park Trailer Court,
  Br. 71446
Lena 71447
Leonville 70551
Lettsworth 70753
Libuse 71348
Lillie 71256
Linville 71257
Lisbon 71048
Livingston 70754
Livonia 70755
Lockport 70374
Logansport 71049
Longleaf 71448
Longstreet 71050
Longville 70652
Loranger 70446
Loreauville 70552
Lottie 70756
Louise Street, Sta. Baton
  Rouge 70802
Louisville, Sta. Monroe 71201
Lucy 70069
Luling (1st) 70070
Lutcher 70071
Lydia 70569
Madison Park, Sta.
  Shreveport 71105
Madisonville 70447
Mamou 70554
Mandeville 70448
Mangham 71259
Mansfield (1st) 71052
Mansura 71350
Many (1st) 71449
Maplewood, Br. Sulphur 70663
Maringouin 70757
Marion 71260
  Haile, R. Br. 71246
Marksville (1st) 71351

Marrero (1st)	70072	
Marthaville	71450	
Mathews	70375	
Maurepas	70449	
Maurice	70555	
Mayna	71352	
Mc Dade	71051	
Meeker, R. Br. Lecompte	71346	
Melder	71451	
Melrose	71452	
Melville	71353	
Mer Rouge	71261	
Meraux	70075	
Mermentau	70556	
Merrydale, Sta. Baton Rouge	70805	
Merryville	70653	
METAIRIE (1st) (see appendix)		
Michoud, Sta. New Orleans	70129	
Mid City, Sta. New Orleans	70119	
Mid City Annex, Sta. Shreveport	71103	
Midland	70557	
Milton	70558	
Minden (1st)	71055	
Mira	71059	
Mitchell	71453	
Mittie	70654	
Mix	70758	
Modeste	70376	
Moisant Airport, Sta. New Orleans	70141	
Monroe (1st)	71201	
Montegut	70377	
Monterey	71354	
Montgomery	71454	
Montpelier, R. Br. Amite	70422	
Mooringsport	71060	
Mora	71455	
Moreauville	71355	
Morgan City (1st)	70380	
Morganza	70759	
Morningside, Sta. Shreveport	71108	
Morrow	71356	
Morse	70559	
Moss Bluff, R. Br. Lake Charles	70601	
Mound	71262	
Mount Airy, R. Br. Reserve	70076	
Mount Hermon	70450	
Nairn	70077	
Napoleonville	70390	
Natalbany	70451	
Natchez	71456	
Natchitoches (1st)	71457	
Negreet	71460	
New Iberia (1st)	70560	
NEW ORLEANS (1st) (see appendix)		
New Roads (1st)	70760	
New Sarpy	70078	
Newellton	71357	
Newllano	71461	
Nicholls University, Sta. Thibodaux	70301	
Noble	71462	
Norco (1st)	70079	
Northeast, Sta. Monroe	71201	
Northwestern, Sta. Natchitoches	71457	
Norwood	70761	

Oak Grove	71263	
Oak Ridge	71264	
Oakdale (1st)	71463	
Oakwood, Br. Gretna	70053	
Oberlin	70655	
Oil Center, Sta. Lafayette	70501	
Oil City	71061	
Olla	71465	
Opelousas (1st)	70570	
Oscar	70762	
Otis	71466	
Paincourtville	70391	
Palmetto	71358	
Paradis	70080	
Park Manor, Sta. Metairie	70003	
Parks, R. Br. Saint Martinville	70582	
Patterson	70392	
Paulina	70763	
Pearl River	70452	
Pelican	71063	
Perry	70575	
Pierre Avenue, Sta. Shreveport	71103	
Pierre Part	70339	
Pilottown	70081	
Pine Grove	70453	
Pine Prairie	70576	
Pineville (1st)	71360	
Pioneer	71266	
Darnell, R. Br.	71231	
Pitkin	70656	
Plain Dealing	71064	
Plaquemine (1st)	70764	
Plattenville	70393	
Plaucheville	71362	
Pleasant Hill	71065	
Point, R. Br. Downsville	71234	
Point Clair, Br. Carville	70721	
Pointe A La Hache	70082	
Pollock	71467	
Ponchatoula (1st)	70454	
Port Allen (1st)	70767	
Port Barre	70577	
Port Sulphur	70083	
Post Trailer Park, Br. Leesville	71446	
Powhatan	71066	
Prairieville	70769	
Pride	70770	
Princeton	71067	
Provencal	71468	
Quitman	71268	
Raceland	70394	
Ragley	70657	
Rayne (1st)	70578	
Rayville (1st)	71269	
Alto, R. Br.	71216	
Reddell	70580	
Reeves	70658	
Bel, R. Br.	70675	
Reserve	70084	
Mount Airy, R. Br.	70076	
Rhinehart	71363	
Ridgecrest, Br. Ferriday	71334	
Ringgold	71068	
Roanoke	70581	
Robeline	71469	
Robert	70455	
Rodessa	71069	
Rosa	71364	
Rosedale	70772	

Roseland	70456	
Rosepine	70659	
Rougon	70773	
Ruby	71365	
Ruston (1st)	71270	
Clay, R. Br.	71228	
Tech, Sta.	71270	
Vienna, R. Br.	71270	
Saint Amant	70774	
Saint Benedict	70457	
Saint Bernard	70085	
Saint Francisville	70775	
Saint Gabriel	70776	
Saint Gertrude, R. Br. Covington	70433	
Saint James	70086	
Saint Joseph	71366	
Saint Landry	71367	
Saint Martinville (1st)	70582	
Saint Maurice	71471	
Saint Rose	70087	
Saline	71070	
Samtown, R. Br. Alexandria	71301	
Sarepta	71071	
Schriever	70395	
Scotlandville, Br. Baton Rouge (see appendix)		
Scott	70583	
Shongaloo	71072	
Shreve Island, Sta. Shreveport	71105	
SHREVEPORT (1st) (see appendix)		
Sibley	71073	
Sicily Island	71368	
Sieper	71472	
Sikes	71473	
Simmesport	71369	
Simpson	71474	
Simsboro	71275	
Singer	70660	
Slagle	71475	
Slaughter	70777	
Slidell (1st)	70458	
Sondheimer	71276	
Sorrento	70778	
South Lafourche, R. Br. Golden Meadow	70338	
South Park, Sta. Alexandria	71301	
South Park Trailer Court, Br. Leesville	71446	
Southeast, Sta. Baton Rouge (see appendix)		
Southern, Br. Baton Rouge	70813	
Southfield, Sta. Shreveport	71105	
Southwestern, Sta. Lafayette	70501	
Spearsville	71277	
Spencer	71278	
Spokane	71370	
Springcreek	70461	
Springfield	70462	
Springhill (1st)	71075	
Starks	70661	
Start	71279	
Sterlington	71280	
Stonewall	71078	
Sugartown	70662	
Sulphur (1st)	70663	
Summer Grove, Br. Shreveport	71108	
Summerfield	71079	

Sun	70463
Sunset	70584
Sunshine	70780
Supreme, R. Br. Labadieville	70396
Swartz	71281
Talisheek	70464
Tallulah (1st)	71282
Tangipahoa	70465
Taylor	71080
Tech, Sta. Ruston	71270
Temple	71476
Terry	71285
Theriot	70397
Thibodaux (1st)	70301
Tickfaw	70466
Tioga	71477
Torbert	70781
Tower Park, Sta. Leesville	71446
Transylvania	71286
Trees	71081
Trout	71371
Tullos	71479
Tunica	70782
Turkey Creek	70585

Twin Cedars, Sta. Baton Rouge	70809
Uncle Sam, R. Br. Convent	70792
Union, R. Br. Convent	70723
University, Sta. Baton Rouge	70803
Urania	71480
Vacherie	70090
Varnado	70467
Venice	70091
Ventress	70783
Verda	71481
Veterans Administration Hosp., Sta. Shreveport	71101
Vick	71372
Vidalia (1st)	71373
Vienna, R. Br. Ruston	71270
Vieux Carre, Sta. New Orleans	70112
Ville Platte (1st)	70586
Vinton	70668
Violet	70092
Vivian	71082
Wakefield	70784

Warden	71289
Washington	70589
Waterproof	71375
Watson	70786
Waverly	71290
Welcome	70093
Welsh	70591
West Monroe (1st)	71291
Westlake	70669
Westport, R. Br. Pitkin	70656
Westwego (1st)	70094
Weyanoke	70787
White Castle	70788
Whiteville	71376
Wildsville	71377
Wilmer	70468
Wilson	70789
Winnfield (1st)	71483
Winnsboro (1st)	71295
Wisner	71378
Woodworth	71485
Youngsville	70592
Zachary (1st)	70791
Zion City, Br. Baton Rouge	70811
Zwolle	71486

Appendix

BATON ROUGE   708

POST OFFICE BOXES

Box Nos.

1-4037	Main Office	21
A-Z-PN	University	03
9201-11999	Southern	13
14501-14999	Southeast	08
15001-15999	Broadview	15
16001-32999	University	03
44001-44999	Capitol	04
52701-53999	Istrouma	05
54901-54999	Louise Street	02
64001-64999	Audubon	06
66001-66999	Central City	06
73001-73999	Scotlandville	07

RURAL ROUTES

2	15
3	08
4	05
5	07
6	15
7	07
8	08

STATIONS, BRANCHES AND UNITS

Audubon Sta.	06
Broadview Sta.	14
Brownfields Br.	07
Capitol Sta.	04
Central City Sta.	06
Highland Road Br.	08
Istrouma Sta.	05
Louise Street Sta.	02
Merrydale Sta.	05

Scotlandville Br.	07
Southeast Sta.	08
Southern Br.	13
Twin Cedars Sta.	09
University Sta.	03
Zion City Br.	11
General Delivery	21
Postmaster	21

APARTMENTS, HOTELS, MOTELS

Alamo Plaza Courts, 4242 Florida	06
Bellemont Motor Courts, 7370 Airline Highway	21
Boyd Lake Apartments, 1150 Boyd Ave	02
Capitol House, 205 Lafayette	21
College Park Apartments, 1500 Aster St	02
Continental Motor, 5180 Airline Hwy	05
Fifth Street Apartments, 439 N 5th St	01
Heidelberg, 206 Lafayette	21
Holiday Inn, 5955 Airline Highway	21
Howard Johnson, 7275 Airline Highway	15
Motor Inn, 4136 Florida Blvd.	21
Oak Manor Courts, Airline Highway	15
Oak Royale Apartments, 450 Cloud Dr	06
Town House Motor, 7361 Airline	05
Vel Rose Motel, 4902 Airline	05

BUILDINGS

Baton Rouge Savings & Loan, 400 North Blvd	01
City National Bank, 124 N 3rd	01
Commerce, 333 Laurel	01
Courthouse Office, 233 St Ferdinand	01
Courthouse, 301 St. Louis	01
Federal Building, Florida St	01
Fidelity Bank, 440 N 3rd	01
Guaranty Income, 929 Government	02
Kean, 207 N 4th	01
Louisiana National Bank, 451 Florida	01
Municipal, 300 North Blvd	01
Old State Capitol, 100 St Philip	01
Post Office And Federal Bldg 700 Florida	21
Reymond, 263 Third	01
Roumain, 343 N 3rd	01
State Capitol Annex, 900 3rd.	04
State Capitol, 9th Block 3rd	04
Taylor, 251 Florida	01
Union Federal, 500 Laurel	01
United States Courthouse	01

HOSPITALS

Baton Rouge General Hospital, 3600 Florida St	21
Earl K Long Charity Hospital, 5825 Airline Hwy	05
Our Lady Of The Lake Hospital, 1500 N 3rd	02

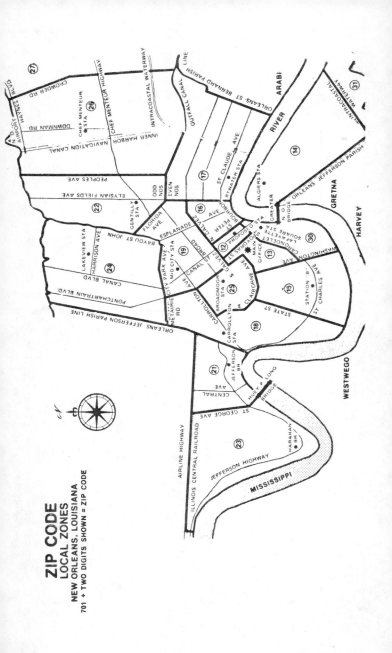

ZIP CODE
LOCAL ZONES
NEW ORLEANS, LOUISIANA
701 + TWO DIGITS SHOWN = ZIP CODE

Baton Rouge (Con.)   708

Womans Hospital, Airline
Hwy 15

UNIVERSITIES AND COLLEGES

Louisiana State University...... 03
Southern University 13

METAIRIE   700

POST OFFICE BOXES

Box Nos.
1-1250   Main Office 04
7001-7999   Lakeside Sta 02
9000-9450   A Sta................ 05
73001-73809   Park Manor
              Sta................ 03

STATIONS, BRANCHES AND UNITS

Lakeside Sta............................ 02
Park Manor Sta 03
General Delivery 01
Postmaster 04

APARTMENTS, HOTELS, MOTELS

Adrian Arms 115 Avenue B 05
Ante Bellum 3201 Belmont
Place 02
Atlantis 2601 Metairie Lawn
Dr....................................... 02
Berkshire Apts 6300 Ackel...... 03
Bissonet Apts 6315 Ackel....... 03
Brittany Apts 3440 Edenborn   02
Bryn Mar Square 1035 Lake
Ave 05
Butterfly Apts 2925 Edenborn
Ave 02
Canterberry Square 3127
Transcontinental Dr............. 02
Causeway Apts 3505 N
Causeway Blvd 02
Charleston Apts 4110
Hessmer Ave 02
Chateau Cleary 3900 I-10
Service Rd.......................... 01
Chateau Romar 3715 Marion . 02
Dorien Apts 3201 Richland..... 02
Drexel House 3340 Edenborn
Ave 02
Edgewater Apts 3901
Ridgelake Dr 02
Elmwood Plantation 6801
Veterans Blvd 03
Fernwood Apts 1010 Lake
Ave 05
Gatehouse Apts 2500
Interstate Hwy..................... 01
Golden Key Apts 4051
Division Ave 02
Hampton Court 1168 Lake
Ave 05
Houma House 3515 Houma
Blvd..................................... 02
Imperial House, 3400 N
Causeway Blvd. 02

Jefferson Town House 1401
Lake Ave 05
Jeffersonian 3500 To 3600
Houma Blvd......................... 02
Jeffersonian 4325
Manhattan 02
Kingston Court 3919
Hessmer 02
Labrias Apts 4021 Hessmer
Ave 02
Laesplanade Apts 3443
Edenborn Ave 02
Lafayette Square 1201 Lake
Ave 05
Lake Castle Apts 222 London 05
Lakeside Apts 01 3333
Edenborn 02
Lakeside Apts 02 3911
Hessmer 02
Lakeside Apts 03 3311
Edenborn 02
Lakeside Apts 04 3225
Ridgelake Dr 02
Lakeside Apts 3500
Edenborn 02
Lakeside Apts 810 Wilshire
Blvd..................................... 05
Malibou Apts 2935 Ridgelake
Dr 02
Marquette Square 1111 Lake
Ave 05
Metairie Plaza 1046 Lake
Ave 05
Metairie Tower Apts 401
Metairie Rd 05
Norgate Apts 3500 Division.... 02
Park Manor Apts 6415 Park
Manor Dr............................. 03
Ridgelake Apts 300
Ridgelake Dr 01
Royal Arms Apts 936 Lake
Ave 05
Sena Apts 615 Sena Dr 05
Surfrider Apts 6416 Park
Manor Dr............................. 03
Townhouse Apts 4804
Quincy 02
Villa D Orleans 01 3030
Edenborn 02
Villa D Orleans 02 3110
Edenborn 02
Village Town House 3425
Edenborn Ave 02
Westchester Apts 4217
Hessmer Ave 02
Whitney Place Apts 2400
Veterans Blvd 02
Yorkshire Arnoult 3320 N
Arnoult Rd........................... 02
Yorkshire Edenborn 3240
Edenborn Ave 02

BUILDINGS

Causeway Interchange Bldg
2456 N Causeway Blvd...... 01
East Bank Parish, 3300
Metairie Rd 01
Imperial Office, 3301 N
Causeway Blvd 02
Jefferson Bank Bldg., 3525 N
Causeway Blvd. 02

Lakeside Plaza Bldg 3425 N
Causeway Blvd 02
Security Homestead Bldg
4900 Veterans Blvd........... 02

HOSPITALS

East Jefferson, 4200 Houma... 02
Lakeside 4700 I 10 Sen
Road.................................... 01
Metairie, 310 Codifer Blvd..... 05

NEW ORLEANS   701

POST OFFICE BOXES

Box Nos.
23A-23J   Harahan Br 23
2000-2999   Custom House
              Sta................ 30
3000-3999   Bywater 17
4000-4999   Carrollton Sta... 18
6000-6999   A Sta 14
8000-8999   Gentilly Sta 82
10000-10999   Jefferson Br..... 21
13000-13999   Broadmoor Sta.. 25
15000-15999   B Sta 15
19000-19999   Mid City Sta 79
23000-23999   Harahan Br 23
24000-24999   Lakeview Sta.... 24
26000-26999   Chef Menteur
              Sta................ 26
29001-29999   Michoud Sta..... 29
30000-30999   Lafayette
              Square Sta 90
50000-50999   Main Office 50
52000-52999   Main Office 52
53000-53999   Main Office 53
60000-60999   Main Office 60
61000-61999   Main Office 61
0020000-
-0020099   New Orleans
              International
              Airport
              Moisant 41

RURAL ROUTES

6 29

STATIONS, BRANCHES AND UNITS

Broadmoor Sta 25
Bywaters Sta 17
Carrollton Sta 18
Chef Menteur Sta.................... 26
Custom House Sta 16
Embarkation Sta...................... 40
Gentilly Sta............................. 22
Harahan Br 23
International Trade Mart Sta 30
Jefferson Br 21
Lafayette Square Sta 30
Lakeview Sta 24
Michoud Sta 29
Mid City Sta 19
Moisant Airport Sta 41
Vieux Carre Sta 12
General Delivery 40
Postmaster 13
Usps No Dist Office 13

New Orleans (Con.)   701

APARTMENTS, HOTELS, MOTELS

Ardens Motel, 6218 Chef
  Menteur Hwy 26
Avalon Motor, 4450 Chef
  Menteur Hwy 26
Brent House, 1512 Jefferson
  Hwy 21
Capri Motel, 2410 Tulane
  Ave 19
Carol, 2100 St Charles Ave 40
Chateau Le Moyne 303
  Dauphine 12
Column Guest House, 3811
  St Charles Ave 15
Congress Inn 13001 Chef
  Menteur Hwy 29
De Ville, 3800 Tulane Ave 19
Del Mar Motel, 8542 Chef
  Menteur Hwy 27
Fontainbleau Motor, 4040
  Tulane Ave 19
French Quarter Patio, 1130
  Chartres 16
Georgian, 2233 St Charles
  Ave 40
Governor House Motor Hotel,
  1630 Canal 12
Greystone, 3701 Canal 19
Holiday Inn 124 Royal St 30
Holiday Inn, 4861 Chef
  Menteur Hwy 26
Howard Johnson 330 Loyola
  Ave 12
Howard Johnson, 4300
  Gentilly Road 26
John Mitchell, 637 Common
  St 30
Jung, 1500 Canal St 40
Lafayette, 628 St Charles St .. 30
Lafitte Guest House, 1003
  Bourbon St 16
Lamothe House, 621
  Esplanade Ave 16
Lasalle, 1113 Canal St 12
Le Pavillon 833 Poydras 40
Le Petit Motel, 2836 Tulane
  Ave 19
London Lodge Motel, 9301
  Airline Hwy 18
Maison De Ville, 727
  Toulouse St 30
Marriott 555 Canal St 40
Mayflower, 2203 St Charles
  Ave 40
Monteleone, 214 Royal St 40
Orleanian, 1205 St Charles
  Ave 30
Pontchartrain, 2031 St
  Charles Ave 40
Prince Conti Motor, 830 Conti
  St 12
Provincial Motel, 1024
  Chartres St 16
Roosevelt, 123 Baronne St 40
Royal Orleans, 621 St Louis
  St 40
Royal Sonesta Hotel 300
  Bourbon 40
Sheraton Charles Hotel 211

St Charles 40
Sheraton Delta Motor Hotel,
  1732 Canal 12
Studio Arms Iv, 200 Deckbar
  Ave 21
Tamanaca Downtown Motel,
  1725 Tulane Ave 12
Town House Motel, 9419
  Airline Hwy 18
Tulane University Dormitory
  Building, 6440 S
  Claiborne Av 25
Warwick, 1315 Gravier 40
Wohl, 2111 St Charles Ave 40

BUILDINGS

Administration, New Orleans
  Airport 26
American Bank, 200
  Carondelet 30
American Red Cross, 2000
  Tulane Ave 12
Audubon, 931 Canal 12
Balter, 403 Camp 30
Balter, 404 St Charles Ave 30
Balter, 618 Commercial Ally ... 30
Bank Of New Orleans 1010
  Common 12
Baronne, 305 Baronne 12
Bienville Street Wharf 30
Board Of Trade Annex, 320
  Board Of Trade Pl 30
California, 1111 Tulane Ave 12
Canal Lasalle 1424 Canal 12
Caribe, 2475 Canal 19
Carondelet, 226 Carondelet ... 30
Celeste Street Wharf 30
Cigali, 107 Camp 30
City Hall 1300 Perdido St 12
Civil Court 421 Loyola Ave 12
Commerce, 821 Gravier 12
Communications, 1215
  Prytania 30
Congress Street Wharf 30
Cotton Exchange, 231
  Carondelet 30
Customhouse, 423 Canal 30
Demontluzin 234 Loyola Ave .. 12
Desire Street Wharf 30
Dodge, 411 Bienville 30
Dumaine Street Wharf 30
Erato Street Wharf 30
Esplanade Avenue Wharf 30
Executive House, 348
  Baronne 12
Federal Office 600 South 30
Federal Office, 701 Loyola 13
First National Life Insurance,
  1000 Howard Ave 13
First Street Wharf 30
Foreign Trade Zone Napoleon
  Ave & River Allfirms ....
Galvez Street Wharf 17
Gateway, 124 Camp 30
Governor Nicholls Street
  Wharf 30
Gravier, 535 Gravier 30
Hancock John 1055 St
  Charles Ave 30
Harmony Street Wharf 30
Hibernia Bank, 812 Gravier 12
Hicks, 316 Baronne 12

Hutchinson Memorial, 143/
  Tulane Ave 12
International Trade Mart, 2
  Canal 30
International, 611 Gravier 30
Julia Street Wharf 30
Louisa Street Wharf 30
Louisiana Southern Life
  Insurance Building 225
  Baronne St 12
Louisiana State Office, 325
  Loyola Ave 12
Lowich, 2026 St Charles Ave .. 30
Maison Blanche, 921 Canal 12
Mandeville Street Wharf 30
Maritime, 203 Carondelet 30
Market Street Wharf 30
Maryland Casualty, 210
  Okeefe Ave 12
Masonic Temple 333 St
  Charles 30
Medallion Towers 344 Camp
  St 30
Miles, 2025 Canal 12
Municipal Auditorium, 1201
  St Peter 16
Nashville Ave Wharf 15
National Bank Of Commerce,
  210 Baronne 12
New Orleans Public Library,
  219 Loyola Ave 12
New Orleans Union
  Passenger Terminal 1001
  Loyola Ave 13
No 1 Shell Square 701
  Poydras St 39
Norman Mayer Memorial, 211
  Camp 30
Odeco, 1600 Canal 12
Oil & Gas 1100 Tulane Ave 12
Orange Street Wharf 30
Pan American Life Insurance,
  2400 Canal 19
Pauline Street Wharf 30
Pere Marquette, 150
  Baronne 12
Pere Marquette, 837
  Common 12
Physicians & Surgeons, 4500
  Magnolia 15
Plaza Towers 1001 Howard
  Ave 13
Plaza, 230 Loyola Ave 12
Poydras Street Wharf 30
Rault Center 1111 Gravier 12
Richards, 837 Gravier 12
Rivergate Exhibition &
  Convention Center, 4 & 6
  Canal 30
Robin Street Wharf 30
Saint Andrew Street Wharf 30
Saratoga, 200 Loyola Ave 12
Security Homestead, 217
  Carondelet 30
Seventh Street Wharf 30
Shell 925 Common 12
Soule, 700 Lafayette 30
Stuyvesant Docks 30
Texaco, 1501 Canal 12
Thalia Street Wharf 30
Third Street Wharf 30
Toulouse Street Wharf 30
Tulane, 3308 Tulane Ave 19

New Orleans (Con.) 701

U S Postal Service 701
Loyola Ave 13
United Fruit, 321 St Charles
Ave 30
Vincent, 325 Camp 30
Vincent, 615 Commercial
Alley 30
Washington Avenue Wharf 30
Whitney Bank 228 St Charles
St 30
Whitney Bank, 624 Common 30
Whitney Bank, 625 Gravier 30
Wild Life & Fisheries, 400
Royal 30
Wirth, 129 Marais 12

GOVERNMENT OFFICES

City Hall, 1300 Perdido 12
Civil Court, 421 Loyola 12
Criminal District Court, 2700
Tulane Ave 19
Supreme Court, 301 Loyola
Ave 12

HOSPITALS

Algiers General, 310
Opelousas Ave 14
Charity, 1532 Tulane Ave 40
Crippled Childrens, 200
Henry Clay Ave 18
De Paul Hosp 1040 Calhoun
St 18
Eye Ear Nose & Throat, 145
Elk Place 12
Flint Goodridge, 2425
Louisiana Ave 15
Hotel Dieu, 2004 Tulane Ave 12
Mercy 301 N Jefferson Davis
Parkway 79
Methodist Hospital, 5620
Read Rd 27
Montelepre Memorial, 3125
Canal 19
Ochsner Foundation, 1516
Jefferson Hwy 21
Saint Claude General, 3501
St Claude Ave 17
Sara Mayo, 609 Jackson Ave .. 30
Southern Baptist, 2700
Napoleon Ave 15
Touro Infirmary, 1400
Foucher 15
United States Public Health
Service, 210 State Street ... 18
Veterans Administration 1601
Perdido 46

MILITARY INSTALLATIONS

Alvin Callender Field, Belle
Chasse La 46
Army Reserve 19th Corp,
5010 Leroy Johnson Dr 40
Eight Naval District, Algiers
La 46
Jackson Barracks Military
Only 6400 Dauphine St 46
Naval Air Station, Belle

Chasse La 46
Navy & Marine Tr Center,
5020 Lakeshore Dr 40
Navy Radio Station, 5000
Lakeshore Dr 46
Port Of Embarkation 4400
Dauphine St 46

UNIVERSITIES AND COLLEGES

Baptist Theological Seminary,
3939 Chef Menteur Hwy 26
Dillard University, 2601
Gentilly Blvd 22
Louisiana State Univ In New
Orleans, 2000 Lakeshore
Dr 22
Louisiana State University
Medical School, 1542
Tulane 12
Loyola University, 6363 St
Charles Ave 18
Newcomb, 1229 Broadway 18
Saint Marys Dominican, 7214
St Charles Ave 18
Southern U. In New Orleans,
6400 Press Dr 26
Tulane University Medical
College, 1430 Tulane Ave ... 12
Tulane University, 6823 St
Charles Ave 18
Ursuline, 2635 State 18
Xavier, 7325 Palmetto 25

SHREVEPORT 711

POST OFFICE BOXES

Box Nos.		
1-199	Main Office Sta	61
200-899	Main Office Sta	62
900-1299	Main Office Sta	63
1300-1499	Main Office Sta	64
1500-1699	Main Office Sta	65
1700-1899	Main Office Sta	66
3001-3706	Main City Annex Sta	03
4001-4999	Centenary Sta ..	04
5001-5999	Southfield Sta ..	05
6001-6999	Cedar Grove Sta	06
7001-7999	Industrial Sta...	07
8001-8999	Morningside Sta	08
9000-9999	Jewella Sta	09

RURAL ROUTES

1	05
2	09
3	06
4	09
5	07

STATIONS, BRANCHES AND UNITS

Barksdale A F B Br 10
Cedar Grove Sta 06
Centenary Sta 04
Cooper Road Br 01
Fair Grounds Sta 09
Industrial Sta 07
Jewella Sta 09
Lakeshore Sta 09
Madison Park Sta 05
Mid City Annex Sta 03
Morningside Sta 08
Pierre Avenue Sta 03
Shreve Island Sta 05
Southfield Sta 05
Summer Grove Br 08
Veterans Administration
HospSta 01
General Delivery 02
Main Office Sta Carriers 01
Postmaster 02

APARTMENTS, HOTELS, MOTELS

Alamo Plaza Courts 1 03
Alamo Plaza Courts 2 07
Brighton Manor 08
Caddo 01
Captain Shreve 01
Colonial Plaza 05
Conquistador 08
Cooper Road Plaza 07
Downtowner 01
Evangeline 06
Fairfield Oaks 04
Fairway Forest Plaza, Rural
Route 2 09
Holiday Inn Of America, 1906
N Market 07
Holiday Inn Of America, 4900
Greenwood 09
Lincoln 01
Mid-City 01
Mikado 03
Normandie Village 04
Northwood 07
Park Villa 05
Pinecrest Mobile Villa 6700
Jefferson Paige Rd 09
Quail Creek 05
Shreveporter 09
Silver Pines 08
Southside Villa 08
The Fountain 01
Town House 01
Town Oak 05
Town South Villa 05
Villa Contessa, 7000
Creswell St 06
Villa Del Lago 09
Washington-Youree 01

BUILDINGS

Barnes 01
Beck 01
Commercial 01
Commercial National Bank 01
Communications 01
Contl-American Bank 01
Fairfield 01

Shreveport (Con.)   711

First National Bank	01
Johnson	01
Lane	01
Louisiana Bank	01
Louisiana State	01
Medical Arts	01
Mid South Towers	01
Municipal Auditorium	01
Oden	01
Oil & Gas	01
Petroleum Bldg	01
Petroleum Tower	01
Pioneer	01
Ricou-Brewster	01
Slattery	01
Texas Eastern	01

Ward	01
Western Union	01

GOVERNMENT OFFICES

Caddo Parish Courthouse	01
City Hall	01

HOSPITALS

Confederate Memorial	01
Doctors	01
Gilmers	04
Gowans	06
Highland	01
Physicians & Surgeons	01
Schumpert	01
Veterans	01

Willis-Knighton Memorial	03

MILITARY INSTALLATIONS

Barksdale Air Force Base	10
Bossier Base	10

UNIVERSITIES AND COLLEGES

Ayers School Of Business	01
Baptist Christian College	08
Centenary College	04
L S U Shreveport Branch	05
Shreveport Draughon-Norton Business College	01
Southern University Shreveport Branch	07

MAINE
(Abbreviation: ME)

Abbot Village	04406
Acton	04001
Addison	04606
Albion	04910
Alfred	04002
Alna	04535
Andover	04216
Anson	04911
Starks, R. Br.	04980
Ashland	04732
Masardis, R. Br.	04759
Ashville	04607
Athens	04912
Atlantic	04608
Auburn (1st)	04210
Augusta (1st)	04330
Aurora	04408
Bailey Island	04003
Bancroft	04409
Bangor (1st)	04401
Bar Harbor (1st)	04609
Bar Mills	04004
Baring, R. Br. Calais	04610
Bass Harbor	04653
Bath (1st)	04530
Bayside, R. Br. Belfast	04915
Bayville, R. Sta. Boothbay Harbor	04536
Beals	04611
Belfast (1st)	04915
Belgrade	04917
Belgrade Lakes	04918
Benedicta	04733
Benton Station	04919
Bernard	04612
Berwick	03901
Bethel	04217
Biddeford (1st)	04005
Biddeford Pool	04006
Bingham	04920
Birch Harbor	04613

Birch Island, R. Br. Brunswick	04011
Blaine	04734
Blue Hill	04614
Blue Hill Falls	04615
Boothbay	04537
Isle Of Springs, R. Br.	04549
Boothbay Harbor	04538
Bayville, R. Sta.	04536
Capitol Island, R. Br.	04538
Southport, R. Br.	04569
Squirrel Island, R. Br.	04570
Bowdoinham	04008
Bradford	04410
Bradley	04411
Brewer (1st)	04412
Bridgewater	04735
Bridgton	04009
Bristol	04539
Brooklin	04616
Brooks	04921
Brooksville	04617
Brookton	04413
Brownfield	04010
Brownville	04414
Brownville Junction	04415
Brunswick (1st)	04011
Birch Island, R. Br.	04011
Cundys Harbor, R. Br.	04011
Merepoint, R. Br.	04053
Bryant Pond	04219
Buckfield	04220
East Sumner, R. Br.	04232
Bucks Harbor	04618
Bucksport	04416
Burkettville	04540
Burlington	04417
Burnham	04922
Bustins Island, R. Br. South Freeport	04013
Calais (1st)	04619
Baring, R. Br.	04610
Milltown, Sta.	04619
Cambridge	04923

Camden (1st)	04843
Hope, R. Br.	04847
Canaan	04924
Canton	04221
Cape Cottage, Br. Portland	04107
Cape Elizabeth, Br. Portland	04107
Cape Neddick	03902
Cape Porpoise, R. Sta. Kennebunkport	04014
Capitol Island, R. Br. Boothbay Harbor	04538
Caratunk	04925
Cardville	04418
Caribou (1st)	04736
Carmel	04419
Carroll	04420
Casco	04015
Castine	04421
Center Lovell	04016
Chamberlain	04541
Charleston	04422
Chebeague Island	04017
Cherryfield	04622
China	04926
Chisholm	04222
Christmas Cove, R. Sta. South Bristol	04542
Clayton Lake	04018
Cliff Island	04019
Clinton	04927
Columbia Falls	04623
Coopers Mills	04341
Corea	04624
Corinna	04928
Cornish	04020
Costigan	04423
Cranberry Isles	04625
Crouseville	04738
Cumberland Center	04021
Cumberland Mills, Sta. Westbrook	04092
Cundys Harbor, R. Br. Brunswick	04011
Cutler	04626

Damariscotta (1st) 04543
Danforth 04424
　　Waite, R. Br. 04492
Danville 04223
Deer Isle 04627
Denmark 04022
Dennysvile 04628
Derby 04425
Detroit 04929
Dexter (1st) 04930
Dixfield 04224
Dixmont 04932
Dover-Foxcroft (1st) 04426
Dresden 04342
Dryden 04225
Eagle Lake 04739
East Andover 04226
East Baldwin 04024
East Blue Hill, R. Br. Surry 04629
East Boothbay 04544
　　Ocean Point, R. Br. 04557
East Corinth 04427
East Dixfield 04227
East Eddington 04428
East Hampden, Br. Bangor 04401
East Holden 04429
East Lebanon 04027
East Livermore 04228
East Machias 04630
East Millinocket 04430
East Newport 04933
East Orland 04431
East Parsonfield 04028
East Peru 04229
East Poland 04230
East Sebago 04029
East Stoneham 04231
East Sullivan 04632
East Sumner. R. Br.
　　Buckfield 04232
East Vassalboro 04935
East Waterboro 04030
East Waterford 04233
East Wilton 04234
East Winthrop 04343
Easton 04740
Eastport 04631
Eaton 04432
Eliot 03903
Ellsworth (1st) 04605
Ellsworth Falls 04633
Emery Mills 04031
Enfield 04433
Estcourt Station 04741
Etna 04434
Eustis 04936
Exeter 04435
Fairfield 04937
Fairmount, Sta. Bangor 04401
Falmouth, Br. Portland 04105
Farmington (1st) 04938
Farmington Falls 04940
Fayette 04344
Five Islands 04546
Forest City, R. Sta. Brookton 04413
Fort Fairfield 04742
Fort Kent 04743
Fort Kent Mills 04744
Frankfort 04438
Franklin 04634
Freedom 04941
Freeport (1st) 04032

Frenchboro 04635
Frenchville 04745
Friendship 04547
Frye 04235
Fryeburg 04037
Gardiner (1st) 04345
Garland 04939
Georgetown 04548
Glen Cove 04846
Gorham (1st) 04038
Gouldsboro 04636
Grand Isle 04746
Grand Lake Stream 04637
Gray 04039
Great Works, Sta. Old Town 04468
Green Lake 04440
Greene 04236
Greenville 04441
Greenville Junction 04442
Grove 04638
Guilford 04443
　　Sebec Lake, R. Br. 04482
Hallowell 04347
Hampden 04444
Hampden Highlands 04445
Hancock 04640
Hanover 04237
Harborside 04642
Harmony 04942
Harrington 04643
Harrison 04040
Hartland 04943
Haynesville 04446
Hebron 04238
Higgins Beach, R. Sta.
　　Scarborough 04074
Hinckley 04944
Hiram 04041
Hollis Center 04042
Hope, R. Br. Camden 04847
Houlton (1st) 04730
Howland 04448
Hudson 04449
Hulls Cove 04644
Island Falls 04747
Isle Au Haut, R. Br.
　　Stonington 04645
Isle Of Springs, R. Br.
　　Boothbay 04549
Islesboro 04848
Islesford 04646
Jackman 04945
Jacksonville 04647
Jay 04239
Jefferson 04348
Jonesboro 04648
Jonesport 04649
Kenduskeag 04450
Kennebunk (1st) 04043
　　Kennebunk Beach, R.
　　Sta. 04045
Kennebunk Beach, R. Sta.
　　Kennebunk 04045
Kennebunkport 04046
　　Cape Porpoise, R. Sta. 04014
Kents Hill 04349
Kezar Falls 04047
Kingfield 04947
Kingman 04451
Kittery (1st) 03904
Kittery Point 03905
La Grange 04453

Lambert Lake 04454
Lee 04455
Levant 04456
Lewiston (1st) 04240
Liberty 04949
Lille 04749
Limerick 04048
Limestone (1st) 04750
Limington 04049
Lincoln 04457
Lincoln Center 04458
Lincolnville 04849
Lincolnville Center 04850
Linneus 04755
Lisbon 04250
Lisbon Center 04251
Lisbon Falls 04252
Litchfield 04350
Little Deer Isle 04650
Livermore 04253
Livermore Falls 04254
Locke Mills 04255
Long Island 04050
Lookout, R. Br. Stonington 04651
Loring A F B, Sta.
　　Limestone 04750
Lovell 04051
Lubec 04652
Mac Mahan, R. Br. Bath 04530
Machias 04654
Machiasport 04655
Madawaska 04756
Madison 04950
Manchester 04351
Manset, R. Br. Southwest
　　Harbor 04656
Mapleton 04757
Maplewood 04052
Mars Hill 04758
Masardis, R. Br. Ashland 04759
Matinicus 04851
Mattawamkeag 04459
Mechanic Falls 04256
Meddybemps 04657
Medomak 04551
Medway 04460
Mercer, R. Br. Norridgewock 04957
Merepoint, R. Br. Brunswick 04053
Mexico 04257
Milbridge 04658
Milford 04461
Millinocket (1st) 04462
Milltown, Sta. Calais 04619
Milo 04463
Minot 04258
Minturn 04659
Monhegan 04852
Monmouth 04259
Monroe 04951
Monson 04464
Monticello 04760
Moody 04054
Morrill 04952
Mount Desert 04660
Mount Vernon 04352
Naples 04055
Naval Base, Br. Portsmouth,
　　N H. 03801
New Gloucester 04260
New Harbor 04554
　　Pemaquid Point, R. Br. 04561
New Limerick 04761

New Portland	04954
New Sharon	04955
New Sweden	04762
New Vineyard	04956
Newagen	04552
Newcastle	04553
Newfield	04056
Newport	04953
Newry	04261
Nobleboro	04555
Norridgewock	04957
North Amity	04465
North Anson	04958
North Belgrade, R. Br. Oakland	04959
North Berwick	03906
North Bridgton	04057
North Brooklin	04661
North Edgecomb	04556
North Fryeburg	04058
North Haven	04853
North Jay	04262
North Leeds	04263
North Lovell	04264
North Lubec	04663
North Monmouth	04265
North New Portland	04961
North Sebago, R. Sta. East Sebago	04029
North Shapleigh	04060
North Sullivan	04664
North Turner	04266
North Vassalboro	04962
North Waterboro	04061
North Waterford	04267
North Whitefield	04353
North Windham	04062
Northeast Harbor	04662
Norway (1st)	04268
Oakfield	04763
Oakland	04963
North Belgrade, R. Br.	04959
Ocean Park, R. Sta. Old Orchard Beach	04063
Ocean Point, R. Br. East Boothbay	04557
Ogunquit	03907
Olamon	04467
Old Orchard Beach (1st)	04064
Ocean Park, R. Sta.	04063
Old Town (1st)	04468
Oquossoc	04964
Orient	04471
Orland	04472
Orono (1st)	04473
Orrington	04474
Orrs Island	04066
Otter Creek	04665
Owls Head	04854
Oxbow	04764
Oxford	04270
Palermo	04354
Palmyra	04965
Paris	04271
Passadumkeag	04475
Patten	04765
Peaks Island, Sta. Portland	04108
Pearl Street, Sta. Portland (see appendix)	
Pejepscot	04067
Pemaquid	04558
Pemaquid Beach	04559
Pemaquid Harbor	04560

Pemaquid Point, R. Br. New Harbor	04561
Pembroke	04666
Pennamaquan, R. Sta. Pembroke	04666
Penobscot	04476
South Penobscott, R. Sta.	04486
Perham	04766
Perry	04667
Peru	04272
Phillips	04966
Phippsburg	04562
Popham Beach, R. Sta.	04562
Small Point, R. Sta.	04567
Pittsfield (1st)	04967
Plaisted	04767
Pleasant Point	04563
Plymouth	04969
Poland	04273
Poland Spring	04274
Popham Beach, R. Sta. Phippsburg	04562
Port Clyde	04855
Portage	04768
Porter	04068
PORTLAND (1st) (see appendix)	
Pownal	04069
Prentiss	04477
Presque Isle (1st)	04769
Princeton	04668
Prospect Harbor	04669
Quimby	04770
Rangeley	04970
Raymond	04071
Readfield	04355
Readfield Depot	04356
Red Beach, R. Br. Robbinston	04670
Richmond	04357
Robbinston	04671
Red Beach, R. Br.	04670
Rockland (1st)	04841
Rockport	04856
Rockwood	04478
Round Pond	04564
Roxbury	04275
Rumford (1st)	04276
Rumford Center	04278
Rumford Point	04279
Sabattus	04280
Saco (1st)	04072
Saint Agatha	04772
Saint Albans	04971
Saint David	04773
Saint Francis	04774
Saint Francis College, Sta. Biddeford	04005
Saint George	04857
Salsbury Cove	04672
Sandy Point	04972
Sanford (1st)	04073
Sangerville	04479
Sargentville	04673
Scarborough (1st)	04074
Seal Cove	04674
Seal Point	04675
Searsmont	04973
Searsport	04974
Sebago Lake	04075
Sebasco Estates	04565
Sebec	04481
Sebec Lake, R. Br. Guilford	04482

Seboeis	04484
Sedgwick	04676
Shapleigh	04076
Shawmut	04975
Sheepscott, R. Br. Wiscasset	04566
Sheridan	04775
Sherman Mills	04776
Sherman Station	04777
Shirley Mills	04485
Sinclair	04779
Skowhegan (1st)	04976
Small Point, R. Sta. Phippsburg	04567
Smithfield	04978
Smyrna Mills	04780
Soldier Pond	04781
Solon	04979
Sorrento	04677
South Berwick	03908
South Bristol	04568
Christmas Cove, R. Sta.	04542
South Casco	04077
South China	04358
South Freeport	04078
Bustins Island, R. Br.	04013
South Gardiner	04359
South Gouldsboro	04678
South Harpswell	04079
South Hiram	04080
South Lewiston, Sta. Lewiston	04240
South Paris	04281
South Penobscott, R. Sta. Penobscot	04486
South Portland, Br. Portland	04106
South Thomaston	04858
South Waterford	04081
South Windham	04082
Southport, R. Br. Boothbay Harbor	04569
Southwest Harbor	04679
Manset, R. Br.	04656
Springfield	04487
Springvale (1st)	04083
Spruce Head	04859
Squirrel Island, R. Br. Boothbay Harbor	04570
Stacyville	04782
Standish	04084
Starks, R. Br. Anson	04980
Steep Falls	04085
Stetson	04488
Steuben	04680
Stillwater	04489
Stockholm	04783
Stockton Springs	04981
Stonington	04681
Isle Au Haut, R. Br.	04645
Lookout, R. Br.	04651
Stratton	04982
Strong	04983
Sullivan	04682
Sunset	04683
Surry	04684
East Blue Hill, R. Br.	04629
Swans Island	04685
Temple	04984
Tenants Harbor	04860
Thomaston	04861
Thorndike	04986

ZIP CODE
PORTLAND, ME.
041 + TWO DIGITS SHOWN = ZIP CODE

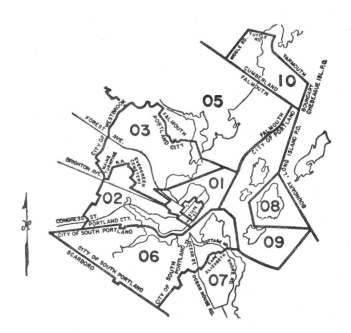

Togus, Br. Augusta	04330
Topsfield	04490
Topsham	04086
Trevett	04571
Troy	04987
Turner	04282

Turner Center, R. Sta.

Turner	04283
Union	04862
Unity	04988
Upper Frenchville	04784
Upton, R. Br. Newry	04261
Van Buren	04785
Vanceboro	04491
Vassalboro	04989
Veazie, Br. Bangor	04401
Vienna	04360
Vinalhaven	04863
Waite, R. Br. Danforth	04492
Waldoboro	04572
Walpole	04573
Warren	04864
Washburn	04786
Washington	04574
Water Street, Sta. Augusta	04330
Waterboro	04087
Waterford	04088

Waterville (1st)	04901
Wayne	04284
Weeks Mills	04361
Weld	04285
Wellington	04990
Wells	04090
Wells Beach, R. Sta. Wells	04090
Wesley	04686
West Baldwin	04091
West Bethel	04286
West Boothbay Harbor	04575
West Bowdoin	04287
West Buxton	04093
West End, Sta. Portland	04102
West Enfield	04493
West Farmington	04992
West Forks	04985

West Jonesport, R. Sta.

Jonesport	04649
West Kennebunk	04094

West Lebanon, R. Sta. East

Lebanon	04027
West Minot	04288
West Newfield	04095
West Paris	04289
West Peru	04290
West Poland	04291
West Rockport	04865

West Scarborough, R. Sta.

Scarborough	04074

West Southport	04576
West Sullivan	04689
West Sumner	04292
West Tremont	04690
Westbrook (1st)	04092
Westfield	04787
Weston	04494

Westpoint, R. Sta. Sebasco

Estates	04565
Whitefield	04362
Whiting	04691
Whitneyville	04692
Wilsons Mills	04293
Wilton (1st)	04294
Windsor	04363
Winn	04495
Winter Harbor	04693
Winterport	04496
Winterville	04788
Winthrop (1st)	04364
Wiscasset	04578

Wiscasset, R. Br.

Sheepscott, R. Br.	04566
Woodfords, Sta. Portland	04101
Woodland	04694
Woolwich	04579
Wytopitlock	04497
Yarmouth (1st)	04096
York	03909
York Beach	03910
York Harbor	03911

PORTLAND   041

POST OFFICE BOXES

Box Nos.

1-600	Pearl Street Sta.	12
601-2011	Main Office	04
2100-2599	South Portland Br.	06
3000-3930	Main Office	04
4000-4368	Sta A	01
4501-4700	Pearl Street Sta.	12
5001-5149	Sta A	01

RURAL ROUTES

1,2	07
3,4	05

STATIONS, BRANCHES AND UNITS

Cape Cottage Br	07
Cape Elizabeth Br	07
Falmouth Br	05
Peaks Island Sta	08
Pearl Street Sta	11
South Portland Br	06
West End Sta	02
Woodfords Sta	01
General Delivery	01
Postmaster	01

APARTMENTS. HOTELS, MOTELS

Albert, 218 Park Ave	02
Alder, 40 Alder	01
Ambassador, 37 Casco	01
Arden, 314 Spring	02
Baxter, 61 Deering	01
Bellevue, 764 Congress	02
Belmead, 398 Forest Ave	01
Berkeley, 72 Park Ave	01
Berry, 88 Park	01
Beverly, 180 Danforth	02
Bowdoin, 131 Chadwick	02
Bramhall, 4 Hill	02
Brightway, 139 William	03
Bristol, 312 Congress	11
Broadview, 344 Broadway S.	06
Calvin, 24 Grant	01
Carleton, 84 Carleton	02
Carroll, 235 Brackett	02
Catir, 284 Congress	11
Chadwick, 135 Chadwick	02
Charter House Motor, 1150 Brighton Ave	02
Clarks, 291 Spring	02
Colby, 123 Sherman	01
Cope, 863 Congress	02
Copely, 485 Cumberland Ave.	01
Corner Lodge, 203 Brackett	02
Court Square, 83 Market	11
Danforth, 132 B Danforth	01
Devon Court, 565 Forest Ave	01
Dora, 152 Grant	01

Dow, 17 Dow	02
Eastland Motor, 157 High	01
Eldridge, 80 Grant	01
Everett, 51 A Oak	01
Faith, 74 Spring	11
Falmouth, 19 Falmouth	03
Fenwick, 133 Grant	01
Fessenden, 15 Shepley	01
Florentine, 41 Chestnut	11
Forest Park, 1 Forest Park	01
Garfield, 505 A Washington Ave	03
Glendon Arms, 563 Cumberland Ave	01
Glendon, 549 Cumberland Ave	01
Hampden, 94 Park Ave	01
Harding, 125 Grant	01
Harlan Annex, 7 A Washington Ave	01
Harlan, 215 Congress	01
Hillside, 16 Weymouth	02
Hindscroft, 108 Noyes	03
Hindscroft, 364 Deering Ave	03
Holiday Inn, 79 Riverside St.	03
Huddersfield, 197 Pine	02
John Alden House, 6 Walker	02
Jones, 116 Pine	02
Kensington, 497 Cumberland Ave	01
Kimball, 776 Congress	02
Knickerbocker, 120 Park Ave	01
Knudsen, 117 Winter	02

Portland (Con.) 041

Lafayette Town House, 638 Congress	01
Lawler, 150 Congress	01
Lincoln, 12 Weymouth	02
Little Weymouth, 851 Congress	02
Longfellow, 658 A Congress	01
Los Angeles, 419 Cumberland Ave	01
Lynden, 407 Cumberland Ave	01
Macarthur Gardens, 16 Walnut	01
Marlborough, 180 High	01
Marlvin, 127 Grant	01
Marstaller, 54 Eastern Promenade	01
Maryland, 385 Cumberland Ave	01
Mc Intyre, 44 Myrtle	01
Mc Kinley, 202 Dartmouth	03
Metropolitan, 439 Congress	11
Miles Standish, 11 Shepley	01
Minot, 30 Preble	01
Monticello, 237 High	01
Morningside, 199 Morning	01
Nathan, 119 Sherman	01
Neal, 168 Neal	02
Northgate, 231 State	01
Oakmont, 128 Park Ave	02
Oakview, 104 Oak St	01
Ocean View, 101 Danforth	01
Oxford, 690 Congress	02
Parkview, 142 Park Ave	02
Parkway, 124 Park Ave	01
Parris, 19 Parris	01
Pilgrim, 30 West	02
Plaza Hotel 21 Preble	01
Plymouth Court, 244 Woodfords	03
Portlander Motel, 645 Congress	01
Raymond, 55 Morning	01
Ricker, 290 Baxter Blvd	01
Ron-Marsh, 12 Pitt	03
Roosevelt, 25 Granite	02
Saint Regis, 196 Middle	11
Shamrock, 21 1/2 Temple	11
Shepley, 18 Casco	01

Sheraton Eastland, 157 High St	01
Sherman, 111 Sherman	01
Six Links, 5 Bishop	03
Somerset, 633 A Congress	01
Southcourt, 51 Park	01
Southgate, 62 State	01
Southport, 36 A S P	06
Stateway, 59 State	01
Sunnyview, 9 Cedar	11
The Oaks, 76 Park Ave	01
Thompson, 97 Emery	02
Tolman House, 6 Tolman Pl	01
Ulysses, 98 Grant	01
Van Brocklin, 55 William	03
Vans, 157 Grant	01
Venetian, 138 Pine	02
Victoria, 939 Congress	02
Vincent, 65 Sherman	01
Warren, 82 Park Ave	01
West View, 193 Clark	02
Whitney, 122 Neal	02
Willard, 84 Eastern Promenade	01
Windsor, 286 State	01
Winslow, 48 State	01
Witham, 130 Brackett	02
Withee, 22 Cedar	11
Woodbury, 111 Franklin	11

BUILDINGS

Baxter Block, 562 Congress	01
Browns Wharf	11
Canal Bank, 192 Middle	01
Casco Bank, 477 Congress	01
Central Wharf	11
City Hall, 389 Congress	11
Clapp Memorial, 443 Congress	11
Commerce, 465 Congress	11
Congress, 615 Congress	01
Cumberland County Courthouse, 142 Federal	11
Custom House Wharf	11
Deakes Wharf	01
Federal, 76 Pearl	11
Gannett, 119 Exchange & 390 Cngrs	11
Holyoke Wharf	01

Libby, 10 Congress Sq	01
Maine State Armory, 772 Stevens Ave	03
Maine State Pier	11
Masonic, 415 Congress	11
Merchants Wharf	11
Merrill Wharf	11
Pinehaven, 100 1st Ave	06
Portland Exposition, 239 Park Ave	02
Portland Pier Wharf	11
Railroad Wharf	01
Richardsons Wharf	11
South Portland Armory, 680 Broadway	06
South Portland Municipal, 25 Cottage Rd	06
Trelawny, 655 Congress	01
Underwood, Underwood Rd	05
Union Mutual Life Insurance Company, Congress	12
Union Mutual Life Insurance Company, Exchange	12
Union Wharf	11
United States Federal, 156 Federal	11
United States Federal, 76 Pearl	11
United States Post Office, 125 Forest Ave	01
Widgery Wharf	11
Wrights Wharf	01

HOSPITALS

Maine Medical Center, 22 Bramhall	02
Mercy, 144 State	01
Osteopathic Hospital Of Maine, 335 Brighton Ave	02

UNIVERSITIES AND COLLEGES

Northeastern Business, 97 Danforth	01
Saint Joseph'S Academy To Catherine Mcauley High	03
University Of Maine, 96 Falmouth	03
Westbrook Junior 716 Stevens Ave To Westbrook College	03

State List of Post Offices

MARYLAND

MARYLAND
(Abbreviation: MD)

Abell	20606
Aberdeen (1st)	21001
Aberdeen Proving Ground (1st)	21005
Abingdon	21009
Accident	21520
Accokeek	20607
Adamstown	21710
Adelphi, Br. Hyattsville	20783
Allen	21810
Andrews A F B, Br. Washington, D C	20331
Andrews Air Force Hospital, Br. Washington, D C	20331

ANNAPOLIS (1st) (see appendix)	
Annapolis Junction	20701
Aquasco	20608
Arlington, Sta. Baltimore	21215
Arnold	21012
Asbury Methodist Home, R. Sta. Gaithersburg	20760
Ashton	20702
Avenue	20609
Bainbridge, Br. Port Deposit	21905
Baldwin	21013
BALTIMORE (1st) (see appendix)	
Barclay	21607
Barnesville	20703
Barstow	20610

Barton	21521
Beallsville	20704
Bel Air (1st)	21014
Bel Alton	20611
Belcamp	21017
Beltsville (1st)	20705
Benedict	20612
Benson	21018
Bentley Springs	21019
Berlin	21811
Berwyn, Sta. College Park	20740
Bethesda, Br. Washington, D C (see appendix)	
Bethlehem	21609
Betterton	21610
Big Pool	21711
Big Spring	21712

Bishops Head 21611
Bishopville 21813
Bittinger 21522
Bivalve 21814
Bladensburg (1st) 20710
Blair, Br. Silver Spring 20910
Bloomington 21523
Boonsboro 21713
Boring 21020
Bowie (1st) 20715
　Mitchellville, Br. 20716
　Pointer Ridge, Br. 20716
　West Bowie, Sta. 20715
Boyds 20720
Bozman 21612
Braddock Heights 21714
Brandywine 20613
Brentwood (1st) 20722
Brinklow 20727
Brookeville 20729
Brooklandville (1st) 21022
Brooklyn-Curtis Bay, Br.
　Baltimore 21225
Broomes Island 20615
Brownsville 21715
Brunswick 21716
Bryans Road 20616
Bryantown 20617
Buckeystown 21717
Burkittsville 21718
Burtonsville 20730
Bushwood 20618
Butler 21023
Cabin John 20731
California 20619
Callaway 20620
Calvert, Sta. Baltimore 21202
Cambridge (1st) 21613
Camp Springs, Br.
　Washington D C 20031
Cape Saint Claire, R. Br.
　Annapolis 21401
Capitol Heights, Br.
　Washington, D C 20027
Capitol Plaza, Br.
　Hyattsville 20784
Cardiff 21024
Carroll, Sta. Baltimore 21229
Carrollton 21025
Cascade 21719
Catonsville, Br. Baltimore .. 21228
Cavetown 21720
Cecilton 21913
Centreville (1st) 21617
Chance 21816
Chaptico 20621
Charlestown 21914
Charlotte Hall 20622
Chase 21027
Cheltenham 20623
Chesapeake Beach 20732
Chesapeake City 21915
Chester 21619
Chestertown (1st) 21620
Cheverly, Br. Hyattsville ... 20785
Chevy Chase, Br.
　Washington, D C 20015
Chewsville 21721
Childs 21916
Chillum, Br. Hyattsville 20783
Church Creek 21622
Church Hill 21623
Churchton 20733

Churchville 21028
Claiborne 21624
Clarksburg 20734
Clarksville 21029
Clear Spring 21722
Clements 20624
Clifton, Sta. Baltimore 21213
Clinton (1st) 20735
Cobb Island 20625
Cockeysville (1st) 21030
Colesville, Br. Silver Spring .. 20904
College, Sta. Westminster .. 21157
College Estates, Sta.
　Frederick 21701
College Park (1st) 20740
　Berwyn, Sta. 20740
Colora 21917
Coltons Point 20626
Columbia, Br. Ellicott City .. 21043
Commerce, Sta. Baltimore .. 21202
Compton 20627
Conowingo 21918
Cooksville 21723
Cordova 21625
Corriganville 21524
Courthouse, Sta. Rockville .. 20850
Crapo 21626
Crellin, R. Br. Oakland 21525
Cresaptown, Br.
　Cumberland 21502
Crisfield (1st) 21817
Crocheron 21627
Crofton, R. Br. Odenton 21113
Crownsville 21032
Crumpton 21628
Cumberland (1st) 21502
Damascus 20750
Dameron 20628
Dames Quarter 21820
Daniels, R. Br. Ellicott City .. 21033
Darlington 21034
Darnestown, R. Br.
　Gaithersburg 20760
Davidsonville 21035
Dayton 21036
Deal Island 21821
Deale 20751
Deer Park, Br. Oakland 21550
Defense Highway, Br.
　Hyattsville 20784
Denton (1st) 21629
Derwood, Br. Rockville 20855
Detour 21725
Dickerson 20753
District Heights, Br.
　Washington, D C 20028
Dowell 20629
Drayden 20630
Druid, Sta. Baltimore 21217
Dundalk, Br. Baltimore 21222
Dunkirk 20754
Earleville 21919
East End, Sta. Baltimore 21205
East New Market 21631
Easton (1st) 21601
Eastport, Sta. Annapolis 21403
Eckhart Mines 21528
Eden 21822
Edgewater 21037
Edgewood 21040
Edgewood Arsenal 21010
Editors Park, Br. Hyattsville .. 20782
Ednor Cloverly, Br. Silver

Spring 20904
Elk Mills 21920
Elkridge, Br. Baltimore 21227
Elkton (1st) 21921
Ellerslie 21529
Ellicott City (1st) 21043
Elliott 21823
Emmitsburg (1st) 21727
Essex, Br. Baltimore 21221
Eudowood, Br. Baltimore 21204
Ewell 21824
Fahrney Keedy Memorial
　Home, R. Br. Boonsboro ... 21713
Fair Play 21733
Fairmount, R. Br. Westover .. 21871
Fallston 21047
Faulkner 20632
Federalsburg (1st) 21632
Ferndale, R. Br. Glen Burnie .. 21061
Finksburg 21048
Fishing Creek 21634
Flintstone 21530
Forest Hill 21050
Fork 21051
Fort George G Meade (1st) .. 20755
Fort Holabird, Sta.
　Baltimore 21219
Fort Howard 21052
Fort Ritchie, Br. Cascade ... 21719
Franklin, Sta. Baltimore 21223
Frederick (1st) 21701
　College Estates, Sta. 21701
　Hood College, Sta. 21701
　Lewistown, R. Br. 21701
　Lime Kiln, R. Br. 21763
Freeland 21053
Friendship 20758
Friendship Airport, Br.
　Baltimore 21240
Friendsville 21531
Frostburg (1st) 21532
Fruitland 21826
Fulton 20759
Funkstown 21734
Gaither 21735
Gaithersburg (1st) 20760
Galena 21635
Galesville 20765
Gambrills 21054
Gapland 21736
Garrett Park 20766
Garrison 21055
Georgetown 21930
Germantown 20767
Gibson Island 21056
Girdletree 21829
Glen Arm 21057
Glen Burnie (1st) 21061
Glen Echo (1st) 20768
Glenelg 21737
Glenn Dale 20769
Glenwood 21738
Glyndon 21071
Goldsboro 21636
Golts 21637
Govans, Sta. Baltimore 21212
Grantsville 21536
Grasonville 21638
Great Mills 20634
Green Haven, R. Br.
　Pasadena 21122
Greenbelt (1st) 20770

Springhill Lake, Sta...........20770
Greensboro...........................21639
Gwynn Oak, Sta. Baltimore....21207
Hagerstown (1st)...................21740
Halethorpe, Br. Baltimore.....21227
Hamilton, Sta. Baltimore......21214
Hampden, Sta. Baltimore......21211
Hampstead (1st)....................21074
Hancock...............................21750
Hanover................................21076
Harmans...............................21077
Harwood...............................20776
Havre De Grace (1st).........21078
Hebron.................................21830
Helen...................................20635
Henderson............................21640
Henryton...............................21080
Highfield..............................21753
Highland...............................20777
Highlandtown, Sta.
  Baltimore.........................21224
Hillsboro..............................21641
Hollywood.............................20636
Hood College, Sta. Frederick...21701
Hoopersville..........................21642
Hospital, R. Br. Crownsville...21032
Hughesville...........................20637
Hunt Valley, Br. Cockeysville...21031
Huntingtown.........................20639
Hurlock................................21643

HYATTSVILLE (1st) (see
  appendix)
Hydes..................................21082
Ijamsville.............................21754
Ilchester..............................21083
Indian Head..........................20640
Ingleside..............................21644
Ironsides..............................20643
Issue...................................20645
Jarrettsville..........................21084
Jefferson..............................21755
Jefferson Heights, Br.
  Hagerstown.......................21740
Jessup (1st)..........................20794
Joppa..................................21085
Keedysville...........................21756
Kenilworth, Br. Riverdale.....20840
Kennedyville..........................21645
Kensington (1st)....................20795
Kent Village, Br. Hyattsville....20785
Keymar................................21757
Kingston...............................21834
Kingsville.............................21087
Kitzmiller.............................21538
Knoxville..............................21758
La Plata (1st)........................20646
La Vale, Br. Cumberland 21502
Ladiesburg............................21759
Lake Shore, Br. Pasadena.....21122
Landover, Br. Hyattsville
  (see appendix)
Landover Hilts, Br.
 . Hyattsville.......................20784
Langley Park, Br. Hyattsville
  (see appendix)
Lanham (1st)........................20801
Lansdowne, Br. Baltimore.....21227
Lantz, R. Br. Sabillasville.....21760
Laurel (1st)..........................20810
Laytonsville, R. Br.
  Gaithersburg....................20760
Le Gore................................21761

Leisure World, Br. Silver
  Spring................................20906
Leonardtown (1st)..................20650
Lewistown, R. Br. Frederick...21701
Lexington Park (1st)...............20653
Libertytown●.........................21762
Lime Kiln, R. Br. Frederick...21763
Lincoln Avenue, Br.
  Hagerstown.......................21740
Lineboro..............................21088
Linkwood..............................21835
Linthicum Heights (1st).........21090
Linwood...............................21764
Lisbon.................................21765
Little Orleans........................21766
Loch Raven, Br. Baltimore....21204
Lonaconing..........................21539
Long Green...........................21092
Lothian................................20820
Loveville..............................20656
Loyola, Sta. Baltimore..........21210
Luke, Br. Westernport...........21562
Lusby..................................20657
Lutherville-Timonium (1st).....21093
Lynch..................................21646
Maddox, R. Br. Chaptico.......20621
Madison...............................21648
Magnolia..............................21101
Main Street, Sta. Salisbury....21801
Manchester...........................21102
Manokin...............................21836
Marbury................................20658
Mardela Springs....................21837
Marion Station......................21838
Marlow Heights, Br.
  Washington, D C.................20031
Marriottsville, R. Br.
  Woodstock........................21104
Marydel...............................21649
Maryland Line.......................21105
Massey.................................21650
Mattapony, Sta.
  Bladensburg.....................20710
Maugansville.........................21767
Mayo...................................21106
Mc Daniel.............................21647
Mc Donough, Br. Baltimore...21208
Mc Henry.............................21541
Mechanicsville......................20659
Merchants, Sta. Baltimore.....21201
Middle River, Br. Baltimore....21220
Middleburg............................21768
Middletown...........................21769
Midland................................21542
Midlothian............................21543
Millers.................................21107
Millersville...........................21108
Millington.............................21651
Mitchellville, Br. Bowie.........20716
Monkton...............................21111
Monrovia..............................21770
Morganza.............................20660
Mount Airy...........................21771
Mount Rainier (1st)...............20822
Mount Savage.......................21545
Mount Victoria......................20661
Mount Washington, Sta.
  Baltimore.........................21209
Mount Wilson........................21112
Mountain Lake Park, Br.
  Oakland...........................21550
Myersville.............................21773

Nanjemoy.............................20662
Nanticoke.............................21840
National Naval Med Center,
  Br. Washington, D C...........20014
Naval Academy, Br.
  Annapolis.........................21402
Naval Air Facility, Br.
  Washington, D C.................20390
Neavitt................................21652
New Carrollton, Br.
  Hyattsville.......................20784
New Market...........................21774
New Midway..........................21775
New Windsor.........................21776
Newark.................................21841
Newburg...............................20664
Newcomb..............................21653
Nikep..................................21546
Normandy, Br. Ellicott City....21043
North Beach..........................20831
North East.............................21901
North Englewood, Br.
  Hyattsville.......................20785
North Ocean City, Br. Ocean
  City.................................21842
Northern, Sta. Hagerstown.....21740
Oakland (1st)........................21550
  .Crellin, R. Br...................21525
  Deer Park, Br....................21550
  Mountain Lake Park, Br......21550
Ocean City (1st)....................21842
Odenton (1st)........................21113
Oldtown...............................21555
Olney...................................20832
Oriole..................................21848
Overlea, Br. Baltimore...........21206
Owings.................................20836
Owings Mills (1st).................21117
Oxford.................................21654
Oxon Hill, Br. Washington, D
  C (see appendix)
Palmer Park, Br. Hyattsville....20785
Parcel Post, Sta. Baltimore....21233
Park Hall..............................20667
Parkton................................21120
Parkville, Br. Baltimore (see
  appendix)
Parsonsburg.........................21849
Pasadena (1st)......................21122
Patapsco..............................21127
Patterson, Sta. Baltimore......21231
Patuxent River (1st)...............20670
Perry Hall (1st).....................21128
Perry Point...........................21902
Perryman.............................21130
Perryville.............................21903
Phoenix................................21131
Pike, Sta. Rockville 20852
Pikesville, Br. Baltimore........21208
Piney Point...........................20674
Pinto...................................21556
Pisgah, R. Br. Indian Head....20640
Pittsville..............................21850
Pocomoke City (1st)...............21851
Point of Rocks......................21777
Pointer Ridge, Br. Bowie.......20716
Pomfret................................20675
Poolesville...........................20837
Port Deposit (1st)..................21904
  Bainbridge, Br...................21905
Port Republic........................20676
Port Tobacco........................20677
Potomac, Br. Rockville..........20854

245

Potomac Heights, Br. Indian
    Head...............................20640
Powellville..............................21852
Preston..................................21655
Price.....................................21656
Prince Frederick.....................20678
Prince Georges Plaza, Br.
    Hyattsville (see appendix)
Princess Anne (1st)................21853
Pylesville...............................21132
Quantico................................21856
Queen Anne............................21657
Queenstown............................21658
Randallstown (1st)..................21133
Randolph Hills, Br.
    Rockville............................20853
Raspeburg, Sta. Baltimore......21206
Rawlings.................................21557
Rehobeth................................21857
Reisterstown (1st)..................21136
Rhodes Point..........................21858
Rhodesdale.............................21659
Riderwood..............................21139
Ridge.....................................20680
Ridgely..................................21660
Rising Sun..............................21911
Rison.....................................20681
Riva......................................21140
Riverdale (1st).......................20840
Riviera Beach, Br.
    Pasadena............................21122
Rock Hall................................21661
Rock Point..............................20682
ROCKVILLE (1st) (see
    appendix)
Rocky Ridge............................21778
Rohrersville............................21779
Roland Park, Sta. Baltimore....21210
Rosedale, Br. Baltimore..........21237
Royal Oak...............................21662
Ruxton, Br. Baltimore.............21204
Sabillasville............................21780
    Lantz, R. Br.......................21760
Saint Inigoes...........................20684
Saint James............................21781
Saint Leonard..........................20685
Saint Marys City......................20686
Saint Michaels.........................21663
Salisbury (1st).........................21801
Sandy Spring...........................20860
Sang Run................................21558
Savage...................................20863
Scotland.................................20687
Seabrook, Br. Lanham............20801
Seat Pleasant, Br.
    Washington, D C.................20027

Secretary................................21664
Security, Br. Baltimore............21235
Severn...................................21144
Severna Park (1st)..................21146
Shady Side..............................20867
Sharpsburg.............................21782
Sharptown..............................21861
Sherwood:...............................21665
Sherwood Forest, R. Br.
    Annapolis...........................21405
Showell..................................21862
SILVER SPRING (1st) (see
    appendix)
Simpsonville............................21150
Smithsburg.............................21783
Snow Hill (1st)........................21863
Solomons................................20688
South, Sta. Baltimore..............21230
Southeast, Sta. Baltimore.......21224
Southwest, Sta. Baltimore.......21230
Sparks Glencoe........................21152
Sparrows Point, Br.
    Baltimore...........................21219
Spencerville............................20868
Spring Gap..............................21560
Springfield State Hospital,
    R. Br. Sykesville................21784
Springhill Lake, Sta.
    Greenbelt...........................20770
Stevenson...............................21153
Stevensville............................21666
Still Pond...............................21667
Stockton.................................21864
Street....................................21154
Sudlersville............................21668
Suitland, Br. Washington, D
    C (see appendix)
Sunderland.............................20689
Swanton.................................21561
Sykesville (1st).......................21784
Takoma Park, Br.
    Washington, D C.................20012
Tall Timbers............................20690
Taneytown..............................21787
Taylors Island.........................21669
Temple Hills, Br.
    Washington, D C.................20031
Templeville.............................21670
Thurmont (1st)........................21788
Tilghman................................21671
Toddville................................21672
Towson, Br. Baltimore............21204
Tracys Landing........................20869
Trappe...................................21673
Tuscarora...............................21790

Twinbrook, Sta. Rockville........20851
Tyaskin..................................21865
Tylerton.................................21866
U S Naval Communications
    Ctr, Br. Washington, D C....20390
Union Bridge...........................21791
Uniontown, R. Br.
    Westminster.......................21157
Unionville...............................21792
Upper Fairmount......................21867
Upper Falls.............................21156
Upper Hill...............................21868
Upper Marlboro (1st)...............20870
Upperco.................................21155
Valley Lee..............................20692
Vienna...................................21869
Walbrook, Sta. Baltimore........21216
Waldorf (1st)..........................20601
Walkersville............................21793
Warwick.................................21912
Washington Dc, Br.
    Washington Dc....................20034
Washington Grove.....................20880
Waverly, Sta. Baltimore...........21218
Welcome.................................20693
Wenona..................................21870
West Annapolis, Sta.
    Annapolis...........................21401
West Bowie, Sta. Bowie...........20715
West End, Br. Annapolis...........21401
West Friendship.......................21794
West Hyattsville, Sta.
    Hyattsville.........................20782
West River..............................20881
Westernport............................21562
Westminster (1st)....................21157
Westover................................21871
Westview, Br. Baltimore..........21228
Westwood...............................20694
Whaleysville............................21872
Wheaton, Br. Silver Spring
    (see appendix)
White Hall..............................21161
White Marsh............................21162
White Plains............................20695
Whiteford...............................21160
Whitehaven.............................21873
Willards.................................21874
Williamsburg...........................21674
Williamsport...........................21795
Wingate.................................21675
Wittman.................................21676
Woodbine...............................21797
Woodmoor, Br. Silver Spring...20901
Woodsboro..............................21798

ANNAPOLIS	214

POST OFFICE BOXES

Box Nos.		
1-1991	Main Office	04

RURAL ROUTES

| 1,2 | .... | 01 |
| 3 | .... | 03 |

4,5,6	....	01
7	....	03
8	....	01

STATIONS, BRANCHES AND UNITS

Cape Saint Claire Rural Br.....	01
Eastport Sta........................	03
Naval Academy Br.................	02
Sherwood Forest Rural Br......	05
West Annapolis Sta...............	01

West End Br........................	01
General Delivery	01
Postmaster	01

GOVERNMENT OFFICES

Agriculture Department Of	
Agricultural Stabilization....	01
All Departments	01
Ann Arundel County	
Agriculture Extension..........	01

Annapolis (Con.)	214
Ann Arundel County Board Of Education	04
Ann Arundel County Civil Defense	04
Ann Arundel County Clerk Circuit Court	04
Ann Arundel County County Commissioners	04
Ann Arundel County Health Department	01
Ann Arundel County Judges Circuit Court	04
Ann Arundel County Juvenile Probation	04
Ann Arundel County Liquor License Board	04
Ann Arundel County Public Works	04
Ann Arundel County Register Of Wills	01
Ann Arundel County Sheriff	04
Ann Arundel County States Attorney	04
Ann Arundel County Supervisor Of Elections	04
Ann Arundel County Welfare Board	04
Bancroft Hall	12
Board Of Natural Resources	01
Board Of Public Works	04
Comptroller Of Treasury	04
Court Of Appeals	04
Department Of Economic Development	01
Department Of Educational Rehabilitation	01
Department Of Employment Security	04
Department Of Forests & Parks	01
Department Of Game, Inland Fish	01
Department Research & Education	01
Department Tidewater Fisheries	01
Federal Bureau Of Investigation	04
Governor	04
Land Commissioner	04
Selective Service System	04
Soil Conservation Service	01
State Library	04
Treasurer	04
Treasury Department Internal Revenue Service	04
Veterans Employment Service	04
Water Pollution Control Commission	01

HOSPITALS

Anne Arundel General Hospital	01
Naval Hospital	02

UNIVERSITIES AND COLLEGES

Naval Academy	02
Saint Johns College	04

BALTIMORE 212

POST OFFICE BOXES

Box Nos.		
1-2499	Main Office	03
ANY	Main Office	33
2501-2699	Arlington Sta	15
2701-2899	Brooklyn-Curtis Bay Br	25
2901-3099	Carroll Sta	29
3101-3299	Catonsville Br	28
3301-3399	Clifton Sta	13
3401-3499	Brooklyn-Curtis Bay Br	25
3501-3699	Hamilton Sta	14
3701-3899	Druid Sta	17
3901-4099	Dundalk Br	22
4101-4299	East End Sta	05
4301-4499	Franklin Sta	23
4501-4699	Govans Sta	12
4701-4899	Hampden Sta	11
4901-5099	Middle River Br	20
5101-5299	Highlandtown Sta	24
5301-5399	Mount Washington Sta	09
5401-5599	Towson Br	04
5601-5699	Roland Park Sta	10
5701-5999	Pikesville Br	08
6001-6199	Patterson Sta	31
6201-6299	Raspeburg Sta	06
6301-6499	South Sta	30
6501-6699	Sparrows Point Br	19
6701-6899	Towson Br	04
6901-7099	Walbrook Sta	16
7101-7299	Waverly Sta	18
7301-7499	Halethorpe Br	27
7501-7699	Gwynn Oak Br	07
7701-7999	Essex Br	21
8001-8399	Ruxton Br	04
8401-8599	Parkville Br	34
8600-8799	Friendship International Airport Br	40
8801-8899	Highlandtown Sta	24
8901-9299	Dundalk Br	22
9301-9499	Catonsville Br	28
9501-9699	Rosedale Br	37
9701-9899	Eudowood Finance Br	04
9901-9999	Highlandtown	24
10001-10199	Towson Br	04
10201-10399	Alameda Station	39
10401-10499	Mount Washington Sta	09

RURAL ROUTES

1	21
2	16
3	37
4	27
5	07
7	08
10	19
13	21

14,15,16	20

STATIONS, BRANCHES AND UNITS

Arlington Sta	15
Brooklyn-Curtis Bay Br	25
Calvert Sta	02
Carroll Sta	29
Catonsville Br	28
Clifton Sta	13
Commerce Sta	02
Druid Sta	17
Dundalk Br	22
East End Sta	05
Elkridge Br	27
Essex Br	21
Eudowood Br	04
Fort Holabird Sta	19
Franklin Sta	23
Friendship Airport Br	40
Govans Sta	12
Gwynn Oak Sta	07
Halethorpe Br	27
Hamilton Sta	14
Hampden Sta	11
Highlandtown Sta	24
Lansdowne Br	27
Loch Raven Br	04
Loyola Sta	10
Mc Donough Br	08
Merchants Sta	01
Middle River Br	20
Mount Washington Sta	09
Overlea Br	06
Parcel Post Sta	33
Parkville Br	34
Patterson Sta	31
Pikesville Br	08
Raspeburg Sta	06
Roland Park Sta	10
Rosedale Br	37
Ruxton Br	04
Security Br	35
South Sta	30
Southeast Sta	24
Southwest Sta	30
Sparrows Point Br	19
Towson Br	04
Walbrook Sta	16
Waverly Sta	18
Westview Br	28
General Delivery	33
Postmaster	33

APARTMENTS, HOTELS, MOTELS

Albion, 900 Cathedral	01
Algonquin, 704 Gladstone Ave	10
Alhambra, 825 Lake Dr	17
Allston, 3111 N Charles	18
Ambassador, 3811 Canterbury Rd	18
Ardmore Arms, 920 W University Pkwy	10
Arlington Park, 6701 Park Heights Ave	15
Armistead, 17 Holliday	02
Baltimorean, 2905 N Charles	18
Bancroft, 6420 Park Heights Av	15
Belvedere Towers, 1190-92 W Northern Pkwy	10
Blackstone Apts 3215 N Charles St	18

247

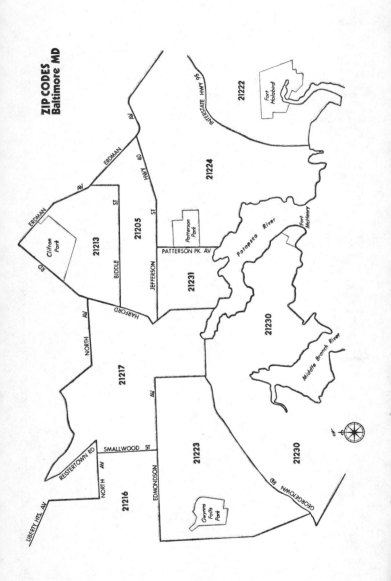

ZIP CODES
Baltimore MD

Baltimore (Con.)   212

Bradford, 3301 St Paul.......... 18
Broadview, 116 W University
   Pkwy........................... 10
Buckingham Arms, 3706 N
   Charles....................... 18
Burford, 3209 N Charles....... 18
Calvert Court, 3024 N
   Calvert........................ 18
Cambridge Arms, 3339 N
   Charles........................ 18
Canterbury Hall, 100 W 39th... 10
Carlton, 3507 N Charles........ 18
Carolina, 108 W University
   Pkwy........................... 18
Carrollton, 3601 Greenway..... 18
Chadford, 909 W University
   Pkwy........................... 10
Chapelgate Apts, 5109
   Williston...................... 29
Charles, 3333 N Charles 18
Charleston Hall, 4500 N
   Charles........................ 10
Claremont, 1201 Brunswick... 23
Club Manor, 7302 Park
   Heights Ave.................. 08
Club, 10 Club Rd.............. 10
Concord, 2500 W Belvedere
   Ave............................. 15
Congress, 306 W Franklin...... 01
Court House Square Apts 1
   Acorn Circle.................. 04
De Soto, 3409 Greenway.. 18
Donnybrook, 7914 Knollwood
   Rd.............................. 04
Dundee Arms, 3902
   Canterbury Rd................ 18
Eden Hall, 3401 Greenway..... 18
Eleven Slade, 11 Slade Ave... 08
Emersonian, 2502 Eutaw Pl .. 17
Esplanade, 2519 Eutaw Pl 17
Eton Hall, 5906 Park Heights
   Ave............................. 15
Executive House, 7011 Park
   Heights Ave.................. 15
Fordleigh, 3800 Fordleigh Rd.. 15
Garden, 230 Stony Run Lane.. 10
Geneva, 3405 Greenway........ 18
Georgian Court, 2516 Linden
   Ave............................. 17
Gilman, 3025-43 N Calvert. ... 18
Goodlow House, 200 Cross
   Keys Rd....................... 10
Greenbriar, 7229 Park
   Heights Ave.................. 08
Greenspring Manor, 7309
   Park Heights Ave........... 08
Greenway, 3401 N Charles 18
Greenwich Gardens,
   Greenwich & Ol Fredk..... 29
Guilford Manor, 2 W
   University Parkway.......... 18
Guilford Towers, 14 W Cold
   Spring Lane.................. 10
Guilford-Homewood, 300 A E
   University Pky............... 18
Hamlyn, 103 W 39th............ 10
Hampton House 204 E Joppa
   Rd.............................. 04
Hampton Plaza 302 E Joppa
   Rd 04

Highfield House, 4000 N
   Charles........................ 18
Hilton Court, 3306 N Hilton.... 16
Hilton Village, 3400 Dolfield
   Ave............................. 15
Holiday Inn, Howard &
   Lombard...................... 01
Homewood, 3003 N Charles.... 18
Hopkins House, 110 W 39th.. 10
Hopkins, 3100 St Paul......... 18
Horizon House, 1101 N
   Calvert..:..................... 02
Ingram Hall, 7301 Park
   Heights Av.................... 08
Ivy Hall, 2 E 33rd.............. 18
Jefferson, 4 E 32nd............ 18
Lake Court, 2517 Linden Ave. 17
Lake Drive, 903 Lake Dr....... 17
Lakeview Towers 727 Druid
   Park Lake Dr................. 17
Linkwood, 4000 Linkwood Rd.. 10
Loch Bend, 8701 Raven Dr.... 34
Loch Raven, 1500 Waverly
   Way............................ 39
Lochwood, 1307 E Belvedere
   Ave............................. 39
Lombardy, 220 Stony Run
   Lane........................... 10
Lord Baltimore, Baltimore &
   Hanover....................... 03
Louiston Court, 2228 Mt
   Royal Ter..................... 04
Madison, 817 St Paul.......... 02
Marjeane, 2437 Lakeview
   Ave............................. 17
Marlborough, 1701 Eutaw Pl.. 17
Marylander, 3501 St Paul...... 18
Melrose East, 100 E Melrose
   Ave............................. 12
Memorial Apts, 301
   Mcmechen.................... 17
Mount Royal, 113 E Mt Royal
   Ave............................. 02
Mount Vernon Place
   Apartment, 101 W
   Monument.................... 01
Navarre, 1700 Eutaw Pl........ 17
New Howard, 8 N Howard...... 01
Normandie, 2624 St Paul...... 18
Northway, 3700 N Charles..... 18
Northwood, 4230 Loch Raven
   Blvd........................... 18
Oaklee Village, 1 Oaklee
   Village........................ 29
Oaklyn, 3317 Liberty Heights
   Ave............................. 15
Park Lynn, 4 Upland Rd 10
Park Plaza, 2 W Madison....... 01
Park Regent, 6414 Park
   Heights Ave.................. 15
Park Towers, 7121 Park
   Heights Ave.................. 15
Pentridge, 1501 Pentridge
   Rd.............................. 39'
Pinkney Court, 6109 Park
   Heights Ave.................. 15
Ralworth, 5702 Beechdl Ave... 39
Ramblewood, 1300 E
   Belvedere Ave............... 39
Ridgemede, 221 Ridgemede
   Rd.............................. 10
Riviera, 901 Lake Dr............ 17
Rochester Court, 2513 Linden

Ave 17
Roland View Towers, 3939
   Roland Ave................... 11
Ruxton Towers, 8415 Bellona
   Ln.............................. 04
Saint Paul Court, 3120 St
   Paul........................... 18
Samester Parkway, 7000
   Park Heights Ave........... 15
Seven Mile Lane, 3901 Seven
   Mile Ln....................... 08
Shelbourne, 3801 Clarks
   Lane........................... 15
Sheraton Baltimore Inn, 400
   N Broadway.................. 31
Sheraton-Belvedere, 1 E
   Chase......................... 02
Stafford, 712 N Charles........ 01
Stanley, 506 N Howard........ 01
Statler Hilton, 101 W Fayette
   St.............................. 01.
Strathmore Towers, 6210
   Park Heights Ave........... 15
Sutton Place Apartments,
   1111 Park Ave............... 01
Temple Court, 233 E
   University Parkway......... 18
Temple Garden, 2601
   Madison Ave................. 17
The Village Of Cross Keys,
   5100 Falls Rd............... 10
The Walters 111 W Centre..... 01
Tudor Arms, 501 W University
   Parkway....................... 10
Tuscany, 221 Stony Run
   Lane........................... 10
University One, 1 E University
   Pkwy........................... 18
University, 104 W University
   Pkwy........................... 10
Victoria, 704 E Baltimore...... 02
Warren Park Apartments........ 08
Warrington, 3908 N Charles... 18
Washington, 700 N Charles.... 01
Wentworth Arms, 311
   Cathedral..................... 01
Westminster House, 524 N
   Charles........................ 01
Westminster, 418 W Fayette... 01
Windsor House, 6503 Park
   Heights Ave.................. 15
Woodcliffe Manor, 108 W
   39th........................... 10
Wyman Park, 3915 Beech
   Ave............................. 11
Wynnewood Towers, 100 W
   Cold Spring Ln.............. 10

BUILDINGS

Abell, 5 South.................. 02
Aero Acres, Martin Blvd........ 20
Alameda, 5600 The Alameda.. 39
Alex Brown & Sons Bldg, 102
   W Penna Ave................. 04
American National, 204 N
   Liberty........................ 01
American Trust, 2 Commerce.. 02
American, 229 E Baltimore..... 02
Arbutus, 1000 Maiden Choice
   Ln.............................. ·29
Association Of Commerce, 22
   Light........................... 02

Baltimore (Con.) 212

Belford, Belair Rd &
Frankford Av 06
Beltway Plaza, 1034 York Rd. 04
Belvedere Gardens Belvedere
Ave And Hillen 39
Blaustein, 1 N Charles 01
Broadway, Caroline &
Orleans 31
Bromo Seltzer Tower, 318 W
Lombard 01
Brookhill, Reistrtwn &
Clarnth Rd 15
Brooklyn Park Plaza, Ritchie
Hy & 11 Ave 25
Candler, 109 Market Place 02
Central Savings Bank, 3 E
Lexington 02
Charing Cross, Baltimore Ntl
Pk & Chrg Crs 29
Cherry Hill, Cherry Hill &
Seabury 25
Cold Spring Lane, Cold
Spring Ln & Lch Rvn 39
Colonial Village, Reisterstwn
& Fallstff 15
Commercial Credit, 300 St
Paul Pl 02
Court Square, 200 E
Lexington 02
Davison Chemical, 101 N
Charles 01
Dolfield, 3500 Dolfield Ave ... 05
Drovers & Mechanics Bank,
100 N Eutaw 01
Drumcastle, 6305 York Rd 12
Dulaney Plaza, 700 Dulaney
Vly Rd 04
Dundalk, Commerce St &
Shpg Pl 22
Eastpoint, N Point Rd &
Eastern Blvd 24
Eastwood, 7500 Eastern
Blvd. 24
Edgemere, 7514 N Point Rd... 19
Edgewater, 1800 Eastern
Blvd. 21
Edmondson Village,
Edmondson & Swann
Aves 29
Equitable Towson Bldg 401
Washington Ave 04
Equitable, 8 N Calvert 02
Erdman, 3901 Erdman Ave..... 13
Essex, 400 Eastern Blvd........ 21
Eudowood Plaza, Goucher
Blvd & Joppa Rd 04
Fallstaff, Reisterstwn &
Labyrnth Rds 15
Farmers Market, Pulaski Hwy
& Mohrs Ln 20
Federal Land Bank, 2315 St
Paul 18
Fidelity, 210 N Charles 01
First National Bank, 7 E
Redwood 02
Frankford, Frankford Av &
Sinclair Ln 06
Frederick Avenue, 2401
Frederick Ave 23
Freedom, 4500 Erdman Ave.... 13

Garrett, 237 E Redwood........ 02
Gas & Electric, 39 W
Lexington 01
Hamilton, 2300 E Northern
Pkwy............................. 14
Hampton Plaza Bldg 300 E
Joppa Rd 04
Hawthorne, 2100 Eastern
Blvd 20
Hillendale, Loch Rvn Blvd &
Tylr SE........................... 04
Hilltop, Reistrstwn Rd &
Rogers........................... 15
Ina, 301 E Fayette 02
Industrial, 501 E Preston....... 02•
Ingleside, Baltimore Ntl Pk &
Inglsd Ave...................... 28
Jefferson 105-07 Chesapeake
Ave W 04
Keyser, 207 E Redwood......... 02
Knickerbocker, 218 E
Lexington 02
Lansdowne, 3900 Hollins
Ferry Rd 27
Liberty Crest, Liberty &
Croydon Rd 07
Loch Raven, Loch Raven Blvd
& Northern Pkwy............... 39
Loch Ridge, Loch Raven Blvd
& Joan Ave...................... 34
Logan, Broening Hwy &
Dundalk Ave.................... 22
Maryland Life, 10 South 02
Maryland National Bank, 10
Light............................. 02
Maryland Trust, 14 S Calvert . 02
Mc Cormick, 414 Light 02
Medical Arts, 101 W Read St.. 01
Mercantile Towson Bldg 409
Washington Ave 04
Mercantile Trust And Bank
Bldg, 2 Hopkins Plaza 01
Merritt Park, Merritt Blvd At
Wise Av.......................... 22
Middle River, Eastern Blvd &
Kingston Rd 20
Middlesex, Eastern Blvd &
Essex Av......................... 21
Mondawmin, Liberty Hts Ave
& Tioga Pky 15
Monumental Life, Charles &
Chase............................ 01
Municipal Office, 300 E
Lexington 02
Munsey, 7 N Calvert 02
National City Bank Bldg, 101
Light............................. 02
North Point Village, 4000
North Point Blvd 22
Northwood, Loch Raven Blvd
& Hvnwd Rd 18
Nottinpham Bldg, 103 W.
Penna Ave....................... 04
Odonnell, Dundalk Ave &
Odonnell 24
Old Town Bank, 321
Fallsway......................... 02
One Charles Center.............. 01
One South Calvert Bldg Is
Calvert 02
Paca-Pratt, 110 S Paca 01
Patterson Village 5/c 4100

Patterson Ave................... 15
Peoples Court, Fayette & Gay. 02
Perry Hall, Belair & Joppa
Rd 36
Pikesville, Reiststwn Rd &
Mchnry Ave 08
Pleasant Plains, 1000 Taylor
Ave 04
Professional, 330 N Charles.... 01
Ravenwood, Loch Raven Blvd
& Tylr NW....................... 04
Reisterstown Plaza,
Reistrstwn Rd & Pttrsn
Ave 15
Riderwood Bldg 1107
Kenilworth Dr................... 04
Ritchie Highway, Ritchie Hwy
& Church St..................... 25
Satyr Hill, Joppa & Satyr Hill
Rd 34
Security S/c, 6600 Security
Blvd.............................. 07
Social Security, 6401 Security
Blvd.............................. 35
Southview, Hmmnds Ln &
Ritchie Hy 25
Standard Oil, 505 St Paul Pl.. 02
Stoney Creek, Ft Smallwood
& Hilltop Rd.................... 26
Sun Life Ins Bldg, 20 S
Charles........................... 01
Super Giant, Liberty &
Milford Mill 07
The Mercantile Trust & Bank
Bldg, 2 Hopkins Plaza 01
Title, 106 St Paul............... 02
Tower, 222 E Baltimore 02
Towson Plaza, 700 Fairmount
Ave 04
U S F & G, 131 E Redwood.... 02
United States Appraisers
Store, 103 S Gay 02
Vickers, 225 E Redwood 02
Victory Villa, 111 Beacon Rd.. 20
Waverly Towers, Greenmount
Av & 29th....................... 18
West Side, 2419 Frederick
Ave 23
Westowne, Edmondson Ave &
N Bend Rd 29
Westview, Baltimore Ntl Pk &
Inglsd Ave...................... 28
Wilkens, 3400 Wilkens Ave..... 29
Woodmoor, Liberty & Essex
Rd 07

GOVERNMENT OFFICES

Baltimore Civic Center, 201
W Baltimore 01
Baltimore Municipal Court,
211 E Madison 02
County Office, 111 W
Chesapeake Ave................ 04
Courthouse 100 N Calvert 02
Federal Bldg., 31 Hopkins
Plaza 01,
State Office Bldg, 301 W
Preston.......................... 01
State Roads Bldg, 300 W
Preston.......................... 01
The City Hall, 100 Holliday.... 02

Baltimore (Con.)   212

United States Court House,
111 N Calvert............... 02
United States Customs
House, 40 S Gay............ 02

HOSPITALS

Augsburg Lutheran Home,
6811 Campfield Rd........ 07
Baltimore City Hospitals,
4940 Eastern Ave.......... 24
Baltimore Eye Ear & Throat
Hospital, 1214 Eutaw Pl.... 17
Bon Secours Hospital, 2025
W Fayette.................. 23
Childrens Hospital, 3825
Greenspring Ave........... 11
Church Home & Hospital,
100 N Broadway............ 31
Franklin Square Hospital,
9000 Franklin Sq Dr....... 37
General German Aged
Peoples Home, 22 S Athol
Ave....................... 29
General German Orphan
Home, 205 Bloomsbury
Ave....................... 28
Good Samaritan, 5601 Loch
Raven Blvd................ 39
Greater Baltimore Medical
Center, 6701 N Charles
St........................ 04
Jenkins Memorial Hospital,
1000 Caton Ave............ 29
Johns Hopkins Hospital, 601
N Broadway................ 05
Kernan Hospital, Forest Park
& Windsor Mill Rd......... 07
Keswick Home, 700 W 40th.... 11
Levindale Hebrew Home &
Infirmary, Belvedere &
Greensprg Av.............. 15
Lutheran Hospital Of
Maryland, 730 Ashburton... 16
Maryland General Hospital,
Linden Ave & Madison...... 01
Mercy Hospital, 331 St Paul
Pl........................ 02
Methodist Home For The
Aged, 2211 W Rogers Ave... 09
Montebello State Hospital,
2201 Argonne Dr........... 18
Mount Pleasant Hospital,
Belevedere & Greenspring
Ave....................... 15
North Charles Gen Hos, 2724
N Charles St.............. 18
Provident Hospital 2600
Liberty Heights Ave....... 15
Saint Agnes Hospital, 1000
Caton Ave................. 29
Saint Elizabeths Home, 3725
Ellerslie Ave............. 18
Saint Josephs Hospital, 7620
York Rd................... 04
Saint Vincents Infant Home,
Reisterstown Rd........... 15
Seton Institute, 6400 Wabash
Ave....................... 15
Sheppard & Enoch Pratt
Hospital, York Rd......... 04

Sinai Hospital, 2401 W
Belvedere Ave............. 15
South Baltimore General
Hospital.................. 30
Spring Grove State Hospital,
Wade Ave.................. 28
Union Memorial Hospital, 200
E 33rd.................... 18
United States Public Health
Service, Wyman Park Dr.... 11
University Hospital, 22 S
Greene.................... 01
Veterans Administration
Hospital, 3900 Loch Raven
Blvd...................... 18

UNIVERSITIES AND COLLEGES

Baltimore Hebrew College,
5800 Park Heights Ave..... 15
Baltimore Junior College,
2901 Liberty Heights Ave... 15
Baltimore Polytechnic
Institute, 1400 W Cold
Spring Ln................. 09
Bard Avon School, 805 N
Charles................... 01
Bryn Mawr School, 109 W
Melrose Ave............... 10
Calvert Hall College High
School, 8100 La Salle Rd... 04
Calvert School, 105 Tuscany
Rd....................... 10
Carnegie Institute Of
Embryology, 115 W
University Pkwy........... 10
Catholic High School, 2810 •
Edison Hwy................ 13
Catonsville Community
College, 800 S Rolling Rd.. 28
Coppin State Teachers
College, 2500 W North
Ave...................... 16
Essex Community College.... 37
Friends School, 5114 N
Charles................... 10
Gilman School Incorporated,
5407 Roland Ave........... 10
Goucher College, Dulaney
Valley Rd................. 04
Johns Hopkins School Of
Hygiene & Health, 615 N.
Wolfe..................... 05
Johns Hopkins University
School Of Medicine, 725 N
Wolfe..................... 05
Johns Hopkins University,
Charles & 34th............ 18
Loyola College, 4501 N
Charles................... 10
Loyola High School, 1000
Boyce Ave................. 04
Maryland Institute, 1300 W
Mt Royal Ave.............. 17
Maryland School For The
Blind, 3501 Taylor Ave.... 36
Maryland Training School For
Boys, 2400 Cub Hill Rd.... 34
Morgan College, Hillen Rd &
Cold Spring Ln............ 39
Mount De Sales Academy Of
The Visitation............ 28

Mount Saint Joseph College,
4403 Frederick Ave........ 29
Mount Washington School For
Boys, Smith Ave........... 09
Ner Israel Rabbinical College,
400 Mt Wilson Ln.......... 08
Notre Dame College, 4701 N
Charles................... 10
Notre Dame Institute, 901
Aisquith.................. 02
Notre Dame Preparatory
School, 815 Hampton
Lane...................... 04
Peabody Dormitory, 606 St.
Paul St................... 02
Peabody Institute &
Conservatory, 1 E Mt
Vernon Pl................. 02
Roland Park Country School,
817 W University Pkwy..... 10
Saint Josephs Passionist
Monastery, 3800 Frederick
Ave...................... 29
Saint Marys Seminary,
Belvedere & Roland........ 10
Saint Marys Seminary, 600 N
Paca..................... 01
Samuel Ready School, 5150
Old Frederick Rd.......... 29
Seton High School, 2800 N
Charles................... 18
Talmudical Academy Of
Baltimore, 4445 Old Court
Rd....................... 08
Towson State College, 8000
York Rd................... 04
University Of Baltimore, 1420
N Charles................. 01
University Of Maryland, 522
W Lombard................. 01

ELLICOTT CITY   210

POST OFFICE BOXES

Box Nos.
1-399   Main Office 43
401-699   Normandy
            Branch............ 43
801-999   Columbia
            Branch............ 44

STATIONS, BRANCHES AND UNITS

Columbia Br................. 43
Daniels Rural Br............ 33
Normandy Br................. 43
General Delivery............ 43
General Delivery Columbia
Br........................ 44
Postmaster.................. 43

APARTMENTS, HOTELS, MOTELS

Concord House 10850 Green
Mountain Cir.............. 44
Cross Keys Inn 10207
Wincopin Cir.............. 44

Ellicott City (Con.)	210

BUILDINGS

American Cities 10227
  Wincopin Cir 44
Awalt S 9051 Baltimore
  National Pike 43
Century Plaza 10630 Little
  Patuxent Pky 44
Columbia Mall 10300 Little
  Patuxent Pky 44
Exhibit 10215 Wincopin Cir 44
Howard County Medical
  Center 3459 St Johns Ln.... 43
Howard County Medical
  Center 3459 St Johns Ln.... 43
Normandy Shopping Center 43
Oakland Mills Shopping
  Center 45
Oakland 9042 Old Annapolis
  Rd 45
Professional 3716 Court Pl..... 43
Ridgely Office 5575 Sterrett
  Pl. 44
Sterrett Pl 5585 Sterrett Pl.... 44
Teachers 10221 Wincopin
  Cir 44
Wilde Lake Village Green 44

GOVERNMENT OFFICES

County Court House 8360
  Court Ave 43
County Jail 1 Emory 43
County Office Building 3450
  Court House Dr 43
County Police 3676 Fells Ave 43
Extension Agents 3450 Court
  House Dr 43

HOSPITALS

Columbia Hospital & Clinic
  5849 Banneker Rd 44
Taylor Manor Hospital College
  Ave 43

HYATTSVILLE	207

POST OFFICE BOXES

Box Nos.		
1-399	Main Office	81
700-999	Adelphi Br	83
1000-1199	Langley Park	
	Br	87
1200-1499	Landover Br	85
1600-1899	Prince Georges	
	Plaza Br	88
2000-2299	Capital Plaza ...	84
2300-2499	Landover Hills	
	Br	84
400-699	West	
	Hyattsville	
	Sta	82

STATIONS, BRANCHES AND UNITS

Adelphi Br 83
Capitol Plaza Br...................... 84
Cheverly Br.............................. 85
Chillum Br................................ 83
Defense Highway Br................ 84
Editors Park Br........................ 82
Kent Village Br........................ 85
Landover Hills Br 84
New Carrollton Br 84
North Englewood Br................ 85
Palmer Park Br........................ 85
West Hyattsville Sta................ 82
General Delivery 80
Postmaster 80

HOSPITALS

Prince Georges General............ 85

ROCKVILLE	208

POST OFFICE BOXES

Box Nos.		
1-599	Court House	
	Sta.................	50
600-799	Twinbrook Sta ..	51
1000-1799	Main Office	50
2000-2299	Pike Sta...........	52

STATIONS, BRANCHES AND UNITS

Courthouse Sta....................... 50
Derwood Br.............................. 55
Pike Sta................................... 52
Potomac Br.............................. 54
Randolph Hills Br 53
Twinbrook Sta.......................... 51
General Delivery 50
Postmaster 50

SILVER SPRING	209

POST OFFICE BOXES

Box Nos.		
1-599	Main Office	07
600-899	Woodmoor Br....	01
900-1199	Blair Br	10
1300-2299	Wheaton Br	02
4000-4499	Colesville Br.....	04

STATIONS, BRANCHES AND UNITS

Blair Br.. 10
Colesville Br............................ 04
Ednor Cloverly Br.................... 04
Leisure World Br...................... 06
Wheaton Br.............................. 02
Woodmoor Br........................... 01
General Delivery 07
Postmaster 07

APARTMENTS, HOTELS, MOTELS

Blair House, 8201 16th 10
Blair Plaza, 1401 Blair Mill
  Rd 10
Blair Towers, 8107 Eastern
  Avenue 10

BUILDINGS

American National Bank,
  8701 Georgia Ave................ 10
Guardian, 8605 Cameron....... 10
Wheaton Plaza Office
  Building 02

MASSACHUSETTS
(Abbreviation: MA)

Abington, Sta. North
   Abington...............................02351
Acoord, Br. Hingham.............02018
Acoaxet, R. Br. Little
   Compton Ri.......................02701
Acton (1st)............................01720
Acushnet, Br. New Bedford....02743
Adams (1st)...........................01220
Agawam (1st)........................01001
Allendale, Sta. Pittsfield........01201
Allerton, Sta. Hull..................02045
Allston, Sta. Boston (see
   appendix)
Amesbury (1st)......................01913
Amherst (1st).........................01002
Andover (1st).........................01810
   Ballardvale, Sta....................01810
   Shawsheen Village, Sta........01810
Annisquam, Sta. Gloucester....01930
Arlington, Br. Boston.............02174
Arlington Heights, Br.
   Boston................................02175
Ashburnham...........................01430
Ashby....................................01431
Ashfield.................................01330
Ashland (1st).........................01721
Ashley Falls...........................01222
Assinippi, R. Sta. Hanover......02339
Assonet.................................02702
Assumption College, Sta.
   Worcester...........................01609
Astor, Sta. Boston.................82123
Athol (1st).............................01331
   Royalston, R. Br..................01368
Attleboro (1st).......................02703
Attleboro Falls, Sta. North
   Attleboro (see appendix)
Auburn (1st)...........................01501
Auburndale, Br. Boston (see
   appendix)
Avon (1st)..............................02322
AYER (1st) (see appendix)
Babson Park, Br. Boston.........02157
Back Back Bay Annex, Sta.
   Boston (see appendix)
Baldwinville...........................01436
Ballardvale, Sta. Andover......01810
Barnstable.............................02630
Barre....................................01005
Barre Plains...........................01006
Barrowsville...........................02710
Bass River, Sta. South
   Yarmouth...........................02664
Beach, Br. Boston..................02151
Becket...................................01223
Bedford (1st).........................01730
Belchertown...........................01007
Bellingham.............................02019
Belmont, Br. Boston...............02178
Berkshire...............................01224
Berlin....................................01503
Bernardston...........................01337
Beverly (1st)..........................01915
Beverly Farms, Sta. Beverly....01915
Billerica (1st).........................01821
Blackstone.............................:01504
Blandford...............................01008
Bolton...................................01740
Bondsville.............................01009
BOSTON (1st) (see appendix)

Boston College, Br. Boston.....02167
Boston University, Sta.
   Boston................................02215
Bourne, Sta. Buzzards Bay.....02532
Boxborough, Br. Acton...........01719
Boxford.................................01921
Boylston................................01505
Bradford, Sta. Haverhill.........01830
Braintree, Br. Boston..............02184
Brant Rock.............................02020
Brewster................................02631
Bridgewater (1st)...................02324
Brighton, Sta. Boston (see
   appendix)
Brightwood, Sta. Springfield...01107
Brimfield...............................01010
BROCKTON (1st) (see
   appendix)
Brookfield..............................01506
Brookline, Br. Boston (see
   appendix)
Brookline Village, Br.
   Boston................................02147
Brookville..............................02326
Bryantville.............................02327
Buckland...............................01338
Burlington (1st)......................01803
Buzzards Bay (1st).................02532
   Bourne, Sta.........................02532
   Otis A F B, Br......................02542
Byfield..................................01922
Cambridge, Br. Boston (see
   appendix)
Cambridge A, Br. Boston
   (see appendix)
Cambridge B, Br. Boston
   (see appendix)
Cambridge C, Br. Boston
   (see appendix)
Campello, Sta. Brockton.........02403
Canton (1st)...........................02021
Carlisle.................................01741
Carver...................................02330
Cataumet...............................02534
Cathedral, Sta. Boston...........02118
Center, Sta. Woburn...............01801
Center Street, Sta. Brockton...02401
Centerville.............................02632
   Craigville, R. Br..................02636
Central Village, Sta.
   Westport............................02790
Charlemont............................01339
Charles Street, Sta. Boston.....02114
Charlestown, Sta. Boston........02129
Charlton................................01507
Charlton City.........................01508
Charlton Depot.......................01509
Chartley................................02712
Chatham (1st)........................02633
Chelmsford (1st)....................01824
Chelsea, Br. Boston................02150
Cherry Valley, Br. Worcester...01611
Cheshire................................01225
Chester.................................01011
Chesterfield...........................01012
Chestnut Hill, Br. Boston
CHICOPEE (1st) (see
   appendix)
Chicopee Center, Sta.
   Chicopee............................01013
Chilmark...............................02535
Cleghorn, Sta. Fitchburg........01420

Cleveland Circle, Br. Boston...02146
Clifton, Sta. Marblehead........01945
Clinton (1st)..........................01510
Cochituate, Sta. Wayland.......01778
Cohasset (1st)........................02025
Colrain..................................01340
Concord (1st).........................01742
Conway.................................01341
Cotuit...................................02635
Craigville, R. Br. Centerville...02636
Cummaquid.............................02637
Cummington...........................01026
Cushman, R. Sta. Amherst......01002
Cuttyhunk..............................02713
Dalton (1st)...........................01226
Danvers (1st).........................01923
Dartmouth.............................02714
Davis, R. Sta. Acton...............01720
Dedham (1st)..........................02026
Deerfield...............................01342
Dennis..................................02638
Dennis Port............................02639
Dighton.................................02715
Division Street, Sta. New
   Bedford..............................02744
Dorchester, Sta. Boston (see
   appendix)
Dorchester Center, Sta.
   Boston (see appendix)
Dover....................................02030
Dracut (1st)...........................01826
Drury....................................01343
Dudley, Br. Webster...............01570
Dudley Hill, Br. Webster.........01570
Dunstable..............................01827
Duxbury (1st).........................02332
East Arlington, Br. Boston......02174
East Boston, Sta. Boston........02128
East Brewster.........................02640
East Bridgewater (1st)...........02333
East Brookfield......................01515
East Dedham, Sta. Dedham....02026
East Dennis............................02641
East Douglas..........................01516
East Falmouth (1st)........ 02536
   Hatchville, R. Br.................02536
   New Seabury, Br. 02536
   Popponesset Beach, R.
   Br......................................02560
   Teaticket, Sta......................02536
   Waquoit, Sta........................02536
East Freetown........................02717
East Harwich, R. Sta.
   Harwich..............................02645
East Longmeadow (1st)..........01028
East Lynn, Sta. Lynn..............01904
East Mansfield.......................02031
East Northfield, Sta.
   Northfield...........................01360
East Orleans..........................02643
East Otis................................01029
East Pembroke.......................02336
East Pepperell........................01437
East Princeton........................01517
East Sandwich........................02537
East Taunton..........................02718
East Templeton.......................01438
East Walpole (1st)..................02032
East Wareham.........................02538
East Watertown, Br. Boston....02172
East Weymouth, Br. Boston
   (see appendix)
Eastham.................................02642

Easthampton (1st)..............01027	(see appendix)
Easton..............02334	Highlands, Sta. Lowell..........01851
Eastondale..............02335	Hingham (1st)..............02043
Edgartown..............02539	Accord, Br...............02018
Elmwood..............02337	Hinsdale..............01235
Erving..............01344	Holbrook (1st)..............02343
Essex..............01929	Holden (1st)..............01520
Essex, Sta. Boston..............02112	Holliston (1st)..............01746
Everett, Br. Boston..............02149	Holyoke (1st)..............01040
Fairhaven (1st)..............02719	Hopedale (1st)..............01747
FALL RIVER (1st) (see appendix)	Hopkinton..............01748
FALMOUTH (1st) (see appendix)	Housatonic..............01236
	Hubbardston..............01452
Fayville..............01745	Hudson (1st)..............01749
Feeding Hills (1st)..............01030	Hull (1st)..............02045
Fiskdale..............01518	Humarock..............02047
Fitchburg (1st)..............01420	Huntington..............01050
Flint, Sta. Fall River..............02723	Hyannis (1st)..............02601
Florence, Sta. Northampton....01060	Hyannis Port..............02647
Forest Park, Sta. Springfield (see appendix)	Hyde Park, Sta. Boston..........02136
	Indian Orchard (1st)..............01051
Forestdale..............02644	Inman Square, Br. Boston (see appendix)
Forge Village..............01828	
Fort Devens, Sta. Ayer..........01433	Ipswich (1st)..............01938
Foxboro (1st)..............02035	Islington, Sta. Westwood..........02090
Framingham (1st)..............01701	Jamaica Plain, Sta. Boston......02130
Framingham Center, Sta. Framingham..............01701	Jefferson..............01522
	John Fitzgerald Kennedy, Sta. Boston..............02203
Franklin (1st)..............02038	Kearney Square, Sta. Lowell....01852
Gardner (1st)..............01440	Kendall Square, Br. Boston......02142
Georgetown, Br. Haverhill......01833	Kenmore, Sta. Boston (see appendix)
Gilbertville..............01031	
Gleasondale, R. Br. Hudson....01749	Kingston, Br. Plymouth..........02364
Glendale..............01229	Lake Pleasant..............01347
Gloucester (1st)..............01930	Lakeville, R. Br. Middleboro....02346
Goshen..............01032	Lancaster..............01523
Grafton..............01519	Lanesboro..............01237
Granby..............01033	Lanesville, Sta. Gloucester......01930
Graniteville..............01829	LAWRENCE (1st) (see appendix)
Granville..............01034	
Great Barrington (1st)..........01230	Lee (1st)..............01238
Green Harbor..............02041	Leeds (1st)..............01053
Greenbush..............02040	Leicester..............01524
Greendale, Sta. Worcester......01606	Lenox (1st)..............01240
Greenfield (1st)..............01301	Lenox Dale..............01242
Greenwood, Sta. Wakefield....01880	Leominster (1st)..............01453
Griswoldville..............01345	Leverett..............01054
Groton..............01450	Lexington, Br. Boston..............02173
Grove Hall, Sta. Boston..........02121	Lincoln (1st)..............01773
Groveland, Br. Haverhill..........01834	Lincoln Center, Sta. Lincoln....01773
Hadley..............01035	Linwood..............01525
Halifax..............02338	Lithia..............01055
Hamilton..............01936	Littleton (1st)..............01460
Hampden..............01036	Long Island, Sta. Boston..........02169
Hancock, R. Br. Lanesboro......01237	Longmeadow, Br. Springfield..............01106
Hanover (1st)..............02339	
Hanover Street, Sta. Boston....02113	LOWELL (1st) (see appendix)
Hanson (1st)..............02341	Ludlow (1st)..............01056
Harding..............02042	Lunds Corner, Sta. New Bedford..............02745
Hardwick..............01037	
Harvard..............01451	Lunenburg..............01462
Harwich..............02645	LYNN (1st) (see appendix)
Harwich Port..............02646	Lynnfield (1st)..............01940
Harwood, Sta. Littleton..........01460	M I T, Br. Boston..............02139
Hatchville, R. Br. East Falmouth..............02536	Magnolia, Sta. Gloucester......01930
	Malden, Br. Boston..............02148
Hatfield..............01038	Manchaug..............01526
Hathorne..............01937	Manchester (1st)..............01944
Haverhill (1st)..............01830	Manomet..............02345
Haydenville..............01039	Mansfield (1st)..............02048
Heath..............01346	Marblehead (1st)..............01945
Highland, Sta. Springfield	Marion..............02738

Marlborough (1st)..............01752
Marshfield (1st)..............02050
Marshfield Hills..............02051
Marstons Mills..............02648
Mashpee..............02649
Mattapan, Sta. Boston..........02126
Mattapoisett..............02739
Maynard (1st)..............01754
Medfield (1st)..............02052
Medford, Br. Boston..............02155
Medway (1st)..............02053
Melrose, Br. Boston..............02176
Melrose Highlands, Br. Boston..............02177
Mendon..............01756
Menemsha..............02552
Merrimac..............01860
Merrimack College, Br. Lawrence..............01845
Methuen, Br. Lawrence..........01844
Middleboro (1st)..............02346
Middlefield..............01243
Middleton (1st)..............01949
Milford (1st)..............01757
Mill River..............01244
Millbury (1st)..............01527
Millers Falls..............01349
Millis (1st)..............02054
Millville..............01529
Milton, Br. Boston..............02186
Milton Village, Br. Boston......02187
Minot..............02055
Mittineague, Sta. West Springfield..............01089
Monponsett..............02350
Monroe Bridge..............01350
Monson (1st)..............01057
Montague..............01351
Montello, Sta. Brockton..........02403
Monterey..............01245
Monument Beach..............02553
Morningdale..............01530
Mount Hermon..............01354
Mount Saint James, Sta. Worcester..............01610
Mount Tom..............01058
Nabnasset..............01861
Nahant, Br. Lynn..............01908
Nantucket (1st)..............02554
Natick (1st)..............01760
Needham, Br. Boston..............02192
Needham Heights, Br. Boston..............02194
NEW BEDFORD (1st) (see appendix)
New Braintree..............01531
New Salem..............01355
New Seabury, Br. East Falmouth..............02536
Newbury, Br. Newburyport......01950
Newburyport (1st)..............01950
Newton, Br. Boston (see appendix)
Newton Center, Br. Boston (see appendix)
Newton Highlands, Br. Boston (see appendix)
Newton Lower Falls, Br. Boston (see appendix)
Newton Upper Falls, Br. Boston (see appendix)
Newtonville, Br. Boston (see appendix)

Nonantum, Br. Boston (see appendix)
Nonquitt, R. Br. New Bedford 02748
Noquochoke, Sta. Westport ..02790
Norfolk 02056
North, Sta. New Bedford 02746
North Abington (1st) 02351
North Adams (1st) 01247
North Amherst, Sta. Amherst 01059
North Andover, Br. Lawrence ..01845
NORTH ATTLEBORO (1st) (see appendix)
North Billerica (1st) 01862
North Brookfield 01535
North Carver 02355
North Chatham 02650
North Chelmsford (1st) 01863
North Cohasset, Sta. Cohasset 02025
North Dartmouth, Br. New Bedford 02747
North Dighton (1st) 02764
North Eastham 02651
North Easton (1st) 02356
North Egremont 01252
North Falmouth 02556
Silver Beach, R. Br. 02565
North Grafton 01536
North Hatfield 01066
North Marshfield 02059
North Oxford 01537
North Pembroke 02358
North Plymouth, Sta. Plymouth 02360
North Quincy, Br. Boston (see appendix)
North Randolph, Sta. Randolph 02368
North Reading (1st) 01864
North Scituate (1st) 02060
North Truro 02652
North Uxbridge 01538
North Weymouth, Br. Boston (see appendix)
North Wilbraham (1st) 01067
North Wilmington, Sta. Wilmington 01887
Northampton (1st) 01060
Northborough (1st) 01532
Northbridge 01534
Northfield 01360
Norton (1st) 02766
Norwell 02061
Norwood (1st) 02062
Nutting Lake 01865
Oak Bluffs 02557
Oakdale 01539
Oakham 01068
Ocean Bluff 02065
Ocean Grove, Sta. Swansea ...02777
Onset 02558
Orange (1st) 01364
Orleans (1st) 02653
Osterville (1st) 02655
Wianno, R. Br. 02674
Otis 01253
Otis A F B, Br. Buzzards Bay 02542
Oxford 01540
Padanaram Village, Br. New Bedford 02748

Palmer (1st) 01069
Parcel Post, Sta. Worcester ...01604
Parcel Post, Sta. Westfield 01085
Parcel Post, Sta. Fitchburg 01420
Paxton, Br. Worcester 01612
Peabody (1st) 01960
Pembroke 02359
Pepperell 01463
Petersham 01366
Pigeon Cove, Sta. Rockport ...01966
Pinehurst 01866
Pittsfield (1st) 01201
Plainfield 01070
Plainville, Br. North Attleboro (see appendix)
Pleasant Lake 02656
Plum Island, Br. Newburyport 01950
PLYMOUTH (1st) (see appendix)
Plympton 02367
Pocasset 02559
Popponesset Beach, R. Br. East Falmouth 02560
Prides Crossing 01965
Princeton 01541
Provincetown (1st) 02657
Prudential Center, Sta. Boston 02199
Quincy, Br. Boston (see appendix)
Randolph (1st) 02368
Raynham 02767
Raynham Center 02768
Reading (1st) 01867
Readville, Sta. Boston 02137
Rehoboth 02769
Revere, Br. Boston 02151
Richmond 01254
Riverdale, Sta. Gloucester 01930
Rochdale 01542
Rochester 02770
Rockland (1st) 02370
Rockport (1st) 01966
Roslindale, Sta. Boston 02131
Rowe 01367
Rowley (1st) 01969
Roxbury, Sta. Boston (see appendix)
Roxbury Crossing, Sta. Boston (see appendix)
Royalston, R. Br. Athol 01368
Russell 01071
Rutland 01543
Sagamore 02561
Sagamore Beach 02562
Salem (1st) 01970
Salem State College, Sta. Salem 01970
Salisbury, Br. Newburyport 01950
Salisbury Beach, Br. Newburyport 01950
Sandisfield 01255
Sandwich 02563
Saugus, Br. Lynn 01906
Savoy 01256
Saxonville, Sta. Framingham 01701
Scituate (1st) 02066
Seekonk (1st) 02771
Segreganset 02773
Sharon (1st) 02067
Shattuckville 01369

Shawsheen Village, Sta. Andover 01810
Sheffield 01257
Shelburne Falls 01370
Sheldonville 02070
Sherborn (1st) 01770
Shirley 01464
Shirley Center 01465
Shrewsbury (1st) 01545
Shutesbury 01072
Siasconset 02564
Silver Beach, R. Br. North Falmouth 02565
Snug Harbor, Sta. Duxbury 02332
Soldiers Field, Sta. Boston (see appendix)
Somerset, Br. Fall River (see appendix)
Somerville, Br. Boston (see appendix)
South, Sta. Fall River 02724
South Ashburnham 01466
South Athol 01372
South Attleboro, Sta. Attleboro 02703
South Barre 01074
South Berlin 01549
South Boston, Sta. Boston 02127
South Carver 02566
South Chatham 02659
South Chelmsford, R. Sta. Chelmsford 01824
South Dartmouth, Br. New Bedford 02748
South Deerfield 01373
South Dennis 02660
South Easton 02375
South Egremont 01258
South Essex 01981
South Framingham, Sta. Framingham 01701
South Gardner, Sta. Gardner ...01440
South Grafton 01560
South Hadley (1st) 01075
South Hadley Falls, Sta. South Hadley 01075
South Hamilton (1st) 01982
South Harwich 02661
South Lancaster 01561
South Lee 01260
South Lynnfield, Sta. Lynnfield 01940
South Natick, Sta. Natick 01760
South Orleans 02662
South Postal Annex, Sta. Boston 02109
South Royalston 01374
South Swansea, Sta. Swansea 02777
South Walpole 02071
South Waltham, Br. Boston 02154
South Wellfleet 02663
South Westport, R. Sta. Westport 02790
South Weymouth, Br. Boston (see appendix)
South Yarmouth (1st) 02664
Southampton 01073
Southborough (1st) 01772
Southbridge (1st) 01550
Southfield 01259
Southwick 01077

Spencer (1st)..............................01562
SPRINGFIELD (1st) (see appendix)
Squantum, Br. Boston (see appendix)
State House, Sta. Boston......02133
Sterling....................................01564
Sterling Junction 01565
Still River................................01467
Stockbridge (1st)....................01262
Stoneham, Br. Boston...........02180
Stoughton (1st)......................02072
Stow..01775
Sturbridge (1st)......................01566
Sudbury (1st)..........................01776
Sunderland..............................01375
Swampscott, Br. Lynn............01907
Swansea (1st).........................02777
Swifts Beach, R. Sta. Wareham.............................02571
Tapley Street Annex, Sta. Springfield..........................01101
Taunton (1st)..........................02780
Teaticket, Sta. East Falmouth............................02536
Templeton................................01468
Tewksbury (1st)......................01876
Thorndike................................01079
Three Rivers............................01080
Topsfield (1st).........................01983
Townsend (1st)........................01469
Tremont, Sta. Boston 02116
Truro..02666
Tufts University, Br. Boston...02153
Turners Falls (1st)..................01376
Turnpike, Sta. Shrewsbury.....01545
Twin Village, Sta. Attleboro...02703
Tyngsboro................................01879
Tyringham................................01264
Uphams Corner, Sta. Boston (see appendix)
Upton.......................................01568
Uxbridge (1st).........................01569
Veterans Administration Hosp., Sta. Boston............02130
Village, Br. Medway................02053
Vineyard Haven (1st)...............02568
West Chop, R. Br...................02573
Waban, Br. Boston (see appendix)
Wakefield (1st)........................01880

Wales.......................................01081
Walpole (1st)...........................02081
Waltham, Br. Boston...............02154
Waquoit, Sta. East Falmouth............................02536
Ward Hill, Sta. Haverhill.........01830
Ware (1st)................................01082
Wareham (1st).........................02571
Warren (1st).............................01083
Watertown, Br. Boston............02172
Waverley, Br. Boston...............02179
Wayland (1st)..........................01778
Webster (1st)...........................01570
Webster Square, Sta. Worcester...........................01603
Wellesley, Br. Boston..............02181
Wellesley Hills, Br. Boston.....02181
Wellfleet..................................02667
Wendell....................................01379
Wendell Depot.........................01380
Wenham (1st)..........................01984
West Acton, Sta. Acton...........01720
West Barnstable.......................02668
West Boxford...........................01885
West Boylston (1st).................01583
West Bridgewater.....................02379
West Brookfield........................01585
West Chatham..........................02669
West Chesterfield.....................01084
West Chop, R. Br. Vineyard Haven.................................02573
West Concord, Sta. Concord ...01742
West Cummington.....................01265
West Dennis.............................02670
West Falmouth..........................02574
West Groton.............................01472
West Hanover, Sta. Hanover....02339
West Harwich............................02671
West Hatfield...........................01088
West Hyannisport......................02672

West Lynn, Sta. Lynn...............01905
West Mansfield.........................02083
West Medford, Br. Boston.........02156
West Millbury...........................01586
West Newbury..........................01985
West Newton, Br. Boston (see appendix)
West Peabody, Sta. Peabody....01960
West Roxbury, Sta. Boston......02132
West Side, Sta. Worcester........01602

West Somerville, Br. Boston....02144
West Springfield (1st)..............01089
West Stockbridge......................01266
West Tisbury.............................02575
West Townsend..........................01474
West Upton..............................01587
West Wareham..........................02576
West Warren (1st).....................01092
West Yarmouth.........................02673
Westborough (1st)....................01581
Westfield (1st).........................01085
Westford..................................01886
Westminster.............................01473
Weston, Br. Boston..................02193
Westover A F B, Sta. Chicopee...........................01022
Westport (1st)..........................02790
Westport Point..........................02791
Westwood (1st)........................02090
Weymouth, Br. Boston (see appendix)
Whately....................................01093
Wheelwright..............................01094
White Horse Beach...................02361
Whitinsville (1st).....................01588
Whitman (1st)..........................02382
Wianno, R. Br. Osterville.........02674
Wilbraham................................01095
Wilkinsonville...........................01590
Williamsburg............................01096
Williamstown (1st)...................01267
Wilmington (1st)......................01887
Winchendon (1st).....................01475
Winchendon Springs.................01477
Winchester (1st).......................01890
Windsor....................................01270
Winter Hill, Br. Boston (see appendix)
Winthrop, Br. Boston................02152
Woburn (1st)............................01801
Wollaston, Br. Boston (see appendix)
Woods Hole, Sta. Falmouth......02543
Woodville..................................01784
WORCESTER (1st) (see appendix)
Woronoco.................................01097
Worthington..............................01098
Wrentham (1st)........................02093
Yarmouth Port..........................02675

Ayer—Boston MASSACHUSETTS

Appendix

AYER 014

POST OFFICE BOXES

Box Nos.		
A-K	Main Office	32
1-469	Main Office	32

STATIONS, BRANCHES AND UNITS

Fort Devens Sta.	33
General Delivery	32
Postmaster	32

BOSTON 021

POST OFFICE BOXES

Box Nos.		
1-400	Main Office	01
401-800	Main Office	02
801-1200	Main Office	03
1201-1600	Main Office	04
1601-2000	Main Office	05
2001-2200	Main Office	06
2201-2400	Main Office	07
8000-8999	John F Kennedy	

	Sta.	14
9001-9188	John F Kennedy	
	Sta.	14

STATIONS, BRANCHES AND UNITS

Allston Sta.	34
Arlington Br.	74
Arlington Heights Br.	75
Astor Sta.	23
Auburndale Br.	66
Babson Park Br.	57
Back Bay Annex Sta.	15

AREA MAP OF COMMUNITIES
COVERED IN THIS INDEX

Stoneham
Melrose
Lexington
Arlington Medford Malden
Revere
Belmont Somerville Everett
Waltham Watertown Cambridge Chelsea
Weston Winthrop
Newton
Wellesley Brookline
BOSTON
Needham
Milton Quincy
Braintree
Weymouth

COMMUNITY
ABBREVIATIONS
USED IN THIS
STREET LISTING

ALL — Allston
ARL — Arlington
AUB — Auburndale
BEL — Belmont
BRA — Braintree
BRI — Brighton
BRO — Brookline
CAM — Cambridge
CHA — Charlestown
CHE — Chelsea
CHH — Chestnut Hill
DOR — Dorchester
EB — East Boston
EV — Everett
EWY — East Weymouth
HP — Hyde Park
JP — Jamaica Plain
LEX — Lexington
MAL — Malden
MAT — Mattapan
MED — Medford
MEL — Melrose
MIL — Milton
N   — Needham
NCE — Newton Center
NEW — Newton
NH — Needham Heights
NLF — Newton Lower Falls
NQ — North Quincy
NUF — Newton Upper Falls

NWH — Newton Highlands
NWV — Newtonville
NWY — North Weymouth
QUI — Quincy
REV — Revere
ROS — Roslindale
ROX — Roxbury
RXC — Roxbury Crossing
SB — South Boston
SF — Soldiers Field
SOM — Somerville
STO — Stoneham
SWY — South Weymouth
WAB — Waban
WAL — Waltham
WAT — Watertown
WAV — Waverley
WEL — Wellesley
WES — Weston
WH — Wellesley Hills
WIN — Winthrop
WNW — West Newton
WOL — Wollaston
WRX — West Roxbury
WS — West Somerville
WY — Weymouth

Boston (Con.)   021

Beach Br	51
Belmont Br	78
Boston College Br	67
Boston University Sta	02215
Braintree Br	84
Brighton Sta	35
Brookline Br	46
Brookline Village Br	47
Cambridge Br	38
Cambridge A Br	39
Cambridge B Br	40
Cambridge C Br	41
Cathedral Sta	18
Charles Street Sta	14
Charlestown Sta	29
Chelsea Br	50
Chestnut Hill Br	67
Cleveland Circle Br	46
Dorchester Sta	22
Dorchester Center Sta	24
East Arlington Br	74
East Boston Sta	28
East Watertown Br	72
East Weymouth Br	89
Essex Sta	12
Everett Br	49
Grove Hall Sta	21
Hanover Street Sta	13
Hyde Park Sta	36
Inman Square Br	39
Jamaica Plain Sta	30
John Fitzgerald Kennedy Sta	02203
Kendall Square Br	42
Kenmore Sta	02215
Lexington Br	73
Long Island Sta	69
Malden Br	48
Mattapan Sta	26
Medford Br	55
Melrose Br	76
Melrose Highlands Br	77
Milton Br	86
Milton Village Br	87
MIT Br	39
Needham Br	92
Needham Heights Br	94
Newton Br	58
Newton Center Br	59
Newton Highlands Br	61
Newton Lower Falls Br	62
Newton Upper Falls Br	64
Newtonville Br	60
Nonantum Br	95
North Quincy Br	71
North Weymount Br	88
Prudential Center Sta	99
Quincy Br	69
Readville Sta	37
Revere Br	51
Roslindale Sta	31
Roxbury Sta	19
Rox Bury Crossing Sta	20
Soldiers Field Sta	63
Somerville Br	43
South Boston Sta	27
South Postal Annex Sta	09
South Waltham Br	54

South Weymouth Br	90
Squantum Br	71
State House Sta	33
Stoneham Br	80
Tremont Sta	16
Tufts University Br	53
Uphams Corner Sta	25
Veterans Administration Hosp Sta	30
Waban Br	63
Waltham Br	54
Watertown Br	72
Waverley Br	79
Wellesley Br	81
ellesley Hills Br	81
West Medford Br	56
West Newton Br	65
West Roxbury Sta	32
West Somerville Br	44
Weston Br	93
Weymouth Br	88
Winter Hill Br	45
Winthrop Br	52
Wollaston Br	70
General Delivery	09
Postmaster	09

APARTMENTS, HOTELS, MOTELS

Bradford, 275 Tremont	16
Essex, 695 Atlantic Ave	11
Lenox, 61 Exeter	16
Madison, 76 Causeway	11
Parker House, 60 School	08
Ritz-Carleton, 15 Arlington	17
Sheraton-Boston, 39 Dalton	99
Sheraton-Plaza, Copley Sq.	16
Somerset, 400 Commonwealth Ave	02215
Statler-Hilton, Park Sq	17

BUILDINGS

Appraisers Stores, 408 Atlantic Ave	10
Beacon Trust, 31 Milk	09
Boston Flour & Grain Exchange, 177 Milk	09
Employers Liability, 33 Broad	09
Federal Reserve Bank, 30 Pearl	10
First National Bank, 1 Federal	10
John B Hynes Memorial Auditorium, 900 Boylston	15
John Hancock, 200 Berkeley	16
Kimball, 18 Tremont	08
Park Square, 31 St James Ave	16
Prudential Center	99
State Street Bank, 225 Franklin	10
Western Union Telegraph, 230 Congress	10

GOVERNMENT OFFICES

City Hall, Gov't Ctr	02201
Court House, 55 Pemberton Square	08
Custom House, 165 State	09

Department Of Public Works, 100 Nashua	14
John F Kennedy Federal Bldg, Gov'T Ctr	02203
Massachusetts Registry Of Motor Vehicles, 100 Nashua	14
State House	33
State Office Bldg, 100 Cambridge	02202
United States Court House, Post Office Sq	09
United States Post Office, Post Office Sq	09

HOSPITALS

Angell Animal, 180 Longwood Ave	15
Baker Clinic, 16 Deaconess Rd	02215
Beth Israel, 330 Brookline Ave	02215
Boston City, 818 Harrison Ave	18
Boston Dispensary, 25 Bennet	11
Boston Evening Clinic, 297 Commonwealth Ave	15
Boston Floating, 20 Ash	11
Boston Hosp For Women, 221 Longwood Ave	15
Boston Industrial Medical Center, Fenway	02215
Boston State, 591 Morton	24
Brookline, 165 Chestnut	46
Carney, 2100 Dorchester Ave	24
Childrens, 300 Longwood Ave	15
Joslin Clinic, Joslin Rd	02215
Lemuel Shattuck, Circuit Dr	30
Long Island, Long Island	69
Massachusetts Eye & Ear, 243 Charles	14
Massachusetts General, 32 Fruit	14
Massachusetts Soldiers Home, 91 Crest Ave	50
New England Baptist, 91 Parker Hill Ave	20
New England Center, 171 Harrison Ave	11
New England Deaconess, 195 Pilgrim Rd	02215
New England Medical Center, 37 Bennet	11
New England, Dimock	19
Palmer Memorial, 195 Pilgrim Rd	02215
Peter Bent Brigham, 721 Huntington Ave	15
Pratt Diagnostic, 30 Bennet	11
Robert Breck Brigham, 125 Parker Hill Ave	20
Saint Elizabeths, 736 Cambridge	35
Saint Margarets, 90 Cushing Ave	25
United States Naval, 1 Broadway	50
United States Public Health Service, 77 Warren	35
University, 750 Harrison Ave	18

Boston (Con.)   021

Veterans Administration,
1400 Vfw Pkwy 32
Veterans Administration, 150
S Huntington Ave................ 30

MILITARY INSTALLATIONS

Army Base, 666 Summer 02210
Coast Guard, 447
Commercial 13
South Boston Annex Navy
Yard, 285 Northern Ave....02210
U S Naval Shipyard, Water 29

UNIVERSITIES AND COLLEGES

Boston College Law School,
St Thomas More................ 35
Boston College, 140
Commonwealth Ave 67
Boston State, 625 Huntington
Ave 15
Boston University Law
School, 11 Ashburton Pl.... 08
Boston University, 755
Commonwealth Ave 02215
Brandeis University, 415
South............................. 54
Bryant & Stratton, 150
Newbury 16
Burdett, 160 Beacon 16
Emerson, 130 Beacon 16
Emmanuel, 400 Fenway.......... 15
Franklin Technical Institute,
41 Berkeley 16
Harvard Business School, 16
N Harvard 63
Harvard Dental School, 188
Longwood Ave 15
Harvard Medical School, 25
Shattuck......................... 15
Harvard School Of Public
Health, 55 Shattuck 15
Harvard University,
Cambridge 38
Mass Inst Of Technology, 77
Massachusetts Ave........... 39
Northeastern University, 360
Huntington Ave 15
Radcliffe, 10 Garden............. 38
Regis, 235 Wellesley 93
Simmons, Fenway................. 15
Suffolk University, 20 Derne... 14
Tufts Medicine & Dental, 136
Harrison Ave 11
Tufts University, Medford 55
University Of Mass At
Boston, 100 Arlington........ 16
Wellesley, 106 Central 81
Wentworth Institute, 550
Huntington Ave 15

NAMED STREETS

A (NH) 94
A (WAV) 79
A (REV) 51
A (HP) 36
A
  1-121 (SB) (ODD) 27
  2-130 (SB) (EVEN) 27

123-OUT (ODD)................02210
132-OUT (EVEN)...............02210
A Ave (WRX) 32
A Dr (EV) 49
Aaron (MEL)......................... 76
Aaron Rd (LEX)..................... 73
Abbey (QUI)......................... 69
Abbey Rd (BRI)..................... 35
Abbot (DOR) 24
Abbotsford (DOR) 21
Abbott (MAL) 48
Abbott (MED) 55
Abbott (WEL) 81
Abbott (NUF) 64
Abbott (N).......................... 92
Abbott (SWY) 90
Abbott (BRA) 84
Abbott Ave (EV).................... 49
Abbott Rd (WAL)................... 54
Abbott Rd (WH) 81
Abbott Rd (LEX).................... 73
Abbottsford Rd (BRO) 46
Abdell (SOM)........................ 43
Aberdeen (NWH).................... 61
Aberdeen 02215
Aberdeen Ave (WAL)............... 54
Aberdeen Ave & Ct (CAM)....... 38
Aberdeen Rd (WS).................. 44
Aberdeen Rd (MIL)................. 87
Aberdeen Rd (WES)................ 93
Aberdeen Rd (WEL)................ 81
Aberdeen Rd (ARL)................ 74
Aberdeen Rd (NQ).................. 71
Abernathy Rd (LEX)............... 73
Abigail Ave (QUI)................... 69
Abigail Adams Cir (NWY)........ 91
Abruzzi (REV)....................... 51
Acacia (CAM)........................ 38
Acacia Ave (CHH).................. 67
Acacia Rd (WRX)................... 32
Academy (ARL)..................... 74
Academy
  1-142 (BRA) 85
  143-OUT (BRA) 84
Academy Ave
  1-107 (EWY) (ODD)........... 89
  2-104 (EWY) (EVEN).......... 89
  106-OUT (WY) (EVEN)........ 88
  109-OUT (WY) (ODD)......... 88
Academy Ct & Ter (ROX) 19
Academy Ln (MIL) 86
Academy Rd (NEW)................ 58
Academy Hill Rd (BRI)........... 35
Acadia (SB) 27
Acadia Park (SOM)................. 43
Access Rd (LEX).................... 73
Accolon Way 14
Achorn Cir (JP).................... 30
Ackers Ave & Ter (BRO)......... 46
Ackley Pl (JP)...................... 30
Acorn (CAM) 39
Acorn (WAL) 54
Acorn 08
Acorn (LEX).......................... 73
Acorn (BEL) 78
Acorn Dr (AUB) 66
Acorn Park (ARL).................. 74
Acorn Park (CAM)................. 40
Acorn St & Cir (BRA)............ 84
Acorn St & Ct (MAL)............. 48
Acron Rd (BRO) 46
Acton (WAL) 54

Acton (HP) 36
Acton (ARL) 74
Acton (WOL)........................ 70
Acton (WAT) 72
Acton 18
Ada (ROS) 31
Adair Rd (BRI) 35
Adamian Park (ARL).............. 74
Adams (ARL) 74
Adams (MEL)........................ 76
Adams (BEL) 78
Adams (LEX) 73
Adams (HP) 36
Adams (WIN) 52
Adams (SOM) 45
Adams (BRO)........................ 46
Adams (MAL)........................ 48
Adams (CHE) 50
Adams (MED) 55
Adams (BRA) 84
Adams
  1-74 (NMV) 60
  1-185 (MIL) 87
  1-773 (DOR) (ODD) 22
  2-770 (DOR) (EVEN) 22
  75-OUT (NEW) 58
  186-OUT (MIL).................. 86
  772-OUT (DOR) (EVEN) 24
  775-OUT (DOR) (ODD) 24
Adams Ave (EV) 49
Adams Ave (WNW)................. 65
Adams Ct & Ter (NEW).......... 58
Adams Pl (SWY).................... 90
Adams Pl (SB)...................... 27
Adams (STO)........................ 80
Adams St & Ave (WAT).......... 72
Adams St & Ave (WAL).......... 54
Adams St, Cir & Ct (QUI)....... 69
Adams St & Ct (REV)............. 51
Adams St & Pl (CHA)............. 29
Adams St & Pl (ROX)............. 19
Adams Ter (DOR) 22
Adams Ter (CAM) 38
Adamson (ALL) 34
Adanac Rd (MIL)................... 86
Adanac Ter (DOR) 24
Adans Ct (REV) 51
Addington Cir (EWY)............. 89
Addington Rd (WRX).............. 32
Addington Rd (BRO).............. 46
Addison (CHE) 50
Addison (BRA)...................... 84
Addison (EB) 28
Addison (ARL)...................... 74
Addison Rd (WAL) 54
Adelaide Rd (SOM)................ 43
Adelaide St & Ter (JP)........... 30
Adele Rd (QUI)..................... 69
Adeline Rd (QUI) 69
Adeline Rd (NCE).................. 59
Adella Ave (WNW)................. 65
Adena Rd (WNW)................... 65
Adirondack Pl (DOR)............. 24
Adorn (WY) 88
Adrian (SOM) 43
Adrian Rd (MIL).................... 86
Aerial (ARL) 74

Aerial (LEX) 73
Agassiz (CAM) 40
Agassiz Park (JP).................. 30
Agassiz St & Ave (WAV)......... 79
Agatha Ave (REV)................. 51

259

Boston (Con.)   021

Agawam (REV) 51
Agawam (DOR) 22
Agawam Rd (QUI) 69
Agawam Rd (WAB) 68
Agnes Ave (MAT) 26
Agneus Ave (WIN) 52
Agry Ter (REV) 51
Ainsley (DOR) 22
Ainsworth (ROS) 31
Ainsworth Pl (MEL) 76
Airport Rd (NQ) 71
Airport Rd Ext (NQ) 71
Airport St & Rd (EB) 28
Airport Service Rd (EB) 28
Akron (CAM) 38
Akron St & Pl (ROX) 19
Alabama (MAT) 26
Alachua Rd (EWY) 89
Alameda Rd (WRX) 32
Alaric St & Ter (WRX) 32
Alaska (ROX) 19
Alba Cir (NEW) 58
Alba Rd (WEL) 81
Alban (DOR) 24
Alban Rd (WAB) 68
Albano (ROS) 31
Albany (CAM) 39
Albany (WOL) 70
Albany
  1-199 11
  200-799 18
  800-OUT (ROX) 19
Albatross Rd (QUI) 69
Albemarle Ave (LEX) 73
Albemarle Rd (WAL) 54
Albemarle St & Ter 15
Albermarle (HP) 36
Albermarle (APL) 74
Albemarle Rd
  1-214 (NWV) 60
  215-215A (WNW) 65
  216-OUT (NWV) 60
Albernathy Rd (LEX) 73
Albert (MEL) 76
Albert Ave (BEL) 78
Albert Ave (WIN) 52
Albert Ave (REV) 51
Albert Park (EV) 49
Albert Rd (WAL) 54
Albert Rd (AUB) 66
Albert Rd (EWY) 89
Alberta (WRX) 32
Alberta Rd (CHH) 67
Alberta Ter (CAM) 40
Albertina (QUI) 69
Albion (MEL) 76
Albion (HP) 36
Albion (EV) 49
Albion (MAL) 48
Albion (MED) 55
Albion (ROX) 19
Albion
  1-91 43
  92-OUT (WS) 44
Albion Ave (STO) 80
Albion Ct, Pl & Ter (WS) 44
Albion Pl (CHE) 50
Albion Pl (CHA) 29
Albion Rd (WH) 81
Albion Rd (WOL) 70
Albion St & Pl (NCE) 59

Albright (WRX) 32
Alcott (ALL) 34
Alcott Park (MAL) 48
Alcott Rd (LEX) 73
Alden (NCE) 59
Alden (MEL) 76
Alden (QUI) 69
Alden (MAL) 48
Alden Ave (REV) 51
Alden Ave (STO) 80
Alden Ln (MED) 55
Alden Pl (WNW) 65
Alden Rd (WH) 81
Alden Rd (LEX) 73
Alden Rd (WAT) 72
Alden Rd (WY) 88
Alden Rd (BRA) 85
Alden Rd (MIL) 86
Alden Rd (N) 92
Alder (ROS) 31
Alder St & Ter (WAL) 54
Aldersey (SOM) 43
Alderwood Rd (WAL) 54
Alderwood Rd (NCE) 59
Aldie (ALL) 34
Aldine 02210
Aldrich (ROS) 31
Aldrich (SOM) 45
Aldrich Rd (WAT) 72
Aldridge Rd (N) 92
Aldwin Rd (ROS) 31
Aldworth (JP) 30
Aletha Rd (N) 92
Alewife Brook Pky (SOM) 44
Alewife Brook Pky
  1-165 (CAM) (ODD) 40
  2-148 (CAM) (EVEN) 40
  150-OUT (CAM) (EVEN) 38
  167-OUT (CAM) (ODD) 38
Alexander (DOR) 25
Alexander Ave (MED) 55
Alexander Ave (BEL) 78
Alexander Rd (NWH) 61
Alexander Rd (BRA) 84
Alford (CHA) 29
Alfred (JP) 30
Alfred (SWY) 90
Alfred (NQ) 71
Alfred Rd (WAT) 72
Alfred Rd (ARL) 74
Alfred Rd (MIL) 86
Alfred Rd (BRA) 84
Alfred St & Ct (EV) 49
Alfred St & Ter (MED) 55
Alger (SB) 27
Algonquin (DOR) 24
Algonquin Rd (CHH) 67
Algonquin Rd (QUI) 69
Alhambra Rd (WEL) 81
Alice (REV) 51
Alice Rd (BRA) 85
Alicia Rd (DOR) 24
Alida St & Rd (BRA) 85
Alkyris Rd (WRX) 32
Allard Ct (RXC) 20
Alleghany (RXC) 20
Allen (HP) 36
Allen (CHE) 50
Allen (ROS) 31
Allen (CAM) 40
Allen (BRA) 84
Allen (N) 92
Allen (ARL) 74

Allen (LEX) 73
Allen Ave (WAB) 68
Allen Cir (MIL) 87
Allen Ct (MED) 55
Allen Pl (WNW) 65
Allen Pl (MEL) 76
Allen Rd (BRI) 35
Allen Rd (WH) 31
Allen Rd (WAL) 54
Allen St & Ct (SOM) 43
Allen Ter (NWH) 61
Allendale (JP) 30
Allendale Rd (MED) 55
Allendale Rd (CHH) 67
Allendale Rd (N) 92
Allenwood (WRX) 32
Allerton (BRO) 46
Allerton (QUI) 69
Allerton (ROX) 19
Allerton Rd (MIL) 87
Allerton Rd
  1-100 (NCE) 59
  101-OUT (NWH) 61
Alleyne (WRX) 32
Alleyne St & Ter (QUI) 69
Allison St & Park (NEW) 58
Allstate Rd (DOR) 25
Allston (DOR) 24
Allston (NWV) 60
Allston (CHA) 29
Allston (REV) 51
Allston
  1-197 (ALL) 34
  198-OUT (BRO) 46
Allston St & Ct (CAM) 39
Allston St, Ct & Ter (MED) 55
Alma Ave (WAV) 79
Almont (WIN) 52
Almont (MAT) 26
Almont St & Ct (MED) 55
Almont St & Ct (MAL) 48
Almquist (QUI) 69
Alna Pl (EB) 28
Alpha Rd (DOR) 24
Alpheus Rd (ROS) 31
Alpine (MAL) 48
Alpine (CAM) 38
Alpine (WS) 44
Alpine (MAT) 26
Alpine (LEX) 73
Alpine Ave & Rd (EV) 49
Alpine Dr (BRA) 84
Alpine Rd (EWY) 89
Alpine St, Pl & Ter (ROX) 19
Alpine St & Ter (ARL) 74
Alpine Ter (N) 92
Alrick Rd (QUI) 69
Alroy Rd (SWY) 90
Alstead (NQ) 71
Alston (SOM) 43
Alta Rd (EWY) 89
Alta Crest Rd (WRX) 32
Altair Ave (BRA) 85
Altair Rd (WRX) 32
Altamont Ave (MEL) 76
Altamount Rd (QUI) 69
Althea (DOR) 22
Alther (ROX) 19
Alton (ARL) 74
Alton Ct (RXC) 20
Alton St & Pl (BRO) 46
Alton Rd (QUI) 69
Alton Ter (EWY) 89

Boston (Con.)   021

Altura Rd (NWY) 91
Alvah Kittredge Park (ROX)........ 19
Alvan Ter (DOR) 25
Alvarado Ave (HP).......................... 36
Alves Ave (BRA)............................. 84
Alveston St & Ter (JP)................... 30
Alvin Ave
  1-25 (NQ) (ODD) 71
  2-108 (NQ) (EVEN).................... 71
  27-OUT (MIL) (ODD) 86
  110-OUT (MIL) (EVEN)............. 86
Alward Rd (ROS) 31
Alwington Rd (CHH)...................... 67
Alwyn St, Ct & Ter (HP).............. 36
Amaranth Ave (MED)..................... 55
Amasa (REV).................................. 51
Amboy (ALL) 34
Ambrose (REV) 51
Ambrose (ROX) 19
Amelia (BEL) 78
Amelia Ave (WIN)......................... 52
Amelia Pl (REV)............................ 51
Amelia Rd (NH)............................. 94
American Legion Hwy (REV).... 51
American Legion Hwy
  1-250 (DOR)............................... 24
  251-OUT (ROS)......................... 31
Ames (MED) 55
Ames (SOM) 45
Ames (CAM) 42
Ames (QUI) 69
Ames (DOR) 24
Ames Ave (LEX)............................ 73
Amesbury (WRX) 32
Amesbury
  1-77 (NQ) 71
  78-OUT (WOL) 70
Amherst (CAM) 42
Amherst (ROS) 31
Amherst (LEX) 73
Amherst (ARL) 74
Amherst Ave (WAL)...................... 54
Amherst Rd (WAB) 68
Amherst Rd (BEL) 78
Amherst Rd (WAT) 72
Amherst Rd (WEL)........................ 81
Amherst Rd (BRA)........................ 85
Amor Rd (MIL) 86
Amory (BRO)................................. 46
Amory
  1-169 (ROX)............................. 19
  170-OUT (JP)............................. 30
Amory Ave & Ter (ROX)............. 19
Amory Rd (WAL) 54
Amory St & Pl (CAM) 39
Amos Ter (EV).............................. 49
Amsden (ARL) 74
Amsterdam Ave (NQ).................... 71
Amy Cir (WAB)............................. 68
Anawan Ave & Ter (WRX) 32
Andem Pl (BRO)............................ 46
Anderson Rd (WOL)...................... 70
Anderson Rd (BRA)....................... 85
Anderson St & Pl 14
Andover Rd (ROS) 31
Andrea Rd (WAL) 54
Andrew (WIN)................................ 52
Andrew (EV).................................. 49
Andrew (CAM) 39
Andrew (WAT) 72
Andrew (ARL)................................ 74

Andrew (NWH) 61
Andrew Sq (SB) 27
Andrew St & Ct (MAL) 48
Andrews (MED) 55
Andrews 18
Andrews Rd (WOL) 70
Andrews Rd (MIL)......................... 86
Andrews Rd (SWY) 90
Andria Rd (MAT).......................... 26
Angela Rd (BRA) 85
Angell (DOR)................................. 24
Angier Cir (AUB).......................... 66
Angier Rd (LEX)........................... 73
Angus (NQ).................................... 71
Anita Cir (WAB) 68
Anita Ter (ROX) 19
Ann (LEX) 73
Ann Rd (REV) 51
Anna Rd (NWY) 91
Annabel (DOR).............................. 25
Annafran (ROS) 31
Annapolis (DOR) 25
Annapolis Rd (MIL) 86
Annapolis Rd (WNW).................... 65
Annavoy (EB)................................. 28
Annawan Rd (WAB)....................... 68
Annese Rd (CHE)........................... 50
Annis Rd (BEL).............................. 78
Annunciation Rd (RXC)................ 20
Ansel Rd (DOR)............................ 24
Anselm Ter (BRI) 35
Anson (JP)...................................... 30
Ansonia Rd (WRX)........................ 32
Anthony Cir & Rd (NWY)............ 60
Anthony Pl 13
Anthony Rd (LEX)......................... 73
Anthony Rd (EWY)........................ 89
Antonellis Cir (NCE)..................... 59
Antrim (EB) 28
Antrim (CAM)................................ 39
Antwerp (BRI)................................ 35
Antwerp (MIL)............................... 86
Apache Trl (MAT) 55
Apache Trl (ARL) 74
Apex (QUI) 69
Appian Dr (WEL).......................... 81
Appian Pl (EB) 28
Appian Way (ALL) 34
Appian Way (CAM) 38
Apple Ln & Rd (MIL) 86
Apple Hill Rd (MEL) 76
Apple Tree Ln (LEX) 73
Apple Tree Ln (WY) 88
Appleby Rd (WEL)........................ 76
Applecrest Rd (WES).................... 93
Applegarth (NCE) 59
Appleton (MEL) 76
Appleton (NQ)............................... 71
Appleton (WAL) 54
Appleton (WS)............................... 44
Appleton 16
Appleton Cir (NCE)....................... 59
Appleton Ct (MAL) 48
Appleton Rd (N)............................ 92
Appleton St, Ct & Ter (EV)......... 49
Appleton St & Pl (ARL)............... 74
Appleton St, Rd & Ter (CAM)..... 38
Appleton St & Ter (WAT)............ 72
April Ln (WES).............................. 93
Apthorp (WOL).............................. 70
Apthorp Rd (MEL)......................... 76
Aquavia Rd (MED)........................ 55
Aramon (EB).................................. 28

Arapahoe Rd (WNW)..................... 65
ArbeHa Rd (DOR).......................... 24
Arbor Ln (WAL) 54
Arbor Rd (WNW) 65
Arborcrest Ter (MAT) 26
Arboretum Rd (ROS)..................... 31
Arborfield Rd (ROS)...................... 31
Arborough Rd (ROS)...................... 31
Arborview Rd (JP)......................... 30
Arborway Dr (BRA)....................... 84
Arborway St, Ct & Ter (JP)......... 30
Arbroth (DOR)............................... 22
Arbutus (DOR)............................... 24
Arbutus Ave (BRA)........................ 85
Arcadia (ROX)............................... 19
Arcadia (CAM) 40
Arcadia (MAL).............................. 48
Arcadia (WRX).............................. 32
Arcadia (REV)............................... 51
Arcadia Ave & Pl (WAL)............. 54
Arcadia (WY)................................. 88
Arcadia St, Park & Ter
  (DOR).. 22
Arch 10
Arch (N)... 92
Arch (MAL)................................... 48
Archdale Rd (ROS)........................ 31
Archer Ave (REV).......................... 51
Archer Ter (ROX) 19
Arcola (JP)..................................... 30
Arcola (MAL)................................ 48
Arcola (LEX).................................. 73
Ardale (ROS)................................. 31
Ardee (EB)..................................... 28
Ardell (NQ).................................... 71
Arden (ALL) 34
Arden (N)....................................... 92
Arden Rd (MED) 55
Arden Rd (WAT)............................ 72
Arden Rd (NWV)........................... 60
Arden Rd (WEL)............................ 81
Ardent (ROS) 31
Ardmore (BRA).............................. 84
Ardmore Rd (NH) 94
Ardmore Rd (WRX)....................... 32
Ardmore Rd & Ter (WNW).......... 65
Argonne (QUI)............................... 69
Argus Pl (BRI) 35
Argyle (EV).................................... 49
Argyle (REV).................................. 51
Argyle (WIN)................................. 52
Argyle (MEL)................................. 76
Argyle Ct (EWY)........................... 89
Argyle Rd (BRA) 84
Argyle Rd (WH)............................. 81
Argyle Rd (ARL)........................... 74
Argyle St & Ter (DOR)................ 24
Arion (DOR)................................... 25
Arizona Ter (ARL) 74
Arklow (JP).................................... 30
Arlene Ave (STO).......................... 80
Arlene Ter (ARL).......................... 74
Arlington (NEW)............................ 58
Arlington (WAT) 72
Arlington (CHE)............................ 50
Arlington (EV).............................. 49
Arlington (HP)............................... 36
Arlington (MED)........................... 55
Arlington (CAM)........................... 40
Arlington (SOM)........................... 45
Arlington (WY).............................. 88
Arlington
  1-13 (NQ)................................... 71

Boston (Con.)	**021**
14-OUT (WOL)	70
Arlington Ave (BRA)	85
Arlington Ave (REV)	51
Arlington Ave (CHA)	29
Arlington Ave	09
Arlington Rd (WAL)	54
Arlington Rd (NH)	94
Arlington Rd (WH)	81
Arlington Rd (CHH)	67
Arlington St & Ct (BRI)	35
Arlington St & Rd (MEL)	76
Arlington St & Sq	16
Arlington St & Ter (MAL)	48
Arlmont (ARL)	74
Arlo Rd (NUF)	64
Arlow Rd (NWH)	61
Armandine (DOR)	24
Armington (ALL)	34
Armory (CHA)	29
Armory (WNW)	65
Armory (QUI)	69
Armstrong (JP)	30
Armstrong Cir (BRA)	85
Arnold (NH)	94
Arnold (REV)	51
Arnold (QUI)	69
Arnold (ARL)	74
Arnold	18
Arnold Ave & Ct (SOM)	43
Arnold Cir (CAM)	39
Arnold Rd (STO)	80
Arnold Rd (WH)	81
Arnold Rd (NQ)	71
Arnold Rd (NCE)	59
Arnold Rd (NWY)	91
Arnold St & Ln (BRA)	84
Arrow (CAM)	38
Arrow (CHA)	29
Arrowhead Ln (ARL)	74
Arrowhead Rd (WES)	93
Arsenal (WAT)	72
Arsenal Sq (CAM)	38
Arthur (NWY)	91
Arthur (BRA)	84
Arthur Ave (EV)	49
Arthur Park (CAM)	39
Arthur Rd (ARL)	74
Arthur Rd (BEL)	78
Arthur St & Ave (QUI)	69
Arthur Ter (WAT)	72
Artwill (MIL)	86
Arundel	02215
Arundel Ter (NEW)	58
Arvale Rd (DOR)	21
Asbury (LEX)	73
Ascenta Ter (WNW)	65
Accot (BRI)	35
Ash (CAM)	38
Ash (CHE)	50
Ash (WAL)	54
Ash (MED)	55
Ash (AUB)	66
Ash (LEX)	73
Ash (NQ)	71
Ash (MEL)	76
Ash (BEL)	78
Ash (STO)	80
Ash	11
Ash (BRA)	84
Ash (WES)	93

Ash Ave (SOM)	45
Ash St Pl (CAM)	38
Ashburton Pl (CAM)	39
Ashburton Pl	08
Ashburton Rd (MEL)	76
Ashcroft (JP)	30
Ashcroft Rd (MED)	55
Ashcroft Rd (MEL)	76
Ashcroft Rd (NWH)	61
Asheville Rd (CHH)	67
Asheville Rd (HP)	36
Ashfield (ROS)	31
Ashford Rd (NCE)	59
Ashford St, Ct & Ter (ALL)	34
Ashland (WS)	44
Ashland (EV)	49
Ashland (WAT)	72
Ashland (QUI)	69
Ashland (ARL)	74
Ashland (DOR)	22
Ashland Ave (WRX)	32
Ashland St & Pl (MAL)	48
Ashland St & Pl (MED)	55
Ashland St & Pl (MEL)	76
Ashley (JP)	30
Ashley St & Ave (EB)	28
Ashmont (EWY)	89
Ashmont	
1-429 (DOR)	24
430-OUT (DOR)	22
Ashmont Ave	
1-12 (NEW)	58
13-OUT (NWV)	60
Ashmont Ct (DOR)	22
Ashmont Park (DOR)	24
Ashmont Rd (WAB)	68
Ashmont Rd (WH)	81
Ashmont St & Park (MEL)	76
Ashton (DOR)	24
Ashton Ave & Park (NCE)	59
Ashton Pl (CAM)	38
Ashton St & Pl (EV)	49
Ashville Rd (NLF)	62
Ashwood Ter (ROS)	31
Ashworth Ave (BRA)	85
Ashworth Park (ROX)	19
Ashworth Rd (NQ)	71
Aspen (ROX)	19
Aspen Ave (AUB)	66
Aspinwall Ave (NWY)	91
Aspinwall Ave (BRO)	46
Aspinwall Rd (BRA)	85
Aspinwall Rd (DOR)	24
Assabet Rd (QUI)	69
Assunta Rd (REV)	51
Aster Cir (WY)	88
Asti Ave (REV)	51
Asticou Rd (JP)	30
Aston Rd (CHH)	67
Astoria (MAT)	26
Athelstane Rd (NCE)	59
Athelwold (DOR)	24
Athenaeum (CAM)	42
Athens (SB)	27
Athens (NWY)	91
Athens St & Ter (CAM)	38
Atherstone (DOR)	24
Atherton (SOM)	43
Atherton (MIL)	86
Atherton (BRA)	84
Atherton (QUI)	69
Atherton	
1-74 (ROX)	19

75-OUT (JP)	30
Atherton Ave (ROS)	31
Atherton Pl (NLF)	62
Atherton Pl (ROX)	19
Atherton Rd (BRO)	46
Athletic Field Rd (WAL)	54
Athol (ALL)	34
Atkins (BRI)	35
Atkinson	18
Atkinson Cir (WIN)	52
Atlanta (SWY)	90
Atlantic (WIN)	52
Atlantic (SB)	27
Atlantic (NQ)	71
Atlantic Ave (REV)	51
Atlantic Ave (MAL)	48
Atlantic Ave	
1-627 (ODD)	10
2-340 (EVEN)	10
342-650 (EVEN)	02210
629-631 (ODD)	02210
633-OUT (ODD)	11
652-OUT (EVEN)	11
Atlantic Rd (ARL)	74
Atlantis (WRX)	32
Atlas Rd (BRA)	84
Atwill Rd (WRX)	32
Atwood (REV)	51
Atwood (WEL)	81
Atwood Ave (STO)	80
Atwood Ave (NWV)	60
Atwood Sq (JP)	30
Aubrey Ter (MAL)	48
Auburn (CHE)	50
Auburn (EV)	49
Auburn (CAM)	39
Auburn (MED)	55
Auburn (MEL)	76
Auburn (RXC)	20
Auburn	
1-57 (WNW)	65
58-OUT (AUB)	66
Auburn Ave (SOM)	45
Auburn Pl (WAT)	72
Auburn Rd (WH)	81
Auburn St & Ct (MAL)	48
Auburn St, Ct & Pl (BRO)	46
Auburn St, Pl, Sq & Ter	
(CHA)	29
Auburn St & Ter (WAL)	54
Auburn Ter (AUB)	66
Auburndale Ave	
1-169 (WNW)	65
170-OUT (AUB)	66
Aucella Ct (REV)	51
Auckland (DOR)	25
Audrey (QUI)	69
Audrey Ave (N)	92
Audrey Rd (BEL)	78
Audubon Ave (BRA)	84
Audubon Cir	02215
Audubon Dr (CHH)	67
Audubon Rd (WEL)	81
Audubon Rd (LEX)	73
Audubon Rd (MIL)	87
Augusta (REV)	51
Augusta Rd (MIL)	86
Augustus (REV)	51
Augustus Ave (ROS)	31
Augustus Rd (WAL)	54
Augustus Rd (LEX)	73
Auriga (DOR)	22
Austin (CHA)	29

Boston (Con.) 021

Austin (SOM) 45
Austin (MAL) 48
Austin (HP) 36
Austin (MIL) 87
Austin
 1-228 (NWV) 60
 229-OUT (WNW) 65
Austin Rd (WY) 88
Austin Rd (MED) 55
Austin St & Park (CAM) 39
Autumn (WRX) 32
Autumn (MAL) 48
Autumn (EV) 49
Autumn (SOM) 45
Autumn 02215
Autumn (BRA) 84
Autumn Ln (WAL) 54
Autumn Rd (WES) 93
Avalon (REV) 51
Avalon Ave (QUI) 69
Avalon Rd (WAB) 68
Avalon Rd (MEL) 76
Avalon Rd (MAL) 48
Avalon Rd (WRX) 32
Avalon Rd (N) 92
Avalon Rd (MIL) 87
Avenue Louis Pasteur 15
Averton (ROS) 31
Avery
 1-23 11
 24-24 12
 25-OUT 11
Avery Path (NCE) 59
Avery Pl (CHA) 29
Avery Pl 11
Avery St & Sq (NH) 94
Avila Rd (HP) 36
Avola (ARL) 74
Avon (MEL) 76
Avon (LEX) 73
Avon (STO) 80
Avon (JP) 30
Avon (EV) 49
Avon (MAL) 48
Avon (REV) 51
Avon (BRO) 46
Avon (SOM) 43
Avon (CAM) 38
Avon 11
Avon Cir (NH) 94
Avon Pl (BRA) 84
Avon Pl (CAM) 40
Avon Pl (SOM) 45
Avon Pl (CHA) 29
Avon Pl (ARL) 74
Avon Pl (NEW) 58
Avon Rd (WEL) 81
Avon Way (WAT) 72
Avon Way (QUI) 69
Avon Hill (CAM) 40
Avondale (DOR) 24
Avondale Rd (NCE) 59
Avonia Ave (WY) 88
Ayer Rd (WEL) 81
Ayles Rd (HP) 36
Ayr Rd (BRO) 46
Azalea Rd (WAL) 54
Azel Rd (BRA) 85
B (NH) 94
B (HP) 36
B (REV) 51

B (EV) 49
B (WAV) 79
B
 1-250 (SB) 27
 251-OUT 02210
Babbitt 02215
Babcock (MIL) 86
Babcock (QUI) 69
Babcock
 1-240 (BRO) 46
 241-OUT 02215
Babcock Ave (NWY) 91
Babson (MAT) 26
Babson Park Ave (BP) 57
Back River Rd (NWY) 91
Bacon (NEW) 58
Bacon (WH) 81
Bacon (WAT) 72
Bacon (ARL) 74
Bacon (LEX) 73
Bacon (WAL) 54
Bacon Ct (HP) 36
Bacon Pl (NUF) 64
Bacon Rd (NWV) 60
Bacon Rd (BEL) 78
Bacon Rd (NWY) 91
Badger Cir (MIL) 86
Badger Pl (CHA) 29
Badger Rd (HP) 36
Badger Rd (MED) 55
Bagnal (ALL) 34
Bailey (MED) 55
Bailey (EV) 49
Bailey (WS) 44
Bailey (QUI) 69
Bailey (DOR) 24
Bailey Ave (MIL) 86
Bailey Ave & Rd (WAT) 72
Bailey Pl (NWV) 60
Bailey Rd (ARL) 74
Bailey Rd (SOM) 45
Bainbridge (MAL) 48
Bainbridge (CHA) 29
Bainbridge (ROX) 19
Baincroft Rd (MAL) 48
Baird (DOR) 24
Baker (MAL) 48
Baker (BEL) 78
Baker Ave (QUI) 69
Baker Ave (LEX) 73
Baker Ave (BRA) 84
Baker Ave (WY) 88
Baker Ave & Ct (DOR) 25
Baker Cir (CHH) 67
Baker Pl (NLF) 62
Baker Rd (ARL) 74
Baker Rd (EV) 49
Baker St & Pl (WRX) 32
Bakers Aly 13
Bakers Hill Rd (WES) 93
Bakersfield (DOR) 25
Balcarres Rd (WNW) 65
Bald Eagle Rd (SWY) 90
Bald Knob Rd (HP) 36
Baldpate Hill Rd (NCE) 59
Baldwin (NEW) 58
Baldwin (MAL) 48
Baldwin (CHA) 29
Baldwin (REV) 51
Baldwin 02210
Baldwin Ave (MEL) 76
Baldwin Ave, Pl & Ter (EV) 49
Baldwin Cir (WES) 93

Baldwin Pl (CAM) 38
Baldwin Pl 13
Baldwin Rd (WAL) 54
Baldwin St Ct (CAM) 38
Balfour (DOR) 25
Balfour (LEX) 73
Balina Pl (DOR) 24
Ball (ROX) 19
Ball Sq (WS) 44
Ballard (NCE) 59
Ballard Pl (CAM) 39
Ballard St & Way (JP) 30
Ballard Ter (LEX) 73
Ballin Pl (JP) 30
Ballou
 1-86 (QUI) 69
 87-OUT (MIL) 86
Ballou Ave (DOR) 24
Balmoral Park (SB) 27
Balsam (DOR) 24
Banbury Ave (WAL) 54
Bancroft (WAL) 54
Bancroft (CAM) 39
Bancroft (ROX) 19
Bancroft (N) 92
Bancroft (WAT) 72
Bancroft Pl (STO) 80
Bancroft Pl (WH) 81
Bancroft Rd (MEL) 76
Banfield Ave (MAT) 26
Bangor Rd (WRX) 32
Banks (WRX) 32
Banks (CAM) 38
Banks (WAL) 54
Banks (WIN) 52
Banks (WS) 44
Banks (REV) 51
Banks (WAV) 79
Banks (NWH) 61
Banks Ave (LEX) 73
Banks Pl (MEL) 76
Banton (DOR) 24
Bantry Way (SB) 27
Baptist Walk (WAT) 72
Barbara (STO) 80
Barbara (JP) 30
Barbara Ln (MED) 55
Barbara Ln (SWY) 90
Barbara Ln (MIL) 86
Barbara Rd (N) 92
Barbara Rd (WAL) 54
Barbara Rd (BEL) 78
Barbara Rd (WNW) 65
Barbara Ter (WAT) 72
Barberry Rd (LEX) 73
Barbour Ter (QUI) 69
Barclay Rd (WRX) 32
Bard Ave (ROX) 19
Bardwell (JP) 30
Barham Ave
 1-133 (NQ) 71
 134-OUT (WOL) 70
Barker (BRI) 35
Barker Rd (MAL) 48
Barlow (JP) 30
Barna Rd (DOR) 24
Barnard Ave (WAT) 72
Barnard Rd (BEL) 78
Barnard Rd (MED) 55
Barnes (WAL) 54
Barnes Ave (MAL) 48
Barnes Ave (EB) 28
Barnes Ave (SWY) 90

Boston (Con.)　　　　　　　　021

Barnes Pl (LEX)	73
Barnes Rd (NEW)	58
Barnstable Rd (WNW)	65
Barnstable Rd (WH)	81
Barrett (N)	92
Barrett (MED)	55
Barrett (REV)	51
Barrett Ave (STO)	80
Barrett Ave (SB)	27
Barrett Rd (LEX)	73
Barrett St & Ln (MAL)	48
Barrieau Ct (NWV)	60
Barrington Rd (DOR)	24
Barrows (ALL)	34
Barry (HP)	36
Barry (QUI)	69
Barry St & Park (DOR)	24
Barrymeade Dr (LEX)	73
Barstow (ALL)	34
Barstow (MAL)	48
Bartlett (MAL)	48
Bartlett (EV)	49
Bartlett (CHA)	29
Bartlett (SOM)	43
Bartlett (BRO)	46
Bartlett (QUI)	69
Bartlett (MEL)	76
Baldwin Pl (CAM)	38
Baldwin Pl	13
Baldwin Rd (WAL)	54
Baldwin St Ct (CAM)	38
Balfour (DOR)	25
Balfour (LEX)	73
Balina Pl (DOR)	24
Ball (ROX)	19
Ball Sq (WS)	44
Ballard (NCE)	59
Ballard (CAM)	39
Ballard Pl (CAM)	39
Ballard St & Way (JP)	30
Ballard Ter (LEX)	73
Ballin Pl (JP)	30
Ballou	
1-86 (QUI)	69
87-OUT (MIL)	86
Ballou Ave (DOR)	24
Balmoral Park (SB)	27
Balsam (DOR)	24
Banbury Ave (WAL)	54
Bancroft (WAL)	54
Bancroft (CAM)	39
Bancroft (ROX)	19
Bancroft (N)	92
Bancroft (WAT)	72
Bancroft Pl (STO)	80
Bancroft Rd (WH)	81
Bancroft Rd (MEL)	76
Banfield Ave (MAT)	26
Bangor Rd (WRX)	32
Banks (WRX)	32
Banks (CAM)	38
Banks (WAL)	54
Banks (WIN)	52
Banks (WS)	44
Banks (REV)	51
Banks (WAV)	79
Banks (NWH)	61
Banks Ave (LEX)	73
Banks Pl (MEL)	76
Banton (DOR)	24
Bantry Way (SB)	27
Baptist Walk (WAT)	72

Bates Rd E (WAT)	72
Bateswell Rd (DOR)	24
Battery	09
Batterymarch	
1-21 (ODD)	09
2-22 (EVEN)	09
23-33 (ODD)	10
24-OUT (EVEN)	10
35-41 (ODD)	09
43-OUT	10
Battle Green Rd (LEX)	73
Baxter (MEL)	76
Baxter (SB)	27
Baxter Pl & Rd (BRO)	46
Baxter St, Ave & Ln (QUI)	69
Baxter St & Ter (MED)	55
Bay (CAM)	39
Bay (WAT)	72
Bay (NQ)	71
Bay (DOR)	25
Bay	16
Bay Rd (WH)	81
Bay Rd (REV)	51
Bay State Ave (WS)	44
Bay State Pl (SB)	27
Bay State Rd (CAM)	38
Bay State Rd (WH)	81
Bay State Rd (NQ)	71
Bay State Rd (BEL)	78
Bay State Rd (MEL)	76
Bay State Rd (ARL)	74
Bay State Rd	02215
Bay State Rd (WES)	93
Bay View (REV)	51
Bay View Ave (WIN)	52
Bay View Pl (SB)	27
Bay View Rd (WH)	81
Bay View St & Ave (QUI)	69
Bayard (ALL)	34
Bayberry Ln (MIL)	86
Bayberry Ln (BRA)	84
Bayberry Rd (NQ)	71
Bayfield Rd N & S (NQ)	71
Baylee Rd (NWY)	91
Bayley Ter (SWY)	90
Bayou (WIN)	52
Bayrd St & Ter (MAL)	48
Bayside (DOR)	25
Bayside Ave (NWY)	91
Bayside Rd (NQ)	71
Bayswater (EB)	28
Bayswater Rd (QUI)	69
Bayview (NWY)	91
Beach (WOL)	70
Beach (NWV)	60
Beach	11
Beach (DOR)	22
Beach (MAL)	48
Beach (CHA)	29
Beach Ave (EWY)	89
Beach Rd (NWY)	91
Beach Rd (WIN)	52
Beach Rd (WH)	81
Beach St, Rd & Ter (REV)	51
Beacham (CHA)	29
Beacham (EV)	49
Beacham (CHE)	50
Beachland Ave (REV)	51
Beachview Ave, Pl & Ter (MAL)	48
Beachview Rd (EB)	28
Beacon (MAL)	48
Beacon (EV)	49

Beacon (WIN)	52
Beacon (STO)	80
Beacon (ARL)	74
Beacon	
1-99	08
1-145 (HP)	36
1-533 (CHH) (ODD)	67
2-548 (CHH) (EVEN)	67
100-400	16
146-OUT (MIL)	86
401-489 (ODD)	15
402-504 (EVEN)	15
491-997 (ODD)	02215
506-998 (EVEN)	02215
535-1089 (NCE) (ODD)	59
550-1090 (NCE) (EVEN)	59
999-2435 (BRO)	46
1091-1199 (NWH)	61
1200-OUT (WAB)	68
2436-2436 (CHH)	67
2437-2495 (BRO)	46
2496-2496 (CHH)	67
2497-2499 (BRO)	46
2500-2500 (CHH)	67
2501-OUT (BRO)	46
Beacon Cir (MIL)	86
Beacon Park (WAT)	72
Beacon St & Pl (MEL)	76
Beacon St & Pl (CHE)	50
Beacon St, Pl & Ter (SOM)	43
Beacon St & Way (QUI)	69
Beaconsfield Rd (BRO)	46
Beaconwood Rd (NWH)	61
Beal (WIN)	52
Beal Rd (WAL)	54
Beale (DOR)	24
Beale	
1-411 (WOL)	70
412-OUT (QUI) (EVEN)	69
413-445 (MIL) (ODD)	86
447-OUT (QUI) (ODD)	69
Beals (NWY)	91
Beals (BRO)	46
Beals Rd (BRA)	85
Bean Ct (ROX)	19
Bear Hill Rd (WAL)	54
Bear Hill Rd (STO)	80
Bearse Ave (DOR)	24
Beatrice Cir (BEL)	78
Beatty Cir (MAT)	26
Beaudreau Ct (MAL)	48
Beaufield (DOR)	24
Beaufort Ave (N)	92
Beaufort Rd (JP)	30
Beaumont (DOR)	24
Beaumont (MEL)	76
Beaumont (LEX)	73
Beaumont Ave (NWV)	60
Beaver (WAL)	54
Beaver (HP)	36
Beaver Rd (WES)	93
Beaver St & Pl	08
Beaver Brook Rd (WAL)	54
Beck (EB)	28
Beck Rd (ARL)	74
Beckert Ave (REV)	51
Becket (NQ)	71
Becket (DOR)	24
Becket Rd (BEL)	78
Beckler Ave (SB)	27
Beckwith Cir (SOM)	43
Bedford (WAL)	54
Bedford	11

Boston (Con.) 021

Bedford (LEX) 73
Bedford (QUI) 69
Bedford
　1-1 (SOM) 43
　2-2 (CAM) 41
　3-OUT (SOM) 43
Beebe Rd (QUI) 69
Beech (LEX) 73
Beech (NEW) 58
Beech (WAY) 79
Beech (NH) 94
Beech (WES) 93
Beech (BRA) 84
Beech (MIL) 86
Beech (WAL) 54
Beech (SOM) 43
Beech (CAM) 40
Beech (EV) 49
Beech
　1-74 (WRX) 32
　75-700 (ROS) 31
　701-OUT (HP) 36
Beech Ave (MEL) 76
Beech Rd (BRO) 46
Beech Glen (ROX) 19
Beechcroft (BRI) 35
Beechcroft Rd (NEW) 58
Beecher (JP) 30
Beecher (EWY) 89
Beecher Pl & Ter (NCE) 59
Beecher Rd (BRO) 46
Beechland (ROS) 31
Beechmont St & Ter (HP) 36
Beechwood (QUI) 69
Beechwood (DOR) 21
Beechwood Ave (WAT) 72
Beechwood Rd (WAL) 54
Beechwood Rd (BRA) 84
Beechwood Rd & Ter (WH) 81
Beethoven (ROX) 19
Beethoven Ave (WAB) 68
Belair Rd (WEL) 81
Belcher Cir (MIL) 86
Belcher St & Pl (WIN) 52
Belcher Gov Ln (MIL) 86
Belden (DOR) 25
Belfort (DOR) 25
Belfry Ter (LEX) 73
Belgrade (REV) 51
Belgrade Ave
　1-347 (ROS) (ODD) 31
　2-338 (ROS) (EVEN) 31
　340-OUT (WRX) (EVEN) 32
　349-OUT (WRX) (ODD) 32
Belgrade Ter (WRX) 32
Belgravia Pl 13
Belknap (WS) 44
Belknap Rd (BRA) 85
Belknap St & Pl (ARL) 74
Belknap Ter (WAT) 72
Bell (QUI) 69
Bell (CHE) 50
Bell Ct (CAM) 39
Bell Ct (SB) 27
Bell Rd (WY) 88
Bell Rock
　1-104 (MAL) 48
　105-OUT (EV) 49
Bell View Ave (EV) 49
Bellaire Rd (ROS) 31
Bellamy (BRI) 35

Belle Ave (WRX) 32
Belle Ave (MED) 55
Belle Isle Ave (REV) 51
Belle Isle Ter (WIN) 52
Bellevue (WRX) 32
Bellevue (DOR) 25
Bellevue (NEW) 58
Bellevue Ave (MEL) 76
Bellevue Ave (REV) 51
Bellevue Ave (CAM) 40
Bellevue Ave (BRA) 85
Bellevue Ave & Ter (WIN) 52
Bellevue Dr (N) 92
Bellevue Rd (BRA) 84
Bellevue Rd (BEL) 78
Bellevue Rd (NQ) 71
Bellevue Rd (ARL) 74
Bellevue Rd (WH) 81
Bellevue Rd & Ter (WAT) 72
Bellevue St & Ave (WAL) 54
Bellevue St & Ter (MED) 55
Bellevue Ter (SOM) 44
Bellevue Hill Rd (WRX) 32
Bellflower (LEX) 73
Bellflower (DOR) 25
Bellingham (NWH) 61
Bellingham (CHE) 50
Bellingham Ave (EV) 49
Bellingham Ave (REV) 51
Bellingham Dr & Rd (CHH) 67
Bellingham Pl 14
Bellington (ARL) 74
Bellington (BEL) 78
Bellis Cir (CAM) 40
Bellows Pl (CHA) 29
Bellvale (MAL) 48
Bellvista Rd (BRO) 46
Belmont (CHA) 29
Belmont (NEW) 58
Belmont (BRA) 84
Belmont (WY) 88
Belmont
　1 68 (NQ) 71
　1-OUT (EV) (ODD) 49
　1-111 (CAM) (ODD) 38
　2-OUT (WAT) (EVEN) 72
　2-OUT (MAL) (EVEN) 48
　69-OUT (WOL) 70
　113-883 (BEL) (ODD) 78
　885-OUT (WAT) (ODD) 72
Belmont Cir (WAV) 40
Belmont Ct (CAM) 39
Belmont Park (EV) 49
Belmont Rd (CHH) 67
Belmont St & Pl (MEL) 76
Belmont St, Pl, Sq & Ter
　(SOM) 43
Belmore Ave (NLF) 62
Belmore Ter (JP) 30
Belnap Rd (HP) 36
Belnel Rd (MAT) 26
Belton (DOR) 24
Belton (ARL) 74
Beltran St & Ter (MAL) 48
Belvidere 15
Belvidere Pl (CAM) 39
Belvoir Rd (DOR) 25
Belvoir Rd (MIL) 87
Bemis (WES) 93
Bemis (MAT) 72
Bemis Ave (WAL) 54
Bemis Rd (WH) 81
Bemis St & Rd (NWV) 60

Bemuth Rd (NWH) 61
Bencliffe Cir (AUB) 66
Benedict (CHA) 29
Benedict St & Ave (SOM) 45
Benefit (WAL) 54
Bengal Rd (SWY) 90
Benham (MED) 55
Benjamin Rd (ARL) 74
Benjamin Rd (BEL) 78
Benjamin Rd (LEX) 73
Benmore (MED) 55
Benner (EB) 28
Benner Ave (MAL) 48
Bennet Pl (EB) 28
Bennet St & Pl 11
Bennett (EV) 49
Bennett (WAL) 54
Bennett (CAM) 38
Bennett (BRI) 35
Bennett (AUB) 66
Bennett (WAT) 72
Bennett Ave (LEX) 73
Bennett Hwy
　75-75 (MAL) 48
　299-299 (MAL) 48
　300-300 (MAL) 48
Bennett Ln (QUI) 69
Bennett St & Ct (SOM) 43
Bennett St & Hwy (REV) 51
Bennett St & Pl (MED) 55
Bennington (REV) 51
Bennington (QUI) 69
Bennington (NEW) 58
Bennington (NH) 94
Bennington (EB) 28
Bennington Rd (LEX) 73
Benson (BRI) 35
Bent (CAM) 41
Bent Ave (MAL) 48
Bent Ct (SB) 27
Bent Ter (QUI) 69
Bentham Rd (DOR) 22
Bentley (BRI) 35
Benton (RXC) 20
Benton (STO) 80
Benton (WEL) 81
Benton Rd (BEL) 78
Benton Rd (SOM) 43
Benton Rd (MED) 55
Benvenue
　1-59 (WEL) 81
　60-OUT (WH) 81
Berkeley (SWY) 90
Berkeley (SOM) 43
Berkeley (MEL) 76
Berkeley (QUI) 69
Berkeley (WAT) 72
Berkeley (ARL) 74
Berkeley 16
Berkeley Ct (BRO) 46
Berkeley Ct & Rd (WH) 81
Berkeley Pl (AUB) 66
Berkeley Rd (WAL) 54
Berkeley St & Pl (CAM) 38
Berkeley (STO) 80
Berkshire (DOR) 24
Berkshire Rd (WH) 81
Berkshire Rd (NWV) 60
Berkshire Rd (WAL) 54
Berkshire Rd (N) 92
Berkshire St & Pl (CAM) 41
Berlin (WOL) 70
Berlin Ave (MIL) 86

Boston (Con.)   021

Bernard (NWH) 61
Bernard (LEX) 73
Bernard (DOR) 24
Bernard Ave (EV) 49
Bernard Ln (WAB) 68
Bernard Rd (WEL) 81
Bernice (DOR) 22
Berresford Rd (CHH) 67
Berry (QUI) 69
Berry (DOR) 22
Berry (MAL) 48
Bersanie Cir (NQ) 71
Bertrand Rd (AUB) 66
Bertson Ave (WRX) 32
Bertwell Rd (LEX) 73
Berwick (BEL) 78
Berwick (WRX) 32
Berwick (SOM) 45
Berwick (BRA) 84
Berwick Ct (EV) 49
Berwick Rd (MED) 55
Berwick Rd (LEX) 73
Berwick Rd (NCE) 59
Berwick St & Pl (MEL) 76
Beryl (ROS) 31
Bess Rd (N) 92
Bestick Rd (BRA) 84
Bethel Rd (WEL) 81
Bethel Beach St & Ter (QUI) 69
Bethune (BRI) 35
Bettinson Ave & Ct (EV) 49
Betts Rd (BEL) 78
Betty (EV) 49
Beverly (REV) 51
Beverly (MEL) 76
Beverly (QUI) 69
Beverly 14
Beverly Ct (BRA) 84
Beverly Rd (WH) 81
Beverly Rd (NWH) 61
Beverly Rd (CHH) 67
Beverly Rd (ARL) 74
Bexley Rd (ROS) 31
Biathrow (MAL) 48
Bickford (JP) 30
Bickford Ave (REV) 51
Bickford Ave (RXC) 20
Bickford Rd (MAL) 48
Bickford Rd (BRA) 84
Bicknell (DOR) 21
Bicknell (QUI) 69
Bicknell Rd & Sq (NWY) 91
Big Blue Dr (MIL) 86
Bigelow (QUI) 69
Bigelow (SOM) 43
Bigelow (CAM) 39
Bigelow Ave & Ter (WAT) 72
Bigelow Rd (WNW) 65
Bigelow Rd (WAL) 54
Bigelow St & Cir (BRI) 35
Billerica 14
Billingham (WS) 44
Billings (WRX) 32
Billings (NQ) 71
Billings Ave (MED) 55
Billings Ln (JP) 30
Billings Park (NEW) 58
Billings Rd
   1-199 (NQ) (ODD) 71
   2-208 (NQ) (EVEN) 71
   201-OUT (WOL) (ODD) 70

210-OUT (WOL) (EVEN) 70
Billows (WIN) 52
Billows Ave (REV) 51
Bills Ct 15
Bilodeau Rd (DOR) 21
Biltmore (JP) 30
Biltmore (MAL) 48
Binford 02210
Binnacle Ln (QUI) 69
Binney 15
Binney
   1-340 (CAM) 42
   341-OUT (CAM) 41
Birch (NH) 94
Birch (BRA) 85
Birch (MIL) 86
Birch (NQ) 71
Birch (BEL) 78
Birch (LEX) 73
Birch (EV) 49
Birch (ROS) 31
Birch (CAM) 38
Birch Ln (MAL) 48
Birch Rd (WIN) 52
Birch Rd (WAL) 54
Birch Rd (WRX) 32
Birch Rd (WAT) 72
Birch Rd (WEL) 81
Birch Rd (STO) 80
Birch Rd (NWY) 91
Birch Hill Ln (LEX) 73
Birch Hill Rd (MED) 76
Birch Hill Rd (BEL) 78
Birch Hill Rd (NWV) 60
Birchbrow Ave (NWY) 91
Birchcliff Rd (EWY) 89
Birchcroft Rd (BRA) 84
Birchcroft Rd (MAT) 26
Birchland Ave & Ter (WRX) 32
Birchwood (WRX) 32
Birchwood Rd (N) 92
Bird (N) 92
Bird (CAM) 38
Bird (DOR) 25
Bird (QUI) 69
Bird Pl (WRX) 32
Bird Hill Ln & Rd (LEX) 73
Birds Hill Ave (N) 92
Birds Hill Rd (WH) 81
Birmingham Pky (BRI) 35
Biscayne Ave (WY) 88
Bishop (JP) 30
Bishop Rd (WAL) 54
Bishop Rd (MAL) 48
Bishop Rd (WOL) 70
Bishops Pl (SOM) 45
Bishopsgate Rd (NCE) 59
Bismarck (JP) 30
Bismarck (MAT) 26
Bispham (DOR) 22
Bither Ave (WAL) 54
Bittern Rd (QUI) 69
Bittersweet Ln (WES) 93
Bixby (REV) 51
Blaban Pl (CHA) 29
Black Hawk Rd (SWY) 90
Black Oak Rd (WES) 93
Black Rock Rd (MEL) 76
Blackfan 15
Blackinton (EB) 28
Blackman Ter (N) 92
Blacksmith Dr (N) 92
Blackstone (CAM) 39

Blackstone
   1-117 (ODD) 09
   2-122 (EVEN) 09
   119-OUT (ODD) 08
   124-OUT (EVEN) 08
Blackstone Rd (NWY) 91
Blackstone Ter (NEW) 58
Blackwell (NQ) 71
Blackwell (DOR) 22
Blackwood 15
Blagden 16
Blaine (MAL) 48
Blaine (ALL) 34
Blair Pl (CAM) 40
Blair Rd (DOR) 25
Blaisdell Rd (MED) 55
Blake (MED) 55
Blake (CAM) 40
Blake (REV) 51
Blake (MAT) 26
Blake (WOL) 70
Blake (NWV) 60
Blake (BEL) 78
Blake (N) 92
Blake Rd (WES) 93
Blake Rd (WY) 88
Blake Rd (BRA) 84
Blake Rd (LEX) 73
Blake Rd (BRO) 46
Blake Ter (N) 49
Blakely Ave (SOM) 45
Blakely Rd (MED) 55
Blakeslee (CAM) 38
Blakeville (DOR) 21
Blanchard (ROX) 19
Blanchard Ave (EV) 49
Blanchard Ave (REV) 51
Blanchard Blvd (BRA) 84
Blanchard Rd (SWY) 90
Blanchard Rd (QUI) 69
Blanchard Rd
   1-OUT (CAM) (ODD) 38
   2-58 (CAM) (EVEN) 38
   60-OUT (BEL) (EVEN) 78
Blanche (CAM) 39
Blanche (DOR) 22
Blanche Rd (WY) 88
Blandford 02215
Blaney (REV) 51
Blantyre Rd (MAL) 48
Blanvon Rd (JP) 30
Bleachery Ct (SOM) 43
Bleakney Rd (NWY) 91
Blenford Rd (BRI) 35
Blinn Rd (LEX) 73
Blithedale (NWV) 60
Block (STO) 80
Blodgett (MAL) 48
Blodgett Rd (LEX) 73
Blomerth (MAL) 48
Bloomfield (LEX) 73
Bloomfield (NQ) 71
Bloomfield (DOR) 24
Bloomingdale (CHE) 50
Bloomington (DOR) 22
Blossom (CHE) 50
Blossom (WAL) 54
Blossom (LEX) 73
Blossom (ARL) 74
Blossom Ln (WES) 93
Blossom Ln (WY) 88
Blossom Rd (BRA) 34
Blossom St & Ct 14

Boston (Con.)   021

Blossom Crest Rd (LEX)	73
Blue Berry Hill Rd (WES)	93
Blue Bird Rd (WH)	81
Blue Hill Ave (MAL)	48
Blue Hill Ave	
1-255 (MIL) (ODD)	87
1-279 (ROX) (ODD)	19
2-292 (ROX) (EVEN)	19
2-294 (MIL) (EVEN)	87
257-OUT (MIL) (ODD)	86
281-759 (DOR) (ODD)	21
294-760 (DOR) (EVEN)	21
296-OUT (MIL) (EVEN)	86
761-1177 (DOR)	24
1178-OUT (MAT)	26
Blue Hill Ter St (MIL)	87
Blue Hill River Rd (MIL)	86
Blue Hills Pky	
1-361 (MIL) (ODD)	87
2-406 (MIL) (EVEN)	87
363-OUT (MtL) (ODD)	86
408-OUT (MIL) (EVEN)	86
Blue Ledge Dr & Ter (ROS)	31
Blue View Cir & Rd (WRX)	32
Blueberry (WY)	88
Blueberry Dr (BRA)	84
Blueberry Ln (LEX)	73
Bluefield Ter (SWY)	90
Bluefield Ter (MAT)	26
Bluff Rd (NWY)	91
Board Aly	13
Boardman (EB)	28
Boardman Ave (MEL)	76
Boardman St & Pl (CAM)	39
Boates Ct	10
Boblink Rd (WH)	81
Bobolink (WRX)	32
Bobsled Dr (NH)	94
Bodwell (DOR)	25
Bogandale Rd (WRX)	32
Bogle (WES)	93
Boland (WAL)	54
Bolster (JP)	30
Bolster (EV)	49
Bolton (WAL)	54
Bolton (SOM)	43
Bolton (CAM)	40
Bolton (SB)	27
Bolton Pl (CHA)	29
Bolton Rd (NWV)	60
Bonad Rd (STO)	80
Bonad Rd (ARL)	74
Bonad Rd (WNW)	65
Bonad Rd (MIL)	86
Bonad Rd	
1-70 (WRX)	32
71-OUT (CHH)	67
Bonair (WRX)	32
Bonair (SOM)	45
Bonair Ave (LEX)	73
Bonaire Cir (WAB)	68
Bond (SOM)	45
Bond (CAM)	38
Bond (MAL)	48
Bond (N)	92
Bond	18
Bond Rd (LEX)	73
Bonell Ter (ROX)	19
Bonita (WNW)	65
Bonmar Cir (AUB)	66
Bonner Ave (SOM)	43

Bonner Ave (MED)	55
Bonnie Rd (SWY)	90
Bonnieview Rd (BRA)	84
Bonnybrook Rd (WAB)	68
Bontempo Rd (NCE)	59
Bonwood (NWV)	60
Bonwood Rd (N)	92
Booth (NH)	94
Booth (QUI)	69
Border (WNW)	65
Border (NQ)	71
Border (EB)	28
Border Rd (N)	92
Borland (BRO)	46
Boscobel (BRA)	85
Bosson (REV)	51
Boston (SOM)	43
Boston (EV)	49
Boston (MAL)	48
Boston	
1-61 (SB)	27
62-OUT (SB)	25
Boston Ave (WS)	44
Boston Ave	
1-514 (MED)	55
515-515 (WS)	44
516-581 (MED)	55
582-OUT (WS)	44
Boston Pl	08
Boston Post Rd (WES)	93
Boston Post Rd Byp (WES)	93
Boston Rock Rd (WH)	76
Bostonia Ave (BRI)	35
Bosworth	08
Bothfield Rd (NCE)	59
Bothwell Rd (BRI)	35
Botolph (MEL)	76
Botolph (NQ)	71
Botsford Rd (CHH)	67
Boulder (MAL)	48
Boulder Rd (NCE)	59
Boulder Rd (LEX)	73
Boulder Rd (WH)	81
Boulder Brook Rd (WH)	81
Boulevard Rd (WH)	81
Boulevard Rd (ARL)	74
Boulevard Ter (ALL)	34
Bound Brook Rd (NWH)	61
Boundary Rd (ARL)	74
Boundary Rd (MAL)	48
Bourne (AUB)	66
Bourne	
1-143 (JP) (ODD)	30
2-122 (JP) (EVEN)	30
124-OUT (ROS) (EVEN)	31
145-OUT (ROS) (ODD)	31
Bourne Rd (JP)	30
Bournedale Rd (JP)	30
Bourneside (DOR)	24
Boutwell (DOR)	22
Bow (EV)	49
Bow (MAL)	48
Bow (HP)	36
Bow (SOM)	43
Bow (CAM)	38
Bow (MED)	55
Bow (WAL)	54
Bow (ARL)	74
Bow (WH)	81
Bow (STO)	80
Bow (LEX)	73
Bow (MEL)	76
Bow Rd (BEL)	78

Bow Rd (NCE)	59
Bow St Ct (STO)	80
Bow St Pl (SOM)	43
Bowditch (BRA)	84
Bowditch Ct (ROX)	19
Bowditch Rd (JP)	30
Bowdoin (SOM)	43
Bowdoin (CAM)	38
Bowdoin (WIN)	52
Bowdoin (MED)	55
Bowdoin (MAL)	48
Bowdoin (EV)	49
Bowdoin (ARL)	74
Bowdoin (NWH)	61
Bowdoin	
1-OUT (ODD)	14
1-100 (NQ)	71
1-123 (DOR) (ODD)	24
2-98 (EVEN)	14
2-126 (DOR) (EVEN)	24
100-OUT (EVEN)	08
101-OUT (WOL)	70
125-OUT (DOR) (ODD)	22
128-OUT (DOR) (EVEN)	22
Bowdoin Ave (WAL)	54
Bowdoin Ave (DOR)	21
Bowdoin Park (DOR)	22
Bowdoin Rd (WH)	81
Bowdoin Sq	14
Bowen (SB)	27
Bowen (NCE)	59
Bowen (NH)	94
Bowen Ave (MED)	55
Bower (MED)	55
Bower (MAL)	48
Bower Rd (BRA)	84
Bower Rd (QUI)	69
Bower St, Park & Pl (ROX)	19
Bower Ter (JP)	30
Bowers (NWV)	60
Bowers Ave (MAL)	48
Bowers Ave (WS)	44
Bowes Ave (QUI)	69
Bowker (LEX)	73
Bowker (BRO)	46
Bowker St & Rd (WAL)	54
Bowman (MAL)	48
Bowman (LEX)	73
Bowman (DOR)	22
Bowser Rd (LEX)	73
Boxford Ter (WRX)	32
Boyd (DOR)	24
Boyd	
1-OUT (WAT) (ODD)	72
2-40 (WAT) (EVEN)	72
42-OUT (NEW) (EVEN)	58
Boyd Park Ter (WAT)	72
Boyden (DOR)	24
Boyle (CHA)	29
Boylston (WAT)	72
Boylston (MAL)	48
Boylston (CAM)	38
Boylston	
1-292 (CHH)	67
1-713	16
1-724 (BRO)	46
293-682 (NCE)	59
683-1102 (NWH)	61
714-878 (NWH)	99
715-877 (ODD)	16
725-OUT (CHH)	67
879-890	16

Boston (Con.)   021

891-1049 15
1050-OUT 02215
1101-OUT (NUF) (ODD) 64
1104-OUT (NUF) (EVEN) 64
Boylston Pl (BRO) 46
Boylston Pl & Sq 16
Boylston Rd (NWH) 61
Boylston St & Pl (JP) 30
Boylston Ter (MED) 55
Boynton (JP) 30
Boynton (WAL) 54
Boynton Rd (MED) 55
Boysen Park (BRA) 85
Bracebridge Rd (NCE) 59
Brackenbury (MAL) 48
Brackett (MED) 55
Brackett (BRI) 35
Brackett (QUI) 69
Brackett (MIL) 86
Brackett (N) 92
Brackett Ave (STO) 80
Brackett Rd (NEW) 58
Bradbury (ALL) 34
Bradbury (CAM) 38
Bradbury Ave (MED) 55
Braddock Park 16
Bradeen (ROS) 31
Bradfield Ave (ROS) 31
Bradford (MAL) 48
Bradford (WAL) 54
Bradford 18
Bradford (QUI) 69
Bradford (N) 92
Bradford Ave (MED) 55
Bradford Ave (SOM) 45
Bradford Cir (ROS) 31
Bradford Ct (NCE) 59
Bradford Park (MEL) 76
Bradford Rd (BEL) 78
Bradford Rd (WH) 81
Bradford Rd (NWH) 61
Bradford Rd (WAT) 72
Bradford Rd (WES) 93
Bradford Rd (BRA) 85
Bradford Rd (MIL) 86
Bradford Rd (SWY) 90
Bradford Rd (MAT) 26
Bradford St, Pl & Ter (EV) .. 49
Bradford Ter (BRO) 46
Bradlee (DOR) 24
Bradlee Rd (MED) 55
Bradlee Rd (MIL) 86
Bradlee St, Ct, Ln & Park
  (HP) 36
Bradley (SOM) 45
Bradley Ave (WEL) 81
Bradley Rd (BEL) 78
Bradley Rd (ARL) 74
Bradley Rd (BRA) 84
Bradley Rd (NWY) 91
Bradmere Way (NWY) 91
Bradshaw (WAT) 72
Bradshaw (MED) 55
Bradshaw (DOR) 21
Bradston 18
Bradstreet Ave (ROS) 31
Bradstreet Ave (REV) 51
Bradwood (ROS) 31
Bradyll Rd (WES) 93
Brae Rd (NWY) 91
Brae Rd (QUI) 69

Brae Burn Rd (AUB) 66
Braeburn Rd (MIL) 86
Braeburn Rd (HP) 36
Braeland Ave (NCE) 59
Braemore Rd (NEW) 58
Braemore Rd (MED) 55
Braemore Rd (BRO) 46
Braemore Rd (WAL) 54
Braemore Rd (BRA) 85
Braemore Ter (LEX) 73
Braeview Rd (BRA) 84
Braewood (HP) 36
Bragdon (ROX) 19
Brahms (ROS) 31
Brainard (HP) 36
Brainerd Rd (ALL) 34
Braintree (ALL) 34
Braintree Ave (QUI) 69
Bramblewood Ln (BRA) 84
Branch (QUI) 69
Branch (MAL) 48
Branch 08
Branch Ave (ARL) 74
Branch Rd (SWY) 90
Branchaud Rd (BEL) 78
Branchfield (DOR) 24
Brand (ARL) 74
Brandeis Cir & Rd (NCE) 59
Brandley Rd (WAT) 72
Brandon (LEX) 73
Brandon Ave (DOR) 25
Brandon Rd (MIL) 87
Brandywyne Dr (EB) 28
Brannon Harris Way 18
Branton (DOR) 22
Brantwood Rd (ARL) 74
Brastow Ave (SOM) 43
Bratley (MEL) 76
Brattle St Pl (ARL) 74
Brattle St, Cir & Sq (CAM) .. 38
Brattle St, Ct, Dr, Ln & Ter
  (ARL) 74
Brattle Way 14
Bray (ROX) 19
Brayton Rd (BRI) 35
Brazil (MEL) 76
Breck (MIL) 86
Breck Ave (BRI) 35
Breed (REV) 51
Breed St & Sq (EB) 28
Breedens Ln (REV) 51
Bremen St & Pl (EB) 28
Bremen Ter (JP) 30
Brennan Ave (WAL) 54
Brent (DOR) 24
Brent Rd (LEX) 73
Brenton (DOR) 21
Brenton (REV) 51
Brenton Rd (WES) 93
Brentwood (ALL) 34
Brentwood (MAL) 48
Brentwood Ave (NCE) 59
Brentwood Cir (N) 92
Brentwood Rd (STO) 80
Brettwood Rd (BEL) 78
Brewer (QUI) 69
Brewer (JP) 30
Brewer (CAM) 38
Brewster (CAM) 38
Brewster (SB) 27
Brewster Ave (WIN) 52
Brewster Ave (BRA) 85
Brewster Pl & Rd (NWY) 91

Brewster Rd (MIL) 86
Brewster Rd (WAL) 54
Brewster Rd (MED) 55
Brewster Rd (WH) 81
Brewster Rd (STO) 80
Brewster Rd (ARL) 74
Brewster Rd (NWH) 61
Brewster Ter (BRO) 46
Briar Ln (NWY) 60
Briar Ln (WES) 93
Briar Wood Trl (WY) 88
Briarcliff Ter (MAT) 26
Briarfield Rd (MIL) 87
Briarwood Cir (NH) 94
Briarwood Rd (MIL) 86
Briarwood Rd (WAL) 54
Bridge (REV) 51
Bridge (CAM) 41
Bridge (ROS) 31
Bridge (EV) 49
Bridge (HP) 36
Bridge (NH) 94
Bridge (NWY) 91
Bridge (NEW) 58
Bridge (QUI) 69
Bridge (LEX) 73
Bridge (WAT) 72
Bridge Ct 14
Bridgeham Ave (WAT) 72
Bridges Ave (NWV) 60
Bridle Path (LEX) 73
Bridle Path (EWY) 89
Bridle Trl Rd (N) 92
Brier Rd (WRX) 32
Brierfield Rd (NWH) 61
Brierwood Rd (BRA) 84
Briggs (WOL) 70
Briggs (MEL) 76
Briggs Pl 18
Briggs Rd (LEX) 73
Brigham (WAT) 72
Brigham (EB) 28
Brigham Rd (LEX) 73
Brigham Rd (WAL) 54
Bright (WAL) 54
Bright Rd (BEL) 78
Brighton (BEL) 78
Brighton (QUI) 69
Brighton (CHA) 29
Brighton Ave (ALL) 34
Brightwood Rd (WAL) 54
Brimmer 08
Brimmer (WAT) 72
Brington Rd (BRO) 46
Brinsley (QUI) 69
Brinsley (DOR) 21
Brinton (ROX) 19
Bristol 18
Bristol
  1-73 (CAM) 41
  74-OUT (CAM) 39
Bristol Rd (WNW) 65
Bristol Rd (WH) 81
Bristol Rd (WS) 44
Broad (QUI) 69
Broad (BEL) 78
Broad (BP) 57
Broad
  1-77 (ODD) 09
  1-514 (WY) 88
  2-72 (EVEN) 09
  74-OUT (EVEN) 10
  79-OUT (ODD) 10

515-OUT (EWY)	89
Broad St Pl (WY)	88
Broad Meadows Rd (N)	92
Broad Sound Ave (REV)	51
Broadlawn Dr & Park (CHH)	67
Broadway (QUI)	69
Broadway (STO)	80
Broadway (WAT)	72
Broadway (ARL)	74
Broadway (REV)	51
Broadway (CHE)	50
Broadway (EV)	49
Broadway (MAL)	48
Broadway	
1-155 (CAM)	42
1-221 (ODD)	16
1-649 (SOM)	45
2-218 (EVEN)	16
156-407 (CAM)	39
220-398 (EVEN)	11
223-399 (ODD)	11
400-OUT (SB)	27
650-OUT (WS)	44
407A-OUT (CAM)	38
Broadway Ext (SB)	27
Broadway Pl (SOM)	45
Broadway St & Ter (NWV)	60
Broadway Ter (CAM)	39
Broady Ave (QUI)	69
Brock (BRI)	35
Brockton (MAT)	26
Brockton Ave (QUI)	69
Brogan Rd (MED)	55
Broken Tree Rd (NCE)	59
Bromfield (WOL)	70
Bromfield (WAT)	72
Bromfield	08
Bromfield Rd (WS)	44
Bromley (JP)	30
Bronsdon (BRI)	35
Bronson Ter (JP)	30
Bronx Rd (WRX)	32
Brook (ROS)	31
Brook (SOM)	45
Brook (BRO)	46
Brook (MAL)	48
Brook (CHE)	50
Brook (WOL)	70
Brook (WEL)	81
Brook (MEL)	76
Brook (LEX)	73
Brook Ave (WAL)	54
Brook Ave	
1-59 (ROX) (ODD)	19
2-66 (ROX) (EVEN)	19
61-OUT (DOR) (ODD)	25
68-OUT (DOR) (EVEN)	25
Brook Rd (NH)	94
Brook Rd (WES)	93
Brook Rd (QUI)	69
Brook Rd	
1-599 (MIL)	87
600-OUT (MIL)	86
Brook Ter (WY)	88
Brook Farm Rd (WRX)	32
Brook Hill Rd (MIL)	87
Brookdale (ROS)	31
Brookdale (REV)	51
Brookdale Ave (WH)	81
Brookdale Rd (NWV)	60
Brookdale Rd (ARL)	74
Brookfield (ROS)	31
Brookfield Cir & Rd (WH)	81

Brookfield Rd (WIN)	52
Brookfield Rd (WAL)	54
Brookford (CAM)	40
Brookford (DOR)	25
Brookings (MED)	55
Brookledge (DOR)	21
Brookledge Rd (MEL)	76
Brookley Rd & Ter (JP)	30
Brookline (CAM)	39
Brookline (REV)	51
Brookline (WAT)	72
Brookline (N)	92
Brookline	
1-175 (CHH)	67
176-OUT (NCE)	59
Brookline Ave	
1-549	02215
550-OUT (BRO)	46
Brookmere Ave (WH)	81
Brookridge Rd (STO)	80
Brooks (ROS)	31
Brooks (BRI)	35
Brooks (EB)	28
Brooks Ave (ARL)	74
Brooks Ave (NWV)	60
Brooks Ave (QUI)	69
Brooks St & Park (MED)	55
Brooksdale Rd (BRI)	35
Brookside Ave (JP)	30
Brookside Ave (NWV)	60
Brookside Ave (WAV)	79
Brookside Ave (LEX)	73
Brookside Park (MIL)	87
Brookside Pky (MED)	55
Brookside Rd (N)	92
Brookside Rd (BRA)	84
Brookside Rd (WH)	81
Brookvale (DOR)	24
Brookview (DOR)	24
Brookview Rd (MED)	55
Brookway (WH)	81
Brookway Ct & Rd (WAL)	54
Brookway Rd & Ter (ROS)	31
Brookwood Rd (LEX)	73
Brow Ave (BRA)	85
Brown (WES)	93
Brown (WAV)	79
Brown (BEL)	78
Brown (MEL)	76
Brown (WAL)	54
Brown (CAM)	38
Brown (EV)	49
Brown (ROX)	19
Brown Ave (ROS)	31
Brown Rd (LEX)	73
Brown Ter (JP)	30
Brown Ter (MAL)	48
Browne (BRO)	46
Browning (WY)	88
Browning Ave (DOR)	24
Browning Rd (SOM)	45
Browning Rd (ARL)	74
Browns Ave (WAL)	54
Bruce (DOR)	24
Bruce Ln (NEW)	58
Bruce Rd (LEX)	73
Bruce Rd (WAL)	54
Brucewood Rd (WRX)	32
Bruno (REV)	51
Brunswick (NQ)	71
Brunswick (DOR)	21
Brunswick Park & Way (MEL)	76

Brunswick Rd (ARL)	74
Brush Hill Ln (MIL)	86
Brush Hill Rd (NWH)	61
Brush Hill Rd	
1-211 (MIL)	87
212-OUT (MIL)	86
Brush Hill Ter (HP)	36
Brushwood Cir (HP)	36
Bryant (REV)	51
Bryant (EV)	49
Bryant (MAL)	48
Bryant (CAM)	38
Bryant Ave (MIL)	86
Bryant Ave (WY)	88
Bryant Ave (QUI)	69
Bryant Rd (CHH)	67
Bryant Rd (LEX)	73
Bryant Rd (WAL)	54
Bryden Rd (WES)	93
Bryer Rd (MAL)	48
Bryn Mawr Rd (WH)	81
Bryon Rd (CHH)	67
Buchanan (WIN)	52
Buchanan Ln (SWY)	90
Buchanan Rd (ROS)	31
Buckingham (SOM)	43
Buckingham (HP)	36
Buckingham	16
Buckingham Rd (MIL)	86
Buckingham Rd (WOL)	70
Buckingham St & Pl (CAM)	38
Buckley (QUI)	69
Buckley Ave (JP)	30
Buckman Ct (ARL)	74
Buckman Dr (LEX)	73
Buckminster Rd (BRO)	46
Bucknam (EV)	49
Bucknam (RXC)	20
Bucknell (WH)	81
Buckskin Dr (WES)	93
Buckthorn Ter (WIN)	52
Buena Vista Park (CAM)	40
Buena Vista Rd (WS)	44
Buena Vista Rd (WH)	81
Buena Vista Rd (ARL)	74
Buff Cir (NCE)	59
Buick (WAT)	72
Buick	02215
Bulfinch Pl	14
Bullard (DOR)	21
Bullard Rd (WES)	93
Bullock	02210
Bullough Park (NWV)	60
Bungalow Rd (WRX)	32
Bunker (HP)	36
Bunker Ln (WNW)	65
Bunker Hill Ln (QUI)	69
Bunker Hill St & Ct (CHA)	29
Bunny Cir (NEW)	58
Bunton (MIL)	86
Burard (WRX)	32
Burbank (REV)	51
Burbank	15
Burbank Rd (MED)	55
Burch (ARL)	74
Burdean Rd (NCE)	59
Burdett Ter (MAL)	48
Burditt (EV)	49
Burgess (NQ)	71
Burgess (DOR)	25
Burget Ave (MED)	55
Burgoyne (DOR)	24

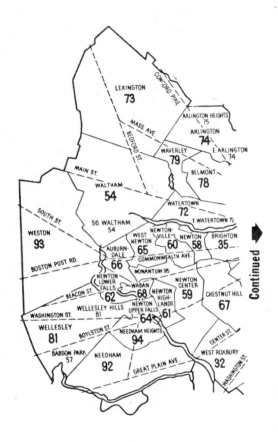

ZIP CODES
BOSTON, Massachusetts
021 + two digits shown = zip code

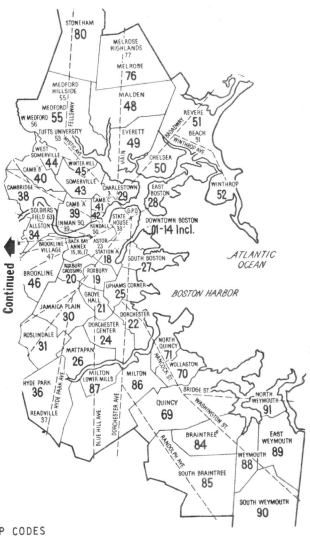

ZIP CODES
BOSTON, Massachusetts
021 + two digits shown = zip code

Burke (RXC)........................... 20
Burke (SB)............................. 27
Burkes Ln (WH)...................... 81
Burkhall (SWY)....................... 90
Burley (ROS)......................... 31
Burlington (LEX)..................... 73
Burlington Ave.....................02215
Burma Rd (CHE)..................... 50
Burmah (MAT)....................... 26
Burnett (JP)......................... 30
Burnett (MEL)....................... 76
Burney (RXC)........................ 20
Burnham (REV)...................... 51
Burnham
  1-59 (WAV) (ODD)............... 79
  2-54 (WAV) (EVEN)............. 79
  56-OUT (WAT) (EVEN)......... 72
  61-OUT (WAT) (ODD).......... 72
Burnham Pl (SB)..................... 27
Burnham Rd (WAT)................. 44
Burnham Rd (LEX).................. 73
Burnham Rd (WNW)............... 65
Burns Ave (QUI)..................... 69
Burns Ct (CAM)..................... 38
Burns Rd (LEX)...................... 73
Burns Sq (EB)....................... 28
Burnside (MED)..................... 55
Burnside Ave (WS)................. 44
Burnside Ave (ROS)............... 31
Burnside Rd (NWH)................ 61
Burnside Rd (NH)................... 94
Burr (JP)............................. 30
Burr Rd (NCE)...................... 59
Burr Oak Park (DOR).............. 21
Burrage (JP)........................ 30
Burrage Rd (NCE).................. 59
Burrell (MEL)....................... 76
Burrell (ROX)....................... 19
Burridge Pl (MAT).................. 48
Burrill Ln (N)........................ 92
Burrill Pl (SB)....................... 27
Burrill Ter (WIN)................... 52
Burroughs Ext & Rd (BRA)....... 84
Burroughs Rd (LEX)............... 73
Burroughs St & Pl (JP)............ 30
Burrwood Rd (ROS)............... 31
Bursely Rd (NWY).................. 91
Burt (DOR).......................... 24
Burton (BRI)........................ 35
Burton (ARL)........................ 74
Burton Ave (ROX)................. 19
Burton (BRA)....................... 84
Burton Ter (SWY).................. 90
Burwell Rd (WRX)................. 32
Bushnell (DOR)..................... 24
Bushnell Ter (BRA)................ 84
Business St & Ter (HP)........... 36
Bussell Rd (MED).................. 55
Buswell...........................02215
Buswell Park (NEW)............... 58
Butler (MED)........................ 55
Butler (REV)........................ 51
Butler (DOR)........................ 24
Butler Ave (LEX)................... 73
Butler Ave (STO).................. 80
Butler Ct (MAL).................... 48
Butler Dr (SOM)................... 45
Butler Rd (QUI).................... 69
Butler Rd (BRA).................... 85
Butler Rd (WY)..................... 89
Buttonwood Ln (WES)............ 93
Buttonwood Rd (STO)............ 80

Buttonwood St & Ct (DOR)...... 25
Buttrick (WAL)...................... 54
Butts (NUF)......................... 64
Buxton Ln (WAL)................... 54
Buzzells Ln (MED)................. 55
Bv French (BRA)................... 84
Byfield Rd (WAB).................. 68
Bynner (JP)......................... 30
Bypass Rd (WES).................. 93
Byrd Ave (ROS).................... 31
Byrd Ave (WNW).................. 65
Byrne Rd (MIL)..................... 87
Byron (MAL)........................ 48
Byron (EB).......................... 28
Byron .... * 08
Byron Ave (LEX)................... 73
Byren Rd (WAL).................... 54
Byron Rd (WY)..................... 88
Byron Rd (WES).................... 93
C (REV).............................. 51
C (WAV)............................. 79
C
  1-368 (SB)...................... 27
  369-OUT 02210
Cabot (NH)......................... 94
Cabot (WY)......................... 88
Cabot (MIL)......................... 86
Cabot (CHH)........................ 67
Cabot (WAL)........................ 54
Cabot (CHE)........................ 50
Cabot (RXC)........................ 20
Cabot
  1-199 (NEW)................... 58
  200-OUT (NWW).............. 60
Cabot Ave (BRA)................... 84
Cabot Ct (NWW).................. 60
Cabot Park (NEW)................. 58
Cabot Rd (STO).................... 80
Cabot Rd (ARL).................... 74
Cabot St & Ct (EV)................ 49
Cadbury (CAM)..................... 40
Caddy Rd (MAT)................... 26
Cady Ave (WS)..................... 44
Cahners Pl.......................... 16
Cain Ave (BRA).................... 85
Cain Ave (EWY).................... 89
Cairn (QUI)......................... 69
Calder (DOR)....................... 24
Calder Pl (JP)...................... 30
Caldon Path (NCE)................ 59
Caldwell (CHA)..................... 29
Caldwell (NWY).................... 91
Caldwell Ave (SOM)............... 43
Caldwell Rd (WAL)................ 54
Caledonia Ave (QUI).............. 69
Caledonian Ave (WRX)........... 32
Calhoun Ave (EV).................. 49
California
  1-121 (WAT)................... 72
  122-395 (NEW)................ 58
  396-OUT (NWW).............. 60
California Ave (MIL)................ 86
California Ave (QUI)................ 69
California Park (WAT)............. 72
Call (JP)............................ 30
Call (CHA).......................... 29
Call Rd (NWY)..................... 91
Call St Pl (CHA)................... 29
Callahan Path (NCE).............. 59
Callender (DOR)................... 24
Callender St & Pl (CAM)......... 39
Calnan Cir (WEY).................. 88
Calnan Sq (CAM).................. 39

Caltha Rd (BRI).................... 35
Calthea (STO)...................... 80
Calumet (WOL)..................... 70
Calumet (REV)...................... 51
Calumet (RXC)..................... 20
Calvary (WAL)...................... 54
Calvary Cemetery (ROS)......... 31
Calvin (SOM)....................... 43
Calvin (LEX)........................ 73
Calvin (BRA)........................ 84
Calvin Rd (WAT)................... 72
Calvin Rd (WEL)................... 81
Calvin Rd (NWV)................... 60
Calvin Rd (QUI).................... 69
Calvin Rd (JP)...................... 30
Cambria (SOM)..................... 43
Cambria 15
Cambria Rd
  1-23 (WNW) (ODD)........... 65
  2-32 (WNW) (EVEN).......... 65
  25-OUT (WAL) (ODD)......... 54
  34-OUT (WAL) (EVEN)........ 54
Cambridge (CHA).................. 29
Cambridge 14
Cambridge (REV)................... 51
Cambridge (WAV).................. 79
Cambridge
  1-599 (ALL) (ODD)............ 34
  1-1040 (CAM).................. 41
  2-630 (ALL) (EVEN)........... 34
  100-100......................02202
  601-OUT (BRI) (ODD)......... 35
  632-OUT (BRI) (EVEN)........ 35
  1041-1563 (CAM).............. 39
  1564-OUT (CAM).............. 38
Cambridge Pky (CAM)............ 42
Cambridge Ter (CAM)............ 40
Cambridge Ter (ALL)............. 34
Camden (LEX)...................... 73
Camden Pl (CAM).................. 38
Camden Rd (AUB)................. 66
Camden St & Pl (QUI)............ 69
Camden St & Pl.................... 18
Camelia Ave (CAM)............... 39
Camelia Pl (LEX)................... 73
Camelia Rd (MAT)................. 26
Camelot Ct (BRI).................. 35
Camelot Way (SWY).............. 90
Cameo Rd (BRA)................... 85
Cameron (EV)...................... 49
Cameron (BRO).................... 46
Cameron (DOR).................... 25
Cameron Ave (WS)............... 44
Cameron Ave (CAM).............. 40
Cameron St & Pl (WEL).......... 81
Camille Rd (REV).................. 51
Camp (CAM)........................ 40
Camp (WY)......................... 88
Camp Rd (WRX)................... 32
Campanelli Dr (BRA).............. 85
Campbell (SWY)................... 90
Campbell (QUI).................... 69
Campbell Ave (REV).............. 51
Campbell Park (WS).............. 44
Campbell Park Pl (WS)........... 44
Campbell Rd (STO)............... 80
Campbell Rd (ARL)............... 74
Canaan (MAT)...................... 26
Canacum Rd (NWY).............. 91
Canal (BRA)........................ 85
Canal 14
Canal (MAL)........................ 48
Canal (MED)....................... 55

Boston (Con.)   021

Canal Ln (SOM) 45
Candace Ave (WAL) 54
Candia (EWY) 89
Candia (ARL) 74
Candlewick Close (LEX) 73
Candlewood Ln (BRA) 84
Candor Pl (JP) 30
Cannell Pl (EV) 49
Cannon (NWH) 61
Canterbury
   1-250 (DOR) 24
   251-OUT (ROS) 31
Canterbury Rd (NWH) 61
Canterbury Rd (WAL) 54
Canton Ave
   1-481 (MIL) (ODD) 87
   2-474 (MIL) (EVEN) 87
   476-OUT (MIL) (EVEN) 86
   483-OUT (MIL) (ODD) 86
Canton Pl 18
Canton Rd (NQ) 71
Cantwell Rd (MIL) 87
Cape Cod Ln (MIL) 87
Cape Cod Ln (BRA) 84
Capen (MIL) 87
Capen (STO) 80
Capen (MED) 55
Capen E (MED) 55
Capen Ct (WS) 44
Capen Rd (BRA) 84
Capen St & Pl (DOR) 24
Capital (WRX) 32
Capital (NEW) 58
Capitol (WAT) 72
Cappy Cir (WNW) 65
Captain Parker Arms (LEX) 73
Captains Walk (QUI) 69
Carberry (MED) 55
Cardinal Ct (BRA) 85
Cardinal Rd (STO) 80
Cardinal Oconnell Way 14
Cardington (ROX) 19
Carey Ave (WAT) 72
Carey Pl & Rd (NH) 94
Cargill (MEL) 76
Carl (NWH) 61
Carl Rd (LEX) 73
Carl Rd (ARL) 74
Carle Rd (WOL) 70
Carleton (NEW) 58
Carleton 16
Carleton (REV) 51
Carleton (CAM) 42
Carleton Cir & Rd (BEL) 78
Carleton Rd (WEL) 81
Carleton Rd (WAL) 54
Carley Rd (LEX) 73
Carlford Rd (JP) 30
Carlida (MEL) 76
Carlida Rd (STO) 80
Carlin Rd (WAL) 54
Carlisle (CAM) 39
Carlisle (NQ) 71
Carlisle (DOR) 21
Carlisle St & Pl (NCE) 59
Carlmark (QUI) 69
Carlos (DOR) 24
Carlotta (DOR) 22
Carlow (ROX) 19
Carlson (QUI) 69

Carlson (EV) 49
Carlson Ave (REV) 51
Carlson Ave (NCE) 59
Carlson Cir (WRX) 32
Carlson Rd (MIL) 86
Carlton (SOM) 43
Carlton Rd (WEL) 81
Carlton Rd (ARL) 74
Carlton Rd (WAB) 68
Carlton St & Path (BRO) 46
Carlton Ter (WAT) 72
Carmel (CHE) 50
Carmel (RXC) 20
Carmel Cir (LEX) 73
Carmela Ln (DOR) 24
Carmen (DOR) 21
Carmen Ave (STO) 80
Carmody Ct (SB) 27
Carnegie Pl (LEX) 73
Carney (MED) 55
Carney Ct (CHA) 29
Carol (STO) 80
Carol Ave (BRO) 46
Carol Cir (WRX) 32
Carol Ln (WAL) 54
Carol Ln (LEX) 73
Carol Rd (N) 92
Carolina (MED) 55
Carolina Ave & Pl (JP) 30
Caroline (WH) 81
Caroline Park (WAB) 68
Carolyn Rd (SWY) 90
Carolyne Ave (BRA) 85
Carpenter (SB) 27
Carriage Dr (LEX) 73
Carrigg Rd (NQ) 71
Carrisbrooke Rd (WH) 81
Carroll (STO) 80
Carroll (WAT) 72
Carroll (EWY) 89
Carroll (WRX) 32
Carroll (CHE) 50
Carrolls Ln (QUI) 69
Carrolton Rd (WRX) 32
Carruth (WOL) 70
Carruth (DOR) 24
Carson (DOR) 25
Carson (WY) 88
Cart Path Rd (WES) 93
Carter (NH) 94
Carter (CHA) 29
Carter (QUI) 69
Carter (NWV) 60
Carter (CHE) 50
Carter (EV) 49
Carter (WAL) 54
Carter Rd (BRA) 85
Carter Ter (SOM) 43
Carthay Cir (NWH) 61
Cartwright Rd (WH) 81
Caruso Rd (REV) 51
Carver (CAM) 38
Carver (SOM) 43
Carver (EWY) 89
Carver 16
Carver Rd (WH) 81
Carver Rd (NWH) 61
Carver Rd (WAT) 72
Carver Rd E (WAT) 72
Carville Ave (LEX) 73
Cary Ave (LEX) 73
Cary Ave (MIL) 86
Cary Ave (REV) 51

Cary Ave (CHE) 50
Cary Pl (CHA) 29
Cary Rd (CHH) 67
Caryll (MAT) 26
Casco (QUI) 69
Case Dr (REV) 51
Caspar (WRX) 32
Caspian Way (DOR) 25
Cass (WRX) 32
Cass (MEL) 76
Cassandra Rd (EWY) 89
Cassnet (DOR) 22
Castle (WAL) 54
Castle Ct (EB) 28
Castle Pl (NH) 94
Castle Rd (EWY) 89
Castle Rd (LEX) 73
Castle St & Ct 18
Castle Rock (WAL) 25
Castlegate (JP) 21
Castleton (JP) 30
Cataldo Dr (REV) 51
Cataumet (JP) 30
Catawba (ROX) 19
Catenaccia Way (JP) 30
Cathedral (ROX) 19
Catherine (ROS) 31
Catherine Rd (MIL) 87
Catlin (BRO) 46
Caton (MAT) 26
Caughey (WAL) 54
Caulfield Cir (NCE) 59
Causeway 14
Cavanaugh Path (NCE) 59
Cavanaugh Rd (WH) 81
Cavanaugh Rd (BRA) 84
Cavel Cir (WRX) 32
Cawfield (DOR) 25
Cazenove 16
Cazenove Pl (EV) 49
Cecelian (REV) 51
Cedar (MAL) 48
Cedar (WAL) 54
Cedar (MAT) 26
Cedar (CHA) 29
Cedar (BRA) 84
Cedar (EWY) 89
Cedar (NCE) 59
Cedar (LEX) 73
Cedar (WOL) 70
Cedar
   1-100 (SOM) 43
   1-249 (WH) 81
   101-163 (WS) 44
   164-OUT (SOM) 45
   250-OUT (NH) 94
Cedar Ave (BRA) 85
Cedar Ave (ARL) 74
Cedar Ave (SOM) 43
Cedar Ave & Way (STO) 80
Cedar Park N & S (MEL) 76
Cedar Pl (QUI) 69
Cedar Pl (DOR) 25
Cedar Rd (BEL) 78
Cedar Rd (CHH) 67
Cedar Rd (WRX) 32
Cedar Rd (MED) 55
Cedar Rd (WES) 93
Cedar St Pl (SOM) 43
Cedar St, Ct & Ter (EV) 49
Cedar St, Park & Sq (ROX) 19
Cedar St & Sq (CAM) 40
Cedar Ter (WH) 81

Boston (Con.)   021

Cedar Ter St (MIL) 86
Cedar Cliff Rd (BRA) 84
Cedar Cliff Ter (MED) 55
Cedar Croft Ln (WAL) 54
Cedar Grove (DOR) 24
Cedar Grove Cemetery (DOR).. 24
Cedar Hill Ln (WAL) 54
Cedar Lane Way 08
Cedarbrook Rd (WH) 81
Cedarcrest Cir & Rd (WRX) 32
Cedarcrest Ter (WRY) 32
Cedarwood Ave (WAL) 54
Cedarwood Rd (JP) 30
Cedarwood Ter (LEX) 73
Cedric (ROX) 19
Cedric Rd (NCE) 59
Cedrus Ave (ROS) 31
Cefalo Rd (WRX) 32
Celestine Ter (STO) 80
Celia Rd (WRX) 32
Celia Rd (BRA) 85
Cemetery (ARL) 74
Cemetery Dr (CHH) 67
Cenacle Rd (BRI) 35
Centennial Ave (REV) 51
Center (WES) 93
Center (EWY) 89
Center Plz 08
Centervale Park (DOR) 24
Centola (BRI) 35
Central (WIN) 52
Central 09
Central (SWY) 90
Central (ARL) 74
Central (WEL) 81
Central
   1-112 (SOM) 43
   113-OUT (SOM) 45
Central Ave (NWV) 60
Central Ave (QUI) 69
Central Ave (MAT) 26
Central Ave (REV) 51
Central Ave (HP) 36
Central Ave (MED) 55
Central Ave (EV) 49
Central Ave (MAL) 48
Central Ave (CHE) 50
Central Ave
   1-425 (MIL) (ODD) 87
   1-763 (NH) 94
   2-434 (MIL) (EVEN) 87
   427-OUT (MIL) (ODD) 86
   436-OUT (MIL) (EVEN) 86
   764-OUT (N) 92
Central Pl (CHA) 29
Central Rd (SOM) 43
Central Sq (CAM) 39
Central Sq (EB) 28
Central St & Ave (WAL) 54
Central St & Ave (BRA) 85
Central St & Sq (STO) 80
Central St & Ter (AUB) 66
Central Ter (MEL) 76
Central Close (AUB) 66
Central Wharf 10
Centre (QUI) 69
Centre (LEX) 73
Centre (WAT) 72
Centre (WAL) 54
Centre (SOM) 43
Centre (CAM) 39

Centre (MAL) 48
Centre (WIN) 52
Centre (BRO) 46
Centre
   1-245 (DOR) 24
   1-249 (ROX) 19
   1-854 (NEW) 58
   246-OUT (DOR) 22
   250-1198 (JP) (EVEN) 30
   251-1193 (JP) (ODD) 30
   855-1457 (NCE) (ODD) 59
   856-1510 (NCE) (EVEN) 59
   1195-1635 (ROS) (ODD) 31
   1200-1634 (ROS) (EVEN) 31
   1459-OUT (NWH) (ODD) 61
   1512-OUT (NWH) (EVEN) ... 61
   1636-OUT (WRX) 32
Centre Ave (BEL) 78
Centre Ave (NEW) 58
Centre Ave (DOR) 24
Centre Ct (DOR) 22
Centre Ln & Ter (WRX) 32
Centre Pl (ROX) 19
Centre St Ter (ROX) 19
Centre St & Ln (MIL) 86
Century (SOM) 45
Century (MED) 55
Century Ln (MIL) 86
Century Rd (SWY) 90
Cerdan Ave (ROS) 31
Cerina Rd (JP) 30
Ceylon
   1-49 (DOR) 25
   50-OUT (DOR) 21
Chadbourne Rd (LEX) 73
Chadbourne Ter (WAT) 72
Chadwick (ROX) 19
Chadwick Rd (WES) 93
Chafee Ave (WAL) 54
Chalke (CAM) 39
Chamber (CHA) 29
Chamberlain (DOR) 24
Chamberlain Ave (WIN) 52
Chamberlain Ave (REV) 51
Chamberlain Rd (NEW) 58
Chamberlain Ter (WAL) 54
Chamblet (DOR) 25
Champa (NUF) 64
Champney (BRI) 35
Champney Pl (ROX) 19
Champney Pl 14
Chandler 16
Chandler (WS) 44
Chandler (NEW) 58
Chandler (WAT) 72
Chandler (LEX) 73
Chandler (BEL) 78
Chandler (ARL) 74
Chandler (WY) 88
Chandler Pl (NUF) 64
Chandler Rd (MED) 55
Chandler Rd (MAL) 48
Change Ave 09
Channing (WOL) 70
Channing (NEW) 58
Channing Rd (NCE) 59
Channing Rd (WAT) 72
Channing Rd (BEL) 78
Channing Rd (BRO) 46
Channing St, Cir & Pl (CAM) .. 38
Chapel (WS) 44
Chapel (BRO) 46

Chapel (NEW) 58
Chapel (QUI) 69
Chapel (N) 92
Chapel Pl (WH) 81
Chapel Rd (HP) 36
Chapin Ave (WRX) 32
Chapin Rd (NCE) 59
Chapman (WAT) 72
Chapman (WOL) 70
Chapman (ARL) 74
Chapman Pl (CAM) 38
Chapman Pl 08
Chapman St & Pl (CHA) 29
Chappie (CHA) 29
Chard (EWY) 89
Chardon Rd (MED) 55
Chardon St & Ct 14
Charger (REV) 51
Charlame St, Ct & Pl (ROX) ... 19
Charlemont (DOR) 22
Charlemont (NWH) 61
Charlemont Rd (MED) 55
Charles (WIN) 52
Charles (CAM) 41
Charles (SOM) 43
Charles (HP) 36
Charles (MAL) 48
Charles (BRO) 46
Charles (CHE) 50
Charles (WAL) 54
Charles (AUB) 66
Charles (NWH) 61
Charles (ARL) 74
Charles (WAT) 72
Charles (STO) 80
Charles (WH) 81
Charles (QUI) 69
Charles (MEL) 76
Charles (BEL) 78
Charles (LEX) 73
Charles (DOR) 22
Charles (CHA) 29
Charles (EWY) 89
Charles (NH) 94
Charles (BRA) 84
Charles
   0-ONLY 16
   1-OUT 14
Charles, S. 16
Charles Ave (REV) 51
Charles Ct E (N) 92
Charles Park Rd (WRX) 32
Charles Rd (DOR) 24
Charles St Ave (WAL) 54
Charles St Pl (MAL) 48
Charles St Pl (CHA) 29
Charles Diersh (EWY) 89
Charles E Ryan Rd (SOM) 45
Charles River (N) 92
Charles River Ave (CHA) 29
Charles River Park & Sq 14
Charles River Rd (WAL) 54
Charles River Rd (WAT) 72
Charles River Ter (NWH) 61
Charlesbank Rd & Ter (NEW) . 58
Charlesbank Way (WAL) 54
Charlesden Park (NWV) 60
Charlesgate St E & W 02215
Charlesmount Ave (QUI) 69
Charlesview (BRI) 35
Charlotte (DOR) 21

Boston (Con.)   021

Charlotte Rd (WAL) 54
Charlotte Rd (NCE) 59
Charlton (ARL) 74
Charlton (EV) 49
Charlton (MED) 55
Charme Ave (ROS) 31
Charnwood Rd (MED) 55
Charnwood Rd (WS) 44
Charter 13
Chase (DOR) 25
Chase (NCE) 59
Chase (QUI) 69
Chase Ave (WNW) 65
Chase Ave (LEX) 73
Chase Rd (STO) 80
Chase Rd (WAL) 54
Chaske Ave (AUB) 66
Chatham (QUI) 69
Chatham (ARL) 74
Chatham (CAM) 39
Chatham Cir (WH) 81
Chatham Ln (WAL) 54
Chatham Rd (EV) 49
Chatham Rd (NWH) 61
Chatham St & Cir (BRO) 46
Chatham St & Ext (MAL) 48
Chatham St & Row 09
Chaucer (EB) 28
Chauncey (WAT) 72
Chauncy 11
Chauncy (SWY) 90
Chauncy St, Ln, Pl & Ter
   (CAM) 38
Cheever (CHE) 50
Cheever (REV) 51
Cheever (MIL) 87
Cheever Ave (NCE) 59
Cheever Ct (EB) 28
Cheever Rd (MAL) 48
Chellman (WRX) 32
Chelmsford (DOR) 22
Chelsea (CHA) 29
Chelsea St, Ct & Ter (EB) 28
Chelsea St & Pl (EV) 49
Chemical Ln (EV) 49
Chenery Ter (BEL) 78
Cheney (DOR) 21
Cheney (NH) 94
Cheney St & Ct (NUF) 64
Cheriton Rd (WOL) 70
Cheriton Rd (WRX) 32
Cherokee (RXC) 20
Cherokee Rd (ARL) 74
Cherry (BEL) 78
Cherry (MEL) 76
Cherry (QUI) 69
Cherry (LEX) 73
Cherry (CHE) 50
Cherry (EV) 49
Cherry (MAL) 48
Cherry (WS) 44
Cherry (WIN) 52
Cherry (WAL) 54
Cherry (BRA) 84
Cherry Ave (STO) 80
Cherry Ln (SWY) 90
Cherry Rd (WRX) 32
Cherry St & Ct (CAM) 39
Cherry St & Ct (MED) 55

Cherry St & Pl (WNW) 65
Cherry Brook Rd (WES) 93
Cheryl Cir & Ln (EWY) 89
Cheryl Dr (MIL) 86
Cheryl Ln (WAL) 54
Cheryl Ln (WIN) 52
Cheryl Ln (HP) 36
Chesbrough Rd (WRX) 32
Chesham Rd (BRO) 46
Cheshire (JP) 30
Chesley Ave (NWV) 60
Chesley Rd (NCE) 59
Chesley Rd (QUI) 69
Chester (.......)" 61
Chester (MEL) 76
Chester (ARL) 74
Chester (WAT) 72
Chester (WOL) 70
Chester (ALL) 34
Chester
   1-18 (CAM) 40
   19-OUT (WS) 44
Chester Ave (REV) 51
Chester Ave (WS) 52
Chester Ave (MED) 55
Chester Ave (SOM) 43
Chester Ave (CHE) 50
Chester Ave & Ln (WAL) 54
Chester Park (MAT) 26
Chester Pl (WRX) 32
Chester Pl (WS) 44
Chester Rd (BEL) 78
Chester St & Pl (MAL) 48
Chester Brook Rd (WAL) 54
Chesterfield (HP) 36
Chesterfield Rd (WNW) 65
Chesterfield Rd (MIL) 86
Chesterton (ROX) 19
Chesterton Rd (WH) 81
Chestnut (WH) 81
Chestnut (STO) 80
Chestnut (WAV) 79
Chestnut (WAT) 72
Chestnut (ARL) 74
Chestnut (QUI) 69
Chestnut 08
Chestnut (WES) 93
Chestnut (HP) 36
Chestnut (MAL) 48
Chestnut (CHE) 50
Chestnut (SOM) 43
Chestnut (CAM) 39
Chestnut (MED) 55
Chestnut
   1-400 (WNW) 65
   401-928 (WAB) 68
   929-OUT (NUF) 64
Chestnut Ave, Pl, Sq & Ter
   (JP) 30
Chestnut Pl (BRI) 35
Chestnut Rd (WRX) 32
Chestnut St, Ave, Park & Pl
   (WAL) 54
Chestnut St & Ct (CHA) 29
Chestnut St & Park (MEL) 76
Chestnut St & Pl (EV) 49
Chestnut St & Pl (BRO) 46
Chestnut St, Pl & Rd (N) 92
Chestnut Ter (NCE) 59
Chestnut Hill Ave
   1-349 (BRI) 35
   350-OUT (BRO) 46

Chestnut Hill Rd & Ter
   (CHH) 67
Cheswick Rd (AUB) 66
Cheswick Rd (ARL) 74
Chetwynd Rd (WS) 44
Chetwynd Rd (CAM) 40
Cheverus Rd (DOR) 24
Cheviot Rd (ARL) 74
Chick (WOL) 70
Chickatawbut (DOR) 22
Chickatawbut Rd (QUI) 69
Chickatawbut Rd (BRA) 84
Chickering Pl 11
Chilcott Pl (JP) 30
Child (JP) 30
Child (HP) 36
Childs Rd (LEX) 73
Chiltern Rd (WES) 93
Chilton (BEL) 78
Chilton (CAM) 38
Chilton (BRO) 46
Chilton Park (MIL) 87
Chilton Pl (NUF) 64
Chilton Rd (WRX) 32
Chinian Path (NCE) 59
Chipman (MED) 55
Chipman (DOR) 24
Chipman Ave & Ter (MEL) 76
Chisholm (EV) 49
Chisholm Ln, Rd & Ter
   (ROS) 31
Chisholm Rd (SWY) 90
Chiswick Rd
   1-99 (BRO) 46
   100-OUT (BRI) 35
Chiswick Ter (BRI) 35
Chittick Rd (HP) 36
Choate Rd (BEL) 78
Christina (NWH) 61
Christine Ave (STO) 80
Christine Rd (ARL) 74
Christine Ter (SWY) 90
Christopher (STO) 80
Christopher (DOR) 22
Christopher Dr (MIL) 86
Christopher Rd (WAL) 54
Chubbuck (QUI) 69
Church (WEL) 81
Church (WAV) 79
Church (STO) 80
Church (MEL) 76
Church (WAT) 72
Church (WAL) 54
Church (HP) 36
Church (WRX) 32
Church (EV) 49
Church (MAL) 48
Church (SOM) 43
Church (CAM) 38
Church (BRA) 84
Church (EWY) 89
Church (WES) 93
Church (DOR) 22
Church 16
Church Ave (SB) 27
Church Ct (CHA) 29
Church Pl (RXC) 20
Church St Pl (WAV) 79
Church St & Pl (MIL) 86
Church St & Rd (NEW) 58
Church Green 10
Church Hill Ln (WAT) 72

Boston (Con.)	021
Churchill (MIL)	87
Churchill (BRO)	46
Churchill Ave (CAM)	40
Churchill Ave (ARL)	74
Churchill Ln (LEX)	73
Churchill Ln (N)	92
Churchill Rd (QUI)	69
Churchill Rd (WRX)	32
Churchill St & Ter (NWV)	60
Churchills Ln (MIL)	86
Cibel Path (NCE)	59
Cimino Rd (NH)	94
Cindy Ln (BRA)	84
Circle Dr (WES)	93
Circle Dr (WY)	88
Circle Rd (WAL)	54
Circle Rd (MAL)	48
Circle Rd (LEX)	73
Circuit Ave (NWH)	61
Circuit Ave (WY)	88
Circuit Dr (JP)	30
Circuit Ln (WAL)	54
Circuit Rd (WIN)	52
Circuit Rd (SWY)	90
Circuit Rd (BRA)	84
Circuit Rd (CHH)	67
Circuit Rd (QUI)	69
Circuit St & Park (MEL)	76
Circuit St & Rd (MED)	55
Circuit St, Sq & Ter (ROX)	19
Citizen Pl (CAM)	41
City Sq (CHA)	29
City Hall Ave	08
City Hall Ave (CHE)	50
City Hall Mall (MED)	55
City Point Ct (SB)	27
City View Rd (BRO)	46
Claflin (BEL)	78
Claflin	02210
Claflin Path & Rd (BRO)	46
Claflin Pl (NWV)	60
Claflin Rd (WH)	81
Claflin Ter (MAL)	48
Clairemont Rd (BEL)	78
Clancy Rd (DOR)	24
Clapp (DOR)	25
Clapp (MAL)	48
Clapp (MIL)	86
Clapp Ave (WY)	88
Clare Ave	
1-85 (ROS) (ODD)	31
2-78 (ROS) (EVEN)	31
80-OUT (HP) (EVEN)	36
87-OUT (HP) (ODD)	36
Claremon (WS)	44
Claremont (MAL)	48
Claremont (WAL)	54
Claremont (BRA)	84
Claremont (NEW)	58
Claremont Ave (QUI)	69
Claremont Ave & Ct (ARL)	74
Claremont St & Park	18
Clarence (ROX)	19
Clarence (BRO)	46
Clarence (EV)	49
Clarence Ter (MAL)	48
Clarendon (MAL)	48
Clarendon	16
Clarendon (QUI)	69
Clarendon (NWV)	60

Clarendon (MEL)	76
Clarendon (WAT)	72
Clarendon (SWY)	90
Clarendon Ave (WS)	44
Clarendon Ave (CAM)	40
Clarendon Ct & Pl (ROS)	31
Clarendon Rd (BEL)	78
Claridge Ter (DOR)	24
Clark (NQ)	09
Clark (NQ)	71
Clark (NCE)	59
Clark (ARL)	74
Clark (SOM)	43
Clark (MAL)	48
Clark (EV)	49
Clark (MED)	55
Clark (BRA)	84
Clark Ave (CHE)	50
Clark Ct & Rd (BRO)	46
Clark Rd (REV)	51
Clark Rd (MIL)	86
Clark Rd (SWY)	90
Clark Rd (WH)	81
Clark Rd (WNW)	65
Clark St Pl (CAM)	39
Clark St & Ln (BEL)	78
Clark St, Ln & Ter (WAL)	54
Clarke (CAM)	39
Clarke (LEX)	73
Clarke Cir & Rd (N)	92
Clarke St Pl (CAM)	39
Clarken Ct (CHA)	29
Clarkson (DOR)	25
Clarkwood (MAT)	26
Claron (ROS)	31
Clary (CAM)	39
Claxton (ROS)	31
Clay (CAM)	40
Clay (MIL)	86
Clay (WOL)	70
Clay Ave (EV)	49
Claybourne (DOR)	24
Claymont Ter (DOR)	22
Claymoss Rd (BRI)	35
Clayton (MAL)	48
Clayton (DOR)	22
Clayton (WAT)	72
Clayton Ave (MED)	55
Clearview Rd (STO)	80
Clearwater Dr (MAT)	26
Clearwater Rd (CHH)	67
Clearwater Rd (NLF)	62
Clearway	15
Cleaves (ROX)	19
Cleaves (WOL)	70
Clelland Rd (LEX)	73
Clematis (DOR)	22
Clematis Ave (WY)	88
Clematis Ave & Rd (WAL)	54
Clematis Rd (MED)	55
Clematis Rd (LEX)	73
Clement (MAL)	48
Clement Ave (WRX)	32
Clement Cir (CAM)	38
Clement Ter (NQ)	71
Clementine Park (DOR)	24
Clements Rd (NEW)	58
Clements Rd (WAL)	54
Clermont (DOR)	24
Cleveland (EB)	28
Cleveland (CAM)	38
Cleveland (SOM)	43
Cleveland (MAL)	48

Cleveland (MED)	55
Cleveland (HP)	36
Cleveland (REV)	51
Cleveland (WNW)	65
Cleveland (MEL)	76
Cleveland (ARL)	74
Cleveland Ave (EV)	49
Cleveland Ave (BRA)	84
Cleveland Cir (BRO)	46
Cleveland Pl	13
Cleveland Rd (WAL)	54
Cleveland Rd (N)	92
Cleveland Rd (WAT)	72
Cleveland Rd (WH)	81
Cleveland Rd	
1-30 (BRO)	46
31-OUT (CHH)	67
Cleveland St & Park (ROX)	19
Clevemont Ave (ALL)	34
Cleverly Ct (QUI)	69
Clewly Rd (MED)	55
Cliff (QUI)	69
Cliff (STO)	80
Cliff (ARL)	74
Cliff (NWY)	91
Cliff Ave (WIN)	52
Cliff Pl (ROX)	19
Cliff Rd (WAL)	54
Cliff Rd (WES)	93
Cliff Rd (BRA)	84
Cliff Rd (MIL)	87
Cliff Rd (WH)	81
Cliff Rd (NUF)	64
Cliff St, Ct & Ter (MAL)	48
Cliff St & Rd (MEL)	76
Cliffe Ave (LEX)	73
Cliffmont (ROS)	31
Clifford (HP)	36
Clifford (MEL)	76
Clifford (WEL)	81
Clifford (ROX)	19
Cliffside Ter (MAL)	48
Clifton (MAL)	48
Clifton (WS)	44
Clifton (REV)	51
Clifton (MED)	55
Clifton (CAM)	40
Clifton (BEL)	78
Clifton (QUI)	69
Clifton	
1-51 (ROX) (ODD)	19
2-56 (ROX) (EVEN)	19
53-OUT (DOR) (ODD)	25
58-OUT (DOR) (EVEN)	25
Clifton Ave (STO)	80
Clifton Ave (EV)	49
Clifton Park (MEL)	76
Clifton Rd (WH)	81
Clifton Rd (NCE)	59
Clifton Rd (MIL)	86
Cliftondale (ROS)	31
Clinton (CAM)	39
Clinton (MAL)	48
Clinton (WAL)	54
Clinton (NEW)	58
Clinton	09
Clinton Path (BRO)	46
Clinton Pl (CHA)	29
Clinton Pl (NCE)	59
Clinton Rd (MEL)	76
Clinton Rd (REV)	51
Clinton Rd (EWY)	89

Boston (Con.)   021

Clinton Rd
  1-440 (BRO)........................ 46
  441-OUT (CHH).................... 67
Clinton St & Ct (CHE)............. 50
Clinton St & Pl (EV)............... 49
Clive (JP)........................... 30
Clive (NQ).......................... 71
Cliveden (QUI)...................... 69
Cloelia Ter (NWV).................. 60
Clovelly Rd (WH)................... 81
Clovelly Rd (CHH).................. 67
Clover (BEL)........................ 78
Clover (DOR)....................... 22.
Cloverdale Rd
  1-34 (NCE)........................ 59
  35-OUT (NWH)..................... 61
Cluney Ct (ROX).................... 19
Clyde (EB).......................... 28
Clyde (N)........................... 92
Clyde (BEL)......................... 78
Clyde (CHH)........................ 67
Clyde (NWV)........................ 60
Clyde (CHE)........................ 50
Clyde (SOM)........................ 45
Clyde (MAL)........................ 48
Clyde Pl (LEX)...................... 73
Clyde Rd (WAT)..................... 72
Clyde Ter (ARL).................... 74
Coach Rd (LEX)..................... 73
Cobb (MED)......................... 55
Cobb Pl (WAB)...................... 68
Cobble Hill Rd (SOM)............... 43
Cobden (ROX)....................... 19
Coburn (MAL)....................... 48
Coburn Ct.......................... 14
Coburn Rd (WES).................... 93
Coburn Ter (EV).................... 49
Cochato (BRA)...................... 85

Cochato Rd (BRA)................... 84
Cochituate Rd (NWH)............... 61
Cochrane (MEL)..................... 76
Codding Ave (MED).................. 55
Coddington (QUI)................... 69
Codman Park & Pl (ROX)............ 19
Codman Rd (BRO)................... 46
Codman St & Sq (DOR).............. 24
Codman Hill Ave (DOR)............. 24
Cody Rd (SWY)...................... 90
Coe (NQ)........................... 71
Coffey (DOR)....................... 22
Cogswell Ave & Pl (CAM)........... 40
Cohasset (ROS)..................... 31
Coker (WAL)........................ 54
Colasanti Rd (NWY)................. 91
Colberg Ave (ROS).................. 31
Colbert (WRX)...................... 32
Colbert Ave (BRA).................. 85
Colbert Rd (WNW)................... 65
Colborne Rd (BRI).................. 35
Colbourne Cres (BRO)............... 46
Colburn (WAL)...................... 54
Colburn Rd (WH).................... 81
Colby (BEL)........................ 78
Colby (MED)........................ 55
Colby (N).......................... 92
Colby (BRA)........................ 84
Colby Rd (ROS)..................... 31
Colby Rd (WH)...................... 81
Colby Rd (NQ)...................... 71
Colby Rd (ARL)..................... 74

Colby Ter (MEL).................... 76
Colchester (BRO)................... 46
Colchester (HP).................... 36
Colchester Rd (WES)................ 93
Colebrook (SB)..................... 27
Colella Rd (NCE)................... 59
Coleman (DOR)...................... 25
Coleman (HP)....................... 36
Coleman (MAL)...................... 48
Coleman Rd (ARL)................... 74
Colerain (ALL)..................... 34
Coleridge (EB)..................... 28
Coles Park (DOR)................... 21
Colgate Park & Rd (NLF)............ 62
Colgate Rd (WEL)................... 81
Colgate Rd (ROS)................... 31
Colgate Rd (N)..................... 92
Collamore (MIL).................... 86
College Ave (MED).................. 55
College Ave (ARL).................. 74
College Ave
  1-200 (WS)........................ 44
  201-OUT (MED)..................... 55
College Cir (WS)................... 44
College Rd (WH).................... 81
College Rd (CHH)................... 67
College Farm Rd (WAL).............. 54
College Hill Rd (WS)............... 44
Collincote (STO)................... 80
Collings Cir (MED)................. 55
Collins (HP)....................... 36
Collins Rd (WAB)................... 68
Colliston Rd (BRO)................. 46
Colman Pl (ALL).................... 35
Colon (BRI)........................ 35
Colonial Ave (WAL)................. 54
Colonial Ave (NWV)................. 60
Colonial Ave (LEX)................. 73
Colonial Ave (DOR)................. 24
Colonial Ct (STO).................. 80
Colonial Dr (ARL).................. 74
Colonial Dr (QUI).................. 69
Colonial Rd (REV).................. 51
Colonial Rd (MIL).................. 86
Colonial Rd (NWY).................. 91
Colonial Rd (N).................... 92
Colonial Ter (BEL)................. 78
Colonial Way (WES)................. 93
Colonial Village Dr (ARL).......... 74
Colony Rd (LEX).................... 73
Colorado (MAT)..................... 26
Colpitts Rd (WES).................. 93
Columbia........................... 11
Columbia (QUI)..................... 69
Columbia (WH)...................... 81
Columbia (WAT)..................... 72
Columbia (REV)..................... 51
Columbia (MAL)..................... 48
Columbia
  1-279 (CAM)....................... 39
  280-462 (CAM) (EVEN).............. 41
  281-459 (CAM) (ODD)............... 41
  461-OUT (SOM) (ODD)............... 43
  464-OUT (SOM) (EVEN).............. 43
Columbia Ave (NWH)................. 61
Columbia Ave (NUF)................. 64
Columbia Park (MIL)................ 87
Columbia Pl & Ter (DOR)............ 25
Columbia Rd (ARL).................. 74
Columbia Rd (MED).................. 55
Columbia Rd
  1-313 (DOR) (ODD)................. 21
  2-310 (DOR) (EVEN)................ 21

  312-898 (DOR) (EVEN).............. 25
  315-899 (DOR) (ODD)............... 25
  900-OUT (SB)...................... 27
Columbia St & Ter (BRO)............ 46
Columbia Ter (CAM)................. 39
Columbia Ter (BRA)................. 84
Columbian
  1-595 (SWY) (ODD)................. 90
  2-580 (SWY) (EVEN)................ 90
  582-OUT (BRA) (EVEN).............. 85
  597-OUT (BRA) (ODD)............... 85
Columbine (DOR).................... 24
Columbine Rd (MIL)................. 87
Columbine Rd (WES)................. 93
Columbine Rd (NCE)................. 59
Columbus (LEX)..................... 73
Columbus (CHE)..................... 50
Columbus Ave (CAM)................. 40
Columbus Ave (SOM)................. 43
Columbus Ave (WAL)................. 54
Columbus Ave (MEL)................. 76
Columbus Ave (BRA)................. 85
Columbus Ave
  1-475 (ODD)....................... 16
  2-472 (EVEN)...................... 16
  474-650 (EVEN).................... 18
  477-649 (ODD)..................... 18
  651-1500 (RXC).................... 20
  1501-OUT (ROX).................... 19
Columbus Pl (WNW).................. 65
Columbus Sq........................ 16
Columbus St & Ter (NWH)............ 61
Colwell Ave (BRI).................. 35
Comeau (WH)........................ 81
Comet Pl........................... 18
Comins Ter (ROX)................... 19
Commander Shea Blvd (NQ)........... 71
Commerce........................... 09
Commercial (EV).................... 49
Commercial (MAL)................... 48
Commercial (MED)................... 55
Commercial
  1-559 (WY)........................ 88
  560-OUT (EWY)..................... 89
Commercial Ave
  1-63 (CAM)........................ 41
  64-OUT (CAM)...................... 42
Commercial Sq (EWY)................ 89
Commercial St & Ct (BRA).......... 84
Commercial St & Ct................. 09
Commercial Wharf................... 10
Common............................. 16
Common (CHA)....................... 29
Common (BRA)....................... 84
Common (WY)........................ 88
Common (WAL)....................... 54
Common (WAT)....................... 72
Common (STO)....................... 80
Common (BEL)....................... 78
Common (QUI)....................... 69
Commonwealth Ave................02210
Commonwealth Ave (QUI)............ 69
Commonwealth Ave
  1-269 (ODD)....................... 16
  1-400 (CHH)....................... 67
  2-282 (EVEN)...................... 16
  271-393 (ODD)..................... 15
  284-368 (EVEN).................... 15
  370-1110 (REV).................02215
  395-1123 (ODD).................02215
  401-1140 (NCE).................... 59
  1112-1400 (ALL) (EVEN)........... 34
  1125-1399 (ALL) (ODD)............ 34

Boston (Con.)	021
1141-1750 (WNW)	65
1401-OUT (BRI)	35
1751-OUT (AUB)	66
Commonwealth Ct (BRI)	35
Commonwealth Park (WH)	81
Commonwealth Park E & W (NCE)	59
Commonwealth Rd (WAT)	72
Commonwealth Ter (BRO)	46
Commonwealth Pier	02210
Como (MAL)	48
Como Rd (HP)	36
Compton (ARL)	74
Compton Cir (LEX)	73
Conant (REV)	51
Conant Rd (NQ)	71
Conant Rd (WAT)	72
Conant Rd (MEL)	76
Conant Rd (CHH)	67
Conant Rd (WES)	93
Conant St & Pl (RXC)	20
Conastoga Rd (LEX)	73
Concolor Ave (NEW)	58
Concord (NLF)	62
Concord (CHA)	29
Concord (NH)	94
Concord (SWY)	90
Concord (MAL)	48
Concord Ave (SOM)	43
Concord Ave (CAM)	38
Concord Ave (MIL)	87
Concord Ave	09
Concord Ave (BEL)	78
Concord Ave & Tpke (LEX)	73
Concord Pl & Sq	18
Concord Rd (WAT)	72
Concord Rd (WES)	93
Concord Tpke	
2-248 (ARL) (EVEN)	74
195-245 (CAM) (ODD)	40
250-258 (CAM) (EVEN)	40
260-398 (BEL) (EVEN)	78
554-1176 (BEL) (EVEN)	78
1178-OUT (ARL) (EVEN)	74
Condor (EB)	28
Confirmation Pl (CHA)	29
Congress (WY)	88
Congress (BRA)	85
Congress (STO)	80
Congress	
1-111 (ODD)	09
2-132 (EVEN)	09
113-261 (ODD)	10
134-268 (EVEN)	10
263-OUT (ODD)	02210
270-OUT (EVEN)	02210
Congress Ave (MED)	55
Congress Ave (CHE)	50
Congress St Pl	10
Congreve (ROS)	31
Coniston Rd (ROS)	31
Conley (DOR)	22
Connecticut Ave (SOM)	45
Connell (BRA)	84
Connell (QUI)	69
Connolly Cir (BRA)	84
Conrad (BRA)	84
Conrad (QUI)	69
Conrad (DOR)	25
Conrad Rd (MEL)	76
Conry Cres (JP)	30
Considine Rd (NCE)	59
Constance (MAL)	48
Constance Rd (WRX)	32
Constitution Ave (REV)	51
Constitution Ave (SWY)	90
Constitution Rd (LEX)	73
Constitution Rd (MAT)	26
Constitution Wharf	09
Continental Rd (CHE)	50
Converse (BRI)	35
Converse Ave (MAL)	48
Converse Ave (NEW)	58
Converse Ln (MEL)	76
Conway Ct (MAL)	48
Conway Rd (MIL)	86
Conway St & Ct (ROS)	31
Conwell (SOM)	43
Conwell Ave (WS)	44
Cook (NEW)	58
Cook (CHA)	29
Cook Ave (CHE)	50
Cook St Ct (CHA)	29
Cook St Pl (CHA)	29
Cooke Rd (LEX)	73
Cookson Ter (MAT)	26
Cooledge St & Ave (REV)	51
Coolidge (EV)	49
Coolidge (BRO)	46
Coolidge (STO)	80
Coolidge Ave (LEX)	73
Coolidge Ave (WAT)	72
Coolidge Ave (CAM)	38
Coolidge Ave (WAL)	54
Coolidge Ave (BRA)	84
Coolidge Ave (WY)	88
Coolidge Ave (N)	92
Coolidge Pl (CAM)	39
Coolidge Rd (MED)	55
Coolidge Rd (ALL)	34
Coolidge Rd (MIL)	86
Coolidge Rd (NCE)	59
Coolidge Rd (MEL)	76
Coolidge Rd (ARL)	74
Coolidge Rd (DOR)	24
Coolidge Hill Rd (WAT)	72
Coolidge Hill St & Rd (CAM)	38
Cooney (SOM)	43
Cooper	13
Cooper Ln (WAL)	54
Cooper Ter (REV)	51
Copeland (WAL)	54
Copeland (WAT)	72
Copeland (QUI)	69
Copeland St, Park & Pl (ROX)	19
Copeland Ter (MAL)	20
Copenger (RXC)	20
Copley (ROX)	19
Copley (BRO)	46
Copley (CAM)	38
Copley (WOL)	70
Copley (NEW)	58
Copley Ter (WAL)	54
Copley Sq	16
Coppersmith Way (EB)	28
Copps Hill Ter	13
Cora (WIN)	52
Coral (REV)	51
Coral (ARL)	74
Coral Ave (WIN)	52
Coral Pl (CHA)	29
Corbet (DOR)	24
Corcoran Dr (HP)	36
Corcoran Park (CAM)	38
Cordis (CHA)	29
Cordis St Ave (CHA)	29
Corey (CHA)	29
Corey (MED)	55
Corey (EV)	49
Corey (MEL)	76
Corey (SWY)	90
Corey Ln (MIL)	86
Corey Rd (MAL)	48
Corey Rd (BRO)	46
Corey St & Ter (WRX)	32
Corina Rd (WIN)	52
Corinth (ROS)	31
Corinthian Rd (WS)	44
Corliss (ROX)	19
Corliss Pl (CAM)	39
Corman Rd (MAT)	26
Cornauba (ROS)	31
Cornauba St Ext (ROS)	31
Cornelia Ct (RXC)	20
Cornell (ROS)	31
Cornell (ARL)	74
Cornell (NLF)	62
Cornell Rd (WH)	81
Corner (MEL)	76
Cornhill St & Ct	08
Cornish (EWY)	89
Cornwall (JP)	30
Cornwallis Pl (WAL)	54
Corona (DOR)	24
Coronado Rd (MAT)	26
Corporal Burns Rd (CAM)	38
Corporal Mc Ternan (CAM)	39
Corporation Way (MED)	55
Corregidor Ct (ROX)	19
Corrine Rd (BRI)	35
Corrinne Rd (MED)	55
Cortes	16
Corwin (DOR)	22
Corwood Dr (WES)	93
Cotswold Rd (BRO)	46
Cotswold Ter (NCE)	59
Cottage (BEL)	78
Cottage (WEL)	81
Cottage (STO)	80
Cottage (NUF)	64
Cottage (LEX)	73
Cottage (BRO)	46
Cottage (MED)	55
Cottage (REV)	51
Cottage (CHE)	50
Cottage (EV)	49
Cottage (EWY)	89
Cottage (EB)	28
Cottage (SB)	27
Cottage Ave (NH)	94
Cottage Ave (WIN)	52
Cottage Ave (ARL)	74
Cottage Ave & Cir (WS)	44
Cottage Ct (NEW)	58
Cottage Ct (DOR)	25
Cottage Ln (WY)	88
Cottage Park Ave (CAM)	40
Cottage Park Rd (WIN)	52
Cottage Pl (HP)	36
Cottage Pl (MIL)	86
Cottage Pl (WNW)	65
Cottage Rd (WRX)	32
Cottage St Pl (EB)	28

Boston (Con.) 021

Cottage St & Ave (QUI)	69
Cottage St, Ct & Row (CAM)	39
Cottage St & Ln (WAT)	72
Cottage St & Park (MEL)	76
Cottage St & Pl (MAL)	48
Cottage Farm Rd (BRO)	46
Cotter Rd (WAB)	68
Cotting (MED)	55
Cotton (ROS)	31
Cotton (NEW)	58
Cotton Ave (BRA)	84
Cottonwood Rd (NCE)	59
Cottonwood Rd (WEL)	81
Cottrell (DOR)	25
Cotuit (WRX)	32
Coulton Park (N)	92
Country Dr (WES)	93
Country Rd (CHH)	67
Country Way (N)	92
Country Club Dr & Ln (ARL)	74
Country Club Ln (BEL)	78
Country Club Rd (MEL)	76
Country Club Rd (STO)	80
Country Club Rd (NCE)	59
Countryside Dr (MAT)	26
Countryside Rd (NCE)	59
County Rd (QUI)	69
County Rd (CHE)	50
County Rd (EV)	49
Courier (SWY)	90
Court (MED)	55
Court (NWV)	60
Court (ARL)	74
Court Rd (WIN)	52
Court Rd (BRA)	85
Court St Pl (ARL)	74
Court St & Sq	08
Courtland (EV)	49
Courtland Cir (MIL)	86
Courtland Rd (MAT)	26
Courtney Rd (WRX)	32
Cousens Cir (NCE)	59
Cove (REV)	51
Coventry (RXC)	20
Covington (SB)	27
Cowasset Ln (WAL)	54
Cowdin (BEL)	78
Cowdrey (STO)	80
Cowing (WRX)	32
Cowper (EB)	28
Cowperthwaite (CAM)	38
Coyne Rd (WAB)	68
Cozy (WAT)	72
Crabtree Rd (NQ)	71
Craddock Ave (MED)	55
Craft Pl (JP)	30
Crafts (WAL)	54
Crafts	
1-409 (NWV)	60
410-OUT (WNW)	65
Crafts Rd (CHH)	67
Craftsland Rd (CHH)	67
Cragmere Ter (MAT)	26
Cragmore Rd (NUF)	64
Craig (MIL)	86
Craig Ave (QUI)	69
Craig Ln (WAL)	54
Craig Pl (BRO)	46
Craigie St & Cir (CAM)	38
Craigie St & Ter (SOM)	43

Craigie Ter (NWV)	60
Craigie Bridge	14
Crammond Rd (CHH)	67
Cranberry Ln (N)	92
Cranberry Rd (WY)	88
Cranch (EWY)	89
Cranch (QUI)	69
Crandall (ROS)	31
Crane (MED)	55
Crane (HP)	36
Crane Rd (QUI)	69
Crane Rd (MIL)	87
Cranmore Ln (MEL)	76
Cranmore Rd (WEL)	81
Cranmore Rd (BRA)	85
Cranmore Rd (HP)	36
Cranston (JP)	30
Craven Cir (WAL)	54
Crawford (CAM)	39
Crawford (MAL)	48
Crawford (BRA)	84
Crawford (NH)	94
Crawford (WAT)	72
Crawford (ARL)	74
Crawford (DOR)	21
Crawford Rd (LEX)	73
Crawford Rd (BRA)	85
Creeley Rd (WAV)	79
Crehore Dr (NLF)	62
Crehore Rd (CHH)	67
Creighton (CAM)	40
Creighton (JP)	30
Cremona Rd (REV)	51
Crescent (WIN)	52
Crescent (CAM)	38
Crescent (MED)	55
Crescent (EV)	49
Crescent (WH)	81
Crescent (QUI)	69
Crescent (WES)	93
Crescent	
1-50 (WNW)	65
1-OUT (CHA) (ODD)	29
2-OUT (SOM) (EVEN)	45
51-OUT (AUB)	66
Crescent Ave (BRA)	85
Crescent Ave (STO)	80
Crescent Ave (NCE)	59
Crescent Ave (CHE)	50
Crescent Ave (REV)	51
Crescent Ave (MAL)	48
Crescent Ave (DOR)	25
Crescent Ave & Pl (MEL)	76
Crescent Rd (BEL)	78
Crescent Rd (LEX)	73
Crescent Rd (NH)	94
Crescent Rd (NWY)	91
Crescent Sq (NEW)	58
Crescent St & Park (WAL)	54
Crescent Hill Ave (LEX)	73
Crescent Hill Ave (ARL)	74
Crest (QUI)	69
Crest (WRX)	32
Crest Ave (WIN)	52
Crest Ave (REV)	51
Crest Ave (CHE)	50
Crest Ave (MEL)	76
Crest Ave (EWY)	89
Crest Rd (WEL)	81
Crest Rd (MED)	55
Crest Hill Rd (SOM)	45
Cresthill Rd (BRI)	35
Cresto Ter. (CAM)	41

Creston St & Park (DOR)	21
Crestview Rd (WAL)	54
Crestview Rd (BEL)	78
Crestway Rd (EB)	28
Crestwood Dr (WH)	81
Crestwood Park (DOR)	21
Crestwood Rd (WNW)	65
Cricket Ln (WRX)	32
Cricklewood Dr (STO)	80
Cricklewood Ln (MEL)	76
Crispus Attucks (ROX)	19
Crocker (SOM)	43
Crocker Cir (WNW)	65
Crocker Rd (MED)	55
Crockers Pl (WRX)	32
Crockett Ave (DOR)	24
Croftdale Rd (NCE)	59
Croftland Ave (DOR)	24
Crofton Rd (WAB)	68
Cromwell Rd (HP)	36
Crosby (STO)	80
Crosby (QUI)	69
Crosby (ARL)	74
Crosby Rd (CHH)	67
Crosby Rd (LEX)	73
Crosby Sq (JP)	30
Cross (HP)	36
Cross (MED)	55
Cross (CAM)	39
Cross (WAL)	54
Cross (MAL)	48
Cross (SOM)	45
Cross (CHE)	50
Cross (EV)	49
Cross (WIN)	52
Cross (REV)	51
Cross (WNW)	65
Cross (ARL)	74
Cross (QUI)	69
Cross (WEL)	81
Cross (BEL)	78
Cross (WAT)	72
Cross (CHA)	29
Cross (EWY)	89
Cross (NH)	94
Cross	
1-71 (ODD)	13
2-68 (EVEN)	13
70-OUT (EVEN)	09
73-OUT (ODD)	09
Cross E (SOM)	45
Cross Rd (WRX)	32
Cross Rd (BRA)	85
Cross St Pl (SOM)	45
Cross Hill Rd (NCE)	59
Crossland (CAM)	39
Crossland Pl (BRI)	35
Crossman (MAT)	26
Crosstown Ave (WRX)	32
Croton (WH)	81
Crowell (DOR)	24
Crowley Ln (BRA)	85
Crowley Rd (MED)	55
Crowley Rogers Way (SB)	27
Crown (MAT)	26
Crown (SOM)	43
Crown (MIL)	87
Crown (AUB)	66
Crown Point Dr (HP)	36
Crown Ridge Rd (WEL)	81
Crowninshield Rd (BRO)	46
Croydon (MAT)	26
Crystal (MAL)	48

Boston (Con.) 021

Crystal (NCE)	59
Crystal (MEL)	76
Crystal Ave (REV)	51
Crystal Pl (CHA)	29
Crystal Cove Ave (WIN)	52
Cuba (WAT)	72
Cudworth (MED)	55
Cufflin (BRI)	35
Culbert (MAT)	26
Cumberland	15
Cumberland (EV)	49
Cumberland Ave (BRO)	46
Cumberland Rd (BEL)	78
Cumberland Rd (WNW)	65
Cummings (MED)	55
Cummings	18
Cummings Ave (REV)	51
Cummings Ave (WOL)	70
Cummings Ave (LEX)	73
Cummings Ave (SWY)	90
Cummings Rd (NCE)	59
Cummings Rd (BRO)	46
Cummington	02215
Cummins Hwy	
1-531 (ROS)	31
532-OUT (MAT)	26
Cumner Ave (MEL)	76
Cunard (RXC)	20
Cunningham (DOR)	25
Cunningham Cir (WAL)	54
Cunningham Park (MIL)	86
Cunningham Rd (WH)	81
Curlew (WRX)	32
Curlew Rd (QUI)	69
Curley (ROS)	31
Curtis (WAL)	54
Curtis (WH)	81
Curtis (NWH)	61
Curtis (NWY)	91
Curtis (EB)	28
Curtis	
1-135 (WS)	44
136-136 (MED)	55
137-OUT (WS)	44
Curtis Ave (WS)	44
Curtis Rd (REV)	51
Curtis Rd (N)	92
Curtis Rd (MIL)	87
Curtis St & Ave (QUI)	69
Curtis St & Pl (MED)	55
Curve (MAL)	48
Curve (WAL)	54
Curve (WNW)	65
Curve (WEL)	81
Curve (LEX)	73
Curve (N)	92
Curve Rd (STO)	80
Cushing (LEX)	73
Cushing (NWH)	61
Cushing (WOL)	70
Cushing (SWY)	90
Cushing (WAL)	54
Cushing (MED)	55
Cushing Ave (REV)	51
Cushing Ave (BEL)	78
Cushing Ave (DOR)	25
Cushing Cir (MEL)	76
Cushing Rd (WH)	81
Cushing Rd (BRO)	46
Cushing Rd (MAL)	48

Cushing Rd (MIL)	86
Cushing St & Ct (CAM)	38
Cushman (WAT)	72
Cushman Ave (REV)	51
Cushman Rd (BRI)	35
Custer (JP)	30
Custom House	10
Cuthbert Rd (WRX)	32
Cutler (WIN)	52
Cutler (SOM)	45
Cutler Ave (CAM)	38
Cutler Ct (WAL)	54
Cutler Ct (SB)	27
Cutler Ln & Rd (CHH)	67
Cutler Rd (N)	92
Cutler Farm Rd (LEX)	73
Cutter (WAV)	79
Cutter (MEL)	76
Cutter (WAL)	54
Cutter (SOM)	45
Cutter Ave, Park, Pl & Sq (WS)	44
Cutter Rd (WRX)	32
Cutterhill Rd (ARL)	74
Cutting Ln (WAL)	54
Cygnet (BRI)	35
Cynthia Cir (WY)	88
Cynthia Rd (NH)	94
Cynthia Rd (NCE)	59
Cypher (SB)	27
Cypress (NCE)	59
Cypress (WAT)	72
Cypress (SWY)	90
Cypress (BRA)	84
Cypress (BRO)	46
Cypress (CAM)	40
Cypress (SOM)	43
Cypress Ct (BRI)	35
Cypress Park (MEL)	76
Cypress Rd (ARL)	74
Cypress Rd (WH)	81
Cypress Rd (MED)	55
Cypress Rd (MIL)	86
Cypress St & Ter (WRX)	32
Cyril (QUI)	69
D	
1-377 (SB) (ODD)	27
2-350 (SB) (EVEN)	27
352-OUT (EVEN)	02210
379-OUT (ODD)	02210
Dabney Pl (ROX)	19
Dacia St & Ter (DOR)	25
Dacy (HP)	36
Dade (ROX)	19
Dahlgren (DOR)	24
Dahlgren (NQ)	71
Dakota (DOR)	24
Dalby (NEW)	58
Dale (NWV)	60
Dale (WH)	81
Dale (LEX)	73
Dale (CHH)	67
Dale (ROX)	19
Dale (ROS)	31
Dale (MAL)	48
Dale (REV)	51
Dale (NH)	94
Dale Ave (QIN)	69
Dale Ct (STG)	80
Dale Rd (EWY)	89
Dale St & Cir (WAL)	54
Dalessio Ct (SB)	27

Daley St & Pl (NH)	94
Dalin Pl (DOR)	25
Dalkeith (DOR)	25
Dallas (RXC)	20
Dalrymple (JP)	30
Dalton	
1-38	15
39-39	99
40-OUT	15
Dalton Rd (NCE)	59
Dalton Rd (BEL)	78
Daly (DOR)	22
Daly Rd (MED)	55
Damien Rd (WH)	81
Damon Ave (MEL)	76
Damon Park (ARL)	74
Damon Rd (MED)	55
Damon Rd (NH)	94
Damon St & Pl (HP)	36
Damrell (SB)	27
Dana (REV)	51
Dana (MAL)	48
Dana (BRO)	46
Dana (SOM)	45
Dana (CAM)	38
Dana Ave	
1-257 (HP)	36
258-OUT (MIL)	86
Dana Ct (WAL)	54
Dana Pl (NH)	94
Dana Rd (WY)	88
Dana Rd (WRX)	32
Dana Rd (BEL)	78
Dana Rd (WEL)	81
Dana Rd (WNW)	65
Dana St, Ct & Pl (ROX)	19
Dana Ter (WAT)	72
Danbury Rd (MAT)	26
Danbury Rd (SWY)	90
Danby Rd (STO)	80
Dane (JP)	30
Dane (EV)	49
Dane Rd (LEX)	73
Dane St & Ave (SOM)	43
Dane Hill Rd (NWH)	61
Daney Rd (HP)	36
Danforth (JP)	30
Danforth Pl (ROX)	19
Dania St & Ter (MAT)	26
Daniel (NCE)	59
Daniel (EWY)	89
Daniel Ct (HP)	36
Daniel Rd (BRA)	85
Daniels (MAL)	48
Daniels (MED)	55
Daniels (LEX)	73
Daniels (ARL)	74
Daniels Ct (WAL)	54
Danny Rd (HP)	36
Dante Ave (WAV)	79
Dante Ter (SOM)	43
Danube (DOR)	25
Danville (WRX)	32
Darby Rd (MIL)	87
Darch Rd (WAT)	72
Darius Ct (SB)	27
Darling (RXC)	20
Darlington (DOR)	24
Darrow (QUI)	69
Dartmouth (QUI)	69
Dartmouth (WAT)	72
Dartmouth (ARL)	74
Dartmouth (WNW)	65

Boston (Con.) 021

Dartmouth (BEL)	78
Dartmouth (MEL)	76
Dartmouth (WAL)	54
Dartmouth (MED)	55
Dartmouth (MAL)	48
Dartmouth (SOM)	45
Dartmouth (EV)	49
Dartmouth Ave (NH)	94
Dartmouth St & Pl	16
Dashwood (REV)	51
Davenport (CAM)	40
Davenport (RXC)	20
Davenport Rd (NH)	94
Davern Ave (DOR)	25
David Rd (NH)	94
David Rd (JP)	30
David Rd (NCE)	59
David Island Rd (NWY)	91
David's Hill Rd (NWY)	91
Davidson Ave (DOR)	25
Davis (WOL)	70
Davis (REV)	51
Davis (EV)	49
Davis Ave & Ct (BRO)	46
Davis Ave & Rd (ARL)	74
Davis Ct (EB)	28
Davis Rd (LEX)	73
Davis Rd (SWY)	90
Davis Rd (BRA)	84
Davis Sq (WS)	44
Davis St, Ave & Ct (WNW)	65
Davis St & Ct (CAM)	39
Davis St & Ct (MAL)	48
Davis St & Rd (WAV)	79
Davison (HP)	36
Davitt (DOR)	25
Dawes (REV)	51
Dawes (WAL)	54
Dawes Rd (LEX)	73
Dawes St & Ter (DOR)	25
Dawson (DOR)	24
Dawson Dr (N)	92
Day (AUB)	66
Day (ARL)	74
Day (MEL)	76
Day (WAL)	54
Day (JP)	30
Day	
1-17 (CAM) (ODD)	40
2-12 (CAM) (EVEN)	40
14-OUT (WS) (EVEN)	44
19-OUT (WS) (ODD)	44
Bay School Ln (BEL)	78
Dayton (QUI)	69
Dayton (DOR)	24
Dayton Ave (ROX)	19
De Forest Rd (NLF)	62
De Francesco Cir (N)	92
De Roma Rd (WRX)	32
De Soto Rd (WRX)	32
De Stephano Rd (ROS)	31
De Wolf (DOR)	25
De Wolf St & Pl (CAM)	38
Deacon (CAM)	42
Deaconess Rd	
1-44	02215
45-OUT	15
Dean (BRA)	84
Dean (EV)	49
Dean (DOR)	25
Dean (BEL)	78

Dean (STO)	80
Dean Rd (BRO)	46
Dean Rd (MIL)	86
Dean Rd	
1-24 (WH)	81
25-OUT (WES)	93
Dean Way (SB)	27
Deane Ave (WIN)	52
Deane Rd (NQ)	71
Dearborn (WH)	81
Dearborn (WNW)	65
Dearborn (ROX)	19
Dearborn St & Rd (MED)	55
Deborah Rd (NCE)	59
Debra Ln (BRA)	84
Decatur (NMV)	60
Decatur (ARL)	74
Decatur (CAM)	39
Decatur (EB)	28
Decatur (CHA)	29
Decher Ave (JP)	30
Deckard (DOR)	21
Decker (MIL)	87
Dedham (WRX)	32
Dedham (REV)	51
Dedham (HP)	36
Dedham	
1-300 (NWH)	61
301-OUT (NCE)	59
Dedham Ave (N)	92
Dee Rd (QUI)	69
Dee Rd (LEX)	73
Deepwater (WIN)	52
Deer (DOR)	25
Deer Path Ln (WES)	93
Deer Island (WIN)	52
Deerfield (N)	92
Deerfield (NQ)	71
Deerfield Rd (WH)	84
Deering Ave (BRA)	84
Deering Ave (LEX)	73
Deering Rd (MAT)	26
Deforest	
1-99 (HP)	36
100-OUT (ROS)	31
Dehon (REV)	51
Deigan Ave (BRA)	85
Delano (EV)	49
Delano Ave (REV)	51
Delano Ave (QUI)	69
Delano Ct & Park (ROS)	31
Delanson Cir (WEL)	81
Delaware (SOM)	45
Delaware Pl (BRI)	35
Deldorf (QUI)	69
Delford (ROS)	31
Delhi (MAT)	26
Delia Walker Rd (SWY)	90
Dell (MAL)	48
Dell (SOM)	45
Dell (WH)	81
Dell Ave (MEL)	76
Dell Ave (MED)	55
Dell Ave (N)	92
Dell Ave & Ter (HP)	36
Delle Ave (RXC)	20
Dellmore Rd (JP)	30
Delmont (DOR)	22
Delmore Rd (NWH)	61
Delnore Pl (MAT)	26
Delore Cir (ROS)	31
Delorey Ave (NWY)	91

Delta Rd (BRA)	84
Demar Rd (LEX)	73
Demerest (WAL)	54
Demers Ln (EV)	49
Deming Rd (LEX)	73
Denby Rd (ALL)	34
Denmark Ave (MIL)	86
Dennis (ROX)	19
Dennis Rd (MAL)	48
Dennis Rd (WH)	81
Dennison (WAL)	54
Dennison (ROX)	19
Denns Pl (NCE)	59
Denny (DOR)	25
Denny Rd (CHH)	67
Densmore (NQ)	71
Dent (WRX)	32
Denton Rd E & W (WEL)	81
Denton Ter (ROS)	31
Denver (LEX)	73
Denvir (DOR)	24
Depot Sq (LEX)	73
Derby (WNW)	65
Derby (WAL)	54
Derby (SOM)	45
Derby (SWY)	90
Derby Ln (WES)	93
Derby Rd (REV)	51
Derby Rd (WAT)	72
Derby Rd (MEL)	76
Dermody Rd (WAL)	54
Derne (EV)	49
Derne	14
Derry (EWY)	89
Derry Rd (HP)	36
Des Moines Rd (QUI)	69
Desmond Ave (WAT)	72
Desmond Rd (MAL)	48
Desmond Rd (MAT)	26
Devens (CHA)	29
Devens (EV)	49
Devens St Pl (CHA)	29
Dever (DOR)	22
Devereaux (ARL)	74
Devine Way (SB)	27
Devir (MAL)	48
Devon (DOR)	21
Devon Rd (CHH)	67
Devon Rd (BRA)	84
Devon Rd & Ter (NCE)	59
Devonshire	
1-135 (ODD)	09
2-100 (EVEN)	09
102-OUT (EVEN)	10
137-OUT (ODD)	10
Devonshire Rd (WAB)	68
Devotion (BRO)	46
Dewar (DOR)	25
Dewey (DOR)	25
Dewey (WAT)	72
Dewey Ave (MED)	55
Dewey Ave (BRA)	85
Dewey Rd (BRA)	84
Dewey Rd (LEX)	73
Dewey Sq	02210
Dewhurst (NQ)	71
Dewitt Rd (STO)	80
Dewson Rd (QUI)	69
Dexter (MIL)	86
Dexter (MED)	55
Dexter (MAL)	48
Dexter (EV)	49
Dexter Ave (WAT)	72

Boston (Con.)	021
Dexter Rd (WEL)	81
Dexter Rd (LEX)	73
Dexter Rd (NWV)	60
Dexter Rd (MEL)	76
Dexter Row (CHA)	29
Dexter St & Ave (WAL)	54
Dexter St & Pl (SB)	27
Diamond Rd (LEX)	73
Diana Ln (LEX)	73
Diane Rd (MED)	55
Dianne Rd (STO)	80
Dickens (WOL)	70
Dickens (DOR)	22
Dickens Rd (LEX)	73
Dickerman Ln (BRA)	84
Dickerman Rd (NWH)	61
Dickinson (SOM)	43
Dickinson (CAM)	39
Dickinson Rd (BRI)	35
Dickson (WS)	44
Dickson Ave (ARL)	74
Diehl Rd (LEX)	73
Dietz Ct & Rd (HP)	36
Dighton (BRI)	35
Dilworth	18
Dimick (SOM)	43
Dimmock (QUI)	69
Dimock (ROX)	19
Dinnano Rd (STO)	80
Dinsmore Ct (CAM)	38
Dinsmore Rd (WH)	81
Ditmar (NQ)	71
Ditmus Ct	18
Ditson (DOR)	22
Divinity Ave (CAM)	38
Division (CHE)	50
Division (MAL)	48
Division (NQ)	71
Division (BRA)	85
Dix (WAL)	54
Dix (WIN)	52
Dix (REV)	51
Dix (DOR)	22
Dixfield (SB)	27
Dixon (WY)	88
Dixon Park Rd (WY)	88
Dixwell (ROX)	19
Dixwell Ave (QUI)	69
Doane (QUI)	69
Doane	09
Doane (CAM)	38
Doane Ave (N)	92
Doane Rd (MED)	55
Dobbins (WAL)	54
Doble (QUI)	69
Doble Ave (MED)	55
Dobson Rd (BRA)	84
Dock (CAM)	42
Dockray (QUI)	69
Dodge (ARL)	74
Dodge (CAM)	39
Dodge (MAL)	48
Dodge Rd (HP)	36
Dogwood Ln (N)	92
Bogwood Rd (WES)	93
Dolan Ave (WNW)	65
Dolans (JP)	30
Dollar Ln (MIL)	86
Dolphin (SWY)	90
Dolphin Ave (WIN)	52
Dolphin Ave (REV)	51

Dolphin Rd (NCE)	59
Don (DOR)	24
Donald (LEX)	73
Donald (WY)	88
Donald Rd (DOR)	24
Donata Rd (BRA)	85
Doncaster (ROS)	31
Donizetti (WEL)	81
Donna Rd (SB)	27
Donna Rd (SWY)	90
Donna Rd (NH)	94
Donna Rd (HP)	94
Donna Ter (HP)	36
Donnell (CAM)	38
Donnellan Cir (NWY)	91
Donnelly Sq (REV)	51
Donnybrook Rd (BRI)	35
Donoghue Pl (HP)	36
Donovan Pl (JP)	30
Donwood Ter (MAT)	26
Doonan Ave (MED)	55
Doone Ave (MAT)	26
Doran Rd (BRO)	46
Dorcar Rd	
1-56 (CHH)	67
57-OUT (NCE)	59
Dorchester (WAL)	54
Dorchester (SB)	27
Dorchester (NQ)	71
Dorchester Ave	
1-48	02210
49-74 (SB)	27
75-75	09
76-699 (SB)	27
700-1246 (DOR)	25
1247-1699 (DOR)	22
1700-OUT (DOR)	24
Doris (DOR)	25
Doris Cir (NEW)	58
Doris Dr & Rd (NWY)	91
Doris Rd (BRA)	84
Dormar Way (ARL)	74
Dorothy Rd (ARL)	74
Dorothy Rd (NCE)	59
Dorr (ROX)	19
Dorr Rd (NEW)	58
Dorrance (CHA)	29
Dorset (DOR)	25
Dorset Ln (WEL)	81
Dorset Rd (WAB)	68
Dorset Rd (BEL)	78
Dothan (ARL)	74
Doty (WAL)	54
Doublett Hill Rd (WES)	93
Douglas (REV)	51
Douglas (QUI)	69
Douglas (SB)	27
Douglas Ave (SOM)	45
Douglas Rd (WAL)	54
Douglas Rd (MED)	55
Douglas Rd (BEL)	78
Douglas Rd (LEX)	73
Douglas Rd (N)	92
Douglas St & Ct (CAM)	39
Douglass (WIN)	52
Douse Rd (WOL)	70
Dove St & Ct (DOR)	25
Dover (MED)	55
Dover	
1-43 (CAM) (ODD)	40
2-46 (CAM) (EVEN)	40
45-OUT (WS) (ODD)	44
48-OUT (WS) (EVEN)	44
Dover Rd (WH)	81

Dow (REV)	51
Dow (WS)	44
Dow Ave (ARL)	74
Dow Rd (WRX)	32
Downer Ave (DOR)	25
Downer Ct (DOR)	22
Downey (MAL)	48
Downey (WAT)	72
Downey Ct (DOR)	25
Downing Rd (LEX)	73
Downing Rd (BRO)	46
Dowse (EV)	49
Doyle Ter (QUI)	69
Drabbington Way (WES)	93
Dracut (DOR)	24
Draelon (ARL)	74
Drake (BRA)	85
Drake Pl (EB)	28
Drake Rd (ARL)	74
Draper (DOR)	22
Draper (MED)	55
Draper Ave (ARL)	74
Drayton Ave (DOR)	25
Dresden (JP)	30
Dresden Cir (WS)	44
Dresser (SB)	27
Drew Ave (LEX)	73
Drew Ave (EWY)	89
Drew Rd (BEL)	78
Drew Rd (CHH)	67
Driftway Rd (NWY)	91
Driftwood Dr (WNW)	85
Driftwood Ln (WES)	93
Driftwood Rd (JP)	30
Drinkwater Ave (BRA)	84
Driscoll Dr (DOR)	24
Dromey (DOR)	25
Druce (BRO)	46
Druid (MAT)	26
Druid Hill Ave (MEL)	76
Druid Hill Rd (NWH)	61
Drumlin Rd (NCE)	59
Drumlin Rd (EB)	28
Drummond (DOR)	21
Drummond Pl (CAM)	40
Drummond Rd (STO)	80
Drury Ln (STO)	80
Drury Ln (WAL)	54
Drury Rd (HP)	36
Duane Ave (WNW)	65
Duane Rd (MED)	55
Duck Ln (EWY)	89
Duddy Ave (WAL)	54
Dudley (MED)	55
Dudley (BRO)	46
Dudley (CHE)	50
Dudley	
1-553 (ROX)	19
554-OUT (DOR)	25
Dudley Ln (MIL)	86
Dudley Rd (WH)	81
Dudley Rd (NCE)	59
Dudley Rd (LEX)	73
Dudley St Pl (ARL)	74
Dudley St & Ct (ARL)	74
Dudley St & Ct (CAM)	40
Dudley Ter (DOR)	25
Duff (WAT)	72
Duffield Rd (AUB)	66
Duffley Ct (CHH)	67
Duggan Ln (MIL)	86
Duke (MAT)	26
Duke (MAL)	48

Boston (Con.)   021

Duke Rd (WEL)	81
Dumas (DOR)	24
Dummer (BRO)	46
Dunbar Ave (MED)	55
Dunbar Ave (DOR)	24
Dunbar Rd (SWY)	90
Dunbarton Rd (N)	92
Dunbarton Rd (WOL)	70
Dunbarton Rd (BEL)	78
Dunboy (BRI)	35
Duncan Rd (EV)	49
Duncan Rd (WNW)	65
Duncan St, Pl & Ter (DOR)	22
Duncklee (NWH)	61
Duncklee (BRI)	35
Duncklee Ave (STO)	80
Dundee Rd (NQ)	71
Dundee Rd (ARL)	74
Dundonald Rd (BEL)	78
Dunedin Pl & Rd (WH)	81
Dunford (ROX)	19
Dunham (LEX)	73
Dunkeld (DOR)	21
Dunlap (DOR)	24
Dunlow St & Pl (RXC)	20
Dunmore (ROX)	19
Dunmore (QUI)	69
Dunn (DOR)	25
Dunn Rd (REV)	51
Dunning Way (JP)	30
Dunns Ct (QUI)	69
Dunns Ter (DOR)	22
Dunns Hill Rd (QUI)	69
Dunreath (ROX)	19
Dunstable (CHA)	29
Dunstable Rd (CAM)	38
Dunstan (WNW)	65
Dunster (ARL)	74
Dunster (CAM)	38
Dunster Rd (JP)	30
Dunster Rd (EV)	49
Dunster Rd (CHH)	67
Dunster Ru (NH)	94
Dunton Rd (WAT)	72
Dunwell (WRX)	32
Durant (WRX)	32
Durant (NEW)	58
Durant (WH)	81
Durant Rd (SWY)	90
Durham (SOM)	43
Durham	15
Durland (BRI)	35
Durnell Ave (ROS)	31
Durso Ave (MAL)	48
Dustin (BRI)	35
Dustin (QUI)	69
Dutton (MAL)	48
Dutton Cir (MED)	55
Duval (BRI)	35
Duxbury Rd (WH)	81
Duxbury Rd (NCE)	59
Duxbury Rd (MAT)	26
Dwhinda Rd (WAB)	68
Dwight (WAT)	72
Dwight	18
Dwight (BRO)	46
Dwight Rd (N)	92
Dwinell (WRX)	32
Dwyer Cir (MED)	55
Dwyer Ln (EWY)	89
Dyer Ave (MIL)	87

Dyer Ave (BRA)	85
Dyer Ave (EV)	49
Dyer Ave (SB)	27
Dyer Ave (MEL)	76
Dyer St & Ct (DOR)	24
Dysart (QUI)	69
E	
1-449 (SB)	27
450-OUT	02210
Eager Rd (MIL)	86
Eagle Sq (EB)	28
Earl (SB)	27
Earl (LEX)	73
Earl (MAL)	48
Earl Ave (MED)	55
Earle (SOM)	43
Earle (WOL)	70
Earle Rd (WH)	81
Early Ave (MED)	55
Early Path (NCE)	59
Earnshaw (WRX)	32
East (CAM)	41
East (STO)	80
East (LEX)	73
East (MEL)	76
East (DOR)	22
East	11
East (EWY)	89
East Blvd Rd (NCE)	59
East Albion (MED)	55
East Albion (SOM)	45
East Berkeley	18
East Border Rd (MAL)	48
East Border Rd (MED)	55
East Boscobel (BRA)	85
East Brookline	18
East Canton	18
East Capen (MED)	55
East Concord	18
East Cottage (DOR)	25
East Dedham	18
East Eagle (EB)	28
East Elm (EV)	49
East Elm Ave (WOL)	70
East Foster (ARL)	76
East Highland Ave (MEL)	76
East Howard (QUI)	69
East Lenox	18
East Locust (EV)	49
East Militia Hts (N)	92
East Milton Rd (BRO)	46
East Newton	18
East Quinobequin Rd (WAB)	68
East Side Pky (NEW)	58
East Springfield	18
East Squantum (NQ)	71
East Summer (EV)	49
East Wyoming Ave (MEL)	76
Eastbourne (ROS)	31
Eastbourne Rd (NCE)	59
Eastburn St, Pl & Ter (BRI)	35
Eastern Ave (CHE)	50
Eastern Ave (MAL)	48
Eastern Ave (REV)	51
Eastern Ave (LEX)	73
Eastern Ave (ARL)	74
Eastern Ave	09
Eastham Rd (NCE)	59
Eastland Rd (JP)	30
Eastman (MED)	55
Eastman (DOR)	25
Eastman Cir (WEL)	81
Eastman Pl (MEL)	76

Eastman Rd (SOM)	43
Eastmont Rd (HP)	36
Easton (ALL)	34
Easton Ave (HP)	36
Eastview Ter (STO)	80
Eastwood Ct (WRX)	32
Eastwood Circuit (WRX)	32
Easy (NWH)	61
Easy (N)	92
Easy (SWY)	90
Eaton (MIL)	86
Eaton (CAM)	39
Eaton (REV)	51
Eaton Ct (WH)	81
Eaton Rd (LEX)	73
Eaton Rd (QUI)	69
Eaton Rd & Sq (N)	92
Ebbets Ave (WOL)	70
Echo (MEL)	76
Echo (MAL)	48
Echo (ROX)	19
Echo Ave (EWY)	89
Echo Rd (WH)	81
Eddie (QUI)	69
Eddy (WNW)	65
Eddy (WAL)	54
Eden (CHE)	50
Eden (CHA)	29
Eden Ave (WNW)	65
Edenfield Ave (WAT)	72
Edgar (RXC)	20
Edgar Ave, Ct & Ter (SOM)	15
Edgar Ter (WIN)	52
Edge Hill (JP)	30
Edge Hill Rd (WAL)	54
Edge Hill Rd (CHH)	67
Edge Hill Rd (QUI)	69
Edge Hill Rd (WH)	81
Edge Hill Rd (BRA)	84
Edge Hill Rd (MIL)	86
Edgebrook Rd (WRX)	32
Edgecliff Rd (WAT)	72
Edgefield Rd (QUI)	69
Edgefield Rd (WAB)	68
Edgehill Rd (ARL)	74
Edgehill Rd (WIN)	52
Edgehill Rd (BRO)	46
Edgemere (MEL)	76
Edgemere Rd (QUI)	69
Edgemere Rd (WRX)	32
Edgemont (ROS)	31
Edgemont Rd (BRA)	84
Edgemoor Ave (WH)	81
Edgemoor Rd (BEL)	78
Edgerly Pl	16
Edgerly Rd	15
Edgewater Dr (MAT)	26
Edgewater Dr (WH)	81
Edgewater Dr (QUI)	69
Edgewater Dr (N)	92
Edgewater Dr (WAL)	54
Edgewater Park (AUB)	66
Edgewood (N)	92
Edgewood Cir (QUI)	69
Edgewood Rd (WNW)	65
Edgewood Rd (LEX)	73
Edgewood St & Park (RO)	19
Edgeworth (CHA)	29
Edgeworth (EWY)	89
Edgeworth Rd (NQ)	71
Edinboro	11
Edinboro Rd (QUI)	69
Edinboro St, Pl & Ter (NWV)	60

Boston (Con.)   021

Edison (WY)	88
Edison Ave (MED)	55
Edison St & Park (QUI)	69
Edison Way (LEX)	73
Edison Green (DOR)	25
Edith (ARL)	74
Edith (HP)	36
Edith Ave (WAT)	72
Edith Rd (EWY)	89
Edith St & Ave (EV)	49
Edmester Ct (EV)	49
Edmonds (SOM)	45
Edmund (MAL)	48
Edmund Rd (ARL)	74
Edmunds (CAM)	40
Edmunds Rd (WH)	81
Edna (LEX)	73
Edna Rd (DOR)	24
Edson (DOR)	24
Edson St, Rd & Ter (HP)	36
Edward (WIN)	52
Edward (BEL)	78
Edward Ave (MIL)	86
Edward Rd (WAT)	72
Edward Rd (WNW)	65
Edward St & Pl (MED)	55
Edward Cody Ln (SWY)	90
Edward Everett Sq (DOR)	25
Edward T Sullivan Rd (CAM)	38
Edward Wilson Sq (SOM)	43
Edwardel Rd (N)	92
Edwards Rd (BRA)	84
Edwards Rd (STO)	80
Edwards St & Ln (QUI)	69
Edwardson (HP)	36
Edwin (BRO)	46
Edwin (NQ)	71
Edwin (DOR)	24
Edwin Rd (WAL)	54
Egan Way (BRI)	35
Egerton Rd (ARL)	74
Egleston (JP)	30
Egleston Sq (ROX)	19
Egleton Park (WIN)	52
Egmont (BRO)	46
Egremont Rd (BRO)	46
Eighth (CAM)	41
Eighth (MED)	55
Eighth (SB)	27
Eileen Rd (MIL)	86
Eisenhower Rd (SWY)	90
Elaine Rd (STO)	80
Elba (BRO)	46
Elba Ter (DOR)	22
Elbert (ROX)	19
Elbow (EB)	28
Elcott Rd (QUI)	69
Elder (DOR)	25
Elder Rd (NH)	94
Elder Ter (ARL)	74
Eldon (DOR)	21
Eldora (RXC)	20
Eldred (LEX)	73
Eldredge (NEW)	58
Eldridge Pl (CHE)	50
Eldridge Rd (JP)	30
Eleanor (CHE)	50
Eleanor (ALL)	34
Eleanor Ct (WIN)	52
Eleanor Dr (BRA)	84
Electric Ave (BRI)	35

Electric Ave (WS)	44
Elena Rd (LEX)	73
Elene (MAT)	26
Elgin (NCE)	59
Elgin (WRX)	32
Elgin (SWY)	90
Elinor Cir (WAL)	54
Elinor Dr (BRA)	84
Elinor Rd (SWY)	90
Elinor Rd (NWH)	61
Eliot (WAT)	72
Eliot (SOM)	43
Eliot (HP)	36
Eliot (MED)	55
Eliot	16
Eliot Ave (WNW)	65
Eliot Cir & Rd (REV)	51
Eliot Ln (WES)	93
Eliot Park & Rd (ARL)	74
Eliot Rd (LEX)	73
Eliot Rd (NH)	94
Eliot Sq & Ter (ROX)	19
Eliot St, Ave & Cres (CHH)	67
Eliot St & Cir (MIL)	87
Eliot St & Pl (JP)	30
Eliot St & Sq (CAM)	38
Eliot Memorial Rd (NEW)	58
Elizabeth (MAT)	26
Elizabeth Cir (WNW)	65
Elizabeth Cir (N)	92
Elizabeth Ln (SWY)	90
Elizabeth Rd (STO)	80
Elizabeth Rd (BEL)	78
Elkins (SB)	27
Elko (BRI)	35
Ellard Rd (HP)	36
Ellen Ave (WY)	88
Ellen Rd (STO)	80
Ellen Ter (WAT)	72
Ellerton (REV)	51
Ellerton Rd (QUI)	69
Ellery (CAM)	38
Ellery (BRA)	85
Ellery (SB)	27
Ellery Rd (WAL)	54
Ellet (DOR)	22
Ellicott (N)	92
Ellington (DOR)	21
Ellington Rd (WS)	44
Ellington Rd (WOL)	70
Ellingwood (RXC)	20
Elliot (WEL)	81
Elliot	
1-14 (WY)	88
1-139 (NWH)	61
15-OUT (NUF)	84
140-OUT (NUF)	64
Elliot Ave (NQ)	71
Elliot Pl & Ter (NUF)	64
Elliott (MEL)	76
Elliott (WIN)	52
Elliott (MAL)	48
Elliott Rd (EV)	49
Elliott Rd (BEL)	78
Ellis (NUF)	64
Ellis (QUI)	69
Ellis (LEX)	73
Ellis (MAL)	48
Ellis (HP)	36
Ellis (ROX)	19
Ellis Ave (MED)	55
Ellis Cir (SWY)	90
Ellis Ln (BRA)	84

Ellis Rd (WES)	93
Ellis Rd (WNW)	65
Ellis Farm Ln (MEL)	76
Ellison Ave (MAT)	26
Ellison Park (WAL)	54
Ellison Rd (LEX)	73
Ellison Rd (NCE)	59
Ells Ave (MEL)	76
Ells Ave (SWY)	90
Ellswood (WRX)	32
Ellsworth (MED)	55
Ellsworth (SOM)	45
Ellsworth (EV)	49
Ellsworth (CHE)	50
Ellsworth (ROX)	19
Ellsworth (DOR)	22
Ellsworth Ave (BRA)	84
Ellsworth Ave (MEL)	76
Ellsworth Ave & Park (CAM)	39
Ellsworth Rd (MIL)	86
Ellwood (CHA)	29
Ellwood Rd (MEL)	76
Elm (MEL)	76
Elm (BEL)	78
Elm (LEX)	73
Elm (QUI)	69
Elm (WAT)	72
Elm (STO)	80
Elm (WH)	81
Elm (CHA)	29
Elm (DOR)	22
Elm (MIL)	86
Elm (SWY)	90
Elm (CAM)	39
Elm (CHE)	50
Elm (BRO)	46
Elm (MED)	55
Elm (JP)	30
Elm (HP)	36
Elm (REV)	51
Elm	
1-53 (SOM)	43
54-98 (WS) (EVEN)	44
55-OUT (WS) (ODD)	44
100-206 (CAM) (EVEN)	40
208-OUT (WS) (EVEN)	44
Elm Ave (WOL)	70
Elm Ct (WNW)	65
Elm Ct (WS)	44
Elm Pl (SOM)	43
Elm Rd (NWV)	60
Elm St, Ave & Ct (WAL)	54
Elm St & Ct (MAL)	48
Elm St, Rd, Ter & Way (EV)	49
Elm St & Ter (BRA)	84
Elm Hill Ave & Park (DOR)	21
Elm Knoll Rd (BRA)	84
Elm Lawn (MIL)	87
Elm Lawn (DOR)	22
Elmcrest Cir (MEL)	76
Elmdale (DOR)	22
Elmer (CAM)	38
Elmer Ave (WIN)	52
Elmer Rd (DOR)	24
Elmer Rd (SWY)	90
Elmhurst (DOR)	24
Elmhurst Rd (NEW)	58
Elmhurst Rd (STO)	80
Elmhurst Rd (ARL)	74
Elmhurst Ter (WAL)	54
Elmira (BRI)	35
Elmlawn Rd (BRA)	84
Elmont (DOR)	21

Boston (Con.)   021

Elmore (ARL) 74
Elmore (NCE) 59
Elmore St & Park (ROX) 19
Elmwood (NEW) 58
Elmwood (EV) 49
Elmwood Ave (WAL) 54
Elmwood Ave (CAM) 38
Elmwood Ave (WAT) 72
Elmwood Ave (MIL) 86
Elmwood Ave (BRA) 85
Elmwood Ave & Ct (WIN) 52
Elmwood Ave & Park (WOL) 70
Elmwood Ct & Park (MAL) 48
Elmwood Park (NWV) 60
Elmwood Park (BRA) 84
Elmwood Rd (N) 92
Elmwood Rd (WH) 81
Elmwood St & Ave (REV) 51
Elmwood St, Ct & Pl (RXC) 20
Elmwood St, Ct & Ter (WS) 44
Elsie (MAL) 48
Elsie (EV) 49
Elsmere Ter (MED) 55
Elsmore Ter (BRA) 84
Elson Rd (WAL) 54
Elston (WS) 44
Elsworth Rd (WNW) 65
Elton (DOR) 25
Elton Ave (WAT) 72
Elton Rd (MIL) 86
Elva Rd (NWY) 91
Elven Rd (ROS) 31
Elwell (MAL) 48
Elwell Rd (JP) 30
Elwern Rd (ARL) 74
Elwood (EV) 49
Elwood Ave (STO) 80
Elwood Dr (SWY) 90
Elwood Pl (REV) 51
Elwyn Rd (DOR) 24
Ely Rd (DOR) 24
Ely Rd (ARL) 74
Emanuel (REV) 51
Embankment Rd
   1-58 14
   59-OUT 08
Embassy Rd (BRI) 35
Emelia Ter (WRX) 32
Emeline Rd (EWY) 89
Emerald (MAL) 48
Emerald (BRO) 46
Emerald (MED) 55
Emerald (NEW) 58
Emerald (QUI) 69
Emerald (LEX) 73
Emerald Ave (BRA) 85
Emerald Ct (STO) 80
Emerald Ct 18
Emerson (SB) 27
Emerson (STO) 80
Emerson (NEW) 58
Emerson (BEL) 78
Emerson (MED) 55
Emerson (BRO) 46
Emerson (SOM) 43
Emerson Pl (MAL) 48
Emerson Pl (MEL) 76
Emerson Pl 14
Emerson Pl & Rd (N) 92
Emerson Rd (MIL) 86
Emerson Rd (WH) 81

Emerson Rd (LEX) 73
Emerson Rd (ARL) 74
Emerson Rd (WAT) 72
Emerson Rd (WIN) 52
Emerson Rd (WAL) 54
Emerson St E & W (MEL) 76
Emerson St & Ter (EWY) 89
Emerson Gardens (LEX) 73
Emery (WAL) 54
Emery (MED) 55
Emery (EV) 49
Emery Ct (STO) 80
Emery Rd (ALL) 34
Emily (CAM) 39
Emmeline Ave (WAL) 54
Emmet (SB) 27
Emmet Pl (EB) 28
Emmet Pl (CAM) 41
Emmet Ter (REV) 51
Emmett (HP) 36
Emmons (EB) 28
Emmons (WNW) 65
Emmons Pl (CAM) 38
Emmonsdale Rd (WRX) 32
Empire (ALL) 34
Empire (QUI) 69
Emrose Ter (DOR) 25
Emsella Ter (JP) 30
Endicott (WAL) 54
Endicott (QUI) 69
Endicott (NWH) 61
Endicott (EWY) 89
Endicott Ave (WS) 44
Endicott Ave (REV) 51
Endicott Rd (STO) 80
Endicott Rd (ARL) 74
Endicott St & Ct 13
Endicott Ter (DOR) 22
Enfield (JP) 30
Enfield Rd (WIN) 52
Englehuft Rd (MED) 55
Englewood Ave (CHE) 50
Englewood Ave (EV) 49
Englewood Ave (BRO) 46
Enmore Rd (MEL) 76
Ennis Rd (ROX) 19
Ensign (REV) 51
Enslin Rd (N) 92
Enterprise (DOR) 25
Epping (DOR) 24
Epping (EWY) 89
Epping (ARL) 74
Eric Rd (ALL) 34
Erickson (MAL) 48
Erickson (STO) 80
Erickson (BRA) 84
Ericson Rd (WY) 88
Ericsson (DOR) 22
Ericsson
   1-9 (BEL) (ODD) 78
   2-OUT (BEL) (EVEN) 78
   11-OUT (CAM) (ODD) 38
Erie (DOR) 21
Erie (CAM) 39
Erie Ave (NWH) 61
Erie Pl (ROX) 19
Erin Way (SWY) 90
Ernest Ave (QUI) 69
Ernest Ave (HP) 36
Ernest Rd (ARL) 74
Ernest Rd (BEL) 78
Ernest Rd (NWY) 91
Ernst (ROX) 19

Erville Ln (EWY) 89
Esmond (DOR) 21
Essex 11
Essex (WY) 88
Essex (MEL) 76
Essex (STO) 80
Essex (LEX) 73
Essex (WAT) 72
Essex (NQ) 71
Essex (MAL) 48
Essex (BRO) 46
Essex (SOM) 45
Essex (REV) 51
Essex (MED) 55
Essex (WAL) 54
Essex Ave 09
Essex Rd (WH) 81
Essex Rd (BEL) 78
Essex Rd (CHH) 67
Essex Rd (MIL) 87
Essex St & Ct (CAM) 39
Essex St, Ct & Pl (CHE) 50
Estabrook Rd (WY) .... 8?
Estabrook Rd (WNW) 65
Estabrook Rd (WOL) 70
Estabrook Rd (LEX) 73
Estella (MAT) 26
Estes Ave (DOR) .... 2?
Estes Pl 02210
Estes St & Ct (EV) 49
Estey (MAL) 48
Estey (RXC) 20
Esther Rd (WRX) 32
Estrello (JP) 30
Esty Farm Rd (NCE) 59
Ethel (ROS) 31
Ethel Ct (MAL) 48
Etna (BRI) 35
Etonia (ALL) 34
Euclid (DOR) 24
Euclid Ave (QUI) 69
Eugene Rd (MED) 55
Eugenia Rd (ROS) 31
Eulita Ter (BRI) 35
Eunice (DOR) 22
Eustis (CHE) 50
Eustis (REV) 51
Eustis (LEX) 73
Eustis (WOL) 70
Eustis (STO) 80
Eustis (ARL) 74
Eustis
   1-72 (CAM) 40
   73-OUT (SOM) 43
Eustis St & Pl (ROX) 19
Euston (BRO) 46
Euston Rd (BRI) 35
Eutaw Ave (BRA) 85
Eutaw St & Pl (EB) 28
Evandale Ter (DOR) 25
Evans (DOR) 24
Evans (NWY) 91
Evans (MED) 55
Evans (NQ) 71
Evans (WAT) 72
Evans Ct (MAL) 48
Evans Rd (BRO) 46
Evans Rd (STO) 80
Evans Rd (N) 92
Evans Way 15
Evelyn (MAT) 26
Evelyn Ave (MED) 55
Evelyn Ave & Pl (MAL) 48

Boston (Con.)   021

Evelyn Ct & Rd (EV)	49
Evelyn Ln (BRA)	85
Evelyn Pl (NQ)	71
Evelyn Rd (WAB)	68
Evelyn Rd (NH)	94
Everard (REV)	51
Everdean (DOR)	22
Everett (DOR)	22
Everett (REV)	51
Everett (MAL)	48
Everett (MED)	55
Everett (HP)	36
Everett (JP)	30
Everett (CAM)	38
Everett (SOM)	43
Everett (WAL)	54
Everett (WOL)	70
Everett (WEL)	81
Everett (STO)	80
Everett (ARL)	74
Everett (NCE)	59
Everett (MEL)	76
Everett Ave (WAT)	72
Everett Ave (SOM)	45
Everett Ave (CHE)	50
Everett Ave (DOR)	25
Everett Pl (NWY)	91
Everett St & Ave (EV)	49
Everett St, Ct & Pl (EB)	28
Everett St & Sq (ALL)	34
Evergreen (JP)	30
Evergreen Ave (SOM)	45
Evergreen Ave (WAL)	54
Evergreen Ave (WES)	93
Evergreen Ave (WH)	81
Evergreen Ave & Rd (BRA)	84
Evergreen Ave & Ter (AUB)	66
Evergreen Ln	
1-16 (LEX)	73
17-OUT (ARL)	74
Evergreen Rd (NH)	94
Evergreen Rd (STO)	80
Evergreen Sq (SOM)	43
Evergreen Way (BEL)	78
Everton (DOR)	21
Ewell Ave (LEX)	73
Ewer (SB)	27
Exchange (MAL)	48
Exchange Ave (MED)	55
Exchange Pl	09
Exchange St, Ct & Pl (WAL)	54
Exeter (MED)	55
Exeter (CHE)	50
Exeter	16
Exeter (BEL)	78
Exeter (WNW)	65
Exeter (WOL)	70
Exeter (ARL)	74
Exeter Ct (CHA)	29
Exeter Park (CAM)	40
Exeter Pl	11
Exmoor Rd (NCE)	59
Export	10
F (SB)	27
Fabiano Dr (BRA)	84
Fabin	18
Fabyan (DOR)	24
Fabyan (ARL)	74
Facotry (HP)	36
Factory (EV)	49

Factory Hill (BRA)	84
Fairwood Cir (CAM)	39
Fair Oaks (CAM)	40
Fair Oaks Ave (NWV)	60
Fair Oaks Dr & Ter (LEX)	73
Fair Oaks Park (N)	92
Fair View (WIN)	52
Fair View Ave & Ter (MAL)	48
Fairbanks (BRO)	46
Fairbanks (BEL)	35
Fairbanks Ave (WH)	81
Fairbanks Rd (LEX)	73
Fairbanks Rd (MIL)	86
Fairbury (DOR)	25
Fairfax (DOR)	24
Fairfax (NWY)	91
Fairfax (WNW)	65
Fairfax (WS)	44
Fairfax Rd (WAL)	54
Fairfax Rd (MIL)	87
Fairfax Rd (N)	92
Fairfield (N)	92
Fairfield (BRA)	84
Fairfield (CAM)	38
Fairfield (REV)	51
Fairfield (MED)	55
Fairfield (NWV)	60
Fairfield (WAT)	72
Fairfield (MEL)	76
Fairfield	16
Fairfield Ave (MAL)	48
Fairfield Dr (LEX)	73
Fairfield Pl	09
Fairgreen Pl (CHH)	67
Fairhaven (NCE)	59
Fairhope Rd (WES)	93
Fairland (LEX)	73
Fairland (ROX)	19
Fairlane Rd (STO)	80
Fairlane Rd (WRX)	32
Fairlawn (MAL)	48
Fairlawn (EV)	49
Fairlawn (N)	92
Fairlawn Ave (NWY)	91
Fairlawn Ave (MIL)	87
Fairlawn Ave (MAT)	26
Fairlawn Ln (LEX)	73
Fairlee (WS)	44
Fairlee Rd & Ter (WAB)	68
Fairmont (BEL)	78
Fairmont (ARL)	74
Fairmont Ave (NEW)	58
Fairmont Ave (WAL)	54
Fairmont St & Ave (CAM)	39
Fairmont St, Ct, Pl & Ter (MAL)	48
Fairmont Way (QUI)	69
Fairmount (MEL)	76
Fairmount (BRO)	46
Fairmount (EV)	49
Fairmount (MED)	55
Fairmount (DOR)	24
Fairmount Ave (WS)	44
Fairmount Ave (EWY)	89
Fairmount Ave (BRA)	84
Fairmount Ave	
1-309 (HP)	36
310-OUT (MIL)	86
Fairmount Ct & Ter (HP)	36
Fairview (ROS)	31
Fairview (NEW)	58
Fairview Ave (MEL)	76

Fairview Ave (ARL)	74
Fairview Ave (LEX)	73
Fairview Ave (WAT)	72
Fairview Ave (HP)	36
Fairview Ave (WAL)	54
Fairview Ave (BRA)	85
Fairview Ave	
1-15 (CAM) (ODD)	38
2-12 (CAM) (EVEN)	38
14-OUT (BEL) (EVEN)	78
17-OUT (BEL) (ODD)	78
Fairview Rd (WES)	93
Fairview Rd (N)	92
Fairview Rd (QUI)	69
Fairview Rd (STO)	80
Fairview Ter (WNW)	65
Fairview Ter (SOM)	45
Fairway (WY)	88
Fairway (MAT)	26
Fairway Dr (WNW)	65
Fairway Rd (CHH)	67
Falcon (EB)	28
Falcon (N)	92
Falcon Ter (QUI)	69
Falkland (BRI)	35
Fall Rd (WRX)	32
Fall St & Park (MAL)	48
Fallgren Ln (EWY)	89
Fallon Cir (BRA)	84
Fallon Pl (CAM)	38
Falmouth (EV)	49
Falmouth (BEL)	78
Falmouth	15
Falmouth Rd (WNW)	65
Falmouth Rd (WH)	81
Falmouth Rd (WAT)	72
Falmouth Rd (ARL)	74
Falmouth Rd (WAL)	54
Falmouth Rd (WES)	93
Falmouth Rd W (ARL)	74
Faneuil (BRI)	35
Faneuil Rd (WAL)	54
Faneuil Hall Sq	09
Faraday (HP)	36
Fargo	02210
Fargo Rd (SWY)	90
Farina Rd (NCE)	59
Farlow Rd (NEW)	58
Farm (SWY)	90
Farm Rd (WES)	93
Farm Rd (BRA)	84
Farm Rd (WEL)	81
Farm Rd (BEL)	78
Farmcrest Ave (LEX)	73
Farmer Rd (ARL)	74
Farmington Rd (WNW)	65
Farmington Rd (WRX)	32
Farnham (BEL)	78
Farnham (ROX)	19
Farnsworth	02210
Farnsworth St & Ave (WAL)	54
Farnum (QUI)	69
Farnum Rd (WAL)	54
Farquhar (ROS)	31
Farquhar Rd (NWV)	60
Farragut (WRX)	32
Farragut Ave (WS)	44
Farragut Ave (MED)	55
Farragut Rd (SB)	27
Farrar (CAM)	38
Farrar Ave (HP)	36
Farrell (QUI)	69
Farren Rd (EWY)	89

Boston (Con.) 021

Farrington (ARL) 74
Farrington (HP) 36
Farrington
  1-56 (NQ) 71
  57-OUT (WOL) 70
Farrington Ave (ALL) 34
Farview Rd (MED) 55
Farwell (WAL) 54
Farwell (NWV) 60
Farwell Ave (MEL) 76
Farwell Ave (HP) 36
Farwell Pl (CAM) 38
Father Carney Dr (MIL) 86
Father Matignon Rd (CAM) .. 40
Fatima Rd (STO) 80
Faulkner Pl (MEL) 76
Faulkner Pl (BRA) 84
Faulkner St & Cir (DOR) 22
Faulkner St & Sq (MAL) 48
Faun Bar Ave (WIN) 52
Faunce Rd (MAT) 26
Favre (MAT) 26
Fawcett (CAM) 38
Fawndale Rd (ROS) 31
Faxon (RXC) 20
Faxon (BRA) 84
Faxon (MEL) 76
Faxon (NEW) 58
Faxon Ave & Ln (QUI) 69
Faxon Park Rd (QUI) 69
Faxon Rd (NQ) 71
Fay 18
Fay Ln (NH) 94
Fay Sq (CHE) 50
Fayerweather (CAM) 38
Fayette 16
Fayette (WAT) 72
Fayette (ARL) 74
Fayette
  1-71 (NQ) (ODD) 71
  2-74 (NQ) (EVEN) 71
  73-OUT (WOL) (ODD) 70
  76-OUT (WOL) (EVEN) ... 70
Fayette Ct 11
Fayette St & Park (CAM) 39
Fayette St & Pl (NEW) 58
Fayston (NEW) 21
Faywood Ave (EB) 28
Federal (WY) 88
Federal Ave (QUI) 69
Federal Dr (BRA) 84
Federal St & Ct. 10
Federal Wharf (EB) 28
Felicia Rd (MEL) 76
Fellows (ROX) 19
Fells Ave (MED) 55
Fells Ave Ter (MED) 55
Fells Rd (WEL) 81
Fells Rd (STO) 80
Fellsmere Ave (STO) 80
Fellsmere Ave (MEL) 76
Fellsmere Rd (NCE) 59
Fellsmere Rd (MAL) 48
Fellsview Ave (MED) 55
Fellsview Rd & Ter (MEL) ... 76
Fellsway (MED) 55
Fellsway
  1020-1250 (MAL) 48
Fellsway E (MAL) 48
Fellsway E (MEL) 76
Fellsway W (MED) 55

Fellsway St E & W (SOM) 45
Felspa Rd (STO) 80
Felton (NQ) 71
Felton (CAM) 38
Felton (WAL) 54
Felton Pl (MEL) 76
Fencourt 15
Fendale Ave (DOR) 24
Fenelon (DOR) 21
Feneno Ter (ALL) 34
Fenley (REV) 51
Fenmere Ave (WH) 81
Fennell (SOM) 45
Fenner (ROX) 19
Fenno (ROX) 19
Fenno (REV) 51
Fenno (CAM) 38
Fenno (CHE) 50
Fenno (WOL) 70
Fenno Rd (NCE) 59
Fensmere Ave (QUI) 69
Fenton (WAL) 54
Fenton Rd (NH) 94
Fenton St & Pl (DOR) 22
Fenway
  1-55 02215
  56-OUT 15
Fenway Ct 15
Fenwick (REV) 51
Fenwick (SOM) 45
Fenwick Pl (ROX) 19
Fenwick Rd (WAB) 68
Fenwick St, Cir & Ter (MAL) .. 48
Fenwood Rd 15
Ferdinand (MEL) 76
Ferguson Rd (MAL) 48
Fermoy Hts Ave (DOR) 24
Fern (WAL) 54
Fern (ALL) 34
Fern (CAM) 38
Fern (AUB) 66
Fern (LEX) 73
Fern Ct (EWY) 89
Fern Rd (SWY) 90
Fern Rd (BRA) 84
Fern Rd (MED) 55
Fernald (LEX) 73
Fernald Dr (CAM) 38
Fernald Ter (DOR) 25
Fernboro (DOR) 21
Ferncroft Rd (WRX) 32
Ferncroft Rd (WAB) 68
Ferncroft Rd (BRA) 84
Ferncroft Rd (MIL) 87
Ferncroft Way (MAL) 48
Ferndale (DOR) 24
Ferndale Rd (N) 92
Ferndale Rd (WES) 93
Ferndale Rd (WOL) 70
Fernwood Ave & Pl (REV) ... 51
Fernwood Rd (WRX) 32
Fernwood Rd (WNW) 65
Fernwood Rd (CHH) 67
Ferrin (CHA) 29
Ferriter (QUI) 69
Ferry 09
Ferry (CHE) 50
Ferry (EV) 49
Ferry St & Pl (MAL) 48
Fessenden (MAT) 26
Fessenden (NWV) 60
Fessenden Rd (ARL) 74
Fessenden Way (LEX) 73

Festa Rd (REV) 51
Fidelis Way (BRI) 35
Field (CAM) 38
Field (MAL) 48
Field (QUI) 69
Field. 15
Field Ave (WY) 88
Field Rd (LEX) 73
Field Rd (ARL) 74
Fieldmont (HP) 36
Fieldmont Rd (BEL) 78
Fields Ct (MEL) 76
Fields Ct (DOR) 25
Fields Corner (DOR) 22
Fields Pond Rd (WES) 93
Fieldstone Dr (STO) 80
Fife Rd (WH) 81
Fifield (WAT) 72
Fifield (DOR) 22
Fifth (SB) 27
Fifth (CHE) 50
Fifth (MED) 55
Fifth
  1-199 (CAM) 41
  200-OUT (CAM) 42
Fifth Ave (WAT) 72
Fifth Ave (QUI) 69
Figurehead Ln (QUI) 69
Filbert (QUI) 69
Fillmore Ter (BRO) 46
Filmore (SWY) 90
Filomena (EWY) 89
Filomena Rd (ROS) 31
Finley (ARL) 74
Fir Ave (WAL) 54
First (WRX) 32
First (MAL) 48
First (MED) 55
First (QUI) 69
First (MEL) 76
First (LEX) 73
First (WY) 88
First
  1-140 (CAM) 41
  141-OUT (CAM) 42
First Ave (NH) 94
First Ave (WAL) 54
First Ave (SOM) 43
Firth Rd (ROS) 31
Fish Pier St & Rd 02210
Fisher (N) 92
Fisher Ave (BRO) 46
Fisher Ave (WEL) 81
Fisher Ave (NWH) 61
Fisher Ave (RXC) 20
Fisher Rd (ARL) 74
Fisher Rd (SWY) 90
Fisher Ter (EV) 49
Fiske (REV) 51
Fiske Ave (SOM) 45
Fiske Ave (EWY) 89
Fiske Ln (WES) 93
Fiske Pl (CAM) 39
Fiske Rd (WH) 81
Fiske Rd (LEX) 73
Fiske St & Ave (WAL) 54
Fiske Ter (ALL) 34
Fiske Wharf 09
Fitchburg (SOM) 43
Fitchburg (WAT) 72
Fitz Ter (CHE) 50
Fitz Henry Sq (REV) 51
Flagg (CAM) 38

Boston (Con.)   021

Flagg (WOL).................. 70
Flagg 18
Flagg Cir (WAL)............ 54
Flagg St Ct (CAM)........ 38
Flaherty Way (SB)........ 27
Flanders Rd (BEL)......... 78
Flavia (DOR)................. 22
Fleet (HP).................... 36
Fleet
  1-29 (ODD)............... 13
  2-34 (EVEN)............. 13
  31-OUT (ODD).......... 09
  36-OUT (EVEN)........ 09
Fleming (MED)............. 55
Fleming Rd (MAL)......... 48
Fletcher (ROS)............. 31
Fletcher Ave (LEX)....... 73
Fletcher Rd (BEL)......... 78
Fletcher Rd (WH)......... 81
Fletcher Rd (N)............ 92
Fletcher Ter (WAT)....... 72
Flett Rd (WAV)............ 79
Flint (REV).................. 51
Flint (MAT).................. 26
Flint Ave (STO)............ 80
Flint Pl (WAL).............. 27
Flint Rd (WAT)............. 72
Flint St & Ave (SOM).... 45
Flintlock Rd (LEX)........ 73
Flood (WAL)................. 54
Flood Sq (SB).............. 27
Floral Ave (MAL).......... 48
Floral Cir (WAL)........... 54
Floral Pl (HP).............. 36
Floral St & Pl (NWH)..... 61
Florence (WOL)............ 70
Florence (MAL)............ 48
Florence (ROS)............ 31
Florence (EV).............. 49
Florence (CAM)........... 39
Florence
  1-50 (NCE)............... 59
  51-OUT (CHH)........... 67
Florence Ave (REV)...... 51
Florence Ave & Ter (ARL) 74
Florence Cir (STO)....... 80
Florence Ct (NWV)....... 60
Florence Rd (WAL)....... 54
Florence St Park (MAL).. 48
Florence St & Ave (MED) 55
Florence St & Ave (MEL) 76
Florence St & Ter (SOM) 45
Florence Ter (WAT)...... 72
Florian
  1-78 (ROS)............... 31
  79-OUT (JP)............. 30
Florian Way (ROS)....... 31
Florida (DOR)............... 24
Floyd (DOR)................. 24
Floyd (WAL)................ 54
Floyd (WIN)................. 52
Floyd (REV)................. 51
Floyd (EV).................. 49
Flynt (NQ).................. 71
Foam (REV).................. 52
Foam Ave (REV)........... 51
Foch (CAM).................. 40
Fogg Rd (SWY)............. 90
Foley (REV)................. 51
Foley (SOM)................ 45
Follen (CAM)................ 38

Follen 16
Follen Rd (LEX)............ 73
Follett (QUI)................ 69
Folsom (QUI)................ 69
Folsom (DOR)............... 25
Folsom (REV)................ 51
Folsom (ROS)............... 31
Folsom Ave (RXC)......... 20
Folsom Ct (MAL)........... 48
Food Mart Rd............... 18
Forbes (JP).................. 30
Forbes (CHE)............... 50
Forbes Rd (LEX)........... 73
Forbes Rd (MIL)........... 86
Forbes Rd (BRA).......... 84
Forbes Hill Rd (WOL)..... 70
Forbush Ave (QUI)........ 69
Ford (QUI)................... 69
Ford (REV).................. 51
Ford (EB).................... 28
Ford Rd (WAT)............. 72
Ford Rd (SWY)............. 90
Ford Ranch Rd (MIL)...... 86
Fordham (ARL)............. 74
Fordham Ct (JP).......... 30
Fordham Rd (ALL)........ 34
Fordham Rd (WNW)...... 65
Fore River Ave (NWY).... 91
Forest (SWY)............... 90
Forest (MIL)................. 86
Forest (BRA)................ 85
Forest (N)................... 92
Forest (CHH)............... 67
Forest (ARL)............... 74
Forest (WAT)............... 72
Forest (MEL)............... 76
Forest (NWH).............. 61
Forest (STO)............... 80
Forest (MAL)............... 48
Forest (MED)............... 55
Forest
  1-27 (CAM)............... 40
  1-167 (WH).............. 81
  28-OUT (SOM)........... 43
  168-249 (BP)............ 57
  250-250 (WH).......... 81
  251-OUT (BP).......... 57
Forest Ave (EV)........... 49
Forest Ave (AUB)......... 66
Forest Ave (WNW)....... 65
Forest Ave (QUI).......... 69
Forest Grv Rd (WAL)..... 54
Forest Pl (CHA)............ 29
Forest St & Cir (WAL).... 54
Forest St & Ct (LEX)..... 73
Forest St & Pl (ROX)..... 19
Forest Hills St & Ave (JP) 30
Forestvale Rd (HP)....... 36
Forrest (WIN).............. 52
Forster (SOM)............. 45
Forsters Ct (CHA)........ 29
Forsyth 15
Forsyth (CHE)............. 50
Fort Ave (ROX)........... 19
Fort Ave Ter (ROX)...... 19
Fort St & Sq (QUI)....... 69
Fort Banks (WIN)......... 52
Fort Dawes (WIN)........ 52
Fort Heath (WIN)......... 52
Fort Hill Sq................ 10
Fort Hill Wharf............02210
Fort Point Rd (NWY)..... 91
Fortunato Dr (MED)...... 55

Forum Rd (QUI)............ 69
Foskett (WS)............... 44
Foss (MED)................. 55
Foss (CHA)................. 29
Fossdale Rd (DOR)....... 24
Foster (REV)............... 51
Foster (EV)................. 49
Foster (BRO).............. 46
Foster (QUI)............... 69
Foster (NWV).............. 60
Foster (ARL)............... 74
Foster Ln (MIL)............ 86
Foster Rd (BRA)........... 85
Foster Rd (LEX)........... 73
Foster Rd (BEL)........... 78
Foster St E & W (MEL)... 76
Foster St & Ct.............. 09
Foster St & Pl (CAM)..... 38
Foster St & Ter (BRI)..... 35
Foster St Ex (BRO)....... 46
Fosters Ct (MED)......... 55
Fosters Wharf............02210
Fottler Ave (LEX)......... 73
Fottler Rd (MAT).......... 26
Foundry (WAL)............. 27
Foundry Ave (WAL)....... 54
Fountain (WAL)............ 54
Fountain (WNW).......... 65
Fountain (BRA)............ 85
Fountain Ave (SOM)...... 45
Fountain Pl................. 13
Fountain Rd (ARL)........ 74
Fountain St, Ct & Ter (MED) 55
Fountain St & Ln (SWY).. 90
Fountain St, Pl & Sq (ROX) 19
Fountain Ter (CAM)....... 38
Fountain Hill (ROX)....... 19
Fourth (SB)................. 27
Fourth (MED).............. 55
Fourth (CHE).............. 50
Fourth (LEX)............... 73
Fourth Ave (WAL)........ 54
Fourth Ave (WY).......... 88
Fourth Ave (NH).......... 94
Fourth St Pl (SB)......... 27
Fowle (ROS)................ 31
Fowler (CAM).............. 39
Fowler (DOR).............. 21
Fowler (QUI)............... 69
Fowler Ave (REV)........ 51
Fox (DOR)................... 22
Fox Ln & Pl (NCE)........ 59
Fox Rd (WAL).............. 54
Fox Chase Ln (WES)..... 93
Fox Hill Ln (MIL).......... 86
Fox Hill Pl & Rd (NCE)... 59
Fox Hill Rd (WH).......... 81
Fox Hill Rd (N)............. 92
Fox Point Rd (DOR)...... 25
Foxmeadow Ln (ARL)..... 74
Foye Ave (WY)............ 88
Framar Ln (WH)........... 81
Frances (NWH)............ 61
Frances Pl (CAM)......... 40
Frances Rd (LEX)......... 73
Francesca (WRX)......... 32
Francesca Ave (WS)..... 44
Francine Rd (BRA)........ 84
Francis (MIL)............... 87
Francis (N).................. 92
Francis (SOM).............. 43
Francis (WAL).............. 54
Francis (REV).............. 51

Boston (Con.) 021

Entry	
Franclaire Dr (WRX)	32
Franconia (DOR)	22
Franey Rd (SOM)	45
Frank (NH)	94
Frank (WAT)	72
Frank Ave (REV)	51
Frank Rd (NWY)	91
Frankfort (EB)	28
Freeport St & Way (DOR)	22
Franklin (DOR)	22
Franklin	10
Franklin (WY)	88
Franklin (NH)	94
Franklin (MIL)	86
Franklin (BRA)	85
Franklin (WIN)	52
Franklin (ALL)	34
Franklin (EV)	49
Franklin (MED)	55
Franklin (WAT)	72
Franklin (BEL)	78
Franklin (NEW)	58
Franklin (ARL)	74
Franklin	
1-215 (STO) (ODD)	80
2-204 (STO) (EVEN)	80
206-OUT (MEL) (EVEN)	76
217-1073 (MEL) (ODD)	76
1075-1075 (STO)	80
1077-OUT (MEL) (ODD)	76
Franklin Ave & Ter (WOL)	70
Franklin Ct (DOR)	25
Franklin Gdns (DOR)	21
Franklin Park (JP)	30
Franklin Pl (ROS)	31
Franklin Pl (STO)	80
Franklin Rd (WH)	81
Franklin St & Ave (CHE)	50
Franklin St, Ave & Pl (REV)	51
Franklin St, Ave & Pl (SOM)	45
Franklin St & Ct (MAL)	48
Franklin St & Ct (BRO)	46
Franklin St & Pl (CAM)	39
Franklin St & Pl (QUI)	69
Franklin St & Ter (HP)	36
Franklin Ter (MEL)	76
Franklin Field (DOR)	24
Franklin Hill Ave (DOR)	24
Franklin Park Zoo (DOR)	21
Frano Ave (BRA)	85
Frawley	15
Frazer (DOR)	24
Frazer (HP)	36
Frazer Rd (ARL)	74
Freca Rd (QUI)	69
Fredana Rd (WAB)	68
Frederick (QUI)	69
Frederick (WAV)	79
Frederick (NWV)	60
Frederick (SB)	27
Frederick Ave (MED)	55
Frederick Park (N)	92
Frederick Rd (BRA)	85
Frederika (DOR)	24
Fredette Rd (NCE)	59
Fredith Rd (EWY)	89
Fredonia (DOR)	24
Freeland (MAT)	26
Freeman (DOR)	22
Freeman (AUB)	66
Freeman (ARL)	74
Freeman (WOL)	70

Entry	
Freeman (BRO)	46
Freeman (REV)	51
Freeman Ave (EV)	49
Freeman Ave (WRX)	32
Freeman Pl	08
Freeman Pl (N)	92
Freemont (SWY)	90
Freemont (LEX)	73
Freemont Ter (WAL)	54
Fremont (MAT)	26
Fremont (WIN)	52
Fremont (MAL)	48
Fremont (SOM)	45
Fremont (NH)	94
Fremont Ave (CHE)	50
Fremont Ave (EV)	49
Fremont Ave (SOM)	43
Fremont Ave (ROX)	19
Fremont St & Ct (ARL)	74
French (NQ)	71
French (MAT)	26
French (SWY)	90
French Ave (BRA)	85
French Rd (WES)	93
French St & Ter (WAT)	72
French Ter (RXC)	20
French Bv (BRA)	85
Fresh Pond Ave, Ln & Pky (CAM)	38
Fresno (ROS)	31
Friend (REV)	51
Friend (WAL)	54
Friend (EWY)	89
Friend	14
Friendship Rd (MAT)	26
Frisbie Rd (CAM)	38
Front (CHE)	50
Front (CHA)	29
Front (BRA)	84
Front	
1-815 (WY)	88
816-OUT (SWY)	90
Frontage Rd	18
Frontenac (DOR)	24
Frost (ARL)	74
Frost Ave (MEL)	76
Frost Ave (DOR)	22
Frost Rd (BEL)	78
Frost St & Ter (CAM)	40
Frothingham (MIL)	87
Frothingham Ave (CHA)	29
Fruean Pl (DOR)	22
Fruit	14
Frye (REV)	51
Frye Rd (MED)	55
Fulbright (MED)	55
Fulda (ROX)	19
Fulkerson (CAM)	41
Fuller (EV)	49
Fuller (WAL)	54
Fuller (MAL)	48
Fuller (BRO)	46
Fuller (DOR)	24
Fuller (STO)	80
Fuller	
1-99 (WAB)	68
100-OUT (WNW)	65
Fuller Ave & Ter (WNW)	65
Fuller Pl (CAM)	38
Fuller Rd (WH)	81
Fuller Rd (WAT)	72
Fuller Rd (LEX)	73

Entry	
Fuller Rd (NWY)	91
Fuller Rd (N)	92
Fuller Brook Rd (N)	92
Fuller Brook Rd (WEL)	81
Fullers Ln (MIL)	86
Fullerton	02215
Fulton (HP)	36
Fulton (MAL)	48
Fulton (MED)	55
Fulton Rd (LEX)	73
Fulton St & Pl	09
Fulton Spring Rd (MED)	55
Fulton Spring Rd Ext (MED)	55
Furber Ln (NCE)	59
Furbush Ave (WNW)	65
Furbush Rd (WRX)	32
Furnace Ave (QUI)	69
Furnace Brook Pky	
1-364 (QUI)	69
365-609 (WOL)	70
610-OUT (QUI)	69
Furness (REV)	51
Furnival Rd (JP)	30
G (SB)	27
Gaffney	02215
Gafford Ave (LEX)	73
Gage (N)	92
Gage Ave (REV)	51
Gail Rd (WES)	93
Gail Rd (NLF)	62
Gainsborough	15
Gale (MAL)	48
Gale (WAL)	54
Gale Ave (BRA)	84
Gale Rd (WY)	88
Gale Rd (BEL)	78
Galen (WAT)	72
Galen (MIL)	86
Galen (WAL)	54
Galena (ROX)	19
Gallivan Blvd	
1-705 (DOR) (ODD)	24
2-718 (DOR) (EVEN)	24
707-OUT (DOR) (ODD)	22
720-OUT (DOR) (EVEN)	22
Galty Ave (DOR)	24
Gambier (AUB)	66
Gammons Rd (WAB)	68
Gannett (DOR)	21
Gannett Rd (QUI)	69
Gannon Ct (WNW)	65
Garden (MEL)	76
Garden (BEL)	78
Garden (ARL)	74
Garden	14
Garden (MIL)	86
Garden (N)	92
Garden (MED)	55
Garden (EV)	49
Garden Ave (LEX)	73
Garden Cir, Ct & Ln (WAL)	54
Garden Ct (SOM)	43
Garden Ct St	13
Garden Park (BRA)	84
Garden Pl & Rd (WH)	81
Garden Rd (STO)	80
Garden Rd (NEW)	58
Garden St Ct (MAL)	48
Garden St, Ct & Ter (CAM)	38
Garden St, Park & Ter (MAL)	48
Gardena (BRI)	35
Gardenside (ROS)	31
Gardiner Rd (QUI)	69

Boston (Con.) 021

Grand View Ave (WIN) 52
Grand View Ave (REV) 51
Grand View Ave (MAL) 48
Grand View Ave (MED) 55
Grand View Ave (SOM) 43
Grand View Ave & Ter (WOL).. 70
Grandview (MEL) 76
Grandview (ROS) 31
Grandview Ave (WAT) 72
Grandview Ave (LEX) 73
Grandview Ave (STO) 80
Grandview Rd (ARL) 74
Grandview Rd (CHE) 50
Grandview Rd (NWY) 91
Granfield Ave (ROS) 31
Granger (WOL) 70
Granger St & Pl (DOR) 22
Granite (WEL) 81
Granite (MEL) 76
Granite (QUI) 69
Granite (SOM) 43
Granite (CAM) 39
Granite (MAL) 48
Granite (WY) 88
Granite
  1-549 (BRA) 84
  550-OUT (BRA) 85
Granite Ave (DOR) 24
Granite Ave & Pl (MIL) 86
Granite Rd (MED) 55
Grannison Rd (WES) 93
Grant (WH) 92
Grant (EWY) 89
Grant (SOM) 45
Grant (CAM) 38
Grant (DOR) 25
Grant (STO) 80
Grant (WNW) 65
Grant Ave (WH) 81
Grant Ave (WAV) 79
Grant Ave (WAT) 72
Grant Ave (NCE) 59
Grant Ave (MED) 55
Grant Pl (QUI) 69
Grant Pl (DOR) 24
Grant Rd (DOR) 21
Grant Rd (MAL) 48
Grant St, Ave & Pl (WAL) 54
Grant St & Pl (LEX) 73
Grantland Rd (WH) 81
Grantley (HP) 36
Granton Park (ARL) 74
Grants Ct (CHA) 29
Granville (DOR) 24
Granville (QUI) 69
Granville Ave (MED) 55
Granville Ave & Pl (MAL) 48
Granville Rd (CAM) 48
Grape (MAL) 73
Grapevine Ave (LEX) 73
Grasmere (NEW) 58
Grasmere Rd (NH) 94
Grassland (LEX) 73
Grassmere (CHH) 67
Grassmere Rd (HP) 36
Graves Rd (REV) 51
Gray (CAM) 38
Gray (CHA) 29
Gray 16
Gray Gdns E & W (CAM) 38
Gray Rd (MEL) 76

Gray St & Cir (ARL) 74
Gray Birch Ter (NWV) 60
Gray Cliff Rd (NCE) 59
Gray Dale Cir (AUB) 66
Grayfield Ave (WRX) 32
Graylynn Rd (NCE) 59
Graymore Rd (WAL) 54
Grayson (DOR) 24
Grayson Ln (NLF) 62
Graystone Rd (STO) 80
Great Hill Dr (NWY) 91
Great Meadow Rd (NCE) 59
Great Plain Ave (WH) 81
Great Plain Ave & Ter (N)........ 92
Great Pond Rd (SWY) 90
Great Republic Ave (SWY) 90
Great Rock Rd (LEX) 73
Greaton Rd (WRX) 32
Greeley Cir (ARL) 74
Greeleys Ct (WAL) 54
Green (WAL) 54
Green (JP) 30
Green (REV) 51
Green (BRO) 46
Green (MAL) 48
Green (CAM) 39
Green (CHE) 50
Green (EV) 49
Green (STO) 80
Green (MEL) 76
Green (WOL) 70
Green (WAT) 72
Green (N) 92
Green (MIL) 86
Green (CHA) 29
Green
  1-456 (NWY) 91
  457-OUT (EWY) 89
Green Ln (WES) 93
Green Ln (NQ) 71
Green Ln (LEX) 73
Green Rd (MED) 55
Green St Ter (WAT) 72
Green St, Ct & Park (NEW) 58
Green Hill (DOR) 22
Green Hill Rd (BRO) 46
Green Hollow Ln (MIL) 86
Green River Way (WAT) 72
Greenbaum (SB) 27
Greenbrier (DOR) 24
Greenbrook Rd (HP) 36
Greendale Ave
  1-379 (NH) 94
  380-OUT (N) 92
Greendale Rd (MAT) 26
Greendale Ter (N) 92
Greene (SOM) 43
Greenfield Ave (MAT) 26
Greenhalge (MED) 55
Greenhalge Ave (EV) 49
Greenheys (DOR) 21
Greenlawn Ave (NCE) 59
Greenlawn Ave (WH) 81
Greenleaf (QUI) 69
Greenleaf (MAL) 48
Greenleaf Ave (MED) 55
Greenleaf Pl (MEL) 76
Greenleaf Rd (MIL) 87
Greenley Pl (JP) 30
Greenmount (DOR) 25
Greenock (DOR) 24
Greenough (NH) 94

Greenough (WNW) 65
Greenough Ave (CAM) 39
Greenough Ave & Park (JP).... 30
Greenough Ln 13
Greenough St & Cir (BRO) 46
Greens Block (CHA) 29
Greensbrook Way (BEL) 78
Greentree Ln (REV) 51
Greentree Ln (SWY) 90
Greenvale Ave (WY) 88
Greenview (QUI) 69
Greenview Ave (JP) 30
Greenview Rd (STO) 80
Greenville (SOM) 43
Greenville (ROX) 19
Greenway Cir (STO) 80
Greenway Ct (BRO) 46
Greenwich (DOR) 22
Greenwich Park 18
Greenwich St & Ct (RXC) 20
Greenwood (DOR) 21
Greenwood (MED) 55
Greenwood (MEL) 76
Greenwood (NCE) 59
Greenwood (LEX) 73
Greenwood Ave (WNW).......... 65
Greenwood Ave (WOL) 70
Greenwood Ave (EWY) 89
Greenwood Ave (N) 92
Greenwood Ave, Cir & Sq
  (HP) 36
Greenwood Ln (WAL) 54
Greenwood Park (DOR) 22
Greenwood Rd (WH) 8
Greenwood Rd (ARL) 7
Greenwood St, Ct & Ter
  (MAL) 4
Greenwood Ter (SOM) 4
Greer (WAL) 5
Gregory (WAL) 5
Grenville Rd (WAT) 7
Grenwold Rd (QUI) 6
Gretter Rd (ROS) 3
Grew Ave (ROS) 58
Grew Hill Rd (ROS) 22
Greybirch Cir & Park (BEL) 3
Greycliff Rd (BRI) 2
Greycliff Rd (EWY) 1
Greylock Rd (ALL) 27
Greylock Rd (WH) 24
Greylock Rd (NWV) 36
Greymere Rd (BRI) ....
Greystone (QUI) ....
Greystone Rd (MEL) ....
Greystone Rd (MAL) ....
Gridley (QUI) ....
Grieco A J Ter (EB) ....
Griffin (REV) ....
Griffin Ter (SWY) ....
Griffin Way (CHE) ....
Griggs Ln (MIL) 59
Griggs Rd & Ter (BRO) 81
Griggs St & Pl (ALL) 69
Grimes (SB) 15
Grimes Rd (LEX) 48
Grimshaw (MAL) 55
Grinnell (RXC) 76
Griswold (CAM) 87
Griswold (EV) 30
Griswold (REV) ....
Grogan Ave (QUI) 25
Groman Pl (MAL) 24
Groom (DOR) 94

Boston (Con.)   **021**

Grossman (QUI)	69
Grosvenor Pl (ROX)	19
Grosvenor Rd (BEL)	78
Grosvenor Rd (WAL)	54
Grosvenor Rd (N)	92
Groton (WOL)	70
Groton	18
Grotto Glen Rd (JP)	30
Grouse (WRX)	32
Grove (MAL)	48
Grove (CHE)	50
Grove (WS)	44
Grove (MED)	55
Grove	14
Grove (WAT)	72
Grove (QUI)	69
Grove (LEX)	73
Grove (ARL)	74
Grove (CHH)	67
Grove (MIL)	87
Grove (EWY)	89
Grove	
1-147 (BEL) (ODD)	78
1-302 (AUB)	66
1-379 (WEL)	81
2-OUT (BEL) (EVEN)	78
149-OUT (CAM) (ODD)	38
303-OUT (NLF)	62
380-418 (N)	92
419-419 (WEL)	81
420-OUT (N)	92
Grove Ave (CAM)	39
Grove St Pl (ARL)	74
Grove St & Cir (BRA)	85
Grove St & Pl (MEL)	76
Grove St & Rd (WAL)	54
Grove St & Ter (WRX)	32
Grove Hill Ave & Park (NWV)	60
Groveland (AUB)	66
Groveland (MAT)	26
Groveland Ave (SWY)	90
Groveland Rd (MEL)	76
Grovenor Rd (JP)	30
Grover (EV)	49
Grover (MAL)	48
Grover (REV)	51
Grover Ave (ROS)	31
Grover Rd (MED)	55
Grover Rd Ext (MED)	55
Grovers Ave (WIN)	52
Grozier Rd (CAM)	38
Guam Rd (CHE)	50
Guernsey (ROS)	31
Guest (BRI)	35
Guild (MED)	55
Guild (QUI)	69
Guild Rd (NH)	94
Guild St & Row (ROX)	19
Guilford (ALL)	34
Guilford Rd (MIL)	86
Guinan (WAL)	54
Gulliver (MIL)	86
Gun Club Ln (WES)	93
Gun Hill (MIL)	86
Gurney (CAM)	38
Gurney (RXC)	20
Gussie Ter (SOM)	43
Gustin (SB)	27
Gwinnett (HP)	36
Gypsy Trl (WES)	93
H (SB)	27

H St Pl (SB)	27
Hackensack Cir, Ct, Rd & Ter (CHH)	67
Hadassah Way	16
Haddon (REV)	51
Hadley (CAM)	40
Hadley (MAL)	48
Hadley (EWY)	89
Hadley Ct (SOM)	45
Hadley Ct (EV)	49
Hadley Ct (ARL)	74
Hadley Rd (LEX)	73
Hadley St & Pl (MED)	55
Hadwin Way (ROS)	31
Hagar (JP)	30
Hagar (WAL)	54
Hagar Rd (NLF)	62
Hagars Ln (WAL)	54
Hagen Rd (NCE)	59
Hagman Rd (WIN)	52
Haines (MED)	55
Haith (REV)	51
Halborn (MAT)	26
Halcyon Rd (NCE)	59
Hale (NUF)	64
Hale (HP)	36
Hale (EWY)	89
Hale Ave (WIN)	52
Hale Ave (MED)	55
Haley (ROX)	19
Haley Rd (BRA)	84
Half Moon (DOR)	25
Halford Rd (WRX)	32
Halifax (JP)	30
Hall (JP)	30
Hall (REV)	51
Hall (MAL)	48
Hall Ave (EV)	49
Hall Ave (BRA)	85
Hall Ave (WAT)	72
Hall Pl (QUI)	69
Hall Pl (SB)	27
Hall Rd (STO)	80
Hall Rd (BRO)	46
Hall St Pl (REV)	51
Hall St & Ave (MED)	55
Hall St & Ave (WS)	44
Hall St & Pl (WAL)	54
Hallam (DOR)	25
Halleck (RXC)	20
Hallen Ave (MIL)	86
Hallet	
1-35 (DOR)	22
36-OUT (DOR)	24
Hallet Sq (DOR)	24
Hallet Hill Rd (WES)	93
Hallet-Davis (DOR)	24
Halliday (ROS)	31
Hallowell (MAT)	26
Hallron (HP)	36
Hallron Rd (NLF)	62
Hallwood Rd (CHH)	67
Halsey Ave (WEL)	81
Halsey Rd (HP)	36
Hamblin (LEX)	73
Hamblin Rd (WAL)	54
Hamden Cir (WOL)	70
Hamilton (WOL)	70
Hamilton (NLF)	62
Hamilton (HP)	36
Hamilton (CAM)	39
Hamilton (MED)	55
Hamilton (EV)	49

Hamilton (BRA)	84
Hamilton	
1-160 (DOR)	25
161-OUT (DOR)	22
Hamilton Ave (NQ)	71
Hamilton Pl (NH)	94
Hamilton Pl	08
Hamilton Rd (LEX)	73
Hamilton Rd (WH)	81
Hamilton Rd (ARL)	74
Hamilton Rd (BEL)	78
Hamilton Rd (WS)	44
Hamilton Rd (WAL)	54
Hamilton Rd (BRO)	46
Hamlet (SOM)	43
Hamlet (ARL)	74
Hamlet (NCE)	59
Hamlet (DOR)	25
Hamlet Pl (MAL)	48
Hamlin (CAM)	41
Hamlin (SB)	27
Hamlin Ave (MED)	55
Hamlin Ln (N)	92
Hamlin Rd (NCE)	59
Hammel Pl (CHH)	67
Hammer (WAL)	54
Hammett (RXC)	20
Hammond (WAL)	54
Hammond (SOM)	43
Hammond (CAM)	38
Hammond (CHH)	67
Hammond Ct (QUI)	69
Hammond Pl (MED)	55
Hammond Rd (BEL)	78
Hammond St & Ter (RXC)	20
Hammond Pond Pky (CHH)	67
Hammondswood Rd (CHH)	67
Hampden (WEL)	81
Hampden (ROX)	19
Hampden Ter (NCE)	59
Hampshire (WNW)	65
Hampshire (RXC)	20
Hampshire (EV)	49
Hampshire Rd (WH)	81
Hampshire St, Ct & Pl (CAM)	39
Hampstead Ln & Rd (JP)	30
Hampton Ave (NH)	94
Hampton Rd (MEL)	76
Hancock (MEL)	76
Hancock (STO)	80
Hancock (AUB)	66
Hancock (ARL)	74
Hancock (WAT)	72
Hancock (WY)	88
Hancock (WS)	44
Hancock (CHE)	50
Hancock (REV)	51
Hancock (DOR)	25
Hancock	14
Hancock	
1-487 (NQ)	71
488-985 (WOL)	70
986-OUT (QUI)	69
Hancock Ave (NCE)	59
Hancock Ct (QUI)	69
Hancock Rd (WES)	93
Hancock Rd (BRO)	46
Hancock St & Ave (BRA)	85
Hancock St & Ave (LEX)	73
Hancock St, Ave & Ct (MED)	55
Hancock St, Park & Pl (CAM)	39
Hancock St, Park & Ter (EV)	49

Boston (Con.)   021

Hancock St & Rd (MAL) 48
Hancock St & Rd (N) 92
Hancock St & Sq (CHA) 29
Hancock Ter (WOL) 70
Hancock Vill (CHH) 67
Hanford Rd (STO) 80
Hanian Dr (EWY) 89
Hanna (QUI) 69
Hannon (DOR) 24
Hano (ALL) 34
Hanover (MAL) 48
Hanover (WY) 88
Hanover
   1-209 (ODD) 08
   2-196 (EVEN) 08
   198-OUT (EVEN) 13
   211-OUT (ODD) 13
Hanover Ave 09
Hansborough (DOR) 24
Hansford Pl (ROX) 19
Hanson 18
Hanson Ave (LEX) 73
Hanson Rd (NCE) 59
Hanson Rd (WAL) 54
Hanson St & Ave (SOM) 43
Harbell (LEX) 73
Harbell Ter (DOR) 22
Harbor 02210
Harbor View (DOR) 25
Harbor View (NQ) 71
Harbor View Ave (NWY) 91
Harbor View Ave (WIN) 52
Harbor View Park & Rd (MIL) . 86
Harbor Villa Ave (BRA) 84
Harcourt 16
Hardan Rd (WS) 44
Harding (CAM) 41
Harding (SOM) 43
Harding (WOL) 70
Harding (WNW) 65
Harding Ave (BEL) 78
Harding Ave (WAL) 54
Harding Ave (MAL) 48
Harding Ave (EV) 49
Harding Ave (BRA) 84
Harding Ave (WY) 88
Harding Ct & Rd (MEL) 76
Harding Rd (LEX) 73
Harding Rd (N) 92
Harding Rd (ROS) 31
Hardwick (CAM) 41
Hardwick Rd (QUI) 69
Hardwick St & Ter (BRI) 35
Hardy (WAL) 54
Hardy (SB) 27
Hardy Ave (WAT) 72
Hardy Rd (WEL) 81
Hardy Pond Rd (WAL) 54
Hargrave Cir (NWH) 61
Harkins (QUI) 69
Harland (MIL) 86
Harland Rd (WY) 88
Harland Rd (WAL) 54
Harlem (DOR) 21
Harlem Rd (NWY) 91
Harley (DOR) 24
Harley Ave & Ct (EV) 49
Harlow (DOR) 25
Harlow (ARL) 74
Harmon (MAT) 26
Harmon Rd (WAL) 54

Harmony (EB) 28
Harnden Ave (WAT) 72
Harnden Rd (MAL) 48
Harold (SOM) 43
Harold (ARL) 74
Harold (MEL) 76
Harold (MIL) 87
Harold
   1-88 (ROX) 19
   89-OUT (DOR) 21
Harold Park (ROX) 19
Harold St & Rd (MED) 55
Harold Ter (WNW) 65
Harriet (BRI) 35
Harriet Ave (NQ) 71
Harriett Ave (WAV) 79
Harrington (WAT) 72
Harrington (NWV) 60
Harrington Ave (QUI) 69
Harrington Ave (ROX) 19
Harrington Cir (WY) 88
Harrington Rd (LEX) 73
Harrington Rd (CAM) 40
Harrington Rd (WAL) 54
Harrington St & Ave (REV) 51
Harrington Ter (MED) 55
Harris (REV) 51
Harris (WAL) 54
Harris (MAL) 48
Harris (BRO) 46
Harris (QUI) 69
Harris (WAV) 79
Harris 09
Harris
   1-35 (SOM) (ODD) 43
   2-30 (CAM) (EVEN) 40
   32-OUT (SOM) (EVEN) 43
   37-37 (CAM) 40
   39-OUT (SOM) (ODD) 43
Harris Ave (N) 92
Harris Ave (WH) 81
Harris Ave (EV) 49
Harris Ave (JP) 30
Harris Cir (ARL) 74
Harris Rd (WNW) 65
Harris Rd (MED) 55
Harrishof
   1-147 (DOR) 21
   148-OUT (ROX) 19
Harrison (MED) 55
Harrison (ROS) 31
Harrison (BRO) 46
Harrison (SOM) 43
Harrison (MEL) 76
Harrison (QUI) 69
Harrison (NWH) 61
Harrison Ave (CAM) 40
Harrison Ave (EV) 49
Harrison Ave (BRA) 84
Harrison Ave
   1-291 11
   292-960 18
   961-OUT (ROX) 19
Harrison Ave Ext. 11
Harrison Park (DOR) 22
Harrison Rd (WS) 44
Harrow (DOR) 25
Hart (BRO) 46
Hart Ave (WY) 88
Hart Pl (SB) 27
Hartford (NWH) 61
Hartford Pl (REV) 51
Hartford Rd (ARL) 74

Hartford St, Ct & Ter (DOR) ... 25
Hartford St & Pl 10
Hartland (DOR) 25
Hartlawn Rd (WRX) 32
Hartley Rd (BEL) 78
Hartley Ter (ALL) 34
Hartman Rd (NCE) 59
Hartshorn St & Ave (MAL) 48
Hartwell (DOR) 21
Hartwell Ave (LEX) 73
Hartwell St & Pl (WAL) 54
Harvard (MAL) 48
Harvard (WIN) 52
Harvard (EV) 49
Harvard (CHE) 50
Harvard (MEL) 76
Harvard (ARL) 74
Harvard (WEL) 81
Harvard. 11
Harvard (WY) 88
Harvard
   1-51 (CAM) 42
   1-100 (NQ) 71
   1-499 (DOR) 24
   52-344 (CAM) (EVEN) 39
   53-339 (CAM) (ODD) 39
   101-OUT (WOL) 70
   341-OUT (CAM) (ODD) 38
   346-OUT (CAM) (EVEN) 38
   500-OUT (MAT) 26
Harvard Ave (DOR) 21
Harvard Ave & Pl (HP) 36
Harvard Ave & Ter (ALL) 34
Harvard Park (DOR) 24
Harvard Rd (BEL) 78
Harvard Sq (CAM) 38
Harvard St, Ave, Ct, Pl & Sq
   (BRO) 46
Harvard St, Ave & Ter (MED).. 55
Harvard St & Cir (NWV) 60
Harvard St & Pl (WAL) 54
Harvard St & Pl (SOM) 43
Harvard St, Pl & Sq (CHA) 29
Harvard Way Ext (SF) 63
Harvest St & Ter (DOR) 25
Harvester (ALL) 34
Harvey (CAM) 40
Harvey (EV) 49
Harvey Pl (WNW) 65
Harvey Steel Rd (ALL) 34
Harveys Ln (QUI) 69
Harwell Dr (CAM) 41
Harwich 16
Harwich Rd (CHH) 67
Harwood (DOR) 24
Hasey (REV) 51
Haskell (CAM) 40
Haskell (A¹L) 34
Haskell (MEL) 76
Haskell (LEX) 73
Haskell Ave (REV) 51
Haskell Ave (EV) 49
Haskins (RXC) 20
Haskins Ct (MAL) 48
Haslet (ROS) 31
Hassett George P Dr (MED) 55
Hastings (WRX) 32
Hastings (WH) 81
Hastings Ln (MED) 55
Hastings Rd (LEX) 73
Hastings Rd (BEL) 78
Hastings Sq (CAM) 39
Hastings St & Ave (WAL) 54

Boston (Con.)   021

Hatch (EV) 49
Hatch (SB) 27
Hatch Rd (MED) 55
Hatfield Rd (WNW) 65
Hathaway (JP) 30
Hathaway 02210
Hathaway Cir (ARL) 74
Hathaway Rd (LEX) 73
Hatherly Rd (WOL) 70
Hatherly Rd (WAL) 54
Hatherly Rd (BRI) 35
Hathon Sq (CHA) 29
Hathorn (SOM) 45
Hauman (REV) 51
Hautevale (ROS) 31
Havana (ROS) 31
Havelock (MAL) 48
Havelock (DOR) 24
Haven (WH) 18
Haven Rd (WH) 81
Haven Rd (BRA) 84
Haverford (JP) 30
Haverhill (CHA) 29
Haverhill Pl (MEL) 76
Havey (ROS) 31
Haviland (WOL) 70
Haviland 15
Havre St & Ct (EB) 28
Hawes 09
Hawes (BRO) 46
Hawes (REV) 51
Hawes Ave (MEL) 76
Hawkins (SOM) 43
Hawkins 14
Hawkins (EWY) 89
Hawley Rd (MEL) 76
Hawley St & Pl 10
Hawthorn (WAV) 79
Hawthorn (NEW) 58
Hawthorn (CAM) 38
Hawthorn (MED) 55
Hawthorn (EV) 49
Hawthorn Rd (BRO) 46
Hawthorn Rd (BRA) 84
Hawthorne (EWY) 89
Hawthorne (MAL) 48
Hawthorne (WS) 44
Hawthorne (MEL) 76
Hawthorne (WAT) 72
Hawthorne (QUI) 69
Hawthorne (ROX) 19
Hawthorne Ave (ARL) 74
Hawthorne Ave (AUB) 66
Hawthorne Ave (WIN) 52
Hawthorne Ave (N) 92
Hawthorne Ln (WES) 93
Hawthorne Park (CAM) 38
Hawthorne Pl 14
Hawthorne Rd (WAL) 54
Hawthorne Rd (MIL) 87
Hawthorne Rd (WH) 81
Hawthorne Rd (LEX) 73
Hawthorne St & Ct (CHE) 50
Hawthorne St & Ter (ROS) 31
Hay Rd (BEL) 78
Hay Rd (NCE) 59
Hayden (QUI) 69
Hayden (RXC) 20
Hayden Ave (LEX) 73
Hayden Pl (WH) 81
Hayden Rd (BRO) 46

Hayden Ter (SOM) 43
Haydn (ROS) 31
Hayes (CAM) 39
Hayes (ARL) 74
Hayes Ave (REV) 51
Hayes Ave & Ln (LEX) 73
Hayes Rd (ROS) 31
Haymarket Pl 11
Haymarket Sq 14
Haynes (EB) 28
Haynes Park (ROX) 19
Haynes Rd (NCE) 59
Hays Rd (WAL) 54
Hayward (CAM) 42
Hayward (MAL) 48
Hayward (NQ) 71
Hayward (BRA) 84
Hayward Ave (LEX) 73
Hayward Pl 11
Hazel (WAT) 72
Hazel (MIL) 86
Hazel (WAL) 54
Hazel (CAM) 38
Hazel Ln (NH) 94
Hazel Park (EV) 49
Hazel Park (ROX) 19
Hazel Rd (MED) 55
Hazel Rd (LEX) 73
Hazel Ter (ARL) 74
Hazelhurst Ave (WNW) 65
Hazelmere Rd (ROS) 31
Hazelton (MAT) 26
Hazelton Ave (N) 92
Hazelton Rd (NCE) 59
Hazelwood (ROX) 19
Hazelwood (MAL) 48
Hazelwood Ave (WNW) 65
Headland Way (MED) 55
Healey (CAM) 38
Healy Rd (WY) 88
Heard (CHE) 50
Heard (WAL) 54
Heard Rd (ARL) 74
Hearn (WAT) 72
Heath (NQ) 71
Heath (EV) 49
Heath (SOM) 45
Heath (N) 92
Heath
   1-99 (BRO) 46
   100-OUT (CHH) 67
Heath Ave (BRO) 46
Heath Ct (CHH) 67
Heath Pl (MAL) 48
Heath Rd (ARL) 74
Heath St & Sq (JP) 30
Heath Hill (BRO) 46
Heathcote (ROS) 31
Heather Ln (SWY) 90
Heather Rd (WAT) 72
Heatherland Rd (NWH) 61
Hebron (MAT) 26
Heckle (WH) 81
Hecla (DOR) 22
Hedge Rd (BRO) 46
Hedlund Ave (BRA) 84
Hefferan (ALL) 34
Held Cir (MED) 55
Heldun (WRX) 32
Helen (WAL) 54
Helen (DOR) 24
Helen Rd (BRA) 84
Helen Rd (N) 92

Helena Rd (DOR) 22
Helene (QUI) 69
Helene Rd (WAB) 68
Helvic Rd (CHH) 67
Hemenway 15
Hemenway Ave (MEL) 76
Hemenway Ave & Ct (MAL) 48
Hemlock (WH) 81
Hemlock (ARL) 74
Hemlock (N) 92
Hemlock Dr (MIL) 86
Hemlock Rd (BRA) 85
Hemlock Rd (WES) 93
Hemlock Rd (NUF) 64
Hemlock Rd (WRX) 32
Hemlock Rd (CAM) 38
Hemlock Ter (WAL) 54
Hemman (ROS) 31
Henchman 13
Henderson (SOM) 45
Henderson (EV) 49
Henderson (ARL) 74
Henderson (N) 92
Henderson Ave (SB) 27
Henderson Rd (WY) 88
Henderson Rd (LEX) 73
Hendry (DOR) 22
Henley (CHA) 29
Henley (MED) 55
Henrici (MAT) 26
Henry (EB) 28
Henry (MED) 55
Henry (EV) 49
Henry (BRO) 46
Henry (CAM) 39
Henry (REV) 51
Henry (ARL) 74
Henry (BEL) 78
Henry (NQ) 71
Henry Ave (MEL) 76
Henry Ave (WS) 44
Henry St & Ct (MAL) 48
Henry Sterling Sq (SB) 27
Henshaw (BRI) 35
Henshaw St, Pl & Ter (WNW) .. 65
Henshaw Ter (WRX) 32
Herald 18
Herbert (DOR) 24
Herbert (WS) 44
Herbert (CAM) 40
Herbert (EV) 49
Herbert (MEL) 76
Herbert Rd (BEL) 78
Herbert Rd (NQ) 71
Herbert Rd (ARL) 74
Herbert Rd (BRA) 84
Herbertson Rd (JP) 30
Hereford 15
Hereford Rd (WAB) 68
Hereward Rd (NCE) 59
Heritage Dr & Rd (LEX) 73
Heritage Ln (BRA) 84
Heritage Ln (MIL) 86
Heritage Ln (EWY) 89
Herman (ROX) 19
Hermon (BEL) 78
Hermon (WIN) 52
Hermon Ter (NEW) 58
Heron (WRX) 32
Heron Rd (QUI) 69
Herrick (BRI) 35
Herrick Rd (NCE) 59
Hersam (STO) 80

Boston (Con.) 021

Hersey (NWH) 61
Hersey (SOM) 43
Hersey Pl (QUI) 69
Hersey Pl 11
Hersom (WAT) 72
Hersum Way (WAL) 54
Hesseltine Ave (MEL) 76
Hesston Ter (DOR) 25
Hester (BRI) 35
Hestia Park (ROX) 19
Hewes (ROX) 19
Hewett Cir (NH) 94
Hewins (DOR) 21
Hewitt Rd (NWY) 91
Hewlett (ROS) 31
Hewmason Rd (BRA) 84
Hews (CAM) 39
Heyward Ave (MEL) 76
Hiawatha Ave (WAL) 54
Hiawatha Ln & Rd (ARL) 74
Hiawatha Rd (MAT) 26
Hibbard (QUI) 69
Hibbard Rd (NEW) 58
Hibbert (ARL) 74
Hibbert (LEX) 73
Hibiscus Ave (WAL) 54
Hibiscus Ave (WY) 88
Hichborn (BRI) 35
Hichborn (REV) 51
Hickory (LEX) 73
Hickory Ave (MED) 55
Hickory Dr (WAL) 54
Hickory Ln (BEL) 78
Hickory Rd (WH) 81
Hickory Rd (BRA) 85
Hickory Rd (WES) 93
Hickory Cliff Rd (NUF) 64
Hicks Ave (MED) 55
Hidden Rd (WES) 93
Higgins (ALL) 34
Higgins (AUB) 66
Higgins (ARL) 74
Higgins Ave (MED) 55
High (MED) 55
High (CAM) 38
High (WAL) 54
High (REV) 51
High (WS) 44
High (CHE) 50
High (EV) 49
High (MAL) 48
High (BRO) 46
High (NUF) 64
High (STO) 80
High (NWH) 61
High (QUI) 69
High (NH) 94
High (MIL) 87
High (EWY) 89
High (CHA) 29
High (DOR) 22
High 10
High Rd (WRX) 32
High St N & S (MEL) 76
High St Pl (BRO) 46
High St Pl (EWY) 89
High St Ter (EV) 49
High Cliff Ter (STO) 80
High Gate (WH) 81
High Gate (N) 92
High Haith Rd (ARL) 74

High Ledge Ave (WH) .... 81'
High Rock (N) 92
High Rock Cir (WAL) 54
High Rock Rd (MAL) 48
High Rock Ter (CHH) 67
High Rock Way (ALL) 34
High School Ave (QUI) 69
High School Ter (EWY) 89
High View Ave (WRX) 32
Highcrest Rd & Ter (ROS) 31
Highfield Cir (MIL) 86
Highfield Rd (QUI) 69
Highfield Rd & Ter (ROS) 31
Highgate (ALL) 34
Highland (HP) 36
Highland (CAM) 38
Highland (WAL) 54
Highland (CHE) 50
Highland (REV) 51
Highland (MIL) 86
Highland (WES) 93
Highland
  1-358 (WNW) 65
  359-OUT (NWV) 60
Highland Ave (WIN) 52
Highland Ave (STO) 80
Highland Ave (ARL) 74
Highland Ave (LEX) 73
Highland Ave (WOL) 70
Highland Ave (WAT) 72
Highland Ave
  1-220 (NWV) 60
  1-288 (SOM) 43
  1-1206 (NH) 94
  -221-OUT (WNW) 65
  289-OUT (WS) 44
  1207-OUT (N) 92
Highland Ave E (BRA) 84
Highland Ave E & W (MEL) ... 76
Highland Ave & Ct (EV) 49
Highland Ave, Ct, Park & Ter
  (MAL) 48
Highland Ave & Park (CAM) ... 39
Highland Ave & Plz (BRA) 85
Highland Ave & Ter (MED) 55
Highland Cir & Ter (NH) 94
Highland Park Ave (ROX) 19
Highland Park St (ROX) 19
Highland Park & Ter (NWV) ... 60
Highland Pl (N) 92
Highland Pl (SWY) 90
Highland Rd (BEL) 78
Highland Rd (WEL) 81
Highland Rd (WS) 44
Highland Rd (BRO) 46
Highland St, Ave, Pl & Ter
  (ROX) 19
Highview (NH) 94
Highview Ave (BRA) 85
Highview Ave (MEL) 76
Hilary (CHA) 29
Hilburn St & Pl (ROS) 31
Hilda (QUI) 69
Hildreth (DOR) 24
Hill (CHA) 29
Hill (QUI) 69
Hill (WAT) 72
Hill (LEX) 73
Hill (WRX) 32
Hill (MAL) 48
Hill (WS) 44
Hill (NH) 94
Hill (EWY) 89

Hill Ave (BRA) 84
Hill Ave (ARL) 74
Hill Rd (BEL) 78
Hill Rd (WAL) 54
Hill St & Ct (STO) 80
Hill Top (DOR) 24
Hill Top Ave (LEX) : 73
Hill Top Rd (WEL) 81
Hill Top Rd (NWY) 91
Hill Top Rd (WES) 93
Hillcrest (ARL) 74
Hillcrest (WRX) 32
Hillcrest Ave (LEX) 73
Hillcrest Ave (MEL) 76
Hillcrest Cir (WAT) 72
Hillcrest Cir (WAB) 68
Hillcrest Rd (NQ) 71
Hillcrest Rd (BEL) 78
Hillcrest Rd (N) 92
Hillcrest Rd (EWY) 89
Hillcrest Rd (MIL) 86
Hillcrest Rd (BRA) 84
Hillcrest St & Rd (WAL) 54
Hillcroft Park (MED) 55
Hillcroft Rd (WAL) 54
Hillcroft Rd (JP) 30
Hillcroft Rd (MAL) 48
Hillcroft Rd (WH) 81
Hilldale Rd (SWY) 90
Hilliard Ct (BRA) 84
Hilliard St & Pl (CAM) 38
Hillis Rd (HP) 36
Hillock (ROS) 31
Hills Ct (MAL) 48
Hillsboro (QUI) 69
Hillsboro (DOR) 25
Hillsboro Rd (MAT) 26
Hillsboro Rd (MED) 55
Hillsdale (DOR) 24
Hillsdale Rd (ARL) 74
Hillsdale Rd
  1-101 (MED) (ODD) 55
  2-96 (MED) (EVEN) 55
  98-OUT (WS) (EVEN) 44
  103-OUT (WS) (ODD) 44
Hillside (MIL) 86
Hillside (RXC) 20
Hillside Ave (NH) 94
Hillside Ave (ARL) 74
Hillside Ave (WOL) 70
Hillside Ave (MED) 55
Hillside Ave (SOM) 45
Hillside Ave (JP) 30
Hillside Ave (CHE) 50
Hillside Ave (EV) 49
Hillside Ave (WIN) 52
Hillside Ave (REV) 51
Hillside Ave & Park (MEL) 76
Hillside Ave & Pl (CAM) 40
Hillside Ave & Rd (STO) 80
Hillside Ave & Rd (BRA) 84
Hillside Ave & Ter (WNW) 65
Hillside Ave & Ter (LEX) 73
Hillside Cir & Park (SOM) 43
Hillside Pl (CHA) 29
Hillside Rd (BRO) 46
Hillside Rd (WH) 81
Hillside Rd (NWH) 61
Hillside St Ext (BEL) 78
Hillside St, Ave, Park, Pl &
  Ter (MAL) 48
Hillside St & Rd (WAT) 72
Hillside St & Ter (BEL) 78

Boston (Con.) 021

Hillsview Rd (MIL)................. 86
Hilltop (MIL)........................ 86
Hilltop (NEW)...................... 58
Hilltop (QUI)........................ 69
Hilltop Rd (WAT).................. 72
Hilltop Rd (CHH).................. 67
Hillview Ave (ROS)............... 31
Hillview Rd (BRA)................. 85
Hilma (NQ).......................... 71
Hilton (ARL)........................ 74
Hilton (HP)......................... 36
Hilton (ROX)....................... 19
Hilton Dr (SWY)................... 90
Hinchey Rd (LEX)................. 73
Hinckley (DOR).................... 25
Hinckley (SOM).................... 45
Hinckley Rd (MIL)................ 87
Hinckley Ter (WAB).............. 68
Hingham (CAM).................... 38
Hingham Ave (SWY).............. 90
Hinsdale.........................02215
Hinsdale (MED).................... 55
Hinston Rd (EWY)................ 89
Hitchcock Ter (QUI).............. 69
Hittinger (BEL).................... 78
Hobart (WOL)...................... 70
Hobart (BRA)...................... 35
Hobart Ave (BRA)................ 85
Hobart Rd (WEL).................. 81
Hobart Rd
  1-OUT (NCE) (ODD)........... 59
  2-100 (NCE) (EVEN).......... 59
  102-OUT (CHH) (EVEN)...... 67
Hobart St & Ter (BRA).......... 84
Hobart Ter (NCE)................. 59
Hobbs Ct (ARL).................... 74
Hobbs Rd (MED).................. 55
Hobbs Rd (WAL).................. 54
Hobbs Brook Rd (WAL).......... 54
Hobbs Brook Rd (WES).......... 93
Hobomac Rd (NWY)............... 91
Hobomack Rd (QUI)............... 69
Hobson (BRI)....................... 35
Hobson (ROS)...................... 31
Hodgdon Ter (WRX).............. 32
Hodge Rd (ARL)................... 74
Hodges Ave (WEL)............... 81
Hodges Ave & Ct (NQ).......... 71
Hodgkinson (QUI)................. 69
Hoffman (JP)....................... 30
Hoitt Rd (BEL)..................... 78
Holborn (MIL)...................... 86
Holborn St, Park & Ter
  (DOR).............................. 21
Holbrook (JP)...................... 30
Holbrook Ave (DOR).............. 22
Holbrook Ave (BRA).............. 85
Holbrook Ct (MEL)................ 76
Holbrook Rd (NWY)............... 91
Holbrook Rd
  1-68 (WOL)...................... 70
  69-OUT (NQ).................... 71
Holden (DOR)...................... 25
Holden (CAM)...................... 38
Holden (BRO)...................... 46
Holden (MAL)...................... 48
Holden Ct........................... 09
Holden Rd (BkA).................. 84
Holden Rd (WAV)................. 79
Holden Rd (WNW)................ 65
Holden Row (CHA)................ 29

Holden Green (CAM)............. 38
Holiday (DOR)..................... 22
Hollace (WAL)..................... 54
Holland (MAL)..................... 48
Holland (WS)...................... 44
Holland (NEW).................... 58
Holland (LEX)..................... 73
Holland Rd (MEL)................. 76
Holland Rd (BRO)................. 46
Holland St & Ter (N)............ 92
Hollander (DOR).................. 21
Hollingsworth (MAT)............. 26
Hollingsworth Ave
  1-149 (BRA).................... 84
  150-OUT (BRA)................ 85
Hollingsworth Rd (MIL).......... 86
Hollis (MIL)........................ 86
Hollis (SWY)....................... 90
Hollis.............................. 16
Hollis (NEW)....................... 58
Hollis (WEL)....................... 81
Hollis Ave (NQ)................... 71
Hollis Ave (BRA)................. 84
Hollis Pl (ALL).................... 34
Hollis St & Park (CAM).......... 40
Holliston (QUI).................... 69
Hollow-Ridge Rd (NH)........... 94
Holly (WAT)........................ 72
Holly Ave (CAM).................. 38
Holly Cir (WES)................... 93
Holly Rd (BRA).................... 85
Holly Rd (ROS).................... 31
Holly Rd (WAB)................... 68
Holly Hill Cir (SWY).............. 90
Hollywood Rd (WRX)............. 32
Holm Ct (MAL).................... 48
Holman (ALL)...................... 34
Holman Rd (AUB)................. 66
Holmberg Rd (EWY).............. 89
Holmes (BRA)..................... 84
Holmes (N)......................... 92
Holmes (CAM)..................... 38
Holmes (ALL)...................... 34
Holmes (MAL)..................... 48
Holmes Ave (NWY)............... 91
Holmes Ln (MIL).................. 86
Holmes Rd (MED)................. 55
Holmes Rd (LEX).................. 73
Holmes St & Pl (NQ)............ 71
Holmfield Ave (MAT)............. 26
Holt
  1-39 (WAV)..................... 79
  40-OUT (WAT).................. 72
Holton (MED)...................... 55
Holton
  1-59 (ALL)...................... 34
  60-OUT (BRI).................. 35
Holton Rd (LEX).................. 73
Holts Ave (SOM).................. 43
Holworthy (DOR).................. 21
Holworthy St, Pl & Ter (CAM). 38
Holyoke (MAL)..................... 48
Holyoke............................ 16
Holyoke (NQ)...................... 71
Holyoke Rd (WS).................. 44
Holyoke St & Pl (CAM).......... 38
Home (MAL)....................... 48
Homer (BRO)...................... 46
Homer (REV)...................... 51
Homer (WAT)...................... 72
Homer (NCE)...................... 59
Homer (EB)........................ 28
Homer (SWY)...................... 90

Homer Cir (MED).................. 55
Homer Rd (QUI).................... 69
Homer Rd (BEL)................... 78
Homer Rd (ARL)................... 74
Homer Sq (SOM).................. 43
Homes Ave (DOR)................ 22
Homestead (DOR)................. 21
Homestead (LEX).................. 73
Homestead Ave (QUI)............ 69
Homestead Ave (WY)............ 88
Homestead Park (NH)............ 94
Homestead Pl (CHA).............. 29
Homestead Rd (ARL)............. 74
Homestead Rd (WEL)............ 81
Homestead St & Rd (WAB)..... 68
Homewood Rd (WRX)............ 32
Hommagen Pl (ROX).............. 19
Hood (QUI)......................... 69
Hood (NEW)....................... 58
Hooker (MED)..................... 55
Hooker (ALL)...................... 34
Hooker (BRA)...................... 84
Hooker Ave (WS)................. 44
Hooper (CHE)...................... 50
Hooper (QUI)...................... 69
Hooper (DOR)..................... 24
Hooten Ct (EB).................... 28
Hooton Way (CHE)............... 50
Hoover Ave (QUI)................. 69
Hoover Ave (BRA)................ 85
Hoover Rd (NH)................... 94
Hope (AUB)........................ 66
Hope Ave (MIL)................... 86
Hope Ave (WAL).................. 54
Hopedale (ALL).................... 34
Hopedale (QUI).................... 69
Hopestiff (DOR)................... 24
Hopewell Rd (MAT)............... 26
Hopkins (DOR)..................... 24
Hopkins (MEL)..................... 76
Hopkins (REV)..................... 51
Hopkins Pl (MAT)................. 26
Hopkins Rd (JP)................... 30
Hopkins Rd (ARL)................ 74
Hopkinson (WH)................... 81
Horace (SOM)...................... 43
Horace (MAL)...................... 48
Horace (EB)........................ 28
Horace (NH)........................ 94
Horace Rd (BEL).................. 78
Horadan Way (RXC)............. 20
Horan Way (JP)................... 30
Horne Ave (MED)................. 55
Horne Rd (BEL)................... 78
Horsford Rd (N)................... 92
Horton Pl (MIL)................... 86
Hosmer (WAT)..................... 72
Hosmer (EV)....................... 49
Hosmer (MAT)..................... 26
Hosmer Cir (WNW)............... 65
Hospital Rd (ARL)................ 74
Hospital Rd (MAL)................ 48
Hotin Rd (STO)................... 80
Hough Rd (WAV).................. 79
Houghton (DOR).................. 22
Houghton
  1-OUT (SOM) (ODD).......... 43
  2-4 (CAM) (EVEN)............ 39
  6-OUT (SOM) (EVEN)........ 43
Houghton Rd (MIL)............... 86
Houghton Rd (BEL)............... 78
House Rock Rd (WY)............. 88
Houston (WRX).................... 32

Boston (Con.) 021

Houston Ave (MIL) ... 87
Houston Park (CAM) ... 40
Hovey (WAT) ... 72
Hovey (NQ) ... 71
Hovey (NEW) ... 58
Hovey Ave (CAM) ... 38
Hovey Rd (WAL) ... 54
Howard (WAL) ... 54
Howard (CAM) ... 39
Howard (WS) ... 44
Howard (REV) ... 51
Howard (NEW) ... 58
Howard (WAT) ... 72
Howard (BEL) ... 78
Howard (MEL) ... 76
Howard (ARL) ... 74
Howard (WNW) ... 65
Howard (MIL) ... 86
Howard (NWY) ... 91
Howard (ROX) ... 19
Howard Ave & Pl (DOR) ... 25
Howard Pl (CHA) ... 29
Howard Rd (MED) ... 55
Howard St & Ct (BRA) ... 84
Howard St & Ter (MAL) ... 48
Howe (SOM) ... 45
Howe (MIL) ... 86
Howe (DOR) ... 25
Howe (WAT) ... 72
Howe (WEL) ... 81
Howe (QUI) ... 69
Howe Ct (RXC) ... 20
Howe Rd (NCE) ... 59
Howe Rd (N) ... 92
Howell (DOR) ... 25
Howell Ct (CHE) ... 50
Howells Rd (BEL) ... 78
Howes (DOR) ... 25
Howie (MEL) ... 76
Howie Rd (BRA) ... 84
Howitt Rd (WRX) ... 32
Howland (CAM) ... 38
Howland (N) ... 92
Howland (DOR) ... 21
Howland Cir (MED) ... 55
Howland Rd (WNW) ... 65
Howley Ave (NCE) ... 59
Hoy Ter (MIL) ... 86
Hoyt (EV) ... 49
Hoyt (DOR) ... 25
Huban Ct (RXC) ... 20
Hubbard (JP) ... 30
Hubbard (MAL) ... 48
Hubbard (SWY) ... 90
Hubbard Ave (CAM) ... 40
Hubbard Park Rd (CAM) ... 38
Hubbard Rd (WES) ... 93
Hubbardston Rd (DOR) ... 25
Hubert (RXC) ... 20
Huckins (ROX) ... 19
Huckins Ave (NQ) ... 71
Hudson (WAT) ... 72
Hudson (QUI) ... 69
Hudson (CHA) ... 29
Hudson ... 11
Hudson (MIL) ... 87
Hudson
　1-92 (SOM) ... 43
　93-OUT (WS) ... 44
Hudson Rd (LEX) ... 73
Hudson St & Pl (CAM) ... 38
Hudson St & Ter (MAL) ... 48

Hughes (QUI) ... 69
Huibert (ROX) ... 19
Hull ... 13
Hull (QUI) ... 69
Hull (NWV) ... 60
Hull (WAV) ... 79
Hull St Ct ... 13
Hull St Pl ... 13
Humboldt (CAM) ... 40
Humboldt (WAL) ... 54
Humboldt Ave
　1-79 (ROX) (ODD) ... 19
　2-90 (ROX) (EVEN) ... 19
　81-OUT (DOR) (ODD) ... 21
　92-OUT (DOR) (EVEN) ... 21
Humboldt Ct & Ter (ROX) ... 19
Humboldt Pl (SB) ... 27*
Hume Ave (MED) ... 55
Humes Rd (DOR) ... 22
Hummock Rd (NQ) ... 71
Humphrey (EWY) ... 89
Humphreys St & Pl (DOR) ... 25
Hundreds Cir & Rd (WH) ... 81
Hunneman (ROX) ... 19
Hunnewell (WH) ... 81
Hunnewell Ave (MEL) ... 76
Hunnewell Ave (MED) ... 55
Hunnewell Ave (BRI) ... 35
Hunnewell Ave & Cir (NEW) ... 58
Hunnewell St & Ter (NH) ... 94
Hunt (WY) ... 88
Hunt (WAT) ... 72
Hunt (NQ) ... 71
Hunt Ave (BRA) ... 84
Hunt Rd (LEX) ... 73
Hunter (WNW) ... 65
Hunter (ROS) ... 31
Hunter (CHA) ... 29
Hunter Ter (SWY) ... 90
Hunting (MAL) ... 48
Hunting (WH) ... 81
Hunting
　1-39 (CAM) (ODD) ... 41
　2-42 (CAM) (EVEN) ... 41
　41-OUT (SOM) (ODD) ... 43
　44-OUT (SOM) (EVEN) ... 43
Hunting Rd (NH) ... 94
Huntington (WAL) ... 54
Huntington Ave (SWY) ... 90
Huntington Ave
　1-85 (ROS) (ODD) ... 31
　1-149 ... 16
　2-76 (ROS) (EVEN) ... 31
　78-OUT (HP) (EVEN) ... 36
　87-OUT (HP) (ODD) ... 36
　150-OUT ... 15
Huntington Rd (MIL) ... 86
Huntington Rd (NEW) ... 58
Huntington Rd (ARL) ... 74
Huntley Rd (QUI) ... 69
Huntley Rd (BRA) ... 84
Huntley St & Ter (MAL) ... 48
Huntoon (DOR) ... 24
Huntress (QUI) ... 69
Hunts Ter (MEL) ... 76
Hurd (MEL) ... 76
Hurd (MAL) ... 48
Hurd Rd (BRO) ... 46
Hurd Rd (BEL) ... 78
Hurlburt (CAM) ... 38
Hurlburt Ct (MAL) ... 48
Hurlcroft Ave (MED) ... 55
Hurlcroft Ave (DOR) ... 24

Hurlcroft Rd (MIL) ... 86
Hurley (CAM) ... 41
Hurley (BEL) ... 78
Hurley Pl (NCE) ... 59
Huron Ave (CAM) ... 38
Huron Cir (DOR) ... 24
Hutchings (DOR) ... 21
Hutchins Rd (MED) ... 55
Hutchinson (CAM) ... 38
Hutchinson (WIN) ... 52
Hutchinson (REV) ... 51
Hutchinson (DOR) ... 24
Hutchinson (MIL) ... 87
Hutchinson Rd (ARL) ... 74
Hutchinson Rd (LEX) ... 73
Hyde (NWH) ... 61
Hyde (QUI) ... 69
Hyde (WY) ... 88
Hyde (MAL) ... 48
Hyde Ave (NEW) ... 58
Hyde Park Ave
　1-336 (JP) ... 30
　337-749 (ROS) ... 31
　750-OUT (HP) ... 36
Hyde Sq (JP) ... 30
Hyde St & Pl (REV) ... 51
Hynes Ave (QUI) ... 69
Hyslop Rd (BRO) ... 46
Hywood (REV) ... 51
I (SB) ... 27
Ibbetson (SOM) ... 43
Ida (QUI) ... 69
Ida Rd (BRA) ... 84
Idaho (MAT) ... 26
Idlewell St & Blvd (WY) ... 88
Iffley Rd (JP) ... 30
Illinois Ave (SOM) ... 45
Imbaro Rd (HP) ... 36
Imrie Rd (ALL) ... 34
Ina Rd (N) ... 92
Incinerator Rd (CHH) ... 67
Independence Ave (QUI) ... 69
Independence Ave (LEX) ... 73
Independence Ave (BRA) ... 84
Independence Dr (CHH) ... 67
India
　1-20 ... 09
　21-47 ... 10
　48-48 ... 09
　49-OUT ... 10
India Pl & Sq ... 10
India Wharf ... 10
Indian Rd (WAL) ... 54
Indian Hill Rd (WES) ... 93
Indian Hill Rd (MIL) ... 96
Indian Hill Rd (ARL) ... 74
Indian Hill Rd (BEL) ... 78
Indian Ridge Rd (NCE) ... 59
Indian Spring Rd (MIL) ... 86
Indian Spring Way (WH) ... 81
Indiana Ave (SOM) ... 45
Indiana Ct & Ter (NUF) ... 64
Industrial Pl (NUF) ... 64
Ingalls Ct (MEL) ... 76
Ingersoll Rd (WH) ... 81
Ingleside (JP) ... 25
Ingleside Ave (MAL) ... 48
ingleside Ave (WIN) ... 52
Ingleside Ave (CHE) ... 50
Ingleside Rd (WH) ... 81
Ingleside Rd (LEX) ... 73
Ingleside Rd (N) ... 92
Inglewood Dr (BRA) ... 84

Boston (Con.)   021

Ingraham Rd (WEL)............... 81
Ingram (QUI) 69
Ingrid Rd (WY) 88
Inis Cir (WNW) 65
Inman 02210
Inman St, Pl & Sq (CAM) 39
Inner Belt Rd (SOM) 43
Institution Ave (NCE) 59
Intervale (QUI) 69
Intervale (REV) 51
Intervale (DOR) 21
Intervale Ave (MED) 55
Intervale Rd (CHH) 67
Intervale Rd (WH) 81
Intervale Rd (ARL) 74
Intervale Rd (N) 92
Intervale Rd (WES) 93
Intervale Rd (EWY) 89
Intervale Rd
   1-91 (NCE) 59
   92-OUT (CHH) 67
Inverness Rd (ARL) 74
Inverness Rd (WH) 81
Inwood (DOR) 25
Iola (DOR) 24
Iona (ROS) 31
Ionia (AUB) 66
Iowa (DOR) 24
Ipswich 02215
Ipswich Pl (EB) 28
Ipswich Rd (NWH) 61
Ireland Rd (NCE) 59
Irena Rd (DOR).................. 24
Ireson Ct (MEL) 76
Irma (DOR) 24
Irma Ave (WAT) 72
Iron Hill (EWY) 89
Iroquois (RXC) 20
Iroquois Rd (ARL) 74
Irving (ARL) 74
Irving (WAV) 79
Irving (MEL) 76
Irving (NCE) 59
Irving (STO) 80
Irving 14
Irving (MED) 55
Irving (REV) 51
Irving (WS) 44
Irving (EV) 49
Irving (BRO) 46
Irving (WAL) 54
Irving Rd (WAB) 68
Irving Rd (NWY) 91
Irving Rd (WES) 93
Irving St, Ct & Pl (MAL) 48
Irving St & Park (WAT) 72
Irving St & Ter (CAM) 38
Irvington (WAB) 68
Irvington Rd (MED) 55
Irwin (WIN) 52
Irwin Ave (ROX) 19
Irwin Rd (WAB) 68
Isabella (MEL) 76
Isabella (QUI) 69
Isabella 16
Island (ROX) 19
Island Ave (QUI) 69
Island Vjew Rd (EWY) 89
Islington Rd (AUB) 66
Islington St & Ter (ALL) 34
Itasca (MAT) 26

Ithaca Cir (NLF) 62
Ivaloo (WAL) 54
Ivaloo (SOM) 43
Ivan (LEX) 73
Ivanhoe (NEW) 58
Ivanhoe 18
Ivory (WRX) 32
Ivy (CAM) 38
Ivy (BRO) 46
Ivy Cir (ARL) 74
Ivy Cir & Rd (WEL) 81
Ivy Ln (LEX) 73
Ivy Ln (WAL) 54
Ivy Rd (MAL) 48
Ivy Rd (MED) 55
Ivy Rd (STO) 80
Ivy Rd (BEL) 78
Ivy St, Ct & Rd (SWY) 90
J Rdwy (NCE) 59
Jackson (NCE) 59
Jackson (QUI) 69
Jackson (MAL) 48
Jackson (HP) 36
Jackson (CAM) 40
Jackson (CHA) 29
Jackson Ave 13
Jackson Ave (EV) 49
Jackson Ct (LEX) 73
Jackson Gdns (CAM) 39
Jackson Rd (SOM) 45
Jackson Rd (MED) 55
Jackson Rd (BEL) 78
Jackson Rd (WH) 81
Jackson Rd & Ter (NEW) 58
Jackson Sq (EWY) 89
Jackson St & Pl (WAL) 54
Jacob (MAL) 48
Jacob (DOR) 24
Jacob (BEL) 78
Jacobs Pl (EV) 49
Jacobs Ter (NCE) 59
Jaconnet (NWH) 61
Jacquelin Rd (WRX) 32
Jacqueline Rd (WAL) 54
Jacquelyn Rd (WY) 88
Jacques (SOM) 45
Jaegar Ter (JP) 30
Jaffrey
   1-114 (EWY) 89
   115-OUT (WY) 88
Jaffrey Cir (WAB) 68
Jalleison (HP) 36
Jamaica Rd (BRO) 46
Jamaica St, Pl & Way (JP)....... 30
Jamaica Way Ct (JP) 30
James (ROS) 31
James (BRO) 46
James (SOM) 45
James (MAL) 48
James (CAM) 38
James (WAL) 54
James (MED) 55
James (WNW) 65
James (LEX) 73
James (QUI) 69
James (ARL) 74
James (WAT) 72
James Ave (WIN) 52
James Ave (NH) 94
James Rd (EWY) 89
Jameson Rd (NEW) 58
Jamestown Ter (MAT) 26
Jane Rd (NCE) 59

Janet Rd (NCE) 59
Janet Rd (ARL) 74
Janet Rd (WOL) 70
Janice Ln (STO) 80
Janvrin Ave (REV) 51
Jarvis (REV) 51
Jarvis (CAM) 38
Jarvis Cir (N) 92
Jarvis (ROX) 19
Jason Rd (BEL) 78
Jason St, Ct & Ter (ARL) 74
Jason Ter (SB) 27
Jasper (SOM) 45
Jasset (NEW) 58
Jay (WS) 44
Jay (CAM) 39
Jay (BRA) 85
Jay Rd (SWY) 90
Jay St Pl (CAM) 39
Jayne Rd (NH) 94
Jean Rd (ARL) 74
Jean Rd (LEX) 73
Jeannette Ave (WAV) 79
Jeffers (ROS) 31
Jefferson (CAM) 41
Jefferson (WIN) 52
Jefferson (NEW) 58
Jefferson (BRA) 85
Jefferson 16
Jefferson Ave (CHA) 29
Jefferson Ave (LEX) 73
Jefferson Ave (WAT) 72
Jefferson Ave (EV) 49
Jefferson Ave (CHE) 50
Jefferson Park (CAM) 40
Jefferson Rd (STO) 80
Jefferson Rd (WH) 81
Jefferson Rd (CHH) 67
Jeffrey Rd (ARL) 74
Jeffrey Ter (LEX) 73
Jeffries (EB) 28
Jefts Ter (MEL) 76
Jenison (NWV) 60
Jenkins (SB) 27
Jenner (CHA) 29
Jenness (QUI) 69
Jenness Rd (BRO) 46
Jennett Ave (WRX) 32
Jennings Rd (WAL) 54
Jensen Rd (WAT) 72
Jepson Ct (WNW) 65
Jerald (WIN) 52
Jeremiah Clancy Rd (DOR) 24
Jericho Hill Rd (WAL) 54
Jerome (SOM) 43
Jerome (MED) 55
Jerome (DOR) 25
Jerome Ave (WNW) 65
Jerome Ct (EV) 49
Jersey 02215
Jersey Ave (BRA) 84
Jeshurun Rd (WRX) 32
Jess (JP) 30
Jewell Pl (ROX) 19
Jewell (ROS) 31
Jewett (QUI) 69
Jewett
   1-19 (WAT) 72
   20-OUT (NEW) 58
Jewett Pl (NEW) 58
Jo Anne Ter (DOR) 24
Joan (STO) 80
Joan Dr (QUI) 69

Boston (Con.)   021

Joan Rd (MED)............... 55
Joan Rd (HP)................. 36
Joan Ter (EWY).............. 89
Joey Rd (REV)................ 51
John (CHE).................... 50
John (WAL).................... 54
John (MAL).................... 48
John (BRO).................... 46
John (NWY)................... 91
John (NH)..................... 94
John (NCE)................... 59
John (NQ).................... 71
John Ave (REV).............. 51
John A Andrew (JP).......... 30
John Alden Rd (WRX)......... 32
John Corcoran Park (CAM).... 38
John Eliot Sq (ROX)......... 19
John F Kennedy Cir (NEW).... 58
John James Rd (MAL)........ 48
John Mooney Rd (REV)....... 51
John Poulter Rd (LEX)....... 73
John Quincy Ln (NWY)....... 91
Johnny Ct................... 11
Johnny Rd (REV)............. 51
Johns Ct (RXC).............. 20
Johnson (WRX)............... 32
Johnson (MIL)............... 86
Johnson Ave (JP)............ 30
Johnson Ave (MED)........... 55
Johnson Ave (CHA)........... 29
Johnson Ave (QUI)........... 69
Johnson Ave & Ter (WIN)..... 52
Johnson Pl (AUB)............ 66
Johnson Rd (ARL)............ 74
Johnson Rd (NWY)............ 91
Johnson Ter (DOR)........... 24
Johnsons Ln (BRA)........... 85
Johnston Park (ROX)......... 19
Johnston Rd (DOR)........... 24
Johnswood Rd (ROS).......... 31
Joiner (CHA)................ 29
Jonathan (WAV).............. 79
Jones (EV).................. 49
Jones Ave (CHE)............. 50
Jones Ave (DOR)............. 24
Jones Ct (NEW).............. 58
Jones Rd (REV).............. 51
Jones Rd (WAL).............. 54
Jones Rd (WES).............. 93
Jordan (WOL)................ 70
Jordan Cir (BRA)............ 85
Jordan Pl (CAM)............. 42
Jordan Rd (BRO)............. 46
Jordan St & Ter (MAL)....... 48
Joseph (MAL)................ 48
Joseph (SOM)................ 43
Joseph (MED)................ 55
Joseph (QUI)................ 69
Joseph (DOR)................ 24
Joseph Rd (NWV)............. 60
Joseph Rd (LEX)............. 73
Joseph Rd (REV)............. 51
Joseph Rd (BRA)............. 84
Joseph A Fern Ct (EWY)...... 89
Josephine (DOR)............. 22
Josephine Ave (WS).......... 44
Josephine Rd (MED).......... 55
Joslin Rd................02215
Josselyn Ter (NWH).......... 61
Joy (SOM)................... 43
Joy (WAL)................... 54

Joy
  1-7.................... V V
  8-OUT................. 14
Joy Pl...................... 08
Joy Ter (MAL)............... 48
Joyce Ave (WY).............. 88
Joyce Rd (WAL).............. 54
Joyce Rd (MED).............. 55
Joyce Rd (HP).............. 36
Joyce Rd (QUI).............. 69
Joyce Rd (ARL).............. 74
Joyce Hayes Way (SB)........ 27
Joyce Kilmer Rd (WRX)....... 32
Judge...................... 15
Judith Rd (NCE)............. 59
Judith Rd (NWY)............. 91
Judkins (NWV)............... 60
Judkins Rd (MED)............ 55
Judson (MAL)................ 48
Judson (BRA)................ 84
Judson (DOR)................ 25
Judson Rd (WY).............. 88
Jules Ter (NCE)............. 59
Julia (MAL)................. 48
Julia Rd (NWY).............. 91
Julia Rd (N)................ 92
Julian (DOR)................ 25
Juliette (DOR).............. 22
Junction (N)................ 92
June (REV).................. 51
June Ln (NCE)............... 59
June Rd (STO).............. 80
June St & Ln (ROS).......... 31
Juniper (BRO)............... 46
Juniper Ln (NCE)............ 59
Juniper Pl & Ter (LEX)...... 73
Juniper Rd (WEL)............ 81
Juniper Rd (BEL)............ 78
Juniper Rd (WAL)............ 54
Juniper Rd (WES)............ 93
Juniper St & Ter (ROX)...... 19
Juniper Hill Rd (WAL)....... 54
Jupiter (WY)................ 88
Justin (LEX)................ 73
Justin Rd (BRI)............. 35
K (EWY).................... 89
K (SB)..................... 27
K St Pl (SB)............... 27
K Way (MED)................. 55
K K Ter (EV)............... 49
Kahler Ave (MIL)............ 87
Kalada Park (DOR)........... 21
Kane (DOR)................. 25
Kaposia (AUB).............. 66
Kappius Path (NCE).......... 59
Kardon Rd (HP).............. 36
Karen Ln (WY).............. 88
Karen Rd (WAB)............. 68
Karlyn Rd (WY).............. 88
Kassul Park (CAM)........... 40
Katherine (NWY)............. 91
Katherine Rd (STO).......... 80
Katherine Rd (WAT).......... 72
Kathleen Rd (SWY)........... 90
Kays Rd (STO).............. 80
Keach (WAL)................. 54
Keane Rd (WRX).............. 32
Kearney (MAL)............... 48
Kearney Rd (NH)............. 94
Kearney Sq.................. 14
Kearsarge Ave & Ter (ROX)... 19
Keating (QUI)............... 69

Keats Rd (ARL).............. 74
Keayne (REV)................ 51
Keefe Ave (NUF)............. 64
Keenan (WAT)................ 72
Keenan Rd (BRI)............. 35
Keene (STO)................. 80
Keith (WAT)................. 72
Keith (WRX)................. 32
Keith (WY).................. 88
Keith Pl (N)................ 92
Keith Rd (MED).............. 55
Keller Path (NCE)........... 59
Kelley Ct (BRI)............. 35
Kelley Ct (CHA)............. 29
Kelley Robert E (CAM)....... 38
Kelly Rd (CAM).............. 39
Kellys Block (CHA).......... 29
Kelton (ALL)................ 34
Kelveden Rd (WAB)........... 68
Kelvin (EV)................. 49
Kemble (ROX)................ 19
Kemble Pl (SB).............. 27
Kemp (SB)................... 27
Kemper (WOL)................ 70
Kempton.................... 15
Kempton Pl (WNW)............ 65
Kenberma Rd (DOR)........... 24
Kendal Ter (NEW)............ 58
Kendall.................... 18
Kendall (NQ)............... 71
Kendall Ave (BRA)........... 85
Kendall Park (WAL).......... 54
Kendall Rd (NCE)............ 59
Kendall Rd (WH)............. 81
Kendall Rd (LEX)............ 73
Kendall Sq (CAM)............ 42
Kendall St & Pl (BRO)....... 46
Kendall Common Rd (WES)..... 93
Kendrick (NH).............. 94
Kendrick Ave (QUI).......... 69
Kenesaw Ter (RXC)........... 20
Kenilworth (ROX)............ 19
Kenilworth (MAL)............ 48
Kenilworth (NEW)............ 58
Kenilworth (EV)............. 49
Kenilworth Cir & Rd (WH).... 81
Kenilworth Rd (ARL)......... 74
Kenilworth Rd (MIL)......... 86
Keniston Rd (MEL)........... 76
Kenmere Rd (MED)............ 55
Kenmere Rd (DOR)............ 24
Kenmore (NCE)............... 59
Kenmore Rd (MEL)............ 76
Kenmore Rd (BEL)............ 78
Kenmore Rd (MAL)............ 48
Kenmore Rd (BRA)............ 85
Kenmore Rd & Ter (WAL)...... 54
Kenmore Sq...............02215
Kennard (MAL)............... 48
Kennard Rd (BRO)............ 46
Kennebec (MAT).............. 26
Kennedy Rd (CAM)............ 38
Kenneson Rd (SOM)........... 45
Kenneth (WRX)............... 32
Kenneth (NWH)............... 61
Kenneth Ter (STO)........... 80
Kenney (JP)................. 30
Kenney (N).................. 92
Kenney Pl (WAB)............. 68
Kenrick (BRI)............... 35
Kenrick St & Ter (NEW)...... 58
Kensington (NWV)............ 60

Boston (Con.) 021

Kensington Ave (SOM)............ 45
Kensington Cir (CHH)............. 67
Kensington Park & Rd (ARL).. 74
Kensington Rd (WY).............. 88
Kensington St & Park (ROX).. 19
Kent (RXC)............................ 20
Kent (WAV)........................... 79
Kent (QUI)............................ 69
Kent Ln (ARL)....................... 74
Kent Rd (WAB)...................... 68
Kent Rd (SWY)...................... 90
Kent Rd (N).......................... 92
Kent St & Ct (SOM)............... 43
Kent St & Sq (BRO)............... 46
Kenton Rd (JP)...................... 30
Kenway (MED)....................... 55
Kenway (CAM)....................... 38
Kenway Ter (ROX)................. 19
Kenwood (DOR)..................... 24
Kenwood (BRO)..................... 46
Kenwood (WS)....................... 44
Kenwood (CAM)..................... 39
Kenwood Ave (NCE)............... 59
Kenwood Ave (STO)............... 80
Kenwood Ln (WAL)................ 54
Kenwood Rd (EV)................... 49
Kenyon (WNW)...................... 65
Kerna Rd (WRX).................... 32
Kernwood (MAL).................... 48
Kerr Path (NCE).................... 59
Kerrigan Pl (BRO)................. 46
Kerrydale Rd (N)................... 92
Kershaw Rd (WRX)................ 32
Kerwin (DOR)....................... 24
Keswick..........................02215
Kevin Rd (MIL)..................... 86
Kevin Rd (DOR)..................... 25
Kew Rd (BRA)....................... 84
Kewadin Rd (WAB)................ 68
Keyes (QUI).......................... 69
Keystone (WRX).................... 32
Kidder (QUI)......................... 69
Kidder Ave (WS)................... 44
Kidney Pond Rd (WES).......... 93
Kiernan Rd (WRX)................. 32
Kilburn (REV)....................... 51
Kilburn Rd (WNW)................ 65
Kilburn Rd (BFI)................... 78
Kilby (QUI).......................... 69
Kilby (SOM)......................... 43
Kilby................................... 09
Kiley Rd (MEL)..................... 76
Kilgore Ave (MED)................. 55
Kilmarnock.......................02215
Kilsyth Rd (MED).................. 55
Kilsyth Rd & Ter (BRO)......... 46
Kilsythe Rd (ARL)................. 74
Kimball (QUI)....................... 69
Kimball (MAL)....................... 48
Kimball (SOM)...................... 43
Kimball (N).......................... 92
Kimball (DOR)...................... 22
Kimball Ave (REV)................. 51
Kimball Ct (MEL).................. 76
Kimball Dr & Rd (STO).......... 80
Kimball Rd (ARL).................. 74
Kimball Rd (LEX).................. 73
Kimball Rd (WAT)................. 72
Kimball Rd (CHE).................. 50
Kimball Rd (BRA).................. 85
Kimball St & Ln (CAM).......... 40

Kimball Ter (NWV)................ 60
Kimlo Rd (WH)..................... 81
Kineo (DOR)......................... 21
King (WAT)........................... 72
King (LEX)............................ 73
King (ARL)........................... 74
King (WAV).......................... 79
King (AUB)........................... 66
King (CAM).......................... 40
King Ave (MED).................... 55
King Ave (WY)...................... 88
King Pl (CAM)....................... 39
King St & Sq (DOR).............. 22
King St & Ter (RXC)............. 20
King Cove Beach St & Rd •
(NWY)............................... 91
King Hill Rd (BRA)................ 85
King Oak Ter (EWY).............. 89
King Phillip (SWY)................ 90
Kingman (WY)...................... 88
Kingman Ave (REV)............... 51
Kingman Rd (SOM)............... 43
Kingman Rd (DOR)................ 24
Kingman Rd (NWH)............... 61
Kings Ln (QUI)..................... 69
Kings Grant Rd (WES)........... 93
Kingsboro Park (JP).............. 30
Kingsbury (N)....................... 92
Kingsbury (WEL)................... 81
Kingsbury (ROX)................... 19
Kingsbury Ln (WES).............. 93
Kingsbury Rd (CHH)............. 67
Kingsdale (DOR)................... 24
Kingsland Rd (WRX).............. 32
Kingsley (ALL)...................... 34
Kingsley Ave (MEL)............... 76
Kingsleys Ct (WAL)............... 54
Kingston (WS)...................... 44
Kingston.............................. 11
Kingston Rd (NWH)............... 61
Kingston Rd & Ter (WAL)....... 54
Kingston St & Pl (CHA)......... 29
Kingswood Rd (AUB)............. 66
Kinmouth Rd (WAB)............... 68
Kinnaird (CAM)..................... 39
Kinross Rd (BRO).................. 46
Kinsman (EV)....................... 49
Kipling Rd (WH)................... 81
Kipling Rd (ARL).................. 74
Kipling Rd (SWY).................. 90
Kippy (EV)........................... 49
Kippy Dr (WAB).................... 68
Kirby (REV).......................... 51
Kirby (BRA).......................... 84
Kirk (WRX).......................... 32
Kirkland.............................. 16
Kirkland Cir (WH)................. 81
Kirkland Rd (SWY)................ 90
Kirkland St, Pl & Rd (CAM)... 39
Kirkstall Rd (NWV)............... 60
Kirkwood Rd (3RI)................ 35
Kirmes Rd (STO).................. 80
Kittredge Ave (QUI).............. 69
Kittredge St, Ct & Ter (ROS). 31
Klasson Ln (WY)................... 88
Knapp (SOM)........................ 43
Knapp.................................. 11
Kneeland............................. 11
Kneeland (MAL).................... 48
Knight (HP).......................... 36
Knights Ct (JP)..................... 30
Knoll (ROS).......................... 31
Knoll (MAL).......................... 48

Knollin (MAL)....................... 48
Knollwood Cir (WY)............... 88
Knollwood Dr (WAL).............. 54
Knollwood Rd (MED)............. 55
Knollwood Rd (NQ)............... 71
Knowles (NCE)..................... 59
Knowles Rd
  1-54 (WAT)....................... 72
  55-OUT (WAV).................. 79
Knowlton (SOM)................... 45
Knowlton (SB)...................... 27
Knox................................... 16
Knox (BEL).......................... 78
Knox Park (EV)..................... 49
Kodaya Rd (WAB).................. 68
Kondazian (WAT)................... 72
Kovey Rd (HP)...................... 36
Kristen Ct (HP)..................... 36
L (SB)................................. 27
La Grange............................ 16
La Grange (WRX).................. 32
La Grange Pl (ROX)............... 19
La Rose Pl (BRI)................... 35
La Salle Rd (NH).................. 94
Labadine (WOL).................... 70
Laban Pratt Rd (DOR)........... 22
Laconia............................... 18
Laconia (LEX)....................... 73
Ladd St & Pl (WAT).............. 72
Lafayette (QUI)..................... 69
Lafayette (ARL).................... 74
Lafayette (MIL).................... 86
Lafayette (EV)...................... 49
Lafayette (WAL)................... 54
Lafayette Ave (CHE)............. 50
Lafayette Ave (EWY)............. 89
Lafayette Cir (WEL).............. 81
Lafayette Rd (NLF)............... 62
Lafayette Sq (CAM)............... 39
Lafield (DOR)....................... 22
Lagrange (CHH).................... 67
Laird Rd (MED)..................... 55
Lake (SOM).......................... 43
Lake (BRI)........................... 35
Lake (MAL).......................... 48
Lake (LEX)........................... 73
Lake (EWY).......................... 89
Lake (BRA).......................... 85
Lake Ave (AUB).................... 66
Lake Ave (MEL).................... 76
Lake Ave
  1-185 (NCE)...................... 59
  186-OUT (NWH)................ 61
Lake Dr (N).......................... 92
Lake Rd (WH)....................... 81
Lake St & Rd (WAL).............. 54
Lake Ter (NCE)..................... 59
Lake Shore Ct, Rd & Ter
  (BRI)............................... 35
Lake Shore Dr (ARL)............. 74
Lake Shore Dr (EWY)............ 89
Lake View Ave (CAM)............ 38
Lakecrest St, Path & Rd
  (EWY).............................. 89
Lakecroft Ct (MEL)............... 76
Lakehill Ave (ARL)............... 74
Lakehurst Ave (EWY)............ 89
Lakeside Ave (EWY).............. 89
Lakeside Ave (QUI)............... 69

Boston (Con.)   **021**

Lakeside Ave (HP) 36
Lakeside Dr (BRA) 84
Lakeview (ARL) 74
Lakeview Ave (NWV) 60
Lakeview Ave (BRA) 85
Lakeview Ave (MED) 55
Lakeview Ave & Ter (WAL) 54
Lakeview Rd (EWY) 89
Lakeville Rd (JP) 30
Lakewood Rd (SWY) 90
Lakewood Rd (NWH) 61
Lakin Rd (NH) 94
Lamar Pl (ROX) 19
Lamartine St, Ct, Ext, Pl & Ter (JP) 30
Lambert (MED) 55
Lambert (CAM) 41
Lambert (REV) 51
Lambert Ave (CHE) 50
Lambert Ave (EWY) 89
Lambert Rd (BEL) 78
Lambert St & Ave (ROX) 19
Lamoine (BEL) 78
Lamont (RXC) 20
Lamont Ave (CAM) 38
Lamson Pl (CAM) 39
Lamson St & Ct (EB) 28
Lanark Rd (BRO) 46
Lanark Rd (MAL) 48
Lanark Rd (ARL) 74
Lanark Rd (WH) 81
Lancaster (QUI) 69
Lancaster (CAM) 40
Lancaster 14
Lancaster Ave (REV) 51
Lancaster Ln (MIL) 87
Lancaster Rd (BRA) 84
Lancaster Rd (N) 92
Lancaster Rd (NEW) 58
Lancaster Rd (ARL) 74
Lancaster Ter (BRO) 46
Landers (SOM) 43
Landers Rd (WOL) 70
Landgrane (NQ) 71
Landon Rd (MIL) 86
Landor Rd (MAT) 26
Landry Rd (MED) 55
Landseer St & Ter (WRX) 32
Lane (WAL) 54
Lane Ave (EWY) 89
Lane Park (BRI) 35
Lanesville Ter (ROS) 31
Langdon (NEW) 58
Langdon (EV) 49
Langdon Ave (WAT) 72
Langdon St & Sq (CAM) 38
Langdon St & Ter (ROX) 19
Langeley Cir (WOL) 70
Langford Park (ROX) 19
Langley Rd (ARL) 74
Langley Rd (NCE) 59
Langley Rd (BRI) 35
Langmaid Ave (SOM) 45
Lansdowne (CAM) 39
Lansdowne (NQ) 71
Lansdowne 02215
Lansdowne Rd (ARL) 74
Lansing (ROX) 19
Lansing Rd (WNW) 65
Lantern Ln (ARL) 74
Lantern Ln (NCE) 59

Lantern Ln (WH) 81
Lantern Ln (LEX) 73
Lantern Ln (WES) 93
Lantern Ln (WY) 88
Lantern Ln (MIL) 87
Lantern Ln (BRA) 84
Lantern Ln (ROS) 31
Lantern Rd (REV) 51
Lantern Rd (BEL) 78
Lapham (MED) 55
Lapland Rd (CHH) 67
Larch (BRI) 35
Larch Cir (BEL) 78
Larch Pl (ROS) 31
Larch Rd (CAM) 38
Larch Rd (WAB) 68
Larch Rd (WH) 81
Larchmont (DOR) 24
Larchmont Ave (WAB) 68
Larchmont Ave (WAL) 54
Larchmont Ln (LEX) 73
Larchmont Rd (MEL) 76
Larchwood Dr (CAM) 38
Laredo (DOR) 21
Lark (SB) 27
Lark (QUI) 69
Larkhill Rd (WRX) 32
Larkin (REV) 51
Larkin Rd (MED) 55
Larkin Rd (CHH) 67
Larkin Rd (WNW) 81
Larkspur Rd (WAB) 68
Larrabee St & Pl (MEL) 76
Larry St & Pl (QUI) 69
Las Casas (MAL) 48
Lasell (WRX) 32
Lasell (AUB) 66
Lash (CHE) 50
Lathrop Pl 13
Lathrop Rd (WEL) 81
Latin Rd (WRX) 32
Latin Way (MED) 55
Lattimore Ct 18
Lauderdale Rd (NWY) 91
Laudholm Rd (NEW) 58
Laurel (MED) 55
Laurel (CHE) 50
Laurel (MAL) 48
Laurel (CAM) 39
Laurel (EWY) 89
Laurel (ROX) 19
Laurel (CHA) 29
Laurel (MEL) 76
Laurel (BEL) 78
Laurel (LEX) 73
Laurel (NCE) 59
Laurel (ARL) 74
Laurel (WAT) 72
Laurel Ave (NWW) 65
Laurel Ave (WAL) 54
Laurel Ave & Ter (WH) 81
Laurel Cir & Dr (N) 92
Laurel Path (WIN) 52
Laurel Rd (WES) 93
Laurel Rd (BRA) 85
Laurel Rd (MIL) 87
Laurel Rd (CHH) 67
Laurel St, Ave & Ter (SOM) 43
Laurel St & Ct (EV) 49
Lauriat (DOR) 24
Lauriat Pl (MED) 55
Laurie Ave (WRX) 32
Lauten Pl (SB) 27
Laval (HP) 36

Lawler Rd (MED) 55
Lawley (DOR) 22
Lawleys Wharf (DOR) 22
Lawmarisa Rd (WAB) 68
Lawn (RXC) 20
Lawn Ave (EB) 28
Lawn Ave (NWV) 60
Lawn Ave (LEX) 73
Lawn Ave (QUI) 69
Lawn St & Ct (CAM) 38
Lawndale (BEL) 78
Lawndale Ave (WAL) 54
Lawndale Rd (STO) 80
Lawndale Rd (MIL) 86
Lawndale Ter (JP) 30
Lawnview Dr (BRA) 84
Lawnwood Pl (CHA) 29
Lawrence 16
Lawrence (SWY) 90
Lawrence (WAL) 54
Lawrence (CHE) 50
Lawrence (EV) 49
Lawrence (CAM) 39
Lawrence (MAL) 48
Lawrence (QUI) 69
Lawrence (WAT) 72
Lawrence Ave (DOR) 21
Lawrence Ave & Rd (CHH) 67
Lawrence Ct (SB) 27
Lawrence Ln (BEL) 78
Lawrence Ln (LEX) 73
Lawrence Ln (ARL) 74
Lawrence Rd (WEL) 81
Lawrence Rd (BRO) 46
Lawrence Rd (REV) 51
Lawrence Rd (MIL) 86
Lawrence Rd (N) 92
Lawrence Rd (WES) 93
Lawrence St & Pl (BRI) 35
Lawrence St & Rd (MED) 55
Lawrence St & Ter (CHA) 29
Lawry (QUI) 69
Lawson Ave (REV) 51
Lawson Ln (BRA) 85
Lawson Pl (EB) 28
Lawson Rd (SWY) 90
Lawson Ter (SOM) 43
Lawton (BRO) 46
Lawton Pl (WAL) 54
Lawton Rd (N) 92
Lawton Rd (QUI) 69
Lawton St & Ter (HP) 36
Le Fevre (MAT) 26
Leah (MEL) 76
Leahaven Rd (MAT) 26
Leahaven Rd (SWY) 90
Leahaven Ter (BRA) 85
Leamington Rd (BRI) 35
Lebanon (DOR) 25
Lebanon (MEL) 76
Lebanon (MAL) 69
Lebanon St & Ter (MAL) 48
Lechmere Sq (CAM) 41
Ledge (MEL) 76
Ledge (STO) 80
Ledge (NH) 94
Ledge Rd (BRA) 84
Ledge Rd (WAL) 54
Ledge Hill Rd & Ter (WY) 98
Ledge Ways (WH) 81
Ledgebrook Rd (SWY) 90
Ledgebrook Rd (MAT) 26
Ledgedale Rd (ROS) 31

Boston (Con.)   021

Ledgelawn Ave (LEX)............... 73
Ledgeriere Rd (BRI)................ 35
Ledges Rd (NCE)..................... 59
Ledgeway (MIL)...................... 86
Ledgeways (WH)..................... 81
Ledgewood Ave (MEL)............. 76
Ledgewood Cir (BEL)............... 78
Ledgewood Rd (NWH)............. 61
Ledgewood Rd (BRA)............... 84
Ledgewood Rd (WES).............. 93
Ledgewood Rd (WRX).............. 32
Ledgewood Ter (MAL).............. 48
Ledyard (WH)......................... 81
Lee (STO)............................... 80
Lee (QUI)............................... 69
Lee (BRO).............................. 46
Lee (JP)................................. 30
Lee (CAM)............................. 39
Lee (SOM)............................. 45
Lee (REV).............................. 51
Lee (MED)............................. 55
Lee (EWY)............................. 89
Lee Rd (NH).......................... 94
Lee Rd (CHH)........................ 67
Lee St & Ave (LEX)................. 73
Lee Ter (ARL)........................ 74

Lee Burbank Hwy (REV).......... 51
Lee Hill Rd (ROS)................... 31
Leeds (SB)............................. 27
Leedsville St & Ct (DOR)......... 22
Leeland Ter (LEX)................... 73
Leeson Ln (NCE).................... 59
Leewood Rd (NWH)................ 61
Leewood Rd (WH).................. 81
Legion Pl (ROS)..................... 31
Legion Rd (WES).................... 93
Lehigh (ARL)......................... 74
Lehigh Rd (WH)..................... 81
Leicester (BRO)...................... 46
Leicester (BRI)....................... 35
Leicester Rd (BEL).................. 78
Leighton (MED)...................... 55
Leighton Ave (LEX)................. 73
Leighton Rd (WEL).................. 81
Leighton Rd (AUB).................. 66
Leighton Rd (HP).................... 36
Leisure Ln (STO).................... 80
Leisure Ter (WY).................... 88
Leitha Dr (WAL)..................... 54
Leland (MAL)......................... 48
Leland (JP)............................ 30
Leland (SOM)........................ 43
Leland Rd (CHH).................... 67
Lemoyne (BRA)...................... 84
Lenglen Rd (NEW).................. 58
Leniston (ROS)....................... 31
Lennaco Rd (JP)..................... 30
Lennon Ct (SB)...................... 27
Lennon Rd (ARL).................... 74
Lenox (WNW)........................ 65
Lenox (QUI)........................... 69
Lenox.................................... 18
Lenox (BRO).......................... 46
Lenox Rd (BRA)..................... 85
Lenoxdale Ave (DOR).............. 24
Leon..................................... 15
Leon (SOM)........................... 43
Leon Cir (MED)...................... 55
Leonard (WS)......................... 44
Leonard (MAL)....................... 48
Leonard (WAL)....................... 54

Leonard (BEL)........................ 78
Leonard Ave (NWV)................ 60
Leonard Ave (CAM)................ 39
Leonard Cir (MED)................. 55
Leonard Pl (SB)..................... 27
Leonard Rd (REV).................. 51
Leonard Rd (NWH)................. 76
Leonard Rd (LEX)................... 73
Leonard Rd (NWY).................. 91
Leonard St & Ct (DOR)............ 22
Leonardo Ave (MAL)............... 48
Leroy (DOR).......................... 22
Leroy Rd (LEX)...................... 73
Leseur Rd (HP)...................... 36
Lesher (ROS)......................... 31
Lesley Ave (WS)..................... 44
Leslie (DOR).......................... 22
Leslie Ave (WY)..................... 88
Leslie Park (ROX).................. 19
Leslie Rd (WAL)..................... 54
Leslie Rd (WAV)..................... 79
Leslie Rd (AUB)..................... 66
Lester (NH)........................... 94
Lester Pl (JP)........................ 30
Lester Ter (WS)...................... 44
Leston (MAT)......................... 26
Letitia Way (BRI)................... 35
Letterfine Ter (DOR)............... 25
Levant (DOR)......................... 22
Levbert Rd (NCE)................... 59
Leverett (EB)......................... 14
Leverett (BRO)....................... 46
Leverett Ave (REV)................. 51
Leverett Ave (EB)................... 28
Lewis (EB)............................. 26
Lewis (SOM).......................... 43
Lewis (MED).......................... 55
Lewis (N).............................. 92
Lewis
   1-11.................................. 09
   12-OUT.............................. 13
Lewis Ave (ARL)..................... 74
Lewis Ave & Ter (WIN)............ 52
Lewis Pl (ROX)....................... 19
Lewis Rd (BEL)...................... 78
Lewis St & Pl (EV).................. 49
Lewis St & Pl (NEW)............... 58
Lewis Wharf........................... 10
Lewiston (HP)........................ 36
Lexington (WAV)..................... 79
Lexington (STO)..................... 80
Lexington (WAT)..................... 72
Lexington (NQ)...................... 71
Lexington (WES).................... 93
Lexington
   1-60 (WNW)....................... 65
   61-OUT (AUB).................... 66
Lexington Ave (NH)................ 94
Lexington Ave (HP)................. 36
Lexington Ave (CAM)............. 38
Lexington Ave (WS)................ 44
Lexington Ave & Rd (LEX)........ 73
Lexington Rd (WH)................. 81
Lexington St & Ave (CHA)........ 29
Lexington St & Park (EV)......... 49
Lexington St, Pl & Sq (EB)....... 28
Lexington St & Ter (WAL)......... 54
Leyden (EB).......................... 28
Leyden St & Ave (MED)........... 55
Leyland (DOR)....................... 25
Libbey (WRX)........................ 32
Libby Rd (MIL)....................... 86
Liberty (WAL)........................ 54

Liberty (EV)........................... 49
Liberty
   1-510 (BRA)...................... 84
   511-OUT (BRA).................. 85
Liberty Ave (MED).................. 55
Liberty Ave (REV).................. 51
Liberty Ave (LEX).................. 73
Liberty Ave & Rd (WS)............ 44
Liberty Park Ave (BRA)........... 85
Liberty Pl (SB)...................... 27
Liberty Sq............................. 09
Liberty St & Sq (SWY)............ 90
Liberty St & Sq (QUI)............. 69
Library (REV)........................ 51
Library (CHE)........................ 50
Life (BRI).............................. 35
Light Guard Dr (MED)............. 55
Lila Ave (MED)...................... 55
Lila Rd (JP).......................... 30
Lilac Cir (WEL)...................... 81
Lilac Ct (CAM)...................... 41
Lilac Ln (WY)........................ 88
Lilac Ter (ROS)...................... 31
Lill Ave (WNW)...................... 65
Lilian (EB)............................ 28
Lillian Rd (WOL).................... 70
Lillian Rd (LEX)..................... 73
Lillian Rd (MAL).................... 48
Lillian Rd (EWY).................... 89
Lillie Way (CHH).................... 67
Lilly (MAL)............................ 48
Lilly (SB).............................. 27
Lime..................................... 08
Lincoln................................. 11
Lincoln (DOR)........................ 22
Lincoln (MAL)........................ 48
Lincoln (HP).......................... 36
Lincoln (EV).......................... 49
Lincoln (REV)........................ 51
Lincoln (STO)........................ 80
Lincoln (WAT)........................ 72
Lincoln (MEL)........................ 76
Lincoln (ARL)........................ 74
Lincoln (NWH)....................... 61
Lincoln (NWY)....................... 91
Lincoln (BRA)........................ 84
Lincoln (MIL)......................... 86
Lincoln (WES)....................... 93
Lincoln (N)........................... 92
Lincoln
   1-199 (BRI)....................... 35
   200-OUT (ALL)................... 34
Lincoln Ave (WOL)................. 70
Lincoln Cir & Rd (WH)............ 81
Lincoln Ln (CAM)................... 38
Lincoln Pky (SOM)................. 43
Lincoln Pl (BRI)..................... 35
Lincoln Rd (BRO)................... 46
Lincoln Rd (NEW).................. 58
Lincoln St, Ave & Pl (SOM)...... 45
Lincoln St & Pl (CAM)............. 41
Lincoln St & Pl (CHA)............. 29
Lincoln St & Rd (MED)............ 55
Lincoln St & Ter (WIN)............ 52
Lincoln St & Ter (WAL)........... 54
Lincoln St & Ter (LEX)............ 73
Lincoln Way (CAM)................ 40
Lincoln Wharf........................ 69
Lind (QUI)............................. 69
Lind Rd (WNW)...................... 65
Linda Ln (NWH)..................... 61
Linda Ln (DOR)...................... 25

Boston (Con.)   021

Linda Ln (WY)	88
Linda Rd (BRA)	85
Lindale Ave (NWY)	91
Lindall (ROS)	31
Lindall Pl	14
Lindbergh Ave (WY)	88
Lindbergh Ave (NH)	94
Lindbergh Ave (WNW)	65
Lindbergh Rd (MIL)	86
Linden (BRA)	84
Linden (N)	92
Linden (NUF)	64
Linden (WOL)	70
Linden (LEX)	73
Linden (STO)	80
Linden (ARL)	74
Linden (WAT)	72
Linden (SB)	27
Linden (ALL)	34
Linden (WIN)	52
Linden (MED)	55
Linden (CAM)	38
Linden 1-330 (WEL)	81
331-OUT (WH)	81
Linden Ave (MAT)	26
Linden Ave (RXC)	20
Linden Ave (BEL)	78
Linden Ave & Pl (MAL)	48
Linden Cir (WES)	93
Linden Ct & Pl (QUI)	69
Linden Gdns & Sq (WEL)	81
Linden Park Dr (WAL)	54
Linden Park St (RXC)	20
Linden Pl (EWY)	89
Linden Rd (WRX)	32
Linden St, Ave, Cir & Pl (SOM)	43
Linden St & Ct (DOR)	22
Linden St, Ct, Park, Pl & Sq (BRO)	46
Linden St & Pl (EV)	49
Linden St & Rd (MEL)	76
Linden St & Ter (WAL)	54
Lindenwood Rd (STO)	80
Linder Ter (NEW)	58
Lindsey (DOR)	24
Lin.dy Ln (WAL)	54
Line 1-45 (CAM) (ODD)	38
2-120 (SOM) (EVEN)	43
47-OUT (CAM) (ODD)	39
122-OUT (CAM) (EVEN)	39
Linehurst Rd (MAL)	48
Linehurst Rd (REV)	51
Lingard (DOR)	25
Linley Ter (LEX)	73
Linmoor Ter (LEX)	73
Linnaean (CAM)	38
Linnet (WRX)	32
Linsky Barry Ct (SB)	27
Linvale Ter (MAT)	26
Linway (SWY)	90
Linwood (HP)	36
Linwood (MAL)	48
Linwood (MED)	55
Linwood (ARL)	74
Linwood Ave (MEL)	76
Linwood Ave (NWV)	60
Linwood Pl (CAM)	39
Linwood Rd (WH)	81

Linwood St & Pl (SOM)	43
Linwood St & Sq (ROX)	19
Lionel Ave (WAL)	54
Lisbeth (LEX)	73
Lisbon (MAL)	48
Lisle (BRA)	84
List Pl (ROS)	31
Liszt (ROS)	31
Litchfield (BRI)	35
Lithgow (DOR)	24
Littell Rd (BRO)	46
Little Pond Rd (BEL)	78
Littledale (ROS)	31
Littlefield (QUI)	69
Littlefield Rd (NCE)	59
Littlejohn (ARL)	74
Livermore (MAT)	26
Livermore Pl (CAM)	41
Livermore Rd (WAL)	54
Livermore Rd (BEL)	78
Livermore Rd (WH)	81
Liverpool Ln (WAL)	54
Liverpool St & Ave (EB)	28
Livesey Rd (NQ)	71
Livingston Ln (WAL)	54
Livingston Rd (WH)	81
Livingston (DOR)	24
Livingstone Cir (N)	92
Livoli Ave (BRA)	85
Llewellyn Rd (WNW)	65
Lloyd Rd (WAT)	72
Lochdale Rd (ROS)	31
Lochland (MIL)	86
Lochland Rd (HP)	36
Lochmere Ave (NWY)	91
Lochstead Ave (JP)	30
Locke (CAM)	40
Locke (CHE)	50
Locke (WAT)	72
Locke (ARL)	74
Locke Ln (LEX)	73
Locke Pl (SB)	27
Locke Rd (WAB)	68
Locke Rd (MED)	55
Lockeland Ave (ARL)	74
Locksley Rd (NCE)	59
Lockwood (HP)	36
Lockwood Dr (SWY)	90
Lockwood Rd (WNW)	65
Lockwood Rd (LEX)	73
Locust (BEL)	78
Locust (MED)	55
Locust (CHE)	50
Locust (WAL)	54
Locust (DOR)	25
Locust Ln (N)	92
Locust Rd 1-2 (WES)	93
3-3 (WH)	81
4-OUT (WES)	93
Locust St & Ave (LEX)	73
Locust St & Park (EV)	49
Locust St & Ter (CAM)	38
Locust St & Way (WIN)	52
Lodge (MIL)	86
Lodge Ave (MEL)	76
Lodge Rd (BEL)	78
Lodge Rd (WNW)	65
Lodgehill Rd (HP)	36
Logan (WAL)	54
Logan (ROX)	19
Logan Ave & Grv (MED)	55
Logan. Rd (BRA)	85

Logan Way (SB)	27
Lois Ln (N)	92
Lois Ter (WOL)	70
Lomasney Way	14
Lombard (DOR)	24
Lombard (NEW)	58
Lombard Ct (MAL)	48
Lombard Rd & Ter (ARL)	74
London Ave (NQ)	71
London St & Ct (EB)	28
Lone Pine Path (WY)	88
Long (MED)	55
Long Ave (ALL)	34
Long Ave (BEL)	78
Long Island (QUI)	69
Long Wharf	10
Longacre Rd (N)	92
Longbow Rd (STO)	80
Longfellow (WAT)	72
Longfellow-(SWY)	90
Longfellow (DOR)	22
Longfellow Park & Rd (CAM)	38
Longfellow Rd (WAL)	54
Longfellow Rd (NH)	94
Longfellow Rd (WH)	81
Longfellow Rd (MEL)	76
Longfellow Rd (ARL)	74
Longfellow Rd (LEX)	73
Longfellow Rd (NLF)	62
Longfellow Rd Ext (WH)	81
Longmeadow (ROX)	19
Longmeadow Rd (WH)	81
Longmeadow Rd (NCE)	59
Longmeadow Rd (ARL)	74
Longmeadow Rd (BEL)	78
Longmeadow Rd (WES)	93
Longview Rd (BRA)	84
Longwell Rd (NLF)	62
Longwood Ave (BRO)	46
Longwood Ave 141-344	15
345-OUT	02215
Longwood Dr (BRA)	84
Longwood Rd (MIL)	87
Longwood Rd (WY)	88
Longwood Rd (QUI)	69
Longwood Rd (CHH)	67
Lonsdale (DOR)	24
Lookout (LEX)	73
Lookout Rd (MED)	55
Loomis (MAL)	48
Loomis (CAM)	38
Loomis (REV)	51
Loomis Ave (WAT)	72
Lopez (CAM)	39
Lopez Ave (CAM)	41
Lora (MAL)	48
Lord (WAL)	64
Lorean Ter (WIN)	52
Loren Park (EV)	49
Lorene Rd (JP)	30
Lorenzo (DOR)	22
Loretta Ave (BRA)	84
Loretta Rd (WAL)	54
Lorette (WRX)	32
Lorimer Pl (ROX)	19
Lorimer Rd (WAV)	79
Loring (WAV)	79
Loring (QUI)	69
Loring (NCE)	59
Loring (SB)	27
Loring (SOM)	43
Loring Pl (MAL)	48

Boston (Con.)   021

Loring Rd (REV).................... 51
Loring Rd (WIN)................... 52
Loring Rd (LEX)................... 73
Loring Rd (WES).................. 93
Loring St & Pl (HP)............. 36
Lorna Rd (NCE)................... 59
Lorna Rd (MAT)................... 26
Lorne (DOR)........................ 24
Lorne Rd (ARL)................... 74
Lorraine (ROS)................... 31
Lorraine (EWY)................... 89
Lorraine Cir (WAB)............. 68
Lorraine Rd (MED)............. 55
Lorraine Ter (ALL)............. 34
Lorraine Ter (ARL)............. 74
Los Angeles (NEW)............. 58
Lothian Rd (BRI)................ 35
Lothrop (BRI)...................... 35
Lothrop (NWV).................... 60
Lothrop Ave (MIL).............. 87
Lotus (JP).......................... 30
Lotus Ave (STO)................ 80
Loud Ave (WY)................... 88
Louders Ln (JP).................. 30
Louis (CHE)........................ 50
Louis (SB).......................... 27
Louis Ter (DOR)................. 24
Louis Pasteur Ave 15
Louis Prang 15
Louisburg Pl (SOM)............ 45
Louisburg Sq 08
Louise (WAT)..................... 72
Louise Ct (MAL)................. 48
Louise Rd (CHH)................ 67
Louise Rd (BEL)................. 78
Louise Rd (BRA)................ 84
Lourdes Ave (JP)............... 30
Love Ln (WES)................... 93
Lovedeed Ct (ROX)............ 19
Lovejoy Pl 14
Loveland Rd (BRO)............ 46
Lovell (WS)........................ 44
Lovell (EB)......................... 28
Lovell (NWY)...................... 91
Lovell Rd (MEL)................. 76
Lovell Rd (WAT)................. 72
Lovell Rd (ARL)................. 74
Lovering Rd (MED)............ 55
Lovett Rd (NCE)................. 59
Lovewell Rd (WEL)............ 81
Lovis (SB).......................... 27
Lowden Ave (WS)............... 44
Lowe (REV)........................ 51
Lowe (QUI)......................... 69
Lowe St Pl (REV)............... 51
Lowell (REV)...................... 51
Lowell (CAM)...................... 38
Lowell (QUI)....................... 69
Lowell (LEX)....................... 73
Lowell (BRA)...................... 84
Lowell
   1-171 (SOM).................. 43
   172-273 (WS)................. 44
   274-OUT (SOM).............. 45
Lowell Ave (NWV).............. 60
Lowell Ave (WAT).............. 72
Lowell Cir (SOM)............... 43
Lowell Ct (MED)................. 55
Lowell Rd (WIN)................. 52
Lowell Rd (BRO)................ 46
Lowell Rd (WH)................. 81

Lowell St Pl (ARL).............. 74
Lowell St, Ave & Ter (MAL).... 48
Lowell St & Pl (WAL).......... 54
Lowell St & Pl (ARL).......... 74
Lowell Ter (SOM)............... 45
Lowland Pl (EB)................. 28
Loyola (ROX)...................... 19
Lubec (EB)......................... 28
Lublin (ARL)....................... 74
Lucas Ct (WNW)................. 65
Lucerne (DOR)................... 24
Lucia Ave (REV)................. 51
Lucille Pl (NUF)................. 64
Lucy (STO)......................... 80
Ludlow (CHA)..................... 29
Ludwig Rd (NH)................. 94
Lufberry (MIL).................... 86
Luke Rd (EV)..................... 49
Lunar Ave (BRA)............... 85
Lund Rd (MED)................... 55
Lunda (WAL)...................... 54
Lundquist Dr (BRA)........... 85
Lunt (NQ)........................... 71
Lura (WAL)......................... 54
Lurton (QUI)....................... 69
Luteman Pl (RXC).............. 50
Luther Pl (CHE)................. 50
Luther Rd (MED)................ 55
Lyall St & Ter (WRX).......... 32
Lyford (DOR)...................... 24
Lyle St & Ter (MAL)........... 48
Lyman (NCE)...................... 59
Lyman Ave (MED).............. 55
Lyman Rd (CHH)................ 67
Lyman Rd (MIL)................. 86
Lyman Ter (WAL)............... 54
Lyme (MAL)........................ 48
Lyme (EWY)....................... 89
Lyme Rd (WNW)................ 65
Lynde (MAL)....................... 48
Lynde (EV)......................... 49
Lynde St & Ave (MEL)........ 76
Lynde St & Ave (CHA)........ 29
Lyndeboro (CHA)............... 29
Lyndeboro Pl...................... 16
Lyndhurst (DOR)................ 24
Lyne Rd (BRI).................... 35
Lynn (CHE)......................... 50
Lynn (EV)........................... 49
Lynn (MAL)......................... 48
Lynn Fells Pky (MEL)......... 76
Lynnville Ter (DOR)........... 21
Lynnway (REV)................... 51
Lyon (DOR)........................ 22
Lyon Rd (CHH)................... 67
Lyons (QUI)........................ 69
Lyons Sq (CHE).................. 50
Lyons St & Ct (WAT).......... 72
Lyra Dr (SWY).................... 90
M (SB)................................ 27
M Ave (WRX)...................... 32
M St Pl (SB)....................... 27
Mabelle Ave (MED)............ 55
Mac Arthur (SOM).............. 45
Mac Arthur Rd (STO)......... 80
Mac Donald (HP)................ 36
Mac Dougal Ct (SWY) 90
Mac Intosh Ave (N)........... 92
Mace Ave (EWY)................ 89
Mackin (BRI)...................... 35
Macklin Rd (MED).............. 55
Macks Ct (WAL)................. 54
Macullar Rd (WRX)............ 32

Macy (QUI)......................... 69
Madden (QUI)..................... 69
Madeleine (QUI)................. 69
Madeline (BRI)................... 35
Madison (HP)..................... 36
Madison (CAM)................... 38
Madison (MED)................... 55
Madison (SOM).................. 43
Madison (REV)................... 51
Madison (MAL)................... 48
Madison (BEL)................... 78
Madison (EWY).................. 89
Madison (ROX)................... 19
Madison Ave (QUI)............. 69
Madison Ave (WAT)........... 72
Madison Ave (NWV)........... 60
Madison Ave (ARL)............ 74
Madison Ave (LEX)............ 73
Madison Ave (WIN)............ 52
Madison Ave (CAM)........... 40
Madison Ave (CHE)........... 50
Madison Ave (EV).............. 49
Madison Rd (WAL)............. 54
Madison Rd (WH)............... 81
Madoc (NCE)...................... 59
Maffa Way (CHA)............... 29
Magazine (ROX)................. 19
Magazine (CAM)................. 39
Magdala (DOR)................... 24
Magee (CAM)..................... 39
Magee (HP)........................ 36
Magees Cor (WIN)............. 52
Maggi Rd (REV)................. 51
Magnolia (MAL)................. 48
Magnolia (ARL).................. 74
Magnolia (MEL).................. 76
Magnolia (BRA).................. 84
Magnolia
   1-189 (DOR)................... 25
   190-OUT (DOR)............... 21
Magnolia Ave (CAM).......... 38
Magnolia Ave (NEW)......... 58
magnolia Ct (EV)............... 49
Magnolia Pl & Sq (DOR).... 25
Magnolia Rd (MIL)............. 86
Magnolia Rd (STO)............ 80
Magnus Ave (SOM)............ 43
Magoun (CAM)................... 40
Magoun Ave (MED)............ 55
Magoun Sq (SOM).............. 45
Mague Ave & Pl (WNW)...... 65
Maguire Ct (NWV).............. 60
Maguire Rd (LEX).............. 73
Mahan Pl............................ 16
Mahler Rd (ROS)............... 31
Maida Ter (HP).................. 36
Main (SOM)........................ 45
Main (MED)........................ 55
Main (EV)........................... 49
Main (MAL)......................... 48
Main (WIN)......................... 52
Main (WAL)........................ 54
Main (CHA)........................ 29
Main (STO)........................ 80
Main (MEL)......................... 76
Main (WAT)........................ 72
Main (QUI).......................... 69
Main (BRA)......................... 85
Main
   1-385 (WY)..................... 88
   1-505 (CAM)................... 42
   386-OUT (SWY).............. 90
   506-OUT (CAM).............. 39

Boston (Con.) 021

Main St Park (MAL)	48
Maine Ave & Ter (SOM)	45
Maitland (MIL)	86
Maitland	02215
Malbert Rd (BRI)	35
Malbon Pl (ROX)	19
Malcolm Rd (CAM)	38
Malcolm Rd (JP)	30
Malcomb Rd (WY)	88
Malden (REV)	51
Malden (EV)	49
Malden (MED)	55
Malden	18
Malden (QUI)	69
Malden (WAT)	72
Malden St Park (MAL)	48
Malden St & Sq (MAL)	48
Malia Ter (CHH)	67
Mall (ROX)	19
Mallard Ave (DOR)	24
Mallard Rd (QUI)	69
Mallard Rd (N)	92
Mallard Way (WAL)	54
Mallet (WS)	44
Mallet (DOR)	24
Mallon Rd (DOR)	21
Malloy Ct (SOM)	43
Malta (MAT)	26
Maltby Ln (NWY)	91
Malubar Ln (NCE)	59
Malvern (QUI)	69
Malvern (MEL)	76
Malvern (WAL)	54
Malvern (ALL)	34
Malvern Ave (WS)	44
Malvern Ter (MED)	55
Malvern Ter (AUB)	66
Malverna Rd (ROS)	31
Mamelon Ct (MAT)	26
Mamie Rd (SWY)	90
Manassas Ave (CAM)	38
Manatee Rd (EWY)	89
Manchester (MAT)	26
Manchester Rd (BRO)	46
Manchester Rd (NWH)	61
Mandalay Rd (NCE)	59
Mandalay Rd (SWY)	90
Manemet Rd (NCE)	59
Manet Ave (QUI)	69
Manet Cir & Rd (CHH)	67
Mangano Ct (WAT)	72
Mangles (MED)	55
Manhattan Rd & Ter (WNW)	65
Manila Ave (HP)	36
Manion Rd (HP)	36
Manison (STO)	80
Manitoba Rd (WAB)	67
Manley (DOR)	22
Manley Ct (LEX)	73
Manley Ter (MAL)	48
Mann (WRX)	32
Mann (BRA)	85
Mann Ave (N)	92
Manning (ROS)	31
Manning (MED)	55
Manning (LEX)	73
Manning	
1-202 (NH)	94
203-OUT (N)	92
Manning Rd (WAL)	54
Manning Ter (EV)	49

Mannix Cir (BEL)	78
Manomet Rd (NWY)	91
Manor (DOR)	22
Manor Ave (WH)	81
Manor Rd (WAL)	54
Manor House Rd (NCE)	59
Mansfield (EV)	49
Mansfield (ALL)	34
Mansfield (SOM)	43
Mansfield Rd (WH)	81
Manson Rd (NH)	94
Mansur (JP)	30
Mansur (ROS)	31
Manthorne Rd (WRX)	32
Manton Ter (ALL)	34
Manzonetta Ave (WY)	88
Mapes (DOR)	22
Maple (MIL)	87
Maple (BRA)	84
Maple (EWY)	89
Maple (CHE)	50
Maple (BRO)	46
Maple (HP)	36
Maple (REV)	51
Maple (STO)	80
Maple (LEX)	73
Maple (QUI)	69
Maple (ARL)	74
Maple	
1-57 (WAT) (ODD)	72
2-52 (WAT) (EVEN)	72
54-OUT (NEW) (EVEN)	58
59-OUT (NEW) (ODD)	58
Maple Ave (EV)	49
Maple Ave (SOM)	45
Maple Ave (CAM)	39
Maple Ave (MED)	55
Maple Grv St (MEL)	76
Maple Park (NCE)	59
Maple Park Ave (MED)	55
Maple Pl (JP)	30
Maple Rd (WIN)	52
Maple Rd (WH)	81
Maple Rd (WES)	93
Maple St Ext (WRX)	32
Maple St, Ave, Cir & Ter	
(NEW)	58
Maple St & Ct (DOR)	21
Maple St, Ct, Pl & Ter (N)	92
Maple St & Park (MAL)	48
Maple St & Ter (WRX)	32
Maple St & Ter (WAL)	54
Maple St & Ter (WAV)	79
Maple St & Ter (MEL)	76
Maple St & Ter (AUB)	66
Mapleton (BRI)	35
Maplewood (WRX)	32
Maplewood (MAL)	48
Maplewood (WAT)	72
Maplewood Ave (NCE)	59
Maplewood Ave (EV)	49
Maplewood Ter (BRA)	85
Marathon (ARL)	74
Marble (STO)	80
Marble (REV)	51
Marble (RXC)	20
Marbury Ter (JP)	30
Marcella (ROX)	19
Marcella St & Ct (CAM)	41
Marcellus Dr (NCE)	59
March Ave, Ter & Way (WRX)	32
Marcia Rd (WAT)	72
Marcia Rd (BRA)	84

Marcy Rd (MAT)	26
Mardell Cir (SOM)	43
Marden Ave (DOR)	24
Margaret	13
Margaret (ARL)	74
Margaret Dr (BRA)	85
Margaret Rd (MIL)	86
Margaret Rd (NWH)	61
Margaret Rd (STO)	80
Margaretta Dr (HP)	36
Margin (HP)	36
Marginal (CHE)	50
Marginal (EB)	28
Marginal Rd (QUI)	69
Margo Rd (BRI)	35
Marguerite Ave (WAL)	54
Maria Ln (ROS)	31
Marianne Rd (WAL)	54
Marida Way (MAL)	48
Marie (DOR)	22
Marie Ave (EV)	49
Marie Ave (CAM)	39
Marie Ave (STO)	80
Marie Ave (SWY)	90
Marieanne Ave (BRA)	85
Marietta Ave (BRA)	84
Marigold Ave (WH)	81
Marilyn Rd (MIL)	87
Marira (SWY)	90
Marine (QUI)	69
Marine (MED)	55
Marine Rd (SB)	27
Marion (MED)	55
Marion (CAM)	41
Marion (SOM)	43
Marion (MAL)	48
Marion (WAL)	54
Marion (ROS)	31
Marion (HP)	36
Marion (WOL)	70
Marion (STO)	80
Marion (WNW)	65
Marion Ave (BRA)	85
Marion Cir & Rd (ARL)	74
Marion Rd (WAT)	72
Marion Rd (BEL)	78
Marion Rd (NWY)	91
Marion St & Pl (EB)	28
Marion St & Ter (BRO)	46
Mariposa (MAT)	26
Marisa Dr (BRA)	85
Marivista Ave (WAL)	54
Marjorie Rd (BRA)	85
Mark (JP)	30
Mark Lee Rd (NH)	94
Marked Tree Rd (N)	92
Market (BRI)	35
Market (CAM)	39
Market (EV)	49
Market (CHE)	50
Market	14
Marks Rd (EWY)	89
Marla Cir (NCE)	59
Marlboro (BEL)	78
Marlboro (WOL)	70
Marlboro (EV)	49
Marlboro (MAL)	48
Marlboro (NEW)	58
Marlboro Rd (LEX)	73
Marlboro Ter (WAT)	72
Marlborough (CHE)	50
Marlborough	
1-325	16

Boston (Con.)	**021**
326-OUT	15
Marlborough Rd (WAL)	54
Marlin Rd (WRX)	32
Marlin Way (DOR)	22
Marlou Ter (JP)	30
Marlowe (DOR)	24
Marlton Rd (WAL)	54
Marmion (JP)	30
Marmion Rd (MEL)	76
Marney (CAM)	41
Marr Crest Dr (MIL)	86
Marrett St & Rd (LEX)	73
Marrigan (ARL)	74
Mars (WY)	88
Marsh (QUI)	69
Marsh (DOR)	24
Marsh	
1-365 (BEL) (ODD)	78
2-396 (BEL) (EVEN)	78
367-OUT (WAV) (ODD)	79
398-OUT (WAV) (EVEN)	79
Marsh Rd (N)	92
Marshall (N)	92
Marshall (BRA)	84
Marshall	08
Marshall (WAT)	72
Marshall (NQ)	71
Marshall (NCE)	59
Marshall (SOM)	45
Marshall (MED)	55
Marshall (BRO)	46
Marshall (REV)	51
Marshall (WIN)	52
Marshall Ave (MAL)	48
Marshall Pl (CHA)	29
Marshall Rd (LEX)	73
Marshall Rd (WEL)	81
Marshall Rd (STO)	80
Marshall St Cir (SOM)	45
Marshall St & Rd (MIL)	86
Marshall Way (WES)	93
Marshfield (ROX)	19
Marshfield Rd (BRA)	85
Marshfield Rd (NCE)	59
Marston (MED)	55
Martell Rd (QUI)	69
Martensen (QUI)	69
Martha Rd	14
Marthas Ln (CHH)	67
Martin (ARL)	74
Martin (MEL)	76
Martin (MED)	55
Martin (REV)	51
Martin (WRX)	32
Martin (CAM)	38
Martin Rd (WH)	81
Martin Rd (WES)	93
Martin Rd & Ter (MIL)	86
Martin Luther King Blvd	
(ROX)	19
Martinwood Rd (JP)	30
Martyn (WAL)	54
Marvin (ROX)	19
Marvin (LEX)	73
Marvin Ln (NCE)	59
Marvin Pl (CAM)	39
Marvin Rd (WEL)	81
Marvin Rd (MEL)	76
Mary (ARL)	74
Mary (QUI)	69
Mary Ann Rd (ROS)	31

Mary Ellen Rd (WAB)	68
Mary Mount Rd (AUB)	66
Maryknoll St & Ter (MAT)	26
Maryland (DOR)	25
Maryland Ave (WIN)	52
Mascoma (DOR)	21
Mascoma (WOL)	70
Mascot (DOR)	24
Mason	11
Mason (WOL)	70
Mason (LEX)	73
Mason (WS)	44
Mason (HP)	36
Mason (CAM)	38
Mason (MED)	55
Mason (MAL)	48
Mason (EV)	49
Mason (SWY)	90
Mason Ct (CHA)	29
Mason Rd (N)	92
Mason Rd (NCE)	59
Mason Rd (WAT)	72
Mason St & Ter (BRO)	46
Massachusetts Ave (MED)	55
Massachusetts Ave (LEX)	73
Massachusetts Ave (QUI)	69
Massachusetts Ave (ARL)	74
Massachusetts Ave (BRA)	85
Massachusetts Ave	
1-400	15
1-975 (CAM) (ODD)	39
2-966 (CAM) (EVEN)	39
401-1099	18
968-1748 (CAM) (EVEN)	38
977-1737 (CAM) (ODD)	38
1100-OUT (DOR)	25
1739-OUT (CAM) (ODD)	40
1750-OUT (CAM) (EVEN)	40
Massapoag (SWY)	90
Massasoit (MAT)	26
Massasoit Rd (NWY)	91
Massasoit Rd (WH)	81
Massasoit St & Ct (WAL)	54
Matchett (BRI)	35
Mathaurs (MIL)	86
Mather St & Ct (DOR)	24
Matignon Rd (DOR)	22
Matignon Rd (CAM)	40
Mattakeeset (MAT)	26
Mattapan St & Sq (MAT)	26
Matthew (DOR)	24
Matthews	10
Mattson (QUI)	69
Maude (MAL)	48
Maude Ter (WAT)	72
Maugus Ave (WH)	81
Maugus Hill Rd (WH)	81
Maureen Rd (LEX)	73
Maurice (MAL)	48
Maurice (MED)	55
Maurice Rd (WEL)	81
Maverick (MED)	55
Maverick (CHE)	50
Maverick St & Sq (EB)	28
Max Ave (CAM)	41
Maxfield (WRX)	32
Maxim Ave (QUI)	69
Maxwell (DOR)	24
Maxwell Rd (MIL)	86
May (N)	92
May (WH)	81
May (LEX)	73
May (JP)	30

May St & Ave (BRA)	84
May Ter (SWY)	90
Mayall Rd (WAL)	54
Maybelle Ave (MED)	55
Mayberry Ave (MED)	55
Maybie (ARL)	74
Maybrook (DOR)	21
Maybury (DOR)	21
Mayfair (ROX)	19
Mayfield (DOR)	25
Mayfield (WAV)	79
Mayflower (LEX)	73
Mayflower (ALL)	34
Mayflower Ave (NWY)	91
Mayflower Dr (STG)	80
Mayflower Rd (ARL)	74
Mayflower Rd (NQ)	71
Mayflower Rd (CHH)	67
Mayflower Rd (BRA)	84
Mayflower Rd (N)	92
Mayflower Ter (NWH)	61
Mayhew (DOR)	25
Maynard (WNW)	65
Maynard (ARL)	74
Maynard (ROS)	31
Maynard (MED)	55
Maynard (MAL)	48
Maynard Pl (CAM)	38
Mayo Ave (N)	92
Mayo Rd (WH)	81
Maypole Rd (QUI)	69
Maywood St & Ter (ROX)	19
Mc Arthur Rd (WEL)	81
Mc Bride (JP)	30
Mc Bride Ct (WAL)	54
Mc Call (MED)	55
Mc Carthy Rd (CAM)	38
Mc Carthy Rd (NCE)	59
Mc Clellan Hwy (EB)	28
Mc Clure (REV)	51
Mc Coba (REV)	51
Mc Cormack (MAL)	48
Mc Cormack Ave (MED)	55
Mc Cormack Sq (EB)	28
Mc Craw (ROS)	31
Mc Culloch Rd (NH)	94
Mc Donald (QUI)	69
Mc Donald Ave (ALL)	34
Mc Donald Rd (MED)	55
Mc Donough Ct (HP)	36
Mc Donough Way (SB)	27
Mc Grath Hwy (QUI)	69
Mc Grath Hwy	
1-463 (SOM) (ODD)	43
2-472 (SOM) (EVEN)	43
465-OUT (SOM) (ODD)	45
474-OUT (SOM) (EVEN)	45
Mc Greevey Way (RXC)	20
Mc Gregor Ave (SOM)	45
Mc Kay Pl (EB)	28
Mc Kenn (WAL)	54
Mc Kenna Ter (WRX)	32
Mc Kenzie Ave (QUI)	69
Mc Kinley (REV)	51
Mc Kinley (EV)	49
Mc Kinley Sq	09
Mc Kinnon Ave (MIL)	86
Mc Kone (DOR)	22
Mc Lean (WEL)	81
Mc Lean Pl (CAM)	40
Mc Lellan (DOR)	21
Mc Neil Way (DOR)	21
Mc Nulty Ct (CHA)	29

Boston (Con.)	021
Mc Tiernan (CAM)	39
Meacham (SOM)	45
Meacham (HP)	36
Meacham (MEL)	76
Meacham Rd	
1-25 (CAM) (ODD)	40
2-28 (CAM) (EVEN)	40
27-OUT (WS) (ODD)	44
30-OUT (WS) (EVEN)	44
Mead (QUI)	69
Mead (CAM)	40
Mead (WS)	44
Mead (EV)	49
Mead (ALL)	34
Mead (CHA)	29
Mead St Ct (CHA)	29
Meade (SWY)	90
Meade St & Rd (ARL)	74
Meader Rd (EV)	49
Meadow (NQ)	71
Meadow Ln (WH)	81
Meadow Ln (WAL)	54
Meadow Ln (SWY)	90
Meadow Ln (MIL)	86
Meadow Ln & Rd (N)	92
Meadow Rd (CHE)	50
Meadow Rd (STO)	80
Meadow Way (CAM)	38
Meadow Brook Ave (LEX)	73
Meadow Brook Rd	
1-60 (CHH)	67
61-OUT (BRO)	46
Meadowbank Ave (MAT)	26
Meadowbrook Rd (WES)	93
Meadowbrook Rd (N)	92
Meadowbrook kd (BRA)	85
Meadowbrook Rd (WH)	81
Meadowbrook Rd (WOL)	70
Meadowbrook Rd (NCE)	59
Meadowview Rd (MEL)	76
Meadowview Rd (MIL)	86
Meadowview Rd (HP)	36
Meadowview Rd (EV)	49
Meagher Ave (MIL)	87
Mears Ave (QUI)	69
Mechanic (QUI)	69
Mechanic (NUF)	64
Mechanic (MIL)	86
Mechanic (WAL)	54
Mechanic St & Ct	13
Medfield	02215
Medford	14
Medford (CHA)	29
Medford (CHE)	50
Medford (ARL)	74
Medford	
1-333 (SOM)	43
334-OUT (SOM)	45
Medford Ct	18
Medford St & Sq (MED)	55
Medford St & Ter (MAL)	48
Medina Way (RXC)	20
Mediterranean Dr (WEY)	88
Medway (DOR)	24
Medway (QUI)	69
Meehan St & Pl (JP)	30
Meeting House Cir (N)	92
Meeting House Ln (EWY)	89
Meigh Rd (CHH)	67
Meisel Path (BEL)	78
Melba Ln (STO)	80
Melba Way (HP)	36
Melbourne (DOR)	24
Melbourne Ave (MEL)	76
Melbourne Ave (NWV)	60
Melbourne Rd (MIL)	86
Melcher	02210
Melendy Ave (WAT)	72
Melina Rd (NCE)	59
Mellen (NH)	94
Mellen (DOR)	24
Mellen (CAM)	38
Mellex Rd (LEX)	73
Mellon Rd (WEL)	81
Melody Ln (WAL)	54
Melody Ln (SWY)	90
Melrose (MEL)	76
Melrose (ARL)	74
Melrose	16
Melrose Ave (LEX)	73
Melrose Ave (N)	92
Melrose St & Ave (AUB)	66
Melton Rd (BRI)	35
Melvern Rd (N)	92
Melville Ave (NWV)	60
Melville Ave & Ln (DOR)	24
Melville Rd (SOM)	45
Melville Ter (WAT)	72
Melvin (SOM)	45
Melvin Ave (BRO)	46
Melvin Rd (ARL)	74
Melvinside Ter (DOR)	25
Memorial Cir (N)	92
Memorial Dr (EWY)	89
Memorial Dr (WAT)	72
Memorial Dr	
1-49 (CAM)	42
50-50 (CAM)	39
51-218 (CAM)	42
219-820 (CAM)	39
821-OUT (CAM)	38
Memorial Rd (SOM)	45
Memorial Way (ARL)	74
Mendell Way (JP)	30
Mendelssohn (ROS)	31
Mendum (ROS)	31
Mendum (MEL)	76
Menlo (BRI)	35
Menotomy Rd & Way (ARL)	74
Menotomy Rocks Dr (ARL)	74
Menton (MAT)	26
Mercantile	09
Mercer (MAT)	26
Mercer (SB)	27
Mercer Cir (CAM)	38
Mercer Rd (NH)	94
Merchants Row	09
Merchants Row (WAT)	72
Mercier Ave (DOR)	24
Mercury (WY)	88
Meredith (WRX)	32
Meredith Ave (NWH)	61
Meredith Cir (MIL)	86
Meredith Cir (N)	92
Meredith Way (WY)	88
Meriam (LEX)	73
Meridian (MEL)	76
Meridian (EB)	28
Meridian St & Pky (MAL)	48
Merilyn Rd (SWY)	90
Merlin (DOR)	24
Mermaid Ave (WIN)	52
Merola Park (MAT)	26
Merriam (JP)	30
Merriam (SOM)	43
Merriam (WES)	93
Merrifield Ave (WAT)	72
Merrill (CAM)	39
Merrill (DOR)	21
Merrill Ave (BEL)	78
Merrill Ave (WOL)	70
Merrill Rd (WAT)	72
Merrill Rd (NCE)	59
Merrimac	14
Merritt Ave (BRA)	84
Merrow Ln (STO)	80
Merrymount Ave (WOL)	70
Merrymount Rd (SWY)	90
Merrymount Rd & Ter (QUI)	69
Merton (NEW)	58
Merton Pl (ROX)	19
Meshaka (WRX)	32
Messenger (REV)	51
Messengers Ct (MEL)	76
Messina (BRA)	85
Messinger (MAT)	26
Metacomet Rd (WAB)	68
Metcalf (ROS)	31
Metcalf (MED)	55
Metcalf Ct (JP)	30
Metcalf Sq (WIN)	52
Metropolitan Ave	
1-427 (ROS)	31
428-999 (HP)	36
1000-OUT (MIL)	86
Metropolitan Cir & Ter (ROS)	31
Meyer St & Ct (ROS)	31
Miami Ave & Ter (WRX)	32
Mica Ln (WH)	81
Michael (ARL)	74
Michael Ave (WAT)	72
Michael Rd (BRI)	35
Michael A Sullivan Sq (CAM)	38
Michelanglo	13
Michelle Ln (BRA)	84
Michigan Ave (DOR)	21
Michigan Ave (SOM)	45
Middle (NEW)	58
Middle (SB)	27
Middle (BRA)	84
Middle (WAT)	72
Middle (STO)	80
Middle (LEX)	73
Middle	
1-661 (EWY)	89
662-1060 (WY)	88
1061-OUT (SWY)	90
Middle St & Ct (WAL)	54
Middle Way (WES)	93
Middleby Rd (LEX)	73
Middlecot (BEL)	78
Middlesex (WEL)	81
Middlesex (NQ)	71
Middlesex (CAM)	40
Middlesex (MAL)	48
Middlesex (CHA)	29
Middlesex Ave (SOM)	45
Middlesex Ave (MED)	55
Middlesex Cir & Rd (WAL)	54
Middlesex Cir & Rd (CHH)	67
Middlesex Rd (WAT)	72
Middlesex Rd (STO)	80
Middleton (DOR)	24
Midland (DOR)	25
Midland (WAT)	72
Midland (BEL)	78

Boston (Con.)	**021**
Midland Ave (NEW)	58
Midland Dr (WAL)	54
Midland Rd (WEL)	81
Midvale Rd (WRX)	32
Midway	02210
Mifflin Pl (CAM)	38
Mignon Rd (WNW)	65
Milano (REV)	51
Mildred Ave (MAT)	26
Mildred Rd (NCE)	59
Miles (ROX)	19
Miles Dr (QUI)	69
Milford	18
Militia Dr (LEX)	73
Milk (LEX)	73
Milk	
1-21 (ODD)	09
2-22 (EVEN)	08
23-66	09
67-67	10
68-OUT	09
Milk Pl (SOM)	43
Mill (REV)	51
Mill (CAM)	38
Mill (WY)	88
Mill (LEX)	73
Mill (QUI)	69
Mill (WAV)	79
Mill (DOR)	22
Mill (CHA)	29
Mill (EB)	28
Mill	
1-160 (NCE)	59
161-OUT (NWV)	60
Mill Ct (CHE)	50
Mill Ln (BRA)	84
Mill Rd (MEL)	76
Mill St Ct (CHA)	29
Mill St Pl (CHA)	29
Mill St Pl (REV)	51
Mill St & Ln (ARL)	74
Millbrook Dr (ARL)	74
Millbrook Rd (LEX)	73
Millen Cir (MAL)	48
Miller (CHE)	50
Miller (EV)	49
Miller (SOM)	43
Miller (QUI)	69
Miller (CHA)	29
Miller (N)	92
Miller Ave (MIL)	86
Miller Ave (CAM)	40
Miller Park (ROX)	19
Miller Rd (NCE)	59
Miller St & Ave (BRA)	84
Millers Ln (DOR)	24
Millers Stile Rd (QUI)	69
Millet (DOR)	24
Millett (ARL)	74
Millett Ave (SWY)	90
Millmont (ROX)	19
Mills (ROX)	19
Mills (MAL)	48
Mills Ave (REV)	51
Mills Rd (NH)	94
Millstone Rd (HP)	36
Milner (WAL)	54
Milo	
1-6 (WNW)	65
7-7 (WAL)	54
8-8 (WNW)	65
9-9 (WAL)	54
10-OUT (WNW)	65
Milton (MIL)	86
Milton (WAL)	54
Milton (MAL)	48
Milton (ARL)	74
Milton (WOL)	70
Milton (BEL)	78
Milton	
1-20 (CAM)	40
21-OUT (WS)	44
Milton Ave (WNW)	65
Milton Pl	10
Milton Rd (NQ)	71
Milton Rd (BRA)	85
Milton Rd (BRO)	46
Milton St & Ave (DOR)	24
Milton St, Ave & Ter (HP)	36
Milton Hill Rd (MIL)	86
Milwood St & Ter (DOR)	24
Minden (JP)	30
Mindora (RXC)	20
Miner (SOM)	45
Miner	02215
Mingo (MIL)	86
Mingo (MAL)	48
Minihans Ln (QUI)	69
Minnesota Ave (WS)	45
Minnie Ct (SB)	27
Minola Rd (LEX)	73
Minot (STO)	80
Minot	
1-209 (DOR)	22
210-OUT (DOR)	24
Minot Park (DOR)	24
Minot Pl (NWV)	60
Minton (JP)	30
Minute Man Ln (WEL)	81
Minute Man Ln (LEX)	73
Miriam (QUI)	69
Miriam Rd (WAL)	54
Mishawum (CHA)	29
Mission	15
Mitchell (SB)	27
Mitchell (QUI)	69
Mitchell Ave (MED)	55
Moccasin Path (ARL)	74
Model Pl (EB)	28
Modena (ARL)	74
Moffat Rd (QUI)	69
Moffat Rd (WAB)	68
Mohan (EV)	49
Mohawk (SB)	27
Mohawk Rd (ARL)	74
Mokena Ave (WAL)	54
Molloy (WAT)	72
Moloney (WRX)	32
Monadnock (DOR)	25
Monadnock Rd (ARL)	74
Monadnock Rd (CHH)	67
Monadnock Rd (WH)	81
Monastery Rd (BRI)	35
Monatiquot (NWY)	91
Monatiquot Ave (BRA)	84
Mondamin Ct (SOM)	43
Monks (SB)	27
Monmouth (SOM)	43
Monmouth (NQ)	71
Monmouth Ave (MED)	55
Monmouth St & Ct (BRO)	46
Monmouth St & Sq (EB)	28
Monponset (MAT)	26
Monroe (MAL)	48
Monroe (NWV)	60
Monroe Rd (QUI)	69
Monsignor Obrien Hwy (CAM)	41
Monsignor Reynolds Way	18
Monsignor Shea Rd	11
Monson (MAT)	26
Montague (DOR)	24
Montague (CAM)	39
Montague (ARL)	74
Montana (DOR)	21
Montcalm Ave (BRI)	35
Montclair Ave (ROS)	31
Montclair Ave (WAL)	54
Montclair Ave (NQ)	71
Montclair Rd (WAB)	68
Montebello Rd (JP)	30
Montello (DOR)	22
Monterey Ave (MAT)	26
Montfern Ave (BRI)	35
Montfern Ave (REV)	51
Montgomery (CAM)	40
Montgomery	16
Montgomery Ave (SOM)	45
Monticello Ave (DOR)	25
Montiltio (QUI)	69
Montmorenci Ave (EB)	28
Montpelier Rd (DOR)	25
Montrose (ROX)	19
Montrose (NEW)	58
Montrose (EV)	49
Montrose Ave (ARL)	74
Montrose St & Ct (SOM)	43
Montrose St & Ct (MAL)	48
Montvale (MAL)	48
Montvale (ROS)	31
Montvale (MEL)	76
Montvale (WES)	93
Montvale Ave (STO)	80
Montvale Rd (WH)	81
Montvale Rd (NCE)	59
Montview (WRX)	32
Montview Ave & Cir (WAL)	54
Monument Ct (SB)	27
Monument St, Ave, Ct & Sq (CHA)	29
Monument St & Ter (MED)	55
Moody (WAL)	54
Moody (DOR)	24
Moody (CHH)	67
Moody Ave (EV)	49
Moon	13
Moon Hill Rd (LEX)	73
Moon Island Rd (NQ)	71
Mooney (CAM)	38
Mooney Rd (REV)	51
Moore (WIN)	52
Moore (WAL)	54
Moore (CAM)	39
Moore (WS)	44
Moore (BEL)	78
Moore (QUI)	69
Moore (EB)	28
Moore	18
Moore Pl (ARL)	74
Moore Rd (EWY)	89
Mooreland Rd (MEL)	76
Mora (DOR)	24
Moraine (JP)	30
Moraine (WAV)	79
Moreland (ROX)	19
Moreland (SOM)	45
Moreland (WRX)	32
Moreland Ave (LEX)	73

Boston (Con.)   021

Moreland Ave (NCE) 59
Moreland Pl (EV) 49
Moreland Rd (QUI) 69
Moreland Rd (BRA) 84
Moreland Rd (NWY) 91
Morey Rd (ROS) 31
Morgan (SOM) 43
Morgan (MEL) 76
Morgan 16
Morgan Ave (STO) 80
Morgan Ave (MED) 55
Morgan Pl (NEW) 58
Morgan Rd (WOL) 70
Morgan Rd (LEX) 73
Morley (ROX) 19
Morley (N) 92
Morley Rd (WOL) 70
Morningside Dr (ARL) 74
Morningside Path (EWY) 89
Morningside Rd (N) 92
Morrell (NWY) 91
Morrill (WNW) 65
Morrill (DOR) 25
Morris (EB) 28
Morris (ARL) 74
Morris (LEX) 73
Morris (EV) 49
Morris (REV) 51
Morris (MAL) 48
Morrison (MED) 55
Morrison (QUI) 69
Morrison Ave & Pl (WS) 44
Morrison Ct (CAM) 40
Morrison Rd (WAT) 72
Morrison St & Rd (BRA) 84
Morrissey Wm T Blvd
   1-620 (DOR) 25
   621-OUT (DOR) 22
Morrissey Wm T Ter (DOR) 25
Morrow Rd (BRI) 35
Morse (DOR) 21
Morse (WAT) 72
Morse (WOL) 70
Morse Rd (NWY) 60
Morse Pond Rd (WH) 81
Morseland Ave (NCE) 59
Mortimer Pl (SOM) 45
Mortimer Ter (QUI) 69
Morton (QUI) 69
Morton (WAT) 72
Morton (SOM) 45
Morton (WIN) 52
Morton (WAL) 54
Morton 13
Morton (NH) 94
Morton
   1-499 (JP) 30
   500-600 (DOR) (EVEN) 24
   501-593 (DOR) (ODD) 24
   595-OUT (MAT) (ODD) 26
   602-OUT (MAT) (EVEN) 26
Morton Ave (MED) 55
Morton Pl (RXC) 20
Morton Pl (EB) 28
Morton Rd (ARL) 74
Morton Rd & Ter (MIL) 87
Morton St & Ave (MAL) 48
Morton St & Cir (WEL) 81
Morton St & Rd (NCE) 59
Morton Village Dr (MAT) 26
Moscow (NQ) 71

Moseley (DOR) 25
Mosely Rd (NCE) 59
Mosgrove Ave (ROS) 31
Mosley Ave (N) 92
Moss Hill Rd (JP) 30
Mossdale Rd (JP) 30
Mossfield Rd (WAB) 68
Mossland (WS) 44
Mossman (WNW) 65
Mother Julian Rd (DOR) 24
Motley (RXC) 20
Mott (ARL) 74
Moulton (NLF) 62
Moulton (CHA) 29
Moulton (CAM) 38
Moulton Ave (STO) 80
Moulton Ave (NWY) 91
Moulton Rd (ARL) 74
Moultrie (DOR) 24
Mound (QUI) 69
Mount Alvernia Rd (CHH) 67
Mount Ararat Rd (QUI) 69
Mount Auburn (WAT) 72
Mount Auburn St & Pl (CAM) 38
Mount Bowdoin Ter (DOR) 21
Mount Calvary Rd (ROS) 31
Mount Cushing Ter (DOR) 25
Mount Everett (DOR) 25
Mount Hood Rd (BRO) 46
Mount Hood Ter (MEL) 76
Mount Hope (ROS) 31
Mount Hope Cemetery (MAT) 26
Mount Ida Rd (DOR) 22
Mount Ida Rd (EWY) 89
Mount Ida St & Ter (NEW) 58
Mount Ida Ter (WAL) 54
Mount Pleasant (WAL) 54
Mount Pleasant (HP) 36
Mount Pleasant (CAM) 40
Mount Pleasant Ave (MAL) 48
Mount Pleasant Ave, Pl & Ter
   (ROX) 19
Mount Pleasant St & Ct
   (SOM) 45
Mount Tabor Rd (LEX) 73
Mount Vernon (QUI) 69
Mount Vernon (ARL) 74
Mount Vernon (STO) 80
Mount Vernon (SOM) 45
Mount Vernon (CAM) 40
Mount Vernon (WRX) 32
Mount Vernon (DOR) 25
Mount Vernon
   1-174 (NWV) 60
   175-OUT (WNW) 65
Mount Vernon Ave (N) 92
Mount Vernon Ave (WAL) 54
Mount Vernon Rd E & W
   (EWY) 89
Mount Vernon St & Ave
   (BRI) 35
Mount Vernon St & Ave
   (CHA) 29
Mount Vernon St & Ave
   (BRA) 84
Mount Vernon St & Ave
   (MEL) 76
Mount Vernon St & Park
   (MAL) 48
Mount Vernon St, Pl & Sq 08
Mount Vernon Ter (NWV) 60
Mount Walley Ave (JP) 30
Mount Walley Rd (WAL) 54

Mount Warren (ROX) 19
Mount Washington (EV) 49
Mount Washington Ave
   (MAL) 48
Mount Washington Ave 02210
Mount Washington Pl (SB) 27
Mount Zion Rd (MED) 76
Mountain Ave (ARL) 74
Mountain Ave (DOR) 24
Mountain Ave (MAL) 48
Mountain Ave (SOM) 43
Mountain Ave (REV) 51
Mountain Ave E (REV) 51
Mountain Ave N & S (MEL) 76
Mountain Rd (LEX) 73
Mountain Rd (WAL) 54
Mountain View Rd (EWY) 89
Mountfort
   1-124 02215
   125-OUT (BRO) 46
Mountfort Rd (NWH) 61
Mountview Rd (WH) 81
Moville (WRX) 32
Mozart (JP) 30
Mugford (WIN) 52
Muirhead (WOL) 70
Mulberry (CHE) 50
Mulberry Pl (ROX) 19
Mulberry Rd (MIL) 87
Muldoons Ct (WAL) 54
Mulford (BRO) 46
Muller Ave (CAM) 40
Mullin Ave (QUI) 69
Mullins Ct (CAM) 41
Mulvey (MAT) 26
Mulvey Ter (ROX) 19
Munroe (ROX) 19
Munroe (CAM) 42
Munroe (SOM) 43
Munroe (BEL) 78
Munroe Ave (WAT) 72
Munroe Ave (WAL) 54
Munroe Rd (WH) 81
Munroe Rd (LEX) 73
Munson 02215
Munster Ter (WAL) 54
Murdock (CAM) 39
Murdock (SOM) 45
Murdock Ave (QUI) 69
Murdock St & Ter (BRI) 35
Murley Ln (NCE) 59
Murphy Ct (NEW) 58
Murphy Rd (N) 92
Murray (SOM) 43
Murray (WAL) 54
Murray (MAL) 48
Murray (CHE) 50
Murray (ARL) 74
Murray Ave (MIL) 86
Murray Ave (ROX) 19
Murray Ct (EB) 28
Murray Rd & Ter (WNW) 65
Murray Ter (DOR) 24
Murray Hill Park & Rd (MAL) 48
Murray Hill Rd (CAM) 40
Murray Hill Rd (MED) 55
Murray Hill Rd (ROS) 31
Museum
   1-111 (CAM) 38
   112-OUT (SOM) 43
Museum Rd 15
Music Hall Ave (WAL) 54

Music Hall Pl................... 08
Muzzey (LEX)................... 73
Myers Ln (MIL)................. 86
Myerson Ln (NCE)............. 59
Myles Standish Rd (WES).... 93
Myles Standish Rd (WRX).... 32
Myopia Rd (HP)................ 36
Myopia Rd (STO).............. 80
Myopia Rd
　1-49 (WOL).................. 70
　50-OUT (QUI)............... 69
Myrick (ALL)................... 34
Myrna Rd (LEX)............... 73
Myrtle (LEX)................... 73
Myrtle (BRA).................. 84
Myrtle (STO).................. 80
Myrtle (WNW)................ 65
Myrtle (WAT).................. 72
Myrtle (NQ)................... 71
Myrtle (BEL).................. 78
Myrtle (MEL).................. 76
Myrtle (WAL).................. 54
Myrtle (MED)................. 55
Myrtle (EV)................... 49
Myrtle (EWY)................. 89
Myrtle.......................... 14
Myrtle (JP)................... 30
Myrtle Ave (BRA)............ 85
Myrtle Ave (CAM)............ 38
Myrtle Ave (WIN)............ 52
Myrtle Ave (AUB)............ 66
Myrtle Pl (ROX).............. 19
Myrtle St & Ct (MAL)........ 48
Myrtle St, Ct & Pl (SOM).... 45
Myrtlebank Ave (DOR)....... 24
Mystic (EV)................... 49
Mystic (ARL)................. 74
Mystic Ave (MEL)............ 76
Mystic Ave (SOM)........... 45
Mystic St Ext (MED)........ 55
Mystic St & Ave (MED)..... 55
Mystic St, Ave & Pl (CHA)... 29
Mystic Bank (ARL).......... 74
Mystic Lake Dr (ARL)....... 74
Mystic River Rd (MED)...... 55
Mystic Valley Pky (ARL).... 74
Mystic Valley Pky
　1-500 (SOM)................ 44
　501-OUT (MED)............ 55
Mystic View Ter (ARL)...... 74
Mystic Wharf (CHA).......... 29
N (SB)......................... 27
Nahant Ave (DOR)........... 22
Nahant Ave (WIN)........... 52
Nahant Ave (REV)........... 51
Nahanton (NCE).............. 59
Nahanton Ave (MIL)......... 86
Nanapashemet Ave (MAL)... 48
Nancia (EB).................. 28
Nancy Rd (MIL).............. 86
Nancy Rd (CHH).............. 67
Nanset Rd (NWY)............ 91
Nantasket Ave (BRI)........ 35
Nantu_et Rd (NWH).......... 61
Nantucket Rd (WH).......... 81
Naomi (MAL)................. 48
Napier Park (DOR)........... 25
Naples Rd (BRO)............. 46
Naples Rd (REV)............. 51
Naples Rd (MEL)............. 76
Nardell Rd (NCE)............ 59
Nardone Rd (NCE)........... 59
Nardone Rd (N)............... 92

Narraganset Ave (WY)....... 88
Narraganset Rd (QUI)........ 69
Narragansett (DOR).......... 22
Nash (WAT)................... 72
Nash (MIL).................... 86
Nash Ave (QUI)............... 69
Nash Ln (WES)................ 93
Nash Ln & Rd (SWY)......... 90
Nash Row (CHA).............. 29
Nash Sq (CHA)................ 90
Nashua......................... 14
Nashua (SOM)................. 45
Nason Dr (MEL)............... 76
Nassau St & Pl................ 11
Natalie Ave (MEL)............ 76
Nathan (ROX)................. 19
Nathan Rd (NCE)............. 59
Nathan Rd (WAL)............. 54
National (SB)................. 27
Naval Hwy & Ter (NQ)....... 71
Navarre
　1-82 (ROS)................. 31
　83-OUT (HP)............... 36
Navarre Pl (HP).............. 36
Navarro Cir (MED)........... 55
Naviens Ln (WAL)............ 54
Navillus Ter (DOR)........... 22
Nay (EB)...................... 28
Nazing St & Ct (DOR)....... 21
Neal (MAL)................... 48
Neal (NLF)................... 62
Neal Ct (CHA)................ 29
Nearen Row (CHA)........... 29
Necco St, Ct & Pl...........02210
Neck (NWY)................... 91
Needham
　1-162 (NWH)............... 61
　163-OUT (NUF)............ 64
Needham Rd (HP)............ 36
Needhamdale Rd (N)........ 92
Neframer Rd (NCE).......... 59
Nehoiden (N)................. 92
Nehoiden Rd (WAB)......... 68
Neighbors Ln (WAL)......... 54
Neillan Cres (JP)............ 30
Neilon Park (MAL).......... 48
Neilson Ave (EV)............ 49
Nell Rd (REV)............... 51
Nelson (HP).................. 36
Nelson (DOR)................ 24
Nelson (QUI)................. 69
Nelson (BRA)................ 84
Nelson Dr (CHH)............. 67
Nelson Rd (SWY)............ 90
Nelson Rd & Ter (MEL)...... 76
Neponset (REV).............. 51
Neponset Ave (HP).......... 36
Neponset Ave & Cir (DOR)... 22
Neponset Ave & Ct (ROS)... 31
Neponset Rd (QUI).......... 69
Neponset Valley Pky (HP)... 36
Neponset Valley Pky (MIL)... 86
Neptune Ave (WIN).......... 52
Neptune Rd (EB)............. 28
Nerious Ave (REV)........... 51
Neshobe Rd (WAB).......... 68
Nestor Ln (WAL)............. 54
Netherlands Rd (BRO)....... 46
Nevada (WIN)................ 52
Nevada (NWV)............... 60
Nevada (DOR)................ 24
Nevada Ave (MAL).......... 48
Nevada Ave (SOM).......... 43

Nevada Rd (QUI)............. 69
Nevada Rd (NH).............. 94
Nevin Rd (SWY).............. 90
New (CAM).................... 38
New (EB)...................... 28
New Park Ave (ROS)......... 31
New Ter Rd (BRO)........... 46
New Acre Rd (HP)........... 36
New Bedford (HP)........... 36
New Bert Ave (SWY)........ 90
New Castle Rd (BEL)........ 78
New Chardon................. 14
New Cross (SOM)............ 45
New England Ave (DOR).... 24
New Hampshire Ave (SOM)... 45
New Haven (WRX)........... 32
New Heath
　1-20 (ROX)................. 19
　21-45 (RXC) (ODD)....... 20
　22-30 (RXC) (EVEN)...... 20
　32-OUT (JP) (EVEN)....... 30
　47-OUT (JP) (ODD)........ 30
New Sudbury................. 14
New Woodcliff (DOR)....... 25
Newark (ROX)................ 19
Newbern (JP)................ 30
Newbern Ave (MED)......... 55
Newbern Pl.................. 16
Newbern St & Ct (RXC)..... 20
Newberne (WS).............. 44
Newbrook Cir (CHH)........ 67
Newburg (ROS).............. 31
Newburgh (WAL)............ 54
Newbury (WS)............... 44
Newbury (MAL).............. 48
Newbury (REV).............. 51
Newbury
　1-279 (ODD)............... 16
　2-282 (EVEN).............. 16
　284-448 (EVEN)........... 15
　450-OUT (ODD)...........02215
　279-449 (ODD)............ 15
Newbury Park (N)........... 92
Newbury St & Ave (NQ)..... 71
Newbury St & Ter (NCE).... 59
Newcastle (MAT)............ 26
Newcastle Ct................ 18
Newcastle Rd (BRI)......... 35
Newcomb (MED)............. 55
Newcomb..................... 18
Newcomb (QUI).............. 69
Newcomb (ARL).............. 74
Newcomb Rd (MEL).......... 76
Newcomb Ter (WY).......... 88
Newcroft Cir (MAT).......... 26
Newell Ave (N).............. 92
Newell Rd (AUB)............ 66
Newell Rd (BRO)............ 46
Newell St & Ter (CAM)...... 40
Newfield (WRX).............. 32
Newfield (WOL).............. 70
Newhall (NQ)................ 71
Newhall (MAL)............... 48
Newhall (REV)............... 51
Newhall St & Pl (DOR)...... 22
Newhill Pl (SB).............. 27
Newkirk (DOR)............... 22
Newland...................... 18
Newland (NQ)................ 71
Newland (AUB).............. 66
Newland Rd (ARL)........... 74
Newland St & Ter (MAL).... 48
Newman (REV)............... 51

Boston (Con.)   021

Newman (CAM) 40
Newman Pl (SOM) 45
Newman Pl (ROX) 19
Newman Rd (MAL) 48
Newman Way (ARL) 74
Newmarket Sq 18
Newport (DOR) 25
Newport (ARL) 74
Newport Ave (MED) 55
Newport Ave (BRA) 85
Newport Ave
  1-115 (NQ) 71
  116-OUT (WOL) 70
Newport Rd (CAM) 40
Newport Ter (WOL) 70
Newsome Park (JP) 30
Newton (QUI) 69
Newton (BEL) 78
Newton (CAM) 39
Newton (MAL) 48
Newton (BRI) 35
Newton (WAL) 54
Newton (EV) 49
Newton (WES) 93
Newton
  1-209 (BRO) (ODD) 46
  2-282 (BRO) (EVEN) 46
  211-OUT (CHH) (ODD) 67
  284-OUT (CHH) (EVEN) 67
Newton Ave (WOL) 70
Newton Rd (ARL) 74
Newton Rd (MED) 55
Newton St & Ave (BRA) 84
Newton St & Ct (NWY) 91
Newton St & Pl (SOM) 43
Newtonville Ave
  1-258 (NEW) 58
  259-OUT (NWV) 60
Newtowne Ct (CAM) 39
Nichol (QUI) 69
Nicholas Rd (BRA) 84
Nichols (EV) 49
Nichols (CHE) 50
Nichols Ave (WAT) 72
Nichols Pl (CAM) 38
Nichols Rd (MAL) 48
Nichols Rd (LEX) 73
Nichols Rd (N) 92
Nickerson Rd (LEX) 73
Nickerson Rd (BRA) 84
Nickerson Rd (CHH) 67
Nickerson Field (WES) 93
Nicod (ARL) 74
Nightingale (DOR) 24
Nightingale Ave (QUI) 69
Nightingale Path (NCE) 59
Nikisch Ave (ROS) 31
Niles (BRI) 35
Niles Rd (NWH) 61
Nilsen Ave (QUI) 69
Nina (MEL) 76
Ninth (MED) 55
Ninth (SB) 27
Nira (MAL) 48
Nira Ave (JP) 30
Nix Point Rd (SWY) 90
Nixon (DOR) 24
Nixon Ln (STO) 80
Nixon Pl (ALL) 34
Noah (MAT) 26
Noanet 11

Noanet (QUI) 69
Noanet Rd (NH) 94
Nob Hill Rd (WY) 88
Noble (WNW) 65
Noble (MAL) 48
Noble (REV) 51
Noble Ct (EB) 28
Nobscot Rd (WH) 81
Nobscot Rd (NCE) 59
Nobscot Rd (WES) 93
Nod Hill Rd (NWH) 61
Nonantum (BRI) 35
Nonantum St, Pl & Rd
  (NEW) 58
None Such Way (WES) 93
Nonquit (DOR) 25
Noonan (WAL) 54
Norcross Pl (SB) 27
Norcross St & Cir (ARL) 74
Norfolk (WOL) 70
Norfolk (ROX) 19
Norfolk (N) 92
Norfolk (WY) 88
Norfolk
  1-409 (CAM) (ODD) 39
  1-430 (DOR) 24
  2-412 (CAM) (EVEN) 39
  411-OUT (SOM) (ODD) 43
  414-OUT (SOM) (EVEN) 43
  431-OUT (MAT) 26
Norfolk Ave
  1-279 (ROX) 19
  280-OUT (DOR) 25
Norfolk Ct, Pl & Ter⁴(CAM) 39
Norfolk Pl 11
Norfolk Rd (ARL) 74
Norfolk Rd (BRA) 84
Norfolk Rd (CHH) 67
Norfolk Ter (WEL) 81
Norfolk Ter (DOR) 24
Norma Ave (WY) 88
Norman (MIL) 86
Norman (CAM) 38
Norman (REV) 51
Norman (EV) 49
Norman Rd (QUI) 69
Norman Rd (NWH) 61
Norman Rd (MEL) 76
Normandy (DOR) 21
Normandy Ave & Ter (CAM) 38
Normandy Rd (CHE) 50
Normandy Rd (AUB) 66
Normandy Rd (LEX) 73
Norris (CAM) 40
Norris Ct (MEL) 76
Norris Rd (HP) 36
Norseman Ave (WAT) 72
North (NQ) 71
North (LEX) 73
North (NCE) 59
North (NWV) 60
North (STO) 80
North (BRA) 84
North (WS) 44
North (MED) 55
North
  1-174 09
  1-514 (NWY) 91
  175-OUT 13
  515-OUT (EWY) 89
North Ave (WES) 93
North Ave (WIN) 52
North Ave (MEL) 76

North St & Ave (REV) 51
North Anderson 14
North Beacon
  1-105 (ALL) 34
  106-OUT (BRI) 35
North Beacon St & Ct (WAT) 72
North Bennet St, Ct & Pl 13
North Border Rd (STO) 80
North Bowditch (BRA) 84
North Cedar Park (MEL) 76
North Central Ave (WOL) 70
North Charlame St, Ct & Ter
  (ROX) 19
North Crescent Circuit (BRI) 35
North Forest (MEL) 76
North Gate Park (WNW) 65
North Gate Rd (WH) 81
North Hancock (LEX) 73
North Hanover Ct 13
North Harvard
  1-94 (SF) 63
  95-OUT (ALL) 34
North Hill Rd (N) 92
North Hudson 13
North Irving Park (WAT) 72
North Margin 13
North Market 09
North Mead (CHA) 29
North Mead St Ct (CHA) 29
North Milton (MAL) 48
North Munroe Ter (DOR) 22
North Park (WAT) 72
North Payne (QUI) 69
North Quincy Pl (CHA) 29
North Russell (MIL) 87
North Shore Rd (REV) 51
North Station 14
North Union (SOM) 45
North Union (ARL) 74
North Washington
  1-221 (ODD) 14
  2-198 (EVEN) 14
  200-OUT (CHA) (EVEN) 29
  223-OUT (CHA) (ODD) 29
Northam Park (DOR) 24
Northampton
  1-28 (ROX) 19
  29-OUT 18
Northampton Pl 18
Northbourne Rd (JP) 30
Northdale Rd (WRX) 32
Northdale Rd Ext (WRX) 32
Northdale Rd Ter (WRX) 32
Northern Ave 02210
Northern Ave (WY) 88
Northern Cir (REV) 51
Northern Rd (MAL) 48
Northfield Ave (QUI) 69
Northgate Rd (STO) 80
Norton (BRA) 84
Norton (HP) 36
Norton (NWY) 91
Norton
  1-68 (DOR) 25
  69-OUT (DOR) 22
Norton Ave (MED) 55
Norton Pl (CAM) 38
Norton Rd (QUI) 69
Norton Rd (LEX) 73
Norumbega (CAM) 38
Norumbega Park (AUB) 66
Norumbega Rd (WES) 93
Norumbega Ter (WAL) 54

Boston (Con.)	**021**
Norval Ave (STO)	80
Norway	15
Norway Park (HP)	36
Norway Rd (MIL)	87
Norwell	
1-155 (DOR)	21
156-OUT (DOR)	24
Norwich Cir (MED)	55
Norwich Rd (N)	92
Norwich Rd (WH)	81
Norwood (EV)	49
Norwood (DOR)	22
Norwood Ave (SOM)	45
Norwood Ave (NCE)	59
Norwood Ave (NWV)	60
Norwood St & Pl (MAL)	48
Notre Dame (ROX)	19
Notre Dame Ave (CAM)	40
Nott (HP)	36
Nottingham (WAL)	54
Nottingham (DOR)	21
Nottingham (NCE)	59
Nottinghill Rd (BRI)	35
Nourse (ARL)	74
Nowell Rd (MEL)	76
Nowers Rd (LEX)	73
Noyes (N)	92
Noyes Pl	13
Nun Buoy Ln (QUI)	69
Nursery Ln (EV)	49
Nut Island Ave & Rd (QUI)	69
Nutting Rd (CAM)	38
Nutting Rd (WAL)	54
Nyack (WAT)	72
O (SB)	27
O St Pl (SB)	27
Oak (CHA)	29
Oak (MEL)	76
Oak (NUF)	64
Oak (WEL)	81
Oak (BRA)	84
Oak (STO)	80
Oak (CAM)	39
Oak (SOM)	43
Oak (WES)	93
Oak (N)	92
Oak (SWY)	90
Oak E (BRA)	84
Oak Ave (NQ)	71
Oak Ave (WNW)	65
Oak Rd (MED)	55
Oak Rd (WRX)	32
Oak Sq (BRI)	35
Oak Sq Ave (BRI)	35
Oak Sq Ter (SOM)	43
Oak St Pl (SOM)	43
Oak St & Ave (BEL)	78
Oak St & Pl (CHH)	67
Oak St & Pl (WAT)	72
Oak St & Pl (HP)	36
Oak St & Pl	11
Oak St & Rd (WAL)	54
Oak St & Rd (QUI)	69
Oak St & Rd (MIL)	87
Oak St & Ter (LEX)	73
Oak St & Ter (MAL)	48
Oak Ter (EV)	49
Oak Ter (NWH)	61
Oak Bluff (MED)	55
Oak Cliff Rd (NWV)	60
Oak Cliff Rd (WH)	81

Oak Cliff Rd (EWY)	89
Oak Grove Ct & Ter (MAL)	48
Oak Grove Ter (QUI)	69
Oak Hill (NCE)	59
Oak Hill Ave (MAT)	26
Oak Hill Dr (ARL)	74
Oak Hill Rd (WAL)	54
Oak Hill Rd (EWY)	89
Oak Hill Rd (BRA)	85
Oak Hill Rd (N)	92
Oak Island St & Rd (REV)	51
Oak Knoll (ARL)	74
Oak Knoll Ter (N)	92
Oak Mill Ave (MAT)	26
Oak Park Cir (LEX)	73
Oak Ridge Rd (MED)	55
Oak Vale Rd (WAB)	68
Oakburn Ave (RXC)	20
Oakcrest Rd (MAT)	26
Oakcrest Rd (N)	92
Oakcrest Rd (SWY)	90
Oakdale Ave (SWY)	90
Oakdale Ave (WES)	93
Oakdale Ave (WH)	81
Oakdale Ave (WR)	32
Oakdale Rd (MAL)	48
Oakdale Rd	
1-92 (NCE)	59
93-OUT (NWH)	61
Oakdale St, Sq & Ter (JP)	30
Oakden Ave (SWY)	90
Oakden Ave (BRA)	85
Oakencroft Rd (WEL)	81
Oakes (EV)	49
Oakhurst (DOR)	24
Oakhurst Cir (N)	92
Oakland (NEW)	58
Oakland (CAM)	39
Oakland (BRA)	84
Oakland (LEX)	73
Oakland (WAT)	72
Oakland (MEL)	76
Oakland Ave (AUB)	66
Oakland Ave (ARL)	74
Oakland Ave (WOL)	70
Oakland Ave (EV)	49
Oakland Ave (SOM)	45
Oakland Ave (N)	92
Oakland Rd (BRO)	46
Oakland Rd Ext (BRO)	46
Oakland St & Cir (WH)	81
Oakland St & Park (MED)	55
Oakland St & Park (ROX)	19
Oakland St & Pl (BRI)	35
Oakledge (ARL)	74
Oakledge Rd (WAL)	54
Oakleigh Rd (NEW)	58
Oakley (DOR)	24
Oakley Ln (WAL)	54
Oakley Rd (BEL)	78
Oakley Rd (WAT)	72
Oakman (DOR)	22
Oakmere (WRX)	32
Oakmont Rd (NCE)	59
Oakmount Cir (LEX)	73
Oakridge (MAT)	26
Oakridge Rd (NQ)	71
Oakridge Rd (WH)	81
Oakridge Rd (STO)	80
Oakridge St & Cir (WEY)	88
Oakton Ave (DOR)	22
Oakvale Ave (MAT)	26

Oakview Ave (ROX)	19
Oakview Ter (JP)	30
Oakville Ave (ROX)	19
Oakwood (DOR)	24
Oakwood (MAT)	26
Oakwood Ave (REV)	51
Oakwood Rd (NWV)	60
Oakwood Rd (QUI)	69
Oakwood Rd (AUB)	66
Oakwood Ter (REV)	59
Ober Rd (NCE)	59
Obierne Pl (ROX)	19
Obrien Ct (CHA)	29
Obrien Msgr Hwy (CAM)	41
Ocallaghan Way (SB)	27
Ocean (DOR)	24
Ocean (NQ)	71
Ocean Ave (NWV)	52
Ocean Ave (REV)	51
Ocean Ave (NWY)	91
Ocean Pier Ave (REV)	51
Ocean Side Park (REV)	51
Ocean View Ave (REV)	51
Ocean View St & Way (WIN)	52
Oconnell Ave (QUI)	69
Oconnell Rd (NCE)	59
Oconnell Rd (DOR)	24
October Ln (WES)	93
Ode (WAL)	54
Odom (QUI)	69
Odonnell Sq & Ter (DOR)	22
Off Lake (EWY)	89
Off Park Ave (SWY)	90
Off Putnam (EWY)	89
Off River (NWY)	91
Off Station (EWY)	89
Off Summer (WY)	88
Ogden (DOR)	24
Ogden Rd (CHH)	67
Ohio	16
Ohio Ave (NUF)	64
Okala Rd (EWY)	89
Olafson (BRA)	85
Olcutt (WAT)	72
Old Rd (WES)	93
Old Rd (DOR)	21
Old Brook Cir (MEL)	76
Old Carriage Ln & Way (BRA)	84
Old Coach Rd (QUI)	69
Old Coach Rd (WES)	93
Old Coach Rd (BRA)	85
Old Colony Ave (SB)	27
Old Colony Ave & Ter (WOL)	70
Old Colony Ln & Rd (ARL)	74
Old Colony Rd (WH)	81
Old Colony Rd (CHH)	67
Old Colony Rd (WES)	93
Old Colony Ter (DOR)	25
Old Concord Rd (BEL)	78
Old Country Way (WY)	88
Old Country Way (BRA)	85
Old Dee Rd (CAM)	38
Old England Rd (CHH)	67
Old Farm Rd (WH)	81
Old Farm Rd (NCE)	59
Old Farm Rd (MIL)	86
Old Farm Rd (N)	92
Old Harbor (SB)	27
Old Heath (JP)	30
Old Ironsides Way (CHA)	29
Old Landing Way (CHA)	29
Old Lexington Rd (WAL)	54

Boston (Con.)   021

Old Middlesex Path (ARL) 74
Old Middlesex Rd (BEL) 78
Old Morton (MAT) 26
Old Mystic (ARL) 74
Old North (BRA) 84
Old Orchard Rd (CHH) 67
Old Shade (LEX) 73
Old Town Rd (WH) 81
Old Winchester (NWH) 61
Olde Field Rd (NCE) 59
Oldfields Rd (DOR) 21
Oldham Rd (WNW) 65
Oldham Rd (ARL) 74
Oleander (DOR) 25
Oleary Way (JP) 30
Oliva Rd (BRI) 35
Olive (BRI) 35
Olive (REV) 51
Olive Ave (MAL) 48
Olive Ave & Sq (SOM) 43
Olive Pl (CAM) 40
Oliver (SOM) 45
Oliver (MAL) 48
Oliver (NQ) 71
Oliver
    1-OUT (ODD) 10
    2-10 (EVEN) 09
    12-OUT (EVEN) 10
Oliver Pl 11
Oliver Rd (EWY) 89
Oliver Rd (WAB) 68
Oliver Rd (BEL) 78
Oliver St & Pl (EV) 49
Oliver St & Rd (WAT) 72
Oliver Ter (REV) 51
Olmstead St & Park (JP) 30
Olney (DOR) 21
Olney (WAT) 72
Omar Ter (NWV) 60
Omeara Ct (CHA) 29
Oneida (QUI) 69
Oneil Pl (BRI) 35
Onslow Ter (SB) 27
Opera Pl 15
Ophir (JP) 30
Orange (CHE) 50
Orange (WAL) 54
Orange (ROS) 31
Orange Ct (EV) 49
Orchard (EV) 49
Orchard (REV) 51
Orchard (MAL) 48
Orchard (NEW) 58
Orchard (MED) 55
Orchard (JP) 30
Orchard (MAT) 26
Orchard (NQ) 71
Orchard (WAT) 72
Orchard (BRA) 84
Orchard (STO) 80
Orchard (WH) 81
Orchard (LEX) 73
Orchard
    1-83 (CAM) (ODD) 40
    2-86 (CAM) (EVEN) 40
    85-OUT (WS) (ODD) 44
    88-OUT (WS) (EVEN) 44
Orchard Ave (WES) 93
Orchard Ave (WNW) 65
Orchard Ave (WAB) 68
Orchard Ave (WAL) 54

Orchard Ln & Pl (MEL) 76
Orchard Park (ROX) 19
Orchard Pl & Ter (ARL) 74
Orchard Rd (BRO) 46
Orchard Rd (SWY) 90
Orchard Rd (MIL) 86
Orchard St & Cir (BEL) 78
Orchardale (DOR) 24
Orchardfield (DOR) 22
Orchardhill Rd (JP) 30
Ordway Rd (WH) 81
Oregon Ave (BRA) 85
Oregon Ct (RXC) 20
Oreilley Way (CHA) 29
Organ Park (ROS) 31
Orient (MAL) 48
Orient Ave (EV) 49
Orient Ave (ARL) 74
Orient Ave (NCE) 59
Orient Ave (LEX) 73
Orient Ave & Hts (EB) 28
Orient Ave, Park & Pl (MEL) 76
Oriental Ct (STO) 80
Oriole (WH) 81
Oriole (WRX) 32
Orkney Rd (BRO) 46
Orlando (MAT) 26
Orlando Ave (WIN) 52
Orlando Ave (ARL) 74
Orlando Ave (NWY) 91
Orleans (QUI) 69
Orleans (EB) 28
Orleans Rd (WY) 88
Ormond (MAT) 26
Orne (DOR) 22
Orono (MIL) 87
Orourke Path (NCE) 59
Orrin (CAM) 38
Orris (AUB) 66
Orris St & Pl (MEL) 76
Ort (BRO) 46
Orton Marotta Way (SB) 27
Ortona (ARL) 74
Orvis Cir & Rd (ARL) 74
Orvis Rd (REV) 51
Osborn Pl 16
Osborne (CAM) 39
Osborne Path (NCE) 59
Osborne Rd (ARL) 74
Osborne Rd (BRO) 46
Osborne Rd (MED) 55
Osborne Rd (MIL) 86
Oscar (RXC) 20
Osceola (MAT) 26
Osceola Path (ARL) 74
Osgood (MED) 55
Osgood (SOM) 43
Osgood Ct (ROX) 19
Ossen (REV) 51
Ossipee Rd (WS) 44
Ossipee Rd (NUF) 64
Oswald (RXC) 20
Oswego (QUI) 69
Otis (WAT) 72
Otis
    1 10
Otis (SOM) 45
Otis (CAM) 41
Otis (WIN) 52
Otis (MED) 55
Otis (MAL) 48
Otis (EV) 49
Otis (MIL) 86
Otis (SWY) 90

Otis (N) 92
Otis
    1-179 (NWV) 60
    180-OUT (WNW) 65
Otis Park & Pl (NWV) 60
Otis Pl (ROS) 31
Otis Pl 08
Otis St & Park (MEL) 76
Otisfield (DOR) 21
Ottawa (ROX) 19
Ottawa Rd (ARL) 74
Outlook Dr (LEX) 73
Outlook Rd (MAT) 26
Outlook Rd (WAL) 54
Oval Rd (WOL) 70
Overbrook Dr (WH) 81
Overland 02215
Overland Rd (WAL) 54
Overlea Ave (CHE) 50
Overlook (EB) 28
Overlook Ave (REV) 51
Overlook Dr & Rd (WES) 93
Overlook Park (MAL) 48
Overlook Park (NCE) 59
Overlook Rd (QUI) 69
Overlook Rd (ARL) 74
Overlook Rd (MEL) 76
Overlook Rd (WAL) 54
Overlook Rd (WRX) 32
Overlook Rd (EWY) 89
Overlook Rd (N) 92
Owaisa Rd (WAB) 68
Owatonna (AUB) 66
Owego Park (MEL) 76
Owen (MAT) 26
Owencroft Rd (DOR) 24
Owens Pl (QUI) 69
Oxbow Rd (LEX) 73
Oxbow Rd (N) 92
Oxbow Rd
    1-40 (WH) 81
    41-OUT (WES) 93
Oxenbridge Rd (WOL) 70
Oxford (LEX) 73
Oxford (MEL) 76
Oxford (ARL) 74
Oxford (MAL) 48
Oxford (SOM) 43
Oxford
    1-110 (CAM) 38
    111-145 (CAM) 40
    146-146 (SOM) 43
    147-147 (CAM) 40
    148-148 (SOM) 43
    149-OUT (CAM) 40
Oxford Ave
    1-69 (BEL) (ODD) 78
    2-72 (BEL) (EVEN) 78
    71-OUT (CAM) (ODD) 38
    74-OUT (CAM) (EVEN) 38
Oxford Cir (BEL) 78
Oxford Rd (NCE) 59
Oxford Rd (WH) 81
Oxford St & Park (REV) 51
Oxford St & Pl 11
Oxford Ter 16
P (SB) 27
Pacific (SB) 27
Pacific (CAM) 39
Packard Ave (DOR) 24
Packard Ave
    1-107 (WS) 44
    108-OUT (MED) 55

Boston (Con.) 021

Packard Dr (BRA)	84
Packard Ln (QUI)	69
Paddock Ln (LEX)	73
Padula Rd (WY)	88
Page (DOR)	21
Page (REV)	51
Page (MAL)	48
Page Rd (WES)	93
Page Rd (N)	92
Page Rd (LEX)	73
Page Rd (NWV)	60
Pages Ct (SB)	27
Pagoda St & Cir (MIL)	87
Pagum (MAL)	48
Paige Ave (SB)	27
Paine (WIN)	52
Paine (ROS)	31
Paine (WH)	81
Paisley Park (DOR)	24
Palace Rd	15
Palermo (EB)	28
Palermo (CAM)	41
Palfrey (ROS)	31
Palfrey (WAT)	72
Palfrey Rd (BEL)	78
Palmer (WAT)	72
Palmer (QUI)	69
Palmer (ARL)	74
Palmer (CAM)	38
Palmer (WAL)	54
Palmer (MED)	55
Palmer (ROX)	19
Palmer (SWY)	90
Palmer Ave (SOM)	45
Palmer Rd (WAB)	68
Palmer St & Ct (CHE)	50
Palmyra (WIN)	52
Pama Gdns (BRI)	35
Pamela Ct (AUB)	66
Pamela Dr (ARL)	74
Pantano (BRA)	84
Panteline Ter (WAT)	72
Paomet Rd (NWY)	91
Paradise Rd (MIL)	86
Paragon Rd (WRX)	32
Parallel (ARL)	74
Paris (MED)	55
Paris (EWY)	89
Paris St & Ct (EV)	49
Paris St, Ct & Pl (EB)	28
Parish (DOR)	22
Parish Rd (NH)	94
Park (MIL)	86
Park (CHA)	29
Park	08
Park (CHE)	50
Park (HP)	36
Park (BRO)	46
Park (BRA)	84
Park (STO)	80
Park (WOL)	70
Park (MEL)	76
Park	
1-199 (DOR)	22
200-OUT (DOR)	24
Park Ave (NH)	94
Park Ave (BRA)	85
Park Ave (SWY)	90
Park Ave (NQ)	71
Park Ave (CAM)	38
Park Ave (REV)	51

Park Ave (WS)	44
Park Ave W (SWY)	90
Park Ave Ext (ARL)	74
Park Ave, Cir, Dr, Pl & Ter (ARL)	74
Park Ave & Dr (WIN)	52
Park Ave & Pl (WH)	81
Park Ave & Rd (BEL)	78
Park Dr (NWH)	61
Park Dr	02215
Park Ln (NCE)	59
Park Ln, Pl & Rd (JP)	30
Park Pl (NWV)	60
Park Rd (WES)	93
Park Rd & Ter (EV)	49
Park Sq	16
Park St Ct (MED)	55
Park St Pl (ARL)	74
Park St & Ave (MED)	55
Park St & Ave (NEW)	58
Park St & Ave (MAL)	48
Park St & Dr (LEX)	73
Park St & Pl (SOM)	43
Park St & Pl (WAL)	54
Park St & Ter (WRX)	32
Park Ter Dr (MEL)	76
Park Front Rd (ROS)	31
Park Vale (BRO)	46
Park Vale Ave (ALL)	34
Park View (DOR)	21
Park View Rd (EV)	49
Park View Ter (MAL)	48
Parkdale (SOM)	43
Parker (MAL)	48
Parker (EV)	49
Parker (CHE)	50
Parker (CAM)	38
Parker (HP)	36
Parker (CHA)	29
Parker (MEL)	76
Parker (LEX)	73
Parker (WAT)	72
Parker (QUI)	69
Parker	
1-510	15
511-889 (RXC)	20
890-OUT (JP)	30
Parker Ave	
1-80 (NCE)	59
81-OUT (NWH)	61
Parker Rd (NH)	94
Parker Rd (NWY)	91
Parker Rd (WH)	81
Parker St & Pl (SOM)	43
Parker St & Rd (ARL)	74
Parker St, Rd & Ter (NCE)	59
Parker Chase Ln & Rd (STO)	80
Parker Hill Ave & Ter (RXC)	20
Parkers Ln (WAL)	54
Parkhurst (QUI)	69
Parking Way (QUI)	69
Parkinson (N)	92
Parkland (BRI)	35
Parkland Rd (NH)	94
Parklawn Rd (WRX)	32
Parkman (BRO)	46
Parkman (WOL)	70
Parkman	14
Parkman St & Pl (DOR)	22
Parkside Ave & Cir (BRA)	84
Parkson (HP)	36
Parkton Rd (JP)	30
Parkvale Rd (N)	92

Parkview Ave (NWV)	60
Parkview Rd (WAL)	54
Parkway (DOR)	24
Parkway Cres (MIL)	87
Parkway Ct (CHE)	50
Parkway Rd (BRO)	46
Parkway Rd (MED)	55
Parkway Rd (NWV)	60
Parkway Rd (STO)	80
Parkway Ter (CAM)	38
Parkwood Ter (JP)	30
Parkwook Dr (MIL)	86
Parley Ave (JP)	30
Parley Vale (JP)	30
Parlin (EV)	49
Parmelee	18
Parmelee	13
Parmenter Pl (QUI)	69
Parmenter Rd (WAL)	54
Parmenter Rd & Ter (WNW)	65
Parnell (NWY)	91
Parrott (HP)	36
Parsonage Rd (MAL)	48
Parsons (BRI)	35
Parsons (WNW)	65
Parsons (QUI)	69
Parsons Ave (WAL)	54
Parsons Ave (SWY)	90
Partridge (WRX)	32
Partridge (WAT)	72
Partridge Ave (SOM)	45
Partridge Cir (WAL)	54
Partridge Ln (WAV)	79
Partridge Pl (ROX)	19
Partridge Rd (WH)	81
Partridge Rd (LEX)	73
Partridge Rd (SWY)	90
Partridge Ter (EV)	49
Partridge Hill Rd (WES)	93
Partridge Hill Rd (BRA)	84
Pasadena Rd (DOR)	21
Pasteur (SWY)	90
Patricia Dr (BRA)	84
Patricia Dr & Ln (MIL)	86
Patricia Ln (SWY)	90
Patrick (ARL)	74
Patrick Rd (QUI)	69
Patriot Pky (REV)	51
Patriots Dr (LEX)	73
Patten (WOL)	70
Patten (WAT)	72
Patten (JP)	30
Patten Ave (BRA)	84
Patterson (DOR)	24
Patterson (EWY)	89
Patterson Rd (LEX)	73
Patterson Way (SB)	27
Patton Cir (NCE)	59
Patton Rd (WEL)	81
Paul (NCE)	59
Paul (WAT)	72
Paul (BRA)	85
Paul Rd (MED)	55
Paul St & Pl	18
Paul Gore St & Ter (JP)	30
Paul Revere Rd (NH)	94
Paul Revere Rd (LEX)	73
Paul Revere Rd (ARL)	74
Paula Ave (STO)	80
Paula Rd (MAT)	26
Paulding (ROX)	19
Paulina (WS)	44
Pauline (WIN)	52

Boston (Con.) 021

Paulman Cir (WRX)	32
Paulson Rd (WAB)	68
Pawnee Cir (MIL)	86
Pawnee Dr (ARL)	74
Pawsey (QUI)	69
Paxton (DOR)	24
Payne (DOR)	22
Payne (QUI)	69
Payne Ave (SWY)	90
Payne Rd (NWH)	61
Payne Ter (MAL)	48
Payson (WIN)	52
Payson (REV)	51
Payson (QUI)	69
Payson (LEX)	73
Payson Ave (DOR)	25
Payson Pl (CHA)	29
Payson Rd (CHH)	67
Payson Rd & Ter (BEL)	78
Peabody (NEW)	58
Peabody	02215
Peabody Rd (ARL)	74
Peabody Rd (STO)	80
Peabody Sq (DOR)	24
Peabody Ter (CAM)	38
Peacedale Cir & Rd (N)	92
Peacevale Rd (DOR)	24
Peach (BRA)	85
Peach Tree Ln (NCE)	59
Peach Tree Rd (LEX)	73
Peacock Ln (WRX)	32
Peacock Farm Rd (LEX)	73
Peak (BRA)	84
Peak Hill Rd (ROS)	31
Pear Tree Dr (LEX)	73
Pearl (LEX)	73
Pearl (STO)	80
Pearl (WAV)	79
Pearl (MEL)	76
Pearl (QUI)	69
Pearl (WAT)	72
Pearl (CAM)	39
Pearl (MED)	55
Pearl (MAL)	48
Pearl (BRO)	46
Pearl (EV)	49
Pearl (CHE)	50
Pearl (WAL)	54
Pearl (NWY)	91
Pearl (DOR)	25
Pearl (CHA)	29
Pearl	10
Pearl Ave (REV)	51
Pearl Ave (WIN)	52
Pearl St Pl (CAM)	39
Pearl St Pl (SOM)	45
Pearl St Pl (CHA)	29
Pearl St & Ct (NEW)	58
Pearl St & Pl (BRA)	85
Pearl St & Ter (SOM)	45
Pearson Ave & Rd (WS)	44
Pearson Rd (BEL)	78
Pearson Ter (MAL)	48
Pebble Ave (WIN)	52
Pebble Rd (MEL)	76
Peck Ave (WH)	81
Peck Ave (ARL)	74
Pecksuat Rd (NWY)	91
Peddock Rd (NWY)	91
Peirce (ARL)	74

Pelham (NCE)	59
Pelham (MAL)	48
Pelham (CAM)	42
Pelham Rd (WAL)	54
Pelham Rd (LEX)	73
Pelham Rd (WES)	93
Pelham St & Ter	18
Pelham Ter (ARL)	74
Pelican Rd (QUI)	69
Pelton (WRX)	32
Pemberton (REV)	51
Pemberton Sq	08
Pemberton St & Ter (CAM)	40
Pembroke (MED)	55
Pembroke (NEW)	58
Pembroke (CHE)	50
Pembroke (QUI)	69
Pembroke Rd (WEL)	81
Pembroke Rd (WES)	93
Pembroke St & Ct (SOM)	45
Pembroke St & Ct	18
Pender (WRX)	32
Penfield (ROS)	31
Penhallow (DOR)	24
Penn (REV)	51
Penn (QUI)	69
Penney Rd (MEL)	76
Penney Hill Rd (MEL)	76
Penniman Rd (ALL)	34
Penniman Rd (BRO)	46
Penniman Ter (BRA)	84
Penns Hill Rd (QUI)	69
Pennsylvania Ave (NUF)	64
Pennsylvania Ave (SOM)	45
Pennsylvania Ave (N)	92
Penny Ln (STO)	80
Penryth (ROX)	19
Pepper Rd (SWY)	90
Pepper Mill Ln (MIL)	86
Pequossette (WAT)	72
Pequossette Rd (BEL)	78
Pequot (RXC)	20
Pequot Rd (QUI)	69
Pequot Rd (NWY)	91
Pera (REV)	51
Perabo Ter (WRX)	32
Perch (ROX)	19
Percival (DOR)	22
Percival Pl (EB)	28
Percy Pl (CAM)	39
Percy Rd (LEX)	73
Peregrin Rd (BRA)	84
Peregrine Rd (NCE)	59
Perham (WRX)	32
Perham Ave (MEL)	76
Perkins (MEL)	76
Perkins (WNW)	65
Perkins (QUI)	69
Perkins (ARL)	74
Perkins (WIN)	52
Perkins (CHA)	29
Perkins Ave (HP)	36
Perkins Ave (MAL)	48
Perkins Rd (CHE)	50
Perkins Rd (EWY)	89
Perkins St & Pl (SOM)	45
Perkins St & Sq (JP)	30
Perley Pl (QUI)	69
Permil Rd (NH)	94
Perrin (ROX)	19
Perrin Rd (BRO)	46
Perry (BRO)	46
Perry (SOM)	43

Perry (CAM)	39
Perry (N)	18
Perry (EWY)	89
Perry (WAT)	72
Perry Dr (N)	92
Perry Ln (WES)	93
Perry Pl (CHA)	29
Perry Pl (EV)	49
Perry Rd (WOL)	70
Perry Rd (BRA)	84
Perry Rd (AUB)	66
Pershing Pl (STO)	80
Pershing Rd (WNW)	65
Pershing Rd (JP)	30
Pershing Rd (NH)	94
Perth (DOR)	21
Perth Rd (ARL)	74
Perthshire Rd (BRI)	35
Peter Rd (NWY)	91
Peter Parley Rd (JP)	30
Peter Tufts Rd (ARL)	74
Peterborough	02215
Peters (SB)	27
Peters (CAM)	39
Peters (ROS)	31
Peters Dr (STO)	80
Peterson Rd (QUI)	69
Peterson Rd (BRA)	85
Peterson Ter (SOM)	43
Petrel Park (WY)	88
Petrel Rd (QUI)	69
Petrini Cir (N)	92
Pettee (NUF)	64
Pevear Pl (ROX)	19
Peverell (DOR)	25
Pheasant (WRX)	32
Pheasant Ave (ARL)	74
Pheasant Rd (NWV)	60
Pheasant Rd (WAL)	54
Pheasant Rd (N)	92
Pheasant Trl (WES)	93
Philbrick (ROS)	31
Philbrick Rd (BRO)	46
Philbrick Rd (NCE)	59
Philemon (ARL)	74
Philip (DOR)	22
Philip Rd (BEL)	78
Philip Rd (LEX)	73
Philips (ARL)	74
Philips Rd (MEL)	76
Phillips (WOL)	70
Phillips (AUB)	66
Phillips (WAT)	72
Phillips	14
Phillips (BRA)	85
Phillips (WY)	88
Phillips Ave (REV)	51
Phillips Cir (WAL)	54
Phillips Cir (MEL)	76
Phillips Ln (NWV)	60
Phillips Pl (SOM)	43
Phillips Pl (CAM)	38
Phillips St & Ct (MAL)	48
Philmore Rd (NEW)	58
Philpot Ter (MEL)	76
Phinney Rd (LEX)	73
Phipps (QUI)	69
Phipps (CHA)	29
Phyllis Ave (BRA)	85
Phyllis Ln (MIL)	86
Pickerel Rd & Ter (WH)	81
Pickering Ave (ROX)	19
Pickering St & Pl (N)	92

Boston (Con.)	021
Pickwick Rd (WNW)	65
Pico Ave (WIN)	52
Pie Aly	08
Piedmont	16
Piedmont (ARL)	74
Piedmont Ave (WAL)	54
Piedmont Rd (MED)	55
Pier View Ave (REV)	51
Pierce (REV)	51
Pierce (WAL)	54
Pierce (MAL)	48
Pierce (BRO)	46
Pierce (HP)	36
Pierce (NQ)	71
Pierce (MIL)	86
Pierce Ave (EV)	49
Pierce Ave (DOR)	22
Pierce Ct (NWY)	91
Pierce Rd (WY)	88
Pierce Rd (WH)	81
Pierce Rd (BEL)	78
Pierce Rd (WAT)	72
Pierce Sq (DOR)	24
Piermont (WAT)	72
Piermont (WOL)	70
Pierpont Rd (WRX)	32
Pierrepont Rd (NLF)	62
Piety Cor Rd (WAL)	54
Pigeon Ln (WAL)	54
Pigeon Hill Rd (WES)	93
Piggott Rd (MED)	55
Pilgrim (CAM)	39
Pilgrim Cir (WEL)	81
Pilgrim Pl (DOR)	25
Pilgrim Rd (BRA)	84
Pilgrim Rd (STO)	80
Pilgrim Rd (WH)	81
Pilgrim Rd (WAT)	72
Pilgrim Rd (BEL)	78
Pilgrim Rd (MEL)	76
Pilgrim Rd (ARL)	74
Pilgrim Rd (WAB)	68
Pilgrim Rd (MED)	55
Pilgrim Rd (WAL)	54
Pilgrim Rd	02215
Pilgrim Rd (NWY)	91
Pilgrim Rd (N)	92
Pilgrim Rd	
1-37 (MIL) (ODD)	86
2-22 (MIL) (EVEN)	86
24-OUT (QUI) (EVEN)	69
39-OUT (QUI) (ODD)	69
Pillion Ct (NWV)	60
Pillon Rd (MIL)	86
Pilsudski Way (SB)	27
Pinckney	14
Pinckney St & Pl (SOM)	45
Pine (WAL)	54
Pine (CAM)	39
Pine (CHE)	50
Pine (MAL)	48
Pine	11
Pine (BRA)	85
Pine (WES)	93
Pine (N)	92
Pine (BEL)	78
Pine (MEL)	76
Pine (WAT)	72
Pine (WH)	81
Pine (STO)	80
Pine (WOL)	70
Pine	
1-84 (WNW)	65
85-OUT (AUB)	66
Pine Ave (MIL)	86
Pine Rd (CHH)	67
Pine St, Ave & Ct (ARL)	74
Pine St, Ave & Ter (HP)	36
Pine St & Cir (SWY)	90
Pine Banks Rd (MAL)	48
Pine Banks Garden (MEL)	76
Pine Cliff Rd (EWY)	89
Pine Crest Rd (BRA)	84
Pine Crest Rd (NCE)	59
Pine Croft Rd (WES)	93
Pine Grove (NH)	94
Pine Grove (MIL)	86
Pine Grove Ave (NLF)	62
Pine Grove Path (EWY)	89
Pine Hill Cir (WAL)	54
Pine Knoll Rd (LEX)	73
Pine Lodge Rd (WRX)	32
Pine Plain Rd (WH)	81
Pine Ridge Rd (WH)	81
Pine Ridge Rd (STO)	80
Pine Ridge Rd (ARL)	74
Pine Ridge Rd (WAB)	68
Pine Ridge Rd (MED)	55
Pine Ridge Rd (EWY)	89
Pine Ridge Rd (MAT)	26
Pine Tree Ave (MAL)	48
Pine Tree Rd (WEL)	81
Pine Vale Rd (WAL)	54
Pinecliff Rd (WRX)	32
Pinecrest (QUI)	69
Pinedale Rd (ROS)	31
Pinefield Ave, Rd & Ter (HP)	36
Pinehurst (ROS)	31
Pinehurst Rd (BEL)	78
Pines Rd (REV)	51
Pinevale Rd (WH)	81
Pinewood (LEX)	73
Pinewood (MAT)	26
Pinewood Rd (MEL)	76
Pinewood Rd (N)	92
Ping On	11
Pingree (HP)	36
Pinkert (MED)	55
Pinkham Rd (MED)	55
Pioneer Rd (ARL)	74
Piper (QUI)	69
Piper Rd (ARL)	74
Pitcairn (REV)	51
Pitcher Ave (MED)	55
Pitman (SOM)	43
Pitsmoor Rd (ROS)	81
Pitts Ave (WOL)	70
Pittsburgh	02210
Placid Rd (NCE)	59
Plain (QUI)	69
Plain (DOR)	22
Plain	
1-128 (BRA)	85
129-OUT (BRA)	84
Plain Rd (WES)	93
Plain Ter (SWY)	90
Plainfield (JP)	30
Plainfield (LEX)	73
Plainfield (WAB)	68
Plainfield Ave (MAL)	48
Plant Ct (JP)	30
Plant Rd (WAL)	54
Platt Rd (BRI)	35
Playstead Rd (MAL)	48
Pleasant (WEL)	81
Pleasant (BRA)	84
Pleasant (LEX)	73
Pleasant (QUI)	69
Pleasant (WNW)	65
Pleasant (NCE)	59
Pleasant (MEL)	76
Pleasant (WAT)	72
Pleasant (DOR)	25
Pleasant (CHA)	29
Pleasant (MED)	55
Pleasant (BRO)	46
Pleasant (MAL)	48
Pleasant (HP)	36
Pleasant (REV)	51
Pleasant (EV)	49
Pleasant (N)	92
Pleasant (MIL)	86
Pleasant	
1-273 (ARL) (ODD)	74
1-599 (SWY)	90
2-278 (ARL) (EVEN)	74
275-727 (BEL) (ODD)	78
280-728 (BEL) (EVEN)	78
600-OUT (EWY)	89
729-OUT (WAV)	79
Pleasant Ave (SOM)	43
Pleasant Park Rd (WIN)	52
Pleasant St Ct (MED)	55
Pleasant St Ct (CHA)	29
Pleasant St Park (MAL)	48
Pleasant St & Ave (WAL)	54
Pleasant St & Ct (WIN)	52
Pleasant St & Pl (CAM)	39
Pleasant St & Ter (STO)	80
Pleasant Hill Ave (MAT)	26
Pleasant Valley Cir (WRX)	32
Pleasant View Ave (EV)	49
Pleasant View Ave (BRA)	84
Pleasant View Ave (WY)	88
Pleasant View Rd (WH)	81
Pleasant View Rd (ARL)	74
Pleasantdale Rd (WRX)	32
Pleasanton (DOR)	21
Pleasantview (ROS)	31
Plover (WRX)	32
Plover Rd (QUI)	69
Plowgate Rd (CHH)	67
Plumer (EV)	49
Plummer Ave (WIN)	52
Plummer Wharf (EB)	28
Plymouth (EV)	49
Plymouth (CAM)	41
Plymouth (QUI)	69
Plymouth (ARL)	74
Plymouth	02215
Plymouth Ave (BEL)	78
Plymouth Ave	
1-120 (MIL)	86
121-OUT (QUI)	69-
Plymouth Ave & Dr (BRA)	85
Plymouth Cir (MEL)	76
Plymouth Dr (WAL)	54
Plymouth Rd (MAL)	48
Plymouth Rd (WH)	81
Plymouth Rd (NWH)	61
Plymouth Rd (LEX)	73
Plymouth Rd (WES)	93
Plymouth Rd (N)	92
Plympton (CAM)	38
Plympton	18
Plympton St Ext (WAL)	54
Plympton St, Ave & Cir	

Boston (Con.)   021

(WAL) 54
Plymton Rd (WNW) 65
Poinsetta Ave (WY) 88
Polk (CHA) 29
Pollywog Ln (WES) 93
Pomeroy (ALL) 34
Pomeworth (STO) 80
Pomfret (WRX) 32
Pomona (REV) 51
Pomona Ave (WRX) 32
Pompeii (ROX) 19
Pond (DOR) 25
Pond (WIN) 52
Pond (WAL) 54
Pond (HP) 36
Pond (STO) 80
Pond (BEL) 78
Pond (MED) 76
Pond (QUI) 69
Pond (WAT) 72
Pond (MIL) 86
Pond (BRA) 85
Pond (N) 92
Pond (SWY) 90
Pond Ave (BRO) 46
Pond Ave (NEW) 58
Pond Cir (MED) 55
Pond Ln & Ter (ARL) 74
Pond Pl (CAM) 39
Pond Rd (WH) 81
Pond St Ct (WAL) 54
Pond St Pl 13
Pond St & Cir (JP) 30
Pond Brook Cir (WES) 93
Pond Brook Rd (CHH) 67
Pond End Ln & Rd (WAL) 54
Pond View Ave (JP) 30
Ponderosa Dr (SWY) 90
Pondred (ROS) 31
Pondside Rd (WEL) 81
Pondview Rd (ARL) 74
Pontiac (RXC) 20
Pontiac Rd (WAB) 68
Pontiac Rd (QUI) 69
Poole (MED) 55
Pope (NQ) 71
Pope Hill Rd (MIL) 86
Popes Hill (DOR) 22
Poplar (BRA) 84
Poplar (STO) 80
Poplar (WAT) 72
Poplar (MEL) 76
Poplar (BEL) 78
Poplar (LEX) 73
Poplar (ROS) 31
Poplar (MAL) 48
Poplar (CHE) 50
Poplar Ave (QUI) 69
Poplar Rd (WH) 81
Poplar Rd (CAM) 38
Poplar St & Ct (SOM) 43
Port Norfolk (DOR) 22
Porter (JP) .... -30
Porter (EB) 28
Porter (CAM) 41
Porter (EV) 49
Porter (MEL) 76
Porter (WAT) 72
Porter Ave (REV) 51
Porter Ave (BRA) 85
Porter Cir, Park, Rd & Sq

(CAM) 40
Porter Rd (MED) 55
Porter Rd (WAL) 54
Porter St & Ave (SOM) 43
Porter St & Ave (MAL) 48
Porter Ter (WRX) 32
Portino Rd (BRI) 35*
Portland 14
Portland
  1-177 (CAM) (ODD) 39
  2-170 (CAM) (EVEN) 39
  172-OUT (CAM) (EVEN) 41
  179-OUT (CAM) (ODD) 41
Portland Rd (BRA) 85
Portsmouth (BRI) 35
Portsmouth (CAM) 41
Possum Rd (WES) 93
Post Island Rd (QUI) 69
Post Office Sq 09
Potomac (WRX) 32
Potosi (DOR) 22
Potter (CAM) 42
Potter (MEL) 76
Potter Park (CAM) 38
Potter Rd (WAL) 54
Poulos Rd (BRA) 85
Powder House Blvd, Sq & Ter

(WS) 44
Powder House Rd (N) 92
Powder House Rd Ext (MED) 55
Powder House Rd & Ter

(MED) 55
Powell (WRX) 32
Powell (BRO) 46
Powellton Rd (DOR) 21
Power House (SB) 27
Powers (N) 92
Powers Ct 09
Poydras (MAT) 26
Prairie (MAT) 26
Prairie Ave (AUB) 66
Pratt (MEL) 76
Pratt (MAL) 48
Pratt (ALL) 34
Pratt (WIN) 52
Pratt Ave (WAL) 54
Pratt Ave (NWY) 91
Pratt Ct (RXC) 20
Pratt Dr (WNW) 65
Pratt Rd (NQ) 71
Pratt St, Ct & Pl (REV) 51
Pray (QUI) 69
Preble (SB) 27
Preble Gardens Rd (BEL) 78
Prendergast Ave (BRO) 46
Prentice (WAL) 54
Prentice Rd (NCE) 59
Prentiss (WAT) 72
Prentiss (MAL) 48
Prentiss
  1-90 (CAM) 40
  91-OUT (SOM) 43
Prentiss Ln (BEL) 78
Prentiss Rd (ARL) 74
Prentiss St & Pl (RXC) 20
Presby Pl (ROX) 19
Prescott (ROX) 19
Prescott (CHA) 29
Prescott (EB) 28
Prescott (ARL) 74
Prescott (MEL) 76
Prescott (WAT) 72
Prescott (NWV) 60

Prescott (WH) 81
Prescott (SWY) 90
Prescott (MAL) 48
Prescott (BRO) 46
Prescott (WIN) 52
Prescott (MED) 55
Prescott (SOM) 43
Prescott (CAM) 38
Prescott (HP) 36
Prescott Ave (CHE) 50
Prescott Ln (BRA) 84
Prescott Ln & Ter (QUI) 69
Prescott Pl (ALL) 34
Prescott St, Rd & Ter (EV) 49
Presentation Rd (BRI) 35
President Rd (ROS) 31
President Ter (ALL) 34
President Gardens Dr (QUI) 69
Presidents Ave & Ln (QUI) 69
Presidents Rd (BRA) 84
Presidents Rd (WY) 88
Presley (MAL) 48
Presley Rd (DOR) 22
Preston (MAL) 48
Preston (EV) 49
Preston Rd (WRX) 32
Preston Rd (SOM) 43
Preston Rd (LEX) 73
Price (NQ) 71
Price (ALL) 34
Prichard Ave (WS) 44
Priesing (JP) 30
Priest Rd (WAT) 72
Primrose (ROS) 31
Primrose Ave (BRA) 84
Primrose Ln (EWY) 89
Primus Ave 14
Prince (JP) 30
Prince (EWY) 89
Prince (N) 92
Prince (MIL) 86
Prince (WNW) 65
Prince (WAV) 79
Prince (BRO) 46
Prince (CAM) 39
Prince (REV) 51
Prince
  1-164 13
  165-165 09
  166-OUT 13
Princess Rd (WNW) 65
Princess Eve Dr (WOL) 70
Princeton (WS) 44
Princeton (NEW) 58
Princeton (MED) 55
Princeton Ave (WAL) 54
Princeton Ave (NWY) 91
Princeton Rd (MAL) 48
Princeton Rd (BEL) 78
Princeton Rd (WH) 81
Princeton Rd (ARL) 74
Princeton Rd (CHH) 67
Princeton St & Pl (EB) 28
Priscilla Cir (WY) 88
Priscilla Cir & Rd (WH) 81
Priscilla Ln (QUI) 69
Priscilla Ln (MIL) 86
Priscilla Ln (WAL) 54
Priscilla Ln (MED) 55
Priscilla Rd (BRI) 35
Priscilla Rd (CHH) 67
Proctor (NWV) 60
Proctor (ROX) 19

Boston (Con.)   021

Proctor Ave (REV).................. 51
Proctor Rd (EV)..................... 49
Proctor Rd (BRA)................... 85
Professors Row (MED)............. 55
Progress (WY)........................ 88
Proprietors Way (ARL)............ 74
Prospect (NQ)........................ 71
Prospect (WH)....................... 81
Prospect (BRA)...................... 84
Prospect (BEL)....................... 78
Prospect (STO)...................... 80
Prospect (MEL)...................... 76
Prospect (WAT)..................... 72
Prospect (N).......................... 92
Prospect (EV)........................ 49
Prospect (CAM)..................... 39
Prospect (WAL)..................... 55
Prospect (BRO)...................... 46
Prospect N (BRA)................... 84
Prospect Ave (WOL)............... 70
Prospect Ave (ARL)................ 74
Prospect Ave (REV)................ 51
Prospect Ave (WIN)............... 52
Prospect Ave (ROS)............... 31
Prospect Ave, Park & Ter
   (NWV)............................. 65
Prospect Pl (WNW) 65
Prospect St Ave (WAL) 54
Prospect St & Ave (CHE)........ 50
Prospect St & Ave (CHA)........ 29
Prospect St & Ct (WY)........... 88
Prospect St & Park (HP).......... 36
Prospect St & Pl (SOM).......... 43
Prospect St & Ter (MAL)......... 48
Prospect Hill (QUI)................. 69
Prospect Hill Ave (SOM)......... 43
Prospect Hill Ave, Ln, Park &
   Rd (WAL)......................... 54
Prospect Hill Dr (NWY)........... 91
Prospect Hill Rd (LEX)............ 73
Prosper (MAL)....................... 48
Prout (QUI)........................... 69
Providence (HP)..................... 36
Providence............................ 16
Province St & Ct.................... 08
Prudential Center................... 99
Puddingstone Ln (NCE)........... 59
Puddingstone Rd (CHH)........... 67
Pulaski Ave (SB).................... 27
Pulsifer (NWV)...................... 60
Purcell Rd (ARL).................... 74
Purchase............................... 10
Puritan Ave (DOR)................. 21
Puritan Dr (QUI).................... 69
Puritan Rd (ARL)................... 74
Puritan Rd (WAT).................. 72
Puritan Rd (EWY).................. 89
Puritan Rd (SOM).................. 45
Puritan Rd
   1-60 (NWH)...................... 61
   61-OUT (WAB)................... 68
Purvis (WAT)........................ 72
Putnam (WAT)...................... 72
Putnam (QUI)........................ 69
Putnam (WNW)..................... 65
Putnam (NH)......................... 94
Putnam (EWY)...................... 89
Putnam (SOM)...................... 43
Putnam (WAL)...................... 54
Putnam (WIN)....................... 52

Putnam (EB)......................... 28
Putnam (CHA)....................... 29
Putnam Ave (BRA) 84
Putnam Ave, Ct & Gdns
   (CAM)............................. 39
Putnam Rd (SOM)................. 45
Putnam Rd (ARL).................. 74
Putnam St & Pl (ROX)........... 19
Putnam St & Rd (REV)........... 51
Putney Ln (WAL)................... 54
Putney Rd (WH).................... 81
Quadrant Cir (QUI)................ 69
Quail (WRX)......................... 32
Quaker Ln............................ 09
Quarley Rd (ROS)................. 31
Quarry (QUI)......................... 69
Quarry Ave (EWY)................ 89
Quarry Ln (MIL).................... 86
Quarter Deck Rd (QUI).......... 22
Queen (MED)........................ 55
Queensberry.........................02215
Queenwood Ter (MAL)........... 48
Quentin (MIL)....................... 86
Quidnic Rd (WAB)................. 68
Quimby (WAT)...................... 72
Quincefield (DOR)................. 25
Quincy (WAT)....................... 72
Quincy (ARL)........................ 74
Quincy (MAL)....................... 48
Quincy (SOM)....................... 43
Quincy (MED)....................... 55
Quincy
   1-269 (DOR) (ODD)............ 21
   2-262 (DOR) (EVEN).......... 21
   264-OUT (DOR) (EVEN)...... 25
   271-OUT (DOR) (ODD)....... 25
Quincy Ave (WIN)................. 52
Quincy Ave (BRA)................. 84
Quincy Ct............................. 13
Quincy Pl & Ter (DOR).......... 21
Quincy St (CHH)................... 67
Quincy Row.......................... 09
Quincy St, Ave, Sq & Ter
   (QUI).............................. 69
Quincy St & Sq (CAM).......... 38
Quincy Mkt........................... 09
Quincy Shore Dr
   1-593 (NQ)....................... 71
   594-1300 (WOL)................ 70
   1301-OUT (QUI)................ 69
Quinn Rd (ARL)..................... 74
Quinn Way (WRX)................. 32
Quinobequin Rd
   1-120 (NLF)...................... 62
   121-OUT (WAB)................. 58
Quint Ave (ALL).................... 58
Quirk (WAT)......................... 72
Quirk Ct (NEW).................... 58
Rachel Rd (NCE)................... 59
Racine Ct (RXC)................... 20
Radcliff (MED)...................... 55
Radcliffe (DOR).................... 21
Radcliffe Rd (MAT)............... 26
Radcliffe Rd (ALL)................ 34
Radcliffe Rd (SOM)............... 45
Radcliffe Rd (ARL)................ 74
Radcliffe Rd (WAB)............... 68
Radcliffe Rd (WEL)............... 81
Radcliffe Rd (BEL)................ 78
Radcliffe Rd (MEL)................ 76
Radcliffe Rd (WES)............... 93
Radford Ln (DOR)................. 24
Radford Pl (HP).................... 36

Radnor Rd (BRI)................... 35
Rae Ave (N).......................... 92
Raeburn Ter (NWH)............... 61
Rafferty Rd (STO)................. 80
Railroad (BRI)....................... 84
Railroad (LEX)...................... 73
Railroad Ave (ARL)............... 74
Railroad Ave (REV)............... 51
Railroad Ave (MAL)............... 48
Rainbow Ln (SWY)................ 90
Rainier Rd (MAT).................. 26
Raldne Rd (HP)..................... 36
Raleigh (SWY)...................... 90
Raleigh...............................02215
Raleigh (ARL)....................... 74
Raleigh Rd (BEL).................. 78
Raleigh Rd (EWY)................. 89
Ralph (WAT)......................... 72
Ralph (MED)......................... 55
Ralph Talbot (SWY).............. 90
Ralston Rd (MAT)................. 26
Ralwood Rd (MAT)............... 26
Rambler Rd (JP).................... 30
Rambler Rd (SWY)................ 90
Ramp................................02210
Ramsdell (NWH)................... 61
Ramsdell Ave (ROS).............. 31
Ramsdell Ct (ARL)................ 74
Ramsdell Rd (MAL)............... 48
Ramsey (DOR)...................... 25
Ramshead Rd (MED).............. 55
Rand (MED).......................... 55
Rand (MAL).......................... 48
Rand (REV).......................... 51
Rand St & Pl (DOR).............. 25
Rand Ter (AUB).................... 66
Randall (ROX)...................... 19
Randall (WAL)...................... 54
Randall Ave (EWY)............... 89
Randall Ave (BRA)................ 85
Randall Rd (REV).................. 51
Randlett (WOL)..................... 70
Randlett Park (WNW)............ 65
Randlett Pl (DOR)................. 25
Rando Ln (WAL).................... 54
Randolph............................. 18
Randolph (NWH)................... 61
Randolph (ARL).................... 74
Randolph (BEL)..................... 78
Randolph (SWY)................... 90
Randolph Ave
   1-299 (MIL)....................... 87
   300-OUT (MIL).................. 86
Randolph Rd (STO)............... 80
Randolph Rd (CHH)............... 67
Ranelegh Rd (BRI)................ 35
Range Rd (DOR)................... 24
Rangeley (DOR).................... 24
Rangeley Rd (WAL)............... 54
Rangeley Rd (CHH)............... 67
Rangeley Rd (ARL)............... 74
Rangeley Rd (WNW)............. 65
Rangeley Rd (WAT).............. 72
Ranger Cir (SWY)................. 90
Rangeway (LEX)................... 73
Ranley Rd (MAT).................. 26
Ransom Rd (NCE)................. 59
Ransom Rd (BRI).................. 35
Rantoule (SWY).................... 90
Ratchford (QUI).................... 69
Raven (DOR)........................ 25
Ravena (REV)....................... 51
Ravenna Rd (ROS)................ 31

Boston (Cón.)　　　021

Ravenswood Rd (WAL) 54
Ravine (ARL) 74
Ravine Rd (WH) 81
Ravine Rd (MED) 55
Ravine Rd & Ter (MEL) 76
Rawson (DOR) 25
Rawson Ave (LEX) 73
Rawson Rd (ARL) 74
Rawson Rd (WOL) 70
Rawson Rd (BRO) 46
Rawston Rd (ROS) 31
Ray (ROX) 19
Ray Ln (BRA) 85
Rayburn Rd (WAV) 79
Raycroft (QUI) 69
Raycroft Ave (WY) 88
Raymond (EWY) 89
Raymond (QUI) 69
Raymond (LEX) 73
Raymond (ALL) 34
Raymond (MAL) 48
Raymond (MED) 55
Raymond (CAM) 40
Raymond (EV) 49
Raymond Ave (WS) 44
Raymond Pl (WNW) 65
Raymond Rd (STO) 80
Raymond St & Rd (REV) 51
Raynes Rd (HP) 36
Raynold Rd (HP) 36
Raynor Cir (STO) 80
Raynor Rd (WES) 93
Read (WIN) 52
Read Ave & Park (QUI) 69
Read Ct (NCE) 59
Reading (ROX) 19
Reading Hill Ave (MEL) 76
Readville (HP) 36
Realton Rd (WRX) 32
Reardon (QUI) 69
Reardon Rd (MED) 55
Record (SOM) 45
Rector Rd (MAT) 26
Red Coat Ln (LEX) 73
Red Devil Ln (WAT) 72
Red Jacket Rd (SWY) 90
Red Pine Rd (HP) 36
Red Wing Rd (WH) 81
Reddington Rd (N) 92
Reddy Ave (HP) 36
Redfield (DOR) 22
Redford (ALL) 34
Redgate Rd (WRX) 32
Redlands Rd (WRX) 32
Redstone Shopping Center
　(STO) 80
Redwood (DOR) 22
Redwood Rd (NCE) 59
Reed (LEX) 73
Reed (ARL) 74
Reed 18
Reed (MIL) 86
Reed Ave (SWY) 90
Reed Ave (EV) 49
Reed St Ter (CAM) 40
Reed St & Ct (CAM) 40
Reed Hill (BRA) 85
Reeds Ct (SOM) 45
Reedsdale (ALL) 34
Reedsdale Rd
　1-125 (MIL) 87

126-OUT (MIL) 86
Regal (BRI) 35
Regan Rd (DOR) 24
Regatta Rd (NWY) 91
Regent (CAM) 40
Regent (WNW) 65
Regent Cir (BRO) 46
Regent Cir (JP) 30
Regent Rd (MAL) 48
Regent Rd (WAV) 79
Regent St, Ct, Pl & Sq
　(ROX) 19
Regina Rd (DOR) 24
Regina. Rd (WEY) 88
Regina Rd & Ter (AUB) 73
Regis Rd (ARL) 74
Regis Rd (WEL) 81
Regis Rd (BRA) 85
Regis Rd (MAT) 26
Regis Rd (MED) 55
Reidy Rd (EWY) 89
Relda Rd (SWY) 90
Remick Ct (SOM) 45
Remick Ter (NEW) 58
Remington (CAM) 38
Remington (DOR) 24
Remington Ct (QUI) 69
Rena (ALL) 34
Rendall Pl (MEL) 76
Rendall Rd (WRX) 32
Renee Ter (NCE) 59
Renfrew (ARL) 74
Renfrew (MED) 55
Renfrew St & Ct (ROX) 19
Renwick Rd (MEL) 76
Reservation Rd (HP) 36
Reservation Rd (MIL) 86
Reserve (MAL) 48
Reservoir (CAM) 38
Reservoir Ave (REV) 51
Reservoir Ave, Dr, Ln & Rd
　(CHH) 67
Reservoir Ct (BRO) 46
Reservoir Rd (WAL) 54
Reservoir Rd (ARL) 74
Reservoir Rd (WOL) 70
Reservoir St, Ave & Ct (BRA) 84
Reservoir St, Ave, Ln & Park
　(NH) 94
Revere (MIL) 87
Revere (ARL) 74
Revere (LEX) 73
Revere (MAL) 48
Revere (REV) 51
Revere (WIN) 52
Revere (CAM) 38
Revere (EV) 49
Revere (JP) 30
Revere. 14
Revere Ave 09
Revere Pl (MED) 55
Revere Rd (QUI) 69
Revere Rd (EWY) 89
Revere Beach Blvd Ct (REV).... 51
Revere Beach Blvd & Pky
　(REV) 51
Revere Beach Pky (MED) 55
Revere Beach Pky (CHE) 50
Revere Beach Pky
　1629-2385 (EV) 49
Revere Beach Pky Ct (CHE).... 50
Reverend Nazareno Properzi
　Way (SOM) 43

Reverend Richard A Burke
　(SB) 27
Revolutionary Rd (LEX) 73
Rex Dr (BRA) 84
Rexford (MAT) 26
Rexhame (ROS) 31
Reyem (WAL) 54
Reynold Rd (HP) 36
Reynolds Ave (EV) 49
Reynolds Ave (CHE) 50
Rhinecliff (ARL) 74
Rhoades (DOR) 24
Rhoda (QUI) 69
Rhoda (WRX) 32
Rhode Island Ave (SOM) 45
Rhodes (LEX) 73
Rhude (QUI) 69
Rhuland Rd (STO) 80
Rice (WEL) 81
Rice (NCE) 59
Rice (BRO) 46
Rice (EB) 28
Rice (DOR) 22
Rice Ave (MED) 55
Rice Ave (REV) 51
Rice Rd (WOL) 70
Rice St & Cir (CAM) 40
Rich (WAL) 54
Rich (MAT) 26
Rich
　1-OUT (EV) (ODD) 49
　2-OUT (MAL) (EVEN) 48
Richard (REV) 51
Richard (MED) 55
Richrd (MAL) 48
Richard (QUI) 69
Richard Rd (LEX) 73
Richard Rd (N) 92
Richard Rd (BRA) 85
Richard Ter (DOR) 24
Richardi Ln (BRA) 85
Richards 02210
Richards Ave (CAM) 40
Richards Cir (WNW) 65
Richards Rd (WAT) 72
Richards Rd (MEL) 86
Richards Rd (EWY) 89
Richardson (MAL) 48
Richardson (NEW) 58
Richardson (CAM) 39
Richardson (BRI) 35
Richardson Ave (ARL) 74
Richardson Dr (N) 92
Richardson Ln & Rd (STO) 80
Richardson Rd (BEL) 78
Richardson Rd (MEL) 76
Richardson Rd (NUF) 64
Richardson St & Ter (SOM) 45
Richdale Ave (SOM) 45
Richdale Ave (CAM) 40
Richdale Ave (EV) 49
Richdale Rd (NH) 94
Richfield (NQ) 71
Richfield Rd (WNW) 65
Richfield Rd (ARL) 74
Richfield St & Park (DOR) 25
Richgrain Ave (WAL) 54
Richie Rd (REV) 51
Richie Rd (QUI) 69
Richland Rd (WH) 81
Richmere Rd (MAT) 26
Richmond (DOR) 24
Richmond 09

Boston (Con.)   021

Richmond (WY)	88
Richmond Rd (BEL)	78
Richmond Rd (NEW)	58
Richview (DOR)	24
Richwood (WRX)	32
Ricker Rd (NEW)	58
Ricker St & Ct (MAL)	48
Ricker Ter	
1-3 (BRI)	35
4-OUT (NEW)	58
Ricker Hill Rd (WRX)	32
Rider Ter (AUB)	66
Ridge (ARL)	74
Ridge (ROS)	31
Ridge Ave (NCE)	59
Ridge Rd (WAB)	68
Ridge Rd (WAV)	79
Ridge Rd (LEX)	73
Ridge Rd (REV)	51
Ridge Rd (MIL)	87
Ridge Hill Ave (MAL)	48
Ridge Hill Farm Rd (WH)	81
Ridgecrest Dr & Ter (WRX)	32
Ridgeley Ct (CAM)	38
Ridgemont (ALL)	34
Ridgeview Ave (MAT)	26
Ridgeway (WOL)	70
Ridgeway Ave & Ter (N.)	92
Ridgeway Dr (QUI)	69
Ridgeway Ln	14
Ridgeway Rd (MED)	55
Ridgeway Rd	
1-3 (WH)	81
4-OUT (WES)	93
Ridgeway Ter (NWH)	61
Ridgewood (DOR)	22
Ridgewood Rd (MEL)	76
Ridgewood Rd (MIL)	86
Ridgewood Rd (WAL)	48
Ridgewood Ter (WAL)	54
Ridgewood Ter (SWY)	90
Ridlon Rd (MAT)	26
Riedesel Ave (CAM)	38
Rifle Ct (WAT)	72
Riley Ave (EWY)	89
Riley Rd (HP)	36
Rill (DOR)	25
Rinaldo Rd (NWY)	91
Rindge (EWY)	89
Rindge Ave (LEX)	73
Rindge Ave Ext (CAM)	40
Rindge Ave & Ter (CAM)	40
Rindgefield (CAM)	40
Ring Ave (QUI)	69
Ringgold	18
Ripley (WAL)	54
Ripley (MAL)	48
Ripley Ln (WES)	93
Ripley Rd (MED)	55
Ripley Rd (DOR)	21
Ripley Rd (WAV)	79
Ripley St & Ter (NCE)	59
Risley Rd (WNW)	65
Risley Rd (CHH)	67
Rita Rd (STO)	80
Rita Rd (BRA)	84
Rita Rd (DOR)	24
Ritchie (ROX)	19
Rivard Rd (N)	92
River (NWY)	91

River	08
River (WH)	81
River (BRA)	84
River (WNW)	65
River (QUI)	69
River (ARL)	74
River (CAM)	39
River	
1-855 (MAT)	26
856-OUT (HP)	36
River Ave (REV)	51
River Ave (NUF)	64
River Park (NH)	94
River St (WES)	93
River Rd (WIN)	52
River Rd (BRO)	46
River Rd (SOM)	45
River St Pl	08
River St Ter (HP)	36
River St & Ave (WAL)	54
River Ridge Rd (WH)	81
River View Pl (NWY)	91
Riverbank Pl (MAT)	26
Riverbank Rd (NWY)	91
Riverbank Rd (QUI)	69
Riverdale (ALL)	34
Riverdale Ave (NEW)	58
Riverdale Rd (WH)	81
Riverdale Rd (MAT)	26
Riverglen Rd (WH)	81
Rivermoor (WRX)	32
Riverside (WAT)	72
Riverside (NH)	94
Riverside Ave (MIL)	86
Riverside Ave (QUI)	69
Riverside Ave (MED)	55
Riverside Dr (WAL)	54
Riverside Pl (CAM)	39
Riverside Rd (WES)	93
Riverside Sq (HP)	36
Riverview Ave (WAL)	54
Riverview Rd (BRI)	35
Riverview Rd (QUI)	69
Riverway (WRX)	32
Riverway	
1-339	02215
340-OUT	15
Roach (DOR)	25
Road A (EV)	49
Road B (EV)	49
Roanoke (QUI)	69
Roanoke Ave (JP)	30
Roanoke Rd (MAT)	26
Roanoke Rd (WEL)	81
Roanoke Rd (ARL)	74
Robbart Ln (HP)	36
Robbie Rd (BRA)	84
Robbins (MAL)	48
Robbins (MIL)	86
Robbins Rd (ARL)	74
Robbins Rd (WAT)	72
Robbins Rd (LEX)	73
Robbins St & Pl (WAL)	54
Robert (ROS)	31
Robert Ter (MAL)	48
Robert E Kelley (CAM)	38
Robert Ford Rd (WAT)	72
Roberta Ln (WOL)	70
Roberta Rd (AUB)	66
Roberts (QUI)	69
Roberts (BRA)	84
Roberts (MAL)	48
Roberts (BRO)	46

Roberts (SOM)	45
Roberts Ave (NWV)	60
Roberts Dr (SWY)	90
Roberts Pl (HP)	36
Roberts Rd (CAM)	38
Roberts Rd (WAL)	54
Roberts Rd (MED)	55
Roberts Rd (WH)	81
Roberts Post Rd (SWY)	90
Robertson St & Ter (QUI)	69
Robeson (JP)	30
Robey	
1-79 (ROX) (ODD)	19
2-74 (ROX) (EVEN)	19
76-OUT (DOR) (EVEN)	25
81-OUT (DOR) (ODD)	25
Robin (WRX)	32
Robin (EV)	49
Robin Rd (WES)	93
Robin Dell (AUB)	66
Robin Hood (DOR)	25
Robin Hood Rd (ARL)	74
Robin Hood Rd (STO)	80
Robinhood (AUB)	66
Robinson (DOR)	22
Robinson (CAM)	38
Robinson (SOM)	45
Robinson Ave (BRA)	84
Robinson Rd (LEX)	73
Robinson Rd (MED)	55
Robinson Rd (MAL)	48
Robinswood Rd (SWY)	90
Robinwood Ave (N)	92
Robinwood Ave (JP)	30
Robinwood Rd (WAV)	79
Robken Rd (ROS)	31
Rochdale (ROX)	19
Roche (QUI)	69
Rochester Rd (NEW)	58
Rock (ROX)	19
Rock Ave (DOR)	24
Rock Rd (MAT)	26
Rock Ter (DOR)	21
Rock Glen Cir & Rd (MED)	55
Rock Hill (MED)	55
Rock Island Rd (QUI)	69
Rock Ledge Rd (NWH)	61
Rock Ridge Rd (WH)	81
Rock Valley Ave (EV)	49
Rockaway Ln (ARL)	74
Rockcroft Rd (WY)	88
Rockdale (MAT)	26
Rockdale Rd (BRA)	84
Rockford (ROX)	19
Rockingham Ave (MAL)	48
Rockingham Ct (EB)	28
Rockingham Rd (MAT)	26
Rockingham St & Pl (CAM)	39
Rockland (NEV)	58
Rockland (WRX)	32
Rockland (WH)	81
Rockland (NWH)	61
Rockland (QUI)	69
Rockland (MEL)	76
Rockland Ave (ARL)	74
Rockland Ave, Park & Pl	
(MAL)	48
Rockland Pl (NUF)	64
Rockland St, Ave & Pl (ROX)	19
Rockledge (ROX)	19
Rockmere (DOR)	25
Rockmont Rd (ARL)	74
Rockmont Rd (BEL)	78

Boston (Con.)　　　　　　　**021**

Rockne Ave (DOR)	24
Rockport Rd (WES)	93
Rockridge Rd (WAL)	54
Rockvale Cir (JP)	30
Rockview Ave (MEL)	76
Rockview Rd (QUI)	69
Rockview Rd (MIL)	87
Rockview St, Pl & Ter (JP)	30
Rockville Ave (LEX)	73
Rockville Park (STO)	80
Rockville Park (ROX)	19
Rockway Ave (WEY)	88
Rockwell (DOR)	24
Rockwell (CAM)	39
Rockwell Ave (MED)	55
Rockwell Ave & Pl (MIL)	86
Rockwell St & Ter (MAL)	48
Rockwood (MEL)	76
Rockwood	
1-100 (JP)	30
101-OUT (BRO)	46
Rockwood Ln (N)	92
Rockwood Ter (AUB)	66
Rockwood Ter (MED)	55
Rockwood Ter (JP)	30
Rocky Nook Ter (JP)	30
Rocsam Park Rd (BRA)	85
Roddy Pl (BRI)	35
Rodgers Rd (STO)	80
Rodman (QUI)	69
Rodman (JP)	30
Rodney (BRI)	35
Rogers (NEW)	58
Rogers (CAM)	42
Rogers (SB)	27
Rogers (NWH)	61
Rogers (EWY)	89
Rogers Ave (WS)	44
Rogers Cir (BRA)	84
Rogers Park Ave (BRI)	35
Rogers Rd (LEX)	73
Rogers St & Ln (QUI)	69
Roine Rd (BRA)	84
Rokeby Rd (WAB)	68
Roland (NWH)	61
Roland (SOM)	43
Roland (SWY)	90
Roland (CHA)	29
Roland Rd (MED)	55
Roland (REV)	51
Rolfe Rd (LEX)	73
Rolling Ln (LEX)	73
Rolling Ln (CHH)	67
Rolling Ln (N)	92
Rolling Ln (WES)	93
Rollins	18
Rollins Ct (CAM)	39
Rollins Pl	14
Romar Ter (ROX)	19
Rome Dr (BRA)	84
Romsey (DOR)	25
Ronaele Rd (MED)	55
Ronald (DOR)	21
Ronald Rd (ARL)	74
Ronan (DOR)	25
Ronan Park (DOR)	22
Roosevelt Rd (LEX)	73
Roosevelt Rd (NCE)	59
Roosevelt Rd (MED)	55
Roosevelt Rd (WY)	88
Roosevelt St & Pl (REV)	51

Roosevelt Towers (CAM)	41
Rosa (HP)	36
Rosalie Rd (NH)	94
Rosalie Rd (NCE)	59
Rosalind Rd (NWY)	91
Rosaria (DOR)	22
Roscoe (NH)	94
Rose (MIL)	86
Rose (WY)	88
Rose (SOM)	43
Rose (REV)	51
Rose Ave (BRA)	85
Rose Ave (WAT)	72
Rose Dr (WNW)	65
Rose Ln (STO)	80
Rose Garden Cir (BRI)	35
Rose Hill Way (WAL)	54
Roseberry Rd (MAT)	26
Roseclair (DOR)	25
Rosecliff St & Ter (ROS)	31
Rosedale (DOR)	24
Rosedale Ave (EV)	49
Rosedale Ave (BRA)	85
Rosedale Rd (WAL)	72
Roseen Ave (WY)	88
Rosegate Rd (NH)	94
Roseglen Rd (MAT)	26
Roseland (DOR)	24
Roseland	
1-55 (CAM) (ODD)	40
2-64 (CAM) (EVEN)	40
57-OUT (SOM) (ODD)	43
66-OUT (SOM) (EVEN)	43
Roselin Ave (QUI)	69
Rosemary (NH)	94
Rosemary (JP)	30
Rosemary Ln (SWY)	90
Rosemary Ln (QUI)	69
Rosemere Ct (ROS)	31
Rosemont (MAL)	48
Rosemont (MAT)	26
Rosemont (DOR)	22
Rosemont Ave (WAL)	54
Rosemont Rd (NWY)	91
Roseway (JP)	30
Rosewood (MAT)	26
Rosewood Dr (WAL)	54
Rosina Rd (EWY)	89
Roslin (DOR)	24
Roslin Rd (ARL)	74
Roslindale Ave (ROS)	31
Roslyn Pl (JP)	30
Roslyn Rd (WAB)	68
Ross (MED)	55
Ross Pl (SB)	27
Ross Rd (BEL)	78
Ross Rd (LEX)	73
Rosselerin Rd (DOR)	22
Rosseter (DOR)	21
Rossetti (REV)	51
Rossmere (NWY)	60
Rossmore (SOM)	43
Rossmore Rd (JP)	30
Roswell (ROX)	19
Rotherwood Rd (NCE)	59
Rotterdam (ALL)	34
Roughan Rd & Ter (CHA)	29
Roughans (REV)	51
Roughans Point (REV)	51
Round Hill (JP)	30
Round Hill Rd (LEX)	73
Round Hill Rd (WES)	93
Roundwood Rd (NUF)	64

Rowe Pl	11
Rowe St & Pl (ROS)	31
Rowe Hill Rd (STO)	80
Rowell (DOR)	25
Rowen Ct (JP)	30
Rowena (DOR)	24
Rowena Rd (NCE)	59
Rowes Wharf	10
Rowland Ave (LEX)	73
Rowley (QUI)	69
Rowley (DOR)	22
Roxana (HP)	36
Roxbury (WIN)	52
Roxbury St, Ct & Ter (ROX)	19
Roxton (DOR)	21
Royal (ALL)	34
Royal (WAL)	54
Royal (WOL)	70
Royal (STO)	80
Royal (WAT)	72
Royal Ave (CAM)	38
Royal Rd (BRO)	46
Royal Rd (BEL)	78
Royall (MED)	55
Royalston Rd (WH)	81
Royce Pl (SOM)	45
Royce Rd (ALL)	34
Royce Rd (NCE)	59
Roys (JP)	30
Rozella (DOR)	22
Ruane Cir & Rd (WNW)	65
Rublee (ARL)	74
Rucille Ave (WY)	88
Rudolph (MAL)	48
Ruffing (HP)	36
Rufo Rd (CAM)	41
Rugby Rd (MAT)	26
Rugdale Rd (DOR)	24
Rugg Rd (ALL)	34
Ruggian Cir (WY)	88
Ruggles (MEL)	76
Ruggles (QUI)	69
Ruggles	
1-41 (ROX)	19
42-OUT (RXC) (EVEN)	20
43-239 (RXC) (ODD)	20
241-OUT (ODD)	15
Ruggles Ct (ROX)	19
Ruggles Ln (MIL)	87
Rumford Ave	
1-142 (WAL)	54
143-143 (AUB)	66
144-152 (WAL)	54
153-153 (AUB)	66
154-160 (WAL)	54
161-161 (AUB)	66
162-162 (WAL)	54
163-163 (AUB)	66
164-OUT (WAL)	54
Rumford Rd (LEX)	73
Rumford Rd (WRX)	32
Rumney Rd (REV)	51
Rundel Park (DOR)	24
Running Brook Rd (WRX)	32
Rural Ave (MED)	55
Rusfield (ROX)	19
Rush (SOM)	45
Rushmore (BRI)	35
Ruskin (WRX)	32
Ruskin (HP)	36
Ruskindale Rd (MAT)	26
Russell (MED)	55
Russell (WIN)	52

Boston (Con.)   021

Russell (BRO) 46
Russell (WAL) 54
Russell (NQ) 71
Russell (MEL) 76
Russell (MIL) 87
Russell
   1-15 (CAM) (ODD) 40
   2-OUT (CAM) (EVEN) 40
   17-OUT (WS) (ODD) 44
Russell Ct (NWY) 60
Russell Park (QUI) 69
Russell Rd (WNW) 65
Russell Rd (LEX) 73
Russell Rd (BRA) 84
Russell Rd (WH) 81
Russell Rd (SWY) 90
Russell Rd (N) 92
Russell Rd (NEW) 58
Russell Rd (WS) 44
Russell St & Ave (WAT) 72
Russell St, Ct & Park (MAL) 48
Russell St, Ct & Pl (CHA) 29
Russell St & Pl (EV) 49
Russell St & Ter (ARL) 74
Russell Ter (WAV) 79
Russett Ln (MEL) 76
Russett Rd
   1-190 (WRX) 32
   191-OUT (CHH) 67
Rustic (NEW) 58
Rustic Dr (SWY) 90
Rustic Pl (QUI) 69
Rustic Rd (WRX) 32
Rustic Rd & Ter (STO) 80
Rustlewood Rd (WRX) 32
Rustlewood Rd (MIL) 87
Rutgers Rd (WH) 81
Rutherford Ave (CHA) 29
Ruthven (NQ) 71
Ruthven Rd (NEW) 58
Ruthven St & Park (DOR) 21
Rutland (MAL) 48
Rutland (CAM) 38
Rutland (WAT) 72
Rutland St & Sq 18
Rutledge (WRX) 32
Rutledge Rd (BEL) 78
Rutledge Rd (WAL) 54
Ruxton Rd (MAT) 26
Ryan Ct (WNW) 65
Ryan Rd (BRI) 35
Ryan Rd (SOM) 45
Rybury Hillway (N) 92
Ryden (QUI) 69
Ryder (ARL) 74
Ryder Ave (MEL) 76
Ryder Rd (SWY) 90
Ryder Hill Rd (BRI) 35
Sabina Way (WAV) 79
Sables Ct (MED) 55
Sabrina Rd (WH) 81
Sabrina Farm Rd (WH) 81
Sachem (RXC) 20
Sachem Ave (ARL) 74
Sachem Rd (NWY) 91
Sachem Rd (NH) 94
Sachem St & Ct (REV) 51
Sachem St & Park (WOL) 70
Sackville (CHA) 29
Saco (DOR) 22
Saco (NUf) 64

Sacramento
   1-74 (CAM) 38
   75-OUT (SOM) 43
Sacramento Pl (CAM) 38
Saddle Brook Dr (N) 92
Saddle Club Rd (LEX) 73
Saddle Hill Rd (WES) 93
Safford (BRA) 85
Safford (HP) 36
Safford
   1-40 (NQ) 71
   41-OUT (WOL) 70
Sagamore (BRA) 85
Sagamore (REV) 51
Sagamore (DOR) 25
Sagamore Ave (WIN) 52
Sagamore Ave (CHE) 50
Sagamore Ave & Park (MED) 55
Sagamore Rd (NWY) 91
Sagamore Rd (NWH) 61
Sagamore Rd (ARL) 74
Sagamore Rd (WH) 81
Sagamore St & Ave (NQ) 71
Sagamore Way (WAL) 54
Saginaw Ave (CAM) 40
Saint Agatha Rd (MIL) 86
Saint Albans Rd 15
Saint Alphonsus (RXC) 20
Saint Andrew Rd (EB) 28
Saint Ann (JP) 30
Saint Annes Rd (EWY) 89
Saint Anns Rd (WOL) 70
Saint Botolph
   1-99 16
   100-OUT 15
Saint Brendon Rd (DOR) 24
Saint Cecelia 15
Saint Charles 16
Saint Claire (BRA) 85
Saint Clare Rd (DOR) 22
Saint Clare Rd (MED) 55
Saint Clements Rd (WS) 44
Saint Cloud Ave (N) 92
Saint Denis Ave (MED) 55
Saint Edward Rd (EB) 28
Saint Francis (MED) 55
Saint Francis Desales (RXC) 20
Saint George 18
Saint Gerard Ter (CAM) 40
Saint Germain 15
Saint Germain (QUI) 69
Saint Gregory Ter (DOR) 24
Saint Gregory St & Ct (DOR) 24
Saint James Ave 16
Saint James Ave (WS) 44
Saint James Rd (MED) 55
Saint James St, Pl & Ter
   (ROX) 19
Saint James St & Ter (NEW) 58
Saint John (JP) 30
Saint Johns Rd (CAM) 38
Saint Joseph (JP) 30
Saint Jude Ter (DOR) 22
Saint Lawrence (BRA) 85
Saint Lukes Rd (ALL) 34
Saint Margaret (EWY) 89
Saint Margaret (DOR) 25
Saint Mark (JP) 30
Saint Marks Rd (DOR) 24
Saint Martin (CHA) 29
Saint Mary
   1-OUT (MED) (ODD) 55
   2-OUT (MAL) (EVEN) 48

Saint Mary Rd (CAM) 39
Saint Marys 02215
Saint Marys (NH) 94
Saint Marys (NLF) 62
Saint Marys (WAT) 72
Saint Marys Ct (BRO) 46
Saint Marys Rd (MIL) 87
Saint Michael Rd (BRA) 85
Saint Paul (CAM) 39
Saint Paul St & Ter (BRO) 46
Saint Pauls Ave (JP) 30
Saint Peter (JP) 30
Saint Richard (ROX) 19
Saint Rose (JP) 30
Saint Sauveur Ct (CAM) 38
Saint Stephen 15
Saint Theresa Ave (WRX) 32
Saint Thomas More Dr (BRI) 35
Saint William (DOR) 25
Saipan Rd (CHE) 50
Salcombe (DOR) 25
Salem (CAM) 39
Salem (MED) 55
Salem (REV) 51
Salem (QUI) 69
Salem Rd (WH) 81
Salem St Ave (CHA) 29
Salem St, Ct & Pl 13
Salem St & Pl (MAL) 48
Salem Hill Ct (CHA) 29
Sales (REV) 51
Salina Rd (DOR) 22
Salisbury Park (DOR) 22
Salisbury Rd (BRO) 46
Salisbury Rd (NEW) 58
Salisbury Rd (WAT) 72
Salman (WRX) 32
Salt Ln 09
Saltonstall Rd (MED) 55
Salutation 09
Sammet (EV) 49
Sammet Ave (ROS) 31
Sammetti (MAL) 48
Samoset (DOR) 24
Samoset (SWY) 90
Samoset Ave (QUI) 69
Samoset Ln (WAL) 54
Samoset Rd (WAB) 68
Sampo Pl (QUI) 69
Sampson St, Ave & Pl (BRA) 84
Samson Rd (MED) 55
Samuel Morse Way (CHA) 29
San Jose Ter (STO) 80
Sanborn Ave (WRX) 32
Sanborn Ave & Ct (SOM) 43
Sanders Ln (WAL) 54
Sanderson Ave (EWY) 89
Sanderson Pl (BRI) 35
Sanderson Rd (WAL) 54
Sanderson Rd (LEX) 73
Sandra Ln (WY) 88
Sandrick Rd (BEL) 78
Sandy Way (NWY) 91
Sanford (MEL) 76
Sanford (HP) 36
Sanford (MAT) 26
Sanger (SB) 27
Sanger (MED) 55
Saning Rd (NWY) 91
Santilli Hwy (EV) 49
Santuit (DOR) 24
Saranac (DOR) 22
Saratoga (NQ) 71

Boston (Con.)   021

Saratoga Rd (ARL) 74
Saratoga St & Pl (EB) 28
Sargent (DOR) 25
Sargent (QUI) 69
Sargent (MEL) 76
Sargent (LEX) 73
Sargent (CAM) 40
Sargent (MAL) 48
Sargent (REV) 51
Sargent (N) 92
Sargent Ave (SOM) 45
Sargent Rd (BRO) 46
Sargent Rd (MED) 55
Sargent Rd (SWY) 90
Sargent Rd (BEL) 78
Sargent St & Park (NEW) 58
Sargent St & Ter (WIN) 52
Sargent Beechwood (BRO) 46
Sargent Crossways (BRO) 46
Sargents Wharf 09
Sarsfield (RXC) 20
Sartell Rd (WAL) 54
Sartwell Ave (WS) 44
Sassaman Ave (MIL) 86
Saunders (NWY) 91
Saunders (MED) 55
Saunders (ALL) 34
Saunders Ter (WH) 81
Savage (REV) 51
Savannah Ave (MAT) 26
Saville (WRX) 32
Saville (CAM) 38
Saville Ave (QUI) 69
Savin (MAL) 48
Savin (ROX) 19
Savin (MIL) 87
Savin Hill Ave, Ct & Ln
  (DOR) 25
Savoy 18
Savoy Rd (N) 92
Saw Mill Brook Pky (NCE) 59
Sawin (ARL) 74
Sawin (WAT) 72
Sawtelle (NWY) 91
Sawyer Ave (DOR) 25
Sawyer Rd (EWY) 89
Sawyer Rd (WH) 81
Sawyer Rd (MEL) 76
Sawyer Rd (WAL) 54
Sawyer St & Ave (MED) 55
Sawyer St & Ct (MAL) 48
Sawyer Ter (ALL) 34
Saxon Rd & Ter (NWH) 61
Saxton (DOR) 25
Saybrook St & Ter (BRI) 35
Sayward (DOR) 25
Sayward Pl (SB) 27
Scammell (QUI) 69
Scarsdale Rd (NWV) 60
Schaller (WH) 81
Schiller (JP) 30
Schiller Rd (WRX) 32
Schirmer Rd (WRX) 32
Schlager Ave (QUI) 69
Schofield Dr (NWV) 60
School (QUI) 69
School (BRA) 84
School (WEL) 81
School (BEL) 78
School (MEL) 76

School (STO) 80
School (ARL) 74
School (LEX) 73
School (CAM) 39
School (BRI) 35
School (BRO) 46
School (MAL) 48
School (NEW) 58
School (REV) 51
School (CHE) 50
School (EV) 49
School (DOR) 24
School 08
School (ROX) 19
School (EWY) 89
School (N) 92
School (MIL) 87
School (WES) 93
School
  1-163 (SOM) 43
  164-OUT (SOM) 45
School St Pl (ROX) 19
School St Pl (CHA) 29
School St Pl (EV) 49
School St & Ave (WAL) 54
School St & Ln (WAT) 72
School House Rd (MED) 55
Schortmanns Ter (WRX) 32
Schouler Ct (ARL) 74
Schrepel Pl (SB) 27
Schubert (ROS) 31
Schuyler (DOR) 21
Sciarappa St & Pl (CAM) 41
Science Park 14
Scituate (ARL) 74
Scotch Pine Cir (WEL) 81
Scotch Pine Rd (WEL) 81
Scotch Pine Rd (WES) 93
Scotch Pond Pl (QUI) 69
Scotia 15
Scotland (LEX) 73
Scotney Rd (CHH) 67
Scott (MED) 55
Scott (CAM) 38
Scott Ln (BRA) 85
Scott Pl (SB) 27
Scott Rd (N) 92
Scott Rd (SWY) 90
Scott Rd (BEL) 78
Scottfield Rd (ALL) 34
Scribner Park (AUB) 66
Scribner Rd (HP) 36
Sea (EV) 49
Sea (MAL) 48
Sea (NWY) 91
Sea St & Ave (QUI) 69
Sea Foam Ave (WIN) 52
Sea View Ave (WIN) 52
Sea View Ave (MAL) 48
Sea View Ave (EB) 28
Sea View Ter (DOR) 25
Seaborn (DOR) 24
Seabury (NWY) 91
Seager Ct (BRI) 35
Seagrave Rd (CAM) 40
Seagull Rd (QUI) 69
Seal Rock Ln (NQ) 71
Sealund Rd (NQ) 71
Searle Ave (BRO) 46
Searle Rd (WRX) 32
Sears (REV) 51
Sears 10

Sears Ave (MEL) 76
Sears Rd (BRO) 46
Sears Rd (MIL) 86
Sears Rd (WES) 93
Seattle (ALL) 34
Seaver (BRO) 46
Seaver (WH) 81
Seaver (EB) 28
Seaver (DOR) 21
Seaver Pl 16
Seaver Rd (EWY) 89
Seaverns Ave (JP) 30
Seaverns Ln (WES) 93
Seaview Ave (REV) 51
Seaward Rd (WH) 81
Seaway Rd (NQ) 71
Seckle (MAL) 41
Second (MAL) 48
Second (WRX) 32
Second (CHE) 50
Second (EV) 49
Second (MED) 55
Second (LEX) 73
Second (WY) 88
Second (SB) 27
Second
  1-159 (CAM) 41
  160-OUT (CAM) 42
Second Ave (NH) 94
Second Ave (WAL) 54
Sedalia Rd (DOR) 24
Sedge Rd (LEX) 73
Sedgewick (JP) 30
Sedgewick Rd (CAM) 38
Seery (MAL) 48
Sefton (MAT) 26
Segel (DOR) 21
Selden (DOR) 24
Selden (WAB) 68
Selkirk Rd (ARL) 74
Selkirk Rd (BRO) 46
Sellers (CAM) 39
Sellon Pl (SOM) 45
Selma (EB) 28
Selwyn (ROS) 31
Selwyn Rd (BEL) 78
Selwyn Rd (NWH) 61
Selwyn Rd (BRA) 85
Seminary (CHA) 29
Seminary Ave (AUB) 66
Seminole (MAT) 26
Seminole Ave (ARL) 74
Seminole Ave (WY) 88
Seminole Ave (WAL) 54
Semont Rd (DOR) 24
Senders Ct (HP) 36
Sentry Hill Pl 14
Service Dr & Rd (WH) 81
Sessions (WH) 81
Seton Hill Rd (AUB) 66
Seven Pines Ave
  1-23 (WS) (ODD) 44
  2-OUT (CAM) (EVEN) 40
  25-OUT (CAM) (ODD) 40
Seventh (SB) 27
Seventh (CAM) 41
Seventh (MED) 55
Sever (CHA) 29
Sevland (NCE) 59
Sewall (WNY) 65
Sewall (MEL) 76
Sewall (WOL) 70
Sewall (RXC) 20

Boston (Con.)   021

Sewall (REV) 51
Sewall Ave (WIN) 52
Sewall Ave (BRO) 46
Sewall Cr (CT) 45
Sewall Woods Rd (MEL) 76
Seward Rd (STO) 80
Seward Rd (WH) 81
Sextant Cir (QUI) 69
Sexton (WAT) 72
Sexton Ct (DOR) 25
Seymour (QUI) 69
Seymour (WIN) 52
Seymour (ROS) 31
Seyon (WAL) 54
Shade (WAL) 54
Shade (LEX) 73
Shadow Ln (WH) 81
Shadow Rd (MEL) 76
Shady Ln (SWY) 90
Shady Ln (N) 92
Shady Brook Ln (BEL) 78
Shady Hill Rd (NWH) 61
Shady Hill Rd (WES) 93
Shady Hill Sq (CAM) 38
Shafter (DOR) 21
Shailer (BRO) 46
Shakespeare Rd (WAL) 54
Shaler Ln (CAM) 38
Shamrock (NEW) 58
Shanahan Pl (ROS) 31
Shandon Rd (DOR) 24
Shanley (BRI) 35
Shannon (BRI) 35
Shapley Ave (MED) 55
Sharon (MED) 55
Sharon (WAL) 54
Sharon (MAL) 48
Sharon Ave (AUB) 66
Sharon Rd (MEL) 76
Sharon Rd (NQ) 71
Sharp (DOR) 24
Sharpe Rd (BEL) 78
Sharpe Rd (NCE) 59
Shattuck 15
Shattuck Rd (WAT) 72
Shaw (WNW) 65
Shaw (QUI) 69
Shaw (WRX) 32
Shaw (NWY) 91
Shaw Pl (LEX) 73
Shaw Rd (BEL) 78
Shaw Rd (CHH) 67
Shaw Rd (WH) 81
Shaw St & Ave (BRA) 84
Shawmut (REV) 51
Shawmut (SOM) 43
Shawmut 16
Shawmut Ave
   1-99 16
   100-652 (EVEN) 18
   101-649 (ODD) 18
   651-OUT (ROX) (ODD) 19
   654-OUT (ROX) (EVEN) 19
Shawmut Park (NUF) 64
Shawmut Rd (WAL) 54
Shawmut St & Ave (EWY) 50
Shawmut St & Pl (CHE) 50
Shawmut St & Pl (QUI) 69
Shawmut St & Ter (MAL) 48
Shawnee Rd (ARL) 74
Shawsheen Rd (EB) 28

Shaylor Ln (WES) 93
Shea (QUI) 69
Shea Rd (CAM) 40
Sheafe (MAL) 48
Sheafe (CHA) 29
Sheafe 13
Sheafe Rd (CHH) 67
Shean Rd (BEL) 78
Shedd (QUI) 69
Sheffield Rd (MEL) 76
Sheffield Rd (NWV) 60
Sheffield Rd (WAL) 54
Sheffield Rd (ROS) 31
Sheila (LEX) 73
Shelburne Rd (WH) 81
Shelby (EB) 28
Sheldon (ROS) 31
Sheldon (MIL) 86
Sheldon Rd (NCE) 59
Sheldon Rd (WAT) 72
Shelley Rd (WH) 81
Shelley Rd (ARL) 74
Shelton Rd (QUI) 69
Shenandoah (DOR) 24
Shennen (QUI) 69
Shepard (NQ) 71
Shepard (CAM) 38
Shepard Ct (HP) 36
Shepard Rd (BRA) 85
Shepard St & Pl (BRI) 35
Shephard Way (BRI) 35
Shepherd Ave (BRI) 15
Shepherd Park (WAB) 68
Shepherd Rd (MED) 55
Sheppard Ave (BRA) 84
Shepton (DOR) 24
Shepton Ter (SB) 27
Sheraton Ave (BRA) 85
Sheraton Park (ARL) 74
Sherborn (ARL) 74
Sherborn 02215
Sherborn Ct (SOM) 45
Sherbrook (WRX) 32
Sherbrook Ave (BRA) 85
Sherbrooke Rd (NEW) 58
Sherburne Cir (WES) 93
Sherburne Cir (QUI) 69
Sherburne Rd (LEX) 73
Sheridan (LEX) 73
Sheridan (WNW) 65
Sheridan (MAL) 48
Sheridan Ave (MED) 55
Sheridan Cir & Rd (WH) 81
Sheridan Dr (MIL) 86
Sheridan Rd (STO) 80
Sheridan Rd (WAL) 54
Sheridan St & Pl (JP) 30
Sheridan St & Sq (CAM) 40
Sherman (ROS) 31
Sherman (EV) 49
Sherman (REV) 51
Sherman (ROX) 19
Sherman (BEL) 78
Sherman (LEX) 73
Sherman (WOL) 70
Sherman (NH) 94
Sherman
   1-43 (CAM) (ODD) 38
   2-40 (CAM) (EVEN) 38
   42-OUT (CAM) (EVEN) 40
   45-OUT (CAM) (ODD) 40
Sherman Pl (AUB) 66
Sherman Rd (CHH) 67

Sherman Rd (STO) 80
Sherman Rd (MEL) 76
Sherman Rd (BRA) 85
Sherman St, Ct & Pl (MED) 55
Sherman St & Sq (CHA) 29
Sherrin (HP) 36
Sherrin Rd (CHH) 67
Sherrin Rd (NLF) 62
Sherwin 18
Sherwood (ROS) 31
Sherwood Ct (ROX) 19
Sherwood Ln (WAL) 54
Sherwood Rd (MED) 55
Sherwood Rd (MEL) 76
Sherwood Rd (STO) 80
Sherwood Rd (NWY) 91
Sheryl Ln (WIN) 52
Shetland (ROX) 19
Ship Ave (MED) 55
Shirley (EV) 49
Shirley (ROX) 19
Shirley (WNW) 65
Shirley (QUI) 69
Shirley (LEX) 73
Shirley Ave (REV) 51
Shirley Rd (MED) 55
Shirley Rd (WAL) 54
Shirley Rd (WH) 81
Shirley Rd (NH) 94
Shirley St & Ave (WIN) 52
Shore Ave (QUI) 69
Shore Dr (SOM) 45
Shore Dr (NWY) 91
Shore Rd (WAL) 54
Shore Rd (WH) 81
Shore Rd (ARL) 74
Shore Side Rd (QUI) 69
Shoreham (NQ) 71
Shornecliffe Rd (NEW) 58
Short (MED) 55
Short (WIN) 52
Short (BRO) 46
Short (MAL) 48
Short (ARL) 74
Short (LEX) 73
Short (MEL) 76
Short (SWY) 90
Short 02215
Short (CHA) 29
Short (EB) 28
Short St Ct (CHA) 29
Short St Pl (CHA) 29
Shrewsbury Rd (ROS) 31
Shumaker Path (NCE) 59
Shuman Cir (NCE) 59
Shurland (JP) 30
Shurtleff (MAL) 48
Shurtleff (REV) 51
Shurtleff St & Pl (CHE) 50
Shute (EV) 49
Shute Path (NCE) 59
Sias Ln (MIL) 86
Sibley Ct (CAM) 38
Sibley Ct & Pl (SOM) 45
Sibley Rd (WAL) 54
Sibley Rd (WES) 93
Sidlaw Rd (BRI) 35
Sidley Rd (WRX) 32
Sidney (CAM) 39
Sidney (WAT) 72
Sierra Rd (HP) 36
Signore Ter (REV) 51

Boston (Con.)   021

Sigourney (REV) 51
Sigourney (JP) 30
Silk (CHE) 50
Silk (ARL) 74
Silloway (DOR) 24
Silva Pl (ROX) 19
Silver (SB) 27
Silver (QUI) 69
Silver (MAL) 48
Silver Pl 14
Silver Rd (EV) 49
Silver Rd (BRA) 84
Silver Birch Rd (WAB) 68
Silver Brook Rd (MIL) 86
Silver Hill Ln (WAL) 54
Silver Hill Rd (WES) 93
Silver Lake Ave (NEW) 58
Silvey Pl (SOM) 43
Simmons (RXC) 20
Simmons Ave (BEL) 78
Simms Ave & Ct (WNW) 65
Simonds Ct (MED) 55
Simonds Rd (MEL) 76
Simonds Rd (LEX) 73
Simonelli Pl (EV) 49
Simpson (NEW) 58
Simpson Ave (WS) 44
Simpson Rd (WEL) 81
Simpson Ter (NWV) 60
Simpsons Ct (CHA) 29
Sims Rd (WOL) 70
Sinclair Rd (ALL) 34
Single Tree Rd (CHH) 67
Sioux Ave (WAL) 54
Siren (WIN) 52
Sixth (MED) 55
Sixth (CHE) 50
Sixth (MEL) 76
Sixth (SB) 27
Sixth
   1-113 (CAM) (ODD) 41
   2-118 (CAM) (EVEN) 41
   115-OUT (CAM) (ODD) 42
   120-OUT (CAM) (EVEN) 42
Sixth Ave (QUI) 69
Skahon Rd (BEL) 78
Skating Pond Rd (WES) 93
Skehan (SOM) 43
Skelly Ave (EWY) 89
Skilton Ave (SOM) 45
Sky Line Dr (WH) 81
Sky View Rd (LEX) 73
Sky View Ter (NCE) 59
Skyline Dr (BRA) 84
Skyline Dr (ARL) 74
Skyline Rd (HP) 36
Skyview Cir (NCE) 59
Slade (BEL) 78
Slayton Rd (MEL) 76
Slayton Way (ROX) 19
Sleeper 02210
Sleepy Hollow Ln (ARL) 74
Slocum Rd (LEX) 73
Slocum Rd (JP) 30
Small (NQ) 71
Smart (CAM) 39
Smart (WAL) 54
Smith (WAL) 54
Smith (REV) 51
Smith (QUI) 69

Smith (ARL) 74
Smith (WEL) 81
Smith (RXC) 20
Smith (N) 92
Smith Ave (LEX) 73
Smith Ave (SOM) 43
Smith Ave & Ct (WNW) 65
Smith Ct 14
Smith Pl (CAM) 38
Smith Rd (MIL) 86
Smith St & Ln (MED) 55
Smith St & Ter (BRA) 85
Smyth (BRO) 46
Snake Hill Rd (BEL) 78
Snelling Pl 13
Snow (BRI) 35
Snow Ter (SOM) 45
Snow Hill 13
Snug Harbor Ct (QUI) 69
Sobin Park 02210
Soden St & Pl (CAM) 39
Solar Ave (BRA) 84
Solaris Rd (HP) 36
Soldiers Field Pl (BRI) 35
Soldiers Field Rd
   1-399 (SF) 63
   400-400 (ALL) 34
   401-1000 (SF) 63
   1001-1200 (ALL) 34
   1201-OUT (BRI) 35
Soley (CHA) 29
Solon (WEL) 81
Solon (NWH) 61
Somerset (BEL) 78
Somerset 08
Somerset (EWY) 89
Somerset (EV) 49
Somerset Ave & Ter (WIN) 52
Somerset Rd (BRO) 46
Somerset Rd (WNW) 65
Somerset Rd (LEX) 73
Somerville Ave (BRA) 84
Somerville Ave
   1-811 (SOM) 43
   812-OUT (SOM) 40
Songin Way (SB) 27
Sonoma (DOR) 21
Sonoma Rd (NQ) 71
Soper Ave (WY) 88
Soper House Ln (BRA) 84
Sorenson Ct (ARL) 74
Sorenti Cir (WEL) 81
Sorrento (ALL) 34
South (BRI) 35
South (CAM) 38
South (SOM) 43
South (MED) 55
South (WAL) 54
South (QUI) 69
South (STO) 80
South (CHH) 67
South (BRA) 85
South (N) 92
South 11
South
   1-400 (JP) 30
   401-OUT (ROS) 31
South Ave (WES) 93
South Ave (EWY) 89
South Ave (MEL) 76
South Ave (WIN) 52
South Ave (REV) 51

South St Ct (MED) 55
South Bay Ave 18
South Bayfield Rd (NQ) 71
South Border Rd (MED) 55
South Cambridge (REV) 51
South Cedar Park (MEL) 76
South Cedar Pl 16
South Central Ave & Ter
   (WOL) 70
South Charlame Ct & Ter
   (ROX) 19
South Crescent Circuit (BRI) .. 35
South Eden (CHA) 29
South Fairview (ROS) 31
South Ferry (EV) 49
South Furness (REV) 51
South Gate Park (WNW) 65
South Genesee (REV) 51
South Hancock (REV) 51
South Hillside (STO) 90
South Hobart (BRI) 35
South Huntington Ave (JP) 30
South Irving (REV) 51
South Irving Park (WAT) 72
South Junior Ter (QUI) 69
South Main (WIN) 52
South Marble (STO) 80
South Market 09
South Munroe Ter (DOR) 22
South Normandy Ave (CAM) 38
South Park (WAT) 72
South Quincy Pl (CHA) 29
South Russell 14
South Shore Plz (BRA) 84
South Station 02210
South Sydney (DOR) 25
South Walnut (QUI) 69
South Walter (ROS) 31
South Washington (MAL) 48
South Waverly (BRI) 35
South Whitney (RXC) 20
Southampton
   1-443 18
   444-OUT (SB) 27
Southbourne Rd (JP) 30
Souther Rd (DOR) 22
Southern Ave (DOR) 24
Southern Ave (WY) 88
Southern Artery
   1-226 (WOL) 70
   227-OUT (QUI) 69
Southgate Rd (WEL) 81
Southmere Rd (MAT) 26
Southview (DOR) 25
Southwick (DOR) 22
Southwick Cir (WH) 81
Southwick Rd (WAB) 68
Southwood (ROX) 19
Spafford Rd (MIL) 86
Sparhawk (BRI) 35
Sparkill (WAL) 54
Sparkill (WAT) 72
Sparks St & Pl (CAM) 38
Sparrow (WRX) 32
Spaulding (EV) 49
Spaulding (QUI) 69
Spaulding (DOR) 22
Spaulding (JP) 30
Spaulding Ln (NCE) 59
Speakman (WOL) 70
Spear (QUI) 69
Spear (MEL) 76
Spear Pl 15

Boston (Con.)   021

Speedway Ave (ALL) 34
Speedwell (DOR) 22
Spence Ave (QUI) 69
Spencer (STO) 80
Spencer (WNW) 65
Spencer (BRA) 84
Spencer (LEX) 73
Spencer (DOR) 24
Spencer (WAL) 54
Spencer (MAL) 48
Spencer Ave (CHE) 50
Spencer Ave (WS) 44
Spencer Rd (MED) 55
Speridakis Ter (CAM) 39
Spevak Ter (MAL) 48
Spice (CHA) 29
Spiers Rd (NCE) 59
Spinney (WRX) 32
Spinney Ter (BEL) 78
Spofford Rd (ALL) 34
Spooner Rd (CHH) 67
Sprague (REV) 51
Sprague Ct (MED) 55
Sprague Rd (WH) 81
Sprague St & Ct (MAL) 48
Sprague St & Pl (HP) 36
Spray Ave (REV) 51
Spring (MAL) 48
Spring (SOM) 43
Spring (EV) 49
Spring (WAL) 54
Spring (WEL) 81
Spring (MEL) 76
Spring (NUF) 64
Spring (LEX) 73
Spring (WY) 88
Spring (BRA) 85
Spring Ct (ROX) 19
Spring Ln 09
Spring Rd (NH) 94
Spring Rd (WES) 93
Spring St Pl (CAM) 41
Spring St & Ave (REV) 51
Spring St, Ave & Rd (ARL) ... 74
Spring St & Ct (WAT) 72
Spring St & Ext (MED) 55
Spring St & Ln (STO) 80
Spring St & Pl (CAM) 41
Spring St & Rd (WRX) 32
Spring St & Ter (QUI) 69
Spring Garden (DOR) 25
Spring Glen Cir (BRA) 85
Spring Hill Rd (HP) 36
Spring Hill Ter (SOM) 43
Spring Park Ave (JP) 30
Spring Valley (ARL) 74
Spring Valley Rd (BEL) 78
Spring Valley Rd (WRX) 32
Springdale (MAL) 48
Springdale (DOR) 25
Springdale Ave (WH) 81
Springer (SB) 27
Springfield (BEL) 78
Springfield (QUI) 69
Springfield (WAT) 72
Springfield
  1-22 (CAM) 39
  23-OUT (SOM) 43
Springvale Ave (NWY) 91
Springvale Ave (WRX) 32
Springvale Ave

1-142 (CHE) 50
143-OUT (EV) 49
Spruce (MIL) 86
Spruce (MAL) 48
Spruce (WAL) 54
Spruce (EV) 49
Spruce (CHE) 50
Spruce (WAT) 72
Spruce (NQ) 71
Spruce (BEL) 78
Spruce (STO) 80
Spruce Ave (CAM) 38
Spruce Park (WH) 81
Spruce St, Ct & Pl 08
Spruce St & Ext (BRA) 84
Spruce Hill Rd (WES) 93
Spurr (ALL) 34
Spy Pond Ln & Pky (ARL) 74
Squanto Rd (QUI) 69
Squanto Rd (NWY) 91
Squantum (MIL) 86
Squire Rd (REV) 51
Squirrel Rd (WH) 81
Stacey (CHA) 29
Stadium Pl & Rd (ALL) 34
Stadium Rd (MAL) 48
Stafford (ROX) 19
Stafford Rd (NCE) 59
Stanbro (HP) 36
Standard (MAT) 26
Standish (DOR) 24
Standish (CAM) 38
Standish (NWH) 61
Standish (NWY) 91
Standish Ave (BRA) 85
Standish Ave (WOL) 70
Standish Cir & Rd (WH) 81
Standish Ct (WAL) 54
Standish Rd (REV) 51
Standish Rd (NQ) 71
Standish Rd (ARL) 74
Standish Rd (STO) 80
Standish Rd (MEL) 76
Standish Rd (WAT) 72
Standish Rd (MIL) 86
Stanford Rd (WEL) 81
Stanford Ter (SOM) 43
Stanhope St & Ct. 16
Staniford 14
Staniford (AUB) 66
Stanley (DOR) 25
Stanley (NWY) 91
Stanley Ave (WAT) 72
Stanley Ave (MED) 55
Stanley Cir (QUI) 69
Stanley Rd (WAB) 68
Stanley Rd (WAV) 79
Stanley Rd (WAL) 54
Stanmore Pl (ROX) 19
Stanton (DOR) 24
Stanton (MAL) 48
Stanton (WOL) 70
Stanton Ave (AUB) 66
Stanton Ave (REV) 51
Stanton Pl (ROX) 19
Stanton Rd (BRO) 46
Stanton Rd (STO) 80
Stanton Rd (MIL) 86
Stanwood St & Ter (DOR) ... 21
Staples (MEL) 76
Staples Ave (EV) 49
Star Rd (WNW) 65
Starbird (MEL) 76

Starbird (MAL) 48
Starbird Ave (ROS) 31
Stark (CHA) 29
Stark Ave (REV) 51
Starr Ln (JP) 30
Starr King Ct (CHA) 29
State 09
State (CAM) 39
State (QUI) 69
State (MIL) 86
State Rd (REV) 51
Staten Rd (BRA) 84
Station (QUI) 69
Station (BRO) 46
Station (EWY) 89
Station (RXC) 20
Station Ave (NWH) 61
Statler Rd (BEL) 78
Staunton (WOL) 70
Staunton Rd (BEL) 78
Stearns (NCE) 59
Stearns (MAL) 48
Stearns (CAM) 38
Stearns (WAL) 54
Stearns Ave (MED) 55
Stearns Rd (BRO) 46
Stearns Rd (WRX) 32
Stearns Rd (BEL) 78
Stearns Rd (WEL) 81
Stearns Rd (WAT) 72
Stearns Rd (LEX) 73
Stearns Ter (REV) 51
Stearns Hill Rd (WAL) 54
Stedman (BRO) 46
Stedman (QUI) 69
Stedman (JP) 30
Stedman Ave (BRA) 84
Stedman Rd (LEX) 73
Steele (STO) 80
Steep Rock Rd (ARL) 74
Steeple (REV) 51
Steeves Cir (WS) 44
Steeves Ct (MAL) 48
Stein Cir (NCE) 59
Stella Dr (WY) 88
Stella Rd (BEL) 78
Stella Rd (ROS) 31
Stellar Rd (BRA) 84
Stellman Rd (ROS) 31
Stephens Pl (NWH) 61
Sterling (WNW) 65
Sterling (NQ) 71
Sterling (MAL) 48
Sterling (WS) 44
Sterling (MED) 55
Sterling
  1-36 (WY) 88
  1-50 (ROX) 19
  37-OUT (BRA) 84
  51-OUT (RXC) 20
Sterling Park (BRA) 84
Sterling Rd (WEL) 81
Sterling Rd (N) 92
Sterling Rd (WAL) 54
Sterling Sq (SB) 27
Stetson (BRO) 46
Stetson (WY) 88
Stetson (BRA) 84
Stetson (LEX) 73
Stetson Ct (WAB) 29
Stetson Way (WAB) 68
Stevens (QUI) 69
Stevens (STO) 80

Boston (Con.)   021

Stevens	18
Stevens (MAL)	48
Stevens (MED)	55
Stevens (REV)	51
Stevens Ave (BRA)	85
Stevens Pl & Rd (MEL)	76
Stevens Rd (LEX)	73
Stevens Rd (WEL)	81
Stevens Rd (N)	92
Stevens Ter (ARL)	74
Stevenson Ave (EV)	49
Stewart (QUI)	69
Stewart Rd (N)	92
Stewart Ter (BEL)	78
Stickney Ave (SOM)	45
Stickney Rd (MED)	55
Stiles Ter (NCE)	59
Still (BRO)	46
Stillings	02210
Stillman (EWY)	89
Stillman Rd (MEL)	76
Stillman St & Pl	13
Stillmeadow Ln (WES)	93
Stimson Ave (LEX)	73
Stimson St & Rd (WRX)	32
Stinson Ct (CAM)	39
Stock (DOR)	22
Stockdale Rd (N)	92
Stockton (DOR)	24
Stockton (CHE)	50
Stockwell (RXC)	20
Stoddard Ln (MIL)	86
Stone (REV)	51
Stone Ave (MEL)	76
Stone Ave (CHH)	67
Stone Ave & Pl (SOM)	43
Stone Rd (WAL)	54
Stone Rd (BEL)	78
Stone Rd (ARL)	74
Stone Ter (DOR)	24
Stone Hill Rd & Ter (HP)	36
Stonecleve Rd (WH)	81
Stonecroft Cir (WES)	93
Stonehill Dr (STO)	80
Stoneholm	15
Stonehurst (DOR)	22
Stonehurst Rd (N)	92
Stoneleigh Cir & Rd (WAT)	72
Stoneleigh Rd (WNW)	65
Stonely Rd (JP)	30
Stonewall Rd (LEX)	73
Stonewood Ave (MEL)	76
Stonewood Dr (NCE)	59
Stonewood Ln (BRA)	84
Stoney Brae Rd (NWH)	61
Stoney Brae Rd (WOL)	70
Stoney Brook Ln (WY)	88
Stony Brook Rd (WES)	93
Stony Brook Rd (BEL)	78
Stony Brook Rd (ARL)	74
Stony Brook Rd (JP)	30
Stony Brook Ter (HP)	36
Storer	10
Storey Pl (JP)	30
Storrs Ave (BRA)	84
Story (SB)	27
Story (CAM)	38
Stoughton (MED)	55
Stoughton	18
Stoughton (QUI)	69
Stoughton St Pl (DOR)	25

Stoughton St & Ter (DOR)	25
Stow (WAL)	54
Stow Rd (MAT)	26
Stowcroft Rd (MEL)	76
Stowe Croft Rd (ARL)	74
Stowers (REV)	51
Stowers Ave (MED)	55
Strandway (WIN)	52
Stratford (WRX)	32
Stratford Rd (MEL)	76
Stratford Rd (WNW)	65
Stratford Rd (N)	92
Stratford Rd (NWY)	91
Stratham Rd (LEX)	73
Strathcona Rd (DOR)	21
Strathmore Cir & Rd (BRA)	84
Strathmore Rd (WEL)	81
Strathmore Rd (MED)	55
Strathmore Rd	
1-130 (BRO)	46
131-OUT (BRI)	35
Stratton (DOR)	24
Stratton Ter (WAL)	54
Strong Pl	14
Stuart	16
Stuart (EV)	49
Stuart (WAT)	72
Stuart Rd (WH)	81
Stuart Rd (NCE)	59
Studio Pl	16
Studio Rd (AUB)	66
Stultz Rd (BEL)	78
Sturbridge (MAT)	26
Sturbridge Rd (WH)	81
Sturges (MED)	55
Sturges Rd (WRX)	32
Sturgis (CHE)	50
Sturgis (WIN)	52
Sturtevant (DOR)	22
Sturtevant Rd (QUI)	69
Sturtevant Ter (MED)	55
Suban Pl (NWH)	61
Sudan (DOR)	25
Sudbury Rd (WH)	81
Sudbury Rd (WES)	93
Suffolk (MED)	55
Suffolk (CHE)	50
Suffolk (CAM)	39
Suffolk (MAL)	48
Suffolk Ave (REV)	51
Suffolk Rd (WH)	81
Suffolk Rd (CHH)	67
Sullivan (LEX)	73
Sullivan (REV)	51
Sullivan Ave (NUF)	64
Sullivan Pl (CAM)	39
Sullivan Rd (QUI)	69
Sullivan Rd & Sq (CAM)	38
Sullivan St & Sq (CHA)	29
Sumac Rd (NQ)	71
Summer (QUI)	69
Summer (NUF)	64
Summer (LEX)	73
Summer (STO)	80
Summer (MEL)	76
Summer (WAT)	72
Summer (ARL)	74
Summer (CHA)	29
Summer (HP)	36
Summer (REV)	51
Summer (CHE)	50
Summer (EV)	49
Summer (MED)	55

Summer (WRX)	32
Summer (WES)	93
Summer (BRA)	85
Summer (WY)	88
Summer	
1-192	10
1-260 (SOM) (ODD)	43
193-701	02210
261-OUT (WS)	44
702-OUT (SB)	27
Summer St Pl (HP)	36
Summer St Pl (ARL)	74
Summer St & Ave (MAL)	48
Summer St & Ave (WAL)	54
Summerhill (STO)	80
Summit (ARL)	74
Summit (ROS)	31
Summit (NEW)	58
Summit (WS)	44
Summit (WY)	88
Summit Ave (SOM)	43
Summit Ave (BRO)	46
Summit Ave (CHE)	50
Summit Ave (EV)	49
Summit Ave (REV)	51
Summit Ave (WIN)	52
Summit Ave (MEL)	76
Summit Ave (WOL)	70
Summit Ave (BRA)	84
Summit Ave & Rd (STO)	80
Summit Rd (WEL)	81
Summit Rd (WAT)	72
Summit Rd (LEX)	73
Summit Rd (MED)	55
Summit Rd (N)	92
Summit St & Ave (WAL)	54
Summit St & Cir (HP)	36
Summit St & Ter (MAL)	48
Summit Ridge Dr (BRA)	84
Sumner (QUI)	69
Sumner (NCE)	59
Sumner (REV)	51
Sumner (MIL)	86
Sumner Ave (BRA)	85
Sumner Ave (MED)	55
Sumner Ave (ROS)	31
Sumner Pl (RXC)	20
Sumner Rd (BRO)	46
Sumner Rd (CAM)	38
Sumner Rd (EWY)	89
Sumner Rd (WH)	81
Sumner St, Ct, Park, Rd, Sq	
& Ter (DOR)	25
Sumner St & Pl (EB)	28
Sun (WAL)	54
Sun Hill Ln (NCE)	59
Sun Valley Dr (BRA)	84
Sunapee Rd (ARL)	74
Suncrest (MAT)	26
Sunderland (DOR)	21
Sundin Rd (WY)	88
Sunny Ct (JP)	30
Sunny Knoll Ave & Ter (LEX)	73
Sunny Plain Ave (WY)	88
Sunnybank Rd (WAT)	72
Sunnybank Rd (WRX)	32
Sunnyside (WAL)	54
Sunnyside (JP)	30
Sunnyside Ave (EV)	49
Sunnyside Ave (SOM)	45
Sunnyside Ave (ARL)	74
Sunnyside Ave (BRA)	84
Sunnyside Ave (WH)	81

Boston (Con.)   021

Sunnyside Ave & Park (WIN)	52
Sunnyside Pl (BEL)	78
Sunnyside Rd (NH)	94
Sunnyside Rd	
1-53 (QUI) (ODD)	69
2-50 (QUI) (EVEN)	69
52-OUT (MIL) (EVEN)	86
55-OUT (MIL) (ODD)	86
Sunnyside St & Ave (HP)	36
Sunnyside Ter (MED)	55
Sunrise Ave (STO)	80
Sunrise Dr (NWY)	91
Sunrise Rd (NQ)	71
Sunset (LEX)	73
Sunset (RXC)	20
Sunset Ave (JP)	30
Sunset Ave (MED)	55
Sunset Ln (DOR)	24
Sunset Rd (NEW)	58
Sunset Rd (CAM)	38
Sunset Rd (WIN)	52
Sunset Rd (WS)	44
Sunset Rd (WAL)	54
Sunset Rd (STO)	80
Sunset Rd (MEL)	76
Sunset Rd (WEL)	81
Sunset Rd (ARL)	74
Sunset Rd (WAT)	72
Sunset Rd (WES)	93
Sunset Rd (EWY)	89
Sunset Rd (BRA)	85
Sunset Hill Path & Rd (ROS)	31
Suomi Rd (QUI)	69
Supple Rd (DOR)	21
Surfside Ave (WIN)	52
Surfside Ln (NQ)	71
Surrey (BRI)	35
Surrey (CAM)	38
Surrey (MED)	55
Surrey Ln (WES)	93
Surrey Rd (NEW)	58
Surrey Rd (ARL)	74
Surry Hill Ln (JP)	30
Susan Rd (SWY)	90
Susanna Ct (HP)	36
Sussex (RXC)	20
Sutcliffe Park (NWH)	61
Sutherland Rd (LEX)	73
Sutherland Rd (BRO)	46
Sutherland Rd & Ter (ARL)	74
Sutton (MAT)	26
Sutton (WY)	88
Sutton Rd (N)	92
Suwanee Rd (EWY)	89
Suzanne Rd (LEX)	.73
Swains Pond Ave (MEL)	76
Swains Pond Ave (MAL)	48
Swallow (SB)	27
Swallow Dr (NLF)	62
Swan (MAL)	48
Swan (MED)	55
Swan (WRX)	32
Swan (EV)	49
Swan Ave (WNW)	65
Swan Ave (SWY)	90
Swan Ct (DOR)	24
Swan Ln (LEX)	73
Swan Rd (QUI)	69
Swan St & Pl (ARL)	74
Swarthmore Rd (WEL)	81
Sweet Fern Ter (DOR)	21

Swett Ct (WAT)	72
Swift St & Ter (EB)	28
Sycamore (EV)	49
Sycamore (ROS)	31
Sycamore (CAM)	40
Sycamore	
1-49 (SOM)	43
1-147 (WAV) (ODD)	79
2-138 (WAV) (EVEN)	79
50-OUT (SOM)	45
140-OUT (WAT) (EVEN)	72
149-OUT (WAT) (ODD)	72
Sycamore Rd (SWY)	90
Sycamore Rd (BRA)	85
Sycamore Rd (NQ)	71
Sycamore Rd (NCE)	59
Sycamore Rd (MEL)	76
Sycamore Rd (STO)	80
Sycamore Ter (SOM)	45
Sydney (SOM)	45
Sydney (MED)	55
Sydney (MAL)	48
Sydney (DOR)	25
Sylvan (MAL)	48
Sylvan (MEL)	76
Sylvan Ave (WNW)	65
Sylvan Ln (WES)	93
Sylvan Rd (N)	92
Sylvan Rd (BEL)	78
Sylvan Rd (WH)	81
Sylvan Rd (WAL)	54
Sylvester Rd (WNW)	65
Sylvester Rd (DOR)	22
Sylvester Ter (WH)	81
Sylvia (ARL)	74
Sylvia (LEX)	73
Sylvia (JP)	30
Sylvia Ct (HP)	36
Sylvia Rd (MED)	55
Symmes (MED)	55
Symmes (ROS)	31
Symphony Rd	15
T Wharf	10
Tabor (OX)	19
Taber (QUI)	69
Tabor Ct (BRA)	84
Tabor Ct (WY)	88
Tabor Pl (BRO)	46
Tacoma (HP)	36
Taft Rd (MIL)	86
Taffiail Rd (QUI)	69
Taft (QUI)	69
Taft (MED)	55
Taft (REV)	51
Taft (DOR)	25
Taft Ave (LEX)	73
Taft Ave (WNW)	65
Taft Ct (ROS)	31
Taft Rd (WY)	88
Taft Hill Park & Ter (ROS)	31
Tafts Ave (WIN)	52
Tainter (MED)	55
Talbot (MAL)	48
Talbot (WNW)	65
Talbot Ave & Pl (DOR)	24
Talbot Rd (BRA)	85
Talbot St & Ave (MED)	55
Talmadge Ave (BRA)	85
Tamarac Ln (N)	92
Tamarac Rd (NUF)	64
Tamarack Rd (WES)	93
Tamarack Trl (SWY)	90
Tamerlane Ridge (SWY)	90

Tampa (MAT)	26
Tamworth	16
Tamworth Rd (WAB)	68
Tanager (ARL)	74
Tanglewood Rd (NCE)	59
Tanglewood Rd (WH)	81
Tanglewood Rd (DOR)	24
Tanglewood Rd (NH)	94
Tapley Ave & Pl (REV)	51
Tappan (WIN)	52
Tappan (BRO)	46
Tappan (ROS)	31
Tappan (EV)	49
Tappan (MEL)	76
Tappan Ave (WAT)	72
Tappan Rd (WEL)	81
Tara Dr (WY)	88
Tarbell Ave (LEX)	73
Tarleton Rd (NCE)	59
Tarleton Rd (WRX)	32
Taunton (SOM)	43
Taunton Ave (MAT)	26
Tavern Ln (LEX)	73
Tavern Rd	15
Tavern Rd & Sq (WAL)	54
Taylor (WAL)	54
Taylor (SOM)	45
Taylor (WIN)	52
Taylor (MED)	55
Taylor	18
Taylor (DOR)	22
Taylor (WAT)	72
Taylor (MEL)	76
Taylor (WOL)	70
Taylor (MIL)	86
Taylor (BRA)	85
Taylor (NH)	94
Taylor (NWY)	91
Taylor	
1-133 (MAL)	48
134-134 (EV)	49
135-OUT (MAL)	48
Taylor Rd (BEL)	78
Taylor Rd (WH)	81
Taylor Sq (CAM)	38
Taylor Ter (MAT)	26
Taylor Crossway (BRO)	46
Tchapitoulas (MAT)	26
Tebroc (DOR)	22
Technology Sq (CAM)	39
Teel (ARL)	74
Teel St Pl (ARL)	74
Teele Ave & Sq (WS)	44
Telegraph (SB)	27
Telford (BRI)	35
Temple (CAM)	39
Temple (MED)	55
Temple (REV)	51
Temple (MAT)	26
Temple	14
Temple (CHA)	29
Temple (ARL)	74
Temple (BEL)	78
Temple (MEL)	76
Temple (QUI)	69
Temple (WNW)	65
Temple Ave (WIN)	52
Temple Pl	11
Temple Rd (WAL)	54
Temple Rd (WEL)	81
Temple St & Rd (SOM)	45
Temple St & Ter (WRX)	32
Templeton Pky (WAT)	72

Boston (Con.)   021

Templeton St & Way (DOR)..... 24
Ten Hills Rd (SOM) 45
Tenean (DOR) 22
Tenney (CAM) 40
Tenney Ct (SOM) 45
Tenney Rd (BRA) 85
Tennis Rd (MAT) 26
Tennyson (SOM) 45
Tennyson (WRX) 32
Tennyson Rd (WAL) 54
Tennyson Rd (WH) 81
Tennyson Rd (WNW) 65
Teregram (EB) 28
Teresa Cir (/.RL) 74
Terminal (CHA) 29
Terminal (EV) 49
Terminal Rd (EB) 28
Termine Ave (JP) 30
Terne Rd (QUI) 69
Terrace Ave (NWH) 61
Terrace Ave (WIN) 52
Terrace Rd (MED) 55
Terrace St & Pl (RXC) 20
Terrell Cres (CHH) 67
Terrier Rd (MED) 55
Terry (RXC) 20
Tesla (MAT) 26
Tesla Ave (MED) 55
Tetlow 15
Teton Ln (MED) 55
Tewksbury (WIN) 52
Tewksbury (LEX) 73
Texas (SWY) 90
Thacher
   1-190 (MIL) 87
   191-OUT (MIL) 86
Thacher St & Ct. 13
Thackery Rd (WH) 81
Thane (DOR) 24
Thatcher (WOL) 70
Thatcher (MED) 55
Thatcher (HP) 36
Thatcher (BRO) 46
Thatcher (MAL) 48
Thaxter Rd (NWV) 60
Thayer (QUI) 69
Thayer 18
Thayer Ave (REV) 51
Thayer Ave (WY) 88
Thayer Ave & Pl (BRA) 85
Thayer Rd (WAL) 54
Thayer Rd (BRA) 84
Thayer St & Pl (BRO) 46
Thayer St & Rd (WAV) 79
The Ledgeway (MIL) 86
The Strand (WOL) 70
The Waterway (WH) 81
Thelma Rd (DOR) 22
Theodore (DOR) 24
Theodore Path & Rd (NCE) 59
Theodore A Glynn Way 18
Theodore Parker Rd (WRX) 32
Theresa Ave (MED) 55
Theresa Ave (LEX) 73
Theresa Ln (S10) 80
Theresa Rd (QUI) 69
Theriault Ct (CAM) 40
Thesda (ARL) 74
Thetford Ave (DOR) 24
Thetford Ave (BRA) 85
Theurer Park (WAT) 72

Thicket (SWY) 90
Thingvalla Ave
   1-73 (CAM) (ODD) 38
   2-OUT (CAM) (EVEN)........... 38
   75-81 (BEL) (ODD).............. 78
   83-OUT (CAM) (ODD)........... 38
Third (WY) 88
Third (ARL) 74
Third (LEX) 73
Third (SB) 27
Third (MED) 55
Third (BRI) 35
Third (MAL) 48
Third (EV) 49
Third (CHE) 50
Third
   1-245 (CAM) (ODD) 41
   2-220 (CAM) (EVEN) 41
   222-OUT (CAM) (EVEN) 42
   247-OUT (CAM) (ODD) 42
Third Ave (NH) 94
Third Ave (WAL) 54
Third Ave (SOM) 43
Third Pl (SB) 27
Third New Way (HP) 36
Thirteenth (MEL) 76
Thistle Ave (MIL) 86
Thistle Rd (BRA) 84
Thomas (BEL) 78
Thomas (ARL) 74
Thomas (QUI) 69
Thomas (MAL) 48
Thomas (MED) 55
Thomas (JP) 30
Thomas Park (SB) 27
Thomas Park (CAM) 38
Thomas Rd (WH) 81
Thomas Rd (SWY) 90
Thompson (QUI) 69
Thompson (HP) 36
Thompson Ln (MIL) 87
Thompson Pl (EV) 49
Thompson Pl (ARL) 74
Thompson Rd (BRA) 85
Thompson Rd (NWY) 91
Thompson St & Sq (CHA) 29
Thompsons Island (SB) 27
Thor Ter (ALL) 34
Thoreau Rd (NQ) 71
Thoreau Rd (LEX) 73
Thorn (MAT) 26
Thorn 18
Thorn Rd (ARL) 74
Thornberry Rd (LEX) 63
Thorndike (ARL) 74
Thorndike (BRA) 84
Thorndike 18
Thorndike (EV) 49
Thorndike (BRO) 46
Thorndike (CAM) 41
Thorndike (WS) 44
Thorndike (REV) 51
Thornley (DOR) 25
Thornton (REV) 51
Thornton (WOL) 70
Thornton Rd (CHH) 67
Thornton Rd (WAL) 54
Thornton Rd (N) 92
Thornton St & Park (WIN) 52
Thornton St & Pl (NEW) 58
Thornton St, Pl & Ter (ROX) ... 19
Thorpe (SOM) 43
Thorpe Rd (NH) 94

Thurlow (WRX) 32
Thurlow Ave (REV) 51
Thurman St & Park (EV) 49
Thurston (SOM) 45
Thurston (EB) 28
Thurston Ave (QUI) 69
Thurston Ln (N) 92
Thurston Rd (NUF) 64
Thurston Rd (MEL) 76
Thurston Rd (WAT) 72
Thwing (ROX) 19
Tibbetts Town Way (CHA)....... 29
Ticknor (SB) 27
Tierney (CAM) 38
Tilden Rd (SWY) 90
Tilesboro (DOR) 22
Tileston (MAT) 26
Tileston (EV) 49
Tileston Rd (WIN) 52
Tileston St & Pl. 13
Tillotson Rd (NH) 94
Tilman (DOR) 24
Timon Ave (CHH) 67
Timothy Ave (EV) 49
Timson Path (NCE) 59
Tina Ave (HP) 36
Tingley Cir & Rd (BRA) 84
Tinson Rd (QUI) 69
Tip Top (BRI) 35
Tip Top Ter (WAL) 54
Tirrell (NQ) 71
Tirrell (WP) 88
Tiverton Rd (MAT) 26
Tobey Rd (BEL) 78
Tobin Ave (REV) 51
Tobin Ct (RXC) 20
Tobin Rd (WRX) 32
Tocci Path (NCE) 59
Todd Rd (LEX) 73
Toland Ct (ROX) 19
Toledo Ter (DOR) 22
Tolman (DOR) 22
Tolman (WNW) 65
Tolman (WAL) 54
Tolman (N) 92
Tolman Pl (ROX) 19
Tomahawk Rd (ARL) 74
Tomlin (WAL) 54
Tonawanda (DOR) 24
Tonset (DOR) 24
Tontine (MED) 55
Topalian (MAT) 26
Topeka 18
Topliff (DOR) 22
Toppan Ave (ROS) 31
Torpie (RXC) 20
Torrey (DOR) 24
Torrey (SWY) 90
Torrey Rd (BRA) 85
Totman (QUI) 69
Totnes Rd (BRA) 84
Totten Cir & Ct (WAL) 54
Totten Pond Rd (WAL) 54
Touro Ave (MED) 55
Tovar (DOR) 22
Tower (EB) 28
Tower (JP) 30
Tower (NH) 94
Tower Ave (SWY) 90
Tower Rd (ARL) 74
Tower Rd (NUF) 64
Tower Rd (LEX) 73
Tower St & Ct (SOM) 43

Boston (Con.)	021	Trescott (DOR)	25	Turner (WAL)	54	
		Tresland Way (QUI)	69	Turner (BRI)	35	
Tower Hill Rd (BRA)	84	Trevalley Rd (REV)	51	Turner (QUI)	69	
Town (BRA)	85	Trevore (NQ)	71	Turner Rd (WEL)	81	
Town Hill (QUI)	69	Trewlawney (MAT)	26	Turner St & Ter (NWV)	60	
Town House Dr (NWV)	60	Tricorne Rd (LEX)	73	Turning Mill Rd (LEX)	73	
Town House Rd (WES)	93	Trident (EB)	28	Turtle Pond Pky & Ter (HP)	36	
Townley Rd (WAT)	72	Trident Ave (WIN)	52	Tuscano Ave (REV)	51	
Townsend (WAL)	54	Trifone (REV)	51	Tuttle (REV)	51	
Townsend (WIN)	52	Trilling Way	02210	Tuttle (DOR)	25	
Townsend (MAL)	48	Trimont Ave (WAL)	54	Tv Pl (NH)	94	
Townsend		Trimount Pl (SB)	27	Twilight Path (EWY)	89	
1-86 (ROX)	19	Trinity Cir (WAL)	54	Twin Cir Dr (ARL)	74	
87-OUT (DOR)	21	Trinity Ct (WH)	81	Twitchell (WEL)	81	
Townsend Ave (BRA)	84	Trinity Ct & Pl	16	Twomey Ct (SB)	27	
Townsend Pl	16	Trinity Ter (NCE)	59	Tyler	11	
Townsend Rd (BEL)	78	Triton Ave (WIN)	52	Tyler (HP)	36	
Toxteth (BRO)	46	Triton Pathway (WIN)	52	Tyler		
Tracton Ave (MAT)	26	Trotter Ct	18	1-54 (NQ)	71	
Trafalgar Ct (SWY)	90	Trotting Horse Dr (LEX)	73	55-OUT (WOL)	70	
Trafford (QUI)	69	Trout Ave (MED)	55	Tyler Ave (MED)	55	
Traill (CAM)	38	Trout Brook Rd (MIL)	86	Tyler Rd (WES)	93	
Train (DOR)	22	Trout Pond Ln (N)	92	Tyler Rd (LEX)	73	
Traincroft (MED)	55	Trowbridge (NCE)	59	Tyler Rd (BEL)	78	
Trainor (MED)	55	Trowbridge (BEL)	78	Tyler St & Ct (MAL)	48	
Trainor Dr (BRA)	84	Trowbridge (ARL)	74	Tyler St, Ct & Pl (SOM)	43	
Transit (SB)	27	Trowbridge Ave (NWV)	60			
Trapelo (BRI)	35	Trowbridge St, Pl & Ter		Tyler Ter (NCE)	59	
Trapelo Rd (WAL)	54	(CAM)	38	Tyndale (ROS)	31	
Trapelo Rd		Troy Ln (WAB)	68	Udine (ARL)	74	
1-232 (BEL)	78	Troy Rd (BEL)	78	Ufford (DOR)	24	
233-OUT (WAV)	79	True (REV)	51	Ulene Ct (CHA)	29	
Trask Ave (QUI)	69	True (EV)	49	Underhill (WIN)	52	
Traveler	18	Trueman (MAL)	48	Underwood (BEL)	78	
Traverse	14	Trueman St & Pl (NH)	94	Underwood Ave (WNW)	65	
Traverse (NEW)	58	Trull (SOM)	45	Underwood Ave (LEX)	73	
Traverse (MAL)	48	Trull (DOR)	25	Underwood Park		
Travis (ALL)	34	Trull Ln (SOM)	43	1-33 (WAL) (ODD)	54	
Travis Dr (CHH)	67	Truman Hwy		2-42 (WAL) (EVEN)	54	
Trayes Ave (MAL)	48	1-475 (MIL)	86	35-OUT (WNW) (ODD)	65	
Traymore (CAM)	40	476-1084 (HP) (EVEN)	36	44-OUT (WNW) (EVEN)	65	
Treadway Rd (DOR)	25	477-OUT (HP) (ODD)	36	Undine Ave (WIN)	52	
Treeland Cir (NEW)	58	1086-OUT (MIL) (EVEN)	86	Undine Ave (REV)	51	
Trefton Ave (WY)	88	Truman Rd (NCE)	59	Undine Rd (BRI)	35	
Trefton Dr (BRA)	84	Trunfio Ln (EV)	49	Unicorn Ave (EWY)	89	
Tremlett (DOR)	24	Truro (QUI)	69	Unicorn Ave (STO)	80	
Tremont (CHA)	29	Truro Ln (MIL)	86	Union (MEL)	76	
Tremont (MEL)	76	Trustman Ter (EB)	28	Union (STO)	80	
Tremont (STO)	80	Tucker (DOR)	24	Union (NCE)	59	
Tremont (WY)	88	Tucker (MIL)	87	Union (QUI)	69	
Tremont (MAL)	48	Tucker Ave (LEX)	73	Union (WAT)	72	
Tremont (CHE)	50	Tucker St & Rd (MED)	55	Union (NH)	94	
Tremont		Tuckerman (REV)	51	Union (SWY)	90	
1-129	08	Tuckerman (SB)	27	Union (BRI)	35	
1-143 (BRI) (ODD)	35	Tudor (SB)	27	Union (REV)	51	
1-168 (CAM)	39	Tudor (REV)	51	Union (CHE)	50	
1-255 (BRA)	85	Tudor (CHE)	50	Union		
2-146 (BRI) (EVEN)	35	Tudor (CAM)	39	1-15 (CAM)	39	
130-186	11	Tudor (WAL)	54	1-55 (ODD)	08	
145-OUT (NEW) (ODD)	58	Tudor Rd (CHH)	67	1-240 (BRA)	85	
148-OUT (NEW) (EVEN)	58	Tudor Rd (N)	92	2-68 (EVEN)	08	
169-OUT (SOM)	43	Tudor Ter (AUB)	66	16-OUT (CAM)	41	
187-555 (ODD)	16	Tufts (ARL)	74	57-OUT (ODD)	14	
188-550 (EVEN)	16	Tufts (CAM)	39	70-OUT (EVEN)	14	
256-OUT (BRA)	84	Tufts (SOM)	45	241-OUT (BRA)	84	
552-920 (EVEN)	18	Tufts (MAL)	48	Union Ave (MIL)	87	
557-921 (ODD)	18	Tufts (CHA)	29	Union Ave (JP)	30	
922-OUT (RXC)	20	Tufts	11	Union Park	18	
Tremont Pl (BRI)	35	Tufts Ave (EV)	49	Union Park St	18	
Tremont Pl (SOM)	43	Tufts Rd (LEX)	73	Union Pl (BRA)	84	
Tremont Pl & Row	08	Tully (CHH)	67	Union Pl & Ter (CAM)	41	
Tremont St & Pl (EV)	49	Tupelo (ROX)	19	Union Sq (SOM)	43	
Trent (DOR)	25	Turell Rd (MED)	55	Union Sq (ALL)	34	
				Union St & Ave (EV)	49	

Boston (Con.)   021

Union St & Ct (MED)	55
Union St & Ct (CHA)	29
Union St & Pl (MAL)	48
Union Wharf	09
Unity (QUI)	69
Unity Ave (BEL)	78
Unity Ave (REV)	51
Unity St & Ct	13
University Ave (MED)	55
University Hts (CHH)	67
University Park (WAL)	54
University Rd (BRO)	46
University Rd (CAM)	38
University Rd (ARL)	74
Unquity Rd (MIL)	86
Upcrest Rd (BRI)	35
Upham (REV)	51
Upham (WNW)	65
Upham Ave (DOR)	25
Upham St & Ter (MEL)	76
Upham St & Ter (MAL)	48
Upland (BRA)	84
Upland Ave (NWH)	61
Upland Ave (DOR)	24
Upland Park (SOM)	45
Upland Rd (WS)	44
Upland Rd (BRO)	46
Upland Rd (MAL)	48
Upland Rd (WIN)	52
Upland Rd (CAM)	40
Upland Rd (WAL)	54
Upland Rd (MED)	55
Upland Rd (EV)	49
Upland Rd (NWV)	60
Upland Rd (WEL)	81
Upland Rd (BEL)	78
Upland Rd (STO)	80
Upland Rd (MEL)	76
Upland Rd (ARL)	74
Upland Rd (WAB)	68
Upland Rd (QUI)	69
Upland Rd (WAT)	72
Upland Rd (LEX)	73
Upland Rd (WY)	88
Upland Rd W (ARL)	74
Upland Rd & Ter (N)	92
Upson Rd (WH)	81
Upton (QUI)	69
Upton (HP)	36
Upton (CAM)	39
Upton	18
Upton Rd (WAL)	54
Upton Ter (MED)	55
Upwey Rd (WH)	81
Usher Rd (MED)	55
Utica (QUI)	69
Utica (LEX)	73
Utica Rd (NH)	94
Utica St & Pl	11
Vail Ct (CAM)	39
Vaille Ave (LEX)	73
Vale (CHE)	50
Vale (ROX)	19
Valencia Rd (HP)	36
Valentine (CAM)	39
Valentine (ROX)	19
Valentine Rd (ARL)	74
Valentine Rd (MIL)	86
Valentine St & Park (WNW)	65
Vallar Rd (EB)	28
Vallero Rd (HP)	36

Valley (EV)	49
Valley (REV)	51
Valley (MAL)	48
Valley Ave (BRA)	85
Valley Park St (MED)	55
Valley Rd (WY)	88
Valley Rd (MIL)	87
Valley Rd (N)	92
Valley Rd (DOR)	24
Valley Rd (ARL)	74
Valley Rd (LEX)	73
Valley Rd (WH)	81
Valley Rd (CHH)	67
Valley Rd (STO)	80
Valley Rd Ext (MIL)	87
Valley St, Pl & Rd (MED)	55
Valley Spring Rd (NEW)	58
Valley View Rd (WAL)	54
Valley View Rd (WES)	93
Valleyfield (LEX)	73
Van Brunt (HP)	36
Van Ness	02215
Van Ness Rd (BEL)	78
Van Norden (CAM)	40
Van Roosen Rd (NCE)	59
Van Vechten (WAL)	54
Van Wart Path (NCE)	59
Van Winkle (DOR)	24
Vancouver	
1-24	15
25-OUT (RXC)	20
Vanderbilt Ave (MAT)	26
Vandine (CAM)	41
Vane (REV)	51
Vane (WEL)	81
Vane (NQ)	71
Vanness Rd (NWY)	91
Vara Ln (NH)	94
Varick Rd (WAB)	68
Varick Rd (WRX)	32
Varick Hill Rd (WAB)	68
Varney (JP)	30
Varnum (ARL)	74
Varnum Park (WAL)	54
Vassall (WOL)	70
Vassall Ln (CAM)	38
Vassar (CAM)	39
Vassar (MED)	55
Vassar (DOR)	21
Vaughan (EV)	49
Vaughan Ave (DOR)	21
Vaughan Ave (NWH)	61
Veda Ct & Rd (SWY)	90
Vega (WY)	88
Vendon Pl (CHA)	29
Venice (EB)	28
Venner Rd (ARL)	74
Ventura (DOR)	24
Venus (WY)	88
Venus Rd (BRA)	84
Vera (DOR)	24
Vera (REV)	51
Vera Ln (STO)	80
Veranda Rd (BRA)	84
Verchild (QUI)	69
Verdun (CAM)	40
Verdun (DOR)	24
Vermont (WRX)	32
Vermont Ave (SOM)	45
Vernal (EV)	49
Verndale (MAT)	26
Verndale Rd (NWH)	61
Verndale Rd (MIL)	87

Verndale Rd (SWY)	90
Verndale St & Ter (BRO)	46
Vernon (BRO)	46
Vernon (MAL)	48
Vernon (CHE)	50
Vernon (SOM)	45
Vernon (HP)	36
Vernon (MED)	55
Vernon (NEW)	58
Vernon (WAL)	54
Vernon (BRA)	85
Vernon (QUI)	69
Vernon	
1-31 (ROX)	19
32-OUT (RXC)	20
Vernon Ave (STO)	80
Vernon Ave (WIN)	52
Vernon Ct & Pl (RXC)	20
Vernon Rd (WAV)	79
Verona (JP)	30
Veronica Rd (EWY)	89
Verrill (MAT)	26
Vershire (NQ)	71
Vershire (WRX)	32
Vesper (WRX)	32
Vesta Rd (DOR)	24
Veterans Ave (EV)	49
Veterans Ln (STO)	80
Veterans Rd (WIN)	52
Veterans Of Foreign Wars	
Hwy (REV)	51
Veterans Of Foreign Wars Pky	
1-300 (ROS)	31
301-683 (CHH) (ODD)	67
302-500 (CHH) (EVEN)	67
502-OUT (WRX) (EVEN)	32
685-OUT (WRX) (ODD)	32
Vicki Rd (EWY)	89
Victor (MED)	55
Victor (MAL)	48
Victor (DOR)	25
Victoria (DOR)	25
Victoria (REV)	51
Victoria (EV)	49
Victoria (WS)	44
Victoria (MIL)	87
Victoria Ave (BRA)	85
Victoria Cir (NCE)	59
Victoria Ln (STO)	80
Victoria Rd (QUI)	69
Victoria Rd (ARL)	74
Victory Ave	
1-29 (QUI) (ODD)	69
2-OUT (MIL) (EVEN)	86
31-OUT (MIL) (ODD)	86
Victory Rd (DOR)	22
Viden Rd (QUI)	69
Vienna (EB)	28
View (REV)	51
View (MAL)	48
View South Ave (JP)	30
Viking Ct & Way (ARL)	74
Viking Gdns (WIN)	52
Viking Pl (SB)	27
Viking Ter (MAT)	26
Vila (CHE)	50
Viles (WES)	93
Viles Ct (WAL)	54
Viles Rd (LEX)	73
Villa (WAL)	54
Villa Ave (EV)	49
Villa Ave (WIN)	52
Villa Ln (BRO)	46

Boston (Con.)   021

Village (CAM)	39
Village Ave (BRA)	84
Village Cir (NCE)	59
Village Ln (ARL)	74
Village Ln (N)	92
Village Ln & Sq (BRO)	46
Village Rd (EWY)	89
Village Rd (NWV)	60
Village St & Ct	18
Village St & Ter (SOM)	43
Village Hill Rd (BEL)	78
Vinal (SOM)	45
Vinal (BRO)	46
Vinal (REV)	51
Vinal Ave (SOM)	43
Vincent (CAM)	40
Vincent (WNW)	65
Vincent Ave (WAV)	79
Vincent Pl (NQ)	71
Vincent Rd (WH)	81
Vincent Rd (ROS)	31
Vine (EV)	49
Vine (MED)	55
Vine (BRA)	84
Vine (MEL)	76
Vine (LEX)	73
Vine (CHH)	67
Vine (CHA)	29
Vine (WY)	88
Vine Ave (QUI)	69
Vine Ave (WIN)	52
Vine Ct & Pl (SOM)	43
Vine St & Ave (ROX)	19
Vine Brook Rd (LEX)	73
Vinedale Rd (BRA)	84
Vineland (BRI)	35
Vinewood Rd (MIL)	86
Vineyard (CAM)	38
Vineyard Ave (LEX)	73
Vineyard Rd (NCE)	59
Vining (MAL)	48
Vining	15
Vinson (DOR)	24
Vinson Rd (SWY)	90
Vinton (SB)	27
Vinton (MEL)	76
Vinton Ave (BRA)	84
Vinton Ct (STO)	80
Viola (MIL)	87
Violante (MAT)	26
Violet (MAT)	26
Violet (WY)	88
Virgil Rd (WRX)	32
Virginia (SOM)	45
Virginia (MIL)	87
Virginia (DOR)	25
Virginia Rd (BRA)	85
Virginia Rd (NH)	94
Virginia Rd (WAL)	54
Virginia Rd (MEL)	76
Virgin: Rd (AUB)	66
Virginia Rd (QUI)	69
Virginia Rd (ARL)	74
Vista (MEL)	76
Vista (ROS)	31
Vista (MAL)	48
Vista Ave (MED)	55
Vista Ave (AUB)	66
Vista Cir (ARL)	74
Vista Rd (WH)	81
Vivian Dr (WAT)	72

Vivien (REV)	51
Vogel (WRX)	32
Vogel Ter (BRO)	46
Volunteer Way (LEX)	73
Volusia Rd (EWY)	89
Von Hillern (DOR)	25
Vose Ave (HP)	36
Vose Ter (NCE)	59
Vose Hill Rd (MIL)	86
Voses Ln (MIL)	87
Waban (WEL)	81
Waban Ave (WAB)	68
Waban Rd (QUI)	69
Waban St & Park (NEW)	58
Waban Hill Rd (CHH)	67
Waban Hill Rd N (CHH)	67
Wabash (MAT)	26
Wabasso Rd (WAL)	54
Wabeno (DOR)	21
Wabon (DOR)	21
Wachusett (MAT)	26
Wachusett (JP)	30
Wachusett Ave (ARL)	74
Wachusett Cir & Dr (LEX)	73
Wachusett Rd (CHH)	67
Wachusett Rd (WH)	81
Wachusett Rd (N)	92
Wachusett Rd (NWY)	91
Wadaga Rd (NWY)	91
Waddell (MED)	55
Wade (BRI)	35
Wade (NWH)	61
Wadleigh Ave (REV)	51
Wadleigh Pl (SB)	27
Wadman Cir (LEX)	73
Wadsworth (NQ)	71
Wadsworth (ALL)	34
Wadsworth (MAL)	48
Wadsworth (CAM)	42
Wadsworth (WY)	88
Wadsworth Ave ,REV)	51
Wadsworth Ave (WIN)	52
Wadsworth Ave (WAL)	54
Wadsworth Rd (ARL)	74
Wagner (STO)	80
Wagner Rd (MED)	55
Wagon Rd (EWY)	99
Wainright Ave (SWY)	90
Wainwright (BRA)	84
Wainwright (DOR)	24
Wart (RXC)	20
Waite (REV)	51
Waite St Ext (MAL)	48
Waite St & Ct (MAL)	48
Waitt Ct & Park (REV)	51
Wakefield Rd (HP)	36
Wakullah (ROX)	19
Walbridge (ALL)	34
Walcott (WAT)	72
Waldeck (DOR)	24
Waldeck Rd (MIL)	86
Waldemar Ave (EB)	28
Waldemar Ave (WIN)	52
Walden (REV)	51
Walden (JP)	30
Walden (NWV)	60
Walden	
1-253 (CAM)	40
254-OUT (CAM)	38
Walden St & Pl (WIN)	52
Waldo (BRO)	46
Waldo Ct (WEL)	81
Waldo Rd (ARL)	74

Waldo Rd (MIL)	87
Waldo St & Ave (SOM)	43
Waldo Ter (BRI)	35
Waldorf (DOR)	24
Waldorf Rd	
1-50 (NWH)	61
51-OUT (NUF)	64
Waldren Rd (ROX)	19
Waldron Rd (BRA)	85
Wales (DOR)	24
Wales (NLF)	62
Walford Way (CHA)	29
Walk Hill	
1-171 (JP)	30
172-349 (ROS)	31
350-399 (MAT)	26
400-400 (DOR)	24
401-OUT (MAT)	26
Walker (WES)	93
Walker (WY)	88
Walker (NWV)	60
Walker (NQ)	71
Walker (WS)	44
Walker (MED)	55
Walker Ln (N)	92
Walker Rd (MEL)	76
Walker St Pl (CAM)	38
Walker St & Ave (CHA)	29
Walker St, Ct & Ter (CAM)	38
Walking Ct (MED)	55
Wall (WAL)	54
Wall (EV)	49
Wall (CHA)	29
Wall (QUI)	69
Wall (ARL)	74
Wall (WEL)	81
Wall's Ct (WAL)	54
Wallace (WS)	44
Wallace (MAL)	48
Wallace (NWH)	61
Wallace Ct (CHA)	29
Wallace Park (JP)	30
Wallace Rd (QUI)	69
Walley (EB)	28
Wallingford Rd (BRI)	35
Wallis Ct (LEX)	73
Wallis Rd (CHH)	67
Wallis Pl (CHA)	29
Walmsley Ln (WEY)	88
Walnut (MIL)	86
Walnut	08
Walnut (LEX)	73
Walnut (NQ)	71
Walnut (BRA)	84
Walnut (MEL)	76
Walnut (WAV)	79
Walnut (STO)	80
Walnut (WAT)	72
Walnut (WAL)	54
Walnut (CHE)	50
Walnut (EV)	49
Walnut (MED)	55
Walnut	
1-97 (SOM)	43
1-649 (NWV)	60
98-OUT (SOM)	45
650-900 (NCE) (EVEN)	59
651-885 (NCE) (ODD)	59
887-OUT (NWH) (ODD)	61
902-OUT (NWH) (EVEN)	61
Walnut Ave (CAM)	40

Boston (Con.)   021

Walnut Ave
   5-42 (WY) 88
   1-452 (ROX) 19
   43-OUT (BRA) 84
   453-OUT (JP) 30
Walnut Ct & Park (ROX) 19
Walnut Park (NEW) 58
Walnut Pl (NWH) 61
Walnut Pl & Ter (NWV) 60
Walnut Rd (SOM) 45
Walnut Rd (WES) 93
Walnut St, Ave & Pl (REV) 51
Walnut St & Ct (DOR) 22
Walnut St, Ct & Pl (N) 92
Walnut St, Ct & Ter (ARL) 74
Walnut St, Path, Pl & Ter
   (BRO) 46
Walnut St & Pl (HP) 36
Walnut St & Pl (WH) 81
Walnut St & Rd (WRX) 32
Walnut St & Ter (MAL) 48
Walnut Ter (QUI) 69
Walnut Hill Rd (CHH) 67
Walnut Hill Rd
   1-70 (NCE) 59
   71-OUT (NWH) 61
Walpole (QUI) 69
Walpole (RXC) 20
Walsh (MED) 55
Walsh Ave (STO) 80
Walsh Pl 09
Welsh Rd (NCE) 59
Walsingham (NLF) 62
Walter (NCE) 59
Walter (MED) 55
Walter (ROS) 31
Walter (HP) 36
Walter Ave (BRO) 46
Walter Ter (SOM) 45
Waltham (WNW) 65
Waltham (WAT) 72
Waltham (LEX) 73
Waltham 18
Walton (DOR) 24
Walton (WAL) 54
Walton Park (MEL) 76
Walworth (ROS) 31
Wamesit Rd (WAB) 68
Wampatuck Rd (QUI) 69
Wampatuck Rd (BRA) 85
Wampum (SWY) 90
Wampum Ave (WAL) 54
Wamsutta Ave (WAL) 54
Wapping (CHA) 29
Ward (RXC) 20
Ward (SOM) 43
Ward (LEX) 73
Ward
   1-149 (CHH) 67
   150-OUT (NCE) 59
Ward St & Ct (SB) 27
Wardman Rd (ROX) 19
Ware (DOR) 25
Ware (WES) 93
Ware (WS) 44
Ware (CAM) 38
Ware Rd (N) 92
Ware Rd (AUB) 66
Wareham (MED) 55
Wareham 18

Wareland Rd (WH) 81
Warner (DOR) 24
Warner (WS) 44
Warner Rd (MIL) 86
Warren (N) 92
Warren (MED) 55
Warren (BRI) 35
Warren (BRO) 46
Warren (REV) 51
Warren (EV) 49
Warren (LEX) 73
Warren (MEL) 76
Warren (STO) 80
Warren (WAT) 72
Warren (ARL) 74
Warren
   1-49 (CAM) 41
   1-443 (ROX) (ODD) 19
   2-432 (ROX) (EVEN) 19
   50-OUT (SOM) 43
   434-OUT (DOR) (EVEN) 21
   445-OUT (DOR) (ODD) 21
Warren Ave (MIL) 87
Warren Ave (BRA) 84
Warren Ave (WNW) 59
Warren Ave (CHE) 50
Warren Ave (MAL) 48
Warren Ave (SOM) 43
Warren Ave 16
Warren Ave, Ln & Pl (WES) 93
Warren Ave & Park (HP) 36
Warren Ave & Ter (WOL) 70
Warren Pl (ROX) 19
Warren Rd (WAB) 68
Warren Sq (JP) 30
Warren St & Ave (CHA) 29
Warren St & Ave (WAL) 54
Warren St & Ter (NCE) 59
Warren Bridge 14
Warrenton 16
Warwick (RXC) 20
Warwick (WOL) 70
Warwick (ARL) 74
Warwick Ave (WAL) 54
Warwick Park (CAM) 40
Warwick Rd (BRO) 46
Warwick Rd (WNW) 65
Warwick Rd (WAT) 72
Warwick Rd (MEL) 76
Warwick Rd (BEL) 78
Warwick St & Pl (SOM) 45
Washburn (EV) 49
Washburn (CHE) 50
Washburn (NEW) 58
Washburn (WAT) 72
Washburn (DOR) 25
Washburn (EWY) 89
Washburn Ave (N) 92
Washburn Ave (AUB) 66
Washburn Ave (WH) 81
Washburn Ave (REV) 51
Washburn Ave & Ter (CAM) ... 40
Washburn Pl & Ter (BRO) 46
Washington (MED) 55
Washington (EV) 49
Washington (BEL) 78
Washington (MEL) 76
Washington (LEX) 73
Washington
   1-59 14
   1-66 (BRO) 46
   1-113 (MIL) 86
   1-345 (DOR) 21

1-440 (WH) 81
1-621 (NEW) 58
1-646 (BRA) 84
1-805 (WY) (ODD) 88
2-774 (WY) (EVEN) 88
60-192 (EVEN) 08
61-441 (ODD) 08
67-OUT (BRI) 35
114-OUT (WOL) 70
194-194 09
206-206 09
208-208 09
210-428 (EVEN) 08
346-OUT (DOR) 24
430-950 (EVEN) 11
441-OUT (WEL) 81
443-949 (ODD) 11
622-1050 (NWV) 60
647-OUT (BRA) 85
776-OUT (EWY) (EVEN) 89
807-OUT (EWY) (ODD) 89
951-1999 18
1051-1700 (WNW) 65
1701-1959 (AUB) 66
1960-OUT (NLF) 62
2000-3134 (ROX) (EVEN) 19
2001-3125 (ROX) (ODD) 19
3127-3799 (JP) (ODD) 30
3136-3798 (JP) (EVEN) 30
3800-4700 (ROS) (EVEN) 31
3801-4699 (ROS) (ODD) 31
4701-OUT (WRX) 32
Washington Ave (N) 92
Washington Ave (WNW) 65
Washington Ave (CHE) 50
Washington Ave (CAM) 40
Washington Ave (WAL) 54
Washington Ave (EB) 28
Washington Ave & Ter (WIN) .. 52
Washington Ct (WH) 81
Washington Park Rd (BRA) 85
Washington Park & Ter
   (NWV) 60
Washington Pl (BRA) 84
Washington Pl (CHA) 55
Washington Sq (WY) 88
Washington St Pl (CHA) 36
Washington St & Ave (ARL) 74
Washington St, Ave & Ct
   (STO) 80
Washington St, Ave & Sq
   (REV) 51
Washington St, Ave & Ter
   (SOM) 43
Washington St & Ct (CAM) 39
Washington St & Ct (QUI) 69
Washington St & Pl (HP) 36
Washington St & Pl (MAL) 48
Washington St, Pl, Sq & Ter
   (CHA) 29
Washington Elms (CAM) 39
Washington Mall 08
Washington Park Blvd (ROX) .. 19
Wason (MED) 55
Water (MED) 55
Water (HP) 36
Water (CAM) 41
Water (SOM) 43
Water (WAL) 54
Water (DOR) 22
Water 09
Water (CHA) 29
Water (QUI) 69

Boston (Con.)	021	
Water (MEL)	76	
Water (ARL)	74	
Water (NCE)	59	
Water (WAT)	72	
Water (EWY)	89	
Water (BRA)	85	
Water St Ct (MED)	55	
Waterford	18	
Waterhouse (WS)	44	
Waterhouse (CAM)	38	
Waterhouse Rd (STO)	80	
Waterston Rd (BEL)	78	
Waterloo (HP)	36	
Waterlow (DOR)	21	
Waterman Rd (CAM)	38	
Waterman Rd (ROS)	31	
Waters Ave (EV)	49	
Waterston Ave (WOL)	70	
Waterston Rd (NEW)	58	
Watertown (LEX)	73	
Watertown		
1-230 (WAT)	72	
231-449 (NEW)	58	
450-749 (NWV)	60	
750-OUT (WNW)	65	
Watertown Sq (WAT)	72	
Watervale Rd (MED)	55	
Watkins (WOL)	70	
Watson (BRA)	84	
Watson (CAM)	39	
Watson (WS)	44	
Watson	18	
Watson Rd (QUI)	69	
Watson Rd (LEX)	73	
Watson Rd (BEL)	78	
Watts (CHE)	50	
Watts St & Pl (MAL)	48	
Wauinbeck (NQ)	71	
Waumbeck (DOR)	21	
Wauwinet Rd (WNW)	65	
Wave (DOR)	25	
Wave Ave (REV)	51	
Wave Way Ave (WIN)	52	
Waverley (WAL)	54	
Waverley		
1-163 (WAV)	79	
164-OUT (BEL)	78	
Waverley Ave (WAT)	72	
Waverley Ave		
1-424 (NEW)	58	
425-OUT (NCE)	59	
Waverley Pl (NLF)	62	
Waverley Ter (WAV)	79	
Waverley Oaks Rd (WAL)	54	
Waverly (BRO)	46	
Waverly (MAL)	48	
Waverly (CAM)	39	
Waverly (BRI)	35	
Waverly (STO)	80	
Waverly (ARL)	74	
Waverly (ROX)	19	
Waverly Ave (REV)	51	
Waverly Ave & Pl (MEL)	76	
Waverly Rd (WRX)	32	
Waverly St, Ave & Pl (EV)	49	
Way (HP)	36	
Way Pl (ROX)	19	
Wayburn Rd (JP)	30	
Wayland (DOR)	25	
Wayland (WOL)	70	
Waymount (RXC)	20	
Wayne (DOR)	21	
Wayne Ave (WAL)	54	
Wayne Ave (BRA)	85	
Wayne Rd (NH)	94	
Wayne Rd (NCE)	59	
Weaver Ct & Way (ROX)	19	
Weaver Rd (EWY)	89	
Webb (BRA)	85	
Webb (WY)	88	
Webb (LEX)	73	
Webb Ave (WH)	81	
Webb Park (SB)	27	
Webber (MAL)	48	
Webber (MED)	55	
Webber St & Pl (ROX)	19	
Webcowet Rd (ARL)	74	
Weber Rd (BEL)	78	
Webley Pl (ALL)	34	
Webster (MED)	55	
Webster (WAL)	54	
Webster (EV)	49	
Webster (REV)	51	
Webster (SOM)	45	
Webster (ARL)	74	
Webster (NQ)	71	
Webster (SWY)	90	
Webster		
1-100 (WAT)	72	
1-251 (WNW)	65	
1-614 (NH)	94	
.01-OUT (WAV)	79	
252-OUT (AUB)	66	
615-OUT (N)	92	
Webster Ave (SOM)	43	
Webster Ave (CAM)	41	
Webster Ave & Ct (CHE)	50	
Webster Ct (STO)	80	
Webster Ct (NCE)	59	
Webster Ct (CHA)	29	
Webster Park (N)	92	
Webster Park & Pl (WNW)	65	
Webster Pl	13	
Webster Rd (BRA)	84	
Webster Rd (LEX)	73	
Webster Rd (WES)	93	
Webster Rd (MIL)	86	
Webster St, Ave & Pl (EB)	28	
Webster St, Ct & Pl (MAL)	48	
Webster St & Pl (BRO)	46	
Webster St & Sq (HP)	36	
Wedgemere Rd (MAL)	48	
Wedgemere Rd (MED)	55	
Wedgemere Rd (WRX)	32	
Wedgewood (EV)	49	
Wedgewood (NQ)	71	
Wedgewood (WH)	81	
Wedgewood Rd (WNW)	65	
Wedgewood Rd (ROS)	31	
Wedmore (DOR)	25	
Weeden Pl (QUI)	69	
Weeks Ave (ROS)	31	
Weir (AUB)	66	
Weir Rd (WAL)	54	
Weitz (ALL)	34	
Welaka Rd (EWY)	89	
Welch Rd (WRX)	32	
Welch Rd (BRO)	46	
Welch Rd (LEX)	73	
Weld		
1-335 (ROS) (ODD)	31	
2-338 (ROS) (EVEN)	31	
337-OUT (WRX) (ODD)	32	
340-OUT (WRX) (EVEN)	32	
Weld Ave (ROX)	19	
Weld Rd (STO)	80	
Weld Hill (JP)	30	
Weldon (DOR)	21	
Weldon Rd (NEW)	58	
Welgate Cir (WOL)	70	
Welgate Rd (MED)	55	
Well	10	
Welland Cir & Rd (WY)	88	
Welland Rd (BRO)	46	
Welles (HP)	36	
Welles Ave (DOR)	24	
Welles Park (ROS)	31	
Wellesley (MED)	55	
Wellesley (WES)	93	
Wellesley Ave (NH)	94	
Wellesley Ave		
1-99 (WEL)	81	
100-OUT (WH)	81	
Wellesley Park (DOR)	24	
Wellesley Rd (BEL)	78	
Wellesley Rd (ARL)	74	
Wellesley Sq (WEL)	81	
Wellington (ARL)	74	
Wellington (BRA)	84	
Wellington	18	
Wellington (MAL)	48	
Wellington Ave (EV)	49	
Wellington Ave (SOM)	45	
Wellington Ct (DOR)	21	
Wellington Ln (CAM)	41	
Wellington Ln (BEL)	78	
Wellington Ln Ave (LEX)	73	
Wellington Pl (CHA)	29	
Wellington Rd (MED)	55	
Wellington St Ext (ARL)	74	
Wellington St, Ave & Grv (WAL)	54	
Wellington Ter (BRO)	46	
Wellington Hill (MAT)	26	
Wellman (BRO)	46	
Wells Ave (NCE)	59	
Wells Ave (WAT)	72	
Wellsmere Park, Rd & Ter (ROS)	31	
Welsh (MAL)	48	
Welton Rd (WRX)	32	
Wendall (WAL)	54	
Wendell (CAM)	38	
Wendell	10	
Wendell Ave (WOL)	70	
Wendell Park E & W (MIL)	86	
Wendell Rd (NCE)	59	
Wendeller (SB)	27	
Wendling Rd (N)	92	
Wendover (DOR)	25	
Wenham (JP)	30	
Wenham Rd (NWH)	61	
Wenlock Rd (DOR)	22	
Wenonah (DOR)	21	
Wensley (RXC)	20	
Wentworth Pl (BRO)	46	
Wentworth Rd (REV)	51	
Wentworth Rd (WOL)	70	
Wentworth Rd (MEL)	76	
Wentworth St, Ct & Ter (MAL)	48	
Wentworth St & Ter (DOR)	24	
Wescott (MAL)	48	
Wesley (MAL)	48	
Wesley (NEW)	58	
Wesley (SOM)	45	
Wesley (CHE)	50	

Boston (Con.) 021

Wesley (CHA)	29
Wesley Park (SOM)	43
Wesley Pl	13
Wesmur Rd (MAL)	48
Wessagusett Rd (NWY)	91
Wessex (DOR)	24
Wessex Rd (NCE)	59
Wesson Ave (QUI)	69
West (QUI)	69
West (MEL)	76
West (ARL)	74
West (BEL)	78
West (STO)	80
West	11
West (CHA)	29
West (MIL)	87
West (NH)	94
West (MAL)	48
West (WS)	44
West (EV)	49
West (MED)	55
West (NEW)	58
West (HP)	36
West (WAL)	54
West	
1-88 (SWY)	90
1-364 (BRA)	84
89-OUT (WY)	88
365-OUT (BRA)	85
West Blvd Rd (NCE)	59
West Ct Ter (ARL)	74
West St & Pl (CAM)	39
West Adams (WS)	44
West Bellflower (DOR)	25
West Border Rd (MAL)	48
West Boundary Rd (WRX)	32
West Brookline	
West Canton	
1-173	18
174-OUT	16
West Cedar	
1-31 (ODD)	08
2-40 (EVEN)	08
33-OUT (ODD)	14
42-OUT (EVEN)	14
West Concord	18
West Cottage (DOR)	25
West Dedham	18
West Eagle (EB)	28
West Elm Ave (WOL)	70
West Foster (MEL)	76
West Fourth (SB)	27
West Hancock (STO)	80
West Hill Ave & Ter (MEL)	76
West Hill Pl	14
West Howard (QUI)	69
West Howell (DOR)	25
West Lake Dr (WY)	88
West Milton (HP)	36
West Newton	
1-183 (ODD)	18
2-200 (EVEN)	18
185-OUT (ODD)	16
202-OUT (EVEN)	16
West Park (DOR)	24
West Pine (AUB)	66
West Quincy (WS)	44
West Riding (WEL)	81
West Roxbury Pky	
1-251 (CHH)	67
252-400 (ROS) (EVEN)	31

253-765 (WRX) (ODD)	32
402-598 (WRX) (EVEN)	32
600-784 (ROS) (EVEN)	31
767-OUT (CHH) (ODD)	67
786-OUT (CHH) (EVEN)	67
West Rutland Sq	18
West Selden (MAT)	26
West Side Rd (MIL)	87
West Sorento (ALL)	34
West Springfield	18
West Squantum (NQ)	71
West Tremlett (DOR)	24
West Walnut Park (ROX)	19
West Wyoming Ave (MEL)	76
Westacott Ct (CAM)	39
Westbourne (ROS)	31
Westbourne (MIL)	86
Westbourne Rd (NCE)	59
Westbourne Ter (BRO)	46
Westbrook (EB)	28
Westbrook Cir (WAL)	54
Westchester Rd (NEW)	58
Westchester Rd (JP)	30
Westcliff Rd (WES)	93
Westcott (DOR)	24
Westcott Rd (STO)	80
Westerley (WEL)	81
Westerley (JP)	30
Westerly Rd (WES)	93
Western Ave (WY)	88
Western Ave (CAM)	39
Western Ave	
1-305 (ALL) (ODD)	34
2-300 (ALL) (EVEN)	34
302-OUT (BRI) (EVEN)	35
307-OUT (BRI)	35
Westfield (N)	92
Westfield	18
Westfield Rd (WNW)	65
Westford (QUI)	69
Westford St & Pl (ALL)	34
Westgate (CAM)	39
Westgate Rd (WAL)	54
Westgate Rd (NCE)	59
Westgate Rd (WEL)	81
Westgate Rd (CHH)	67
Westglow (DOR)	22
Westland Ave	15
Westland Ave & Ter (WNW)	65
Westland Rd (WAT)	72
Westland Rd (WES)	93
Westley Ave (CAM)	40
Westlund Rd (BEL)	78
Westminster (HP)	36
Westminster (WS)	44
Westminster (RXC)	20
Westminster Ave (WAT)	72
Westminster Ave (ARL)	74
Westminster Ave (LEX)	73
Westminster Ave & Ter (ROX)	19
Westminster Rd (NCE)	59
Westminster Rd (EWY)	89
Westminster Ter (BRI)	35
Westmoor Cir, Rd & Ter (WRX)	32
Westmore Rd (MAT)	26
Westmoreland (DOR)	24
Westmoreland Ave (ARL)	74
Westmount Ave (WRX)	32
Weston (HP)	36
Weston (WAL)	54
Weston (LEX)	73

Weston (MIL)	87
Weston Ave (WOL)	70
Weston Ave (WS)	44
Weston Ave & Ct (BRA)	84
Weston Rd	
1-309 (WEL)	81
310-OUT (WEL)	81
Weston St & Pl (RXC)	20
Weston Ter (WEL)	81
Westover (WRX)	32
Westover (EV)	49
Westvale Rd (MED)	55
Westvale Rd (MIL)	86
Westview (LEX)	73
Westview St & Ext (DOR)	24
Westview Ter (WNW)	65
Westville	
1-130 (DOR)	24
131-OUT (DOR)	22
Westville Ter (DOR)	24
Westwood (DOR)	21
Westwood (WNW)	65
Westwood Rd (LEX)	73
Westwood Rd (STO)	80
Westwood Rd (WEL)	81
Westwood Rd (MED)	55
Westwood Rd (SOM)	43
Wetherbee Rd (WAL)	54
Wetherell (NUF)	64
Wexford (NH)	94
Weyanoke (DOR)	24
Weybosset (MAT)	26
Weybosset (NWY)	91
Weybridge Rd (BRO)	46
Weyham Rd (NWY)	91
Weymouth (QUI)	69
Weymouth Ave (WRX)	32
Wharf (CHE)	50
Wharf (QUI)	69
Wharf (EWY)	89
Wharf (MIL)	87
Wharf	10
Wharf	09
Wharton Ct (HP)	36
Wheatland (SOM)	45
Wheatland Ave (DOR)	24
Wheaton (ARL)	74
Wheaton Sq (JP)	30
Wheeler (SOM)	45
Wheeler (CAM)	38
Wheeler (MAL)	48
Wheeler Ave (MED)	55
Wheeler Ave (MEL)	76
Wheeler Ct & Ln (WAT)	72
Wheeler Ln (ARL)	74
Wheeler Rd (NCE)	59
Wheeler Rd (LEX)	73
Wheelock (WIN)	52
Wheelock Ave (DOR)	25
Wheelock Rd & Ter (WAL)	54
Wheelwright Rd (MED)	55
Whip Hill Rd (MEL)	76
Whipple (MAL)	48
Whipple (WS)	44
Whipple	15
Whipple Ave (ROS)	31
Whipple Ave (STO)	80
Whipple Rd (LEX)	73
Whipple St & Cir (SWY)	90
Whitby (EB)	28
Whitby Ter (DOR)	25
Whitcomb (WAL)	54

Boston (Con.)   021

Whitcomb
  1-27 (WAV) (ODD) 79
  2-24 (WAV) (EVEN) 79
  26-OUT (WAT) (EVEN) 72
  29-OUT (WAT) (ODD) 72
Whitcomb Ave (JP) 30
Whitcomb Ter (SWY) 90
White (SWY) 90
White (EB) 28
White (ARL) 74
White (QUI) 69
White
  1-OUT (CAM) (ODD) 40
  2-30 (CAM) (EVEN) 40
  32-OUT (WS) (EVEN) 44
White Ave (NCE) 59
White Ave (CHH) 67
White Ln (WES) 93
White Pl (BRO) 46
White Rd (BRA) 84
White St Pl (EB) 28
White St Pl
  1-OUT (CAM) (ODD) 40
  2-12 (CAM) (EVEN) 40
  14-22 (WS) (EVEN) 44
  24-OUT (CAM) (EVEN) 40
White St & Ter (WAV) 79
White Ter (LEX) 73
White Oak Ln (EWY) 89
White Oak Rd (WH) 81
White Oak Rd (WAB) 68
White Oak Rd (WRX) 32
White Pine Ln (LEX) 73
White Pine Rd (NUF) 64
White Pine Rd (N) 92
Whitelawn Ave (MIL) 87
Whites Ave (WAT) 72
Whitfield (DOR) 24
Whitfield Rd (WS) 44
Whitford (ROS) 31
Whitford Ter (WAL) .... 54·
Whitin Ave (REV) 51
Whitin Ave Ext (REV) 51
Whiting (ROX) 19
Whiting Rd (WH) 81
Whiting Way (N) 92
Whitlow Rd (WNW) 65
Whitman (EWY) 89
Whitman (DOR) 24
Whitman (WS) 44
Whitman (MAL) 48
Whitman Ave (MEL) 76
Whitman Cir (LEX) 73
Whitman Rd (QUI) 69
Whitman Rd (MED) 55
Whitman Rd (MIL) 86
Whitman Rd (N) 92
Whitman Rd
  1-37 (WAT) (ODC) 72
  2-OUT (WAL) (EVEN) 54
  3S-OUT (WAL) (ODD) 54
Whitney (WAT) 72
Whitney (CHH) 67
Whitney Ave (CAM) 39
Whitney Rd (MED) 55
Whitney Rd (QUI) 69
Whitney Rd (NWV) 60
Whitney Tavern Rd (WES) 93
Whiton Ave (QUI) 69
Whitridge (DOR) .... 24·

Whittemore (ARL) 74
Whittemore (MED) 55
Whittemore (WRX) 32
Whittemore Ave (CAM) 40
Whittemore Rd (NEW) 58
Whittemore Ter (DOR) 25
Whittemore Ter (WES) 93
Whitten (DOR) 22
Whittier (RXC) 20
Whittier (CAM) 40
Whittier (WIN) 52
Whittier (MEL) 76
Whittier Ave (WAL) 54
Whittier Dr (EV) 49
Whittier Pl 14
Whittier Rd (MED) 55
Whittier Rd (NWV) 60
Whittier Rd (LEX) 73
Whittier Rd (WH) 81
Whittier Rd (BRA) 84
Whittier Rd (N) 92
Whittier Rd (MIL) 86
Whittlesey Rd (NCE) 59
Whitwell (MEL) 76
Whitwell (QUI) 69
Whyte (MED) 55
Wichita Ter (MAT) 26
Wickfield Ct (EV) 49
Wicklow (MAL) 48
Wicklow Ave (MED) 55
Widett Cir 18
Wiget 13
Wiggin 13
Wigglesworth (MAL) 48
Wigglesworth (SOM) 45
Wigglesworth
  1-35 (RXC) (ODD) 20
  2-22 (RXC) (EVEN) 20
  24-OUT (EVEN) 15
  37-OUT (ODD) 15
Wight (WAL) 54
Wigwam Cir (ARL) 74
Wilbur (WAL) 54
Wilbur (MAL) 48
Wilbur (EV) 49
Wilbur (SWY) 90
Wilbur (DOR) 25
Wilbur Ave (ARL) 74
Wilbur Ct (EB) 28
Wilcock (MAL) 24
Wilcox Rd (DOR) 24
Wilde (WH) 81
Wilde Rd (WAB) 68
Wilder (DOR) 21
Wildon Rd (WEL) 81
Wildwood
  1-53 (DOR) (ODD) 24
  2-64 (DOR) (EVEN) 24
  55-OUT (MAT) (ODD) 26
  66-OUT (MAT) (EVEN) 26
Wildwood Ave (BRA) 85
Wildwood Ave (ARL) 74
Wildwood Ave (NWV) 60
Wildwood Dr (N) 92
Wildwood Ln (WES) 93
Wildwood Ln (STO) 80
Wildwood Ln (WAL) 54
Wildwood Rd (WEL) 55
Wildwood Rd (WH) 81
Wildwood Rd (MEL) 76
Wildwood Rd (LEX) 73
Wildwood. Rd (MIL) 86

Wildwood Rd (EWY) 89
Wiley (MAL) 48
Wiley Rd (WAV) 79
Wilgus Rd (QUI) 69
Wilkes 18
Wilkins Pl (ROS) 31
Wilkins Rd (BRA) 84
Wilkinson Park (DOR) 22
Willard (BRA) 84
Willard (MEL) 76
Willard (NWH) 61
Willard (MAL) 48
Willard (NEW) 58
Willard (MAL) 50
Willard (CHE) 50
Willard (CAM) 38
Willard Ave (MED) 55
Willard Pl. 18
Willard Rd (BRO) 46
Willard Rd (WES) 93
Willard St Ct (CAM) 38
Willard St & Ter (QUI) 69
Willcut Rd (DOR) 21
Willers (WRX) 32
Willet (WOL) 70
William (WNW) 65
William (WH) 81
William (STO) 80
William (CAM) 39
William (WS) 44
William St & Pl (MED) 55
William F Mc LeHan Hwy
  (EB) 28
William H Devine Way (SB) 27
William J Day Blvd (SB) 27
William Jackson Ave (BRI) 35
William Roger Greeley Vil
  (LEX) 73
William T Morrissey Blvd
  1-620 (DOR) 25
  621-OUT (DOR) 22
Williams (NQ) 71
Williams (ARL) 74
Williams (WAT) 72
Williams (MAL) 48
Williams (BRO) 46
Williams (CHE) 50
Williams (EV) 49
Williams (WAL) 54
Williams (WIN) 52
Williams (JP) 30
Williams
  1-50 (ROX) 19
  51-OUT (RXC) 20
Williams Ave (SWY) 90
Williams Ave
  1-174 (HP) 36
  175-OUT (MIL) 86
Williams Ct (EV) 88
Williams Ct (SOM) 43
Williams Rd (LEX) 73
Williams Sq (RXC) 20
Williams St & Ct (BRA) 84
Williams St & Ct (NUF) 64
Willis (DOR) 25
Willis Ave (WIN) 52
Willis Ave (MED) 55
Willis Ter (ROX) 19
Williston Rd (BRO) 46
Williston Rd (AUB) 66
Williston Rd (BEL) 78
Willoughby (SOM) 43

Boston (Con.)   021

Willoughby (BRI)	35
Willoughby Pl (ROX)	19
Willoughby Rd (MIL)	87
Willow (N)	92
Willow	08
Willow (MAL)	48
Willow (WAL)	54
Willow (CHE)	50
Willow (BEL)	78
Willow (STO)	80
Willow (BRA)	84
Willow (WH)	81
Willow (LEX)	73
Willow	
1-174 (CAM)	41
175-175 (SOM)	43
176-OUT (CAM)	41
Willow Ave (NWY)	91
Willow Ave (WS)	44
Willow Ave (HP)	36
Willow Ave & Ter (WIN)	52
Willow Cres (BRO)	46
Willow Ct (ARL)	74
Willow Ct (DOR)	25
Willow Ln (EWY)	89
Willow Park (WAT)	72
Willow Park & Rd (WEL)	81
Willow Rd (WES)	93
Willow St & Ave (WOL)	70
Willow St & Park (MEL)	76
Willow St & Ter (NCE)	59
Willow St & Ter (WRX)	32
Willowdean Ave (WRX)	32
Willowwood (DOR)	24
Wilmarth Rd (BRA)	84
Wilmington Ave (DOR)	24
Wilmore (MAT)	26
Wilmot (WAT)	72
Wilmot (ROS)	31
Wilmot (WAL)	54
Wilna Ct (WRX)	32
Wilrose (DOR)	21
Wilshire (WIN)	52
Wilshire Park (N)	92
Wilson (REV)	51
Wilson (MED)	55
Wilson (DOR)	24
Wilson (WEL)	81
Wilson Ave (WAV)	79
Wilson Ave (WAT)	72
Wilson Ave (BRA)	84
Wilson Ave (ARL)	74
Wilson Ave (WOL)	70
Wilson Ave (MAL)	48
Wilson Ave (CAM)	40
Wilson Ave (SOM)	45
Wilson Ave (WY)	88
Wilson Ct (NQ)	71
Wilson Park (BRI)	35
Wilson Rd (WAL)	54
Wilson Rd (STO)	80
Wilson Rd (LEX)	73
Wilsons Ln (N)	92
Wilton (WAL)	54
Wilton (SOM)	45
Wilton (HP)	36
Wilton St & Ter (ALL)	34
Wiltshire Ct & Rd (NEW)	58
Wiltshire Rd (BRI)	35
Wimbledon Cir (WNW)	65
Winborough (MAT)	26

Winchester	16
Winchester (NWH)	61
Winchester (BRO)	46
Winchester (MAL)	48
Winchester Dr (LEX)	73
Winchester Rd (ARL)	74
Winchester Rd (NEW)	58
Winchester St, Ct & Pl (MED)	55
Winchester Ter (JP)	30
Windemere Cir (BRA)	84
Windemere Rd (WH)	81
Windermere Ave, Ln & Park (ARL)	74
Windermere Rd (AUB)	66
Windermere Rd (DOR)	25
Windham Rd (HP)	36
Winding River Cir (WH)	81
Winding River Rd	
1-157 (N)	92
158-OUT (WH)	81
Windmill Ln (ARL)	74
Windom (ALL)	34
Windom (WS)	44
Windsor (SOM)	43
Windsor (EV)	49
Windsor (ARL)	74
Windsor (RXC)	20
Windsor	
1-300 (CAM)	39
301-548 (CAM)	41
549-OUT (SOM)	43
Windsor Rd (SWY)	90
Windsor Rd (N)	92
Windsor Rd (MIL)	87
Windsor Rd (WH)	81
Windsor Rd (NQ)	71
Windsor Rd (WAB)	68
Windsor Rd (WS)	44
Windsor Rd (MED)	55
Windsor Rd (BRO)	46
Windsor St & Rd (MEL)	76
Windsor Ter (WAL)	54
Winfield (N)	92
Winfield (SB)	27
Winford Way (MED)	55
Wingate Rd (WAL)	54
Wingate Rd (HP)	36
Wingate Rd (EWY)	89
Wingate Rd (WH)	81
Wingate Rd (LEX)	73
Winn (BEL)	78
Winn Ave (LEX)	73
Winn Ter (MAL)	48
Winnemere (MAL)	48
Winnetaska Rd (WAB)	68
Winnisimmet (CHE)	50
Winona (AUB)	66
Winona Way (NWY)	91
Winship (LEX)	73
Winship (MAL)	48
Winship St & Pl (BRI)	35
Winslow (EV)	49
Winslow (HP)	36
Winslow (CAM)	38
Winslow (ARL)	74
Winslow Ave (MED)	55
Winslow Ave (WS)	44
Winslow Rd (BRO)	46
Winslow Rd (WAB)	68
Winslow Rd (WAV)	79
Winslow Rd (BRA)	84
Winslow Rd (WH)	81

Winslow Rd (NQ)	71
Winslow St & Pl (ROX)	19
Winsom Ave (WAL)	54
Winsor Ave (WAT)	72
Winsor Way (WES)	93
Winstead Rd (EWY)	89
Winston Rd (LEX)	73
Winston Rd (NCE)	59
Winston Rd (DOR)	24
Winter (DOR)	22
Winter (NUF)	64
Winter (LEX)	73
Winter (WAT)	72
Winter (QUI)	69
Winter (BRA)	85
Winter (STO)	80
Winter (WAV)	79
Winter (ARL)	74
Winter (WY)	88
Winter (WES)	93
Winter (WAL)	54
Winter (WS)	44
Winter (MED)	55
Winter (CAM)	41
Winter (HP)	36
Winter (EV)	49
Winter St Pl (CAM)	41
Winter St & Ave (MAL)	48
Winter St & Pl (MEL)	76
Winter St & Pl	08
Winter Hill Cir (SOM)	45
Winter Hill Rd (MED)	55
Winthrop (HP)	36
Winthrop (CHE)	50
Winthrop (WAL)	54
Winthrop (WIN)	52
Winthrop (ROX)	19
Winthrop (EB)	28
Winthrop (CHA)	29
Winthrop (MEL)	76
Winthrop (STO)	80
Winthrop (WAT)	72
Winthrop (WNW)	65
Winthrop (MIL)	87
Winthrop Ave (WOL)	70
Winthrop Ave (NEW)	58
Winthrop Ave, Pky & Pl (REV)	51
Winthrop Ave & Rd (BRA)	85
Winthrop Rd (BEL)	78
Winthrop Rd (WEL)	81
Winthrop Rd (ARL)	74
Winthrop Rd (LEX)	73
Winthrop Rd (BRO)	46
Winthrop Sq	10
Winthrop St, Ct, Pl & Sq (MED)	55
Winthrop St & Park (MAL)	48
Winthrop St, Park & Pl (QUI)	69
Winthrop St & Rd (EV)	49
Winthrop St & Sq (CAM)	38
Winthrop Shore Dr (WIN)	52
Winton (ROS)	31
Wirt (BRI)	35
Wisconsin Ave (SOM)	45
Wise (JP)	30
Wistar Pl (CHA)	29
Wiswall (WNW)	65
Wiswall Cir (WEL)	81
Wiswall Rd (NCE)	59
Witherbee Ave (REV)	51
Withington (DOR)	24
Withington Rd (NWV)	60

Boston (Con.)   021

Wittawaumet Rd (NWY)	91
Woburn (LEX)	73
Woburn (MED)	55
Woburn (WAL)	54
Woerd Ave (WAL)	54
Wolcott (EV)	49
Wolcott (DOR)	21
Wolcott Rd (REV)	51
Wolcott Rd (STO)	80
Wolcott Rd (WAT)	72
Wolcott Rd (CHH)	67
Wolcott Rd (MIL)	86
Wolcott Rd Ext (CHH)	67
Wolcott St, Ct & Sq (HP)	36
Wolcott St & Park (MED)	55
Wolcott St & Park (AUB)	66
Wolcott St & Ter (MAL)	48
Wolfe (WRX)	32
Wollaston Ave (WOL)	70
Wollaston Ave (ARL)	74
Wollaston Ter (DOR)	24
Wollitzer Ln (WAT)	72
Wood (LEX)	73
Wood (CHA)	29
Wood (CAM)	40
Wood (MIL)	86
Wood Ave (EWY)	89
Wood Ave	
1-135 (MAT) (ODD)	26
2-122 (MAT) (EVEN)	26
124-OUT (HP) (EVEN)	36
137-OUT (HP) (ODD)	36
Wood Rd (BRA)	84
Wood End Rd (NWH)	61
Wood Haven Rd (WAB)	68
Woodard Rd (WRX)	32
Woodberry Rd (LEX)	73
Woodbine (WOL)	70
Woodbine (WAL)	54
Woodbine (SOM)	43
Woodbine (ROX)	19
Woodbine Cir (NH)	94
Woodbine Rd (EWY)	89
Woodbine Rd (MED)	55
Woodbine Rd (WH)	81
Woodbine Rd (BEL)	78
Woodbine St & Ter (AUB)	66
Woodbole Ave (MAT)	26
Woodbourne Rd (JP)	30
Woodbriar Rd (MEL)	76
Woodbridge (CAM)	40
Woodbrier Rd (WRX)	32
Woodbrier Rd (NQ)	71
Woodbury (ARL)	74
Woodbury	18
Woodbury Dr (N)	92
Woodchester Cir & Rd (WAL)	54
Woodchester Dr (MIL)	86
Woodchester Dr (WES)	93
Woodchester Dr (CHH)	67
Woodchester Rd (WH)	81
Woodcliff (DOR)	25
Woodcliff Dr (WAL)	54
Woodcliff Rd (WH)	81
Woodcliff Rd (CHH)	67
Woodcliff Rd (QUI)	69
Woodcliff Rd (NWH)	61
Woodcliffe Rd (LEX)	73
Woodcrest Ct (SWY)	90
Woodcrest Dr E, N & W	
(MEL)	76

Wooddale Ave (MAT)	26
Woodedge Ave, Cir & Ln	
(BRA)	85
Woodfall (BEL)	78
Woodfield (DOR)	22
Woodfield Rd (WH)	81
Woodford (DOR)	25
Woodgate (MAT)	26
Woodglen Rd (HP)	36
Woodhaven (MAT)	26
Woodland (EV)	49
Woodland (BEL)	78
Woodland (ARL)	74
Woodland Ave (MEL)	76
Woodland Ave (BRA)	85
Woodland Ave & Rd (MED)	55
Woodland Dr (SWY)	90
Woodland Pl (HP)	36
Woodland Rd (WAL)	54
Woodland Rd (REV)	51
Woodland Rd (WES)	93
Woodland Rd (MIL)	86
Woodland Rd (BRA)	84
Woodland Rd (WH)	81
Woodland Rd (STO)	80
Woodland Rd (LEX)	73
Woodland Rd (AUB)	66
Woodland Rd (CHH)	67
Woodland Rd (JP)	30
Woodland St & Rd (MAL)	48
Woodland Hill (WH)	81
Woodlawn (JP)	30
Woodlawn Ave (WAL)	54
Woodlawn Ave (CHE)	50
Woodlawn Ave (N)	92
Woodlawn Ave & Oval (WH)	81
Woodlawn Dr (CHH)	67
Woodlawn St & Ave (EV)	49
Woodledge (DOR)	25
Woodledge Rd (N)	92
Woodleigh Rd (WAT)	72
Woodley Ave (WRX)	32
Woodman (QUI)	69
Woodman (JP)	30
Woodman Cir (SWY)	90
Woodman Rd (CHH)	67
Woodmont (BRI)	35
Woodridge Cir & Rd (WES)	93
Woodridge Rd (WEL)	81
Woodrock Rd (EWY)	89
Woodrow Ave (NWV)	60
Woodrow Ave (MAL)	48
Woodrow Ave (MED)	55
Woodrow Ave (DOR)	24
Woodrow Wilson Ct (ROX)	19
Woodrow Wilson Ct (CAM)	39
Woodruff Ave (MED)	55
Woodruff Ave (MEL)	76
Woodruff Way (MAT)	26
Woods Ave (REV)	51
Woods Ave (WS)	44
Woods Ln (MAL)	48
Woods Pl (CHA)	29
Woods Rd (MED)	55
Woods Rd (BEL)	78
Woods Edge Rd (MED)	55
Woodside Ave (EV)	49
Woodside Ave (BRA)	85
Woodside Ave (WH)	81
Woodside Ave (JP)	30
Woodside Ave & Park (WIN)	52
Woodside Dr (MIL)	86
Woodside Ln (ARL)	74

Woodside Path (EWY)	89
Woodside Rd (NWV)	60
Woodside Rd (MED)	55
Woodsom Dr (BRA)	85
Woodstock (WS)	44
Woodstock Ave (BRO)	46
Woodville (EV)	49
Woodville Ave (MIL)	86
Woodville St, Park & Ter	
(ROX)	19
Woodville Ter (MAL)	48
Woodward (EV)	49
Woodward	
1-186 (NWH)	51
187-OUT (WAB)	68
Woodward Ave (ROX)	19
Woodward Ave (QUI)	69
Woodward Ct (MIL)	86
Woodward Ln (WES)	93
Woodward Park St (DOR)	25
Woodward St & Pl (SB)	27
Woodway Rd (WEL)	81
Woodworth (DOR)	22
Woolsey Sq (JP)	30
Woolson (MAT)	26
Worcester (WEL)	81
Worcester (BEL)	78
Worcester (WAT)	72
Worcester (CAM)	39
Worcester Ln (WAL)	54
Worcester St & Pl	18
Wordsworth St & Ter (EB)	28
Worley (WRX)	32
Wormwood	02210
Woronoco Rd (NWY)	91
Worster (MED)	55
Worster Ter (WY)	88
Worth (MEL)	76
Worth Cir (NEW)	58
Worthen Rd (LEX)	73
Worthern Ave (WY)	88
Worthington (CAM)	38
Worthington (RXC)	20
Worthington Cir (BRA)	84
Worthington Rd (BRO)	46
Wren (WRX)	32
Wren Ter (QUI)	69
Wrentham (DOR)	24
Wright (LEX)	73
Wright (ARL)	74
Wright (STO)	80
Wright (CAM)	38
Wright (SWY)	90
Wright Ave (MED)	55
Wright Rd (NCE)	59
Wyatt St & Cir (SOM)	43
Wycliff (WRX)	32
Wycliff Rd (EWY)	89
Wycoma Way (WAL)	54
Wyeth St & Ct (MAL)	48
Wykeham Rd (WNW)	65
Wyllis Ave	
1-OUT (MAL) (ODD)	48
2-OUT (EV) (EVEN)	49
Wyman (WAB)	68
Wyman (WAL)	54
Wyman (MED)	55
Wyman (CAM)	40
Wyman (WIN)	52
Wyman Pl	16
Wyman Rd (LEX)	73
Wyman Rd (BRA)	84
Wyman Rd & Sq (CAM)	38

Boston (Con.)	021
Wyndmere Rd (MIL)	86
Wynnewood Rd (WEL)	81
Wynot Rd (BRA)	84
Wyola Pl (DOR)	21
Wyola Prospect (WAL)	54
Wyoming (DOR)	21
Wyoming Ave (N)	92
Wyoming Ave E & W (MEL)	76
Wyoming Ave & Pl (MAL)	48
Wyoming Hts & Ter (MEL)	76
Wyoming Rd (NWV)	60
Wyvern (ROS)	31
Yale (MED)	55
Yale Rd (ARL)	74
Yale Rd (NH)	94
Yale Ter (JP)	30
Yard Way (SB)	27
Yard Arm Ln (QUI)	69
Yarmouth	16
Yarmouth (EV)	49
Yarmouth Rd (WH)	81
Yarmouth Rd (CHH)	67
Yeamans (REV)	51
Yeoman St, Ct & Pl (ROX)	55
Yeomans Ave (MED)	55
Yerxa Rd (CAM)	40
Yerxa Rd (ARL)	74
Yetten Ter (WAL)	54
York (REV)	51
York (LEX)	73
York (DOR)	21
York Ave (WAT)	72
York Rd (WAB)	68
York Rd (BEL)	78
York St & Pl (CAM)	41
York Ter (BRO)	46
York Ter (MEL)	76
Yorktown (NQ)	71
Yorktown (WRX)	32
Yorktown (WS)	44
Youle (MEL)	76
Young (NQ)	71
Young (LEX)	73
Young Path (NCE)	59
Young Rd (WES)	93
Yuill Cir (HP)	36
Yukon Ave (WAT)	72
Yurick Rd (N)	92
Zamora St & Ct (JP)	30
Zeigler St & Pl (ROX)	19
Zeller (ROS)	31
Zoar Ave (LEX)	73

NUMBERED STREETS

1st (MEL)	76
1st (QUI)	69
1st	
1-140 (CAM)	41
141-OUT (CAM)	42
1st Ave (SOM)	43
1st thru 2nd St (WRX)	32
1st thru 3rd St (MAL)	48
1st thru 3rd St (SB)	27
1st thru 3rd St (WY)	88
1st thru 4th Ave (WAL)	54
1st thru 4th Ave (NH)	94
1st thru 4th St (LEX)	73
1st thru 9th St (MED)	55
2nd	
1-159 (CAM)	41

160-OUT (CAM)	42
2nd thru 3rd St (EV)	49
2nd thru 6th St (CHE)	50
3rd (ARL)	74
3rd	
1-245 (CAM) (ODD)	41
2-220 (CAM) (EVEN)	41
222-OUT (CAM) (EVEN)	42
247-OUT (CAM) (ODD)	42
3rd Ave (SOM)	43
3rd St Pl (SB)	27
4th (SB)	27
4th Ave (WY)	88
4th St Pl (SB)	27
5th	
1-199 (CAM)	41
200-OUT (CAM)	42
5th Ave (WAT)	72
5th thru 6th Ave (QUI)	69
5th thru 9th St (SB)	27
6th (MEL)	76
6th	
1-113 (CAM) (ODD)	41
2-118 (CAM) (EVEN)	41
115-OUT (CAM) (ODD)	42
120-OUT (CAM) (EVEN)	42
7th thru 8th St (CAM)	41
13th (MEL)	76

BROCKTON 024

POST OFFICE BOXES

Box Nos.		
1-128	Montello Sta	03
1-296	Campello Sta	03
1-972	Main Office	03

STATIONS, BRANCHES AND UNITS

Campello Sta	03
Center Street Sta	01
Montello Sta	03
General Delivery	03
Postmaster	03

APARTMENTS, HOTELS, MOTELS

Ardmore, 93 High	01
Bryant, 33 West Elm	01
Central 40 West Elm	01
Congress Inn, 1005 Belmont	01
Grayson, 32 High	01
Holiday Inn, Westgate Dr	01
West Elm, 56 West Elm	01

BUILDINGS

Ashland Heights Shopping Center, 466-72 E Ashland	02
Colonial Village, 626-32 Pleasant	01
Del'S Shopping Center, 459-465 Centre	02
East Shopping Plaza, 672-766 Crescent	02
East Side Shopping Center, 581-605 Center	02
Oak Village Shopping Center, 180-196 Oak	01

South Shopping Center 2071-2077 Main	01
Southgate Plaza 1640-1670 Main	01
West Shopping Center, 593-709 Belmont	01
Westgate Gardens Shopping Plaza, Westgate Drive	01

HOSPITALS

Brockton, 680 Center	02
Cardinal Cushing Gen Hospital, 235 No Pearl	01
Veterans Administration Hospital, 945 Belmont	01

CHICOPEE 010

POST OFFICE BOXES

Box Nos.		
A-V	Main Office	21
1-420	Chicopee Center Sta	14
1-680	Main Office	21

STATIONS, BRANCHES AND UNITS

Chicopee Center Sta	13
Westover A F B Sta	22
General Delivery	21
Postmaster	21

FALL RIVER 027

POST OFFICE BOXES

Box Nos.		
A-F	Somerset Br	26
A-O	South Sta	24
1-298	Flint Sta	23
1-326	Somerset Br	26
1-356	South Sta	24
1-2410	Main Office	22

STATIONS, BRANCHES AND UNITS

Flint Sta	23
Somerset Br	25
South Sta	24
General Delivery	22
Postmaster	22

HOSPITALS

Saint Anne's, 795 Middle St	22
Truesdale, 1820 Highland Ave	22
Union, Highland Ave	20

FALMOUTH 025

POST OFFICE BOXES

Box Nos.		
A-Z	Falmouth	41
1-736	Falmouth	41

Falmouth (Con.)   025

| 1-747 | Woods Hole Sta | 43 |
| AA-JJ | Falmouth | 41 |

STATIONS, BRANCHES AND UNITS

Woods Hole Sta	43
General Delivery	40
Postmaster	40

APARTMENTS, HOTELS, MOTELS

| Admiralty Apts | 40 |
| Greengate Apts | 40 |

BUILDINGS

| Marine Biological Lab | 43 |
| Woods Hole Oceanographic Inst | 43 |

HOSPITALS

| Falmouth | 40 |

LAWRENCE   018

POST OFFICE BOXES

Box Nos.
1-446	North Andover Br	45
1-518	Methuen Br	44
1-1517	Main Office	42

RURAL ROUTES

| 1,2 | 44 |
| 3 | 45 |

STATIONS, BRANCHES AND UNITS

Merrimack College Br	45
Methuen Br	44
North Andover Br	45
General Delivery	42
Postmaster	42

UNIVERSITIES AND COLLEGES

| Merrimack College | 45 |

LOWELL   018

POST OFFICE BOXES

Box Nos.
| 1-1600 | Main Office | 53 |
| 2001-2999 | Highland Sta | 51 |

STATIONS, BRANCHES AND UNITS

Highlands Sta	51
Kearney Square Sta	52
General Delivery	53
Postmaster	53

UNIVERSITIES AND COLLEGES

| Lowell State College | 54 |
| Lowell Technical Institute | 54 |

LYNN   019

POST OFFICE BOXES

Box Nos.
1-74	East Lynn Sta	04
1-86	Nahant Br	08
1-219	West Lynn Sta	05
1-294	Swampscott Br	07
1-951	Main Office	03
1001-1231	Saugus Br	06

STATIONS, BRANCHES AND UNITS

East Lynn Sta	04
Nahant Br	08
Saugus Br	06
Swampscott Br	07
West Lynn Sta	05
General Delivery	01
Postmaster	01

NEW BEDFORD   027

POST OFFICE BOXES

Box Nos.
A-A	Main Office	41
B-B	Main Office	41
C-C	Main Office	41
D-D	Main Office	42
E-E	Main Office	42
F-F	Main Office	42
G-G	Main Office	42
L-L	Lunds Corner Sta	45
M-M	Division Sta	44
N-N	North Sta	46
P-P	Padanaram Br	48
1-98	Nonquitt Br	48
1-118	Acushnet Br	43
1-237	North Dartmouth Br	47
1-268	South Dartmouth	48

RURAL ROUTES

1	43
2	48
3	47

STATIONS, BRANCHES AND UNITS

Acushnet Br	43
Division Street Sta	44
Lunds Corner Sta	45
Nonquitt Rural Br	48
North Sta	46
North Dartmouth Br	47
Padanaram Village Br	48
South Dartmouth Br	48
General Delivery	40
Postmaster	41

NORTH ATTLEBORO   027

POST OFFICE BOXES

Box Nos.
1-1112	Main Office	61
1201-1349	Attleboro Falls Sta	63
1501-1828	Plainville Br	62

RURAL ROUTES

| 1,2 | 60 |
| 3 | 62 |

STATIONS, BRANCHES AND UNITS

Attleboro Falls Sta	63
Plainville Br	62
General Delivery	60
Postmaster	60

PLYMOUTH   023

POST OFFICE BOXES

Box Nos.
1-128	No Ply Sta	60
1-260	Kingston Br	64
1-537	Main Office	60

RURAL ROUTES

1	60
2	64
3,4	60

STATIONS, BRANCHES AND UNITS

Kingston Br	64
North Plymouth Sta	60
General Delivery	60
Postmaster	60

SPRINGFIELD   011

POST OFFICE BOXES

Box Nos.
1-265	Brightwood Sta	07
1-317	Forest Park Sta	08
1-447	Highland Sta	09
1-3580	Main Office	01

STATIONS, BRANCHES AND UNITS

Brightwood Sta	07
Forest Park Sta	08
Highland Sta	09
Longmeadow Br	06
Tapley Street Annex Sta	01
General Delivery	01
Postmaster	01

HOSPITALS

Mercy, 233 Carew	04
Municipal, 1414 State	09
Shriners, 516 Carew	04
Springfield Medical Center, 759 Chestnut	07

Springfield (Con.)   011

Wesson Memorial, 140 High... 01
Wesson Womens, 735
    Chestnut 07

UNIVERSITIES AND COLLEGES

American International, 170
    Wilbraham Rd..................... 09
Junior Bay Path, 588
    Longmeadow...................... 06
Springfield, 263 Alden............ 09
Western New England, 1215
    Wilbraham Rd..................... 19

WORCESTER   016

POST OFFICE BOXES

Box Nos.
1-240   West Side Sta .. 02

1-295   Greendale Sta .. 06
1-1160   G P O
          Worcester........ 13
1601-1728   C Sta................ 07

0000149-
-0001591   Federal Sta....... 01

STATIONS, BRANCHES AND UNITS

Assumption College Sta.......... 09
Cherry Valley Br.................... 11
Greendale Sta........................ 06
Mount Saint James Sta........... 10
Parcel Post Sta...................... 04
Paxton Br.............................. 12
Webster Square Sta................ 03
West Side Sta........................ 02
Postmaster............................. 13

HOSPITALS

Doctors, 107 Lincoln 05
Fairlawn, 189 May 02
Hahnemann, 281 Lincoln....... 05

Memorial, 119 Belmont........... 05
Saint Vincent, 25 Winthrop..... 10
Worcester City, 71 Jaques
    Ave...................................... 10
Worcester State, 305
    Belmont............................... 04

UNIVERSITIES AND COLLEGES

Anna Maria............................ 12
Assumption, 500 Salisbury..... 09
Becker Junior, 61 Sever.......... 09
Clark University, 950 Main..... 10
Holy Cross, College St............ 10
Notre Dame Academy,
    Salisbury............................. 09
Quinsigamond Community
    College 670 Boylston W...... 06
State Teachers, 486
    Chandler.............................. 02
Worcester Academy, 81
    Providence........................... 04
Worcester Junior, 766 Main ... 08
Worcester Polytechnic
    Institute, Institute Rd.......... 09

MICHIGAN   State List of Post Offices

MICHIGAN
(Abbreviation: MI)

Acme....................................49610
Ada (1st)..............................49301
Addison................................49220
Adrian (1st)..........................49221
Afton....................................49705
Ahmeek................................49901
Airport, Br. Ypsilanti.............48197
Akron...................................48701
Alabaster, R. Br. Tawas City..48764
Alanson................................49706
Alba.....................................49611
Albion (1st)...........................49224
Alden...................................49612
Alger....................................48610
Algonac (1st)........................48001
Allegan (1st).........................49010
Allen....................................49227
Allen Park (1st).....................48101
Allendale..............................49401
Allenton...............................48002
Allouez.................................49805
Alma (1st).............................48801
Almont.................................48003
Alpena (1st)..........................49707
Alpha...................................49902
Alto.....................................49302
Amasa..................................49903
Anchorville...........................48004
Andrews, R. Br. Berrien
    Springs.............................49104
ANN ARBOR (1st) (see
    appendix)
Applegate.............................48401
Arcadia.................................49613
Argyle...................................48410
Armada.................................48005
Arnold, R. Br. Cornell............49819
Ashley..................................48806

Athens..................................49011
Atlanta..................................49709
Atlantic Mine.........................49905
Atlas....................................48411
Attica....................................48412
Au Gres................................48703
Au Train................................49806
Auburn..................................48611
Auburn Heights, Br. Pontiac...48057
Augusta.................................49012
Aura.....................................49906
Avoca...................................48006
Azalia...................................48110
Bach.....................................48704
Bad Axe (1st)........................48413
Bailey...................................49303
Baldwin.................................49304
Baltic....................................49907
Bancroft................................48414
Bangor (1st)..........................49013
Bannister...............................48807
Baraga..................................49908
Barbeau.................................49710
Bark River.............................49807
Baroda..................................49101
Barron Lake, R. Br. Niles.......49120
Barryton................................49305
Barton City............................48705
Bath......................................48808
BATTLE CREEK (1st) (see
    appendix)
Bay City (1st)........................48706
    A, Sta...............................48706
    University Center, R. Br......48710
Bay Port...............................48720
Bay View, Br. Petoskey.........49770
Bayshore, R. Br. Charlevoix...49711
Bear Lake.............................49614
Beaverton..............................48612
Bedford.................................49020

Beech, Br. Detroit..................48239
Beechwood............................49909
Belding (1st)..........................48809
Bellaire.................................49615
Belle River, R. Br. Saint
    Clair.................................48079
Belleville (1st).......................48111
Bellevue................................49021
Belmont................................49306
Bentley.................................48613
Benton Harbor (1st)...............49022
Benzonia...............................49616
Bergland...............................49910
Berkley, Br. Royal Oak..........48072
Berrien Center.......................49102
Berrien Springs (1st)..............49103
    Andrews, R. Br.................49104
Berville, R. Br. Allenton.........48002
Bessemer..............................49911
Beulah..................................49617
Big Bay.................................49808
Big Rapids (1st).....................49307
Birch Run..............................48415
BIRMINGHAM (1st) (see
    appendix)
Bitely....................................49309
Black River............................48721
Blanchard..............................49310
Blaney Park...........................49809
Blissfield (1st)........................49228
Bloomfield Hills (1st).............48013
Bloomingdale.........................49026
Boon....................................49618
Boyne City (1st)....................49712
Boyne Falls...........................49713
Bradley.................................49311
Brampton...............................49810
Branch..................................49402
Brant....................................48614
Breckenridge.........................48615

Breedsville.................................49027
Brethren....................................49619
Bridgeport (1st).........................48722
Bridgewater...............................48115
Bridgman (1st)...........................49106
Brightmoor, Sta. Detroit...........48223
Brighton (1st)............................48116
Brimley.....................................49715
Britton......................................49229
Brohman...................................49312
Bronson....................................49028
Brooklands, Br. Rochester........48063
Brooklyn...................................49230
Brown City................................48416
Bruce Crossing..........................49912
Brunswick.................................49313
Brutus......................................49716
Buchanan (1st)..........................49107
   Glendora, R. Br...................49114
Buckley.....................................49620
Burlington.................................49029
Burnips.....................................49314
Burr Oak...................................49030
Burt..48417
Burt Lake..................................49717
Byron..48418
Byron Center.............................49315
Cadillac (1st)............................49601
Cadmus....................................49231
Caledonia.................................49316
Calumet (1st)............................49913
   Kearsarge, R. Br..................49942
   Laurium, R. Br.....................49913
Camden.....................................49232
Canal, Sta. Sault Sainte
   Marie..................................49783
Cannonsburg.............................49317
Capac.......................................48014
Carland....................................48810
Carleton....................................48117
Carlshend.................................49811
Carney......................................49812
Caro (1st).................................48723
Carp Lake.................................49718
Carrollton.................................48724
Carson City...............................48811
Carsonville................................48419
Caseville...................................48725
Casnovia...................................49318
Caspian....................................49915
Cass City (1st)..........................48726
Cassopolis (1st)........................49031
Castle, Sta. Saginaw.................48606
Castle Park, R. Br. Holland.......49422
Cedar..49621
Cedar Lake...............................48812
Cedar River..............................49813
Cedar Springs...........................49319
Cedarville.................................49719
   Coryell Islands, R. Br..........49719
   Les Cheneaux Club, R.
   Br......................................49754
Cement City..............................49233
Center Line (1st).......................48015
Central Lake..............................49622
Centreville.................................49032
Ceresco.....................................49033
Champion..................................49814
Channing...................................49815
Charlevoix (1st).........................49720
   Bayshore, R. Br...................49711
Charlotte (1st)...........................48813

Chase..49623
Chassell....................................49916
Chatham....................................49816
Cheboygan (1st)........................49721
Chelsea (1st).............................48118
Chesaning (1st).........................48616
Chief...49624
Chippewa Lake.........................49320
Christmas, R. Br. Munising.......49862
Church Street, Sta. Flint...........48502
Clare (1st).................................48617
Clarklake...................................49234
Clarkston (1st)..........................48016
Clarksville.................................48815
Clawson (1st)............................48017
Clayton.....................................49235
Clifford.....................................48727
Climax......................................49034
Clinton......................................49236
Clio (1st)...................................48420
Cloverdale.................................49035
Cody, Sta. Flint.........................48507
Cohoctah...................................48816
Coldwater (1st).........................49036
Coleman....................................48618
College Park, Sta. Detroit.........48221
Coloma (1st).............................49038
   Hagar Shores, R. Br............49039
Colon..49040
Columbiaville............................48421
Comins......................................48619
Commerce, R. Br. Union
   Lake...................................48085
Comstock..................................49041
Comstock Park (1st)..................49321
Concord....................................49237
Conklin.....................................49403
Constantine...............................49042
Conway.....................................49722
Cooks..49817
Coopersville (1st)......................49404
Copemish...................................49625
Copper City...............................49917
Copper Harbor...........................49918
Coral...49322
Cornell......................................49818
   Arnold, R. Br.......................49819
Corunna....................................48817
Coryell Islands, R. Br.
   Cedarville...........................49719
Court, Sta. Kalamazoo (see
   appendix)
Covert..49043
   Palisades Park, R. Br...........49044
Covington...................................49919
Cross Village.............................49723
Croswell.....................................48422
Crystal......................................48818
Crystal Falls..............................49920
Curran.......................................48728
Curtis..49820
Custer.......................................49405
Dafter.......................................49724
Daggett.....................................49821
Dalton, R. Br. Muskegon..........49445
Dansville...................................48819
Davisburg..................................48019
Davison (1st).............................48423
De Tour Village.........................49725
De Witt.....................................48820
DEARBORN (1st) (see
   appendix)

Dearborn Heights (1st)..............48127
Decatur.....................................49045
Decker.......................................48426
Deckerville................................48427
Deerfield...................................49238
Deerton.....................................49822
Deford.......................................48729
Dolton.......................................49046
Denton, R. Br. Belleville...........48111
DETROIT (1st) (see
   appendix)
Detroit River, Sta. Detroit........48222
Dexter (1st)...............................48130
Dimondale................................48821
Dodgeville.................................49921
Dollar Bay................................49922
Dominican, Sta. Adrian............49221
Donken......................................49923
Dorr..49323
Doster, R. Br. Plainwell...........49080
Douglas.....................................49406
Dowagiac (1st).........................49047
Dowling.....................................49040
Downtown, Sta. Ann Arbor
   (see appendix)
Drayton Plains (1st)..................48020
Drummond Island.....................49726
Dryden......................................48428
Dundee......................................48131
Durand (1st)..............................48429
Dutton, R. Br. Grand Rapids....49511
Eagle..48822
Eagle Harbor, R. Br.
   Mohawk..............................49951
Eagle River................................49924

East Detroit (1st).......................48021
East Jordan...............................49727
East Lansing (1st).....................48823
East Leroy.................................49051
East Side, Sta. Flint..................48508
East Tawas................................48730
Eastlake....................................49626
Eastland Center, Br. Detroit......48236
Eastport.....................................49627
Eaton Rapids (1st).....................48827
Eau Claire.................................49111
Eben Junction...........................49825
   Rumely, R. Br.....................49826
Eckerman...................................49728
   Strongs, R. Br.....................49790
Ecorse, Br. Detroit....................48229
Edenville...................................48620
Edmore......................................48829
Edwardsburg..............................49112
   Union, R. Br........................49130
Elberta......................................49628
Elk Rapids.................................49629
Elkton.......................................48731
Ellsworth...................................49729
Elm Hall....................................48830
Elmira.......................................49730
Eloise..48132
Elsie..48831
Elwell..48832
Emmett......................................48022
Empire.......................................49630
Engadine...................................49827
Erie...48133
Escanaba (1st)..........................49829
Essexville (1st).........................48732
Eureka.......................................48833

Evart....................................49631
Ewen....................................49925
Fair Haven............................48023
Fairgrove..............................48733
Fairplain Plaza, Br. Benton
  Harbor................................49022
Fairview................................48621
Falmouth................................49632
Farmington (1st).....................48024
Farwell..................................48622
Fayette..................................49830
Federal Station, Br. Pontiac
  (see appendix)
Felch....................................49831
Fenkell, Sta. Detroit...............48238
Fennville................................49408
Fenton (1st)...........................48430
Fenwick..................................48834
Ferndale, Br. Detroit...............48220
Ferry, R. Br. Shelby...............49455
Ferrysburg............................49409
Fibre....................................49732
Fife Lake................................49633
Filer City..............................49634
Filion....................................48432
Fisher Building, Sta. Detroit....48202
Flat Rock (1st).......................48134
FLINT (1st) (see appendix)
Flushing (1st).........................48433
Forest Lake............................49832
Forestville............................48434
Fort Dearborn, Sta. Dearborn
  (see appendix)
Fort Shelby, Sta. Detroit (see
  appendix)
Foster City............................49834
Fostoria................................48435
Fountain................................49410
Fowler..................................48835
Fowlerville............................48836
Frandor, Br. Lansing...............48912
Frankenmuth (1st)...................48734
Frankfort..............................49635
Franklin, Br. Birmingham........48025
Fraser (1st)...........................48026
Frederic................................49733
Free Soil..............................49411
Freeland (1st).......................48623
Freeport................................49325
Fremont (1st).........................49412
Frontier................................49239
Fruitport..............................49415
Fulton..................................49052
Gaastra................................49927
Gagetown..............................48735
Gaines..................................48436
Galesburg (1st).....................49053
Galien..................................49113
Garden..................................49835
Garden City (1st)...................48135
Garnet, R. Br. Naubinway......49734
Gay......................................49928
Gaylord (1st).........................49735

General Post Office, Sta.
  Detroit................................48232
Genesee................................48437
Germfask..............................49836
Gibraltar, R. Br. Rockwood....48173
Gilford..................................48736
Gladstone (1st).....................49837
Gladwin (1st).........................48624

Glen Arbor............................49636
Glendora, R. Br. Buchanan....49114
Glenn....................................49416
Glennie..................................48737
Glenside, Br. Muskegon........49441
Gobles..................................49055
Goetzville..............................49736
Good Hart..............................49737
Goodells................................48027
Goodrich................................48438
Gould City............................49838
Gowen..................................49326
Grand Blanc (1st)...................48439
Grand Circus Park, Sta.
  Detroit................................48226
Grand Haven (1st)..................49417
Grand Junction.......................49056
Grand Ledge (1st)..................48837
Grand Marais.........................49839
GRAND RAPIDS (1st) (see
  appendix)
Grand River, Sta. Detroit.......48208
Grandville (1st).......................49418
Grant....................................49327
Grass Lake............................49240
Gratiot, Sta. Detroit...............48207
Grawn..................................49637
Grayling (1st).........................49738
Greenbush..............................48738
Greenfield Village, Sta.
  Dearborn..............................48120
Greenland..............................49929
Greenville (1st).......................48838
Gregory................................48137
Grind Stone City, R. Br. Port
  Austin................................48467
Grosse Ile (1st).......................48138
Grosse Pointe, Br. Detroit......48236
Gulliver................................49840
Gwinn (1st)...........................49841
  K I Sawyer A F B, Br.......49843
  Princeton, R. Br...............49875
Hadley..................................48440
Hagar Shores, R. Br.
  Coloma................................49039
Hale......................................48739
Hamburg................................48139
Hamilton................................49419
Hammond Bay, R. Br.
  Ocqueoc..............................49763
Hamtramck, Br. Detroit..........48212
Hancock (1st).........................49930
Hanover................................49241
Harbert................................49115
Harbor Beach.........................48441
Harbor Point, Br. Harbor
  Springs................................49740
Harbor Springs.......................49740
Hardwood..............................49844
Harper, Sta. Detroit...............48213
Harper Woods, Br. Detroit......48236
Harrietta................................49638
Harris..................................49845
Harrison................................48625
Harrisville..............................48740
Harsens Island.......................48028
Hart......................................49420
Hartford (1st).........................49057
Hartland................................48029
Harvey, Br. Marquette............49855
Haslett..................................48840
Hastings (1st).........................49058

Hawks..................................49743
Hazel Park (1st).....................48030
Hell, R. Br. Pinckney.............48169
Hemlock................................48626
Henderson..............................48841
Henry Street, Br. Muskegon....49441
Hermansville.........................49847
Herron..................................49744
Hersey..................................49639
Hesperia................................49421
Hessel..................................49745
Hickory Corners.....................49060
Higgins Lake.........................48627
Highland................................48031
Highland Park, Br. Detroit......48203
Hillman..................................49746
Hillsdale (1st).........................49242
Holland (1st).........................49423
  Castle Park, R. Br...........49422
  Windmill Island, Sta.........49423
Holly (1st)............................48442
Holt (1st)..............................48842
Holton..................................49425
Homer..................................49245
Honor..................................49640
Hope....................................48628
Hopkins................................49328
Horton..................................49246
Houghton (1st).......................49931
Houghton Lake.......................48629
Houghton Lake Heights..........48630
Howard City..........................49329
Howell (1st)...........................48843
Hoxeyville............................49641
Hubbard Lake.........................49747
Hubbardston..........................48845
Hubbell..................................49934
Hudson..................................49247
Hudsonville............................49426
Hulbert..................................49748
Huntington Woods, Br. Royal
  Oak......................................48070
Ida......................................48140
Idlewild................................49642
Imlay City..............................48444
Indian River...........................49749
Ingalls..................................49848
Inkster (1st)...........................48141
Interlochen............................49643
Ionia (1st)............................48846
Iron Mountain (1st)................49801
Iron River (1st).......................49935
  Alvin, R. Br.......................49936
Irons....................................49644
Ironwood (1st).......................49938
Ishpeming (1st)......................49849
Isle Royale National Park, R.
  Br. Grand Portage M N.......55617
Ithaca..................................48847
JACKSON (1st) (see
  appendix)
Jamestown............................49427
Jasper..................................49248
Jeddo..................................48032
Jefferson, Sta. Detroit...........48214
Jenison (1st)..........................49428
Jerome..................................49249
Johannesburg.........................49751
Jones....................................49061
Jonesville (1st).......................49250
Joyfield, Sta. Detroit.............48228
K I Sawyer A F B, Br. Gwinn..49843

KALAMAZOO (1st) (see appendix)
Kaleva.................................49645
Kalkaska..............................49646
Karlin..................................49647
Kawkawlin............................48631
Kearsarge, R. Br. Calumet......49942
Keego Harbor (1st)................48033
Kendall................................49062
Kensington, Sta. Detroit.........48224
Kent City..............................49330
Kenton................................49943
Kentwood, Br. Grand Rapids....49508
Kercheval, Sta. Detroit (see appendix)
Kewadin..............................49648
Keweenaw Bay.......................49944
Kincheloe A F B, Br. Sault Sainte Marie.......................49788
Kinde..................................48445
Kingsford, Br. Iron Mountain....49801
Kingsley...............................49649
Kingston..............................48741
Kinross................................49752
L'Anse.................................49946
La Salle...............................48145
Lachine...............................49753
Lacota.................................49063
Laingsburg...........................48848
Lake....................................48632
Lake Ann.............................49650
Lake City.............................49651
Lake George.........................48633
Lake Leelanau.......................49653
Lake Linden..........................49945
Lake Odessa.........................48849
Lake Orion (1st)....................48035
Lakeland..............................48143
Lakeport, R. Br. Port Huron.....48060
Lakeside..............................49116
Lakeview.............................48850
Lakeville..............................48036
Lambertville..........................48144
Lamont................................49430
LANSING (1st) (see appendix)
Lapeer (1st).........................48446
   Lum, R. Br..........................48452
Lathrup Village, Br. Southfield.........................48075
Laurium, Br. Calumet.............49913
Lawrence.............................49064
Lawton.................................49065
Le Graph, Br. Dearborn..........48125
Le Roy.................................49655
Leland.................................49654
Lennon................................48449
Leonard...............................48038
Leonidas.............................49066
Les Cheneaux Club, R. Br. Cedarville.........................49754
Leslie..................................49251
Levering..............................49755
Lewiston..............................49756
Lexington.............................48450
Limestone............................49851
Lincoln................................48742
Lincoln Park (1st)..................48146
Linden.................................48451
Linwood, Sta. Detroit.............48206
Linwood...............................48634
Litchfield.............................49252
Little Lake...........................49833

Livernois, Sta. Detroit............48210
LIVONIA (1st) (see appendix)
Long Lake............................48743
Loretto, R. Br. Vulcan............49852
Lowell (1st)..........................49331
Ludington (1st).....................49431
Lum, R. Br. Lapeer................48452
Luna Pier.............................48157
Lupton.................................48635
Luther.................................49656
Luzerne...............................48636
Lyons..................................48851
M Fifty Nine Plaza, Br. Pontiac............................48054
Macatawa............................49434
Mackinac Island....................49757
Mackinaw City......................49701
Madison Heights, Br. Royal Oak.................................48071
Mancelona...........................49659
Manchester..........................48158
Manistee (1st)......................49660
Manistique (1st)....................49854
   Thompson, R. Br................49889
Manitou Beach......................49253
Manton................................49663
Maple, Sta. Dearborn.............48120
Maple City............................49664
Maple Rapids........................48853
Marcellus.............................49067
Marenisco............................49947
Marine City (1st)...................48039
Marion.................................49665
Marlette (1st).......................48453
Marne.................................49435
Marquette (1st).....................49855
Marshall (1st).......................49068
Martin.................................49070
Marysville (1st).....................48040
Mason (1st)..........................48854
Mass...................................49948
Mattawan............................49071
Maybee, Br. Monroe...............48161
Mayfield..............................49666
Mayville...............................48744
Mc Bain..............................49657
Mc Brides............................48852
Mc Gregor, R. Br. Deckerville........................48427
Mc Millan.............................49853
Mears..................................49436
Mecosta..............................49332
Melvin.................................48454
Melvindale, Br. Dearborn........48122
Memphis..............................48041
Mendon...............................49072
Menominee (1st)...................49858
Merrill.................................48637
Merritt.................................49667
Merriweather........................49949
Mesick................................49668
Metamora............................48455
Metropolitan Airport, Br Detroit.............................48242
Metz, R. Br. Posen................49758
Michigamme..........................49861
Michigan Avenue, Sta. Lansing (see appendix)
Michigan Center....................49254
Middlebelt, R. Br. Romulus......48174
Middleton.............................48856
Middleville............................49333
Midland (1st)........................48640

Milan (1st)...........................48160
Milburg, R. Br. Benton Harbor.............................49022
Milford (1st).........................48042
Millbrook..............................49334
Millersburg..........................49759
Millington............................48746
Milwaukee Junction, Sta. Detroit.............................48211
Minden City..........................48456
Mio.....................................48647
Mohawk Eagle Harbor, R. Br..........49951
Moline.................................49335
Monroe (1st)........................48161
Montague (1st)......................49437
Montgomery..........................49255
Montrose.............................48457
Moore Park, R. Br. Three Rivers.............................49093
Moorestown, R. Br. Lake City.................................49651
Moran.................................49760
Morenci...............................49256
Morley.................................49336
Morrice...............................48857
Moscow...............................49257
Mosherville..........................49258
Mott Park, Sta. Flint..............48504
Mount Clemens (1st)..............48043
   Selfridge A F B, Br.............48045
Mount Elliott, Sta. Detroit.......48234
Mount Morris (1st).................48458
Mount Pleasant (1st)..............48858
Muir....................................48860
Mullett Lake.........................49761
Mulliken...............................48861
Munger................................48747
Munising (1st).......................49862
Munith.................................49259
Munson...............................49260
MUSKEGON (1st) (see appendix)
Muskegon Heights, Br. Muskegon..........................49444
Nadeau................................49863
Nahma.................................49864
Napoleon..............................49261
Nashville..............................49073
National City.........................48748
National Mine........................49865
Naubinway............................49762
Nazareth..............................49074
Negaunee (1st)......................49866
Nestoria..............................49867
New Baltimore.......................48047
New Boston..........................48164
New Buffalo (1st)...................49117
New Era...............................49446
New Haven...........................48048
New Hudson..........................48165
New Lothrop..........................48460
New Richmond.......................49447
New Troy..............................49119
Newaygo..............................49337
Newberry (1st)......................49868
Newport...............................48166
Niles (1st)............................49120
Nisula.................................49952
North Adams.........................49262
North Bradley........................48648
North Branch........................48461
North End, Sta. Detroit (see

appendix)
North Escanaba, Sta.
  Escanaba 49829
North Lansing, Sta. Lansing
  (see appendix)
North Muskegon, Br.
  Muskegon 49445
North Side, Sta. Flint 48505
North Star 48862
North Street 48049
Northeast, Sta. Livonia 48152
Northgate, Br. Grand
  Rapids 49505
Northland 49869
Northland Center, Sta.
  Southfield 48075
Northport 49670
Northville (1st) 48167
Northwestern, Sta. Detroit ..48204
Norvell 49263
Norway 49870
Nottawa 49075
Novi (1st) 48050
Nunica 49448
Oak Grove 48863
Oak Park, Br. Detroit 48237
Oak Ridge, Sta. Royal Oak ..48073
Oakley 48649
Ocqueoc 49763
Oden 49764
Okemos (1st) 48864
Old Mission 49673
Olivet 49076
Omena 49674
Omer 48749
Onaway 49765
Onekama 49675
Onondaga 49264
Onsted 49265
Ontonagon 49953
Orchard Lake, Br. Keego
  Harbor 48033
Orleans 48865
Ortonville 48462
Oscoda (1st) 48750
  Wurtsmith A F B, Br. 48753
Oshtemo 49077
Osseo 49266
Ossineke 49766
Otisville 48463
Otsego (1st) 49078
Ottawa Lake 49267
Otter Lake 48464
Ovid 48866
Owasippe, R. Br. Twin Lake ..49457
Owendale 48754
Owosso (1st) 48867
Oxford (1st) 48051
Painesdale 49955
Palisades Park, R. Br.
  Covert 49044
Palmer 49871
Palms 48465
Palmyra 49268
Palo 48870
Paradise 49768
Parchment, Br. Kalamazoo ..49004
Paris 49338
Park Grove, Sta. Detroit 48205
Park Plaza, Sta. Lincoln
  Park 48146
Parma 49269
Paulding, R. Br. Bruce

Crossing 49956
Paw Paw (1st) 49079
Pearl Beach 48052
Peck 48466
Pelkie 49958
Pellston 49769
Penobscot, Sta. Detroit 48226
Pentwater 49449
Perkins 49872
Perrinton 48871
Perronville 49873
Perry 48872
Petersburg 49270
Petoskey (1st) 49770
Pewamo 48873
Pickford 49774
Pierson 49339
Pigeon 48755
Pinckney 48169
Pinconning (1st) 48650
Pittsford 49271
Plainwell (1st) 49080
Plaza, Br. Battle Creek 49015
Pleasant Lake 49272
Pleasant Ridge, Br. Royal
  Oak 48069
Plymouth (1st) 48170
Pointe Aux Barques, R. Br.
  Port Austin 48467
Pointe Aux Pins 49775
Pompeii 48874
PONTIAC (1st) (see
  appendix)
Port Austin 48467
Port Hope 48468
Port Huron (1st) 48060
Port Sanilac 48469
Portage (1st) 49081
Portland (1st) 48875
Posen 49776
  Metz, R. Br. 49758
Potterville 48876
Powers 49874
Prattville 49273
Prescott 48756
Presque Isle 49777
Princeton, R. Br. Gwinn 49875
Prudenville 48651
Pullman 49450
Quincy 49082
Quinnesec 49876
Raco 49778
Raisinville, R. Br. Monroe ..48161
Ralph 49877
Ramsay 49959
Rapid City 49676
Rapid River 49878
Ravenna 49451
Reading 49274
Redford, Sta. Detroit 48219
Redford Heights, Br. Detroit ..48240
Reed City (1st) 49677
Reeds Lake, Br. Grand
  Rapids 49506
Reese 48757
Remus 49340
Republic 49879
Rhodes 48652
Richland 49083
Richmond (1st) 48062
Richville 48758
Ridgeway 49275
Riga 49276

River Rouge, Br. Detroit 48218
Riverdale 48877
Riverside 49084
Riverview, Br. Wyandotte 48192
Rives Junction 49277
Rochester (1st) 48063
Rock 49880
Rockford (1st) 49341
Rockland 49960
Rockwood 48173
Rodney 49342
Rogers City (1st) 49779
Rollin 49278
Romeo (1st) 48065
Romulus (1st) 48174
Roosevelt Park, Br.
  Muskegon 49444
Roscommon 48653
Rose City 48654
Rosebush 48878
Roseville (1st) 48066
Rothbury 49452
ROYAL OAK (1st) (see
  appendix)
Ruby, R. Br. Goodells 48027
Rudyard 49780
Rumely, R. Br. Eben
  Junction 49826
Ruth 48470
SAGINAW (1st) (see
  appendix)
Sagola 49881
Saint Charles 48655
Saint Clair (1st) 48079
SAINT CLAIR SHORES (1st)
  (see appendix)
Saint Helen 48656
Saint Ignace 49781
Saint James 49782
Saint Johns (1st) 48879
Saint Joseph (1st) 49085
Saint Louis (1st) 48880
Salem 48175
Saline (1st) 48176
Samaria 48177
Sand Creek 49279
Sand Lake 49343
Sandusky (1st) 48471
Sanford 48657
Saranac (1st) 48881
Saugatuck 49453
Sault Sainte Marie (1st) 49783
  Canal, Sta. 49783
  Kincheloe A F B, Br. 49788
Sawyer 49125
Schaffer 49882
Schoolcraft 49087
Scotts 49088
Scottville 49454
Sears 49679
Sebewaing 48759
Selfridge A F B, Br. Mount
  Clemens 48045
Seneca 49280
Seney 49883
Seven Oaks, Sta. Detroit 48235
Seymour Square, Sta. Grand
  Rapids 49510
Shaftsburg 48882
Shelby 49455
Shelbyville 49344
Shepherd 48883

346

Sheridan	48884
Sherwood	49089
Shingleton	49884
Shopping Center, Br. Monroe	48161
Sidnaw	49961
Sidney	48885
Silverwood	48760
Sister Lakes, R. Br. Dowagiac	49047
Six Lakes	48886
Skandia	49885
Skanee	49962
Skidway Lake, R. Br. Prescott	48756
Smiths Creek	48074
Smyrna	48887
Snover	48472
Sodus	49126
Somerset	49281
Somerset Center	49282
South, Sta. Warren (see appendix)	
South Boardman	49680
South Branch	48761
South Cedar Street Annex, Sta. Lansing (see appendix)	
South Haven (1st)	49090
South Lyon (1st)	48178
South Range	49963
South Rockwood	48179
Southfield (1st)	48075
Southgate, Br. Wyandotte	48192
Southkent, Br. Grand Rapids	49508
Southland Center, Sta. Taylor	48180
Spalding	49886
Sparta (1st)	49345
Spring Arbor	49283
Spring Lake (1st)	49456
Springfield, Br. Battle Creek	49015
Springport	49284
Springwells, Sta. Detroit	48209
Spruce	48762
Stalwart	49789
Stambaugh	49964
Standish	48658
Stanton	48888
Stanwood	49346
State Center, Br. Saginaw	48602
Stephenson	49887
Sterling	48659
STERLING HEIGHTS (see appendix)	
Stevensville (1st)	49127
Stockbridge	49285
Stony Lake, R. Br. Shelby	49455
Strathmoor, Sta. Detroit	48227
Stronach	49681
Strongs, R. Br. Eckerman	49790
Sturgis (1st)	49091
Sumner	48889
Sunfield	48890
Suttons Bay	49682
Swartz Creek (1st)	48473

Tawas City (1st)	48763
Alabaster, R. Br.	48764
Taylor (1st)	48180
Tecumseh (1st)	49286
Tekonsha	49092
Teleford, Sta. Dearborn	48128
Temperance (1st)	48182
Thompson, R. Br. Manistique	49889
Thompsonville	49683
Three Oaks	49128
Three Rivers (1st)	49093
Tipton	49287
Toivola	49965
Topinabee	49791
Tower	49792
Township, Br. Ypsilanti	48197
Traunik	49890
Traverse City (1st)	49684
Trenary	49891
Trenton (1st)	48183
Trimountain	49966
Trout Creek	49967
Trout Lake	49793
Troy (1st)	48084
Trufant	49347
Turner	48765
Tuscola, R. Br. Vassar	48769
Tustin	49688
Twin Lake	49457
Twining	48766
Ubly	48475
Union, R. Br. Edwardsburg	49130
Union City	49094
Union Lake (1st)	48085
Commerce, R. Br.	48085
White Lake, R. Br.	48086
Union Pier	49129
Unionville	48767
University Center, R. Br. Bay City	48710
Urbandale, Sta. Battle Creek	49017
Utica (1st)	48087
Sterling Heights, Br.	48077
Vandalia	49095
Vanderbilt	49795
Vandercook Lake, Br. Jackson	49203
Vassar (1st)	48768
Tuscola, R. Br.	48769
Vermontville	49096
Vernon	48476
Vestaburg	48891
Veterans Administration Hosp, Sta. Iron Mountain	49801
Vicksburg (1st)	49097
Vulcan	49892
Loretto, R. Br.	49852
Wabaningo, R. Br. Whitehall	49463
Wakefield	49968
Waldron	49288
Walhalla	49458
Walker, Br. Grand Rapids	49504
Walkerville	49459
Wallace	49893
Walled Lake (1st)	48088

WARREN (1st) (see appendix)	
Washington	48094
Waterford (1st)	48095
Waters	49797
Watersmeet	49969
Watervliet	49098
Watton	49970
Waverly, Br. Lansing	48917
Wayland (1st)	49348
Wayne (1st)	48184
Westland, Br.	48185
Webberville	48892
Weidman	48893
Wells	49894
Wellston	49689
Wequetonsing, Br. Harbor Springs	49740
West Bay, Br. Traverse City	49684
West Branch (1st)	48661
West Main Street, Sta. Midland	48640
West Olive	49460
Westland, Br. Wayne	48185
Weston	49289
Westphalia	48894
Wetmore	49895
Wheeler	48662
White Cloud	49349
White Lake, R. Br. Union Lake	48086
White Pigeon	49099
White Pine	49971
Whitefish Point	49798
Whitehall (1st)	49461
Wabaningo, R. Br.	49463
Whitmore Lake	48189
Whittaker	48190
Whittemore	48770
Williamsburg	49690
Williamston	48895
Willis	48191
Wilson	49896
Windmill Island, Sta. Holland	49423
Winn	48896
Winona	49972
Wixom (1st)	48096
Wolf Lake, Br. Muskegon	49442
Wolverine	49799
Woodhaven, Br. Trenton	48183
Woodland	48897
Wurtsmith A F B, Br. Oscoda	48753
Wyandotte (1st)	48192
Wyoming, Br. Grand Rapids	49509
Wyoming Park, Br. Grand Rapids	49509
Yale	48097
Ypsilanti (1st)	48197
Zeeland (1st)	49464

ANN ARBOR 481

POST OFFICE BOXES

Box Nos.
A-D	Main Office	06
1-999	Downtown Sta	07
A-1-D-I	Main Office	06
1000-2199	Main Office Sta	06

RURAL ROUTES

1	03
2	05
3,4	03
5	04
6	05

STATIONS, BRANCHES AND UNITS

Downtown Sta	07
General Delivery	06
Postmaster	06

APARTMENTS, HOTELS, MOTELS

Alpine Manor, 1500 Pine Valley	04
Ann Arbor, Woods, 2167 Medford	04
Apartments Limited, 611 Church	04
Arbor Forest, 721 Forest Ave	04
Arbor Hills, 2000 Huron Pky	04
Arbor Lodge, 3245 Washtenaw Ave	04
Arbor Park, 2505 Ellsworth Rd E	04
Arbor Valley, 1500 Plymouth Rd	05
Bell Tower Motor Inn, 300 S Thayer	04
Brookside, 1513 Jones Dr	05
Campus Inn, 605 E Huron	08
Chapel Hill Townhouses, 300 Green Rd	05
Chatham Village, 2000 Pauline Blvd	03
Colonial Square, 3012 Williamsburg	04
Forest Plaza, 715 Forest Ave	04
Geddes Lakes Townhouses, Lakehaven Dr	05
Georgetown Manor, 2800 Page Ave	04
Glencoe Hills, 2236 Glencoe Hills Dr	04
Greenbrier, 3505 Greenbrier Dr	05
Hearth Stone, 1500 Pine Valley	04
Hillside Manor, 2000 Commerce	03
Holiday Inn-East, 3750 Washtenaw Ave	04
Holiday Inn-West, 2900 Jackson Ave	03
Howard Johnsons Motor Lodge, 2380 Carpenter Rd	04
Huron Towers, 2220 Fuller Rd	05
Imperial, 2315 Packard	04

Independence, 2407 Packard	04
Inn America, 3250 Washtenaw Ave	04
Island Drive, 1000 Island Dr	05
Lamp Post, 2424 E Stadium Blvd	04
Longshore Town Houses, 517 Kellogg	05
Maiden Lane, 1102 Maiden Ln Ct	05
Maple Ridge Manor, 2200 Dexter Ave	03
Maynard House, 400 Maynard	08
Michigan League, 227 S Ingalls	04
Michigan Union, 530 S State	04
Park Plaza, 1320 S University	04
Pontiac Hts Cooperative, 2319 Arrow Wood Trl	05
Ramada Inn, 126 E Huron	08
Ramada Inn, 2800 Jackson Ave	03
River House, 1200 Island Dr	05
Riverside Park Pl, 1050 Wall	05
Spruce Knob, 2960 Birch Hollow Dr	04
Statler Hilton Inn, 610 Hilton Dr	04
Strawberry Hill, 2738 Golfside	04
Tiffany 1 & 2 731 & 736 Packard	04
Tower Plaza, 555 E. William	08
Town & Country, 2578 Carpenter Rd	04
Traver Knoll, 1023 Barton Dr	05
University Towers, 536 Forest Ave	04
University Towne Houses, 2505 Ellsworth Rd E	04
University, 1000 Broadway	05
Village Green, Village Green Ln	05
Village Green, 4800 Washtenaw Ave	04
Walden Hills, 2102-2120 Pauline Blvd	03
Weber'S Inn, 3050 Jackson Ave	03
Woodbury Gardens, 1865 Woodbury Ave	04
Woodland Hills, 4300 Packard	04
Ym-Ywca, 350 S 5th Ave	08

BUILDINGS

Ann Arbor Trust, 100 S Main	08
Brooks, 201 E Liberty	08
City Center, 220 E Huron	08
City Hall, 100 N 5th Ave	08
County, 101 E Huron	08
First National, 201 S Main	08
Fritz, 103 E Liberty	08
Gunn, 506 E Liberty	08
Huron Valley Bank, 125 S 5th Ave	08
Hutzel, 110 E Liberty	08
Kresge, 204 S Main	08
Michigan Theatre, 601 E Liberty	08

Municipal Court, 110 W Huron	08
National Bank & Trust, 125 S Main	08
National Sanitation Foundation, 3475 Plymouth Rd	06
Nickels Arcade, 300 Maynard	08
Professional, 425 E Washington	08
Trick, 725 N University	04
Wolverine, 202 E Washington	08

HOSPITALS

Mercywood, 4038 Jackson Rd Po Box 1127	06
Parkview Medical Center, 1000 Wall	05
St Joseph Mercy, 326 N Ingalls	04
University, 1405 E Ann	04
Veterans, 2215 Fuller	05

UNIVERSITIES AND COLLEGES

Concordia, 4090 Geddes Rd	05
University Of Michigan, Central Campus	04
University Of Michigan, North Campus	05
Washtenaw Community, 204 E Huron Po Box 345	07

BATTLE CREEK 490

RURAL ROUTES

1,2,3,4,5,6,7,8,9,10,11,12,13, 14	17

STATIONS, BRANCHES AND UNITS

Plaza Br	15
Springfield Br	15
Urbandale Sta	17
General Delivery	16
Postmaster	16

APARTMENTS, HOTELS, MOTELS

Cherry Hill Manor	17
Hart Hotel, 31 N Washington	14
Holiday Inn, Capital Ave & I 94	15
Howard Johnson'S Motor Lodge, 2590 Capital Ave SW	15
Kellogg Inn, 258 Champion	17
Williams House, 46 E Michigan Ave	14

BUILDINGS

Capital, 37 Capital Ave NE	14
City Hall, E Michigan Ave	14
Federal Bldg, 50 N Washington	17
Michigan Nat Bank Bldg, 1 W Michigan Ave	14

Battle Creek (Con.) 490

Post Bldg, 65 W Michigan
Ave 14
Security Tower, 25 W
Michigan Ave.............. 14
Wolverine Tower, 70 W
Michigan Ave.............. 14

HOSPITALS

American Legion, Evergreen
Rd 16
Battle Creek Sanitarium, 197
N Washington 16
Community, 200 Tompkins 16
Lakeview General, 80 N 20th... 15
Leila Y Post, 9 Emmett.......... 16
Veterans Administration......... 16

BIRMINGHAM 480

POST OFFICE BOXES

Box Nos.
1-547   Main Office 12

STATIONS, BRANCHES AND UNITS

Franklin Br 25
General Delivery 12
Postmaster 12

DEARBORN 481

POST OFFICE BOXES

Box Nos.
1-1999   Main Office 21
2001-2599   Fort Dearborn
            Sta.................. 23
3001-3399   Melvindale Br.... 22
4001-4699   Maple St Sta...... 26
5001-5399   Teleford Sta...... 28

STATIONS, BRANCHES AND UNITS

Fort Dearborn Sta.................... 23
Greenfield Village Sta.............. 20
Le Graph Br............................ 25
Maple Sta................................ 20
Melvindale Br 22
Teleford Sta 28
General Delivery 20
Postmaster 20

APARTMENTS, HOTELS, MOTELS

Congress Inn 12800
Michigan Avenue 26
Dearborn Inn 20301 Oakwood
Blvd...................................... 24
Dearborn Towers 22700
Garrison 24
Dearborn Towne House 2101
S Telegraph Rd 24

DETROIT 482

POST OFFICE BOXES

Box Nos.
A-D   Kensington
            Sta................ 24
A-L   Grand River
            Sta................ 08
U-Z   North End Sta.. 02
1-86   Kensington
            Sta................ 24
1-87   Brightmoor
            Sta................ 23
1-120   Ferndale Br 20
1-121   River Rouge
            Br.................. 18
1-149   Hamtramck Br.... 12
1-1130   College Park
            Sta................ 21
1-3199   Fort Shelby
            Sta................ 31
A 1/2
1-A-1599   General Post
            Office Sta....... 32
401-548   Northwestern
            Sta................ 04
601-746   Linwood Sta 06
1962-1968   Seven Oaks
            Sta................ 35
3201-3389   Jefferson Sta.... 14
3401-3671   Highland Park
            Br.................. 03
3701-3786   Kercheval Sta.... 15
3701-3846   Oak Park Br 37
3801-3886   Park Grove Sta.... 05
3901-4016   Strathmoor
            Sta................ 27
4401-4486   Joyfield Sta...... 28
4501-4587   Ecorse Br.......... 29
4601-6486   Mount Elliott
            Sta................ 34
4701-4949   Redford Sta 19
5001-5244   Grosse Pointe
            Br.................. 36
5001-5399   Seven Oaks
            Sta................ 35
5301-5446   Milwaukee
            Junction Sta..... 11
5501-5616   Fenkell Sta 38
5701-5816   Beech Br 39
5901-6017   Livernois Sta 10
6501-6724   Redford
            Heights Br....... 40
6801-6884   Grosse Pointe
            Br.................. 36
7001-7499   North End Sta 02
7501-7699   Springwells
            Sta................ 09
7701-7899   Gratiot Sta....... 07
7901-8017   Kercheval Sta.... 15
8100-8399   Harper Sta........ 13
8501-8699   Kensington
            Sta................ 24
8851-8938   Oak Park Br 37
9101-9154   Springwells
            Sta................ 09
9501-9590   North End Sta 02
03001-03999 Highland Park
            Br.................. 03
05001-05999 Park Grove Sta.... 05
08001-08999 Grand River
            Sta................ 08

10001-10199 Livernois......... 10
14001-14999 Jefferson Sta 14
27001-27999 Strathmoor
            Sta................ 27
35001-35999 Seven Oaks
            Sta................ 35

STATIONS, BRANCHES AND UNITS

Beech Br 39
Brightmoor Sta 23
College Park Sta 21
Detroit River Sta 22
Eastland Center Br 36
Ecorse Br............................... 29
Fenkell Sta 38
Ferndale Br............................ 20
Fisher Building Sta 02
Fort Shelby Sta....................... 26
General Post Office Sta 32
Grand Circus Park Sta 26
Grand River Sta 08
Gratiot Sta 07
Grosse Pointe Br 36
Hamtramck Br........................ 12
Harper Sta 13
Harper Woods Br 36
Highland Park Br 03
Jefferson Sta 14
Joyfield Sta 28
Kensington Sta 24
Kercheval Sta......................... 15
Linwood Sta........................... 06
Livernois Sta 10
Metropolitan Airport Br.......... 42
Milwaukee Junction Sta 11
Mount Elliott Sta.................... 34
North End Sta......................... 01
Northwestern Sta.................... 04
Oak Park Br............................ 37
Park Grove Sta 05
Penobscot Sta 26
Redford Sta 19
Redford Heights Br 40
River Rouge Br........................ 18
Seven Oaks Sta 35
Springwells Sta...................... 09
Strathmoor Sta 27
General Delivery 26
Postmaster 33

APARTMENTS, HOTELS, MOTELS

Abington, 700 Seward............. 02
Alden Park Manor, 8100
Jefferson E........................... 14
American, 408 Temple............. 01
Chateau Frontenac, 10410
Jefferson E........................... 14
Executive House, 114 Adams
W... 26
International Inn, 5440 Cass.. 02
Jeffersonian, 9000 Jefferson
E... 14
Lafayette Towers, 1321
Orleans................................ 07
Lafayette Townhouses, 1321
Nicolet Pl 07
Leland House, 1701 Cass........ 26
Madison-Lenox, 230 Madison.. 26
Park Shelton, 15 Kirby E......... 02
Pavilion, 1 Lafayette
Plaisance.............................. 07

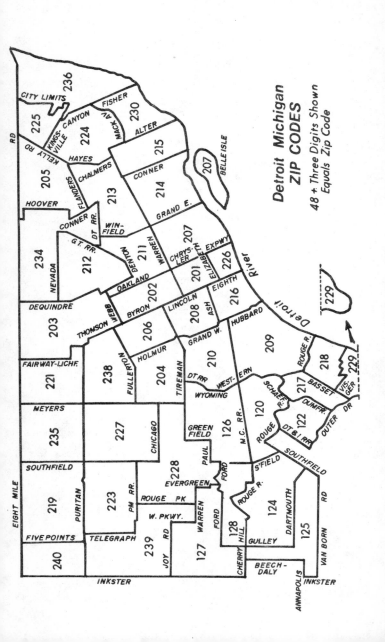

Detroit Michigan ZIP CODES

48 + Three Digits Shown Equals Zip Code

Detroit (Con.) 482

Pick-Fort Shelby, 525
  Lafayette Blvd..................... 31
Pontchartrain, 2 Washington
  Blvd.................................... 26
River House Cooperative
  Incorporated, 8900
  Jefferson E......................... 14
Saint Regis, 3017 Grand
  Blvd W............................... 02
Seventy West Apts, 70
  Alexandrine W.................... 01
Seville, 3160 2nd Blvd.......... 01
Sheraton-Cadillac, 1114
  Washington Blvd................. 31
Statler Hilton, 1539
  Washington Blvd................. 31
Town House, 1511 1st........... 26
Tuller, 521 Park Ave............. 26
Whittier, 415 Burns Dr.......... 14

BUILDINGS

Book Or Tower, 1249
  Washington Blvd................. 26
Boulevard Center, 6560
  Cass.................................. 02
Boulevard, 7310 Woodward ... 02
Broderick Tower, 10 Witherell. 26
Buhl, 535 Griswold................ 26
Cadillac Square Or Tower,
  Cadillac Sq & Bates............ 26
City-County, 2 Woodward 26
Club-Exchange, 150 Bagley ... 26
Commonwealth, 719
  Griswold............................ 26
David Stott, 1150 Griswold.... 26
David Whitney, 1553
  Woodward........................... 26
Federal, 231 Lafayette Blvd... 26
First Federal, 1001
  Woodward........................... 26
First National, 660
  Woodward........................... 26
Fisher, 3011 Grand Blvd W ... 02
Ford, 615 Griswold................ 26
Free Press, 321 Lafayette
  Blvd.................................. 26
General Motors, 3044 Grand
  Blvd W............................... 02
Griswold Building, 1214
  Griswold............................ 26
Guardian, 500 Griswold......... 26
Kales, 76 Adams W................ 26
Lafayette, 149 Michigan........ 26
Metropolitan, 33 John R......... 26
Michigan, 220 Bagley............ 26
New Center, 7430 2nd Blvd.... 02
Penobscot, 645 Griswold........ 26
Professional, 10 Peterboro 01
Water Board, 735 Randolph ... 26

HOSPITALS

Detroit General, Macomb &
  St Antoine.......................... 26
Grace, 4160 John R............... 01
Harper, 3825 Brush............... 01
Henry Ford, 2799 Grand Blvd
  W...................................... 02
Herman Kiefer, Hamilton &
  Taylor................................ 02
Highland Park General, 369

Glendale.............................. 03
Hutzel, 432 Hancock E.......... 01
Mt Carmel Mercy, 6071 Outer
  Dr W.................................. 35
Saint John, 22101 Moross
  Rd..................................... 36
Saint Joseph Mercy, 2200
  Grand Blvd E...................... 11
Sinai, 6767 Outer Dr W 35

UNIVERSITIES AND COLLEGES

Detroit College Of Law, 130
  Elizabeth E......................... 01
Detroit Institute Of
  Technology, 2300 Park
  Ave.................................... 01
Marygrove, 8425 Mc Nichols
  Rd W.................................. 21
Mercy College, 8200 Outer Dr
  W...................................... 19
University Of Detroit, 4001
  Mcnichols Rd W.................. 21
Wayne State College Of
  Medicine, 540 Canfield E..... 01
Wayne State University, 4841
  Cass.................................. 02

NAMED STREETS

A Ct.................................... 20
Aaron.................................. 07
Abbott
  1-199................................ 18
  400-1399........................... 26
  1400-OUT.......................... 16
Abington Ave
  6300-9499......................... 28
  9500-OUT.......................... 27
Abington Rd
  6300-9499......................... 28
  9500-OUT.......................... 27
Acacia
  15500-18099...................... 27
  18100-23999...................... 23
  24000-25499...................... 39
Academy.............................. 20
Ackley................................. 11
Adair.................................. 07
Adams Ct............................. 20
Adams St E & W.................... 26
Addison............................... 10
Adelaide
  1-899................................ 01
  900-OUT............................ 07
Adele.................................. 11
Adeline............................... 03
Afton Rd.............................. 03
Agnes
  200-499............................. 29
  6800-7199......................... 07
  7200-OUT.......................... 14
Akron.................................. 12
Alameda.............................. 03
Alaska................................ 04
Albany
  100-1799........................... 20
  8200-15499........................ 37
  18000-20699...................... 34
Albert................................. 19
Alberta............................... 20
Albion................................. 34

Alcoy.................................. 05
Alden.................................. 38
Alderton.............................. 19
Alexander............................ 18
Alexander Ct........................ 29
Alexandrine E
  1-899................................ 01
  900-OUT............................ 07
Alexandrine W
  1-1399............................... 01
  1400-OUT.......................... 08
Alexis St E & W.................... 29
Alfred
  1-899................................ 01
  900-OUT............................ 07
Alger
  1-899................................ 02
  900-OUT............................ 11
Alger Pl
  1-99.................................. 30
Algonac
  12000-17099...................... 05
  17100-OUT......................... 34
Algonquin............................ 15
Alice.................................. 12
Aline Dr.............................. 36
Allard Ave & Rd................... 36
Allen
  100-1799........................... 20
  13600-OUT......................... 37
Allen Pl.............................. 04
Allendale............................. 04
Allonby............................... 27
Alma................................... 05
Almont
  1800-2199......................... 20
  8000-OUT.......................... 34
Alpena................................ 12
Alpha.................................. 12
Alpine................................. 04
Alstead............................... 36
Alter Rd
  1-4999............................... 15
  5000-OUT.......................... 24
Alton.................................. 39
Alwar.................................. 05
Alwyne Ln............................ 03
American
  7200-7999......................... 10
  8000-OUT.......................... 04
Amherst............................... 09
Amity.................................. 14
Amrad................................. 34
Amsterdam........................... 02
Anatole............................... 36
Anchor St E & W................... 18
Anderdon
  2100-4999......................... 15
  5000-OUT.......................... 13
Anderson S........................... 09
Andover.............................. 03
Andrus................................ 12
Anglin
  13400-17999...................... 12
  18000-OUT......................... 34
Anita
  500-2299........................... 36
  19600-OUT......................... 25
Ann Arbor Trl
  20000-20198 (EVEN) 28
  22700-23299...................... 39
Anna Pl............................... 11

Detroit (Con.)   482

Annabelle
  1200-2499.................... 20
Annabelle S
  1000-3799.................... 17
Annapolis....................... 04
Annchester Rd................. 19
Annin........................... 03
Annland........................ 04
Annott......................... 05
Annsbury
  9000-11499................... 13
  11500-OUT.................... 05
Anson.......................... 09
Anstell........................ 13
Anthen......................... 09
Anthony Wayne Dr
  4800-4999.................... 01
  5000-OUT..................... 02
Antietam Ave & Rd............. 07
Antoinette
  1-1399....................... 02
  1400-OUT..................... 08
Antwerp........................ 34
Anvil.......................... 05
Apple.......................... 10
Applegrove..................... 29
Appleton
  8800-12599................... 39
  12600-16099.................. 23
  16100-OUT.................... 19
Appoline
  8000-9499.................... 28
  9500-16099................... 27
  16100-OUT.................... 35
Arcadia........................ 04
Archdale
  6300-9499.................... 28
  9500-16099................... 27
  16100-OUT.................... 35
Archer......................... 19
Arcola......................... 34
Arden Park Blvd................ 02
Ardmore
  12600-16099.................. 27
  16100-OUT.................... 35
Ardmore Dr..................... 20
Argus.......................... 19
Argyle Cres.................... 03
Arizona St E & W............... 03
Arlington...................... 12
Armada......................... 12
Armour......................... 13
Army........................... 09
Arndt.......................... 07
Arnold
  8100-8599.................... 10
  8800-OUT..................... 39
Artesian
  5600-12599................... 28
  12600-OUT.................... 23
Arthur......................... 25
Asa............................ 04
Asbury Park
  6300-9499.................... 28
  9500-16099................... 27
  16100-OUT.................... 35
Ash............................ 08
Ashland........................ 15
Ashley......................... 36
Ashton Ave

5600-12599..................... 28
  12600-16099.................. 23
  16100-OUT.................... 19
Ashton Rd
  5600-12599................... 28
  12600-16099.................. 23
  16100-OUT.................... 19
Astor.......................... 13
Athens.a....................... 13
Atkinson
  1-1399....................... 02
  1400-OUT..................... 06
Atlanta........................ 13
Atlas.......................... 11
Atwater
  1-899........................ 26
  900-OUT...................... 07
Aubrey......................... 39
Auburn
  5800-12599................... 28
  12600-OUT.................... 23
Auburn St E & W................ 29
Auburndale..................... 03
Audrey......................... 35
Audubon Ave
  1000-3399.................... 30
  3400-OUT..................... 24
Audubon Rd
  1000-3399.................... 30
  3400-OUT..................... 24
August......................... 05
Aurora......................... 04
Austin......................... 16
Avalon......................... 03
Averhill Ct.................... 15
Avery.......................... 08
Avis........................... 09
Avon Ave
  15400-16099.................. 23
  16100-20699.................. 19
  20700-OUT.................... 37
Avon Ct
  500-1199..................... 36
Avon Rd
  15400-16099.................. 23
  16100-20699.................. 19
  20700-OUT.................... 37
Avondale
  12300-14999.................. 15
  15000-OUT.................... 30
B.............................. 16
B Ct........................... 20
Bacon.......................... 09
Badger......................... 13
Bagley
  100-1399..................... 26
  1400-OUT..................... 16
  4000-OUT..................... 09
Baker.......................... 09
Baldwin
  500-4999..................... 14
  5000-OUT..................... 13
Balfour Ave
  600-3399..................... 30
  3400-11999.................. 24
  13600-14999 (OP)............. 37
  19200-OUT.................... 25
Balfour Rd
  600-3399..................... 30
  3400-11999................... 24
  13600-14999 (OP)............. 37
  19200-OUT.................... 25
Ballantyne Ct E & W............ 36

Ballantyne Rd.................. 36
Balmoral Ave & Dr.............. 03
Baltimore St E & W............. 02
Baltree Ct..................... 36
Bangor Ave & Ct................ 10
Bank........................... 09
Banmoor....................... 28
Barbara
  21400-22699.................. 23
  26000-27399.................. 39
Barclay Rd..................... 36
Barham......................... 24
Barker......................... 13
Barlow......................... 05
Barlum......................... 10
Barnes......................... 09
Barr........................... 04
Barrett........................ 13
Barrington Rd.................. 30
Barron......................... 09
Barry.......................... 14
Bartlett....................... 03
Barton......................... 10
Basil.......................... 35
Bassett S...................... 17
Batavia........................ 18
Bates.......................... 26
Baubee......................... 10
Bauman......................... 03
Baylis
  15300-16099.................. 38
  16100-OUT.................... 21
Bayside S...................... 17
Beach.......................... 29
Beacon......................... 26
Beacon Hill Rd................. 36
Beaconsfield Ave
  500-3399..................... 30
  3400-19199.................. 24
  19200-20699.................. 25
Beaconsfield Rd
  500-3399..................... 30
  3400-19199................... 24
  19200-20699.................. 25
Beals.......................... 14
Beaman......................... 14
Beard.......................... 09
Beatrice S..................... 17
Beaubien
  200-2099..................... 26
  2100-4999.................... 01
  5000-OUT..................... 02
Beaufait
  400-4999..................... 07
  5000-6199.................... 11
  19800-21799 (HW)............. 25
Beaufait Dr
  1700-2199 (GPW).............. 36
Beaufield...................... 20
Beaumont....................... 09
Beaupre Ln & Rd................ 36
Beaverland
  7200-12599................... 39
  12600-16099.................. 23
  16100-OUT.................... 19
Bedford Ave
  700-3399..................... 30
  3400-OUT..................... 24
Bedford Ln
  600-599...................... 30
Bedford Ln
  700-3399..................... 30

Detroit (Con.)   482

3400-OUT .... 2'
Beech 26
Beech Ct. 39
Beech Daly Rd
  8800-16099 39
  16100-20699 40
Beechdale 04
Beechton 10
Beechwood
  200-599 18
  5700-7299 10
  7300-OUT 04
Begole 10
Beland 34
Belanger 36
Belden
  15400-16099 38
  16100-OUT 21
Belfast 10
Bell 29
Belle 09
Belleterre 04
Bellevue
  400-4999 07
  5000-OUT 11
Belmont
  1-899 02
  1900-OUT 12
Belton
  2100-12669 04
  12700-21959 28
  22000-OUT 39
Belvid
  1200-4999 14
  5000-OUT 13
Benham 11
Beniteau
  1-4999 14
  5000-OUT 13
Bennett
  21300-24999 19
  25000-27399 40
Bennette St E & W 20
Benson 07
Benson St E & W 29
Bentler Ave
  12600-16099 23
  16100-20699 19
Bentler Ct. 19
Benton
  400-899 01
  900-OUT 07
Berden
  16500-18899 24
  18900-19199 36
  19200-OUT 25
Beresford 03
Berg Rd 19
Berkeley Rd 21
Berkley 37
Berkshire Ave
  700-3399 30
  3400-OUT 24
Berkshire Pl 36
Berkshire Rd
  700-3399 30
  3400-OUT 24
Bermuda 20
Bernard 12
Berns Ct. 36

Berres 12
Berry 34
Bertha 20
Berwyn 39
Bessemore 13
Bethlawn 20
Bethune E 02
Bethune W
  1-1399 02
  1400-OUT 06
Bethune Pl N
  21000-21499 20
Bethune Pl S
  21000-21499 20
Beverly 37
Beverly Ct 04
Beverly Rd 36
Bewick
  1400-4999 14
  5000-OUT 13
Biarritz Cir. 37
Biddle 06
Biltmore
  14800-16099 27
  16100-OUT 31
Binder
  17800-17999 12
  18000-OUT 34
Bingham 28
Birch 27
Birch Ln 36
Birchcrest Dr 21
Birwood
  8000-12599 04
  12600-16099 38
  16100-OUT 21
Bishop Ave
  1-3399 30
  3400-11099 24
  14400-OUT 37
Bishop Ln 30
Bishop Rd
  1-3399 30
  3400-11099 24
  14400-OUT 37
Bivouac 09
Blackmoor 34
Blackstone Ave
  12600-16099 23
  16100-20699 19
  21900-OUT 37
Blackstone Ct. 19
Blaine
  1-1399 02
  1400-3999 06
  4000-OUT 04
Blair 13
Blairmoor Ave & Ct. 36
Blake 03
Bliss 34
Bloom
  11800-17999 12
  18000-OUT 34
Bloomfield Rd 21
Bloomsburg Pl 07
Blossom Ln 36
Blowers 04
Bluehill 28
Blythe 24
Boeing 39
Boleyn 24
Bondie 29

Bonita 24
Bonner 20
Bonzanno 29
Bordeau 04
Borgman 37
Borman 28
Bortle 14
Boston Blvd E 02
Boston Blvd W
  1-1399 02
  1400-3999 06
  4000-OUT 04
Bostwick 09
Bosworth Ct. 19
Botsford 12
Boulder 05
Bourassa 29
Bourke 38
Bournemouth 25
Bournemouth Cir & Rd 36
Boxwood 10
Boyd 09
Brace 28
Braden 10
Bradford
  11400-11499 13
  11500-OUT 05
Bradley 14
Brady Ave
  900-1399 07
  8800-16099 39
  16100-OUT 40
Brady Ct 39
Braile
  7200-12599 28
  12600-16099 23
  16100-OUT 19
Brainard
  400-1399 01
  1400-OUT 08
Bramell
  7200-12599 39
  12600-16099 23
  16100-OUT 19
Bramford 34
Brandon 73
Breakfast Dr 39
Breckenridge
  3200-3399 08
  8100-OUT 37
Breckenridge St E & W 20
Bremen 24
Brennan 09
Brentwood E
  400-1899 03
  1900-OUT 34
Brentwood W 03
Bretton Dr............................. 23
Brewster
  400-899 01
  900-OUT 07
Briar Dr 37
Briarcliff Dr
  1-1199 (GPS) 36
Briarcliff Pl
  1-1199 (GPS) 36
Briarcliff Rd
  19900-20499 21
Brickley 20
Brierstone 25
Brighton 03
Brimson 12

Detroit (Con.)	482
Bringard Dr	05
Brinker	34
Brinket	14
Bristol Pl	16
Bristow	12
Britain	24
Broadstone Ave	25
Broadstone Rd	36
Broadstreet Ave	
9200-12599	04
12600-OUT	38
Broadstreet Blvd	
9200-12599	04
12600-OUT	38
Broadway	
1-99	29
1200-OUT	26
Brock	05
Brockton	11
Brombach	12
Brooklyn	
1200-2099	26
2100-4999	01
5000-OUT	02
Brooks	15
Brown Pl	08
Browning	20
Brownlee	18
Bruce	14
Bruckner	10
Brunswick	24
Brush	
200-2099	26
2100-4999	01
5000-11699	02
11700-OUT	03
Bryanston Cres	07
Bryant	08
Bryden	
7200-7999	10
8000-OUT	04
Brys Dr N & S	36
Bryson	03
Buchanan	
2000-3999	08
4000-OUT	10
Buckingham Ave	
1000-3399	30
3400-OUT	24
Buckingham Rd	
1000-3399	30
3400-OUT	24
Buelow Ct	09
Buena Vis E	03
Buena Vis W	
1-1399	03
1400-12699	38
12700-OUT	27
Buffalo Ave	
5500-17999	12
18000-OUT	34
Buffalo Ct	12
Buhl	14
Buhr	12
Bulwer	10
Burchill Ct	13
Burdeno	09
Burdette	20
Burger	12
Burgess Ave	

13900-16099	23
16100-OUT	19
Burgess Ct	19
Burke	18
Burlage Pl	07
Burlingame	
1-1399	02
1400-3999	06
4000-OUT	04
Burlington Dr	03
Burnette	
7200-7999	10
8000-OUT	04
Burns Ave	
1-4999	14
5000-OUT	13
Burns Dr	14
Burnside	12
Burrell Pl	08
Burroughs	02
Burt Ct	
20900-20999	23
Burt Rd	
8000-12599	28
12600-16099	23
16100-20699	19
Burton	
4400-4799	10
10000-OUT	37
Burwell	10
Bushey	10
Butler	11
Butternut	16
Byron	
1-399	18
7300-11699	02
11700-OUT	03
C	16
Cabot	
1900-3599	09
3600-OUT	10
Cadet	09
Cadieux Rd	
300-3399	30
3400-OUT	24
Cadillac Ave	
1300-4999	14
5000-OUT	13
Cadillac Blvd	
1300-4999	14
5000-OUT	13
Cadillac Sq	26
Caely	12
Cahalan	09
Cairney	13
Caldwell	
12800-17999	12
18000-OUT	34
California	03
Calumet	
800-1399	01
1400-OUT	08
Calvert	
1-1399	02
1400-OUT	06
Calvin	36
Cambourne St E & W	20
Cambridge Ave	
1-199	36
2800-12699	21
12700-18099	35
18100-24999	19
25000-27399	40

Cambridge Rd	
1-199	36
2800-12699	21
12700-18099	35
18100-24999	19
25000-27399	40
Cambridge St N & S	21
Camden	
300-1899	20
11300-OUT	13
Cameron	
7300-11699	11
11700-OUT	03
Cameron Pl	30
Camille	15
Camley	24
Campbell	
1-599 (RR)	18
100-2699	09
Campbell S	
100-599	09
Campus Martius	26
Candler	03
Canfield E	
1-899	01
900-7199	07
7200-11999	14
12000-OUT	15
Canfield W	
1-1399	01
1400-OUT	08
Caniff	
900-1619	11
1620-OUT	12
Canonbury	05
Canterbury Rd	
400-1199	36
19100-OUT	21
Canton	
400-4999	07
5000-OUT	11
Canyon	36
Capital	37
Capitol	
12700-18099	27
18100-21999	28
22000-26599	39
Carbon	09
Carbondale	04
Cardoni	
8700-11699	11
11700-OUT	03
Carleton	14
Carlin	
8000-9499	28
9500-OUT	27
Carlisle	05
Carman	03
Carmel	
900-1199	03
Carmel Ln	
1-99	36
Carol	
16000-16099	39
20000-OUT	35
Caroline	
1-99	30
1900-OUT	08
Carpenter	12
Carrie	
6500-10499	11
10500-17999	12
18000-OUT	34

Detroit (Con.)　482

Carson 09
Carten 14
Carter
　2600-3999 06
　4000-OUT 04
Cartridge 09
Carver 36
Cascade 04
Casgrain 09
Casino 24
Casmere 12
Casper
　2300-3599 09
　3600-OUT 10
Cass
　500-2099 26
　2100-4999 01
　5000-OUT 02
Castle 34
Castleton 27
Catalpa Ct 20
Cathedral
　15500-21999 28
　22000-27399 39
Catherine 18
Cavalry 09
Cavalry S 09
Cecil 10
Cedar 09
Cedar Ct 25
Cedargrove 05
Cedarhurst Pl 03
Cedarlawn 04
Celeron 09
Celestine 05
Celia 08
Centerbrook 36
Central
　700-3599 09
　900-2099 (FER) 20
　3600-7999 10
　8000-OUT 04
Centralia
　8800-16099 39
　16100-20699 40
Centre 26
Chadwick 27
Chalfonte
　1-599 36
　3100-12699 38
　12700-18099 27
　17500-17799 (GPC) 30
　18100-OUT 23
Chalmers
　200-4999 15
　5000-11499 13
　11500-OUT 05
Chamberlain 09
Champine Pl 36
Chandler 02
Chandler Park Dr
　13000-14399 13
　14400-18599 24
　18600-OUT 36
Channing 20
Chapel
　12600-16099 23
　16100-OUT 19
Chapin 13
Chapman 37
Charest

9300-17999 12
18000-OUT 34
Charlemagne 13
Charles
　1-299 18
　3800-6299 12
　17500-OUT 30
Charleston 03
Charlevoix
　1-299 36
　2600-7199 07
　7200-11999 14
　12000-14999 15
　15000-17899 30
　20700-OUT 36
Charlotta 20
Charlotte
　1-899 01
Charlotte E
　1-99 29
Charlotte W
　1-99 29
Chateaufort Pl 07
Chatfield 09
Chatham
　7200-12599 39
　12600-16099 23
　16100-OUT 19
Chatsworth 24
Chelsea
　10700-14999 13
　15400-OUT 39
Chene
　200-4999 07
　5000-OUT 11
Chenlot 04
Cherboneau Pl 07
Cherokee 19
Cherry
　600-1399 01
　1400-OUT 16
Cherrygrove 29
Cherrylawn
　11200-12599 04
　12600-16099 38
　16100-OUT 21
Chesapeake 39
Cheshire 36
Chester
　2700-3399 20
　17400-18899 24
　18900-19199 36
　19200-OUT 25
Chesterfield Rd 21
Chesterfield St E & W 20
Chestnut
　1-199 18
　1400-3199 07
　2100-2499 (FER) 20
Cheyenne
　8000-9499 28
　9500-16099 27
　16100-OUT 35
Chicago Blvd
　1-1399 02
　1400-2599 06
Chipman 16
Chippewa
　3700-12699 21
　12700-18099 35
　18100-OUT 19
Chope Pl 08
Chopin 10

Christ Church Ln 36
Christiancy 09
Christine Ct & Dr 36
Christopher 11
Christy 05
Chrysler Fwy
　400-4998 (EVEN) 07
　401-2099 (ODD) 26
　2101-4999 (ODD) 01
　5000-9799 11
　9800-12899 12
　12900-20699 03
Church Ave
　1-299 03
　1400-1899 16
　20700-OUT 37
Church Ct 25
Church Rd
　1-299 03
　1400-1899 16
　20700-OUT 37
Churchill 06
Cicotte
　1-499 29
　3200-OUT 10
Cicotte E
　1-199 18
Cicotte W
　1-199 18
Cincinnati 24
Civic Pl
　10800-12699 04
　12700-OUT 28
Civic Center Dr 26
Claireview Rd 36
Clairmount
　1-1399 02
　1400-3999 06
　4000-OUT 04
Clairpointe 15
Clairview 24
Clairview Ct E & W 36
Clarendon St N & S 04
Clarion 13
Clarita
　3100-12699 21
　12700-18099 35
　18100-24999 19
　25000-27399 40
Clark
　100-2599 09
　2600-OUT 10
Clark S 09
Clark Ct 09
Clarkdale 11
Clay 28
Clayburn 10
Clayton 10
Clements 38
Cliff
　17100-17999 12
　18000-OUT 34
Clifford
　1-2099 26
　2100-OUT 01
Clifton 10
Clinton
　400-899 26
　900-OUT 07
Clippert 10
Clough
　11300-11599 34
　11600-OUT 05

Detroit (Con.)   482

Cloverdale
- 8000-10899 (FER) 20
- 10600-12599 04
- 12600-14999 38
- 12700-15499 (OP) 37

Cloverlawn
- 8000-12599 04
- 12600-16099 38
- 20700-OUT 37

Cloverly Rd 36
Cobalt S 09
Cobb Pl 10

Cochrane
- 2200-3299 16
- 3300-OUT 08

Codding 19
Cody 12
Coe 14

Colfax
- 5800-7299 10
- 7300-OUT 04

Colgate 37
Colleen 37

College
- 100-2099 20
- 11000-OUT 05

Collingham Br 05

Collingwood
- 1-1399 02
- 1400-3999 06
- 4000-OUT 04

Colonial S 17
Colonial Ct & Rd 36
Colorado 03
Colton 03
Columbia 39

Columbia E
- 1-899 01
- 900-OUT 07

Columbia W 01

Columbus
- 2600-3999 06
- 4000-OUT 04

Commercial 09
Commonwealth 08
Commor 12
Compass 27

Comstock
- 3300-5899 12
- 5900-OUT 11

Conant
- 7700-8899 11
- 8900-17999 12
- 18000-OUT 34

Concord
- 400-4999 07
- 5000-10499 11
- 10500-17999 12
- 18000-OUT 34

Condon 37
Conger 13

Congress E
- 1-899 26
- 900-7199 07
- 7200-W 14

Congress W 26

Conley
- 13400-17999 12
- 18000-OUT 34

Connecticut 03
Conner

400-4999 15
5000-11499 13
11500-17099 05
17100-OUT 34

Conner Ln 14
Conrad 10

Constance
- 10600-12699 37
- 16100-21999 28
- 22000-OUT 39

Continental 15
Conway 17
Cook 10
Cook Rd 36
Cooley 19

Coolidge
- 1-1954 18
- 20700-24999 37
- 25001-26799 (ODD) 37

Coolidge Hwy
- 1-1954 18
- 20700-24999 37
- 25001-26799 (ODD) 37

Cooper
- 4500-4999 14
- 5000-OUT 13

Cope 15
Copland 09

Coplin
- 400-4999 15
- 5000-11499 13
- 11500-OUT 05

Cora 18
Coram 05
Corbett 13
Corbin 17
Cordell 05
Cordova 34
Corey 15
Corning 37
Cornwall 24

Cortland
- 1-1399 03
- 1400-3999 06
- 4000-OUT 04

Cottrell S 09
Council 12

Country Club Dr
- 100-2199 36
- 19600-OUT 25

Country Club Ln 36
Courtland 37
Courville 24

Coventry
- 500-599 36
- 19100-OUT 03

Covert 12
Covington Dr 03
Coy 20

Coyle
- 8000-9499 28
- 9500-16099 27
- 16100-19999 35
- 23600-OUT 37

Craft 24
Craig 11
Cranbrook Dr 21

Crane
- 900-4999 14
- 5000-OUT 13

Cranford Ln 30
Cranshaw 04
Crawford 09

Crawford S 09
Crescent Dr 23
Crescent Ln 36
Cresswell 13
Crestwood Dr 36
Crocuslawn 04
Cromwell 16
Crosley 39
Cross 26
Crossley S 09
Crowley 10
Crown 09
Crusade 05

Cruse
- 14200-16099 27
- 16100-OUT 35

Culver 13
Cumberland Way 03
Curt 13

Curtis
- 3100-12699 21
- 12700-18099 35
- 18100-24999 19
- 25000-27399 40

Curwood 03
Cushing 05

Custer
- 1-899 02
- 900-OUT 11

Cutler 11
Cymbal 14
Cypress 10
D 16

Dacosta
- 7200-12599 39
- 12600-OUT 23

Dailey Ave & Ct 04
Dakota St E & W 03

Dalby
- 15900-16099 39
- 16100-OUT 40

Dale
- 8800-12599 39
- 12600-16099 23
- 16100-OUT 19

Dallas 11
Dalrymple 04
Dalzelle 16
Damman 25
Dan 12
Danbury 03
Danbury Ln 25
Dane 11
Danforth 12
Daniels 10
Dante 37
Darcy 23
Dartmouth 37
Dartmouth S 17
Darwin 36
Davenport 01
David 14
Davis Pl 11

Davison E
- 1-1899 03
- 1900-OUT 12

Davison W
- 1-1399 03
- 1400-12699 38
- 12700-18099 27
- 18100-23999 23
- 24000-OUT 39

Dawes 04

Detroit (Con.)   482

Dayton
- 7600-8799 10
- 18100-OUT 28

De Buel 11
De Soto 38
Deacon S 17

Dean
- 13400-17999 12
- 18000-20699 34

Dean Ln 36
Dearborn 09
Dearing 12
Deborah 39

Decatur
- 8000-9499 28
- 9500-OUT 27

Deeplands Ct 36
Deeplands Rd N & S 36
Defer Pl 14
Dehner 19

Delaware
- 1-1399 02
- 1400-2099 06
- 14800-16099 39
- 16100-20699 40

Delisle 18
Delmar 11
Delta 12
Deming 09
Deming Ln 36

Denby
- 15300-16099 39
- 16100-OUT 40

Denmark 17
Dennis 10
Dennison 10

Denton
- 2100-2899 12
- 2900-OUT 11

Denver 24

Dequindre
- 100-4999 07
- 5000-8399 11
- 8400-17999 12
- 18000-20699 34

Derby 03
Desmond 09
Desner 12
Detroit 24
Devereaux 10
Devine 13
Devon 05

Devonshire Ave
- 1000-3399 30
- 3400-OUT 24

Devonshire Rd
- 1000-3399 30
- 3400-OUT 24

Dewey 02

Dexter Ave
- 7300-12599 06
- 12600-16099 38
- 16100-OUT 21

Dexter Blvd
- 7300-12599 06
- 12600-16099 38
- 16100-OUT 21

Dey 09
Dey S 09
Dickerson

- 400-4999 15
- 5000-11499 13
- 11500-OUT 05

Dill Pl 09
Distel 09

Diversey
- 6300-7599 10
- 15500-OUT 28

Division
- 1-299 18
- 400-899 01
- 900-OUT 07

Dix 09
Dix S 17
Dixie 39
Dobel 34
Dodge 11

Dolphin
- 7200-12599 39
- 12600-16099 23
- 16100-20599 19

Dolson 23
Domine 11
Donald Ave & Ct 39
Donald Pl 07
Dorchester 14

Doremus
- 3300-5899 12
- 5900-OUT 11

Doris
- 1-1399 03
- 1400-OUT 38

Doris Ct 39
Dorothy 11
Dorthen 36

Dover
- 1500-1799 20
- 6300-12699 04
- 12700-21999 28
- 22000-27399 39

Dow 39
Downing 17
Doyle 34
Doyle Ct 36
Doyle Pl E & W 36
Dragoon 09
Dragoon S 09
Drake 12
Drayton St E & W 20
Drennen 29
Dresden 05

Drexel
- 300-4999 15
- 5000-OUT 13

Drifton 05
Driggs 09

Duane
- 3700-3999 06
- 4000-OUT 04

Dubay 34

Dubois
- 100-4999 07
- 5000-8399 11
- 8400-OUT 12

Ducharme Pl 07
Duchess 24
Dumbarton Rd 04
Dumfries S 17
Dundee 04
Dunedin 06
Dunkirk S 17

Dwyer
- 8000-10499 11
- 10500-17999 12
- 18000-OUT 34

Dyar 12
Dyar Ln 36
Eagle 10
Earl Blvd 20
Earl Ct 36
Earle 08
Eason 03

Eastborne
- 19200-19399 25
- 19400-OUT 36

Eastbrook 36
Eastburn 05
Eastern Pl 08
Eastland Village Dr 25

Eastlawn
- 100-4999 15
- 5000-OUT 13

Eastwood
- 11000-11599 34
- 11600-16199 05
- 21900-OUT 37

Eastwood Dr 25

Eaton
- 500-599 18
- 6300-12699 38
- 12700-18099 27
- 18100-OUT 23

Edgefield
- 18900-19199 36
- 19200-OUT 25

Edgemere Rd 36
Edgemont Park 30
Edgeton 12
Edgevale 03

Edgewood
- 100-599 20
- 8000-OUT 13

Edgewood Dr N & S 36
Edgeworth 20
Edinborough Rd 19

Edison
- 1-1399 02
- 1400-OUT 06

Edlie 14
Edmonton 04
Edmore Dr 05
Edmund Pl 01
Edmunton Dr 36
Edsel S 17

Edsel Ford Fwy E
- 1-899 02
- 900-7199 11
- 7200-14399 13
- 14400-19199 24
- 19200-OUT 25

Edsel Ford Fwy W
- 400-1399 02
- 1400-3999 08
- 4000-OUT 10

Edshire Ln 36

Edward
- 6300-7699 10
- 16000-OUT 03

Edwin
- 1900-5899 12
- 5900-OUT 11

Eileen 39
Elaine Ct 37

357

Detroit (Con:)   482

Elba
3600-3799 07
25500-OUT 39
Eldon 34
Eldred 09
Eldridge 12
Electric S 17
Elford Ct 36
Elgin
8000-8599 34
13600-OUT 37
Eliot
1-899 01
900-OUT 07
Eliza 29
Elizabeth
1-99 (RR) 18
Elizabeth E
1-999 01
909-921 (ODD) 26
Elizabeth W
1-1399 01
1400-OUT 16
Elizabeth Ct 36
Elkhart 25
Ellair Pl 30
Ellen 38
Ellery Ave
2400-4999 07
5000-8399 11
8400-OUT 12
Ellery Pl 07
Elliott 18
Ellis
10400-12699 04
12700-OUT 28
Ellsworth
6300-12699 38
12700-OUT 27
Elm
1-199 18
1300-2099 16
14400-OUT 37
Elm Ct
1-99 36
19800-OUT 25
Elmdale
11100-15199 13
15200-OUT 24
Elmer 10
Elmhurst
1-1399 03
1400-3999 06
4000-OUT 04
Elmira
8500-12699 04
12700-18099 27
18100-21999 28
22000-27399 39
Elmo 05
Elmsleigh Pl 30
Elmwood
400-4999 07
5000-OUT 11
Elmwood Park Dr 07
Elsa 14
Elsinore 39
Elsmere 09
Elton 29
Emeline 12

Emerson 15
Emery
1-1899 03
1900-OUT 34
Emiline 18
Emily 34
Emmons 14
Emory Ct E & W 36
Emwill 20
Endicott 02
Engle 14
Engleside 05
Englewood 34
Epworth
5900-7299 10
7300-OUT 04
Erbie 13
Erie 09
Erle 03
Erskine
1-899 01
900-OUT 07
Erwin
8800-9899 13
9900-OUT 34
Esper 04
Essex Ave
12300-14999 15
15000-OUT 30
Essex Blvd
12300-14999 15
15000-OUT 30
Ethel S 1
Euclid E
1-899 02
900-OUT 11
Euclid W
1-1399 02
1400-3999 06
4000-OUT 04
Eugene 15
Eureka
13400-17999 12
18000-OUT 34
Evaline
1900-5899 12
5900-OUT 11
Evans 09
Evanston
11200-14399 13
14400-OUT 24
Evergreen Ave
5600-6298 (EVEN) 28
6300-12599 28
12600-16099 23
16100-20699 19
Evergreen Rd
5600-6298 (EVEN) 28
6300-12599 28
12600-16099 23
16100-20699 19
Evers Pl N & S 20
Everts 24
Ewald Cir
1800-3419 38
3420-OUT 04
Ewers 10
Exeter 03
F 16
Faber 12
Fair 20
Fair Ct 36
Fairacies Dr 36

Fairchild S 17
Faircrest 05
Fairfax
14800-14999 15
15000-OUT 30
Fairfield
600-699 20
14700-16099 38
16100-Rd 21
Fairford Rd 36
Fairholme Rd 36
Fairlake Ln 36
Fairmont 18
Fairmount Dr 05
Fairport 05
Fairview
1-4999 14
5000-OUT 13
Fairway Dr
17100-19099 21
19800-OUT 36
Fairway Ln 36
Fairwood 20
Falcon
8700-9299 09
9800-OUT 12
Fargo
15500-18099 35
18100-24999 19
25000-27399 40
Farley 39
Farmbrook 24
Farmdale 20
Farmer 26
Farnsworth
1-899 02
900-7199 11
7200-OUT 13
Farr 11
Farrand Park 03
Farrow 20
Faust Ave
5600-12599 28
12600-16099 23
16100-OUT 19
Faust Rd
5600-12599 28
12600-16099 23
16100-OUT 19
Fayette 03
Federal 09
Felch 13
Fenelon
11300-17999 12
18000-OUT 34
Fenkell
1800-12699 38
12700-18099 27
18100-OUT 23
Fenmore 35
Fenton
8800-16099 39
16100-OUT 19
Fenwick 09
Ferdinand 09
Ferdinand S 09
Ferguson
14700-16099 27
16100-OUT 35
Fern
6600-6799 10
20700-OUT 37
Fernhill 03

Detroit (Con.) 482

Ferry W 02
Ferry Park 08
Field
  400-4999 14
  5000-OUT 13
Fielding
  100-1499 20
  7200-12599 28
  12600-16099 23
  16100-OUT 19
Filbert 05
Filer
  9100-10499 11
  10500-17999 12
  18000-OUT 34
Findlay 05
Finley 11
Firwood
  6300-7299 10
  7300-OUT 04
Fischer
  900-4999 14
  5000-OUT 13
Fisher Fwy E
  1-899 01
  900-2299 07
Fisher Fwy W
  1-1399 01
  1400-3999 16
  4000-9399 09
Fisher Rd 30
Fiske Dr 14
Fitzgerald Blvd 20
Fitzpatrick Ave & Ct 28
Five Points 40
Flanders 05
Fleet 38
Fleetwood Ave
  19600-OUT 25
Fleetwood Dr 36
Fleming
  11300-17999 12
  18000-OUT 34
Flora 09
Florence
  1-99 (RR) 18
  1-2199 03
  2200-12699 21
  3900-3999 (EC) 29
  12700-18099 35
  18100-24999 19
  25000-OUT 40
Florian 12
Florida 10
Flower Ct 07
Flowerdale 20
Floyd 10
Foley
  10500-12699 04
  12700-OUT 27
Fontaine Pl 37
Fontana Ln 36
Ford
  1-1399 03
  1400-OUT 38
Ford Ct 36
Ford Rd
  18100-18954 (EVEN) 28
Fordale 17
Fordcroft 36

Fordham 05
Fordson S 17
Fordson Hwy 39
Fordyce 11
Forest
  1-99 (RR) 18
  23000-OUT 37
Forest E
  1-899 01
  900-7199 07
  7200-12599 14
  12000-OUT 15
Forest W
  1-1399 01
  1400-OUT 08
Forest Ct 01
Forestlawn 34
Forman 09
Forman S 09
Forrer
  6300-9499 28
  9500-16099 27
  16100-OUT 35
Forsyth 02
Fort E
  300-899 26
  900-OUT 07
Fort S 7
Fort W
  100-1399 26
  1400-3999 16
  4000-OUT 09
Fortune S 09
Foster 11
Fournier 05
Fox
  1300-1499 20
  14500-16099 39
  16100-OUT 40
Frances 29
Francis 17
Frank 01
Frankfort Ave
  12000-14399 13
  14400-OUT 24
Frankfort Ct
  5200-5499 13
Franklin
  300-899 26
  900-OUT 07
Frazer Pl 02
Frazier 18
Freda 04
Frederick
  200-899 02
  900-7199 11
  7200-OUT 13
Fredro 12
Freeland
  8000-9499 28
  9500-16099 27
  16100-OUT 35
Freer 10
Fremont Pl 07
French Rd
  3700-4999 14
  5000-10099 13
  10100-OUT 34
Freud
  10400-11999 14
  12000-OUT 15
Frisbee 19

Frontenac 11
Fullerton
  1500-12699 38
  12700-18099 27
  18100-23999 23
  24000-OUT 39
Fulton 09
G A R 10
Gable
  11300-17999 12
  18000-OUT 34
Gainsboro 20
Gainsborough Rd 23
Galaxie 20
Gale 17
Gallagher
  8900-17999 12
  18000-OUT 34
Galster 07
Garden
  6300-8099 04
  25900-OUT 37
Garden Ln 20
Gardendale
  100-999 20
  20100-OUT 21
Gardner 37
Garfield Ave
  1-899 01
  900-7099 07
  1200-2399 (FER) 20
  8800-16099 39
  16100-OUT 40
Garfield Ct 39
Garfield Pl 07
Garland
  1400-4999 14
  5000-OUT 13
Garnet 05
Gartner 09
Garvin 12
Gary 03
Gates 09
Gates S 09
Gateshead 36
Gavel 27
Gaylord
  2900-3899 12
  15000-16099 39
  16100-OUT 40
Gaynor Ct 09
Geimer 12
Geitzen
  11300-11599 34
  11600-OUT 05
Genessee
  1-499 18
  9200-OUT 06
Geneva
  1-2099 03
  23000-OUT 37
Genoa 13
Geoffrey Ct 37
George 03
Georgeland 04
Georgia
  4000-7199 11
  7200-OUT 13
Gerald 03
Gerisch 09
Ghesquiere Ct 36
Gibbs 09
Gibson 01

Detroit (Con.)	482
Gilbert	10
Gilbo	34
Gilchrist	
15000-16099	27
16100-OUT	35
Gillett	11
Gilroy	17
Giltner Ct	20
Girardin	
7600-10499	11
10500-17999	12
18000-OUT	34
Gitre	05
Gladstone	
1-1399	02
1400-3999	06
4000-OUT	04
Gladwin	14
Gladys	10
Glastonbury Ave	
11600-12599	28
12600-16099	23
16100-OUT	19
Glastonbury Rd	
11600-12599	28
12600-16099	23
16100-OUT	19
Gleason	17
Glen Arbor Ln	36
Glen Lodge	20
Glenco	19
Glendale	
1-1399	03
1400-12699	38
12700-18099	27
18100-23999	23
24000-OUT	39
Glenfield	13
Glenhurst	19
Glenmore	40
Glenwood	05
Glenwood St E & W	29
Glinnan	09
Globe	38
Gloucester Dr	03
Glover	14
Glynn Ct	
1-1399	02
1400-OUT	06
Goddard	
12200-17999	12
18000-OUT	34
Goethe	
7200-11999	14
12000-14999	15
15000-17799	30
21400-OUT	36
Golden Gate St E & W	03
Goldner	10
Goldsmith	09
Goodell	18
Goodell St E & W	29
Goodrich	20
Goodson	12
Goodwin	
8900-11699	11
11700-OUT	03
Gordon	14
Gore	19
Goulburn	05
Gould	09

Grand Blvd E	
1-1164	07
1165-2851	11
2852-OUT	02
Grand Blvd W	
1-887	16
888-2749	08
2750-OUT	02
Grand Haven	12
Grand Marais	30
Grand River E	26
Grand River W	
1-2099	26
2100-3099	01
3100-7299	08
7300-12699	04
12700-18099	27
18100-19999	23
20000-24999	19
25000-27399	40
Grandmont Ave	
6300-9499	28
9500-OUT	27
Grandmont Rd	
6300-9499	28
9500-OUT	27
Grandview	19
Grandville Ave	
5600-12599	28
12600-16099	23
16100-OUT	19
Grandville Rd	
5600-12599	28
12600-16099	23
16100-OUT	19
Grandy	
3400-4999	07
5000-OUT	11
Granger	13
Grant	12
Granzon	37
Gratiot	
1-899	26
900-7199	07
7200-11999	13
12000-15599	05
Graves	14
Gravier	24
Gray	
1100-4999	15
5000-OUT	13
Grayfield	
8800-12599	39
12600-16099	23
16100-OUT	19
Grayling	12
Grayson	20
Grayton Ave	
1000-3399	30
3400-OUT	24
Grayton Rd	
1000-3399	30
3400-OUT	24
Great Lakes St E & W	18
Greeley	
8500-11699	11
11700-OUT	03
Green S	09
Green St & Pl	09
Greenbriar	
1-99	36
13900-OUT	37
Greendale St E & W	03

Greenfield	
6301-7999 (ODD)	28
8000-9499	28
9500-16099	27
16100-20699	35
20700-26700 (EVEN)	37
Greenlawn	
8000-12599	04
12600-16099	38
16100-OUT	21
Greensboro	24
Greenspan	16
Greenview Ave	
5600-12599	28
12600-16099	23
16100-20699	19
Greenview Rd	
5600-12599	28
12600-16099	23
16100-20699	19
Greenway	04
Gregorie	14
Greiner	
11000-11599	34
11600-OUT	05
Greusel	10
Greydale Ave	
12600-16099	23
16100-OUT	19
Greydale Ct	19
Greyfriars S	17
Griffin	11
Griggs	
8600-12599	04
12600-16099	38
16100-OUT	21
Grinnell	13
Griswold	26
Grixdale E	
1-1899	03
1900-OUT	34
Grixdale W	03
Groesbeck Hwy	05
Grosse Pointe Blvd	36
Grosse Pointe Ct	30
Grotto Ct	05
Grove	
1-2199	03
2200-12699	21
12700-18099	35
18100-24999	19
25000-27399	40
Grover	05
Groveview	20
Gruebner	34
Guilford	24
Gunston	
5800-11499	13
11500-OUT	05
Guoin	07
Guthrie	15
Hackett	27
Hafeli	13
Hague	
1-899	02
900-OUT	11
Hale	07
Hall	13
Hall Pl	36
Halleck	12
Halley	23
Haltiner	18
Hamata	20

Detroit (Con.) 482

Hamilton Ave	
9500-11699	02
11700-OUT	03
Hamilton Ct	36
Hamilton Rd	
9500-11699	02
11700-OUT	03
Hamlet	34
Hammond	
2300-2999	09
3000-OUT	10
Hampshire	13
Hampton	
1-2299	36
14900-14999	15
15000-15199	30
20700-OUT	25
Hampton Rd	
1-2299	36
14900-14999	15
15000-15199	30
20700-OUT	25
Hancock E	
1-899	01
900-OUT	07
Hancock W	
1-1399	01
1400-3999	08
4000-OUT	10
Hancock Ct	20
Handy Pl	36
Hanley	12
Hanna	03
Hanover	06
Hanson	10
Harbaugh	09
Harbaugh S	09
Harbor Ct	36
Harbor Hill Rd	36
Harbor Island	15
Harcourt Rd	30
Harding	
400-4999	14
5000-8999	13
21600-OUT	37
Hardyke	13
Harlow	35
Harmon	02
Harned	34
Harnor Ct	06
Harold	12
Harper Ave	
1-899	02
900-7199	11
7200-14399	13
14400-19199	24
19200-20999	25
19600-19698 (EVEN)	36
Harper Ct	
1-899	02
900-7199	11
7200-14399	13
14400-19199	24
19200-20999	25
19600-19698 (EVEN)	36
Harrell	13
Harriett Ct	37
Harrington	09
Harrington S	09
Harris	20
Harrison	

2200-3299	16
3300-3999	08
6400-6499	09
Harry	13
Hart	
600-3799	14
13600-OUT	37
Hart Pl N	
21000-21499	20
Hart Pl S	
21000-21499	20
Hartford	10
Hartwell	
8000-9499	28
9500-16099	27
16100-OUT	35
Hartwick	11
Harvard Rd	
1000-3399	30
3400-OUT	24
Harvey	09
Hasse	
13400-17999	12
18000-OUT	34
Hastings	11
Hathon	13
Havana	03
Haverhill	24
Hawthorne	
11300-11699	11
11700-20599	03
20600-OUT	25
Hawthorne Rd	36
Hayes	
9000-11499	13
11500-20699	05
Hazel	08
Hazelhurst St E & W	20
Hazelridge	05
Hazelton	
8800-12599	39
12600-16099	23
16100-OUT	19
Hazelwood	
1-1399	02
1400-3999	06
4000-OUT	04
Hazlett	10
Healy	
13400-17999	12
18000-OUT	34
Heather Ln	36
Heck Pl	07
Hecla	08
Hedge	11
Heidelberg	07
Heidt S	17
Heintz	11
Helen	
400-4999	07
5000-10499	11
10500-17999	12
18000-20599	34
Helen Ave	
19800-19999 (HW)	25
Helen Ct	
19800-19999 (HW)	25
Hemingway	39
Hemlock	35
Henderson	10
Hendricks	07
Hendrie	
1-899	02

900-7199	11
7200-OUT	13
Hendrie Ln	36
Henry	
1-1399	01
Henry St E & W	18
Herbert	10
Hereford	24
Herkimer	09
Hern	13
Hershey	03
Hessel Ave	
15600-18099	35
18100-OUT	19
Hessel Ct	19
Hewitt	12
Heyden Ave	
6300-7198 (EVEN)	28
7200-12599	28
12600-16099	23
16100-OUT	19
Heyden Ct	28
Hibbard	14
Hickory	05
Hidden Ln	36
Higbie Pl N & S	36
High	29
Highland	
1-1399	03
1400-OUT	06
Hildale E	
1-1899	03
1900-OUT	34
Hildale W	03
Hill	
1-99 (RR)	18
1-2099	03
Hillcrest Ln & Rd	36
Hillger	14
Hillsboro	04
Hillview	27
Hilton Rd	20
Hindle	11
Hobart	02
Hobson	01
Hogarth	
2600-3999	06
4000-OUT	04
Holborn	11
Holbrook	
1-899	02
900-1799	11
1800-OUT	12
Holcomb	
1100-4999	14
5000-OUT	13
Holden	
800-1399	02
1400-OUT	08
Holford	18
Holiday Rd	36
Holly	09
Hollywood	
500-2399	36
19500-OUT	25
Hollywood E	
400-1899	03
1900-OUT	34
Hollywood W	03
Holmes	
2300-2799	12
7000-OUT	18

Detroit (Con.)   482

Holmur
  7500-12599 04
  12600-16099 38
  16100-OUT 21
Homedale 10
Homer 09
Homestead Pl 11
Honorah 09
Hooker 08
Hoover 05
Hope 39
Horatio 10
Horton
  1-899 02
  900-2499 11
  2700-OUT 20
Hosmer 14
Houghton 19
House 34
Houston Whittier 05
Howard
  400-1399 26
  1400-3999 16
  4000-OUT 09
Howe Ct 14
Howell
  4700-7299 10
  7300-9099 04
  26900-27399 39
Hoyt 05
Hubbard
  700-2599 09
  2600-OUT 10
Hubbell
  8000-9499 28
  9500-16099 27
  16100-20699 35
  20700-OUT 37
Huber
  5900-7199 11
  7200-OUT 13
Hudson 08
Hughes 38
Hughes Ter 08
Hull 03
Humboldt
  2600-3299 16
  3300-OUT 08
Humphrey
  3700-3999 06
  4000-OUT 04
Hunt 07
Hunt Club Dr
  1800-2199 36
  19600-OUT 25
Huntington Ave
  18500-21299 (HW) 25
Huntington Blvd 36
Huntington Rd
  18500-21299 (HW) 25
Huntington (First Choice) Rd
  16100-20699 19
Hurlbut
  1400-4999 14
  5000-OUT 13
Huron 16
Hussar 09
Hyacinthe 29
Hyde 11
Hyde Park Rd 07

Hyland 20
Ida 09
Ida Ln E & W 36
Idaho 38
Ilene
  11600-12599 04
  12600-16099 38
  16100-OUT 21
Iliad
  15300-16099 23
  16100-16599 19
Iliad Ct
  15700-16199 23
Illinois
  900-OUT 07
Imperial Hwy 40
Indian
  15700-16099 39
  16100-20699 40
Indiana
  8000-12599 04
  12600-16099 38
  16100-OUT 21
Indiandale 38
Infantry 09
Inglis 09
Inkster Rd
  8800-16098 (EVEN) 39
  16100-20698 (EVEN) 40
Inman 20
Intervale
  6300-12699 38
  12700-OUT 27
Inverness
  15300-16099 38
  16100-OUT 21
Iowa 12
Iris 27
Iron 07
Ironside 10
Ironwood
  6000-7299 10
  7300-OUT 04
Iroquois
  700-4999 14
  5000-OUT 13
Irvine Blvd 37
Irvine Ln 36
Irvington
  19100-20599 03
  26800-OUT 39
Isham 13
Ithaca
  20700-22999 20
  23000-OUT 37
Ivanhoe
  4700-5699 04
  25300-OUT 39
Jackson 10
Jacob 12
James
  14000-15499 37
James Ct 13
James St E & W 18
James Couzens Fwy
  15400-16099 38
  16100-16774 21
  16775-OUT 35
Jameson 14
Jan 39
Jane 05
Jarvis 20

Jason 23
Jay 07
Jean 20
Jefferson E
  1-899 26
  900-7199 07
  7200-11999 14
  12000-14999 15
  15000-17899 30
Jefferson W
  1-1399 26
  1400-3999 16
  4000-9999 09
  10000-11453 18
Jefferson Ct 07
Jeffries Fwy
  2600-3299 16
  3300-7299 08
  7300-12699 04
  12700-18099 27
  18100-19999 28
  20000-23999 23
  24000-27399 39
Jennie 10
Jennifer Ave & Ct 39
Jennings 27
Jerome
  2000-3699 12
  8800-9499 39
  22000-OUT 37
Jewell 20
Joan 37
Joann 05
Joe 10
John C Lodge Fwy
  100-2099 26
  2100-4999 01
  5000-11699 02
  11700-12199 03
  12200-OUT 38
John F Kennedy Pl 03
John Glenn Pl 03
John Kronk 10
John R
  1-2099 26
  2100-4999 01
  5000-11699 02
  11700-20599 03
Johnson 16
Joliet Pl 07
Jones 26
Jordan 34
Joseph 29
Joseph Campau
  100-4999 07
  5000-8399 11
  8400-17999 12
  18000-OUT 34
Josephine 02
Josephine St E & W 29
Joslyn 03
Joy Rd
  2600-3999 06
  4000-12699 04
  12700-21999 28
  22000-23226 39
  23228-27398 (EVEN) 39
Julian 04
Junction
  100-2999 09
  3000-OUT 10
Junction S 09

Detroit (Con.)   482

Justine
  12200-17999.......................... 12
  18000-OUT 34
Kaier 09
Kalsh 34
Kane St N & S 23
Kanter 11
Karen 37
Karl 19
Kay 04
Keal 27
Keating 03
Keeler
  12700-18099.......................... 27
  18100-23999.......................... 23
  24000-OUT 39
Keelson Dr............................ 15
Keibler 27
Keller 09
Kellogg Pl 11
Kelly Rd
  11300-19199.......................... 24
  19200-20699.......................... 25
Kempa 34
Kenberton Ave, Ct & Dr 37
Kendall Ave
  1-1399................................. 03
  1400-12699.......................... 38
  12700-18099.......................... 27
  18100-23999.......................... 23
  24000-OUT 39
Kendall Ct 39
Kenilworth............................ 02
Kenmoor............................... 05
Kenmore Ave......................... 25
Kenmore Dr........................... 36
Kennebec 05
Kenneth
  20600-20699.......................... 03
  26200-OUT 39
Kenney 34
Kenosha
  18500-20899 (HW)................. 25
  20700-26799 (OP)................. 37
Kensington Ave
  100-999............................... 20
  1000-3399.......................... 30
  3400-OUT 24
Kensington Rd
  100-999............................... 20
  1000-3399.......................... 30
  3400-OUT 24
Kent 13
Kentfield
  12600-16099.......................... 23
  16100-OUT 19
Kentfurd............................... 23
Kenton
  1500-1799.......................... 20
  14400-OUT 37
Kentucky
  8000-12599.......................... 04
  12600-16099.......................... 38
  16100-OUT 21
Kenwood
  1400-1651.......................... 11
  1652-1899............................ 12
  3100-3399.......................... 20
  8100-OUT 37
Kenwood Ct & Rd. 36
Kerby Ln & Rd....................... 36

Kercheval Ave
  1-499................................. 36
  6300-7199............................ 07
  7200-11999.......................... 14
  12000-14999.......................... 15
  15000-OUT 30
Kercheval Pl 30
Kern 13
Kessler 19
Keystone
  13400-17999.......................... 12
  18000-OUT 34
Kilbourne 13
Kimberly Ct........................... 04
Kimland Ct 39
King
  1-899................................. 02
  900-OUT 11
King Pl, N
  21000-21499.......................... 20
King Pl, S
  21000-21499.......................... 20
King Richard 24
Kings Ct E & W....................... 36
Kingsley Ct 02
Kingston 37
Kingston Rd 21
Kingsville
  18500-21899.......................... 25
  21900-OUT 36
Kingswood 21
Kinloch
  8800-16099.......................... 39
  16100-20699.......................... 40
Kinsman 10
Kipke 39
Kipling
  7300-7699............................ 06
  20700-OUT 37
Kirby E
  1-899................................. 02
  900-7199............................ 11
  7200-OUT 13
Kirby W
  1-1399................................. 02
  1400-OUT 08
Kirkwood
  6600-8799............................ 10
  18100-OUT 28
Kitchener 15
Klein 18
Kleinow 15
Klenk 15
Klinger
  8200-8899............................ 11
  8900-17999.......................... 12
  18000-OUT 34
Knight 39
Knodell................................. 13
Knox
  1-99................................... 29
  8900-OUT 11
Kolb 14
Konkel 10
Kopernick.............................. 10
Korte
  13100-14999.......................... 15
  15000-OUT 30
Krakow Pl 07
Kramer
  10200-12699.......................... 04
  12700-OUT 28
Kresge.................................. 13

Kress.................................... 19
Kulick................................... 10
La Belle Ave
  1-1399................................. 03
  400-499 (GPS) 36
  1400-2599.......................... 38
  13600-OUT 37
La Belle Rd
  1-1399................................. 03
  400-499 (GPS) 36
  1400-2599.......................... 38
  13600-OUT 37
La Prairie 20
La Salle Blvd
  7300-12599.......................... 06
  12600-16099.......................... 38
  16100-OUT 21
La Salle Ct 38
La Salle Gdns N & S 06
La Salle Pl............................. 36
Labadie Ave & Ct.................... 29
Labrosse
  900-1399............................. 26
  1400-OUT 16
Lafayette E
  300-899............................... 26
  900-7199............................ 07
  7200-OUT 14
Lafayette Blvd
  10C-1399.............................. 26
  1400-3999.......................... 16
  4000-OUT 09
Lafayette Plaisance................. 07
Lafferty Pl............................. 16
Lafontaine 36
Lahser Ave
  8800-12599.......................... 39
  12600-16099.......................... 23
  16100-20699.......................... 19
Lahser Rd
  8800-12599.......................... 39
  12600-16099.......................... 23
  16100-20699.......................... 19
Laing
  11400-19199.......................... 24
  19200-OUT 25
Lake Ct................................. 30
Lake Shore Ln & Rd................ 36
Lakecrest Ln.......................... 36
Lakeland Ave & Ct.................. 30
Lakepointe
  500-3399............................. 30
  3400-OUT 24
Lakeview
  1-299................................. 36
  1000-4999.......................... 15
  5000-OUT 13
Lakeview Ct........................... 30
Lakewood
  1-4999................................. 15
  5000-OUT 13
Lambert
  6300-7199............................ 11
  7200-OUT 13
Lambie Pl.............................. 16
Lamont
  17100-17999.......................... 12
  18000-OUT 34
Lamothe............................... 06
Lamphere
  7200-12599.......................... 39
  12600-16099.......................... 23
  16100-OUT 19

Detroit (Con.)   482

Lanark	24
Lancashire	23
Lancaster	
1800-2199	36
19600-OUT	25
Lanco	04
Lane	09
Lang	17
Langholm	34
Lanman	08
Lannette	13
Lannoo	36
Lansdowne	
11100-19199	24
19200-OUT	25
Lansing	09
Lantz E	
1-1899	03
1900-OUT	34
Lantz W	03
Lappin	
11000-11599	34
11600-OUT	05
Larchmont	04
Larchwood	03
Lark	13
Larkins	10
Larned E	
1-899	26
900-OUT	07
Larned W	26
Latham	12
Lauder	
8000-9499	28
9500-16099	27
16100-OUT	35
Lauderdale	09
Laura	14
Laurel	05
Law	24
Lawley	12
Lawndale	
200-3599	09
3600-OUT	10
Lawrence	
1-1399	02
1400-3999	06
4000-OUT	04
Lawton	
2600-3299	16
3300-7299	08
7300-12599	06
12600-16099	38
16100-OUT	21
Le Blanc	
1-99 (RR)	18
1-99 (EC)	29
Le Grand	11
Le Roy	
1-199 (RR)	18
100-1799 (FER)	20
8200-9999	37
11000-11499	13
11500-OUT	05
Leach	14
Leander	34
Ledyard	01
Lee Ct	36
Lee Pl	06
Lee Gate Ln	36
Leewin	19

Lehman	12
Leib	07
Leicester Ct	02
Leidich	13
Leigh S	09
Leitch Rd	20
Leland	
900-3599	07
1800-2199 (FER)	20
Lemay	
400-4999	14
5000-OUT	13
Lennane	
14700-16099	39
16100-OUT	40
Lennon	
1800-2199	36
19600-OUT	25
Lennox	
(ODD)	20
Lenoir	18
Lenore	
8800-16099	39
16100-OUT	19
Lenox	
1-4999	15
5000-OUT	13
Leona Dr	39
Leonard	17
Leota	01
Lernoult	13
Leslie	
1-1399	03
1400-4899	38
14400-OUT	37
Lessing	14
Lesure	
13500-16099	27
16100-OUT	35
Leverette	
1300-1399	26
1400-OUT	16
Leverne	39
Lewerenz	09
Lewiston Rd	36
Lewiston St E & W	20
Lexington Ave	
400-499	36
7000-7199	09
13900-16099	39
16100-OUT	40
Lexington Rd	
400-499	36
7000-7199	09
13900-16099	39
16100-OUT	40
Liberal	05
Liberty	11
Library	26
Lichfield Rd	21
Liddesdale S	17
Liebold S	17
Lilac	21
Lillibridge	
400-4999	14
5000-OUT	13
Lincoln Ave	
3400-6199	08
6200-11699	02
11700-14499	03
13600-15499	37
Lincoln Blvd & Ter	37
Lincoln Rd	30

Lincolnshire Dr	03
Linden	18
Lindsay	
14800-16099	27
16100-OUT	35
Linnhurst	
11000-11599	34
11600-OUT	05
Linsdale	04
Linville	
12900-14399	13
14400-18599	24
18600-OUT	36
Linwood	
5200-7299	08
7300-12599	06
12600-16099	38
16100-OUT	21
Linzee	10
Liptori	04
Lisbon	09
Littlefield	
8000-9499	28
9500-16099	27
16100-OUT	35
Littlestone Ave	
1600-2199	36
19600-OUT	25
Littlestone Rd	
1600-2199	36
19600-OUT	25
Livernois	
100-2699 (FER)	20
100-2999	09
3000-7999	10
8000-12599	04
12600-16099	38
16100-OUT	21
Livernois S	
100-699	09
Livingstone	07
Lochmoor	25
Lochmoor Blvd	36
Lockwood	10
Lodewyck	24
Lodge Dr	14
Lodi	11
Log Cabin	
15300-16099	38
16100-OUT	03
Logan	09
Lola Ave	
5900-5999	10
15300-16099	39
16100-OUT	40
Lola Dr	
5900-5999	10
15300-16099	39
16100-OUT	40
Lombard Ter	08
London	21
Longacre	
6300-9499	28
9500-OUT	27
Longfellow	
1-1399	02
1400-OUT	06
Longview	13
Longwood Ave E	03
Longwood Ave & Pl	03
Longwood Pl W	03
Longworth	09
Longyear	11

Detroit (Con.)   482

Lons................................... 39
Lonyo
  2900-3599......................... 09
  3600-6226......................... 10
Loraine
  700-899........................... 30
  5000-OUT......................... 08
Loretta Pl........................... 37
Loretto............................... 05
Lorman............................... 14
Lorne................................. 24
Lothrop Ave
  1-499 (GPS)...................... 36
  1-1399............................ 02
  1400-OUT......................... 06
Lothrop Rd
  1-499 (GPS)...................... 36
  1-1399............................ 02
  1400-OUT......................... 06
Louis
  1-99.............................. 18
  8800-9299......................... 03
  9200-9499......................... 39
Louis First Choice
  8800-9299......................... 14
Louisiana............................ 03
Lovett................................ 10
Lowdell.............................. 17
Lowell Dr............................ 03
Lozier
  13100-14899....................... 15
  14900-OUT........................ 24
Luce................................. 12
Lucerne Ave
  8800-14299........................ 39
  19000-OUT........................ 03
Lucerne Dr
  8800-14299........................ 39
  19000-OUT........................ 03
Lucky Pl............................. 11
Ludden.............................. 07
Ludlow............................... 37
Lumley............................... 10
Lumpkin
  8400-17999........................ 12
  18000-OUT........................ 34
Luther S............................. 17
Lycaste.............................. 14
Lyford............................... 34
Lyle................................. 09
Lyman Pl............................. 11
Lynch Rd............................ 34
Lyndon
  6300-12699........................ 38
  12700-18099....................... 27
  18100-23999....................... 23
  24000-27399....................... 39
Lynn................................. 11
Lyon................................. 09
Lyons................................ 37
Lysander
  900-1399.......................... 01
  1400-OUT......................... 08
Mabel................................ 03
Mac Arthur
  13900-16099....................... 39
  16100-OUT........................ 40
Mac Crary........................... 05
Mack Ave
  1-899............................. 01
  900-7199.......................... 07

7200-11999......................... 14
12000-14899........................ 15
14900-18199........................ 24
18200-21401........................ 36
Mack Rd
  1-899............................. 01
  900-7199.......................... 07
  7200-11999........................ 14
  12000-14899....................... 15
  14900-18199....................... 24
  18200-21401....................... 36
Mackay
  11300-17999....................... 12
  18000-OUT........................ 34
Mackenzie
  6300-12699........................ 04
  12700-OUT........................ 28
Mackinaw............................ 04
Macomb
  300-899........................... 26
  900-OUT.......................... 07
Macon............................... 13
Maddelein........................... 05
Madeira.............................. 03
Madison
  1-899............................. 26
  400-499 (GPS)..................... 36
  900-OUT.......................... 07
Madola.............................. 34
Magnolia
  1600-3999......................... 08
  4000-OUT......................... 10
Mahan............................... 20
Maiden.............................. 13
Maine
  12200-17999....................... 12
  18000-OUT........................ 34
Maison Rd........................... 36
Majestic
  6300-8099......................... 10
  15500-21999....................... 28
  20700-22999 (FER)................. 20
  22000-22799....................... 39
  23000-OUT........................ 37
Major............................... 17
Malcolm............................. 13
Mallina.............................. 36
Malta................................ 23
Malvern............................. 13
Manatee............................. 20
Manchester Ave
  1-299............................. 03
  1600-2199......................... 36
  20800-OUT........................ 25
Manchester Blvd
  1-299............................. 03
  1600-2199......................... 36
  20800-OUT........................ 25
Mandalay............................ 04
Mandale............................. 09
Manderson Rd........................ 03
Manhattan
  8400-8599......................... 11
  13600-OUT........................ 37
Manhattan Pl........................ 37
Manila............................... 14
Manistee............................ 37
Manistique
  200-4999.......................... 15
  5000-OUT......................... 24
Manning
  11100-11599....................... 34
  11600-OUT........................ 05

Manor
  400-499........................... 36
  8000-12599....................... 04
  12600-16099....................... 38
  16100-OUT........................ 21
Mansfield
  6300-9499......................... 28
  9500-16099........................ 27
  16100-OUT........................ 35
Manson.............................. 09
Mansur.............................. 11
Manuel.............................. 11
Maple
  1-199............................. 18
  900-OUT.......................... 07
Maple Ln............................ 36
Mapledale........................... 20
Maplehurst St E & W................. 20
Maplelawn........................... 04
Mapleridge.......................... 05
Mapleton Rd......................... 36
Mapleview........................... 05
Maplewood........................... 04
Marantette.......................... 16
Marbud.............................. 05
Marcus
  5900-7199......................... 11
  7200-OUT......................... 13
Marene.............................. 19
Marford Ct.......................... 36
Margaret St E & W................... 03
Margareta
  3100-12699........................ 21
  12700-18099....................... 35
  18100-24999....................... 19
  25000-27399....................... 40
Marian Ct........................... 36
Marian Pl........................... 19
Marie
  1-99.............................. 29
  1300-OUT......................... 20
Marietta............................ 14
Marion
  1-999............................. 18
  8000-8699......................... 13
  8800-OUT......................... 39
Marion Cres......................... 39
Marjorie............................ 13
Mark................................ 08
Mark Twain
  8000-9499......................... 28
  9500-16099........................ 27
  16100-OUT........................ 35
Market.............................. 07
Marlborough
  200-4999.......................... 15
  5000-OUT......................... 24
Marlin Dr........................... 39
Marlow St & Pl...................... 37
Marlowe
  8000-9499......................... 28
  9500-16099........................ 27
  16100-OUT........................ 35
Marne............................... 24
Marquette........................... 08
Marquette Dr........................ 14
Marseilles.......................... 24
Marshall
  800-1099.......................... 17
Marshall E
  100-1899.......................... 20
Marshall W
  100-1799.......................... 20

Detroit (Con.) 482

Marshfield ... 20
Marston
  1-899 ... 02
  900-OUT ... 11
Marter Rd ... 36
Martin ... 10
Martin Rd ... 20
Martindale St N & S ... 04
Marx ... 03
Mary ... 36
Marygrove Dr ... 21
Maryland
  1-3399 ... 30
  3400-OUT ... 24
Mason Pl ... 09
Massachusetts ... 03
Mather ... 10
Matthews ... 07
Maumee ... 30
Maxwell
  2100-4999 ... 14
  5000-OUT ... 13
May ... 13
Maybury Grand
  3300-OUT ... 08
Mayfield ... 05
Maynard ... 15
Maywood ... 13
Mc Bride Pl ... 27
Mc Clain Dr ... 37
Mc Clellan
  1200-4999 ... 14
  5000-OUT ... 13
Mc Cormick
  18500-20799 ... 24
  20800-OUT ... 36
Mc Donald ... 10
Mc Donald Pl ... 08
Mc Dougall
  1-4999 ... 07
  5000-8399 ... 11
  8400-17999 ... 12
  18000-OUT ... 34
Mc Dowell ... 20
Mc Graw
  1900-3999 ... 08
  4000-OUT ... 10
Mc Gregor ... 09
Mc Intyre ... 19
Mc Kinley ... 08
Mc Kinley Pl & Rd ... 36
Mc Kinney ... 24
Mc Kinstry ... 09
Mc Kinstry S ... 09
Mc Lean
  1-1899 ... 03
  1900-OUT ... 12
Mc Millan
  4600-OUT ... 09
Mc Millan Rd
  1-399 ... 36
Mc Nichols Rd E
  1-1899 ... 03
  1900-7399 ... 12
  7400-11499 ... 34
  11500-OUT ... 05
Mc Nichols Rd W
  1-2199 ... 03
  2200-12699 ... 21
  12700-18099 ... 35
  18100-OUT ... 19

Mc Quade ... 06
Meade ... 12
Meadow Ln ... 36
Meadow Park ... 39
Meadow Lark ... 37
Meadowbrook Ave
  1-1399 ... 14
  14700-16099 ... 39
  16100-16199 ... 40
  25000-27399 ... 39
Meadowbrook Rd
  1-1399 ... 14
  14700-16099 ... 39
  16100-16199 ... 40
  25000-27399 ... 39
Meadowdale
  100-999 ... 20
  8200-OUT ... 28
Mecca ... 27
Mechanic ... 26
Medbury
  1300-7199 ... 11
  7200-OUT ... 13
Medina ... 09
Meige ... 09
Melbourne
  1-899 ... 02
  900-OUT ... 11
Meldrum Ave & Ct ... 07
Mellon ... 17
Melrose ... 09
Melville ... 09
Melvin ... 18
Memorial Ave
  6300-9499 ... 28
  9500-13699 ... 27
  17100-OUT ... 40
Memorial Dr
  6300-9499 ... 28
  9500-13699 ... 27
  17100-OUT ... 40
Mendota
  8000-12599 ... 04
  12600-16099 ... 38
  16100-20699 ... 21
  20700-OUT ... 20
Mercedes ... 39
Mercier ... 10
Merkel ... 13
Merlin ... 24
Merrick
  400-1399 ... 02
  1400-OUT ... 08
Merrill ... 02
Merrill Plaisance ... 03
Merritt ... 09
Merriweather Rd ... 36
Merton Rd ... 03
Merwin ... 10
Mettetal
  6300-9499 ... 28
  9500-OUT ... 27
Meuse ... 24
Meyers Rd
  8000-9499 ... 28
  9500-16099 ... 27
  16100-20699 ... 35
  20700-OUT ... 27
Miami ... 17
Michaux Ln ... 36
Michigan
  1-1399 ... 26
  1400-3999 ... 16

  4000-9999 ... 10
Middle ... 26
Middlepoint ... 04
Middlesex Rd ... 30
Midfield ... 27
Midland
  1-1399 ... 03
  1400-12699 ... 38
  12700-18099 ... 27
  18100-23999 ... 23
  24000-OUT ... 39
Milbank ... 34
Miles ... 11
Milford
  3700-3999 ... 08
  4000-OUT ... 10
Military
  100-2999 ... 09
  3000-7999 ... 10
  8000-OUT ... 04
Military S ... 09
Mill ... 29
Miller
  2900-7199 ... 11
  7200-7999 ... 13
  14000-OUT ... 37
Miller Ct ... 07
Miller Rd ... 09
Milner ... 13
Milo ... 12
Milton ... 34
Milwaukee E
  1-899 ... 02
  900-OUT ... 11
Milwaukee W ... 02
Minden ... 05
Minerva
  3000-3399 ... 20
  17200-OUT ... 24
Minneapolis ... 24
Minnesota
  1-1899 ... 03
  1900-OUT ... 12
Minock
  5600-12599 ... 28
  12600-OUT ... 23
Minock Cir & Dr ... 39
Mint ... 09
Mirabeau Pl ... 36
Missouri ... 08
Mitcheldale ... 20
Mitchell
  3400-4999 ... 07
  5000-8399 ... 11
  8400-17999 ... 12
  18000-OUT ... 34
Modern
  1600-1899 ... 03
  1900-OUT ... 12
Moenart
  11900-17999 ... 12
  18000-OUT ... 34
Moffat ... 13
Mogul ... 24
Mohawk ... 08
Mohican ... 05
Molena ... 34
Monarch ... 05
Monica
  8800-12599 ... 04
  12600-16099 ... 38
  16100-OUT ... 21

Detroit (Con.)	482
Monitor	34
Monroe	
1-899	26
900-3799	07
4200-OUT	29
Montana St E & W	03
Montcalm E	
1-899	01
900-OUT	07
Montcalm W	01
Montclair	
300-4999	14
5000-OUT	13
Monte Vis	
12600-16099	38
16100-OUT	21
Monterey	
1-1399	03
1400-3999	06
4000-OUT	04
Montgomery	
2600-3999	06
4000-OUT	04
Montlieu	34
Montmartre Ct	37
Montrose	
6300-9499	28
9500-16099	27
16100-OUT	35
Montville Pl	38
Moon	36
Moore Pl	
3500-3999	08
4000-OUT	10
Moorhouse	20
Moorland Dr	36
Moran	
1-499	36
3800-4999	07
5000-8399	11
8400-OUT	12
Moran Rd	
1-499	36
3800-4999	07
5000-8399	11
8400-OUT	12
Morang Dr	
9000-18299	24
18300-OUT	05
Morgan	34
Moritz	37
Morley	04
Morningside Dr	36
Moross Pl	
1-499	36
16000-18499	05
18500-20799	24
20800-OUT	36
Moross Rd	
1-499	36
16000-18499	05
18500-20799	24
20800-OUT	36
Morrell	09
Morrell S	09
Morrow	
300-399	18
7800-OUT	11
Morrow Cir E	
8000-8399	04

Morse	10
Morton	
6300-6499	10
21900-OUT	37
Moselle Pl	36
Moss	03
Motor Boat Ln	14
Mound	
11300-17999	12
18000-20699	34
Mount Elliott Ave	
1-4999	07
5000-10499	11
10500-17999	12
18000-OUT	34
Mount Elliott Ct	12
Mount Olivet	34
Mount Vernon	
1-899	02
200-499 (GPS)	36
900-OUT	11
Moyes	10
Muir Rd	36
Muirland	
14800-16099	38
16100-OUT	21
Mulberry	08
Mullane	09
Mullet	
600-899	26
900-OUT	07
Muncey	24
Munich	24
Murat	13
Murray	13
Murray Hill	
15300-16099	27
16100-OUT	35
Musket	09
Muskoka Rd	36
Myrtle	
1-99 (RR)	18
1-1399	01
700-899 (FER)	20
1400-OUT	08
Nadine	37
Nagel	12
Nagle	13
Nall	
3800-3999	08
4000-OUT	10
Nancy	12
Naples	11
Napoleon	
400-899	01
900-OUT	07
Nardin	04
Nashville	05
Nathaline	39
Naumann	12
Navahoe	15
Navarre	14
Navarre Pl	14
Navy	09
Neal	14
Nebraska	08
Neff Ln	30
Neff Rd	
300-3399	30
3400-OUT	24
Negaunee	
15800-16099	39
16100-20699	40

Neibel	12
Nelson	27
Nett	13
Netting	24
Nevada E	
1-1899	03
1900-OUT	34
Nevada W	03
Neveux	24
New York	24
Newark	16
Newbern	12
Newberry	09
Newberry Pl	36
Newcastle Rd	
1500-1899	36
21200-OUT	25
Newhall	11
Newport	
100-4999	15
5000-11499	13
11500-OUT	05
Newton	11
Nichols	13
Nicolet Pl	07
Nieman	18
Noble	
900-1399	01
Norborne	
8800-16099	39
16100-20699	40
Norcross	13
Norfolk	
3100-12699	21
12700-18099	35
18100-24999	19
25000-27399	40
Norfolk St N & S	35
Norman	09
Normandy	
15300-16099	38
16100-OUT	21
Normile	04
North	03
North Campbell	10
North End	
1100-12699	20
8500-9998 (EVEN)	37
12700-OUT	37
North Oak Dr	20
Northampton	17
Northfield	
5800-7299	10
7300-9599	04
8400-15499 (OP)	37
Northgate	37
Northlawn	
8000-12599	04
12600-16099	38
16100-OUT	21
Northrop	19
Northway	20
Northwestern	06
Norton Ct	36
Norvell Ct	14
Norwalk	
1800-5899	12
5900-OUT	11
Norway	17
Norwood	
1700-2199 (GPW)	36
17800-17999	12
18000-20599	34

Detroit (Con.)   **482**

19600-21299 (HW)	25
23000-OUT	37
Norwood Dr	
1700-2199 (GPW)	36
17800-17999	12
18000-20599	34
19600-21299 (HW)	25
23000-OUT	37
Notre Dame	30
Nottingham Rd	
800-3399	30
3400-OUT	24
Novara	05
Nowak	10
Nuernberg	34
Oak	18
Oak Dr	21
Oak Park Blvd	37
Oak Crest Ave & Ct	37
Oakdale	09
Oakfield	
14800-16099	27
16100-OUT	35
Oakland	
6200-7299	02
7300-11699	11
11700-OUT	03
Oakman Blvd	
1-799	03
800-3419	38
3420-5969	04
5970-6799	28
Oakman Ct	
1-799	03
800-3419	38
3420-5969	04
5970-6799	28
Oakridge St E & W	20
Oakwood Dr	37
Ogden	
4800-5999	18
15400-OUT	39
Ohio	
8000-12599	04
12600-16099	38
16100-OUT	21
Oklahoma	12
Old Homestead Dr	25
Old Mill Pl	38
Oldbrook Ln	36
Oldtown	24
Olga	13
Oliver	11
Olivet	09
Olympia	
8000-8399	13
17100-OUT	40
Omaha	17
Omara Ct	36
Omira	03
Oneida	37
Ontario	24
Opal	36
Orangelawn	
8500-12699	04
12700-18099	27
18100-21999	28
22000-27399	39
Orchard	
1-99	18

700-2499	20
21100-OUT	19
Oregon	04
Orion	34
Orleans	
100-4999	07
5000-11699	11
11700-OUT	03
Ormond	17
Otis	10
Otsego	04
Otto	04
Outer Dr E	
1400-6499	34
6500-9819	13
9820-OUT	24
Outer Dr W	
2900-4471	21
4472-8059	35
8060-9400	19
9401-13199	23
13200-14299	39
25691-26585 (ODD)	17
26600-27727	29
Owen	
1-899	02
900-OUT	11
Oxford Rd N & S	36
Oxley	35
Pacific	04
Packard	34
Page	09
Paget Ct	36
Pallister	
1-1399	02
1400-OUT	06
Palmer E	
1-899	02
900-7199	11
7200-OUT	13
Palmer W	02
Palmerston	18
Palmetto	34
Palms	09
Panama	10
Park Ave	
500-2099	26
2100-3199	01
9000-11499	13
11500-12699	05
14400-OUT	37
Park Dr	
500-2099	26
2100-3199	01
9000-11499	13
11500-12699	05
14400-OUT	37
Park Grv	
11000-11599	34
11600-OUT	05
Park Ln	30
Park Pl E	26
Park Ter	04
Park Lawn	37
Parkcrest Dr	25
Parkdale Ter	10
Parker	
500-4999	14
5000-OUT	13
Parkhurst Pl E & W	03
Parkinson	10
Parkland	39

Parkside	
14800-16099	38
16100-19599	21
20700-OUT	20
Parkview Ave & Dr	14
Parkway Dr	36
Parkwood	10
Parsons	01
Pasadena	
1-1399	03
1400-4399	38
8000-12699	20
12700-OUT	37
Patricia S	17
Patton	
7200-12599	28
12600-16099	23
16100-20699	19
Patton Ct	
20600-20699	28
Paul	
15500-18098 (EVEN)	28
18100-19999	28
Paxton	20
Payton	24
Peach Tree Ln	36
Pear	38
Pear Tree Ln	36
Pearl	09
Pearson	
100-1899	20
13600-OUT	37
Pease	11
Peerless	
10600-19199	24
19200-OUT	25
Pelham	09
Pelham S	09
Pelkey	05
Pelouze	10
Pemberton Rd	30
Pembridge Pl	07
Pembroke Ave	
3000-12699	21
12700-18099	35
18100-24999	19
25000-27399	40
Pembroke Rd	
3000-12699	21
12700-18099	35
18100-24999	19
25000-27399	40
Pennington Dr	21
Pennsylvania	
1200-4999	14
5000-OUT	13
Penrod	
5600-12599	28
12600-OUT	23
Penrose	03
Peoria	05
Pepper Rd	29
Perkins	10
Perrien	36
Perrin	18
Perry	
1000-1399	01
1400-OUT	16
Peter Hunt	13
Peterboro	01
Peters	17

Detroit (Con.) | 482

Petoskey Ave
8700-12599 | 04
12600-16099 | 38
16100-OUT | 21

Petoskey Rd
8700-12599 | 04
12600-16099 | 38
16100-OUT | 21

Pfent | 05
Phelps | 13

Philadelphia E
1-899 | 02
900-OUT | 11

Philadelphia W
1-1399 | 02
1400-3999 | 06
4000-OUT | 04

Philip
200-4999 | 15
5000-OUT | 24

Phyllis | 12
Picadilly Rd | 21
Piche | 36

Pickford
3100-12699 | 21
12700-18099 | 35
18100-24999 | 49
25000-27399 | 40

Piedmont
6000-12599 | 28
12600-OUT | 23

Pierce | 07

Pierson
7200-12599 | 28
12600-16099 | 23
16100-OUT | 19

Pierson Ct N & S | 28

Pilgrim
1-1399 | 03
1400-12699 | 38
1801-2899 (FER) (ODD) | 20
12700-18099 | 27
18100-23999 | 23
24000-OUT | 39

Pine
1-199 | 18
900-1399 | 01
1400-OUT | 16

Pine Ct | 36
Pinecrest Dr | 20

Pinehurst
8000-12599 | 04
12600-16099 | 38
16100-OUT | 21

Pinewood | 05

Pingree
1-1399 | 02
1400-3999 | 06
4000-OUT | 04

Piper Blvd | 15

Piquette
1-899 | 02
900-OUT | 11

Pitkin | 03

Pitt
4200-4299 | 29
7100-OUT | 09

Pittsburg | 10

Plainview Ave
5600-12599 | 28
12600-16099 | 23
16100-OUT | 19

Plainview Rd
5600-12599 | 28
12600-16099 | 23
16100-OUT | 19

Planavon | 20
Platt | 07

Pleasant
500-699 | 20
11800-OUT | 17

Pleasant St E & W | 18

Plum
600-1399 | 01
1400-OUT | 16

Plumer | 09

Plymouth Rd
8300-12699 | 04
12700-18099 | 27
18100-21999 | 28
22000-27399 | 39

Poe | 06
Poinciana | 40
Pointer | 34
Poland | 12
Polk | 18

Pomona Ave
15300-16099 | 39
16100-16799 | 40
17400-OUT | 24

Pomona Dr
15300-16099 | 39
16100-16799 | 40
17400-OUT | 24

Pontchartrain Blvd | 03
Pontiac | 14
Poplar | 08
Port Dr | 15
Portage | 03

Porter
600-1399 | 26
1400-3999 | 05
4000-OUT | 09

Portlance | 09
Portland | 09
Posen | 09
Post | 09
Post S | 09
Powell | 17

Prairie
7100-7999 | 10
8000-12599 | 04
12600-16099 | 38
16100-OUT | 21

Prentis | 01
Prescott | 12
Pressler | 13

Prest
8000-9499 | 28
9500-16099 | 27
16100-OUT | 35

Preston
1-99 | 36
3000-7199 | 07
7200-OUT | 14

Prestwick Ave | 25
Prestwick Rd | 36

Prevost
8000-9499 | 28
9500-16099 | 27
16100-OUT | 35

Princeton
15300-16099 | 38
16100-OUT | 21

Proctor | 10

Promenade
11000-15199 | 13
15200-OUT | 24

Prospect | 03
Provencal Rd | 36
Pryor | 14

Pulaski
2100-2799 | 12
8600-9199 | 09

Pulford | 07

Puritan
1-2199 | 03
2200-12699 | 38
12700-18099 | 27
18100-23999 | 23
24000-27399 | 39

Putnam
1-1399 | 02
1400-OUT | 08

Putnam Pl | 36

Queen
9200-11499 | 13
11500-OUT | 05

Queenston Pl | 03

Quincy
8400-12599 | 04
12600-16099 | 38
16100-OUT | 21

Quinn | 34
Racine | 05

Radcliffe
7500-8299 | 10
15500-OUT | 28

Radclift St & Pl | 37

Rademacher
100-1999 | 09

Rademacher S
100-799 | 09

Radford | 04
Radio Pl | 28
Radnor | 24
Radnor Cir | 36
Radom | 12
Raine | 37
Ralston | 03
Randall | 16
Randolph | 26

Rangoon
6500-7999 | 10
8000-OUT | 04

Rankin | 09
Ranspach | 09
Rathbone | 09
Rathbone Pl | 30
Ravenswood | 04
Ray | 23

Raymond
6600-9699 | 13
19200-OUT | 36

Raynor | 26
Redfern | 19
Redford | 19
Redmond | 05
Reed Pl | 02
Reeder | 09
Regent Dr | 05
Regular | 09
Reid S | 09
Reimanville | 20
Reisener | 09
Reissman | 09

Remington E
1-1899 | 03

Detroit (Con.)   482

1900-OUT	34
Remington W	03
Renaud Rd	36
Renaud Rd N & S	36
Renfrew Rd	21
Reno	
100-199	29
18400-OUT	05
Reno Ln	36
Rensselaer	37
Renville	10
Republic	
21600-22998 (EVEN)	20
21601-22999 (ODD)	37
23000-OUT	37
Reva	27
Revere	34
Rex	05
Reynolds	12
Rhode Island	03
Riad	
11600-19199	24
19200-OUT	25
Rich	10
Richard	09
Richardson	11
Richmond	11
Richter	
1-399	18
9300-OUT	14
Richton	
1-1399	03
1400-3999	06
4000-OUT	04
Ridge	
1-99	29
16200-OUT	19
Ridge Rd	
1-399	36
Ridgedale	37
Ridgemont Ave	
1-2299	36
19800-OUT	25
Ridgemont Rd	
1-2299	36
19800-OUT	25
Ridgewood	04
Rieden	09
Ries	17
Riopelle	
100-4999	07
5000-11699	11
11700-OUT	03
Risdon	16
Rivard	
100-4999	07
5000-OUT	11
Rivard Blvd	
200-999	30
River Cir	39
River Ct	14
River Rd	36
Riverdale Ave	
8800-12599	39
12600-16099	23
16100-OUT	19
Riverdale Dr N	
16100-OUT	19
Riverdale Dr S	
16100-OUT	19

Riverdale Dr W	
16100-OUT	19
Riverdale Rd	
8800-12599	39
12600-16099	23
16100-OUT	19
Riverpark	39
Riverside Blvd & Dr	15
Riverview	
8800-12599	39
12600-16099	23
16100-OUT	19
Riviera	04
Roanoke	37
Robert	13
Robert John Ave & Rd	36
Robindale	39
Robinwood E	
1-1899	03
1900-OUT	34
Robinwood W	03
Robson	
8000-9499	28
9500-16099	27
16100-OUT	35
Roby	11
Rochelle	05
Rochester	06
Rockcastle	
17800-18899	24
18900-19199	36
19200-OUT	25
Rockdale	
7200-12599	39
12600-16099	23
16100-OUT	19
Rockland	39
Rockwood	11
Rockwood St E & W	29
Rogers	09
Rogge	34
Rohns	
3400-4999	14
5000-OUT	13
Roland	13
Roland Ct & Rd	36
Rolandale	
18900-19199	36
19200-OUT	25
Rolf Pl	14
Rolyat	34
Romeo	20
Romeyn	09
Ronald Ct	37
Rondo	05
Roosevelt	
2400-3299	16
2900-3299 (HAM)	12
3300-OUT	08
Roosevelt Pl	30
Roscommon	25
Rose	16
Rose Ct	25
Roseberry	13
Rosedale Ct	
1-899	02
900-OUT	03
Rosedale Ct N & S	36
Roseland Ct	37
Roselawn	
8000-12599	04
12600-16099	38

16100-OUT	21
Rosemary	13
Rosemary Blvd	37
Rosemont Ave	
5600 12599	28
12600-16099	23
16100-OUT	19
Rosemont Rd	
5600-12599	28
12600-16099	23
16100-OUT	19
Rosewood	
100-1699	20
16300-17099	24
22000-OUT	37
Rosewood Ct	37
Roslyn Pl	
3300-3399	21
Roslyn Rd	
1-2299	36
21700-OUT	25
Roslyn (First Choice) Rd	
19500-19999	21
Ross Ct & Dr	39
Rossini Dr	05
Rossiter	
10900-19199	24
19200-OUT	25
Rouge S	17
Rouge Dr	17
Roulo Pl	09
Rowan	09
Rowe	05
Rowley	12
Roxbury	24
Roxford	19
Roy	16
Royal Grand	39
Rue Versailles	37
Ruedisale Ct	14
Rugg	11
Runyon	34
Rupert	12
Ruskin	16
Russell	
400-4999	07
5000-11699	11
11700-OUT	03
Ruth	
1-99	29
8600-OUT	13
Rutherford	
6300-9499	28
9500-16099	27
16100-OUT	35
Rutland	
6300-9499	28
9500-OUT	27
Ryan	
13400-17999	12
18000-20699	34
Ryland	
15500-16099	39
16100-OUT	40
Saddle Ln	36
Saginaw	11
Saint Albertus Pl	07
Saint Antoine	
400-2099	26
2100-4999	01
5000-OUT	02
Saint Aubin	
100-4999	07

Detroit (Con.)	482
5000-8399	11
8400-17999	12
18000-OUT	34
Saint Aubin Pl	
1100-1299	07
Saint Clair	
100-4999	14
300-999 (GPC)	30
5000-OUT	13
Saint Cyril	13
Saint Hedwig	10
Saint Ignace Pl	07
Saint James	10
Saint Jean	
1-4999	14
5000-OUT	13
Saint John	10
Saint Josafats Ct	
600-899	01
900-OUT	07
Saint Joseph	07
Saint Lawrence	10
Saint Louis	
100-999	20
11600-17999	12
18000-OUT	34
Saint Maron	07
Saint Martins Ave	
3600-12699	21
12700-18099	35
18100-24999	19
25000-27399	40
Saint Martins Rd	
3600-12699	21
12700-18099	35
18100-24999	19
25000-27399	40
Saint Martins St N & S	21
Saint Marys	
6300-9499	28
9500-16099	27
16100-OUT	35
Saint Patrick	05
Saint Paul	
6300-7199	07
7200-11999	14
12000-14999	15
15000-OUT	30
Saint Stephens	10
Saint Thomas	4
Sainte Anne	16
Salem	
8800-16099	39
16100-OUT	19
Sallan	11
Salliotte	17
Salliotte Rd	29
Salter	05
Sampson	16
San Jose	39
San Juan Dr	
14000-16099	38
16100-OUT	21
Sanders	17
Sanford	05
Sanger	10
Sanilac	
9300-19199	24
19200-OUT	25
Santa Barbara Dr	21

Santa Clara	
3100-12699	21
12700-18099	35
18100-OUT	19
Santa Maria	
3100-12699	21
12700-18099	35
18100-24999	19
25000-OUT	40
Santa Rosa Dr	
12000-12599	04
12600-16099	38
16100-OUT	21
Sarasota Ave & Ct	39
Saratoga	
8200-12999	37
13600-OUT	05
Saratoga St E & W	20
Sarena	10
Sargent	11
Sarsfield	16
Sauer	
11300-11599	34
11600-OUT	05
Savage	34
Savannah St E & W	03
Savery	06
Savoy	16
Sawyer	
18100-21999	28
22000-OUT	39
Saxon	10
Scarsdale	23
Schaefer Hwy	
8000-9499	28
9500-16099	27
16100-OUT	35
Schaefer Hwy S	
101-1499 (ODD)	17
1500-2899	17
Scheffer Pl	11
Schiller	14
Schoenherr	05
School	12
Schoolcraft	
7400-12699	38
12700-18099	27
18100-23999	23
24000-27399	39
Schroeder S	09
Schuper	24
Schweizers Pl	26
Scotia	37
Scotia Ln	20
Scott	07
Scotten	
100-2599	09
2600-7299	10
7300-OUT	04
Scotten S	09
Scovel Pl	
3300-3999	08
4000-OUT	10
Scripps	15
Sears	03
Secor Pl	11
Seebaldt	04
Selden Ave	
1-1399	01
1400-OUT	08
Selden Ct	
1-1399	01
1400-OUT	08

Selfridge	12
Selkirk	11
Seminole	
700-4999	14
5000-6899	13
8800-16099	39
16100-20659	40
Senator	09
Seneca	
3700-4999	14
5000-6799	13
14800-15299	39
23000-OUT	37
Service	07
Severn Rd	
1500-2199	36
21200-OUT	25
Seward	
1-1399	02
1400-OUT	06
Seyburn	
500-4999	14
5000-OUT	13
Seymour	05
Shady Ln	16
Shaftsbury Ave & Rd	19
Shakespeare	05
Sharon	
1900-3599	09
3600-OUT	10
Shasta Pl	20
Shaw	10
Shawcross Pl	03
Sheehan	13
Sheffield Rd	21
Shelbourne Rd	36
Shelby	26
Shelden Rd	36
Sherbourne Rd	21
Sheridan	
500-4999	14
5000-OUT	13
Sherman	
900-3199	07
22600-OUT	37
Sherwood	
6400-10499	11
10500-17999	12
13600-15099 (OP)	37
18000-20599	34
Shevlin	20
Shiawassee Dr	
18300-24999	19
Shiawassee Rd	
18300-24999	19
Shields	
13400-17999	12
18000-OUT	34
Shipherd Ave & Ct	14
Shirley	27
Shoemaker	13
Shorecrest Cir	36
Shoreham Rd	36
Short	19
Shrewsbury Rd	21
Sibley	01
Siebert	34
Signet	15
Silman	20
Simms	05
Simon K	12
Sioux	
8800-13899	39

Detroit (Con.)   482

17100-OUT 24
Sire 09
Sirron 34
Sloan S 09
Sloan Dr 25
Sloman
  1400-1499 11
  21900-OUT 37
Smart 10
Smith
  1-899 02
  900-OUT 11
Snowden Ave
  14500-16099 27
  16100-OUT 35
Snowden Ct
  14500-16099 27
  16100-OUT 35
Sobieski 12
Solvay 09
Solvay S 09
Somerset Ave
  1-3399 30
  3400-OUT 24
Sonoma 20
Sorrento
  8000-9499 28
  9500-16099 27
  16100-OUT 35
South 09
South Cary 09
South Oakwood 17
Southampton
  12900-14399 13
  14400-OUT 24
Southfield Fwy
  1-399 29
  5601-6299 (ODD) 28
  6300-12599 28
  12600-16099 23
  16100-20699 35
Southwestern Hwy 39
Southwick 40
Sparling 12
Sparta 10
Spaulding Ct 16
Spencer
  100-1899 20
  19100-20599 34
Spinoza Dr 28
Spokane 04
Sprague 14
Springarden 05
Springfield 13
Springle 15
Springwells
  500-3599 09
  3600-OUT 10
Springwells S 09
Sproat 01
Spruce
  1000-1399 01
  1400-OUT 16
Stafford Pl 07
Stahelin Ave
  5600-12599 28
  12600-16099 23
  16100-20699 19

Stahelin Rd
  5600-12599 28
  12600-16099 23
  16100-20699 19
Stair 09
Standish 16
Stanford 10
Stanhope 36
Stanley
  900-1399 02
  1400-OUT 08
Stansbury
  13300-16099 27
  16100-OUT 35
Stanton 08
Stanton Ln 36
Starboard Dr 15
Stark 10
State 26
State Fair E
  1-1899 03
  1900-11599 34
  11600-OUT 05
State Fair W 03
Stawell 04
Stearns 04
Steel
  8500-9499 28
  9500-16099 27
  16100-OUT 35
Steger Ct 38
Stegner 23
Stender
  1300-1899 03
  1900-OUT 12
Stephens Rd 36
Sterling 02
Sterling Ct 37
Sterritt 13
Stevens 03
Stillmeadow Ln 36
Stimson 01
Stocker 17
Stockton 34
Stockwell 24
Stoepel
  8800-12599 04
  12600-16099 38
  16100-OUT 21
Stoepel Pl 07
Stone 09
Stonehurst Rd 36
Stoner 18
Stotter 34
Stout
  7200-12599 28
  12600-16099 23
  16100-OUT 19
Stovell Pl 01
Strasburg 05
Stratford
  100-799 20
  19100-20699 21
  20700-OUT 37
Stratford Pl
  1-99 30
  25900-OUT 37
Stratford Rd
  100-799 20
  19100-20699 21
  20700-OUT 37
Strathcona Dr 03
Strathmoor

8000-9499 26
9500-16099 27
16100-OUT 35
Stratman 24
Stratton 09
Stratton Pl 36
Stringham Ct 13
Strong
  6300-7199 11
  7200-OUT 13
Stuart 07
Student 39
Sturgis 34
Sturtevant
  1-1399 03
  1400-3999 06
  4000-OUT 04
Suburban 29
Suffolk Dr 03
Summit
  100-299 (RR) 18
  100-299 09
Summit S 09
Sumner
  7700-8099 10
  14900-16099 39
  16100-OUT 40
Sunderland Rd 19
Sunningdale Dr & Park 36
Sunnyside
  1-99 29
  23200-OUT 23
Sunset
  13300-17999 12
  18000-20699 34
  21900-OUT 37
Sunset Blvd
  13300-17999 12
  18000-20699 34
  21900-OUT 37
Sunset Ln 36
Superior
  400-599 (RR) 18
  900-OUT 07
Sussex
  8000-9499 28
  9500-16099 27
  16100-19999 35
  20700-24999 (OP) 37
Sutherland 37
Suzanne 34
Swain 09
Swain S 09
Swan 39
Swift 03
Sycamore 08
Sylbert Ct 39
Sylbert St N & S 39
Sylvan 08
Sylvan Ct 37
Sylvester
  3600-7199 07
  7200-OUT 14
Symes Rd 20
Syracuse
  12800-17999 12
  18000-20699 34
Tacoma 05
Taft 08
Talbot
  3800-5899 12
  13600-OUT 37

Detroit (Con.)	482
Tappan	34
Tarnow	10
Tate	39
Taylor	
1-1399	02
1400-3999	06
4000-OUT	04
Teaco	15
Tecumseh	
1-199	29
8800-OUT	39
Telegraph Rd	
8800-16099	39
16100-20699	19
Temple	
1-1399	01
1400-OUT	16
Tennessee	15
Tennyson	03
Teppert	34
Terminal	14
Ternes	10
Terrell	34
Terry	
8000-9499	28
9500-OUT	27
Thaddeus	09
Thatcher	
2900-12699	21
12700-18099	35
18100-OUT	19
Theodore	
200-899	02
900-7199	11
7200-OUT	13
Thole Ct	38
Thompson Ct	07
Thomson	03
Thorn Tree Rd	36
Thornhill Pl	07
Thornton	27
Tillman	
2800-3299	16
3300-OUT	08
Times Sq	26
Tireman	
4000-7999	04
8000-12698 (EVEN)	04
12700-15498 (EVEN)	28
15500-21999	28
22000-23199	39
Toledo	
3500-3999	16
4000-OUT	09
Toles Ln	36
Tonnancour Pl	36
Toronto	17
Torrey Ave & Ct	10
Torrey Rd	36
Touraine Rd	36
Tournier	27
Townsend	
400-4999	14
5000-OUT	13
Tracey	
14500-16099	27
16100-OUT	35
Tractor	17
Traverse	13
Treadway Pl	14
Trenton	10
Trevor Pl	07
Trinity	
8000-12599	28
12600-16099	23
16100-OUT	19
Troester	05
Trojan	
14600-18099	35
18100-OUT	19
Trombley Rd	30
Trombly	11
Trowbridge	
1-1899	02
1900-OUT	12
Troy Pl	37
Troy Pl	03
Troy St E & W	20
Trumbull	
700-3299	16
3300-6199	08
6200-11699	02
11700-OUT	03
Tulare	37
Tuller	
12200-12599	04
12600-16099	38
16100-OUT	21
Tumey	34
Turner	
10500-12599	04
12600-16099	38
16100-OUT	21
Turner Pl	07
Tuscola	01
Tuxedo	
1-1399	03
1400-3999	06
4000-OUT	04
Tyler	
1-1399	03
1400-OUT	38
12700-15499	27
25000-OUT	37
Tyrone	
18900-19199	36
19200-OUT	25
Ulster	19
Underwood	04
Union	
1-99	29
900-OUT	01
University	
100-1899	20
University Pl	
200-3399	30
3400-OUT	24
Uthes	09
Utica	04
Vale	37
Van Antwerp	
1800-2199	36
19900-OUT	25
Van Buren	
6300-12699	04
12700-21999	28
22000-23299	39
Van Dyke	
500-4999	14
5000-9899	13
9900-20561	34
Van Dyke Pl	
7800-7999	14
Van K Dr	36
Vancourt	10
Vancouver	04
Vanderbilt	09
Varjo	12
Varney	11
Vassar Ave	
13200-18099	35
18100-24999	19
25000-27399	40
Vassar Dr	
13200-18099	35
18100-24999	19
25000-27399	40
Vaughan	
6300-12599	28
12600-16099	23
16100-OUT	19
Veach	34
Vendome Ct & Rd	36
Venice	13
Verdun	19
Vermont	
500-3299	16
3300-OUT	08
Verne	
15500-18099	35
18100-OUT	19
Vernier Cir	36
Vernier Rd	
1-2299	36
17700-21599	25
Vernon	37
Vernor Hwy E	
1-899	01
900-7199	07
7200-11999	14
12000-14999	15
15000-OUT	30
Vernor Hwy W	
1-1399	01
1400-3999	16
4000-9399	09
Verona	05
Vester	20
Vicksburg	
2600-3999	06
4000-OUT	04
Victor	03
Victoria	
1-99	18
2000-3699	12
13600-OUT	37
Vigo	10
Village Ln	30
Vincennes Pl	36
Vincent	11
Vinewood	
100-3299	16
3300-OUT	08
Vinewood S	16
Vinton	13
Violetlawn	04
Virgil	
8800-12599	39
12600-16099	23
16100-OUT	19
Virginia Ct	29
Virginia Ln	36
Virginia Park	
1-1399	02
1400-3999	06
4000-OUT	04

Detroit (Con.)   482

Visger
1-601 (ODD) 29
2-98 (EVEN) 29
100-598 (EVEN) 18
11700-OUT 17
Visger Rd
1-599 (ODD) 29
2-98 (EVEN) 29
100-598 (EVEN) 18
11700-OUT 17
Vista Ct 09
Voight 24
Voltaire Pl 36
Volte 27
Voss 09
Votrobeck Ct & Dr 19
Vulcan 11
Wabash
1400-3299 16
3300-7299 08
7300-12599 06
12600-OUT 38
Wade
11200-14499 13
14500-OUT 24
Wadsworth
10300-12699 04
12700-18099 27
18100-21999 28
22000-27399 39
Wager 06
Wagner 10
Wakefield Rd 21
Wakenden
15300-16099 39
16100-20699 40
Walbridge 13
Walden 13
Waldo 10
Wales 37
Walker 07
Wallace 13
Wallick Pl 07
Wallingford 24
Walnut 18
Walter P Chrysler Fwy
400-4998 (EVEN) 07
401-2099 (ODD) 26
2101-4999 (ODD) 01
5000-9799 11
9800-12899 12
12900-20699 03
Waltham 05
Walton 10
Wanamaker Pl 23
Wanda
100-1799 20
17100-OUT 03
Ward
8000-9499 28
9500-16099 27
16100-OUT 35
Waring S 17
Warner 14
Warner Rd 36
Warren E
1-899 01
900-7199 07
7200-11999 14
12000-14899 15
14900-18399 24

Warren W
1-1399 01
1400-3999 08
4000-8099 10
15500-20200 28
2020z-21998 (EVEN) 28
22000-22798 (EVEN) 39
Warren Ct 07
Warrington Dr 21
Warsaw Pl 07
Warwick
5600-12599 28
12600-16099 23
16100-OUT 19
Washburn
11600-12599 04
12600-16099 38
16100-OUT 21
Washington Blvd 26
Washington Rd 30
Washtenaw 25
Waterloo
1900-7199 07
7200-11999 14
12000-14999 15
15000-OUT 30
Waterman 09
Waterman S 09
Watko 12
Watson
1-899 01
900-OUT 07
Waveney
12500-14899 15
14900-OUT 24
Waverly
1-1399 03
1400-OUT 38
Waverly Ln 36
Wayburn
1000-3399 30
3400-OUT 24
Wayne 09
Weaver 28
Webb
1-1399 02
1400-3999 06
4000-OUT 04
Webber Dr 25
Webber Ln 36
Webster
4400-4699 29
23000-OUT 37
Webster Rd 36
Webster St E & W 20
Wedgewood Dr 36
Weitzel Ct 11
Wellesley Dr 03
Wellington 11
Wellington Pl 30
Welton 04
Wendell 09
Wendy Ln 36
Wesson 10
West Chicago
2600-3999 06
4000-12699 04
12700-21999 28
22000-27399 39
West End
100-299 09
101-1799 (FER) (ODD) 20

West End S 09
West Jefferson 29
West Parkway
7300-12599 39
12600-16099 23
16100-OUT 19
West Point 04
West Wind Ln 36
Westbrook
12600-16099 23
16100-20699 19
21600-OUT 36
Westchester Rd 30
Western
2800-3599 09
3600-OUT 10
Westfield
6300-12699 04
12700-21999 28
22000-27399 39
Westfield St E & W 29
Westgate Dr 39
Westhampton 37
Westland Rd 40
Westminster
1-899 02
900-OUT 11
Westmoreland Rd 19
Westover 04
Westphalia 05
Westridge Ct 20
Westview 20
Westwood
5800-12599 28
12600-OUT 23
Wetherby
7100-7999 10
8000-OUT 04
Wexford
17800-17999 12
18000-OUT 34
Weyher 14
Whalen 12
Wheeler 10
Wheelock 09
Whipple 13
Whitcomb
8000-9499 28
9500-16099 27
16100-OUT 35
Whitcomb Dr 36
White
1-399 29
8500-OUT 09
Whitehead 10
Whitehill 24
Whitewood 10
Whitfield 04
Whithorn 05
Whitlock 28
Whitmore
300-1099 03
21600-OUT 37
Whitmore Rd
300-1099 03
21600-OUT 37
Whitney
2600-3999 06
4000-OUT 04
Whittaker 09
Whittier Ave
700-3399 30
3400-11799 24

Detroit (Con.)   482

Whittier Rd
  700-3399 30
  3400-11799 24
Wicks Ln 36
Widman Pl 11
Wight 07
Wilbur 02
Wilbur Ct 39
Wilcox 28
Wilde 09
Wildemere
  7300-12599 06
  12600-16099 38
  16100-OUT 21
Wildwood
  900-1099 03
  20700-OUT 37
Wildwood Dr 25
Wilfred 13
Wilkie 09
Wilkins
  400-899 01
  900-OUT 07
Willard 14
Willette 10
William Ct E & W 36
Williams
  1-399 36
  2700-3299 16
  3300-OUT 08
Williamsburg Ct 25
Willis E
  1-899 01
  900-OUT 07
Willis W
  1-1399 01
  1400-OUT 08
Willison Rd 36
Willmarth 19
Willow Ln 36
Willow Tree Ln & Pl 36
Wilshire Dr 13
Winchester 37
Winchester E
  1-1899 03
  1900-OUT 34
Winchester W 03
Winder
  1-899 01
  900-OUT 07
Windmill Pointe Dr 30
Windsor 24
Winfield
  8500-9699 13
  9800-OUT 12
Wing Pl 16
Winger 12
Winkleman 11
Winona 03
Winslow 08
Winston
  8800-16099 39
  16100-OUT 19
Winter 07
Winthrop
  6300-9499 28
  9500-16099 27
  16100-OUT 35
Winthrop Pl 36
Wisconsin
  8000-12599 04

  12600-16099 38
  16100-OUT 21
Wisner 34
Witherell
  1-2099 26
  2100-OUT 01
Withington 20
Witt 09
Wolcott 20
Wolff 09
Wood 34
Woodbine
  8800-16099 39
  16100-OUT 19
Woodbridge
  100-899 26
  900-OUT 07
Woodcrest 25
Woodhall 24
Woodingham Dr
  15300-16099 38
  16100-OUT 21
Woodland
  1-899 02
  900-1499 11
  1500-1899 12
  18500-OUT 25
Woodland Ct 37
Woodland Pl 30
Woodland St E & W 20
Woodland Shores Dr 36
Woodlawn 13
Woodmere 09
Woodmont Ave
  6300-9499 28
  9500-15099 27
  18900-OUT 25
Woodmont Rd
  6300-9499 28
  9500-15099 27
  18900-OUT 25
Woodrow
  5600-6699 10
  26200-OUT 40
Woodrow Wilson
  7300-12599 06
  12600-OUT 38
Woods Ct & Ln 36
Woodside
  8200-8599 37
  9200-10099 04
  18500-20799 (HW) 25
  20700-21499 (FER) 20
Woodside Ct & Dr 37
Woodstock Dr
  2300-2999 03
  3000-OUT 21
Woodston Rd 03
Woodvale 37
Woodward
  1-2099 26
  2100-4999 01
  5000-11699 02
  11700-20699 03
  20700-23625 20
Woodward Hts 20
Woodward St E & W 29
Woodworth
  14800-16099 39
  16100-20699 40
Worcester Pl 03
Worden 24
Wordsworth 20

Wormer
  8800-16099 39
  16100-OUT 19
Wreford 08
Wrenson 20
Wyandotte 12
Wykes
  7200-7999 10
  8000-OUT 04
Wyman 19
Wyoming
  5202-6400 (EVEN) 10
  8000-12599 04
  12600-16099 38
  16100-20699 21
  20700-21799 20
  21600-21798 (EVEN) 37
  21800-21999 37
Yacama Rd 03
Yale 37
Yale S 09
Yates 14
Yellowstone 04
Yemans
  1900-5899 12
  5900-OUT 11
Yolanda 34
Yonka
  17800-17999 12
  18000-OUT 34
York 02
Yorkshire Ave
  1000-3399 30
  3400-OUT 24
Yorkshire Rd
  1000-3399 30
  3400-OUT 24
Yorktown 36
Yosemite 04
Young 05
Young Ln 36
Zender Pl 07
Zinow 12
Zug Island Rd 09

NUMBERED STREETS

1st
  500-1999 26
  4400-OUT 29
2nd Ave
  600-2099 26
  2100-4999 01
  4300-4599 (EC) 29
  5000-11699 02
  11700-OUT 03
2nd Blvd
  600-2099 26
  2100-4999 01
  4300-4599 (EC) 29
  5000-11699 02
  11700-OUT 03
3 Mile Dr
  800-3399 30
  3400-OUT 24
3rd
  500-2099 26
  2100-4999 01
  4300-4599 (EC) 29
  5000-11699 02
  11700-OUT 03
4th
  1200-2099 26

Detroit (Con.)   482

2100-4999	01
4400-4699 (EC)	29
5000-OUT	02
5 Mile Rd	39
5th	
1400-2099	26
2100-2799	01
4100-OUT	29
6 Mile Rd	40
6th	
1200-2099	26
2100-4899	01
4100-4699 (EC)	29
7 Mile Rd E	
1-1899	03
1900-11599	34
11600-OUT	05
7 Mile Rd W	
1-2199	03
2200-12699	21
12700-18099	35
18100-24999	19
25000-27399	40
7th	29
8 Mile Rd E	
2-1898 (EVEN)	03
101-1899 (FER) (ODD)	20
1701-2241 (GPW) (ODD)	36
1900-9998 (EVEN)	34
10000-17050 (EVEN)	05
17052-OUT (EVEN)	25
8 Mile Rd W (ODD)	
1-2999 (ODD)	03
100-12698 (EVEN)	20
3001-12699 (ODD)	21
12700-15498 (EVEN)	37
12701-18099 (ODD)	35
18101-24999 (ODD)	19
25001-27399 (ODD)	40
8th	
500-2299	16
3700-OUT	29
9 Mile Rd E	
100-2099	20
9 Mile Rd W	
100-1699	20
8100-15499	37
9th	29
10 Mile Rd E	
600-2498 (EVEN)	20
10 Mile Rd W	
8201-13599 (ODD)	37
13600-15499	37
10th	
500-2099	16
3700-OUT	29
11 Mile Rd W	
13601-15499 (ODD)	37
11th	
1900-2099	16
3700-OUT	29
12th	
100-3299	16
3300-7299	08
3700-4399 (EC)	29
7300-12599	06
12600-16099	38
16100-OUT	03
13th	29
14th	

700-3299	16
3300-7299	08
3700-4099 (EC)	29
7300-12599	06
12600-OUT	38
15th	
300-3299	16
3300-6599	08
3700-4299 (EC)	29
16th	
500-3299	16
3300-6599	08
3700-4299 (EC)	29
17th	
500-3299	16
3300-5099	08
3700-4299 (EC)	29
18th	
500-3299	16
3300-4799	08
3700-4299 (EC)	29
19th	29
20th thru 22nd St	1E
23rd	
1-3299	16
3300-OUT	08
24th	
1-3299	16
3300-OUT	08
25th	
1-3299	16
3300-OUT	08
28th thru 33rd St	10
35th	10
51st thru 52nd St	10

FLINT   485

POST OFFICE BOXES

Box Nos.		
1-1999	Main Office	01
3000-3999	Church Street Sta.	02
4000-4999	Mott Park Sta.	04
5000-5999	North Side Sta.	05
6000-6999	East Side Sta.	08
7000-7999	Cody Sta.	07

STATIONS, BRANCHES AND UNITS

Church Street Sta	02
Cody Sta	07
East Side Sta	08
Mott Park Sta	04
North Side Sta	05
General Deliver	02
Postmaster	02

APARTMENTS, HOTELS, MOTELS

Airport, 3040 W Bristol Rd	07
Ambassador Arms West, G 1/2 3348 Flushing Rd	04
Autorams, 2002 S Dort Hwy	03
Ballenger Manor, 810 S Ballenger Hwy	04
Beecher, G5326 N Saginaw	05
Berridge, 421 Garland	01
Bervean, 318 W 2nd	02
Capitol, 139 E 2nd	01
Chase, 906 Garland	03

College Inn, 505 Detroit	02
Colonial, G5661 S Saginaw	07
Country Club Manor, 1902 Woodslea St	07
Dort, G3370 S Dort Hwy	07
Durant, 607 E 2nd Ave	01
Ehrnst, 6550 N Dort Hwy	05
Elms, 2701 S Dort Hwy	07
Flint, G5452 N Dort Hwy	05
Forest Park Manor, 4060 Detroit	05
Hardy, 613 Clifford	02
Holiday Inn, 2207 W. Bristol Rd.	07
Howard Johnson, G3129 Miller Rd	07
Hunters Ridge, 3020 Ridgecliffe St	04
Imperial 400, 902 Stevens	03
Kearsley Lake Terrace, 3465 Benmarks Pl	06
Lawrence Manor, 5515 Detroit St	05
Mar-Jo, 1760 S Dort Hwy	03
Marvanette, 711 Mary	03
Miller West Thirty 1/2 one Hundred, G 1/2 3100 Miller Rd	07
North West Manor, 5515 Detroit St	05
Oakview Manor, 125 W Gracelawn St	05
Orchard Lane, 2645 Orchard Lane	04
Parkview Manor, 915 E Court	03
Regency Park Cooperative, 2112 Trout Dr	07
River Forest, 3500 Riverforest St	04
Sheffield Manor, 328 Sheffield St	03
Stone, 222 E 1st	02
Sussex Arms, 1910 W Pierson Rd	04
Swayze, 224 E Court	02
Westgate Terrace, 3901 Hammerberg St	07
Westwood Manor, 4201 Clio Rd	04

BUILDINGS

A C Spark Plug	56
Atwood, 436 S Saginaw	02
Buick Motor Division	50
Capitol, 134 E 2nd	02
Center, 201 N Saginaw	02
Chevrolet Engine Plant	52
Chevrolet Flint Assembly Division	51
Chevrolet Flint Manufacturing	55
Chevrolet Frame & Stamping Plant	53
Chevrolet National Parts	54
Chevrolet Zone Sales	01
Citizens Bank, 328 S Saginaw	02
College & Cultural Center, E Kearsley & Crapa	02
Commerce, 242 S Saginaw St	02

Flint (Con.)	485

Community Service, 202 E.
Boulvard Dr.......................... 02
Dryden, 601 S Saginaw 02
Fisher Body Coldwater Rd
Plant 59
Fisher Body 1 57
Fisher Body 2 58
Genesee Bank, 346 S
Saginaw 02
Genesee Towers, 120 E 1st ... 02
Kresge, 108 E Kearsley........... 02
Metropolitan, 428 N Saginaw. 02
Mott, 501 S Saginaw 02
National, 460 S Saginaw......... 02
North Flint Plaza, 102 W
Pierson Rd 05
Northwest Plaza, W Pierson &
Clio Rd 04
Palace Theatre Bldg, 201
Kearsley St 02
Paterson, 653 S Saginaw 02
Phoenix Bldg, 801 S Saginaw
St 02
Public Library, 1026 E
Kearsley.............................. 02
Sill, 257 S Saginaw................. 02
South Flint Plaza, Hemphill &
Fenton Rd 07
Walsh Bldg, 310 N Saginaw
St 02

GOVERNMENT OFFICES

City Hall, 1101 S Saginaw 02
Federal Building, 600
Church 02
State Police Headquarters,
G3478 Corunna Rd............. 04

HOSPITALS

Flint General, 765 E
Hamilton 05
Flint Osteopathic, 3921
Beecher Rd 02
Genesee Memorial, 702 S
Ballenger Hwy..................... 02
Hurley, 6th Ave & Begole....... 02
Mc Laren General, 401 S
Ballenger Hwy..................... 02
Saint Josephs, 302
Kensington 02
Walter Winchester, G4562
Flushing Rd 04

UNIVERSITIES AND COLLEGES

Baker Business
University,1110 Manitou..... 07
Flint Junior College, 1401 E
Ct 02
General Motors Institute, 3rd
Ave & Chevrolet................. 02
University Of Michigan Flint
Branch, 1321 E Ct.............. 02

GRAND RAPIDS	495

POST OFFICE BOXES

Box Nos.
A-T	Main Office	01
1000-2999	Main Office	01
6000-6999	Station C........	06
7000-7999	Seymour	
	Square Sta	10
8000-8999	South Kent Br ..	08
9000-9999	Wyoming Br......	09

RURAL ROUTES

1 08
2 04
3 06
4 04
5 05
6 09
7,8 08

STATIONS, BRANCHES AND UNITS

Dutton Rural Br...................... 11
Kentwood Br........................... 08
Northgate Br............................ 05
Reeds Lake Br......................... 06
Seymour Square Sta............... 10
Southkent Br 08
Walker Br................................ 04
Wyoming Br 09
Wyoming Park Br.................... 09
General Delivery 01
Postmaster 01

APARTMENTS, HOTELS, MOTELS

Fountain Hill, 301 Fountain
St NE 03
Herkimer, 323 Division Ave S. 02
Hillmount, 505 Cherry St SE... 03
Holland Home, 1450 Fulton,
East.................................... 03
Lakeshore, 2311 Wealthy St
SE....................................... 06
Milner, 74 Ionia Ave SW 02
Morton House, 72 Monroe Ave
NW..................................... 02
Oakway, 35 Oakes St SW........ 02
Oakwood Manor, 547 Cherry
St SE 02
Olds Manor, 201 Michigan St
NW..................................... 02
Pantlind, 187 Monroe Ave St
NW..................................... 02
Stuyvesant, 413 Cherry St
SE....................................... 03
Waters House, 500 Fulton St
E... 03
Y M C A, 33 Library St NE 02
Y W C A, 25 Sheldon Ave SE... 02

BUILDINGS

A & G Terminal, 900 Monroe
Ave NW............................... 02
Castle,the, 455 Cherry SE....... 02
Commerce 5 Lyon NW 02
Exhibitors, 220 Lyon NW 02
Federal Square, 29 Pearl NW.. 02

G M A C, 345 State SE............ 02
Goodspeed, 190 Monroe Ave
NW..................................... 02
Grand Rapids Mutual, 201
Monroe Ave, NW................. 02
Grand Rapids Press, 155
Michigan St NW.................. 02
Helmer, 21 Ottawa Ave NW 02
Keeler, 60 Division Ave N 02
Kendall, 16 Monroe Ave NE 02
Loraine, 124 Fulton St E......... 02
Luman, 45 Monroe Ave NW..... 02
Mckay Tower, 146 Monroe
Ave NW.............................. 02
Medical Arts, 26 Sheldon
Ave, SE 02
Michigan Consolidated Gas,
200 Monroe Ave NW........... 02
Michigan National Bank, 77
Monroe Ave NW.................. 02
Old Kent Bank, 111 Lyon St
NW..................................... 02
Peoples, 60 Monroe Ave NW ... 02
Prudential Insurance, 252
State St SE 02
Tanglefoot, 314 Straight Ave
SW..................................... 02
Tower Medical, 21 Michigan
St., NE................................ 02
Trust, 40 Pearl St NW............ 02
Union Bank, 200 Ottawa Ave
NW..................................... 02
Waters, 161 Ottawa Ave NW... 02

GOVERNMENT OFFICES

City Hall, 300 Monroe Ave,
NW..................................... 02
County Building, 300 Monroe
Ave, NW.............................. 02
Federal Building, 150 Ionia
Ave, NW.............................. 02
Hall Of Justice, 333 Monroe
Ave, NW.............................. 02

HOSPITALS

Blodgett, 1840 Wealthy St
SE....................................... 06
Butterworth, 100 Michigan St
NE...................................... 03
Ferguson-Droste-Ferguson, 72
Sheldon Ave SE.................. 02
Grand Rapids Osteopathic,
1919 Boston St SE.............. 06
Kent Community, 750 Fuller
Ave, NE 03
Michigan Veterans Facility,
3000 Monroe Ave NE.......... 05
Pine Rest Chr, 6850 Division
Ave S 08
Saint Mary'S, 201 Lafayette
Ave SE................................ 03

UNIVERSITIES AND COLLEGES

Aquinas, 1607 Robinson Rd
SE....................................... 06
Calvin Seminary, 3233
Burton St SE....................... 06
Calvin-Knollcrest Campus,
3215 Burton St SE.............. 06
Calvin, 1331 Franklin St SE... 06

Grand Rapids (Con.)   495

Grace Bible, 1011 Aldon St
SW 09
Grand Rapids Baptist Bible
Col, 1001 E Beltline Ave
NE 05

JACKSON   492

POST OFFICE BOXES

Box Nos.
1-1324   Main Office 04

RURAL ROUTES

1,2,3,4,5,6,7,8,9,10,11,12,13,
14 01

STATIONS, BRANCHES AND UNITS

Vandercook Lake Br 03
General Delivery 01
Postmaster 01

KALAMAZOO   490

POST OFFICE BOXES

Box Nos.
1-117   Parchment Br... 04
1-1071   Court Sta.... 05
2001-2858   Main Office 03

RURAL ROUTES

1 09
2 04
3,4,5 01
6 07
7 09
8 01
9 09
10 04
11,12 09
14 01

STATIONS, BRANCHES AND UNITS

Court Sta. 06
Parchment Br 04
General Delivery 03
Postmaster 01

LANSING   489

POST OFFICE BOXES

Box Nos.
1-210   Lansing 01
211-510   Lansing 02
511-810   Lansing 03
811-1410   Lansing 04

2001-2364   Michigan
    Avenue Sta... 11
5001-5314   North Lansing
    Sta............. 05
9001-9577   South Cedar
    Annex Sta...... 09

RURAL ROUTES

1 06
2 17
3 10
4 06
5 17

STATIONS, BRANCHES AND UNITS

Frandor Br...................................... 12
Michigan Avenue Sta...................... 11
North Lansing Sta............................ 05
South Cedar Street Annex Sta. 09
Waverly Br...................................... 17
General Delivery............................. 24
Postmaster...................................... 24

APARTMENTS, HOTELS, MOTELS

Capitol Club, 222 Seymour
Ave. 33
Capitol Park Motor, 501
Townsend 14
Central, 212 West
Kalamazoo 33
Country Club Manor, 1815
Potomac Cir 10
Dean, 727 North Capitol Ave.. 06
Embassy, 524-526 South
Chestnut 33
Ferris Park Towers, 323 N
Walnut 33
Grand River Terrace, 2603-
2727 E Grand River...................... 12
Grand, 403 East Grand River
Ave 06
Heritage Arms, 3031 S
Washington Ave 10
Holiday Inn 3131 East Grand
Rive Ave 12
Holiday Inn, 1031 Pierpont 10
Horne'S Motor Lodge, 6501 S
Cedar 10
Hospitality Motor Inn, I 496
At Dunckel 10
Howard Johnson Motor Lodge,
6741 S Cedar 10
Lansing Towers, 610 W
Ottawa 33
Manor House, 920 S
Washington Ave 10
Motel 6, 112 E. Main...................... 33
Olds Plaza, 125 W. Michigan
Ave. 02
Ramada Inn, 1000 Ramada
Dr 10
Washington, 917 S
Washington Ave 10

BUILDINGS

American Bank And Trust
101 S Washington Sq. 33
Bank Of Lansing, 101 N
Washington Sq............................... 33
Bauch, 115 West Allegan 33

Board Of Water & Light, 123
W Ottawa 33
Builders & Traders, 1240 E
Saginaw 06
Capitol Savings & Loan, 112
East Allegan 33
Civic Center, 505 West
Allegan 33
Commerce Center, 300 S
Capitol Ave. 33
County, 118 West Ottawa 33
Davenport, 144 West Ottawa.. 33
Federal, 315 West Allegan 33
Hollister, 108 West Allegan 33
Labor, 300 East Michigan
Ave. 33
Lansing City Library, 401 S
Capitol Ave 14
Lansing Medical - Dental,
2909 E Grand River Ave............... 12
Leonard Plaza 309 N
Washington Sq. 33
Medical Arts, 1322 E
Michigan Ave 12
Medical Center West, 701 N
Logan 15
Michigan Dental, 230 N.
Washington Ave 33
Michigan National Tower,
124 West Allegan 33
Michigan Theatre Arcade,
215 S Washington Ave 33
State Employees Credit
Union, 501 S. Capitol
Ave. 33
Stoddard, 125 West Allegan 33
Union Savings & Loan, 121
West Allegan 33
Washington Sq Bldg. 109
West Michigan Ave 33
Ywca 217 Townsend 33

HOSPITALS

Edward W Sparrow, 1215
East Michigan Ave.............. 02
Ingham Medical, 401 West
Greenlawn 10
Lansing General, 2800
Devonshire Ave 09
Saint Lawrence, 1210 West
Saginaw 14

UNIVERSITIES AND COLLEGES

Great Lakes Bible College,
6211 W Willow Hwy............ 17
Lansing Business University,
200 North Capitol Ave.................. 33
Lansing Community College,
419 North Capitol Ave........ 14

LIVONIA   481

POST OFFICE BOXES

Box Nos.
2001-2952   Main Office 51

STATIONS, BRANCHES AND UNITS

Northeast Sta 52
General Delivery 50

MUSKEGO‡I 494

POST OFFICE BOXES

Box Nos.
1-1024	Main Office	43
4001-4432	Muskegon Heights Br	44
5001-5128	North Muskegon Br	45

RURAL ROUTES

1	44
2,3	45
4	42
5	45
6	42

STATIONS, BRANCHES AND UNITS

Dalton Rural Br	45
Glenside Br	41
Henry Street Br	41
Muskegon Heights Br	44
North Muskegon Br	45
Roosevelt Park Br	44
Wolf Lake Br	42
General Delivery	40
Postmaster	40

PONTIAC 480

POST OFFICE BOXES

Box Nos.
1-1072	Main Office	56
3001-3793	Federal Sta	59
4109-4700	Auburn Heights Br	57

RURAL ROUTES

1	57
2	54
3,4	55
5	54
6	55

STATIONS, BRANCHES AND UNITS

Auburn Heights Br	57
Federal Station Br	58
M Fifty Nine Plaza Br	54
General Delivery	56
Postmaster	53

APARTMENTS, HOTELS, MOTELS

Canterbury Apts., 900 East Blvd. S	53
Embassy East & West, 5367 Highland	54
Fountainbleau Apts., 995 N. Cass Lake	54
Grand Prix Apts., 311 S. Telegraph	53

BUILDINGS

Community National Bank Bldg., 30 N. Saginaw	58
County Court House, 1200 N. Telegraph	53
Federal Building, 35 E. Huron	58
Pontiac State Bank Bldg., 28 N. Saginaw	58
Riker Building, 35 E. Huron	58

HOSPITALS

Pontiac General Hospital, Seminole At W. Huron	53
Pontiac Osteopathic Hospital, 50 N. Perry	53
Pontiac State Hospital, 140 Elizabeth Lake	53
St. Joseph Mercy Hospital, 900 Woodward	53

ROYAL OAK 480

POST OFFICE BOXES

Box Nos.
A-H	Main Office	68
1-499	Main Office	68
1-699	Madison Heights Br	71
500	Oak Ridge Sta	73
701-947	Main Office	68
1000-1299	Berkley Br	72

STATIONS, BRANCHES AND UNITS

Berkley Br	72
Huntington Woods Br	70
Madison Heights Br	71
Oak Ridge Sta	73
Pleasant Ridge Br	69
General Delivery	67
Postmaster	67

SAGINAW 486

POST OFFICE BOXES

Box Nos.
501-1291	Castle Sta	06
1341-3306	Main Office	05

RURAL ROUTES

1	01
2	04
3,4	01
5,6,7,8	03
9	01

STATIONS, BRANCHES AND UNITS

Castle Sta	06

State Center Br

State Center Br	02
General Delivery	05
Postmaster	05

APARTMENTS, HOTELS, MOTELS

Amadore, 518 Thompson	07
Green Acres Village, 4545 Colonial	03
Hidden Hollow, 1800 Beacon Dr	02
Mac Arthur Square, 332 South Center Rd	03
Maplewood Manor, 535 S Warren	07
Poplar, 4440 State	03

BUILDINGS

Bearinger, 126 S Franklin	07
Chamber Of Commerce, Washington At Johnson	07
Eddy, 102 N Washington	07
First Savings & Loan, 124 S Jefferson	07
Second National Bank, 121 E Genesee	07
Wiechmann, 112 S Jefferson	07

GOVERNMENT OFFICES

Saginaw City Hall, 1315 S Washington	01
Saginaw County Court House, 111 S Michigan	02

HOSPITALS

Saginaw County, Hospital Rd.	05
Saginaw General, 1447 N Harrison	02
Saginaw Osteopathic, 515 N Michigan	02
Saint Lukes, 705 Cooper	02
Saint Marys, 830 S Jefferson	01

SOUTHFIELD 480

POST OFFICE BOXES

Box Nos.
1-200	Lathrup Village Branch	76
1-999	Main Office	75
1000-1399	Northland Center Station	75

STATIONS, BRANCHES AND UNITS

Lathrup Village Br	75
Northland Center Sta	75
General Delivery	75
Postmaster	75

SAINT CLAIR SHORES 480

POST OFFICE BOXES

Box Nos.
A-H	Main Office	83

| St. Clair Shores (Con.) | 480 | **WARREN** | 480 | **WYANDOTTE** | 481 |

STATIONS, BRANCHES AND UNITS

| General Delivery | 83 |
| Postmaster | 83 |

POST OFFICE BOXES

Box Nos.
| 1-464 | South Sta | 90 |
| 501-1269 | Main Office Sta | 90 |

POST OFFICE BOXES

Box Nos.
1-409	Main Office	92
AA-FF	Southgate Br	95
1001-1280	Southgate Br	92
2001-2154	Riverview Br	92

STERLING HEIGHTS 480

STATIONS, BRANCHES AND UNITS

| Sterling Heights Br | 77 |
| Postmaster | 77 |

STATIONS, BRANCHES AND UNITS

South Sta	92
General Delivery	89
Postmaster	89

STATIONS, BRANCHES AND UNITS

Riverview Br	92
Southgate Br	92
General Delivery	92
Postmaster	92

MINNESOTA

State List of Post Offices

MINNESOTA
(Abbreviation: MN)

Ada	56510
Adams	55909
Adolph	55701
Adrian	56110
Afton	55001
Ah-Gwah-Ching	56430
Aitkin (1st)	56431
Akeley	56433
Albany	56307
Albert Lea (1st)	56007
Alberta	56207
Albertville	55301
Alborn	55702
Alden	56009
Aldrich	56434
Alexandria (1st)	56308
Almelund	55002
Alpha	56111
Altura	55910
Alvarado	56710
Alvwood	56620
Amboy	56010
Amiret	56112
Angle Inlet	56711
Angora	55703
Angus	56712
Annandale	55302
Anoka (1st)	55303
Soderville, R. Br.	55304
Apache, Br. Minneapolis	55421
Appleton	56208
Arco	56113
Argyle	56713
Arlington	55307
Ashby	56309
Askov	55704
Atwater	56209
Audubon	56511
Aurora	55705
Austin (1st)	55912
Avoca	56114
Avon	56310
Babbitt	55706
Backus	56435
Badger	56714
Bagley	56621
Baker	56513
Balaton	56115

Ball Club, R. Br. Deer River	56622
Barnesville	56514
Barnum	55707
Barrett	56311
Barry	56210
Battle Lake	56515
Baudette (1st)	56623
Bayport (1st)	55003
Beardsley	56211
Beaver Bay	55601
Beaver Creek	56116
Becida	56625
Becker	55308
Bejou	56516
Belgrade	56312
Belle Plaine	56011
Bellingham	56212
Beltrami	56517
Belview	56214
Bemidji (1st)	56601
Bena	56626
Benedict	56436
Benson (1st)	56215
Beroun	55004
Bertha	56437
Bethel	55005
Bible College, R. Br. Saint Bonifacius	55375
Big Falls	56627
Big Lake	55309
Bigelow	56117
Bigfork	56628
Bingham Lake	56118
Birchdale	56629
Bird Island	55310
Biwabik	55708
Bixby	55916
Blackduck	56630
Blomkest	56216
Bloom Dale, Br. Minneapolis	55431
Blooming Prairie	55917
Bloomington, Br. Minneapolis (see appendix)	
Blue Earth (1st)	56013
Bluffton	56518
Bock	56313
Bongards	55311
Borup	56519
Bovey	55709
Bowlus	56314

Bowstring	56631
Boy River	56632
Boyd	56218
Braham	55006
Brainerd (1st)	56401
Brandon	56315
Breckenridge (1st)	56520
Brewster	56119
Bricelyn	56014
Brimson	55602
Britt	55710
Brook Park	55007
Quamba, R. Br.	55064
Brooklyn Center, Br. Minneapolis	55429
Brooks	56715
Brookston	55711
Brooten	56316
Browerville	56438
Browns Valley	56219
Brownsdale	55918
Brownsville	55919
Brownton	55312
Bruno	55712
Buckman	56317
Buffalo (1st)	55313
Buffalo Lake	55314
Buhl	55713
Burnett	55714
Burnsville, Br. Savage	55378
Burtrum	56318
Butterfield	56120
Buyck, R. Br. Orr	55771
Byron	55920
Caledonia	55921
Callaway	56521
Calumet	55716
Cambridge (1st)	55008
Camden, Sta. Minneapolis (see appendix)	
Campbell	56522
Canby	56220
Cannon Falls (1st)	55009
Canton	55922
Canyon	55717
Carlisle, R. Br. Fergus Falls	56538
Carlos	56319
Carlton	55718
Carver	55315
Cass Lake	56633
Castle Rock	55010

Cedar	55011
Cedar Mills, R. Br. Hutchinson	55351
Center City	55012
Central Avenue, Sta. Minneapolis	55418
Ceylon	56121
Champlin	55316
Chandler	56122
Chanhassen	55317
Chaska (1st)	55318
Chatfield	55923
Chester, R. Br. Rochester	55904
Chicago Lake, Sta. Minneapolis	55407
Chisago City	55013
Chisholm (1st)	55719
Chokio	56221
Circle Pines (1st)	55014
City, Sta. Rochester	55901
Civic Center, Sta. Duluth	55802
Clara City (1st)	56222
Claremont	55924
Clarissa	56440
Clarkfield	56223
Clarks Grove	56016
Clear Lake	55319
Clearbrook	56634
Clearwater	55320
Clements	56224
Clementson, R. Br. Baudette	56623
Cleveland	56017
Climax	56523
Eldred, R. Br.	56532
Clinton	56225
Clitherall	56524
Clontarf	56226
Cloquet (1st)	55720
Cloverton	55015
Cobden	56018
Cohasset	55721
Cokato	55321
Cold Spring	56320
Coleraine	55722
Collegeville (1st)	56321
Cologne	55322
Columbia Heights, Br. Minneapolis	55421
Comfrey	56019
Commerce, Sta. Minneapolis	55415
Como, Sta. Saint Paul	55108
Comstock	56525
Conger	56020
Cook	55723
Coon Rapids, Br. Minneapolis (see appendix)	
Correll	56227
Cosmos	56228
Cottage Grove	55016
Cotton	55724
Cottonwood	56229
Courtland	56021
Crane Lake	55725
Cromwell	55726
Crookston (1st)	56716
Gentilly, R. Br.	56717
Crosby	56441
Crosslake	56442
Crystal, Br. Minneapolis (see appendix)	
Crystal Bay	55323

Culver	55727
Currie	56123
Cushing	56443
Cyrus	56323
Dakota	55925
Dalbo	55017
Dalton	56324
Danube	56230
Danvers	56231
Darfur	56022
Darwin	55324
Dassel	55325
Kingston, R. Br.	55326
Dawson	56232
Dayton	55327
Daytons Bluff, Sta. Saint Paul	55106
De Graff	56233
Deephaven, Br. Wayzata	55391
Deer Creek	56527
Deer River	56636
Ball Club, R. Br.	56622
Talmoon, R. Br.	56637
Deerwood	56444
Delano	55328
Delavan	56023
Delft	56124
Delhi	56234
Denham	55728
Dennison	55018
Dent	56528
Detroit Lakes (1st)	56501
Dexter	55926
Diamond Lake, Sta. Minneapolis (see appendix)	
Dilworth	56529
Dodge Center	55927
Donaldson	56720
Donnelly	56235
Doran	56530
Douglas, R. Br. Oronoco	55960
Dover	55929
Dovray	56125
Dresbach	55930
DULUTH (1st) (see appendix)	
Dumont	56236
Dundas	55019
Dundee	56126
Dunnell	56127
Duquette	55729
Eagle Bend	56446
Eagle Lake	56024
East End, Sta. Duluth	55802
East Grand Forks (1st)	56721
Eastern Heights, Sta. Saint Paul	55119
Easton	56025
Ebro	56638
Echo	56237
Eden Prairie, Br. Hopkins	55343
Eden Valley	55329
Edgerton	56128
Edina, Br. Minneapolis (see appendix)	
Effie	56639
Egan, Br. Saint Paul	55111
Eitzen	55931
Elbow Lake	56531
Eldred, R. Br. Climax	56532
Elgin	55932
Elizabeth	56533
Elk River (1st)	55330
Elko	55020

Elkton	55933
Ellendale	56026
Ellsworth	56129
Elmer	55730
Elmore	56027
Elmwood, Br. Minneapolis	55416
Elrosa	56325
Ely (1st)	55731
Elysian	56028
Embarrass	55732
Emily	56447
Emmons	56029
Erhard	56534
Ericksburg, R. Br. International Falls	56640
Erskine	56535
Esko	55733
Essig	56030
Euclid	56722
Evan	56238
Evansville	56326
Eveleth (1st)	55734
Excelsior (1st)	55331
Eyota	55934
Fairfax	55332
Fairhaven, R. Br. South Haven	55383
Fairmont (1st)	56031
Falcon Heights, Br. Saint Paul	55113
Faribault (1st)	55021
Farmington (1st)	55024
Farwell	56327
Federal Dam	56641
Felton	56536
Fergus Falls (1st)	56537
Carlisle, R. Br.	56538
Fertile	56540
Fifty Lakes	56448
Finland	55603
Isabella, R. Br.	55607
Finlayson	55735
Fisher	56723
Flensburg	56328
Flom	56541
Floodwood	55736
Florence	56130
Foley	56329
Forbes	55738
Forest Lake (1st)	55025
Foreston	56330
Fort Ripley	56449
Fosston	56542
Fountain	55935
Foxhome	56543
Franklin	55333
Franklin Avenue, Sta. Minneapolis	55404
Frazee	56544
Freeborn	56032
Freeport	56331
Fridley, Br. Minneapolis	55421
Frontenac	55026
Frost	56033
Fulda	56131
Garden City	56034
Garfield	56332
Garrison	56450
Garvin	56132
Gary	56545
Gatzke	56724
Gaylord (1st)	55334
Gemmell	56643
Geneva	56035

Genola, R. Br. Pierz	56365
Gentilly, R. Br. Crookston	56717
Georgetown	56546
Gheen	55740
Ghent	56239
Gibbon	55335
Gilbert	55741
Gilman	56333
Glencoe (1st)	55336
Glenville	56036
Glenwood (1st)	56334
Gluek, R. Br. Maynard	56261
Glyndon	56547
Golden Hills, Br. Minneapolis	55416
Golden Valley, Br. Minneapolis	55427
Gonvick	56644
Good Thunder	56037
Goodhue	55027
Goodland	55742
Goodridge	56725
Graceton	56645
Graceville	56240
Granada	56039
Grand Marais	55604
Grand Meadow	55936
Grand Portage	55605
Isle Royale National Park, R. Br.	55617
Grand Rapids (1st)	55744
Grandy	55029
Granger	55937
Granite Falls (1st)	56241
Grasston	55030
Henriette, R. Br.	55036
Green Isle	55338
Green Valley, R. Br. Marshall	56242
Greenbush	56726
Greenwald	56335
Grey Eagle	56336
Grove City	56243
Grygla	56727
Guckeen	56040
Gully	56646
Guthrie	56451
Hackensack	56452
Hadley	56133
Hallock	56728
Halma	56729
Halstad	56548
Hamburg	55339
Hamel	55340
Hammond, R. Br. Rochester	55938
Hampton	55031
Hancock	56244
Hanley Falls	56245
Hanover	55341
Hanska	56041
Harding, R. Br. Pierz	56364
Hardwick	56134
Harmony	55939
Harris	55032
Hartland	56042
Hastings (1st)	55033
Hatfield	56135
Hawick	56246
Hawley	56549
Hayfield	55940
Hayward	56043
Hazel Run	56247
Hector	55342

Henderson	56044
Hendricks	56136
Hendrum	56550
Henning	56551
Henriette, R. Br. Grasston	55036
Herman	56248
Heron Lake	56137
Hewitt	56453
Hibbing (1st)	55746
Highland, Sta. Minneapolis	55411
Highland Park, Sta. Saint Paul	55116
Hill City	55748
Hillman	56338
Hills	56138
Hillside, Sta. Duluth	55805
Hinckley	55037
Hines	56647
Hitterdal	56552
Hoffman	56339
Hokah	55941
Holdingford	56340
Holland	56139
Hollandale	56045
Holloway	56249
Holmes City	56341
Holyoke	55749
Homer, R. Br. Winona	55942
Hope	56046
Hopkins (1st)	55343
Houston	55943
Hovland	55606
Howard Lake	55349
Hoyt Lakes	55750
Hugo	55038
Humboldt	56731
Hunters Park, Sta. Duluth	55803
Huntley	56047
Hutchinson (1st)	55350
Cedar Mills, R. Br.	55351
Ihlen	56140
Indus	56648
Industrial, Sta. Saint Paul	55104
International Falls (1st)	56649
Ericksburg, R. Br.	56640
Inver Grove Heights, Br. South Saint Paul	55075
Iona	56141
Iron	55751
Ironton	56455
Isabella, R. Br. Finland	55607
Isanti	55040
Island Park, R. Sta. Mound	55364
Isle	56342
Ivanhoe	56142
Jackson (1st)	56143
Jacobson	55752
Janesville	56048
Jasper	56144
Jeffers	56145
Jenkins	56456
Johnson	56250
Jordan	55352
Judson	56049
Kanaranzi	56146
Kandiyohi	56251
Karlstad	56732
Kasota	56050
Kasson	55944
Keewatin	55753
Kelliher	56650
Kellogg	55945
Kelly Lake	55754

Kelsey	55755
Kennedy	56733
Kenneth	56147
Kensington	56343
Kent	56553
Kenwood, Sta. Duluth	55811
Kenyon	55946
Kerkhoven	56252
Kerrick	55756
Kettle River	55757
Kiester	56051
Kilkenny	56052
Kimball	55353
Kimberly	56457
Kingston, R. Br. Dassel	55326
Kinney	55758
Klossner	56053
Knife River	55609
La Crescent	55947
La Salle	56056
Lafayette	56054
Lake Benton	56149
Lake Bronson	56734
Lake City (1st)	55041
Lake Crystal	56055
Lake Elmo	55042
Lake George	56458
Lake Hubert	56459
Lake Itasca	56460
Lake Lillian	56253
Lake Park	56554
Lake Street, Sta. Minneapolis (see appendix)	
Lake Wilson	56151
Lakefield	56150
Lakeland	55043
Lakeside, Sta. Duluth	55804
Lakeville	55044
Lamberton	56152
Lamoille	55948
Lancaster	56735
Lanesboro	55949
Lansing	55950
Laporte	56461
Larsmont, R. Br. Two Harbors	55610
Lastrup	56344
Le Center (1st)	56057
Le Roy	55951
Le Sueur (1st)	56058
Leader, R. Br. Motley	56462
Lengby	56651
Leonard	56652
Leota	56153
Lester Prairie	55354
Lewiston	55952
Lewisville	56060
Linden Hills, Sta. Minneapolis	55410
Lindstrom	55045
Lismore	56155
Litchfield (1st)	55355
Little Falls (1st)	56345
Little Marais, R. Br. Silver Bay	55611
Little Sauk	56346
Littlefork	56653
Lockhart	56555
Loman	56654
London	56061
Long Lake	55356
Long Prairie (1st)	56347

Longville........................56655
Lonsdale.........................55046
Loop, Sta. Minneapolis........55402
Loretto..........................55357
Loring, Sta. Minneapolis
  (see appendix)
Louisburg........................56254
Lowry............................56349
Lowry Hill, Sta. Minneapolis...55405
Lucan...........................56255
Lutsen..........................55612
Luverne (1st)...................56156
Lyle............................55953
Lynd............................56157
Mabel...........................55954
Madelia (1st)...................56062
Madison.........................56256
Madison Lake....................56063
Magnolia........................56158
Mahnomen........................56557
Mahtomedi, Br. Saint Paul.......55115
Mahtowa.........................55762
Makinen.........................55763
Manchester......................56064
Manhattan Beach.................56463
Manitou.........................56656
Mankato (1st)...................56001
  North Mankato, Br..........56001
  Rapidan, R. Br.............56079
Mantorville.....................55955
Maple Lake......................55358
Maple Plain (1st)...............55359
Mapleton :......................56065
Maplewood, Br. Saint Paul.......55109
Marble..........................55764
Marcell.........................56657
Margie..........................56658
Marietta........................56257
Marine On Saint Croix...........55047
Markville.......................55048
Marshall (1st)..................56258
  Green Valley, R. Br........56242
Matawan.........................56066
Max.............................56659
Mayer...........................55360
Maynard.........................56260
  Gluek, R. Br...............56261
Mazeppa.........................55956
Mc Grath........................56350
Mc Gregor.......................55760
Mc Intosh.......................56556
Mc Kinley.......................55761
Meadowlands.....................55765
Medford.........................55049
Medicine Lake, Br.
  Minneapolis................55427
Melby...........................56351
Melrose.........................56352
Melrude.........................55766
Menahga.........................56464
Mendota, Br. Saint Paul.........55050
Mentor..........................56736
Meriden.........................56067
Merrifield......................56465
Middle River....................56737
Midway, Sta. Saint Paul.........55104
Milaca (1st)....................56353
Milan...........................56262
Millville.......................55957
Milroy..........................56263
Miltona.........................56354
MINNEAPOLIS (1st) (see
  appendix)

Minnehaha, Sta.
  Minneapolis................55406
Minneiska.......................55958
Minneota........................56264
Minnesota City..................55959
Minnesota Lake..................56068
Minnesota Transfer, Sta.
  Saint Paul.................55114
Minnetonka, Br. Hopkins.........55343
Minnetonka Beach................55361
Minnetonka Mills, Br.
  Hopkins....................55343
Mizpah..........................56660
Montevideo (1st)................56265
Montgomery......................56069
Monticello......................56362
Montrose........................55363
Moorhead (1st)..................56560
Moose Lake......................55767
Mora (1st)......................55051
Morgan..........................56266
Morgan Park, Sta. Duluth........55808
Morris (1st)....................56267
Morristown......................55052
Morton..........................56270
Motley..........................56466
  Leader, R. Br..............56462
Mound (1st).....................55364
Mountain Iron...................55768
Mountain Lake...................56159
Murdock.........................56271
Myrtle..........................56070
Nashua..........................56565
Nashwauk........................55769
Nassau..........................56272
Navarre, R. Br. Wayzata.........55392
Naytahwaush.....................56566
Nelson..........................56355
Nerstrand.......................55053
Nett Lake, R. Br. Orr...........55772
Nevis...........................56467
New Auburn......................55366
New Brighton, Br. Saint
  Paul.......................55112
New Germany.....................55367
New Hope, Br. Minneapolis.......55428
New London......................56273
New Market......................55054
New Munich......................56356
New Prague (1st)................56071
New Richland....................56072
New Ulm (1st)...................56073
New York Mills..................56567
Newfolden.......................56738
Newport (1st)...................55055
Nicollet........................56074
Nielsville......................56568
Nimrod, R. Br. Sebeka...........56478
Nisswa..........................56468
Nokomis, Sta. Minneapolis.......55417
Nopeming, R. Br. Duluth.........55770
Norcross........................56274
Normandale, Br. Minneapolis
  (see appendix)
North Branch....................55056
North Douglas, Br.
  Minneapolis................55422
North Mankato, Br. Mankato......56001
North Redwood...................56275
North Saint Paul, Br. Saint
  Paul.......................55109
Northcote.......................56739
Northfield (1st)................55057

Northome........................56661
Northrop, Br. Fairmont..........56075
Northside, Sta. Albert Lea......56007
Northwest Terminal, Sta.
  Minneapolis................55413
Norwood.........................55368
Noyes...........................56740
Number Five, Sta. Duluth........55802
Oak Island......................56741
Oak Knoll, Br. Hopkins..........55343
Oak Park........................56357
Oak Street, Sta.
  Minneapolis................55414
Oakland.........................56076
Odessa..........................56276
Odin............................56160
Ogema...........................56569
Ogilvie.........................56358
Okabena.........................56161
Oklee...........................56742
Olivia (1st)....................56277
Onamia..........................56359
Orleans.........................56743
Ormsby..........................56162
Oronoco.........................55960
Orr.............................55771
  Buyck, R. Br...............55771
  Nett Lake, R. Br...........55772
Ortonville......................56278
Osage...........................56570
Osakis..........................56360
Oslo............................56744
Osseo (1st).....................55369
Ostrander.......................55961
Otisco..........................56077
Ottertail.......................56571
Outing..........................56662
Owatonna (1st)..................55060
Palisade........................56469
Park Rapids (1st)...............56470
Parkers Prairie.................56361
Parkville.......................55773
Payne...........................55774
Payne Avenue, Sta. Saint
  Paul.......................55101
Paynesville.....................56362
Pease...........................56363
Pelican Rapids..................56572
Pemberton.......................56078
Pencer..........................56746
Pengilly........................55775
Pennington......................56663
Pennock.........................56279
Pequaywan Lake, R. Br.
  Duluth.....................55803
Pequot Lakes....................56472
Perham..........................56573
Perley..........................56574
Peterson........................55962
Pierz...........................56364
  Genola, R. Br..............56365
  Harding, R. Br.............56364
Pike Lake, Br. Duluth...........55811
Pillager........................56473
Pine City.......................55063
Pine Island.....................55963
Pine River......................56474
Pinecreek.......................56747
Pinewood........................56664
Pioneer, Sta. Saint Paul........55101
Pipestone (1st).................56164
Pitt............................56665
Plainview.......................55964

Plato.................................55370
Plummer...........................56748
Ponemah...........................56666
Ponsford...........................56575
Porter................................56280
Powderhorn, Sta.
  Minneapolis...................55407
Preston.............................55965
Princeton (1st).................55371
Prinsburg.........................56281
Prior Lake........................55372
Procter, Br. Duluth...........55810
Prosper.............................55966
Puposky............................56667
Quamba, R. Br. Brook Park ...55064
Racine...............................55967
Radium.............................56749
Randall.............................56475
Randolph...........................55065
Ranier...............................56668
Rapidan, R. Br. Mankato ...56079
Ray...................................56669
Raymond...........................56282
Reading.............................56165
Reads Landing..................55968
Red Lake Falls..................56750
Red Wing (1st).................55066
Redby................................56670
Redlake.............................56671
Redwood Falls (1st)..........56283
Regal................................56366
Remer...............................56672
Renville.............................56284
Revere..............................56166
Rice..................................56367
Rice Street, Sta. Saint Paul ...55117
Richfield, Br. Minneapolis ...55423
Richmond..........................56368
Richville...........................56576
Richwood..........................56577
Riverside, Sta. Minneapolis ...55404
Riverview, Sta. Saint Paul ...55107
Robbinsdale, Br.
  Minneapolis (see
  appendix)
Rochert.............................56578
Rochester (1st)..................55901
  Chester, R. Br...............55904
  City, Sta........................55901
  Hammond, R. Br............55938
  Viola, R. Br...................55980
Rock Creek........................55067
Rockford............................55373
Rockville...........................56369
Rogers..............................55374
Rollingstone......................55969
Ronneby............................56370
Roosevelt..........................56673
Roscoe..............................56371
Rose Creek........................55970
Roseau (1st)......................56751
Rosemount (1st)................55068
Roseville, Br. Saint Paul ...55113
Ross.................................56753
Rothsay............................56579
Round Lake.......................56167
Royalton............................56373
Rush City..........................55069
Rushford............................55971
Rushmore..........................56168
Russell..............................56169
Ruthton.............................56170
Rutledge...........................55778

Sabin................................56580
Sacred Heart.....................56285
Saginaw............................55779
Saint Anthony Falls, Sta.
  Minneapolis...................55414
Saint Bonifacius................55375
Saint Charles.....................55972
Saint Clair, Sta. Saint Paul ...55105
Saint Clair.........................56080
Saint Cloud (1st)...............56301
Saint Francis......................55070
Saint Hilaire......................56754
Saint James (1st)..............56081
Saint Joseph......................56374
  Saint Stephen, R. Br......56375
Saint Leo...........................56286
Saint Louis Park, Br.
  Minneapolis (see
  appendix)
Saint Martin.......................56376
Saint Michael....................55376
SAINT PAUL (1st) (see
  appendix)
Saint Paul Park (1st)..........55071
Saint Peter (1st)................56082
Saint Stephen, R. Br. Saint
  Joseph............................56375
Saint Vincent.....................56755
Salol.................................56756
Sanborn............................56083
Sandstone.........................55072
Santiago............................55377
Sargeant...........................55973
Sartell..............................56377
Sauk Centre (1st).............56378
Sauk Rapids, Br. Saint
  Cloud.............................56379
Saum................................56674
Savage (1st)......................55378
Sawyer..............................55780
Scandia.............................55073
Schroeder..........................55613
Seaforth............................56287
Searles..............................56084
Sebeka..............................56477
  Nimrod, R. Br...............56478
Sedan................................56380
Shafer...............................55074
Shakopee (1st)..................55379
Shelly...............................56581
Sherburn...........................56171
Shevlin.............................56676
Side Lake..........................55781
Silver Bay.........................55614
  Little Marais, R. Br........55611
Silver Creek......................55380
Silver Lake........................55381
Slayton..............................56172
Sleepy Eye (1st)................56085
Soderville, R. Br. Anoka ...55304
Solway..............................56678
Soudan..............................55782
South Haven......................55382
  Fairhaven, R. Br............55383
South International Falls ...56679
South Saint Paul (1st).......55075
Spicer...............................56288
Spring Grove.....................55974
Spring Lake......................56680
Spring Lake Park, Br.
  Minneapolis...................55432
Spring Park (1st)...............55384
Spring Valley....................55975

Springfield........................56087
Squaw Lake.......................56681
Stacy................................55079
Stanchfield.......................55080
Stanton.............................55081
Staples..............................56479
Starbuck............................56381
Steen................................56173
Stephen.............................56757
Stewart.............................55385
Stewartville.......................55976
Stillwater (1st)..................55082
Stockton, R. Br. Winona ...55988
Storden.............................56174
Strandquist.......................56758
Strathcona........................56759
Sturgeon Lake...................55783
Sunburg............................56289
Svea.................................56290
Swan River........................55784
Swanville..........................56382
Swatara............................55785
Swift.................................56682
Taconite............................55786
Talmoon, R. Br. Deer River ...56637
Tamarack..........................55787
Taopi................................55977
Taunton.............................56291
Taylors Falls.....................55084
Tenney..............................56582
Tenstrike...........................56683
Terrace..............................56383
Theilman...........................55978
Thief River Falls (1st)........56701
Thompson Park, Br.
  Minneapolis...................55433
Tintah...............................56583
Tofte.................................55615
Togo.................................55788
Toivola..............................55789
Tower................................55790
Tracy................................56175
Traffic, Sta. Minneapolis ...55403
Trail.................................56684
Trimont.............................56176
Trosky..............................56177
Truman.............................56088
Twig.................................55791
Twin Cities, Br. Saint Paul ...55111
Twin Lakes........................56089
Twin Valley.......................56584
Two Harbors (1st)..............55616
  Larsmont, R. Br.............55610
Tyler.................................56178
U S Air Force, Br. Duluth ...55814
Ulen.................................56585
Underwood.........................56586
University, Sta. Minneapolis ...55414
Upper Nicollet, Sta.
  Minneapolis...................55403
Upsala..............................56384
Uptown, Sta. Minneapolis ...55408
Uptown, Sta. Saint Paul (see
  appendix)
Utica.................................55979
Valley Ridge, Br. Savage ...55378
Verdi................................56179
Vergas..............................56587
Vermillion.........................55085
Verndale...........................56481
Vernon Center...................56090
Veseli...............................55086
Vesta................................56292

Victoria	55386
Viking	56760
Villard	56385
Vining	56588
Viola, R. Br. Rochester	55980
Virginia (1st)	55792
Wabasha	55981
Wabasso	56293
Waconia (1st)	55387
Wadena (1st)	56482
Wahkon	56386
Waite Park, Br. Saint Cloud	56387
Waldorf	56091
Walker	56484
Walnut Grove	56180
Walters	56092
Waltham	55982
Wanamingo	55983
Wanda	56294
Wannaska	56761
Warba	55793
Warren	56762
Warroad	56763
Warsaw	55087
Waseca (1st)	56093
Waskish	56685
Watertown	55388
Waterville	56096
Watkins	55389
Watson	56295
Waubun	56589
Waverly	55390
Wawina	55794
Wayzata (1st)	55391
Deephaven, Br.	55391
Navarre, R. Br.	55392
Webster	55088
Welch	55089
Welcome	56181
Wells	56097
Wendell	56590
West Concord	55985
West Duluth, Sta. Duluth	55807
West End, Sta. Saint Paul	55102
West Saint Paul, Br. Saint Paul	55118
West Union	56389
Westbrook	56183
Whalan	55986
Wheaton	56296
Whipholt	56485
White Bear Lake, Br. Saint Paul	55110
White Earth	56591
Wilder	56184
Willernie	55090
Williams	56686
Willmar (1st)	56201
Willow River	55795
Wilmont	56185
Wilton	56687
Windom (1st)	56101
Winger	56592
Winnebago	56098
Winona (1st)	55987
Homer, R. Br.	55942
Stockton, R. Br.	55988
Winsted	55395
Winthrop	55396
Winton	55796
Wirt	56688
Wolf Lake	56593
Wolverton	56594
Wood Lake	56297
Woodland, Sta. Duluth	55803
Woodstock	56186
Worthington (1st)	56187
Wrenshall	55797
Wright	55798
Wykoff	55990
Wyoming	55092
Young America	55397
Zim	55799
Zimmerman	55398
Zumbro Falls	55991
Zumbrota	55992

DULUTH 558

POST OFFICE BOXES

Box Nos.

A-D	Proctor Br	10
A-E	West Duluth Sta.	07
1-750	Civic Center Sta.	01
1001-1096	Proctor Br	10
3000-3999	Mount Royal Sta.	03
6001-6999	Main Office	06
7001-7216	West Duluth Sta.	07
8001-8116	Morgan Park Sta.	08

RURAL ROUTES

1,2	11
3,4	03
5	10
6	04
7	10

STATIONS, BRANCHES AND UNITS

Civic Center Sta	02
East End Sta	02
Hillside Sta	05
Hunters Park Sta	03
Kenwood Sta	11
Lakeside Sta	04
Morgan Park Sta	08
Nopeming Rural Br	55770
Number Five Sta	02
Pequaywan Lake Rural Br.	03
Pike Lake Br	11
Procter Br	10
U S Air Force Br	14
West Duluth Sta	07
Woodland Sta	03
General Delivery	06
Postmaster	06

APARTMENTS, HOTELS, MOTELS

Arrowhead, 225 N 1st Ave W.	06
Buena Vista, 1144 Mesaba Ave.	11
Cascade, 103 W 3rd	06
Devonshire, 1321 E 1st	05
Downtown, 131 W 2nd	02
Duluth Hotel, 231 E Superior.	02
Duluth Motel, 4415 Grand Ave.	07
Edgewater, 2330 London Rd.	12
Fifth Avenue Apt, 501 E 3rd.	05
Grand View Manor, 301 E 2nd.	05
Grand, 4312 Grand Ave	07
Hillcrest, 1721 E 3rd	12
Holiday Inn, 250 S 1st Ave E.	01
Lake Aire, 2416 London Rd	12
Lakeview, 1703 E 3rd	12
Lincoln, 317 W 2nd	02
London Manor, 1801 London Rd	12
London Road Court, 2521 London Rd	12
Mount Royal Manor, 100 Elizabeth	03
Munger Terrace, 405 Mesaba Ave	06
Radisson-Duluth 503 West Superior	02
Saint Ann'S Home, 330 E 3rd	05
Seaway, 2001 W Superior	06
Select Homes, 801 E 2nd	05
Skyline Court, 2930 Miller Trunk Hwy	11
Yorkleigh, 1017 London Rd.	02

BUILDINGS

A M Clure Public Marine Terminal, 1200 Garfield Ave	02
Aetna, 403 N Central Ave	07
Alworth, 306 W Superior	02
Armory, 1305 London Rd	05
Beal, 3 N 3rd Ave W	02
Board Of Trade, 301 W 1st	02
Bradley, 10 E Superior	02
Christie, 120 N 4th Ave W	02
Duluth Clinic, 205 W 2nd	02
Duluth International Airport	11
Duluth National Bank, 2002 W Superior	06
Engineers, 600 Lake Ave S	02
Federal, 5th Ave W & 1st	02
Fidelity, 14 W Superior	02

ZIP CODE

Minneapolis, Minn.
554 + Two Digits Shown = Zip Code

Duluth (Con.)   558

First American National
   Bank, 230 W Superior 02
Harbrace, 1 East 1st 02
Lonsdale, 302 W Superior.... 02
Medical Arts, 324 W
   Superior.............................. 02
Missabe 227 West 1st............. 02
New Garrick, 128 W 1st........ 02
Northland, 410 W Superior..... 02
Palladio, 5 North 4th Ave W.... 02
Phoenix, 333 W Superior....... 02
Providence, 334 W Superior.... 02
Public Library, 101 W 2nd...... 02
Sellwood, 200 W Superior 02
Terminal Public Marine, 1200
   Garfield Ave 02
Torrey, 314 W Superior........... 02
Winthrop, 325 W 1st............. 02
Y M C A, 302 W 1st.............. 02
Y W C A, 202 West 2nd......... 02

GOVERNMENT OFFICES

City Hall, 4th Ave W & 1st..... 02
Courthouse County, 5th Ave
   W & 1st................................ 02
Courthouse Federal, 5th Ave
   W & 1st................................ 02
U S Engineers, 600 Lake Ave
   S... 02

HOSPITALS

Miller Dwan, 504 E 2nd......... 05
Saint Lukes, 915 E 1st.......... 05
Saint Marys, 407 E 3rd 05

UNIVERSITIES AND COLLEGES

Duluth Business University,
   418 W Superior.................... 02
Saint Scholastica.................... 11
University Of Minnesota
   Duluth, 2400 Oakland Ave . 12

MINNEAPOLIS   554
POST OFFICE BOXES

Box Nos.
1-1999   Main Office 40
3101-3499   Traffic Sta........ 03
3501-3599   Upper Nicollet
               Sta................. 03
3601-3999   Loring Sta 03
4201-4299   Saint Anthony
               Falls Sta........ 14
4401-4499   Columbia
               Heights Br..... 21
9501-9899   Main Office 40
02001-02999 Loop Sta........... 02
06001-06999 Minnehaha
               Sta................. 06
07001-07999 Powderhorn
               Sta................. 07
08001-08999 Lake Street
               Sta................. 08
11001-11999 Highland Sta..... 11
12001-12999 Camden Sta 12

14001-14999 University Sta... 14
15001-15999 Commerce Sta.... 15
16001-16999 Elmwood Br...... 16
17001-17999 Nokomis Sta..... 17
18001-18999 Central Ave
               Sta................. 18
19001-19999 Diamond Lake
               Sta................. 19
20001-20999 Bloomington
               Br.................. 20
21001-21999 Columbia
               Heights Br...... 21
22001-22999 Robbinsdale
               Br.................. 22
23001-23999 Richfield Br...... 23
24001-24999 Edina Br.......... 24
26001-26999 Saint Louis
               Park Br.......... 26
27001-27299 Golden Valley
               Br.................. 27
32001-32999 Fridley Br........ 32
33001-33999 Coon Rapids
               Br.................. 33
35501-35999 Normandale Br.. 35

STATIONS, BRANCHES AND UNITS

Apache Br.................................. 21
Bloom Dale Br........................... 31
Bloomington Br......................... 20
Brooklyn Center Br................... 29
Camden Sta............................... 12
Central Avenue Sta................... 18
Chicago Lake Sta...................... 07
Columbia Heights Br................ 21
Commerce Sta........................... 15
Coon Rapids Br......................... 33
Crystal Br.................................. 28
Diamond Lake Sta..................... 19
Edina Br.................................... 24
Elmwood Br............................... 16
Franklin Avenue Sta................. 04
Fridley Br.................................. 21
Golden Hills Br......................... 16
Golden Valley Br....................... 27
Highland Sta............................. 11
Lake Street Sta......................... 04
Linden Hills Br......................... 10
Loop Sta.................................... 02
Loring Sta................................. 03
Lowry Hill Sta........................... 03
Medicine Lake Br...................... 27
Minnehaha Sta.......................... 06
New Hope Br............................. 28
Nokomis Sta.............................. 17
Normandale Br.......................... 35
North Douglas Br...................... 22
Northwest Terminal Sta............ 13
Oak Street Sta.......................... 14
Powderhorn Sta......................... 07
Richfield Br.............................. 23
Riverside Sta............................. 04
Robbinsdale Br......................... 22
Saint Anthony Falls Sta........... 14
Saint Louis Park Br.................. 26
Spring Lake Park Br................. 32
Thompson Park Br.................... 33
Traffic Sta................................ 03
University Sta............................ 14
Upper Nicollet Sta.................... 03
Uptown Sta................................ 08
General Delivery........................ 01

Postmaster................................. 01

APARTMENTS, HOTELS, MOTELS

Andrews, 5 S 4th...................... 01
Curtis, 327 S 10th.................... 04
Dyckman, 27 S 6th.................... 02
Hampshire Arms, 900 4th
   Ave S.................................. 04
Holiday Central, 1313
   Nicollet Ave........................ 03
Leamington, 1014 3rd Ave S... 04
Nicollet, 230 Nicollet Ave....... 01
Northstar Inn, 618 2nd Ave
   So....................................... 02
Radisson, 45 S 7th................... 02
Sheraton-Ritz, 315 Nicollet
   Ave..................................... 01
Sheridan, 1112 Marquette
   Ave..................................... 03

BUILDINGS

American Hardware Mutual,
   3033 Excelsior Blvd............ 16
Apache Plaza............................. 21
Auditorium, 211 E Grant......... 03
Baker Arcade, 733 Marquette
   Ave..................................... 02
Baker, 706 2nd Ave S.............. 02
Builders Exchange, 609 2nd
   Ave S.................................. 02
Cargill, 110 S 7th.................... 02
Chamber Of Commerce............ 02
Citizens Aid, 404 S 8th........... 04
Dain Tower, 527 Marquette 02
Doctors, 90 S 9th..................... 02
Donaldson, 80 S 7th................ 02
Farmers & Mechanics Bank,
   88 S 6th Street.................... 02
First Federal Savings & Loan,
   634 Nieqiiet Mall................. 02
First National Bank Bldg,
   120 S 6th............................ 02
First National Concourse, 515
   Marquette Ave..................... 02
Flour Exchange, 310 4th Ave
   S... 15
Foshay Tower, 821 Marquette
   Ave..................................... 02
Gamble-Skogmo, 5100
   Gamble Dr........................... 16
Grain Exchange, 400 S 4th 15
International Business
   Machines, 245 Marquette
   Ave..................................... 01
Investors, 733 Marquette
   Ave..................................... 02
Kresge, 628 Nicollet Ave......... 02
Loring Medical, 1409 Willow.... 03
Marquette Bank, 91 S 7th
   Street.................................. 02
Mc Knight, 415 2nd Ave S....... 01
Medical Arts, 825 Nicollet
   Ave..................................... 02
Merchandise Mart, 400 1st
   Ave N.................................. 01
Merchandise, 528 Hennepin
   Ave..................................... 03
Metropolitan Med Office Bldg
   825 S 8th............................ 04
Midland Bank, 405 2nd Ave
   S... 01
Midwest Federal Savings &
   Loan, 801 Nicollet Mall....... 02

Minneapolis (Con.)   554

Midwest Plaza, 801 Nicollet Mall 02
Minnesota Federal, 603 Marquette Ave. 02
National, 527 2nd Ave S. 02
Northstar Center, 110 S 7th... 02
Northwestern Bank, 620 Marquette Ave. 02
Northwestern Bell Telephone, 224 S 5th 02
Northwestern Federal, 730 Hennepin Ave. 03
Northwestern Terminal, 600 Stinson Blvd 13
Physicians & Surgeons, 63 S 9th 02
Pillsbury, 608 2nd Ave S. 02
Plymouth, 12 S 6th. 02
Produce Bank, 100 N 7th. 03
Public Library, 316 Nicollet Ave. 01
Roanoke, 109 S 7th. 02
Sexton, 529 S 7th. 15
Six-Hundred, 600 1st Ave N. ... 03
Soo Line, 105 S 5th. 02
Southdale 35
Southdale Medical, 6545 France Ave S. 35
Southgate Plaza 5001 W 78th 37
Syndicate, 84 S 6th. 02
Thorpe, 519 Marquette Ave..... 02
Title Insurance, 400 2nd Ave S. 01
Twin City Federal, 811 Marquette Ave. 02
Union Bus Depot, 29 N 9th..... 03
Upper Midwest, 425 Hennepin Ave. .... 0.
W C C 0, 625 2nd Ave S. 02
Wesley Temple, 115 E Grant.... 03
Western Union, 317 2nd Ave S. 01
Y M C A, 30 S 9th. 02
Y W C A, 1130 Nicollet Ave..... 03

GOVERNMENT OFFICES

City Hall & Court House 15
Minneapolis St Paul Metro Center 99
Public Health, 312 3rd Ave S. 15
United States Courthouse, 110 S 4th. 01
United States Federal Building, 110 S 4th. 01
United States Federal Office, 200 Washington Ave S. 01
United States Post Office, 100 S 1st. 01

HOSPITALS

Abbott, 110 E 18th. 03
Doctors Memorial, 1375 Willow. 03
Eitel, 1375 Willow. 03
Elizabeth Kenny Institute, 1800 Chicago Ave. 04
Fairview, 2312 S 6th. 06
Glenwood Hills, 3901 Golden

Valley Rd. 22
Hennepin County General, 619 S 5th. 15
Lutheran Deaconess, 2315 14th Ave S. 04
Methodist, 6500 Excelsior Blvd. 26
Metropolitan Medical Center 900 S 8th. 04
Mount Sinai, 2215 Park Ave... 04
North Memorial, 3220 Lowry Ave N. 22
Northwestern, 810 E 27th. 07
Saint Marys, 2414 S 7th. 06
Sheltering Arms, 4330 W River Rd. 06
Shriners, 2025 E River Rd...... 14
Southdale Fairview, 6401 France Ave S. 35
Unity, 550 Osborne Rd NE. 32
University, 412 Union SE........ 55
Veterans, 4801 E 54th. 17

UNIVERSITIES AND COLLEGES

Augsburg College, 707 21st Ave S. 04
Bunwoody Institute, 816 Wayzata Blvd 03
University Of Minnesota 55

SAINT PAUL   551

POST OFFICE BOXES

Box Nos.
1-1000   Uptown Sta 02
1001-1499   Saint Clair Sta. 05
1500-1999   Twin Cities Br.... 11
2000-2499   North Saint Paul Br. 09
2500-2999   New Brighton Br 12
3000-3999   Main Office 65
4000-4499   Highland Park Sta. 16
4500-4999   Mahtomedi Br.... 15
5000-5999   Industrial Sta.... 04
6000-6499   West Saint Paul Br. 18
6500-6999   Daytons Bluff Sta. 06
7000-7499   Rice Street Sta. 17
7500-7999   Eastern Heights Sta. ... 19
8000-8499   Roseville Br...... 13
8500-8999   White Bear Lake Br. 10
9000-9999   New Brighton Br 77
30000-30999 Main Office 75
80000-80499 Como Station ... 08

STATIONS, BRANCHES AND UNITS

Como Sta. 08
Daytons Bluff Sta. 06

Eastern Heights Sta 19
Egan Br. 11
Falcon Heights Br. 13
Highland Park Sta. 16
Industrial Sta. 04
Mahtomedi Br. 15
Maplewood Br. 09
Mendota Br. 55050
Midway Sta. 04
Minnesota Transfer Sta. 14
New Brighton Br. 12
North Saint Paul Br 09
Payne Avenue Sta. 01
Pioneer Sta. 01
Rice Street Sta. 17
Riverview Sta. 07
Roseville Br. 13
Saint Clair Sta. 05
Twin Cities Br. 11
Uptown Sta. 02
West End Sta. 02
West Saint Paul Br 18
White Bear Lake Br. 10
General Delivery 01
Postmaster 01

APARTMENTS, HOTELS, MOTELS

Capp Towers, 77 E 9th. 01
Commodore, 79 N Western Ave. 02
Hilton, 11 E Kellogg Blvd 01
Holiday Inn, 161 St Anthony Ave. 03
Lowry, 339 N Wabasha 02
Midway Motor Lodge, 1964 University Ave. 04
Paul Bunyan, 2965 N Snelling Ave. 13
Saint Paul Travelodge, 149 E University Ave. 01
Saint Paul, 363 St Peter.......... 02
Twins Motor Motel, 1975 University Ave. 04

BUILDINGS

Arts & Science Center, 30 E 10th. 01
Bremer Arcade, 419 N Robert. 01
Burlington Northern, 176 E 5th. 01
Centennial, 658 Cedar. 01
Central Medical, 393 N Dunlap 04
Commerce, 8 E 4th. 01
Degree Of Honor, 325 Cedar... 01
Dispatch, 55 E 4th. 01
Endicott, 350 N Robert........... 01
Federal Land Bank, 375 Jackson 01
Fire, 101 E 10th. 01
First National Bank, 332 Minnesota 01
Griggs Midway, 1821 University Ave W. 04
Guardian, 84 E 4th. 01
Hamm, 408 St Peter. 02
Lowry, 75 W 4th. 02

St. Paul (Con.)   551

Lowry, 350 St Peter	02
Metro Square, 121 E 7th	01
Minnesota, 46 E 4th	01
Nalpac, 333 Sibley	01
Northwestern Bank, 55 E 5th.	01
Osborn, 370 N Wabasha	02
Pioneer, 336 N Robert	01
Public Library, 90 W 4th	02
Public Safety, 101 E 10th	01
State Highway, John Ireland Blvd	01

GOVERNMENT OFFICES

Armory, 600 Cedar	01
Courthouse, 15 W Kellogg Blvd	02
Federal Bldg & U. S. Court House, 316 N. Robert	01
Federal Bldg, Ft Snelling, Mn	11
Post Office & Custom House, 180 E Kellogg Blvd	01
State Capitol, Aurora Ave & Park	03

HOSPITALS

Bethesda, 559 Capitol Blvd	03
Childrens, 311 Pleasant Ave	02
Gillette State Hospital For Crippled Children, 1003 E Ivy	06
Midway, 1700 University Ave W	04
Miller, 125 W College Ave	02
Mounds Park, 200 Earl	06
Riverview Memorial, 225 Prescott	07
Saint Johns, 403 Maria	06
Saint Josephs, 69 W Exchange	02
Saint Lukes, 287 Smith Ave	02
Saint Paul Ramsey, 640 Jackson	01
Salvation Army Booth Memorial, 1471 Como Ave	08
Samaritan Hospital, 1515 Charles	04

MILITARY INSTALLATIONS

Armory, 600 Cedar	01

UNIVERSITIES AND COLLEGES

Bethel College & Seminary, 1480 N Snelling Ave	08
Concordia, 275 N Syndicate	04
Hamline University, 1536 Hewitt Ave	04
Luther Seminary, 2375 Como Ave	08
Macalester, 1600 Grand Ave	05
Saint Catherines, 2004 Randolph Ave	05
Saint Paul Bible, 1361 Englewood Ave	04
Saint Paul Seminary, 2200 Grand Ave	05
Saint Thomas, 2115 Summit Ave	05
U-Farm, 1444 N Cleveland Ave	08
William Mitchell College Of Law, 2100 Summit Ave	05

State List of Post Offices   MISSISSIPPI

MISSISSIPPI
(Abbreviation: MS)

Abbeville	38601
Aberdeen (1st)	39730
Ackerman	39735
Agricola, R. Br. Lucedale	39452
Alcorn College, R. Br. Lorman	39096
Algoma	38820
Alligator	38720
Amory (1st)	38821
Anguilla	38721
Apple Ridge, Sta. Jackson	39204
Arcola	38722
Arkabutla	38602
Artesia	39736
Ashland	38603
Askew	38604
Avalon	38912
Avon	38723
Bailey	39320
Baird	38724
Baldwyn	38824
Banner	38913
Bassfield	39421
Batesville (1st)	38606
Battlefield, Sta. Jackson	39204
Baxterville, R. Br. Lumberton	39455
Bay Saint Louis (1st)	39520
Bay Springs	39422
Beaumont	39423
Becker	38825
Belden	38826
Belen	38609
Bellefontaine	39737
Belmont	38827

Belzoni (1st)	39038
Benoit	38725
Stringtown, R. Br.	38777
Benton	39039
Bentonia	39040
Beulah	38726
Bexley, R. Br. Lucedale	39453
Big Creek	38914
Bigbee Valley	39738
BILOXI (1st) (see appendix)	
Black Hawk, R. Br. Carrollton	38918
Blaine, R. Br. Sunflower	38727
Blue Mountain	38610
Blue Springs	38828
Bobo, R. Br. Clarksdale	38728
Bogue Chitto	39629
Bolton	39041
Bond, R. Br. Wiggins	39550
Bonita	39321
Booneville (1st)	38829
Bourbon	38729
Boyle	38730
Brandon (1st)	39042
Johns, R. Br.	39042
Value, R. Br.	39178
Braxton	39044
Brazil	38956
Brookhaven (1st)	39601
Brooklyn	39425
Brooksville	39739
Bruce	38915
Buckatunna	39322
Buge	39630
Burns, R. Br. Raleigh	39153
Burnsville	38833
Byhalia	38611
Caledonia	39740

Calhoun City	38916
Slate Spring, R. Br.	38955
Camden	39045
Canaan	38612
Candlestick, Br. Jackson	39212
Canton (1st)	39046
Carlisle	39049
Carpenter	39050
Carriere	39426
Carrollton	38917
Black Hawk, R. Br.	38918
Carson	39427
Carthage (1st)	39051
Cary	39054
Cascilla	38920
Cedarbluff	39741
Centreville	39631
Chalybeate, R. Br. Walnut	38684
Charleston	38921
Chatawa	39632
Chatham	38731
Choctaw, Sta. Laurel	39440
Chunky	39323
Church Hill	39055
Clara	39324
Clarksdale (1st)	38614
Bobo, R. Br.	38728
Farrell, R. Br.	38630
Clermont Harbor	39551
Cleveland (1st)	38732
Cliftonville	39742
Clinton (1st)	39056
Clinton Plaza, Sta. Clinton	39056
Coahoma	38617
Cockrum, R. Br. Hernando	38632
Coffeeville	38922
Coila	38923
Coldwater	38618

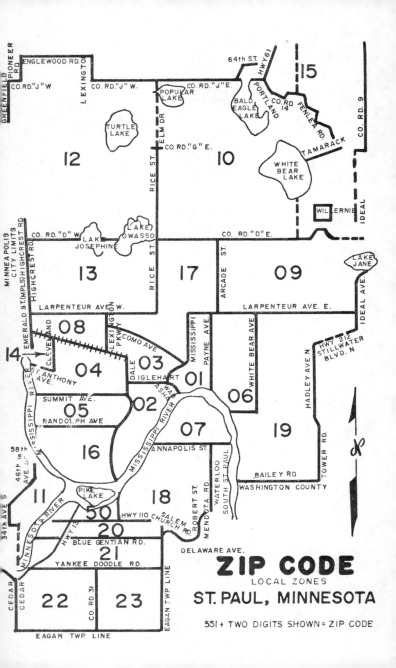

ZIP CODE
LOCAL ZONES
ST. PAUL, MINNESOTA

551 + TWO DIGITS SHOWN = ZIP CODE

Coles, R. Br. Gloster 39639
College, Sta. Columbus..........39701
Collins 39428
Collinsville 39325
Colonial, Sta. Jackson...........39211
Columbia (1st) 39429
Columbus (1st) 39701
Columbus A F B, Br.
　　Columbus.......................39701
Como 38619
Conehatta 39057
Corinth (1st)..........................38834
Courtland...............................38620
Crawford................................39743
Crenshaw...............................38621
Crosby....................................39633
Crossroads, Sta. Greenville...38701
Crowder 38622
Cruger....................................38924
Crystal Springs (1st).............39059
Cuevas, R. Br. Pass
　　Christian..........................39571
D'Iberville, Sta. Biloxi............39532
D'Lo 39062
Daleville.................................39326
Darling...................................38623
Darlove..................................38734
De Kalb..................................39328
De Lisle, R. Br. Pass
　　Christian..........................39571
De Soto, R. Br. Shubuta 39360
Decatur..................................39327
Delta City 39061
Delta Drive, Sta. Jackson......39213
Delta State College, Sta.
　　Cleveland.........................38732
Dennis 38838
Derma 38839
Doddsville..............................38736
Drew 38737
　　Parchman, R. Br..............38738
Dublin 38739
Duck Hill................................38925
Dumas....................................38625
Duncan...................................38740
Dundee...................................38626
Durant....................................39063
Eastabuchie...........................39436
Eastlawn, Sta. Pascagoula....39567
Ebenezer................................39064
Ecru.......................................38841
Eddiceton, R. Br. Mc Call
　　Creek...............................39634
Eden, R. Br. Yazoo City.........39065
Edinburg, R. Br. Carthage......39051
Edwards.................................39066
Egypt, R. Br. Okolona............38842
Electric Mills 39329
Elizabeth................................38742
Elliott, R. Br. Grenada..........38926
Ellisville.................................39437
Enid.......................................38927
Enterprise..............................39330
Escatawpa..............................39552
Ethel......................................39067
Etta..38627
Eupora...................................39744
Evergreen, Sta. Gulfport........39501
Fairlane, Sta. Columbus 39701
Falcon, R. Br. Sledge............38628
Falkner...................................38629
Farmington, R. Br. Corinth 38834
Farrell, R. Br. Clarksdale.......38630

Fayette...................................39069
Fernwood 39635
Fitler.....................................39070
Flora......................................39071
　　Pocahontas, R. Br...........39072
Florence.................................39073
Fondren, Sta. Jackson...........39216
Forest (1st)............................39074
Forkville.................................39076
Fort Adams............................39636
Foxworth................................39483
French Camp..........................39745
Friars Point............................38631
Fruitland Park 39438
Fulton (1st)............................38843
Gallman.................................39077
Gattman.................................38844
Gautier...................................39553
Georgetown............................39078
Gholson.................................39331
Gibson, R. Br. Aberdeen........39730
Glen 38846
Glen Allan..............................38744
Glendora................................38928
Gloster...................................39638
　　Coles, R. Br....................39639
Golden...................................38847
Goodman................................39079
Gore Springs..........................38929
Grace.....................................38745
Greenville (1st).......................38701
　　Crossroads, Sta...............38701
　　Winterville, R. Br............38782
Greenwood (1st).....................39930
Greenwood Springs.................39848
Grenada (1st).........................38901
　　Elliott, R. Br..................38926
Gulfport (1st).........................39501
Gunnison................................38746
Guntown.................................38849
Hamburg, R. Br. Roxie...........39661
Hamilton.................................39746
Handsboro, Sta. Gulfport 39501
Harperville.............................39080
Harriston................................39081
Harrisville...............................39082
Hatley, R. Br. Amory..............38821
Hattiesburg (1st).....................39401
Hazlehurst (1st)......................39083
Heidelberg..............................39439
Hermanville............................39086
Hernando (1st)........................38632
Hickory...................................39332
Hickory Flat 38633
Hillhouse................................38747
Hillsboro.................................39087
Hiwannee...............................39333
Holcomb.................................38940
Hollandale..............................38748
Holly Bluff..............................39088
Holly Ridge.............................38749
Holly Springs (1st)..................38635
　　Mount Pleasant, R. Br.....38649
Homewood.............................39089
Horn Lake...............................38637
Houlka...................................38850
Houston (1st) 38851
Hurley....................................39555
Independence.........................38638
Indianola (1st)........................38751
Inverness................................38753
Isola.......................................38754
Itta Bena................................38941

Iuka (1st) 38852
JACKSON (1st) (see
　　appendix)
Jayess....................................39641
Johns, R. Br. Brandon............39042
Johnstons Station 39642
Jonestown..............................38639
Keesler A F B, Sta. Biloxi.......39534
Kilmichael..............................39747
Kiln 39556
Kokomo..................................39643
Kosciusko (1st)......................39090
Kossuth, R. Br. Corinth..........38834
Kreole, Sta. Moss Point..........39563
Lafayette Springs 38640
Lake.......................................39092
Lake Cormorant......................38641
Lakeshore..............................39558
Lamar.....................................38642
Lambert..................................38643
Lamont...................................38755
Lauderdale.............................39335
Laurel (1st)............................39440
Lawrence................................39336
Le Flore.................................38942
Le Tourneau, R. Br.
　　Vicksburg.........................39180-
Leaf.......................................39450
Leakesville.............................39451
Learned..................................39093
Leavell Woods, Sta. Jackson...39212
Leland (1st)............................38756
　　Tralake, R. Br..................38757
Lena.......................................39094
Lexington................................39095
Liberty....................................39645
Little Rock..............................39337
Long Beach (1st) 39560
Longview, R. Br. Starkville.....39749
Lorman...................................39096
Louin.....................................39338
Louise....................................39097
Louisville (1st)........................39339
Lucedale (1st).........................39452
　　Agricola, R. Br................39452
　　Bexley, R. Br...................39453
Ludlow....................................39098
Lula.......................................38644
Lumberton..............................39455
Lyman, R. Br. Gulfport...........39501
Lyon.......................................38645
Maben....................................39750
Macon (1st)............................39341
Madden..................................39109
Madison..................................39110
Magee (1st) 39111
　　Sanitorium, Br................39112
Magnolia................................39652
Mantachie..............................38855
Mantee...................................39751
Marietta.................................38856
Marion....................................39342
Marks.....................................38646
Mary Holmes, R. Br. West
　　Point...............................39773
Matherville, R. Br. Shubuta ...39360
Mathiston...............................39752
Mattson..................................38758
Mayersville.............................39113
Mayhew..................................39753
Mc Adams..............................39107
Mc Call Creek.........................39647
　　Eddiceton, R. Br.............39634

Mc Carley 38943
Mc Comb (1st) 39648
Mc Condy 38854
Mc Cool 39108
Mc Henry 39561
Mc Lain 39456
Mc Laurin, R. Br.
  Hattiesburg 39401
Mc Neill 39457
Mc Willie, Sta. Jackson 39206
Meadville 39653
Mendenhall 39114
Meridian (1st) 39301
Merigold 38759
Metcalfe 38760
Michigan City 38647
Midnight 39115
Mineral Wells 38648
Minter City 38944
Miss Valley State College, R.
  Br. Itta Bena 38941
Mississippi City, Sta.
  Gulfport 39501
Mississippi College, Br.
  Clinton 39058
Mize 39116
Money 38945
Monticello 39654
Montpelier 39754
Montrose 39343
Mooreville 38857
Moorhead 38761
Morgan City 38946
Morgantown 39484
Morton 39117
  Polkville, R. Br. 39118
Moselle 39459
Moss 39460
Moss Point (1st) 39563
Mound Bayou 38762
Mount Olive 39119
Mount Pleasant, R. Br. Holly
  Springs 38649
Myrtle 38650
Natchez (1st) 39120
Naval Air Station, Br.
  Meridian 39301
Neely 39461
Nesbit 38651
Neshoba 39344
Nettleton 38858
New Albany (1st) 38652
New Augusta 39462
New Site 38859
Newhebron 39140
Newton (1st) 39345
Nicholson 39463
Nitta Yuma 38763
North, Sta. Jackson 39206
North, Sta. Meridian 39301
North Carrollton 38947
Northwest Jr College, Sta.
  Senatobia 38668
Norwood Village, R. Br.
  Gulfport 39501
Noxapater 39346
Oak Vale 39656
Oakland 38948
Ocean Springs (1st) 39564
Ofahoma 39141
Okolona (1st) 38860
  Egypt, R. Br. 38842
Olive Branch 38654

Oma 39142
Onward 39143
Osyka 39657
Ovett 39464
Oxford (1st) 38655
Pace 38764
Pachuta 39347
Palmers Crossing, R. Br.
  Hattiesburg 39401
Panther Burn 38765
Parchman, R. Br. Drew 38738
Paris 38949
Pascagoula (1st) 39567
Pass Christian (1st) 39571
Pattison 39144
Paulding 39348
Paulette 39349
Pearl, Br. Jackson 39208
Pearlington 39572
Pelahatchie 39145
Percy, R. Br. Hollandale 38748
Perkinston 39573
Petal 39465
Pheba 39755
Philadelphia (1st) 39350
Philipp 38950
Picayune (1st) 39466
Pickens 39146
Pinckneyville 39658
Piney Woods 39148
Pinola 39149
Pittsboro 38951
Plain, R. Br. Jackson 39218
Plantersville 38862
Pocahontas, R. Br. Flora 39072
Polkville, R. Br. Morton 39118
Pontotoc (1st) 38863
Pope 38658
Poplarville (1st) 39470
Port Gibson 39150
Porterville 39352
Potts Camp 38659
Prairie 39756
Prairie Point 39353
Prentiss 39474
Preston 39354
Prichard, R. Br. Tunica 38660
Puckett 39151
Pulaski 39152
Purvis 39475
Quentin 39660
Quitman 39355
Raleigh 39153
Randolph 38864
Raymond 39154
Red Banks 38661
Redwood 39156
Reform 39757
Rena Lara 38767
Rich 38662
Richton 39476
Ridgeland 39157
Rienzi 38865
Ripley (1st) 38663
Robinsonville 38664
Rolling Fork 39159
Rome 38768
Rose Hill 39356
Rosedale 38769
Roxie 39661
Ruleville 38771
Russell 39357
Ruth 39662

Sallis 39160
Saltillo 38866
Sandersville 39477
Sandhill 39161
Sandy Hook 39478
Sanford, R. Br. Seminary 39479
Sanitorium, Br. Magee 39112
Sarah 38665
Sardis 38666
Sarepta 38867
Satartia 39162
Saucier 39574
Savage 38667
Schlater 38952
Scobey 38953
Scooba 39358
Scott 38772
Sebastopol 39359
Seminary 39479
Senatobia (1st) 38668
Sessums 39758
Shannon 38868
Sharon 39163
Shaw 38773
Shelby 38774
Sherard 38669
Sherman 38869
Shivers 39164
Shubuta 39360
Shuqualak 39361
Sibley 39165
Sidon 38954
Silver City 39166
Silver Creek 39663
Skene 38775
Slate Spring, R. Br. Calhoun
  City 38955
Sledge 38670
  Falcon, R. Br. 38628
Smithdale 39664
Smithville 38870
Sontag 39665
Soso 39480
Southaven 38671
Southern, Sta. Hattiesburg 39401
Star 39167
Starkville (1st) 39759
  Longview, R. Br. 39749
State College (1st) 39762
State Line 39362
Steens 39766
Stewart 39767
Stoneville 38776
Stonewall 39363
Stovall 38672
Stringer 39481
Stringtown, R. Br. Benoit 38777
Sturgis 39769
Summit 39666
Sumner 38957
Sumrall 39482
Sunflower 38778
  Blaine, R. Br. 38727
Swan Lake 38958
Swiftown 38959
Sylvarena, R. Br. Raleigh 39153
Taylor 38673
Taylorsville (1st) 39168
Tchula 39169
Terry 39170
Thaxton 38871
The Mall, Sta. Vicksburg 39180
Thomastown 39171

Thornton	39172
Tie Plant	38960
Tillatoba	38961
Tinsley	39173
Tiplersville	38674
Tippo	38962
Tishomingo	38873
Toccopola	38874
Tomnolen	39770
Toomsuba	39364
Tougaloo	39174
Tralake, R. Br. Leland	38757
Trebloc	38875
Tremont	38876
Triangle Hospital, Sta. Biloxi	39530
Tribbett	38779
Tula	38675
Tunica	38676
Prichard, R. Br.	38660
Tupelo (1st)	38801
Tutwiler	38963
Tylertown	39667
U S Naval Construction Batt, Sta. Gulfport	39501
Union	39365
Union Church	39668

Utica Junior College, R. Br. Utica	39175
Vaiden	39176
Valley Park	39177
Value, R. Br. Brandon	39178
Van Vleet	38877
Vance	38964
Vancleave, R. Br. Ocean Springs	39564
Vardaman	38878
Vaughan	39179
Verona	38879
Veterans Administration Cent, Sta. Biloxi	39531
Vicksburg (1st)	39180
Victoria	38679
Vossburg	39366
Wade, R. Br. Pascagoula	39575
Walls (1st)	38680
Walnut	38683
Chalybeate, R. Br.	38684
Walnut Grove	39189
Walthall	39771
Washington	39190
Water Valley (1st)	38965
Waterford	38685
Waveland	39576

Waynesboro (1st)	39367
Wayside	38780
Webb	38966
Weir	39772
Wenasoga	38886
Wesson	39191
West	39192
West, Sta. Meridian	39301
West Biloxi, Sta. Biloxi	39531
West Jackson, Sta. Jackson (see appendix)	
West Point (1st)	39773
West Union, R. Br. Myrtle	38650
Westland, Sta. Jackson	39209
Wheeler	38880
Whitfield	39193
Wiggins	39577
Bond, R. Br.	39550
Willis Heights, Sta. Tupelo	38801
Winona (1st)	38967
Winstonville	38781
Winterville, R. Br. Greenville	38782
Woodland	39776
Woodville	39669
Woolmarket, R. Br. Biloxi	39532
Yazoo City (1st)	39194
Eden, R. Br.	39065

BILOXI 395

POST OFFICE BOXES

Box Nos.

1-1209	Main Office	33
K65-K299	Keesler Afb Station	34
4001-4597	West Biloxi Sta	31

RURAL ROUTES

1,2,3,4,5,6	32

STATIONS, BRANCHES AND UNITS

D'Iberville Sta	32
Keesler A F B Sta	34
Triangle Hospital Sta	30
Veterans Administration CentSta	31
West Biloxi Sta	31
Woolmarket Rural Br	32
General Delivery	30
Postmaster	30

JACKSON 392

POST OFFICE BOXES

Box Nos.

1-2500	Main Office	05
2501-4198	West Jackson Sta	07
4201-5047	Fondren Sta	16

5501-6127	Pearl Br	08
6501-7000	Leavell Woods Sta	12
8001-8999	Battlefield Sta	04
9561-10194	North	06
10201-10995	Westland Sta	09
11001-11297	Delta Drive Sta	13
12001-13000	Colonial Sta	11
15001-16000	A Sta	10
16001-16500	Mc Willie	06
17001-19000	Station C	17

RURAL ROUTES

1,2	09
3	13
4	08
5	12
6	08

STATIONS, BRANCHES AND UNITS

Apple Ridge Sta	04
Battlefield Sta	04
Candlestick Br	12
Colonial Sta	11
Delta Drive Sta	13
Fondren Sta	16
Leavell Woods Sta	12
Mc Willie Sta	06
North Sta	06
Pearl Br	08
Plain Rural Br	18
West Jackson Sta	03
Westland Sta	09
General Delivery	05
Postmaster	05

APARTMENTS, HOTELS, MOTELS

Camelot Apartments, 2840 Robinson Road	09
Canton Road Manor, 4911 Old Canton Rd	11
Capitol, 1315 W Capitol	03
Chateau, 1576 W Capitol	03
De Ville, 700 N Jefferson	02
Downtowner, 225 E Capitol	01
Hallmark, 987 E Northside Dr	06
Heidelberg, 131 E Capitol	01
Hylan Garden, 1297 Whitfield Mill Rd	03
Lakeland, 760 Lakeland Dr	16
Magnolia Towers Apts, 809 N State	01
Park Towne, 3895 Northview Dr	06
Park Hill, 624 Ellis Ave	09
Raymond Garden, 386 Raymond Rd	04
Sterling Towers Apts, 170 E Griffith	02
Sun N Sand, 401 N Lamar	01
University, 707 Lakeland Dr	16
Vieux Carre Apts, 3961 Hwy 55, N	16

BUILDINGS

Bankers Trust-Plaza, 120 N Congress	01
Barnett, 200 S President	01
Court Square South, 429 Tombigbee	01
Deposit Guaranty Bank, 200 E Capitol	01

Jackson (Con.)　　　　392

East Amite, 145 E Amite	01
Eight O Two, 802 N State	01
Electric, 126 S West	01
Federal, 245 E Capitol	01
First Federal Savings & Loan, 525 E Capitol	01
First National Bank, 248 E Capitol	01
Gale, 126 S President	01
Hinds Professional, 1815 Hospital Dr	04
Lamar Life Insurance, 317 E Capitol	01
Magnolia State Savings & Loan, 202 N Congress	01
Medical Arts, 1151 N State	01
Medical Towers, 440 E Woodrow Wilson	16
Milner, 210 S Lamar	01

Mississippi Farm Bureau, 429 Mississippi	01
Morgan, 3100 Old Canton Rd	06
Petroleum, 200 E Pascagoula	01
Primos Fondren, 603 Duling	16
Primos, 414 N State	01
Six Fifty Six, 656 N State	01
Southern Farm Bureau, 501 E Amite	01
Standard Life, 127 S Roach	01
Three O One, 301 N Lamar	02
Two O Three 203 W Capitol	01
Two Thirty Six, 236 E Capitol	01
University Plaza, 500 E Woodrow Wilson	16
Woolfolk State Office, 501 N West	01

HOSPITALS

Baptist, 1190 N State	01
Doctors, 2949 University Dr	16
Hinds General, 1850 Chadwick Dr	04
Saint Dominic'S, 969 Lakeland Dr	16
University Medical Center, 2500 N State	16
Veterans Administration, 1500 E Woodrow Wilson Ave	16

UNIVERSITIES AND COLLEGES

Belhaven, 1500 Peachtree	02
Jackson State, 1325 Lynch	03
Millsaps, 1701 N State	02
University Medical Center, 2500 N State	16

MISSOURI　　　　　　　　　　　　　　　**State List of Post Offices**

MISSOURI
(Abbreviation: MO)

Adrian	64720
Advance	63730
Affton, Br. Saint Louis	63123
Agency	64401
Alba	64830
Albany (1st)	64402
Aldrich	65601
Alexandria	63430
Allendale	64420
Allenton	63001
Allenville, R. Br. Chaffee	63741
Alley Spring	65431
Alma	64001
Altamont	64620
Altenburg	63732
Alton	65606
Amazonia	64421
Amity	64422
Amoret	64722
Amsterdam	64723
Anabel	63431
Anderson	64831
Annada	63330
Annapolis	63620
Anniston	63820
Antioch, Sta. Kansas City (see appendix)	
Antonia, R. Br. Imperial	63052
Appleton City	64724
Arab	63733
Arbela	63432
Granger, R. Br.	63442
Arbyrd	63821
Arcadia	63621
Archie	64725
Arcola	65603
Argyle	65001
Armstrong	65230
Arnold (1st)	63010
Arrow Rock	65320
Asbury	64832
Ash Grove	65604

Ashburn	63433
Ashland	65010
Atherton, R. Br. Independence	64050
Atlanta	63530
Augusta	63332
Aurora (1st)	65605
Jenkins, R. Br.	65677
Auxvasse	65231
Ava	65608
Avalon	64621
Avilla	64833
Avondale	64010
Baden, Sta. Saint Louis	63147
Bakersfield	65609
Ballwin (1st)	63011
Baring	63531
Barnard	64423
Barnett	65011
Barnhart	63012
Bates City	64011
Bay, R. Br. Hermann	65041
Beaufort	63013
Belgrade	63622
Bell City	63735
Belle	65013
Belleview	63623
Bellflower	63333
Belton (1st)	64012
Bendavis	65433
Benton	63736
Benton City	65232
Benton Park, Sta. Saint Louis (see appendix)	
Berger	63014
Berkeley, Br. Saint Louis	63134
Bernie	63822
Berryman	65445
Bertrand	63823
Bethany (1st)	64424
Bethel	63434
Beulah	65436
Bevier	63532
Bigelow	64425
Billings	65610

Birch Tree	65438
Thomasville, R. Br.	65578
Bismarck	63624
Bixby	65439
Black	63625
Blackburn	65321
Blackwater	65322
Blackwell	63626
Blairstown	64726
Bland	65014
Mount Sterling, R. Br.	65062
Blodgett	63824
Bloomfield	63825
Bloomsdale	63627
Blue Eye	65611
Blue Springs (1st)	64015
Blythedale	64426
Bogard	64622
Bois D Arc	65612
Bolckow	64427
Bolivar (1st)	65613
Bonne Terre (1st)	63628
Bonnots Mill	65016
Boonville (1st)	65233
Boss	65440
Boston	64727
Bosworth	64623
Bourbon	65441
Bowling Green (1st)	63334
Cyrene, R. Br.	63340
Bradleyville	65614
Bragg City	63827
Braggadocio	63826
Brandsville	65688
Branson (1st)	65616
Brashear	63533
Braymer	64624
Brazeau	63737
Breckenridge	64625
Bremen, Sta. Saint Louis	63160
Brentwood, Br. Saint Louis	63144
Briar	63931
Bridgeton, Br. Hazelwood	63044
Brighton	65617
Brimson	64626

Brinktown 65443
Brixey 65618
Broadway, Sta. Saint Louis....63147
Bronaugh 64728
Brookfield (1st) 64628
Brookline Station 65619
Broseley 63932
Brownbranch, R. Br. Ava 65608
Browning 64630
Brownington 64729
Brownwood 63738
Brumley 65017
Bruner 65620
Brunswick 65236
Bucklin 64631
Buckner 64016
Bucyrus 65444
Buell, R. Br. Montgomery
    City 63361
Buffalo 65622
Bunceton 65237
Bunker 63629
Burfordville 63739
Burlington Junction 64428
Butler (1st) 64730
Butterfield, R. Br. Cassville.....65623
Bynumville, R. Br. Salisbury.....65238
Cabanne, Sta. Saint Louis........63161
Cabool 65689
Cadet 63630
Cainsville 64632
Cairo 65239
Caledonia 63631
Calhoun 65323
California (1st) 65018
Callao 63534
Camden 64017
Camden Point 64018
Camdenton (1st) 65020
Cameron (1st) 64429
Campbell 63933
Canalou 63828
Canton 63435
Cape Fair 65624
Cape Girardeau (1st) 63701
Caplinger Mills 65607
Cardwell 63829
Carl Junction 64834
Carondelet, Sta. Saint Louis.....63111
Carr, Sta. Florissant 63031
Carrollton (1st) 64633
Carterville 64835
Carthage (1st) 64836
Caruthersville (1st) 63830
Cascade 63632
Cassville (1st) 65625
    Butterfield, R. Br. 65623
Catawissa 63015
Catron 63833
Caulfield 65626
Cedar City 65022
Cedar Hill 63016
Cedarcreek 65627
Center 63436
Centertown 65023
Centerview 64019
Centerville 63633
    Corridon, R. Br. 63635
Central, Sta. Saint Louis
    (see appendix)
Central, Sta. Kansas City
    (see appendix)
Centralia (1st) 65240

Centropolis, Sta. Kansas
    City 64126
Chadwick 65629
Chaffee 63740
    Allenville, R. Br. 63741
Chamois 65024
Charles Nagel, Sta. Saint
    Louis (see appendix)
Charleston (1st) 63834
Cherryville 65446
Chesterfield (1st) 63017
Chestnutridge 65630
Chilhowee 64733
Chillicothe (1st) 64601
Chouteau, Sta. Saint Louis.....63110
Christian Bechtold, Sta.
    Saint Louis 63118
Chula 64635
Civic Center, Sta. Kansas
    City 64106
Clara 65447
Clarence 63437
Clark 65243
Clarksburg 65025
Clarksdale 64430
Clarksville 63336
Clarkton 63837
Claycomo, Br. Kansas City.....64119
Clayton, Br. Saint Louis.....63105
Clearmont 64431
Clearwater 63634
Cleveland 64734
Clever 65631
Clifton Hill 65244
Climax Springs 65324
Clinton (1st) 64735
Clubb, R. Br. Piedmont 63934
Clyde 64432
Coatsville 63555
Coffey 64636
Coldwater, R. Br. Piedmont 63934
Cole Camp 65325
College Mound, R. Br.
    Excello 65245
Collins 64738
Columbia (1st) 65201
Commerce 63742
Commerce Tower, Sta.
    Kansas City 64199
Commercial, Sta.
    Springfield 65803
Conception 64433
Conception Junction 64434
Conclay, Br. Saint Louis 63124
Concordia 64020
Conran 63838
Conway 65632
Cook Station 65449
Cooter 63839
Corder 64021
Corning, R. Br. Craig 64435
Corridon, R. Br. Centerville.....63635
Corso 63337
Cosby 64436
Cottleville 63338
Couch 65690
Country Club, Sta. Kansas
    City 64113
Courtois 65451
Cowgill 64637
Craig 64437
    Corning, R. Br. 64435
Crane 65633

Creighton 64739
Crescent, R. Br. Eureka 63018
Creve Coeur, Br. Saint Louis ...63141
Crocker 65452
Cross Timbers 65634
Crystal City (1st) 63019
Cuba (1st) 65453
Curryville 63339
Cyrene, R. Br. Bowling
    Green 63340
Dadeville 65635
Daisy 63743
Dalton 65246
Darlington 64438
Davisville 64556
Dawn 64638
De Kalb 64440
De Soto (1st) 63020
De Witt 64639
Dearborn 64439
Deepwater 64740
Deerfield 64741
Deering 63840
Defiance 63341
Delta 63744
Denver 64441
Des Arc 63636
Des Peres, Br. Saint Louis 63131
Desloge, Br. Flat River 63601
Devils Elbow 65457
Dexter (1st) 63841
Diamond 64840
Diehlstadt, R. Br.
    Charleston 63834
Diggins 65636
Dillard 65458
Dittmer 63023
Dixon 65459
Doe Run 63637
Doniphan (1st) 63935
Dora 65637
Dorena 63844
Dover 64022
Downing 63536
Drexel 64742
Drury 65638
Dudley 63936
Duenweg 64841
Dugginsville 65639
Duke 65461
Dunnegan 65640
Durham 63438
Dutchtown 63745
Dutzow 63342
Eagle Rock 65641
Eagleville 64442
East Lynne 64743
East Prairie 63845
Easton 64443
Edgar Springs 65462
Edgerton 64444
Edina 63537
Edwards 65326
El Dorado Springs (1st) 64744
Eldon (1st) 65026
Eldridge 65463
Elijal 65642
Elk Creek 65464
Elkhead, R. Br. Sparta 65753
Elkland 65644
Ellington 63638
    Sweetwater, R. Br. 63680
Ellis Prairie 65465

Ellisville, Br. Ballwin............63011
Ellsinore.................................63937
Elmer.....................................63538
Elmo......................................64445
Elsberry.................................63343
Elvins, Br. Flat River.............63639
Emden....................................63439
Eminence...............................65466
   Round Spring, R. Br..........65467
Emma.....................................65327
Englewood, Sta.
   Independence...................64052
Eolia......................................63344
Essex.....................................63846
Ethel......................................63539
Etterville................................65031
Eudora, R. Br. Morrisville......65645
Eugene...................................65032
Eunice....................................65468
Eureka (1st)...........................63025
   Crescent, R. Br.................63018
Everton...................................65646
Ewing.....................................63440
Excello...................................65247
   College Mound, R. Br........65245
Excelsior Springs (1st)...........64024
Exeter....................................65647
Fagus.....................................63938
Fair Grove..............................65648
Fair Play.................................65649
Fairdealing.............................63939
Fairfax...................................64446
Fairgrounds, Sta. Saint
   Louis.................................63107
Fairleigh, Sta. Saint Joseph....64506
Fairmount, Sta.
   Independence..................64053
Fairport, R. Br. Maysville......64447
Fairview..................................64842
Falcon....................................65470
   Nebo, R. Br.......................65471
Farber.....................................63345
Farley.....................................64028
Farmington (1st).....................63640
Farrar.....................................63746
Faucett...................................64448
Fayette...................................65248
Federal Reserve, Sta.
   Kansas City.......................64198
Fenton (1st)............................63026
Ferguson, Br. Saint Louis.......63135
Ferrelview, R. Br. Kansas
   City...................................64163
Festus (1st)............................63028
Field, Sta. Saint Louis............63108
Fillmore..................................64449
Fisk..63940
Flat River (1st).......................63601
   Desloge, Br.......................63601
   Elvins, Br..........................63639
   Frankclay, R. Br................63644
   Leadwood, R. Br................63653
Flemington.............................65650
Fletcher..................................63030
Flinthill..................................63346
Florence.................................65329
FLORISSANT (1st) (see
   appendix)
Foley......................................63347
Forbes....................................64450
Fordland.................................65652
Forest City..............................64451
   Fortescue, R. Br...............64452

Forest Green, R. Br.
   Salisbury..........................65249
Foristell..................................63348
Forsyth...................................65653
   Hilda, R. Br.......................65670
Fort Leonard Wood (1st)........65473
Fortescue, R. Br. Forest City..64452
Fortuna...................................65034
Foster.....................................64745
Frankclay, R. Br. Flat River....63644
Frankford................................63441
Franklin..................................62250
Fredericktown (1st)................63645
Freeburg.................................65035
Freeman.................................64746
Freistatt.................................65654
Fremont..................................63941
French Village.........................63036
Friedheim...............................63747
Fristoe, R. Br. Warsaw...........65356
Frohna...................................63748
Fulton (1st)............................65251
Gainesville.............................65655
   Howards Ridge, R. Br........65673
Galena....................................65656
Gallatin..................................64640
Galt..64641
Garden City............................64747
Gardner, Sta. Saint Louis........63109
Garrison..................................65657
Gasconade..............................65036
Gashland, Sta. Kansas City......64118
Gatewood...............................63942
Gentry....................................64453
Gerald....................................63037
Gibbs.....................................63540
Gibson....................................63847
Gideon....................................63848
Gilliam...................................65330
Gilman City.............................64642
Gipsy.....................................63750
Gladden..................................65478
Gladstone, Br. Kansas City
   (see appendix)
Glasgow..................................65254
Glenallen................................63751
Glencoe..................................63038
Glendale, Br. Saint Louis........63122
Glenstone, Sta. Springfield.....65804
Glenwood...............................63541
Glover....................................63646
Gobler....................................63849
Golden....................................65658
Golden City.............................64748
Goldsberry.............................63542
Goodman................................64843
Goodson.................................65659
Gordonville.............................63752
Gorin......................................63543
Gower.....................................64454
Graff.......................................65660
Graham...................................64455
Grain Valley............................64029
Granby....................................64844
Grand Pass.............................65331
Grandin...................................63943
Grandview (1st).......................64030
Granger, R. Br. Arbela............63442
Graniteville, R. Br. Ironton......63650
Grant City...............................64456
Grassy....................................63754
Gravois, Sta. Saint Louis........63116
Gravois Mills...........................65037

Laurie, R. Br..........................65038
Gray Summit...........................63039
Grayridge................................63850
Green Castle...........................63544
Green City...............................63545
Green Ridge............................65332
Greenfield...............................65661
Greentop.................................63546
Greenville...............................63944
Greenwood..............................64034
Grover....................................63040
Grovespring............................65662
Grubville.................................63041
Guilford..................................64457
Hale.......................................64643
Half Way.................................65663
Hallsville................................65255
Halltown.................................65664
Hamilton.................................64644
   Nettleton, R. Br................64666
Hammond................................65665
Hannibal (1st).........................63401
Hardenville.............................65666
Hardin....................................64035
Harding, Sta. Kansas City.......64111
Harris.....................................64645
Harrisburg..............................65256
Harrisonville (1st)...................64701
Hartsburg...............................65039
Hartshorn................................65479
Hartville.................................65667
Harvester, R. Br. Saint
   Charles..............................63303
Harviell...................................63945
Harwood.................................64750
Hatfield..................................64458
Hawk Point.............................63349
Hayti......................................63851
HAZELWOOD (1st) (see
   appendix)
Helena....................................64459
Hematite.................................63047
Hemple, R. Br. Stewartsville....64460
Hendrickson, R. Br. Poplar
   Bluff..................................63946
Henley....................................65040
Henrietta................................64036
Herculaneum...........................63048
Hermann (1st).........................65041
   Bay, R. Br........................65041
   Mc Kittrick, R. Br..............65056
Hermitage...............................65668
Hickman Mills, Sta. Kansas
   City (see appendix)
Higbee....................................65257
Higginsville (1st).....................64037
High Hill.................................63350
High Point...............................65042
High Ridge..............................63049
Highlandville...........................65669
Hilda, R. Br. Forsyth...............65670
Hillsboro (1st).........................63050
Hiram.....................................63947
Hocomo..................................65691
Holcomb..................................63852
Holden....................................64040
Holland...................................63853
Holliday..................................65258
Hollister.................................65672
Hollywood...............................63854
Holt..64048
Holts Summit..........................65043

Hope, R. Br. Morrison...........65044
Hopewell, R. Br. Mineral
  Point.............................63660
Hopkins...............................64461
Hornersville.........................63855
Horton................................64751
House Springs.......................63051
Houston..............................65483
Houstonia............................65333
Howards Ridge, R. Br.
  Gainesville......................65673
Howardville, R. Br. New
  Madrid............................63869
Huggins...............................65484
Hughesville...........................65334
Humansville..........................65574
Hume.................................64752
Humphreys...........................64646
Hunnewell............................63443
Hunter................................63948
Huntsville.............................65259
Hurdland..............................63547
Hurley.................................65675
Iantha.................................64753
Iberia.................................65486
Illmo.................................63754
Imperial..............................63052
INDEPENDENCE (1st) (see
  appendix)
Inza, Sta. Saint Joseph...........64508
Ionia..................................65335
Iron Mountain.......................63649
Irondale..............................63648
Ironton...............................63650
Irwin..................................64754
Isabella...............................65676
Jackson (1st)........................63755
Jacksonville..........................65260
Jadwin...............................65501
James Crews, Sta. Kansas
  City................................64108
Jameson..............................64647
Jamesport............................64648
Jamestown...........................65046
Jane, R. Br. Pineville..............64846
Jasper................................64755
Jefferson City (1st)................65101
Jefferson Memorial, Sta.
  Saint Louis.....................63102
Jenkins, R. Br. Aurora.............65677
Jennings, Br. Saint Louis..........63136
Jerico Springs.......................64756
Jerome...............................65529
Jesse James Territory, R. Br.
  Sullivan..........................63080
Jonesburg............................63351
Joplin (1st)..........................64801
Jordan W Chambers, Sta.
  Saint Louis.....................63106
Kahoka...............................63445
  Medill, R. Br....................63455
Kaiser................................65047
KANSAS CITY (1st) (see
  appendix)
Kearney..............................64060
Kelso.................................63758
Keltner...............................65678
Kennett (1st)........................63857
Kenoma, R. Br. Lamar.............64759
Kersey Coates, Sta. Kansas
  City................................64105
Kewanee.............................63860

Keytesville...........................65261
Kidder................................64649
Kimberling City, R. Br.
  Reeds Spring....................65686
Kimmswick...........................63053
Kinder, R. Br. Puxico..............63759
King City.............................64463
Kingdom City........................65262
Kingston.............................64650
Kingsville.............................64061
Kinloch, Br. Saint Louis...........63140
Kirbyville.............................65679
Kirksville (1st)......................63501
Kirkwood, Br. Saint Louis
  (see appendix)
Kissee Mills..........................65680
Knob Lick............................63651
Knob Noster.........................65336
Knox City.............................63446
Koch..................................63054
Koeltztown...........................65048
Koshkonong..........................65692
La Belle..............................63447
La Due...............................64758
La Grange............................63448
La Monte.............................65337
La Plata..............................63549
  South Gifford, R. Br...........63564
La Russell............................64848
Labadie...............................63055
Laclede...............................64651
Laddonia.............................63352
Lake Lotawana, R. Br. Lees
  Summit...........................64063
Lake Ozark (1st)....................65049
Lake Sherwood, R. Br.
  Marthasville.....................63357
Lake Spring..........................65532
Lamar (1st)..........................64759
Lambert Airport, Br. Saint
  Louis..............................63145
Lampe................................65681
Lanagan..............................64847
Lancaster.............................63548
Langdon, R. Br. Rock Port........64464
Lanton, R. Br. Thayer..............65792
Laquey...............................65534
Laredo................................64652
Latham...............................65050
Lathrop...............................64465
Latour................................64760
Laurie, R. Br. Gravois Mills.......65038
Lawson...............................64062
Leadwood, R. Br. Flat River.......63653

Leasburg.............................65535
Lebanon (1st).......................65536
Lecoma...............................65540
Leeds, Sta. Kansas City...........64129
Lees Summit (1st)..................64063
Leeton................................64761
Lemay, Br. Saint Louis............63125
Lemons...............................63550
Lenox................................65541
Lentner...............................63450
Leonard..............................63451
Leopold..............................63760
Leslie.................................63056
Lesterville............................63654
Levasy................................64066
Lewistown............................63452
Lexington (1st)......................64067
Liberal................................64762

Liberty (1st).........................64068
Licking...............................65542
Liguori (1st).........................63057
Lilbourn..............................63862
Lincoln................................65338
Linn..................................65051
Linn Creek...........................65052
Linneus..............................64653
Livonia...............................63551
Lock Springs.........................64654
Lockwood.............................65682
Lodi..................................63950
Lohman...............................65053
Lone Jack............................64070
Lonedell..............................63060
Long Lane............................65590
Longrun, R. Br. Theodosia.........65684
Longview, Sta. Kansas City
  (see appendix)
Loose Creek..........................65054
Louisburg.............................65685
Louisiana (1st).......................63353
Lowndes..............................63951
Lowry City............................64763
Lucerne...............................64655
Ludlow................................64656
Luebbering...........................63061
Luray.................................63453
Lutesville.............................63762
Lynchburg.............................65543
Macks Creek.........................65786
Macomb..............................65702
Macon (1st)..........................63552
Madison..............................65263
Maitland..............................64466
Malden (1st).........................63863
Malta Bend...........................65339
Manchester, Br. Ballwin...........63011
Manes, R. Br. Mountain
  Grove.............................65703
Mansfield.............................65704
Mapaville.............................63065
Maplewood, Br. Saint Louis.......63143
Marble Hill............................63764
Marceline (1st)......................64658
Marionville...........................65705
Marquand.............................63655
Marshall (1st)........................65340
Marshfield (1st).....................65706
Marston...............................63866
Marthasville..........................63357
Martinsburg...........................65264
Martinsville...........................64467
Maryland Heights, Br.
  Hazelwood.......................63043
Maryville (1st)......................64468
Matthews.............................63867
Maysville.............................64469
  Fairport, R. Br..................64447
Mayview..............................64071
Maywood.............................63454
Mc Bride, R. Br. Perryville.......63776
Mc Clurg..............................65701
Mc Fall...............................64657
Mc Gee...............................63763
Mc Girk..............................65055
Mc Kittrick, R. Br. Hermann......65056
Meadville.............................64659
Medill, R. Br. Kahoka.............63455
Mehlville, Br. Saint Louis.........63129
Memphis..............................63555
Mendon...............................64660
Menfro...............................63765

Mercer	64661
Meta	65058
Metz	64765
Mexico (1st)	65265
Miami	65344
Middle Brook	63656
Middletown	63359
Midway, R. Br. Columbia	65201
Milan	63556
Milford	64766
Mill Grove	64662
Mill Spring	63952
Millcreek	63658
Miller	65707
Millersville	63766
Milo	64767
Mindenmines	64769
Mine La Motte	63659
Mineola, R. Br. Montgomery City	63360
Mineral Point	63660
Missouri City	64072
Moberly (1st)	65270
Mokane	65059
Monett (1st)	65708
Monroe City	63456
Montauk	65545
Montgomery City	63361
Buell, R. Br.	63361
Mineola, R. Br.	63360
Monticello	63457
Montier	65546
Montreal	65591
Montrose	64770
Moody	65777
Mooresville	64664
Mora	65345
Morehouse	63868
Morgan	65709
Morley	63767
Morrison	65061
Hope, R. Br.	65044
Morrisville	65710
Eudora, R. Br.	65645
Morse Mill	63066
Mosby	64073
Moscow Mills	63362
Moselle, R. Br. Union	63067
Mound City	64470
Moundville	64771
Mount Moriah	64665
Mount Sterling, R. Br. Bland	65062
Mount Vernon (1st)	65712
Mountain Grove (1st)	65711
Manes, R. Br.	65703
Mountain View	65548
Myrtle	65778
Napoleon	64074
Napton	65346
Nashua, Sta. Kansas City	64155
Naylor	63953
Nebo, R. Br. Falcon	65471
Neck City	64849
Neelyville	63954
Nelson	65347
Neosho (1st)	64850
Nettleton, R. Br. Hamilton	64666
Nevada (1st)	64772
New Bloomfield	65063
New Boston	63557
New Cambria	63558
New Florence	63363

New Franklin	65274
New Hamburg, R. Br. Benton	63736
New Hampton	64471
New Hartford	63364
New Haven (1st)	63068
New London	63459
New Madrid	63869
New Melle	63365
New Offenburg	63661
New Point	64472
New Wells	63768
Newark	63458
Newburg	65550
Newtonia	64853
Newtown	64667
Niangua	65713
Nixa	65714
Noble	65715
Noel	64854
Norborne	64668
Normandy, Br. Saint Louis	63121
North County, Br. Saint Louis (see appendix)	
North Kansas City, Br. Kansas City (see appendix)	
Northeast, Sta. Kansas City	64123
Northview	65716
Northwest Plaza, Sta. Saint Ann	63074
Norwood	65717
Nottinghill	65718
Novelty	63460
Novinger	63559
O'Fallon (1st)	63366
Oak Grove	64075
Oak Ridge	63769
Oakwood, Sta. Hannibal	63401
Ocie, R. Br. Theodosia	65719
Odessa (1st)	64076
Old Appleton	63770
Old Monroe	63369
Old Town, Sta. Florissant	63031
Oldfield	65720
Olean	65064
Olive, Sta. Saint Louis	63101
Olivette, Br. Saint Louis (see appendix)	
Olney	63370
Oran	63771
Oregon	64473
Oronogo	64855
Orrick	64077
Osage Beach	65065
Osborn	64474
Osceola	64776
Otterville	65348
Otto, R. Br. Imperial	63052
Overland, Br. Saint Louis	63114
Owensville	65066
Oxly	63955
Ozark	65721
Pacific (1st)	63069
Painton	63772
Palmyra	63461
Paris	65275
Parkville, Br. Kansas City (see appendix)	
Parkway, Sta. Kansas City	64130
Parma	63870
Parnell	64475
Pascola	63871

Passaic	64777
Patterson	63956
Patton	63662
Pattonsburg	64670
Paynesville	63371
Peace Valley	65788
Peach Orchard	63872
Peculiar	64078
Perkins	63774
Perry	63462
Perryville (1st)	63775
Mc Bride, R. Br.	63776
Uniontown, R. Br.	63783
Peruque, R. Br. Saint Charles	63372
Pevely	63070
Philadelphia	63463
Phillipsburg	65722
Pickering	64476
Piedmont	63957
Clubb, R. Br.	63934
Coldwater, R. Br.	63934
Pierce City	65723
Pierre Laclede, Sta. Saint Louis	63108
Pilot Grove	65276
Pilot Knob	63663
Pine	63958
Pine Lawn, Br. Saint Louis	63120
Pineville	64856
Jane, R. Br.	64846
Pittsburg	65724
Plato	65552
Platte City	64079
Plattsburg	64477
Plaza, Sta. Kansas City	64112
Plaza, Sta. Saint Louis	63199
Pleasant Hill (1st)	64080
Pleasant Hope	65725
Plevna	63464
Pocahontas	63779
Point Lookout	65726
Point Pleasant, R. Br. Portageville	63873
Polk	65727
Pollock	63560
Polo	64671
Pomona	65789
Ponce De Leon	65728
Pontiac	65729
Poplar Bluff (1st)	63901
Hendrickson, R. Br.	63946,
Portage Des Sioux	63373
Portageville	63873
Portland	65067
Potosi (1st)	63664
Pottersville	65790
Powell	65730
Powersite	65731
Powersville	64672
Poynor	63959
Prairie Home	65068
Preston	65732
Princeton	64673
Principia, Br. Saint Louis	63131
Progress, Sta. Saint Louis	63159
Protem	65733
Purcell	64857
Purdin	64674
Purdy	65734
Puxico	63960
Kinder, R. Br.	63759
Queen City	63561

Quincy.................................65735
Quitman...............................64478
Qulin...................................63961
Racine.................................64858
Ravenwood..........................64479
Raymondville........................65555
Raymore..............................64083
Raytown, Br. Kansas City
  (see appendix)
Rayville...............................64084
Rea.....................................64480
Redford...............................63665
Reeds..................................64859
Reeds Spring........................65737
Renick.................................65278
Republic..............................65738
Revere.................................63465
Reynolds..............................63666
Rhineland............................65069
Rich Hill..............................64779
Richards..............................64778
Richards Gebaur A F B, Br.
  Grandview........................64030
Richland..............................65556
Richmond (1st).....................64085
Richmond Heights, Br. Saint
  Louis...............................63117
Richwoods............................63071
Ridgedale.............................65739
Ridgeway..............................64481
Risco...................................63874
Ritchey................................64860
River Roads, Br. Saint Louis...63136
Riverside, Br. Kansas City......64168
Riverton, R. Br. Alton............65606
Rives................................63875
Roach..................................65787
Robert E Hannegan, Sta.
  Saint Louis.......................63139
Robertsville..........................63072
Roby...................................65557
Rocheport............................65279
Rock Port.............................64482
  Langdon, R. Br................64464
  Watson, R. Br..................64496
Rockaway Beach....................65740
Rockbridge...........................65741
Rockville..............................64780
  Taberville, R. Br...............64787
Rocky Comfort......................64861
Rocky Mount.........................65072
Rocky Ridge, R. Br. Sainte
  Genevieve........................63676
Rogersville...........................65742
Rolla (1st)............................65401
  Vida, R. Br.......................65581
Rombauer.............................63962
Roscoe................................64781
Rosebud...............................63091
Roselle, R. Br. Ironton............63650
Rosendale.............................64483
Rothville..............................64676
Round Spring, R. Br.
  Eminence.........................65467
Rueter.................................65744
Rush Hill..............................65280
Rushville..............................64484
Russellville...........................65074
Rutledge...............................63563
Saco....................................63669
Saginaw...............................64864

Saint Albans.........................63073
Saint Ann (1st).....................63074
Saint Catharine.....................64677
Saint Charles (1st).................63301
  Harvester, R. Br...............63303
  Peruque, R. Br.................63372
Saint Clair (1st)....................63077
Saint Elizabeth......................65075
Saint James..........................65559
Saint Johns, Br. Saint Louis....63114
SAINT JOSEPH (1st) (see
  appendix)
SAINT LOUIS (1st) (see
  appendix)
Saint Marys..........................63673
Saint Patrick.........................63466
Saint Paul, R. Br. O'Fallon......63366
Saint Peters..........................63376
Saint Robert, R. Br.
  Waynesville......................65583
Saint Thomas........................65076
Sainte Genevieve (1st)...........63670
  Rocky Ridge, R. Br...........63676
  Weingarten, R. Br.............63676
Salem (1st)...........................65560
Salisbury..............................65281
  Bynumville, R. Br.............65238
  Forest Green, R. Br...........65249
Santa Fe..............................65282
Sappington, Br. Saint Louis
  (see appendix)
Sarcoxie..............................64862
Savannah.............................64485
Saverton..............................63467
Schell City...........................64783
Scopus, R. Br. Lutesville........63762
Scott City.............................63780
Sedalia (1st).........................65301
Sedgewickville......................63781
Seligman..............................65745
Senath.................................63876
Seneca................................64865
Seymour..............................65746
Shelbina..............................63468
Shelbyville............................63469
Sheldon...............................64784
Shell Knob............................65747
  Viola, R. Br......................65748
Sheridan..............................64486
Sherman..............................63078
Shook..................................63963
Sibley..................................64088
Sikeston (1st).......................63801
Silex...................................63377
Silva...................................63964
Silver Dollar City, R. Br.
  Branson...........................65616
Skidmore.............................64487
Slater..................................65349
Smithton..............................65350
Smithville.............................64089
Snyder.................................65288
Solo....................................65564
Souder.................................65751
Soulard, Sta. Saint Louis........63157
South Fork, R. Br. West
  Plains.............................65776
South Gifford, R. Br. La
  Plata..............................63564
South Greenfield....................65752
South Mall, Sta.

Warrensburg.........................64093
South Saint Joseph (1st)........64488
South Side, Sta. Springfield
  (see appendix)
South Troost, Sta. Kansas
  City.................................64131
South West City.....................64863
Southeast, Sta. Kansas City....64132
Sparta.................................65753
Spickard..............................64679
Spokane..............................65754
SPRINGFIELD (1st) (see
  appendix)
Squires................................65755
Stanberry.............................64489
Stanton................................63079
Stark City.............................64866
State Hospital, Br.
  Farmington.......................63640
Steedman.............................65077
Steele..................................63877
Steelville..............................65565
  Viburnum, R. Br...............65566
Steffenville...........................63470
Stella..................................64867
Stet....................................64680
Stewartsville.........................64490
  Hemple, R. Br..................64460
Stockton..............................65785
Stockyards, Sta. Kansas
  City.................................64102
Stotesbury............................64786
Stotts City............................65756
Stoutland.............................65567
Stoutsville............................65283
Stover.................................65078
Strafford..............................65757
Strasburg.............................64090
Sturdivant............................63782
Sturgeon..............................65284
Success...............................65570
Sugar Creek, Br.
  Independence....................64054
Sullivan (1st)........................63080
Sulphur Springs.....................63083
Summersville........................65571
Sumner................................64681
Sunny Slope, Sta. Kansas
  City.................................64110
Sunrise Beach.......................65079
Swedeborg............................65572
Sweet Springs (1st)...............65351
Sweetwater, R. Br. Ellington....63680
Sycamore.............................65758
Syracuse..............................65354
Taberville, R. Br. Rockville......64787
Tallapoosa............................63878
Taneyville............................65759
Tarkio.................................64491
Taylor..................................63471
Tebbetts..............................65080
Tecumseh.............................65766
Teresita...............................65573
Thayer.................................65791
  Lanton, R. Br...................65792
Theodosia.............................65761
  Longrun, R. Br.................65684
  Ocie, R. Br......................65719
Thomasville, R. Br. Birch
  Tree................................65578
Thompson.............................65285

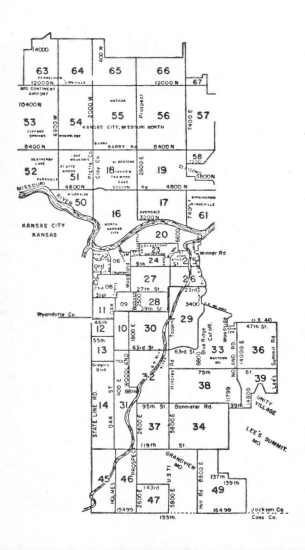

ZIP CODES
KANSAS CITY, Missouri
641 + two digits shown = zip code

Thornfield	65762
Tiff	63674
Tiff City	64868
Tina	64682
Tipton	65081
Tower Grove, Sta. Saint	
Louis	63163
Tracy	64091
Treloar	63378
Trenton (1st)	64683
Trimble	64492
Triplett	65286
Troy (1st)	63379
Truesdail, R. Br. Warrenton	63380
Truxton	63381
Tunas	65764
Turners	65765
Turney	64493
Tuscumbia	65082
Udall	65766
Ulman	65083
Union (1st)	63084
Moselle, R. Br.	63067
Union Star	64494
Uniontown, R. Br. Perryville	63783
Unionville	63565
Unity Village, Br. Lees	
Summit	64063
University City, Br. Saint	
Louis	63130
Upton	65579
Urbana	65767
Urich	64788
Utica	64686
Valles Mines	63087
Valley Park	63088
Van Buren	63965
Vandalia	63382
Vanduser	63784
Vanzant	65768
Verona	65769
Versailles	65084
Veterans Hospital, Sta.	
Kansas City	64128

Viburnum, R. Br. Steelville	65566
Vichy	65580
Vida, R. Br. Rolla	65581
Vienna	65582
Villa Ridge	63089
Village Of St Francois, R.	
Br. Farmington	63640
Viola, R. Br. Shell Knob	65748
Vista	64789
Vulcan	63675
Waco	64869
Wakenda	64687
Waldron	64092
Walker	64790
Walnut Grove	65770
Walnut Shade	65771
Wappapello	63966
Wardell	63879
Warrensburg (1st)	64093
Warrenton	63383
Truesdail, R. Br.	63380
Warsaw (1st)	65355
Fristoe, R. Br.	65356
Washburn	65772
Washington (1st)	63090
Wasola	65773
Watson, R. Br. Rock Port	64496
Waverly	64096
Wayland	63472
Waynesville (1st)	65583
Weatherby	64497
Weaubleau	65774
Webb City (1st)	64870
Webster Groves, Br. Saint	
Louis	63119
Weingarten, R. Br. Sainte	
Genevieve	63676
Wellington	64097
Wellston, Sta. Saint Louis	
(see appendix)	
Wellsville	63384
Wentworth	64873
Wentzville (1st)	63385
Wesco	65586
West Line	64791

West Plains (1st)	65775
South Fork, R. Br.	65776
Westalton	63386
Westboro	64498
Weston	64098
Westphalia	65085
Westport, Sta. Kansas City	64111
Wheatland	65779
Wheaton	64874
Wheeling	64688
Whiteman A F B, Br.	
Sedalia	65301
Whiteoak	63880
Whiteside	63387
Whitewater	63785
Willard	65781
Willhoit	65782
William M Chick, Sta.	
Kansas City	64124
Williamsburg	63388
Williamstown	63473
Williamsville	63967
Willow Springs (1st)	65793
Windsor (1st)	65360
Windyville	65783
Winfield	63389
Winigan	63566
Winona	65588
Winston	64689
Wittenberg	63786
Wolf Island	63881
Womack	63677
Wooldridge	65287
Wornall, Sta. Kansas City	
(see appendix)	
Worth	64499
Worthington	63567
Wright City	63390
Wyaconda	63474
Wyatt	63882
Wyatt Park, Sta. Saint	
Joseph	64507
Yukon	65589
Zalma	63787
Zanoni	65784

Appendix

Florissant — Hazelwood
Independence — Kansas City MISSOURI

FLORISSANT 630

POST OFFICE BOXES

Box Nos.		
A-U	Carr Sta	31
1-399	Old Town Station	32
AA-AB	Carr Sta	31
500-999	Florissant	33
1001-1499	Carr Sta	31

RURAL ROUTES

2		31

STATIONS, BRANCHES AND UNITS

Carr Sta	31
Old Town Sta	31
General Delivery	33
Postmaster	33

HAZELWOOD 630

STATIONS, BRANCHES AND UNITS

Bridgeton Br	44
Maryland Heights Br	43
General Delivery	42

INDEPENDENCE 640

POST OFFICE BOXES

Box Nos.		
A-C	Main Office	51
1-499	Main Office	51
600-900	Englewood Sta	52
1001-1249	Main Office	51
7700-7899	Fairmount Sta	53
8500-8699	Sugar Creek Br	54

RURAL ROUTES

1,2,3		50

STATIONS, BRANCHES AND UNITS

Atherton Rural Br	50

KANSAS CITY 641

POST OFFICE BOXES

Box Nos.		
1-1999	Main Office	41
2000-3999	Central Sta	42
4000-4299	A Sta	01
4300-4499	B Sta	27
4500-4599	William M Chick Sta	24
4600-4899	E Sta	09

Kansas City (Con.)   641

4900-4999	F Sta	20
5000-5199	Southeast Sta	32
5200-5299	Plaza Sta	12
5300-5499	South Troost Sta	31
5500-5599	E Sta	09
5600-5799	Stockyards Sta	02
5800-5999	Westport Sta	11
6000-6199	Sunny Slope Sta	10
6200-6599	Centropolis Sta	26
6600-6799	Northeast Sta	23
6800-6999	Parkway Sta	30
7000-7299	Country Club Sta	13
7300-7599	North Kansas City Br	16
7600-7699	D Sta	28
7900-8099	Leeds Sta	29
8100-8199	Plaza Sta	12
8200-8399	Kersey Coates Sta	05
8400-8799	Wornall Sta	14
9000-9299	Riverside Br	68
9300-9599	Raytown Br	33
9600-9999	Hickman Mills Sta	34
10000-10499	Westport Sta	11
10500-10899	Gladstone Br	18
11000-11299	Antioch Sta	19
11300-11499	Plaza Sta	12
11500-11999	Longview Sta	38
12000-12299	Parkville Br	52
12300-12799	North Kansas City Br	16
12800-12999	William M Chick Sta	24
13000-13999	Commerce Tower Sta	99
15000-15999	Civic Center	06
16000-16499	Plaza	12
16500-16999	Raytown Br	33
17000-17299	Southeast	32
17300-17599	Parkway Sta	30
17700-17999	Hickman Mills Sta	34
9000-19999	Main Office	41

RURAL ROUTES

2,3	33
6	26
9	29
13	16
15	29
17	38
18,19	34
20	18
21	19
22,23,24,25,27	52
28,29	18
30	34
31	14

STATIONS, BRANCHES AND UNITS

Antioch Sta	19
Centropolis Sta	26
Civic Center Sta	06
Claycomo Br	19
Commerce Tower Sta	99
Country Club Sta	13
Federal Reserve Sta	98
Ferrelview Rural Br	63
Gashland Sta	18
Gladstone Br	18
Harding Sta	11
Hickman Mills Sta	34
James Crews Sta	08
Kersey Coates Sta	05
Leeds Sta	29
Longview Sta	38
Nashua Sta	55
North Kansas City Br	16
Northeast Sta	23
Parkville Br	50
Parkway Sta	30
Plaza Sta	12
Raytown Br	33
Riverside Br	68
South Troost Sta	31
Southeast Sta	32
Stockyards Sta	02
Sunny Slope Sta	10
Veterans Hospital Sta	28
Westport Sta	11
William M Chick Sta	24
Wornall Sta	14
General Delivery	08
Postmaster	08

APARTMENTS, HOTELS, MOTELS

Aladdin, 1215 Wyandotte	05
Ambassador, 3560 Broadway	11
Bellerive, 214 E Armour Blvd	11
Biarritz, 121 Ward Parkway	12
Boulevard Manor, 1115 E Armour Blvd	09
Casa Loma, 105 Ward Parkway	12
Cavalier, 1109 E Armour Blvd	09
Chatham, 3701 Broadway	11
Commodore, 1217 E Linwood Blvd	09
Continental, 106 W 11th	05
Dixon Inn, 1205 Baltimore	05
Downtowner, 1234 Central	05
Ellison, 300 W Armour Blvd	05
Executive, 509 W 13th	05
Georgian Court, 400 E Armour Blvd	09
Haven Hill, 700 W 47th	12
Hilton Inn, 610 Washington	05
Holiday Inn, At Municipal Airport	16
Howard Johnson0s, 1600 .e. Russell Rd	16
Hyde Park, 336 W 36th	11
Kansas Citian, 1216 Broadway	05
Locarno, 235 Ward Parkway	12
Mayfair, 1224 E Linwood Blvd	09
Montrose, 6 E 40th	11
Muehlebach, 107 W 12th	05
Netherlands, 3835 Main	11
New Yorker, 1114 Baltimore	05
Oak Hall, 4550 Warwick	11
Park Lane, 4600 J C Nichols Pkwy	12
Parkway Towers, 4545 Wornall	11
Plaza Inn, 1 E 45th	11
President, 1329 Baltimore	05
Prom, 5 E 6th Trafficway	06
Ramada Inn, 5100 E Linwood Blvd	28
Rasbach, 1116 Wyandotte	05
Riviera, 229 Ward Pkwy	12
Rodeway Inn, 1211 Armour Rd	16
Senate, 1015 E Armour Blvd	09
Southland, 3517 Main	11
Valentine On Broadway, 3724 Broadway	11
Villa Serena, 321 Ward Pkwy.	12
Westport Arms, 301 W Armour Blvd	11

BUILDINGS

Altman, 103 E 11th	06
Argyle, 306 E 12th	06
B M A Tower, 700 Karnes	08
Balcony, 300 W 47th	12
Board Of Trade, 1005 Wyandotte	05
Bryant, 1102 Grand Ave	06
Centennial, 210 W 10th	05
City National Bank, 926 Grand Ave	06
Columbia Bank, 921 Walnut	06
Commerce Tower, 911 Main	05
Commerce, 922 Walnut	06
Congress, 3525 Broadway	11
Corrigan, 1828 Walnut	08
Davidson, 1627 Main	08
Doctor'S, 701-51 E 63rd	10
Dwight, 1004 Baltimore Ave	05
Fairfax, 101 W 11th	05
Farm & Home, 1021 Grand Ave	06
Federal Reserve, 925 Grand Ave	06
Finance, 1009 Baltimore Ave.	05
First National Bank, 14 W 10th	05
Garden, 409 E 63rd	10
Grand Avenue Bank, 1805 Grand Ave	08
Graphic Arts, 934 Wyandotte	05
Hanover, 15 W 10th	05
Home Savings, 1006 Grand Ave	06
Insurance Exchange, 21 W 10th	05
Jason, 1211 Walnut	06
John Hancock, 800 W 47th	12
K C Board of Trade, 4800 Main	12
K C Southern, 114 W 11th	05
Lathrop, 1005 Grand Ave	06
Law, 1207 Grand Ave	06
Lillis, 18 E 11th	06
Lincoln, 1605 E 18th	08
Live Stock Exchange, 1600 Genesee	02
Medical Plaza, 4320 Wornall Rd	11
Merchandise Mart, 2201 Grand Ave	08
Merchants Produce Bank, 531 Walnut	06

Kansas City (Con.)   641

Municipal Auditorium, 211 W
13th 05
National Fidelity Life, 1002
Walnut 06
Ozark National Life, 906
Grand Ave 06
Pershing, 215 W Pershing
Rd 08
Plaza Medical, 315 Nichols
Rd 12
Plaza Parkway, 4620 Nichols
Pkwy 12
Plaza Time, 411 Nichols Rd ... 12
Power & Light, 106 W 14th 05
Professional, 1103 Grand
Ave 06
Prudential, 427 W 12th 05
Public Library, 311 E 12th 06
Puritan, 405 E 13th 06
Scarritt Arcade, 817 Walnut ... 06
Scarritt, 818 Grand Ave 06
Telephone, 324 E 11th 06
Temple, 903 Grand Ave 06
Tenmain Center, 920 Main 05
Title, 112 E 10th 06
Tower, 116 W 47th 12
Traders National Bank, 1125
Grand Ave 06
Union Carbide, 910 Baltimore
Ave 05
Union Station, 30 W Pershing
Rd 08
Uptown, 3706 Broadway 11
V F W, 406 W 34th 11
Waldheim, 6 E 11th 06
Waltower, 823 Walnut 06
Wirthman, 3100 Troost Ave ... 09

GOVERNMENT OFFICES

City Hall, 414 E 12th 06
Courthouse, 415 E 12th 06
Federal Office Bldg, 911
Walnut 06
Gsa Federal Office Bldg,
1500 E Bannister Rd 31
Main Post Office, 315 W
Pershing Rd 08
Midwest Service Center, 2306
E Bannister Rd 70
Missouri State Employment
Security, 1411 Main 05
Missouri State Office, 615 E
13th 06
New Federal Office Bldg, 601
E 12th 06
US Marine Corps Finance
Center, 1500 E Bannister
Rd 97
United States Courthouse,
811 Grand Ave 06

HOSPITALS

Baptist Memorial, 6601
Rockhill Rd 31
Conley Maternity, 619
Garfield 24
Doctors, 2501 Gillham Rd 08
Downtown, 918 Oak 06
Florence Crittenton Home,

225 W 43rd................................. 11
General, 2400 Cherry............... 08
Lakeside, 8701 Troost Ave...... 31
Menorah Medical Center,
4949 Rockhill Rd.................. 10
Mercy 2415 Locust................... 08
N K C Memorial, 2800
Hospital Dr............................ 16
Neurological, 2625 Paseo 08
Northeast Osteopathic, 620
Bennington Ave..................... 25
Osteopathic, 926 E 11th.......... 06
Psychiatric Receiving Center,
600 E 22nd............................ 08
Ralph Clinic, 529 Highland
Ave 06
Research, 2316 E Meyer
Blvd... 32
Saint Joseph's, 2510 Linwood
Blvd... 28
Saint Luke's, 4401 Wornall
Rd 41
Saint Mary's, 101 Memorial
Dr 08
Trinity Lutheran, 3001
Wyandotte.............................. 08
Veterans Administration,
4801 Linwood Blvd.............. 28
Wheatley Provident, 1826
Forest Ave.............................. 08

SAINT JOSEPH   645

POST OFFICE BOXES

Box Nos.		
1-108	E Sta	05
1-114	A Sta	03
1-117	Inza Sta.........	08
1-189	D Sta	04
1-1105	Main Office	02
41-710	Fairleigh Sta ..	06
301-356	A Sta	03
1601-1648	Wyatt Park Sta.	07
1701-1728	Wyatt Park Sta.	07

RURAL ROUTES

1	06
2	05
3	06
4,5	03
6,8	04

STATIONS, BRANCHES AND UNITS

Fairleigh Sta...........................	06
Inza Sta...................................	08
Wyatt Park Sta........................	07
General Delivery	01
Postmaster	01

APARTMENTS, HOTELS, MOTELS

Ambassador, 30th & Parkway
A.. 07
Baxters Black Angus Motel,
1216 N Belt Hwy..................... 06
Century, 627 N 25th.................. 06
Charleston, 615 Robidoux....... 01

Chateau 25, 702 N 25th......... 06
Clay Hill, 1816 Clay................. 01
Colonial, 2604 Frederick......... 06
Cook, 1025 Penn...................... 03
Crestview Village, 2901
Frederick................................. 06
Del Rosa, 312 Noyes Blvd 01
Eastern Gardens 3414 - 48
Messanie................................ 01
Eastside 1401 N 36th.............. 06
El Cid, 3515 Gene Field Rd..... 06
Field Eugene, 2124 Marion..... 01
Francis Street, 1307 Francis .. 01
Frederick Garden, 2602
Frederick................................. 06
Georgian Court, 422 N 7th..... 01
Goff, 416 N 7th......................... 01
Gray, 2202 Duncan 07
Hall Manor, 801 Hall................ 01
Herman, 2522 Frederick.......... 06
Hillcrest, 2709 Frederick.......... 06
Holiday Inn Motel, 4312
Frederick Ave......................... 06
Jesse James Motel, 807 S
Belt Hwy.................................. 07
Lorraine, 521 N 7th.................. 01
Mary Gale, 421 1/2 25 N
25th 01
Mertland, 210 N 8th................. 01
Northwood Pl 1100-1499
Maxwell Rd............................. 05
Oakridge 1200-1299
Angelique............................... 01
Park Lane, 128 Park Ln........... 06
Parkview, 902 Seneca............. 03
Parkwood, 1202 N 22nd.......... 06
Pembroke Gardens, 2807 1/2
11 Pembroke Ln..................... 06
Plaza, 1821 Clay...................... 01
Pony Express Motel, 1225 N
Belt Hwy.................................. 06
Ramada Inn 4016 Frederick
Ave 06
Ritchey, 801 N 25.................... 06
Robidoux, 5th & Francis.......... 01
Rose Lawn, 708 Hall................ 01
San Regis, 1015 Faraon.......... 01
Senate, 2511 Mitchell Ave...... 07
Shamrock Motel, 3301 N Belt
Hwy.. 06
Shangri-La Motel, 2201 N
Belt Hwy.................................. 02
Summit Place, 516 N 10th....... 01
Tik-Tok Motel, 1414 S Belt
Hwy.. 07
Travelodge, 1320 N Belt Hwy 06
Victorian Court, 809 N 25th..... 06
Winston, 104 Winston Pl......... 06

BUILDINGS

American National Bank, 106
S 7th... 01
Arcade, 216 N 7th.................... 01
Belt Professional Bldg, 908 N
Belt 06
Commerce Bank, 419
Edmond.................................... 01
Corby, 5th & Felix..................... 01
Donnell Court, 507 Francis...... 01
East Hills Shopping Ctr........... 06
Edmond Plaza, 708 Edmond... 01
Empire Trust, 602 Edmond..... 01

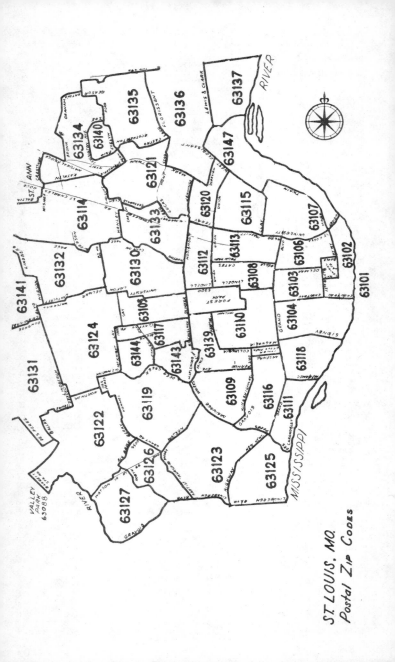

ST. LOUIS, MO.
Postal Zip Codes

Saint Joseph (Con.)   **645**

Federal, 8th & Edmond........... 01
First National Bank, 4th &
   Felix.................................. 01
Frederick Towers, 2400
   Frederick............................. 06
Herman, 622 Edmond............. 01
King Hill, 819 1/2 Francis...... 01
Kirkpatrick, 620 Francis......... 01
Light & Power, 520 Francis..... 01
Missouri Valley Trust, 400
   Felix.................................. 01
Physicians & Surgeons, 700
   Francis................................ 01

GOVERNMENT OFFICES

City Hall, 11th & Frederick
   Ave.................................... 01
Court House, 302 N 5th.......... 01
U S Post Office & Court
   House, 8th & Edmond 01

HOSPITALS

General Osteopathic, 117 S
   15th................................... 01
Methodist, 8th & Faraon......... 01
Saint Josephs, 923 Powell...... 01
State Hospital 2, Box 263 02
Thompson-Brumm-Knepper
   Clinic, Box 8 02

UNIVERSITIES AND COLLEGES

Gards Business University,
   514 Francis.......................... 01
Missouri Western College,
   Downs Dr 07
Platt College Of Commerce,
   8th & Felix.......................... 01

SAINT LOUIS   **631**

POST OFFICE BOXES

Box Nos.
A-B   Normandy Br...... 21
A-C   Carondelet Sta.... 11
A-J   Webster Groves
           Br 19
1-530   Main Office........ 66
AA-AC   Clayton Br......... 05
541-1626   Central Sta....... 88
1801-1987   Christian
           Bechtold Sta .. 18
2001-2199   Benton Park
           Sta................. 58
2201-2288   Gardner Sta. 09
2301-2599   Overland Br...... 14
2601-2687   Gravois Sta 16
2801-2889   Carondelet Sta. .. 11
2901-3199   University City
           Br 30
3401-3599   Maplewood Br.... 43
3751-3898   Kirkwood Br...... 22
3900-4196   Jennings Br....... 36
4201-4290   Tower Grove
           Sta................. 63

4301-4399   Affton Br.......... 23
4701-4996   Field Sta.......... 08
5001-5114   Nagel Sta.......... 15
5121-5194   Hannegan Sta.. 39
5201-5234   Hannegan Sta .. 39
5241-5394   Nagel Sta......... 15
5401-5599   Bremen Sta....... 60
5601-5799   Normandy Br..... 21
5801-5999   Berkeley Br....... 34
6001-6116   Hannegan Sta... 39
6301-6479   Fairgrounds
           Sta................. 07
6501-6699   Lemay Br.......... 25
6701-6877   Brentwood Br ... 44
6900-6920   Affton Br.......... 23
7001-7499   Main Office....... 77
7501-7741   Progress Sta...... 59
7801-7974   Jordan W
           Chambers
           Sta................. 06
8001-8299   Pierre Laclede
           Sta................. 56
8301-8499   Olivette Br........ 32
8501-8646   Sappington Br.. 26
8701-8999   Jefferson
           Memorial Sta.. 02
9101-9399   Richmond
           Heights Br...... 17
9401-9599   Cabanne Sta.... 61
9601-9699   Kirkwood Br..... 22
9701-9899   Kinloch Br 40
9901-9999   Kirkwood Br..... 22
10001-10599   Lambert Airport
           Br 45
10601-10899   Mehlville Br...... 29
10901-11100   Ferguson Br...... 35
11201-11899   Clayton Br........ 05
11901-12199   Wellston Sta 12
12201-12399   Soulard Sta 57
12401-12499   Olivette Br........ 32
12501-12999   Creve Coeur
           Br 41
13001-13199   Webster Groves
           Br 19
13201-13399   Soulard Sta....... 57
13401-13699   North County
           Br 38
13800-13999   Baden Sta 47
14001-14999   Main Office....... 78
15001-15599   Chouteau Sta ... 10
15701-15799   Tower Grove
           Sta................. 63
15800-15999   Overland Br...... 14
16501-16999   Clayton Br........ 05
20001-20099   Brentwood Br ... 44
20101-20299   Affton Br.......... 23
20300-20499   Wellston Sta 12
20501-20699   Hannegan Sta... 39
21100-21299   Baden Sta 47
21301-21418   Nagel Sta.......... 15
21501-21599   Olivette Br........ 32
21601-21999   Gardner Sta....... 09
22001-22087   Sappington Br.. 26
22100-22299   Gravois Sta 16
22401-22499   Sappington Br.. 26
22501-22889   Broadway Sta... 47
23001-23999   Pierre Laclede
           Sta................. 56
23501-23590   Wellston Sta 12
23700-23899   Normandy Br..... 21
23901-23999   Webster Groves
           Br 19
24100-24299   University City

           Br 30
24501-24699   Creve Coeur
           Br 41
24701-24899   Nagel Sta......... 15
26001-26199   Jennings Br...... 36

RURAL ROUTES

1.. 41
9.. 29
13.. 41

STATIONS, BRANCHES AND UNITS

Affton Br............................... 23
Baden Sta.............................. 47
Benton Park Sta..................... 04
Berkeley Br............................ 34
Bremen Sta............................ 60
Brentwood Br......................... 44
Broadway Sta......................... 47
Cabanne Sta.......................... 61
Carondelet Sta....................... 11
Central Sta............................. 01
Charles Nagel Sta................... 13
Chouteau Sta......................... 10
Christian Bechtold Sta............ 18
Clayton Br............................. 05
Conclay Br............................. 24
Creve Coeur Br....................... 41
Des Peres Br.......................... 31
Fairgrounds Sta...................... 07
Ferguson Br........................... 35
Field Sta................................ 08
Gardner Sta........................... 09
Glendale Br............................ 22
Gravois Sta............................ 16
Jefferson Memorial Sta........... 02
Jennings Br............................ 36
Jordan W. Chambers Sta......... 06
Kinloch Br............................. 40
Kirkwood Br........................... 22
Lambert Airport Br................. 45
Lemay Br............................... 25
Maplewood Br........................ 43
Mehlville Br........................... 29
Normandy Br.......................... 21
North County Br..................... 37
Olive Sta............................... 04
Olivette Br............................. 24
Overland Br........................... 14
Pierre Laclede Sta.................. 20
Pine Lawn Br......................... 20
Plaza Sta............................... 99
Principia Br............................ 31
Progress Sta........................... 59
Richmond Heights Br.............. 17
River Roads Br....................... 36
Robert E. Hannegan Sta.......... 39
Saint Johns Sta...................... 14
Sappington Br........................ 26
Soulard Sta............................ 57
Tower Grove Sta..................... 63
University City Br................... 30
Webster Groves Br.................. 19
Wellston Sta........................... 12
General Delivery...................... 66
Postmaster............................. 55

APARTMENTS, HOTELS, MOTELS

A B C D, 4 N Kingshighway
   Blvd................................... 08
Adlon, 3438 Russell Blvd........ 04

Saint Louis (Con.) 631

Adolphus, 5004 Delmar Blvd.... 08
Airline Motel, 10124 Natural
Brdge Rd....................... 34
Alverne, 1014 Locust 01
Ambassador, 5340 Delmar
Blvd................................ 12
Baden, 8220 N Broadway....... 47
Baltimore, 205 N 9th............ 01
Bel Air Motel, 9745 Highway
66................................. 26
Biltmore, 3643 Washington
Blvd................................ 08
Blue Haven Motel, 10000
Highway 66..................... 26
Branscome, 5370 Pershing
Ave................................ 12
Browning, 5536 Pershing
Ave................................ 12
Cambridge Ct, 4917
Mcpherson Ave................ 08
Canterbury Hall, 4132
Washington Ave............... 08
Carr Square, 1500 Carr Dr..... 06
Castle Point Auto Court
Motel, 2468 Chambers Rd . 36
Castlereagh, 6820 Delmar
Blvd................................ 30
Cathedral Court, 4362 Lindell
Blvd................................ 08
Catherine Springer Home,
220 N Spring Ave.............. 08
Chase Park Plaza, 212 N
Kingshighway Blvd............ 08
Chase, 4931 Lindell Blvd 08
Chippewa Motel, 7880
Watson Rd...................... 19
Claridge, 1800 Locust............ 03
Clemens Hall, 3640 W Pine
Blvd................................ 08
Colonial Motel, 11777
Highway 67..................... 38
Congress, 275 Union Blvd 08
Convent Garden, 4497
Pershing Ave................... 08
Coral Court Motel, 7755
Watson Rd...................... 19
Crystal Motel, 7746 Watson
Rd.................................. 19
Daniel Boone, 3733 Lindell
Blvd................................ 08
De Soto, 200 N 11th............ 01
Delmonte, 5622 Delmar Blvd.. 12
Diplomat Motel, 433 N
Kingshighway Blvd............ 08
Ellington, 4961 Laclede Ave.... 08
Embassy, 530 Union Blvd....... 08
Eugene Field, 4339 Olive........ 08
Evangeline Residence 205 N
18th................................ 03
Evergreen Motel, 8715
Watson Rd...................... 19
Fairmount, 7 Maryland Plaza.. 08
Ford, 1405 Pine.................... 03
Forest Park, 4910 West Pine
Blvd................................ 08
Fremont, 4066 Lindell Blvd 08
Frontenac, 40 N
Kingshighway Blvd............ 08
Fusz Memorial, 3700 W Pine
Blvd................................ 08

Gatesworth, 245 Union Blvd... 08
George Washington, 600 N
Kingshighway Blvd............ 08
Grand Towers 3520 Laclede
Ave................................ 03
Grays Cottage Camp, 7474
St Charles Rock Rd........... 33
Greater Saint Louis Trailer
Park, 6825 St Charles Rck
Rd.................................. 33
Gregorian, 5374 Delmar Blvd. 12
Harlan Court, 5455 Delmar
Blvd................................ 12
Hawthorne, 4475 W Pine
Blvd................................ 08
Holiday Inn Motel Downtown
2211 Market................... 03
Holiday Inn Motel Midtown
4483 Lindell Blvd............. 08
Holiday Inn Motel South,
3660 S Lindbergh Blvd 27
Hollywood Tourist Court
Motel, 10336 Manchester
Rd.................................. 22
Howard Johnson Motor Lodge
Motel, 6929 S Lindbergh
Blvd................................ 25
Hutchinson Arms, 2107 S
Grand Blvd...................... 04
Ivy Motel, 10143 Olive Street
Rd.................................. 41
Jefferson, 415 N 12th............ 01
John J Cochran, 1418 N 8th.... 06
Katherine, 4432 Washington
Blvd................................ 08
Kenrick Square, 3853 Lindell
Blvd................................ 08
King Bros Motel, 1335 S
Lindbergh Blvd................. 31
Kingsway, 108 N
Kingshighway Blvd............ 08
Knotty Pine Auto Court Motel,
10130 Olive Street Rd...... 41
Lennox 825 Washington Ave... 01
Lindell Tower, 3745 Lindell
Blvd................................ 08
Lowell, 4140 Washington
Blvd................................ 08
Lucas & Hunt Village, 5303
Lucas & Hunt Rd............... 21
Mac Arthur, 100 N Broadway.. 02
Manhasset Village, 8915
Eager Rd......................... 44
Mansion House Ctr 400
Mansion House Ctr........... 02
Mark Twain, 116 N 8th.......... 01
Marlborough, 5696 Kingsbury
Blvd................................ 12
Mayfair, 806 St Charles.......... 01
Mc Auley Hall, 325 N
Newstead Ave.................. 08
Mc Kinley, 806 N 12th........... 01
Montclair, 18 S Kinshighway
Blvd................................ 08
Monticello, 4535 Lindell Blvd.. 08
Neighborhood Gardens, 1201
N 8th.............................. 06
Northwestern, 4919 Natural
Bridge Av........................ 15
Ozark Plaza Motor Motel,
10705 Highway 66............ 27
Park Manor, 5560 Pershing

Ave................................ 12
Park Plaza, 220 N
Kingshighway Blvd............ 08
Parkedge, 4907 W Pine.......... 08
Parkhurst, 228 N Taylor Ave... 08
Pierre Chouteau, 4440 Lindell
Blvd................................ 08
Plaza Square Apartments, 10
Plaza Sq......................... 03
President, 4615 Lindell Blvd .. 08
Ranelagh, 5707 Mcpherson
Ave................................ 12
Roosevelt, 4903 Delmar Blvd . 08
Rose Bowl Motel, 9982
Manchester Rd................ 22
Royal Motel, 9282 Watson
Rd.................................. 26
Saint Louis Gateway, 822
Washington Av................. 01
Saint Regis, 4950 Lindell
Blvd................................ 08
Sarah Belle, 4125 W Belle Pl.. 08
Saum, 1919 S Grand Blvd...... 04
Sherman, 6188 Mcpherson
Ave................................ 12
Sir Walter Raleigh, 3664
Washington Blvd.............. 08
Sixty-Six Auto Court Motel,
8730 Watson Rd............... 19
Springdale Motel, 4121
Springdale Ave................ 34
Tower Motel, Highway 40 &
Ballas Rd........................ 41
Town & Country, 8801 Eager
Rd.................................. 44
Tramore Castle, 4525 Lindell
Blvd................................ 08
Twin-Six Auto Court Motel,
10230 Highway 66............ 27
Ulysses S Grant Motel, 8498
Watson Rd...................... 19
University, 3703 Washington
Blvd................................ 08
Versailles, 709 So Skinker
Blvd................................ 05
Walsh Hall, 3622 W Pine
Blvd................................ 08
Warwick, 1428 Locust............ 03
Wayside Motel, 7800 Watson
Rd.................................. 19
Wendell Pruitt 2407 Ofallon ... 06
Westgate, 706 N
Kingshighway Blvd............ 08
Westmoreland, 5330 Pershing
Ave................................ 12
Westward Motel, 1580 S
Lindbergh Blvd................. 27
Wiltshire, 725 S Skinker
Blvd................................ 05
Windsor, 4209 Lindell Blvd..... 08
Winston Churchill, 5475
Cabanne Ave.................... 12

BUILDINGS

Ambassador, 411 N 7th.......... 01
Arcade, 812 Olive.................. 01
Beaumont Medical, 3720
Washington Blvd.............. 08
Bell Telephone, 1010 Pine 01
Beltmar, 5473 Delmar Blvd.... 12
Boatmens Bank, 314 N
Broadway........................ 02

Saint Louis (Con.)   **631**

Boulevard, 508 N Grand
    Blvd.............................. 03
Brune, 806-808 Chestnut........ 01
Buder, 707 Market................. 01
Cambridge Medical, 150 N.
    Meramec Ave. 05
Centennial, 1139 Olive........... 01
Century, 313 N 9th................ 01
Chemical, 721 Olive............... 01
Chouteau, 4030 Chouteau
    Ave.................................... 10
Clayton Central, 110 So
    Central Ave........................ 05
Columbia, 318 N 8th.............. 01
Commerce, 418 Olive.............. 02
Continental, 3615 Olive.......... 08
Cotton Belt, 111 N 4th........... 02
Farm & Home, 411 N 10th..... 01
Fashion Square, 1307
    Washington Ave.................. 03
Federal Commerce Trust 208
    N Broadway........................ 02
Fidelity, 820 N Grand Blvd..... 06
Field 4485 Olive.................... 08
Frisco 906 Olive.................... 01
General American Life, 1505
    Locust 03
General Van, 4908 Delmar
    Blvd.................................. 08
Ghio, 506 N Vandeventer
    Ave.................................. 08
Globe Democrat, 710 N 12th.. 01
Goldman, 709 Pine 01
Holland, 211 N 7th................ 01
Imperial, 922 Pine 01
International Office, 722
    Chestnut 01
La Salle, 509 Olive 01
Laclede Gas, 720 Olive.......... 01
Leather Trades, 1602 Locust.. 03
Lindell Trust, 2739 N Grand
    Blvd.................................. 06
Lister, 4500 Olive.................. 08
Louderman, 317 N 11th.......... 01
Martin, 923 Washington Ave .. 01
Mary Muffet, 1627 Locust...... 03
Merchants Exchange, 5100
    Oakland Ave...................... 10
Merchants Laclede, 408
    Olive.................................. 02
Mid City, 320 N Grand Blvd.... 03
Mississippi Valley, 506 Olive.. 03
Missouri Pacific Annex, 1218
    Olive.................................. 03
Missouri Pacific, 210 N 13th... 03
Monogram, 1718 Washington
    Ave.................................... 03
Musical Art, 459 N Boyle
    Ave.................................... 08
Nicholas, 1504 S Grand Blvd... 04
Old Federal, 815 Olive............ 01
Olivia, 1023 N Grand Blvd 06
Paul Brown, 818 Olive............ 01
Pierce, 112 N 4th.................. 02
Pineate, 804 Pine.................. 01
Poe, 1492 Hodiamont Ave....... 12
Post-Dispatch, 1111 Olive....... 01
Railway Exchange, 611 Olive.. 01
Roosevelt, 4903 Delmar Blvd . 08
Sacks, 8008 Carondelet Ave... 05
Saint Charles, 505 N 7th 01

Security, 319 N 4th................ 02
Seven-O-Five Olive, 705 Olive. 01
Shell, 1221 Locust................. 03
Silk Exchange, 503 N 12th..... 01
South Side National Bank,
    3606 Gravois Ave 16
State National Life, 4 No 8th. 01
Syndicate Trust, 915 Olive..... 01
Taylor-Olive, 4505 Olive 08
Title Guaranty, 706 Chestnut . 01
Travelers, 522 Olive............... 01
University City, 6635 Delmar
    Blvd.................................. 30
University Club 607 N Grand
    Blvd.................................. 03
Victoria, 401 N 8th................ 01
Wainwright, 705 Chestnut 01
Wall, 3903 Olive.................... 08
Western Union, 910
    Chestnut 01

GOVERNMENT OFFICES

Chamber Of Commerce, 511
    Locust 01
City Hall, 1206 Market........... 03
Civil Courts, 10 N 12th 01
Federal 1520 Market.............. 03
Municipal Courts, 1320
    Market.............................. 03
United States Courthouse,
    1114 Market 01
United States Customhouse,
    1114 Market 01

HOSPITALS

Alexian Bros., 3933 S.
    Broadway............................ 18
Barnard Free Skin & Cancer,
    600 S Kingshighway Blvd .. 10
Barnes, 600 S Kingshighway
    Blvd.................................. 10
Bethesda, 3655 Vista Ave 10
Booth Memorial, 3740
    Marine.............................. 18
Cardinal Glennon Memorial,
    1465 S Grand Blvd............. 04
Christian, 4411 N Newstead
    Ave.................................... 15
City, 1515 Lafayette Ave........ 04
De Paul, 2415 N
    Kingshighway Blvd 13
Deaconess, 6150 Oakland
    Ave.................................... 39
Faith West 12634 Olive
    Street Rd.......................... 41
Faith, 3300 N Kingshighway
    Blvd.................................. 15
Firmin Desloge, 1325 S
    Grand Blvd........................ 04
Homer G Phillips, 2601
    Whittier............................ 13
Incarnate Word 3545
    Lafayette Ave.................... 04
Jewish, 216 S Kingshighway
    Blvd.................................. 10
Lutheran, 2639 Miami 18
Malcolm A Bliss, 1420
    Grattan............................ 04
Masonic Home, 5351 Delmar
    Blvd.................................. 12
Mc Millan, 640 S

Kingshighway Blvd 10
Missouri Baptist, 3015
    Ballas Rd N........................ 31
Missouri Pacific, 1755 S
    Grand Blvd........................ 04
Mount Saint Rose, 9101 S
    Broadway............................ 25
Normandy Osteopathic, 7840
    Natural Bridge Rd 21
Park Lane Memorial, 4930
    Lindell Blvd........................ 08
Public Health Service, 1520
    Market.............................. 03
Saint Anne'S Home, 5351
    Page Blvd.......................... 12
Saint Anthonys, 3520
    Chippewa............................ 18
Saint Johns Mercy, 615 New
    Ballas Rd S........................ 41
Saint Josephs, 525 Couch
    Ave.................................... 22
Saint Louis Childrens, 500 S
    Kingshighway Blvd 10
Saint Louis City, 1515
    Lafayette Ave.................... 04
Saint Louis County, 601 S
    Brentwood Blvd.................. 05
Saint Louis Maternity, 630 S
    Kingshighway Blvd 10
Saint Lukes, 5535 Delmar
    Blvd.................................. 12
Saint Marys Infirmary, 1536
    Papin................................ 03
Saint Marys, 6420 Clayton
    Rd...................................... 17
Saint Vincents, 7301 St
    Charles Rock Rd................ 33
Shriners Hospital For
    Crippled Chi, 2001 S
    Lindbergh Blvd 31
State, 5400 Arsenal............... 39
Veterans Administration, 915
    N Grand Blvd...................... 06
Veterans, Jefferson Barracks.. 25
Washington University Nurses
    Res, 416 S Kingshighway
    Blv..................................... 10
Wohl Memorial, 4960
    Audubon Blvd 10

UNIVERSITIES AND COLLEGES

Christian Brothers, 6501
    Clayton Rd........................ 17
Concordia Seminary, 801 De
    Mun Ave............................ 05
Covenant College &
    Theological Seminary,
    12330 Conway Rd 41
David Ranken School, 4431
    Finney Ave........................ 13
Eden Seminary, 475 E
    Lockwood Ave.................... 19
Florissant Valley Community
    3400 Pershall Rd............... 35
Fontbonne, 6800 Wydown
    Blvd.................................. 05
Forest Park Community
    College, 5600 Oakland
    Ave.................................... 10
Harris Teacher, 3026 Laclede
    Ave.................................... 03

Saint Louis (Con.) 631

Incarnate Word Convent,
2800 Normandy Ave 21
Junior College Dist Office St
Louis, 7508 Forsyth Blvd.... 05
Kenrick Seminary, 7800
Kenrick Rd 19
Marillac Seminary, 7800
Natural Bridge Rd. 21
Maryhurst Normal, 1101 S
Lindbergh Blvd 22
Maryville College Of The
Sacred Heart, 13550
Conway Rd 41
Meramec Community, 11333
Big Bend Blvd 22
Missouri U. Stlouis Campus,
8001 Natural Bridge Rd 21
Principia, 13201 Clayton Rd... 31.
Saint Louis County
Vocational School, 5600
Countryday Ln .... 34.
Saint Louis Preparatory
Seminary, 5200
Shrewsbury Ave. 19
Saint Louis University, 221 N
Grand Blvd 03
South Campus, 3230
Hartford 18
Ursuline Convent & Academy,
800 E Monroe Ave 22
Visitation Academy, 3020 N
Ballas Rd 31
Washington Univ Medical
School, 660 S
Kingshighway Blvd 10
Washington University,
Lindell & Skinker Blvd. 30
Webster, 470 E Lockwood
Ave 19

SPRINGFIELD 658

POST OFFICE BOXES

Box Nos.
A-E	Glenstone Sta..	04
1-992	Harry S Jewell	
	Sta..............	01
901-1106	Commercial	
	Sta..............	03
1001-2004	South Side Sta.	05
2751-2894	Commercial	
	Sta..............	03

| 3001-3987 | Glenstone Sta... | 04 |
| 4281-4352 | Glenstone Sta... | 04 |

RURAL ROUTES

1	03
2	02
3	04
4	02
5,6	03
7	02
8	07
9	04
10,11	03
12	04

STATIONS, BRANCHES AND UNITS

Commercial Sta.	03
Glenstone Sta.	04
South Side Sta.	05
General Delivery	01
Postmaster	01

APARTMENTS, HOTELS, MOTELS

Arrowhead, 2501 N
Glenstone 03
Battlefield Inn, 2114 S
Glenstone 04
Beverly, 529 Cherry 06
Camp Manor, 423 E Elm 06
Coach House Inn, 2535 N
Glenstone 03
Colonial Motor Lodge,
Highway 166 07
Colonial, 330 St Louis 05
Elms, 527 St Louis 06
Empire Inn North, 2555 N
Glenstone 03
Englenook, 700 E Walnut..... 06
Executive Arms, 2355 N
Glenstone 03
Hawks, 1839 E Sunshine...... 04
Hillcrest Ninety, 2444 N
Delaware 03
Holiday Inn, 2700 N
Glenstone 03
Howard Johnsons, 2610 N
Glenstone 03
Imperial 400, 1001 St Louis... 06
Kelley Jane, 835 E Walnut ... 06
Kentwood Arms Motor, 700 St
Louis 05
Kingsbarde, 937 E Lombard... 04
Lamplighter, 1839 E

| Sunshine | 04 |
Lorraine, 527 E Walnut 06
Maple, 2233 N Glenstone 03
Missouri, 412 Commercial 03
North Terrace, 1646 E North... 03
Queen Anne, 1750 Cherry 06
Rail Haven, 203 S Glenstone.. 02
Ramada Inn, 2715 N
Glenstone 03
Rock Castle, 401 Mt Vernon... 06
Sands, 1824 N Glenstone 03
Seville, 218 E Walnut 06
Ship & Anchor, 2137 N
Glenstone 03
Sir Robert, 1403 E Elm.......... 02
State, 400 S Jefferson 06
Sunvilla Tower, 833 E Elm 06
Travelodge, 503 St Louis....... 06

BUILDINGS

Empire, 430 South 06
Frisco, 3253 E Trafficway 02
Holland, 205 St Louis 06
Landers, 149 Public Sq 06
Landmark, 317 St Louis. 06
Mc Daniel, 318 St Louis......... 06
Professional, 609 Cherry........ 06
Wilhoit, 300 E Pershing 06
Woodruff, 331 St Louis.......... 06

GOVERNMENT OFFICES

City Hall, 830 Boonville 02
Court House, 940 Boonville 02
Federal Building, 870
Boonville 01

HOSPITALS

Baptist, 440 S Market 06
Cox Lester E Medical Center,
1423 N Jefferson 02
Saint John'S, 1235 E
Cherokee 02
Springfield Gen Osteopathic,
2828 N National 01

UNIVERSITIES AND COLLEGES

Baptist Bible, 628 E Kearney . 02
Central Bible, 3000 N Grant... 02
Draughon'S Business, Wilhoit
Bldg 05
Drury, 900 N Benton 02
Evangel, 1111 N Glenstone ... 02
Southwest Missouri State,
901 S National 02

MONTANA
(Abbreviation: MT)

Absarokee 59001
  Nye, R. Br 59061
Acton 59002
Alberton 59820
Alder 59710
Alzada 59311
Anaconda (1st) 59711
Angela 59312
Antelope 59211
Arlee 59821
Ashland (1st) 59003
Augusta 59410
Avon 59713
Babb 59411
Bainville 59212
Baker 59313
Ballantine 59006
Basin 59631
Bearcreek 59007
Belfry 59008
Belgrade 59714
Belknap, R. Br. Trout Creek....59822
Belle Creek, Br. Broadus........59317
Belt 59412
Biddle 59314
Big Arm 59910
Big Sandy 59520
Big Timber 59011
Bigfork 59911
Bighorn 59010
BILLINGS (1st) (see
  appendix)
Billings Heights, Br.
  Billings...............................59101
Birney 59012
Black Eagle 59414
Blackfoot 59415
Bloomfield 59315
Bonner 59823
Boulder 59632
Box Elder 59521
Boyd, R. Br. Roberts 59013
Boyes 59316
Bozeman (1st) 59715
Brady 59416
Bridger 59014
Broadus 59317
  Belle Creek, Br..................59317
  Sonnette, R. Br..................59348
Broadview 59015
Brockton 59213
Brockway 59214
Browning 59417
Brusett 59318
Buffalo 59418
Busby 59016
Butte (1st) 59701
Bynum 59419
Cameron 59720
Canyon Creek 59633
Capitol 59319
Cardwell 59721
Carlyle 59320
Carter 59420
Cascade 59421
Cat Creek, R. Br. Winnett 59017
Charlo 59824
Chester 59522
Chinook 59523

Choteau 59422
Christina 59423
Circle 59215
Clancy 59634
Clinton 59825
Clyde Park 59018
Coalridge 59216
Coalwood, R. Br. Miles City....59321
Coffee Creek 59424
Cohagen 59322
Colstrip 59323
Columbia Falls (1st) 59912
Columbus 59019
Condon 59826
Conner 59827
Conrad (1st) 59425
Cooke City 59020
Coram 59913
Corvallis 59828
Corwin Springs 59021
Crane 59217
Creston, R. Br. Kalispell 59902
Crow Agency 59022
Culbertson 59218
Cushman 59023
Custer 59024
Cut Bank (1st) 59427
Dagmar 59219
Danvers 59429
Darby 59829
Dayton 59914
De Borgia 59830
Decker 59025
Deer Lodge (1st) 59722
Dell 59724
Delphia, R. Br. Roundup........59073
Denton 59430
Devon 59431
Dillon (1st) 59725
Divide 59727
Dixon 59831
Dodson 59524
Drummond 59832
Dupuyer 59432
Dutton 59433
East Glacier Park 59434
East Helena 59635
Edgar 59026
Ekalaka 59324
Elliston 59728
Elmo 59915
Emigrant, R. Br. 59027
Enid 59220
Ennis 59729
Epsie 59325
Essex 59916
Ethridge 59435
Eureka 59917
Evergreen, Br. Kalispell 59901
Fairfield 59436
Fairview 59221
Fallon 59326
Ferdig 59437
Fergus 59438
Fishtail 59028
Flaxville 59222
Florence 59833
Floweree 59440
Forestgrove 59441
Forsyth 59327
Fort Benton 59442
Fort Harrison 59636
Fort Peck 59223

Fort Shaw 59443
Fortine 59918
Four Buttes 59224
Frazer 59225
Frenchtown 59834
Froid 59226
Fromberg 59029
Galata 59444
Gallatin Gateway 59730
Gardiner 59030
Garneill 59445
Garrison 59731
Garryowen 59031
Geraldine 59446
Geyser 59447
Gildford 59525
Glasgow (1st) 59230
  Glasgow Air Base, R. Br.....59231
Glasgow Air Base, R. Br.
  Glasgow 59231
Glen 59732
Glendive (1st) 59330
  Intake, R. Br......................59335
Glentana 59240
Goldcreek 59733
Grantsdale 59835
Grassrange 59032
GREAT FALLS (1st) (see
  appendix)
Greenough 59836
Greycliff 59033
Hall 59837
Hamilton (1st) 59840
Hammond 59332
Hardin (1st) 59034
  Yellowtail, R. Br.................59035
Harlem 59526
Harlowton 59036
Harrison 59735
Hathaway 59333
Haugan 59842
Havre (1st) 59501
Hays 59527
Heart Butte 59448
Helena (1st) 59601
  Montana City, R. Br............59602
  State Capitol, Sta...............59601
Helmville 59843
Heron 59844
Highwood 59450
Hilger 59451
Hingham 59528
Hinsdale 59241
Hobson 59452
Hogeland 59529
Homestead 59242
Hot Springs 59845
Hungry Horse 59919
Huntley 59037
Huson 59846
Hysham 59038
Ingomar 59039
Intake, R. Br. Glendive 59335
Inverness 59530
Ismay 59336
Jackson 59736
Jeffers 59737
Jefferson City 59638
Joliet 59041
Joplin 59531
Jordan 59337
Judith Gap 59453
Kalispell (1st) 59901

Creston, R. Br.....................59902
Evergreen, Br........................59901
Kevin..................................59454
Kila....................................59920
Kinsey................................59338
Kolin..................................59455
Kremlin...............................59532
Lake Mc Donald, R. Br. West
  Glacier...............................59921
Lakeside..............................59922
Lambert...............................59243
Lame Deer............................59043
Landusky..............................59533
Larslan................................59244
Laurel (1st)...........................59044
Laurin.................................59738
Lavina.................................59046
Ledger.................................59456
Lewistown (1st)......................59457
Libby (1st)............................59923
Lima...................................59739
Lincoln.................................59639
Lindsay................................59339
Livingston (1st)......................59047
Lloyd..................................59535
Locate.................................59340
Lodge Grass..........................59050
Lolo....................................59847
Loma..................................59460
Lonepine..............................59848
Loring.................................59537
Lothair................................59461
Lustre, R. Br. Frazer................59225
Luther.................................59051
Malmstrom A F B, Br. Great
  Falls..................................59402
Malta..................................59538
Manhattan............................59741
Marion................................59925
Martin City............................59926
Martinsdale...........................59053
Marysville.............................59640
Maudlow..............................59742
Maxville...............................59850
Mc Allister............................59740
Mc Cabe..............................59245
Mc Leod..............................59052
Medicine Lake........................59247
Melrose................................59743
Melstone..............................59054
Melville................................59055
Mildred................................59341
Miles City (1st).......................59301
  Coalwood, R. Br....................59321
Mill Iron...............................59342
Milltown...............................59851
Missoula (1st)........................59801
Moccasin..............................59462
Moiese, R. Br. Charlo................59824
Molt....................................59057
Monarch...............................59463
Montana City, R. Br. Helena........59602
Moore.................................59464
Mosby.................................59058
Musselshell............................59059
Myers..................................59060
Nashua................................59248
Neihart................................59465
Niarada................................59852
Norris..................................59745
Noxon.................................59853
Nye, R. Br. Absarokee...............59061
Oilmont...............................59466

Olive...................................59343
Olney..................................59927
Opheim................................59250
Otter...................................59062
Outlook...............................59252
Ovando................................59854
Pablo..................................59855
Paradise...............................59856
Park City..............................59063
Peerless...............................59253
Pendroy...............................59467
Perma.................................59857
Philipsburg............................59858
Pioneer, Sta. Billings................59102
Plains.................................59859
Plentywood............................59254
Plevna.................................59344
Polaris.................................59746
Polebridge.............................59928
Polson (1st)...........................59860
Pompeys Pillar........................59064
Pony...................................59747
Poplar.................................59255
Potomac..............................59862
Powderville............................59345
Power..................................59468
Pray...................................59065
Proctor................................59929
Pryor..................................59066
Radersburg, R. Br.
  Townsend...........................59641
Ramsay...............................59748
Rapelje................................59067
Ravalli.................................59863
Raymond..............................59256
Raynesford............................59469
Red Lodge............................59068
Redstone..............................59257
Reedpoint.............................59069
Regina.................................59539
Reserve................................59258
Rexford................................59930
Richey.................................59259
Richland...............................59260
Ringling...............................59642
Roberts................................59070
  Boyd, R. Br..........................59013
Rock Springs..........................59346
Rollins.................................59931
Ronan.................................59864
Roscoe................................59071
Rosebud...............................59347
Roundup...............................59072
  Delphia, R. Br........................59073
Roy....................................59471
Rudyard...............................59540
Russell, Sta. Great Falls............59405
Ryegate................................59074
Saco...................................59261
Saint Ignatius.........................59865
Saint Mary, R. Br. Browning........59417
Saint Regis............................59866
Saint Xavier...........................59075
Saltese................................59867
Sand Coulee..........................59472
Sand Springs..........................59077
Sanders...............................59076
Santa Rita.............................59473
Savage.................................59262
Scobey................................59263
Seeley Lake...........................59868
Shawmut..............................59078
Shelby (1st)...........................59474

Shepherd..............................59079
Sheridan...............................59749
Shonkin...............................59476
Sidney (1st)...........................59270
Silesia.................................59080
Silver Gate............................59081
Silver Star.............................59751
Silverbow..............................59750
Simms.................................59477
Simpson...............................59541
Somers................................59932
Sonnette, R. Br. Broadus...........59348
Springdale.............................59082
Stanford...............................59479
State Capitol, Sta. Helena..........59601
Stevensville...........................59870
Stockett...............................59480
Stryker................................59933
Suffolk.................................59481
Sula...................................59871
Sumatra...............................59083
Sun River.............................59483
Sunburst...............................59482
Superior...............................59872
Swan Lake, R. Br. Bigfork..........59911
Sweetgrass............................59484
Tampico...............................59272
Teigen.................................59084
Terminal Annex, Sta.
  Billings...............................59101
Terry...................................59349
Thompson Falls.......................59873
Three Forks...........................59752
Toston.................................59643
Townsend..............................59644
  Radersburg, R. Br..................59641
Trego..................................59934
Trident................................59753
Trout Creek...........................59874
  Belknap, R. Br......................59822
Troy...................................59935
Turner................................59542
Twin Bridges..........................59754
Twodot................................59085
Ulm....................................59485
Utica, R. Br. Hobson................59452
Valier..................................59486
Vandalia...............................59273
Vaughn................................59487
Victor..................................59875
Vida...................................59274
Virginia City..........................59755
Volborg...............................59351
Wagner................................59543
Walkerville, Br. Butte...............59701
Warmsprings..........................59756
Waterloo..............................59757
West Glacier..........................59936
  Lake Mc Donald, R. Br............59921
West Yellowstone....................59758
Westby................................59275
White Sulphur Springs..............59645
Whitefish (1st)........................59937
Whitehall..............................59759
Whitetail..............................59276
Whitewater............................59544
Whitlash...............................59545
Wibaux................................59353
Willard................................59354
Willow Creek..........................59760
Witsall.................................59086
Winifred...............................59489
Winnett...............................59087

Cat Creek, R. Br	59017	Wise River	59762	Wyola	59089
Winston	59647	Wolf Creek	59648	Yellowtail, R. Br. Hardin	59035
Wisdom	59761	Wolf Point (1st)	59201	Zortman	59546
		Worden	59088	Zurich	59547

Appendix

BILLINGS 591

POST OFFICE BOXES

Box Nos.
1-2565   Main Office 03
20001 20869 Pioneer Sta 02

RURAL ROUTES

1	02
2;3	01
4	02
5	01

STATIONS, BRANCHES AND UNITS

Billings Heights Br.	01
Pioneer Sta.	02
Terminal Annex Sta	01
General Delivery	01
Postmaster	01

APARTMENTS, HOTELS, MOTELS

Acme, 109 1/2 N Broadway	01
Alexandra, 104 N 31st	01
Ardmore, 3010 N 2nd Ave	01
Arnatt, 3020 N 7th Ave	01
B & B, 524 N 23rd	01
Babcock, 118 1/2 N Broadway	01
Bede Apts, 1111 Main	01
Berger, 222 N 25th	01
Beta House, 2908 N 1st Ave	01
Carlin, 2501 Montana Ave	01
Colonial Courts Motel, 580 Main	01
Colonial, 223 S 27th	01
Darryl, 114 1/2 N 26th	01
Driftwood Court, 932 Ave B	02
Dude Rancher Lodge, 415 N 29th	01
Dupre Manor, 721 14th W	02
Executive, 445 Lordwith Dr	02
Gage, 2325 Montana Ave	01
General Custer, 106 N 27th	01
Grand, 16 S 27th	01
Hedgemere, 2803 N 7th Ave	01
Holiday Inn, Highway 10 E	01
James, 19 1/2 N 27th	01
Jean, 3405 N 1st Ave	01
Lee, 118 N 24th	01
Lincoln, 2520 1st Ave N	01
Lordwith Courts, 1601 Virginia Lane	02
Middleton Arms, 707 N 31	01
Mustang Motel, R 1/2 3	01
Northern, 19 N Broadway	01
Okerman, 23 Yellowstone Ave	02

(continued)

Parkview, 420 Lordwith Dr	02
Ponderosa Acres Apartments, 1301 Industrial Ave	02
Ponderosa Inn, 2511 1st Ave N	01
Prior, 19 N 26th	01
Rex, 2401 Montana Ave	01
Reynolds, 224 S 30th	01
Ross, 1615 N 2nd Ave	01
Roxy, 15 1/2 N 29th	01
Santa Fe Arms, 2207 Central	02
Shaffer, 4 Lewis Ave	02
Sherton Arms, 1616 Ave E	02
Shield, 43 Broadwater Ave	02
Stratford, 2817 N 6th Ave	01
Terry Park, 421 W 5th	02
Thomas, 715 N 29th	01
Western Towers	01
Wreford, 3317 N 2nd Ave	01
Young Womens Apartment, 16 N 29th	01

BUILDINGS

Behner, 2822 N 3rd Ave	01
Doctors, 1231 N 29th	01
Electric, 113 N Broadway	01
Executive, 1925 Grand Ave	02
First National Bank, 2715 N 2nd Ave	01
Fratt, 2819 N 2nd Ave	01
Hart-Albin, 208 N Broadway	01
Hedden, 2911 N 2nd Ave	01
Kook, 3203 3rd Ave N	01
M & R, 1002 Division	02
Midland National Bank, 303 N Broadway	01
Petroleum, 2812 N 1st Ave	01
Professional, 1236 N Broadway	01
Securities, 2708 N 1st Ave	01
Security Bank, 2813 N 3rd Ave	01
Selvidge-Babcock, 2718 Montana Ave	01
Stapleton, 104 N Broadway	01
Transwestern Life Insurance, 404 N 31st	01
Treasure State, 2906 N 2nd Ave	01
West Professional, 17th W & Ave D	02
Wilcox, 3302 N 4th Ave	01

GOVERNMENT OFFICES

Chamber Of Commerce, 301 N 27th	01
City Hall, 220 N 27th	01
Court House, 2620 N 3rd Ave	01

(continued)

Federal Building & U S Court House, 310 N 26th	01
United States Post Office, 2602 N 1st Ave	01

HOSPITALS

Billings Deaconess, 2813 N 9th Ave	01
New Western Manor, 2115 Central Ave	02
Saint Johns Lutheran Home, 3940 Rimrock Rd	02
Saint Vincents, 2915 N 12th Ave	01
Valley View Nursing Home, 1807 1/2 24 W	02
Yellowstone County, Yell River Blvd	01

UNIVERSITIES AND COLLEGES

Eastern Montana College Of Education, 1500 N 30th	01
Rocky Mountain, 1511 Poly Dr	02

GREAT FALLS 594

POST OFFICE BOXES

Box Nos.
1-3499   Main Office 03
1-5000   Malmstrom AFB 02

RURAL ROUTES

1,2	01

STATIONS, BRANCHES AND UNITS

Malmstrom A F B Br	02
Russell Sta	05
General Delivery	01
Postmaster	01

APARTMENTS, HOTELS, MOTELS

Adele Apts, 426 1st Ave SW	04
Bitterroot Apts, 400 5th St N	03
Blackstone Apts, 314 3rd St N	01
Cambridge Apts, 520 4th Ave N	01
Centaur Apts, 3345 11th Ave S	05
Country Club Motel, Country Club Addition	04

Great Falls (Con.)   594

Country Club Tower Apts,
1536 Meadowlark Dr 04
Dearborn Apts, 121 5th St N.. 01
Devonshire Homes, 1200
32nd St S 05
Don Plaza Motel, 1224 10th
Ave S 05
Eagles Manor, 1421 9th St
S 05
Elmore Hotel, 6 6th St S 01
Executive Apts, 3500 11th
Ave S 05
Fergus Motel, 299 3rd St NW. 04

Geraldine Apts, 706 3rd Ave
N 01
Glacier Apts, 505 3rd Ave N.. 01
Glendale Apts, 3161/2
Central Ave 01
Harden Court Apts, 2525
12th Ave S 05
Holiday Apts 3320 11th Ave
S 05
Holiday Inn, 1411 10th Ave
S 05
Imperial 400 Motel, 601 2nd
Ave N 01
Jensen Apts, 801 4th Ave N... 01
Leigland Apts, 11 9th St S..... 01
Leland Annex, 718 1st Ave N. 01

Leland Apts, 726 1st Ave N.... 01
Lexington Apts, 800 2nd Ave
N 01
Marland Apts, 512 2nd Ave
N 01
Midtown Motel, 525 2nd Ave
N 01
New Villa Motel, 726 10th
Ave S 05
O Haire Manor, 17 7th St S.... 01
Pennsylvania Apts, 116 3rd
Ave N 01
Ponderosa Motel, 226
Central 01
Racine Apts, 119 13th St N.... 01
Rainbow Motel, 20 3rd St N... 01

NEBRASKA

State List of Post Offices

NEBRASKA
(Abbreviation: NE)

Abie, R. Br. Bruno	68001
Adams	68301
Agnew	68302
Ainsworth	69210
Albion (1st)	68620
Alda	68810
Alexandria	68303
Allen	68710
Alliance (1st)	69301
Alma	68920
Almeria	68811
Alvo	68304
Amelia	68711
Ames	68621
Ames Avenue, Sta. Omaha	68111
Amherst	68812
Angora	69331
Angus	68921
Anselmo	68813
Ansley	68814
Antioch	69332
Arapahoe	68922
Arcadia	68815
Archer	68816
Arlington	68002
Arnold	69120
Arthur	69121
Ashby	69333
Ashland	68003
Ashton	68817
Atkinson	68713
Atlanta	68923
Auburn (1st)	68305
Aurora (1st)	68818
Avoca	68307
Axtell	68924
Ayr	68925
Bancroft	68004
Barneston	68309
Bartlett	68622
Bartley	69020
Bassett	68714
Battle Creek	68715
Bayard	69334
Beatrice (1st)	68310
Beaver City	68926
Beaver Crossing	68313
Bee	68314

Beemer	68716
Belden	68717
Belgrade	68623
Bellevue (1st)	68005
Bellwood	68624
Belvidere	68315
Benedict	68316
Benkelman	69021
Bennet	68317
Bennington	68007
Benson, Sta. Omaha (see appendix)	
Bertrand	68927
Berwyn	68819
Big Springs	69122
Bingham	69335
Bladen	68928
Blair (1st)	68008
Bloomfield	68718
Bloomington	68929
Blue Hill	68930
Blue Springs	68318
Boelus	68820
Boone	68625
Boys Town (1st)	68010
Bradshaw	68319
Brady	69123
Brainard	68626
Brandon, R. Br. Grant	69102
Brewster	68821
Bridgeport	69336
Bristow	68719
Broadwater	69125
Brock	68320
Broken Bow (1st)	68822
Brownlee	69126
Brownville	68321
Brule	69127
Bruning	68322
Bruno	68014
Abie, R. Br.	68001
Brunswick	68720
Bucktail, R. Br. Paxton	69155
Burchard	68323
Burkett, Sta. Grand Island	68801
Burr	68324
Burton	68721
Burwell	68823
Bushnell	69128
Butte	68722
Byron	68325

Cairo	68824
Callaway	68825
Cambridge	69022
Campbell	68932
Carleton	68326
Carroll	68723
Cedar Bluffs	68015
Cedar Creek	68016
Cedar Rapids	68627
Center	68724
Central City	68826
Ceresco	68017
Chadron (1st)	69337
Chambers	68725
Champion	69023
Chapman	68827
Chappell	69129
Chester	68327
Clarks	68628
Clarkson	68629
Clatonia	68328
Clay Center	68933
Clearwater	68726
Cody	69211
Eli, R. Br.	69213
Coleridge	68727
College View, Sta. Lincoln (see appendix)	
Colon	68018
Columbus (1st)	68601
Comstock	68828
Concord	68728
Cook	68329
Cordova	68330
Cornlea	68630
Cortland	68331
Cotesfield	68829
Cozad (1st)	69130
Crab Orchard	68332
Craig	68019
Crawford	69339
Creighton	68729
Creston	68631
Crete (1st)	68333
Crofton	68730
Crookston	69212
Culbertson	69024
Curtis	69025
Dakota City	68731
Dalton	69131
Danbury	69026

Dannebrog	68831
Davenport	68335
Davey	68336
David City	68632
Garrison, R. Br.	68639
Dawson	68337
Daykin	68338
De Witt	68341
Decatur	68020
Denton	68339
Deshler	68340
Deweese	68934
Dickens	69132
Diller	68342
Dix	69133
Dixon	68732
Dodge	68633
Doniphan	68832
Dorchester	68343
Douglas	68344
Downtown, Sta. Omaha (see appendix)	
Du Bois	68345
Dunbar	68346
Duncan	68634
Dunning	68833
Dwight	68635
Eagle	68347
Eddyville	68834
Edgar	68935
Edison	68936
Elba	68835
Elgin	68636
Eli, R. Br. Cody	69213
Elk Creek	68348
Elkhorn	68022
Ellsworth	69340
Elm Creek	68836
Elmwood	68349
Elmwood Park, Sta. Omaha (see appendix)	
Elsie	69134
Elsmere	69135
Elwood	68937
Elyria	68837
Emerson	68733
Emmet	68734
Enders	69027
Endicott	68350
Ericson	68637
Eustis	69028
Ewing	68735
Exeter	68351
Fairbury (1st)	68352
Gladstone, R. Br.	68363
Powell, R. Br.	68425
Fairfield	68938
Fairmont	68354
Falls City (1st)	68355
Farnam	69029
Farwell	68838
Filley	68357
Firth	68358
Flats	69136
Florence, Sta. Omaha (see appendix)	
Fordyce	68736
Fort Calhoun	68023
Foster	68737
Franklin	68939
Fremont (1st)	68025
Friend	68359
Fullerton	68638

Funk	68940
Gandy	69137
Garland	68360
Garrison, R. Br. David City	68639
Gates	68839
Geneva	68361
Genoa	68640
Gering (1st)	69341
Gibbon	68840
Gilead	68362
Giltner	68841
Gladstone, R. Br. Fairbury	68363
Glenvil	68941
Goehner	68364
Gordon	69343
Gothenburg	69138
Grafton	68365
Grainton	69139
Grand Island (1st)	68801
Grant	69140
Brandon, R. Br.	69102
Greeley	68842
Greenwood	68366
Gresham	68367
Gretna	68028
Guide Rock	68942
Gurley	69141
Hadar, R. Br. Norfolk	68738
Haigler	69030
Hallam	68368
Halsey	69142
Hamlet	69031
Hampton	68843
Harbine, R. Br. Jansen	68369
Hardy	68943
Harrisburg	69345
Harrison	69346
Hartington	68739
Harvard	68944
Hastings (1st)	68901
Havelock, Sta. Lincoln	68529
Hay Springs	69347
Hayes Center	69032
Hazard	68844
Heartwell	68945
Hebron	68370
Hemingford	69348
Henderson	68371
Hendley	68946
Henry	69349
Herman	68029
Hershey	69143
Hickman	68372
Hildreth	68947
Holbrook	68948
Holdrege (1st)	68949
Holland	68373
Holmesville	68374
Holstein	68950
Homer	68030
Hooper	68031
Hordville	68846
Hoskins	68740
Howells	68641
Hubbard	68741
Hubbell	68375
Humboldt	68376
Humphrey	68642
Huntley	68951
Hyannis	69350
Imperial	69033
Inavale	68952
Indianola	69034

Inland	68954
Inman	68742
Ithaca	68033
Jackson	68743
Jamison	68744
Jansen	68377
Harbine, R Br.	68369
Johnson	68378
Johnstown	69214
Julian	68379
Juniata	68955
Kearney (1st)	68847
Kenesaw	68956
Kennard	68034
Keystone	69144
Kilgore	69216
Kimball (1st)	69145
Lakeside	69351
Lamar	69035
Laurel	68745
Lawrence	68957
Lebanon	69036
Leigh	68643
Lemoyne	69146
Leshara, R. Br. Valley	68035
Lewellen	69147
Lewiston	68380
Lexington (1st)	68850
Liberty	68381
LINCOLN (1st) (see appendix)	
Lindsay	68644
Linwood	68036
Lisco	69148
Litchfield	68852
Lodgepole	69149
Long Pine	69217
Loomis	68958
Lorton	68382
Louisville	68037
Loup City	68853
Lushton, R. Br. Mc Cool Junction	68383
Lyman	69352
Lynch	68746
Lyons	68038
Macy	68039
Madison	68748
Madrid	69150
Magnet	68749
Malcolm	68402
Malmo	68040
Manley	68403
Marquette	68854
Marsland	69354
Martell	68404
Maskell	68751
Mason City	68855
Max	69037
Maxwell	69151
Maywood	69038
Mc Cook (1st)	69001
Mc Cool Junction	68401
Lushton, R. Br.	68383
Mc Grew	69353
Mc Lean	68747
Mead	68041
Meadow Grove	68752
Melbeta	69355
Memphis	68042
Merna	68856
Merriman	69218
Milburn	68857

Milford	68405
Millard, Br. Omaha	68137
Miller	68858
Milligan	68406
Mills	68753
Minatare	69356
Minden (1st)	68959
Mitchell	69357
Monroe	68647
Moorefield	69039
Morrill	69358
Morse Bluff	68648
Mount Michael, R. Br. Elkhorn	68022
Mullen	69152
Murdock	68407
Murray	68409
Naper	68755
Naponee	68960
Nebraska City (1st)	68410
Nehawka	68413
Neligh	68756
Nelson	68961
Nemaha	68414
Nenzel	69219
Newcastle	68757
Newman Grove	68758
Newport	68759
Nickerson	68044
Niobrara	68760
Nora	68962
Norden, R. Br. Springview	68778
Norfolk (1st)	68701
Hadar, R. Br.	68738
Norman	68963
North Bend	68649
North Loup	68859
North Platte (1st)	69101
Northport	69359
Northwest, Br. Omaha	68134
O'Neill (1st)	68763
Oak	68964
Oakdale	68761
Oakland	68045
Obert	68762
Oconto	68860
Octavia	68650
Odell	68415
Odessa	68861
Offutt A F B, Br. Omaha (see appendix)	
Ogallala (1st)	69153
Ohiowa	68416
OMAHA (1st) (see appendix)	
Ong, R. Br. Shickley	68452
Orchard	68764
Ord	68862
Orleans	68966
Osceola	68651
Oshkosh	69154
Osmond	68765
Otoe	68417
Overton	68863
Oxford	68967
Page	68766
Palisade	69040
Palmer	68864
Palmyra	68418
Panama	68419
Papillion (1st)	68046
Parks	69041
Pawnee City	68420
Paxton	69155
Pender	68047
Peru	68421
Petersburg	68652
Phillips	68865
Pickrell	68422
Pierce	68767
Pilger	68768
Plainview	68769
Platte Center	68653
Plattsmouth (1st)	68048
Pleasant Dale	68423
Pleasanton	68866
Plymouth	68424
Polk	68654
Ponca	68770
Poole	68867
Potter	69156
Powell, R. Br. Fairbury	68425
Prague	68050
Preston, R. Br. Falls City	68427
Primrose	68655
Prosser	68868
Purdum	69157
Raeville	68656
Ragan	68969
Ralston, Br. Omaha (see appendix)	
Randolph	68771
Ravenna	68869
Raymond	68428
Red Cloud	68970
Republican City	68971
Reynolds	68429
Richfield	68054
Richland	68657
Rising City	68658
Riverdale	68870
Riverton	68972
Roca	68430
Rockville	68871
Rogers	68659
Rosalie	68055
Roscoe	69159
Rose	68772
Roseland	68973
Royal	68773
Rulo	68431
Rushville	69360
Ruskin	68974
Saint Columbans (1st)	68056
Saint Edward	68660
Saint Helena	68774
Saint Libory	68872
Saint Mary	68432
Saint Paul	68873
Salem	68433
Sargent	68874
Saronville, R. Br. Sutton	68975
Schuyler (1st)	68661
Scotia	68875
Scottsbluff (1st)	69361
Scribner	68057
Seneca	69161
Seward (1st)	68434
Shelby	68662
Shelton	68876
Shickley	68436
Ong, R. Br.	68452
Shubert	68437
Sidney (1st)	69162
Silver Creek	68663
Smithfield	68976
Snyder	68664
South Bend	68058
South Omaha, Sta. Omaha (see appendix)	
South Sioux City (1st)	68776
Spalding	68665
Sparks	69220
Spencer	68777
Sprague	68438
Springfield	68059
Springview	68778
Stamford	68977
Stanton	68779
Staplehurst	68439
Stapleton	69163
State House, Sta. Lincoln	68509
Steele City	68440
Steinauer	68441
Stella	68442
Sterling	68443
Stock Yards, Sta. Omaha	68107
Stockham, R. Br. Aurora	68818
Stockville	69042
Strang	68444
Stratton	69043
Stromsburg	68666
Stuart	68780
Sumner	68878
Sunol	69164
Superior (1st)	68978
Surprise	68667
Sutherland	69165
Sutton	68979
Saronville, R. Br.	68975
Swanton	68445
Syracuse	68446
Table Rock	68447
Talmage	68448
Tarnov, R. Br. Humphrey	68642
Taylor	68879
Tecumseh	68450
Tekamah	68061
Thedford	69166
Thurston	68062
Tilden	68781
Tobias	68453
Trenton	69044
Trumbull	68980
Tryon	69167
Uehling	68063
Ulysses	68669
Unadilla	68454
Union	68455
University Place, Sta. Lincoln (see appendix)	
Upland	68981
Utica	68456
Valentine (1st)	69201
Valley	68064
Valparaiso	68065
Venango	69168
Verdel	68782
Verdigre	68783
Verdon	68457
Veterans Administration Hosp., Sta. Omaha	68105
Virginia	68458
Waco	68460
Wahoo (1st)	68066
Wakefield	68784
Wallace	69169

Walthill	68067
Walton	68461
Washington	68068
Waterbury	68785
Waterloo	68069
Wauneta	69045
Wausa	68786
Waverly	68462
Wayne (1st)	68787
Weeping Water	68463
Weissert	68880
Wellfleet	69170
West Dodge, Sta. Omaha	

(see appendix)	
West Omaha, Sta. Omaha	
(see appendix)	
West Point (1st)	68788
Western	68464
Westerville	68881
Weston	68070
Whiteclay	69365
Whitman	69366
Whitney	69367
Wilber	68465
Wilcox	68982
Willow Island	69171

Wilsonville	69046
Winnebago	68071
Winnetoon	68789
Winside	68790
Winslow	68072
Wisner	68791
Wolbach	68882
Wood Lake	69221
Wood River	68883
Wymore	68466
Wynot	68792
York (1st)	68467
Yutan	68073

Appendix   Lincoln — Omaha NEBRASKA

LINCOLN   685

POST OFFICE BOXES

Box Nos.

2300-2999	Sta B	02
4400-4699	University Place Sta	04
5000-5599	Sta C	05
6000-6399	College View Sta	06
29100-29399	Havelock Sta	29
30000-30399	Sta A	03
80001-83399	Main Office	01
94600-94899	State House Sta	09

RURAL ROUTES

1	02
2,3	05
5	08
6	02
8	06

STATIONS, BRANCHES AND UNITS

College View Sta	06
Havelock Sta	29
State House Sta	09
University Place Sta	04
General Delivery	01
Postmaster	01

APARTMENTS, HOTELS, MOTELS

Ambassador, 1330 J	08
Clayton House, 1020 O	08
Gateway Manor, 225 N 56	04
Lincoln, 147 N 9	01
Metropolitan, 502 S 12	08
Palisade, 1035 S 17	08
President, 1340 J	08
Radisson Cornhusker, 309 S 13	08
Regent, 1626 D	02
Sky Park Manor, 1301 J	08
Tower View, 1631-41 J	08
Trenridge Garden	05
University Park, 4300 Holdredge	03

BUILDINGS

Anderson, 116 N 12	08
First National Bank, 233 S 13	08
Gateway Shopping Area	05
Lincoln Benefit Life, 134 S 13	08
Lincoln, 1001 O	08
Rudge & Guenzel, 134 S 12	08
Sharp, 206 S 13	08
Stuart, 128 N 13	08
Terminal, 941 O	08

GOVERNMENT OFFICES

County-City, 555 S 10	08
Federal, 129 N 10	08
State Capitol, 1445 K	09

HOSPITALS

Bryan Memorial, 4848 Sumner	06
Lincoln General, 2300 S 16	02
Lincoln Regional Center, 2705 S Folsom	01
Providence, 4600 Valley Rd	10
Saint Elizabeth Community Health Center, 555 S 70th	10
Veterans Administration, 600 S 70th	01

UNIVERSITIES AND COLLEGES

Nebraska School Of Religion, 1237 R	08
Nebraska Wesleyan, 2630 N 50	04
Union, 3800 S 48	06
University Of Nebraska (City Campus)	08
University Of Nebraska (East Campus)	03
University Of Nebraska Agriculture College	03

OMAHA   681

POST OFFICE BOXES

Box Nos.

1-1999	Downtown Sta	01
2001-2999	A Sta	20
3001-3999	Main Office	03
4001-4999	Benson Sta	04
6001-6999	Elmwood Park Sta	06
7001-7999	South Omaha Sta	07
9001-9999	C Sta	09
11001-11999	Ames Avenue Sta	11
12001-12999	Florence Sta	12
13001-13999	Offutt Afb Br	13
14001-14999	West Omaha Sta	14
19001-19999	Air Mail Facility	19
27001-27999	Ralston	27
31001-31999	West Dodge Sta	31
34001-34299	Northwest Sta	34
37001-37999	Millard Br	37
55001-55999	B Sta	55

RURAL ROUTES

1	14
2	34
3	23
4	37
6	12

STATIONS, BRANCHES AND UNITS

Ames Avenue Sta	11
Benson Sta	04
Downtown Sta	01
Elmwood Park Sta	05
Florence Sta	02
Millard Br	37
Northwest Br	34
Offutt AFB Br	13
Ralston Br	27
South Omaha Sta	07
Stock Yards Sta	07
Veterans Administration Hosp. Sta	05

Omaha (Con.)   681

West Dodge Sta.................................. 31
West Omaha....................................... 14
General Delivery................................ 08
Postmaster... 08

APARTMENTS, HOTELS, MOTELS

Adelphia, 836 Park Ave.............. 05
Austin, 205 N 38.......................... 31
Austin, 206 N 37th....................... 31
Austin, 3701 Davenport............... 31
Beverly Arms, 3420 Jones........... 05
Beverly Manor, 128 N 31st......... 31
Buckingham Manor, 4817
  Chicago..................................... 32
Carberry, 3910 Cass.................... 31
Carberry, 501 N 40th................... 31
Castle, 632 S 16th....................... 02
Cherry Garden Court, 813 S
  38th... 05
Cherry Garden Court, 814 S
  37th Ave.................................. 05
Chula Vista, 1141 S 30th
  Ave.. 05
Chula Vista, 2968 Ponpleton
  Ave.. 05
Colonial, 3804 Farnam................ 31
Commodore, 2410 Dodge............ 31
Conant, 1913 Farnam.................. 02
Covert Ave 2235 St Marys
  Ave.. 02
Cox, 2235 St Marys Ave............. 02
Delmar, 219 S 24th..................... 02
Diplomat, 1511 Farnam............... 02
Drake Court Annex, 2201
  Jones....................................... 02
Drake Court Office, 701 S
  22nd... 02
Drake Court, 20th To 22nd &
  Jones....................................... 02
Dundee Court, 4728 Chicago..... 32
Dundee Manor, 106 N 49th......... 32
Dundee Towers, 110 S 49th........ 32
Dundee, 5019 Underwood
  Ave.. 32
Farnam, 3252 Farnam.................. 31
Flatiron, 1722 St Marys............... 02
Hamilton, 2406 Farnam............... 31
Hill, 505 S 16th............................ 02
Holiday Inn, 3321 S 72nd............ 24
Howard Johnsons 72nd & I-
  80... 24
Imperial 400, 2211 Douglas........ 02
Knickerbocker, 3801 Jones......... 05
Knickerbocker, 702 S 38th.......... 05
Landon Court, 519 S 24th............ 02
Logan, 1804 Dodge..................... 02
Masonic Manor, 801 S 52 06
New Paxton 1405 Farnam............ 02
New Tower, 7764 Dodge............. 14
O E A Manor, 22nd &

Chicago..................................... 02
Omaha Hilton 1616 Dodge......... 02
Paxton Court, 25th Ave
  Douglas.................................... 31
Prom Town House, 7000
  Dodge...................................... 14
Radisson Blackstone, 302 S
  36th... 31
Rorick, 604 S 22nd..................... 02
Travelodge, 3902 Dodge............. 31
Tudor Arms, 131 S 39th............. 31
Twin Towers, 3000 Farnam........ 31
Windsor Arms, 544 S 25th
  Ave.. 05

BUILDINGS

Ames Plaza, 56th & Ames.......... 04
Aquila Court, 1615 Howard....... 02
Baird, 1704 Douglas.................... 02
Barker, 306 S 15th...................... 02
Beverly Hills, 79th & Dodge...... 14
Blondo Plaza, 80th & Blondo..... 34
Capitol Plaza, 1815 Capitol
  Ave.. 02
Center, 42nd & Center................ 05
City National Bank, 405 S
  16th... 02
Continental, 209 So 19............... 02
Country Side Village, 87th &
  Pacific...................................... 14
Crossroads Shopping Center,
  72nd & Dodge......................... 14
Doctors Building, 4239
  Farnam..................................... 31
Electric, 409 S 17th.................... 02
Executive, 1624 Douglas............ 02
Faidley, 121 S 16th..................... 02
Farm Credit, 206 S 19th............. 02
Farnam, 1613 Farnam................. 02
Federal Office, 106 S 15th......... 02
Federal, 215 N 17th.................... 02
First National Bank, 1603
  Farnam..................................... 02
First National Center 16th
  And Dodge............................... 02
Grain Exchange, 1905
  Harney..................................... 02
Karbach, 209 S 15th.................... 02
Keeline, 319 S 17th..................... 02
Kiewit Plaza, 3555 Farnam........ 31
Kilpatrick, 222 S 15th................. 02
Lawyers 3535 Harney................. 31
Live Stock Exchange, 29th O... 07
Loveland Shopping Center,
  90th & Center.......................... 24
Lyric, 221 S 19th........................ 02
Masonic Temple, 117 S 19th..... 02
Medical Arts Building, 105 S
  17th... 02
Mid American Plaza, 71st &
  W Center Rd............................ 06
Omaha, 1620 Farnam.................. 02
Physicians Building, 3601

Dodge.. 31
Professional, 3510 Dodge.......... 31

Redick Tower, 1504 Harney...... 02
Securities, 305 S 16th................. 02
Service Life, 1904 Farnam......... 02
South Omaha City Hall, 5002
  S 24th...................................... 07
Swanson, 8401 Dodge................ 14
Westgate Plaza, 84th &
  Hascall.................................... 24
Westroads Shopping Center,
  102nd West Dodge Rd............ 14
Woodmen Of The World, 1319
  Farnam..................................... 02
Woodmen Tower, 1700
  Farnam..................................... 02
Xerox, 7002 W Center Rd.......... 06

GOVERNMENT OFFICES

City Hall, 108 So 18.................... 02
County Court House, 1715
  Farnam..................................... 02

HOSPITALS

Archbishop Bergan-Mercy......... 24
Bishop Clarkson Memorial........ 05
Booth Memorial, 426 So.
  40th... 31
Childrens Memorial, 502 S
  44th... 05
Doctors, 501 Park Ave............... 05
Douglas County, 4102
  Woolworth............................... 05
Eppley Care Center, 3612
  Cuming.................................... 31
Immanuel, 36th & Meredith ... 11
Lutheran, 515 S 26th.................. 31
Nebraska Methodist, 8303 &
  Dodge...................................... 14
Richard A Young Memorial,
  402 S 24th Ave........................ 31
Saint Catharines, 9th &
  Forest Ave............................... 08
Saint Josephs, 2305 S 10th....... 08
Univ Of Nebraska College Of
  Medicine, 42nd Dewey
  Ave.. 05
Veterans Administration,
  42nd & Woolworth Ave........... 05

UNIVERSITIES AND COLLEGES

Ave... 05
Creighton Medical School
  639 N 27th.............................. 31
Creighton University, 2500
  California................................. 31
Saint Marys, 1901 S 72nd......... 24
University Of Nebr. At
  Omaha, 60th & Dodge............ 32
University Of Nebraska
  College Of Medicine 42nd
  & Dewey Ave........................... 05

NEVADA
(Abbreviation: NV)

Airport, Br. Las Vegas	89111
Alamo	89001
Austin	89310
Babbitt, Br. Hawthorne	89416
Baker	89311
Battle Mountain	89820
Beatty	89003
Beowawe	89821
Black Spring, Br. Reno	89508
Blue Diamond	89004
Bonanza Annex, Sta. Las Vegas (see appendix)	
Boulder City (1st)	89005
Bunkerville	89007
Caliente	89008
Carlin	89822
Carp	89009
Carson City (1st)	89701
Cherry Creek	89312
Crescent Valley, R. Br. Beowawe	89821
Crystal Bay	89402
Incline Village, Br.	89450
Currie	89313
Dayton	89403
Deeth	89823
Denio	89404
Downtown, Sta. Las Vegas	89101
Duckwater	89314
Dyer	89010
East Ely	89315
East Las Vegas, Br. Las Vegas	89112
Elko (1st)	89801
Ely (1st)	89301
Empire	89405
Eureka	89316
Fallon (1st)	89406
Federal, Sta. Las Vegas	89101
Fernley	89408
Gabbs	89409
Galena, Sta. Reno	89501

Gardnerville	89410
Garside, Sta. Las Vegas (see appendix)	
Genoa	89411
Gerlach	89412
Glenbrook	89413
Golconda	89414
Goldfield	89013
Goodsprings, R. Sta. Jean	89019
Halleck	89824
Hawthorne (1st)	89415
Babbitt, Br.	89416
Hazen	89417
Henderson (1st)	89015
Hiko	89017
Huntridge, Sta. Las Vegas (see appendix)	
Imlay	89418
Incline Village, Br. Crystal Bay	89450
Indian Springs	89018
Jackass Flats, Br. Mercury	89023
Jackpot	89825
Jarbidge	89826
Jean	89019
Jiggs	89827
Lake Mead Base, Br. Las Vegas	89110
Lamoille	89828
LAS VEGAS (1st) (see appendix)	
Lathrop Wells	89020
Laughlin, R. Br. Searchlight	89046
Lee	89829
Logandale	89021
Lovelock	89419
Lund	89317
Luning	89420
Manhattan	89022
Mc Dermitt	89421
Mc Gill	89318
Mercury	89023
Mesquite	89024
Mina	89422
Minden	89423

Moapa	89025
Montello	89830
Mountain City	89831
Nellis A F B, Br. Las Vegas	89110
Nixon	89424
North Las Vegas (1st)	89030
Orovada	89425
Overton	89040
Owyhee	89832
Pahrump	89041
Panaca	89042
Paradise Valley	89426
Peavine, Sta. Reno	89502
Pioche	89043
Pittman	89044
RENO (1st) (see appendix)	
Round Mountain	89045
Ruby Valley	89833
Ruth	89319
Schurz	89427
Searchlight	89046
Silver City	89428
Silver Springs	89429
Silverpeak	89047
Smith	89430
Sparks (1st)	89431
Stateline, Br. Zephyr Cove	89449
Steamboat	89436
Stewart	89437
Tonopah	89049
Tracy Clark, R. Sta. Sparks	89431
Tuscarora	89834
University, Sta. Reno	89507
Valmy	89438
Verdi	89439
Virginia City	89440
Wadsworth	89442
Washington, Sta. Reno	89503
Weed Heights	89443
Wellington	89444
Wells	89835
Winnemucca (1st)	89445
Yerington (1st)	89447
Zephyr Cove (1st)	89448
Stateline, Br.	89449

Appendix
Las Vegas NEVADA

LAS VEGAS   891

POST OFFICE BOXES

Box Nos.

1-2196	Downtown Sta	01
2201-2987	Huntridge Sta	04
4001-4427	Bonanza Sta	06
5301-5746	Garside Sta	02
7331-7545	Downtown Sta	01
9701-9789	Nellis A F B Br	10
11001-11400	Airport Sta	11
12051-12949	East Las Vegas Br	12
14001-15555	Main Office	14
16000-16043	Federal Sta	01

STATIONS, BRANCHES AND UNITS

Airport Br	11
Bonanza Annex Sta	06
Downtown Sta	01
East Las Vegas Br	12
Federal Sta	01
Garside Sta	02
Huntridge Sta	04
Lake Mead Base Br	10
Nellis A F B Br	10
General Delivery	14
Postmaster	14

APARTMENTS, HOTELS, MOTELS

Aladdin, 3667 Las Vegas Blvd S	09
Bonanza Hotel, 3645 Las Vegas Blvd S	09
Caesar's Palace, 3570 Las Vegas Blvd S	09
Circus Circus, 2880 Las Vegas Blvd S	09
Desert Inn, 3145 Las Vegas Blvd S	09
El Cortez, 600 Fremont	01
Flamingo, 3680 Las Vegas Blvd S	09
Four Queens, 202 E Fremont	01
Fremont, 200 Fremont	01
Frontier, 3120 Las Vegas Blvd S	09
International Hotel, 3000 Paradise Rd	09
Landmark Hotel, 364 Convention Ctr Dr	09
Las Vegas Hacienda, 3950 Las Vegas Blvd S	19
Riviera, 3200 Las Vegas Blvd S	09
Sahara, 2800 Las Vegas Blvd S	09
Showboat, 2800 E Fremont Ave	04
Stardust, 3000 Las Vegas Blvd S	09
The Dunes, 3700 Las Vegas	

Las Vegas (Con.)	891
Blvd S	09
The Mint, 110 Fremont	01
The Sands, 3317 Las Vegas Blvd S	09
Thunderbird, 2800 Las Vegas Blvd S	09
Tropicana, 3801 Las Vegas Blvd S	09
Union Plaza, 1 Main	01

HOSPITALS

Las Vegas, 201 N 8th	01
Southern Nevada Memorial Hospital, 1800 W Charleston Blvd	02
Sunrise, 3186 Maryland Pky	09
Womens, 2025 E Sahara Ave	05

UNIVERSITIES AND COLLEGES

University Of Nevada Las Vegas, 4505 Maryland Pky	09

RENO   895

POST OFFICE BOXES

Box Nos.		
1-1399	Main Office	04

1400-4999	Main Office	05
5000-6999	Washington Sta	03
7000-7999	Peavine Sta	02
8000-9999	University Of Nevada Sta	07
10000-10999	Riverside Annex	10
13001-14999	University Of Nevada Station	07

RURAL ROUTES

1,2	02
3	03
4	02
5	08

STATIONS, BRANCHES AND UNITS

Black Spring Br	08
Galena Sta	01
Peavine Sta	02
University Sta	07
Washington Sta	03
General Delivery	01
Postmaster	01

APARTMENTS, HOTELS, MOTELS

El Cortez, 239 West 2nd	01
Harrahs, 219 North Center	01
Holiday, 111 Mill	01
Mapes, 10 North Virginia	01
Overland, 246 North Center	01
Pioneer Inn, 221 S. Virginia	01
Ponderosa, 515 S Virginia	01
Riverside, 17 South Virginia	01

BUILDINGS

Arlington Towers, 100 N Arlington	01
First National Bank, 1 E 1st	01
Professional, 150 N Center	01

GOVERNMENT OFFICES

Court House, S Virginia	01
Federal Bldg, 300 Booth	02

HOSPITALS

Nevada State, Galletti Way	02
Saint Marys, 235 W 6th	03
Veterans, 1000 Locust	02
Washoe Medical Center, 90 Kirman Ave	02

NEW HAMPSHIRE
(Abbreviation: NH)

Acworth	03601
Alstead	03602
South Acworth, R. Br.	03607
Alton	03809
Alton Bay	03810
Amherst	03031
Andover	03216
Antrim	03440
Ashland	03217
Ashuelot	03441
Atkinson	03811
Auburn	03032
Barnstead	03218
Barrington	03825
Bartlett	03812
Bath	03740
Bedford, R. Br. Manchester	03102
Beebe River, R. Br. Campton	03219
Belmont	03220
Bennington	03442
Berlin (1st)	03570
Bethlehem	03574
Blodgett Landing, Br. Newbury	03255
Boscawen, Br. Concord	03301
Bradford	03221

Bretton Woods, R. Br. Twin Mountain	03575
Bristol	03222
Brookline	03033
Burkehaven, Br. Sunapee	03782
Campton	03223
Beebe River, R. Br.	03219
Waterville Valley, R. Br.	03223
West Campton, R. Sta.	03228
West Thornton, R. Br.	03285
Canaan	03741
Candia	03034
Canterbury	03224
Center Barnstead	03225
Center Conway	03813
Center Harbor	03226
Center Ossipee	03814
Center Sandwich	03227
Center Strafford	03815
Center Tuftonboro, R. Br. Wolfeboro	03816
Charlestown	03603
Chester	03036
Chesterfield	03443
Chocorua	03817
Claremont (1st)	03743
Colebrook	03576
Concord (1st)	03301
Contoocook	03229

Conway	03818
Cornish Flat	03746
Crawford House, R. Br. Twin Mountain	03577
Danbury	03230
Danville	03819
Deerfield	03037
Derry (1st)	03038
Dover (1st)	03820
Drewsville	03604
Dublin (1st)	03444
Durham (1st)	03824
East Andover	03231
East Candia	03040
East Derry	03041
East Hampstead	03826
East Hebron	03232
East Kingston	03827
East Lempster	03605
East Madison	03828
East Rochester, Sta. Rochester	03867
East Sullivan	03445
East Swanzey	03446
East Wakefield	03830
Eaton Center, R. Br. Madison	03832
Elkins	03233

Enfield 03748
Enfield Center 03749
Epping 03042
Epsom 03234
Errol 03579
Etna 03750
Exeter (1st) 03833
Fabyan House, R. Sta. Twin
   Mountain 03595
Farmington 03835
Fitzwilliam 03447
Fitzwilliam Depot, R. Sta.
   Fitzwilliam 03447
Francestown 03043
Franconia 03580
Franklin (1st) 03235
Franklin Pierce College, R.
   Sta. Rindge 03461
•Freedom 03836
Fremont 03044
Georges Mills 03751
Gilmanton 03237
Gilmanton Iron Works 03837
Gilsum 03448
Glen 03838
Glencliff 03238
Goffstown 03045
Gonic, Sta. Rochester 03867
Gorham 03581
Goshen 03752
Gossville 03239
Grafton 03240
Grantham 03753
Greenfield 03047
Greenland 03840
Greenville 03048
Groveton 03582
Guild 03754
Hampstead 03841
Hampton (1st) 03842
Hampton Beach, Sta.
   Hampton 03842
Hampton Falls 03844
Hancock 03449
Hanover (1st) 03755
Harrisville 03450
Haverhill 03765
Hebron 03241
Hedding, R. Sta. Epping 03042
Henniker 03242
Hill 03243
Hillsboro (1st) 03244
Hinsdale 03451
Holderness 03245
Hollis 03049
Hooksett, Br. Manchester 03106
Hopkinton, Br. Concord 03301
Hudson (1st) 03051
Intervale 03845
Jackson 03846
Jaffrey (1st) 03452
   Jaffrey Center, R. Sta. 03454
Jaffrey Center, R. Sta.
   Jaffrey 03454
Jefferson 03583
Kearsarge 03847
Keene 03431
Kingston 03848
Laconia (1st) 03246
Lakeport, Sta. Laconia 03246
Lancaster (1st) 03584
Lebanon (1st) 03766

Lempster 03606
Lincoln 03251
Lisbon 03585
Littleton (1st) 03561
Lochmere 03252
Londonderry 03053
Loudon, Br. Concord 03301
Lyme 03768
Lyme Center 03769
Madison 03849
   Eaton Center, R. Br. 03832
MANCHESTER (1st) (see
   appendix)
Marlborough 03455
Marlow 03456
Meadows 03587
Melvin Village 03850
Meredith (1st) 03253
Meriden 03770
Merrimack 03054
Milan 03588
Milford (1st) 03055
Milton 03851
Milton Mills 03852
Mirror Lake 03853
Monroe 03771
Mont Vernon 03057
Moultonboro 03254
Mount Sunapee 03772
Mount Washington, R. Br.
   Twin Mountain 03589
Munsonville 03457
Nashua (1st) 03060
   South Merrimack, R. Br. 03083
New Boston 03070
New Castle 03854
New Durham 03855
New Hampton 03256
New Ipswich 03071
New London (1st) 03257
Newbury 03255
Newfields 03856
Newmarket (1st) 03857
Newport (1st) 03773
Newton 03858
Newton Junction 03859
North Chichester 03258
North Conway (1st) 03860
North Hampton 03862
North Haverhill 03774
North Salem 03073
North Sandwich 03259
North Stratford 03590
North Sutton 03260
North Woodstock 03262
   Woodstock, R. Sta. 03293
Northwood 03261
Nottingham 03290
Orford 03777
Orfordville 03778
Ossipee 03864
Pease A F B, Sta.
   Portsmouth 03801
Pelham 03076
Penacook, Sta. Concord 03301
Percy 03591
Peterborough (1st) 03458
Piermont 03779
Pike 03780
Pittsburg 03592
Pittsfield 03263
Plainfield 03781
Plaistow (1st) 03865

Plymouth (1st) 03264
Portsmouth (1st) 03801
Potter Place 03265
Randolph 03593
Raymond 03077
Redstone (1st) 03866
Reeds Ferry, Sta. Merrimack ... 03054
Rindge 03461
Rochester (1st)* 03867
Rollinsford 03869
Rumney 03266
   Stinson Lake, R. Sta. 03274
Rye 03870
Rye Beach 03871
Salem (1st) 03079
Salisbury 03268
Sanbornton 03269
Sanbornville 03872
Sandown 03873
Sandwich 03270
Seabrook 03874
Silver Lake 03875
Snowville 03877
Somersworth (1st) 03878
South Acworth, R. Br.
   Alstead 03607
South Chatham, R. Br.
   Fryeburg, M E 04037
South Danville 03881
South Effingham 03882
South Lyndeboro 03082
South Merrimack, R. Br.
   Nashua 03083
South Newbury 03272
South Sutton 03273
South Tamworth 03883
Spofford 03462
Stinson Lake, R Sta.
   Rumney 03274
Stoddard 03464
Strafford 03884
Stratham 03885
Strawbery Banke, Sta.
   Portsmouth 03801
Sugar Hill, Br. Lisbon 03585
Sunapee 03782
Suncook 03275
Surry, R Br. Keene 03431
Tamworth 03886
Temple 03084
Tilton 03276
Troy 03465
Twin Mountain 03595
   Bretton Woods, R. Br. 03575
   Crawford House, R. Br. 03577
   Fabyan House, R. Sta. 03595
   Mount Washington, R.
     Br. 03589
Union 03887
Wakefield 03888
Walpole 03608
Warner 03278
Warren 03279
Washington 03280
Waterville Valley, R. Br.
   Campton 03223
Weare 03281
Weirs Beach, Sta. Laconia 03246
Wendell 03783
Wentworth 03282
Wentworth By The Sea, Sta.
   New Castle 03854

West Campton, R. Sta.		West Rye	03891		
Campton	03228	West Springfield	03284	Winchester	03470
West Canaan, R. Sta.		West Stewartstown	03597	Windham	03087
Canaan	03741	West Swanzey	03469	Winnisquam	03289
West Chesterfield	03466	West Thornton, R. Br.		Wolfeboro (1st)	03894
West Franklin, Sta. Franklin	03235	Campton	03285	Center Tuftonboro, R. Br.	03816
West Hampstead	03889	Westmoreland	03467	Wolfeboro Falls	03896
West Hopkinton	03283	Westville	03892	Wonalancet	03897
West Lebanon	03784	Whitefield	03598	Woodstock, R. Sta. North	
West Nottingham	03291	Willey House	03893		
West Ossipee	03890	Wilmot Flat	03287	Woodstock	03293
West Peterborough	03468	Wilton	03086	Woodsville	03785

MANCHESTER   031

POST OFFICE BOXES

Box Nos.
1-1080	Main Office	05
2001-2399	Hooksett Br	06

RURAL ROUTES

1	04
2	02
3	03
4,5	02

STATIONS, BRANCHES AND UNITS

Bedford Rural Br	02
Hooksett Br	06
General Delivery	01

Postmaster   01

APARTMENTS, HOTELS, MOTELS

Carpenter Motor, 323 Franklin	01
China Dragon, Hooksett	06
Holiday Inn, Amoskeag	02
Howard Johnson Motel Queen City Ave	02
Queen City Motel, Queen City Ave	01
Wayfarer Inn, S River Rd	02

GOVERNMENT OFFICES

City Hall, 908 Elm	01
County Court House, 300 Chestnut	01
Veterans Adminstration, 497 Silver	03

HOSPITALS

Elliot, 955 Auburn	03
Notre Dame, 337 Notre Dame Ave	02
Sacred Heart, 200 Hanover	04
United States Government Veterans Administration, Smyth	04

UNIVERSITIES AND COLLEGES

Mount Saint Marys College, Hooksett	06
N H College 2500 River Rd	04
Notre Dame College, 2321 Elm	04
Saint Anselms College, College Rd	02

NEW JERSEY
(Abbreviation: NJ)

Absecon (1st)	08201	appendix)		Belvidere (1st)	07823
Academy, Sta. Newark	07102	Atlantic Highlands (1st)	07716	Bergen, Sta. Jersey City	07304
Adelphia	07710	Audubon, Br. Camden	08106	Bergen Mall, Sta. Paramus	07652
Alfred Vail, Br. Eatontown	07724	Augusta	07822	Bergen Point, Sta. Bayonne	07002
Allaire, R. Br. Farmingdale	07727	Avalon	08202	Bergenfield (1st)	07621
Allamuchy	07820	Avenel (1st)	07001	Bergenline, Sta. Union City	07087
Allendale (1st)	0740:	Avon By The Sea (1st)	07717	Berkeley Heights (1st)	07922
Allenhurst (1st)	07711	Baptistown	08803	Berlin (1st)	08009
Allentown	08501	Barnegat	08005	Bernardsville (1st)	07924
Allenwood	08720	Barnegat Light	08006	Betsytown, Sta. Elizabeth	07201
Alloway	08001	Barrington (1st)	08007	Beverly (1st)	08010
Allwood, Sta. Clifton	07012	Basking Ridge (1st)	07920	Birmingham	08011
Alpha, Br. Phillipsburg.	08865	Lyons, Br.	07939	Blackwood (1st)	08012
Alpine	07620	Batsto, R. Br. Hammonton	08037	Blackwood Terrace, Br.	
Ampere, Sta. East Orange		Bay Head, Br. Point		Woodbury	08096
(see appendix)		Pleasant Beach	08742	Blairstown	07825
Ancora, Br. Hammonton	08037	Bayonne (1st)	0700:	Blawenburg	08504
Andover	07821	Bayville	08721	Bloomfield (1st)	07003
Annandale	08801	Bayway, Sta. Elizabeth	07202	Bloomingdale (1st)	07403
Arlington, Sta. Kearny	07032	Beach Haven (1st)	08008	Bloomsbury (1st)	08804
Asbury	08802	Beachwood	08722	Bogota, Br. Hackensack	07603
Asbury Park (1st)	07712	Bedminster	07921	Boonton (1st)	07005
Atco	08004	Belford	07718	Bordentown (1st)	08505
Athenia, Sta. Clifton	07013	Belle Mead (1st)	08502	Bound Brook (1st)	08805
ATLANTIC CITY (1st) (see		Belleville, Br. Newark	07109	Bradley Beach (1st)	07720
		Bellmawr, Br. Gloucester		Brainy Boro, Sta. Metuchen	08840
		City	08030	Branchville (1st)	07826
		Belmar (1st)	07719	Breton Woods, Br. Brick	

Town...............................08723
Brick Church, Sta. East
Orange (see appendix)
Brick Town (1st)...............08723
Bridgeport........................08014
Bridgeton (1st)................08302
Brielle.............................08730
Brigantine........................08203
Broadway.........................08808
Brookdale, Sta. Bloomfield.....07003
Brooklawn, Br. Gloucester
City.............................08030
Brookside........................07926
Browns Mills (1st)............08015
Browntown, Br. Old Bridge...08857
Budd Lake........................07828
Buena.............................08310
Burlington (1st)...............08016
Butler (1st)......................07405
Buttzville.........................07829
Caldwell (1st)..................07006
Califon............................07830
CAMDEN (1st) (see
appendix)
Cape May (1st)................08204
Cape May Court House (1st)..08210
Cape May Point..................08212
Carlstadt, Br. Rutherford.....07072
Carneys Point, Br. Penns
Grove...........................08069
• Carteret (1st).................07008
Castle Point, Sta. Hoboken...07030
Cedar Brook.....................08018
Cedar Grove (1st)............07009
Cedar Knolls (1st)............07927
Cedarville........................08311
Center, Sta. Trenton............08608
Central, Sta. East Orange
(see appendix)
Chambersburg, Sta. Trenton...08611
Changewater....................07831
Chatham (1st)..................07928
Chatsworth......................08019
Cheesequake, Br. South
Amboy..........................08879
Cherry Hill (1st)...............08002
Cherry Mall, Sta. Cherry Hill..08034
Chester (1st)...................07930
Chestnut, Sta. Union...........07083
Cinnaminson, Br. Riverton.....08077
Circle, Br. Trenton.............08638
Circle City, Br. Phillipsburg...08865
Circle Plaza,
Nanasquan.....................08736
Clark, Br. Rahway.............07066
Clarksboro.......................08020
Clarksburg.......................08510
Clayton...........................08312
Clementon (1st)...............08021
Cliffside Park (1st)...........07010
Cliffwood.........................07721
Cliffwood Beach, Br.
Keyport........................07735
•CLIFTON (1st) (see
appendix)
Clinton (1st)....................08809
Clinton Hill, Sta. Newark.....07108
Closter (1st)....................07624
Collingswood, Br. Camden....08108
Cologne...........................08213
Colonia, Br. Rahway..........07067
Colts Neck.......................07722
Columbia..........................07832

Columbus.........................08022
Convent Station, Br.
Morristown.....................07961
Cookstown.......................08511
Coytesville, Br. Fort Lee.......07024
Cranbury (1st)..................08512
Cranford (1st)..................07016
Creamridge......................08514
Cresskill (1st)..................07626
Crosswicks.......................08515
Dayton (1st)....................08810
Deal...............................07723
Deepwater (1st)................08023
Deerfield Street.................08313
Delair, Br. Camden............08110
Delanco, Br. Riverside.........08075
Delawanna, Sta. Clifton.......07014
Delaware.........................07833
Delmont..........................08314
Delran, Br. Riverside..........08075
Demarest (1st).................07627
Dennisville.......................08214
Denville (1st)...................07834
Deptford, Br. Woodbury.......08096
Dividing Creek..................08315
Doddtown, Sta. East Orange..07017
Dorchester.......................08316
Dorothy...........................08317
Dover (1st)......................07801
Drew University, Br.
Madison........................07940
Dumont (1st)...................07628
Dundee, Sta. Passaic.........07055
Dunellen (1st)..................08812
East, Sta. Paterson............07514
East Brunswick (1st)..........08816
East Camden, Sta. Camden...08105
East Hanover (1st).............07936
East Keansburg, Br.
Keansburg......................07734
East Millstone, Br. Somerset..08873
EAST ORANGE (1st) (see
appendix)
East Paterson (1st)............07407
East Rutherford, Br.
Rutherford......................07073
East Side, Sta. Bridgeton.....08302
East Windsor, Br.
Hightstown....................08520
Eatontown (1st)................07724
Edgewater (1st)................07020
Edison (1st).....................08817
Egg Harbor City (1st)........08215
Elberon, Br. Long Branch.....07740
ELIZABETH (1st) (see
appendix)
Elizabethport, Sta. Elizabeth..07206
Elmer.............................08318
Elmora, Sta. Elizabeth........07202
Elwood............................08217
Emerson (1st)...................07630
ENGLEWOOD (1st) (see
appendix)
Englewood Cliffs, Br.
Englewood.....................07632
Englishtown (1st)..............07726
Ernston, Sta. Parlin...........08859
Essex Fells.......................07021
Estell Manor.....................08319
Ewan..............................08025
Fair Haven, Br. Red Bank.....07701
Fair Lawn (1st).................07410
Fairfield, Br. Caldwell.........07006

Fairton............................08320
Fairview (1st)...................07022
Fanwood (1st)..................07023
Far Hills..........................07931
Farmingdale (1st)..............07727
Five Corners, Sta. Jersey
City.............................07308
Flagtown.........................08821
Flanders..........................07836
Flemington (1st)...............08822
Florence..........................08518
Florham Park (1st)............07932
Fords, Br. Perth Amboy.......08863
•Forked River...................08731
Fort Dix, Br. Trenton..........08640
Fort Lee (1st)...................07024
Fort Monmouth, Br. Red
Bank.............................07703
Fortescue........................08321
Forty Eighth Street, Br.
Union City......................07087
Forty Third Street, Sta.
Union City......................07087
Foster Village, Sta.
Bergenfield....................07621
Franklin (1st)...................07416
Franklin Lakes (1st)...........07417
Franklin Park....................08823
Franklinville.....................08322
Freehold (1st)..................07728
Frenchtown......................08825
Garden State, Sta. Paramus..07652
Garfield (1st)...................07026
Garwood (1st)..................07027
General Lafayette, Sta.
Jersey City.....................07304
Gibbsboro.......................08026
Gibbstown.......................08027
Gillette...........................07933
Gladstone........................07934
Glassboro (1si).................08028
Glasser...........................07837
Glen Gardner....................08826
Glen Ridge (1st)...............07028
Glen Rock, Br. Ridgewood....07452
Glendora.........................08029
Glenwood........................07418
Gloucester City (1st).........08030
Goshen...........................08218
Grantwood, Sta. Cliffside
Park.............................07010
Grasselli, Sta. Linden.........07036
Great Meadows..................07838
Green Brook, Br. Dunellen.....08812
Green Creek.....................08219
Green Pond, R. Br.
Newfoundland..................07435
Green Village....................07935
Greendell.........................07839
Greenville, Sta. Jersey City...07305
Greenwich........................08323
Grenloch.........................08032
Greystone Park, Br. Morris
Plains...........................07950
Grove, Sta. Bloomfield........07003
Groveville, Br. Trenton........08620
Guttenberg, Br. West New
York............................07093
HACKENSACK (1st) (see
appendix)
Hackettstown (1st)............07840
Haddon Heights (1st)........08035
Haddonfield (1st)..............08033

Hainesport.................................08036
Haledon-North Haledon, Br.
 Paterson...............................07508
Hamburg...................................07419
Hamilton Square, Br.
 Trenton................................08690
Hammonton (1st).......................08037
Hampton (1st)...........................08827
Haneocks Bridge.......................08038
Harrington Park.........................07640
Harrison (1st)...........................07029
Harrisonville.............................08039
Harvey Cedars, Br. Beach
 Haven..................................08008
Hasbrouck Heights, Br.
 Hackensack...........................07604
Haskell (1st)............................07420
Haworth...................................07641
Hawthorne, Br. Paterson
 (see appendix)
Hazlet (1st).............................07730
Heislerville...............................08324
Helmetta..................................08828
Hewitt.....................................07421
Hibernia...................................07842
High Bridge..............................08829
Highland Lakes..........................07422
Highland Park, Br. New
 Brunswick.............................08904
Highlands.................................07732
Hightstown (1st).......................08520
Hillcrest, Sta. Paterson...............07502
Hillsdale (1st)..........................07642
Hillside, Br. Elizabeth.................07205
Ho Ho Kus (1st)........................07423
Hoboken (1st)...........................07030
Holmdel (1st)...........................07733
Hopatcong (1st)........................07843
Hope.......................................07844
Hopewell (1st)..........................08525
Howell, Br. Farmingdale..............07727
Hudson City, Sta. Jersey
 City......................................07307
Hudson Heights, Sta. North
 Bergen..................................07047
Imlaystown...............................08526
Industrial Hillside, Br.
 Elizabeth...............................07205
Ironbound, Sta. Newark...............07105
Ironia.....................................07845
Irvington, Br. Newark..................07111
Iselin (1st)..............................08830
Island Heights...........................08732
Jackson (1st)...........................08527
Jackson Avenue, Sta. Jersey
 City......................................07305
Jamesburg (1st)........................08831
JERSEY CITY (1st) (see
 appendix)
Jobstown.................................08041
Johnsonburg.............................07846
Journal Square, Sta. Jersey
 City......................................07306
Juliustown................................08042
Jutland, R. Br. Clinton................08809
Keansburg (1st)........................07734
Kearny (1st).............................07032
Keasbey...................................08832
Kendall Park (1st)......................08824
Kenilworth (1st)........................07033
Kenvil....................................07847
Keyport (1st)...........................07735
Kingston..................................08528

Kinnelon, Br. Butler....................07405
Kirkwood..................................08043
Lafayette..................................07848
Lake Hiawatha (1st)...................07034
Lake Hopatcong.........................07849
Lakehurst (1st).........................08733
Lakehurst Naval Air Station,
 Br. Lakehurst.........................08733
Lakeland, R. Sta.
 Blackwood.............................08012
Lakewood (1st).........................08701
Lambertville (1st)......................08530
Landing...................................07850
Landisville................................08326
Lanoka Harbor...........................08734
Laurel Springs, Br.
 Clementon.............................08021
Laurence Harbor, Br. South
 Amboy..................................08879
Lavallette.................................08735
Lawnside..................................08045
Lawrenceville, Br. Trenton...........08648
Layton....................................07851
Lebanon (1st)...........................08833
Ledgewood...............................07852
Leeds Point..............................08220
Leesburg..................................08327
Leonardo..................................07737
Leonia, Br. Hackensack...............07605
Liberty Corner...........................07938
Lincoln Park..............................07035
Lincroft (1st)...........................07738
Linden (1st).............................07036
Lindenwold, Br. Clementon...........08021
Linwood (1st)...........................08221
Little Falls (1st).......................07424
Little Ferry (1st).......................07643
Little Silver (1st)......................07739
Little York................................08834
Livingston (1st)........................07039
Locust, Br. Rumson....................07760
Lodi (1st)................................07644
Long Beach, Br. Beach
 Haven..................................08008
Long Branch (1st)......................07740
Long Valley..............................07853
Longport, Br. Atlantic City..........08403
Lopatcong, Br. Phillipsburg..........08865
Lumberton................................08048
Lyndhurst, Br. Rutherford............07071
Lyons, Br. Basking Ridge............07939
Madison (1st)...........................07940
Magnolia..................................08049
Mahwah (1st)...........................07430
Malaga....................................08328
Mall, Sta. Short Hills.................07078
Manahawkin.............................08050
Manasquan (1st).......................08736
Manor Park, Br. Brick Town.........08723
Mantoloking..............................08738
Mantua (1st)............................08051
Manville (1st)...........................08835
Maple Shade (1st).....................08052
Maplecrest, Sta. Maplewood........07040
Maplewood (1st)........................07040
Margate City, Br. Atlantic
 City......................................08402
Marlboro..................................07746
Marlton (1st)............................08053
Marmora..................................08223
Martinsville...............................08836
Masonville................................08054
Matawan (1st)..........................07747

Mauricetown..............................08329
Mays Landing (1st).....................08330
Maywood, Br. Hackensack...........07607
Mc Afee..................................07428
Mc Guire A F B, Br. Trenton........08641
Meadowview, Sta. North
 Bergen..................................07047
Medford (1st)...........................08055
Medford Lakes, Br. Medford........08055
Mendham (1st).........................07945
Menlo Park, Sta. Edison.............08817
Mercerville, Br. Trenton..............08619
Merchantville, Br. Camden
 (see appendix)
Metuchen (1st).........................08840
Mickleton................................08056
Middlebush, Br. Somerset...........08873
Middlesex (1st).........................08846
Middletown (1st).......................07748
Middleville................................07855
Midland Park (1st).....................07432
Midtown, Sta. Newark.................07102
Milford (1st)............................08848
Military Ocean Terminal,
 Sta. Bayonne.........................07002
Millburn (1st)...........................07041
Millington.................................07946
Milltown (1st)...........................08850
Millville (1st)............................08332
Milmay....................................08340
Milton, Sta. Oak Ridge...............07438
Minotola..................................08341
Mizpah....................................08342
Monitor, Sta. West New York......07093
Monmouth Beach.......................07750
Monmouth Junction....................08852
Monroe....................................07430
Monroeville..............................08343
MONTCLAIR (1st) (see
 appendix)
Montvale (1st)..........................07645
Montville (1st)..........................07045
Moonachie, Br. Rutherford..........07074
Moorestown (1st)......................08057
Morganville..............................07751
Morris Plains (1st).....................07950
Morris Street, Sta.
 Morristown.............................07960
Morristown (1st).......................07960
 Convent Station, Br.................07961
 Morris Street, Sta..................07960
Mount Arlington........................07856
Mount Ephraim (1st)..................08059
Mount Freedom.........................07970
Mount Holly (1st)......................08060
Mount Royal.............................08061
Mountain Lakes (1st).................07046
Mountainside, Br. Westfield.........07092
Muhlenburg, Sta. Plainfield..........07060
Mullica Hill..............................08062
Murray Hill, Br. New
 Providence............................07974
National Park............................08063
Navesink..................................07752
Neptune (1st)...........................07753
Neptune City, Br. Neptune..........07753
Neshanic Station.......................08853
Netcong..................................07857
Netherwood, Sta. Plainfield.........07062
NEW BRUNSWICK (1st) (see
 appendix)
New Egypt...............................08533
New Gretna..............................08224
New Lisbon...............................08064

New Milford (1st) 07646
New Monmouth, Br.
  Middletown 07748
New Providence (1st) 07974
New Shrewsbury, Br.
  Eatontown 07724
New Vernon 07976
NEWARK (1st) (see
  appendix)
Newfield 08344
Newfoundland 07435
Newport 08345
Newton (1st) 07860
Newtonville 08346
Nixon, Sta. Edison 08817
Norma 08347
Normandy Beach 08739
North, Sta. Newark 07104
North Arlington, Br. Kearny ...07032
North Bergen (1st) 07047
North Branch, Br.
  Somerville 08876
North Brunswick, Br. New
  Brunswick 08902
North Cape May, Br. Cape
  May 08204
North Center, Sta.
  Bloomfield 07003
North Elizabeth, Sta.
  Elizabeth 07208
North Hackensack, Sta.
  River Edge 07661
North Plainfield, Br.
  Plainfield 07060
North Wildwood, Br.
  Wildwood 08260
Northfield (1st) 08225
*Northvale (1st) 07647
Norwood (1st) 07648
Number Five, Sta. Asbury
  Park 07712
Number One, Sta. Ocean
  Grove 07756
Nutley, Br. Newark 07110
Oak Ridge (1st) 07438
Oakhurst (1st) 07755
Oakland (1st) 07436
Oaklyn, Br. Camden 08107
Ocean, Br. Asbury Park 07712
Ocean City (1st) 08226
Ocean Gate 08740
Ocean Grove 07756
Ocean View 08230
Oceanport 07757
Oceanville 08231
Ogdensburg 07439
Old Bridge (1st) 08857
Old Tappan, Br. Westwood ...07675
Oldwick 08858
Oradell (1st) 07649
ORANGE (1st) (see
  appendix)
Osbornsville, Br. Brick Town ...08723
Outwater, Sta. Garfield 07026
Overbrook, Sta. Cedar Grove ...07009
Oxford 07863
Packanack Lake, Sta.
  Wayne 07470
Palisade, Sta. Fort Lee 07024
Palisades Park (1st) 07650
Palmyra (1st) 08065
Pamrapo, Sta. Bayonne 07002
Paramus (1st) 07652

Park, Sta. Paterson 07513
Park Ridge (1st) 07656
Parlin (1st) 08859
Parsippany (1st) 07054
PASSAIC (1st) (see
  appendix)
Passaic Park, Sta. Passaic ...07055
PATERSON (1st) (see
  appendix)
Pattenburg 08860
Paulsboro (1st) 08066
Peapack 07977
Pedricktown 08067
Pemberton 08068
Pennington (1st) 08534
Penns Grove (1st) 08069
Pennsauken, Br. Camden 08110
Pennsville (1st) 08070
Pequannock (1st) 07440
Perrineville 08535
PERTH AMBOY (1st) (see
  appendix)
Phillipsburg (1st) 08865
Pine Beach 08741
Pine Brook (1st) 07058
Pine Hill, Br. Clementon 08021
Piscataway (1st) 08854
Pitman (1st) 08071
Pittstown 08867
PLAINFIELD (1st) (see
  appendix)
Plainsboro 08536
Plaza, Sta. Willingboro 08046
Pleasantville (1st) 08232
Pluckemin 07978
Point Pleasant, Br. Point
  Pleasant Beach 08742
Point Pleasant Beach (1st) ...08742
Pomona 08240
Pompton Lakes (1st) 07442
Pompton Plains (1st) 07444
Port Elizabeth 08348
Port Monmouth 07758
Port Murray 07865
Port Norris 08349
Port Reading 07064
Port Republic 08241
Pottersville 07979
Preakness, Sta. Wayne 07470
Presidential Lakes, R. Br.
  Browns Mills 08015
Princeton (1st) 08540
Princeton Junction 08550
Quakertown 08868
Quinton 08072
RAHWAY (1st) (see
  appendix)
Ramsey (1st) 07446
Rancocas 08073
Randolph, Sta. Dover 07801
Raritan (1st) 08869
Readington 08870
Red Bank (1st) 07701
  Fair Haven, Br. 07701
  Fort Monmouth, Br. 07703
  Shrewsbury, Br. 07701
  Suburban, Br. 07701
  Westboro, Sta. 07701
Richland 08350
Richwood 08074
Ridgefield (1st) 07657
Ridgefield Park (1st) 07660
RIDGEWOOD (1st) (see

appendix)
Ringoes 08551
Ringwood 07456
Rio Grande 08242
Ritz, Sta. Garfield 07026
River Edge (1st) 07661
River Road, Sta. Fair Lawn ...07410
River Street, Sta. Paterson ...07524
River Vale, Br. Westwood 07675
Riverdale (1st) 07457
Riverside (1st) 08075
Riverton (1st) 08077
Roadstown 08351
Robbinsville, Br. Trenton 08691
Rochelle Park (1st) 07662
Rockaway (1st) 07866
Rockleigh, Br. Northvale 07647
Rocky Hill 08553
Roebling 08554
Roosevelt 08555
Roseland (1st) 07068
Roselle, Br. Elizabeth 07203
Roselle Park, Br. Elizabeth ...07204
Rosemont 08556
Rosenhayn 08352
Roseville, Sta. Newark 07107
Rumson (1st) 07760
Runnemede (1st) 08078
RUTHERFORD (1st) (see,
  appendix)
Saddle Brook, Br. Rochelle
  Park 07662
Saddle River (1st) 07458
Salem (1st) 08079
Sayreville (1st) 08872
Schooleys Mountain 07870
Scobeyville, R. Br.
  Eatontown 07724
Scotch Plains (1st) 07076
Sea Bright, Br. Rumson 07760
Sea Girt 08750
Sea Isle City (1st) 08243
Seabrook, Br. Bridgeton 08302
Seaside Heights 08751
Seaside Park 08752
Secaucus (1st) 07094
Sergeantsville 08557
Sewaren 07077
Sewell 08080
Shiloh 08353
Ship Bottom, Br. Beach
  Haven 08008
Shore Acres, Br. Brick Town ...08723
Short Hills (1st) 07078
Shrewsbury, Br. Red Bank 07701
Sicklerville 08081
Skillman 08558
Smithville, Br. Absecon 08201
Somerdale (1st) 08083
Somers Point (1st) 08244
Somerset (1st) 08873
Somerville (1st) 08876
  North Branch, Br. 08876
South, Sta. Newark 07114
South Amboy (1st) 08879
South Bound Brook (1st) 08880
South Branch 08881
South Camden, Sta.
  Camden 08104
South Dennis 08245
South Hackensack, Br.
  Hackensack 07606
South Livingston, Sta.
  Livingston 07039

423

South Orange (1st) 07079
South Paterson, Sta.
  Paterson 07503
South Plainfield (1st) 07080
South River (1st) 08882
South Seaville 08246
South Toms River, Br. Toms
  River 08753
South Vineland, Sta.
  Vineland 08360
Sparta (1st) 07871
Spotswood (1st) 08884
Spring Lake (1st) 07762
Spring Lake Heights, Br.
  Spring Lake 07762
Springfield (1st) 07081
Stanhope (1st) 07874
Stanton 08885
State Hospital, Br. Trenton ...08625
Stewartsville 08886
Stillwater 07875
Stirling (1st) 07980
Stockholm 07460
Stockton 08559
Stone Harbor 08247
Stratford (1st) 08084
Strathmere 08248
Suburban, Br. Red Bank 07701
Succasunna (1st) 07876
Summit (1st) 07901
Summit Avenue, Sta. Union
  City 07087
Surf City, Br. Beach Haven ...08008
Sussex (1st) 07461
Swartswood 07877
Swedesboro 08085
Tabor 07878
Taurus, Sta. West New York ...07093
Teaneck (1st) 07666
Tenafly (1st) 07670
Tennent 07763
Teterboro, Br. Hackensack ...07608
Thorofare 08086
Three Bridges 08887
Titusville 08560
Toms River (1st) 08753
Totowa, Br. Paterson (see
  appendix)
Towaco 07082
Town Center, Br. Orange 07052
Townley, Sta. Union 07083
Townsends Inlet, Br. Sea
  Isle City 08243
Tranquility 07879
TRENTON (1st) (see
  appendix)

Tuckahoe 08250
Tuckerton 08087
Turnersville, Br. Blackwood ...08012
Tyler Park, Sta. North
  Bergen 07047
Union (1st) 07083
Union Beach, Br. Keyport 07735
Union Center, Sta. Union 07083
Union City (1st) 07087
Union Square, Sta.
  Elizabeth 07201
Upper Montclair, Sta.
  Montclair 07043
Uptown, Sta. Hoboken 07030
V A Hospital, Sta. East
  Orange 07018
Vailsburg, Sta. Newark 07106
Valley, Sta. Wayne 07470
Vauxhall (1st) 07088
Ventnor City, Br. Atlantic
  City 08406
Vernon 07462
Verona, Br. Montclair 07044
Vienna 07880
Villas 08251
Vincentown 08088
Vineland (1st) 08360
Voorhees, R. Br. Kirkwood ...08043
Waldwick (1st) 07463

Wall, Br. Belmar 07719
Wallington, Br. Passaic 07057
Wallpack Center 07881
Wanaque 07465
Waretown 08758
Warren, Br. Plainfield 07060
Warren Point, Sta. Fair
  Lawn 07410
Washington (1st) 07882
Washington Park, Sta.
  Newark 07102
Washington Street, Sta.
  Hoboken 07030
Watchung, Br. Plainfield 07060
Waterford Works 08089
Watsessing, Sta. Bloomfield ...07003
Wayne (1st) 07470
Weehawken, Br. Union City ...07087
Weequahic, Sta. Newark 07112
Wenonah 08090
West, Sta. Newark 07103
West Berlin 08091
West Caldwell, Br. Caldwell ...07006
West Carteret, Br. Carteret ...07008
West Collingswood, Br.

Camden 08107
West Creek 08092
West End, Sta. Long Branch ...07740
West Englewood, Sta.
  Teaneck 07666
West Hudson, Sta. Kearny 07032
West Keansburg, Br.
  Keansburg 07734
West Long Branch (1st) 07764
West Milford 07480
West New York (1st) 07093
West Orange, Br. Orange 07052
West Paterson, Br. Little
  Falls 07424
West Side, Sta. Jersey City ...07304
West Side, Sta. Hoboken 07030
West Trenton, Br. Trenton 08628
Westboro, Sta. Red Bank 07701
WESTFIELD (1st) (see
  appendix)
Westmont, Br. Camden 08108
Westville (1st) 08093
Westwood (1st) 07675
Wharton (1st) 07885
Whippany (1st) 07981
White House Station 08889
Whitehouse 08888
Whitesboro 08252
Whiting, Br. Lakehurst 08759
Wickatunk 07765
Wildwood (1st) 08260
Wildwood Crest, Br.
  Wildwood 08260
Williamstown (1st) 08094
Willingboro (1st) 08046
Windsor 08561
Winslow 08095
Wood-Ridge, Br. Rutherford
  (see appendix)
Woodbine 08270
Woodbridge (1st) 07095
Woodbury (1st) 08096
  Blackwood Terrace, Br. ...08096
  Deptford, Br. 08096
  Woodbury Heights, Br. 08097
Woodbury Heights, Br.
  Woodbury 08097
Woodcliff, Sta. North Bergen ...07047
Woodcliff Lake, Br.
  Westwood 07675
Woodcrest, Sta. Cherry Hill ...08003
Woodlynne, Br. Camden 08107
Woodstown (1st) 08098
Wrightstown (1st) 08562
Wyckoff (1st) 07481
Yardville, Br. Trenton 08620
Zarephath 08890

ATLANTIC CITY   084

POST OFFICE BOXES

B ox Nos.		
A-1	Main Office	04
1-1430	Main Office	04
421-597	Longport Br	03
2000-2999	Ventnor Br	06
3001-3246	Margate Br	02

STATIONS, BRANCHES AND UNITS

Longport Br	03
Margate City Br	02
Ventnor City Br	06
General Delivery	01
Postmaster	01

APARTMENTS, HOTELS, MOTELS

Admiral Apartments, 2 S Hartford Ave	01
Barclay Court Apartments, 9 S Penna Ave	01
Best Of Life Apartments, 129 S Va Ave	01
Biarritz Apartments, 37 S Iowa Ave	01

Atlantic City (Con.)   084

Chelsea Towers, 3817 Ventnor Ave.	01
Emmanuel Apartments, 1526 Pacific Ave.	01
Galbreath Apartments, 1500 Pacific Ave.	01
Grammercy Court Apartments, 14 Maine Ave.	01
Haverford Apartments, 114 S Va Ave.	01
Loumar Apartments, 1329 Pacific Ave.	01
Manhattan Apartments, 1106 Atl Ave.	01
Mayfair Apartments, S Albany Ave.	01
Ocean Manor Apartments, 101 Boardwalk.	01
Park Lane Apartments, 117 S Illinois Ave.	01
Plaza Apartments, Plaza And Boardwalk.	01
Preston Apartments, 3 N Penna Ave.	01
Riviera Apartments, 116 S Raleigh Ave.	01
Town House Apartments, 64 S S Car Ave.	01
Vermont Apartments, 245 S Vermont Ave.	01

GOVERNMENT OFFICES

NAFEC	05

CAMDEN   081

POST OFFICE BOXES

Box Nos.

1-148	Audubon Br	06
1-218	Oaklyn Br	07
1-246	Pennsauken Br.	10
1-349	Collingswood Br	08
1-415	Delair Br	10
1-899	Main Office	01
1000-1099	Main Office	01
1001-1399	Merchantville Br	09
1201-1367	East Camden Sta	05
1900-1999	Main Office	01

STATIONS, BRANCHES AND UNITS

Audubon Br	06
Collingswood Br	08
Delair Br	10
East Camden Sta	05
Merchantville Br	09
Oaklyn Br	07
Pennsauken Br	10
South Camden Sta	04
West Collingswood Br	07

Westmont Br	08
Woodlynne Br	07
General Delivery	01
Postmaster	01

APARTMENTS, HOTELS, MOTELS

Ablett Village Housing Unit, E State & River Rd.	05
Audubon Park Housing Unit	06
Beacon Place, 1440 Sheridan.	04
Branch Village Housing Unit, 9th &. Van Hook.	04
Canterbury, 9th & Morgan.	04
Chelton Terr Housing Unit 7th & Chelton.	04
Cooper River Plaza, 5105 North Park Drive	09
Crescent, 1624 Independence Rd	04
Crestfair, 8th & Morgan.	04
Crestwood, 301 Champion Ave.	07
Cuthbert Manor, East Cuthbert Rd.	08
East State Village, East State & Harrison Ave.	05
Eldridge Gardens, Eldridge & Taylor.	07
Everett Gardens Housing Unit, 1507 S 7th St.	04
Ferry Station, Ferry Ave : Old White Horse Pike.	04
Franklin Place, Hull Rd.	04
Haddon View, 1 Macarthur Blvd.	04
Heather House, 201 Cuthbert Rd	07
Hillcrest, 215 E Garfield Ave.	08
John F Kennedy Housing Unit, 21st & Westminister.	04
John Wesley Village, 805 N. Front.	02
Marina Park, Cooper River Dr.	08
Mc Guire Gardens Housing Unit, 21st & Westminister.	05
Northgate, 7th & Linden.	02
Parkview, White Hrs Pk & Collins Ave.	07
Penn Gardens, 46th & Amon Ave.	10
Penn Manor, Union & Stockton Ave.	09
Plaza Motor, 5th & Cooper.	02
Roosevelt Manor Housing Unit, 8th & Central Ave.	04
Stockton Station, Dudley & Pleasant.	05
Towne Park, 8th & Market.	02
Walt Whitman, Broadway & Cooper.	02
Washington Park, 342 Marlton Ave.	05
Westfield Acres, 31st & Westfield Ave.	05
Westfield Gardens, 32nd & Westfield Ave.	05
Westfield Towers 32nd And Westfield Ave.	05

GOVERNMENT OFFICES

City Hall, 6th & Market	01
Post Office, 401 Market	01

HOSPITALS

Cooper, 6th & Stevens	03
Our Lady Of Lourdes, Haddon & Vesper Blvd.	03
West Jersey, Mt Ephraim & Lansdowne	04

UNIVERSITIES AND COLLEGES

Rutgers College Of South Jersey, 406 Penn.	02

CHERRY HILL   080

POST OFFICE BOXES

Box Nos.

A-D	Main Office	02
1-499	Main Office	02
500-899	Woodcrest Station	03

STATIONS, BRANCHES AND UNITS

Cherry Mall Sta	34
Woodcrest Sta	03
General Delivery	02
Postmaster	02

APARTMENTS, HOTELS, MOTELS

Chapel Manor 606 Cooper Landing Rd	34
Cherry Hill Apartments E & W Route 38.	34
Cherry Hill Inn Route 38	34
Cherry Hill Lodge Route 38.	34
Colonial Apartments E & W 836 Cooper Landing Rd	34
Colonial Motel Route 38	34
Country Squire Motel Route 70.	34
Hillside Motel Route 38	34
Holiday Inn Route 70	34
King George Motel Route 70	34
Landmark Apartments Route 70 & Interstate 295	34
Parkway Apartments Park Blvd & Kings Hwy.	34
Plaza Towers 1200 Marlton Pk E	34
Provincial Apartments E & W Chestnut St.	34
Rickshaw Inn Route 70.	34
Sheraton Poste Inn Route 70.	34
Somerset House Apartments Cooper Landing Rd	34
Stuyvesant Terrace Apartments Cooper Landing.	34
Sussex House Apartments Kings Hwy E.	34
Towers Of Windsor Apartments Chapel Ave.	34
Wallworth Park Apartments Park Blvd & Kings Hwy.	34

Cherry Hill (Con.) — 080

BUILDINGS

Barclay Pavilion Route 70 34
Barclay Shopping Center
Route 70 34
Cherry Hill Mall Route 38 &
Haddonfield Rd 34
Cherry Hill Plaza Route 70 34
Ellisburg Shopping Center
Kings Hwy N 34
One Cherry Hill Mall Route
38 & Haddonfield Rd 34
Provincial Executive Bldg
Route 38 34
Woodcrest Shopping Center
Berlin Rd & Browning Ln 03
523 Building Route 38 &
Hollywood Ave 34

GOVERNMENT OFFICES

Cherry Hill Post Office 1588
Kings Hwy N ..... 0.
Cherry Hill Township Bldg
820 Mercer St 34
Woodcrest Station Cherry Hill
Post Office Woodcrest 03

HOSPITALS

Cherry Hill Medical Center
Chapel Ave & Cooper
Landing Rd 34

CLIFTON — 070

POST OFFICE BOXES

Box Nos.
1-417   Main Office 15
501-699   Allwood Sta 12
701-899   Athenia Sta 13
901-1125   Delawanna
    Sta 14

STATIONS, BRANCHES AND UNITS

Allwood Sta 12
Athenia Sta 13
Delawanna Sta 14
General Delivery 15
Postmaster 15

APARTMENTS, HOTELS, MOTELS

Colonial Gardens, 470 Piaget
Ave 11
Country Club Towers, 100-
140 Hepburn Rd 12
Franklin Gardens 11
Garret Village, 948 Valley Rd. 13
Jefferson Gardens 11
Maple Gardens, 765 Clifton
Ave 13
Martha Washington, 1401
Van Houten Ave 13
Middle Village, 24 Day 11

Richfield Village Gardens 12
Styertowne 12
Williamsburg N, 565 Grove 13
Williamsburg S, 605 Grove 13

EAST ORANGE — 070

POST OFFICE BOXES

Box Nos.
1-1999   Main Office 19
2001-2999   Central Sta 19
3001-3999   Brick Church
     Sta ..... 19·
4001-4999   Ampere 19

STATIONS, BRANCHES AND UNITS

Ampere Sta 17
Brick Church Sta 18
Central Sta 18
Doddtown Sta 17
V A Hospital Sta 18
General Delivery 19
Postmaster 19

HOSPITALS

East Orange General
Hospital, 300 Central Ave 19
Veterans Administration
Hospital, Tremont Ave 19

MILITARY INSTALLATIONS

National Guard Armory, 215
N Oraton Pkwy 17

UNIVERSITIES AND COLLEGES

Upsala College, 345
Prospect 19

ELIZABETH — 072

POST OFFICE BOXES

Box Nos.
A-L   Industrial Br 05
A-Z   Main Office 07
1-85   Hillside Br 05
1-196   Roselle Park
   Sta 04
1-230   Elizabethport
   Sta 06
1-264   Roselle Sta 03
1-697   Main Office 07
601-728   Industrial Br 05
901-954   North Elizabeth
    Sta 08

STATIONS, BRANCHES AND UNITS

Bayway Sta 02
Betsytown Sta 01
Elizabethport Sta 06
Elmora Sta 02
Hillside Br 05
Industrial Hillside Br 05
North Elizabeth Sta 08
Roselle Br 03
Roselle Park Br 04
Union Square Sta 01
General Delivery 07
Postmaster 07

APARTMENTS, HOTELS, MOTELS

Chilton Hall Apartments 02
Chilton Towers, 220 W Jersey 02
Elizabeth Carteret, 1155 E
Jersey 07
Ford Leonard Towers, 71
Division 01
Golden Age, 31 Cherry 02
Hancock House, 1380 North
Ave 08
Hayes House, 330 W Jersey 02
John F Kennedy Arms, 70
Westfield Ave 08
Park East, 1065 E Jersey 01
Pierce Manor Apartments,
Irvington Ave 08
Queen Elizabeth, 801 N
Broad 08
Queen Mary, 1341 North Ave 08
Salem Park Apartments,
Salem Park 08
Templeton Arms, N Broad 08
Tudor Court Apartments, 800
N Broad 08
Winfield Scott, 323 N Broad 07

BUILDINGS

Albender, 1143 E Jersey 01
American Type, 200 Elmora
Ave 07
Bayway Terminal, 666 S
Front 02
Elizabethtown Plaza, 2
Elizabethtown Plaza 02
Hersh Tower, 125 Broad 01
Industrial Park, 107
Trumbull 06
Martin, 1139 E Jersey 01
Medical Arts, 230 W Jersey 02
New Jersey Employment
Office, 1115 E Jersey 01
Public Library, 1 S Broad 02
Social Security, 268 N Broad 01
Y M C A, 135 Madison Ave 01
Y W C A, 1131 E Jersey 01

GOVERNMENT OFFICES

City Hall, 50 W Scott Pl 07
Court House, 2 Broad 07

HOSPITALS

Alexian Brothers, 655 E
Jersey 06

Elizabeth (Con.)   072

Elizabeth General, 925 E
  Jersey 01
Saint Elizabeths, 204 S
  Broad 07

ENGLEWOOD   076

POST OFFICE BOXES

Box Nos.
1-752	Englewood	31
900-1264	Englewood Cliffs Br	32

STATIONS, BRANCHES AND UNITS

Englewood Cliffs Br	32
General Delivery	31
Postmaster	31

HACKENSACK   076

POST OFFICE BOXES

Box Nos.
1-237	Leonia Br	05
1-347	Bogota	03
1-454	Hasbrouck Heights	04
1-970	Main Office	02
31-54	Maywood	07
801-947	Maywood	07
1501-2388	South Hackensack	06

STATIONS, BRANCHES AND UNITS

Bogota Br	03
Hasbrouck Heights Br	04
Leonia Br	05
Maywood Br	07
South Hackensack Br	06
Teterboro Br	08
General Delivery	01
Postmaster	02

HOSPITALS

Hackensack Hospital, 22
  Hospital Pl Hackensack..... 01
South Bergen Hospital, 214
  Terrace Ave Hasbrouck
  Heights............................... 04

JERSEY CITY   073

POST OFFICE BOXES

Box Nos.
A-M	Bergen Sta	04
A-P	Hudson City Sta	07
A-Q	General Lafayette Sta	04
1-900	Main Office	03
7A-7DDD	Hudson City Sta	07
4001-4419	Bergen	04
5001-5148	Greenville Sta	05
6471-6950	Journal Square Sta	06
7001-7900	Hudson City Sta	07
8001-8207	Five Corners Sta	08
9001-9168	General Lafayette Sta	04

STATIONS, BRANCHES AND UNITS

Bergen Sta	04
Five Corners Sta	08
General Lafayette Sta	04
Greenville Sta	05
Hudson City Sta	07
Jackson Avenue Sta	05
Journal Square Sta	06
West Side Sta	04
General Delivery	03
Postmaster	03

APARTMENTS, HOTELS, MOTELS

Alban Court, 2540 Boulevard	04
Annabee, 28 Sherman Pl	07
Ariston, 63 Sherman Pl	07
Duncan, 2600 Boulevard	06
Embassy, 151 Sip Ave	06
Fairmount, 2595 Boulevard	06
Garrison Apartments, 121 Garrison Ave	06
Gifford Court, 9 Gifford Ave	04
Gifford Gardens, 25 Gifford Ave	04
Gifford Hall, 17 Gifford Ave	04
Gifford Towers, 2465 Boulevard	04
Glenwood, 2677 Boulevard	06
Gloria Gables, 131 Kensington Ave	04
Gothic Towers, 50 Glenwood	06
Granada, 129 Magnolia Ave	06
Green Gables, 7 Tonnele Ave	06
Gregory Park, 280 Henderson	02
Hampshire House, 20 Tonnele Ave	06
Holiday Inn, 180 12th	02
Holland, 9 Journal Sq	06
Jamid Court, 2520 Blvd	04
Lincoln, 137 Kensington Ave	04
Madeline Gardens, 40 Glenwood Ave	06
Madrid, 821 Bergen Ave	06
Mayflower, 65 Tonnele Ave	06
Melbro Towers, 340 Fairmount Ave	06
Melrita, 107 Kensington Ave	04
Mitchell, 31 Gifford Ave	04
Park Lane, 70 Danforth Ave	05
Plaza, 91 Sip Ave	06
Rosemont, 321 Fairmount Ave	06

Royal Park, 145 Kensington Ave	04
Saint Johns Apartment 2, 225 St Pauls Ave	06
Saint Johns Apartments, 10 Huron Ave	06
Stockadian, 88 Van Reypen	06
Sunny Towers, 2500 Boulevard	04
The Bentley, 9 Bentley Ave	04
The Britton, 320 Fairmount Ave	06
The Dorian, 5 Bentley Ave	04
The Gifford, 11 Gifford Ave	04
The Netherlands, 2695 Blvd	06
The Sevilla, 2801 Blvd	06
The Shelbourne, 85 Van Reypen	06
The Summit	06
The Washington, 2671 Blvd	06
Towne House, 57 Sip Ave	06
Windsor, 305 Academy	06

BUILDINGS

Administration, 595 Newark Ave	06
Catholic Youth Organization, 380 Bergen Ave	04
Commercial Trust Company, 15 Exchange Pl	02
First Jersey National Bank, 1 Exchange Pl	02
Garden State National Bank	02
Harborside Terminal, 34 Exchange Pl	02
Jersey Journal, 30 Journal Sq	06
Labor Bank, 26 Journal Sq	06
Lackawanna Terminal, 629 Grove	02
Medical Arts, 8-12 Clifton Pl	04
New Jersey Employment Agency, 363 Summit Ave	06
Public Library, 472 Jersey Ave	02
Spingarn Arcade, 591 Summit Ave	06
Trust Company Of New Jersey, 921 Bergen Ave	06
Ymca, 654 Bergen Ave	04
Ymca, 604 Bergen Ave	04
Ywca, 270 Fairmount Ave	06

GOVERNMENT OFFICES

Board Of Education, 2 Harrison Ave	04
City Hall, 280 Grove	02
County Jail, 578 Pavonia Ave	06
Court House, Newark Ave	06

HOSPITALS

Christ, 176 Palisade Ave	06
Door Of Hope Home & Hospital, 503 Garfield Ave	05
Elizabeth Kenny Institute, Baldwin Ave	04
Fairmount, 136 Summit Ave	04
Greenville, 1825 Boulevard	05
Hudson County Tuberculosis,

427

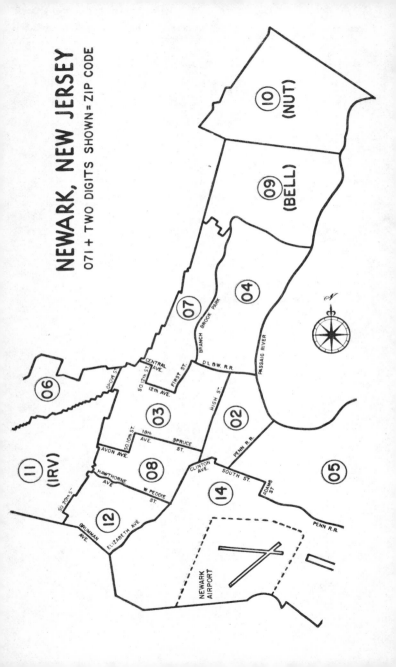

Jersey City (Con.)   **073**

100 Clifton Pl 04
Margaret Hague Maternity,
Clifton Pl 04
Medical Center, Baldwin Ave.. 02
Mothers Institute, 400 3rd...... 02
Pollack, 100 Clifton Pl......... 04
Saint Francis, 25 Mc
Williams Pl...................... 02

UNIVERSITIES AND COLLEGES

College Of Medicine &
Dentistry, 24 Baldwin Ave.. 04
Jersey City State College,
2039 Boulevard 05
Rutgers University, 168 Sip
Ave 06
Saint Peters, 2641 Blvd......... 06

MONTCLAIR   **070**

POST OFFICE BOXES

Box Nos.
A-J '   Verona 44
A-T   Main Office 42
A-Z   Main Office 42
1-341   Verona Br 44
AA-AK   Main Office 42
98-700   Main Office 42
701-937   Upper
Montclair Sta . 43

STATIONS, BRANCHES AND UNITS

Upper Montclair Sta 43
Verona Br 44
General Delivery 42
Postmaster 42

APARTMENTS, HOTELS, MOTELS

Clairidge House, Clairidge Dr.. 44
Rockcliffe 42

HOSPITALS

Community, 120 Harrison
Ave 42
Mountainside, Bay Ave &
Highland Ave 42
Saint Vincents, 45 Elm St 42

UNIVERSITIES AND COLLEGES

Montclair State, Normal Ave
& Valley Rd..................... 43

NEWARK   **071**

POST OFFICE BOXES

Box Nos.
A-N   Irvington............. 11
1-264   Belleville Br...... 09

1-268   Nutley Br......... 10
1-320   Irvington Br...... 11
1-2000   Main Office 01
2001-2999   South Sta......... 14
3001-3500   West Sta.......... 03
4001-4400   Weequahic Sta.. 12
5001-5146   Ironbound Sta ... 05
6001-6144   Vailsburg Sta.... 06
7001-7209   Roseville Sta 07
8001-8236   Clinton Hill
Sta.............. 08
9001-9207   North Sta......... 04
10000-10187 Main Office 01

STATIONS, BRANCHES AND UNITS

Academy Sta 02
Belleville Br 09
Clinton Hill Sta..................... 08
Ironbound Sta....................... 05
Irvington Br 11
Midtown Sta 02
North Sta 04
Nutley Br 10
Roseville Sta 07
South Sta 14
Vailsburg Sta 06
Washington Park Sta 02
Weequahic Sta 12
West Sta 03
General Delivery 01
Postmaster 02

APARTMENTS, HOTELS, MOTELS

Archbishop Thomas J Walsh
Homes, 1945 Mc Carter
Hwy 04
Belmont, 1007 Broad............. 02
Christopher Columbus
Homes, 112 8th Ave......... 04
Colonnade, 381 Broad 04
Devine Riviera, 169 Clinton
Ave 08
Douglas, 15 Hill 01
Essex House, 1050 Broad 02
Felix Fuld Court, 80 Jelliff
Ave 08
Franklin D Roosevelt Homes,
35 Riverview Ct 05
Holiday Inn, 430 Broad St 02
Ivy Hill Park, 5 Manor Dr....... 06
James M Baxter Terrace, 202
Orange 03
Joseph B Bradley Court, 46 N
Munn Ave....................... 06
Lincoln Park, 105 Lincoln
Park.............................. 02
Mac Evoy Court, 140
Roseville Ave 07
Military Park, 16 Park Pl 01
New Tremont, 16 Fulton......... 01
Normandie, 103 Chancellor
Ave 12
Otto Kretchmer Homes, 71
Ludlow........................... 14
Park Lane, 79 Lincoln Park 02
Rev W P Hayes Homes, 71
Boyd.............................. 03
Robert Treat, 50 Park Pl......... 01
Seth Boyden Court, 124 Seth
Boyden Ter 14
Stella Windsor Wright Homes,

159 Spruce........................ 08
Stephen Crane Village, 1
Stephen Crane Plaza 07
Weequahic Park Tower, 455
Elizabeth Ave 12

BUILDINGS

Academy, 17 Academy........... 02
American Insurance, 15
Washington...................... 02
Broad & Market, 784 Broad ... 02
Chamber Of Commerce, 24
Branford Pl 02
Commerce Court, 10
Commerce Ct................... 02
Fatzler, 9 Hill 02
Federal Trust, 24 Commerce... 02
Griffith, 605 Broad................ 02
Kinney, 790 Broad................. 02
Medical Tower, 31 Lincoln
Park.............................. 02
Military Park, 60 Park Pl 02
Mutual Benefit Life
Insurance, 520 Broad 02
National Newark & Essex,
744 Broad 02
National State Bank, 810
Broad 02
Prudential Insurance
Company, 763 Broad......... 02
Raymond-Commerce, 1180
Raymond Blvd.................. 02
Union, 9 Clinton 02
Wiss, 665 Broad.................... 02

GOVERNMENT OFFICES

Federal Building, 970 Broad
St 02
N J State Building, 1100
Raymond Blvd.................. 02
United States Court House,
Federal Square................. 02
United States Post Office,
Federal Square................. 02
Veterans Administration, 20
Washington Pl................. 02

HOSPITALS

American Legion Memorial,
741 Broadway.................. 04
Babies, 15 Roseville Ave 07
Beth Isreal, 201 Lyons Ave 12
Clara Maass, Franklin Ave.
Belleville 09
Columbus, 495 N 13th........... 07
Doctors, 65 Avon Ave............ 08
Hospital & Home For
Crippled Children, 89 Park
Ave 04
Irvington General, 832
Chancellor Ave. Irvington ... 11
Martland Medical Center, 65
Bergen........................... 07
Newark Convalescent, Ivy
Hill 06
Newark Eye & Ear Infirmary,
77 Central Ave................. 02
Presbyterian, 27 S 9th........... 07
Saint James, 155 Jefferson..... 05
Saint Michaels, 306 High....... 02

Newark (Con.)   071

UNIVERSITIES AND COLLEGES

Essex County Community, 31 Clinton St	02
Newark College Of Engineering, 323 High	02
Rutgers University	02
Rutgers University College Of Pharmacy, 1 Lincoln Ave	04
Seton Hall University Law School, 40 Clinton St	02

NEW BRUNSWICK   089

POST OFFICE BOXES

Box Nos.

1-1806	North Brunswick Br	02
1-2020	Main Office	03
1200-1410	Highland Park Br	04

RURAL ROUTES

4	02

STATIONS, BRANCHES AND UNITS

Highland Park Br	04
North Brunswick Br	02
General Delivery	01
Postmaster	01

APARTMENTS, HOTELS, MOTELS

Bishop Towers	01
Colony House	01
Georgetown	02
Holiday Inn	02
Howard Johnson	01
Lionel Village	02
Park Lane	04
Park Town	04

BUILDINGS

National Bank Building	03

GOVERNMENT OFFICES

Highland Park Borough	04
Middlesex County Offices	01
New Brunswick City Hall	03
North Brunswick Township	02

HOSPITALS

Middlesex County Rehabilatation Center, Georges Rd	02
Middlesex General, 180 Somerset St	01
Saint Peters, Easton Ave	03

UNIVERSITIES AND COLLEGES

College Of Agriculture	03
Douglas College	03
Highland Park High	04
Livingston College	03
Middlesex County Vocational	01
New Brunswick Junior High	02
New Brunswick Senior High	02
New Brunswick Theological Seminary	01
Rutgers University	03
Saint Peters High	01

ORANGE   070

POST OFFICE BOXES

Box Nos.

1-116	Town Center Br	52
1-717	Main Office	51

STATIONS, BRANCHES AND UNITS

Town Center Br	52
West Orange Br	52
General Delivery	50
Postmaster	50

PASSAIC   070

POST OFFICE BOXES

Box Nos.

1-2999	Main Office	55
3101-3999	Wallington Br	57

STATIONS, BRANCHES AND UNITS

Dundee Sta	55
Passaic Park Sta	55
Wallington Br	57

HOSPITALS

Beth Israel Hospital, 70 Parker Ave	55
Passaic General Hospital, 350 Boulevard	55
Saint Mary Hospital, 211 Pennington Ave	55

PATERSON   075

POST OFFICE BOXES

Box Nos.

1-296	Park Sta	13
1-352	Totowa Br	11
1-506	Hawthorne Br	07
1-600	Haledon No Haledon Br	08
AA-BM	Main Office	09

301-644	River Street Sta	24
701-1057	South Paterson	03
1101-3250	Main Office	09

STATIONS, BRANCHES AND UNITS

East Sta	14
Haledon-North Haledon Br	08
Hillcrest Sta	02
Park Sta	13
River Street Sta	24
South Paterson Sta	03
Totowa Br	12
General Delivery	10
Postmaster	10

APARTMENTS, HOTELS, MOTELS

Alexander Hamilton, 55 Church	05
Emperor Motel Lodge, US Highway 46	12
Kent Village, 769 11th Ave	14
Lido Arms Court, 154 Paterson	01
Mayfair, 185 E 33rd	04
Park East Terrace, E 43rd & 11th Ave	03
Riverview Towers, 85 Presidential Blvd	22
Stratford Motor Court, US Highway 46 Totowa	12
Thunderbird, 411 Broadway	01

BUILDINGS

Administration, 71 Hamilton	05
Colt 5, Colt	05
Fabian, 45 Church	05
First National Bank, 125 Ellison	05
Law, 64 Hamilton	05
Mainmark, 262 Main	05
Romaine, 136 Washington	05

GOVERNMENT OFFICES

City Hall Annex, 137 Ellison	05,
Court House, 75 Hamilton	05

HOSPITALS

Barnert Memorial, 680 Broadway	14
Paterson General, 528 Market	01
Saint Josephs, 703 Main St	03
Valley View Or Preakness, Valley View Rd	09

PERTH AMBOY   088

POST OFFICE BOXES

Box Nos.

1-299	Fords Br	63
1-1030	Perth Amboy	62

Perth Amboy (Con.) 088

STATIONS, BRANCHES AND UNITS

Fords Br................................. 63
General Delivery 61
Postmaster 61

GOVERNMENT OFFICES

Internal Revenue...................... 61
Social Security......................... 61

HOSPITALS

Perth Amboy General Hosp 61

PLAINFIELD 070

POST OFFICE BOXES

Box Nos.
1-1474   Main Office 61
2500-2699   Muhlenberg
                      Sta................ 60
2700-2974   Netherwood
                      Sta............... 62
3000-3100   Station A 60
4001-4337   Warren Br......... 60

RURAL ROUTES

1,2 60

STATIONS, BRANCHES AND UNITS

Muhlenburg Sta....................... 60
Netherwood Sta....................... 62
North Plainfield Br.................... 60
Warren Br............................... 60
Watchung Br............................ 60
General Delivery 61
Postmaster 61

APARTMENTS, HOTELS, MOTELS

Cyprus Gardens, 1165
   Hgihway 22........................... 60
Greenbrook Gardens, 1275
   Rock Ave.............................. 60
Greenwood Gardens, 1300
   Highway 22........................... 60
Leland Gardens, 1227 E
   Front.................................... 62
Malcolm Gardens, 450 Little
   Pl.. 60
Meadowbrook Village, 1001 E
   Front.................................... 62
Pineview Gardens, 1000-1100
   W 7th.................................. 63
Regency Village, 401
   Highway 22........................... 60
Terrace View, 300-301 Maple
   Ave...................................... 60
Windsor Terrace, 1300 Rock
   Ave...................................... 60

GOVERNMENT OFFICES

Selective Service Board 44,
   325 E Front........................... 60

HOSPITALS

Muhlenberg Hosipital,
   Randolph Rd.......................... 61

UNIVERSITIES AND COLLEGES

Mount Saint Mary'S Academy,
   Highway 22........................... 61
Mount Saint Mary'S College,
   Highway 22........................... 61

RAHWAY 070

POST OFFICE BOXES

Box Nos.
A-F   Main Office 65
AA-AK   Main Office 65
1-1274   Main Office 65
2-215   Colonia Br........ 67
701-978   Clark Br........... 66

STATIONS, BRANCHES AND UNITS

Clark Br.................................. 66
Colonia Br............................... 67
General Delivery 65
Postmaster 65

RIDGEWOOD 074

POST OFFICE BOXES

Box Nos.
1-832   Main Office 51
1-1104   Glen Rock Br.... 52

STATIONS, BRANCHES AND UNITS

Glen Rock Br........................... 52
General Delivery 51
Postmaster 51

BUILDINGS

C F Post Building, 20 Wilsey
   Sq....................................... 51
Glen Rock Professional, 66
   Glen Ave............................... 52
Glen Rock Public Library, 315
   Rock Rd................................ 52
Lincoln Building, 45 N Broad ... 50
Mallard Building, 1156 E
   Ridgewood Ave....................... 51
Mcentegart-Melehan Bldg-139
   Harristown Rd Glen Rock
   Nj.. 52
Medical Arts Building, 385 S
   Maple Ave............................. 50
Reynolds, 125-127 E

Ridgewood Ave........................ 50
Ridgewood Public Library,
   125 N Maple Ave.................... 50
Teal, 1172 E Ridgewood Ave.. 51
Wilcox-Sithens, 75 N Maple
   Ave...................................... 51
Y M C A - Y W C A, 112 Oak
   St.. 51
Zecher Building, 1250 E
   Ridgewood Ave....................... 51

HOSPITALS

Valley, Linwood & North Van
   Dien Ave............................... 51

RUTHERFORD 070

POST OFFICE BOXES

Box Nos.
1-247   Wood Ridge Br . 75
1-284   East
                      Rutherford Br . 73
1-317   Carlstadt Br..... 72
1-460   Rutherford 70
81-465   Lyndhurst Br 71

STATIONS, BRANCHES AND UNITS

Carlstadt Br............................ 72
East Rutherford Br................... 73
Lyndhurst Br............................ 71
Moonachie Br........................... 74
Wood-Ridge Br......................... 75
General Delivery 70
Postmaster 70

TRENTON 086

POST OFFICE BOXES

Box Nos.
1-181   Main Office 01
1-266   West Trenton
                      Br 28
1-328   Yardville Br 20
1-428   Lawrenceville
                      Br 48
1-514   Robbinsville
                      Br 91
191-321   Main Office 02
331-511   Main Office 03
521-751   Main Office 04
761-970   Main Office 05
971-1201   Main Office 06
1211-2499   Main Office 07
2500-2699   Hamilton
                      Square Br..... 90
2700-2768   Main Office 07
3001-3248   Mercerville Br... 19
4000-4400   C Sta............... 10
4500-4599   Chambersburg
                      Sta............... 11
5000-5999   Circle Br 38

Trenton (Con.)   086

RURAL ROUTES

1	48
2	20
3,4	91

STATIONS, BRANCHES AND UNITS

Center Sta	08
Chambersburg Sta	11
Circle Br	38
Fort Dix Br	40
Groveville Br	20
Hamilton Square Br	90
Lawrenceville Br	48
Mc Guire A F B Br	41
Mercerville Br	19
Robbinsville Br	91
State Hospital Br	25
West Trenton Br	20
Yardville Br	20
General Delivery	08
Postmaster	08

APARTMENTS, HOTELS, MOTELS

Brookville, 1920 Riverside Dr.	18
Brookville, 321 Clearfield Ave	18
Cadwalader, 640 W State	18
Carteret Arms, 333 W State	18
Colonial Gardens, 455 W State	18
East Gate, 1501 Parkside Ave	38
Elmhurst, 879 Bellevue Ave	18
Hamilton Arms, Ward Ave Ext	19
Hamilton Arms, 1500 Nottingham Way	09
Hamilton Gardens, 2300 S Broad	10
Hamilton Park, 500 Arena Dr.	10
Hanover, 137 E Hanover	08

Hildebrecht, 27 W State	0b
Holiday Inn Of Trenton, 240 W State	08
Hotel Fitchway, 200 S Broad	08
Imperial 400, 350 S Broad	08
Lalor Gardens, 700 Lalor	10
Leonard, 85 S Clinton Ave	09
Mayfair, 583 Bellevue Ave	18
Midtown Motel, 541 E State	09
Parkside Manor, 1400 Parkside Ave	38
Penn, 81 S Clinton Ave	09
Scudders Falls East, 325 W Upper Ferry Rd	28
West Gate, 550 Lawrenceville Rd	38
Woodbrook House, 865 Lower Ferry Rd	28

BUILDINGS

Commonwealth, 150 E State	08
Federal, 402 E State	08
First-Mechanics Bank, 1 West State	08
Hamilton Township Municipal, 2090 Greenwood Ave	09
Mercer County Airport	28
N J National Bank	08
National State Bank	08
Professional, 1100 S Broad	11
Wallach, 86 E State	08
War Memorial, Memorial Dr	08

GOVERNMENT OFFICES

All Offices & Divisions, Trenton New Jersey	25
Div Of Motor Vehicles	66
Ewing Township Municipal, 1872 Pennington Ave	18
Lawrence Township Municipal, 2207 Lawrenceville Rd	38
Mercer County Court House, 209 S Broad	07
Trenton City Hall, E State	08

HOSPITALS

Donnelly Memorial, Hamilton Ave & Klockner Rd	19
Hamilton White Horse - Ham Sq Rd	90
Helene Fuld, Brunswick Ave At Fuld	38
Mercer, 446 Bellevue Ave	07
New Jersey State Hospital, Sullivan Way	25
Saint Francis, 601 Hamilton Ave	29

MILITARY INSTALLATIONS

Fort Dix New Jersey	40
Mc Guire Afb, New Jersey	41
U. S. Naval Air Propulsion Test Center	28

UNIVERSITIES AND COLLEGES

Board Of Education, 9 S Stockton	11
Mercer County Community College, 101 W State	08
Rider College, 2083 Lawrenceville Rd	02
Trenton State College, Hillwood Lakes	25

WESTFIELD   070

POST OFFICE BOXES

Box Nos.		
A-N	Mountainside Branch	92
A-W	Main Office	91
1-880	Main Office	91
1001-1221	Mountainside Br	92

STATIONS, BRANCHES AND UNITS

Mountainside Br	92
General Delivery	91
Postmaster	91

NEW MEXICO
(Abbreviation: NM)

Abiquiu	87510
Alameda, Br. Albuquerque (see appendix)	
Alamo, R. Br. Magdalena	87825
Alamogordo (1st)	88310
Albert, R. Br. Mosquero	87733
ALBUQUERQUE (1st) (see appendix)	
Alcalde	87511
Algodones, R. Br. Bernalillo	87001
Alto	88312
Amalia	87512
Ambrosia Lake, R. Br. Grants	87020
Amistad	88410

Ancho, R. Br. Carrizozo	88313
Animas	88020
Anthony	88021
Berino. R. Br.	88024
Anton Chico	87711
Apache Creek, R. Br. Reserve	87830
Aragon	87820
Arenas Valley	88022
Arrey	87930
Arroyo Hondo	87513
Arroyo Seco	87514
Artesia (1st)	88210
Aztec	87410
Bard	88411
Bayard	88023
Belen (1st)	87002

Bell Ranch, R. Br. Tucumcari	88441
Bellview	88111
Bent	88314
Berino, R. Br. Anthony	88024
Bernalillo	87004
Algodones, R. Br.	87001
Bingham	87815
Blanco	87412
Bloomfield	87413
Bluewater	87005
Boles, R. Br. Alamogordo	88310
Bosque	87006
Brimhall	87310
Broadmoor, Sta. Roswell	88201
Broadview	88112
Buckeye	88212

Buckhorn 88025
Buena Vista 87712
Bueyeros 88412
Caballo 87931
Campus, Sta. Socorro 87801
Canjilon 87515
Cannon A F B, Br. Clovis.......88101
Canoncito, R. Br. Laguna.......87026
Canones 87516
Capitan 88316
Caprock 88213
Capulin 88414
Carlsbad (1st) 88220
Carrizozo 88301
　　Ancho, R. Br. 88313
Carson 87517
Casa Blanca 87007
Causey 88113
Cebolla 87518
Cedar Crest 87008
Cedarvale 87009
Central 88026
Cerrillos 87010
Cerro 87519
Chacon 87713
Chama 87520
Chamberino 88027
Chamisal 87521
Chimayo 87522
Church Rock 87311
Cimarron 87714
Claunch 87011
Clayton 88415
Cleveland 87715
Cliff 88028
Clines Corners, R. Br.
　Moriarty 87070
Cloudcroft 88317
Clovis (1st) 88101
Cochiti, R. Br. Penablanca 87041
Columbus 88029
Conchas Dam, R. Br.
　Tucumcari 88416
Continental Divide..................87312
Cordova 87523
Corona 88318
Coronado, Sta. Santa Fe........87501
Corrales 87048
Costilla 87524
Counselor, R. Br. Cuba 87018
Coyote 87012
Crossroads 88114
Crownpoint 87313
Cuba 87013
　Counselor, R. Br. 87018
　Regina, R. Br. 87046
Cubero 87014
Cuchillo 87932
Cuervo 88417
Cundiyo, R. Br. Chimayo.........87522
Datil 87821
Deming (1st) 88030
Derry 87933
Des Moines 88418
Dexter 88230
Dixon 87527
Dona Ana 88032
Dora 88115
Downtown, Sta. Albuquerque
　(see appendix)
Dulce 87528
Duran 88319
Dusty 87934

Eagle Nest 87718
East Vaughn 88320
Edgewood 87015
El Prado 87529
El Rito 87530
Elephant Butte 87935
Elida 88116
Elkins 88117
Embudo 87531
Encino 88321
Espanola (1st) 87532
　　Fairview, Sta. 87532
　　Hernandez, R. Br. 87537
　　Truchas, R. Br. 87578
Estancia 87016
　　Tajique, R. Br. 87057
Eunice 88231
Fairacres. 88033
Fairview, Sta. Espanola 87532
Farley, R. Br. Springer 87720
Farmington (1st) 87401
Faywood 88034
Fence Lake 87315
Flora Vista 87415
Floyd 88118
Flying H 88322
Folsom 88419
Fort Bayard, R. Br. Silver
　City 88036
Fort Stanton 88323
Fort Sumner 88119
Fort Wingate 87316
Fruitland 87416
Gabaldon 87721
Gallina 87017
Gallup (1st) 87301
　Gamerco, R. Br. 87317
　Navajo, R. Br. 87328
　Vander Wagen, R. Br. 87326
Gamerco, R. Br. Gallup 87317
Garfield 87936
Garita 88421
Gila 88038
Gila Hot Springs, R. Br.
　Silver City 88061
Gladstone 88422
Glencoe 88324
Glenrio 88423
Glenwood 88039
Glorieta 87535
Gonzales Ranch......................87536
Grady 88120
Grants (1st) 87020
Grenville 88424
Guadalupita 87722
Hachita 88040
Hagerman 88232
Hanover 88041
Hatch 87937
Hayden 88425
Hernandez, R. Br Espanola....87537
High Rolls Mountain Park.......88325
Hillsboro 88042
Hobbs (1st) 88240
Holloman Air Force Base
　(1st 88330
Holman 87723
Hondo 88336
Hope 88250
Horse Springs 87822
House..88121
Humble City 88251
Hurley 88043

Ilfeld, R. Br. Santa Fe............87538
Isleta 87022
Jal 88252
Jarales 87023
Jemez Pueblo 87024
Jemez Springs 87025
Kenna 88122
Kirtland 87417
Kirtland A F B, Br.
　Albuquerque (see
　appendix)
La Jara 87027
La Loma 87724
La Luz 88337
La Madera 87539
La Mesa 88044
　　Vado, R. Br. 88072
La Plata 87418
Laguna 87026
Lajoya 87028
Lake Arthur 88253
Lakewood 88254
Lamy, R. Br. Santa Fe 87540
Las Cruces (1st) 88001
　University Park, Br..............88001
　White Sands Missle
　Range, Br..............................88002
Las Tablas 87541
Las Vegas (1st) 87701
Ledoux 87725
Lemitar 87823
Leyba 87542
Lincoln 88338
Linda Vista, Sta. Roswell.......88201
Lindrith 87029
Lingo 88123
Llano, R. Br. Penasco.............87543
Llaves 87030
Loco Hills 88255
Logan 88426
Lordsburg 88045
　Redrock, R. Br. 88055
Los Alamos (1st) 87544
Los Lunas 87031
Los Ranchos De
　Albuquerque, Br.
　Albuquerque (see
　appendix)
Loving 88256
Lovington (1st) 88260
Lumberton 88547
Luna 87824
Magdalena 87825
Malaga 88263
Maljamar 88264
Manuelito 87318
Maxwell 87728
Mayhill 88339
Mc Alister 88427
Mc Donald 88262
Mc Intosh 87032
Medanales 87548
Melrose 88124
Mentmore 87319
Mescalero 88340
Mesilla 88046
Mesilla Park 88047
Mesquite 88048
Mexican Springs 87320
Miami 87729
Milan, Br. Grants 87020
Mills 87730
Milnesand 88125

Mimbres.............................88049
Mogollon...........................88050
Montezuma.........................88731
Monticello.........................87939
Montoya............................88428
Monument..........................88265
Mora...............................87732
Moriarty...........................87035
  Clines Corners, R. Br..........87070
  Stanley, R. Br................87056
Mosquero..........................87733
Mount Dora........................88429
Mountainair.......................87036
Mule Creek........................88051
Nageezi...........................87037
Nara Visa.........................88430
Navajo, R. Br. Gallup.............87328
Navajo Dam........................87419
New Laguna........................87038
Newkirk...........................88431
Nogal.............................88341
Ocate.............................87734
Oil Center........................88266
Ojo Caliente......................87549
Ojo Feliz.........................87735
Ojo Sarco.........................87550
Old Albuquerque, Sta.
  Albuquerque...................87104
Organ.............................88052
Orogrande.........................88342
Paguate...........................87040
Paradise Hills, R. Br.
  Albuquerque...................87114
Park View.........................87551
Pastura, R. Br. Santa Rosa........88435
Pecos.............................87552
Penablanca........................87041
Penasco...........................87553
  Llano, R. Br..................87543
  Rodarte, R. Br................87561
Pep...............................88126
Peralta...........................87042
Petaca............................87554
Picacho...........................88343
Pie Town..........................87827
Pinon.............................88344
Pinos Altos, R. Br. Silver
  City..........................88053
Placitas..........................87043
Pojoaque Valley, R. Br.
  Santa Fe......................87501
Polvadera.........................87828
Ponderosa.........................87044
Portales (1st)....................88130
Prewitt...........................87045
Puerto De Luna, R. Br.
  Santa Rosa....................88432
Quay..............................88433
Quemado...........................87829
Questa............................87556
Radium Springs....................88054
Rainsville........................87736
Ramah.............................87321
Ranches Of Taos...................87557
Raton (1st).......................87740
Red River.........................87558
Redrock, R. Br. Lordsburg.........88055
Regina, R. Br. Cuba...............87046
Rehoboth..........................87322
Rencona...........................87559

Reserve...........................87830
Ribera............................87560
Rincon............................87940
Rio Rancho Estates, Br.
  Albuquerque...................87114
Rociada...........................87742
Rodarte, R. Br. Penasco...........87561
Rodeo.............................88056
Rogers............................88132
Roswell (1st).....................88201
Rowe..............................87562
Roy...............................87743
Ruidoso (1st).....................88345
Ruidoso Downs.....................88346
Rutheron..........................87563
Sabinoso..........................87744
Sacramento........................88347
Saint Vrain.......................88133
Salem.............................87941
San Acacia........................87831
San Antonio.......................87832
San Cristobal.....................87564
San Fidel.........................87049
San Jon...........................88434
San Jose..........................87565
San Juan Pueblo...................87566
San Lorenzo, R. Br. Santa
  Rita..........................88057
San Mateo.........................87020
San Miguel........................88058
San Patricio......................88348
San Rafael........................87051
San Ysidro........................87053
Sandia Base, Br.
  Albuquerque (see
  appendix)
Sandia Park.......................87047
Sanostee, R. Br. Shiprock.........87420
Santa Cruz........................87567
Santa Fe (1st)....................87501
  Coronado, Sta.................87501
  Ilfeld, R. Br.................87538

  Lamy, R. Br...................87540
  Pojoaque Valley, R. Br........87501
Santa Rita........................88059
  San Lorenzo, R. Br............88057
Santa Rosa........................88435
  Pastura, R. Br................88435
  Puerto De Luna, R. Br.........88432
Santo Domingo Pueblo..............87052
Sapello...........................87745
Scholle...........................87054
Seboyeta..........................87055
Sedan.............................88436
Sena..............................87568
Seneca............................88437
Serafina..........................87569
Shiprock..........................87420
Silver City (1st).................88061
  Fort Bayard, R. Br............88036
  Gila Hot Springs, R. Br.......88061
  Pinos Altos, R. Br............88053
Socorro (1st).....................87801
Solano............................87746
Springer..........................87747
  Farley, R. Br.................87720
Stanley, R. Br. Moriarty..........87056
Stead.............................88438
Sunland Park......................88063

Sunspot...........................88349
Taiban............................88134
Tajique, R. Br. Estancia..........87057
Taos (1st)........................87571
Taos Ski Valley, R. Br. Taos......87571
Tatum.............................88267
Tererro...........................87573
Tesuque...........................87574
Texico............................88135
Thoreau...........................87323
Three Rivers, R. Br.
  Tularosa......................88350
Tierra Amarilla...................87575
Tijeras...........................87059
Tinnie............................88351
Toadlena..........................87324
Tohatchi..........................87325
Tome..............................87060
Torreon...........................87061
Trampas...........................87576
Trementina........................88439
Tres Piedras......................87577
Truchas, R. Br. Espanola..........87578
Trujillo..........................87748
Truth Or Consequences
  (1st).........................87901
Tucumcari (1st)...................88401
  Bell Ranch, R. Br.............88441
  Conchas Dam, R. Br............88416
Tularosa..........................88352
  Three Rivers, R. Br...........88350
Turnerville.......................88064
Tyrone............................88065
University, Sta. Portales.........88130
University Park, Br. Las
  Cruces........................88001
Ute Park..........................87749
Vadito............................87579
Vado, R. Br. La Mesa..............88072
Valdez............................87580
Vallecitos........................87581
Valmora...........................87750
Vanadium..........................88073
Vander Wagen, R. Br.
  Gallup........................87326
Vaughn............................88353
Veguita...........................87062
Velarde...........................87582
Veterans Hospital, Br.
  Albuquerque...................87108
Villanueva........................87583
Wagon Mound.......................87752
Walker, Br. Roswell...............88201
Waterflow.........................87421
Watrous...........................87753
Weed..............................88354
West Las Vegas, Br. Las
  Vegas.........................87701
White Rock, Sta. Los
  Alamos........................87544
White Sands Missle Range,
  Br. Las Cruces................88002
Whites City.......................88268
Willard...........................87063
Williamsburg......................87942
Winston...........................87943
Yeso..............................88136
Youngsville.......................87064
Zuni..............................87327

ALBUQUERQUE 871

POST OFFICE BOXES

Box Nos.

1-2999	Downtown Station	03
3000-3999	D Sta	10
4000-4999	A Sta	06
5001-5999	Sandia Base Br	15
6001-6999	B Sta	07
7000-7999	Old Albuquérque Sta	04
8001-8999	C Sta	08
9001-9999	Airport Mail Facility Sta	19
10001-10999	Alameda Br	14
11001-11999	E Sta	12
12001-12999	F	05
14000-14999	G	11
15000-15999	Rio Rancho Estates Br	24
18000-18999	Kirtland A F Base Br	18
25001-26999	Main Office	25

RURAL ROUTES

1	05
2	14
3	05
4	07
5	23
6	05
7	13
8,9	05
10	23
11,12	14
13	13
14,15	23

STATIONS, BRANCHES AND UNITS

Alameda Br	14
Downtown Sta	01
Kirtland AFB Br	17
Los Ranchos De Albuquerque Br	07
Old Alburquerque Sta	04
Paradise Hills Rural Br	14
Rio Rancho Estates Br	14
Sandia Base Br	15
Veterans Hospital Br	08
General Delivery	03
Postmaster	01

APARTMENTS, HOTELS, MOTELS

Albuquerque Lorlodge, 801 Central Ave NE	02
Alvarado, 110 1st SW	01
Ambassador East, 8911 Northeastrn Blvd NE	12
Broadmoor, 1115 Grand NE	06
Casa Del Norte, 900 Louisiana Blvd NE	10
Casa Grande Lodge, 2625 Central Ave NW	04
Chaparral, 521 Spruce SE	06
Cole, 123 5th NW	02
College Inn, 303 Ash NE	06
Continental Arms, 1200 Madeira Dr SE	08
Continental East, 1101 Madeira Dr SE	08
Crossroads Motel, 1001 Central Ave SE	06
Desert Sands Motor, 5000 Central Ave SE	08
Downtowner Motor Inn, 717 Central Ave NW	01
El Camino Lodge, 6801 4th NW	07
Embassy House, 1330 Louisiana Blvd NE	10
Encino House, 601 Encino Pl NE	02
Gales, 6231 Gibson Blvd SE	08
Holiday Inn Of Albuquerque, 12901 Central Ave NE	23
Lanai, 1033 Madeira Dr SE	08
Landmark, 6303 Indian School Rd NE	10
Mitchell, 405 14th NW	04
Mountainview, 2323 Kathryn Ave SE	06
Nine-O-Nine, 909 Tijeras Ave NW	02
Ramada Inn, 4501 Central Ave NE	08
Sahara, 5915 Gibson Blvd SE	08
Six-Hundred Alcalde West, 1411 Coal Ave SW	04
Sundowner Motor, 6101 Central Ave NE	08
Trade Winds Motor, 5400 Central Ave NE	08
Virginian, 1400 Virginia NE	10
Western Gardens, 7310 Natalie Ave NE	10
Western Palasades, 1720 Atrisco Dr NW	05
Western Skies Motor, 13400 Central Av SE	23
White-Winrock, Winrock Center NE	10

BUILDINGS

Albuquerque National Bank, 123 Central Ave NW	01
Bank Of New Mexico, 222 Fourth SW	02
Civic Center, Cor Elm & Fruit NE	02
Del Castillo, 2933 Monte Vista Blvd NE	06
Federal, 517 Gold Ave SW	01
First National Bank East, 5301 Central Ave E	08
First National Bank, 219 Central Ave W	02
Fox, 120 Madeira Dr NE	01
Insurance, 610 Gold Ave SW	01
Korber, 208 2nd NW	01
Lawyers, 416 2nd NW	01
Mc Intosh, 220 Copper Ave NW	02
National, 505 Marquette Ave NW	01
Occidental Life, 3rd ' Gold NE	02
Oil Center, 3010 Monte Vista Blvd NE	06
Public Service, 414 Silver Ave SW	01

GOVERNMENT OFFICES

City Hall, 400 Marquette Ave NW	02
Old United States Courthouse, 421 Gold Ave SW	01

HOSPITALS

A T ' S F Association, 800 Central Ave SW	02
Albuquerque Medical Center, 109 Elm SE	01
Bataan Memorial Methodist, 5400 Gibson Blvd SE	08
Bernalillo County Medical Center, 2211 Lomas Blvd NE	06
Docotrs, 1010 Tijeras Ave NW	02
Encino Medical Plaza, 717 Encino Pl NE	06
La Mesa Medical Laboratory, 7000 Cutler Ave NE	
Lomas Medical, 718 Encino Pl NE	
Lovelace Clinic, 5200 Gibson Blvd SE	
Medical & Dental, 106 Girard Blvd NE	
Medical Arts Square, Lomas & Encino Pl NE	06
Nazareth, Alameda Road NE	13
Osteopathic, 1127 University NE	02
Presbyterian, 1012 Gold Ave SE	06
Saint Josephs, 715 Grand Ave NE	01
Sandia Ranch Sanitorium 6900 Edith Blvd NE	13
Southwest Dental, 123 Quincy NE	08

UNIVERSITIES AND COLLEGES

Albuquerque Business College, 221 San Pedro Dr NE	08
Browning Commercial School, 210 Yale Blvd SE	06
Draughons Business College, 110 Central Ave SW	02
Mc Caulley School Of Business, 115 Maple NE	06
University Of Albuquerque, Saint Joseph'S Pl NW	20
University Of New Mexico, University Hill NE	06
Western School For Secretaries, 805 Tiieras Ave NW	01

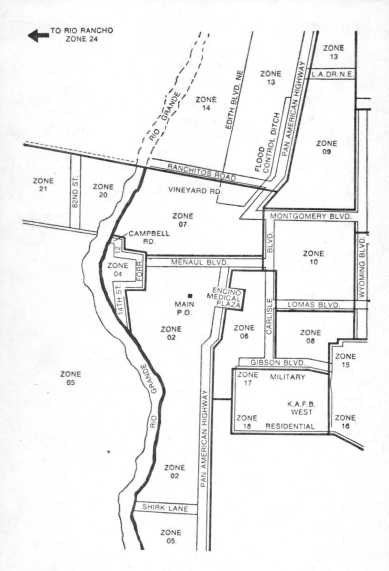

ZIP CODES
Albuquerque NM

871 + Two Digits Shown = ZIP Code

NEW YORK
(Abbreviation: NY)

Academy, Sta. Albany 12208
Accord.................................12404
Acra.....................................12405
Adams (1st).........................13605
Adams Basin.........................14410
Adams Center........................13606
Addison................................14801
Adelphi, Sta. Brooklyn...........11238
Adirondack............................12808
Afton...................................13730
Akron (1st)...........................14001
Alabama...............................14003
ALBANY (1st) (see appendix)
Albertson (1st) 11507
Albion (1st)..........................14411
Alcove.................................12007
Alden (1st)...........................14004
Alden Manor, Br. Floral Park ..11003
Alder Creek...........................13301
Alexander..............................14005
Alexandria Bay......................13607
Alfred (1st)...........................14802
Alfred Station........................14803
Allegany...............................14706
Allentown.............................14707
Allerton, Sta. Bronx 10467
Alma...................................14708
Almond.................................14804
Alpine..................................14805
Alplaus................................12008
Altamont..............................12009
Altmar.................................13302
Alton...................................14413
Altona.................................12910
Amagansett...........................11930
Amawalk..............................10501
Amenia.................................12501
Ames, R. Br. Canajoharie 13317
Amherst, Br. Buffalo..............14226
Amityville (1st).....................11701
Amsterdam (1st)....................12010
Ancram................................12502
Ancramdale...........................12503
Andes..................................13731
Andover................................14806
Angelica...............................14709
Angola (1st)..........................14006
Annandale-on-Hudson.............12504
Ansonia, Sta. New York..........10023
Antwerp...............................13608
    Oxbow, R. Sta. 13671
Apalachin.............................13732
Appleton...............................14008
Apulia Station........................13020
Aquebogue............................11931
Arcade (1st)..........................14009
Arden...................................10910
Ardonia................................12505
Ardsley (1st).........................10502
Ardsley-on-Hudson 10503
Argyle..................................12809
Arkport................................14807
Arkville................................12406
Arlington, Br. Poughkeepsie 12603
Armonk (1st).........................10504
Arverne, Sta. Far Rockaway 11692
Ashland................................12407
Ashville................................14710

Astoria, Sta. Long Island
    City.................................11102
Athens.................................12015
Athol...................................12810
Athol Springs........................14010
Atlanta.................................14808
Atlantic Beach.......................11509
Attica (1st)...........................14011
Au Sable Forks.......................12912
Auburn (1st)..........................13021
Audubon, Sta. New York 10032
Auriesville............................12016
Aurora.................................13026
Ausable Chasm 12911
Austerlitz.............................12017
Ava.....................................13303
Averill Park...........................12018
Avoca..................................14809
Avon (1st).............................14414
BABYLON (1st) (see
    appendix)
Bainbridge (1st).....................13733
Bakers Mills..........................12811
Baldwin (1st).........................11510
Baldwin Place........................10505
Baldwinsville (1st)..................13027
Ballston Lake.........................12019
Ballston Spa (1st)...................12020
Balmat.................................13609
Bangall................................12506
Bangor, R. Br. North Bangor ..12966
Bank Plaza, Sta. Merrick 11566
Bardonia, Br. Nanuet..............10954
Barker.................................14012
Barnes Corners......................13610
Barneveld.............................13304
Barrytown............................12507
Barryville.............................12719
Barton.................................13734
Basom.................................14013
Batavia (1st).........................14020
Bath (1st).............................14810
Bath Beach, Sta. Brooklyn......11214
Bay, Sta. Brooklyn.................11235
Bay Ridge, Sta. Brooklyn........11220
Bay Shore (1st).....................11706
    Fair Harbor, R. Br.:..........11734
    Kismet, R. Br. 11706
    Mall, Sta. 11706
    Penataquit, Sta. 11707
    Saltaire, R. Br. 11706
Bay Terrace, Sta. Flushing......11360
Baychester, Sta. Bronx...........10469
Bayport................................11705
Bayside, Sta. Flushing (see
    appendix)
Bayville...............................11709
Beacon (1st)..........................12508
Bear Mountain.......................10911
Bearsville.............................12409
Beaver Dams.........................14812
Beaver Falls.........................13305
Beaver River, R. Br.
    Lowville...........................13306
Bedford (1st).........................10506
Bedford Hills (1st)..................10507
Beechwood, Sta. Rochester......14609
Belfast.................................14711
Bellerose, Sta. Jamaica...........11426

Belleville..............................13611
Bellevue, Sta. Schenectady......12306
Bellmore (1st).......................11710
Bellona................................14415
Bellport (1st).........................11713
Bellvale................................10912
Belmont................................14813
Bemus Point.........................14712
Bergen.................................14416
Berkshire..............................13736
Berlin..................................12022
Berne..................................12023
Bernhards Bay.......................13028
Bethel.................................12720
Bethpage (1st).......................11714
Bible School Park...................13737
Bidwell, Sta. Buffalo..............14222
Big Flats...............................14814
Big Indian.............................12410
Big Moose.............................13307
Billings................................12510
BINGHAMTON (1st) (see
    appendix)
Black Creek...........................14714
Black River...........................13612
Blasdell, Br. Buffalo...............14219
Biauvelt (1st).........................10913
Bliss....................................14024
Blodgett Mills........................13738
Blooming Grove......................10914
Bloomingburg........................12721
Bloomingdale.........................12913
Bloomington..........................12411
Bloomville............................13739
Blossvale.............................13306
Blue Mountain Lake 12812
Blue Point (1st)......................11715
Bluff Point............................14417
Blythebourne, Sta. Brooklyn....11219
Bohemia (1st)........................11716
Boiceville.............................12412
Bolivar.................................14715
Bolton Landing......................12814
Bombay................................12914
Boonville (1st).......................13309
Borough Hall, Sta. Jamaica 11424
Boston.................................14025
Botanical, Sta. Bronx.............10458
Bouckville............................13310
Boulevard, Sta. Bronx (see
    appendix)
Bovina Center........................13740
Bowling Green, Sta. New
    York................................10004
Bowmansville........................14026
Bradford..............................14815
Brainard...............................12024
Brainardsville........................12915
Branchport............................14418
Brandywine, Sta.
    Schenectady.....................12304
Brant...................................14027
Brant Lake............................12815
Brantingham.........................13312
Brasher Falls.........................13613
Breesport..............................14816
Brentwood (1st).....................11717
Brevoort, Sta. Brooklyn..........11216
Brewerton.............................13029
Brewster (1st).......................10509
Briarcliff Manor (1st)..............10510
Bridge, Sta. Niagara Falls......14305

437

Bridgehampton 11932
Bridgeport 13030
Bridgewater 13313
Brier Hill 13614
Brighton, Sta. Brooklyn 11235
Brighton, Sta. Rochester 14610
Brightwaters (1st) 11718
Brisben 13741
Bristol Center 14419
Broad Channel, Sta. Far
    Rockaway 11693
Broadalbin 12025
Broadway, Sta. Long Island
    City 11106
Brockport (1st) 14420
Brocton 14716
BRONX (1st) (see appendix)
Bronxville, Br. Yonkers 10708
Brookfield 13314
Brookhaven 11719
BROOKLYN (1st) (see
    appendix)
Brooktondale 14817
Brookview 12026
Brownsville, Sta. Brooklyn 11212
Brownville 13615
Brushton 12916
Bryant, Sta. New York 10036
Buchanan 10511
BUFFALO (1st) (see
    appendix)
Bulls Head, Sta. Rochester 14611
Bullville 10915
Burdett 14818
Burke 12917
Burlingham 12722
Burlington Flats 13315
Burnt Hills (1st) 12027
Burt 14028
Bush Terminal, Sta.
    Brooklyn 11232
Bushwick, Sta. Brooklyn 11221
Buskirk 12028
Butterfield, Br. Utica 13502
Byron 14422
Cadosia 13742
Cadyville 12918
Cairo 12413
Calcium 13616
Caledonia (1st) 14423
Callicoon 12723
Callicoon Center 12724
Calverton 11933
Cambria Heights, Sta.
    Jamaica 11411
Cambridge (1st) 12816
Camden (1st) 13316
Cameron 14819
Cameron Mills 14820
Camillus (1st) 13031
Camp Drum, MOU.
    Watertown 13601
Camp Smith, Br. Peekskill 10566
Campbell 14821
Campbell Hall 10916
Campus Plaza, Sta. Vestal 13850
Canaan 12029
Canada Lake, R. Br. Caroga
    Lake 12030
Canajoharie (1st) 13317
Canal Street, Sta. New York 10013
Canandaigua (1st) 14424
Canarsie, Sta. Brooklyn 11236

Canaseraga 14822
Canastota (1st) 13032
Candor 13743
Caneadea 14717
Canisteo 14823
Canton (1st) 13617
Cape Vincent 13618
Capitol, Sta. Albany (see
    appendix)
Carle Place (1st) 11514
Carlisle 12031
Carmel (1st) 10512
Caroga Lake 12032
    Canada Lake, R. Br. 12030
Carthage (1st) 13619
Cass, Br. Buffalo 14206
Cassadaga 14718
Cassville 13318
Castile 14427
Castle, Sta. New Rochelle 10801
Castle Creek 13744
Castle Hill, Sta. Bronx 10462
Castle Point 12511
Castleton on Hudson 12033
Castorland 13620
Cathedral, Sta. New York 10025
Cato 13033
Catskill (1st) 12414
Cattaraugus 14719
Cayuga 13034
Cayuta 14824
Cazenovia (1st) 13035
Cedarhurst (1st) 11516
Celoron 14720
Cementon 12415
Center Berlin, R. Sta. Berlin 12022
Center Moriches (1st) 11934
Centereach (1st) 11720
Centerport (1st) 11721
Centerville 14029
Central, Sta. Jamaica 11435
Central Bridge 12035
Central Islip (1st) 11722
Central Square 13036
Central Valley (1st) 10917
Central White Plains, Sta.
    White Plains (see
    appendix)
Centuck, Sta. Yonkers 10710
Ceres 14721
Chadwicks 13319
Chaffee 14030
Champlain (1st) 12919
Chappaqua (1st) 10514
Charlotte, Sta. Rochester 14612
Charlotteville 12036
Chase Mills 13621
Chateaugay 12920
Chatham (1st) 12037
Chaumont 13622
Chautauqua 14722
Chazy 12921
Cheektowaga, Br. Buffalo 14225
Chelsea 12512
Chemung 14825
Chenango Bridge (1st) 13745
Chenango Forks 13746
Cherokee, Sta. New York 10028
Cherry Creek 14723
Cherry Grove, R. Br. Sayville 11782
Cherry Valley 13320
Cherryplain 12040
Chester (1st) 10918

Cnestertown 12817
Chestnut Ridge, Br.
    Lockport 14094
Chichester 12416
Childwold 12922
Chinatown, Sta. New York 10013
Chippewa Bay 13623
Chittenango 13037
Church Street, Sta. New
    York (see appendix)
Churchville 14428
Churubusco 12923
Cicero 13039
Cincinnatus 13040
Circleville 10919
City Island, Sta. Bronx 10464
Claremont Park, Sta. Bronx 10457
Clarence (1st) 14031
Clarence Center 14032
Clarendon 14429
Clark Mills 13321
Clarkson 14430
Clarksville 12041
Claryville 12725
Classon, Sta. Brooklyn 11238
Claverack 12513
Clay 13041
Clayton 13624
Clayville 13322
Clearfield, Br. Buffalo 14221
Clemons 12819
Cleveland 13042
Cleverdale 12820
Clifton 14431
Clifton Springs 14432
Climax 12042
Clinton (1st) 13323
Clinton Corners 12514
Clintondale 12515
Clintonville, R. Br.
    Keeseville 12924
Clockville 13043
Clyde 14433
Clymer 14724
Cobleskill (1st) 12043
    Hyndsville, R. Br. 12044
Cochecton 12726
Cochecton Center 12727
Coeymans 12045
Coeymans Hollow 12046
Cohocton 14826
Cohoes (1st) 12047
Cold Brook 13324
Cold Spring 10516
Cold Spring Harbor (1st) 11724
Colden 14033
Colgate, Sta. Hamilton 13346
College, Sta. New York 10030
College Point, Sta. Flushing 11356
Colliersville 13747
Collins 14034
Collins Center 14035
Colonial Park, Sta. New
    York 10039
Colton 13625
Columbia University, Sta.
    New York 10025
Columbiaville 12050
Columbus, Sta. Mount
    Vernon 10553
Columbus Circle, Sta. New
    York 10023
Colvin, Sta. Syracuse 13205

Colvin Eggert, Br.	
Tonawanda	14150
Commack (1st)	11725
Comstock	12821
Conesus	14435
Conewango Valley	14726
Coney Island, Sta. Brooklyn	11224
Congers	10920
Conklin	13748
Connelly	12417
Constable	12926
Constableville	13325
Constantia	13044
Cooks Falls	12728
Cooper, Sta. New York	10003
Coopers Plains	14827
Cooperstown (1st)	13326
Middlefield, R. Br.	13405
Copake	12516
Copake Falls	12517
Copenhagen	13626
Copiague (1st)	11726
Coram	11727
Corbettsville	13749
Corfu	14036
Corinth	12822
Corners, Br. Ithaca	14850
Corning (1st)	14830
Cornwall	12518
Cornwall on the Hudson	12520
Cornwallville	12418
Corona-A, Sta. Flushing	11368
Corona-Elmhurst, Sta.	
Flushing	11373
Cortland (1st)	13045
Cossayuna	12823
Cottekill	12419
Cowlesville	14037
Coxsackie	12051
Cragsmoor	12420
Cranberry Lake	12927
Crane Street, Sta.	
Schenectady	12303
Cranford, Sta. Bronx	10470
Craryville	12521
Crittenden	14038
Croghan	13327
Crompond	10517
Cropseyville	12052
Cross River	10518
Croton Falls	10519
Croton-on-Hudson (1st)	10520
Crugers, Br.	10521
Crotona Park, Sta. Bronx	10460
Crown Point	12928
Crugers, Br.	
Croton-on-Hudson	10521
Cuba (1st)	14727
Cuddebackville	12729
Cutchogue (1st)	11935
Cuyler	13050
Cypress Hills, Sta Brooklyn	11208
Dale	14039
Dalton	14836
Dannemora	12929
Dansville (1st)	14437
Scottsburg, R. Br.	14545
Darien Center	14040
Davenport	13750
Davenport Center	13751
Davis Park, R. Br.	
Patchogue	11728
Dayton	14041

De Kalb Junction	13630
De Lancey	13752
De Peyster	13633
De Ruyter	13052
De Witt, Br. Syracuse (see	
appendix)	
Deansboro	13328
Deer Park (1st)	11729
Deer River	13627
Deferiet	13628
Degrasse	13629
Delanson	12053
Delaware, Sta. Albany	12209
Delevan	14042
Delhi (1st)	13753
Delmar (1st)	12054
Delphi Falls	13051
Delray, Br. Buffalo	14224
Denmark	13631
Denver	12421
Depauville	13632
Depew (1st)	14043
Deposit (1st)	13754
Derby	14047
Dewey, Sta. Rochester	14613
Dewittville	14728
Dexter	13634
Diamond Point	12824
Dick Urban, Br. Depew	14043
Dickinson Center	12930
Dobbs Ferry (1st)	10522
Dolgeville (1st)	13329
Dorloo	12099
Dormansville	12055
Douglaston, Sta. Flushing	11363
Dover Plains	12522
Downsville	13755
Dresden	14441
Dryden	13053
Duanesburg	12056
Dundee	14837
Dunham, Sta. Utica	13502
Dunkirk (1st)	14048
Van Buren Point, R. Br.	14166
Durham	12422
Durhamville	13054
Dyker Heights, Sta. Brooklyn	11228
Eagle Bay	13331
Eagle Bridge	12057
Eagle Harbor	14442
Earlton	12058
Earlville	13332
East, Sta. Yonkers	10704
East Amherst	14051
East Aurora (1st)	14052
East Berne	12059
East Bethany	14054
East Bloomfield	14443
East Branch	13756
East Chatham	12060
East Concord	14055
East Durham	12423
East Elmhurst, Sta.	
Flushing	11369
East Freetown	13055
East Greenbush (1st)	12061
East Greenwich	12826
East Hampton (1st)	11937
East Homer	13056
East Islip (1st)	11730
East Jewett	12424
East Marion	11939
East Meadow, Br.	

Hempstead	11554
East Meredith	13757
East Moriches	11940
East Nassau	12062
East New York, Sta.	
Brooklyn	11207
East Northport (1st)	11731
East Norwich (1st)	11732
East Otto	14729
East Palmyra	14444
East Patchogue, Br.	
Patchogue	11772
East Pembroke	14056
East Pharsalia	13758
East Quogue	11942
East Randolph	14730
East Rochester (1st)	14445
East Rockaway (1st)	11518
East Schodack	12063
East Setauket (1st)	11733
East Side, Sta. Binghamton	13904
East Springfield	13333
East Syracuse (1st)	13057
East White Plains, Br. White	
Plains	10604
East Williamson	14449
East Williston, Br. Williston	
Park	11596
East Windham	12425
East Worcester	12064
Eastchester, Br. Yonkers	10709
Eastport	11941
Eastwood, Sta. Syracuse	13206
Eaton	13334
Eddyville	12426
Eden (1st)	14057
Edinburg, R. Br. Northville	12134
Edmeston	13335
Edwards	13635
Elba	14058
Elbridge	13060
Eldred	12732
Elizabethtown	12932
Elizaville	12523
Elka Park	12427
Ellenburg	12933
Ellenburg Center	12934
Ellenburg Depot	12935
Ellenville (1st)	12428
Ellicott, Sta. Buffalo	14205
Ellicottville	14731
Ellington	14732
Ellisburg	13636
Elma	14059
Elmhurst-A, Sta. Flushing	11373
ELMIRA (1st) (see appendix)	
Elmira Heights, Br. Elmira	14903
Elmont, Br. Floral Park	11003
Elmsford (1st)	10523
Elmwood, Sta. Syracuse	13207
Elnora	12065
Elsmere, Br. Delmar	12054
Eltingville, Sta. Staten	
Island	10312
Elwood, Sta. East Northport	11731
Embarkation, Sta. Brooklyn	11250
Empire State, Sta. New York	10001
Endicott (1st)	13760
Endwell, Br. Endicott	13760
Erieville	13061
Erin	14838
Esopus	12429
Esperance	12066

Esplanade, Sta. Bronx..........10469
Essex..........12936
Etna..........13062
Evans Mills..........13637
Fabius..........13063
Fair Harbor, R. Br. Bay
　　Shore..........11734
Fair Haven..........13064
Fairfield..........13336
Fairport (1st)..........14450
Falconer (1st)..........14733
Falls, Sta. Niagara Falls..........14303
Fallsburg..........12733
Fancher..........14452
FAR ROCKAWAY (1st) (see
　　appendix)
Farmersville Station..........14060
Farmingdale (1st)..........11735
Farmingville..........11738
Farnham..........14061
Farragut, Sta. Brooklyn..........11203
Fayette..........13065
Fayetteville (1st)..........13066
Federal, Sta. Rochester (see
　　appendix)
Federal Reserve, Sta. New
　　York..........10045
Felts Mills..........13638
Ferndale..........12734
Feura Bush..........12067
Fieldston, Sta. Bronx..........10463
Fillmore..........14735
Findley Lake..........14736
Fine..........13639
Fineview..........13640
Fire Island Pines, Br.
　　Sayville..........11782
Fishers..........14453
Fishers Island..........06390
Fishers Landing..........13641
Fishkill (1st)..........12524
Fishs Eddy..........13774
Flatbush, Sta. Brooklyn..........11226
Fleetwood, Sta. Mount
　　Vernon..........10552
Fleischmanns..........12430
FLORAL PARK (1st) (see
　　appendix)
Florida..........10921
FLUSHING (1st) (see
　　appendix)
Fly Creek..........13337
Fonda..........12068
Fordham, Sta. Bronx..........10458
Forest Hills, Sta. Flushing..........11375
Forestport..........13338
　　Otter Lake, R. Br...........13427
Forestville..........14062
Fort Ann..........12827
Fort Covington..........12937
Fort Edward (1st)..........12828
Fort George, Sta. New York..........10040
Fort Hamilton, Sta. Brooklyn..........11209
Fort Hunter..........12069
Fort Jackson, R. Br. North
　　Lawrence..........12938
Fort Johnson..........12070
Fort Montgomery..........10922
Fort Plain (1st)..........13339
Fort Tilden, Sta. Far
　　Rockaway..........11695
Fort Washington, Sta. New
　　York..........10032
Fosterdale..........12735

Fpo 09517, Br. New York..........09517
Frankfort..........13340
Franklin..........13775
Franklin D Roosevelt, Sta.
　　New York..........10022
Franklin Springs..........13341
Franklin Square (1st)..........11010
Franklinville..........14737
Fraser, R. Br. Delhi..........13753
Fredonia (1st)..........14063
Freedom..........14065
Freehold..........12431
Freeport (1st)..........11520
Freeville..........13068
Fremont Center..........12736
Fresh Meadows, Sta.
　　Flushing..........11365
Fresh Pond, Sta. Brooklyn..........11227
Frewsburg..........14738
Friendship..........14739
Front Street, Br.
　　Binghamton..........13905
Frontenac, R. Br. Clayton..........13624
Fulton (1st)..........13069
Fultonham..........12071
Fultonville..........12072
　　Randall, R. Br...........12142
Gabriels..........12939
Gainesville..........14066
Gallupville..........12073
Galway..........12074
Gansevoort..........12831
Garden City (1st)..........11530
Gardiner..........12525
Garnerville (1st)..........10923
Garrattsville..........13342
Garrison (1st)..........10524
Gasport..........14067
Gedney, Sta. White Plains..........10605
Geneseo (1st)..........14454
Geneva (1st)..........14456
Genoa..........13071
Georgetown..........13072
Georgetown Square, Br.
　　Buffalo..........14221
Germantown..........12526
Gerry..........14740
Getzville..........14068
Ghent..........12075
Gilbertsville..........13776
Gilboa..........12076
Gimbels Number One, Sta.
　　Valley Stream..........11581
Glasco..........12432
Glen Aubrey..........13777
Glen Cove (1st)..........11542
Glen Head (1st)..........11545
Glen Island, R. Sta. Bolton
　　Landing..........12814
Glen Oaks, Br. Floral Park..........11004
Glen Spey..........12737
Glen Wild..........12738
Glendale, Sta. Brooklyn..........11227
Glenfield..........13343
Glenford..........12433
Glenham..........12527
Glenmont..........12077
Glens Falls (1st)..........12801
Glenwood..........14069
Glenwood Landing..........11547
Gloversville (1st)..........12078
Godeffroy..........12739
Goldens Bridge..........10526
Gorham..........14461

Goshen (1st)..........10924
Gouverneur (1st)..........13642
　　Spragueville, R. Br...........13689
Governors Island, Br. New
　　York..........10004
Gowanda (1st)..........14070
Gracie, Sta. New York..........10028
Grafton..........12082
Grahamsville..........12740
　　Sundown, R. Br...........12782
Grand Central, Sta. New
　　York..........10017
Grand Gorge..........12434
Grand Island (1st)..........14072
Granite Springs..........10527
Granville (1st)..........12832
Gravesend, Sta. Brooklyn..........11223
Great Bend..........13643
Great Kills, Sta. Staten
　　Island..........10308
GREAT NECK (1st) (see
　　appendix)
Great River..........11739
Great Valley..........14741
Greece, Br. Rochester..........14616
Greeley Square, Sta. New
　　York..........10001
Green Island, Br. Troy..........12183
Greene (1st)..........13778
Greenfield Center..........12833
Greenfield Park..........12435
Greenhurst..........14742
Greenlawn (1st)..........11740
Greenpoint, Sta. Brooklyn..........11222
Greenport (1st)..........11944
Greenvale (1st)..........11548
Greenville..........12083
Greenwich (1st)..........12834
Greenwood..........14839
Greenwood Lake..........10925
Greig..........13345
Grenell, R. Br. Clayton..........13624
Griffiss A F B, Br. Rome..........13440
Grindstone..........13644
Grossinger, Br. Ferndale..........12734
Groton (1st)..........13073
Groveland..........14462
Grover, Br. Buffalo..........14226
Guilderland (1st)..........12084
Guilderland Center..........12085
Guilford..........13780
Hadley..........12835
Hagaman..........12086
Hague..........12836
Hailesboro..........13645
Haines Falls..........12436
Halcott Center..........12437
Halcottsville..........12438
Halesite, Br. Huntington..........11743
Hall..........14463
Halsey, Sta. Brooklyn..........11233
Hamburg (1st)..........14075
Hamden..........13782
Hamilton (1st)..........13346
Hamilton Grange, Sta. New
　　York..........10031
Hamlin..........14464
Hammond..........13646
Hammondsport (1st)..........14840
Hampton..........12837
Hampton Bays (1st)..........11946
Hancock..........13783
Hancock Field, MOU.
　　Syracuse..........13225

Hankins 12741
Hannacroix.............................12087
Hannawa Falls 13647
Hannibal.................................13074
Harford..................................13784
Harford Mills 13785
Harlem, Br. Buffalo................14226
Harpersfield 13786
Harpursville............................13787
Harriman...............................10926
Harris.....................................12742
Harrison (1st).........................10528
Harrisville...............................13648
Hart Lot.................................13075
Hartford.................................12838
Hartsdale (1st).......................10530
Hartwick................................13348
Hartwick Seminary 13349
Hastings.................................13076
Hastings On Hudson, Br.
 - Yonkers...........................10706
Hauppauge, Br. Smithtown....11787
Haverstraw (1st) 10927
Hawkeye, R. Br. Au Sable
 Forks.................................12912
Hawthorne (1st) 10532
Hayt Corners..........................14465
Heathcote, Br. Scarsdale 10583
Hector 14841
Helena 13649
Hell Gate, Sta. New York.......10029
Helmuth.................................14079
Hemlock.................................14466
HEMPSTEAD (1st) (see
 appendix)
Henderson..............................13650
Henderson Harbor..................13651
Henrietta (1st)........................14467
Hensonville.............................12439
Herkimer (1st).........................13350
Hermon..................................13652
Herrings.................................13653
Hertel, Sta. Buffalo................14216
Heuvelton...............................13654
Hewlett (1st)..........................11557
HICKSVILLE (1st) (see
 appendix)
Higgins Bay, R. Br. Lake
 Pleasant...........................12108
High Bridge, Sta. Bronx.........10452
High Falls...............................12440
Highland (1st).........................12528
Highland Falls (1st)................10928
Highland Lake.........................12743
Highland Mills........................10930
Highlawn, Sta. Brooklyn........11223
Highmount.............................12441
Hiler, Br. Buffalo....................14223
Hill, Sta. Middletown............10940
Hillburn..................................10931
Hillsdale.................................12529
Hillside, Sta. Bronx................10469
Hillside Manor, Br. New
 Hyde Park.........................11040
Hilton (1st).............................14468
Himrod...................................14842
Hinckley.................................13352
Hinsdale.................................14743
 Ischua, R. Br. 14746
Hobart....................................13788
Hoffmans...............................12088
Hoffmeister............................13353
Hogansburg............................13655

Holbrook (1st)........................11741
Holcomb.................................14469
Holland...................................14080
Holland Patent........................13354
Holley.....................................14470
Hollis, Sta. Jamaica................11423
Hollowville.............................12530
Holmes...................................12531
Holmesville.............................13789
Holtsville................................11742
Homecrest, Sta. Brooklyn......11229
Homer (1st).............................13077
Homer Folks Hospital, R. Br.
 Oneonta...........................13820
Honeoye.................................14471
Honeoye Falls (1st)................14472
Hoosick..................................12089
Hoosick Falls (1st).................12090
Hope Farm, R. Br. Millbrook..12532
Hopewell Junction (1st).........12533
Hopkinton, R. Br. North
 Lawrence..........................12940
Horace Harding, Sta.
 Flushing...........................11362
Hornell (1st)...........................14843
Horseheads (1st).....................14845
Hortonville.............................12745
Hospital, Sta. Binghamton.....13904
Houghton...............................14744
Howard, Sta. New York..........10013
Howard Beach, Sta.
 Jamaica............................11414
Howells..................................10932
Howes Cave............................12092
Hub, Sta. Bronx......................10455
Hubbardsville.........................13355
Hudson (1st)...........................12534
Hudson Falls (1st)..................12839
Hughsonville...........................12537
Huguenot...............................12746
Hulberton...............................14473
Huletts Landing......................12841
Hume.....................................14745
Hunt......................................14846
Hunter...................................12442
Huntington (1st).....................11743
Huntington Station (1st).........11746
Hurley....................................12443
Hurleyville.............................12747
Hyde Park (1st).......................12538
Hyndsville, R. Br. Cobleskill...12044
Ilion (1st)...............................13357
Indian Lake............................12842
Industry.................................14474
Inlet......................................13360
Interlaken..............................14847
Inwood, Sta. New York..........10034
Inwood L I, Br. Far
 Rockaway..........................11696
Ionia......................................14475
Irondequoit, Br. Rochester.....14617
Irving.....................................14081
Irvington (1st).........................10533
Ischua, R. Br. Hinsdale..........14746
Island Park (1st)..................... 11558
Islip (1st)...............................11751
Islip Terrace (1st)...................11752
Ithaca (1st).............................14850
Ithaca College, Br. Ithaca.....14850
Jackson Heights, Sta.
 Flushing 11372
Jacksonville...........................14854
JAMAICA (1st) (see

 appendix)
Jamesport..............................11947
Jamestown (1st).....................14701
Jamesville..............................13078
Jasper....................................14855
Java Center............................14082
Java Village...........................14083
Jay...12941
Jefferson................................12093
Jefferson Valley.....................10535
Jeffersonville..........................12748
Jericho (1st)...........................11753
Jerome Avenue, Sta. Bronx...10468
Jewett....................................12444
John F Kennedy Airport, Sta.
 Jamaica............................11430
Johnsburg..............................12843
Johnson.................................10933
Johnson City (1st)..................13790
Johnsonburg...........................12084
Johnsonville...........................12094
Johnstown (1st)......................12095
Jonesville...............................12098
Jordan....................................13080
Jordanville.............................13361
Junction Boulevard, Sta.
 Flushing...........................11372
Kanona..................................14856
Katonah (1st).........................10536
Kattskill Bay...........................12844
Kauneonga Lake.....................12749
Keene.....................................12942
Keene Valley...........................12943
Keeseville...............................12944
 Clintonville, R. Br. 12924
Kelly Corners..........................12445
Kelsey, R. Br. Hancock..........13783
Kendall..................................14476
Kenmore, Br. Buffalo.............14217
Kennedy.................................14747
Kenoza Lake...........................12750
Kensington, Sta. Brooklyn......11218
Kensington, Sta. Buffalo.........14215
Kent.......................................14477
Kenwood, Sta. Oneida...........13421
Kerhonkson............................12446
Kernan, Sta. Utica..................13502
Keuka Park.............................14478
Kew Gardens, Sta. Jamaica....11415
Kiamesha Lake.......................12751
Kill Buck................................14748
Killawog.................................13794
Kinderhook.............................12106
King Ferry..............................13081
Kings Bridge, Sta. Bronx........10463
Kings Park (1st).......................11754
Kings Point, Br. Great Neck....11024
Kingston (1st).........................12401
Kingsway, Sta. Brooklyn........11229
Kirkville.................................13082
Kirkwood................................13795
Kismet, R. Br. Bay Shore.......11706
Knapp Creek...........................14749
Knickerbocker, Sta. New
 York..................................10002
Knowlesville...........................14479
Knox......................................12107
Knoxboro...............................13362
Krumville...............................12447
 Samsonville, R. Sta. 12476
La Fargeville...........................13656
La Fayette..............................13084
La Guarda Airport, Sta.

Flushing 11371
La Salle, Sta. Niagara Falls 14304
Lackawanna, Br. Buffalo 14218
Lacona 12083
Lagrangeville 12540
Lake Carmel, Br. Carmel 10512
Lake Clear 12945
Lake George (1st) 12845
Lake Grove (1st) 11755
Lake Hill 12448
Lake Huntington 12752
Lake Katrine 12449
Lake Luzerne 12846
Lake Minnewaska, Br. New
　　Paltz 12561
Lake Peekskill 10537
Lake Placid (1st) 12946
Lake Placid Club, Sta. Lake
　　Placid 12946
Lake Pleasant 12108
Lake Ronkonkoma, Br.
　　Ronkonkoma 11779
Lake Success, Sta. New
　　Hyde Park 11040
Lake View 14085
Lakemont 14857
Lakeville 14480
Lakewood 14750
Lancaster (1st) 14086
　　Town Line, R. Br. 14165
Lanesville 12450
Lansingburg, Sta. Troy 12182
Larchmont (1st) 10538
Latham (1st) 12110
Laurel 11948
Laurens 13796
Lawrence (1st) 11559
Lawrenceville 12949
Lawtons 14091
Lawyersville 12113
Le Roy (1st) 14482
Lebanon 13085
Lebanon Springs 12114
Lee Center 13363
Leeds 12451
Lefferts, Sta. Brooklyn 11225
Leicester 14481
Lenox Hill, Sta. New York 10021
Leon 14751
Leonardsville 13364
Levittown (1st) 11756
Lewbeach 12753
Lewis 12950
Lewiston (1st) 14092
Lexington 12452
Liberty (1st) 12754
Lily Dale 14752
Lima 14485
Limerick 13657
Limestone 14753
Lincoln Park, Br. Buffalo 14223
Lincolndale 10540
Lincolnton, Sta. New York 10037
Linden Hill, Sta. Flushing 11354
Lindenhurst (1st) 11757
Lindley 14858
Linwood 14486
Lisbon 13658
Lisle 13797
Little Falls (1st) 13365
Little Genesee 14754
Little Neck, Sta. Flushing
　　(see appendix)

Little Valley 14755
Little York 13087
Liverpool (1st) 13038
Livingston 12541
Livingston Manor 12758
Livonia 14487
Livonia Center 14488
Loch Sheldrake 12759
Locke 13092
Lockport (1st) 14094
Lockwood 14859
Locust Valley (1st) 11560
Lodi 14860
London Terrace, Sta. New
　　York 10011
Long Beach (1st) 11561
Long Eddy 12760
LONG ISLAND CITY (1st) (see
　　appendix)
Long Lake 12847
Longwood, Sta. Bronx 10459
Loon Lake, R. Br. Onchiota 12951
Lorraine 13659
Loudonville, Br. Albany 12211
Lowman 14861
Lowville (1st) 13367
　　Beaver River, R. Br. 13306
Ludlowville 14862
Lycoming 13093
Lyell, Sta. Rochester 14606
Lynbrook (1st) 11563
Lyndonville 14098
Lyon Mountain 12952
　　Merrill, R. Br. 12955
Lyons (1st) 14489
Lyons Falls 13368
Lysander 13094
Mac Dougall 14501
Macedon (1st) 14502
Machias 14101
Madison 13402
Madison Square, Sta. New
　　York 10010
Madrid 13660
Mahopac (1st) 10541
Mahopac Falls 10542
Main Mill, Br. Buffalo 14221
Maine 13802
Malden on Hudson 12453
Malden Bridge 12115
Mall, Sta. Bay Shore 11706
Mallory 13103
Malone (1st) 12953
Malverne (1st) 11565
Mamaroneck (1st) 10543
Manchester 14504
Manhasset (1st) 11030
Manhasset Hills, Sta. New
　　Hyde Park 11040
Manhattanville, Sta. New
　　York 10027
Manhattanville College, Sta.
　　Purchase 10577
Manlius (1st) 13104
Mannsville 13661
Manorville 11949
Maple Springs 14756
Maple View 13107
Maplecrest 12454
Marathon 13803
Marcellus 13108
Marcy 13403
Margaretville 12455

Mariaville, R. Sta. Delanson ...12053
Marietta 13110
Marilla 14102
Mariners Harbor, Sta. Staten
　　Island 10303
Marion 14505
Market, Sta. Buffalo 14203
Marlboro 12542
Marquette, Br. Buffalo 14217
Martinsburg 13404
Martville 13111
Maryknoll (1st) 10545
Maryland 12116
Marymount, Sta. Tarrytown 10591
Masonville 13804
Maspeth, Sta. Flushing 11378
Massapequa (1st) 11758
Massapequa Park (1st) 11762
Massawepie, R. Br. Tupper
　　Lake 12986
Massena (1st) 13662
Mastic 11950
Mastic Beach 11951
Mattituck 11952
Mattydale, Br. Syracuse 13211
Maybrook 12543
Mayfair, Br. Schenectady 12302
Mayfield 12117
Mayville (1st) 14757
Mc Connellsville 13401
Mc Donough 13801
Mc Graw (1st) 13101
Mc Kownville, Br. Albany 12203
Mc Lean 13102
Meacham, Br. Floral Park 11003
Mechanicville (1st) 12118
Mecklenburg 14863
Medford (1st) 11763
Medina (1st) 14103
Medusa 12120
Melcourt, Sta. Bronx 10451
Mellenville 12544
Melrose 12121
Melville, Br. Huntington
　　Station 11746
Memphis 13112
Mendon 14506
Meredith 13805
Meridale 13806
Meridian 13113
Merrick (1st) 11566
Merrill, R. Br. Lyon
　　Mountain 12955
Merriweather Campus, Br.
　　Greenvale 11548
Metropolitan, Sta. Brooklyn 11206
Mexico 13114
Middle Falls 12848
Middle Granville 12849
Middle Grove 12850
Middle Hope, Br. Newburgh 12550
Middle Island 11953
Middle Village, Sta.
　　Flushing 11379
Middleburg 12122
Middlefield, R. Br.
　　Cooperstown 13405
Middleport (1st) 14105
Middlesex 14507
Middletown (1st) 10940
Middleville 13406
Midland Beach, Sta. Staten
　　Island 10306

Midtown, Sta. New York 10018
Midtown Plaza, Sta.
   Rochester.........................14604
Midwood, Sta. Brooklyn........11230
Mileses..................................12761
Milford..................................13807
Mill Neck...............................11765
Millbrook (1st).......................12545
Miller Place............................11764
Millerton................................12546
Millport..................................14864
Millwood................................10546
Milton....................................12547
Mineola (1st)..........................11501
Minerva..................................12851
Minetto...................................13115
Mineville.................................12956
Minoa.....................................13116
Model City..............................14107
Modena...................................12548
Mohawk (1st)..........................13407
Mohegan Lake.........................10547
Mohonk Lake, Br. New Paltz....12561
Moira......................................12957
Mongaup Valley.......................12762
Monroe (1st)...........................10950
Monsey (1st)...........................10952
Montauk..................................11954
Montezuma..............................13117
Montgomery.............................12549
Monticello (1st).......................12701
Montour Falls..........................14865
Montrose.................................10548
Mooers....................................12958
Mooers Forks...........................12959
Moravia (1st)...........................13118
Morgan, Sta. New York.............10001
Moriah....................................12960
Moriah Center..........................12961
Moriches..................................11955
Morley, R. Br. Canton..............13617
Morningside, Sta. New York......10026
Morris.....................................13808
Morris Heights, Sta. Bronx........10453
Morris Park, Sta. Bronx............10461
Morrisania, Sta. Bronx..............10456
Morrisonville............................12962
Morristown..............................13664
Morrisville...............................13408
Morton....................................14508
Mosholu, Sta. Bronx.................10467
Mott Haven, Sta. Bronx............10454
Mottville..................................13119
Mount Carmel, Sta. Bronx.........10458
Mount Kisco (1st)....................10549
Mount Marion...........................12456
Mount Morris...........................14510
Mount Pleasant, R. Br.
   Mount Tremper....................12457
Mount Sinai.............................11766
Mount Tremper.........................12457
Mount Upton............................13809
MOUNT VERNON (1st) (see
   appendix)
Mount Vision............................13810
Mountain Dale..........................12763
Mountain View, R. Br. Owls
   Head..................................12963
Mountainville...........................10953
Mumford..................................14511
Municipal Building, Sta.
   Brooklyn.............................11201
Munnsville...............................13409

Murray Hill, Sta. New York.....10016
Murray Isle, R. Br. Clayton.....13624
Myers....................................14866
Nanuet (1st)...........................10954
Napanoch...............................12458
Naples...................................14512
Narrowsburg...........................12764
Nassau..................................12123
Natural Bridge........................13665
Naval Hospital, Sta.
   Jamaica..............................11425
Nedrow..................................13120
Nelliston................................13410
Nelsonville, Br. Cold Spring.....10516
Nesconset..............................11767
Neversink...............................12765
New Baltimore.........................12124
New Berlin..............................13411
New Bremen............................13412
New City (1st).........................10956
New Dorp, Sta. Staten
   Island.................................10306
New Hamburg..........................12560
New Hampton...........................10958
New Hartford (1st)....................13413
New Haven..............................13121
New Hyde Park (1st).................11040
New Kingston...........................12459
New Lebanon............................12125
New Lebanon Center..................12126
New Lisbon..............................13415
New Lots, Sta. Brooklyn............11208
New Market, Sta. Niagara
   Falls...................................14301
New Milford.............................10959
New Paltz (1st).........................12561
NEW ROCHELLE (1st) (see
   appendix)
New Russia...............................12964
New Scotland............................12127
New Suffolk..............................11956
New Windsor, Br. Newburgh.......12550
New Woodstock.........................13122
NEW YORK (1st) (see
   appendix)
New York Mills.........................13417
Newark (1st)............................14513
Newark Valley...........................13811
Newburgh (1st).........................12550
Newcomb.................................12852
   Tahawus, R. Br...................12879
Newfane..................................14108
Newfield..................................14867
Newkirk, Sta. Brooklyn..............11226
Newport...................................13416
Newton Falls............................13666
Newtonville..............................12128
NIAGARA FALLS (1st) (see
   appendix)
Niagara Square, Sta. Buffalo
   (see appendix)
Niagara University.....................14109
Nichols....................................13812
Nicholville................................12965
Nineveh...................................13813
Niobe......................................14758
Niverville.................................12130
No One Hundred Thirty
   Eight, Sta. New York...........10001
Norfolk....................................13667
North, Sta. Yonkers..................10703
North Babylon, Br. Babylon.....11703
North Baldwin, Sta. Baldwin...11510

North Bangor............................12966
   Bangor, R. Br.....................12966
   West Bangor, R. Br.............12991
North Bay................................13123
North Bellmore, Br.
   Bellmore............................11710
North Blenheim........................12131
North Boston...........................14110
North Branch...........................12766
North Brookfield......................13418
North Chatham........................12132
North Chili...............................14514
North Clymer...........................14759
North Cohocton.......................14868
North Collins............................14111
North Creek.............................12853
North End, Br. Middletown.......10940
North Evans.............................14112
North Granville.........................12854
North Greece............................14515
North Hoosick..........................12133
North Hudson..........................12855
North Java...............................14113
North Lawrence........................12967
   Fort Jackson, R. Br.............12938
   Hopkinton, R. Br.................12940
North Massapequa, Br.
   Massapequa........................11758
North Merrick, Sta. Merrick.....11566
North New Hyde Park, Br.
   New Hyde Park...................11040
North Norwich..........................13814
North Pitcher...........................13124
North Pole, R. Br. Lake
   Placid...............................12946
North River..............................12856
North Rose..............................14516
North Salem.............................10560

North Syracuse, Br.
   Syracuse............................13212
North Tarrytown, Br.
   Tarrytown..........................10591
North Tonawanda (1st)............14120
North Western..........................13419
North White Plains, Sta.
   White Plains (see
   appendix)
Northport (1st)........................11768
Northside, Sta. Corning............14830
Northtown, Br. Buffalo.............14226
Northville................................12134
Northwood, Br. Buffalo............14223
Norton Hill..............................12135
Norwich (1st)..........................13815
Norwood.................................13668
Nostrand, Sta. Brooklyn...........11235
Number Eighteen, Sta. New
   York..................................10016
Number Eighty Two, Sta.
   New York............................10022
Number Forty, Sta. New
   York..................................10001
Nunda....................................14517
Nyack (1st).............................10960
Oak Beach, Br. Babylon...........11702
Oak Hill..................................12460
Oak Point, Sta. Bronx.............10455
Oakdale (1st)...........................11769
Oakfield.................................14125
Oakland Gardens, Sta.
   Flushing.............................11364
Oaks Corners..........................14518
Obernburg..............................12767

Ocean Beach	11770
Oceanside, Br. Rockville Centre	11572
Odessa	14869
Ogden, Sta. Bronx	10452
Ogdensburg (1st)	13669
Olcott	14126
Old Bethpage Branch, Br. Hicksville:	11804
Old Chatham	12136
Old Chelsea, Sta. New York	10011
Old Forge	13420
Old Village, Sta. Great Neck (see appendix)	
Old Westbury, Br. Westbury	11568
Olean (1st)	14760
Olivebridge	12461
Oliverea	12462
Olmstedville	12857
Onchiota	12968
Loon Lake, R. Br.	12951
Oneida (1st)	13421
Oneonta (1st)	13820
Onondaga, Br. Syracuse	13215
Ontario	14519
Ontario Center	14520
Oran	13125
Orangeburg (1st)	10962
Orchard Park (1st)	14127
Orient	11957
Oriskany	13424
Oriskany Falls	13425
Orwell	13426
Ossining (1st)	10562
Oswegatchie	13670
Oswego (1st)	13126
Otego	13825
Otisville	10963
Otselic	13129
Otter Lake, R. Br. Forestport	13427
Otto	14766
Ouaquaga	13826
Ovid	14521
Ovington, Sta. Brooklyn	11220
Owasco	13130
Owego (1st)	13827
Owls Head	12969
Mountain View, R. Br.	12963
Oxbow, R. Sta. Antwerp	13671
Oxford	13830
Oyster Bay (1st)	11771
Ozone Park, Sta. Jamaica (see appendix)	
Painted Post (1st)	14870
Palatine Bridge	13428
Palenville	12463
Palisades (1st)	10964
Palmer, Sta. Corinth	12822
Palmyra (1st)	14522
Panama	14767
Panorama, Br. Rochester	14625
Paradox	12858
Parcel Post, Sta. Far Rockaway	11691
Parcel Post, Sta. Long Island City	11101
Parcel Post, Sta. Hempstead	11550
Parcel Post, Sta. Jamaica	11418
Parcel Post, Sta. Brooklyn	11215
Paris	13429
Paris Station	13430
Parish	13131
Parishville	13672
Park Slope, Sta. Brooklyn	11215
Parkchester, Sta. Bronx	10462
Parkside, Sta. Flushing	11375
Parksville	12768
Parkville, Sta. Brooklyn	11204
Parkway, Sta. Bronx	10462
Patchin, Sta. New York	10011
Patchogue (1st)	11772
Davis Park, R. Br.	11728
East Patchogue, Br.	11772
Patroon, Sta. Albany	12204
Patterson	12563
Pattersonville	12137
Paul Smiths	12970
Pavilion	14525
Pawling (1st)	12564
Peakville	13831
Pearl River (1st)	10965
Peck Slip, Sta. New York	10038
Peconic	11958
Peekskill (1st)	10566
Pelham, Br. New Rochelle	10803
Penataquit, Sta. Bay Shore	11707
Penfield (1st)	14526
Penn Yan (1st)	14527
Pennellville	13132
Perkinsville	14529
Perry (1st)	14530
Perrysburg	14129
Perryville	13138
Peru	12972
Peter Stuyvesant, Sta. New York	10009
Peterboro	13134
Petersburg	12138
Phelps	14532
Philadelphia	13673
Phillipsport	12769
Philmont	12565
Phoenicia	12464
Phoenix	13135
Piercefield	12973
Piermont	10968
Pierrepont Manor	13674
Piffard	14533
Pike	14130
Pilgrim, Sta. Bronx	10461
Pilot Knob, R. Sta. Kattskill Bay	12844
Pine, Sta. Albany	12203
Pine Bush	12566
Pine City	14871
Pine Hill	12465
Pine Island	10969
Pine Plains	12567
Pine Valley	14872
Piseco	12139
Pitcher	13136
Pitt, Sta. New York	10002
Pittsford (1st)	14534
Plainview, Br. Hicksville	11803
Plainville	13137
Plandome, Br. Manhasset	11030
Planetarium, Sta. New York	10024
Plattekill	12568
Plattsburgh (1st)	12901
Plattsburgh A F B, Br.	12903
Plattsburgh A F B, Br. Plattsburgh	12903
Plaza, Sta. Long Island City	11101
Pleasant Valley (1st)	12569
Pleasantville (1st)	10570
Plessis	13675
Plymouth	13832
Poestenkill	12140
Point Lookout	11569
Point Pleasant, Br. Rochester	14622
Point Vivian, R. Br. Alexandria Bay	13607
Poland	13431
Pomona	10970
Pomonok, Sta. Flushing	11365
Pompey	13138
Pond Eddy	12770
Poolville	13432
Poplar Ridge	13139
Port Authority, Sta. New York	10011
Port Byron	13140
Port Chester (1st)	10573
Port Crane	13833
Port Ewen	12466
Port Gibson	14537
Port Henry	12974
Port Jefferson Station (1st)	11776
Port Jervis (1st)	12771
Westbrookville, R. Br.	12785
Port Kent	12975
Port Leyden	13433
Port Richmond, Sta. Staten Island	10302
Port Washington (1st)	11050
Portageville	14536
Porter Corners	12859
Portland	14769
Portlandville	13834
Portville	14770
Postal Concentration Center, Sta. New York	11101
Potsdam (1st)	13676
Pottersville	12860
POUGHKEEPSIE (1st) (see appendix)	
Poughquag	12570
Pound Ridge (1st)	10576
Pratt, Sta. Brooklyn	11205
Pratts Hollow	13434
Prattsburg	14873
Prattsville	12468
Preble	13141
Preston Hollow	12469
Prince, Sta. New York	10012
Princes Bay, Sta. Staten Island	10309
Prospect	13435
Prospect Park West, Sta. Brooklyn	11215
Pulaski (1st)	13142
Pulteney	14874
Pultneyville	14538
Purchase (1st)	10577
Purdy Station	10578
Purling	12470
Putnam Station	12861
Putnam Valley	10579
Pyrites	13677
Quail, Sta. Albany	12206
Quaker Street	12141
Queens Village, Sta. Jamaica (see appendix)	
Queensbury, Br. Glens Falls	12801
Quogue	11959
Radio City, Sta. New York	10019

Rainbow Lake................12976
Randall, R. Br. Fultonville....12142
Randolph................14772
Ransomville................14131
Raquette Lake................13436
Ravena................12143
Ravenwood, Br. Albany........12205
Ray Brook................12977
Raymondville................13678
Reading Center................14876
Red Creek................13143
Red Hook (1st)................12571
Red Hook, Sta. Brooklyn........11231
Redfield................13437
Redford................12978
Redwood................13679
Rego Park, Sta. Flushing........11374
Remsen................13438
Remsenburg................11960
Rensselaer (1st)................12144
Rensselaer Falls................13680
Rensselaerville................12147
Retsof................14539
Rexford................12148
Rexville................14877
Rhinebeck (1st)................12572
Rhinecliff................12574
Richburg................14774
Richfield Springs................13439
Richford................13835
Richland................13144
Richmond Hill, Sta. Jamaica....11418
Richmondville................12149
Richville................13681
Ridge................11961
Ridgemont Plaza, Br.
  Rochester................14626
Ridgewood, Sta. Brooklyn........11227
Rifton................12471
Riparius................12862
Ripley................14775
River Campus, Sta.
  Rochester................14627
Riverdale, Sta. Bronx........10471
Riverhead (1st)................11901
Rochdale Village, Sta.
  Jamaica (see appendix)
ROCHESTER (1st) (see
  appendix)
Rock City Falls................12863
Rock Glen................14540
Rock Hill................12775
Rock Stream................14878
Rock Tavern................12575
Rockaway Beach, Sta. Far
  Rockaway................11693
Rockaway Park, Sta. Far
  Rockaway................11694
Rockaway Point, Sta. Far
  Rockaway................11697
Rockefeller Center, Sta. New
  York................10020
ROCKVILLE CENTRE (1st)
  (see appendix)
Rocky Point................11778
Rodman................13682
Roessleville, Br. Albany........12205
Rome (1st)................13440
Romulus................14541
Ronkonkoma (1st)................11779
Roosevelt (1st)................11575
Roosevelt Field, Sta. Garden
  City................11530

Rooseveltown................13683
Roscoe................12776
Rose................14542
Rosebank, Sta. Staten
  Island................10305
Roseboom................13450
Rosedale, Sta. Jamaica........11422
Rosendale................12472
Roseton................12576
Roslyn (1st)................11576
Roslyn Heights (1st)................11577
Rossburg................14776
Rossie, R. Br. Hammond........13646
Rotterdam, Br. Schenectady....12303
Rotterdam Junction................12150
Round Lake................12151
Round Top................12473
Rouses Point (1st)................12979
Roxbury................12474
Ruby................12475
Rugby, Sta. Brooklyn........11203
Rush................14543
Rushford................14777
Rushville................14544
Russell................13684
Ryder, Sta. Brooklyn........11234
Rye (1st)................10580
S U N Y, Sta. Albany........12203
Sabael................12864
Sackets Harbor................13685
Sag Harbor (1st)................11963
Sagaponack................11962
Saint Albans, Sta. Jamaica....11412
Saint Bonaventure................14778
Saint George, Sta. Staten
  Island................10301
Saint Huberts, R. Br. Keene
  Valley................12943
Saint James (1st)................11780
Saint Johns Place, Sta.
  Brooklyn................11213
Saint Johnsville................13452
Saint Josephs................12777
Saint Regis Falls................12980
Saint Remy, R. Br. Kingston....12401
Salamanca (1st)................14779
Salem................12865
Salina, Sta. Syracuse........13208
Salisbury Center................13454
Salisbury Mills................12577
Salt Point................12578
Saltaire, R. Br. Bay Shore....11706
Samsonville, R. Sta.
  Krumville................12476
Sanborn................14132
Sand Lake................12153
Sandusky................14133
Sandy Creek................13145
Sangerfield................13455
Sanitaria Springs................13836
Santapogue, Br. Babylon........11704
Saranac................12981
Saranac Inn, R. Br. Saranac
  Lake................12982
Saranac Lake (1st)................12983
  Saranac Inn, R. Br.........12982
Saratoga Springs (1st)........12866
Sardinia................14134
Saugerties (1st)................12477
Sauquoit................13456
Savannah................13146
Savona................14879
Sayville (1st)................11782

Scarborough, Sta. Briarcliff
  Manor................10510
Scarsdale (1st)................10583
Schaghticoke................12154
SCHENECTADY (1st) (see
  appendix)
Schenevus................12155
Schodack Landing................12156
Schoharie................12157
Schroon Lake................12870
Schuyler, R. Br. Utica........13502
Schuyler Falls................12985
Schuyler Lake................13457
Schuylerville................12871
Scio................14880
Scipio Center................13147
Scotia, Br. Schenectady........12302
Scottsburg, R. Br. Dansville....14545
Scottsville................14546
Sea Cliff (1st)................11579
Seaford (1st)................11783
Seamens Church Institute,
  Sta. New York................10004
Seaway Plaza, Br.
  Watertown................13601
Selden (1st)................11784
Selkirk................12158
Seneca Castle................14547
Seneca Falls (1st)................13148
Sennett................13150
Setauket, Br. East Setauket....11733
Severance................12872
Seward................12199
Shady................12479
Shandaken................12480
Sharon Springs................13459
Sheds................13151
Shelter Island................11964
Shelter Island Heights........11965
Shenorock................10587
Sherburne................13460
Sheridan................14135
Sherman................14781
Sherrill (1st)................13461
Shinhopple................13837
Shirley................11967
Shokan................12481
Shoreham................11786
Shortsville................14548
Shrub Oak................10588
Shushan................12873
Sidney (1st)................13838
Sidney Center................13839
Siena, Br. Albany................12211
Silver Bay................12874
Silver Creek (1st)................14136
Silver Lake................14549
Silver Springs................14550
Sinclairville................14782
Skaneateles (1st)................13152
Skaneateles Falls................13153
Slate Hill................10973
Slaterville Springs................14881
Slingerlands................12159
Sloansville................12160
Sloatsburg................10974
Smallwood................12778
Smithboro................13840
Smithtown (1st)................11787
Smithville................13686
Smithville Flats................13841
Smyrna................13464
Snyder, Br. Buffalo................14226

Sodus (1st).................................14551
Sodus Center..........................14554
Sodus Point............................14555
Solsville..................................13465
Solvay, Br. Syracuse.............13209
Somers.....................................10589
Sonyea......................................14556
Sound Beach..........................11789
Soundview, Sta. Bronx (see appendix)
South, Sta. Yonkers...............10705
South Bethlehem...................12161
South Buffalo, Sta. Buffalo....14210
South Butler............................13154
South Byron............................14557
South Cairo.............................12482
South Colton...........................13687
South Corning, Br. Corning....14830
South Dayton..........................14138
South Edmeston.....................13466
South Fallsburg (1st)............12779
South Farmingdale, Br. Farmingdale........................11735
South Jamesport....................11970
South Kortright.......................13842
South Lansing.........................14882
South Lima..............................14558
South New Berlin...................13843
South Otselic..........................13155
South Ozone Park, Sta. Jamaica.................................11420
South Park, Sta. Buffalo........14220
South Plymouth......................13844
South Richmond Hill, Sta. Jamaica.................................11419
South Road, Br. Poughkeepsie.......................12601
South Rutland.........................13688
South Salem............................10590
South Schodack.....................12162
South Schroon.......................12877
South Side, Sta. Elmira..........14904
South Wales............................14139
South Westerlo.......................12163
Southampton (1st).................11968
Southfields.............................10975
Southold (1st).........................11971
Southtown, Br. Rochester.....14623
Southview, Sta. Binghamton....13903
Sparkill...................................10976
Sparrow Bush.........................12780
Speculator..............................12164
Spencer...................................14883
Spencerport (1st)...................14559
Spencertown...........................12165
Speonk...................................11972
Spragueville, R. Br. Gouverneur........................13689
Sprakers..................................12166
Spring Brook..........................14140
Spring Glen.............................12483
Spring Valley (1st).................10977
Springfield Center..................13468
Springfield Gardens, Sta. Jamaica.................................11413
Springville (1st).....................14141
Springwater.............................14560
Staatsburg..............................12580
Stadium, Sta. Bronx...............10452
Stafford...................................14143
Stamford (1st)........................12167
Stanfordville...........................12581
Stanley....................................14561

Stanwix Heights, R. Br. Rome.....................................13440
Stapleton, Sta. Staten Island..................................10304
Star Lake.................................13690
State University, Sta. Westbury..............................11568
STATEN ISLAND (1st) (see appendix)
Steamburg..............................14783
Steel City, Br. Buffalo............14218
Steinway, Sta. Long Island City.....................................11103
Stella Niagara.........................14144
Stephentown...........................12168
Stephentown Center..............12169
Sterling...................................13156
Sterling Forest.......................10979
Stewart A F B, Br. Newburgh............................12550
Stillwater................................12170
Stittville..................................13469
Stockport................................12171
Stockton..................................14784
Stone Ridge............................12484
Stony Brook (1st)...................11790
Stony Creek............................12878
Stony Point (1st)....................10980
Stormville...............................12582
Stottville.................................12172
Stow..14785
Stratford.................................13470
Strathmore, Sta. Manhasset....11030
Strykersville...........................14145
Stuyvesant..............................12173
Stuyvesant, Sta. Brooklyn.....11233
Stuyvesant Falls.....................12174

Suffern (1st)...........................10901
Suffolk County A F B, MOU. Westhampton Beach............11978
Sugar Loaf..............................10981
Summit....................................12175
Summitville.............................12781
Sundown, R. Br. Graamsville.........................12782
Sunmount, Br. Tupper Lake....12986
Sunnyside, Sta. Long Island City.....................................11104
Sunset, Sta. Brooklyn............11220
Surprise...................................12176
Swain.......................................14884
Swan Lake...............................12783
Swormville...............................14146
Sylvan Beach..........................13157
Syosset (1st)..........................11791
SYRACUSE (1st) (see appendix)
Taberg....................................13471
Taconic Lakes, R. Br. Petersburg..........................12138
Tahawus, R. Br. Newcomb....12879
Tallman...................................10982
Tannersville............................12485
Tappan (1st)...........................10983
Tarrytown (1st).......................10591
Ten Mile River, R. Br. Narrowsburg......................12764
Terminal, Sta. Staten Island....10301
Thendara................................13472
Theresa...................................13691
Thiells.....................................10984
Thompson Ridge.....................10985
Thompsonville........................12784

Thomson.................................12881
Thornwood (1st)....................10594
Thousand Island Park............13692
Three Mile Bay.......................13693
Throggs Neck, Sta. Bronx.....10465
Thurston Road, Sta. Rochester.........................14619
Ticonderoga (1st)..................12883
Tillson.....................................12486
Times Plaza, Sta. Brooklyn....11217
Times Square, Sta. New York.....................................10036
Tioga Center...........................13845
Tivoli.......................................12583
Tomkins Cove.........................10986
Tompkins Square, Sta. New York.....................................10009
Tonawanda (1st)....................14150
Tottenville, Sta. Staten Island....................................10307
Town Line, R. Br. Lancaster....14165
Trainsmeadow, Sta. Flushing..............................11370
Transitown, Br. Buffalo..........14221
Treadwell................................13846
Tremont, Sta. Bronx..............10457
Tri Willow, Br. Rome..............13440
Tribes Hill...............................12177
Triborough, Sta. New York....10035
Troupsburg.............................14885
Trout Creek............................13847
TROY (1st) (see appendix)
Trumansburg..........................14886
Truxton...................................13158
Tuckahoe, Br. Yonkers..........10707
Tudor, Sta. New York:............10017
Tully..13159
Tunnel.....................................13848
Tupper Lake (1st)..................12986
    Massawepie, R. Br.............12986
    Sunmount, Br....................12986
Turin.......................................13473
Tuscarora................................14562
Tuxedo Park............................10987
Twelve Corners, Br. Rochester.........................14618
Tyrone.....................................14887
U S C C, Sta. West Point........10996
U S Public Health Hosp, Sta. Staten Island.....................10304
Ulster Park.............................12487
Unadilla..................................13849
Union, Sta. Endicott..............13760
Union Center, Br. Endicott....13760
Union Hill................................14563
Union Springs.........................13160
Uniondale, Br. Hempstead....11553
Unionville................................10988
United Nations New York, Sta. New York.....................10017
University, Sta. Syracuse.......13210
University Heights, Sta. Bronx.................................10452
Upper Jay................................12987
Upper Saint Regis, R. Br. Lake Clear.........................12945
Upper Union, Br. Schenectady......................12309
Upton (1st).............................11973
Uptown, Sta. Kingston..........12401
UTICA (1st) (see appendix)
Utopia, Sta. Flushing............11366
Vails Gate (1st)......................12584

Valatie 12184
Valhalla (1st) 10595
Valley Cottage 10989
Valley Falls 12185
VALLEY STREAM (1st) (see appendix)
Valois 14888
Van Brunt, Sta. Brooklyn 11215
Van Buren Point, R. Br. Dunkirk 14166
Van Cott, Sta. Bronx 10467
Van Del, Br. Buffalo 14217
Van Etten 14889
Van Hornesville 13475
Van Nest, Sta. Bronx 10462
Vanderveer, Sta. Brooklyn 11210
Varna, Br. Ithaca 14850
Varysburg 14167
Venice Center 13161
Verbank 12585
Vermontville 12989
Vernon 13476
Vernon Center 13477
Verona 13478
Verona Beach 13162
Verplanck 10596
Versailles 14168
Vestal (1st) 13850
Veterans Administration, Br. Bath 14810
Veterans Administration Faci. Sta. Batavia 14020
Veterans Administration Hosp. Sta. Buffalo 14215
Veterans Hospital, Sta. Syracuse 13210
Victor 14564
Victory Mills 12884
Village, Sta. New York 10014
Voorheesville 12186
Waccabuc 10597
Waddington 13694
Wadhams 12990
Wading River 11792
Wadsworth 14565
Wainscott 11975
Wakefield, Sta. Bronx 10466
Walden (1st) 12586
Wales Center 14169
Walker 14566
Walker Valley 12588
Wall Street, Sta. New York 10005
Wallace 14890
Wallkill 12589
Walton (1st) 13856
Walworth 14568
Wampsville 13163
Wanakena 13695
Wantagh (1st) 11793
Wappingers Falls (1st) 12590
Warners 13164
Warnerville 12187
Warrensburg 12885
Warsaw (1st) 14569
Warwick (1st) 10990
Washington Bridge, Sta. New York 10033
Washington Mills 13479
Washingtonville 10992
Wassaic 12592
Wassaic State School, R. Sta. Wassaic 12592
Water Mill 11976

Waterford (1st) 12188
Waterloo (1st) 13165
Waterport 14571
Watertown (1st) 13601
Waterville 13480
Watervliet (1st) 12189
Watkins Glen (1st) 14891
Waverly (1st) 14892
Wawarsing 12489
Wayland 14572
Wayne 14893
Webster (1st) 14580
Webster Crossing 14584
Weedsport 13166
Wells 12190
Wells Bridge 13859
Wellsburg 14894
Wellsville (1st) 14895
West Babylon, Br. Babylon 11704
West Bangor, R. Br. North Bangor 12991
West Berne 12191
West Bloomfield 14585
West Brentwood, Br. Brentwood 11717
West Burlington 13482
West Camp 12490
West Chazy 12992
West Clarksville 14786
West Copake 12593
West Corners, Br. Endicott 13760
West Coxsackie 12192
West Danby 14896
West Davenport 13860
West Eaton 13484
West Edmeston 13485
West Exeter 13487
West Falls 14170
West Farms, Sta. Bronx 10460
West Fulton 12194
West Gilgo Beach, Br. Babylon 11702
West Haverstraw (1st) 10993
West Hempstead, Br. Hempstead 11552
West Henrietta 14586
West Hurley 12491
West Islip (1st) 11795
West Kill 12492
West Lebanon 12195
West Leyden 13489
West Monroe 13167
West New Brighton, Sta. Staten Island 10310
West Newburgh, Sta. Newburgh 12550
West Nyack (1st) 10994
West Oneonta 13861
West Park 12493
West Point (1st) 10996
West Ridge, Sta. Rochester 14615
West Rush 14587
West Sand Lake 12196
West Sayville 11796
West Seneca, Br. Buffalo 14224
West Shokan 12494
West Side, Sta. Elmira 14905
West Stockholm 13696
West Valley 14171
West Webster, Br. Webster 14580
West Winfield 13491
Westbrookville, R. Br. Port Jervis 12785

Westbury (1st) 11590
Old Westbury, Br. 11568
State University, Sta. 11568
Westchester, Sta. Bronx 10461
Westdale 13483
Westerlo 12193
Westernville 13486
Westfield (1st) 14787
Westford 13438
Westgate, Br. Rochester 14624
Westhampton 11977
Westhampton Beach (1st) 11978
Westmoreland 13490
Westons Mills 14788
Westport 12993
Westtown 10998
Westview, Sta. Binghamton 13905
Wevertown 12886
Whallonsburg 12994
Whippleville 12995
White Creek, R. Br. Eagle Bridge 12057
White Lake 12786
WHITE PLAINS (1st) (see appendix)
White Sulphur Springs 12787
Whiteface, R. Br. Lake Placid 12946
Whitehall 12887
Whitesboro (1st) 13492
Whitestone, Sta. Flushing 11357
Whitesville 14897
Whitney Point 13862
Willard 14588
Willet 13863
Williams Bridge, Sta. Bronx 10467
Williamsburg, Sta. Brooklyn 11211
Williamson 14589
Williamstown 13493
Williamsville, Br. Buffalo 14221
Williston Park (1st) 11596
Willow 12495
Willsboro 12996
Willseyville 13864
Wilmington 12997
Wilson 14172
Wilton, R. Br. Saratoga Springs 12866
Windham 12496
Windsor 13865
Wingdale 12594
Winthrop 13697
Witherbee 12998
Wolcott 14590
Wood Haven, Sta. Jamaica 11421
Woodbourne 12788
Woodbury (1st) 11797
Woodgate 13494
Woodhull 14898
Woodlawn, Sta. Bronx 10470
Woodmere (1st) 11598
Woodridge 12789
Woodside, Sta. Flushing 11377
Woodstock (1st) 12498
Woodville 13698
Woolsey, Sta. Long Island City 11105
Worcester 12197
Wurtsboro 12790
Wyandanch (1st) 11798
Wyckoff Heights, Sta. Brooklyn 11237
Wykagyl, Sta. New Rochelle 10804

447

Wynantskill (1st)	12198
Wyoming	14591
Yaphank	11980
YONKERS (1st) (see	
appendix)	
York	14592
Yorkshire	14173
Yorktown Heights (1st)	10598
Yorkville (1st)	13495
Youngstown	14174
Youngsville	12791
Yulan	12792

Albany NEW YORK

Appendix

ALBANY   122

POST OFFICE BOXES

Box Nos.

1-2000	Main Office	01
4001-4200	Patroon Sta	04
5001-5200	Roessleville Br	05
6001-6200	Quail Sta	06
7001-7100	Capitol Annex Sta	25
7101-7400	Capitol Sta	24
8001-8200	Pine Sta	03
8501-8700	Academy Sta	08
9001-9100	Delaware Sta	09
11001-11790	Loudonville Br	11

RURAL ROUTES

| 1 | 03 |
| 2 | 05 |

STATIONS, BRANCHES AND UNITS

Academy Sta	08
Capitol Sta	24
Delaware Sta	09
Loudonville Br	11
Mc Kownville Br	03
Patroon Sta	04
Pine Sta	03
Quail Sta	06
Ravenwood Br	05
Roessleville Br	05
S U N Y Sta	03
Siena Br	11
General Delivery	01
Postmaster	07

APARTMENTS, HOTELS, MOTELS

Adams Park, 550 New Scotland Ave	08
Berkshire, 140 State	07
Cameo Apartments 12 California Ave	05
Danker Village, 129 Lincoln Ave	06
De Witt Clinton, 142 State	07
Dutch Village, Van Rensselaer Ave	04
Elouise, 11 South Lake Ave	03
Harmony Hill	03
Holiday Inn Of America, 1614 Central	05
Holiday Inn Of America, 575 Broadway, Menands	04
Howard Johnson Motor Lodge, Southern Blvd	09
Inn Towne Motel, 300 Broadway	07
Knickerbocker, 175 Jay	10
Lake, 47 South Lake Ave	03
Livingston Village, 421 Livingston Ave	06
Loudon Arms, 308 Northern Blvd	04
Mayflower, 6 South Lake Ave	03
Menands Garden	04
New Kenmore, 76 North Pearl	07
Park Lane	04
Philip Schuyler, 75 Willett	10
Riverhill, Van Rensselaer Blvd	04
Stonehenge, Circle Lane	03
Thruway, 1375 Washington Ave	06
Tom Sawyer Motor Inn, 1444 Western Ave	03
Towers Of Colonie Center, 420 Sandcreek Road	05
Town House Motor, Northern Blvd & Shaker Rd	04
Wellington, 136 State	07
Willett, 84 Willet	10

BUILDINGS

Albany County Airport, Albany Shaker Rd	11
Albany County Jail, Shaker Road	11
Albany Institute Of History & Art, 125 Washington Ave	10
Ann Lee Home	11
City & Country Savings Bank, 100 State	07
City Hall, Eagle Street	07
City Parks, Hoffman Ave	09
Colonie Center Central Ave At Wolf Road	05
County, Eagle	07
Delaware & Hudson, The Plaza	07
Executive Park, Western Ave Fuller Rd	03
Federal, Broadway	07
Harmanus Bleecker Library, Washington Ave & Dove	10
Home Savings Bank, 11 North Pearl	07
K-Mart 1860 Central Ave	05
National Savings Bank, 90 State	07
Nelson House, 5 Samaritan Rd	08
New York State Campus Site, Washington Ave	26
New York State Capitol, Eagle State & Washington Ave	24
New York State Education, Washington Ave	24
New York State Office, S Swan	25
New York Telephone	
Company, 158 State	07
Northway Mall 1440 Central Ave	05
Standard, 112 State	07
State Bank, 75 State	07
Stuyvesant Plaza, Western Ave & Fuller Rd	03
University Plaza, 1215 Western Ave	03
West Mall Plaza, Central Ave	06
Westgate, Central Ave & Colvin Ave	06

GOVERNMENT OFFICES

Court Of Appeals Hall, 20 Eagle	07
Internal Revenue Service, 161 Washington Ave	10
Old Post Office, Broadway & State	07

HOSPITALS

Albany Hospital For Incurables, Mc Carty Ave	02
Albany Palsy Center, 100 New Scotland Ave	08
Albany, 43 New Scotland Ave	08
Childs, University Heights	08
Memorial, Northern Blvd	04
Saint Margarets, 27 Hackett Blvd	08
Saint Peters, 632 New Scotland Ave	08
Veterans Administration, 113 Holland Ave	08

UNIVERSITIES AND COLLEGES

Albany Business, 130 Washington Ave	10
Albany College Of Pharmacy, 106 New Scotland Ave	08
Albany Law School, 80 New Scotland Ave	08
Albany Medical College, 47 New Scotland Ave	08
College Of St Rose, 979 Madison Ave	03
Maria College, 700 New Scotland Ave	08
Russell Sage	10
Siena College, Rt 9 Loudonville	11
State University Of New York At Alba, 1400 Washington Ave	03

BABYLON   117

POST OFFICE BOXES

Box Nos.

1-600	Main Office	02
1001-1128	West Babylon Br	04
2001-2310	North Babylon Br	03

STATIONS, BRANCHES AND UNITS

North Babylon Br	03
Oak Beach Br	02
Santapogue Br	04
West Babylon Br	04
West Gilgo Beach Br	02
General Delivery	02
Postmaster	02

BINGHAMTON   139

POST OFFICE BOXES

Box Nos.

1-117	East Side Sta	04
1-144	Southview Sta	03
1-235	Westview Sta	05
301-1895	Main Office	02

RURAL ROUTES

1,2	03
3	04
4	01
5	05
6	04

STATIONS, BRANCHES AND UNITS

East Side Sta	04
Front Street Br	05
Hospital Sta	04
Southview Sta	03
Westview Sta	05
General Delivery	02
Postmaster	02

APARTMENTS, HOTELS, MOTELS

Banner Motel, 1169 Front	05
Carlisle Apartments, 150 Moeller	04
Chenango Apartments, 100 Robert	01
Clayton Village Apartments, 412 Clubhouse Rd	03
Colonial Motor Inn, Vestal Pkwy	03
Country Towne, 100 Robert	01
Dixie, 106 Henry	01
Foothills Motel, Upper Court	04
Holiday Inn, Upper Court	04
Holiday Inn, Vestal Pkwy	01
Mayfair Motel, 1424 Front	01
Ramada Inn 65 Front	05
River House, 40 Front	05

Riverside Towers, 5 Riverside Dr	05
Saratoga Heights Apartments, Saratoga Hts	03
Saratoga Terrace Apartments, Saratoga Ter	03
Sheraton Inn, 50 Front	02
Terry Town Apartments, 414 Clubhouse Rd	03
Thruway Motel, 399 Court	04
Treadway Inn 2-4 Hawley St	02
Windermere, 260 Washington	01

BUILDINGS

Binghamton Plaza, West State	01
Chenango Plaza, Upper Front	01
Colonial Plaza 32 West State St	01
Fowler Dick & Walker, 19 Court	02
Marine Midland, 84 Court	01
Mc Leans Department Stores, 89 Court	02
Montgomery Ward Company, 38 Main	02
Oneil, 70 Court	01
Press, 19 Chenango	01
Public Library, 78 Exchange	01
Sears Roebuck & Company, 174 Court	02
Security Mutual, 84 Exchange	01
Vestal Plaza, Vestal Pkwy	03

GOVERNMENT OFFICES

Binghamton City School District, 98 Oak	05
City Hall, 95 Collier	01
County Welfare Dept, 901 Front	05
Courthouse, Courthouse Square	01
Department Of Education, 98 Oak	05
Department Of Motor Vehicles District Office, 184 Court	01
Department Of Public Works, 71 Fredrick	01
Department Of Taxation & Finance, 184 Court	01
Fire Headquarters, 74 Carroll	01
General Services Administration, Hoyt Ave	01
Internal Revenue Service, 15 Henry	02
Labor, 221 Washington	01
Main Post Office, 115 Henry	02
Police Headquarters, 62 Water	01
Public Library, 78 Exchange	01
Social Security Administration, 107 Chenango	02
United States Courthouse, 15 Henry	02
Welfare Department, 251 Water	01

Workmans Compensation Board, 221 Washington	01

HOSPITALS

Binghamton General Hospital, 25 Park Ave	01
Binghamton State Hospital, 425 Robinson	01
County Home & Hospital Box 1704	02
Our Lady Of Lourdes Hospital, 169 Riverside Dr	05

UNIVERSITIES AND COLLEGES

Broome Technical Community College, 907 Front	02
Harpur College State University Of New York, Vestal Pkwy	01

BRONX   104

POST OFFICE BOXES

Box Nos.

1-54	City Island Sta	64
1-90	Wakefield Sta	66
1-102	Morris Heights Sta	53
1-102	West Farms Sta	60
1-108	Baychester Sta	69
1-108	Fordham Sta	58
1-108	Parkchester Sta	62
1-108	Riverdale Sta	71
1-108	Throggs Neck Sta	65
1-108	Tremont Sta	57
1-108	Westchester Sta	61
1-108	Williams Bridge Sta	67
1-108	Woodlawn Sta	70
1-210	Boulevard Sta	59
1-216	High Bridge Sta	52
1-216	Hub Sta	55
1-216	Jerome Avenue Sta	68
1-216	Kings Bridge Sta	63
1-230	Mott Haven Sta	54
1-237	Morrisania Sta	56
1-243	Soundview Sta	72
1-252	Main Office	51

STATIONS, BRANCHES AND UNITS

Allerton Sta	67
Baychester Sta	69
Botanical Sta	58
Boulevard Sta	59
Castle Hill Sta	62
City Island Sta	64
Claremont Park Sta	57
Cranford Sta	70

Bronx (Con.)   104

Crotona Park Sta	60
Esplanade Sta	69
Fieldston Sta	63
Fordham Sta	58
High Bridge Sta	52
Hillside Sta	69
Hub Sta	55
Jerome Avenue Sta	68
Kings Bridge Sta	63
Longwood Sta	59
Melcourt Sta	51
Morris Heights Sta	53
Morris Park Sta	61
Morrisania Sta	56
Mosholu Sta	67*
Mott Haven Sta	54
Mount Carmel Sta	58
Oak Point Sta	55
Ogden Sta	52
Parkchester Sta	62
Parkway Sta	62
Pilgrim Sta	61
Riverdale Sta	71
Soundview Sta	72
Stadium Sta	52
Throggs Neck Sta	65
Tremont Sta	57
University Heights Sta	52
Van Cott Sta	67
Van Nest Sta	62
Wakefield Sta	66
West Farms Sta	60
Westchester Sta	62
Williams Bridge Sta	67
Woodlawn Sta	70
General Delivery	51
Postmaster	51

BUILDINGS

Bronx Terminal Market, E.150th St & Cromwell Ave	51
N.Y.C. Terminal Market (Hunts P'T Mkt), Hunts Pt & E. Bay Av	74

HOSPITALS

Abraham Jacobi, Pelham Pkwy S & Eastchstr Rd	61
Albert Einstein, 1825 Eastchester Rd	61
Bronx Eye & Ear Infirmary, 321 E Tremont Ave	57
Bronx Municipal, Pelham Pkwy S & Eastchstr Rd	61
Bronx State Hospital, Haswell & Industrial	61
Bronx-Lebanon Concourse Div. Grand Concourse & E Mt Eden Av	57
Bronx-Lebanon Fulton Division, 1276 Fulton Ave	56
Fordham, Southern Blvd & E Fordham Rd	58
Frances Schervier, Independence Ave & W 227	63
Home Of Daughters Of Jacob, Findlay Ave & E 167th	56

House Of Calvary, 1600 Macombs Rd	52
Lincoln, Concord Ave & E 141st	54
Misericordia, 600 E 233rd	66
Montefiore, E Gunhill & Bainbridge Ave	67
Morrisania City, Walton Ave & E 168th	52
Mount Eden, 199 E Mt Eden Ave	57
Nathan B Van Etten, Morris Park Ave & Eastchstr Rd	61
Parkchester General, 1425 Zerega Ave	62
Pelham Bay General Hospital, 1870 Pelham Pkwy S	61
Prospect, 730 Kelly	55
Royal, 2021 Grand Concourse	53
Saint Barnabas Hosp For Chrodiseases, 4422 3rd Ave	57
Union, 260 E 188th	58
United States Veterans Administration.,130 W Kingsbridge Rd	68
University Heights, 76 W Tremont Ave	53
Westchester Square, 2475 Saint Raymonds Ave	61

UNIVERSITIES AND COLLEGES

Albert Einstein College Of Medicine, 1300 Morris Park Ave	61
Bronx Community College, 120 E 184th	68
Fordham, E Fordham Rd	58
Herbert H. Lehman, Bedford Park Blvd	68
Manhattan, Manhattan College Pkwy	71
Mount Saint Ursula, 330 Bedford Park Blvd	58
Mount Saint Vincent, Riverdale Av & W 261st	71
New York State Maritime College, Fort Schuyler	65
New York University, University Heights	53

BROOKLYN   112

POST OFFICE BOXES

Box Nos.

1-89	New Lots Sta	08
1-89	Parkville Sta	04
1-100	Gravesend Sta	23
1-100	Stuyvesant Sta	33
1-108	Bushwick Sta	21
1-119	Canarsie Sta	36
1-119	Wyckoff Heights Sta	37
1-138	East New York Sta	07
1-140	Bush Terminal Sta	32

1-148	Bath Beach Sta	14
1-148	Blythebourne Sta	19
1-148	Dyker Heights Sta	28
1-148	Fort Hamilton Sta	09
1-148	Vanderveer Sta	10
1-149	Pratt Sta	05
1-149	Red Hook Sta	31
1-149	Ridgewood Sta	27
1-150	Kensington Sta	18
1-159	Bay Sta	35
1-179	Greenpoint Sta	22
1-179	Homecrest Sta	29
1-179	Saint Johns Place Sta	13
1-180	Metropolitan Sta	06
1-206	Flatbush Sta	26
1-208	Bay Ridge Sta	20
1-219	Coney Island Sta	24
1-227	Brevoort Sta	16
1-229	Rugby Sta	03
1-238	Brownsville Sta	12
1-239	Lefferts Sta	25
1-259	Midwood Sta	30
1-265	Ryder Sta	34
1-269	Van Brunt Sta	15
1-329	Adelphi Sta	38
1-359	Times Plaza Sta	17
1-374	Williamsburg Sta	11
1-1818	Main Office	02

STATIONS, BRANCHES AND UNITS

Adelphi Sta	38
Bath Beach Sta	14
Bay Sta	35
Bay Ridge Sta	20
Blythebourne Sta	19
Brevoort Sta	16
Brighton Sta	35
Brownsville Sta	12
Bush Terminal Sta	32
Bushwick Sta	21
Canarsie Sta	36
Classon Sta	38
Coney Island Sta	24
Cypress Hills Sta	08
Dyker Heights Sta	28
East New York Sta	07
Embarkation Sta	50
Farragut Sta	03
Flatbush Sta	26
Fort Hamilton Sta	09
Fresh Pond Sta	27
Glendale Sta	27
Gravesend Sta	23
Greenpoint Sta	22
Halsey Sta	33
Highlawn Sta	23
Homecrest Sta	29
Kensington Sta	18
Kingsway Sta	29

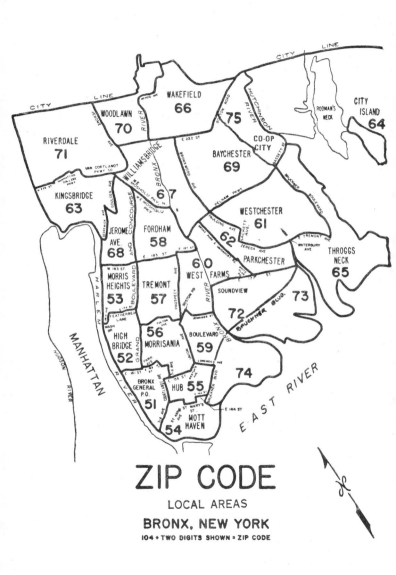

ZIP CODE

LOCAL AREAS

BRONX, NEW YORK

104 + TWO DIGITS SHOWN = ZIP CODE

ZIP CODE
LOCAL AREAS
BROOKLYN, NEW YORK

Brooklyn (Con.)   112

Lefferts Sta	25
Metropolitan Sta	06
Midwood Sta	30
Municipal Building Sta	01
New Lots Sta	08
Newkirk Sta	26
Nostrand Sta	35
Ovington Sta	20
Parcel Post Sta	15
Park Slope Sta	15
Parkville Sta	04
Pratt Sta	05
Prospect Park West Sta	15
Red Hook Sta	31
Ridgewood Sta	27
Rugby Sta	03
Ryder Sta	34
Saint Johns Place Sta	13
Stuyvesant Sta	33
Sunset Sta	20
Times Plaza Sta	17
Van Brunt Sta	15
Vanderveer Sta	10
Williamsburg Sta	11
Wyckoff Heights Sta	37
General Delivery	01
Postmaster	01

APARTMENTS, HOTELS, MOTELS

Albany Houses, 1229 Park Pl.	13
Atlantic Towers Plaza East, 216 Rockaway Ave	33
Atlantic Towers Plaza West, 249 Hopkinson Ave	33
Bay View Houses, 9800 Seaview Ave	36
Beach Haven, 2611 West 2nd	23
Bossert, 98 Montague	01
Boulevard Houses, 812 Ashford	07
Breukelen Houses, 618 East 108th	36
Brevoort Houses, 296 Ralph Ave	33
Brownsville Houses, 307 Blake Ave	12
Bushwick Houses, 372 Bushwick Ave	06
Clinton Hill Apartments, 345 Clinton Ave	38
Concord Village, 215 Adams	01
Coney Island Houses, 2793 West 33rd	24
Cooper Park, 40 Debevoise Ave	11
Cypress Hills Houses, 600 Euclid Ave	08
Dayton Manor, 9315 Ft Hamilton Pkwy	09
Ebbets Field Apartments, 1720 Bedford Ave	25
Eleanor Roosevelt Houses, 314 Pulaski	06
Farragut Houses, 251 Nassau	01
Flagg Court, 7200 Ridge Blvd	09
Forest Crescent, 9060 Union Turnpike	27
Fort Hamilton Manor, 405 Battery Ave	09
Fort Hamilton Manor, 620 Poly Pl	09
Franklin Arms, 66 Orange	01
Glenwood Houses, 1660 Ralph Ave	36
Golden Gate Inn, 3867 Shore Pkwy	35
German Apartments, 1371 Linden Blvd	12
Gowanus Houses, 211 Hoyt	17
Granada, Ashland Pl & Lafayette Ave	17
Gravesend Houses, 2793 West 33rd	24
Howard Houses, 1562 East New York Ave	12
Independence Houses, 80 Taylor	11
Jimerson Houses, 1407 Linden Blvd	12
John F Hylan Houses, 372 Bushwick Ave	06
Jonathan Williams Plaza, 227 Division Ave	11
Kings Bay Houses, 2520 Batchelder	35
Kingsboro Houses, 1880 Pacific	33
Kingsview Homes, 115 Ashland Pl	01
Lafayette Garden, 387 Lafayette Ave	38
Lafayette, 25 Lafayette Ave	17
Linden Houses, 914 Van Siclen Ave	07
Lindsay Park Co-Op, 555 Broadway	06
Louis Heaton Pink House, 2632 Linden Blvd	08
Luna Park Houses, 2880 West 12th	24
Majestic, 230 Duffield	01
Manhattan Beach, 156 West End Ave	35
Marcy Houses, 648 Marcy Ave	06
Margaret, 97 Columbia Hts	01
Marlboro Houses, 2740 86th	23
Mohawk, 379 Washington Ave	38
Nostrand Houses, 2955 Avenue W	29
Palm, 82 Pierrepont	01
Patio Gardens, 580 Flatbush Ave	25
Philip Howard Apartments, 1655 Flatbush Ave	10
Pierrepont, 55 Pierrepont	01
Raymond V Ingersoll, 120 Navy Walk	01
Red Hook Houses, 62 Mill	31
Ryerson Towers, 309 Lafayette Ave	38
Saint George, 51 Clark	01
Samuel J Tilden Houses, 282 Dumont Ave	12
Sheepshead Bay Houses, 2955 Avenue W	29
Shorehaven, 2064 Cropsey Ave	14
Standish Arms, 169 Columbia Hts	01
Sumner Houses, 20 Lewis Ave	06
Times Plaza, 510 Atlantic Ave	17
Tompkins Houses, 105 Tompkins Ave	06
Towers, 25 Clark	01
Trump Village, 2942 West 5th	24
University Terrace, 21 St James Pl	38
University Towers, 175 Willoughby	01
Van Dyke Houses, 370 Blake Ave	12
Vanderveer Estates, 1352 New York Ave	03
Walt Whitman Houses, 287 Myrtle Ave	05
Warbasse Houses, 425 Neptune Ave	24
Williamsburg Houses, 176 Maujer	06
Willoughby Walk Apartments, 195 Willoughby Ave	05
Zeckendorf Residence, 190 Willoughby	01

BUILDINGS

Albee, Albee Square	01
Board Of Education, 110 Livingston	01
Board Of Health, 295 Flatbush Ave Ext	01
Borough Hall, 205 Joralemon	01
Brooklyn Academy Of Music, 30 Lafayette Ave	17
Brooklyn Botanic Garden, 1000 Washington Ave	25
Brooklyn Eastern District Terminal, 86 Kent Ave	11
Brooklyn Museum, 178 Eastern Pkwy	38
Brooklyn Savings Bank 211, Montague	01
Brooklyn Waterfront Terminal Dock, Foot Of Clinton	31
Chamber Of Commerce, 26 Court	42
Chanin, 105 Court	01
Civic Center Brooklyn War Memorial, Cadman Plaza West	01
Clinton Wharf Dock	31
Commercial Wharf Dock	31
Department Of Welfare, 330 Jay	01
Dime Savings Bank Of New York, 9 Dekalb Ave	01
Domestic Relations, 383 Adams	01
Eighty Hanson Place Professional, 80 Hanson Pl	17
Fox Medical, 1 Nevins	17
Fulton Savings Bank, 395 Jay	01

Brooklyn (Con.) 112

Galen Hall, 184 Joralemon...... 01
Gowanus Lumber Terminal
Dock, Foot Of Columbia..... 31
Greenpoint Terminal Dock,
Foot Of Greenpoint Ave....... 22
Hall Of Records, 360 Adams.. 01
Kings Lafayette Bank, 200
Montague......................... 01
Lumber Exchange Terminal
Dock................................ 22
Manufacturers Trust, 177
Montague......................... 01.
Medical Arts, 142 Joralemon .. 01
Montague Court, 16 Court...... 41
Municipal, Joralemon &
Court................................ 01
New York Docks Trade
Facilities, 360 Furman 01
North Pier Dock...................... 31
Pier A Dock............................ 31
Pier B Dock............................ 31
Red Cross, 1 Red Cross Pl...... 01
Supreme Court, 360 Adams.... 01
Temple Bar, 44 Court............. 01
Terminal, 50 Court................. 01
Transit Authority, 370 Jay....... 01
U S Internal Revenue Bldg,
35 Tillary.......................... 01
U S Post Office & Federal
Bldg, 271 Cadman Plaza
-East.................................. 01
U.S. Courthouse, 225
Cadman Plaza East............ 01
Williamsburg Savings Bank,
1 Hanson Pl....................... 43

GOVERNMENT OFFICES

Immigration And
Naturalization Service, 250
Adams............................... 01

HOSPITALS

Adelphi, 50 Greene Ave.......... 38
Bay Ridge, 437 Ovington
Ave.................................. 09
Bethany Deaconess, 237 St
Nicholas Ave..................... 37
Brookdale Hospital Center,
Linden Blvd & Rockaway
Pkwy................................ 12
Brooklyn Cancer Institute,
451 Clarkson Ave.............. 03
Brooklyn Doctors, 4421 15th
Ave.................................. 19
Brooklyn Eye & Ear, 29
Greene Ave....................... 38
Brooklyn State Hospital For
Mentally Ill, 681 Clarkson.. 03
Brooklyn Thoracic, 121 De
Kalb Ave.......................... 01
Brooklyn Womens, 1395
Eastern Pkwy.................... 33
Brooklyn, De Kalb Ave &
Ashland............................. 01
Caledonian, Parkside Ave &
St Pauls........................... 26
Carson C Peck Memorial,
Crown & Albany Ave.......... 13

Community Hospital, 2525
Kings Hwy......................... 29
Coney Island, Ocean Pkwy &
Avenue Z.......................... 35
Cumberland, 39 Auburn Pl..... 05
Downstate Medical Center,
450 Clarkson Ave.............. 03
Flatbush.General Hospital,
719 Linden Blvd................ 03
Greenpoint, Kingsland Ave &
Jackson............................ 11
Holy Family, 155 Dean........... 17
House Of Saint Giles The
Cripple, 1346 President...... 13
Interboro General, 2749
Linden Blvd....................... 08
Jewish Hospital Of Brooklyn,
555 Prospect Pl................. 38
Kings County, 451 Clarkson
Ave.................................. 03
Kings Highway, 3201 Kings
Hwy.................................. 34
Kingsbrook Jewish Med Ctr,
East 49th & Rutland Rd.... 03
Kingsway, 4422 Avenue J...... 34
Lefferts General Hospital,
460 Lefferts Ave............... 25
Linden General, 501 New
Lots Ave........................... 07
Long Island College, Henry &
Pacific.............................. 01
Lutheran Hospital Of
Brooklyn, E New York Ave
& Junius........................... 12
Lutheran Medical Center
Maternity Division, 362 51
St..................................... 20
Lutheran Medical Center,
4520 4th Ave.................... 20
Maimonides Medical Center
4802 10th Avenue.............. 19
Methodist Hospital Of
Brooklyn, 6th.................... 15
Metropolitan-Jewish Geriatric
Center-Parshelsky Pavilion,
2....................................... 24
Metropolitan-Jewish Geriatric
Center, 813 Howard Ave.... 12
Midwood, 19 Winthrop .... 25.
Prospect Heights, 775
Washington Ave................. 38
Saint Charles, 277 Hicks........ 01
Saint Giles, 1346 President..... 13
Saint Johns Episcopal
Hospital Of Brooklyn, 480
Herkimer........................... 13
Saint Marys, 1298 St. Marks
Ave.................................. 13
Samaritan, 759 President....... 15
Shore Road, Shore Rd &
91st.................................. 09
Sister Elizabeth Maternity,
362 51st........................... 20
Swedish, 1350 Bedford Ave.... 16
Unity, 1545 St Johns Pl......... 13
Veterans Admin Hospital Of
Brooklyn, 800 Poly Pl........ 09
Victory Memorial, 9036 7th
Ave.................................. 28
Williamsburg General, 757

Bushwick Ave......................... 21
Wyckoff Heights Hospital Of
Brooklyn, 142 St Nicholas
Ave.................................. 37

MILITARY INSTALLATIONS

Embarkation (Brooklyn Army
Terminal).......................... 50
Fort Ham Military
Reservation....................... 52
J.s. Naval Station, 136
Flushing Ave..................... 51

UNIVERSITIES AND COLLEGES

Brooklyn College Of
Pharmacy, 600 Lafayette
Ave.................................. 16
Brooklyn Law School, 250
Joralemon......................... 01
Brooklyn Polytechnic
Institute, 333 Jay St.......... 01
Brooklyn, Bedford Ave &
Avenue H........................... 10
Cathedral College Of
Immaculate Conception,
555 Washington................. 38
Long Island University, 385
Flatbush Ave Ext............... 01
New York City Community
College Arts & Science,
300 Pearl.......................... 01
Packer Collegiate Institute,
170 Joralemon.................. 01
Pratt Institute, 215 Ryerson... 05
Saint Francis, 180 Remsen 01
Saint Johns University
Center, 96 Schermerhorn.... 01
Saint Josephs College For
Women, 245 Clinton Ave.... 05
State University Of N Y
College Of Med, 450
Clarkson Ave..................... 03
Zeckendorf Campus, 385
Flatbush Ave Ext............... 01

BUFFALO 142

POST OFFICE BOXES

Box Nos.		
A-H	Kenmore Br	17
A-I	West Seneca Br	24
A-J	B Sta...............	07
1-47	South Park Sta.	20
1-54	Cheektowaga Br	25
1-67	Kensington Sta.	15
1-99	Lackawanna Br	18
1-99	South Cheektowaga Br	27
1-117	Bidwell Sta......	22
1-117	C Sta..............	09
1-117	J Sta..............	08

Buffalo (Con.)　　　　142

1-119	G Sta	13
1-144	Market Sta.	03
1-154	B Sta	07
1-177	Hiler Br	23
1-216	West Seneca Br	24
1-240	Kenmore Br	17
1-266	F Sta.	12
1-267	Williamsville Br	21
1-270	Niagara Square Sta	01
1-1212	Main Office	40
1-3045	Ellicott Sta	05
900-999	C Sta	09
1000-1099	D Sta	10
1100-1199	E Sta	11
1400-1499	H Sta	14
1600-1699	Hertel Sta	16
1901-2047	Blasdell Br	19
2501-2599	Cheektowaga Br	25
2601-2747	Amherst Br	26

STATIONS, BRANCHES AND UNITS

Amherst Br	26
Bidwell Sta	22
Blasdell Br	19
Cass Br	06
Cheektowaga Br	25
Clearfield Br	24
Delray Br	24
Ellicott Sta	05
Georgetown Square Br	21
Grover Br	26
Harlem Br	26
Hertel Sta	16
Hiler Br	23
Kenmore Br	17
Kensington Sta	15
Lackawanna Br	18
Lincoln Park Br	23
Main Mill Br	21
Market Sta.	03
Marquette Br	17
Niagara Square Sta	01
Northtown Br	26
Northwood Br	23
Snyder Br	26
South Buffalo Sta	18
South Park Sta	20
Steel City Br	18
Transitown Br	21
Van Del Br	17
Veterans Administration HospSta	15
West Seneca Br	24
Williamsville Br	21
General Delivery	40
Postmaster	40

APARTMENTS, HOTELS, MOTELS

Airways, Genesee & Airport Dr	25
Alfred D. Price Cts, 406 Jefferson Ave	04
Algonquin, 76 Johnson Pk	01
Ambassador, 535 North	01
Ashland, 712-718 Ashland Ave	22

Bennett, 2727 Main	14
Best, 4-16 Best	09
Boulevard Towers 90 Meyer Rd	26
Buffalo Travelodge, 984 Main	02
Campanile, 925 Delaware Ave	09
Canterbury Court, 2 Lexington Ave	22
Cathedral, 1022 Delaware Ave	09
Chapel Court, 71 Linda Dr	25
Chippewa, 47 W Chippewa	02
Clinton-Aire, 4237 Genesee	25
Colonial, 401 Delaware Ave	02
Commodore, 1240 Delaware Ave	09
Continental Inn, 3456 Delaware Ave	17
Delaware Park, 1995 Delaware Ave	16
Delaware Towers Apts, 1088 Delaware Ave	09
Elliott, 175 Delaware Ave	09
Elm-Nor, 209 Elmwood Ave	22
Executive Motor, 4243 Genesee	25
Executive Tower Apts, 849 Delaware Ave	09
Fairfax Motor Inn, 715 Delaware Ave	09
Gates Circle, 1306 Delaware Ave	09
Genesee, 308 Pearl	02
Graystone, 24 Johnson Park	01
High Street, 23 High	03
Holiday Inn - Airport, 4600 Genesee, E	25
Holiday Inn - Downtown, 620 Delaware Ave	02
Holiday Inn, Dingens & Rossler	06
Hyde Park, 196 North	01
Jewett, 4 Jewett Parkway	14
Kensington Heights, 32 Glenny Dr	14
La Salle, 186 W Chippewa	01
Lackawanna, 727 Ridge Rd	18
Lafayette, Washington & Clinton	05
Lenox, 140 North	01
Lin-Nor, 3 Linwood Ave	02
Lord Amherst Motor, 5000 Main	26
Mayflower, 66 Summer	02
Mohawk Motor Inn, Main & Michigan Ave	09
New Ashland, 7 Ashland Ave	22
North Court, 197 North	01
Park Lane, 33 Gates Cir	09
Pomeroy Lane, 3901 Main	26
Prince Edward, 490 Pearl	02
Princeton Court, 165 Princeton Ave	26
Regency Motor Hotel, 4408 Mile Strip Rd	19
Roosevelt, 12 Carlton	03
Sherwood, 140 Linwood Ave	09
Statler Hilton, Niagara Sq	02
Stratford Arms, 25 W Utica	09
Stuyvesant, 245 Elmwood Ave	22

Towne House, 999 Main	03
Tudor Arms, 354 Franklin	02
Tudor Plaza, 731-751 West Ferry	22
Twelve Ninety Delaware Apts, 1290 Delaware Ave	09
Villa Nova, 234 Franklin	02
Virginia, 520 Virginia	02
Westbrook House, 675 Delaware Ave	02
Williamsville Motel & Inn, 5447 Main	21
Windsor, 703 W Ferry	22
Y M C A, 45 W Mohawk	02
Y W C A Residence, 245 North	01
400 Elmwood Avenue, 400 Elmwood Ave	22

BUILDINGS

Albright-Knox Art Gallery, 1285 Elmwood Ave	22
Andrews, 35 Court	02
Bank Of Buffalo, 17 Court	02
Blue Cross, 298 Main	02
Bowen, 36 W Huron	02
Brisbane, 403 Main	03
Buffalo & Erie County Historical Society, 25 Nottingham Ct	16
Buffalo & Erie County Public Library, 1 Broadway	03
Buffalo Catholic Institute, 836 Main	02
Buffalo Museum Of Science, Humboldt Parkway	11
Byers, 505 Pearl	02
Byers, 700 Main	02
Central Terminal, 495 Paderewski Dr	12
Corn Exchange, 100 South Elmwood Ave	02
Crosby, 170 Franklin	02
Delaware, 361 Delaware Ave	02
Dun, 110 Pearl	02
Edwards, 155 Franklin	02
Electric, 535 Washington	02
Ellicott Square, 295 Main	03
Erie County Savings Bank, Main Pl	02
Genesee, 1 W Genesee	02
Greater Buffalo Intl Airport, Genesee & Cayuga Rd	25
Henkel, 1377 Main	09
Hurst, 47 W Huron	02
Huyler, 374 Delaware Ave	02
Jackson, 220 Delaware Ave	02
Kleinhans Music Hall, Symphony Cir	01
Lafayette, 6 Broadway	03
Liberty Bank, 422 Main	02
Linwood Medical Ctr, 333 Linwood Ave	09
Lockwood, 80 W Genesee	02
M & T Plaza, 1 M & T Plaza	03
Main Place Tower	03
Marine Trust, 237 Main	03
Market Arcade, 617 Main	03
Memorial Auditorium, 140 Main	02
Merchants Mutual, 250 Main	02
Nellany, 485 Main	03
New York Telephone, 44	

Buffalo (Con.)   142

Church 02
Niagara Frontier Food
  Terminal, 1500 Clinton 06
Niagara Frontier, 290 Main 02
Peace Bridge Plaza 13
Prudential, 28 Church 02
Rand, 14 Lafayette Sq 03
Roosevelt Apt, 921 Main 02
Root, 70 W Chippewa 02
Sidway, 775 Main 03
Statler-Hilton Hotel, Niagara
  Sq 02
Thomas Industrial Center,
  1200 Niagara 13
Tishman, 10 Lafayette Sq 03
Two Ten Franklin, Two Ten
  Franklin 02
Vars, 344 Delaware Ave 02
Walbridge, 43 Court 02
Western, 15 Court 02
White, 292 Main 02
Ymca, 45 W.mohawk 02
Ywca, 190 Franklin 02

GOVERNMENT OFFICES

Buffalo City Hall, 65 Niagara
  Sq 02
Chamber Of Commerce, 238
  Main 02
City Court, 42 Delaware Ave ... 02
County Court, 25 Delaware
  Ave 02
County Hall, Franklin & W
  Eagle 02
Donovan State Office, 125
  Main 03
Erie County, 134 West Eagle .. 02
Federal 111 West Huron 02
Federal, 121 Ellicott 03
Hud, Fha Office, 560 Main 02
Rath County Office, 95
  Franklin 02
Social Security Office, 560
  Main 02
State Office, 65 Court 02
U S Court House, 64 Court 02
U S Veterans Administration
  111 W Huron 02

HOSPITALS

Booth Memorial, 740
  Jefferson Ave 04
Buffalo Columbus, 300
  Niagara 01
Buffalo General, 100 High 03
Buffalo State, 400 Forest
  Ave 13
Childrens, 219 Bryant 22
Deaconess, 1001 Humboldt
  Parkway 08
Emergency, 108 Pine 04
Kenmore Mercy, 2950
  Elmwood Ave 17
Lafayette General, 113
  Lafayette Ave 13
Mercy, 565 Abbott Rd 20
Meyer Memorial E J, 462
  Grider 15

Millard Fillmore, 3 Gates Cir .. 09
Our Lady Of Victory, 55
  Melroy 18
Roswell Park Memorial
  Institute, 666 Elm 03
Saint Francis, 2787 Main 14
Saint Josephs
  Intercommunity, 2605
  Harlem Rd 25
Sisters Of Charity, 2157
  Main 14
Veterans Administration,
  3495 Bailey Ave 15

UNIVERSITIES AND COLLEGES

Bryant & Stratton, 1028
  Main 02
Canisius 2001 Main 08
Dyouville, 320 Porter Ave 01
Erie Community, (Ecti), Main
  & Youngs Rd 21
Houghton College, Buffalo
  Campus, 910 Union Rd 24
Medaille College, 18 Agassiz
  Cir 14
Rosary Hill, 4380 Main 26
State U Of N Y Interim
  Campus, 4224 - 4250
  Ridge Lea Rd 26
State University College At
  Buffalo, 1300 Elmwood
  Ave 22
State University Of New York
  At Buffalo 14
State University Of New York
  Dentistry School, 3435
  Main 14
State University Of New York
  Law School, 77 W Eagle 02
State University Of New York
  Medical School, 3435
  Main 14
Trocaire, 110 Red Jacket Pky .. 20
Villa Maria College, 240 Pine
  Ridge Rd 25

ELMIRA   149

POST OFFICE BOXES

Box Nos.
1-1999   Main Office 02
2001-2117 Elmira Heights
             Br 03
3001-3118 Westside Sta 05
4001-4119 Southside Sta ... 04

RURAL ROUTES

1 03
2 01

STATIONS, BRANCHES AND UNITS

Elmira Heights Br 03
South Side Sta 04
West Side Sta 05
General Delivery 02
Postmaster 01

APARTMENTS, HOTELS, MOTELS

Centennial, 511-519
  Westwater 05
Cherrywood Manor, Maple
  Ave 04
Dades 03
Elms, 310 Walnut 01
Evans, 211 Walnut 05
Highland Terrace Ashland
  Ave & Mulberry 03
Holiday Inn, Box 64 02
Howard Johnson, Box 85 02
Mark Twain, Box 178 02
Newtown Towers, Dewitt Ave .. 01
Red Jacket, Box 489 02
Tom Sawyer, Box 1046 02
Woodland, 1849 West Water 05
Yorkshire, R D 01 03

BUILDINGS

Hulett, 338 East Water 01
M C I, 212-214 College Ave 01
Perry, Box 345 02
Robinson, 159-167 Lake 01

HOSPITALS

Arnot Ogden, Grove St & Roe
  Ave 01
Saint Josephs, Box 247 02

UNIVERSITIES AND COLLEGES

Elmira College, College Ave
  & Washington Ave 01

FAR ROCKAWAY   116

POST OFFICE BOXES

Box Nos.
1-21   Broad Channel
             Sta 93
1-116   Rockaway Park
             Sta 94
1-119   Arverne Sta 92
1-140   Fort Tilden Sta . 95
1-176   Inwood Long
             Island Br 96
1-205   Rockaway Point
             Sta 97
1-599   Far Rockaway 90
151-386   Rockaway
             Beach Sta 93

STATIONS, BRANCHES AND UNITS

Arverne Sta 92
Broad Channel Sta 93
Fort Tilden Sta 95
Inwood L I Br 96
Parcel Post Sta 91
Rockaway Beach Sta 93
Rockaway Park Sta 94
Rockaway Point Sta 97

Far Rockaway (Con.)   116
APARTMENTS, HOTELS, MOTELS

Allens, 163 Beach 98............ 94
Arlington, 430 Beach 20........ 91
Arverne Houses, 349 Beach
54.................................... 92
Balfour Arms, 1170
Nameoake.......................... 91
Barocrest, 121 Ocean
Promenade........................ 94
Bayswater Gardens, 2334
Mott Ave........................... 91
Beatrice Gardens, 2220
Cornaga Ave...................... 91
Belle Harbor Gardens, 128
Newport Ave...................... 94
Bermuda, 20 Elk Dr............. 91
Beyers, 179 Beach 129......... 94
Boulevard, 196 Beach 97...... 93
Catalina, 22 Brookhaven Ave. 91
Commodore, 126 Rockaway
Beach Blvd........................ 94
Cornaga Apartments, 2311
Cornaga Ave...................... 91
Cornell Hall, 22 Brookhaven
Ave.................................. 91
Crossway, 1502 Mott Ave..... 91
Crystal, 188 Beach 102......... 94
Dayton Beach Park............... 93
Daytona, 22 New Haven Ave.. 91
Dinsmore Towers, 10 Neilson
Ave.................................. 91
Edgemere Houses, 434 Beach
54.................................... 92
Fitzgeralds, 159 Beach 108.... 94
Garden House, 133 Rockaway
Beach Blvd........................ 94
Grand Apartments, 1001
Nameoake St...................... 91
Grassy Point, 18 Crossbay
Blvd................................. 93
Greenwood Gardens, 1430
Greenport Rd..................... 91
H.i.l.i., 1742 Seagirt Blvd...... 91
Hammel Houses, 85
Rockaway Beach Blvd 93
Homestaed Apartments, 1012
Nameoke........................... 91
Kay Rock Gardens, 1420
Greenport Rd..................... 91
Lawrence Arms, 1261 Central
Ave.................................. 91
Lawrence T.a.i, 833 Central
Ave.................................. 91
Lawrence, 158 Beach 116...... 94
Loyard, 122 Ocean
Promenade........................ 94
Manor, 259 Watjean Ct........ 91
Marguerita, 536 Beach 22..... 91
Marina Apartments, 2240
Mott Ave........................... 91
Martinique, 2204 Collier Ave.. 91
Mc Nultys Ocean, 108
Rockaway Beach Blvd 94
Monte Carlo, 631 Beach 9..... 91
Muriel Arms, 22 Mott Ave..... 91
Nassau, 407 B 20................. 91
Neilson Apartments, 1011
Neilson Ave....................... 91
Neilson Gardens, 1014
Neilson Ave....................... 91

Neilson Imperial, 1040
Neilson Ave....................... 91
Newport Inn, 129 Newport
Ave.................................. 94
Nordeck Houses, 349 Beach
57.................................... 92
Ocean Country Apartments,
705 Empire Ave.................. 91
Ocean Park, 169 Beach 115... 94
Oceancrest Apartments, 2944
Beach Chl Dr..................... 91
Oceanview Garden, 2316
Mott Ave........................... 91
Park Inn, 115 Ocean
Promenade........................ 94
Park Plaza, 170 Beach 121.... 94
Peninsula Apartments........... 91
Pickwick Arms, 160 Beach
117.................................. 94
Redfern Houses, 1456 Beach
Channel Dr........................ 91
Riviera, 707 Beach 9............ 91
Robert Arms, 2308 Mott Ave . 91
Rogers, 116 Rockaway Beach
Blvd................................. 94
Rosoff Terrace, 123
Rockaway Beach Blvd 94
Sea Isle, 133 Beach 120........ 94
Seagirt Apartments, 1430
Seagirt Ave........................ 91
Seville, 128 Rockaway Beach
Blvd................................. 94
Sheldon Terrace, 1007
Hartman Lane.................... 91
Shoreview Apartments, 2287
Mott Ave........................... 91
Shoreview Cooperative, 1141
Mcbride............................ 91
Surf House, 130 Beach 133.... 94
Surfside Park...................... 94
The Leizabeth, 123 Ocean
Promenade........................ 94
Washington, 124 Rockaway
Beach Blvd........................ 94
Wavecrest Gardens, 20
Seagirt Blvd....................... 91
White House, 109 Rockaway
Beach Blvd........................ 94
William, 1054 Beach 22........ 91

BUILDINGS

Chase Manhattan, 720
Beach 20........................... 91
Chase Manhattan, 84
Rockaway Beach Blvd 93
Jamaica Saving Bank 1525
Central Av......................... 91
National Bank, 1624 Central
Ave.................................. 91
Rockaway Savings Bank,
1600 Central Ave................ 91
Smith, 19 Mott Ave............. 91
Telephone, 1311 Bayport Pl... 91

HOSPITALS

Peninsula General Hospital,
51 Beach Channel Dr.......... 91
Saint Josephs, 327 Beach
19.................................... 91

FLORAL PARK   110

POST OFFICE BOXES

Box Nos.
1-72   Meacham Br...... 03
1-234   Glen Oaks Br..... 04
1-448   Elmont Br.......... 03
1-807   Main Office 02
301-389   Alden Manor
Br 03

STATIONS, BRANCHES AND UNITS

Alden Manor Br................... 03
Elmont Br.......................... 03
Glen Oaks Br...................... 04
Meacham Br....................... 03
General Delivery.................. 02
Postmaster......................... 01

FLUSHING   113

POST OFFICE BOXES

Box Nos.
A-Z   Corona-
Elmhurst Sta.... 73
1-72   Middle Village
Sta................ 79
1-87   Rego Park Sta.. 74
1-146   Flushing A Sta. 58
1-146   Oakland
Gardens Sta 64
1-147   Corona A Sta ... 68
1-163   Whitestone Sta. 57
1-171   College Point
Sta................. 56
1-175   Elmhurst A
Sta................. 73
1-176   Fresh Meadows
Sta................. 65
1-194   Maspeth Sta.... 78
1-234   Little Neck....... 63
1-375   Bayside Sta..... 61
1-439   East Elmhurst
Sta................. 69
1-574   Jackson
Heights Sta 72
1-597   Forest Hills...... 75
1-619   Woodside Sta... 77
1-832   Main Office 52
1-1039   La Guardia
Airport Sta...... 71
AA-AG   Corona-
Elmhurst Sta.. 73
400-440   Station C........ 67
501-1002   Corona-
Elmhurst Sta.. 73
801-1197   Linden Hill Sta. 54

STATIONS, BRANCHES AND UNITS

Bayside Sta........................ 60
Bay Terrace Sta................... 60
College Point Sta................. 56
Corona-A Sta 68
Corona-Elmhurst Sta 73
Douglaston Sta.................... 63
East Elmhurst Sta................ 69
Elmhurst-A Sta.................... 73

Flushing (Con.)   113

Forest Hills Sta......................   75
Fresh Meadows Sta................   65
Horace Harding Sta...............   62
Jackson Heights Sta..............   72
Junction Boulevard Sta.........   72
La Guarda Airport Sta...........   71
Linden Hill Sta......................   54
Little Neck Sta......................   62
Maspeth Sta..........................   78
Middle Village Sta.................   79
Oakland Gardens Sta............   64
Parkside Sta..........................   75
Pomonok Sta.........................   65
Rego Park Sta........................   74
Trainsmeadow Sta.................   70
Utopia Sta.............................   66
Whitestone Sta......................   57
Woodside Sta........................   77
General Delivery....................   52
Postmaster............................   51

APARTMENTS, HOTELS, MOTELS

Anchor Motor Inn, 204-10
    Northern Blvd....................   61
Chateau Chapin, 35-14
    Parsons Blvd.....................   54
Crossway La Guardia Inn,
    100-30 Ditmars Blvd   69
El Capitan Motel, 87-02 23rd
    Ave..................................   69
Fair Motor Inn, Long Island
    Exp & Gd Cent..................   68
Forest Hills Inn, 1 Station
    Square.............................   75
Haven Motel, 68-05
    Woodhaven Blvd................   74
Holiday Fair Apts, 97-11
    Horace Harding..................   68
La Guardia Hotel, 99-11
    Ditmars Blvd.....................   69
Midway Motor, Long Island
    Exp & 108 St.....................   68
New York Trades Council, 74-
    09 37th Ave......................   72
Pan American Motor Inn, 79-
    00 Queens Blvd.................   73
Queens Motor Inn, 64-11
    Queens Blvd......................   77
Sanford Motor, 140-40
    Sanford Ave......................   55
Sheraton Tenney Inn, 90-10
    Grand Central Pky.............   69
Skyway La Guardia, 102-10
    Ditmars Blvd.....................   69
Stadium View.Inn, 37-10
    114th...............................   68
Sunchester, 37-52 80 St.........   72
Travelers, 94-00 Ditmars
    Blvd.................................   69
Treadway Inn, 37-10 114th.....   68
Whitestone, 31st Ave &
    131st St............................   54

HOSPITALS

Booth Memorial, 56-45 Main ..   55
Deepdale, 55-15 Little Neck
    Parkway...........................   62
Elmhurst General, 79th St &
    Broadway..........................   73

Flushing, 44-14 Parsons
    Blvd.................................   55
Hillcrest General, 158-40
    79th Ave...........................   66
Parkway, 70-35 113th.............   75
Parsons, 35-06 Parsons Blvd..   54
Physicians, 34-01 73rd...........   72
Saint Johns, 90-02 Queens
    Blvd.................................   73
Saint Marys Hospital For
    Children, 29-01 216th.........   60
Salvation Army Maternity
    Home, 56-10 141st.............   55
Whitestone, 166th St Corner
    12 Ave..............................   57
Wyckoff Heights, 102-01 66th
    Road................................   75

UNIVERSITIES AND COLLEGES

Queens, 65-30 Kissena Blvd..   67
Queensboro Community, 56-X
    Springfield Blvd.................   64

GREAT NECK   110

POST OFFICE BOXES

Box Nos.
261-1000   Great Neck.......   22
1000-OUT   Old Village
                Sta....................   23

STATIONS, BRANCHES AND UNITS

Kings Point Br........................   24
Old Village Sta.......................   23
General Delivery.....................   22
Postmaster............................   22

APARTMENTS, HOTELS, MOTELS

Bayberry, 75 No Station
    Plaza................................   21
Belgrave, 37 Brompton Rd   21
Clent, Clent Rd......................   21
Colony, 10 Bond.....................   21
Kenwood, 160 Middle Neck
    Rd....................................   21
Knightsbridge, Knightsbridge
    Rd....................................   21
Summit House........................   21
Terrace, Terrace Circle............   21
Towers, 2-4 Spruce.................   21
Town House, Cutter Mill Rd.....   21
Tuscan Court, 215 Middle
    Neck Rd............................   21
Windsor, 21 Barstow Rd..........   21
Wychwood Gardens, 28 So
    Station Plaza.....................   21

BUILDINGS

Lake Success Industrial Park,
    Community Drive................   21
Sperry Gyroscope, Marcus &
    Lakeville...........................   20

HOSPITALS

Great Neck Medical Center,

Community Dr.......................   21
Great Neck Nursing Home,
    Community Dr....................   21

UNIVERSITIES AND COLLEGES

United States Merchant
    Marine Academy, Kings
    Point...............................   24

HEMPSTEAD   115

POST OFFICE BOXES

Box Nos.
1-147   Uniondale Br....   53
1-175   East Meadow
            Br..................   54
1-528   West
            Hempstead
            Br..................   52
1-642   Main Office......   51

STATIONS, BRANCHES AND UNITS

East Meadow Br.....................   54
Parcel Post Sta......................   50
Uniondale Br..........................   53
West Hempstead Br................   52
General Delivery.....................   51
Postmaster............................   51

UNIVERSITIES AND COLLEGES

Hofstra University-1000
    Fulton Ave........................   50

HICKSVILLE   118

POST OFFICE BOXES

Box Nos.
A-F   Main Office......   02
1-237   Plainview Br.....   03
1-297   Old Bethpage
            Br..................   04
1-774   Main Office......   02

STATIONS, BRANCHES AND UNITS

Old Bethpage Branch Br..........   04
Plainview Br...........................   03
General Delivery.....................   02
General Delivery Old
    Bethpag............................   04
General Delivery Plainview B....   03
Postmaster............................   02

APARTMENTS, HOTELS, MOTELS

Astro Motor-Inn, 828 S Oyster
    Bay Rd..............................   01
Fairhaven Garden
    Apartments, Richard Ave....   01
Hicksville Motor Lodge, Old
    Country&wantagh Pky........   01

Hicksville (Con.)   118

Holiday Inn, Sunnyside Blvd...   03
Kings Grant Motor Inn, 150
  Sunnyside Blvd   03
Pickwick Motor Inn,
  Roundswamp Rd.................   03

BUILDINGS

Gertz, Mid-Island Plaza   01
J C Penny, S Oyster Bay Rd....   03
Mid Island Herald, 1
  Jonathan Avenue.................   01
Mid-Island Times, 22 W
  Nicholai.................   01
Sears Roebuck, 185-195 N
  Broadway   02

GOVERNMENT OFFICES

Bureau Of Motor Vehicles......   01
Department Of Agriculture......   02
Hicksville Board Of
  Education.................   01
Hicksville Fire Department......   01
Hicksville Water District.........   02
Office Of Civil Defense   01
Plainview Board Of
  Education.................   03
Plainview Fire Department......   03
Plainview Water District.........   03
Post Office Department.........   02
Town Of Oyster Bay.............   01

HOSPITALS

Central General Of Plainview,
  888 Old Country Rd...........   03
East Nassau Medical Center,
  350 S Broadway   01

JAMAICA   114

POST OFFICE BOXES

Box Nos.
1-85   Rosedale Stà....   22
1-87   Cambria
    Heights Sta   11
1-87   Springfield
    Gardens Sta   13
1-117   Bellerose Sta....   26
1-146   Queens Village
    Sta.................   29
1-146   Saint Albans
    Sta.................   12
1-146   South Ozone
    Park Sta   20
1-158   South
    Richmond Hill
    Sta.................   19
1-176   Hollis Sta   23
1-186   Ozone Park
    Sta.................   17
1-227   Central Sta......   35
1-384   Richmond Hill
    Sta.................   18
1-386   Kew Gardens
    Sta.................   15

1-589   Rochdale
    Village Sta   34
1-752   J F K Internatl
    Airport Sta......   30
1-1080   Main Office   31
101-249   Howard Beach
    Sta.................   14
501-587   Borough Hall
    Sta.................   24
101-1295   Woodhaven
    Sta.................   21

STATIONS, BRANCHES AND UNITS

Bellerose Sta................   26
Borough Hall Sta..........   24
Cambria Heights Sta   11
Central Sta................   35
Hollis Sta................   23
Howard Beach Sta   14
John F Kennedy Airport Sta....   30
Kew Gardens Sta.............   15
Naval Hospital Sta.............   25
Ozone Park Sta.............   16
Parcel Post Sta................   18
Queens Village Sta.............   27
Richmond Hill Sta.............   18
Rochdale Village Sta.........   34
Rosedale Sta................   22
Saint Albans Sta.............   12
South Ozone Park Sta   20
South Richmond Hill Sta   19
Springfield Gardens Sta.........   13
Wood Haven Sta.............   21
General Delivery   31
Postmaster.................   31

APARTMENTS, HOTELS, MOTELS

Air Host Inn 152-25 138 Ave....   34
Bristol 161-01 89 Ave.........   32
Franklin, 89-05 163rd.........   32
Holiday Inn Of America, Inc.,
  175-15 Rockaway Blvd......   34
International, Van Wyck Exp
  & S Cndt Av   30
Riviera Idlewild, 151-20
  Baisley Blvd.................   34
Skyway, 132-10 S Conduit
  Av.................   30
Statler Hilton Inn, 138-10
  135 Ave.................   36
Whitman, 160-11 89th Ave....   32

BUILDINGS

Borough Hall, 120-55 Queens
  Blvd.................   24
Domestic Relations, 105-34
  Union Hall.................   33

GOVERNMENT OFFICES

Board Of Health, 90-37
  Parsons Blvd.................   32

HOSPITALS

Creedmoor State, Winchester
  Blvd & Hillside Ave   27
Interfaith Hospital Of
  Queens, 175-10 88 Ave......   32
Jamaica. 89th Ave & Van

Wyck Expway.................   18
Kew Gardens General, 80-02
  Kew Gardens Rd.................   15
Mary Immaculate, 152-11
  89th Ave.................   32
Queens General, 82-68
  164th.................   32
Queens Village Sanatorium,
  218-15 103 Rd Ave.........   29
Terrace Heights, 87-37
  Palermo Ave.................   23
Triboro, Parsons Blvd &
  Goethals Dr.................   32
United States Naval Hospital,
  Linden Bd & 180th St......   25

UNIVERSITIES AND COLLEGES

Saint Johns University, 81-10
  Utopia Pkwy.................   32

LONG ISLAND CITY   111

POST OFFICE BOXES

Box Nos.
1001-1999   Main Office   01
2001-2999   Astoria Sta.....   02
3001-3999   Steinway Sta   03
4001-4999   Sunnyside Sta ..   04
5001-5999   Woolsey Sta   05
6001-6999   Broadway Sta....   06

STATIONS, BRANCHES AND UNITS

Astoria Sta................   02
Broadway Sta.................   06
Parcel Post Sta.................   01
Plaza Sta.................   01
Steinway Sta.................   03
Sunnyside Sta.................   04
Woolsey Sta.................   05
General Delivery   01
Postmaster.................   01

APARTMENTS, HOTELS, MOTELS

Astoria Housing Project.........   02
Crystal Gardens.................   02
Essex House, 42 43rd Ave........   04
Golden Gate, 41 43rd Ave   04
Marine Terrace.................   05
Phipps Gardens, 51 39th
  Ave.................   04
Queensbridge Housing   01
Queensview Housing   06
Ravenswood Housing Project..   06
Sunnyside Towers, 46 39th
  Ave.................   04

BUILDINGS

Boys Club Of Queens, 21-12
  30th Road.................   02

GOVERNMENT OFFICES

Board Of Education, 28
  Bridge Plaza N.................   01
City Prison, Court Square   01

Long Island City (Con.)	111
Criminal Court, 25 Court Sq..	01
Fire College, 48 35th	01
Health Center, 12 31st Ave....	06
Labor Department, Bank Manhattan Bldg	01
Magistrates Court, 25 Court Sq	01
Police Dep'T. 108 Pct	01
Police Dep'T. 114 Pct	02
Postal Concentration Center, 48th & N Boulevard	01
Salvation Army, 45 Broadway	03
Sanitation Department, 3 Crescent	01
Sanitation Department, 34 21st	06
Selective Service, 29 41st Ave	01
Traffic Court, 25 Court Sq	01
United States Selective Service, 29 41st Ave	01

HOSPITALS

Astoria General, 25 30th Ave .	02
Boulevard, 46 31st Ave	03

MILITARY INSTALLATIONS

United States Army Pictoral Center, 35 35th Ave	06

MOUNT VERNON   105

POST OFFICE BOXES

Box Nos.		
1-147	Fleetwood Sta...	52
1-1500	Main Office	51

STATIONS, BRANCHES AND UNITS

Columbus Sta	53
Fleetwood Sta	52
General Delivery	51
Postmaster	51

NEW ROCHELLE   108

POST OFFICE BOXES

Box Nos.		
1-119	Wykagyl Sta	04
1-209	Pelham Br	03
1-1590	Main Office	02

STATIONS, BRANCHES AND UNITS

Castle Sta	01
Pelham Br	03
Wykagyl Sta	04
General Delivery	02
Postmaster	02

UNIVERSITIES AND COLLEGES

Iona College	01
New Rochelle College	01

NEW YORK   100

POST OFFICE BOXES

Box Nos.		
1-104	Prince Sta	12
1-154	Peck Slip Sta	38
1-216	Fort George Sta	40
1-224	Inwood Sta	34
1-250	Knickerbocker Sta	02
1-300	Village Sta	14
1-324	Lincolnton Sta	37
1-360	Audubon Sta	32
1-425	Bowling Green Sta	04
1-448	College Sta	30
1-456	Murray Hill Sta	16
1-475	Hell Gate Sta	29
1-503	Old Chelsea Sta	11
1-518	Hamilton Grange Sta	31
1-526	Washington Bridge Sta	33
1-539	Gracie Sta	28
1-554	Planetarium Sta	24
1-575	Canal Street Sta	13
1-575	Cooper Sta	03
1-600	Lenox Hill Sta	21
1-600	Midtown Sta	18
1-600	Triborough Sta	35
1-615	Colonial Park Sta	39
1-650	Cathedral Sta	25
1-670	Morningside Sta	26
1-756	Manhattanville Sta	27
1-779	Times Square Sta	36
1-927	Madison Square Sta	10
1-950	Wall Street Sta	05
1-1039	Peter Stuyvesant Sta	09
1-1175	Ansonia Sta	23
1-1200	Radio City Sta.	19
1-1236	Seamans Ch Inst Sta	04
1-1299	Franklin D. Roosevelt Sta	22
1-3000	Main Office	01
1-3999	Church Street Sta	08
1-6000	Grand Central Sta	17
4000-15000	Church Street Sta	49

STATIONS, BRANCHES AND UNITS

Ansonia Sta	23
Audubon Sta	32
Bowling Green Sta	04
Bryant Sta	36
Canal Street Sta	13
Cathedral Sta	25
Cherokee Sta	28
Chinatown Sta	13
Church Street Sta	07
College Sta	30
Colonial Park Sta	39
Columbia University Sta	25
Columbus Circle Sta	23
Cooper Sta	03
Empire State Sta	01
Federal Reserve Sta	45
Fort George Sta	40
Fort Washington Sta	32
Franklin D Roosevelt Sta	22
Governors Island Br	04
Gracie Sta	28
Grand Central Sta	17
Greeley Square Sta	01
Hamilton Grange Sta	31
Hell Gate Sta	29
Howard Sta	13
Inwood Sta	34
Knickerbocker Sta	02
Lenox Hill Sta	21
Lincolnton Sta	37
London Terrace Sta	11
Madison Square Sta	10
Manhattanville Sta	27
Midtown Sta	18
Morgan Sta	01
Morningside Sta	26
Murray Hill Sta	16
No One Hundred Thirty Eight Sta	01
Number Eighteen Sta	16
Number Eighty Two Sta	22
Number Forty Sta	01
Old Chelsea Sta	11
Patchin Sta	11
Peck Slip Sta	38
Peter Stuyvesant Sta	09
Pitt Sta	02
Planetarium Sta	24
Port Authority Sta	11
Postal Concentration Center Sta	11101
Prince Sta	12
Radio City Sta	19
Rockefeller Center Sta	20
Seamens Church Institute Sta	04
Times Square Sta	36
Tompkins Square Sta	09
Triborough Sta	35
Tudor Sta	17
United Nations New York Sta	17
Village Sta	14
Wall Street Sta	05
Washington Bridge Sta	33
General Delivery	01

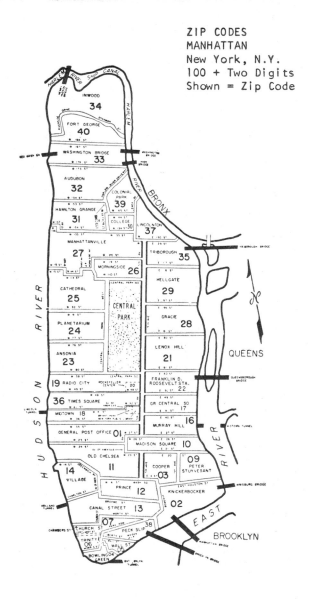

ZIP CODES
MANHATTAN
New York, N.Y.
100 + Two Digits
Shown = Zip Code

New York (Con.)   100

Postmaster   01

APARTMENTS, HOTELS, MOTELS

Abbey Victoria, 151 W 51st.... 19
Aberdeen, 17 W 32nd............ 01
Adams, 2 E 86th.................... 03
Alamac, Broadway & W 71st.. 23
Albert, 23 E 10th................... 03
Alden, 225 Central Pk W....... 24
Alexandria, 250 W 103rd...... 25
Algonquin, 59 W 44th........... 36
Allerton, 130 E 57th............. 22
Alrae, 37 E 64th................... 21
America, 331 E 86th.............. 28
Americana, 801 7th Ave........ 19
Amsterdam, 57 Lexington
  Ave 10
Ansonia, Broadway & W
  73rd 23
Arlington, 18 W 25th............ 10
Ashley, 157 W 47th.............. 36
Bancroft, 40 W 72nd............ 23
Barbizon Plaza, 106 Central
  Pk S 19
Barbizon, Lexington Ave & E
  63rd 21
Barclay, 111 E 48th.............. 17
Beacon, Broadway & W 75th.. 23
Bedford, 118 E 40th............. 16
Beekman Tower, 3 Mitchell
  Pl....................................... 17
Beekman, 575 Park Ave........ 21
Belair, 349 W 48th............... 36
Belleclaire, Broadway & W
  77th 24
Belmont Plaza, Lexington Ave
  & E 49th............................ 22
Belmore, 61 Lexington Ave.... 10
Belvedere, 319 W 48th......... 36
Benjamin Franklin, 222 W
  77th 24
Berkley, 170 W 74th............. 23
Berkshire, 21 E 52nd............ 22
Beverly, 125 E 50th.............. 22
Biltmore, Madison Ave & E
  43rd 17
Blackstone, 50 E 58th........... 22
Bolivar, 230 Central Park W... 24
Bond, 125 Chambers............ 07
Braddock, 272 W 126th........ 27
Bradford, 210 W 70th........... 23
Breslin, Broadway & W 29th.. 01
Bretton Hall, Broadway & W
  86th 24
Brevort, 11 5th Ave.............. 03
Brewster, 21 W 86th............. 24
Broadmoor, Broadway & W
  102nd................................ 25
Bryant, W 54th & Broadway... 19
Buckingham, 101 W 57th...... 19
Butler Hall, 400 W 119......... 27
Cambridge House, 333 W
  86th 24
Cambridge, 141 W 110th...... 26
Cameron, 41 W 86th............ 24
Carlton House, 680 Madison
  Ave 21
Carlyle, 35 E 76th................ 21
Carriage House, 200 E 38th... 16
Cecil, 208 W 118th.............. 26

Chalfonte, 200 W 70th......... 23
Chelsea, 222 W 23rd............ 11
Claremont, 140 Claremont
  Ave 27
Clifton, 127 W 79th.............. 24
Coliseum House, 228 W 71st. 23
Collingwood, 45 W 35th....... 01
Colony, 30 E 65................... 21
Columbia, 70 W 46th........... 36
Commander, 240 W 73rd...... 23
Commodore, Lexington Ave &
  E 42nd.............................. 17
Consulate, 224 W 49th......... 19
Cornish Arms, 311 W 23rd.... 11
Cort, 301 W 48th................. 36
Croyden, 12 E 86th.............. 28
Delmonico, 502 Park Ave...... 22
Des Artistes, 1 W 67th.......... 23
Diplomat, 108 W 43rd.......... 36
Dixie, 250 W 43rd................ 36
Doral, 70 Park Ave............... 16
Dorset, 30 W 54th............... 19
Dover, 687 Lexington Ave..... 22
Downtown Athletic Club, 19
  West 04
Drake, 440 Park Ave............ 22
Dryden, 150 E 39th............. 16
Earle, 103 Waverly Pl........... 11
East End, 541 E 78th............ 21
Edison, 228 W 47th.............. 36
Elton, 101 E 26th................. 10
Elysee, 60 E 54th................. 21
Embassy, 154 W 70th........... 23
Empire, Broadway & W 63rd.. 23
Endicott Apartment, 53 W
  72nd 23
Esplanade, 305 West End
  Ave 23
Essex House, 160 Central
  Park S 19
Excelsior, 45 W 81st............. 24
Executive, 237 Madison Ave... 16
Fifth Avenue, 5th Ave & 9th... 11
Franconia, 20 W 72nd.......... 23
Franklin, 164 E 87th............. 28
Fulton, 266 W 46th.............. 36
George Washington,
  Lexington Ave & E 23rd 10
George, 112 W 47th............. 36
Globe, 300 W 44th............... 36
Gorham, 136 W 55th........... 19
Gotham, 5th Ave & W 55th... 19
Gramercy Park, 52 Gramercy
  Park N 10
Grand Union, 1815 Park Ave.. 35
Grand Union, 34 E 32nd....... 16
Great Northern, 118 W 57th... 19
Greystone, Broadway & W
  91st.................................... 24
Grosvenor, 35 5th Ave.......... 03
Hadson, W 31st & Broadway.. 01
Hamilton, 143 W 73rd.......... 23
Hampshire House, 150
  Central Park S 19
Hampton House, 28 E 70th... 21
Hargrave, 112 W 72nd......... 23
Harmony, 544 W 110th........ 26
Hatfield, 103 E 29th............. 16
Henry Hudson, 353 W 57th... 19
Holland, 351 W 42nd........... 36
Hutton Hall, 304 W 92nd...... 25
Hyde Park, 25 E 77th 21
International House, 500

Riverside Dr...................... 27
Iroquois, 49 W 44th............. 36
Irving, 26 Gramercy Pk......... 03
John Murray House, 220
  Madison Ave 16
Johnson Hall, 411 W 116th... 27
Kenmore Hall, 145 E 23rd..... 10
Kent, 31 West 71st............... 23
Keystone, 161 W 36th.......... 18
Kimberly, Broadway & W
  74th 23
King Edward, 120 W 44th...... 36
Kings Crown, 420 W 116th.... 27
Knickerbocker, 120 W 45th... 36
Lancaster, Madison Ave &
  38th 16
Latham, 4 E 28th................. 16
Le Marquis, 12 E 31st.......... 16
Lenox, 151 W 44th.............. 36
Leonari, 26 E 63rd............... 21
Lexington, Lexington Ave & E
  48th 17
Lincoln Square, 166 W 75th... 23
Lombardy, 111 E 56th.......... 22
Lowell, 28 E 63rd................. 21
Lucerne, Amsterdam Ave & W
  79th 24
Manger Windsor, 100 W
  58th 19
Manhattan Towers, Broadway
  & W 76th............................ 24
Manhattan, 700 8th Ave....... 36
Mansfield, 12 W 44th........... 36
Marlton, 5 W 8th................. 11
Marseilles, Broadway & W
  103rd 25
Martha Washington, 29 E
  29th 16
Martinique, Broadway & W
  32nd 01
Master, 310 Riverside Dr...... 25
Mayfair, 610 Park Ave.......... 21
Mayflower, 15 Central Park
  West 23
Meurice, 145 W 58th............ 19
Midway, Broadway & W
  100th.................................. 25
Milburn, 242 W 76th............ 23
Monterey, Broadway & W
  94th 25
Morningside, 100
  Morningside Dr 27
Motel City, 510 W 42nd........ 36
Murray Hill, 42 W 35th......... 01
Narragansett, 2510
  Broadway 25
Nassau, 56 E 59th............... 22
National, 7th Ave & W 42nd... 36
Navarro, 112 Central Park S... 19
New Endicott, Columbus Ave
  & W 81st............................ 24
New York Hilton, 1335 Ave Of
  The Amer............................ 19
New Yorker, 8th Ave & W
  34th 01
Newton, 2528 Broadway...... 25
Olcott, 27 W 72nd............... 23
Oliver Cromwell, 12 W 72nd.. 23
One Fifth Avenue................. 03
One-Twenty-Three, 123 W
  44th 36
Orleans 416 Columbus Ave... 24
Paramount, 235 W 46th........ 36

New York (Con.)   100

Paris, West End Ave & W
97th 25
Park Plaza, 50 W 77th......... 24
Park Royal, 23 W 73rd......... 23
Park Sheraton, 7th Ave & W
56th 19
Park Wald, 117 W 58th......... 19
Peerless, 116 W 45th............ 36
Penn Garden, 391 7th Ave...... 01
Penn Post, 304 W 31st.......... 01
Peter Cooper, 130 E 39th....... 16
Piccadilly, 227 W 45th.......... 36
Pickwick Arms, 230 E 51st..... 22
Pierre, 5th Ave & E 61st........ 21
Plaza, 5th Ave & W 59th........ 19
President, 234 W 48th............ 36
Prince George, 14 E 28th....... 16
Regency, 540 Park Ave 21
Regent, Broadway & W
104th 25
Remington, 129 W 46th.......... 36
Rio, 132 W 47th.................. 36
Ritz Tower, Park Ave & E
57th 22
Riverside Plaza, 253 W 73rd.. 23
Roger Smith, Lexington Ave
& E 47th........................ 17
Roger Williams, 28 E 31st...... 16
Roosevelt, Madison Ave & E
45th 17
Rosoff, 147 W 43rd.............. 36
Roy, 535 W 112th................ 25
Royalton, 44 W 44th............. 36
Rutledge, 161 Lexington Ave.. 16
Ruxton, 50 W 72nd............... 23
Saint Agnes Residence, 237
W 74th.......................... 23
Saint Francis, 124 W 47th 36
Saint George, Broadway & E
12th 03
Saint James, 109 W 45th....... 36
Saint Moritz, 50 Central Pk
S................................. 19
Saint Regis, 5th Ave & E
55th 22
Salisbury, 123 W 57th........... 19
Salvation Army Retirement
Home West End Ave And
W 95th.......................... 25
San Carlos, 150 E 50th.......... 22
Scott, 132 W 45th................ 36
Seamans Church Institute,
15 State........................ 04
Seville, Madison Ave & E
29th 16
Shelton, Lexington Ave & E
49th 17
Sheraton Motor Motel, 42nd
& 12th Ave..................... 36
Sheraton-Atlantic, Broadway
& W 34th........................ 01
Sheraton-Russell, Park Ave &
E 37th.......................... 16
Sherry-Netherland, 5th Ave &
E 59th.......................... 22
Simmons House, 350 W 88th.. 24
Skyline Motel, 721 10th Ave... 19
Somerset, 150 W 47th........... 36
Spencer Arms, Broadway & W
69th 23
Stanhope, 995 5th Ave 28

Strand, 206 W 43rd.............. 36
Stratford Arms, 117 W 70th.... 23
Stratford, 11 E 32nd............. 16
Studio Club, 210 E 77th......... 21
Summit, Lexington Ave &
51st 22
Surrey, 20 E 76th................ 21
Sutton Plaza, 116 E 58th....... 22
Sutton, 330 E 56th............... 22
Taft, 7th Ave & W 50th.......... 19
Times Square, 8th Ave & W
43rd 36
Tudor, 304 E 42nd............... 17
Tuscany, 120 E 39th............. 16
University Broadway And W
3rd 12
Van Rensselaer, 17 E 11th...... 03
Victoria, 7th Ave & W 51st..... 19
Volney, 23 E 74th................ 21
Waldorf Astoria, Park Ave &
E 50th.......................... 22
Wales, 1295 Madison Ave....... 28
Walton, 104 W 70th.............. 23
Warrington, 161 Madison
Ave 16
Warwick, 65 W 54th............. 19
Washington & Jefferson, 318
W 51 St......................... 19
Wellington, 7th Ave & W
55th 19
Wentworth, 59 W 46th........... 36
Westbury, Madison Ave & E
69th 21
Westley, 126 W 73rd............. 23
Whitby, 325 W 45th.............. 36
Whitehall, 100 100th........... 25
Willard, 330 West End Ave 23
Wilson, 308 W 58th.............. 19
Windemere, 666 West End
Ave 25
Winslow, Madison Ave & E
55th 22
Wolcott, 4 W 31st................ 01
Woodstock, 127 W 43rd......... 36
Woodward, Broadway & W
55th 19
York, 7th Ave & W 36th......... 18

BUILDINGS

Associated Press, 50
Rockefeller Plaza 20
Astor Plz........................ 36
Battery Park Plz................ 04
China Daily News, 20
Elizabeth 13
China Tribune, 210 Canal...... 13
Daily News Record, 7 E 12..... 03
Daily News, 220 E 42........... 17
El Dario, 181 Hudson........... 13
Forward, 175 E Broadway...... 02
Four Sherman Plz............... 23
Gulf & Western Olz. 15
Columbus Cir.................. 23
Hammarskjold Plz............... 17
Il Progresso, 260 Audubon
Ave 33
Journal Of Commerce, 99
Wall 05
La Prensa, 181 Hudson 13

Liberty Plz...................... 06
Lincoln Sq. Plz................. 23
Madison Sq. Plz................ 10
Morning Telegraph, 525 W
52................................. 19
New York Amsterdam News,
2340 8th Ave.................. 27
New York Courier, 15 W
125th 27
New York Plz.................... 04
New York Post 210 South...... 02
New York Times, 229 W 43 36
One Pennsylvania Plz........... 01
One Sherman Plz............... 23
Pace Plz 41 Park Row......... 38
State Street Plz................. 04
Stevem Plz...................... 36
United Journal, 199 Canal...... 13
Wall Street Journal, 30
Broad 04
Womens Wear, 7 E 12.......... 03
World Trade Center 48
World Trade Center, New York
State Agencies................ 47
75 Rockefeller Plz. 19

GOVERNMENT OFFICES

Alcoholic Beverage Control
Board 07
Athletic Commission, 226 W
47................................. 36
Banking Department, 100
Church 07
Board Of Elections............. 13
Board Of Estimate.............. 07
Bureau Of Motor Vehicles,
155 Worth 13
Chief Medical Examiner........ 16
City Civil Service
Commission 13
City Clerk........................ 07
City Collector................... 07
Commerce & Industrial
Development 17
Customs House, Broadway &
Bowling Grn 04
Depart. Of Consumer Affairs .. 13
Department Of Buildings....... 07
Department Of Commerce,
230 Park Ave.................. 17
Department Of Correction...... 13
Department Of Finance......... 07
Department Of Health.......... 13
Department Of Hospitals....... 13
Department Of Housing &
Building 38
Department Of Insurance,
123 William.................... 38
Department Of License......... 13
Department Of Markets......... 13
Department Of Public Events .. 22
Department Of Public Works.... 07
Department Of Purchases...... 07
Department Of Sanitation...... 13
Department Of Taxation &
Finance, 80 Center........... 13
Department Of Water Supply
Gas & Electricity.............. 07
Department Of Welfare 13
District Attorney................ 13

New York (Con.) 100

Federal Building, 641 Washington ... 14
Federal Bureau Of Investigation, 201 E 69th ... 21
Federal Communications Commission, 641 Washington ... 14
Fire Department ... 07
Harness Racing Commission, 820 2nd Ave. ... 17
Housing Authority ... 07
Human Rights Commission ... 13
Immigration & Naturalization Service, 20 W Broadway ... 07
Interior Department Bureau Of Commerce, 155 John ... 38
Internal Revenue Service, 120 Church ... 07
Marriage Licenses ... 07
Mayors Office ... 07
Office Of Civil Defense ... 22
Police Department ... 13
Police Hack Bureau ... 13
Port Of New York Authority, 111 8th Ave ... 11
Post Office Department, 419 8th Ave ... 01
Racing Commission, 598 Madison Ave ... 22
Railroad Retirement Board, 341 9th Ave ... 01
Reconstruction Finance Corporation, 20 Exchange Pl. ... 05
Rent Commision Temporary State Housing, 50 Park Pl. ... 07
Selective Service System, 26 Federal Plz ... 07
Social Security Adminstration, 39 Broadway ... 06
State Insurance Fund, 199 Church ... 07
Third Naval District, 90 Church ... 07
Veterans Administration, 252 7 Ave. ... 01
Weather Bureau, 30 Rockefeller Center ... 20
Workmans Compensation, 50 Park Pl ... 07

HOSPITALS

Animal Medical Center, York Ave & 62nd ... 21
Babies, Broadway & 167th ... 32
Beekman Downtown, 170 William ... 38
Bellevue Medical, Foot Of E 26th ... 16
Bernstein Institute, 307 2nd Ave ... 03
Beth Israel, Stuyvesant Sq & E 17th ... 03
Bird S Coler, Welfare Island ... 17
Burke Foundation, 164 E 124th ... 35
College View Nursing Home, 421 W 144th ... 31

Columbia Presbyterian, 622 W 168th ... 32
Columbus, 227 E 19th ... 03
Cornell Medical, 1300 York Ave ... 21
Delafield Hospital, 99 Ft Washington Ave ... 32
Doctors, East End Ave & E 87th ... 28
East Harlem Center, 2294 3rd Ave ... 35
Eye Institute, 635 W 165th ... 32
Flower & Fifth, 5th Ave & E 105th ... 29
French, 324 W 30th W ... 01
Goldwater Memorial, Welfare Island ... 17
Gouverneur, Gouverneur Slip ... 02
Gracie Square, 420 E 76th ... 21
Guggenheim Hosp Mount Sinai Hospital, 1176 5th Ave ... 29
Harkness Pavilion, 180 Ft Washington Ave ... 32
Harlem Health Center, 2238 5th Ave ... 37
Harlem Uptown Med., 2099 Lexington Ave ... 35
Harlem, Lenox Ave & W 136th ... 37
Home & Hospital Of The Daughters Of Israel, 1260 5th Ave ... 29
Hospital For Joint Diseases, 1919 Madison Ave ... 35
Hospital For Special Surgery, 535 E 70th ... 21
Italian, 123 W 110th ... 26
James Ewing, 1250 1st Ave ... 21
Jewish Board Of Guardians, 120 W 57th ... 19
Jewish Memorial, Broadway & W 196th ... 40
Klingen Stein Pavilion Mount Sinai, 1176 5th Ave ... 29
Knickerbocker, 70 Convent Ave ... 27
Lenox Hill, 100 E 77th ... 21
Leroy, 40 E 61st ... 21
Madison, 30 E 76th ... 21
Manhattan Eye Ear & Throat, 210 E 64th ... 21
Mayflower Nursing Home, 601 West End Ave ... 24
Medical Arts Center, 57 W 57th ... 19
Memorial Clinic, 1269 York Ave ... 21
Memorial, 444 E 68th ... 21
Metropolitan, 1901 1st Ave ... 29
Midtown, 309 E 49th ... 17
Mother Cabrini Memorial, 611 Edgecombe Ave ... 32
Mount Sinai, 5th Ave & E 100th ... 29
Neurological Institute, Ft Wash Ave & W 168th ... 32
New York Eye & Ear Infirmary, 310 E 14th ... 03
New York Foundling, 1175 3rd Ave ... 21

New York Hospital, 525 E 68th ... 21
New York Infirmary, 321 E 15th ... 03
New York University Bellevue Medical, 550 1st Ave ... 16
Park East, 112 E 83rd ... 28
Park West, 170 W 76th ... 23
Parkway, 123 W 110th ... 26
Physical Medicine & Rehabilitation Institution, 400 E 34. ... 16
Polyclinic, 345 W 50th ... 19
Regent, 115 E 61st ... 21
Rockefeller Hospital, York Ave & E 66th ... 21
Roosevelt, 9th Ave & W 59th ... 19
Saint Clares, 415 W 51st ... 19
Saint Elizabeths, 689 Ft Washington Ave ... 40
Saint Lukes, 421 W 113th ... 25
Saint Vincents, 7th Ave & W 11th ... 11
Sanger Home, 500 W 57th ... 19
Sloan Maternity, 622 W 168th ... 32
Sydenham, 565 Manhattan Ave ... 27
Trafalgar, 161 E 90th ... 28
University, 560 1st Ave ... 16
Veterans Administration, 408 1st Ave ... 10
Wadsworth, 629 W 185th ... 33
Wickersham, 133 E 58th ... 22
Womans, 1111 Amsterdam Ave ... 25

UNIVERSITIES AND COLLEGES

Barnard, Broadway & W 119th ... 27
Bellevue Medical, 550 1st Ave ... 16
Borough Of Manhattan Community College, 134 W 51st ... 20
Cathedral, 555 West End Ave ... 24
City College Of New York, B. Baruch Br, 17 Lexington Ave ... 10
City University, Graduate Center, 33 W 42nd ... 36
College Of Physicians & Surgeons, 630 W 168th ... 32
College Of The City Of New York, Convent Ave & W 139th ... 31
Columbia University College Of Pharmacy, 121 W 68th ... 23
Columbia University New York School Of Social, 2 E 91 St ... 28
Columbia University, Broadway & W 116th ... 27
Convent Of The Sacred Heart, 1 E 91st ... 28
Cooper Union, 50 Astor Place ... 03
Cornell University Medical, 1300 York Ave ... 21
Fordham Law School, 140 W 62nd ... 23

New York (Con.)   **100**

Fordham, 302 Broadway	07
General Theological Seminary, 175 9th Ave	11
Hebrew College, 40 W 68	23
Hunter, 695 Park Ave	21
Jewish Theological Seminary Of America, Broadway & 122nd	27
New School, 66 W 12th	11
New York College Of Dentistry, 421 First Ave	10
New York Medical College, 1249 5th Ave	29
New York Theological Seminary, 335 E 49th	17
New York Univ Courant Inst Of Math Sciences, 251 Mercer	12
New York University College Of Medicine, 550 1st Ave	16
New York University, Washington Sq	03
Pace, 41 Park Row	38
Rhodes School, 11 W 54th	19
Rockefeller University, York Ave & E 66th	21
Teachers, 525 W 120th	27
Union Theological Seminary, Broadway & W 120th	27
Yeshiva Univ., Graduate Center, 55 5th Ave	03
Yeshiva Univ., Main Center, 500 W 185th	33
Yeshiva Univ., Midtown Center, 253 Lexington Ave	16

NAMED STREETS

Abingdon Pl & Sq	14
Academy	34
Albany	06
Allen	02
Amsterdam Ave	
1-339	23
340-639	24
640-1098 (EVEN)	25
641-1139 (ODD)	25
1100-1478 (EVEN)	27
1141-1479 (ODD)	27
1480-1880	31
1881-2268	32
2269-2565	33
2566-OUT	40
Ann	38
Arden	40
Asser Levy Pl	10
Astor Pl	03
Astor Plz	36
Attorney	02
Audubon Ave	
1-160	32
161-439	33
440-OUT	40
Avenue A	09
Avenue B	09
Avenue C	09
Avenue D	09
Avenue Of Americas	
1-204	13
205-415 (ODD)	14
206-334 (EVEN)	14

336-650 (EVEN)	11
417-649 (ODD)	11
651-773	10
774-960	01
961-1080	18
1081-1219	36
1220-1279 (EVEN)	20
1280-OUT	19
Bank	14
Barclay	07
Barrow	14
Baruch Dr & Pl	02
Battery Pl	04
Baxter	
25-OUT (ODD)	13
28-OUT (EVEN)	13
Bayard	
1-38	02
39-OUT	13
Beach	13
Beak	34
Beaver	
1-53 (ODD)	04
2-74 (EVEN)	04
55-OUT (ODD)	05
76-OUT (EVEN)	05
Bedford	14
Beekman	38
Beekman Pl	22
Bennett Ave	
1-131	33
132-OUT	40
Benson	13
Bethune	14
Birmingham	02
Bishops Ln	07
Bleecker	
1-226	12
227-OUT	14
Bloomfield	14
Bogardus Pl	40
Bond	12
Bowery	
1-279 (ODD)	02
2-148 (EVEN)	13
150-364 (EVEN)	12
281-OUT (ODD)	03
366-OUT (EVEN)	03
Bowling Green	04
Bradhurst Ave	
1-63	30
64-OUT	39
Bridge	04
Broad	
1-23	05
24-OUT	04
Broadway	
1-27 (ODD)	04
2-70 (EVEN)	04
29-171 (ODD)	06
72-148 (EVEN)	05
150-222 (EVEN)	38
173-331 (ODD)	07
224-334 (EVEN)	07
333-487 (ODD)	13
336-486 (EVEN)	13
488-694 (EVEN)	12
489-697 (ODD)	12
696-900 (EVEN)	03
699-901 (ODD)	03
902-1139	10
1140-1330	01
1331-1450	18

1451-1589 (ODD)	36
1452-1592 (EVEN)	36
1591-1809 (ODD)	19
1594-1810 (EVEN)	19
1811-2160	23
2161-2459	24
2460-2918 (EVEN)	25
2461-2959 (ODD)	25
2920-3298 (EVEN)	27
2961-3299 (ODD)	27
3300-3699	31
3700-4100	32
4101-4379	33
4380-4759	40
4760-5170	34
Broadway Aly	16
Broadway Ter	40
Broome	
1-338	02
339-OUT	13
Burling Slip	38
Cabrini Blvd	
1-250	33
251-OUT	40
Canal	
1-151 (ODD)	02
2-142 (EVEN)	02
144-OUT (EVEN)	13
153-OUT (ODD)	13
Cannon	02
Cardinal Hayes Pl	07
Carl Schurz Park	28
Carlisle	06
Carmine	14
Caroline	13
Cathedral Cir	26
Cathedral Hts	25
Cathedral Pky	
1-399 (ODD)	26
2-348 (EVEN)	26
350-OUT (EVEN)	25
401-OUT (ODD)	25
Catherine	38
Catherine Ln	13
Catherine Slip	38
Cedar	
1-1	05
2-88 (EVEN)	05
3-27 (ODD)	38
29-87 (ODD)	05
89-OUT	06
Central Park N	26
Central Park S	19
Central Park W	
1-160	23
161-310	24
311-OUT	25
Centre	
1-73 (ODD)	07
2-68 (EVEN)	07
70-OUT (EVEN)	13
75-OUT (ODD)	13
Centre Market Pl	13
Chambers	07
Charles St & Ln	14
Charlton	14
Chase Manhattan Plz	05
Chatham Sq	38
Chelsea Sq	11
Cherokee Pl	21
Cherry	02
Cherry Ln	14
Chisum Pl	37

Chittenden Ave & Pl	33
Christopher	14
Chrystie	02
Church	
1-18	06
19-225 (ODD)	07
20-168 (EVEN)	07
170-OUT (EVEN)	13
227-OUT (ODD)	13
City Hall	07
Claremont Ave	27
Clarkson	14
Cleveland Pl	12
Cliff	38
Clinton	02
Coenties Slip	04
Collister	13
Columbia	02
Columbus Ave	
1-339	23
340-639	24
640-OUT	25
Columbus Cir	
1-10	19
11-OUT	23
Commerce	14
Convent Ave	
1-116	27
117-OUT	31
Cooper	34
Cooper Sq	03
Cornelia	14
Cortlandt	07
Cortlandt Aly	13
Crosby	
1-40	13
41-OUT	12
Cumming	34
Delamater Sq	14
Delancey	02
Depeyster	05
Desbrosses	13
Dey	07
Division	02
Dominick	13
Dongan Pl	40
Dover	38
Downing	14
Doyers	13
Duane	
20-125	07
126-OUT	13
Duffy Sq	36
Dutch	38
Dyckman	
1-99	34
100-217	40
218-OUT	34
East Broadway	
1-15 (ODD)	38
2-10 (EVEN)	38
12-OUT (EVEN)	02
17-OUT (ODD)	02
East End Ave	
1-23 (ODD)	21
2-18 (EVEN)	21
20-OUT (EVEN)	28
25-OUT (ODD)	28
East Houston	
1-91 (ODD)	12
2-88 (EVEN)	12
90-OUT (EVEN)	02
93-OUT (ODD)	02

East River Dr	
1-611	02
612-765	09
8-01-19-100	09
20-01-25-100	10
26-01-39-100	16
40-01-48-100	17
49-01-59-100	22
60-01-79-100	21
80-01-95-100	28
96-01-115-100	29
116-01-130-100	35
East River Piers	
1-9	04
10-14	05
15-26	38
27-54	02
55-68	09
69-73	10
Edgecombe Ave	
1-231	30
232-394	31
395-OUT	32
Edward M Morgan Pl	32
Eldridge	02
Elizabeth	
1-136	13
137-OUT	12
Elk	07
Ellis Island	04
Ellwood	40
Elm	07
Ericsson Pl	13
Esplanade Gdns Plz	39
Essex	02
Exchange Aly	06
Exchange Pl	
1-67 (ODD)	05
2-42 (EVEN)	05
44-OUT (EVEN)	04
69-OUT (ODD)	04
Fairview Ave	40
Federal Plz	07
Federal Reserve Bank	45
Fletcher	38
Foley Sq	07
Forsyth	02
Fort George Ave	40
Fort George Hill	40
Fort Jay	04
Fort Tryon Park	40
Fort Washington Ave	
1-300	32
301-599	33
600-OUT	40
Fort Washington Park	33
Frankfort	38
Franklin St & Pl	13
Franklin Ter	01
Franklin D Roosevelt Dr	
1-611	02
612-765	09
8-01-19-100	09
20-01-25-100	10
26-01-39-100	16
40-01-48-100	17
49-01-59-100	22
60-01-79-100	21
80-01-95-100	28
96-01-115-100	29
116-01-130-100	35
Frederick Douglas Cir	26

Front	
1-73 (ODD)	04
2-76 (EVEN)	04
75-151 (ODD)	05
78-154 (EVEN)	05
153-OUT (ODD)	38
156-OUT (EVEN)	38
Fulton	
1-167 (ODD)	38
2-158 (EVEN)	38
160-OUT (EVEN)	07
169-OUT (ODD)	07
Fulton Market	38
Gansevoort	14
Gansevoort Market	14
Gay	14
Gold	38
Gouverneur	02
Gouverneur Ln	05
Gouverneur Slip	02
Governors Island	04
Gracie Sq & Ter	28
Gramercy Park	
1-37	03
38-OUT	10
Grand	
1-235	13
236-OUT	02
Great Jones	12
Greene	
1-55	13
56-228	12
229-OUT	03
Greenwich	
1-40	04
41-169 (ODD)	06
42-164 (EVEN)	06
166-292 (EVEN)	07
171-301 (ODD)	07
294-552 (EVEN)	13
303-549 (ODD)	13
551-OUT (ODD)	14
554-OUT (EVEN)	14
Greenwich Ave	
1-OUT (ODD)	14
2-OUT (EVEN)	11
Grove St & Ct	14
Hall Pl	03
Hamill Pl	07
Hamilton Pl & Ter	31
Hancock Pl & Sq	27
Hanover	
1-OUT (ODD)	05
2-6 (EVEN)	05
8-OUT (EVEN)	04
Hanover Sq	
1-5 (ODD)	04
2-2	04
4-OUT (EVEN)	05
7-OUT (ODD)	05
Harlem Market	29
Harlem River Dr	39
Harlem River Driveway	
155-01-160-100	39
161-01-172-100	32
173-01-186-100	33
187-01-192-100	40
193-01-OUT	34
Harrison	13
Harry Howard Sq	13
Haven Ave	
1-162	32
163-OUT	33

New York (Con.)   100

Haven Plz 09
Henderson Pl 28
Henry
  1-11 38
  12-OUT 02
Henry Hudson Pky 34
Henshaw 34
Herald Sq 01
Hester
  1-149 1/2 (ODD) 02
  2-134 (EVEN) 02
  136-OUT (EVEN) 13
  151-OUT (ODD) 13
High Bridge Park 33
Hillside Ave 40
Horatio 14
Howard 13
Hubert 13
Hudson
  1-339 (ODD) 13
  2-344 (EVEN) 13
  341-OUT (ODD) 14
  346-OUT (EVEN) 14
Indian Rd 34
Irving Pl 03
Isham St & Park 34
Jackson 02
James 38
Jane 14
Jay 13
Jefferson 02
Jersey 12
John 38
Jones 14
Jumel Pl & Ter 32
Kenmore 12
King
  1-5 12
  6-OUT 14
Knickerbocker Village 02
La Guardia Pl 12
La Salle 27
Lafayette
  1-39 (ODD) 07
  2-34 (EVEN) 07
  36-192 (EVEN) 13
  41-193 (ODD) 13
  194-372 12
  373-OUT 03
Laight 13
Laurel Hill Ter
  1-120 33
  121-OUT 40
Lenox Ave
  1-199 26
  200-402 (EVEN) 27
  201-399 (ODD) 27
  401-699 (ODD) 37
  404-698 (EVEN) 37
  700-OUT 39
Lenox Ter Pl 37
Leonard 13
Leroy 14
Lewis 02
Lexington Ave
  1-79 10
  80-353 16
  354-538 17
  539-765 (ODD) 22
  540-762 (EVEN) 22
  764-1162 (EVEN) 21

767-1171 (ODD) 21
1164-1486 (EVEN) 28
1173-1489 (ODD) 28
1488-1870 (EVEN) 29
1491-1869 (ODD) 29
1871-2169 35
2170-OUT 37
Liberty
  1-76 05
  77-OUT 06
Liberty Ct & Pl 38
Liberty Island 04
Lillian Wald Dr 09
Lincoln Sq Plz 23
Lispenard 13
Little West 12th 14
Ludlow 02
Mac Dougal
  1-7 (ODD) 13
  2-154 (EVEN) 12
  9-141 (ODD) 12
  143-OUT (ODD) 11
  156-OUT (EVEN) 11
Mac Dougal Aly 11
Macombs Pl 39
Madison
  1-67 (ODD) 38
  2-72 (EVEN) 38
  69-OUT (ODD) 02
  74-OUT (EVEN) 02
Madison Ave
  1-61 10
  62-280 (EVEN) 16
  63-277 (ODD) 16
  279-429 (ODD) 17
  282-430 (EVEN) 17
  431-651 22
  652-1056 (EVEN) 21
  653-1047 (ODD) 21
  1049-1379 (ODD) 28
  1058-1378 (EVEN) 28
  1380-1767 29
  1768-2059 35
  2060-OUT 37
Magaw Pl 33
Maiden Ln
  1-101 38
  102-134 (EVEN) 05
  103-133 (ODD) 38
  135-OUT 38
Mangin 02
Manhattan Ave
  1-239 25
  240-488 (EVEN) 26
  241-479 (ODD) 26
  481-OUT (ODD) 27
  490-OUT (EVEN) 27
Manhattan Pl 07
Marie Curie Ave 21
Market 02
Market Slip 02
Marketfield 04
Mercer
  1-63 13
  64-260 12
  261-OUT 03
Mill Ln 04
Milligan Pl 11
Minetta St, Ln & Pl 12
Mitchell Pl
  1-15 17
Mitchell Sq 32
Monroe 02

Montgomery 02
Moore 04
Morningside Ave
  1-58 26
  59-OUT 27
Morningside Dr
  1-59 25
  60-OUT 27
Morris
  1-9 (ODD) 04
  2-OUT (EVEN) 06
  11-OUT (ODD) 06
Morton 14
Mott
  1-173 (ODD) 13
  2-168 (EVEN) 13
  170-OUT (EVEN) 12
  175-OUT (ODD) 12
Mount Morris Park W 27
Mulberry
  10-176 (EVEN) 13
  13-177 (ODD) 13
  178-OUT 12
Murray 07
Nagle Ave
  1-169 40
  170-OUT 34
Nassau
  1-47 (ODD) 05
  2-40 (EVEN) 05
  42-OUT (EVEN) 38
  49-OUT (ODD) 38
Nathan D Perlman Pl 03
New
  1-11 (ODD) 05
  2-28 (EVEN) 05
  13-OUT (ODD) 04
  30-OUT (EVEN) 04
Norfolk 02
North Moore 13
North River Piers
  A-2 04
  3-11 06
  12-20 07
  21-36 13
  37-56 14
  57-64 11
  65-75 01
  76-80 18
  81-88 36
  89-99 19
Old Broadway 27
Old Slip 05
Oliver 38
Orchard 02
Overlook Ter
  1-65 33
  66-OUT 40
Paladino Ave 35
Park
  1-84 07
  85-OUT 13
Park Ave
  1-99 16
  100-299 17
  300-519 22
  520-914 (EVEN) 21
  521-923 (ODD) 21
  916-1240 (EVEN) 28
  925-1245 (ODD) 28
  1242-1636 (EVEN) 29
  1247-1637 (ODD) 29
  1638-1914 (EVEN) 35

New York (Con.)	100
1639-1919 (ODD)	35
1916-2298 (EVEN)	37
1921-2299 (ODD)	37
Park Ave S	
200-250	03
251-363 (ODD)	10
252-384 (EVEN)	10
365-OUT (ODD)	16
386-OUT (EVEN)	16
Park Pl	07
Park Row	
1-43	38
44-166 (EVEN)	07
45-165 (ODD)	38
167-OUT	38
Park Ter E & W	34
Patchin Pl	11
Payson Ave	34
Pearl	
1-117 (ODD)	04
2-100 (EVEN)	04
102-194 (EVEN)	05
119-197 (ODD)	05
196-462 (EVEN)	38
199-463 (ODD)	38
464-OUT	07
Peck Slip	38
Pell	13
Pennsylvania Plz	01
Perry	14
Peter Cooper Rd	10
Pike	02
Pike Slip	02
Pine	05
Pinehurst Ave	33
Pitt	02
Platt	38
Plaza Lafayette	33
Pleasant Ave	
1-299	29
300-OUT	35
Pomander Walk	25
Post Ave	34
Prince	12
Randalls Island	35
Reade	
1-83	07
84-OUT	13
Rector	06
Renwick	13
Ridge	02
Riverside Dr	
1-40	23
41-190	24
191-439	25
440-569	27
570-762	31
763-1150	32
1151-1599	33
1600-1780	40
1781-OUT	34
Riverside Dr W	
155-01-159-100	32
Riverview Ter	22
Rivington	02
Robert F Wagner Sr Pl	38
Rockefeller Plz	20
Roosevelt Sq	27
Rutgers	02
Rutgers Slip	02
Rutherford Pl	03

Saint Clair Pl	27
Saint James Pl	38
Saint Johns Ln	13
Saint Lukes Pl	14
Saint Marks Pl	
1-85 (ODD)	03
2-82 (EVEN)	03
84-OUT (EVEN)	09
87-OUT (ODD)	09
Saint Nicholas Ave	
1-201 (ODD)	26
2-198 (EVEN)	26
200-456 (EVEN)	27
203-455 (ODD)	27
457-699 (ODD)	30
458-690 (EVEN)	30
692-860 (EVEN)	31
701-861 (ODD)	31
862-1259	32
1260-1539	33
1540-OUT	40
Saint Nicholas Pl	
1-60	31
61-OUT	32
Saint Nicholas Ter	
1-55	27
56-OUT	31
Schiff Pky	02
Seaman Ave	34
Sheridan Sq	14
Sheriff	02
Sherman Ave	
1-84	40
85-801	34
Sherman Sq	23
Sickles	40
Sniffen Ct	16
South	
1-39	04
40-75	05
76-202	38
203-OUT	02
South Ferry	04
South Pinehurst Ave	33
South William	04
Spring	
1-220	12
221-OUT	13
Spruce	38
Staff	34
Stanton	02
Staple	13
State	04
Staten Island Ferry	04
Statue Of Liberty	04
Stone	04
Stuyvesant Oval	09
Stuyvesant St & Aly	03
Suffolk	02
Sullivan	12
Sutton Pl S	22
Sutton Pl & Sq	22
Sylvan Ct & Pl	35
Sylvan Ter	32
Szold Pl	09
Thames	06
Thayer	40
Thomas	
1-42	07
43-OUT	13
Thompson	
1-49	13
50-OUT	12

Tieman Pl	27
Times Sq	36
Transverse Rd	24
Trimble Pl	07
Trinity Pl	06
Tudor City Pl	17
Union Sq	03
United Nations Plz	17
University Pl	03
Van Nest Pl	14
Vandam	13
Vanderbilt Ave	17
Vanderbilt Concourse	17
Varick	
1-169 (ODD)	13
2-172 (EVEN)	13
171-OUT (ODD)	14
174-OUT (EVEN)	14
Vermilyea Ave	34
Vesey	07
Vestry	13
Wadsworth Ave	
1-279	33
280-OUT	40
Wadsworth Ter	40
Walker	13
Wall	05
Wanamaker Pl	03
Wards Island	35
Warren	07
Washington	
1-39 (ODD)	04
2-32 (EVEN)	04
34-170 (EVEN)	06
41-169 (ODD)	06
171-286	07
287-531	13
532-OUT	14
Washington Pl	
1-60	03
61-90	11
91-OUT	14
Washington Sq E	
77-OUT	03
Washington Sq N	
1-13	03
14-27	11
Washington Sq S	
39 1/2 -76	12
Washington Sq W	
28-39	11
Washington Ter	33
Washington Mews	03
Washington Sq Village	12
Water	
1-53 (ODD)	04
2-56 (EVEN)	04
55-55	41
57-69 (ODD)	04
58-152 (EVEN)	05
71-153 (ODD)	05
154-399	38
400-OUT	02
Watts	13
Waverly Pl	
1-99	03
100-130 (EVEN)	11
101-133 (ODD)	11
132-OUT (EVEN)	14
135-OUT (ODD)	14
Weehawken	14
Welfare Island	17

New York (Con.)   100

West
1-20	04
21-114	06
115-185	07
186-324	13
325-OUT	14

West Broadway
1-95	07
96-368 (EVEN)	13
97-373 (ODD)	13
370-OUT (EVEN)	12
375-OUT (ODD)	12

West End Ave
1-341	23
342-640 (EVEN)	24
343-637 (ODD)	24
639-OUT (ODD)	25
642-OUT (EVEN)	25

West Houston
1-177 (ODD)	12
2-170 (EVEN)	12
172-OUT (EVEN)	14
179-OUT (ODD)	14

West Washington Market	14
White	13
Whitehall	04
Willett	02

William
1-9 (ODD)	04
2-6 (EVEN)	04
8-78 (EVEN)	05
11-83 (ODD)	05
80-OUT (EVEN)	38
85-OUT (ODD)	38

Wooster
1-55 (ODD)	13
2-58 (EVEN)	13
57-OUT (ODD)	12
60-OUT (EVEN)	12

World Trade Center	48
World Trade Center (Ny St)	47
Worth	13
York	13

York Ave
1-1509 (ODD)	21
2-1512 (EVEN)	2?
1511-OUT (ODD)	
1514-OUT (EVEN)	

NUMBERED STREETS

1st
1-73	03
74-OUT	09

1st Ave
1-343 (ODD)	03
2-346 (EVEN)	09
345-443 (ODD)	10
348-444 (EVEN)	10
445-699	16
700-876	17
877-1095 (ODD)	22
878-1100 (EVEN)	22
1097-1531 (ODD)	21
1102-1538 (EVEN)	21
1533-1855 (ODD)	28
1540-1854 (EVEN)	28
1856-2254 (EVEN)	29
1857-2255 (ODD)	29
2256-OUT (EVEN)	35
2259-OUT (ODD)	35

2nd
1-87 (ODD)	03
2-98 (EVEN)	03
89-OUT (ODD)	09
100-OUT (EVEN)	09

2nd Ave
1-343	03
344-459	10
460-746	16
747-922	17
923-1141 (ODD)	22
924-1138 (EVEN)	22
1140-1536 (EVEN)	21
1143-1541 (ODD)	21
1538-1854 (EVEN)	28
1543-1863 (ODD)	28
1856-2258 (EVEN)	29
1865-2259 (ODD)	29
2260-OUT	35

3rd E
1-99	03
100-OUT	09

3rd W	12

3rd Ave
1-243	03
244-356	10
357-618	16
619-796	17
797-1009	22
1010-1409	21
1410-1709	28
1710-2120 (EVEN)	29
1711-2123 (ODD)	29
2122-2398 (EVEN)	35
2125-2399 (ODD)	35

4th E
1-133 (ODD)	03
2-20 (EVEN)	12
22-130 (EVEN)	03
132-OUT (EVEN)	09
135-OUT (ODD)	09

4th W
1-151 (ODD)	12
2-154 (EVEN)	12
153-OUT (ODD)	14
156-OUT (EVEN)	14

4th Ave
1-OUT	03

4th Walk E	09

5th
1-399	03
400-OUT	09

5th Ave
1-133 (ODD)	03
2-152 (EVEN)	11
135-231 (ODD)	10
154-216 (EVEN)	10
218-370 (EVEN)	01
233-459 (ODD)	16
372-498 (EVEN)	18
461-609 (ODD)	17
500-594 (EVEN)	36
596-638 (EVEN)	20
611-787 (ODD)	22
640-770 (EVEN)	19
772-786 (EVEN)	22
788-990	21
991-1150	28
1151-1415 (ODD)	29
1152-1312 (EVEN)	29
1314-1416 (EVEN)	29
1417-2119 (ODD)	35

1418-2116 (EVEN)	35
2118-OUT (EVEN)	37
2121-OUT (ODD)	37

6th
1-399	03
400-OUT	09

7th
1-99	03
90-OUT	09

7th Ave
1-243 (ODD)	11
2-240 (EVEN)	11
242-460 (EVEN)	01
245-461 (ODD)	01
462-576	18
577-720	36
721-941	19
942-2000	26
2001-2259	27
2260-2499	30
2500-OUT	39

7th Ave S	14

8th E
1-199	03
200-OUT	09

8th Ave
1-79 (ODD)	14
2-66 (EVEN)	14
68-278 (EVEN)	11
81-277 (ODD)	11
279-499	01
500-637	18
638-789	36
790-996	19
997-2223 (ODD)	26
998-2226 (EVEN)	26
2225-2481 (ODD)	27
2228-2488 (EVEN)	27
2483-2727 (ODD)	30
2490-2728 (EVEN)	30
2729-OUT	39

8th thru 9th St W	11

9th E
1-399	03
400-OUT	09

9th Ave
1-43	14
44-227	11
228-449	01
450-559	18
560-700	36
701-925	19
926-OUT	34

10th E
1-244	03
245-OUT	09

10th W
1-127	11
128-OUT	14

10th Ave
1-59	14
60-240 (EVEN)	11
61-235 (ODD)	11
237-449 (ODD)	01
242-448 (EVEN)	01
450-555	18
556-684 (EVEN)	36
557-703 (ODD)	36
686-906 (EVEN)	19
705-905 (ODD)	19
907-OUT	34

11th E
1-399	03

New York (Con.)	100
400-OUT	09
11th W	
1-199	11
200-OUT	14
11th Ave	
1-2	14
3-200 (ODD)	11
201-419 (ODD)	01
202-426 (EVEN)	01
421-533 (ODD)	18
428-538 (EVEN)	18
535-661 (ODD)	36
540-662 (EVEN)	36
663-OUT	19
12th E	
1-399	03
400-OUT	09
12th W	
1-229	11
230-OUT	14
12th Ave	
1-99	14
100-164	11
165-360	01
361-499	18
500-639	36
640-874	19
875-2351	27
2352-OUT	31
13th E	
1-399	03
400-OUT	09
13th W	
1-299	11
300-OUT	14
14th E	
1-399	03
400-OUT	09
14th W	
1-299	11
300-OUT	14
15th E	
1-399	03
400-OUT	09
15th thru 20th St W	11
16th E	
1-399	03
400-OUT	09
17th E	
1-399	03
400-OUT	09
18th E	
1-399	03
400-OUT	09
19th E	
1-399	03
400-OUT	09
20th E	
1-399	03
400-OUT (EVEN)	09
401-OUT (ODD)	10
21st W	
1-99	10
100-OUT	11
21st thru 25th St E	10
22nd W	
1-99	10
100-OUT	11
23rd W	
1-99	10
100-OUT	11
24th W	
1-99	10
100-OUT	11
25th W	
1-99	10
100-OUT	01
26th E	
1-399 (ODD)	10
2-OUT (EVEN)	10
401-OUT (ODD)	16
26th W	
1-99	10
100-OUT	01
27th St & Dr W	01
27th thru 40th St E	16
28th thru 35th St W	01
36th thru 40th St W	18
41st W	
1-99	18
100-OUT	36
41st thru 49th St E	17
42nd thru 47th St W	36
48th W	
1-145 (ODD)	20
2-OUT (EVEN)	36
48th. W	
147-OUT (ODD)	36
49th W	
1-139 (ODD)	20
2-138 (EVEN)	20
49th. W	
140-OUT	19
50th W	
1-157 (ODD)	20
2-134 (EVEN)	20
136-OUT (EVEN)	19
159-OUT (ODD)	19
50th thru 60th St E	22
51st W	
1-145 (ODD)	19
2-146 (EVEN)	20
147-OUT	19
52nd thru 59th St W	19
60th thru 61st St W	23
61st Dr W	23
61st thru 80th St E	21
62nd thru 76th St W	23
77th thru 91st St W	24
81st thru 96th St E	28
92nd thru 109th St W	25
97th thru 116th St E	29
110th W	
1-399 (ODD)	26
2-348 (EVEN)	26
350-OUT (EVEN)	25
401-OUT (ODD)	25
111th W	
1-399	26
400-OUT	25
112th W	
1-399	26
400-OUT	25
113th W	
1-399	26
400-OUT	25
114th W	
1-399	26
400-500	25
501-599 (ODD)	27
600-OUT	25
115th W	
1-399	26
400-499	25
500-599	27
600-OUT	25
116th W	
1-399	26
400-OUT	27
117th W	
1-399	26
400-OUT	27
117th thru 129th St E	35
118th W	
1-399	26
400-OUT	27
119th W	
1-399	26
400-OUT	27
120th thru 129th St W	27
130th W	
1-99	37
100-OUT	27
130th thru 131st St E	37
131st W	
1-99	37
100-OUT	27
132nd E	
1-199	37
132nd W	
1-99	37
100-OUT	27
133rd E	
1-199	37
133rd W	
1-99	37
100-349	30
350-OUT	27
134th E	
1-199	37
134th W	
1-99	37
100-399	30
400-699	31
700-OUT	27
135th E	
1-99	37
135th W	
1-99	37
100-399	30
400-699	31
700-OUT	27
136th E	
1-99	37
136th W	
1-99	37
100-399	30
400-699	31
700-OUT	27
137th E	
1-99	37
137th W	
1-99	37
100-399	30
400-OUT	31
138th E	
1-99	37
138th W	
1-97	37
98-399	30
400-OUT	31
139th E	
1-99	37
139th W	
1-99	37
100-399	30
403-OUT	31

New York (Con.)   100

140th E
1-99 37
140th W
1-99 37
100-399 30
400-OUT 31
141st E
1-99 37
141st W
1-99 37
100-399 30
400-OUT 31
142nd E
1-99 37
142nd W
1-99 37
100-399 30
400-OUT 31
143rd W
1-99 37
100-399 30
400-OUT 31
144th W
1-99 37
100-399 30
400-OUT 31
145th W
1-399 (ODD) 39
2-356 (EVEN) 39
341-OUT (ODD) 31
358-OUT (EVEN) 31
146th W
1-349 39
350-OUT 31
147th W
1-349 39
350-OUT 31
148th W
1-349 39
350-OUT 31
149th W
1-349 39
350-OUT 31
150th W
1-349 39
350-OUT 31
151st W
1-349 39
350-OUT 31
152nd W
1-349 39
350-OUT 31
153rd W
1-349 39
350-OUT 31
154th W
1-349 39
350-OUT 32
155th W
1-349 39
350-OUT 32
156th W
1-349 39
350-OUT 32
157th W
1-349 39
350-OUT 32
158th W
1-349 39
350-OUT 32

159th W
1-349 39
350-OUT 32
160th W
1-349 39
350-OUT 32
161st W
300-399 39
400-OUT 32
162nd thru 173rd St W 32
174th thru 187th St W 33
188th thru 199th St W 40
200th W
1-99 34
100-217 40
218-OUT 34
201st thru 223rd St W 34

NIAGARA FALLS   143

POST OFFICE BOXES

Box Nos.
1-286   La Salle Sta 04
1-314   Bridge Sta 05
1-1102   Main Office 02
651-1147   Falls Sta 03
2001-2154   New Market
                    Sta 01

STATIONS, BRANCHES AND UNITS

Bridge Sta 05
Falls Sta 03
La Salle Sta 04
New Market Sta 01
General Delivery 02
Postmaster 02

APARTMENTS, HOTELS, MOTELS

Beaton, 334 1st 03
Belmont, 411 2nd 01
Clifton, 18 W Falls 03
Converse, 325 1st 03
Eleanor, 702 8th 01
Estella, 942 Niagara Ave 05
Falls, 109 Falls 03
Hall, 552 3rd 01
Hennepin, 649 Jefferson Ave .. 03
Holiday Inn, 114 Buffalo Ave .. 03
Jefferson, 250 Jefferson Ave .. 03
Lincoln, 1967 Niagara 03
Lochiel, 302 Buffalo Ave 03
Marquette, 505 Walnut Ave ... 01
Mathews, 918 Niagara Ave 05
Mc Kinstry, 308 Ferry Ave 01
Niagara, 1st St & Jefferson
   Ave 03
Park Place, 723 3rd 01
Parkway Inn, 401 Buffalo
   Ave 03
Parkway, 151 Buffalo Ave 03
Red Coach Inn, 2 Buffalo
   Ave 03
Sagamore, 528 Main 01
Sandra Court, 6627 Buffalo
   Ave 04
Schrafft'S Motor Inn, 443
   Main 02
Simon, 230 1st 03
Spallino Towers, 720-10th 01
Stratford Arms, 555 7th 01

Stratford Arms, 703 Walnut
   Ave 01
Travelers Lodge, 200
   Jefferson Ave 03
Treadway Inn, 7001 Buffalo
   Ave 04
Waldorf-Niagara, 130 Quay 03
Yorkshire, 630 9th 01

BUILDINGS

Federal, 615 Main 02
Hancock, 43 Falls 03
Lozina, 217 Falls 03
Medical Arts, 457 3rd 01
Neisner, 8 W Falls 03
Rieckhoff, 910 South Ave 05
United Office, 222 1st 03

GOVERNMENT OFFICES

City Hall, 745 Main 02
Niagara County, 775 3rd 02
Public Service, 520 Hyde
   Park Blvd 02

HOSPITALS

Niagara Falls Memorial
   Medical Ctr, 621-10th 02
Saint Marys Manor, 515 6th ... 01

UNIVERSITIES AND COLLEGES

Niagara County Community,
   430 Buffalo Ave 03

POUGHKEEPSIE   126

POST OFFICE BOXES

Box Nos.
1-1299   Main Office 02
1601-1799   South Road Br . 01
3000-3999   Arlington Br 03
5001-5327   Main Office 02

RURAL ROUTES

1 01
2,3 03

STATIONS, BRANCHES AND UNITS

Arlington Br 03
South Road Br 01
General Delivery 01
Postmaster 01

APARTMENTS, HOTELS, MOTELS

Beechwood South, 363 South
   Rd 01
Binders Motel, 62 Haight
   Ave 03
Boulevard Knolls Court Apts ... 01
Camelot Inn, South Road 01
Canterbury Gardens, Janet
   Dr 03
Charles St Apts, Charles St 01

Poughkeepsie (Con.) 126

Collegeview, 119-131 Fulton
Ave 03
Colonial Gardens, Corlies Ave
Ext 01
Corlies Manor, Corlies Ave..... 01
Country Club Terrace,
Anthony Dr 01
Delafield Ct Apt Delafield St... 01
Dorchester Motor Lodge,
South Rd............................. 01
Dr Martin Luther King Apts
Washington St 01
Dutch Garden Apts Hook
Road................................... 01
Dutchess Motel, South Rd 01
Dutchess, Van Wagner Rd....... 03
Eden Roc, 166 Academy.......... 01
Edison Motor Inn, Route 55..... 03
Envoy Plaza, 131 Beechwood
Ave 01
Executive Towers Academy
St 01
Forbus Hill, 31 Forbus............ 01
Franklin - Carroll, 55 Carroll .. 01
Franklin-Carroll, 115 Franklin. 01
Georgetown Square Apts 274
Hooker Ave 03
Hamilton Garden, 94 S
Hamilton 01
Hilbrae, Titusville Rd 03
Kings Court Hotel, 40
Cannon 02
Manchester Gardens, 46
Manchester Rd.................... 03
Poughkeepsie Inn, 23
Cannon 01
Poughkeepsie Motor Hotel,
418 South Rd 01
Red Bull Motor Inn, 576
South Rd............................. 01
Ridge Field Apts Innis Ave 03
Rip Van Winkle House............. 01
River Terrace Apts Riverview
Blvd.................................... 01
Rivercrest Apts., Rivercrest
Court 01
Rochambeau Motel, South
Rd 01
Rolling Hill Estates Maloney
Rd 03
Rombout 01

St Simeon Apts 24
Beechwood Ave 01
Vassar Garden, Lewis Ave 03

HOSPITALS

Hudson River State Hospital,
North Rd 01
Saint Francis Hospital, North
Rd 01
Vassar Brothers Hospital,
Reade Pl 01

UNIVERSITIES AND COLLEGES

Dutchess Community College,
Pendell Rd 01
Marist College, 82 North

Road............................... 01
Vassar College, Raymond
Ave 01

ROCHESTER 146

POST OFFICE BOXES

Box Nos.
1-335   Main Office 01
336-675   Main Office 02
676-2105   Main Office 03
2701-3000   Ridgemont
                Plaza 26
3001-3500   Federal 14
3501-3800   Beechwood
                Sta 09
3801-4100   Brighton Sta 10
4101-4400   Bulls Head
                Sta 11
4401-4700   Dewey Sta 13
4701-5000   Charlotte Sta ... 12
5001-7100   River Campus
                Sta 27
7101-7400   Greece Br 16
7401-7600   West Ridge
                Sta 15
7601-7800   Point Pleasant
                Br 22
7801-8100   Lyell Sta 06
8101-8300   Irondequoit Br .. 17
8301-8500   Twelve Corners
                Br 18
8501-8700   Thurston Rd
                Sta 19
8701-8999   Westgate Br 24
9101-9300   Panorama Br 25
9301-9697   Midtown Plaza
                Sta 04
9701-9980   Southtown Br 23
18001-18089   Twelve Corners
                Br 18

STATIONS, BRANCHES AND UNITS

Beechwood Sta 09
Brighton Sta 10
Bulls Head Sta 11
Charlotte Sta 12
Dewey Sta 13
Federal Sta.......................... 08
Greece Br............................ 16
Irondequoit Br...................... 17
Lyell Sta 06
Midtown Plaza Sta 04
Panorama Br 25
Point Pleasant Br 22
Ridgemont Plaza Br 26
River Campus Sta 27
Southtown Br........................ 23
Thurston Road Sta 19
Twelve Corners Br 18
West Ridge Sta 15
Westgate Br.......................... 24
General Delivery 03
Postmaster 03

APARTMENTS, HOTELS, MOTELS

Ainslow, 56 Chestnut............. 07
Alexandrian, 300 Alexander 07

Algonquin, 34 S Goodman....... 07
Ambassador, 86 S Union......... 07
Ardsley, 699 Main E............... 05
Argyle, 154 Clinton Ave S....... 04
Barrington, 152 Barrington..... 07
Biltmore, 357 Alexander......... 07
Bretton Hall, 325 Alexander.... 07
Brown Stone, 241 Alexander.... 07
Buckingham, 713 Park Ave 07
Cadillac, 45 Chestnut............. 08
Campus, 1126 Dewey Ave 13
Claridge, 149 Clinton Ave N.... 04
Clintwood, Clintwood Dr......... 20
Clover East, 2410-2458 East
Ave 10
Clover Garden, Clover Park
Dr 18
Colby Park, 1225 Park Ave...... 10
Colonial Manor, Cornelia Dr.... 06
Colonial, 28-30 Park Ave 07
Coolidge, 1650 East Ave.......... 10
Country Club Manor, 2405-
2415 East Ave..................... 10
East Avenue Court, 1625
East Ave............................. 10
East Avenue Towers, 2501
East Ave............................. 10
East Boulevard Manor, 76
East Blvd 10
Eastman, 215 Chestnut........... 07
Ellison Park, Bobrich Dr......... 10
Elmwood Manor, 1308-1412
Elmwood Ave...................... 20
Fairway, 4000 East River Rd.... 23
Falmouth, Falmouth 15
Fernwood Park, 1000
Fernwood Pk....................... 09
Five-Twenty East Avenue, 520
E Ave.................................. 07
Flagship Rochester, 70 State.... 03
Fredrick, 1640 East Ave.......... 10
Gibbs, 53 Gibbs 04
Glenora Gardens, Glenora
Gardens 15
Grecian Gardens, Grecian
Gardens 26
Haddon Hall, 505 University
Ave 07
Highland Manor, 14 Manor
Pkwy 20
Highlander, 1307 South Ave..... 20
Hill Court, Hill Court Cir 21
Holiday Inn Downtown 120
Main E................................ 04
Holleycroft, 400 Broad E......... 07
Holyoke, 86 Holyoke.............. 15
Imperial, 1693 Stone Rd.......... 15
Landing Heights, 22
Knollbrook Rd..................... 10
Lee Garden, Lee Garden Pk 24
Lost Mountain, Lost Mountain
Trail................................... 25
Manor Parkway, 90 Manor
Pkwy 20
Manor, 14 Manor Pkwy 20
Mariner Motor Inn 95 Main
W 14
Mc Call Manor, 1131-1151
Stone Rd 16
Midtown Towers, Midtown
Plaza 04
Milford, 86 Milford 15

Rochester (Con.)   146

Mohawk Manor Motor Inn, 55
  Troup.. 08
Nathaniel Rochester Motor
  Inn 155 Broad E...................... 04
Ninety Five Troup, 95 Troup..... 08
Normandie, 253 Alexander....... 07
Northgate Manor, Northgate
  Manor.. 16
Northside, 720-740 Carter....... 21
Norton Village, 1979 Norton 09
Parliament Arms, 2120 St
  Paul.. 21
Plymouth Gardens, 1400
  Plymouth Ave S....................... 11
Poplar Way, 1011 University
  Ave... 07
Portland Manor, Portland Ct.... 21
Ramona Park, 800 Ramona....... 15
Ridgemont Park, Brambury
  Dr.. 21
Ridgeway, 1368 Ridgeway
  Ave... 15
Roosevelt, 267 Oxford............. 07
Royal Manor, 75 East Blvd...... 10
Rushmore Estates, 68-138
  Floverton.................................. 10
Saegers Edison, 93 Elm............ 04
Saint Paul Court, 1564 St
  Paul.. 21
Shelbourne, 517 University
  Ave... 07
Sheraton, 111 East Ave.......... 04
Six-Eighty-Eight East Avenue,
  688 East Ave........................... 07
Sixteen-Forty East Avenue,
  1640 East Ave......................... 10
Sixteen-Hundred East Avenue,
  1600 East Ave......................... 10
Spencerport Manor, Gates
  Manor Dr.................................. 06
Stone Road, 1684-1746 Stone
  Rd... 15
Strathmore, 970 Monroe Ave .. 20
Suburban Court, Suburban
  Ct.. 20
Thirty S Goodman
  Incorporated, 30 S
  Goodman................................... 07
Thurston, 447 Thurston Rd..... 19
Town House Motel, 1325 Mt
  Hope Ave.................................. 02
Travelodge Motel, 390 South
  Ave... 20
Treadway Inn, 384 East Ave... 07
Two-Forty Goodman S, 240 S
  Goodman................................... 07
Valley Court, 1170 Genesee.... 11
Vassar, 593 Park Ave.............. 07
Wedgewood West, 2001-2057
  E Henrietta Rd......................... 23
Westmoor, 327 West Ave........ 11
Whittier, 270 S Goodman........ 07
Wilsonia, 62 Chestnut.............. 07
Winslow, 565 Chili Ave............ 11

BUILDINGS

Abstract, 31 Exchange............. 14
Case, 82 St Paul....................... 04
Columbus, 50 Chestnut............ 04
Commerce, 119 Main E............ 04

Community Savings, 235
  Main E....................................... 04
Copeland, 133 Clinton Ave S... 04
Cox, 36 St Paul......................... 04
Crossroads, 2 State.................. 14
Cutler, 42 East Ave.................. 04
East Avenue, 49 East Ave 04
Educational, 13 Fitzhugh S 14
Ellwanger & Barry, 39 State.... 14
Engineering, 77 South Ave 04
Executive Office, 34 Main W.... 14
First Federal Savings, 328
  Main E....................................... 04
Fitch, 315 Alexander................. 04
Gas & Electric, 89 East Ave.... 04
Granite, 130 Main E.................. 04
Hiram Sibley, 311 Alexander.... 04
I.B.M., 180 State....................... 14
Kenning, 426 Main E................. 04
Lincoln, 10 Gibbs...................... 04
Marine Midland, Marine
  Midland Plz............................... 04
Midtown Tower, Midtown
  Plaza... 04
Monroe County Office, 39
  Main W...................................... 14
National, 32 South Ave............ 14
Powers, 16 Main W.................. 14
Present, 27 Clinton Ave S........ 04
Professional, 35 Chestnut........ 04
Public Library, 115 South
  Ave... 04
Reynolds Arcade, 16 Main E.... 14
Rochester Savings Bank, 40
  Franklin..................................... 04
Rochester Savings Bank, 5
  Fitzhugh S................................ 14
Rundel Memorial, 115 South
  Ave... 04
Searle, 183 St Paul................... 04
Security Tower, 1 East Ave 04
Sibley Tower, 25 North............. 04
Temple, 14 Franklin.................. 04
Terminal, 65 Broad................... 14
Times Square, 45 Exchange..... 14
Triangle, 335 Main E................ 04
Union Trust, 19 Main W........... 14
War Memorial, 100 Exchange... 14
Washington Square, 172 S
  Clinton....................................... 04
Washington, 155 W Main......... 14
Wilder, 8 Exchange.................. 14
Xerox Square, Xerox Sq.......... 03

GOVERNMENT OFFICES

City Hall, 20 Fitzhugh S 14
City Public Safety Building,
  Civic Center Plaza................... 14
Federal, Church & N
  Fitzhugh..................................... 14
Hall Of Justice, Civic Center
  Plaza... 14

HOSPITALS

Community County Home,
  435 E. Henrietta Rd 20
Dale Sanitarium, 1040 Lake
  Ave... 13
Eastman Dental Dispensary,
  800 Main E............................... 03
Field Sanitarium, 525 Lake

Ave... 13
Genesee, 224 Alexander.......... 07
Highland, Bellevue Dr.............. 20
Knorr Sanitarium, 139 Troup.... 08
Lake Avenue, 179 Lake Ave.... 08
Municipal, Crittenden Blvd...... 20
Park Avenue, 789 Park Ave 07
Residential Treatment Center,
  2075 Scottsville Rd 23
Rochester General, 1425
  Portland Ave............................ 21
Rochester State, 1600 South
  Ave... 20
Saint Marys, 89 Genesee........ 11
State, 1600 South Ave............. 20
Strong Memorial, 260
  Crittenden Blvd....................... 20

UNIVERSITIES AND COLLEGES

Colgate Rochester Divinity,
  1100 Goodman S..................... 20
Monroe Community College,
  1000 East Henrietta Rd......... 23
Nazareth, 4245 East Ave........ 10
Roberts Wesleyan 2301 West
  Side Dr..................................... 24
Rochester Business Institute,
  172 Clinton Ave S................... 04
Rochester Institute Of
  Technology, 1 Lomb
  Memorial Dr............................. 23
Saint Bernards Seminary,
  2260 Lake Ave........................ 12
Saint John Fisher, 3690 East
  Ave... 18
Sch Of Medicine & Dentistry,
  U. Of R., 260 Crittenden
  Blvd... 20
University Of Rochester River
  Sta... 27

ROCKVILLE CENTRE   115

POST OFFICE BOXES

Box Nos.
1-356   Oceanside Br..... 72
1-420   Main Office 71

STATIONS, BRANCHES AND UNITS

Oceanside Br.............................. 72
General Delivery......................... 71
General Delivery Oceanside...... 72
Postmaster.................................. 70

SCHENECTADY   123

POST OFFICE BOXES

Box Nos.
1-87   Bellevue Sta...... 06
1-97   Crane Street
                  Sta................... 03
1-147   Brandywine
                  Sta................... 04
1-699   Main Office 01

Schenectady (Con.)   123

900-1090	Main Office	01
1101-1256	Scotia Br	02
2501-2697	Upper Union Br	09

RURAL ROUTES

1,2	02
3	06
4	02
5	06

STATIONS, BRANCHES AND UNITS

Bellevue Sta	06
Brandywine Sta	04
Crane Street Sta	03
Mayfair Br	02
Rotterdam Br	03
Scotia Br	02
Upper Union Br	09
General Delivery	05
Postmaster	05

APARTMENTS, HOTELS, MOTELS

Colonial, 9 N Church	05
Douglas, 875 State	07
Foster, 508 State	05
Governor Yates, 206 Union	07
Griesmer	07
Hilliard, 243 Union	05
Jackson Avenue, Jackson Ave.	04
Jackson, 1100 Union	08
Lincoln, 114 Union	05
Mahoney, 133 S Brandywine Ave	07
Mohawk Gardens, Jackson Ave	04
Mohawk Manor, Duanesbura Rd	06
Netherlands Village, Mills Eyck Eyck Pky	08
Patroon, 223 Union	05
Queensbury, Queens Dr	04
Randi Gardens, Randi Rd	09
Roosevelt, 110 Union	05
Saint Regis, 602 Union	05
Schanowee Village, Hamilton & Millard	05
Schenectady, Broadway	05
Sheridan Village, Rosa Rd & Gerlino	08
Southgate, Watt	04
Steinmetz, Watt & Henry	04
Suellan, Suellan Rd	09
Ten Byck, Broadway	05
Van Antwerp, Van Antwerp Rd	09
Van Buren, Eastern Pkwy	09
Wade Lupe Towne Houses, 15 Lafayette	05
Westinghouse, 244 Union	05

BUILDINGS

| Education, 108 Union | 05 |
| Lorraine Block, 505 State | 05 |

Phillips, 434 State	05
Picotte, 530 Franklin	05
Proctor Arcade, 434 State	05
Wedgeway, 277 State	05

GOVERNMENT OFFICES

| City Hall, 105 Jay | 05 |
| Court House, 620 State | 07 |

HOSPITALS

Bellevue Maternity, Troy Rd Stop 11	09
Eastern New York Orthopedic School, 124 Rosa Rd	08
Ellis, Nott & Rosa Rd	08
Glenridge Tuberculosis, Glenridge Rd	02
Saint Clares, 514 Mcclellan	04
Schenectady County Tuberculosis, Glenridge Rd	02

UNIVERSITIES AND COLLEGES

| Schenectady Cty Community College | 05 |
| Union, Union | 08 |

STATEN ISLAND   103

POST OFFICE BOXES

Box Nos.

1-117	Rosebank Sta	05
1-119	Tottenville Sta	07
1-147	Mariners Harbor Sta	03
1-149	Eltingville Sta	12
1-178	West New Brighton Sta	10
1-236	Princes Bay Sta	09
1-239	Stapleton Sta	04
1-296	New Dorp Sta	06
1-391	Saint George	01
1-600	Gpo Sta	01
231-444	Great Kills Sta	08
301-537	Port Richmond Sta	02

STATIONS, BRANCHES AND UNITS

Eltingville Sta	12
Great Kills Sta	08
Mariners Harbor Sta	03
Midland Beach Sta	06
New Dorp Sta	06
Port Richmond Sta	02
Princes Bay Sta	09
Rosebank Sta	05
Saint George Sta	01
Stapleton Sta	04
Terminal Sta	01
Tottenville Sta	07
U S Public Health Hosp Sta	04
West New Brighton Sta	10
General Delivery	14
Postmaster	14

APARTMENTS, HOTELS, MOTELS

Adlon, 4 Chester Pl	04
Ambassador, 30 Daniel Low Ter	01
Avon Place, 29 Avon Pl	01
Bard Manor, 162 Bard Ave	10
Bayview, 299 St Marks Pl	01
Berry Homes, 1718 Richmond Rd	06
Beverly, 273 St Marks Pl	01
Bon-Aire, 15 Central Ave	01
Boulevard, 2071 Hylan Blvd	06
Carolina Gardens, 2862 Hylan Blvd	06
Castleton Avenue, 585 Castleton Ave	01
Castleton, 153 St Marks Pl	01
Century, 650 Victory Blvd	01
Christmas Tree Inn, 51 Wilbur	09
Clifton, 630 Victory Blvd	01
Clove Lake Arms, 830 & 850 Howard Ave	01
Columbia, 200 Victory Blvd	01
Court Plaza, 136 Stuyvesant Pl	01
Crestmont, 325 Westervelt Ave	01
Curtis Lodge, 261 Hamilton Ave	01
Fort Place Towers, Fort Place & Monroe Av	01
Golf Court, 215 Hart Blvd	01
Grey Court, 50 Wall	01
Grymes Hill Gardens, 6 Arlo Rd	01
Grymes Hill Manor Estates, 25 Seth Ct	01
Heberton, 137 Heberton Ave	02
Hylan Motel, 481 Hylan Blvd	05
Imperial Towers, 55 Austin Pl	04
La Toja, 4408 Hylan Blvd	12
Lincoln, 630 Midland Ave	06
Mariners Harbor Housing, 200 Lockman Ave	03
Markham Homes, 35 Markham Rd	10
Mc Gregor Manors, 115 Stuyvesant Pl	01
Motel Knickerbocker, 25 Russell	08
Park Hills Gardens, 184 Vanderbilt Ave	04
Park-View House, 700 Victory Blvd	01
Pentz, 33 Central Ave	01
Prospect Gables, 155 Prospect Ave	01
Richmond, 71 Central Ave	01
Saint George Court, 100 Stuyvesant Pl	01
Saint George Gardens, St Marks Pl & Hamilton	01
Saint Marks, 191 St Marks Pl	01
Silver Lake Arms, 800 Victory Blvd	01
Silver Lake Court, 459 Victory Blvd	01

Staten Island (Con.)   103

Skyline Terrace Co-Op, 350
  Richmond Ter..............   01
South Beach Housing, 84
  Lamport Blvd..............   05
Stapleton Housing, Broad &
  Tompkins Ave.............   04
Staten, 610 Victory Blvd........   01
The Castleton, 153 St Marks
  Pl.............................   01
The Sherman, 25 Sherman
  Ave...........................   01
Todt Hill Housing, 801 Manor
  Rd............................   14
Walker Parks Apartments,
  102 Bard Ave.............   10
Walker Parks Apartments, 91
  Davis Ave..................   10
West Brighton Housing, 210
  Broadway...................   10
Willowbrook, 125 Willowbrook
  Rd............................   02
Wisteria, 141 St Marks Pl......   01

BUILDINGS

Borough Hall, Hyatt &
  Stuyvesant Pl.............   01
Crabtree, 42 Richmond Ter.....   01
Hugot, 36 Richmond Ter.........   01
New York Telephone, 130
  Stuyvesant Pl.............   01
Pape, 15 Beach..................   04
Richmond, 350 St Marks Pl...   01
S I Plaza Shopping Center,
  Barrett & Decker Aves.......   02
Staten Island Medical Arts,
  100 Central Ave...........   01
Staten Island Museum, 75
  Stuyvesant Pl.............   01
Staten Island Zoo, Broadway..   10

GOVERNMENT OFFICES

Chamber Of Commerce, 130
  Bay..........................   01
City Court House, 927
  Castleton Ave.............   10
County Court House, 10
  Richmond Terr.............   01
Court House, 71 Targee.........   04
General Post Office, 550
  Manor Rd..................   14
Motor Vehicle Bureau, 450
  Saint Marks Pl............   01
Police Precinct 0120, 58
  Richmond Terr.............   01
Police Precinct 0122.............   06
Police Precinct 0123, 116
  Main.........................   07
Traffic, 71 Targee................   04

HOSPITALS

Doctors Hospital, 1050
  Targee St..................   04
Farm Colony, 460 Brielle Ave.   14
Lakeview Home, 77 Chicago
  Ave..........................   05

Richmond Boro, 460 Brielle
  Ave...........................   14
Richmond Memorial, 375
  Seguine Ave...............   09
Saint Vincents Medical Ctr O,
  Bard & Castleton Aves.....   10
Sea View, 460 Brielle Ave.....   14
Staten Island Medical Center,
  307 Victory Blvd...........   01
Staten Island, 101 Castleton
  Ave...........................   01
US Public Health Service
  Hosp, Bay St & Vanderbilt
  Ave...........................   04
Willowbrook State, Victory
  Blvd..........................   14

MILITARY INSTALLATIONS

Fort Wadsworth   05
Miller Field   06

UNIVERSITIES AND COLLEGES

Notre Dame, 300 Howard
  Ave...........................   01
Richmond, 130 Stuyvesant
  Pl.............................   01
Staten Island Community
  College, 715 Ocean Ter.....   01
Wagner, 631 Howard Ave......   01

SYRACUSE   132

POST OFFICE BOXES

Box Nos.
1-89   Mattydale Br   11
1-116   Solvay Br..........   09
1-118   Elmwood Sta   07
1-157   Colvin Sta   05
1-177   Onondaga Br......   15
1-207   Salina Sta   08
1-209   University Sta...   10
1-278   Eastwood Sta ...   06
1-297   Dewitt Br.........   14
1-304   North Syracuse
      Br   12
1-1400   Main Office   01

RURAL ROUTES

1.................................   09
2,3..............................   15

STATIONS, BRANCHES AND UNITS

Colvin Sta   05
Dewitt Br...........................   14
Eastwood Sta   06
Elmwood Sta   07
Hancock Field MOU...............   25
Mattydale Br.......................   11
North Syracuse Br.................   12
Onondaga Br.......................   15
Salina Sta   08
Solvay Br...........................   09
University Sta   10
Veterans Hospital Sta   10
General Delivery   01

Postmaster.......................   01

APARTMENTS, HOTELS, MOTELS

Alabama, 606 University Ave..   10
Ambassador, 417 University
  Ave...........................   10
Ambassador, 901 Madison   10
Belmore, 100 Wood Ave.........   05
Berkeley, 735 W Onondaga....   04
Castle, 124 W Castle............   05
Chancellor, 2508 S Salina.....   05
Chatham, 644 W Onondaga ..   04
Commodore, 1505 E Genese..   10
Crown Arms, 307 Hawley
  Ave...........................   03
Dewitt Arms, 401 Smith........   24
Edward, 1210 Bellevue Ave....   04
Ellis Court, 101 Woodbine
  Ave...........................   06
Frontenac, 1802 W Genese.....   04
Genesee, 1804 W Genesee......   04
Grant Village, 814 117 Edtim
  Rd............................   06
Highland, 814 Bellevue Ave....   04
Hillside, 1530 E Genese..,....   10
Huntley, 407 Stolp Ave   07
Imperial Gardens, 989
  James.......................   03
James Plaza, 622 James.........   03
Kasson, 622 James..............   03
Leavenworth, 828 SW............   02
Leonard A, 828 SW..............   02
Leonard B, 400 W Onondaga..   02
Leonard C, 410 W Onondaga..   02
Mayflower, 1030 E Genese....   10
Moore, 308 James................   03
Parkwood, 140 Washington
  Sq............................   08
Plaza, 1108 E Genesee..........   10
Roosevelt, 1301 E Genese......   10
Sagamore, 666 W Onondaga..   04
Schopfer Court, 708 James.....   03
Sherbrooke, 604 Walnut........   10
Sherbrooke, 920 Madison.......   10
Skyline, 753 James..............   03
Snowden, 400 James............   03
Swiss Village, Alpine Dr.........   14
Tower, 770 James................   03
University Arms, 613
  University Ave.............   10
Valley Court, 300 Mains Ave..   07
Walnut Arms, 514 Walnut
  Ave...........................   10
Washington Square, 1706
  Park.........................   08
Woodbine, 100 Woodbine Ave.   06
111 & 121 Lafayette Rd.........   05

BUILDINGS

Chimes, 109 W Onondaga....   02
Daniel, 433 S Salina............   02
Eckel, 214 E Fayette............   02
Empire, 472 S Salina............   02
Federal, Clinton Sq.............   02
First Trust & Deposit, 212 E
  Washington................   02
Gridley, 115 E Genesee.........   02
Herald, 332 S Warren...........   02
Hills, 217 Montgomery..........   02
Jefferson, 204 E Jefferson.....   02
Lafayette, 210 E Fayette.......   02

Syracuse (Con.) 132

Larned, 114 S Warren	02
Lincoln Bank, 105 W Water	02
Marine Midland, 344 S Warren	02
Mc Carthy, 113 E Onondaga	02
Merchants Bank, 214 S Warren	10
Midtown Plaza, 700 E Water	10
Mony Plaza, 100 Madison Street	02
Onondaga County Savings Bank, 113 S Salina	02
Pickard, 5858 E Malloy Rd	11
Presidential Plaza, 600 E Genesee St	02
Public Safety, 511 S State	02
Romax, 731 James	03
S A & K, 206 E Genesee	02
Seitz, 201 E Jefferson	02
State Office, 333 E Washington	02
State Tower, 109 S warren	02
Syracuse-Kemper, 224 Harrison	02

GOVERNMENT OFFICES

Chamber Of Commerce, 351 S Warren	02
City Hall, 233 E Washington	02
County Courthouse, 401 Montgomery	02

HOSPITALS

Community Hosp, Broad Rd	15
Crouse-Irving Memorial Hosp, 736 Irving Ave	10
Saint Josephs, 301 Prospect Ave	03
Saint Marys, 1601 Court	08
Upstate Medical Center Building, 766 Irving Ave	10
Van Duyn Hosp, W Seneca Tpk	15
Veterans Hosp, 800 Irving Ave	10
345 Renwick Ave	10

TROY 121

POST OFFICE BOXES

Box Nos.		
1-1079	Main Office	81
91-299	Lansingburgh Sta	82
1501-1530	Green Island Br	83

RURAL ROUTES

1	80
2	82
3,4,5,6	80

APARTMENTS, HOTELS, MOTELS

Ahern Apts, 127 Ferry	80
Corliss Park, Northern Dr	82
Fallon Arnold Apts Glen Ave	80
Griswold Hts, Madison Ave	80

STATIONS, BRANCHES AND UNITS

Green Island Br	83
Lansingburg Sta	82
General Delivery	80
Postmaster	80
Hendrick Hudson Hotel, 200 Broadway	80
Holiday Inn, 1800 Sixth Ave	80
Hotel Troy, 2 First	80
Kennedy Towers, 2100 Sixth Ave	80
Martin Luther King Apts Eddys Ln	80
Phelan Margaret Apts Phelan Ct	80
Sweeney Catherine M Apts 4th St	80
Taylor Apts, 125 River	80
Trojan Hotel, 43 Third	80
Troy Garden Apts, 275 Hoosick	80
Troy Hills Apts, Marvin Ave	80
Troy Rose Garden Apts, 25th	80
Twin Towers Apts 1900 Sixth Ave	80

HOSPITALS

Leonard New Turnpike Rd	82
Saint Mary'S, 1300 Massachusetts Ave	80
Samaritan, Peoples Ave	80

UNIVERSITIES AND COLLEGES

Emma Willard, Pawling Ave	80
Hudson Valley Community, 80 Vandenburgh Ave	80
Rensselaer Polytechnic, 110 Eighth	81
Russell Sage, 45 Ferry	80

UTICA 135

POST OFFICE BOXES

Box Nos.		
1-874	Main Office	03

RURAL ROUTES

1,2	02

STATIONS, BRANCHES AND UNITS

Butterfield Br	02
Dunham Sta	02
Kernan Sta	02
Schuyler Rural Br	02

General Delivery	03
Postmaster	03

APARTMENTS, HOTELS, MOTELS

Algonquin, 1434 Genesee	02
Amlott, 1420 Genesee	02
Genesee Court, 1426 Genesee	02
Genesee Manor, 1400 Genesee	02
Georgian Courts, 2400 Oneida	01
Goldbas, 440 Whitesboro	02
Holland House Apts., 1629 Genesee	01
Kanatenah, 1504 Genesee	02
Olbiston, 1440 Genesee	01
Roosevelt, 1514 Genesee	02
Ropewalk, 1427 Oneida	01
Southwind Terrace, 141 Marlboro Rd	01
Utica Hotel, 102 Lafayette	03

BUILDINGS

Brock, 276 Genesee	02
Central N Y Power, 258 Genesee	02
Devereaux Block, 134 Genesee	02
First National Bank, 187 Genesee	01
Gardner, 190 Genesee	01
Genesee Corporation, 258 Genesee	02
Insurance, 110 Genesee	02
Kempf, 250 Genesee	02
Martin, 115 Genesee	01
Mayro, 239 Genesee	01
N.Y. State Office Bldg. 201 Genesee	01
Oneida County Office Bldg. 800 Park Ave	01
Paul, 209 Elizabeth	01
Security, 124 Bleecker	01

HOSPITALS

Childrens, 1675 Bennett	02
Faxton, 1676 Sunset Ave	02
Masonic Home, 2150 Bleecker	03
St Elizabeths, 2209 Genesee	01
St Lukes Memorial, Champlin Rd	03
State Hospital, 1213 Court	02

UNIVERSITIES AND COLLEGES

M V C C, 1101 Sherman Dr	01
Utica College, Burrstone Rd	02

VALLEY STREAM 115

POST OFFICE BOXES

Box Nos.		
A-L	Main Office	82

Valley Stream (Con.)   115

1-517   Main Office   32

STATIONS, BRANCHES AND UNITS

Gimbels Number One Sta   81
General Delivery   80
Postmaster   80

HOSPITALS

Franklin General Hospital,
900 Franklin Ave   80

YONKERS   107

POST OFFICE BOXES

Box Nos.
1-128   Eastchester Br.   09
1-144   North   03
1-177   Centuck Sta ...   10
1-297   Hastings Br   06
1-338   South   05
1-386   East Sta   04
1-514   Bronxville
           Branch.........   08
1-632   Yonkers..........   02
121-506   Tuckahoe Br.....   07

STATIONS, BRANCHES AND UNITS

Bronxville Br............................   08
Centuck Sta.............................   10
East Sta..................................   04
Eastchester Br.........................   09
Hastings On Hudson Br   06
North Sta.................................   03
South Sta.................................   05
Tuckahoe Br.............................   07
General Delivery   01
Postmaster   01

APARTMENTS, HOTELS, MOTELS

Dunwoodie Motor Court,
  Yonkers Ave   01
Gramatan, Pondfield Rd
  Bronxville   08
Holiday Inn Motel, Tuckahoe
  Rd   10
Rockledge Manor, 124 Bruce
  Ave   05
Trade Winds Motel, Yonkers
  Ave   04
Tuckahoe Motel, Tuckahoe
  Rd   10
Westchester Town House,
  Tuckahoe Rd   10
Windham, Hudson   01

HOSPITALS

Andrus Paviaion, North
  Broadway.........................   01
Bates Memorial Hospital,
  Sprain Rd..........................   10
Cross County Hospital, Cross
  County Center   04
Lawrence Hospital, Palmer
  Rd Bronxville.....................   08
Professional Hospital,
  Ludlow..............................   05
Saint Johns Riverside
  Hospital, North Broadway...   01
Saint Josephs Hospital...........   01
Yonkers General Hospital,
  Ashburton Ave...................   01

UNIVERSITIES AND COLLEGES

Concordia College, White
  Plains Rd Bronxville   08
Saint Josephs Seminary,
  Seminary Avenue   04
Sarah Lawrence College,
  Kimball Av Bronxville..........   08
Seton College, North
  Broadway   01

WHITE PLAINS   106

POST OFFICE BOXES

Box Nos.
1-89   Gedney Sta......   05
1-149   East White
            Plains Br.......   04
1-149   North White
            Plains Sta   03
1-1252   Main Office   02

STATIONS, BRANCHES AND UNITS

Central White Plains Sta..........   06
East White Plains Br..............   04
Gedney Sta..............................   05
North White Plains Sta............   03
General Delivery   02
Postmaster..............................   02

APARTMENTS, HOTELS, MOTELS

Alton Gardens, 23
  Mamaroneck Rd..................   05
Benjamin Franklin, 1 Broad
  Pkwy................................   01
Brentwood, 300 Main............   01
Briarview Manor, 10 Nosband
  Ave.................................   05

Broad Park Lodge, 292 Main..   01
Bryant Gardens, 1 Bryant
  Cres................................   05
Edgebrook Estates, 1
  Lawrence Dr......................   03
Fulton Park Apartments, Co
  Ctr Rd..............................   07
Gedney House, 59
  Mamaroneck Rd..................   05
Greenridge Court, 1
  Greenridge Ave..................   05
Netherlands, 205 W Post Rd..   06
River Park, 1 Virginia Rd.......   03
Surrey Strathmore, 90 Bryant
  Ave.................................   05
Westview Gardens, 7
  Westview Ave....................   03
White Swan, 1 S Broadway.....   01
Woodlands Hill   03

BUILDINGS

Bar, 199 Main........................   01
County Center, 198 Central
  Ave..................................   07
Macys, 220 Main....................   01
Municipal, 279 Hamilton Ave.   01
Northcourt, 175 Main..............   01
Peoples Bank, 31
  Mamaroneck Ave.................   01
White Plains Plaza, 1 No.
  Broadway...........................   01

GOVERNMENT OFFICES

City Hall 255 Main St............   01
County Court House, 166
  Main.................................   01
County Office, 148 Martine
  Ave..................................   01

HOSPITALS

Burke Foundation, 785
  Mamaroneck Ave.................   05
Saint Agnes Hospital, North ...   05
White Plains Hospital, 41 E
  Post Rd.............................   01

UNIVERSITIES AND COLLEGES

Battle Avenue, 155 Battle
  Ave..................................   06
College Of White Plains, 76
  No. Broadway.....................   03
Dobbs Ferry Road, Dobbs
  Ferry Rd............................   07
Eastview, 25 Eastview Ave.....   01
George Washington, 100
  Orchard............................   04
Greenburgh Junior High, 33
  W Hillside Ave....................   07
Jewish Community Center,
  252 Soundview Ave   06
Mamaroneck Avenue, 9
  Nosband Ave.....................   05

NORTH CAROLINA
(Abbreviation: NC)

Abbottsburg, R. Br.
  Bladenboro............................28321
Aberdeen (1st)............................28315
Advance............................27006
Ahoskie (1st)............................27910
Akers Center, Sta. Gastonia....28052
Alamance............................27201
Albemarle (1st)............................28001
Albertson............................28508
Alexander............................28701
Alexander Mills, R. Br.
  Forest City............................28043
Alexis............................28006
Alliance............................28509
Almond............................28702
Altamahaw............................27202
Anderson, R. Br. Kitty Hawk....27949
Andrews............................28901
Angier............................27501
Ansonville............................28007
Apex (1st)............................27502
Apple Grove............................28602
Aquone............................28703
Arapahoe............................28510
Ararat............................27007
Archdale, Br. High Point............27263
Arcola, R. Br. Warrenton............27589
Arden (1st)............................28704
Ardmore, Sta. Winston-Salem
  (see appendix)
Ash............................28420
  Freeland, R. Br. 28440
Asheboro (1st)............................27203
ASHEVILLE (1st) (see
  appendix)
Ashford............................28603
Assembly, R. Br. Lake
  Junaluska............................28745
Atando, Sta. Charlotte............28206
Atkinson............................28421
Atlantic............................28511
Atlantic Beach............................28½ 2
Atlantic Christian College,
  Sta. Wilson............................27893
Aulander............................27805
Aurora............................27806
Autryville............................28318
Avon............................27915
Ayden............................28513
Aydlett............................27916
Azalea, Sta. Wilmington............28401
Badin............................28009
Bahama............................27503
Bailey............................27807
Bakersville............................28705
Bald Creek, R. Br.
  Burnsville............................28714
Balfour............................28706
Balsam............................28707
Balsam Grove............................28708
Banner Elk............................28604
Barber............................27008
Barco............................27917
Barium Springs............................28010
Barnardsville............................28709
Barnesville............................28319
Bat Cave............................28710
Bath............................27808
Battleboro............................27809
Bayboro............................28515

Bear Creek............................27207
Bear Poplar, R. Br.
  Salisbury............................28011
Beaufort (1st)............................28516
Belcross............................27918
Belew Creek............................27009
Belhaven............................27810
Bellarthur............................27811
Belmont (1st)............................28012
Belvidere............................27919
Bennett............................27208
Benson............................27504
Bessemer City............................28016
Bethabara, Sta.
  Winston-Salem............................27106
Bethania............................27010
Bethel............................27812
Bethlehem, R. Br. Hickory....28601
Beulaville............................28518
Biggs Park, Sta. Lumberton....28358
Biltmore, Sta. Asheville....28803
Biscoe............................27209
Black Creek............................27813
Black Mountain (1st)............................28711
Black Mountain Sanatorium,
  R. Br. Black Mountain....28711
Bladenboro............................28320
  Abbottsburg, R. Br............................28321
Blanch............................27212
Blounts Creek............................27814
Blowing Rock............................28605
Blue Ridge, R. Br. Black
  Mountain............................28711
Boger City, Br. Lincolnton......28092
Boiling Spring Lakes, R. Br.
  Southport............................28461
Boiling Springs............................28017
Bolivia............................28422
Bolton............................28423
Bonlee............................27213
Bonnie Doone, Br.
  Fayetteville............................28303
Boomer............................28606
Boone (1st)............................28607
  Valle Crucis, R. Br............................28691
Boonville............................27011
Bostic............................28018
Boulevard, Sta. Eden............27288
Bowdens............................28322
Brasstown............................28902
Brevard (1st)............................28712
Bridgeton............................28519
Broadway............................27505
Brookford, R. Br. Hickory....28601
Brookside, Br. Goldsboro....27530
Browns Summit............................27214
Brunswick............................28424
Bryson City (1st)............................28713
Buies Creek............................27506
Bullock............................27507
Bunn............................27508
Bunnlevel............................28323
Burgaw (1st)............................28425
Burlington (1st)............................27215
Burnsville............................28714
Butner............................27509
Butters............................28324
Buxton............................27920
Bynum, R. Br. Pittsboro....27228
Ca Vel............................27512
Calypso............................28325
Camden............................27921
Cameron............................28326

Cameron Village, Sta.
  Raleigh............................27605
Camp Lejeune, Br.
  Jacksonville............................28542
Candler............................28715
Candor............................27229
Cane River, R. Br.
  Burnsville............................28714
Canton (1st)............................28716
Cape Fear, Br. Wilmington......28401
Caroleen............................28019
Carolina Beach............................28428
Carolina Hills, R. Br.
  Fletcher............................28732
Carrboro (1st)............................27510
Carthage............................28327
Cary (1st)............................27511
Casar............................28020
Cashiers............................28717
Castalia............................27816
Castle Hayne............................28429
Casville, R. Br. Ruffin............27326
Caswell, Br. Kinston............28501
Catawba............................28609
Catawba Heights, Br.
  Belmont............................28012
Cedar Falls............................27230
Cedar Grove............................27231
Cedar Island............................28520
Cedar Mountain............................28718
Central Falls............................27232
Century, Sta. Raleigh............27602
Cerro Gordo............................28430
Chadbourn............................28431
Chadwick, Sta. Charlotte....28208
Chapel Hill (1st)............................27514
CHARLOTTE (1st) (see
  appendix)
Charlottetown, Sta. Charlotte
  (see appendix)
Cherokee............................28719
Cherry Point, Br. Havelock....28533
Cherryville (1st)............................28021
Chimney Rock............................28720
China Grove............................28023
Chinquapin............................28521
Chocowinity............................27817
Claremont............................28610
Clarendon............................28432
Clarkton............................28433
Clayton............................27520
Clemmons (1st)............................27012
Cleveland............................27013
Cliffside............................28024
Climax............................27233
Clinton (1st)............................28328
Clyde............................28721
Coats............................27521
Cofield............................27922
Coinjock............................27923
Colerain............................27924
Coleridge............................27234
Colfax............................27235
College, Sta. Durham............27708
Collettsville............................28611
Colon............................27236
Columbia............................27925
Columbus............................28722
Comfort............................28522
Como............................27818
Concord (1st)............................28025
Conetoe............................27819
Connellys Springs............................28612

Conover (1st)........................28613
Conway................................27820
Cooleemee...........................27014
Corapeake............................27926
Cordova...............................28330
Cornelius.............................28031
Corolla...............................27927
Cottonae, Br. Fayetteville.....28303
Council...............................28434
Court House, Sta. Asheville....28807
Cove City.............................28523
Cramerton............................28032
Cranberry............................28614
Creedmoor............................27522
Creston...............................28615
Creswell..............................27928
Crisp, R. Br. Macclesfield.....27852
Crossnore............................28616
Crouse................................28033
Crumpler..............................28617
Culberson.............................28903
Cullowhee.............................28723
Cumberland...........................28331
Cumnock, R. Br. Sanford........27237
Currie................................28435
Currituck.............................27929
Dallas................................28034
Dana..................................28724
Danbury...............................27016
Davidson (1st).......................28036
Davis.................................28524
Deep Gap.............................28618
Deep Run.............................28525
Delco.................................28436
Denton................................27239
Denver................................28037
Derita, Br. Charlotte.............28213
Dillsboro.............................28725
Dilworth, Sta. Charlotte........28203
Dobson................................27017
Dover.................................28526
Downtown, Sta. Charlotte........28202
Draper, Sta. Eden..................27288
Drexel (1st).........................28619
Dublin................................28332
Dudley................................28333
Duke, Sta. Durham..................27706
Dunn (1st)...........................28334
Durants Neck, R. Br.
   Hertford...........................27930
DURHAM (1st) (see
   appendix)
Eagle Rock...........................27523
Eagle Springs.......................27242
Earl..................................2803?
East Bend.............................270
East Carolina University,
   Sta. Greenville..................278
East Durham, Sta. Durham........2770.
East Fayetteville, Br.
   Fayetteville......................28301
East Flat Rock.......................29726
East Gastonia, R. Sta.
   Gastonia...........................28052
East Lake.............................27931
East Laurinburg, R. Br.
   Laurinburg........................28352
East Lumberton, Sta.
   Lumberton..........................28358
East Rockingham, Br.
   Rockingham.........................28379
East Rocky Mount, Sta.
   Rocky Mount........................27801

East Spencer.........................28039
Eastgate, Sta. Chapel Hill.....27514
Eastway, Sta. Charlotte (see
   appendix)
Eden (1st)...........................27288
Edenton (1st)........................27932
Edgemont..............................28620
Edneyville...........................28727
Edward................................27821
Efland................................27243
Elizabeth, Sta. Charlotte.......28204
Elizabeth City (1st)...............27909
Elizabethtown (1st)................28337
Elk Park.............................28622
Elkin (1st)..........................28621
Ellenboro............................28040
Ellerbe...............................28338
Elm City (1st).......................27822
Elon College (1st).................27244
Emerson...............................28237
Emerywood, Sta. High Point.....27262
Encas, R. Br. Wilson...............27893
Enfield...............................27823
Engelhard.............................27824
Englewood, Sta. Rocky
   Mount..............................27801
Enka..................................28728
Ennice................................28623
Erlanger, Sta. Lexington........27292
Ernul.................................28527
Erwin.................................28339
Ether.................................27247
Etowah................................28729
Eure..................................2794?
Eureka, R. Br. Fremont...........27830
Eutaw, Sta. Fayetteville (see
   appendix)
Everetts..............................27825
Evergreen.............................28438
Fair Bluff...........................28439
Fairfield.............................27826
Fairmont.............................28340
Fairview..............................28730
Faison................................28341
Faith.................................28041
Falcon................................28342
Falkland..............................27827
Fallston..............................28042
Farmer, R. Br. Asheboro.........27203
Farmville (1st)......................27828
FAYETTEVILLE (1st) (see
   appendix)
Federal Building, Sta.
   Elizabeth City....................27909
Ferguson..............................28624
Five Point, Sta. Raleigh........27608
Flat Rock.............................28731
Fleetwood.............................28626
Fletcher..............................28732
Fontana Dam..........................28733
Forest City (1st)...................28043
Forest Hills, Sta. Durham.......27707
Fort Bragg, Br. Fayetteville....28307
Fountain..............................27829
Four Oaks.............................27524
Frank, R. Br. Newland.............28657
Franklin (1st).......................28734
Franklin Street, Sta. Chapel
   Hill...............................27514
Franklinton...........................27525
Franklinville........................27248
Freedom, Sta. Charlotte (see
   appendix)

Freeland, R. Br. Ash..............28440
Fremont...............................27830
Friendly, Sta. Greensboro.......27404
Frisco................................27936
Fuquay-Varina (1st)................27526
Gardner Webb College, R.
   Sta. Boiling Springs............28017
Garland...............................28441
Garner (1st).........................27529
Garysburg.............................27831
Gaston................................27832
Gastonia (1st).......................28052
Gates.................................27937
Gatesville............................27938
George................................27833
Germanton.............................27019
Gerton................................28735
Gibson................................28343
Gibsonville..........................27249
Gilkey, R. Br. Rutherfordton....28141
Glade Valley.........................28627
Glen Alpine..........................28628
Glen Lennox, Sta. Chapel
   Hill...............................27514
Glen Raven, Br. Burlington.....27215
Glendale Springs....................28629
Glendon...............................27251
Glenrock, Sta. Asheville........28802
Glenville.............................28736
Glenwood..............................28737
Gloucester............................28528
Godwin................................28344
Gold Hill.............................28071
Golden Gate, Sta.
   Greensboro.........................27405
Goldsboro (1st)......................27530
Goldston..............................27252
Grace, Sta. Asheville.............28804
Graham (1st).........................27253
Grandy................................27939
Granite Falls........................28630
Granite Quarry.......................28072
Grantham, R. Br. Goldsboro......27530
Grantsboro............................28529
Grassy Creek.........................28631
Grayson...............................28632
Greenmountain........................28740
GREENSBORO (1st) (see
   appendix)
Greenville (1st).....................27834
Gregory...............................27940
Grifton...............................28530
Grimesland............................27837
Grover................................28073
Guilford, Br. Greensboro........27409
Guilford College, Br.
   Greensboro.........................27410
Gulf..................................27256
Gumberry..............................27838
Half Moon, R. Br.
   Jacksonville.......................28540
Halifax...............................27839
Hallsboro.............................28442
Hamilton..............................27840
Hamlet (1st).........................28345
Hampstead.............................28443
Hamptonville..........................27020
Hanes, Sta. Winston-Salem.......27103
Harbinger.............................27941
Harkers Island.......................28531
Harmony...............................28634
Harrells..............................28444
Harrellsville........................27942

Harris....................................28074
Harrisburg............................28075
Hassell..................................2784J
Hatteras................................2794 j
Havelock (1st)......................2853?
  Cherry Point, Br.............2853 i
Haw River.............................2925&
Hayesville.............................2890'4
Haymount, Sta. Fayetteville..28305
Hays......................................2863S
Hayti, Sta. Durham..............27701
Haywood Road, Sta.
  Asheville...........................28806
Hazelwood (1st)...................28738
Henderson (1st)....................27536
Hendersonville (1st)............28739
Henrico.................................27842
Henrietta..............................28076
Henry River, R. Br. Hickory..28601
Hertford................................27944
  Durants Neck, R. Br..........27930
Hickory (1st).........................28601
Hickory Grove, Br. Charlotte..28215
Hiddenite..............................28636
HIGH POINT (1st) (see
  appendix)
High Rock, R. Br. Denton......27239
High Shoals...........................28077
Highfalls...............................27259
Highlands..............................28741
Hildebran.............................2863?
Hillsborough (1st)................27278
Hilltop, Sta. Greensboro......27407
Hobbsville.............................27946
Hobgood...............................27843
Hobucken..............................28537
Hoffman...............................28347
Holden Beach, R. Br. Supply..28462
Hollister................................27844
Holly Ridge...........................28445
Holly Springs........................27540
Hookerton.............................28538
Hope Mills............................28348
Horse Shoe...........................28742
Hot Springs...........................28743
Hubert...................................28539
Hudson.................................28638
Huntersville..........................28078
Hurdle Mills.........................27541
Husk......................................28639
Icard.....................................28666
Idlewild, Br. Charlotte..........28212
Indian Trail...........................28079
Ingalls, R. Br. Newland.........28657
Ingold...................................28446
Iron Station..........................28080
Ivanhoe.................................28447
Jackson.................................27845
Jackson Hill...........................27280
Jackson Park, Br.
  Kannapolis........................28081
Jackson Springs....................27281
Jacksonville (1st)..................28540
  Camp Lejeune, Br.............28542
  Half Moon, R. Br..............28540
  M C A F New River, Br......28540
  Midway Park, Br...............28544
  New River Plaza, Sta........28540
  Northwoods, Sta...............28540
  Tarawa Terrace, Br...........28543
  Verona, R. Br...................28540
James City, R. Br. New Bern..28550
Jamestown.............................27282

Jamesville.............................27846
Jarvisburg.............................27947
Jefferson...............................28640
Jonas Ridge...........................28641
Jonesboro Heights, Sta.
  Sanford.............................27330
Jonesville..............................28642
Julian....................................27283
Kannapolis (1st)...................28081
Kelford..................................27847
Kelly.....................................28448
Kenansville...........................28349
Kenly....................................27542
Kernersville (1st)..................27284
Kill Devil Hills......................27948
King......................................27021
King Charles, Sta. Raleigh....27610
Kings Mountain (1st)...........28086
Kinston (1st).........................28501
Kipling..................................27543
Kittrell..................................27544
Kitty Hawk............................27949
Knightdale............................27545
Knotts Island........................27950
Kure Beach...........................28449
La Grange (1st).....................28551
Lafayette, Br. Fayetteville....28304
Lake Junaluska.....................28745
Lake Lure..............................28746
Lake Toxaway.......................28747
Lake Waccamaw....................28450
Lakedale, Sta. Fayetteville....28306
Lakeview...............................28350
Lakewood, Sta. Durham........27707
Landis...................................28088
Lansing..................................28643
Lasker...................................27848
Lattimore.............................28089
Laurel Hill............................28351
Laurel Springs......................28644
Laurinburg (1st)....................28352
Lawndale..............................28090
Lawsonville...........................27022
Leasburg...............................27291
Leicester...............................28748
Leland...................................28451
Lemon Springs......................28355
Lenoir (1st)...........................28645
Lenoir Rhyne, Sta. Hickory..28601
Lester, Sta. Kinston..............28501
Lewiston................................27849
Lewisville..............................27023
Lexington (1st)......................27292
Liberty..................................27298
Lilesville...............................28091
Lillington..............................27546
Lincolnton (1st)....................28092
Linden..................................28356
Linville..................................28646
Linville Falls..........................28647
Linwood................................27299
Little Switzerland.................28749
Littleton................................27850
Locust...................................28097
Long Beach, R. Br.
  Southport.........................28461
Long View, Br. Hickory.........28601
Longhurst.............................27548
Longisland............................28648
Longwood.............................28452
Louisburg (1st).....................27549
Love Valley, R. Br.
  Statesville.........................28677

Lowell...................................28098
Lowgap.................................27024
Lowland.................................28552
Lucama..................................27851
Lumber Bridge......................28357
Lumberton (1st)....................28358
Lynn.....................................28750
M C A F New River, Br.
  Jacksonville.......................28540
Macclesfield..........................27852
Macon...................................27551
Madison (1st)........................27025
Maggie..................................28751
Magnolia...............................28453
Maiden..................................28650
Main Street, Sta. Garner.......27529
Mamers.................................27552
Manns Harbor.......................27953
Manson.................................27553
Manteo..................................27954
Maple....................................27956
Maple Hill.............................28454
Marble..................................28905
Margarettsville......................27853
Marietta................................28362
Marion (1st)..........................28752
Mars Hill..............................28754
Marshall................................28753
Marshallberg.........................28553
Marshville.............................28103
Marston.................................28363
Matthews (1st)......................28105
Maury....................................28554
Maxton..................................28364
Mayodan...............................27027
Maysville...............................28555
Mc Adenville.........................28101
Mc Cain.................................28361
Mc Donalds, R. Br.
  Fairmont...........................28340
Mc Farlan.............................28102
Mc Grady..............................28649
Mc Leansville........................27301
Mebane (1st).........................27302
Meredith College, R. Sta.
  Raleigh.............................27602
Merritt..................................28556
Merry Hill.............................27957
Method (1st).........................27554
Methodist College, Br.
  Fayetteville.......................28301
Micaville...............................28755
Micro....................................27555
Middleburg...........................27556
Middlesex..............................27557
Middletown, R. Br.
  Engelhard..........................27824
Midland.................................28107
Midway, Br. Kannapolis........28081
Midway Park, Br.
  Jacksonville.......................28544
Mill Spring............................28756
Millbrook..............................27558
Millers Creek........................28651
Millside, R. Sta. Shelby.........28150
Milton...................................27305
Milwaukee............................27854
Mineral Springs....................28108
Minneapolis..........................28652
Minpro, R. Br. Spruce Pine...28777
Mint Hill, R. Br. Charlotte....28212
Misenheimer.........................28109
Mocksville (1st).....................27028

Moncure 27559
Monroe (1st) 28110
Montezuma 28653
Montreat 28757
Mooresboro 28114
Mooresville (1st) 28115
Moravian Falls 28654
Mordecai, Sta. Raleigh 27604
Morehead City (1st) 28557
Morgans Corner, R. Br.
  Elizabeth City 27909
Morganton (1st) 28655
Morrisville 27560
Morven 28119
Mount Airy (1st) 27030
  White Plains, R. Br. 27031
Mount Gilead (1st) 27306
Mount Holly (1st) 28120
Mount Mourne 28123
Mount Olive (1st) 28365
Mount Pleasant 28124
Mount Tabor, Sta.
  Winston-Salem 27106
Mount Ulla 28125
Mount Vernon Springs, R.
  Br. Siler City 27345
Mountain Home 28758
Moyock 27958
Municipal Airport, Br.
  Charlotte 28208
Murfreesboro 27855
Murphy (1st) 28906
Myers Park, Sta. Charlotte .. 28207
Nags Head 27959
Nakina 28455
Naples 28760
Nashville 27856
Navassa, R. Br. Wilmington .. 28404
Nebo 28761
Neuse 27561
Neuse Forest, Br. New Bern .. 28560
New Bern (1st) 28560
  James City, R. Br. 28550
  Neuse Forest, Br. 28560
  West New Bern, Sta. 28560
New Hill 27562
New Holland, R. Br.
  Swanquarter 27885
New Hope, Br. Raleigh 27604
New London 28127
New River Plaza, Sta.
  Jacksonville 28540
Newbold, Sta. Fayetteville .. 28301
Newell 28126
Newland 28657
Newport 28570
Newton (1st) 28658
Newton Grove 28366
Niagara, R. Br. Southern
  Pines 28388
Norlina 27563
Norman 28367
North, Sta. Winston-Salem ... 27105
North Asheboro, Br.
  Asheboro 27203
North Belmont, Br. Belmont .. 28012
North Burlington, Sta.
  Burlington 27215
North Charlotte, Sta.
  Charlotte 28206
North Durham, Sta. Durham .. 27704
North Hills, Sta. Raleigh 27609
North Wilkesboro (1st) 28659

Northgate, Sta. Durham 27701
Northside 27564
Northwoods, Sta.
  Jacksonville 28540
Norwood (1st) 28128
Oak City 27857
Oak Ridge 27310
Oakboro 28129
Ocean Isle Beach, R. Br.
  Shallotte 28459
Ocracoke 27960
Old Fort (1st) 28762
Old Trap 27961
Olin 28660
Olivia 28368
Oriental 28571
Orrum 28369
Oteen, Br. Asheville 28805
Otto 28763
Overhills 28370
Oxford (1st) 27565
Pactolus 27858
Palmyra 27859
Pantego 27860
Park Road, Sta. Charlotte 28209
Park View, Sta. Kinston 28501
Parkton 28371
Parkwood, Br. Durham 27707
Parmele 27861
Patterson 28661
Paw Creek (1st) 28130
Peachland 28133
Pelham 27311
Pembroke 28372
Pendleton 27862
Penland 28765
Penrose 28766
Pensacola, R. Br. Burnsville .. 28714
Pfafftown 27040
Pike Road, R. Br. Pantego ... 27860
Pikeville 27863
Pilot Mountain 27041
Pine Hall 27042
Pine Level 27568
Pinebluff 28373
Pinehurst (1st) 28374
Pineola 28662
Pinetops 27864
Pinetown 27865
Pineville 28134
Piney Creek 28663
Pink Hill 28572
Pinkney, R. Br. Gastonia 28052
Pinnacle 27043
Pisgah Forest 28768
Pittsboro 27312
Plaza, Sta. Greensboro 27408
Plaza, Sta. Charlotte (see
  appendix)
Pleasant Garden 27313
Pleasant Hill 27866
Plumtree 28664
Plymouth (1st) 27962
Point Harbor 27964
Polkton 28135
Polkville 28136
Pollocksville 28573
Pomona, Sta. Greensboro 27407
Pope A F B, MOU.
  Fayetteville 28308
Poplar Branch 27965
Potecasi 27867
Powells Point 27966

Powellsville 27967
Princeton 27569
Proctorville 28375
Prospect Hill 27314
Providence 27315
Purlear 28665
Raeford (1st) 28376
RALEIGH (1st) (see
  appendix)
Ramseur 27316
Randleman 27317
  Worthville, R. Br. 27378
Randolph, Sta. Charlotte 28211
Ranlo Smyre, Br. Gastonia .. 28052
Ransomville, R. Br.
  Belhaven 27810
Red Oak 27868
Red Springs (1st) 28377
Reidsville (1st) 27320
Relief 28769
Research Triangle Park, Br.
  Durham 27709
Rex 28378
Reynolda, Sta.
  Winston-Salem 27109
Rhodhiss 28667
Rich Square (1st) 27869
Richfield 28137
Richlands 28574
Ridgecrest 28770
Ridgeway 27570
Riegelwood 28456
Rivermont, Br. Kinston 28501
Roanoke Rapids (1st) 27870
Roaring Gap 28668
Roaring River 28669
Robbins 27325
Robbinsville 28771
Robersonville 27871
Rockford 27044
Rockingham (1st) 28379
Rockwell 28138
Rocky Mount (1st) 27801
Rocky Point 28457
Rodanthe 27968
Roduco 27969
Rolesville 27571
Ronda 28670
Roper 27970
Rose Hill 28458
Roseboro 28382
Rosman 28772
Rougemont 27572
Rowan Mill, R. Br. Salisbury .. 28144
Rowland 28383
Roxboro (1st) 27573
Roxobel 27872
Ruffin 27326
Rural Hall 27045
Rutherford College 28671
Rutherfordton (1st) 28139
  Gilkey, R. Br. 28141
Saint Pauls 28384
Salem, Sta. Winston-Salem .. 27108
Salemburg 28385
Salisbury (1st) 28144
  Bear Poplar, R. Br. 28011
  Rowan Mill, R. Br. 28144
Salter Path 28575
Saluda 28773
Salvo 27972
Sandy Ridge 27046
Sanford (1st) 27330

Cumnock, R. Br. 27237
Jonesboro Heights, Sta. 27330
Sapphire 28774
Saratoga 27873
Saxapahaw 27340
Scaly Mountain 28775
Scotland Neck 27874
Scotts 28699
Scottville 28672
Scranton 27875
Seaboard 27876
Seagrove 27341
Sealevel 28577
Sedalia 27342
Sedgefield, Sta. Charlotte 28209
Selma 27576
Semora 27343
Seven Springs 28578
Severn 27877
Seymour Johnson A F B, Br.
   Goldsboro 27530
Shallotte (1st) 28459
Shamrock, Sta. Charlotte 28215
Shannon 28386
Sharon, Sta. Charlotte 28210
Sharpsburg 27878
Shawboro 27973
Shelby (1st) 28150
Shepard, Sta. Durham 27707
Sherrills Ford 28673
Shiloh 27974
Siler City (1st) 27344
   Mount Vernon Springs, R.
   Br. 27345
Siloam 27047
Simpson 27879
Sims 27880
Skyland 28776
Smithfield (1st) 27577
Smyrna 28579
Sneads Ferry 28460
Snow Camp 27349
Snow Hill 28580
Sophia 27350
South Greensboro, Sta.
   Greensboro 27406
South Mills 27976
South Wilson, Sta. Wilson 27893
Southern Pines (1st) 28387
   Niagara, R. Br. 28388
Southmont 27351
Southport 28461
Southside, Sta.
   Hendersonville 28739
Sparta 28675
Speed 27881
Spencer 28159
Spindale (1st) 28160
Spot 27977
Spray, Sta. Eden 27288
Spring Hope 27882
Spring Lake (1st) 28390
Spruce Pine (1st) 28777
Stacy 28581
Staley 27355
Stanfield 28163
Stanley 28164
Stantonsburg 27883
Star 27356
Starmount, Sta. Charlotte
   (see appendix)
State Road 28676

State University, Sta.
   Raleigh 27607
Statesville (1st) 28677
Stedman 28391
Stella 28582
Stem 27581
Stokes 27884
Stokesdale 27357
Stoneville 27048
Stonewall 28583
Stony Point 28678
Stovall 27582
Stumpy Point 27978
Sugar Grove 28679
Suit, R. Br. Murphy 28906
Summerfield 27358
Summit, Sta. Greensboro 27405
Sunbury 27979
Sunrise, Sta. Goldsboro 27530
Sunset Beach, R. Br.
   Shallotte 28459
Supply 28462
Surf City, R. Br. Holly Ridge ...28445
Swannanoa (1st) 28778
Swanquarter 27885
Swansboro 28584
Swepsonville 27359
Sylva (1st) 28779
Tabor City (1st) 28463
Tapoco 28780
Tar Heel 28392
Tarawa Terrace, Br.
   Jacksonville 28543
Tarboro (1st) 27886
Tate Street, Sta. Greensboro ...27403
Taylorsville (1st) 28681
Teachey 28464
Terrell 28682
Thomasville (1st) 27360
Thurmond 28683
Tillery 27887
Timberlake 27583
Toast 27049
Tobaccoville 27050
Todd 28684
Tomahawk, R. Br. Harrells 28465
Topsail Beach, R. Br. Holly
   Ridge 28445
Topton 28781
Townsville 27584
Traphill 28685
Trenton 28585
Trinity 27370
Triplett 28686
Troutman 28166
Troy (1st) 27371
Tryon (1st) 28782
Tuckasegee 28783
Turkey 28393
Turnersburg 28688
Tuxedo 28784
Tyner 27980
U N C C, R. Br. Charlotte 28213
U S S North Carolina, R. Br.
   Wilmington 28401
Unaka 28908
Union, R. Br. Ahoskie 27910
Union Grove 28689
Union Mills 28167
University Park, Sta.
   Charlotte (see appendix)
Valdese (1st) 28690
Vale 28168

Valle Crucis, R. Br. Boone 28691
Vanceboro 28586
Vandemere 28587
Vass 28394
Vaughan 27586
Verona, R. Br. Jacksonville 28540
Viewmont, Br. Hickory 28601
Vilas 28692
Waco 28169
Wade 28395
Wadesboro (1st) 28170
Wagram 28396
Wake Forest (1st) 27587
Wakulla 28397
Walkertown 27051
Wallace (1st) 28466
Wallburg 27373
Walnut, R. Br. Marshall 28753
Walnut Cove 27052
Walstonburg 27888
Wanchese 27981
Warne 28909
Warren Wilson College, R.
   Br. Swannanoa 28778
Warrensville 28693
Warrenton 27589
Warsaw 28398
Washington (1st) 27889
Watha 28471
Waughtown, Sta.
   Winston-Salem 27107
Waves 27982
Waxhaw 28173
Waynesville (1st) 28786
Weaverville (1st) 28787
Webster 28788
Weeksville, R. Br. Elizabeth
   City 27909
Welcome 27374
Weldon (1st) 27890
Wellons Village, Sta.
   Durham 27703
Wendell 27591
Wentworth 27375
Wesleyan College, R. Br.
   Rocky Mount 27801
West Asheville, Sta.
   Asheville 28806
West Concord, Br. Concord 28025
West Durham, Sta. Durham 27705
West End 27376
West Gastonia, Sta.
   Gastonia 28052
West Jefferson 28694
West Market Street, Sta.
   Greensboro 27402
West New Bern, Sta. New
   Bern 28560
West Rocky Mount, Sta.
   Rocky Mount 27801
West Statesville, Sta.
   Statesville 28677
Westfield 27053
Whispering Pines, R. Br.
   Carthage 28389
Whitakers 27891
White Lake, R. Br.
   Elizabethtown 28337
White Oak 28399
White Plains, R. Br. Mount
   Airy 27031
Whitehead 28695

Whiteville (1st).....................28472
Whitnel, Br. Lenoir 28645
Whitsett................................27377
Whittier................................28789
Wil-Mar Park, Sta. Concord....28025
Wilbar..................................28696
Wildwood.............................28588
Wilkesboro...........................28697
Wilkinson Boulevard, Sta.
   Charlotte..........................28208
Willard.................................28478
Williamston (1st)...................27892
Williston...............................28589
Willow Spring 27592
Wilmington, (1st)..................28401

Azalea, Sta............................28401
Cape Fear, Br. 28401
Navassa, R. Br. 28404
U S S North Carolina, R.
   Br....................................28401
Wilson (1st)..........................27893
Wilsons Mills........................27593
Windsor................................27983
Winfall.................................27985
Wingate................................28174
Winnabow.............................28479
WINSTON-SALEM (1st) (see
   appendix)
Winterville............................28590

Winton 27986
Wise.....................................27594
Woodard, Sta. Wilson 27893
Woodland..............................27897
Woodlawn, Sta. Lowell 28098
Woodleaf..............................27054
Woodsdale............................27595
Worthville, R. Br.
   Randleman.........................27378
Wrightsville Beach 28480
Yadkinville............................27055
Yanceyville............................27379
Youngsville...........................27596
Zebulon................................27597
Zionville...............................28698
Zirconia...............................28790

ASHEVILLE   288

POST OFFICE BOXES

Box Nos.
1-3110	Asheville...........	02
4001-4296	Glenrock Sta.....	02
5001-5977	Biltmore Sta.....	03
6001-6964	West Asheville Sta................	06
7001-7667	Court House Sta.................	07
8001--0008518	Grace Sta	04
9001-9727	Oteen Br...........	05
10501-10655	Biltmore Station..........	03

RURAL ROUTES

1...	04
2...	05
3,4......................................	06
5,6,7...................................	03
8...	06

STATIONS, BRANCHES AND UNITS

Biltmore Sta.............................	03
Court House Sta........................	07
Glenrock Sta.............................	02
Grace Sta.................................	04
Haywood Road Sta....................	06
Oteen Br..................................	05
West Asheville Sta....................	06
General Delivery........................	01
Postmaster...............................	01

APARTMENTS, HOTELS, MOTELS

Alaine, 480 Tunnel Rd............	05
Alamo Plaza, 90 Tunnel Rd.....	05
Alpine, 985 Patton Ave...........	06
Altamount 72 N. Market St......	01

Amber Court, 850 Hendersonville Rd..............	03
American Court, 85 Merrimon Ave...............................	01
Asheville Arms, 102 Furman Ave................................	01
Asheville Court, 130 Merrimon Ave..................	01
Aston Park Towers, 165 French Broad Ave S..........	01
Battery Park, Battle Sq..........	02
Beaver Lake Court, 959 Merrimon Ave.................	04
Bennett'S, 107 Merrimon Ave.	01
Beverly, 615 Biltmore Ave......	03
Biltmore Gardens, 700 Biltmore Ave...................	03
Biltmore, R-5 Sweeten Cr Rd..	03
Blue Ridge Motor Lodge, 60 Tunnel Rd............................	05
Buena Vista, 1080 Hendersonville Rd..............	03
Carolinian Court, 929 Merrimon Ave.................	04
Cavalier, Hiawassee St...........	01
Cavalier, 2 Tunnel Rd............	05
Central, 77 Central Ave.........	01
College Park...........................	04
Deaverview 275 Deaverview Rd..................................	06
Downtown, 65 Merrimon Ave..	01
Downtowner Motor Inn 120 Patton Ave.........................	02
Dunbar, 1 Conestee St...........	01
Edge-O-Town, 2 Weaverville Hi-Way.............................	04
Edgewood Court, 1435 Merrimon Ave.................	04
Edgewood Knoll, 600 Merrimon Ave.................	04
Erskine Black	01
Evergreen, 612 Merrimon Ave.................................	04
Farwood, 549 Merrimon Ave...	04

Florida Court, 121 Tunnel Rd.	05
Forest Manor, 866 Hendersonville Rd..............	03
Gracelyn Garden, 30 Clairmont Ave...................	04
Grove Court, 55 Grove St.......	01
Grove Park Inn & Motor Lodge, 290 Macon Ave.......	02
Grove Park, 28-30 Edgemont Rd..................................	01
Hamiltonian, 1526 Patton Ave................................	06
Hillcrest, Atkinson St.............	01
Holiday Inn Of America, 201 Tunnel Rd...........................	05
Holiday Inn Of America, 275 Smoky Park Highway..........	06
Hollywood, 875 Tunnel Rd......	05
Horne'S Motor Lodge, 166 Tunnel Rd...........................	05
Host Of America Motor Lodge, 200 Tunnel Rd........	05
Howard Johnson'S Motor Lodge, 190 Hendersonville Rd...................................	03
Howard Johnson'S Motor Lodge, 29 Tunnel Rd.........	05
Lakeshore Gardens, 77 Lakeshore Dr....................	04
Laurel Terrace, 100 Tunnel Rd	05
Lee Walker Heights, 30 Wilbar Ave........................	01
Longchamps, 185 Macon Ave.................................	04
Malvern Springs, 1616patton Ave................................	06
Manor, 265 Charlotte.............	01
Milestone Court, 300 Tunnel Rd..................................	05
Mount-Vue, 15 Tunnel Rd	05
Mountaineer Court, 155 Tunnel Rd...........................	05
Mountainside 56 Hunthill Pl...	01

Parkway, 1060 Tunnel Rd...... 05
Pines, R-1weaverville Hi-Way .. 04
Pisgah View, Cordova,
  Granada, Hanover.............. 06
Plaza Hotel Court, 111
  Hendersonville Rd.............. 03
Quality Court(Intown), 100
  Tunnel Rd 05
Quality Court(Redmon), 501
  Tunnel Rd 05
Ridge Town House, Wynne
  Way 05
Rock Haven Terrace, 1464
  Patton Ave 06
Rockola Court & Trailer Park,
  1655 Patton Ave................ 06
Royal Terrace 90 Tunnel
  Road 05
Shady Rest, 740
  Hendersonville Rd.............. 03
Shamrock Court, 140 Tunnel
  Rd 05
Sheraton Motor Inn 22
  Woodfin 01
Singing Hills, 157 Smoky
  Park Hi-Way...................... 06
Skyview, 37 Sunset Dr............ 04
Skyway, 135 Tunnel Rd........... 05
Sunset Court, 688 Merrimon
  Ave 04
Thunderbird, 835 Tunnel Rd... 05
Tiara, 647 Town Mtn Rd......... 04
Tour-O-Tel, 640 Merrimon
  Ave 04
Town Motor Lodge, 820
  Merrimon Ave 04
Vanderbilt 75 Haywood St....... 01
Walton 01
West Terrace, 1043 Haywood
  Rd 06
Whispering Pines, 140 Smoky
  Park Hi-Way...................... 06

BUILDINGS

Biltmore Plaza, 3 Biltmore
  Plaza 03
Castanea, 55 1 1/2
  2haywood St 01
Doctors, 50 Doctors Dr........... 01
First Union Bank, 82 Patton
  Ave 01
Flat Iron, 20 Battery Park
  Ave 01
Gennett, 29 N Market St......... 01
Haywood, 46 Haywood St........ 01
Jackson, 22 S Pack Sq............ 01
Legal, 10 S Pack Sq............... 01
Medical Center, 86 Victoria
  Rd 01
Medical Dental, 675 Biltmore
  Ave 03
Northwestern Bank, 1-11
  Pack Sq NW...................... 01
Parkway Office, 170-174
  Woodfin St 01
Public Service, 91-93 Patton
  Ave 01
The Doctors Park, 400
  Biltmore Ave 01
Wachovia Bank, 1 Haywood.... 01
York, 108 College.................. 01

GOVERNMENT OFFICES

City Hall, 70 Court Plaza..... 01
County Court House, 60
  Court Plaza 01
Eastern Aerial Photo Lab, 45
  S French Broad Ave............ 01
Environmental Science Servs,
  37 Battery Park Ave............ 01
Post Office, Post & Otis
  Streets............................. 01

HOSPITALS

Asheville Orthopedic, 95
  London Rd........................ 03
Aston Park, 298 Hilliard Ave .. 02
Memorial Mission, 509
  Biltmore Ave 01
Oteen-Va, Riceville & Tunnel
  Rds.................................. 05
Saint Josephs, 428 Biltmore
  Ave.................................. 01

UNIVERSITIES AND COLLEGES

Allen, 331 College................ 01
Asheville School For Boys,
  School Rd.......................... 06
Ben Lippen, Route 4 Box
  100.................................. 06
Saint Genevieve-Of-The-Pines,
  103 Victoria Rd 01
U N C At Asheville, College
  Hts.................................. 04

CHARLOTTE 282

POST OFFICE BOXES

Box Nos.
1-720   Main Office 30
721-1300   Main Office 31
1301-1849   Main Office 32
1850-2190   Main Office 4.... 33
2331-2757   Main Office 34
3000-3999   Dilworth Sta..... 03
4000-4999   Charlottetown
             Sta.................. 04
5000-5999   North Charlotte
             Sta.................. 05
6000-6499   Myers Park
             Sta.................. 07
8000-8999   Freedom Sta..... 08
9000-9999   Plaza Sta......... 05
10001-10628 Main Office 37
10631-10897 Main Office 34
11000-11999 Park Road Sta... 09
12000-12999 Eastway Sta...... 05
15000-15999 Starmount
             Sta.................. 10
16000-16999 University Park
             Sta.................. 16
17001-17999 Randolph Sta ... 11
20001-20535 Downtown Sta... 02
21000-21199 Atando Sta 06
23000-23199 Mint Hill R Br... 12
24000-24199 Chadwick Sta.... 16
25000-25999 Idlewild Br....... 12
26001-26999 Derita Br 13
27000-27999 Municipal
             Airport Br 08

RURAL ROUTES

1.. 12
2,3 10
4,5,6..................................... 08
7.. 13
8.. 12
9.. 08
10,11.................................... 13

STATIONS, BRANCHES AND UNITS

Atando Sta.......................... 06
Chadwick Sta....................... 08
Charlottetown Sta................. 04
Derita Br............................ 13
Dilworth Sta........................ 03
Downtown Sta...................... 02
Eastway Sta......................... 05
Elizabeth Sta....................... 04
Freedom Sta........................ 08
Hickory Grove Br.................. 15
Idlewild Br.......................... 12
Mint Hill Rural Br................. 12
Municipal Airport Br............. 08
Myers Park Sta..................... 07
North Charlotte Sta............... 05
Park Road Sta...................... 09
Plaza Sta............................ 05
Randolph Sta....................... 11
Sedgefield Sta...................... 09
Shamrock Sta....................... 15
Sharon Sta.......................... 10
Starmount Sta...................... 10
University Park Sta................ 08
UNCC Rural Br..................... 13
Wilkinson Boulevard Sta......... 08
General Delivery................... 02
Postmaster.......................... 02

APARTMENTS, HOTELS, MOTELS

Aaloha 3770 Frew Rd 06
Alamo Plaza Courts, 2309 N
  Tryon 31
Alpine Lodge........................ 10
Barcelona 3500 Sharon Amity
  Rd 05
Belvedere Homes 321 Judson
  Ave 08
Bordeaux 6600 Wisteria.......... 10
Boulevard Homes West
  Boulevard 08
Briarcreek 3041 Karen Ct 05
Brookhill Village 606
  Remount Rd...................... 03
Camelot 1500 Eastcrest Dr 05
Canterbury Woods 2107
  Canterwood Dr 13
Catalina Motor Lodge, 2403
  Wilkinson Blvd 33
Cavalier Court 2800 Monroe
  Rd 05
Central Square 3101 Central
  Ave 05
Charlotte Woods 1116
  Scalybark Rd..................... 09
Chateau Villa 9700
  University City Blvd 13
Claridge Nations Ford &
  Arrowhead Rd 10

Coliseum Motor Court, 3016
E Independence Blvd.......... 05
Cotswold 4425 Randolph Rd.. 11
Dalton Village West
Boulevard............................ 08
Darby Terrace, 4501 Central
Ave..................................... 05
Double Oaks 2623 Double
Oaks Rd.............................. 06
Dutch Village 1900 Eastway
Dr.. 05
Earle Village 610 East 7th..... 02
East Forest Monroe &
Idlewild Rds..................... 12
East Lake Village
Independence Blvd 12
Edwin Towers 210 West 10th. 02
Elmhurst Dorchester Pl......... 09
Fairview Homes 1026
Oaklawn Ave..................... 06
Forest Brook 5600
Tuckaseegee Rd................ 08
Fountain Square 2400
Eastway Dr......................... 05
Four Seasons 5800 Albemarle
Rd....................................... 12
Foxfire 6700 Idlewild Rd....... 12
Green Oaks, 1400-2831
Eastcrest Dr....................... 05
Guthrey, 508 N Tryon............ 02
Hope Valley 2609 Milton Rd.. 15
Idlewild 6507 Idlewild Rd..... 12
Italian Village 5600
Providence Rd.................... 11
Jackson Park 5509 Airport
Dr.. 08
Jamestowne, 1201 Green
Oaks Ln.............................. 05
Kings Creek........................... 10
L Atriums North 1600 Tom
Hunter Rd.......................... 13
Lake Hills 2326 Shade Valley
Rd....................................... 05
Lake Plaza............................. 15
Lemon Tree 5900 Monroe Rd.. 12
Little Rock Homes West
Boulevard............................ 08
Manger Motor Inn, 631 N
Tryon................................... 32
Marlborough Homes
Marlborough Rd................. 08
Milner Mecklinburg, 516 W
Trade................................... 32
Milton Road 1951 Milton Rd.. 15
Morningside 2500 Mcclintock
Rd....................................... 05
Oak Crest 217 Elmhurst Rd ... 09
Orvin Motor Court, 307 N
Graham............................... 31
Piedmont Courts 831 Seigle
Ave..................................... 04
Pinehurst, 3910-4132
Providence Rd.................... 11
Plaza Terrace 3224 The
Plaza................................... 05
Providence Square................. 11
Quail Hill 5901 Quail Hollow
Rd....................................... 10
Queens Tower, 1300 Queens
Rd....................................... 07
Randolph Park 4516
Randolph Rd...................... 11
Roseland 1210 Pressley Rd... 10

Sandhurst, 1701 W
Boulevard............................ 08
Selwyn Village 300
Walkefield Dr..................... 09
Shamrock Gardens 3779
Michigan Ave..................... 15
Sharon Lakes, Sharon Road
West.................................... 10
Southgate, 3910-4300
Conway Ave........................ 09
Southside Homes 3400
Griffith............................... 03
Strawn 500 Butternut Ct........ 03
The Lake 5503 Albemarle Rd.. 12
Tree Top Archdale Dr & 177.... 03
Tryon Forest 300 Lambeth Dr. 13
Tryon Hill 200 W 26th............ 06
Versailles 2600 Park Rd......... 09
Vista Villa 6400 The Plaza..... 15
Westwood 1501 Evergreen Dr. 08
White House Inn, 237 W
Trade................................... 34
Williamsburg, 1210-1513
Green Oaks Ln.................... 05
Yorktown 254 Tyvola Rd......... 10

BUILDINGS

Albemarle Center 4822
Albemarle Rd...................... 05
American, 201 S Tryon........... 86
Attorneys, 806 E Trade.......... 02
Bank Of N C Bldg 112 S
Tryon................................... 84
Builders, 312-14 W Trade....... 02
Charlotte Civic Center 101 S
College............................... 02
City National Bank, 237 S.
Tryon................................... 02
Cole 207 Hawthorne Ln 04
Colwick Towers 4401 Colwick
Rd....................................... 11
Court Plaza 901 Elizabeth
Ave..................................... 04
Doctors, 1012 S Kings Dr....... 83
Equity, 701 E Trade................ 02
Ervin 4037 E Independence
Blvd.................................... 05
Executive Office Park 800
Baxter.................................. 02
Executive, 623 E Trade.......... 02
Home Federal, 139 S Tryon.... 02
Ina 4425 Randolph Rd 11
Independence, 102 W Trade... 02
Jefferson First Union Plaza
300 S College.................... 82
Jefferson Standard 301 - 307
S Tryon............................... 02
Johnston, 212 S Tryon........... 81
Law, 730 E Trade................... 02
Merchandise Mart 2500 E
Independence Blvd 05
North Carolina National
Bank, 200 S Tryon............. 55
Professional, 403 N Tryon...... 02
Tryon Plaza 301-307 S Tryon.. 82
Wachovia Bank, 129 W
Trade................................... 02

GOVERNMENT OFFICES

City Hall, 600 E. Trade.......... 02
Mecklenburg County Court
House, 700 E. Trade.......... 02
Mecklenburg County Office,
720 E. 4th.......................... 02
United States Courthouse,
401 W Trade....................... 02
United States Post Office,
401 W Trade....................... 02

HOSPITALS

Charlotte Community, 801 S
Graham............................... 02
Charlotte Eye Ear Nose &
Throat................................. 04
Charlotte Memorial, 1000
Blythe Blvd........................ 01
Mercy, 2000 E 5th................. 01
Presbyterian, 200 Hawthorne
Ln.. 01

UNIVERSITIES AND COLLEGES

Central Piedmont Comm,
1141 Elizabeth Ave............ 04
Johnson C Smith University,
100 Beatties Ford Rd......... 16
Kings Business, 322 Lamar
Ave..................................... 01
Queens, 1900 Selwyn Ave..... 74
U N C At Charlotte, Highway
49 N.................................... 13

DURHAM   277

POST OFFICE BOXES

Box Nos.		
1-2332	Main Office......	02
2401-3205	West Durham Sta..................	05
3801-3880	Durham	02
4001-5999	Duke Sta...........	06
6001-7699	College Sta.......	08
8001–8499	North Durham Sta..................	04
8501–8999	Forest Hills Sta..................	07
9001-9669	Duke Sta...........	06
11001-0011637	East Durham Sta..................	03
12001-12275	Research Triangle Park Br....................	09
18001-19919	Shepard Sta	07

RURAL ROUTES

1,2...............................	05
3..................................	07
4..................................	03
5..................................	04
6..................................	03
7..................................	07
8..................................	04

STATIONS, BRANCHES AND UNITS

College Sta	08
Duke Sta	06
East Durham Sta	03
Forest Hills Sta	07
Hayti Sta	01
Lakewood Sta	07
North Durham Sta	04
Northgate Sta	01
Parkwood Br	07
Research Triangle Park Br	09
Shepard Sta	07
Wellons Village Sta	03
West Durham Sta	05
General Delivery	01
Postmaster	01

APARTMENTS, HOTELS, MOTELS

Alastair Court, 300 Swift	05
Ambassador, 916 W Trinity Ave	01
Anderson St, 1600 Anderson	07
Atlas, 200 Atlas	05
Bickett, 806 Gregson	01
Bristol, 1100 Douglas	05
Campus, Elf	05
Capri	07
Carolee, 2200 Elder	05
Carriage House	04
Carstelle, 1911 House Ave	07
Carwin, 2213 Elder	05
Channing Court, Channing Ave	04
Chesterfield Apts, 1808 Chapel Hill Rd	07
Chesterfield Motel, 1900 N Roxboro	02
Churchill Court, 315 - 317 W Trinity	01
College Plaza, 415 Pilot	07
Colonial Terrace, 3022 Chapel Hill Rd	07
Confederate, Hwy 70 West	05
Damar Court, Morreene Rd	05
Duke & Duchess, House Ave	07
Duke Manor Morreene Rd	05
Duke Motor Lodge, Durham - Chapel Hill Blvd	07
Dutch Village, 2306 Elder	05
Eden Rock, Durham - Chapel Hill Blvd	07
El Rancho, Elf	05
Erwin, 312 Buchanan Blvd	01
Executive, 900 W Trinity Ave	01
Few Gardens	03
Four Seasons, 2007 House Ave	07
General Joseph Johnston, Intersection Jct 70 W - Inter 85	05
Georgetown Manor, 1000 N Duke	01
Glenn, 922 - 926 Dacian Ave	01
Holiday Inn (Downtown), 605 W Chapel Hill	02
Holiday Inn (West), 3460 Hillsborough Rd	05
Holly Hills	05
Homestead, Durham - Chapel Hill Blvd	07

Howard Johnson, 1 - 85 &hillandale Rd	05
Imperial, 301 W Trinity Ave	01
Jack Tar, 207 N Corcoran	02
Lincoln, Lakeland Ave	01
Manor Court	07
Mcdougald Terrace	01
Morreene, 3600 Tremont	05
Murchison, 809 Demerius	01
Nortwood Circle, 300 Northwood Cir	01
Palomina Park, 1306 Leon	05
Poplar, Erwin Rd	05
Presidential, 1000 Ruby	04
Princeton, Chapel Hill & Morehead	07
Sedgefield Court, 1615 Sedgefield	05
Seven Eleven, 711 N Duke	01
Statler Hilton, 2424 Erwin Rd	05
Town & Campus Of Durham, 4216 Garrett Rd	07
Town & Campus, 910 W Trinity	01
Town House, 301 Swift	05
Triangle	05
Trinity North, 300 W Trinity	01
University, Duke University Rd	01
Valley Terrace, 2820 Chapel Hill Rd	07
Vance, 922 - 926 Dacian Ave	01
Voyager Inn, 15 - 501 By-Pass	05
Weaver, 3000 Weaver	07
Wellcraft Garden	03
Westover Park, 2312 Pratt	05
1100 Leon, 1100 Leon	04
1200 Leon, 1200 Leon	05

BUILDINGS

Central Carolina Bank, N Corcoran	01
Environmental Protection Agency Davis Dr	11
First Union Bank, 301 W Main	01
North Carolina National Bank, 123 W Main	01
Trust, 212 W Main	01
Wachovia Bank, 130 W Main	01

HOSPITALS

Duke West Campus	10
Lincoln, 1301 Fayetteville	07
Mc Pherson, 1110 W Main	01
North Carolina Cerebral Palsy, 2910 Erwin Rd	05
Veterans, 2500 Erwin Rd	05
Watts, 2000 W Club Blvd	05

UNIVERSITIES AND COLLEGES

Croft Business College, 111 Orange	01
Duke University Mens Campus, Campus Dr	06
Duke University Womens Campus, W Main	08

Durham Business College, 3128 Fayetteville	07
North Carolina College, 1805 Fayetteville	07
Southeastern Business College, 603 S Alston Ave	01

FAYETTEVILLE 283 -

POST OFFICE BOXES

Box Nos.		
A-Z	Fayetteville	02
1-2000	Fayetteville	02
3000-3999	Haymount Sta	05
4000-4999	Lakedale Sta	06
5000-5999	Eutaw Sta	03

RURAL ROUTES

1,2	01
3	06
4	04
5,6	01
7	06
8	04
9,10	01
11	04

STATIONS, BRANCHES AND UNITS

Bonnie Doone Br	03
Cottonade Br	03
East Fayetteville Br	01
Eutaw Sta	03
Fort Bragg Br	07
Haymount Sta	05
Lafayette Br	04
Lakedale Sta	06
Methodist College Br	01
Newbold Sta	01
Pope A F B Mou	08
General Delivery	02
Postmaster	02

BUILDINGS

First Union National Bank, Donaldson St	01
First-Citzens Bank, 109 Green St	01
Grace Pittman, 431 Hay St	01
Highland Office, 2504 Raeford Rd	05
Huske, 417 Hay St	01
Jessup, 2606 Raeford Rd	03
Lawyers, Market Sq	01
Professional, 155 Gillespie St	01
Tolar, 1239 Fort Bragg Rd	05
Wooten, 1220 Fort Bragg Rd	05

GOVERNMENT OFFICES

Cumberland County Courthouse, Gillesepie St	01
Federal, 301 Green St	01

HOSPITALS

Cape Fear Valley, Owen Dr....	02
Highsmith-Rainey, Bradford Ave..................	01
Veterans Administration, Ramsey St..................	01
Womack Army..................	07

MILITARY INSTALLATIONS

Fort Bragg..................	07
Pope AFB..................	08

UNIVERSITIES AND COLLEGES

Fayetteville State, Murchison Rd..................	01
Fayetteville Technical Institue, Hull Rd..................	03
Methodist, Ramsey St..	01

GREENSBORO   274

POST OFFICE BOXES

Box Nos.		
A-ZI	West Market St Sta..................	02
1-3999	West Market St Sta..................	02
4001-4999	South Greensboro Sta..................	06
5001-5999	Tate Street Sta..................	03
6001-6999	Summit Sta......	05
7001-7999	Hilltop Sta........	07
8001-8999	Guilford College Br	10
9001-9999	Plaza Sta..........	08
10001-10999	Friendly Sta,.....	04
11001-11999	Guilford Br......	09
13000-13999	Golden Gate ..	05
20001-22144	Main Office	20

RURAL ROUTES

1..................	06
2..................	05
3..................	10
4..................	06
5,6..................	05
7..................	07
8..................	09
9..................	06
10..................	06
11..................	10
12,13..................	06

STATIONS, BRANCHES AND UNITS

Friendly Sta..................	04
Golden Gate Sta..................	05
Guilford Br..................	09
Guilford College Br..................	10
Hilltop Sta..................	07
Plaza Sta..................	08
Pomona Sta..................	06
South Greensboro Sta..................	06
Summit Sta..................	05

Tate Street Sta..................	03
West Market Street Sta..........	02
General Delivery..................	20
Postmaster..................	20

APARTMENTS, HOTELS, MOTELS

Alonzo Towers, 2314 Church..	05
Bob Pettys Court, 2228 Osborne Rd..................	07
Bob Pettys, 3710 Oakwood Dr..................	07
Cabana Club, 2821 N O'Henry Blvd..................	05
Cannon Court, 828 N Elm..	01
Carolina, 121 W Mc Gee..	01
Churchill Arms, 301 N Mendenhall..................	01
Cool Spring, 3200 Spring	05
Country Club Mobile Home, Rt 6 Box 188..................	05
Country Club, 1700 N Elm....	08
Diplomat 1/2 thunderbird, 29 & 70 S..................	06
Dixie, 336 Bellemeade..................	01
Dolly Madison, 1015 N Elm	01
Donnells Lodge, 1112 W Market..................	03
Fairfax, 203 E Bessemer Ave..	01
Francisco, 23 1/2 2499 Patriot Way..................	08
Frazier..................	10
Friendly Hills, Hunt Club Rd..	10
Gambles, Rt 1 Boxes 1-39.....	06
Garretts, 5704 High Point Rd..................	07
General Greene, US Highway 29 S..................	02
Greensboro Travelodge, 225 Church..................	01
Greenwich, 111 W Washington..................	01
Henry Louis Smith Homes, 743 W Florida..................	06
Henrys, Rt 6 Box 509..............	05
Hidden Valley, 6001 W Market..................	09
Holiday Inn N, US 29 At 16th..................	05
Holiday Inn S, US 29 & 17....	05
Howard Johnsons, U S Hwy 855..................	02
Irving Park Manor, 1800 N Elm..................	08
Jamison, 2500 Hiatt..................	03
Journeys End, 2310 Battleground Ave..................	08
Kent Court, Hwy 29 N.............	01
Kings Arms, 1831 1/2 41 Banking..................	08
Kings Inn, 1103 N Elm..........	01
Madison Woods, 5500 Tomahawk..................	10'
Manor, 1045 W Market..........	01
Maplewood, 2500 Battleground Ave..................	08
Mark-Rand, 230 S Park Dr......	01
Midtown, 817 Summit Ave......	05
Morgan Court, 6706 W Market..................	09
Morningside Homes, 1843 Everitt..................	01
O Henry, 101 Bellemeade	02

Oaks, 1118 Summit Ave........	05
Oakwood, 3701 High Point Rd..................	07
Palms The, 3100-3299 Lawndale Dr..................	08
Piedmont, 209 N Cedar	01
Plantation, 3404 High Point Rd..................	04
Pleasant Acres, 814 Robs Ct..	06
Powhatan, 906 W Market......	01
Sands, 3114 O Henry Blvd	05
Sans Souci, 912 E Cone Blvd..................	05
Scott, 318 Asheboro..............	06
Sedgefield Inn, 5704 High Point Rd..................	07
Shady Lane, Rt 5 Box 30........	05
Shady Lawn, 1020 W Market..	01
Sheraton Motor Inn, 2838 S Elm..................	06
Shirley, 203 E Bessemer Ave..	01
Smith Ranch, 2210 Randleman Rd..................	06
Stancils 421 No-1 & No 2, 4309 Liberty Rd..................	06
Three Fountains North Mcknight Mill Rd Rt Utah..	05
Towers, 1101 N Elm..............	01
Towne House Motor Lodge, 1000 W Market..................	02
Travel Inn, Highway 29 S	07
Troxlers, 1005 Alamance Rd....	06
Twin Maple, 4638 W Market....	07
Vanee, 1104 Magnolia..........	01
Victoria, 301 Mc Iver............	03
Victory, 1045 W Market........	01
Voyager Inn, 830 W Market	02
Whites, Rt 5 Box 39..............	05
Wildwood, 3521 Mc Cuistan Rd..................	07
Winburn Court, 203 Tate	03
Yesteroaks Pisgah Church Rd Rt Yesteroaks..................	05

BUILDINGS

Banner, 119 N Elm..................	01
Beaman, 2820 Lawndale Dr....	08
Brown, 438 W Market..........	01
Butler, 430 W Gaston............	01
Dixie, 125 S Elm..................	01
Edgeworth, 232 N Edgeworth .	01
Federal, 324 W Market..........	02
Five-Hundred West Gaston, 500 W Gaston..................	01
Freeman, 612 Pasteur Dr........	03
Jefferson Standard, 101 N Elm..................	01
Piedmont, 114 N Elm..........	01
Professional, 1030 Church......	01
Southeastern, 102 N Elm......	01
Three Thirty-Eight North Elm, 338 N Elm..................	01
Wachovia Bank, 201 N Elm....	01
Watson, 124 W Sycamore......	01

GOVERNMENT OFFICES

City Offices, 210 N Greene.....	02
Municipal Offices, 210 N Greene..................	02

HOSPITALS

Moses H. Cone Memorial, Po
Box 13227............................ 05
Richardson L Memorial, 2600
Southside Blvd.................... 06
Wesley Long Community, 501
N Elam Ave......................... 02

UNIVERSITIES AND COLLEGES

Agricultural & Technical Of
North Carolina, 312 N
Dudley.................................. 11
Bennett College, Washington
& Macon.............................. 20
Greensboro Division Of
Guilford College, 501 W
Washington.......................... 02
Greensboro, W Market........... 20
Guilford, Friendly Rd............. 10
Kings Business, 415 W
Friendly Ave....................... 01
Womens College U Of N
Carolina, 1000 Spring
Garden 12

HIGH POINT   272

POST OFFICE BOXES

Box Nos.
1-2152   Main Office 61
4001-4399   Archdale Br 63
5001-5619   Emerywood
               Sta................ 62

RURAL ROUTES

1,2 60
3,4,5 63

STATIONS, BRANCHES AND UNITS

Archdale Br 63
Emerywood Sta 62
General Delivery 60
Postmaster 60

RALEIGH   276

POST OFFICE BOXES

Box Nos.
1-3069   Century Sta 02
5001-5937   State College.... 07
6001-6527   Five Point Sta .. 08
7400-7599   B Sta.............. 11
10001-10977   Cameron
               Village Sta 05
11001-11524   Mordecai Sta.... 04
12000-12595   Cameron
               Village Sta 05
14001-14467   King Charles
               Sta.............. 10
17001-17885   North Hills Sta. 09
25001-28272   Main Office 11

RURAL ROUTES

1 09
2 10

3 03
4 06
5 04
6,7 09
8 07
10 03

STATIONS, BRANCHES AND UNITS

Cameron Village Sta 05
Century Sta 02
Five Point Sta......................... 08
King Charles Sta..................... 10
Meredith College Rural Sta..... 02
Mordecai Sta........................... 04
New Hope Br 04
North Hills Sta 09
State University Sta 07
General Delivery...................... 11
Postmaster.............................. 11

APARTMENTS, HOTELS, MOTELS

Alamo Plaza, 1816 Louisburg
Rd 02
Anclote Arms, 3609-21
Anclote Pl........................... 07
Andrew Johnson, 100 W
Martin 02
Baily Apartments, 200 E
Edenton............................... 01
Beckanna Apartments, 3939
Glenwood Ave..................... 09
Belvidere Motel, 2729 S
Wilmington.......................... 03
Boylan Apartments, 753
Hillsboro............................. 03
Brookhill Townhouse, 5425
Dana Dr 06
Cabanna Motel, 514 S
Salisbury............................. 02
Cameron Courts Apartments,
783 Hillsboro...................... 03
Cameron Parks Apartments,
1213 Hillsboro.................... 03
Capital Apartments, 127 New
Bern Ave............................. 01
Carolina, 228 W Hargett........ 02
College Inn, 2717 Western
Blvd.................................... 07
Country Club Homes,
Fairview & Oberlin Rd......... 08
Crabtree Manor Apartments,
200 E Six Forks Rd............. 09
Dods Motel, 1403 S
Wilmington.......................... 03
Downtown Plaza, 531 N
Blount 04
Downtowner, 309 Hillsboro 11
Fairfield, 1817 Louisburg Rd.. 04
Fincastle Apartments, 3109
Hillsboro............................. 07
Glenwood Arms Apartments,
2612 Glenwood Ave............ 08
Glenwood Gardens
Apartments, 2550
Glenwood Ave..................... 08
Golden Eagle Motor Inn, 525
Fayetteville......................... 01
Greystone Apartments, 701 N
Blount 04

Grosvenor Garden
Apartments, 825 Hillsboro.. 03
Hillyer Apartments, 8 St
Marys 05
Holiday Inn 0 2, 306-18
Hillsboro............................. 02
Holiday Inn, 2813 North Blvd. 04
Johnnys Motor Lodge, 1625
North Blvd........................... 04
Joslin Apartments, 705 W
Morgan................................ 03
Mc Kimmon Village, Gorman
& Jackson 07
Montecito, 3939 Wake Forest
Rd 09
North Carolina State College
Married Student Housing...... 07
Park Central, 130 W Martin..... 02
Parkview Apartments, 216 E
Jones 01
Penwood Apartments,
Penwood Rd......................... 06
Plantation Inn, US 1 North...... 04
Raleigh Apartments, 1020 W
Peace.................................. 05
Raleigh Towne House, 519-25
Wade Ave............................ 05
Ranch Motel, 6129 Glenwood
Ave 09
Royal Hill Garden, 4315
Leesville Rd........................ 09
Simpson Apartments, 2402
Clark Ave............................ 07
Sir Walter, 400 Fayetteville..... 02
Spanish Trace, 800 Dixie Trl... 07
Swain Apartments, 121 N
Person 01
Tara Apartments, 109
Ramblewood Dr................... 09
Town & Campus, 2700-2810
Conifer Dr 06
Travelodge, 300 N Dawson..... 11
Vance Apartments, 105 E
Edenton............................... 01
Velvet Cloak Inn, 1505
Hillsboro............................. 05
Voyager Motel Inn, Hillsboro
& Cox Ave........................... 05
Webb Motel, 2718 S
Wilmington.......................... 03
Wedgwood Apratments, 740
Smallwood Dr...................... 05
Western Manor Apartments,
2300 Avent Ferry Rd........... 06
White Apartments, 217 E
North 01
Wilmont Apartments, 3200
Hillsboro............................. 07

BUILDINGS

Agriculture, Edenton &
Halifax................................ 01
Alexander, 133 Fayetteville..... 01
Baptist Convention, 301
Hillsboro............................. 03
Branch Bank, 333
Fayetteville......................... 01
Brown-Rogers, 115 Hillsboro... 03
Bryan, 2113 Cameron............. 05
C-E E, 333 Wade Ave............. 05

Cameron-Brown, 900 Wade Ave	05
Cameron, 400 Oberlin Rd	05
Capital Club, 16 W Martin	01
Doctors, Wade Ave & St Mary'S	05
Education, W Edenton & Salisbury	03
First Citizens Bank, 14 E Martin	01
First Federal Savings & Loan, 300 S Salisbury	01
First Union National Bank, 234 Fayetteville	01
Glenwood Prof Village, Glenwood Ave Essex Cir	08
Insurance, 336 Fayetteville	01
Koger Executive Center	12
Lawyers, 320 S Salisbury	01
Ligon, 800 St Marys	05
Medical Arts, 1110 Wake Forest Rd	04
Methodists, Glenwood & Wade Ave	05
N C National Bank, 239 Fayetteville	01
Odd Fellows, 15 W Hargett	01
Phillips, 401 Oberlin Rd	05
Professional, 127 W Hargett	01
Raleigh Savings & Loan, 219 Fayetteville	01
Raleigh, 5 W Hargett	01
Wachovia Bank, 227 Fayetteville	01
Y M C A, 1601 Hillsboro	05
Y M C A, 217 W Jones	03
York, 2016 Cameron	05
1330, 1330 Saint Marys	05

HOSPITALS

Dorothea Dix State, S Boylan Ave	11
Mary Elizabeth, 1100 Wake Forest Rd	04
Medicenter, 616 Wade Ave	05
Rex Hospital, 1311 St Marys	03
Wake Memorial Hospital, 3000 New Bern Ave	10

UNIVERSITIES AND COLLEGES

Blind School, Ashe & Park Ave	06
Governor Morehead School, Ashe Ave & Park Ave	06
Meredith, 3800 Hillsboro	11
Methodist Orphanage, 1001 Glenwood Ave	05
Nazareth Orphanage, Avent Ferry Rd & Price	11
North Carolina State College, 2205 Hillsboro	07
Peace College, 15 E Peace	04
Saint Augustine College, 1315 Oakwood Ave	11
Saint Marys College, 900 Hillsboro	11
Shaw University, 11 W South	02

WINSTON SALEM 271

POST OFFICE BOXES

Box Nos.		
A-Z	Salem	08
1-3199	Main Office	02
N-1-99	North	05
4001-4499	North Sta	05
4501-4999	Waughtown Sta	07
5001-5999	Ardmore Sta	03
6001-9099	Reynolda Sta	09
10001-10999	Salem Sta	08
11001-11999	Bethabara	06
12001-12999	Waughtown	07
15001-15074	Ardmore	03

RURAL ROUTES

1	06
2	03
3	05
4,5,6	07
7	05
8	06
9,10	07
11	03

STATIONS, BRANCHES AND UNITS

Ardmore Sta	03
Bethabara Sta	06
Hanes Sta	03
Mount Tabor Sta	06
North Sta	05
Reynolda Sta	09
Salem Sta	08
Waughtown Sta	07
General Delivery	02
Postmaster	02

APARTMENTS, HOTELS, MOTELS

Ardmore Terrace Apts, 224 Melrose	03
Balcony Courts Apartments, 1606-1610 Northwest Blvd	04
Baptist Home Apts, Reynolds Park Rd	07
Carolina, 407 W 4th St	02
Chermar Apts, Bethania Sta Rd	06
Cloverdale Apts, 224 Melrose	03
College Villiage Apartments, 741 Avalon Rd	04
Colonial Villiage Apartments, 110 Martin St	03
Country Club Apts, N. Peace Haven Rd	04
Downtowner Motor Inn, 128 N Cherry St	01
Faculty Apartments, 2200 Faculty Dr	06
Georgetown Apts, Carriage Dr	06
Graycourt Apartments, 450 N Broad St	01
Greystone Downtown Motel, 650 W 4th St	01

Hawthorne Ct Apts, 1835 S Hawthorne Rd	03
Holiday Inn, Trentwest	03
Holiday Inn, 127 S Cherry St	01
Howard Johnson'S Motor Lodge, 150 S Stratford Rd	04
Johnsborough Town House Apts, 3629 Old Vineyard Rd	04
Lee Apts, Miller & Silas Creek Pky	03
Medical Foundation Apts, Hawthorne Rd	03
Miller Park Apartments, 2500-35 Miller Park Cir	03
Monticello Apartments, 755 Anson St	03
Parkland Apts, Hutton	03
Parkway Chalet Motor Lodge, 600 Peters Creek Pkwy	03
Plaza Apartments, 900 Thurmond St	05
Regency Apts, Old Vineyard Rd	03
Salem Square Apts, 3812 Country Club Rd	04
Sheraton Motor Inn, 380 Knollwood Ave	03
Spainhour Apts, Indiana Ave	06
Statler Hilton Inn, Marshall & High St	01
Students Apartments, 2300 Faculty Dr	06
Twin Castles Apartments, 2000 Beach St	03
Villas Apts, Old Vineyard Rd	04
Vineyard Garden Apts, Old Vineyard Rd	04
Wedgewood Apts, 1620 W 1st St	04
Westgate Luxury Apts, Westgate Cir	06
Winston Apartments, 654 W 4th St	01

BUILDINGS

Bolick Arcade, 119 W 2nd St	01
First Union 310 W 4th St	01
Forsyth Medical Park, 1900 S Hawthorne Rd	03
North Carolina National Bank, 10 N Liberty St	01
Northwestern Bank 235 Cherry NW	01
O Hanlon, 105 W 4th St	01
Pepper, 104 W 4th St	01
Professional, 2240 Cloverdale Ave	03
Public Library, 660 W 5th St	01
Reynolds, 401-405 N Main St	01
Stratford Medical Center, 107 S Stratford Rd	04
Wachovia, 301 N Main St	01

GOVERNMENT OFFICES

City Hall	01
County Court House	01
Government Center	01

HOSPITALS

Baptist Homes, Reynolds
Park Rd............................ 07
Casstevens Hospital, 514 S
Stratford Rd...................... 03
Forsyth County, Rt 7.............. 05
Forsyth Memorial Hospital,
3333 Silas Creek Pkwy....... 03
Graylyn Hospital, 2539
Robinhood Rd.................... 06

Kate Bitting Hospital, 1101 E
7th St............................... 01
North Carolina Baptist
Hospital, 300 S Hawthorne
Rd 03

UNIVERSITIES AND COLLEGES

Bowman Gray School Of Med
Wake Forest, 300 S
Hawthorne Rd.................... 03

Salem College, Salem
Square............................... 08
Wake Forest Univ, Reynolda
Rd 09
Winston-Salem State College,
Columbia Hts..................... 02

NORTH DAKOTA
(Abbreviation: ND)

Abercrombie........................58001
Absaraka............................58002
Adams................................58210
Adrian................................58410
Agate, R. Br. Bisbee..........58310
Akra...................................58211
Alamo................................58830
Alexander...........................58831
Alfred................................58411
Alice..................................58003
Alkabo...............................58832
Almont...............................58520
Alsen.................................58311
Ambrose............................58833
Amenia...............................58004
Amidon..............................58620
Anamoose...........................58710
Aneta.................................58212
Antler................................58711
Appam...............................58834
Ardoch...............................58213
Arena.................................58412
Argusville...........................58005
Arnegard............................58835
Arthur................................58006
Arvilla................................58214
Ashley................................58413
Ayr....................................58007
Backoo...............................58215
Baker.................................58312
Baldwin..............................58521
Balfour...............................58712
Balta..................................58313
Bantry................................58713
Barney...............................58008
Bartlett...............................58314
Barton, R. Br. Rugby...........58315
Bathgate.............................58216
Battleview...........................58714
Beach.................................58621
Belcourt..............................58316
Belden................................58715
Belfield...............................58622
Benedict.............................58716
Bentley...............................58522
Bergen...............................58717
Berlin.................................58415
Berthold.............................58718
Beulah...............................58523
Binford...............................58416
Bisbee................................58317
　Agate, R. Br.....................58310
Bismarck (1st).....................58501
　Livona, R. Br...................58501
　Mc Kenzie, R. Br..............58553
Blaisdell.............................58720
Blanchard...........................58009
Bonetraill...........................58836
Bordulac............................58417
Bottineau (1st)....................58318
Bowbells............................58721
Bowdon..............................58418
Bowesmont.........................58217
Bowman..............................58623
Braddock............................58524
Brampton............................58010
Brantford............................58419
Breien................................58525
Bremen...............................58319

Brinsmade..........................58320
Brocket...............................58321
Buchanan............................58420
Bucyrus..............................58624
Buffalo...............................58011
Buford................................58837
Burlington...........................58722
　Foxholm, R. Br................58738
Burnstad.............................58526
Burt...................................58527
Butte..................................58723
Buxton...............................58218
Caledonia............................58219
Calio..................................58322
Calvin................................58323
Cando.................................58324
Cannon Ball, R. Br. Fort
　Yates..............................58528
Carbury..............................58724
Carpio................................58725
Carrington...........................58421
Carson...............................58529
Cartwright...........................58838
Casselton............................58012
Cathay................................58422
Cavalier..............................58220
Cayuga...............................58013
Center................................58530
Chaffee, R. Br. Wheatland....58014
Charlson.............................58726
Chaseley.............................58423
Christine.............................58015
Churchs Ferry......................58325
Cleveland............................58424
Clifford...............................58016
Cogswell.............................58017
Coleharbor..........................58531
Colfax................................58018
Colgan...............................58840
Colgate..............................58019
Columbus............................58727
Concrete.............................58221
Conway, R. Br. Fordville......58232
Cooperstown........................58425
Coteau...............................58728
Coulee...............................58729
Courtenay...........................58426
Crary.................................58327
Crete..................................58020
Crosby...............................58730
Crystal...............................58222
Crystal Springs....................58427
Cummings...........................58223
Dahlen...............................58224
Davenport...........................58021
Dawson..............................58428
Dazey................................58429
De Lamere, R. Br. Milnor.....58022
Deering..............................58731
Denbigh..............................58732
Denhoff..............................58430
Des Lacs............................58733
Devils Lake (1st)..................58301
Dickey................................58431
Dickinson (1st).....................58601
Dodge................................58625
Donnybrook.........................58734
Douglas..............................58735
Downtown, Sta. Minot..........58701
Doyon................................58328
Drake.................................58736
Drayton..............................58225

Dresden..............................58226
Driscoll..............................58532
Dunn Center........................58626
Dunseith.............................58329
Durbin...............................58023
Dwight...............................58024
Eckelson, R. Br. Jamestown...58432
Edgeley..............................58433
Edinburg.............................58227
Edmore...............................58330
Edmunds.............................58434
Egeland..............................58331
Eldridge.............................58435
Elgin..................................58533
Ellendale............................58436
Emerado.............................58228
Emmet................................58534
Emrick................................58437
Enderlin..............................58027
Englevale............................58028
Epping................................58843
Erie....................................58029
Esmond..............................58332
Fairdale..............................58229
Fairfield..............................58627
Fairmount...........................58030
Fargo (1st)..........................58102
Fessenden...........................58438
Fillmore..............................58333
Fingal................................58031
Finley.................................58230
Flasher...............................58535
　Raleigh, R. Br.................58564
　Shields, R. Br.................58569
Flaxton...............................58737
Forbes................................58439
Fordville.............................58231
　Conway, R. Br................58232
Forest River........................58233
Forman...............................58032
Fort Ransom........................58033
Fort Rice............................58537
Fort Totten..........................58335
Fort Yates...........................58538
　Cannon Ball, R. Br..........58528
Fortuna..............................58844
Foxholm, R. Br. Burlington....58738
Freda.................................58539
Fredonia.............................58440
Fullerton.............................58441
Gackle................................58442
Galchutt.............................58034
Galesburg...........................58035
Gardar...............................58234
Gardena, R. Br. Kramer.......58739
Gardner..............................58036
Garrison.............................58540
Gascoyne............................58629
Geneseo.............................58037
Gilby..................................58235
　Honeyford, R. Br.............58242
　Johnstown, R. Br.............58245
Gladstone............................58630
Glasston.............................58236
Glen Ullin...........................58631
Glenburn.............................58740
Glenfield.............................58443
Goldenvalley........................58541
Golva.................................58632
Goodrich.............................58444
Gorham...............................58633
Grace City..........................58445

Grafton (1st)	58237
Grand Forks (1st)	58201
Grand Forks A F B, Br.	
Grand Forks	58201
Grand Rapids, R. Br. La	
Moure	58446
Grandin	58038
Granville	58741
Grassy Butte	58634
Great Bend	58039
Grenora	58845
Guelph	58447
Gwinner	58040
Hague	58542
Halliday	58636
Hamar	58336
Hamberg	58337
Hamilton	58238
Hamlet	58742
Hampden	58338
Hankinson	58041
Hannaford	58448
Hannah	58239
Hannover	58543
Hansboro, R. Br. Rocklake	58339
Harlow	58340
Harvey	58341
Harwood	58042
Hatton	58240
Havana	58043
Haynes	58637
Hazelton	58544
Hazen	58545
Heaton	58450
Hebron	58638
Heil	58546
Heimdal	58342
Hensel	58241
Hensler	58547
Hettinger	58639
Hickson	58044
Hillsboro	58045
Honeyford, R. Br. Gilby	58242
Hoople	58243
Hope	58046
Horace	58047
Huff, R. Br. Mandan	58555
Hunter	58048
Hurdsfield	58451
Inkster	58244
Jamestown (1st)	58401
Eckelson, R. Br.	58432
Nortonville, R. Br.	58473
Jessie	58452
Johnstown, R. Br. Gilby	58245
Joliette	58246
Juanita	58453
Jud	58454
Judson, R. Br. New Salem	58548
Karlsruhe	58744
Kathryn	58049
Keene	58847
Kenmare	58746
Kensal	58455
Kief	58747
Killdeer	58640
Kindred	58051
Kintyre	58549
Kloten	58248
Knox	58343
Kramer	58748
Gardena, R. Br.	58739
Kulm	58456

La Moure	58458
Grand Rapids, R. Br.	58446
Lakota	58344
Landa	58749
Langdon	58249
Maida, R. Br.	58255
Lankin	58250
Lansford	58750
Larimore	58251
Lark	58550
Larson	58751
Lawton	58345
Leal	58459
Leeds	58346
Lefor	58641
Lehr	58460
Leith	58551
Leonard	58052
Leroy	58252
Lidgerwood	58053
Lignite	58752
Linton	58552
Lisbon	58054
Litchville	58461
Livona, R. Br. Bismarck	58501
Loraine	58753
Lostwood	58754
Ludden	58462
Luverne	58056
Maddock	58348
Maida, R. Br. Langdon	58255
Makoti	58756
Mandan (1st)	58554
Huff, R. Br.	58555
Mandaree	58757
Manfred	58465
Manning	58642
Mantador	58058
Manvel	58256
Mapes	58349
Mapleton	58059
Marion	58466
Marmarth	58643
Marshall	58644
Martin	58758
Max	58759
Maxbass	58760
Mayville	58257
Mc Canna	58253
Mc Clusky	58463
Mc Gregor	58755
Mc Henry	58464
Mc Kenzie, R. Br. Bismarck	58553
Mc Leod	58057
Mc Ville	58254
Medina	58467
Medora	58645
Mekinock	58258
Menoken	58558
Mercer	58559
Merricourt	58469
Michigan	58259
Millarton	58470
Milnor	58060
De Lamere, R. Br.	58022
Milton	58260
Minnewaukan	58351
Minot (1st)	58701
Minot A F B, Br. Minot	58701
Minto	58261
Moffit	58560
Mohall	58761
Monango	58471

Montpelier	58472
Mooreton	58061
Mott	58646
Mountain	58262
Munich	58352
Mylo	58353
Nanson	58354
Napoleon	58561
Nash	58264
Neche	58265
Nekoma	58355
New England	58647
New Hradec	58648
New Leipzig	58562
New Rockford	58356
New Salem	58563
Judson, R. Br.	58548
New Town	58763
Newburg	58762
Niagara	58266
Niobe	58764
Nome	58062
Noonan	58765
Norma	58766
Northgate	58767
Northwood	58267
Nortonville, R. Br.	
Jamestown	58473
Norwich	58768
Oakes	58474
Oberon	58357
Oriska	58063
Orr	58268
Orrin	58359
Osnabrock	58269
Overly	58360
Page	58064
Palermo	58769
Park River	58270
Parshall	58770
Pekin	58361
Pembina (1st)	58271
Penn	58362
Perth	58363
Petersburg	58272
Pettibone	58475
Pillsbury	58065
Pingree	58476
Pisek	58273
Plaza	58771
Pleasant Lake	58364
Portal	58772
Portland	58274
Powers Lake	58773
Raleigh, R. Br. Flasher	58564
Raub	58774
Rawson	58848
Ray	58849
Wheelock, R. Br.	58855
Reeder	58649
Regan	58477
Regent	58650
Reynolds	58275
Rhame	58651
Richardton	58652
Riverdale	58565
Robinson	58478
Rocklake	58365
Hansboro, R. Br.	58339
Rogers	58479
Rolette	58366
Rolla	58367
Roseglen	58775

Ross.................................58776
Rugby (1st)........................58368
   Barton, R. Br. 58315
Ruso................................58778
Rutland.............................58067
Ryder...............................58779
Saint Anthony......................58566
Saint John.........................58369
Saint Michael......................58370
Saint Thomas.......................58276
San Haven..........................58371
Sanborn............................58480
Sanish.............................58780
Sarles.............................58372
Sawyer.............................58781
Scranton...........................58653
Selfridge..........................58568
Selz...............................58373
Sentinel Butte.....................58654
Sharon.............................58277
Sheldon............................58068
Sherwood...........................58782

Sheyenne...........................58374
Shields, R. Br. Flasher............58569
Silva..............................58375
Silver Strip, Sta. Williston.......58801
Solen..............................58570
Souris.............................58783
South Heart........................58655
South Washington, Sta.
   Grand Forks.................58201
Spiritwood.........................58481
Spring Brook.......................58850
Stanley............................58784
Stanton............................58571
Starkweather.......................58377
State University, Sta. Fargo.......58102
Steele.............................58482
Sterling...........................58572
Stirum.............................58069
Strasburg..........................58573
Straubville........................58070
Streeter...........................58483
Surrey.............................58785

Sutton.............................58484
Sydney.............................58485
Sykeston...........................58486
Tappen.............................58487
Taylor.............................58656
Thompson...........................58278
Tioga..............................58852
Tokio..............................58379
Tolley.............................58787
Tolna..............................58380
Tower City.........................58071
Towner.............................58788
Trenton............................58853
Trotters...........................58657
Turtle Lake........................58575
Tuttle.............................58488
Underwood..........................58576
Union..............................58279
University, Sta. Grand Forks.......58201
Upham..............................58789
Valley City (1st). 58072

OHIO
(Abbreviation: OH)

(the) Delta Queen, Sta.
Cincinnati 45202
Aberdeen 45101
Ada (1st) 45810
Adams Mills 43801
Adamsville 43802
Addison 45610
Addyston 45001
Adelphi 43101
Adena 43901
Adrian 44801
Air Materiel Command, Br.
Dayton 45433
Airport, Sta. Columbus 43219
Airport, Br. Cleveland 44181
AKRON (1st) (see appendix)
Albany ....r.....................45710
Alexandria 43001
Alger 45812
Alledonia 43902
Allensville 45611
Alliance (1st) 44601
Alpha 45301
Alvada 44802
Alvordton 43501
Amanda 43102
Amelia 45102
Amesville 45711
Amherst (1st) 44001
Amlin 43002
Amsden 44803
Amsterdam 43903
Andover 44003
Anna 45302
Ansonia 45303
Antioch 43710
Antwerp 45813
Apple Creek 44606
Arcadia 44804
Arcanum 45304
Archbold (1st) 43502
Arlington 45814
Armstrongs Mills 43904
Ashland (1st) 44805
Ashley 43003
Ashtabula (1st) 44004
Ashville 43103
Athens (1st) 45701
Atlanta 43104
Attica 44807
Atwater 44201
Augusta 44607
Aurora (1st) 44202
Austinburg 44010
Austintown, Br. Youngstown 44515
Ava 43711
Avon 44011
Avon Lake (1st) 44012
Bainbridge (1st) 45612
Bakersville 43803
Baltic 43804
Baltimore 43105
Bannock 43972
Barberton (1st) 44203
Barlow 45712
Barnesville (1st) 43713
Bartlett 45713
Barton 43905
Bascom 44809
Batavia (1st) 45103

Batesville 43715
Bath (1st) 44210
Bay Village, Br. Cleveland 44140
Beach City 44608
Beachland, Sta. Cleveland 44119
Beachwood, Br. Cleveland
(see appendix)
Beallsville 43716
Beaver 45613
Beaverdam, R. Br. Lima 45808
Bedford, Br. Cleveland 44146
Beechwold, Sta. Columbus 43214
Bellaire (1st) 43906
Bellbrook 45305
Belle Center 43310
Belle Valley 43717
Bellefontaine (1st) 43311
Bellevue (1st) 44811
Bellville 44813
Belmont 43718
Belmore, R. Br. Leipsic 45815
Beloit 44609
Belpre (1st) 45714
Benton, R. Br. Millersburg 44654
Benton Ridge 45816
Bentonville 45105
Berea (1st) 44017
Bergholz 43908
Berkey 43504
Berlin 44610
Berlin Center 44401
Berlin Heights 44814
Bethel 45106
Bethesda 43719
Bettsville 44815
Beverly 45715
Bexley, Br. Columbus 43209
Bidwell 45614
Big Prairie 44611
Birmingham 44816
Blackfork 45615
Blacklick 43004
Bladensburg 43005
Blaine 43909
Blakeslee 43505
Blanchester (1st) 45107
Blissfield 43805
Bloomdale 44817
Bloomingburg 43106
Bloomingdale 43910
Bloomville 44818
Blue Creek 45616
Blue Rock 43720
Bluffton (1st) 45817
Boardman, Br. Youngstown 44512
Bolivar 44612
Bono ....4340!
Botkins 45306
Bourneville 45617
Bowerston 44695
Bowersville 45307
Bowling Green (1st) 43402
Bradford 45308
Bradner 43406
Brady Lake, R. Br. Kent 44211
Branch Hill 45108
Brecksville, Br. Cleveland 44141
Bremen (1st) 43107
Brewster 44613
Brice 43109
Bridgeport (1st) 43912
Briggs, Br. Cleveland 44134
Brilliant 43913

Brimfield, Br. Kent 44240
Brinkhaven 43006
Bristolville 44402
Broadway 43007
Brook Park, Br. Cleveland 44142
Brookfield 44403
Brooklyn, Br. Cleveland 44144
Brookville (1st) 45309
Brownsville 43721
Brunswick (1st) 44212
Bryan (1st) 43506
Buchtel 45716
Buckeye Lake 43008
Buckland, R. Br. Lima 45819
Bucyrus (1st) 44820
Buffalo 43722
Buford 45110
Burbank 44214
Burghill 44404
Burgoon 43407
Burkettsville 45310
Burnet Woods, Sta.
Cincinnati 45220
Burton 44021
Butler 44822
Byesville 43723
Cable 43009
Cadiz (1st) 43907
Cairo 45820
Calcutta, Br. East Liverpool 43920
Caldwell 43724
Caledonia 43314
Cambridge (1st) 43725
Camden 45311
Cameron 43914
Camp Dennison 45111
Camp Ground, Br.
Lancaster 43130
Campbell 44405
Campus, Sta. Cincinnati 45221
Canal Fulton 44614
Canal Winchester 43110
Canfield (1st) 44406
CANTON (1st) (see appendix)
Carbon Hill 43111
Carbondale, R. Br.
Nelsonville 45717
Cardington 43315
Carey (1st) 43316
Carlisle, Br. Franklin 45005
Carroll 43112
Carrollton (1st) 44615
Carrothers 44823
Carthagena, R. Br. Celina 45822
Casstown 45312
Castalia 44824
Castine 45313
Catawba 43010
Cecil 45821
Cedarville 45314
Celina (1st) 45822
Carthagena, R. Br. 45822
Chickasaw, R. Br. 45826
Centerburg 43011
Centerville, Br. Dayton 45459
Central, Sta. Toledo (see
appendix)
Chagrin Falls (1st) 44022
Chandlersville 43727
Chardon (1st) 44024
Charm 44617
Chatfield 44825
Chauncey 45719

Cherry Fork................................45618
Chesapeake................................45619
Cheshire.....................................45620
Chester......................................45720
Chesterhill..................................43728
Chesterland (1st)........................44026
Chesterville................................44317
Chickasaw, R. Br. Celina............45826
Chillicothe (1st)..........................45601
Chilo..45112
Chippewa Lake...........................44215
Christiansburg.............................45389
CINCINNATI (1st) (see
  appendix)
Circleville (1st)............................43113
Clarington..................................43915
Clark...43810
Clarksburg..................................43115
Clarksville..................................45113
Clay Center................................43408
Claysville...................................43729
Clayton......................................45315
CLEVELAND (1st) (see
  appendix)
Cleveland Heights, Br.
  Cleveland (see appendix)
Cleves.......................................45002
Clifton.......................................45316
Clinton.......................................44216
Cloverdale..................................45827
Clyde (1st).................................43410
Coal Run....................................45721
Coalton......................................45621
Coldwater (1st)...........................45828
Colerain.....................................43916
College Corner............................45003
College Hill, Sta. Cincinnati..........45224
College Springs, Br.
  Columbus.................................43219
Collins.......................................44826
Collinsville..................................45004
Collinwood, Sta. Cleveland...........44110
Colton.......................................43510
Columbia Station.........................44028
Columbiana (1st).........................44408
COLUMBUS (1st) (see
  appendix)
Columbus Grove..........................45830
Commercial Point.........................43116
Conesville..................................43811
Conneaut (1st)............................44030
Conover.....................................45317
Constitution................................45722
Continental.................................45831
Dupont, R. Br.............................45837
Convoy.......................................45832
Coolville (1st)..............................45723
Copley, Br. Akron........................44321
Corning......................................43730
Corryville, Sta. Cincinnati.............45219
Cortland (1st).............................44410
Coshocton (1st)...........................43812
Covington (1st)...........................45318
Cranwood, Sta. Cleveland............44128
Creola.......................................45622
Crestline (1st).............................44827
Creston......................................44217
Cridersville, Br. Lima...................45806
Crooksville..................................43731
Croton.......................................43013
Crown City.................................45623
Cuba..45114
Cumberland................................43732

Cumminsville, Sta.
  Cincinnati...............................45223
Curtice......................................43412
Custar.......................................43511
Cutler..45724
CUYAHOGA FALLS (1st) (see
  appendix)
Cygnet......................................43413
Cynthiana...................................45624
Dabel, Sta. Dayton (see
  appendix)
Dalton.......................................44618
Damascus...................................44619
Danville.....................................43014
Darbydale, R. Br. Grove City..43123
Dart..45725
Day Heights, Br. Milford...........45150
DAYTON (1st) (see appendix)
Dayton View, Sta. Dayton..........45406
De Graff.....................................45318
Decatur......................................45115
Deer Park, Br. Cincinnati............45236
Deerfield....................................44411
Deersville...................................44693
Defiance (1st)..............................43512
Del Fair, Br. Cincinnati...............45238
Delaware (1st).............................43015
Dellroy......................................44620
Delphos (1st)..............................45833
Delta...43515
Dennison....................................44621
Derby...43117
Derwent.....................................43733
Deshler......................................43516
Devola, Br. Marietta...................45750
Dexter.......................................45726
Dexter City.................................45727
Diamond....................................44412
Dillonvale...................................43917
  Dunglen, R. Br........................43918
Dola..45835
Donnelsville................................45319
Dorset.......................................44032
Dover (1st).................................44622
Downtown, Sta. Akron................44302
Downtown, Sta. Canton................44702
Doylestown................................44230
Dresden.....................................43821
Dublin..43017
Dunbridge...................................43414
Duncan Falls..............................43734
Dundas......................................45625
Dundee......................................44624
Dunglen, R. Br. Dillonvale..........43918
Dunkirk......................................45836
Dupont, R. Br. Continental..........45837
East Akron, Sta. Akron...............44305
East Canton, Br. Canton.............44730
East Claridon..............................44033
East Cleveland, Br.
  Cleveland (see appendix)
East End, Sta. Cincinnati............45226
East Fultonham...........................43735
East Liberty................................43319
East Liverpool (1st).....................43920
East Monroe...............................45116
East Orwell.................................44034
East Palestine (1st).....................44413
East Rochester............................44625
East Side, Sta. Youngstown........44506
East Sparta................................44626
East Springfield..........................43925
Eastlake, Br. Willoughby.............44094

Eaton (1st).................................45320
Edenton......................................45117
Edgerton....................................43517
Edgewater, Br. Cleveland............44107
Edgewood, Br. Ashtabula............44004
Edison..43320
Edon..43518
Elba...45728
Eldorado....................................45321
Elgin..45838
Elida, Br. Lima............................45807
Elkton..44415
Ellet, Sta. Akron.........................44312
Elliston.......................................43415
Ellsworth....................................44416
Elm Grove..................................45626
Elmore.......................................43416
Elmwood Place, Br.
  Cincinnati...............................45216
ELYRIA (1st) (see appendix)
Empire..43926
Englewood (1st)..........................45322
Enon..45323
Erieview, Sta. Cleveland (see
  appendix)
Etna..43018
Euclid, Br. Cleveland (see
  appendix)
Evansport...................................43519
Ewington....................................45627
Excello, Br. Middletown...............45042
Fairborn (1st).............................45324
Fairfield, Br. Hamilton.................45014
Fairlawn, Br. Akron.....................44313
Fairpoint.....................................43927
Fairport Harbor, Br.
  Painesville...............................44077
Fairview.....................................43736
Fairview Park, Br. Cleveland....44126
Far Hills, Br. Dayton..................45419
Farmdale....................................44417
Farmer.......................................43520
Farmersville, Br.
  Germantown............................45325
Fayette.......................................43521
Fayetteville.................................45118
Federal Reserve, Sta.
  Cincinnati...............................45201
Federal Reserve, Sta.
  Cleveland................................44101
Feesburg....................................45119
Felicity.......................................45120
Findlay (1st)...............................45840
  Jenera, R. Br..........................45841
Firebrick, R. Br. Oak Hill............45656
Firestone Park, Sta. Akron
  (see appendix)
Flat Rock....................................44828
Fleming......................................45729
Fletcher......................................45326
Flushing.....................................43977
Fly...45730
Forest..45843
Forest Park, Br. Dayton (see
  appendix)
Fort Jennings..............................45844
Fort Loramie...............................45845
Fort Recovery.............................45846
Fort Scott Camps, R. Br.
  Harrison..................................45030
Fort Seneca................................44829
Fosterville, Sta. Youngstown......44511
Fostoria (1st)..............................44830

Fountain Square, Sta.
　Cincinnati 45202
Fowler 44418
Frankfort 45628
Franklin (1st) 45005
Franklin Furnace 45629
Frazeysburg 43822
Fredericksburg 44627
Fredericktown 43019
Freeport 43973
Fremont (1st) 43420
Fresno 43824
Friendship..................................45630
Frost 45731
Fulton 43321
Fultonham 43738
Gahanna, Br. Columbus 43230
Galena 43021
Galion (1st) 44833
Gallipolis (1st) 45631
Galloway 43119
Gambier 43022
Garfield Heights, Br.
　Cleveland (see appendix)
Garrettsville (1st) 44231
Gates Mills 44040
Geneva (1st) 44041
　Geneva-on-the-Lake, R.
　Br. 44043
Geneva-on-the-Lake, R. Br.
　Geneva 44043
Genoa (1st) 43430
Georgetown 45121
Germano, R. Br. Jewett 43987
Germantown (1st) 45327
　Farmersville, Br. 45325
Gettysburg 45328
Gibsonburg 43431
Gilboa 45847
Girard (1st) 44420
Glandorf 45848
Glencoe 43928
Glendale, Br. Cincinnati 45246
Glenford 43739
Glenmary, Br. Cincinnati 45246
Glenmont 44628
Glouster 45732
Gnadenhutten 44629
Gomer, R. Br. Lima 45809
Good Hope, R. Br.
　Washington Court House 43121
Goodrich Street, Sta. Akron...44311
Gordon 45329
Gore 43122
Goshen 45122
Grafton 44044
Grand Rapids 43522
Grand River 44045
Granville (1st) 43023
Gratiot 43740
Gratis 45330
Graysville 45734
Graytown 43432
Green Camp 43322
Green Springs 44836
Greenfield (1st) 45123
　Rainsboro, R. Br. 45165
Greenford 44422
Greenhills, Br. Cincinnati 45218
Greensburg 44232
Greentown 44630
Greenville (1st) 45331
Greenwich 44837

Grelton, R. Br. Mc Clure 43523
Groesbeck, Br. Cincinnati 45239
Grove City (1st) 43123
Groveport 43125
Grover Hill 45849
Guernsey 43741
Guysville 45735
Gypsum 43433
Hallsville 45653
Hamden 45634
Hamersville 45130
HAMILTON (1st) (see
　appendix)
Hamler 43524
Hammondsville 43930
Hanging Rock 45635
Hannibal 43931
Hanoverton 44423
Harbor, Sta. Ashtabula 44004
Harbor View 43434
Harlem Springs 44631
Harpster 43323
Harrisburg 43126
Harrison (1st) 45030
Harrisonville, R. Br.
　Pomeroy 45737
Harrisville 43974
Harrod 45850
Hartford 44424
Hartville (1st) 44632
Harveysburg 45032
Haskins 43525
Haverhill 45636
Haviland 45851
Haydenville 43127
Hayesville 44838
Heath, Br. Newark 43055
Heathersdowns, Sta. Toledo...43614
Hebron 43025
Helena 43435
　Millersville, R. Br. 43448
Hemlock 43743
Hemlock Grove 45738
Hendrysburg 43744
Hicksville 43526
Hide-A-Way Hills, R. Br.
　Bremen 43107
Higginsport 45131
Highland 45132
Hilliard (1st) 43026
Hillsboro (1st) 45133
Hilltop, Sta. Columbus 43204
Hinckley 44233
Hiram 44234
Hocking, Sta. Lancaster 43130
Hockingport 45739
Holgate 43527
Holland 43528
Hollansburg 45332
Holloway 43985
Holmesville 43633
Homer 43027
Homerville 44235
Homeworth 44634
Hooven 45033
Hopedale 43976
Hopewell 43746
Houston 45333
Howard 43028
Hoytville 43529
Hubbard (1st) 44425
Huber Heights, Br. Dayton.....45424
Hudson (1st) 44236

Huntsburg 44046
Huntsville 43324
Huron (1st) 44839
Hyde Park, Sta. Cincinnati.....45208
Iberia 43325
Idaho, R. Br. Piketon.............45661
Independence, Br. Cleveland ..44131
Irondale 43932
Ironton (1st) 45638
Irwin 43029
Isle Saint George......................43436
Ivorydale, Br. Cincinnati 45217
Jackson (1st) 45640
Jackson Center..........................45334
Jacksontown 43030
Jacksonville 45740
Jacobsburg 43933
Jamestown 45335
Jasper 45642
Jefferson (1st) 44047
Jeffersonville 43128
Jenera, R. Br. Findlay.............45841
Jeromesville 44840
Jerry City 43437
Jerusalem 43747
Jewell 43530
Jewett 43986
　Germano, R. Br. 43987
Johnstown 43031
Junction City.............................43748
Kalida 45853
Kamms, Sta. Cleveland...........44111
Kansas 44841
Keene 43828
Kelleys Island 43438
Kenmore, Sta. Akron..............44314
Kensington 44427
Kent (1st) 44240
　Brady Lake, R. Br. 44211
　Brimfield, Br. 44240
　Streetsboro, Br. 44240
Kenton (1st) 43326
Kenwood, Sta. Toledo.............43606
Kerr 45643
Kettering, Br. Dayton.............45429
Kettlersville 45336
Kidron 44636
Kilbourne 43032
Killbuck 44637
Kimbolton 43749
Kings Mills 45034
Kingston 45644
Kingsville 44048
Kinsman 44428
Kipling 43750
Kipton 44049
Kirby 43330
Kirkersville 43033
Kirtland, Br. Willoughby.........44094
Kitts Hill 45645
Kunkle 43531
La Rue 43332
Lacarne 43439
Lafayette, R. Br. Lima............45854
Lafferty 43951
Lagrange 44050
Laings 43752
Lake Milton 44429
Lakemore 44250
Lakeside-Marblehead...............43440
Lakeview 43331
Lakeville 44638
Lakewood, Br. Cleveland........44107

Lancaster (1st)...............43130
Langsville.......................45741
Lansing..........................43934
Latham...........................45646
Latty..............................45855
Laura..............................45337
Laurelville......................43135
Leavittsburg...................44430
Lebanon (1st).................45036
Lee Road, Br. Cleveland...44120
Lees Creek......................45138
Leesburg.........................45135
Leesville.........................44639
Leetonia.........................44431
Leipsic...........................45856
Belmore, R. Br..............45815
Lemoyne.........................43441
Leonardsburg..................43034
Lewis Center...................43035
Lewisburg.......................45338
Lewistown.......................43333
Lewisville........................43754
Lexington, Br. Mansfield...44904
Liberty, Br. Youngstown...44505
Liberty Center.................43532
LIMA (1st) (see appendix)
Limaville.........................44640
Lincoln, Br. Mansfield......44905
Lincoln Village, Br.
Columbus....................43228
Lindenwald, Sta. Hamilton...45015
Lindsey...........................43442
Lisbon (1st)....................44432
Litchfield........................44253
Lithopolis.......................43136
Little Hocking..................45742
Livingston, Sta. Columbus...43227
Lockbourne.....................43137
Lockbourne A F B, Br.
Columbus....................43217
Lockland, Br. Cincinnati...45215
Lodi...............................44254
Logan (1st).....................43138
London (1st)....................43140
Londonderry....................45647
Long Bottom...................45743
LORAIN (1st) (see appendix)
Lore City.........................43755
Loudonville (1st).............44842
Louisville (1st)................44641
Loveland (1st).................45140
Lowell.............................45744
Lowellville......................44436
Lower Salem....................45745
Lucas.............................44843
Lucasville........................45648
Luckey...........................43443
Ludlow Falls...................45339
Lynchburg.......................45142
Lyndhurst-Mayfield, Br.
Cleveland....................44124
Lyndon...........................45649
Lynx..............................45650
Lyons.............................43533
Macedonia, Br. Northfield...44056
Macksburg......................45746
Macon, R. Br. Sardinia.....45143
Madeira, Br. Cincinnati....45243
Madison (1st)..................44057
Madison Avenue, Sta.
Toledo........................43624
Madisonville, Sta.
Cincinnati...................45227

Magnetic Springs.............43036
Magnolia.........................44643
Maineville........................45039
Malaga............................43757
Malinta...........................43535
Malta..............................43758
Malvern...........................44644
Manchester......................45144
MANSFIELD (1st) (see
appendix)
Mantua (1st)...................44255
Maple Heights, Br.
Cleveland....................44137
Maple Valley, Sta. Akron...44320
Maplewood......................45340
Marathon........................45145
Marengo.........................43334
Maria Stein.....................45860
Mariemont, Br. Cincinnati...45227
Marietta (1st)..................45750
Marion (1st)....................43302
Marion Plaza, Br. Marion...43302
Mark Center....................43536
Marshallville....................44645
Martel............................43335
Martin............................43445
Martins Ferry (1st)...........43935
Martinsburg.....................43037
Martinsville.....................45146
Marysville (1st)................43040
Mason (1st).....................45040
Massillon (1st).................44646
Masury...........................44438
Maud, R. Br. West Chester...45069
Maumee (1st)..................43537
Maximo...........................44650
Maynard..........................43937
Mc Arthur.......................45651
Mc Clure.........................43534
Grelton, R. Br...............43523
Mc Comb........................45858
Mc Connelsville...............43756
Mc Cutchenville...............44844
Mc Dermott.....................45652
Mc Donald.......................44437
Mc Guffey......................45859
Mc Kinley Heights, Br. Niles...44446
Mechanicsburg.................43044
Mechanicstown.................44651
Medina (1st)....................44256
Medway..........................45341
Melmore..........................44845
Melrose...........................45861
Mendon...........................45862
Mentor (1st)....................44060
Mentor-on-the-Lake, Br.
Mentor........................44060
Mesopotamia...................44439
Metals Park, R. Br. Novelty...44073
Metamora........................43540
Miami University, Sta.
Oxford.........................45056
Miamisburg (1st).............45342
Miamitown.......................45041
Miamiville........................45147
Mid City, Sta. Dayton.......45402
Middle Bass.....................43446
Middle Point....................45863
Middlebranch...................44652
Middleburg......................43336
Middlefield (1st)...............44062
Middleport.......................45760
Middletown (1st)..............45042

Midland...........................45148
Midpark, Br. Cleveland......44130
Midtown, Sta. Zanesville...43701
Midvale...........................44653
Milan..............................44846
Milford (1st)....................45150
Day Heights, Br...........45150
Mulberry, R. Br............45150
Perintown, R. Br..........45161
Milford Center..................43045
Millbury..........................43447
Milledgeville....................43142
Miller City.......................45864
Millersburg (1st)..............44654
Millersport......................43046
Millersville, R. Br. Helena...43448
Millfield.........................45761
Millville, Br. Hamilton.......45013
Milton Center...................43541
Mineral City.....................44656
Mineral Ridge...................44440
Minersville.......................45763
Minerva (1st)...................44657
Minford...........................45653
Mingo.............................43047
Mingo Junction................43928
Minster...........................45865
Mogadore (1st)................44260
Monclova........................43542
Monroe...........................45050
Monroeville.....................44847
Montezuma......................45866
Montgomery, Br. Cincinnati...45242
Montpelier (1st)...............43543
Montville.........................44064
Moorefield.......................43979
Moraine, Br. Dayton.........45439
Morral............................43337
Morristown......................43759
Morrow (1st)....................45152
Moscow..........................45153
Moundbuilders, Sta. Newark...43055
Mount Airy, Sta. Cincinnati...45239
Mount Blanchard..............45867
Mount Carmel, Br.
Cincinnati...................45244
Mount Cory.....................45868
Mount Eaton...................44659
Mount Gilead (1st)...........43338
Mount Healthy, Br.
Cincinnati...................45231
Mount Hope....................44660
Mount Liberty..................43048
Mount Orab....................45154
Mount Perry....................43760
Mount Pleasant...............43939
Mount Saint Joseph..........45051
Mount Sterling.................43143
Mount Union, Sta. Alliance...44601
Mount Vernon (1st)..........43050
Mount Vernon Avenue, Sta.
Columbus....................43203
Mount Victory..................43340
Mount Washington, Sta.
Cincinnati (see appendix)
Mowrystown....................45155
Moxahala........................43761
Mulberry, R. Br. Milford....45150
Munroe Falls...................44262
Murray City.....................43144
Nankin............................44848
Napoleon (1st).................43545
Nashport.........................43830

497

Nashville	44661	
Navarre	44662	
Neapolis	43547	
Neffs	43940	
Negley	44441	
Nelsonville	45764	
Carbondale, R. Br.	45717	
Nevada	44849	
Neville	45156	
New Albany	43054	
New Athens	43981	
New Bavaria	43548	
New Bloomington	43341	
New Boston, Br. Portsmouth	45662	
New Bremen (1st)	45869	
New Carlisle (1st)	45344	
New Concord (1st)	43762	
New Hampshire	45870	
New Haven	44850	
New Holland	43145	
New Knoxville	45871	
New Lebanon	45345	
New Lexington (1st)	43764	
New London (1st)	44851	
New Lyme	44066	
New Madison	45346	
New Marshfield	45766	
New Matamoras	45767	
New Miami, Br. Hamilton	45011	
New Middletown	44442	
New Paris	45347	
New Philadelphia (1st)	44663	
Wainwright, R. Br.	44686	
New Plymouth	45654	
New Richmond	45157	
New Riegel	44853	
New Rumley	43984	
New Springfield	44443	
New Straitsville	43766	
New Vienna	45159	
New Washington	44854	
New Waterford	44445	
New Weston, R. Br.		
Rossburg	45348	
Newark (1st)	43055	
Newburg, Sta. Cleveland	44105	
Newbury	44065	
Newcomerstown (1st)	43832	
Newport	45768	
Newton Falls (1st)	44444	
Newtonsville	45158	
Newtown, Br. Cincinnati	45244	
Ney	43549	
Niles (1st)	44446	
Nimisila, R. Br. Clinton	44216	
Noble, Br. Cleveland	44132	
North Baltimore	45872	
North Bend	45052	
North Benton	44449	
North Bloomfield	44450	
North Canton, Br. Canton (see appendix)		
North College Hill, Br. Cincinnati	45239	
North Dayton, Sta. Dayton (see appendix)		
North Fairfield	44855	
North Georgetown	44665	
North Hampton	45349	
North Hill, Sta. Akron	44310	
North Industry, Br. Canton	44707	
North Jackson	44451	
North Kingsville	44068	
North Lawrence	44666	
North Lewisburg	43060	
North Lima	44452	
North Madison, Br. Madison	44057	
North Olmsted (1st)	44070	
North Ridgeville, Br. Elyria	44035	
North Robinson	44856	
North Royalton, Br. Cleveland	44133	
North Side, Sta. Youngstown (see appendix)		
North Star	45350	
Northfield (1st)	44067	
Macedonia, Br.	44056	
Northridge, Br. Dayton	45414	
Northup	45655	
Northwest, Sta. Columbus	43220	
Norton, Br. Barberton	44203	
Norwalk (1st)	44857	
Norwich	43767	
Norwood, Br. Cincinnati (see appendix)		
Nova	44859	
Novelty (1st)	44072	
Metals Park, R. Br.	44073	
Oak Harbor (1st)	43449	
Oak Hill	45656	
Oakland Park, Br. Columbus	43224	
Oakley, Sta. Cincinnati	45209	
Oakwood	45873	
Oberlin (1st)	44074	
Obetz, Br. Columbus	43207	
Oceola	44860	
Ohio City	45874	
Okeana	45053	
Okolona	43550	
Old Fort	44861	
Old Washington	43768	
Old West End, Sta. Toledo (see appendix)		
Olmsted Falls, Br. Cleveland	44138	
Ontario	44862	
Orangeville	44453	
Oregon, Br. Toledo (see appendix)		
Oregonia	45054	
Orient	43146	
Orrville (1st)	44667	
Orwell	44076	
Osgood	45351	
Ostrander	43061	
Ottawa (1st)	45875	
Ottoville	45876	
Otway	45657	
Outville, R. Br. Pataskala	43062	
Overlook, Br. Dayton (see appendix)		
Overpeck	45055	
Owensville	45160	
Oxford (1st)	45056	
Painesville (1st)	44077	
Palestine	45352	
Pandora	45877	
Parcel Post, Sta. Steubenville	43952	
Parcel Post, Sta. Youngstown	44505	
Parcel Post Annex, Sta. Warren	44484	
Parcel Post Annex, Sta. Sandusky	44870	
Parcel Post Annex, Sta. Cleveland	44101	
Parcel Post Annex, Sta. Mansfield	44903	
Parcel Post Annex, Sta. Elyria	44035	
Paris	44669	
Parkdale, Br. Cincinnati (see appendix)		
Parkman	44080	
Parma, Br. Cleveland (see appendix)		
Pataskala	43062	
Patriot	45658	
Patterson	45878	
Paulding (1st)	45879	
Pavonia	44863	
Payne	45880	
Pearlbrook, Sta. Cleveland	44109	
Pedro	45659	
Peebles	45660	
Pemberton	45353	
Pemberville	43450	
Peninsula	44264	
Pennsville	43770	
Pepper Pike, Br. Cleveland	44124	
Perintown, R. Br. Milford	45161	
Perry	44081	
Perrysburg (1st)	43551	
Perrysville	44864	
Petersburg	44454	
Pettisville	43553	
Phillipsburg	45354	
Philo	43771	
Phoneton	45355	
Pickerington	43147	
Piedmont	43983	
Pierpont	44082	
Piketon	45661	
Piney Fork	43941	
Pioneer	43554	
Piqua (1st)	45356	
Pitsburg	45358	
Plain City	43064	
Plainfield	43836	
Piaza, Br. Youngstown	44512	
Pleasant City	43772	
Pleasant Hill	45359	
Pleasant Plain	45162	
Pleasantville	43148	
Plymouth	44865	
Point, Sta. Columbus (see appendix)		
Point Place, Sta. Toledo	43611	
Point Pleasant	45163	
Poland, Br. Youngstown	44514	
Polk	44866	
Pomeroy	45769	
Harrisonville, R. Br.	45737	
Port Clinton (1st)	43452	
Port Jefferson	45360	
Port Washington	43837	
Port William	45164	
Portage	43451	
Portland	45770	
Portsmouth (1st)	45662	
Post Office Annex, Sta. Cincinnati	45214	
Potsdam	45361	
Potter Village, Sta. Fremont	43420	
Powell	43065	

Powhatan Point	43942
Price Hill, Sta. Cincinnati	45205
Proctor "le	45669
Prospect	43342
Public Square, Sta. Cleveland	44114
Puritas Parks, Sta. Cleveland	44135
Put-in-Bay	43456
Quaker City	43773
Quincy	43343
Racine	45771
Radcliff	45670
Radnor	43066
Rainsboro, R. Br. Greenfield	45165
Randolph	44265
Rarden	45671
Ravenna (1st)	44266
Rawson	45881
Ray	45672
Rayland	43943
Raymond	43067
Reading, Br. Cincinnati	45215
Reedsville	45772
Reesville	45166
Reily, R. Br. Hamilton	45060
Reinersville	43774
Rendville	43775
Reno	45773
Republic	44867
Reynolds Corners, Sta. Toledo (see appendix)	
Reynoldsburg (1st)	43068
Richfield (1st)	44286
Richmond	43944
Richmond Dale	45673
Richmond Heights, Br. Cleveland	44143
Richwood	43344
Ridgeville Corners	43555
Ridgeway	43345
Rinard Mills	45774
Rio Grande	45674
Ripley	45167
Risingsun	43457
Rittman (1st)	44270
Robertsville	44670
Rock Camp	45675
Rock Creek	44084
Rockbridge	43149
Rockford	45882
Rockland, Sta. Belpre	45714
Rocky Ridge	43458
Rocky River, Br. Cleveland	44116
Rodney	45676
Rogers	44455
Rome	44085
Roosevelt, Sta. Dayton (see appendix)	
Rootstown	44272
Roselawn, Sta. Cincinnati	45237
Roseville	43777
Rosewood	43070
Ross	45061
Rossburg	45362
New Weston, R. Br.	45348
Rossford (1st)	43460
Rossmoyne, Br. Cincinnati	45236
Rossville, Sta. Hamilton	45013
Roundhead	43346
Rudolph	43462
Rushsylvania	43347

Rushville	43150
Russells Point	43346
Russellville	45168
Russia	45363
Rutland	45775
Sabina	45169
Saint Bernard, Br. Cincinnati	45217
Saint Clairsville (1st)	43950
Saint Henry	45883
Saint Johns	45884
Saint Louisville	43071
Saint Martin	45170
Saint Marys (1st)	45885
Saint Paris	43072
Salem (1st)	44460
Salesville	43778
Salineville	43945
Sandusky (1st)	44870
Sandyville	44671
Sarahsville	43779
Sardinia	45171
Macon, R. Br.	45143
Sardis	43946
Savannah	44874
Saylor Park, Sta. Cincinnati	45233
Scio	43988
Scioto Furnace	45677
Sciotoville, Sta. Portsmouth	45662
Scott	45886
Scottown	45678
Seaman	45679
Sebring (1st)	44672
Sedalia	43151
Selma, R. Br. South Charleston	45364
Senecaville	43780
Seven Mile	45062
Seville	44273
Shade	45776
Shadyside	43947
Shaker Heights, Sta. Cleveland	44120
Shandon	45063
Shanesville, Sta. Sugarcreek	44681
Sharon	43781
Sharon Center	44274
Sharonville, Br. Cincinnati	45241
Sharpsburg	45777
Shauck	43349
Shawnee	43782
Shawnee Hills, R. Br. Powell	43065
Sheffield Lake, Br. Lorain	44054
Shelby (1st)	44875
Shepard, Sta. Columbus	43219
Sherman, Sta. Mansfield	44906
Sherrodsville	44675
Sherwood	43556
Shiloh	44878
Shinrock	44879
Shore, Br. Cleveland	44123
Short Creek	43989
Shreve	44676
Sidney (1st)	45365
Sinking Spring	45172
Smithfield	43948
Smithville	44677
Solon, Br. Cleveland	44139
Somerdale	44678
Somerset	43783
Somerton	43784

Somerville	45064
Sonora	43785
South Arlington, Sta. Akron	44306
South Bloomingville	43152
South Charleston	45368
Selma, R. Br.	45364
South Euclid, Br. Cleveland (see appendix)	
South Lebanon	45065
South Lorain, Sta. Lorain	44055
South Olive, R. Br. Caldwell	43724
South Point	45680
South Salem	45681
South Side, Sta. Youngstown	44507
South Solon	43153
South Vienna	45369
South Webster	45682
South Zanesville, Br. Zanesville	43701
Southington	44470
Southwest, Sta. Mansfield	44907
Sparta	43350
Spencer	44275
Spencerville	45887
Spring Valley	45370
Springboro	45066
Springdale, Br. Cincinnati	45246
SPRINGFIELD (1st) (see appendix)	
Stafford	43786
State Road, Sta. Cuyahoga Falls	44223
State Street, Sta. Columbus	43215
Sterling	44276
Steubenville (1st)	43952
Stewart	45778
Stewartsville	43960
Stillwater	44679
Stock Yards, Sta. Cincinnati	45225
Stockdale	45683
Stockport	43787
Stone Creek	43840
Stony Ridge	43463
Stout	45684
Stoutsville	43154
Stow, Br. Cuyahoga Falls	44224
Strasburg	44680
Stratton	43961
Streetsboro, Br. Kent	44240
Strongsville, Br. Cleveland	44136
Struthers (1st)	44471
Stryker	43557
Sugar Grove	43155
Sugar Tree Ridge, R. Br. Hillsboro	45133
Sugarcreek	44681
Sullivan	44880
Sulphur Springs	44881
Summerfield	43788
Summit Station	43073
Summitville	43962
Sunbury	43074
Surfside, Br. Willoughby	44094
Swanton (1st)	43558
Sycamore	44882
Sycamore Valley	43789
Sylvania (1st)	43560
Syracuse	45779
Taft, Br. Cincinnati (see appendix)	

Tallmadge (1st).................44278
Tarlton.............................43156
Terrace Park....................45174
The Avenue, R. Br. Masury....44438
The Delta Queen, Sta
  Cincinnati.....................45202
The Plains........................45780
Thompson.........................44086
Thornville.........................43076
Thurman...........................45685
Thurston...........................43157
Tiffin (1st).......................44883
Tiltonsville.......................43963
Tipp City (1st)..................45371
Tippecanoe.......................44699
Tiro..................................44887
TOLEDO (1st) (see appendix)
Tontogany........................43565
Torch................................45781
Toronto (1st)....................43964
Tremont City.....................45372
Trenton.............................45067
Tri Village, Sta. Columbus....43212
Trimble.............................45782
Trinway............................43842
Trotwood, Br. Dayton (see
  appendix)
Troy (1st).........................45373
Tuppers Plains...................45783
Tuscarawas.......................44682
Twinsburg (1st).................44087
Uhrichsville (1st)...............44683
Union, Br. Englewood..........45322
Union Furnace....................44158
Unionport..........................43966
Uniontown.........................44685
Unionville..........................44088
Urionville Center................43077
Uniopolis...........................45888
University, Sta. Columbus.....43210
University Center, Sta.
  Cleveland.....................44106
University Heights, Br.
  Cleveland.....................44118
Upper Arlington, Br.
  Columbus......................43221
Upper Sandusky (1st)..........43351
Uptown, Sta. Cleveland.......44114
Urbana (1st).....................43078
Utica................................43080
Valley City........................44280
Van Buren.........................45889
Van Wert (1st)...................45891
Vandalia (1st)....................45377
Vanlue..............................45890
Vaughnsville......................45893
Venedocia.........................45894
Venice, Sta. Sandusky.........44870
Vermilion (1st)...................44089
Verona.............................45378
Versailles..........................45380
Veterans Administration, Br.
  Dayton........................45428
Vickery.............................43464
Vienna..............................44473
Vincent.............................45784
Vine Street, Br. Willoughby....44094
Vinton..............................45686
Wadsworth (1st)................44281
Wainwright, R. Br. New
  Philadelphia.................44686
Wakefield.........................45687
Wakeman...........................44889

Walbridge.........................43465
Waldo...............................43356
Walhonding.......................43843
Walnut Creek.....................44687
Walnut Hills, Sta.
  Cincinnati.....................45206
Wapakoneta (1st)...............45895
Warner.............................45785
Warnock............................43967
WARREN (1st) (see
  appendix)
Warsaw.............................43844
Washington Court House
  (1st)...........................43160
  Good Hope, R. Br..........43121
Washingtonville..................44490
Waterford.........................45786
Waterloo...........................45688
Watertown........................45787
Waterville.........................43566
Wauseon (1st)...................43567
Waverly (1st)....................45690
Wayland...........................44285
Wayne..............................43466
Waynesburg......................44688
Waynesfield.......................45896
Waynesville.......................45068
Wellington (1st).................44090
Wellston (1st)....................45692
Wellsville (1st)...................43968
Wernert, Sta. Toledo (see
  appendix)
West Akron, Sta. Akron........44307
West Alexandria..................45381
West Carrollton, Br. Dayton
  (see appendix)
West Chester.....................45069
West Elkton.......................45070
West End, Sta. Ashtabula......44004
West Farmington.................44491
West Jefferson....................43162
West Lafayette...................43845
West Liberty......................43357
West Manchester.................45382
West Mansfield...................43358
West Middletown, R. Br.
  Middletown...................45042
West Millgrove...................43467
West Milton........................45383
West Park, Sta. Cleveland.....44111
West Point.........................44492
West Rushville....................43163
West Salem........................44287
West Side, Sta. Youngstown....44509
West Toledo, Sta. Toledo......43612
West Town, Sta. Marion........43302
West Union........................45693
West Unity.........................43570
West Warren, Sta. Warren....44485
Western College, Br. Oxford....45056
Western Hills, Br. Cincinnati....45238
Westerville (1st).................43081
Westfield Center (1st)..........44251
Westlake, Br. Cleveland.......44145
Weston.............................43569
Westville...........................43083
Westwood, Br. Cincinnati......45211
Wharton............................43359
Wheelersburg.....................45694
Whipple............................45788
White Cottage....................43791
Whitehall, Br. Columbus.......43213

Whitehouse........................43571
Wickliffe (1st)....................44092
Wilberforce........................45384
Wilkesville.........................45695
Willard (1st)......................44890
Williamsburg......................45176
Williamsfield......................44093
Williamsport.......................43164
Williamstown......................45897
Williston............................43468
Willoughby (1st).................44094
Willow, Sta. Cleveland.........44127
Willow Wood.......................45696
Willowick, Br. Willoughby.....44094
Willshire............................45898
Wilmington (1st).................45177
Wilmot..............................44689
Winchester.........................45697
Windham............................44288
Windsor.............................44099
Winesburg.........................44690
Wingett Run.......................45789
Winona..............................44493
Wintersville, Br.
  Steubenville..................43952
Winton Place, Sta.
  Cincinnati.....................45232
Withamsville, Br. Cincinnati....45245
Wolf Run...........................43970
Wonderland, R. Br.
  Columbus......................43230
Woodsfield.........................43793
Woodstock.........................43084
Woodville..........................43469
Wooster (1st).....................44691
Worthington, Br. Columbus....43085
Wren................................45899
Wright Patterson'A F B, Br.
  Dayton........................45433
Wyoming, Br. Cincinnati.......45215
Xavier, Sta. Cincinnati.........45207
Xenia (1st)........................45385
Yellow Springs (1st)............45387
Yorkshire...........................45388
Yorkville............................43971
YOUNGSTOWN (1st) (see appendix)
Zaleski..............................45698
Zanesfield.........................43360
Zanesville (1st)..................43701
Zoar................................44697
Zoarville............................44698

AKRON 443

POST OFFICE BOXES

Box Nos.

A-P	East Akron	05
1-1590	Akron	09
2601-2794	Firestone Park Sta	01
2999-2314	Goodrich Sta	11
3301-3499	West Akron Sta	07
3500-3699	North Hill Sta	10
3701-3864	Kenmore Sta	14
4000-4499	Copley Br	21
5108-5999	Fairlawn Br	13
6001-6389	Ellet Sta	12
7001-7999	South Arlington Sta	06
8001-8184	Maple Valley Sta	20
9001-9499	East Akron Sta.	05

RURAL ROUTES

7,14	13

STATIONS, BRANCHES AND UNITS

Copley Br	21
Downtown Sta	02
East Akron Sta	05
Ellet Sta	12
Fairlawn Br	13
Firestone Park Sta	01
Goodrich Street Sta	11
Kenmore Sta	14
Maple Valley Sta	20
North Hill Sta	10
South Arlington Sta	06
West Akron Sta	07
General Delivery	09
Postmaster	09

APARTMENTS, HOTELS, MOTELS

Akron Tower Motor Inn, 50 W State	08
Alcazar, 627 W Market	03
Ambassador, 753 W Market	03
Arcadia, 322 W Market	03
Auldfarm, 345 Diagonal Rd	20
Avalon, 214 N Portage Path	03
Belvidere, 630 W Market	03
Blair House, 255 N Portage Path	03
Carlton House, 275 N Portage Path	03
Chesterfield, 1032 W Market	13
Crescent, 795 W Market	03
Diplomat House, 1350 N Howard	10
Highland Towers, 900 W Market	13
Hill Chateau, 26 E Tallmadge Ave	10
Holiday Inn, li Cascade Plaza	08
Mayfield, 222 Twin Oaks Rd	13
Midtown Motel, 219 E Market	08
New Portage, 10 N Main	08
Ontario, 264 W Market	03

Parkview, 1620 W Sunset View Dr	20
Pasadena, 218 Twin Oaks Rd	13
Plaza, 173 N Portage Path	03
Seville, 715 W Market	03
Twin Oaks, 202 Twin Oaks Rd	13
Westgate Manor, 64 Eastgay Dr	13
Y M C A, 80 W Center	08
Y W C A, 146 S High	08

BUILDINGS

A C & Y, 12 E Exchange	08
Akron Art Institute, 69 E Market	08
Akron Center, I Cascade Plaza	08
Akron Savings & Loan, 7 W Bowery	08
Cascade Plaza, S Main & W Bowery	08
City Bldg., 166 S High	08
Delaware, 137 S Main	08
Evans Savings, 333 S Main	08
Everst', 39 E Market	08
First Federal Savings, 326 S Main	08
First National Tower, 106 S Main	08
Metropolitan, 39 S Main	08
Ohio Bell Telephone, 50 W Bowery	08
Ohio, 175 S Main	08
Oneils, 226 S Main	08
Permanent Federal, 55 E Mill	08
Polskys, 225 S Main	08
Public Library, 55 S. Main	08
Ruhlin, li Cascade Plaza	08
Second National, 159 S Main	08
Union Depot, 220 Grant	08
United Rubber Workers, 87 S High	08
United, 9 S Main	08

GOVERNMENT OFFICES

City-County Safety Bldg, 217 S High	08
Courthouse, 209 S High	08
Municipal Bldg, 166 S High	08
Ohio Bureau Of Employment Services, 150 E Market	08

HOSPITALS

Akron City, 525 E Market	09
Akron General, 400 Wabash	07
Childrens, W Bowery & W Buchtel	08
Edwin Shaw Sanatorium, 2600 Sanatorium Rd	12
Saint Thomas, 444 N Main	10

MILITARY INSTALLATIONS

Akron Armory, 161 S High	08

Army Reserve Training Center, 1011 Gorge Blvd	10
Naval Reserve Training Center, 800 Dan	10

UNIVERSITIES AND COLLEGES

University Of Akron, 302 E Buchtel Ave	04

CANTON 447

POST OFFICE BOXES

Box Nos.

1-236	B Sta	06
1-327	North Industry Br	07
1-1031	Downtown Sta	01
1201-1430	C Sta	08
1401-1684	East Canton Br	30
1701-1900	A Sta	05
2101-2449	North Canton Br	20
8001-9200	Main Office	11

RURAL ROUTES

2,4	30

STATIONS, BRANCHES AND UNITS

Downtown Sta	02
East Canton Br	30
North Canton Br	20
North Industry Br	07
General Delivery	11
Postmaster	11

APARTMENTS, HOTELS, MOTELS

Ambassador, 2901 Tuscarawas E	07
Arcade, 133 4th NW	02
Belden, 103 6th NE	02
Canton Travelodge, 1031 Tuscarawas W	02
Downtowner Motor Inn, 621 Market Ave N	02
Harleigh Inn, 500 Main St N	20
Holiday Inn, 800 Tuscarawas W	02
Imperial House, 4343 Everhard Rd NW	18
Moon Mist, 4411 Tuscarawas E	30
Motel Quiet, 3205 Lincoln E	07
Onesto, 225 2nd NW	02
Stanley, 2801 Tuscarawas E	07
Top-O-The-Mark, 4135 Tuscarawas E	30
Towne Manor, 926 Tuscarawas W	02
Washington, 305 Mckinley Ave SW	01

BUILDINGS

Arcade Market, 135 3rd NW	02
Citizens, 110 Central Plz S	02

501

Cleve-Tusc, 121 Cleveland
Ave SW 02
Commercial, 205 Market Ave
S 02
Dime Bank, 307 Tuscarawas
E 02
First Federal Savings & Loan,
200 Tuscarawas W 02
First National Bank, 120
Tuscarawas W 02
Harter Bank, 138 2nd NE 02
Home Savings And Loan, 315
Tuscarawas W 02
Mellett, 115 Dewalt Ave NW 02
Nationwide, 1020 Market Ave
N 02
Peoples-Merchant Trust, 116
Cleveland Ave NW 02
Professional, 816 Market Ave
N 02
Renkert, 306 Market Ave N 02
Wells Professional, 515 3rd
NW 03

GOVERNMENT OFFICES

Chamber Of Commerce, 229
Wells Ave NW 03
City Hall, 218 Cleveland Ave.
S. W. 02
Stark County Court House
Office, 209 Tuscarawas W . 02

HOSPITALS

Aultman, 2600 6th SW 10
Shadyside, 932 Main N Onc ... 20
Timken-Mercy, 2015 12th NW . 08

UNIVERSITIES AND COLLEGES

Kent State Univ, 6000 Frank
Ave NW 20
Malone College, 515 25th
NW 09
Walsh College, 2020 Easton
NW 20

CINCINNATI 452

POST OFFICE BOXES

Box Nos.
1-2550	Fountain Square Sta....	01
5A-5E	Price Hill Sta....	05
15A-15Q	Lockland Br.....	15
24A-24I	College Hill Sta....	24
26A-26H	East End Sta....	26
30A-30I	Mount Washington Sta....	30
31A-31H	Mount Healthy Br..........	31
36A-36L	Taft Br....	36
42A-42L	Montgomery Br....	42
4601-4116	F Sta	04
5601-5149	Price Hill Sta.....	05

6001-6417	Walnut Hills Sta..............	06
8001-8959	Hyde Park Sta ..	08
9001-9143	Oakley Sta........	09
10001-10214	V Sta	10
11001-11328	Westwood Br.....	11
12001-12480	Norwood Br.....	12
14001-14717	Annex Sta........	14
15001-15460	Lockland Br......	15
16001-16115	Elmwood Place Br..............	17
1700A-1700I	Saint Bernard Br..............	17
17001-17134	Saint Bernard Br..............	17
18001-18116	Parkdale Br.....	40
19001-19297	Corryville Sta...	19
20001-20138	Burnet Woods Sta..............	20
21001-21116	Campus Sta	21
23001-23206	Cumminsville Sta..............	23
24001-24199	College Hill Sta..............	24
25001-25146	Stock Yards Sta..............	25
26001-26116	East End Sta....	26
27001-27155	Madisonville Sta..............	27
29001-29269	I Sta	29
30001-30279	Mount Washington Sta..............	30
31001-31158	Mount Healthy Br	31
32001-32115	Winton Place Sta..............	17
33101-33157	Sayler Park Sta..............	33
36001-36280	Taft Br..............	36
37001-37908	Roselawn Sta....	22
38001-38204	Western Hills Branch..........	38
39001-39518	Groesbeck Br.....	39
40101-40274	Parkdale Br.....	40
41001-41316	Sharonville Br...	41
42001-42320	Montgomery Br.	42
43001-43699	Madeira Br....	43
44001-44147	Newtown Br......	44
46001-46472	Parkdale Br.....	40
75000-75131	Airport Br	75

STATIONS, BRANCHES AND UNITS

Airport Br 75
Burnet Woods Sta 20
Campus Sta 21
College Hill Sta 24
Corryville Sta 19
Cumminsville Sta 23
Deer Park Br............................ 36
Del Fair Br................................ 38
East End Sta 26
Elmwood Place Br 16
Federal Reserve Sta 01
Fountain Square Sta 02
Glendale Br.............................. 46
Glenmary Br............................ 46
Greenhills Br............................ 18
Groesbeck Br 39
Hyde Park Sta 08

Ivorydale Br.............................. 17
Lockland Br.............................. 15
Madeira Br................................ 43
Madisonville Sta...................... 27
Mariemont Br 27
Montgomery Br........................ 42
Mount Airy Sta........................ 39
Mount Carmel Br...................... 44
Mount Healthy Br.................... 31
Mount Washington Sta............ 30
Newtown Br.............................. 44
North College Hill Br............... 39
Norwood Br.............................. 12
Oakley Sta................................ 09
Parkdale Br.............................. 40
Post Office Annex Sta.............. 14
Price Hill Sta............................ 05
Reading Br 15
Roselawn Sta 37
Rossmoyne Br.......................... 36
Saint Bernard Br...................... 17
Saylor Park Sta 33
Sharonville Br.......................... 41
Springdale Br.......................... 46
Stock Yards Sta........................ 25
Taft Br...................................... 36
The Delta Queen Sta................ 02
Walnut Hills Br........................ 06
Western Hills Br 38
Westwood Br............................ 11
Winton Place Sta...................... 32
Withamsville Br........................ 45
Wyoming Br.............................. 15
Xavier Sta................................ 07
General Delivery 02
Postmaster 02

APARTMENTS, HOTELS, MOTELS

Alms Motor Hotel, 2525
Victory Pkwy............................ 06
Anna Louise Inn, 300 Lytle..... 02
Barkley House, Greater
Cincinnati Airport 75
Belvedere, 3851 Reading Rd.. 29
Blue Fountain, 1673 Cedar
Ave 24
Boulevard Lawn, 2630 Victory
Pkwy.. 06
Carrousel Inn, 8001 Reading
Rd 37
Cincinnati Club, 30 Garfield
Pl... 02
Cincinnatian, 16 W 6th 02
Clifton House, 2971
Deckebach Ave........................ 20
Clovernook Home For The
Blind, 6990 Hamilton Ave.. 31
Colonial Inn, 10200 Reading
Rd 41
Columbia Towers, 1815 Wm
Howard Taft Rd 06
Deupree House East, 3939
Erie Ave 08
East Oak Manor, 310 Oak 19
El Rancho Rankin, 5218
Beechmont Ave........................ 30
Essex House, 7610 Reading
Rd 37
Executive, 621 Mc Alpin Ave .. 20
Fenwick, 423 Commercial Sq . 02
Fessel Garden, 3242
Whitfield Ave.......................... 20
Fontbonne, 410 E 5th 02

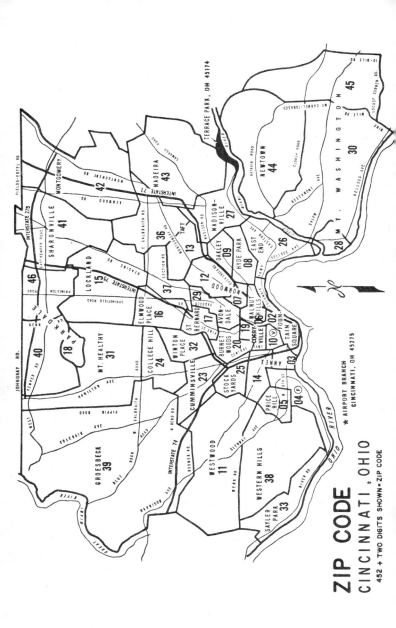

ZIP CODE
CINCINNATI, OHIO
452 + TWO DIGITS SHOWN = ZIP CODE

Fort Washington, 621 Main 02
Fountain Square, 420 Vine 01
Georgetown East 484 Batavia
   Rd 44
Grasmoor House, 2370
   Madison Rd......................... 08
Haddon Hall, 3418 Reading
   Rd 29
Hammond North, 5300
   Hamilton Ave...................... 24
Highland Towers, 380
   Oregon................................. 02
Holiday Inn Downtown, 802
   W 8th................................... 03
Holiday Inn North, 2235 E
   Sharon Rd 41
Howard Johnson'S, 11440
   Chester Rd........................... 46
Imperial House Motel, 1717
   Glendale - Milford Rd......... 15
Interstate Motel, I-275 41
Kemper Lane, 2500 Kemper
   Ln 06
Kensington Lane Town House,
   7752 Montgomery Road...... 36
Lytle Towers, 405 Broadway ... 02
Madison House, 2324
   Madison Rd.......................... 08
Mariemont Inn, 6839 Wooster
   Rd 27
Milner Highlander, 108
   Garfield Pl............................ 02
Mont Michel, 688 Riddle
   Road...................................... 20
Netherland Hilton, 63 W 5th... 01
New Dennison, 716 Main........ 02
Panorama, 2375 Montana
   Ave.. 11
Park-Lane Apartments, 4201
   Victory Pkwy 29
Phelps Apts, 506 E 4th 02
Princeton, 431 Elm 02
Quality Courts Motel, 4747
   Montgomery Rd................... 12
Queen'S Tower, 810 Matson
   Pl... 04
Regency, 2444 Madison Rd 08
River Terrace, 2401
   Ingleside 06
Riverview, 2538 Hackberry...... 06
Rowe Towers Stanley G, 1609
   Linn....................................... 14
Rowe Towers Stanley, 822
   Poplar Walk......................... 14
Saint Margaret Hall, 1960
   Madison Rd.......................... 06
Sheraton Gibson, 421
   Walnut................................... 01
Shullers Motel, 7759 Reading
   Rd 37
Stouffer'S Cincinnati Inn,
   150 W 5 Th........................... 02
Summit View, 2701 Lehman
   Rd 04
Terrace Hilton, 15 W 6th 01
Travelodge Motel, 3244
   Central Pkwy........................ 25
Vernon Manor, 2810 Burnet
   Ave.. 19
Victory Lane, 2210 Victory
   Pkwy...................................... 06
Williamsburg Of Cincinnati,
   200 W Galbraith Rd 15

Y M C A, 1105 Elm................. 10
Y W C A, 898 Walnut.............. 02

BUILDINGS

American, 30 E Central Pkwy.
Ashtree Village Shopping
   Center, 4781 Hamilton
   Ave... 23
Atlas Bank, 524 Walnut.......... 02
B & O Railroad Freight
   Station, Nwc 2nd & Smith. 02
Becker, 705 Sycamore............ 02
Beechmont Mall Shopping
   Center, 7500 Beechmont
   Avenue.................................. 30
Bell Telephone, 225 E 4th..... 02
Big Four Office, 517 W 3rd 02
Brentwood Plaza Shopping
   Center................................... 31
Brotherhood Of Railway
   Clerk, 1015 Vine.................. 02
Building Industries Bldg, 626
   Broadway.............................. 02
Carew Tower Arcade, 435
   Vine....................................... 02
Carew Tower, 441 Vine............ 02
Carrousel Towers, 8075
   Reading Rd........................... 37
Central Trust Towers Annex,
   309 Vine................................ 02
Central Trust Towers, 5 W
   4th... 02
Cherry Grove Plaza Shopping
   Center................................... 30
Cincinnati Art Museum, Eden
   Park...................................... 02
Cincinnati Convention
   Exposition Center, 525
   Elm.. 02
Cincinnati Gas & Electric,
   319 Main............................... 02
Cincinnati Music Hall, 1245
   Elm.. 10
Cincinnati Observatory, 3489
   Observatory Pl..................... 08
Cincinnati Union Terminal
   Service, W Liberty At
   Mclean Av............................ 14
Cincinnati Union Terminal
   1301 Western Ave............... 03
Commerce 100 E 8th.............. 02
Daylight, 659 E 6th................. 02
Del-Fair Shopping Ctr............. 38
Dillonvale Shopping Ctr.......... 36
Dixie Terminal, 49 E 4th........ 02
Doctors, 19 Garfield Pl.......... 02
Dubois Tower, 511 Walnut...... 02
Duttenhoefer, 299 E 6th........ 02
Eagle Savings, 914 Main........ 02
Elet Hall, Dana & Winding
   Way....................................... 29
Enquirer, 617 Vine.................. 02
Executive Bldg, 35 E 7th....... 02
Federal Office 550 Main 02
Federal Reserve Bank, 105 W
   4th... 02
Federated, 707 Race............... 02
Fifth Third Center, 511
   Walnut................................... 02
Film Center, 1632 Central
   Pkwy...................................... 10

Film Mart, 1635 Central
   Pkwy...................................... 14
First National Bank, 105 E
   4th... 02
Formica 120 E 4th.................. 02
Fourth & Walnut, 36 E 4th..... 02
Fruit Exchange, 27 W Front ... 02
Garfield Tower, 111 Garfield
   Pl... 02
Greater Cincinnati Airport..... 75
Greenhills Shopping Ctr......... 18
Gwynne, 602 Main 02
Hartford Insurance, 630
   Main...................................... 02
Hillcrest Square, 7162
   Reading Rd........................... 37
Hyde Park Plaza Shopping
   Ctr 3822 Paxton Ave.......... 09
Inter-Ocean Insurance, 2600
   Victory Pkwy........................ 06
Kenwood Mall Shopping Ctr,
   7800 Montgomery Rd 36
Kenwood Plaza Shopping Ctr
   7801 Montgomery Rd 36
Kenwood Shopping Ctr 7565
   Kenwood Rd......................... 36
Krippendorf, 628 Sycamore.... 02
Kroger, 1014 Vine................... 02
Masonic Temple, 317 E 5th.... 02
Mercantile Library, 414
   Walnut................................... 02
Merchants, 34 W 6th............... 02
Methodist Book Concern, 420
   Plum...................................... 02
Mills, 31 E 4th........................ 02
Montgomery Square Shopping
   Ctr... 42
Morgens Hall, 2930 Scioto..... 19
Northbrook Shopping Ctr........ 31
Northgate Mall........................ 39
Northland Shopping Center..... 41
Norwood Plaza Shopping Ctr .. 12
Palace, 12 E 6th..................... 02
Post-Times Star Tower, 800
   Broadway.............................. 02
Power, 224 E 8th..................... 02
Procter-Gamble, SE Cor 6th &
   Sycamore.............................. 02
Provident Bank, 632 Vine....... 02
Provident Towers, 1 E 4th...... 02
Public Library, 800 Vine......... 02
Pugh, 400 Pike........................ 02
Railway Express, Findlay At
   Mc Lean Ave........................ 14
Resor, 37 W 7th...................... 02
Riverfront Stadium 201 E
   2nd.. 02
Rookwood, 1077 Celestial...... 02
Roselawn Center, 1701
   Section Rd 37
Salvation Army Citadel, 114
   E Central Pkwy.................... 10
Sawyer Hall, 2910 Scioto....... 19
Schwartz, 906 Main 02
Scioto Hall, 2920 Scioto 19
Second National, 830 Main 02
Seven-O-Seven Race, 707
   Race...................................... 02
Southern Ohio Bank, 519
   Main... 02

Swift, 230 E 9th	02
Swifton Shopping Ctr.	37
Telephone 4th Street, 225 E 4th	02
Telephone 7th Street, 209 W 7th	02
Temple Bar, 138 E Court	02
Terrace-Hilton Bldg, 15 W 6th	02
Textile, 205 W 4th	02
Transit, 6 E 4th	02
Transportation, 307 E 4th	02
Tri County Shopping Ctr, 11700 Princeton Rd	46
Tri-State, 432 Walnut	02
Twenty Six East Sixth 26 E 6th	02
U S Post Office And Court House 100 E 5th	02
University Plaza Shopping Ctr, 1 Corry	19
Western Hills Plaza Shopping Ctr	11
Western Village Shopping Ctr	11
Western Woods Shopping Ctr	11
White Oak Shopping Ctr.	39
Wiggins Block, 7 E 5th	02

GOVERNMENT OFFICES

Chamber Of Commerce, 309 Vine	02
Cincinnati Post Office Annex Bldg A, 1601 Dalton Ave.	34
Cincinnati Post Office Annex Bldg B, 1589 Dalton Ave.	34
Cincinnati Post Office Annex Office Tower, 1591 Dalton Ave.	34
City Hall, 800 Central Ave.	02
Environmental Protection Agency	68
Hamilton County Court House, 1000 Main	02
United States Courthouse, 100 E 5th	02
United States Post Office, 100 E 5th	02

HOSPITALS

Bethesda Suburban, 10500 Montgomery Rd	42
Bethesda, 619 Oak	06
Catherine Booth, 3595 Washington Ave.	29
Childrens, 240 Bethesda	29
Christ, 2139 Auburn Ave	19
Cincinnati General, 234 Goodman	29
Deaconess, 311 Straight	19
Drake Memorial,151 W. Galbraith Rd	16
Dunham, Guerley Rd	05
Emerson A North, 5642 Hamilton Ave	24
Epp Memorial, 8000 Kenwood Rd	36

Good Samaritan, 3217 Clifton Ave	20
Holmes, Eden & Bethesda	19
Jewish, 3212 Burnet Ave	29
Longview, 6600 Paddock Rd	16
Maple Knoll, 11174 Springfield Rd	46
Our Lady Of Mercy, 7010 Rowan Hills Dr	27
Providence, 2366 Kipling Rd	39
Rollman Receiving, 3009 Burnet Ave	19
Saint Francis, 1860 Queen City Avenue	14
Saint George, 3156 Glenmore Ave	11
Shriner0s Burns Institute 202 Goodman	19
Veterans, 3200 Vine	20

UNIVERSITIES AND COLLEGES

Cincinnati Bible Seminary, 2700 Glenway Ave	04
Cincinnati College Of Pharmacy, University Of Cincinnati	21
Cincinnati Law School, University Of Cincinnati	21
Cincinnati Technical Inst.,3520 Central Parkway	23
College Conservatory Of Music Of Cincinnati	21
College Of Medicine University Of Cincinnati	19
Edgecliff College, Edgecliff And Victory Parkway	06
Glenmary Seminary, 10295 Princeton Rd	46
Gods Bible School & College, 1810 Young	10
Hebrew Union College, 3101 Clifton Ave	20
Mount Saint Mary Seminary, 5440 Moeller Ave.	12
Ohio College Of Applied Science, 100 E Central Parkway	10
Saint Gregory'S Seminary, 6616 Beechmont Ave	30
Salmon P Chase Law School, 1105 Elm	10
Teachers College Athenaeum Of Ohio, 5418 Moeller Ave.	12
Teachers College University Of Cincinnati, Clifton Ave.	21
University Of Cincinnati, Clifton Ave	21
Xavier University, Dana & Victory Pkwy	07

CLEVELAND 441

POST OFFICE BOXES

Box Nos.		
1-299	Brecksville Br	41
1-299	South Euclid Br	21
300-499	Willow Sta	27
500-699	Edgewater Br	07
700-899	Beachwood Br	22
1000-1099	A Sta	02
1100-1499	B Sta	03
1500-1699	C Sta	04
1700-1799	Newburg Sta	05
1800-2099	University Center Sta	06
2100-2199	H Sta	08
2200-2299	Pearlbrook Sta.	09
2300-2399	Collinwood Sta	10
2400-2599	East Cleveland Br	12
2600-2699	Lakewood Br	07
2700-2799	West Park Sta	11
2800-2999	Rocky River Br	16
3000-3299	Euclid Br	17
3500-3599	Cleveland Heights Br	18
3600-3799	Beachland Sta	19
3800-3899	Collinwood Sta.	10
3900-3999	Shaker Heights Sta	20
4000-4199	Shore Br	23
4200-4399	Noble Br	32
4400-4499	Garfield Heights Br	25
4500-4699	Lyndhurst-Mayfield Br	24
4700-4999	Fairview Park Br	26
5000-6999	Main Office	01
7000-7199	Cranwood Sta	28
7200-7399	Parma Br	29
7400-7599	Midpark Br	30
7600-7899	Independence Br	31
8200-8399	North Royalton Br	33
8400-8599	Briggs Br	34
8600-8799	Puritas Park Sta	35
8800-8999	Strongsville Br	36
9000-9199	Maple Heights Br	37
9200-9399	Olmsted Falls Br	38
9400-9599	Solon Br	39
9600-9799	Bay Village Br	40
9800-9999	Brook Park Br	42
02000-02999	A Sta	02
03000-03999	B Sta	03
05000-05999	Newburg Sta	05
08000-08999	H Sta	08
09000-09999	Pearlbrook	09
10000-10999	Collingwood Sta	10
16000-16999	Rocky River Br	16
18000-18999	Cleveland Heights Br	18
20000-20999	Shaker Heights Sta	20
22000-22999	Beachwood Br	22

24000-24999 Lyndhurst-Mayfield	24
29000-29999 Parma	29
30000-30999 Midpark Br	30
33000-33999 North Royalton	33
36000-36999 Strongsville Br	36
39000-39999 Solon	39
41000-41999 Brecksville	41
42000-42999 Brook Park	42
43000-43999 Richmond Heights	43
44000-44999 Brooklyn	44
45000-45999 Westlake	45
46000-46999 Bedford	46
81000-81999 Airport Mail Facility	81
91000-91999 Main Office	01

STATIONS, BRANCHES AND UNITS

Airport Br	81
Bay Village Br	40
Beachland Sta	19
Beachwood Br	22
Bedford Br	46
Brecksville Br	41
Briggs Br	34
Brook Park Br	42
Brooklyn Br	44
Cleveland Heights Br	18
Collinwood Sta	10
Cranwood Br	28
East Cleveland Br	12
Edgewater Br	07
Erieview Sta	99
Euclid Br	17
Fairview Park Br	26
Federal Reserve Sta	01
Garfield Heights Br	25
Independence Br	31
Kamms Sta	11
Lakewood Br	07
Lee Road Br	20
Lyndhurst-Mayfield Br	24
Maple Heights Br	37
Midpark Br	30
Newburg Sta	05
Noble Br	32
North Royalton Br	33
Olmsted Falls Br	38
Parcel Post Annex Sta	01
Parma Br	29
Pearlbrook Sta	09
Pepper Pike Br	24
Public Square Sta	14
Puritas Parks Sta	35
Richmond Heights Br	43
Rocky River Br	16
Shaker Heights Sta	20
Shore Br	23
Solon Br	39
South Euclid Br	21
Strongsville Br	36
University Center Br	06
University Heights Br	18
Uptown Sta	14
West Park Sta	11
Westlake Br	45
Willow Sta	27
General Delivery	01
Postmaster	01

APARTMENTS, HOTELS, MOTELS

Alcazar, 2450 Derbyshire Rd	06
Belden, 1903 E 70th	03
Belmont, 3844 Euclid Ave	15
Bolton Square, 8907 Carnegie Ave	06
Commodore, 1990 Ford Dr	06
Fenway Motor Inn, 1986 E 107th	06
Graduate House, 10660 Carnegie Ave	06
Haddam, 10510 Euclid Ave	06
Knickerbocker, 8314 Euclid	03
Lake Shore, 12506 Edgewater Dr	07
Manger, 1802 E 13th	14
New Amsterdam, 2142 Euclid Ave	15
Park Lane Villa, 10510 Park Ln	06
Pick-Carter, 1012 Prospect Ave E	15
Regent, 10539 Euclid Ave	06
Sheraton-Cldeveland, 219 Superior Ave W	01
Statler-Hilton, 1127 Euclid Ave	01
Sterling, 3002 Prospect Ave E	15
University Towers, 1575 East Blvd	06
Wade Park Manor, 1890 E 107th	06
Westlake, 19030 Lake Rd	16

BUILDINGS

Airport Mail Facility, 19801 Five Points Rd	81
Arcade, 401 Euclid Ave	14
Bulkley Bldg Annex, 1501 Euclid Ave	15
Bulkley, 1501 Euclid	15
C T S, 1404 E 9th	14
Carnegie Medical Bldg, 10515 Carnegie Ave	06
Caxton, 812 Huron Rd E	15
Central National Bank Bldg, 800 Superior Ave	14
Chester-Twelfth, 1120 Chester Ave	14
Citizens, 850 Euclid Ave	14
Cleveland Athletic Club, 1118 Euclid Ave	15
Cleveland Stadium	14
Colonial Arcade, 530 Euclid Ave	15
Columbia, 112 Prospect Ave E	15
Continental Bank Bldg, 1255 Euclid Ave	15
Crown, 310 Lakeside Ave E	13
Cuyahoga, 216 Superior Ave E	14
East Ohio, 1717 E 9th	14
Engineers, 1365 Ontario	14
Euclid Arcade, 510 Euclid	14
Euclid Ninth Tower, 214 E 9th	15
Federal Reserve Bank, 1455 E 6th	01
Federal, 210 Superior Ave E	14
Fidelity, 1940 E 6th	14

Film Exchange, 2108 Payne Ave	14
Finance, 750 Prospect Ave E	15
Guildhall, 45 Prospect Ave W	15
Hanna, 1422 Euclid Ave	15
Hippodrome Annex, 715 Prospect Ave E	15
Hippodrome, 720 Euclid Ave	14
Illuminating, 55 Public Square	13
Investment Insurance, 601 Rockwell Ave	14
Investment Plaza, 1801 E 9th	14
Keith, 1621 Euclid	15
Leader, 526 Superior Ave East	14
Lincoln, 1367 E 6th	14
Livestock Exchange, 3200 W 65th	02
Mall, 118 St Clair Ave E	14
Marion, 1276 W 3rd	13
Merchandise Mart, 420 Prospect Ave	15
Midland, 101 Prospect Ave W	15
Midwestern National, 75 Public Square	13
National City Bank, 629 Euclid Ave	14
National City East Sixth, 1953 E 6th	14
Nineteen-Hundred Euclid, 1900 Euclid Ave	15
Northern Ohio Food Terminal, 3800 Orange Ave	15
One Erieview Plaza, 1 Erieview Plaza	14
One Hundred Erieview Plaza, 100 Erieview Plaza	14
One Public Square Bldg, 1 Public Square	13
Osborne, 1020 Huron Rd E	15
Park-Chester Medical, 10605 Chester Ave	06
Park, 140 Public Square	14
Penton, 1213 E 3rd	13
Perry-Payne, 740 Superior Ave E	13
Plaza 9 Bldg	14
Post Office Bldg, 301 Prospect Ave W	01
Prospect East Bldg, 1514 Prospect Ave	15
Prospect Fourth, 2077 E 4th	15
Public Auditorium Bldg, 1220 E 6th	14
Public Library, 325 Superior Ave E	14
Public Square, 33 Public Square	13
Republic, 25 Prospect Ave W	15
Rockefeller Physics Bldg, 10900 Euclid Ave	06
Rockefeller, 614 Superior Ave W	13
Rose, 2060 E 9th	15
Schofield, 2014 E 9th	15
Severance Medical Arts Bldg, 5 Severance Cir	18
Six-Sixty-Six Bldg, 666 Euclid Ave	14

Society National Bank, 145 Public Square 14
Standard, 1370 Ontario 13
Superior, 815 Superior Ave E.. 14
Ten-Ten Euclid, 1010 Euclid Ave 15
Terminal Tower, 50 Public Sq 13
Thirty-Three Public Square, 33 Public Square 13
Twelve-Twenty Huron, 1220 Huron Rd E 15
Union Commerce Annex, 1100 Chester Ave 14
Union Commerce Arcade, 1030 Chester Ave 14
Union Commerce, 925 Euclid Ave 15
Union, 1836 Euclid Ave 15
United Office, 2012 W 25th... 13
Western Reserve, 1468 W 9th 13
Williamson, 215 Euclid 14

GOVERNMENT OFFICES

City Hall, 601 Lakeside Ave E 14
Courthouse, 1 Lakeside Ave ... 13
Federal Office Bldg, 1240 E 9th St 99
United States Post Office, 301 Prospect Ave W 13

HOSPITALS

Babies & Children, 2103 Adelbert Rd 06
Bay View, 23200 Lake Rd 40
Bedford Municipal, 44 Blaine Ave 46
Benjamin Rose, 2073 Abington Rd 06
Booth Memorial, 1881 Torbenson Dr 12
Brecksville Veterans Admin, 10000 Brecksville Rd 41
Brentwood, 4110 Warrensville Center Rd 22
Cleveland Clinic, 2050 E 93rd St 06
Cleveland Metropolitan General, 3395 S Cranton Rd 09
Cleveland State, 4455 Turney Rd 05
Euclid-General, 101 E 185th.. 19
Evangelical Deaconess, 4233 Pearl Rd 09
Fairhill Psychiatric, 12200 Fairhill Rd 20
Fairview General, 18101 Lorain Ave 11
Forest City, 701 Parkwood Dr. 08
Grace, 2307 W 14th 13
Hanna House, 2045 Adelbert Rd 06
Highland View, 3901 Ireland Dr 22
Hillcrest, 6760 Mayfield Rd.... 24
Huron Road, 13951 Terrace Rd 12
Ingleside, 8811 Euclid Ave ... 06

Jewish Convalescent, 18810 Harvard Ave 22
Lakeside, 2065 Adelbert Rd.... 06
Lakewood, 14519 Detroit Ave . 07
Lutheran, 2609 Franklin Ave .. 13
Macdonald House, 2105 Adelbert Rd 06
Marymount, 12300 Mc Cracken Rd 25
Mount Sinai, 1800 E 105th... 06
Parma Community General, 7007 Powers Blvd 29
Polyclinic, 6606 Carnegie Ave 03
Rainbow, 1605 South Green Rd 21
Richmond Heights General, 27100 Chardon Rd 43
Saint Ann, 2475 East Blvd 06
Saint Johns, 7911 Detroit Ave 02
Saint Lukes, 11311 Shaker Blvd 04
Saint Vincent Charity, 2222 Central Ave 15
Saints Alexis, 5163 Broadway 27
Suburban Community, 4180 Warrensville Center Rd...... 22
Sunny Acres, 4310 Richmond Rd 22
University, 2065 Adelbert Rd.. 06
Veterans Administration Hospital, 10701 East Blvd. 06
Womans, 1940 E 101th.......... 06

UNIVERSITIES AND COLLEGES

Case Western Reserve University, 10900 Euclid Ave 06
Cleveland Institute Of Art, 11141 East Blvd 06
Cleveland State University, 1983 E 24th 15
Cleveland-Marshall Law School, 1240 Ontario 13
Cuyahoga Community College, 2214 E 14th 15
Dyke & Spencerian College, 1375 E 6th 14
Great Lakes College & Clinic, 1900 Superior Ave 14
Griswold Institute, 2031 Euclid Ave 15
John Carroll University, 20700 North Park Blvd...... 18
Lincoln Extension Institute Incorporated, 1401 W 75th 02
Notre Dame College, 4545 College Rd 21
Ohio College Of Podiatry, 2057 Cornell Rd 06
Saint John College, 1033 Superior Ave E 14
Ursuline College, 2600 Lander Rd 24

COLUMBUS　　432

POST OFFICE BOXES

Box Nos.
A-E　　Worthington Branch..........43085
A-H　　Mount Vernon Avenue Sta.... 03
1-797　Worthington Branch..........43085
1-2519　Main Office 16
2731-2944　Hilltop Sta 04
3001-3179　University Sta.... 10
3451-3796　Beechwold Sta .. 14
4001-4089　H Sta 15
4391-4697　Tri-Village Sta .. 12
4701-4994　B Sta 02
5001-5254　Tri-Village Sta .. 12
5501-5874　Upper Arlington Br 21
6301-6494　Oakland Park Br 24
6501-6798　Bexley Br 09
6801-7124　E Sta 05
7301-7368　Bexley Br 09
7601-7892　G Sta 07
8001-8448　A Sta 01
8501-8799　State Street...... 15
9601-9807　F Sta 06
11301-11447　C Sta 11
13001-13500　Whitehall Br..... 13
14501-14774　Mount Vernon Avenue Sta.... 03
15001-15949　Civic Center 15
17000-17450　Lockbourne Air Force Br.......... 17
19001-19244　Shepard Sta 19
19701-19999　Airport Sta....... 19
20001-20999　Northwest 20
23081-23424　Point Sta.......... 23
27001-27990　Livingston Sta.. 27
28001-28999　Lincoln Village Br 28
29001-29999　Northland 29
30100-30999　Gahanna.......... 30

RURAL ROUTES

1 30
4 28

STATIONS, BRANCHES AND UNITS

Airport Sta 19
Beechwold Sta 14
Bexley Br 09
College Springs Br 19
Gahanna Br 30
Hilltop Sta 04
Lincoln Village Br 28
Livingston Sta 27
Lockbourne A F B Br 17
Mount Vernon Avenue Sta 03
Northwest Sta 20
Oakland Park Br 24
Obetz Br 07
Point Sta 23
Shepard Sta 19
State Street Sta 15
Tri Village Sta 12
University Sta 10
Upper Arlington Br 21

Whitehall Br 13
Wonderland Rural Br 30
Worthington Br 43085
General Delivery 16
Postmaster 16

APARTMENTS, HOTELS, MOTELS

Arlington Arms, 1335 Dublin
  Rd 15
Beverly Manor, 374 N
  Virginia Lee 09
Bolivar Arms, Caldwell Pl 03
Broad Hampton, 42 N
  Hampton Rd 13
Broad-Garfield, 775 E Broad ... 05
Broad-Ohio, 1160 E Broad 05
Broadwin, 1312 E Broad 05
Cambridge Arms, 926 E
  Broad 05
Charminel, 342 E State 15
Christopher Inn, 300 E
  Broad 15
Clarmont Motor Inn, 650 S
  High 15
Clifton Court, 179 Clifton Ct .. 03
Clifton Park, 1761 Clifton
  Ave 03
Columbus Plaza, 50 N 3rd 15
Columbus Travelodge, 1070
  Dublin Rd 15
Fairport Gardens, Fairway
  Blvd 13
First Community Village,
  1800 Riverside Dr 12
Fort Hayes, 31 W Spring 15
Frambes Hall, 47 E Frambes
  Ave 01
Greystone Court, 815 N High .. 15
Holiday Inn Of America
  Airport, 4300 E 17th Ave ... 19
Holiday Inn Of America
  Downtown, 175 E Town St .. 15
Holiday Inn Of America East,
  4801 E Broad 13
Holiday Inn Of America
  North, 1212 E Granville
  Rd 29
Holiday Inn Of America West,
  4601 W Broad 28
Howard Johnson East, 5000
  E Main 13
Howard Johnson North, 999 E
  Granville Rd 29
Howard Johnson West, 3833
  W Broad 28
Indianola Court, 1770 N
  High 01
International House-Men, 104
  15th Ave E 01
International House-Women,
  1875 Summit 01
Jefferson, 17 E Spring 15
Leafy Dale, 789 Dennison
  Ave 15
Lincoln Lodge, 4950 W
  Broad 28
Lutheran Senior City, 977
  Parkview Blvd 19
Madonna, 79 Taylor Ave 03
Mayfair, 226 Mayfair Blvd 13
Mid-City, 950 E Broad 05
Nationwide Inn, 4101 W
  Broad 28

Neil Hall, 1634 Neil Ave 10
Neil House Motor Hotel, 41 S
  High 15
Neil-Wood Gables, 2090 Neil
  Ave 01
Northern, 493 1/2 N High 15
Norwick, State & 4th 15
Ohio Stater Inn, 2060 N
  High 01
Olentangy Inn, 1299
  Olentangy Rvr Rd 12
Park Tower, 1620 E Broad 03
Royal York, 1445 E Broad 05
Seneca, Broad & Grant 15
Southern, Main & High 15
Southgate Manor, 2207
  Winslow Dr 07
Stouffers University Inn,
  3025 Olentangy River Rd ... 02
Thurber Towers, 645 Neil
  Ave 15
Town Terrace, 518 E Town 15
Townley Court, 580 E Town 15
University Arms, 505 Harley
  Dr 02
Virginia Lee Gardens, 3016
  Maryland Ave 09
Westgate Manor, 587
  Wedgewood Dr 28
Westminster Hall, 52 15th
  Ave E 01
Y M C A, 40 W Long St 15
Y W C A, 65 S 4th St 15

BUILDINGS

Atlas, 8 E Long 15
Beacon Mutual, 52 W Gay 15
Beggs, 21 E State 15
Blue Cross, 174 E Long 15
Brunson, 145 N High 15
Bryson, 156 Parsons Ave 15
Bryson, 700 Bryden Rd 15
Buckeye & Loan, 36 E Gay 15
Catholic Center, 80 S 6th St ... 15
City National Bank, 20 E
  Broad 15
Columbus Public Library, 96
  S Grant Ave 15
Continental, 11 E Gay 15
Curl, 1309 E Broad 05
Eighty-Eight East Broad, 88
  E Broad 15
Empire, 150 E Broad 15
First National, 33 N High 15
Franklin Federal Savings &
  Loan, 297 S High 15
Guarantee Title & Trust, 22
  W Gay 15
Hartman Theatre, 79 E State
  St 15
High-Long, 5 E Long 15
Huntington Bank, 17 S High 15
Lanman, 20 S 3rd 15
Lincoln-Le Veque Tower, 50 W
  Broad 15
Masonic Temple, 34 N 4th
  St 15
Medical Arts, 327 E State St ... 15
Medical Science, 9 Buttles
  Ave 15
Nationwide, 246 N High 16
Nitschke, 35 E Gay 15

Ohio State Federal Savings &
  Loan, 85 E Gay 15
Outlook, 44 E Broad 15
Physicians & Surgeons, 350
  E Broad 15
Physicians, 683 E Broad St 15
Spahr, 50 E Broad St 15
Stoneman, 335 S High 15
Three Ninety Five East Broad,
  395 E Broad St 15
Trautman, 209 S High 15
University Club, 40 S 3rd 15

GOVERNMENT OFFICES

Chamber Of Commerce, 50 W
  Broad 15
City Hall, 90 W Broad 15
Court House, Mound & High ... 15
Federal Bldg, 85 Marconi
  Blvd 15
Main Post Office, 850 Twin
  Rivers Dr 15
State House, Broad & High
  St 15
State Office Bldg, 65 S Front
  St 15

HOSPITALS

Benjamin Franklin, 1755
  Alum Creek Dr 07
Childrens, 561 S 17th 05
Columbus State School, 1601
  W Broad 23
Columbus State, 1960 W
  Broad 23
Doctors Lincoln Village, 5100
  W Broad 28
Doctors Main Hospital, 1087
  Denninson Ave 01
Grant, 309 E State 15
Harding, 445 E Granville Rd .. 43085
Lincoln Memorial, 3341 E
  Livingston Ave 27
Mercy, 1430 S High 07
Mount Carmel, 793 W State 22
Ohio State University, 410 W
  10th Ave 10
Ohio Tuberculosis, 466 W
  10th Ave 10
Riverside Methodist, 3535
  Olentangy Rvr Rd 14
Saint Anns Maternity, 1555
  Bryden Rd 05
Saint Anthony, 1450
  Hawthorne Ave 03

MILITARY INSTALLATIONS

Fort Hayes Military
  Reservation 15
Lockbourne Air Force Base 17

UNIVERSITIES AND COLLEGES

Bliss Business, 131 E State ... 15
Capital University, 2199 E
  Main 09
Columbus Business
  University, 208 N High 15
Franklin University, 201 S.
  Grant 15

Ohio Dominican, 1016 Sunbury Rd		19
Ohio State University, 1659 N High		10
Saint Charles, 2010 E Broad..		09
Saint Mary Of The Springs, 1016 Sunbury Rd		19

CUYAHOGA FALLS 442

POST OFFICE BOXES

Box Nos.		
1-600	Cuyahoga Falls	22
900-1200	State Road	23
1300-1900	Stow Br	24

STATIONS, BRANCHES AND UNITS

State Road Sta	23
Stow Br	24
General Delivery	22
Postmaster	22

DAYTON 454

POST OFFICE BOXES

Box Nos.		
1-176	Dabel Br	20
1-207	Centerville Br	59
1-268	West Carrollton Br	49
1-297	Dayton View Sta	06
1-297	Roosevelt Sta	17
1-324	North Dayton Sta	04
1-429	Forest Park Br	05
1-597	Veterans Administration Br	
1-646	Far Hills Br	19
1-1061	Mid City Sta	02
1-1477	Main Office	01
1401-14229	Northridge-Br	14
2001-2384	Kettering Br	29
3001-3175	Overlcok Br	31
3001-4077	Trotwood Br	26
7001-7296	B Sta	07
33001-33499	Wpafb Br	33
33501-33619	Amc Br	33

STATIONS, BRANCHES AND UNITS

Air Materiel Command Br	33
Centerville Br	59
Dabel Sta	20
Dayton View Sta	06
Far Hills Br	19
Forest Park Br	05
Huber Heights Br	24
Kettering Br	29
Mid City Sta	02
Moraine Br	39
North Dayton Sta	04
Northridge Br	14
Overlook Br	31
Roosevelt Sta	17

Trotwood Br		26
Veterans Administration Br		28
Wright Patterson AFB Br		33
General Delivery		01
Postmaster		01

APARTMENTS, HOTELS, MOTELS

Commodore, 522 Grand Ave	05
Gibbons Arcade, 26 W 3rd	02
Holden, 200 W 5th	02
Holiday Inn, 2301 Wagoner Ford Rd	14
Howard Johnson'S, 2221 Wagoner Ford Rd	14
Imperial House North, 2401 Needmore Rd	14
Matl Motor Inn, 21 S Jefferson St	02
Oakwood Manor, 1211 Far Hills Ave	19
Red Horse Motor Inn, 4625 S Dixie Hgwy	39
Sheraton-Dayton, 210 N Main	02
Statler-Hilton, 11 S Ludlow	01
Stratford House, 330 W 1st	02
Stratford Motel, 225 W 1st	02
Travelodge North, 2833 N Dixie Dr	14
Travelodge South, 4530 S Dixie Hgwy	39
Travelodge, 222 E First St	02

BUILDINGS

American, 4 S Main	02
Century 11i W 1st	02
Commercial, 44 S Ludlow	02
Dayco 333 W 1st	02
Eleven West Monument, 11 W Monument Ave	02
Fidelity 219 S Main	02
Gas & Electric, 25 N Main	02
Gem City Savings, 4 N Main	02
Grant Denau Towers 40 W 4th St	02
Harries, 137 N Main	02
Hulman, 120 W 2nd	02
I B M, 33 W 1st St	02
Municipal, 101 W 3rd	01
Reibold, 117 S Main	02
Safety, 325 W 3rd	02
Talbott Towers, 118 W 1st	02
Talbott, 131 N Ludlow	02
Third National, 34 N Main	02
Twenty-Five South Main, 25 S Main	02
Winters Bank, 40 N Main	02

GOVERNMENT OFFICES

Court House, 15 N Main	02
Federal Bureau Of Investigation 40 W 4th	02
Internal Revenue Service 40 W 4th	02
Recruiting Offices, Centre City Bldg	02
Selective Service Board, Knott Bldg	02
Social Security Agency, 333 W 1st	02

Treasury Department Collector Of Customs 118 W 3rd		02

28

HOSPITALS

Dayton Childrens Psychiatric, 141 Firwood Dr	19
Dayton State, 2335 Wayne Ave	20
Good Samaritan, 1425 W Fairview Ave	06
Grandview, 405 Grand Ave	05
Kettering Memorial, 3535 Southern Blvd	29
Miami Valley, 1 Wyoming	09
Saint Elizabeth, 49 Hopeland	08
Stillwater Sanitarium, 8100 N Main	15
Veterans Administration, 4100 W 3rd	28

MILITARY INSTALLATIONS

Defense Electronic Supply Center	44
Wright Patterson A F B	33

UNIVERSITIES AND COLLEGES

University Of Bayton, 300 College Park Ave	69
Wright State University 7751 Col Glenn Hwy	31

ELYRIA 440

POST OFFICE BOXES

Box Nos.		
A-M	Parcel Post Annex	35
1-145	North Ridgeville Br	39
1-760	Main Office	35
901-1048	Parcel Post Annex	35

RURAL ROUTES

1,2,3	35

STATIONS, BRANCHES AND UNITS

North Ridgeville Br	35
Parcel Post Annex Sta	35
General Delivery	35
Postmaster	35

HAMILTON 450

POST OFFICE BOXES

Box Nos.		
1-170	Fairfield Br	14
1-958	Main Office	12
2001-2199	Lindenwald Sta	15
3001-3090	Rossville Sta	13

RURAL ROUTES

1	11
2	13
3	15
4,5,6	13
7	11

STATIONS, BRANCHES AND UNITS

Fairfield Br	14
Lindenwald Sta	15
Millville Br	13
New Miami Br	11
Reily Rural Br	60
Rossville Sta	13
General Delivery	12
Postmaster	12

LIMA 458

POST OFFICE BOXES

Box Nos		
1-162	Gomer R. Sta	09
1-170	Buckland R. Sta	19
1-197	Beaverdam R. Sta	08
1-1318	Main Office	02
2001-2086	Cridersville Br	06
3001-3116	Elida	07
7001-7250	Lafayette	54

RURAL ROUTES

1,2,3	07
4	06
5	01
6	06
7	54

STATIONS, BRANCHES AND UNITS

Beaverdam Rural Br	08
Buckland Rural Br	19
Cridersville Br	06
Elida Br	07
Gomer Rural Br	09
Lafayette Rural Br	54
General Delivery	01
Postmaster	02

LORAIN 440

POST OFFICE BOXES

Box Nos		
1-570	Main Office	52
1001-1203	South Lorain Sta	55
2001-2095	Sheffield Lake Br	54

STATIONS, BRANCHES AND UNITS

Sheffield Lake Br	54
South Lorain Sta	55
General Delivery	52
Postmaster	52

MANSFIELD 449

POST OFFICE BOXES

Box Nos.		
1-790	Mansfield	01
1000-1499	Mansfield Annex Sta	03
1500-1999	Southwest Sta	07
2000-2499	Lincoln Sta	05
2500-2999	Sherman Sta	06
3000-3499	Lexington Br	04

RURAL ROUTES

1,2,3,4,5,6	03
7,8	04

STATIONS, BRANCHES AND UNITS

Lexington Br	04
Lincoln Br	05
Parcel Post Annex Sta	03
Sherman Sta	06
Southwest Sta	07
General Delivery	01
Postmaster	01

APARTMENTS, HOTELS, MOTELS

Base Apartments, 270 N Main	02
Carriage Hill, 72 N Linden Rd	06
Charford Apts 74 Bowman St	02
Court, 115 N Main	02
Creamers, 304 N Main	02
Downtown Motor Lodge, 191 Park Ave W	02
Ebony, 831 Bowman	05
Forty-Two Motel, 2444 Lexington Ave	07
Gardner Apts 114 Park Avenue West	02
Holiday Inn Of America, Laver Rd	05
King Apts 616 King St	06
Leland Motor Hotel, 27 Park Ave W	02
Mansfield Apartments, 151 W 2nd	02
Newman, 316 N Main	02
Phoenix, 323 N Main	02
Ramada Inn, P.o. Box 2007	05
Southern, 2 S Park	02
Travel Lodge Of Mansfield, 137 Park Ave W	02
Zediker Apartments, 100 Blymer Ave	03
Zediker Apartments, 160 W 2nd	02
Zediker Apartments, 458 Woodward	03

BUILDINGS

City Bldg 27 West Second St	02
Courthouse 50 Park Avenue East	02
Farmers Bank, 28 Park Ave W	02

Richland Trust, 3 N Main	02
Stewart Towers, 13 Park Ave W	02

HOSPITALS

Beatty Clinic, 1695 Lucas Rd	03
Madison Hospital, 73 Madison Rd	05
Mansfield General Hospital, 335 Glessner Ave	03
Peoples Hospital, 597 Park Ave E	05

UNIVERSITIES AND COLLEGES

Mansfield Campus Ohio State U, 2275 Springmill Rd	06

SPRINGFIELD 455

POST OFFICE BOXES

Box Nos.		
1-1594	Springfield	01

RURAL ROUTES

1,2,3,4,5,6,7,8	02

STATIONS, BRANCHES AND UNITS

General Delivery	01
Postmaster	01

APARTMENTS, HOTELS, MOTELS

Allan Apartments, 1001 E High	05
Belmont Apartments, 1920 E High	05
Fairfax Motel, 2418 E Main	03
Governors Manor Apartments, 2100 E High	05
High Royal Apartments, 1590-1592 E High	05
Holiday Inn Motel, 1715 W North	04
Northridge Apartments, 4761-4953 Ridgewood Rd E	03
Ridgewood Apartments, 1009 E Home Rd	03
Scots Inn Motel 11 W Leffel Ln	06
Shawnee Apartments, 102 E Main	02
Southern Apartments, 501 S Limestone	05
Travelodge Motel, 325 W Columbia	04
Troy Plaza Apartments, 2107 Troy Rd	04
Williamsburg Apartments, 2650 E High	05

BUILDINGS

Arcade, 1 E High	02
Arcue, 6 W High	02

First National Bank, 4 W Main	02
Mc Adams, 31 E High	02
Mitchell, 42 S Limestone	02
New Merchants & Mechanics, 20 S Limestone	02
Tecumseh, 34 W High	02
Winwood, 49 W High	02
Woolworth, 34 E High	02

HOSPITALS

Community Hospital, 2615 E High	01
Ioof Home Hospital, 404 E Mccreight Ave	01
Knights Of Pythian Home Hospital, 901 W High	01
Mercy Medical Center, 1343 N Fountain Ave	01
Rickley Memorial Hospital, West National Rd	01
Springview Hospital, 3130 E National Rd	01

UNIVERSITIES AND COLLEGES

Wittenberg University	01

TOLEDO   436

POST OFFICE BOXES

Box Nos.

1-357	A Sta	05
1-1080	Main Office	01
1101-1290	Madison Avenue Sta	24
1501-2368	Central Sta	03
2501-2914	Sta Kenwood	06
3001-3499	C Sta	07
3501-3678	D Sta	08
4001-4317	E Sta	09
4500-4716	Old West End Sta	20
5001-5299	Point Place Sta	11
5501-5897	Wernert Sta	13
6001-6399	Heatherdowns Sta	14
6401-6764	West Toledo Sta	12
7001-7392	Reynolds Corners Sta	15
7501-7596	Oregon Br	16

RURAL ROUTES

5	18

STATIONS, BRANCHES AND UNITS

Central Sta	04
Heathersdowns Sta	14
Kenwood Sta	06
Madison Avenue Sta	24
Old West End Br	20
Oregon Br	16
Point Place Sta	11
Reynolds Corners Sta	15
Wernert Sta	13
West Toledo Sta	12
General Delivery	01
Postmaster	01

APARTMENTS, HOTELS, MOTELS

Albertus Brown Homes, 300 Avondale Ave	02
Birmingham Terrace, 2100 Consaul	05
Brand Whitlock Homes, 392 Nebraska Ave	02
Commodore Perry, 505 Jefferson Ave	03
Executive Towers, 1920 Collingwood Blvd	24
Globe, 1001 Jefferson Ave	24
Hillcrest, 231 16th	24
Holiday Inn N, 1821 E Manhattan Blvd	08
Hospitality Motor Inn, 1800 Miami	05
Lorraine, 1117 Jefferson Ave	24
Mid City, 111 S Summit	02
Port Lawrence Homes, 200 Indiana Ave	02
Ravine Park Village, 2300 Seaman	05
Secor, 425 Jefferson Ave	04
Southern, 5430 Telegraph Rd	12
Spieker Terrace, 385 Earl	05
Toledo Travel Lodge, 1919 Collingwood Blvd	24
Town House, 1111 W Bancroft	06
Waldorf, 310 Summit	03
Weiler Homes, 601 Fassett	05
Willard Motor Lodge, 415 St Clair	03

BUILDINGS

Board Of Trade, 205 St Clair	04
Community Services, 1 Stranahan Sq	04
Edison, 420 Madison Ave	04
Federal Office, 234 Summit	04
Fiberglass Tower, 1 Levis Sq	04
Gardner, 506 Madison Ave	04
Great Eastern, 2500 Woodville Rd	16
Lamb, 406 Madison Ave	04
Lof, 811 Madison Ave	24
Lucas County Bank, 515 Madison Ave	04
Lucas County, C H Adams At Erie	24
Miracle Mile, 4925 Jackman Rd	13
National Bank, 606 Madison Ave	04
Owens-Illinois, 405 Madison Ave	04
Professional, 1838 Parkwood Ave	24
Security, 243 Huron	04
Southland, 3300 Glendale	14
Spitzer, 520 Madison Ave	04
Toledo Trust, 241 Summit	04
United Savings, 240 Huron	04
Westgate, 3301 W Central Ave	06
Woodville Mall, 3725 Williston Rd	16

GOVERNMENT OFFICES

Chamber Of Commerce, 218 Huron	04
City Hall Safety, Erie & Jackson	24
United States Courthouse & Customs, 1710 Spielbush Blvd	24

HOSPITALS

Flower, 3350 Collingwood Blvd	10
Maumee Valley, 2025 Arlington Ave	09
Mercy, 2221 Madison Ave	24
Parkview, 1920 Parkwood Ave	24
Riverside, 1609 Summit	04
Roche Memorial, 945 S Detroit	14
Saint Charles, 2600 Navarre Ave	16
Saint Lukes, 2517 Robinwood	10
Saint Vincents, 2213 Cherry	08
Toledo State, 930 S Detroit Ave	03
Toledo, 2142 N Cove Blvd	06

UNIVERSITIES AND COLLEGES

Davis Business, 701 Adams	24
Mary Manse, 2443 Collingwood Blvd	20
Stautzenberger Business, 331 1/2 St Clair	04
University Of Toledo, 2801 W Bancroft	06

WARREN   444

POST OFFICE BOXES

Box Nos.

100-1431	Main Office	82
2001-2999	Warren Annex Sta	84
3000-3999	West Warren Sta	85

RURAL ROUTES

1,2,3,4,6	81

STATIONS, BRANCHES AND UNITS

Parcel Post Annex Sta	84
West Warren Sta	85
General Delivery	82
Postmaster	81

YOUNGSTOWN 445

POST OFFICE BOXES

Box Nos.

1-1590	Main Office	01
1900-2099	East Side Sta..	06
2100-2299	North Side Sta.	04
2300-2499	West Side Sta	09
2500-2799	South Side Sta.	07
2900-3099	Fosterville Sta..	11
3100-3799	Boardman Br....	12
3800-3999	Parcel Post Sta	12
4000-4199	Austintown Br..	15
5000-5399	Poland Br........	14

STATIONS, BRANCHES AND UNITS

Austintown Br	15
Boardman Br	12
East Side Sta	06
Fosterville Sta	11
Liberty Br	05
North Side Sta	04
Parcel Post Sta	12
Plaza Br	12
Poland Br	14
South Side Sta	07
West Side Sta	09
General Delivery	01
Postmaster	01

APARTMENTS, HOTELS, MOTELS

Alberta Terrace, 1918 Hillman	07
Belmont, 929 Belmont Ave	04
Buechner Hall, 620 Bryson	02
Canfield, 12-14 West Delason Ave	07
Caroline, 2116 Market	05
Colonial, 725 Bryson	02
Della, 2406 Market	07
Dora Terrace, 2145-55 Oak Hill Ave	07
Dorothy, 3325 Market	07
Edgewood, 55 E Dewey	07
Edna Terrace, 524-538 Belmont Ave	02
Elm Terrace, 200 West Scott..	02
Elm, 1745 Elm	02
Evans Terrace, 204-214 Grant	02
Fifth Avenue, 804-812 Fifth Ave	04
Fithian, 145 East Midlothian Bd	07
Glenoir Terrace, 1501-15 Kennedy Ave	06
Home, 238 West Rayen Ave..	02
Kalsander The, 374 E Boardman-Poland Rd	12
Kane, 511 West Indianola	11
Kennedy Terrace, 1731-41 Hillman	07
Lillian Flats, 102 Benita Ave..	05
Linberg Dwellings, 3820 Mahoning Ave	15
Lincoln Towers, 257 Lincoln Ave	03
Lo-Rayen, 143 W Rayen	03
Lora, 218-226 Lora Ave	04
Lorena Terrace, 1435-39 Wick Ave	05
Lustig, 802-812 5th Ave	04
Mar-Phil, 16 West Madison Ave	05
Mayfair, 5312 Glenwood Ave	12
Mc Vey Terrace, 108 W Madison Ave	05
Mellinger Terrace, 2201-09 Hillman	07
Merle Terrace, 240-48 Lincoln Park	06
Metro Plaza, 151 S Hazel	03
Newport, 3711 Glenwood Ave.	11
Newport, 4000 Hillman Way..	12
North Heights, 273-5 North Heights Ave	04
Ohio Hotel, 121 West Boardman	01
Parkway Tower, 291 Park Ave	04
Pelton, 224 West Wood	02
Rayen, 305 Elm	03
Renner, 277 Park Ave	03
Ryder Terrace, 2129-39 Hillman	07
Shagrin, 204 West Madison Ave	04
Sunset, 369 East Midlothian Blvd	07
Valley, 31 Spring Common	03
Vindy, 32 E Front	03
Voyager Motor Inn, 129 Market	03
West, 308 Lincoln	02
Westlake Terrace, 976 W Federal St	10
Wickcliffe Manor, 28 Yorkshire Blvd	15
Williams Terrace, 2144 Oak Hill Ave	07
Youngstown, 311 W Boardman	03

BUILDINGS

American Legion Home, 34 West Spring	02
American Red Cross, 266 West Wood	02
Armory Ohio State, 325 West Rayen Ave	02
Binema Bldg, 112 W Commerce	03
Boardman Medical Arts, 7330 Market	12
Butler Art Institute, 524 Wick Ave	02
Central Tower, 11 Central Sq.	03
Diocese Of Youngstown, 144 West Wood	03
Dollar Bank, 16 Wick Ave	03
Eagles, 272 West Rayen	03
Executive Bldg 123-25 W. Commerce	03
Federal, 18 N Phelps	03
Home Savings & Loan, 277 West Federal	03
Jewish Community Center, 505 Gypsy Lane	01
K Of C, 25 South Hazel	03
K Of P Hall, 247 West Federal	03
Lederer, 450 West Commerce.	03
Legal Arts, 101 Market	03
Mahoning Bank, 26 Market	03
Market Street Professional, 3718 Market	07
Masonic Temple, 233 Wick Ave	03
Medical Arts, 3031 Market	07
Ohio Edison, 25 East Boardman	03
Proffessional, 226 North Phelps	03
Public Library, 305 Wick Ave..	03
Realty, 47 Central Sq	03
Renner Block, 33 North Hazel	03
Republic, 335 Market	03
South Side Bank, 1509 Market	07
Stambaugh Auditorium, 1000 Fifth Ave	04
Stambaugh, 44 Central Sq.	03
Union Bank, 16 Central Sq.....	03
W F M J, 101 West Boardman	03
Wick, 30 W. Federal	03
Y W C A, 25 West Rayen Ave.	03
Ymca	01
Youngstown Catholic Action Center, 141 West Rayen Ave	03
Youngstown Symphony Center, 266 West Federal...	03

GOVERNMENT OFFICES

City Hall, 106 W Boardman....	03
City Jail, 116 West Boardman	03
County Jail, 21 West Boardman	03
Court House Mahoning County, 120 Market	03
U S Post Office And Court House, 9 West Front	03

HOSPITALS

Blackburn Home For Aged, 6 Botsford	14
Cafaro Memorial Hospital	61
Florence Crittendon Home, 1161 Mcguffey Rd	05
Mahoning County Tuberculosis Sanatorium, 4880 Kirk Rd	15
Saint Elizabeth, 1044 Belmont Ave	05
Stambaugh Nurses Home	01
Tod Nurses Home	01
Woodside Receiving, 800 E Indianola Ave	02
Youngstown North Side Unit..	01
Youngstown Osteopathic	01
Youngstown South Side Unit..	01

UNIVERSITIES AND COLLEGES

| Penn Ohio, 3517 Market | 07 |
| Youngstown State University, 410 Wick Ave | 03 |

OKLAHOMA
(Abbreviation: OK)

Achille	74720
Ada (1st)	74820
Adair	74330
Adams	73901
Adamson, R. Br. Hartshorne	74520
Addington	73520
Admiral, Sta. Tulsa (see appendix)	
Afton	74331
Agra	74824
Airpark, Br. Ardmore	73401
Albany	74721
Albert	73001
Albion	74521
Alderson	74522
Alex	73002
Aline	73716
Allen	74825
Alluwe, R. Br. Nowata	74049
Alma	73003
Altus (1st)	73521
Altus A F B, Br. Altus	73521
Alva (1st)	73717
Amber	73004
Ames	73718
Amorita	73719
Anadarko (1st)	73005
Antlers	74523
Apache	73006
Arapaho	73620
Arcadia	73007
Ardmore (1st)	73401
Arkoma	74901
Arnett	73832
Asher	74826
Pearson, R. Br.	74861
Ashland	74524
Atoka	74525
Bentley, R. Br.	74527
Farris, R. Br.	74542
Atwood	74827
Avant	74001
Bache	74526
Bacone	74420
Baker	73930
Balko	73931
Barnsdall	74002
Bartlesville (1st)	74003
East Side, Sta.	74003
Battiest	74722
Bearden	74828
Beaver	73932
Beggs	74421
Bengal	74929
Bennington	74723
Bentley, R. Br. Atoka	74527
Bernice, R. Br. Afton	74331
Bessie	73622
Bethany (1st)	73008
Bethel	74724
Big Cabin	74332
Billings	74630
Binger	73009
Bison	73720
Bixby	74008
Blackburn, R. Cr. Pawnee	74058
Blackwell (1st)	74631
Blair	73526
Blanchard	73010
Blanco	74528

Blocker	74529
Blue	74725
Bluejacket	74333
Boise City	73933
Wheeless, R. Br.	73952
Bokchito	74726
Bokoshe	74930
Boley	74829
Boswell	74727
Boulevard, Sta. Norman	73069
Bowlegs	74830
Bowring, R. Br. Pawhuska	74009
Boynton	74422
Bradley	73011
Braggs	74423
Braman	74632
Bray	73012
Breckinridge, R. Br. Enid	73721
Briartown, R. Br. Porum	74424
Bridgeport	73013
Bristow (1st)	74010
Britton, Sta. Oklahoma City	73114
Broken Arrow (1st)	74012
Broken Bow	74728
Bromide	74530
Buffalo	73834
Bunch	74931
Burbank	74633
Burlington	73722
Burneyville	73430
Burns Flat	73624
Butler	73625
Byars	74831
Byron	73723
Cache	73527
Caddo	74729
Calera	74730
Calumet	73014
Calvin	74531
Gerty, R. Br.	74544
Camargo	73835
Cameron	74932
Pocola, R. Br.	74902
Cameron College, Sta. Lawton	73501
Canadian	74425
Caney	74533
Canton	73724
Canute	73626
Capitol Hill, Sta. Oklahoma City (see appendix)	
Capron	73725
Cardin	74335
Carmen	73726
Carnegie	73015
Carney	74832
Carrier	73727
Carter	73627
Cartersville	74934
Cartwright	74731
Cashion	73016
Castle	74833
Catoosa	74015
Cement	73017
Centrahoma	74534
Centralia	74336
Chandler	74834
Chattanooga	73528
Checotah	74426
Chelsea	74016
Cherokee	73728
Chester	73838
Cheyenne	73628

Chickasha (1st)	73018
Chilocco	74635
Choctaw	73020
Chouteau	74337
Mazie, R. Br.	74353
Cimarron, Sta. Oklahoma City (see appendix)	
Claremore (1st)	74017
Clarita	74535
Clayton	74536
Clearview	74835
Clebit	74732
Cleo Springs	73729
Cleveland	74020
Clinton (1st)	73601
Cloudy	74537
Coalgate	74538
Colbert	74733
Colcord	74338
Coleman	73432
College, Sta. Stillwater	74074
Collinsville (1st)	74021
Colony	73021
Comanche	73529
Commerce	74339
Concho	73022
Connerville	74836
Cookson	74427
Cooperton, R. Br. Gotebo	73023
Copan	74022
Cordell (1st)	73632
Corn	73024
Council Hill	74428
Countyline	73025
Covington	73730
Coweta	74429
Cox City, R. Br. Rush Springs	73082
Coyle	73027
Crawford	73638
Crescent	73028
Cromwell	74837
Crowder	74430
Cumberland	74333
Cushing (1st)	74023
Custer	73639
Cyril	73029
Dacoma	73731
Daisy	74540
Dale, R. Br. Shawnee	74838
Davenport	74026
Davidson	73530
Davis	73030
Dawson, Sta. Tulsa	74151
Deer Creek	74636
Del City, Br. Oklahoma City (see appendix)	
Delaware	74027
Delhi	73640
Depew	74028
Depot, Br. Mc Alester	74501
Devol	73531
Dewar	74431
Dewey	74029
Dibble	73031
Dill City	73641
Disney	74340
Donaldson, Sta. Tulsa	74104
Dougherty	73032
Douglas	73733
Dover	73734
Dow, R. Br. Hartshorne	74541

Downtown, Sta. Oklahoma City (see appendix)
Drummond 73735
Drumright 74030
Duke 73532
Duncan (1st) 73533
Durant (1st) 74701
Durham 73642
Dustin 74839
Eagle City 73643
Eagletown 74734
Eakly 73033
Earlsboro 74840
East Side, Sta. Bartlesville 74003
Eastern, Sta. Oklahoma City ... 73117
Eastern Okla A M College,
  Br. Wilburton 74578
Edmond (1st) 73034
El Reno (1st) 73036
Eldorado 73537
Elgin 73538
Elk City (1st) 73644
Elmer 73539
Elmore City 73035
Elmwood 73935
Enid (1st) 73701
  Breckinridge, R. Br. 73721
  University, Sta. 73701
  Vance A F B, Br. 73701
  3, Sta. 73701
Erick 73645
Eucha 74342
Eufaula 74432
  Lenna, R. Br. 74443
Evo 73936
Fairfax 74637
Fairland 74343
Fairmont 73736
Fairview 73737
Fanshawe 74935
Fargo 73840
Farley, Sta. Oklahoma City
  (see appendix)
Farris, R. Br. Atoka 74542
Faxon 73540
Fay 73646
Felt 73937
Fillmore, R. Br. Milburn 73434
Finley 74543
Fittstown 74842
Fitzhugh 74843
Fletcher 73541
Foraker 74638
Forgan 73938
Fort Cobb 73038
Fort Gibson 74434
Fort Sill, Br. Lawton 73503
Fort Supply 73841
Fort Towson 74735
Foss 73647
Foster 73039
Fox 73435
Foyil 74031
Francis 74844
Frederick (1st) 73542
Freedom 73842
Gage 73843
Gans 74936
Garber 73738
Garvin 74736
Gate 73844
Geary 73040
Gene Autry 73436

Geronimo 73543
Gerty, R. Br. Calvin 74544
Glencoe 74032
Glenpool 74033
Glover, R. Br. Broken Bow 74728
Golden 74737
Goltry 73739
Goodwell 73939
Gore 74435
Gotebo 73041
  Cooperton, R. Br. 73023
Gould 73544
Gowen 74545
Gracemont 73042
Grady 73545
Graham 73437
Grainola 74639
Grandfield 73546
Granite 73547
Grant 74738
Greenfield 73043
Greenwood, Sta. Tulsa 74120
Griggs 73941
Grove 74344
Guthrie (1st) 73044
Guymon (1st) 73942
Haileyville 74546
Hallett 74034
Hammon 73650
Hanna 74845
Harden City 74846
Hardesty 73944
Harmon 73845
Harrah 73045
Harris, R. Br. Haworth 74739
Hartshorne 74547
  Adamson, R. Br. 74520
  Dow, R. Br. 74541
Haskell 74436
Hastings 73548
Haworth 74740
  Harris, R. Br. 74739
Haywood 74548
Headrick 73549
Healdton 73438
Heavener 74937
Helena 73741
Hendrix 74741
Hennepin 73046
Hennessey 73742
Henryetta (1st) 74437
Hillsdale 73743
Hinton 73047
Hitchcock 73744
Hitchita 74438
Hobart (1st) 73651
Hockerville, R. Br. Picher 74345
Hodgen 74939
Hoffman 74439
Holdenville (1st) 74848
Hollis 73550
Hollister 73551
Homestead 73745
Hominy 74035
Honobia 74549
Hooker 73945
Hopeton 73746
Howe 74940
Hoyt 74440
Hugo (1st) 74743
Hulbert 74441
Hunter 74640
Hydro 73048

Idabel (1st) 74745
Indiahoma 73552
Indianola 74442
  nola 74036
Isabella 73747
Jay 74346
Jefferson 73748
Jenks 74037
Jennings 74038
Jet 73749
Jones 73049
Jumbo 74551
Kansas 74347
Kaw 74641
Kellyville 74039
Kemp 74747
Kendrick 74040
Kenefic 74748
Kenton 73946
Kenwood 74348
Keota 74941
Ketchum 74349
Keyes 73947
Kiefer 74041
Kildare 74642
Kingfisher (1st) 73750
Kingston 73439
Kinta 74552
Kiowa 74553
Knowles 73847
Konawa 74849
Krebs 74554
Kremlin 73753
Lahoma 73754
Lakeside, Sta. Oklahoma
  City 73116
Lamar 74850
Lamont 74643
Lane 74555
Langley 74350
Langston 73050
Laverne 73848
Lawton (1st) 73501
  Cameron College, Sta. 73501
  Fort Sill, Br. 73503
  Meers, R. Br. 73558
  Sheridan, Sta. 73501
  Sullivan Village, R. Br. 73501
Leach 74351
Lebanon 73440
Leedey 73654
Leflore 74942
Lehigh 74556
Lenapah 74042
Lenna, R. Br. Eufaula 74443
Leon 73441
Leonard 74043
Lequire 74943
Lexington 73051
Lindsay (1st) 73052
Loco 73442
Locust Grove 74352
Logan 73849
Lone Grove 73443
Lone Wolf 73655
Longdale 73755
Lookeba 73053
Lookout 73850
Loveland 73553
Loyal 73756
Lucien 73757
Luther 73054
Macomb 74852

Madill	73446
Manchester	73758
Mangum	73554
Manitou	73555
Mannford	74044
Mannsville	73447
Maramec	74045
Marble City	74945
Marietta	73448
Marland	74644
Marlow	73055
Marshall	73056
Martha	73556
Mason	74853
Maud	74854
May	73851
Mayfield	73656
Maysville	73057
Mazie, R. Br. Chouteau	74353
Mc Alester (1st)	74501
Mc Curtain	74944
Mc Loud	74851
Mc Millan	73445
Mead	73449
Medford	73759
Medicine Park	73557
Meeker	74855
Meers, R. Br. Lawton	73558
Memorial, Sta. Muskogee	74401
Meno	73760
Meridian	73058
Miami (1st)	74354
Midwest City, Br. Oklahoma City (see appendix)	
Milburn	73450
Fillmore, R. Br.	73434
Milfay	74046
Mill Creek	74856
Millerton	74750
Milo	73451
Minco	73059
Moffett	74946
Monroe	74947
Moodys	74444
Moore, Br. Oklahoma City	73160
Mooreland	73852
Morris	74445
Morrison	73061
Mounds	74047
Mountain Park	73559
Mountain View	73062
Moyers	74557
Muldrow	74948
Mulhall	73063
Muse	74949
Muskogee (1st)	74401
Mustang	73064
Mutual	73853
Nardin	74646
Nash	73761
Nashoba	74558
New Lima	74858
Newalla	74857
Newcastle	73065
Newkirk	74647
Nichols Hills, Br. Oklahoma City	73116
Nicoma Park	73066
Ninnekah	73067
Noble	73068
Norman (1st)	73069
North Mc Alester, Sta. Mc Alester	74501
North Miami	74358
Northside, Sta. Tulsa (see appendix)	
Northwest, Sta. Oklahoma City	73106
Nowata (1st)	74048
Alluwe, R. Br.	74049
Oakhurst	74050
Oakland	73452
Oaks	74359
Oakwood	73658
Ochelata	74051
Octavia, R. Br. Smithville	74958
Oilton	74052
Okarche	73762
Okay	74446
Okeene	73763
Okemah	74859
Okla College For Women, Sta. Chickasha	73018
OKLAHOMA CITY (1st) (see appendix)	
Okmulgee (1st)	74447
Oktaha	74450
Oleta	74751
Olustee	73560
Omega	73764
Oologah	74053
Optima	73948
Orienta	73765
Orlando	73073
Osage	74054
Oscar	73561
Overbrook	73453
Owasso	74055
Paden	74860
Page	74950
Panama	74951
Panola	74559
Paoli	73074
Park Hill	74451
Pauls Valley (1st)	73075
Pawhuska (1st)	74056
Bowring, R. Br.	74009
Pawnee	74058
Blackburn, R. Br.	74058
Pearson, R. Br. Asher	74861
Peckham	74648
Peggs	74452
Perkins	74059
Pernell	73076
Perry (1st)	73077
Pharoah	74862
Picher	74360
Hockerville, R. Br.	74345
Pickens	74752
Piedmont	73078
Pittsburg	74560
Platter	74753
Plunkettville	74952
Pocasset	73079
Pocola, R. Br. Cameron	74902
Ponca City (1st)	74601
Pondcreek	73766
Pontotoc	74863
Pooleville	73454
Porter	74454
Porum	74455
Briartown, R. Br.	74424
Poteau (1st)	74953
Prague	74864
Preston	74456
Proctor	74457
Prue	74060
Pryor (1st)	74361
Purcell (1st)	73080
Putnam	73659
Quapaw	74363
Quinton	74561
Ralston	74650
Ramona	74061
Ranch Acres, Sta. Tulsa (see appendix)	
Randlett	73562
Ratliff City	73081
Rattan	74562
Ravia	73455
Red Fork, Sta. Tulsa	74153
Red Oak	74563
Redbird	74458
Redrock	74651
Reed	73563
Reeves, Sta. Muskogee	74401
Renfrow	73767
Rentiesville	74459
Reydon	73660
Ringling	73456
Ringold	74754
Ringwood	73768
Ripley	74062
Rocky	73661
Roff	74865
Roland	74954
Roosevelt	73564
Rose	74364
Rosedale, R. Br. Byars	74831
Rosston	73855
Rubottom	73457
Rufe	74755
Rush Springs	73082
Ryan	73565
Saint Louis	74866
Salina	74365
Sallisaw (1st)	74955
Sanatorium, R. Br. Talihina	74571
Sand Springs (1st)	74063
Sapulpa (1st)	74066
Sardis	74564
Sasakwa	74867
Savanna	74565
Sawyer	74756
Sayre	73562
Schulter	74460
Scipio	74566
Seiling	73663
Selman	73856
Seminole (1st)	74868
Sentinel	73664
Shady Point	74956
Shamrock	74068
Sharon	73857
Shartel, Sta. Oklahoma City	73118
Shattuck	73858
Shawnee (1st)	74801
Dale, R. Br.	74838
University, Sta.	74801
Shepherd Mall, Sta. Oklahoma City	73107
Sheridan, Sta. Lawton	73501
Sherwood	74757
Shidler	74652
Skiatook	74070
Slick	74071
Smithville	74957
Octavia, R. Br.	74958
Snow	74567

Snyder.....................................73566
Soper......................................74759
South Coffeyville...................74072
Southard................................73770
Southeast, Sta. Tulsa (see appendix)
Southside, Sta. Tulsa (see appendix)
Southwest, Sta. Oklahoma City (see appendix)
Sparks....................................74869
Spavinaw................................74366
Spencer..................................73084
Spencerville...........................74760
Sperry....................................74073
Spiro......................................74959
Springer.................................73458
State Capitol, Sta. Oklahoma City...................73105
Sterling..................................73567
Stidham..................................74461
Stigler....................................74462
Stillwater (1st).......................74074
Stilwell...................................74960
Stockyards, Sta. Oklahoma City (see appendix)
Stonewall...............................74871
Strang....................................74367
Stratford................................74872
Stringtown.............................74569*
Strong City.............................73665
Stroud....................................74079
Stuart.....................................74570
Sullivan Village, R. Br. Lawton..................................73501
Sulphur (1st).........................73086
Summerfield, R. Br. Wister....74966
Sweetwater............................73666
Swink.....................................74761
Taft..74463
Tahlequah (1st)......................74464
Talala.....................................74080
Talihina..................................74571
Taloga....................................73667
Tatums...................................73087
Tecumseh...............................74873
Temple....................................73568
Terlton....................................74081
Terral......................................73569
Texhoma................................73949
Texola....................................73668
Thackerville............................73459
Thirty Ninth Street, Sta. Oklahoma City (see appendix)
Thomas...................................73669
Tinker A F B, Br. Oklahoma City.......................................73145
Tipton.....................................73570
Tishomingo.............................73460
Tom..74762
Tonkawa..................................74653
Tryon......................................74875
Tullahassee.............................74466
TULSA (1st) (see appendix)
Tupelo....................................74572
Turley, Br. Tulsa......................74156
Turpin.....................................73950
Tushka....................................74573
Tuskahoma..............................74574
Tussy......................................73088
Tuttle.....................................73089
Twin Oaks...............................74368

Tyrone....................................73951
Uncas, R. Br. Ponca City........74601
Union......................................73090
University, Sta. Enid................73701
University, Sta. Shawnee.........74801
Utica.......................................74763
Utica Square, Sta. Tulsa.........74152
Valliant....................................74764
Vance A F B, Br. Enid..............73701
Vanoss....................................74876
Velma......................................73091
Vera..74082
Verden.....................................73092
Vernon.....................................74877
Vian..74962
Vici...73859
Village, Br. Oklahoma City.......73120
Vinita (1st).............................74301
Vinson.....................................73571
Wagoner (1st).........................74467
Wainwright..............................74468
Wakita.....................................73771
Walters....................................73572
Wanette...................................74878
Wann.......................................74083
Wapanucka...............................73461
Wardville..................................74576
Warner.....................................74469
Warr Acres, Br. Oklahoma City.......................................73123
Warwick...................................74879
Washington..............................73093
Washita....................................73094
Watonga...................................73772
Watson.....................................74963
Watts.......................................74964
Waukomis.................................73773
Waurika....................................73573
Wayne......................................73095
Waynoka...................................73860
Weatherford (1st)....................73096
Webb City................................74654
Webbers Falls..........................74470
Welch......................................74369
Weleetka..................................74880
Welling....................................74471
Wellston...................................74881
Welty.......................................74882
West Tulsa, Sta. Tulsa (see appendix)
Westville..................................74965
Wetumka..................................74883
Wewoka (1st)...........................74884
Wheatland................................73097
Wheeless, R. Br. Boise City.....73952
Whitefield................................74472
Whitesboro...............................74577
Whittier, Sta. Tulsa.................74150
Wilburton.................................74578
Will Rogers, Sta. Oklahoma City.......................................73159
Willis.......................................73462
Willow.....................................73673
Wilson.....................................73463
Wirt..73464
Wister.....................................74966
Woodford.................................73465
Woodville.................................73466
Woodward (1st)........................73801
Wright City..............................74766
Wyandotte................................74370
Wynnewood..............................73098
Wynona....................................74084

Yale..74085
Yeager.....................................74885
Yukon (1st).............................73099

OKLAHOMA CITY 731

POST OFFICE BOXES

Box Nos.
1-1999	Downtown Sta...	01
6001-6999	Moore Branch...	60
10000-10999	Midwest City Br...	10
11000-11999	Cimarron Sta....	11
12000-12999	39th Street Sta...............	12
14000-14999	Britton Sta	14
15000-15999	Del City Br......	15
17000-17999	Eastern Sta......	17
18000-18999	Shartel Sta......	18
19000-19999	Southwest Sta...	19
20000-20999	Village Br......	20
24000-24999	Main Office	24
25000-25999	Main Office	25
26000-26999	Main Office	26
32000-32999	Warr Acres Br...	32
52000-53999	State Capitol....	05
59900-59999	Will Rogers World Airport Sta..................	59
60000-69999	Northwest......	06
75000-75999	Farley Sta	07
82000-82999	Stockyards Sta .	08
94000-94999	Capitol Hill Sta..................	09

RURAL ROUTES

1..............................		11
2..............................		14
3..............................		07
4..............................		11
5..............................		08
6..............................		19
7,8..........................		-09
10,11.......................		60
12............................		15

STATIONS, BRANCHES AND UNITS

Britton Sta......................	14
Capitol Hill Sta..............	09
Cimarron Sta..................	11
Del City Br....................	15
Downtown Sta................	01
Eastern Sta....................	17
Farley Sta......................	07
Lakeside Sta...................	16
Midwest City Br.............	10
Moore Br........................	60
Nichols Hills Br..............	16
Northwest Sta.................	06
Shartel Sta.....................	18
Shepherd Mall Sta...........	07
Southwest Mall Sta..........	19
State Capitol Sta.............	05
Stockyards Sta................	08
Thirty Ninth Street Sta.....	12
Tinker AFB Br................	45
Village Br......................	20
Warr Acres Br................	23
Will Rogers Br...............	59
General Delivery..............	25
Postmaster.....................	25

APARTMENTS, HOTELS, MOTELS

Aberdeen, 125, NW 15th........	03
Black, 5 N Hudson..............	02
Downtowner Motor, 1305 Classen Dr..................	03
Hotel Oklahoma Motor Inn, 228 W Sheridan..........	02
Lakeview Towers, 6001 N Brookline................	12
Leonhardt, 1125 N Lee......	03
Regency Tower 333 NW 5th....	02
Roberts, 15 N Broadway........	02
Sieber, 1305 N Hudson......	03
Skirvin Tower Park Ave And Bradway	02
Skirvin Tower, Park Ave. & Broadway	02
Tower, 125 NW 9th...............	02

BUILDINGS

American National 32 N Robinson......................	02
Citizens Bank Tower, 2200 Classen Blvd..............	06
City National Bank, 101 W Main......................	02
Civic Center Music Hall, 201 N Dewey..................	02
Colcord, 15 N Robinson........	02
County Court House 321 Park Ave......................	02
Cravens, 119 N Robinson......	02
Dan Lenniger, 3545 N W 58th......................	12
Doctors Medical, 5700 NW Grand Blvd................	12
Fidelity Bank Plaza 201 Roberts Kerr Ave..............	02 ●
Fidelity National Park 0 N Harvey....................	02
First National, 120 N Robinson..................	02
Hales, 109 N Robinson	02
Hightower, 105 N Hudson	02
Jim Thorpe, 2101 N Lincoln Blvd......................	05
Kermac, 134 Robert S Kerr Ave......................	02
Kerr Mc Gee, 133 NW Robert S Ave......................	02
Leonhardt, 228 NW Robert S Kerr......................	02
Lincoln Plaza, 4601 N Lincoln Blvd................	05
Livestock Exchange, 2401 Exchange Ave..............	08
Local Federal, 203 Park Ave....	02
May-Ex, 3020 NW Expressway.................	12
Medical Tower, 3141 NW Expressway.................	12
Municipal, 200 N Walker	02
National Foundation Life, 3521 N W 58th............	12
Oklahoma Gas & Electric, 321 N Harvey................	02
Oklahoma Mortgage, 324 N Robinson, ...	02
Oklahoma Natural Gas, 407 N Harvey	02

Old Federal, 215 NW 3rd........	02
Osler Bldg 1200 N Walker......	03
Pasteur Bldg 1111 N Lee	03
Petroleum Club, 120 NW Robert S Kerr..............	02
Physicians &surgeons, 1211 N Shartel................	03
Security Federal Savings, 301 N Harvey................	02
Sequoyah Memorial, 2400 N Lincoln..................	05
South Community Medical Center, 4200 S Douglas.....	09
Southwestern Bell Telephone, 405 N Broadway	02
Southwestern Bell Telephone, 707 N Robinson..........	02
U S Court & Federal, 200 NW 4th......................	02
United Founders Tower, 5900 Mosteller Dr	12
Will Rogers Memorial, 2401 N Lincoln................	05
Y M C A, 125 NW 5th............	02
Y W C A, 320 Park Ave..........	02

GOVERNMENT OFFICES

Post Office, 320 SW 5th.........	25
State Capitol, 2302 Lincoln Blvd......................	05
United States Court House, 200 NW 4th..............	02
United States Federal Building, 200 NW 4th........	02

HOSPITALS

Baptist Memorial, 5800 NW Grand Blvd..............	12
Bone& Joint 605 NW 10th	03
Crippled Childrens, 800 NE 13th......................	04
Deaconess, 5401 N Portland ..	12
Doctors General 1407 N Robinson..................	03
Hillcrest Osteopathic, 2129 SW 59th..................	19
Medicenter 700 N Lee............	02
Mercy, 501 NW 12th............	03
Midwest City, 2825 Park Lawn Dr..................	10
Moore Municipal Hosp 1500 SE 4th..................	60
Presbyterian, 300 NW 12......	03
Saint Anthony, 601 NW 9th	02
South Community, 1001 SW 44th......................	09
University, 800 NE 13th.........	04
Veterans Administration, 921 NE 13..................	06

UNIVERSITIES AND COLLEGES

Midwest Christian 6600 N Kelley..................	11
Oklahoma Christian, N Eastern&memorial Road..	11
Oklahoma City University, 2501 N Blackwelder.......	06
Southwestern 4700 NW 10th..	27

TULSA   741

POST OFFICE BOXES

Box Nos.

A-Y	Admiral Sta	15
1-3500	Main Office	01
AA-JJ	Admiral Sta	15
3501-4099	Utica Square Sta	52
4100-4999	Donaldson Sta	04
6001-6499	Northside Sta	06
6501-6999	Turley Br	56
7001-7795	Southside Sta	05
9001-9799	West Tulsa Sta	07
15001-15899	Admiral Sta	15
45001-45999	Southeast	45
50000-50999	Whittier	50
51000-51999	Dawson	51

RURAL ROUTES

1	15
2	35
3	15
4	45
5	07
6	27
7	06
8	07
9	07
10	15
13	07

STATIONS, BRANCHES AND UNITS

Admiral Sta	08
Dawson Sta	51
Donaldson Sta	04
Greenwood Sta	20
Northside Sta	06
Ranch Acres Sta	14
Red Fork Sta	53
Southeast Sta	45
Southside Sta	05
Turley Br	56
Utica Square Sta	52
West Tulsa Sta	07
Whittier Sta	50
General Delivery	01
Postmaster	01

APARTMENTS, HOTELS, MOTELS

Adams, 403 S Cheyenne Ave	03
Albany, 518 S Cheyenne Ave	01
Alvin Plaza, 631 S Main	01
Ambassador, 7 W 14th	19
Baltimore Arms, 24 E 17th	19
Barcelona 5126 So. Yale	35
Boulder Park, 7 W 18th	19
Center Plaza 100-200 401 W 11th	01
Chalet, 3903 Riverside Drive	05
Cheyenne Arms, 1210 S Cheyenne Ave	19
City Gardens 3200 Hudson	35
Country Club, 1120 N Osage Drive	06
Country Estates 1900-2100 East Skelly Dr	05
De Ville 1100 East 48th	05
French Villa 4700 So.	

Harvard	35
Gardens Of Cortez 100 No. Garnett	16
Georgetown 5500 East 47th Pl	35
Harbor 9700-9800 East 12th	28
Hewgley Terrace 624 So. Lawton	27
Mansion House 1633 So. Carson	19
Marquis 1700 So. Memorial	12
Mayo, 115 W 5th	01
Memorial Manor 1232 So. Memorial	12
Metro	03
Mingo Circle 300 So. Mingo	28
Mingo Valley 1301 So. 107th East Ave	28
Mohawk Manor 3600 No. Birmingham	10
Monaco 5000 So. 72nd East Ave	45
Morning Star Village 2100 No. Hartford	06
Park Place 4901 So. Braden	35
Pioneer Plaza 901 No. Elgin	06
Place One 3200 Riverside Dr	05
Plaza Del Leon 8302 East 25th Pl	29
Pythian Manor 6568 East 21st Pl	29
Riverview Park 2300 So. MaybeHe	07
Shamrock Lodge, 340 E 11th	20
Sophian Plaza, 1500 S Frisco Ave	19
Southern Hills Villa 6600 So. Lewis	36
Spanish Gardens 2434 East 51st	05
Spanish Villa 1050 East 61st	36
Stratford House East 4300 East 51st	35
Stratford House 4100 East 51st	35
Trenton Terrace, 1607 E 12th	20
Trimble, 215 S Boulder Ave	01
Tulsa, 9 W 9th	19
United Methodist Square 1600 East Young	06
University Club Towers 1720 So. Carson	19
Utica Square, 1724 E 22nd Pl	14
Vernon Manor 500 East 32nd St. No.	06
Versailles 4800 So. Sheridan	45
Villa Fontana 7405 East 49th	45
Williamsburg Plaza 6801 So. Lewis	36
Woodstock 3200 So. Lakewood	35
Yorktown Village 4900 So. Yorktown	05

BUILDINGS

Amoco	03

Atlas	03
Beacon	03
Community Ins Center	03
County Court House, 5th And Denver	03
Court Arcade	03
Enterprise	03
Federal	03
First National Bank	03
Fourth National Bank	19
Home Federal	03
Mayo	03
Mid-Continent	03
National Bank Of Commerce	03
National Bank Of Tulsa	03
Oil Capital	03
Palace	03
Petroleum	03
Philtower	03
Plaza	03
Resource Sciences	03
Shell	19
Thompson	03
Thurston NatOl.	03
Tri-State	19
Tulsa	03
World	03
Wright	03

GOVERNMENT OFFICES

Corp. Of Engrs., 224 So. Boulder	03
Geol. Survey, 333 W. 4th	03
Internal Revenue, 15 W. 6th	19
Social Security, 333 W. 4th	03

HOSPITALS

Childrens Medical Center, 4900 S Lewis Ave	05
Doctors Hospital, 2323 S Harvard	14
Glass Nelson Clinic, 2020 S Xanthus Ave	04
Hillcrest Medical Center, 1120 S Utica Ave	04
Mercy-Sisler-Bone & Joint, 807 So Elgin Ave	20
Moton Memorial, 603 E Pine	06
Oklahoma Osteopathic, 744 W 9th	27
Saint Francis, 61st & Yale Ave	35
Saint Johns, 1923 S Utica Ave	04
Springer Clinic, 6160 S Yale Ave	36
Tulsa Clinic, 915 S Cincinnati Ave	19
Utica Square Medical Center, 1980 Utica Square	14

UNIVERSITIES AND COLLEGES

Oral Roberts University	02
University Of Tulsa, 600 S College Ave	04

OREGON
(Abbreviation: OR)

Adams 97810
Adel 97620
Adrian 97901
Agness 97406
Albany (1st) 97321
Alicel 97811
Allegany 97407
Aloha, Br. Beaverton 97006
Alpine, R. Br. Monroe 97408
Alsea 97324
Alvadore 97409
Amity 97101
Antelope 97001
Applegate, R. Br.
    Jacksonville 97530
Arago, R. Br. Myrtle Point 97458
Arch Cape 97102
Arlington 97812
    Mikkalo, R. Br. 97861
    Olex, R. Br. 97812
Arock 97902
Ashland (1st) 97520
Ashwood 97711
Astoria (1st) 97103
Athena 97813
Aumsville 97325
Aurora 97002
Azalea 97410
Baker (1st) 97814
    Bridgeport, R. Br. 97819
Bandon 97411
Banks 97106
Barlow 97003
Bates 97817
Bay City, R. Br. Tillamook 97107
Beatty 97621
Beaver, R. Br. Cloverdale 97108
Beavercreek 97004
Beaverton (1st) 97005
    Aloha, Br. 97006
Bend (1st) 97701
Birkenfeld, R. Br.
    Clatskanie 97016
Blachly 97412
Black Butte Ranch, R. Br.
    Sisters 97759
Blodgett 97326
Blue River 97413
Bly 97622
Boardman 97818
Bonanza 97623
Bonneville 97008
Boring (1st) 97009
Bridal Veil 97010
Bridgeport, R. Br. Baker 97819
Brightwood 97011
Broadbent 97414
Brogan 97903
Brookings (1st) 97415
Brooklyn, Sta. Portland 97242
Brooks, Br. Salem 97305
Brothers 97712
Brownsmead, R. Br.
    Clatskanie 97012
Brownsville 97327
Burns (1st) 97720
    Diamond, R. Br. 97722
    Fields, R. Br. 97710
    Princeton, R. Br. 97721
Burnt Woods, R. Br.

Eddyville 97328
Butte Falls 97522
Buxton 97109
Camas Valley 97416
Camp Sherman 97730
Campus, Sta. Corvallis 97331
Canby (1st) 97013
Cannon Beach 97110
Canyon City 97820
Canyonville 97417
Carlton 97111
Cascade Locks 97014
Cascade Summit 97418
Cascadia 97329
Cave Junction 97523
    Kerby, R. Br. 97531
    Oregon Caves, R. Br. 97523
Cayuse 97821
Cecil, R. Br. Ione 97822
Cedar Hills, Br. Portland 97225
Central, Sta. Portland (see
    appendix)
Central Point, Br. Medford 97501
Charleston, R. Br. Coos Bay 97420
Chemawa, Br. Salem 97306
Chemult 97731
Cherry Grove, R. Br. Gaston 97119
Cheshire 97419
Chiloquin 97624
    Crater Lake, R. Br. 97604
    Sprague River, R. Br. 97639
Christmas Valley, R. Br.
    Silver Lake 97638
Clackamas 97015
Clatskanie 97016
    Birkenfeld, R. Br. 97016
    Brownsmead, R. Br. 97012
    Mist, R. Br. 97016
    Westport, R. Br. 97016
Cloverdale 97112
    Beaver, R. Br. 97108
    Neskowin, R. Br. 97149
Coburg, R. Br. Eugene 97401
Colton 97017
Columbia City 97018
Condon 97823
Coos Bay (1st) 97420
Coquille (1st) 97423
Corbett 97019
Cornelius 97113
Corvallis (1st) 97330
    Campus, Sta. 97331
Cottage Grove (1st) 97424
    Saginaw, R. Br. 97472
Cove 97824
Crabtree 97335
Crane 97732
Crater Lake, R. Br.
    Chiloquin 97604
Crawfordsville 97336
Crescent 97733
Crescent Lake 97425
Creston, Sta. Portland 97206
Creswell 97426
Culp Creek 97427
Culver 97734
Curtin 97428
Dairy, R. Br. Klamath Falls 97625
Dale, R. Br. Ukiah 97880
Dallas (1st) 97338
Days Creek 97429
Dayton 97114
Dayville 97825

Deadwood 97430
Deer Island, R. Br. Saint
    Helens 97054
Depoe Bay 97341
Detroit 97342
Dexter 97431
Diamond, R. Br. Burns 97722
Diamond Lake, R. Br.
    Chemult 97731
Dillard 97432
Disston 97433
Donald 97020
Dorena 97434
Drain 97435
Drewsey 97904
Dufur 97021
Dundee 97115
Durkee 97905
Eagle Creek 97022
Eagle Point 97524
East Portland, Sta. Portland
    (see appendix)
Eastside, R. Br. Coos Bay 97420
Echo 97826
Eddyville 97343
    Burnt Woods, R. Br. 97328
Elgin 97827
Elkton 97436
Elmira 97437
Empire, Sta. Coos Bay 97420
Enterprise 97828
Estacada 97023
EUGENE (1st) (see appendix)
Fairview 97024
Fall Creek 97438
Falls City 97344
Federal, Sta. Portland (see
    appendix)
Fields, R. Br. Burns 97710
Finn Rock, R. Br. Eugene 97401
Florence (1st) 97439
Forest Grove (1st) 97116
    Gales Creek, R. Br. 97117
Forest Park, Sta. Portland 97210
Fort Klamath 97626
Fort Rock 97735
Fossil 97830
Foster 97345
Four Corners, Br. Salem 97301
Fox 97831
Frenchglen 97736
Friend 97025
Gales Creek, R. Br. Forest
    Grove 97117
Garden Home, Br. Portland
    (see appendix)
Gardiner 97441
Garibaldi 97118
Gaston 97119
Gates, R. Br. Mill City 97346
Gaylord, R. Br. Myrtle Point 97458
Gearhart, Br. Seaside 97138
Gervais 97026
Gilchrist 97737
Gladstone (1st) 97027
Glendale 97442
Gleneden Beach, R. Br.
    Lincoln City 97388
Glenwood 97120
Glide 97443
Goble, R. Br. Rainier 97048
Gold Beach 97444
Gold Hill 97525

Goshen, R. Br. Eugene.............97401
Government Camp...................97028
Grand Ronde............................97347
Grants Pass (1st)...................97526
　Wilderville, R. Br................97543
Grass Valley.............................97029
Greenleaf.................................97445
Gresham (1st)........................97030
Haines......................................97833
Halfway....................................97834
Halsey......................................97348
Hammond.................................97121
Harbor, R. Br. Brookings.......97415
Harper....................................97906
Harrisburg...............................97446
Hebo...97122
Helix...97835
Heppner...................................97836
　Lexington, R. Br..................97839
Hereford..................................97837
Hermiston (1st)......................97838
High School, Br. Saint
　Helens..................................97051
Highway, Sta. Woodburn.......97071
Hillsboro (1st).........................97123
　Manning, R. Br...................97125
Hines..97738
Holladay Park, Sta. Portland
　(see appendix)
Hollywood, Sta. Salem..........97303
Hood River (1st)....................97031
Horton, R. Br. Junction City...97448
Hubbard...................................97032
Huntington...............................97907
Idanha.....................................97350
Idleyld Park.............................97447
Imbler......................................97841
Imnaha.....................................97842
Independence..........................97351
Ione..97843
　Cecil, R. Br..........................97822
Ironside....................................97908
Irrigon.....................................97844
Island City, R. Br. La
　Grande.................................97851
Jacksonville.............................97530
Jamieson..................................97909
Jasper, R. Br. Eugene...........97401
Jefferson..................................97352
　Marion, R. Br......................97359
Jennings Lodge, Br.
　Portland...............................97267
John Day..................................97845
Jordan Valley...........................97910
Joseph......................................97846
Junction City (1st).................97448
Juntura.....................................97911
Keating.....................................97847
Keizer, Br. Salem....................97303
Keno...97627
Kent..97033
Kenton, Sta. Portland............97217
Kerby, R. Br. Cave Junction...97531
Kimberly...................................97848
Kings Valley.............................97353
Kingsley Field, Br. Klamath
　Falls.....................................97601
Kingwood, Sta. Salem...........97304
Kinzua......................................97849
Klamath Falls (1st)................97601
　Dairy, R. Br.........................97625
　Kingsley Field, Br.............97601

Lake Of The Woods, R.
　Br...97603
　Oretech, Br..........................97601
La Grande (1st).......................97850
　Island City, R. Br...............97851
La Pine....................................97739
Lacomb, R. Br. Lebanon.......97354
Lafayette.................................97127
Lake Grove, Sta. Lake
　Oswego.................................97034
Lake Of The Woods, R. Br.
　Klamath Falls......................97603
Lake Oswego (1st)................97034
Lakeside...................................97449
Lakeview (1st)........................97630
Langlois....................................97450
Lawen......................................97740
Leaburg, R. Br. Eugene.........97401
Lebanon (1st).........................97355
　Lacomb, R. Br.....................97354
Lees Camp, R. Br.
　Tillamook.............................97142
Lents, Sta. Portland (see
　appendix)
Lexington, R. Br. Heppner......97839
Lincoln City (1st)...................97367
　Gleneden Beach, R. Br.......97388
　Taft, Sta...............................97367
Linnton, Sta. Portland...........97231
Logsden...................................97357
Long Creek..............................97856
Lorane.....................................97451
Lostine....................................97857
Lowell.......................................97452
Lyons.......................................97358
Madras (1st)...........................97741
　Metolius, R. Br....................97742
Malin..97632
Manhattan Beach, R. Br.
　Rockaway.............................97136
Manning, R. Br. Hillsboro......97125
Manzanita...............................97130
Mapleton.................................97453
Maplewood, Br. Portland
　(see appendix)
Marcola....................................97454
Marion, R. Br. Jefferson.........97359
Market, Br. Coos Bay.............97420
Marquam, R. Br. Mount
　Angel....................................97362
Marylhurst...............................97036
Maupin.....................................97037
　South Junction, R. Br........97074
Mayville, R. Br. Fossil...........97830
Mc Kenzie Bridge, R. Br.
　Eugene.................................97401
Mc Minnville (1st)..................97128
Mc Nary...................................97858
Meacham, R. Br. Pendleton...97859
Medford (1st).........................97501
Medical Springs......................97860
Mehama, R. Br. Stayton........97384
Merlin......................................97532
Merrill......................................97633
Metolius, R. Br. Madras.........97742
Midland....................................97634
Midway, Br. Portland (see
　appendix)
Mikkalo, R. Br. Arlington.......97861
Mill City...................................97360
　Gates, R. Br........................97346
Milo, R. Br. Canyonville.........97455

Milton-Freewater (1st)..........97862
　Umapine, R. Br...................97881
Milwaukie, Br. Portland.........97222
Mist, R. Br. Clatskanie..........97016
Mitchell....................................97750
Molalla.....................................97038
Monitor, R. Br. Woodburn......97072
Monmouth (1st)......................97361
Monroe.....................................97456
　Alpine, R. Br........................97408
Monument.................................97864
Moro...97039
Mosier......................................97040
Mount Angel............................97362
Mount Hood.............................97041
Mount Vernon..........................97865
Mulino......................................97042
Multnomah, Sta. Portland
　(see appendix)
Murphy.....................................97533
Myrtle Creek............................97457
Myrtle Point.............................97458
Nashville, R. Br. Philomath...97370
Nehalem...................................97131
Neotsu.....................................97364
Neskowin, R. Br. Cloverdale...97149
Netarts, R. Br. Tillamook.......97143
New Pine Creek.......................97635
Newberg (1st)........................97132
Newport (1st).........................97365
　Otter Rock, R. Br...............97369
　Southbeach, R. Br..............97366
North Bend (1st)....................97459
North Plains.............................97133
North Portland.........................97043
North Powder..........................97867
North Roseburg, Br.
　Roseburg..............................97470
Norway.....................................97460
Noti..97461
Nyssa.......................................97913
O'Brien.....................................97534
Oak Grove, Br. Portland.........97268
Oakland....................................97462
Oakridge..................................97463
Oceanside................................97134
Odell..97044
Olex, R. Br. Arlington............97812
Ontario (1st)...........................97914
Ophir..97464
Oregon Caves, R. Br. Cave
　Junction...............................97523
Oregon City (1st)...................97045
Oretech, Br. Klamath Falls....97601
Otis..97368
　Rose Lodge, R. Br..............97372
Otter Rock, R. Br. Newport...97369
Oxbow......................................97840
Pacific City..............................97135
Paisley......................................97636
Parkdale...................................97047
Parkrose, Br. Portland (see
　appendix)
Paulina.....................................97751
Pendleton (1st).......................97801
　Meacham, R. Br...................97859
Perrydale, R. Br. Amity..........97101
Philomath.................................97370
Phoenix....................................97535
Piedmont, Sta. Portland.........97211
Pilot Rock................................97868
Pioneer, Sta. Portland (see
　appendix)

Pistol River, R. Br. Gold
  Beach.................................97444
Pleasant Hill, R. Br. Eugene...97401
Plush.......................................97637
Port Orford.............................97465
PORTLAND (1st) (see
  appendix)
Portland Zoo Railway, Sta.
  Portland (see appendix)
Post...97752
Powell Butte............................97753
Powers....................................97466
Prairie City.............................97869
Princeton, R. Br. Burns..........97721
Prineville (1st)........................97754
Prospect..................................97536
Rainier....................................97048
Raleigh Hills, Br. Portland......97225
Redmond (1st)........................97756
Reedsport (1st).......................97467
Remote....................................97468
Rhododendron..........................97049
  Zigzag, R. Br. 97073
Richland..................................97870
Rickreall.................................97371
Riddle.....................................97469
Riley.......................................97758
Ritter......................................97872
Riverside.................................97917
Riverton, R. Br. Coquille.........97423
Rockaway................................97136
Rogue River.............................97537
Rose City Park, Sta.
  Portland (see appendix)
Rose Lodge, R. Br. Otis..........97372
Roseburg (1st).........................97470
Rufus......................................97050
Saginaw, R. Br. Cottage
  Grove...............................97472
Saint Benedict.........................97373
Saint Helens (1st)...................97051
  Deer Island, R. Br...............97054
  High School, Br...................97051
  Warren, R. Br. 97053
Saint Johns, Sta. Portland
  (see appendix)
Saint Paul...............................97137
SALEM (1st) (see appendix)
Sandy......................................97055
Scappoose................................97056
Scio..97374
Scotts Mills.............................97375
Scottsburg...............................97473
Seal Rock, R. Br. Waldport......97376
Seaside (1st)...........................97138
Sellwood Moreland, Sta.
  Portland............................97202
Selma.....................................97538
Seneca....................................97873
Shady Cove.............................97539
Shaniko..................................97057
Shedd 97377
Sheridan.................................97378
Sherwood................................97140
Siletz......................................97380
Silver Lake..............................97638
Silverton (1st).........................97381
Sisters....................................97759
Sixes......................................97476
South Junction, R. Br.
  Maupin..............................97074
Southbeach, R. Br. Newport...97366
Southside, Sta. Eugene..........97405

Sprague River, R. Br.
  Chiloquin...........................97639
Spray......................................97874
Springfield (1st)......................97477
Stanfield.................................97875
Stayton (1st)...........................97383
  Mehama, R. Br. 97384
Sublimity.................................97385
Summer Lake...........................97640
Summerville.............................97876
Sumpter..................................97877
Sunny Valley, R Br. Wolf
  Creek...............................97478
Sunriver, R. Br. Bend..............97701
Sutherlin.................................97479
Sweet Home (1st)....................97386
Swisshome...............................97480
Taft, Sta. Lincoln City............97367
Talent.....................................97540
Tangent...................................97389
Telocaset.................................97878
Tenmile...................................97481
Terrebonne..............................97760
The Dalles (1st).......................97058
Thurston..................................97482
Tidewater................................97390
Tigard, Br. Portland (see
  appendix)
Tillamook (1st)........................97141
  Bay City, R. Br...................97107
  Lees Camp, R. Br. 97142
  Netarts, R. Br. 97143
Tiller......................................97484
Timber....................................97144
Toledo.....................................97391
Tolovana Park..........................97145
Trail.......................................97541
Troutdale................................97060
Tualatin..................................97062
Turner.....................................97392
Twelve Mile, R. Br. Gresham ..97030
Tygh Valley..............................97063
Ukiah....................................≥97880
Umapine, R. Br.
  Milton-Freewater.................97881
Umatilla..................................97882
Umpqua...................................97486
Union......................................97883
Unity......................................97884
University, Sta. Eugene...........97403
University Park, Sta.
  Portland (see appendix)
Vale..97918
Valsetz....................................97393
Veneta....................................97487
Vernonia..................................97064
Vida.......................................97488
Vista, Sta. Salem....................97302
Waldport.................................97394
  Seal Rock, R. Br. 97376
Wallowa..................................97885
Walterville...............................97489
Walton....................................97490
Wamic, R. Br. Tygh Valley......97063
Warm Springs..........................97761
Warren, R. Br. Saint Helens....97053
Warrenton...............................97146
Wasco.....................................97065
Waterloo.................................97395
Wedderburn.............................97491
Wemme...................................97067

West Linn (1st)........................97068
West Main, Br. Medford..........97501
West Oak, R. Sta. Oakridge....97463
West Side, Sta. Eugene...........97402
West Slope, Br. Portland
  (see appendix)
West Stayton, R. Br.
  Aumsville...........................97325
Westfall...................................97920
Westfir....................................97492
Westlake..................................97493
Weston....................................97886
Westport, R. Br. Clatskanie ...97016
Wheeler...................................97147
White City, Br. Medford..........97501
Wilbur.....................................97494
Wilderville, R. Br. Grants
  Pass.................................97543
Willamette, Sta. West Linn 97068
Willamina.................................97396
Williams..................................97544
Wilsonville...............................97070*
Winchester...............................97495
Winchester Bay, R. Br.
  Reedsport..........................97467
Winston...................................97496
Wolf Creek...............................97497
  Sunny Valley, R. Br. 97478
Woodburn (1st)........................97071
  Highway, Sta. 97071
  Monitor, R. Br. 97072
Yachats...................................97498
Yamhill....................................97148
Yoncalla..................................97499
Zigzag, R. Br.
  Rhododendron.....................97073

EUGENE 974

POST OFFICE BOXES

Box Nos.
1-1999	Main Office	01
2000-2999	Westside Sta	02
3000-3999	University Sta	03
5000-5999	Southside	05
10000-10999	Main Office	01

RURAL ROUTES

1	02
2	01
3,4	05
5,6	02
7	05
8	01

STATIONS, BRANCHES AND UNITS

Coburg Rural Br	01
Finn Rock Rural Br	01
Goshen Rural Br	01
Jasper Rural Br	01
Leaburg Rural Br	01
Mc Kenzie Bridge Rural Br	01
Pleasant Hill Rural Br	01
Southside Sta	05
University Sta	03
West Side Sta	02
General Delivery	01
Postmaster	01

PORTLAND 972

POST OFFICE BOXES

Box Nos.
1-1799	Federal Sta	07
G-1-G-159	Garden Home Br	23
M-1-M-65	Maplewood Br	13
2700-4499	Main Office	08
6100-6299	Linnton Sta	31
8000-8599	Federal Sta	07
8700-9000	Main Office	08
02001-02999	Sellwood-Moreland	02
03001-03999	Saint Johns	03
06001-06999	Creston	06
10001-10999	Forest Park Sta	10
11001-11999	Piedmont Sta	11
12001-12999	Holladay Park Sta	12
13001-13999	Rose City Park	13
14000-14999	East Portland	14
16001-16999	Midway	16
17001-17999	Kenton Sta	17
19001-19999	Multnomah Sta	19
20001-20999	Parkrose	20
22001-22999	Milwaukie Br	22
23001-23999	Tigard Br	23
25001-25999	West Slope Br	25
42001-42999	Brooklyn Sta	42
66001-66999	Lents Sta	66
67001-67999	Jennings Lodge Br	67

68001-68999 Oak Grove Br	68

RURAL ROUTES

1,2	31
3	23

STATIONS, BRANCHES AND UNITS

Brooklyn Sta	42
Cedar Hills Br	25
Central Sta	04
Creston Sta	06
East Portland Sta	14
Federal Sta	07
Forest Park Sta	10
Garden Home Br	23
Holladay Park Sta	12
Jennings Lodge Br	67
Kenton Sta	17
Lents Sta	66
Linnton Sta	31
Maplewood Br	13
Midway Sta	17
Milwaukie Br	22
Multnomah Sta	19
Oak Grove Br	68
Parkrose Br	20
Piedmont Sta	11
Pioneer Sta	04
Portland Zoo Railway Sta	21
Raleigh Hills Br	25
Rose City Park Sta	13
Saint Johns Br	03
Sellwood Moreland Sta	02
Tigard Br	23
University Park Sta	03
West Slope Br	25
General Delivery	08
Postmaster	08

APARTMENTS, HOTELS, MOTELS

Benson	05
Congress	04
Cosmopolitan Portland Motor	32
Envoy	05
Fontaine	32
Heathman	05
Highlander Inn	07
Holiday Inn Of America	27
Hollywood Towne House	13
Hoyt	09
Imperial	05
Ione Plaza	01
King Tower	05
Mallory	05
Northwest Towers	09
Ongford	07
Panorama	05
Park Haviland	05
Park Plaza	01
Park Vista	07
Portland Hilton	05
Portland Towers	05
Riverside West Motor	04
Roosevelt	05
Sheraton Motor Inn	08
Terwilliger Plaza	01
Vista Saint Clair	05
Willamette View Manor	22

Attorneys, 1123 SW Yamhill	05
Blue Cross 100 SW Market	01
Board Of Trade, 310 SW 4 Ave	04
Boise Cascade 1600 SW 4 Ave	01
Bullier, 420 SW Washington	04
California Towers 707 SW Washington	05
Cascade Plaza 2828 SW Corbett	01
Commerce, 225 SW Broadway	05
Crown Plaza, 1520 SW 1 Ave.	01
Equitable, 1300 SW 6 Ave	01
Executive, 811 SW 6 Ave	04
Failing, 618 SW 5 Ave	04
First National Bank, 1300 SW 5 Ave.	01
Franklin, 333 SW 5 Ave	04
Georgia Pacific 900 SW 5 Ave	04
Henry, 309 SW 4 Ave	04
Jackson Tower, 808 SW Broadway	05
Labor Center 201 SW Arthur	01
Lawyers, 521 SW Clay	01
Lewis, 333 SW Oak	04
Lincoln, 208 SW 5 Ave	04
Lloyd Center	32
Lloyd, 700 NE Multnomah	32
Mead, 421 SW 5 Ave	04
Mohawk, 222 SW Morrison	04
Morgan, 720 SW Washington	05
Oregon Bank, 319 SW Washington	04
Oregonian, 1320 SW Broadway	01
Pacific, 520 SW Yamhill	04
Pittock Block, 921 SW Washington	05
Portland, 425 SW Washington	04
Professional, 1033 SW Yamhill	05
Public Service, 920 SW 6 Ave	04
Riviera Plaza 1618 SW 1 Ave	01
Standard Plaza, 1100 SW 6 Ave	04
State Office, 1400 SW 5 Ave.	01
Terminal Sales, 1220 SW Morrison	05
United States National Bank, 309 SW 6th Ave	04
Weatherly, 516 SE Morrison	14
Willamette, 534 SW 3 Ave	04
Yeon, 522 SW 5 Ave	04

GOVERNMENT OFFICES

United States Court House, 620 SW Main	05

HOSPITALS

Bess Kaiser, 5055 N Greeley Ave	17
City Of Roses Memorial, 1329 SE Harney	02

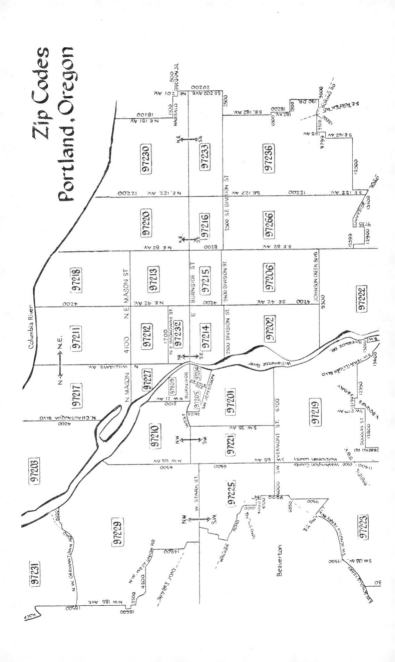

Zip Codes
Portland, Oregon

Doernbecher Memorial For
  Children, 3181 SW Sam
  Jackson Pk 01
Emanuel, 2801 N Gantenbein
  Ave 27
Fairlawn, 10404 SE Foster
  Rd 66
Good Samaritan, 1015 N W
  22 Ave 10
Holladay Park, 220 N E
  Multnomah 32
Multnomah County, 3171 SW
  Jackson Pk Rd 01
Physicians & Surgeons, 1927
  NW Lovejoy 09
Portland Adventist, 6040 SE
  Belmont 15
Portland Osteopathic, 2900
  SE Steele 02
Providence, 700 NE 47 Ave 13
Saint Vincents, 2447 NW
  Westover Rd 10
United States Veterans, SW U
  S Vets Hospital Rd 07
Wilcox Memorial, 1022 NW
  22 Ave 10
Woodland Park, 10300 NE
  Hancock 20

UNIVERSITIES AND COLLEGES

Concordia 11
Conquerors Bible 03

Judson Baptist 20
Lewis & Clark 19
Multnomah School Of
  Engineering Of The Univer
  Of Portland 03
Multnomah School Of The
  Bible 20
Pacific Bible 16
Portland State 07
Portland State Extension
  Division 01
Reed 02
University Of Oregon Medical
  School, 3181 SW Sam
  Jackson 01
University Of Portland 03
Warner Pacific Bible 15
Western Conservative Baptist
  Theological 15
Western Evangelical
  Seminary 22
Western States College Of
  Chiropractic 06

SALEM   973

POST OFFICE BOXES

Box Nos.
1-2999   Salem 08
3001-3999   Vista Sta 02
5001-5999   Kingwood Sta ... 04

7001-7999   Hollywood Sta ... 03
9001-9999   Brooks Br 05

RURAL ROUTES

1 04
2 03
3,4 02
5 01
6 05
8 01
9 03

STATIONS, BRANCHES AND UNITS

Brooks Br 05
Chemawa Br 06
Four Corners Br 01
Hollywood Sta 03
Keizer Br 03
Kingwood Sta 04
Vista Sta 02
General Delivery 01
Postmaster 01

GOVERNMENT OFFICES

State Offices 10

PENNSYLVANIA
(Abbreviation: PA)

Aaronsburg......................................16820
Abbottstown...................................17301
Abington (1st).................................19001
Ackermanville, R. Br.
   Bangor.....................................18010
Acme...15610
Acosta...15520
Adah..15410
Adamsburg......................................15611
Adamstown......................................19501
Adamsville......................................16110
Addison...15411
Adrian...16210
Airville..17302
Aitch...16610
Akron..17501
Aladdin, Br. Schenley.....................15682
Alba..16910
Albion...16401
Albrightsville...................................18210
Alburtis..18011
Aldan, Br. Clifton Heights...............19018
Alden, Br. Nanticoke.....................18634
Aldenville, R. Br. Forest City.........18401
Aleppo..15310
Alexandria.......................................16611
Aliquippa (1st)................................15001
Allegheny, Sta. Pittsburgh.............15212
Allen, R. Br. Boiling Springs..........17001
Allenport...15412
Allensville.......................................17002
ALLENTOWN (1st) (see
   appendix)
Allenwood.......................................17810
Allison...15413
Allison Park (1st)............................15101
Allport...16821
ALTOONA (1st) (see
   appendix)
Alum Bank......................................15521
Alverda...15710
Alverton..15612
Amaranth, R. Br.
   Warfordsburg...........................17267
Amberson..17210
Ambler (1st)....................................19002
Ambridge (1st)................................15003
Amity..15311
Analomink.......................................18320
Andalusia, Sta. Cornwells
   Heights.....................................19020
Andreas..18211
Anita...15711
Annville (1st)..................................17003
Ansonville.......................................16612
Antes Fort.......................................17720
Apollo (1st).....................................15613
Aquashicola.....................................18012
Arcadia..15712
Archbald (1st).................................18403
Arcola..19420
Ardara...15615
Ardmore (1st).................................19003
Ardsley, Sta. Glenside....................19038
Arendtsville.....................................17303
Aristes..17920
Armagh..15920
Armbrust...15616
Arnold, Br. New Kensington......15068

Arnot..16911
Arona..15617
Arsenal, Sta. Pittsburgh...............15201
Artemas..17211
Ashfield...18212
Ashland (1st)..................................17921
Ashley, Br. Wilkes-Barre...............18706
Ashville...16613
   Coupon, R. Br......................16629
Aspers...17304
Aspinwall, Br. Pittsburgh..............15215
Aston, Br. Chester..........................19014
Atglen...19310
Athens (1st)....................................18810
Athol...19502
Atlantic...16111
Atlas, Br. Mount Carmel................17851
Atlasburg..15004
Auburn..17922
Audubon, Br. Norristown...............19407
Aultman..15713
Austin..16720
   Keating Summit, R. Br.........16737
Avalon, Br. Pittsburgh...................15202
Avella...15312
Avis...17721
Avoca, Br. Pittston.........................18641
Avon, Br. Lebanon..........................17042
Avondale...19311
Avonmore..15618
Baden (1st).....................................15005
Bainbridge.......................................17502
Bair...17305
Bairdford...15006
Bakers Summit...............................16614
Bakerstown.....................................15007
Bala-Cynwyd (1st)..........................19004
Bally...19503
Bangor (1st)....................................18013
   Ackermanville, R. Br............18010
   East Bangor, R. Br.............18013
   Roseto, Br............................18013
Banning...15414
Barking..15008
Barnesboro......................................15714
Barnesville......................................18214
Barree...16615
Bart...17503
Barto...19504
Bartonsville.....................................18321
Bath..18014
Bausman...17504
Beach Haven...................................18601
Beach Lake......................................18405
Beallsville.......................................15313
Bear Creek, R. Br.
   Wilkes-Barre...........................18602
Bear Lake..16402
Beaver (1st)....................................15009
Beaver Brook, R. Br.
   Hazleton..................................18215
Beaver Falls (1st)...........................15010
Beaver Meadows.............................18216
Beaver Springs...............................17812
Beaverdale......................................15921
Beavertown......................................17813
Beccaria..16616
Bechtelsville...................................19505
Bedford (1st)..................................15522
Bedminster......................................18910
Beech Creek....................................16822
   Orviston, R. Br.....................16864

Bell Acres, R. Br. Sewickley....15143
Belle Vernon (1st)..........................15012
Bellefonte (1st)...............................16823
   Pleasant Gap, Br..................16823
   Wingate, R. Br.....................16880
Belleville..17004
Bellevue, Br. Pittsburgh................15202
Bellwood..16617
Belsano..15922
Bendersville....................................17306
Benezett..15821
Benson East, Br. Jenkintown...19046
Bentleyville.....................................15314
Benton...17814
Berkeley Hills, Br.
   Pittsburgh...............................15237
Berlin..15530
Bernville..19506
Berrysburg......................................17005
Berwick (1st)..................................18603
Berwyn (1st)...................................19312
Bessemer...16112
Bethel..19507
Bethel Park (1st)............................15102
BETHLEHEM (1st) (see
   appendix)
Bethton, Br. Souderton..................18964
Beulah, Br. Turtle Creek...............15145
Beyer...16211
Big Cove Tannery, R. Br.
   Needmore................................17212
Big Run...15715
Bigler..16825
Biglerville..17307
Birchrunville....................................19421
Bird In Hand...................................17505
Birdsboro (1st)...............................19508
Black Lick..15716
Blain...17006
Blair, Sta. Clairton........................15025
Blairs Mills......................................17213
Blairsville (1st)...............................15717
Blakely, Br. Olyphant....................18447
Blakeslee...18610
Blanchard..16826
Blandburg..16619
Blandon...19510
Blawnox, Br. Pittsburgh................15238
Bloomfield, Sta. Pittsburgh...........15224
Blooming Glen.................................18911
Bloomsburg (1st)............................17815
   Espy, Br.................................17815
   Light Street, R. Br..............17839
Blossburg..16912
Blue Ball...17506
Blue Bell (1st)................................19422
Blue Ridge Summit (1st)...............17214
Boalsburg..16827
Bobtown..15315
Bodines, R. Br. Trout Run............17722
Boiling Springs...............................17007
   Allen, R. Br...........................17001
Bolivar...15923
Bon Aire, Br. Butler......................16001
Boothwyn, Br. Marcus Hook.........19061
Boston, Br. Mc Keesport...............15135
Boswell..15531
   Jenners, R. Br.....................15546
Boulevard, Sta. Philadelphia........19149
Bovard...15619
Bowers..19511
Bowmansdale...................................17008

Bowmanstown	18030	
Bowmansville	17507	
Boyds Mills	18406	
Boyers	16020	
Boyertown (1st)	19512	
Boynton	15532	
Brackenridge (1st)	15014	
Brackney	18812	
Braddock (1st)	15104	
Bradenville	15620	
Bradford (1st)	16701	
Bradfordwoods	15015	
Braeburn, R. R. New Kensington	15016	
Branch Dale	17923	
Branchton	16021	
Brandamore	19316	
Brandy Camp	15822	
Brave	15316	
Breezewood	15533	
Breinigsville	18031	
Brentwood, Br. Pittsburgh	15227	
Bridesburg, Sta. Philadelphia	19137	
Bridgeport, Br. Norristown	19405	
Bridgeville (1st)	15017	
Brier Hill	15415	
Brisbin	16620	
Bristol (1st)	19007	
Broad Street, Sta. Hazleton	18201	
Broad Top	16621	
Brockport	15823	
Brockton	17925	
Brockway (1st)	15824	
Brodbecks	17308	
Brodheadsville	18322	
Brogue	17309	
Brookhaven, Br. Chester	19015	
Brookline, Sta. Pittsburgh	15226	
Brooklyn	18813	
Brookville (1st)	15825	
Broomall (1st)	19008	
Broughton, Br. Pittsburgh	15236	
Brownfield	15416	
Brownstown	17508	
Brownsville (1st)	15417	
Bruin	16022	
Brunnerville, R. Br. Lititz	17543	
Brush Valley	15720	
Bryn Athyn	19009	
Bryn Mawr (1st)	19010	
Buck Hill Falls	18323	
Buck Run	17926	
Buckingham	18912	
Buena Vista	15018	
Buffalo Mills	15534	
Buhl, Sta. Sharon	16146	
Bulger	15019	
Bunola	15020	
Burgettstown (1st)	15021	
Florence, R. Br.	15040	
Paris, R. Br.	15021	
Burlington	18814	
Burnham	17009	
Burnside	15721	
Burnt Cabins	17215	
Burtville	16721	
Bushkill	18324	
Tamiment, R. Br.	18371	
Unity House, R. Br.	18373	
Bustleton, Sta. Philadelphia (see appendix)		
Butler (1st)	16001	

Butztown, Br. Bethlehem	18017	
Byrnedale	15827	
Cabot	16023	
Cadogan	16212	
Cairnbrook	15924	
California (1st)	15419	
Callensburg	16213	
Callery	16024	
Calumet	15621	
Calvin	16622	
Cambra	18611	
Cambridge Springs	16403	
Cammal	17723	
Camp Curtin, Sta. Harrisburg	17110	
Camp Hill (1st)	17011	
Campbelltown	17010	
Camptown	18815	
Canadensis	18325	
Canonsburg (1st)	15317	
Canton (1st)	17724	
Ellenton, R. Br.	17732	
Carbondale (1st)	18407	
Cardale	15420	
Carlisle (1st)	17013	
Carlisle Barracks, MOU. Carlisle	17013	
Carlton	16311	
Carmichaels	15320	
Carnegie (1st)	15106	
Carrolltown	15722	
Carson, Sta. Pittsburgh	15203	
Carversville	18913	
Cascade, Br. New Castle	16101	
Cashtown	17310	
Cassandra	15925	
Cassville	16623	
Castanea	17726	
Caste Village, Br. Pittsburgh	15236	
Castle Shannon, Br. Pittsburgh	15234	
Castor, Sta. Philadelphia	19149	
Catasauqua (1st)	18032	
Catawissa	17820	
Cecil	15321	
Cedar Run, R. Br. Jersey Shore	17727	
Cedarhurst, Br. Pittsburgh	15243	
Cedars	19423	
Cementon, Br. Whitehall	18052	
Center Moreland, R. Br. Tunkhannock	18657	
Center Square, R. Sta. Blue Bell	19422	
Center Valley	18034	
Centerport	19516	
Centerville	16404	
Central, Sta. Washington	15301	
Central, Sta. Mc Keesport	15132	
Central City	15926	
Central Highlands, Br. Elizabeth	15037	
Centralia	17927	
Centre Hall	16828	
Chadds Ford	19317	
Chalfont (1st)	18914	
Chalkhill	15421	
Chambers Hill, Br. Harrisburg	17111	
Chambersburg (1st)	17201	
Chambersville	15723	
Champion	15622	

Chandlers Valley	16312	
Chapman Lake, R. Br. Jermyn	18433	
Charleroi (1st)	15022	
Chatham	19318	
Cheltenham (1st)	19012	
Cherry Tree	15724	
Cherryville	18035	
Chest Springs	16624	
CHESTER (1st) (see appendix)		
Chester Heights	19017	
Chester Springs	19425	
Chestnut Hill, Sta. Philadelphia	19118	
Chestnut Ridge	15422	
Cheswick (1st)	15024	
Cheyney	19319	
Chicora	16025	
Kaylor, R. Br.	16042	
Childs, Br. Carbondale	18407	
Chinchilla	18410	
Christiana	17509	
Churchtown	17510	
Churchville, Br. Southampton	18966	
Clairton (1st)	15025	
Clarence	16829	
Clarendon	16313	
Claridge	15623	
Clarington	15828	
Clarion (1st)	16214	
Clark	16113	
Clarks Mills	16114	
Clarks Summit (1st)	18411	
Clarksburg	15725	
Clarksville	15322	
Claysburg	16625	
Claysville	15323	
Clearfield (1st)	16830	
Clearville	15535	
Cleona, Br. Lebanon	17042	
Clermont, R. Br. Mount Jewett	16722	
Clifford	18413	
Clifton Heights (1st)	19018	
Climax	16216	
Clinton	15026	
Clintonville	16372	
Clune	15727	
Clymer	15728	
Coal Center	15423	
Coaldale	18218	
Coalport	16627	
Coatesville (1st)	19320	
Coburn	16832	
Cochranton (1st)	16314	
Cochranville	19330	
Cocolamus	17014	
Codorus	17311	
Cogan Station	17728	
Cokeburg	15324	
Colebrook	17015	
College, Sta. Easton	18042	
College Misericordia, Br. Dallas	18612	
Collegeville (1st)	19426	
Collingdale, Br. Darby	19023	
Colmar (1st)	18915	
Colonial Park, Br. Harrisburg	17109	
Columbia (1st)	17512	
Columbia Cross Roads	16914	

Columbus 16405
Colver 15927
Commerce, Sta.
  Philadelphia 19108
Commodore 15729
Concord 17217
Concordville (1st) 19331
Conemaugh, Br. Johnstown 15909
Conestoga 17516
Confluence 15424
Conneaut Lake 16316
Conneaut Lake Park, Br.
  Conneaut Lake 16316
Conneautville 16406
Connellsville (1st) 15425
Connoquenessing 16027
Conshohocken (1st) 19428
Continental, Sta.
  Philadelphia 19106
Conway 15027
Conyngham 18219
Cooksburg 16217
Coolspring, R. Br.
  Punxsutawney 15730
Coopersburg 18036
Cooperstown 16317
Coplay 18037
Coral 15731
Coraopolis (1st) 15108
Corliss, Sta. Pittsburgh 15204
Cornwall 17016
  Quentin, R. Br. 17083
Cornwells Heights (1st) 19020
Corry (1st) 16407
Corsica 15829
Coryville, R. Br. Eldred 16723
Coudersport (1st) 16915
Coulters 15028
Coupon, R. Br. Ashville 16629
Courtney 15029
Covington 16917
Cowanesque 16918
Cowansville 16218
Crabtree 15624
Crafton, Br. Pittsburgh 15205
Craigsville 16219
Craley 17312
Cramer, R. Br. Seward 15954
Cranberry 16319
Cranesville 16410
Creamery 19430
Creekside 15732
Creighton 15030
Cresco 18326
Cresson (1st) 16630
Cressona 17929
Crooked Creek 16919
Crosby 16724
Cross Fork 17729
Crown 16220
Croydon, Br. Cornwells
  Heights 19020
Crucible 15325
Crum Lynne 19022
Crystal Spring 15536
Cuddy 15031
Cumbola 17930
Curllisville 16221
Curryville 16631
Curtisville 15032
Curwensville 16833
Custer City 16725
Cyclone 16726

Ormsby, R. Br. 16741
Dagus Mines 15831
Daisytown 15427
Dallas (1st) 18612
Dallastown (1st) 17313
Dalmatia 17017
Dalton 18414
Damascus 18415
  Galilee, R. Br. 18423
Danboro 18916
Danielsville 18038
Danville (1st) 17821
Darby (1st) 19023
Darling, R. Br. Media 19063
Darlington 16115
Darragh 15625
Dauberville, R. Br. Leesport ...19517
Dauphin 17018
Davidsville 15928
Davistown 15326
Dawson 15428
Dayton 16222
De Lancey 15733
De Young 16728
Deep Valley, R. Br. .New
  Freeport 15352
Defiance 16633
Delano 18220
Delaware Water Gap (1st) 18327
Delmont 15626
Delta 17314
Denbo 15429
Denver (1st) 17517
Derrick City 16727
Derry 15627
Devault 19432
Devon (1st) 19333
Dewart 17730
Dickerson Run 15430
Dickinson 17218
Dickson City, Br. Scranton 18519
Dilliner 15327
Dillsburg (1st) 17019
Dilltown 15929
Dimock 18816
Dingmans Ferry 18328
Distant 16223
Dixonville 15734
Donaldson, Br. Tremont 17981
Donegal 15628
Donora (1st) 15033
Dora 15735
Dormont, Br. Pittsburgh 15216
Dornsife 17823
Douglassville 19518
Dover (1st) 17315
Downingtown (1st) 19335
Downtown, Sta. Uniontown 15401
Doylesburg, R. Br. Dry Run 17219
Doylestown (1st) 18901
  Lumberville, R. Br. 18933
  New Britain, Br. 18901
Dravosburg 15034
Dresher, Br. Fort
  Washington 19025
Drexel Hill (1st) 19026
Drifting 16834
Drifton 18221
Driftwood 15832
Drumore 17518
Drums 18222
Dry Run 17220
  Doylesburg, R. Br. 17219

Du Bois (1st) 15801
Dublin 18917
Dudley 16634
Duke Center 16729
Dunbar 15431
Duncannon 17020
Duncansville (1st) 16635
Dunlevy 15432
Dunlo 15930
Dunmore, Br. Scranton 18512
Dupont, Br. Pittston 18641
Duquesne (1st) 15110
Durham 18039
Duryea, Br. Pittston 18642
Dushore 18614
Dysart 16636
Eagles Mere 17731
Eagles Mere Park, R. Sta.
  Eagles Mere 17731
Eagleville, Br. Norristown 19408
Earlington 18918
Earlville 19519
East Bangor, R. Br. Bangor 18013
East Berlin 17316
East Brady 16028
East Butler 16029
East Earl 17519
East Falls, Sta.
  Philadelphia 19129
East Freedom 16637
East Germantown, Sta.
  Philadelphia 19138
East Greenville 18041
East Hickory 16321
East Hills, Br. Johnstown 15904
East Liberty, Sta. Pittsburgh ..15206
East Mc Keesport (1st) 15035
East Millsboro 15433
East Petersburg (1st) 17520
East Pittsburgh (1st) 15112
East Prospect 17317
East Side, Sta. Nanticoke 18634
East Smethport 16730
East Smithfield 18817
East Springfield 16411
East Stroudsburg (1st) 18301
East Texas (1st) 18046
East Vandergrift 15629
East Waterford 17021
East York, Br. York 17402
Easton (1st) 18042
  College, Sta. 18042
  Raubsville, R. Br. 18075
Eau Claire 16030
Ebensburg (1st) 15931
Ebervale 18223
Eddington, Br. Cornwells
  Heights 19020
Eddystone, Br. Chester 19013
Edgemont 19028
Edinboro (1st) 16412
Edinburg 16116
Edison 18919
Edmon 15630
Edwardsville, Br.
  Wilkes-Barre 18704
Effort 18330
Egypt, Sta. Whitehall 18052
Eighty Four 15330
Elco 15434
Eldersville 15036
Elderton 15736
Eldred 16731

Coryville, R. Br..............16723
Elgin...............................16413
Elizabeth (1st)...............15037
Elizabethtown (1st).........17022
Elizabethville.................17023
Elkins Park, Br.
   Philadelphia................19117
Elkland..........................16920
Ellenton, R. Br. Canton...17732
Elliottsburg....................17024
Ellport, Br. Ellwood City...16117
Ellsworth........................15331
Ellwood City (1st)...........16117
Elm...............................17521
Elmhurst........................18416
Elmora...........................15737
Elrama...........................15038
Elroy, Br. Souderton.......18964
Elton.............................15934
Elverson........................19520
Elwyn, Br. Media............19063
Elysburg........................17824
Emeigh..........................15738
Emerald.........................18048
Emigsville......................17318
Emlenton.......................16373
Emmaus (1st).................18049
Emporium (1st)...............15834
Emsworth, Br. Pittsburgh..15202
Endeavor........................16322
English Center................17733
Enola (1st).....................17025
Enon Valley....................16120
Entriken.........................16638
Ephrata (1st)..................17522
   Martindale, R. Br.........17549
Equinunk........................18417
ERIE (1st) (see appendix)
Ernest............................15739
Erwinna.........................18920
Espy, Br. Bloomsburg......17815
Espyville Station, R. Br.
   Linesville...................16414
Essington (1st)...............19029
Etna, Br. Pittsburgh........15223
Etters............................17319
Evans City......................16033
Evansville.......................19521
Everett (1st)...................15537
Everson..........................15631
Ewalt, Sta. Pittsburgh.....15212
Excelsior........................17825
Exeter, Br. Pittston.........18643
Export............................15632
Exton (1st).....................19341
   Lionville, R. Br...........19353
Eyers Grove, R. Br. Millville..17826
Eynon, Sta. Archbald.......18403
Factoryville....................18419
Fairbank........................15435
Fairchance......................15436
Fairfield.........................17320
Fairhill, Sta. Philadelphia..19133
Fairhope........................15538
Fairless Hills (1st)..........19030
Fairmount, Sta. Philadelphia
   (see appendix)
Fairmount City................16224
Fairoaks, Br. Ambridge....15003
Fairview (1st).................16415
Fairview Village, Br.
   Norristown.................19409
Fallentimber...................16639

Falls.............................18615
Falls Creek....................15840
Fallsington, Br. Levittown..19054
Fannettsburg.................17221
Farmington.....................15437
Farrandsville..................17734
Farrell (1st)...................16121
Fawn Grove....................17321
Fayette City...................15438
Fayetteville....................17222
Feasterville-Trevose, Br.
   Langhorne..................19047
Federal Reserve, Sta.
   Pittsburgh..................15230
Federal Reserve, Sta.
   Philadelphia................19107
Federal Square, Sta.
   Harrisburg.................17108
Felton...........................17322
Fenelton.........................16034
Fern Glen, R. Br. Nuremberg..18241
Ferndale.........................18921
Fernway, Br. Zelienople...16063
Fernwood, Br. Lansdowne..19050
Fidelity, Sta. Philadelphia..19109
Finleyville......................15332
Fisher...........................16225
Fishertown.....................15539
Fleetville........................18420
Fleetwood......................19522
Fleming..........................16835
Flemington, Br. Lock Haven..17745
Flicksville.......................18050
Flinton...........................16640
Floreffe..........................15039
Florence, R. Br.
   Burgettstown..............15040
Flourtown (1st)..............19031
Fogelsville.....................18051
Folcroft (1st).................19032
Folsom (1st)...................19033
Fombell.........................16123
Forbes Road...................15633
Force.............................15841
Ford City (1st)................16226
Ford Cliff.......................16228
Forest City (1st).............18421
   Aldenville, R. Br.........18401
   Vandling, Br...............18421
Forest Grove..................18922
Forest Hills, Br. Pittsburgh..15221
Forestville......................16035
Forksville.......................18616
Fort Hill.........................15540
Fort Littleton, R. Br. Mc
   Connellsburg..............17223
Fort Loudon...................17224
Fort Washington (1st)......19034
Fortieth Street, Sta.
   Philadelphia................19104
Forty Fort, Br. Wilkes-Barre..18704
Foster Brook, Br. Bradford..16701
Fountainville...................18923
Fourth Avenue, Sta.
   Pittsburgh..................15222
Fox Chapel, Br. Pittsburgh..15238
Fox Chase, Sta.
   Philadelphia................19111
Foxburg.........................16036
Frackville (1st)...............17931
Franconia, R. Br. Souderton..18924
Frankford, Sta. Philadelphia..19124
Franklin (1st).................16323

Franklin Center, R. Br.
   Media.......................19063
Franklintown..................17323
Frazer, Br. Malvern.........19355
Frederick........................19135
Fredericksburg...............17026
Fredericktown.................15333
Fredonia.........................16124
Freeburg........................17827
Freedom.........................15042
Freeland (1st).................18224
Freemansburg, Br.
   Bethlehem.................18017
Freeport.........................16229
Frenchville......................16836
   Lecontes Mills, R. Br...16850
Friedens.........................15541
Friedensburg..................17933
Friedensville...................18818
Frostburg, R. Br.
   Punxsutawney............15740
Fryburg..........................16326
Fullerton, Sta. Whitehall...18052
Furlong..........................18925
Gaines...........................16921
Galeton..........................16922
Galilee, R. Br. Damascus..18423
Gallitzin.........................16641
Ganister.........................16642
Gans, R. Br. Lake Lynn....15439
Gap...............................17527
Garards Fort...................15334
Garden Mart, Br. Pottstown..19464
Gardenville.....................18926
Gardners........................17324
Garland..........................16416
Garrett..........................15542
Gastonville.....................15336
Gateway, Br. Wilkes-Barre..18704
Gateway Center, Sta.
   Pittsburgh..................15222
Geigertown.....................19523
Geistown, Br. Johnstown..15904
Genesee.........................16923
Geneva, R. Br. Conneaut
   Lake.........................16316
George School, Br. Newtown..18940
Georgetown....................15043
Germania, R. Br. Galeton..16922
Germansville...................18053
Germantown, Sta.
   Philadelphia................19144
Gettysburg (1st).............17325
Gibbon Glade..................15440
Gibraltar........................19524
Gibson...........................18820
Gibsonia (1st).................15044
Gifford..........................16732
Gilbert...........................18331
Gilberton.......................17934
Gilbertsville....................19525
Gillett............................16925
Ginter............................16643
Gipsy.............................15741
Girard (1st)....................16417
Girard Avenue, Sta.
   Philadelphia................19122
Girardville......................17935
Gladwyne (1st)...............19035
Glasgow.........................16644
Glassport (1st)................15045
Glen Campbell.................15742
Glen Lyon......................18617

Glen Mills	19342
Glen Richey	16837
Glen Riddle	19037
Glen Rock (1st)	17327
Glencoe	15543
Glenhope, R. Br. Irvona	16645
Glenmoore	19343
Glenolden (1st)	19036
Glenshaw (1st)	15116
Glenside (1st)	19038
Glenville	17329
Glenwillard	15046
Wireton, R. Br.	15092
Goodville	17528
Gordon	17936
Gordonville	17529
Gouldsboro	18424
Gowen City	17828
Graceton	15743
Gradyville	19039
Grampian	16838
Grand Valley	16420
Grantham	17027
Grantville	17028
Granville	17029
Granville Summit	16926
Grapeville	15634
Grassflat	16839
Gratz	17030
Gray	15544
Grays Landing, R. Br.	
Masontown	15461
Graysville	15337
Great Bend	18821
Great Southern, Br.	
Bridgeville	15017
Greater Pittsburgh Airport,	
Br. Pittsburgh	15231
Greeley	18425
Green Hills, Br. Sharon Hill	19079
Green Lane	18054
Green Park	17031
Greencastle (1st)	17225
Greene	17530
Greengate, Br. Greensburg	15601
Greenock	15047
Greensboro	15338
Greensburg (1st)	15601
Greenstone	17227
Greentown	18426
Greenville (1st)	16125
Grindstone	15442
Grove City (1st)	16127
Grover	17735
Guys Mills	16327
Gwynedd	19436
Gwynedd Valley	19437
Hadley	16130
Halifax	17032
Hallstead	18822
Hallton	15842
Hamburg (1st)	19526
Hamilton	15744
Hamlin	18427
Hammersley Fork	17736
Hampden, Sta. Reading	19604
Hampton, R. Br. New Oxford	17330
Hannastown	15635
Hanover (1st)	17331
Harborcreek	16421
Harford	18823
Harleigh	18225
Harleysville (1st)	19438

Harmonsburg	16422
Harmonville, Br.	
Conshohocken	19428
Harmony	16037
Harriman, Sta. Bristol	19007
HARRISBURG (1st) (see	
appendix)	
Harrison City	15636
Harrison Valley, R. Br.	
Westfield	16927
Harrisonville, R. Br.	
Hustontown	17228
Harrisville	16038
Hartleton	17829
Hartstown	16131
Harveys Lake	18618
Harwick	15049
Harwood Mines, R. Br.	
Hazleton	18201
Hastings	16646
Hatboro (1st)	19040
Hatfield (1st)	19440
Haverford (1st)	19041
Havertown, Br. Upper Darby	19083
Hawk Run	16840
Hawley (1st)	18428
Lakeville, R. Br.	18438
Hawthorn	16230
Hazel Hurst	16733
Hazelwood, Sta. Pittsburgh	15207
Hazen	15843
Hazleton (1st)	18201
Beaver Brook, R. Br.	18215
Broad Street, Sta.	18201
Harwood Mines, R. Br.	18201
Jeanesville, R. Br.	18227
West Hazelton, Br.	18201
Heckscherville	17937
Hegins	17938
Heidelberg, Br. Carnegie	15106
Heilwood	15745
Helfenstein	17939
Hellam, Br. York	17406
Hellertown (1st)	18055
Hendersonville	15339
Hendricks, R. Br. Woxall	18979
Henryville	18332
Hepburnville, R. Br. Cogan	
Station	17728
Hereford	18056
Herman	16039
Herminie	15637
Hermitage, Br. Sharon	16146
Herndon	17830
Herrick Center	18430
Hershey (1st)	17033
Hessdale	17531
Hesston	16647
Hibbs	15443
Hickory	15340
High Spire	17034
Hill, Sta. Harrisburg (see	
appendix)	
Hilcrest, Sta. Bethel Park	15102
Hiller	15444
Hilliards	16040
Hillsdale	15746
Hillsgrove	18619
Hillsville	16132
Hilltown	18927
Hoban Heights	18620
Hokendauqua, Sta.	
Whitehall	18052

Holbrook	15341
Holicong	18928
Holiday Park, Br. Pittsburgh	15239
Hollidaysburg (1st)	16648
Hollsopple	15935
Holmes	13043
Holmesburg, Sta.	
Philadelphia	19136
Holtwood	17532
Home	15747
Homer City (1st)	15748
Homestead (1st)	15120
Hometown, R. Br. Tamaqua	18252
Homewood, Sta. Pittsburgh	15208
Honesdale (1st)	18431
Honey Brook	19344
Honey Grove	17035
Hookstown	15050
Hooversville	15936
Hop Bottom	18824
Hopeland	17533
Hopewell	16650
Hopwood	15445
Horsham (1st)	19044
Hospital, Sta. Norristown	19401
Hostetter	15638
Houston	15342
Houtzdale	16651
Howard	16841
Hublersburg	16842
Huey	16231
Hughesville	17737
Hummels Wharf	17831
Hummelstown (1st)	17036
Hummer	15639
Hunlock Creek	18621
Hunting Park, Sta.	
Philadelphia	19140
Huntingdon (1st)	16652
Huntingdon Valley (1st)	19006
Huntington Mills	18622
Hustontown	17229
Harrisonville, R. Br.	17228
Hutchinson	15640
Hyde	16843
Hyde Park	15641
Hydetown	16328
Hyndman	15545
Wellersburg, R. Br.	15564
Hyner, R. Br. North Bend	17738
Ickesburg	17037
Idaville	17337
Imler	16655
Immaculata	19345
Imperial	15126
Independence	15343
Indian Head	15446
Indiana (1st)	15701
Indianola	15051
Industry	15052
Ingomar	15127
Ingram, Br. Pittsburgh	15205
Intercourse	17534
Irvine	16329
Irvona	16656
Glenhope, R. Br.	16645
Irwin (1st)	15642
Isabella	15447
Iselin, R. Br. Saltsburg	15681
Ivyland, Br. Warminster	18974
Jackson	18825
Jackson Center	16133
Jacobs Creek	15448

529

Jacobus, Br. York.................17407
James City.........................16734
James Creek.......................16657
Jamestown.........................16134
Jamison............................18929
Jeanesville, R. Br. Hazleton 18227
Jeannette (1st)...................15644
Jefferson..........................15344
Jenkins, Br. Pittston.............18640
Jenkintown (1st).................19046
Jenners, R. Br. Boswell..........15546
Jennerstown.......................15547
Jermyn............................18433
Jerome............................15937
Jersey Mills......................17739
Jersey Shore (1st)...............17740
  Cedar Run, R. Br...............17727
  Salladasburg, R. Br............17740
Jessup............................18434
Jim Thorpe........................18229
Joffre............................15053
John Wanamaker, Sta.
  Philadelphia....................19107
Johnsonburg.......................15845
JOHNSTOWN (1st) (see
  appendix)
Jones Mills.......................15646
Jonestown.........................17038
Josephine.........................15750
Julian............................16844
Juneau............................15751
Junedale..........................18230
Juniata, Sta. Altoona............16601
Kane (1st)........................16735
Kantner...........................15548
Karns City........................16041
Karthaus..........................16845
  Piper, R. Br...................16845
  Pottersdale, R. Br.............16871
Kaska.............................17940
Kaylor, R. Br. Chicora...........16042
Kaywin, Br. Bethlehem............18018
Keating Summit, R. Br.
  Austin..........................16737
Keisterville......................15449
Kelayres..........................18231
Kellers Church, R. Br.
  Perkasie........................18944
Kelton............................19346
Kemblesville......................19347
Kempton...........................19529
Kendall Creek, Sta.
  Bradford........................16701
Kennedy, Br. Mc Kees Rocks.......15136
Kennerdell........................16374
Kennett Square (1st).............19348
Kensington, Sta.
  Philadelphia....................19125
Kent..............................15752
Kersey............................15846
Keystone, Br. Chambersburg.......17201
Kilbuck, Sta. Pittsburgh.........15233
Kimberton.........................19442
King Of Prussia, Br.
  Norristown......................19406
Kingsessing, Sta.
  Philadelphia....................19143
Kingsley..........................18826
Kingston, Br. Wilkes-Barre.......18704
Kintnersville.....................18930
Kinzers...........................17535
Kirkwood..........................17536
Kittanning (1st).................16201

Kleinfeltersville................17039
Klingerstown.....................17941
Knox 16232
Knox Dale.........................15847
Knoxville.........................16928
Koppel............................16136
Kossuth...........................16331
Kreamer...........................17833
Kresgeville.......................18333
Kulpmont..........................17834
Kulpsville........................19443
Kunkletown........................18058
Kutztown (1st)...................19530
Kylertown.........................16847
La Belle..........................15450
La Jose...........................15753
La Plume..........................18440
Laceyville........................18623
Lackawaxen........................18435
Lafayette Hill (1st).............19444
Lahaska...........................18931
Lairdsville.......................17742
Lake Ariel........................18436
Lake City (1st)..................16423
Lake Como.........................18437
Lake Harmony......................18624
Lake Lynn.........................15451
  Gans, R. Br....................15439
Lake Winola.......................18625
Lakemont, Br. Altoona............16602
Lakeville, R. Br. Hawley.........18438
Lakewood..........................18439
Lamar.............................16848
Lamartine.........................16375
Lamberton.........................15452
Lampeter..........................17537
LANCASTER (1st) (see
  appendix)
Landenberg........................19350
Landingville......................17942
Landisburg........................17040
Landisville (1st)................17538
Lanesboro.........................18827
Langdondale.......................16658
Langeloth.........................15054
Langhorne (1st)..................19047
Lansdale (1st)...................19446
Lansdowne (1st)..................19050
Lanse.............................16849
Lansford (1st)...................18232
Laporte...........................18626
Large, Br. Clairton..............15025
Larimer...........................15647
Latrobe (1st)....................15650
Lattimer Mines....................18234
Laughlintown......................15655
Laurel Gardens, Br.
  Pittsburgh......................15229
Laureldale, Br. Reading..........19605
Laurelton.........................17835
Laurys Station....................18059
Lavelle...........................17943
Lawn..............................17041
Lawrence..........................15055
Lawrenceville.....................16929
Lawton............................18828
Layton............................15453
Le Raysville......................18829
Le Roy............................17743
Lebanon (1st)....................17042
Lebanon Church, Sta.
  Pittsburgh......................15122
Leck Kill.........................17836

Leckrone..........................15454
Lecontes Mills, R. Br.
  Frenchville.....................16850
Lederach..........................19450
Leechburg (1st)..................15656
Leeper............................16233
Leesport, (1st)..................19533
  Dauberville, R. Br.............19517
Leetsdale (1st)..................15056
Lehigh University, Sta.
  Bethlehem.......................18015
Lehigh Valley, Br. Bethlehem
  (see appendix)
Lehighton (1st)..................18235
Lehman............................18627
Leisenring........................15455
Lemasters.........................17231
Lemont............................16851
Lemont Furnace....................15456
Lemoyne (1st)....................17043
Lenhartsville.....................19534
Lenni (1st)......................19052
Lenoxville, R. Br. Nicholson.....18441
Leola (1st)......................17540
Lester, Br. Philadelphia.........19113
Level Green, R. Br. Trafford.....15085
LEVITTOWN (1st) (see
  appendix)
Lewis Run.........................16738
Lewisberry........................17339
Lewisburg (1st)..................17837
Lewistown (1st)..................17044
Lewisville........................19351
Liberty...........................16930
Library...........................15129
Lickingville......................16332
Light Street, R. Br.
  Bloomsburg......................17839
Ligonier (1st)...................15658
Lilly.............................15938
Lima..............................19060
Limekiln..........................19535
Limeport..........................18060
Limerick, Br. Royersford.........19468
Limestone.........................16234
Lincoln Place, Sta.
  Pittsburgh......................15207
Lincoln University...............19352
Linden............................17744
Lindsey, Sta. Punxsutawney.......15767
Line Lexington....................18932
Linesville........................16424
Linfield, Br. Royersford.........19468
Linglestown, Br. Harrisburg
  (see appendix)
Linwood, Br. Marcus Hook.........19061
Lionville, R. Br. Exton..........19353
Listie............................15549
Listonburg........................15457
Lititz (1st).....................17543
  Brunnerville, R. Br...........17543
  Rothsville, R. Br.............17573
Little Marsh......................16931
Little Meadows....................18830
Littlestown (1st)................17340
Liverpool.........................17045
Llewellyn.........................17944
Lock Haven (1st).................17745
Locust Gap........................17840
Locustdale........................17945
Logan, Sta. Philadelphia.........19141
Loganton..........................17747
Loganville........................17342

Long Pond 18334
Lopez 18628
'Loretto (1st) 15940
Lost Creek 17946
Lowber 15660
Lower Burrell, Br. New
    Kensington 15068
Lower Paxton, Br.
    Harrisburg 17109
Loyalhanna 15661
Loysburg 16659
Loysville 17047
Lucernemines 15754
Lucinda 16235
Ludlow 16333
Lumberville, R. Br.
    Doylestown 18933
Lurgan 17232
Luthersburg 15848
Luxor 15662
Luzerne, Br. Wilkes-Barre 18709
Lykens (1st) 17048
Lyndell 19354
Lyndora 16045
Lynnewood, Br. Philadelphia ...19150
Lynnport 18061
Lyon Station 19536
Mac Arthur, Sta. Aliquippa 15001
Macdonaldton, R. Br. Berlin ...15530
Mackeyville 17750
Macungie 18062
Madera 16661
Madison 15663
Madisonburg 16852
Mahaffey 15757
Mahanoy City (1st) 17948
Mahanoy Plane 17949
Mahoningtown, Sta. New
    Castle 16102
Mainesburg 16932
Mainland 19451
Malvern (1st) 19355
Mammoth 15664
Manayunk, Sta.
    Philadelphia 19127
Manchester 17345
Manheim (1st) 17545
Manns Choice 15550
Manoa, Br. Upper Darby 19083
Manor 15665
Manor Oak, Br. Pittsburgh 15220
Manorville 16238
Mansfield (1st) 16933
Maple Glen, Br. Ambler 19002
Mapleton Depot 17052
Mar Lin 17951
Marble 16334
Marchand 15758
Marcus Hook (1st) 19061
Marianna 15345
Marienville 16239
Marietta (1st) 17547
Marion 17235
Marion Center 15759
Marion Heights 17832
Marion Hill, Br. New
    Brighton 15066
Market Street, Sta. West
    Chester 19380
Markleton 15551
Marklysburg 15459
Mars (1st) 16046
Marshalls Creek 18335

Marsteller 15760
Martin 15460
Martindale, R. Br. Ephrata 17549
Martins Creek 18063
Martinsburg 16662
Marwood 16047
Mary D. 17952
Marysville 17053
Marywood College, Sta.
    Scranton 18509
Masontown 15461
Matamoras 18336
Mather 15346
Mattawana 17054
Maxatawny 19538
Mayfair, Sta. Philadelphia 19136
Mayfield, Br. Jermyn 18433
Mayport 16240
Maytown 17550
Mc Adoo (1st) 18237
Mc Alisterville 17049
Mc Clellandtown 15458
Mc Clure 17841
Mc Connellsburg 17233
    Fort Littleton, R. Br. 17223
Mc Connellstown 16660
Mc Coysville 17050
Mc Donald 15057
Mc Elhattan 17748
Mc Ewensville 17749
Mc Gees Mills 15755
Mc Grann 16236
Mc Intyre 15756
Mc Kean 16426
Mc Kees Rocks (1st) 15136
MC KEESPORT (1st) (see
    appendix)
Mc Knight, Br. Pittsburgh 15237
Mc Knightstown 17343
Mc Murray, Br. Canonsburg ...15317
Mc Sherrystown 17344
Mc Veytown 17051
Meadow Lands 15347
Meadowbrook, Br.
    Jenkintown 19046
Meadville (1st) 16335
Mechanicsburg (1st) 17055
Mechanicsville 18934
MEDIA (1st) (see appendix)
Mehoopany 18629
Melcroft 15462
Mendenhall 19357
Menges Mills 17346
Mentcle 15761
Mercer (1st) 16137
Mercersburg (1st) 17236
Meridian, R. Br. Butler 16001
Merion Station (1st) 19066
Merrittstown 15463
Mertztown 19539
Meshoppen 18630
Mexico 17056
Meyersdale 15552
Middle City, Sta.
    Philadelphia (see
    appendix)
Middle Creek 17843
Middleburg (1st) 17842
Middlebury Center 16935
Middleport 17953
Middletown (1st) 17057
Midland (1st) 15059
Midway 15060

Mifflin 17058
Mifflinburg 17844
Mifflintown 17059
Mifflinville 18631
Milan 18831
Milanville 18443
Mildred 18632
Milesburg 16853
Milford (1st) 18337
Milford Square........................18935
Mill Creek 17060
Mill Hall
    Salona, R. Br. 17767
Mill Run 15464
Mill Village 16427
Millersburg (1st) 17061
Millerstown 17062
Millersville (1st) 17551
Millerton 16936
Millheim 16854
Millmont 17845
Millport, R. Br.
    Shinglehouse 16739
Millrift 18340
Mills 16937
Millsboro 15348
Millvale, Br. Pittsburgh 15209
Millville 17846
    Eyers Grove, R. Br. 17826
Milmont Park, Br. Folsom 19033
Milnesville 18239
Milroy 17063
Milton (1st) 17847
Mineral Point 15942
Mineral Springs 16855
Minersville (1st) 17954
Mingoville 16856
Minisink Hills 18341
Miquon 19452
Mocanaqua, R. Br.
    Shickshinny 18655
Modena 19358
Mohnton 19540
Mohrsville 19541
Monaca (1st) 15061
Monessen (1st) 15062
Monocacy Station 19542
Monongahela (1st) 15063
Monroeton 18832
Mont Alto 17237
Mont Clare 19453
Montandon 17850
Montgomery (1st) 17752
Montgomeryville (1st)............18936
Montour, Br. Pittsburgh 15244
Montoursville (1st) 17754
Montrose (1st) 18801
Moosic, Br. Scranton 18507
Morann 16663
Moravian, Sta. Bethlehem 18018
Morea Colliery 17955
Morgan 15064
Morgantown 19543
Morris 16938
Morris Run 16939
Morrisdale. 16858
Morrisville (1st) 19067
Morton (1st) 19070
Morwood 18937
Moscow 18444
Moshannon 16859
Mount Aetna 19544
Mount Airy, Sta.

Philadelphia..............19119
Mount Bethel..............18343
Mount Braddock..............15465
Mount Carmel (1st)..............17851
Mount Gretna..............17064
Mount Holly Springs..............17065
Mount Jewett..............16740
Clermont, R. Br..............16722
Mount Joy (1st)..............17552
Mount Lebanon, Br.
Pittsburgh..............15228
Mount Morris..............15349
Mount Nebo, R. Br.
Sewickley..............15143
Mount Oliver, Sta.
Pittsburgh..............15210
Mount Penn, Br. Reading..............19606
Mount Pleasant (1st)..............15666
Mount Pleasant Mills..............17853
Mount Pocono (1st)..............18344
Mount Union..............17066
Mount Washington, Sta.
Pittsburgh..............15211
Mount Wolf..............17347
Mountain Top, Br.
Wilkes-Barre..............18707
Mountainhome..............18342
Mountville..............17554
Mowry..............17956
Moylan, Br. Media..............19065
Muir..............17957
Muncy (1st)..............17756
Pennsdale, R. Br..............17761
Muncy Valley..............17758
Sonestown, R. Br..............17770
Munhall, Br. Homestead..............15120
Munson..............16860
Murrysville (1st)..............15668
Muse..............15350
Myerstown (1st)..............17067
Nagle Road, Br. Erie..............16510
Nanticoke (1st)..............18634
Nanty Glo..............15943
Narberth (1st)..............19072
Narrows, Br. Wilkes-Barre..............18704
Narvon..............17555
Natalie..............17854
Natrona, Br. Natrona
Heights..............15065
Natrona Heights (1st)..............15065
Naval Hospital, Sta.
Philadelphia..............19145
Nazareth (1st)..............18064
Needmore..............17238
Big Cove Tannery, R. Br...17212
Neelyton..............17239
Neffs..............18065
Neffsville, Br. Lancaster..............17601
Nelson..............16940
Nemacolin..............15351
Nescopeck..............18635
Neshannock, Br. New Castle..............16105
Nesquehoning..............18240
Neville Island, Br.
Pittsburgh..............15225
New Albany..............18833
New Alexandria..............15670
New Baltimore..............15553
New Bedford..............16140
New Berlin..............17855
New Berlinville..............19545
New Bethlehem..............16242
New Bloomfield..............17068

New Brighton (1st)..............15066
New Britain, Br. Doylestown..18901
New Buffalo..............17069
NEW CASTLE (1st) (see
appendix)
New Columbia, R. Br. West
Milton..............17856
New Cumberland (1st)..............17070
New Derry..............15671
New Eagle..............15067
New Enterprise..............16664
New Florence..............15944
New Freedom..............17349
New Freeport..............15352
New Galilee..............16141
New Geneva..............15467
New Germantown..............17071
New Holland (1st)..............17557
New Hope (1st)..............18938
New Kensington (1st)..............15068
Arnold, Br..............15068
Braeburn, R. Br..............15016
Lower Burrell, Br..............15068
Parnassus, Sta..............15068
New Kingstown..............17072
New London..............19360
New Milford..............18834
New Millport..............16861
New Oxford..............17350
Hampton, R. Br..............17330
New Paris..............15554
New Park..............17352
New Philadelphia..............17959
New Providence..............17560
New Ringgold..............17960
New Salem..............15468
New Stanton..............15672
New Tripoli..............18066
New Wilmington..............16142
Newberry, Sta. Williamsport..17701
Newburg..............17240
Newell..............15466
Newfield, Br. Verona..............15147
Newfoundland..............18445
Newmanstown..............17073
Newport..............17074
Newportville, Br. Levittown....19056
Newry..............16665
Newton Hamilton..............17075
Newtown (1st)..............18940
Newtown Square (1st)..............19073
Newville (1st)..............17241
Niantic..............19546
Nicetown, Sta. Philadelphia....19140
Nicholson..............18446
Lenoxville, R. Br..............18441
Nicktown..............15762
Ninepoints..............17561
Nineveh..............15353
Nisbet..............17759
Nittany Mall, Br. State
College..............16801
Nixon, Br. Butler..............16001
Noblestown, R. Br. Oakdale..15071
Normalville..............15469
NORRISTOWN (1st) (see
appendix)
North Apollo..............15673
North Bend..............17760
Hyner, R. Br..............17738
North Bessemer, Br.
Pittsburgh..............15235
North Bingham..............16941

North Braddock, Br.
Braddock..............15104
North Charleroi, Br.
Charleroi..............15022
North East (1st)..............16428
North End, Sta. Wilkes-Barre..18705
North Hills, Sta. Glenside........19038
North Huntingdon, Br. Irwin....15642
North Philadelphia, Sta.
Philadelphia..............19133
North Pine Grove..............16243
North Scranton, Sta.
Scranton..............18508
North Springfield..............16430
North Versailles (1st)..............15137
North Wales (1st)..............19454
North Warren, Br. Warren........16365
North Washington..............16048
Northampton (1st)..............18067
Northbrook..............19361
Northpoint..............15763
Northumberland (1st)..............17857
Northwest, Br. State College..16801
Norvelt..............15674
Norwood (1st)..............19074
Nottingham..............19362
Noxen..............18636
Nu Mine..............16244
Nuangola..............18637
Number Fifty Six, Sta.
Philadelphia..............19107
Numidia..............17858
Nuremberg..............18241
Oak Hall..............16862
Oak Lane, Sta. Philadelphia..19126
Oak Ridge..............16245
Oakdale..............15071
Oakland, Sta. Pittsburgh........15213
Oakland Mills..............17076
Oakmont (1st)..............15139
Oaks (1st)..............19456
Obelisk, R. Br. Zieglerville......19492
Observatory, Sta. Pittsburgh..15214
Ogontz Campus, Br.
Abington..............19001
Ohiopyle..............15470
Oil City (1st)..............16301
Oil Creek, Sta. Oil City..........16301
Olanta..............16863
Old Forge, Br. Scranton..........18518
Old Zionsville..............18068
Oley..............19547
Oliphant Furnace..............15471
Oliveburg..............15764
Oliver..............15472
Olney, Sta. Philadelphia..........19120
Olyphant (1st)..............18447
Oneida..............18242
Ono..............17077
Orangeville..............17859
Orbisonia..............17243
Orefield..............18069
Oreland (1st)..............19075
Ormsby, R. Br. Cyclone..........16741
Orrstown..............17244
Orrtanna..............17353
Orson..............18449
Orviston, R. Br. Beech
Creek..............16864
Orwigsburg (1st)..............17961
Orwin, R. Br. Tower City........17980
Osceola..............16942
Osceola Mills..............16666

Sandy Ridge, R. Br.	16677
Osterburg	16667
Saint Clairsville, R. Br.	16676
Oswayo, R. Br. Coudersport	16915
Ottsville	18942
Overbrook, Sta. Philadelphia	19151
Oxford (1st)	19363
Palm	18070
Palmerton (1st)	18071
Palmyra (1st)	17078
Paoli (1st)	19301
Paradise	17562
Parcel Post, Sta. Reading	19603
Parcel Post, Sta. Pittsburgh	15233
Pardeesville	18243
Paris, R. Br. Burgettstown	15021
Park, Sta. Vandergrift	15690
Park Ridge, Br. Norristown	19401
Parker	16049
Parker Ford	19457
Parkesburg	19365
Parkhill	15945
Parkway Center, Br. Pittsburgh	15220
Parnassus, Sta. New Kensington	15068
Parryville	18244
Paschall, Sta. Philadelphia (see appendix)	
Patton	16668
Paupack	18451
Paxinos	17860
Paxtang, Br. Harrisburg	17111
Paxtonville	17861
Peach Bottom	17563
Peach Glen, R. Br. Bendersville	17306
Peckville	18452
Peely, Br. Wilkes-Barre	18706
Pen Argyl (1st)	18072
Penbrook, Br. Harrisburg	17103
Penfield	15849
Penllyn, Br. Blue Bell	19422
Penn	15675
Penn Center, Sta. Philadelphia	19103
Penn Hills, Br. Pittsburgh (see appendix)	
Penn Rose, Br. Verona	15147
Penn Run	15765
Penndel, Br. Langhorne	19047
Penns Creek	17862
Penns Park	18943
Pennsburg	18073
Pennsdale, R. Br. Muncy	17761
Pennsylvania Furnace	16865
Penryn	17564
Pequea	17565
Perkasie (1st)	18944
Perkiomenville	18074
Perry Square, Sta. Erie	16507
Perryopolis	15473
Perrysville, Br. Pittsburgh	15237
Perulack, R. Br. East Waterford	17021
Petersburg	16669
Petrolia	16050
PHILADELPHIA (1st) (see appendix)	
Philipsburg (1st)	16866
Phoenixville (1st)	19460
Picture Rocks	17762
Pilgrim Gardens, Sta. Drexel	

Hill	19026
Pillow	17080
Pine Avenue, Sta. Erie	16504
Pine Bank	15354
Pine Forge	19548
Pine Grove	17963
Pine Grove Mills	16868
Pineville	18946
Piper, R. Br. Karthaus	16645
Pipersville	18947
Pitman	17964
PITTSBURGH (1st) (see appendix)	
Pittsfield	16340
PITTSTON (1st) (see appendix)	
Plainfield	17081
Plains, Br. Wilkes-Barre	18705
Plainsville	18650
Plaza, Sta. Butler	16001
Pleasant Gap, Br. Bellefonte	16823
Pleasant Hall	17246
Pleasant Hills, Br. Pittsburgh	15236
Pleasant Mount	18453
Pleasant Unity	15676
Pleasant Valley	18948
Pleasantville	16341
Plum, Br. Pittsburgh	15239
Plumsteadville	18949
Plumville	16246
Plymouth (1st)	18651
Plymouth Meeting (1st)	19462
Pocono Lake	18347
Pocono Lake Preserve, R. Br.	18348
Pocono Lake Preserve, R. Br. Pocono Lake	18348
Pocono Manor	18349
Pocono Pines	18350
Pocono Summit	18346
Pocopson	19366
Point, Br. Butler	16001
Point Breeze, Sta. Philadelphia	19145
Point Marion	15474
Point Pleasant	18950
Polk	16342
Pomeroy	19367
Port Allegany (1st)	16743
Wrights, R. Br.	16752
Port Carbon	17965
Port Clinton	19549
Port Kennedy	19463
Port Matilda	16870
Port Royal	17082
Port Trevorton	17864
Port Vue, Br. Mc KEesport	15133
Portage	15946
Porter	15766
Porters Sideling, R. Br. Spring Grove	17354
Portersville	16051
Portland	18351
Portland Mills	15850
Pottersdale, R. Br. Karthaus	16871
Potts Grove	17865
Pottstown (1st)	19464
Pottsville (1st)	17901
Poyntelle	18454
Presque Isle, Br. Erie (see appendix)	
Presto	15142

Preston Park	18455
Pricedale	15072
Primos Secane, Br. Clifton Heights	19018
Prompton	18456
Prospect	16052
Prospect Park (1st)	19076
Prosperity	15329
Pulaski	16143
Punxsutawney (1st)	15767
Coolspring, R. Br.	15730
Frostburg, R. Br.	15740
Lindsey, Sta.	15767
Puritan, R. Br. Portage	15946
Quakake	18245
Quakertown (1st)	18951
Quarryville (1st)	17566
Quecreek	15555
Queen	16670
Quentin, R. Br. Cornwall	17083
Quincy	17247
Racine, R. Br. Beaver Falls	15010
Radnor, Br. Wayne	19087
Railroad	17355
Ralston	17763
Ramey	16671
Ranshaw, R. Br. Shamokin	17866
Ransom	18653
Raubsville, R. Br. Easton	18075
Ravine	17966
Rea	15356
READING (1st) (see appendix)	
Reamstown	17567
Rebersburg	16872
Rebuck	17867
Rector	15677
Red Hill	18076
Red Lion (1st)	17356
Reeders	18352
Reedsville	17084
Refton	·15·,·q
Regency Mall, Br. Indiana	1570.
Rehrersburg	19550
Reinerton, Br. Tower City	17980
Reinholds	17569
Renfrew	16053
Reno	16343
Renovo	17764
Renton, Br. Pittsburgh	15239
Republic	15475
Revere	18953
Revloc	15948
Rew	16744
Rexmont	17085
Reynoldsville	15851
Rheems	17570
Rhone, Sta. Nanticoke	18634
Rices Landing	15357
Riceville	16432
Richboro, Br. Southampton	18954
Richeyville	15358
Richfield	17086
Richland	17087
Richlandtown	18955
Richmond, Sta. Philadelphia	19134
Riddlesburg	16672
Ridgway (1st)	15853
Ridley Park (1st)	19078
Riegelsville	18077
Rillton	15678
Rimersburg	16248
Ringgold	15770

Ringtown 17967
Riverside 17868
Rixford 16745
Roaring Branch 17765
Roaring Spring (1st) 16673
Robertsdale 16674
Robesonia (1st) 19551
Robinson 15949
Rochester (1st) 15074
Rochester Mills 15771
Rock Glen 18246
Rockhill Furnace 17249
Rockledge, Br. Philadelphia 19111
Rockton 15856
Rockwood 15557
Rogersville 15359
Rohrerstown (1st) 17571
Rome 18837
Ronco 15476
Ronks 17572
Roscoe 15477
Rosehill, Sta. Philadelphia 19140
Rosemont, Br. Bryn Mawr 19010
Roseto, Br. Bangor 18013
Roslyn, Br. Abington 19001
Rossiter 15772
Rossville 17358
Rostraver, Br. Belle Vernon 15012
Rothsville, R. Br. Lititz 17573
Roulette 16746
Rouseville 16344
Rouzerville 17250
Rowland 18457
Roxborough, Sta.
   Philadelphia 19128
Roxbury 17251
Royersford (1st) 19468
Ruffs Dale 15679
Rural Ridge 15075
Rural Valley 16249
Rushland 18956
Rushville 18839
Russell 16345
Russellton 15076
Rutherford Heights, Br.
   Harrisburg 17111
Rutledge, Br. Morton 19070
Rydal, Br. Jenkintown 19046
Sabinsville 16943
Sacramento 17968
Sadsburyville 19369
Saegertown 16433
Sagamore 16250
Saint Benedict 15773
Saint Boniface 16675
Saint Charles 16251
Saint Clair 17970
Saint Clairsville, R. Br.
   Osterburg 16676
Saint Davids, Br. Wayne 19087
Saint Johns 18247
Saint Marys (1st) 15857
Saint Michael 15951
Saint Peters 19470
Saint Petersburg 16054
Saint Thomas 17252
Salford 18957
Salfordville 18958
Salina 15680
Salisbury 15558
Salix 15952
Salladasburg, R. Br. Jersey
   Shore 17740

Salona, R. Br. Mill Hall 17767
Saltillo 17253
Saltsburg (1st) 15681
Salunga, Br. Landisville 17538
Sandy Lake 16145
Sandy Ridge, R. Br. Osceola
   Mills 16677
Sarver 16055
Sassamansville 19472
Saxonburg 16056
Saxton 16678
Saylorsburg 18353
Sayre (1st) 18840
Scalp Level, Br. Windber 15963
Scenery Hill 15360
Schaefferstown 17088
Schellsburg 15559
Schenley 15682
Schnecksville 18078
Schoeneck 17574
Schuylkill, Sta. Philadelphia ...19146
Schuylkill Haven (1st) 17972
Schwenksville 19473
Sciota 18354
Scotland 17254
Scotrun 18355
Scottdale (1st) 15683
SCRANTON (1st) (see
   appendix)
Seanor 15953
Seelyville, Br. Honesdale 18431
Selinsgrove (1st) 17870
Sellersville (1st) 18960
Seltzer 17974
Seminole 16253
Seneca 16346
Sergeant 16747
Seven Valleys 17360
Seward 15954
Sewickley (1st) 15143
Shade Gap 17255
Shady Grove 17256
Shadyside, Sta. Pittsburgh 15232
Shaft 17975
Shamokin (1st) 17872
   Ranshaw, R. Br. 17866
Shamokin Dam 17876
Shamrock Station 19552
Shanesville 19553
Shanksville 15560
Sharon (1st) 16146
Sharon Hill (1st) 19079
Sharpsburg, Br. Pittsburgh 15215
Sharpsville 16150
Shartlesville 19554
Shavertown, Br.
   Wilkes-Barre 18708
Shawanese 18654
Shawnee On Delaware 18356
Shawville 16873
Sheakleyville 16151
Sheffield 16347
Sheiocta 15774
Shenandoah (1st) 17976
Shenango 16152
Sheppton 18248
Shermans Dale 17090
Shickshinny 18655
Shillington, Br. Reading 19607
Shinglehouse 16748
   Millport, R. Br. 16739
Shippensburg (1st) 17257
Shippenville 16254

Shippingport 15077
Shiremanstown, Br. Camp
   Hill 17011
Shirleysburg 17260
Shoemakersville 19555
Shohola 18458
Shrewsbury 17361
Shunk 17768
Sidman 15955
Sigel 15860
Silver Spring 17575
Silverdale 18962
Simpson, Br. Carbondale 18407
Sinking Spring, Br. Reading 19608
Sinnamahoning 15861
Sipesville 15561
Six Mile Run 16679
Sixtieth Street, Sta.
   Philadelphia 19139
Skippack 19474
Skytop 18357
Slate Run 17769
Slatedale 18079
Slatington (1st) 18080
Slickville 15684
Sligo 16255
Slippery Rock (1st) 16057
Slovan 15078
Smethport 16749
Smicksburg 16256
Smithfield 15478
Smithmill 16680
Smithton 15479
Smock 15480
Smokerun 16681
Smoketown 17576
Snow Shoe 16874
Snydersburg 16257
Snydertown 17877
Solebury 18963
Somerset (1st) 15501
Somerton, Sta. Philadelphia 19116
Sonestown, R. Br. Muncy
   Valley 17770
Souderburg 17577
Souderton (1st) 18964
   Bethton, Br. 18964
   Elroy, Br. 18964
   Franconia, R. Br. 18924
South, Sta. Butler 16001
South Canaan 18459
South Connellsville, Br.
   Connellsville 15425
South Erie, Sta. Erie (see
   appendix)
South Fork 15956
South Gibson 18842
South Heights 15081
South Hills, Br. Pittsburgh 15216
South Montrose 18843
South Mountain 17261
South New Castle, Sta. New
   Castle 16101
South Plaza, Br. Indiana 15701
South Side, Sta. Scranton 18505
South Sterling 18460
South Williamsport, Br.
   Williamsport 17701
Southampton (1st) 18966
Southview 15361
Southwark, Sta. Philadelphia
   (see appendix)
Southwest 15685

Spangler	15775
Spartansburg	16434
Spinnerstown	18968
Spraggs	15362
Sprankle Mills	15776
Spring Church	15686
Spring City (1st)	19475
Spring Creek	16436
Spring Garden, Sta. Philadelphia (see appendix)	
Spring Glen	17978
Spring Grove (1st)	17362
Porters Sideling, R. Br.	17354
Spring House (1st)	19477
Spring Mills	16875
Spring Mount	19478
Spring Run	17262
Springboro	16435
Springdale (1st)	15144
Springfield, Br. Media	19064
Springs	15562
Springtown	18081
Springville	18844
Sproul	16682
Spruce Creek	16683
Squirrel Hill, Sta. Pittsburgh	15217
Stahlstown	15687
Star Junction	15482
Starford	15777
Starlight	18461
Starr	16348
Starrucca	18462
State College (1st)	16801
Nittany Mall, Br.	16801
Northwest, Br.	16801
Toftrees, Br.	16801
University Park, Sta.	16802
State Line	17263
Steelton, Br. Harrisburg	17113
Steelville	19370
Sterling	18463
Stevens	17578
Stevensville	18845
Stewartstown	17363
Stiles, Sta. Whitehall	18052
Stillwater	17878
Stockdale	15483
Stockertown	16083
Stoneboro	16153
Stony Run	19557
Stouchsburg, R. Br. Womelsdorf	19558
Stowe, Br. Pottstown	19464
Stoystown	15563
Strabane	15363
Strasburg	17579
Strattanville	16258
Strausstown	19559
Strong	17879
Strongstown, R. Br. Twin Rocks	15957
Stroudsburg (1st)	18360
Stump Creek	15863
Sturgeon	15082
Suburbia, Br. Pottstown	19464
Sugar Notch, Br. Wilkes-Barre	18706
Sugar Run	18846
Sugargrove	16350
Sugarloaf	18249
Summerdale	17093
Summerhill	15958

Summerville	15864
Summit Hill	18250
Summit Station	17979
Sumneytown	18084
Sunbury (1st)	17801
Suplee	19371
Susquehanna	18847
Sutersville	15083
Swarthmore (1st)	19081
Swedeland	19479
Sweet Valley	18656
Swengel	17880
Swiftwater	18370
Swissvale, Br. Pittsburgh	15218
Swoyerville, Br. Wilkes-Barre	18704
Sybertsville	18251
Sycamore	15364
Sykesville	15865
Sylvania	16945
Tacony, Sta. Philadelphia	19135
Tafton	18464
Talmage	17580
Tamaqua (1st)	18252
Tamiment, R. Br. Bushkill	18371
Tannersville	18372
Tarentum (1st)	15084
Tarrs	15688
Tatamy	18085
Taylor-Old Forge, Br. Scranton (see appendix)	
Taylorstown	15365
Telford (1st)	18969
Temple (1st)	19560
Templeton	16259
Tenth Avenue, Sta. Bethlehem	18018
Terminal, Sta. Upper Darby	19082
Terre Hill	17581
Thomasville	17364
Thompson	18465
Thompsontown	17094
Thorndale (1st)	19372
Thornton	19373
Three Springs	17264
Throop, Br. Scranton	18512
Tidioute	16351
Timblin	15778
Tioga	16946
Tiona	16352
Tionesta	16353
Tipton	16684
Tire Hill	15559
Titusville (1st)	16354
Tobyhanna (1st)	18466
Todd	16685
Toftrees, Br. State College	16801
Topton (1st)	19562
Torrance	15779
Torresdale, Sta. Philadelphia (see appendix)	
Toughkenamon	19374
Towanda (1st)	18848
Tower City	17980
Townville	16360
Trafford (1st)	15085
Transfer	16154
Treehaven, Sta. Bethel Park	15102
Treichlers	18086
Tremont	17981
Tresckow	18254
Trevorton	17881
Trevose, Br. Langhorne	19047
Trexlertown	18087

Trout Run	17771
Bodines, R. Br.	17722
Troutville	15866
Troxelville	17882
Troy (1st)	16947
Trucksville, Br. Wilkes-Barre	18708
Trumbauersville	18970
Tullytown, Br. Bristol	19007
Tunkhannock (1st)	18657
Turbotville	17772
Turkey City	16058
Turtle Creek (1st)	15145
Turtlepoint	16750
Tuscarora	17982
Twin Rocks	15960
Strongstown, R. Br.	15957
Tyler Hill	18469
Tylersburg	16361
Tylersport	18971
Tylersville	17773
Tyre, R. Br. Imperial	15126
Tyrone (1st)	16686
U S Naval Base, Sta. Philadelphia	19112
Uledi	15484
Ulster	18850
Ulysses	16948
Union City (1st)	16438
Union Dale	18470
Union Trust, Sta. Pittsburgh	15219
Uniontown (1st)	15401
Unionville	19375
United	15689
Unity House, R. Br. Bushkill	18373
Unityville	17774
Universal, Br. Pittsburgh	15235
University Park, Sta. State College	16802
Upper Black Eddy	18972
UPPER DARBY (1st) (see appendix)	
Upper Saint Clair, Br. Pittsburgh	15241
Upper Strasburg	17265
Uptown, Sta. Pittsburgh	15219
Ursina	15485
Utica	16362
Uwchland	19480
Valencia	16059
Valier	15780
Valley Forge (1st)	19481
Valley Forge Army Hospital, Br. Phoenixville	19460
Valley View	17983
Van	16363
Van Meter	15487
Van Voorhis	15366
Vanderbilt	15486
Vandergrift (1st)	15690
Vandling, Br. Forest City	18421
Venango	16440
Venetia	15367
Venus	16364
Vera Cruz, R. Br. Emmaus	18049
Vernfield	18973
Vernon Park, Sta. Philadelphia	19144
Verona (1st)	15147
Versailles, Br. Mc Keesport	15132
Vestaburg	15368
Veterans Administration Hosp, Br. Butler	16001

Veterans Administration
  Hosp. Sta. Altoona............16603
Veterans Hospital, Sta.
  Wilkes-Barre....................18703
Veterans Hospital, Br.
  Coatesville.......................19320
Veterans Hospital, Sta.
  Pittsburgh........................15240
Vicksburg................................17883
Villa Maria..............................16155
Village, Br. Pittsburgh.........15241
Villanova (1st)........................19085
Vintondale..............................15961
Virginville...............................19564
Volant.....................................16156
Vowinckel...............................16260
Wabash Sta. Pittsburgh.......15220
Wadsworth, Sta.
  Philadelphia.....................19150
Wagontown.............................19376
Wahnetah, Sta. Jim Thorpe..18229
Wallaceton..............................16876
Wallingford, Br. Media.........19086
Walnut Bottom.......................17266
Walnutport..............................18088
Walston...................................15781
Waltersburg............................15488
Wampum.................................16157
Wapwallopen..........................18660
Ward..19377
Warfordsburg..........................17267
Warminster (1st).....................18974
Warren (1st)............................16365
Warren Center.........................18851
Warrendale..............................15086
Warrington (1st).....................18976
Warriors Mark.........................16877
Washington (1st).....................15301
Washington Boro.....................17582
Washington Crossing.............18977
Washingtonville.......................17884
Waterfall.................................16689
Waterford................................16441
Waterman, R. Br. Homer
  City................................15748
Waterville................................17776
Watsontown............................17777
Wattsburg...............................16442
Waverly...................................18471
Wawa, R. Br. Media...............19063
Waymart.................................18472
Wayne (1st)............................19087
Waynesboro (1st)....................17268
Waynesburg (1st)....................15370
Weatherly................................18255
Webster...................................15087
Weedville................................15868
Weikert...................................17885
Weissport, Br. Lehighton.......18235
Wellersburg, R. Br.
  Hyndman.........................15564
Wells Tannery.........................16691
Wellsboro (1st)........................16901
Wellsville................................17365
Wendel....................................15691
Wernersville............................19565
Wescosville, Br. Allentown....18106
Wesleyville, Br. Erie (see
  appendix)
West Alexander.......................15376
West Aliquippa, Sta.
  Aliquippa.........................15001

West Bridgewater, Br.
  Beaver.............................15009
West Bristol, Br. Bristol........19007
West Brownsville, Br.
  Brownsville......................15417
West Chester (1st).................19380
West Conshohocken, Br.
  Conshohocken..................19428
West Decatur..........................16878
West Elizabeth........................15088
West End, Sta. Harrisburg....17102
West Fairview, Br. Enola.......17025
West Finley.............................15377
West Goshen, Br. West
  Chester............................19380
West Grove (1st).....................19390
West Hazelton, Br. Hazleton..18201
West Hickory...........................16370
West Hills, Br. Coraopolis....15108
West Lawn, Br. Reading........19609
West Lebanon.........................15783
West Leisenring.......................15489
West Market Street, Sta.
  Philadelphia.....................19139
West Middlesex.......................16159
West Middletown.....................15379
West Milton.............................17886
  New Columbia, R. Br........17856
West Monterey........................16060
West Nanticoke, Br.
  Nanticoke........................18634
West Newton (1st)...................15089
West Park, Sta.
  Philadelphia.....................19131
West Pittsburg........................16160
West Pittston, Br. Pittston....18643
West Plaza, Br. Erie..............16505
West Point (1st)......................19486
West Reading, Br. Reading....19602
West Ridge, Br. Erie.............16506
West Salisbury........................15565
West Scranton, Sta.
  Scranton..........................18504
West Side, Sta. Nanticoke....18634
West Springfield......................16443
West Sunbury..........................16061
West View, Br. Pittsburgh.....15229
West Willow............................17583
West Winfield...........................16062
West Wyoming, Br. Pittston..18644
Westfield.................................16950
  Harrison Valley, R. Br.....16927
Westford, R. Br. Jamestown..16134
Westland.................................15378
Westline..................................16751
Westmoreland City.................15692
Weston....................................18256
Westover.................................16692
Westport..................................17778
Westtown................................19395
Westville.................................15869
Westwood, Br. Johnstown....15905
Wexford (1st)..........................15090
Wheatland...............................16161
Whitaker, Br. Homestead......15120
White.......................................15490
White Deer..............................17887
White Haven............................18661
White Mills..............................18473
White Oak, Br. Mc Keesport..15131
Whitehall (1st)........................18052
Whites Crossing, Br.
  Carbondale......................18407

Whitney...................................15693
Whitsett...................................15491
Wickhaven...............................15492
Wiconisco................................17097
Widener College, Sta.
  Chester............................19013
Widnoon..................................16261
Wila, R. Br. Newport.............17074
Wilburton................................17888
Wilcox.....................................15870
Wildwood................................15091
WILKES-BARRE (1st) (see
  appendix)
Wilkinsburg, Br. Pittsburgh....15221
William Penn Annex, Sta.
  Philadelphia (see
  appendix)
Williamsburg...........................16693
Williamson...............................17270
Williamsport (1st)...................17701
Williamstown..........................17098
Willow Grove (1st)..................19090
Willow Hill..............................17271
Willow Street..........................17584
Wilmerding (1st).....................15148
Wilmore...................................15962
Wilpen.....................................15694
Wilson, Sta. Clairton.............15025
Winburne.................................16879
Wind Ridge.............................15380
Windber (1st)..........................15963
Windgap (1st).........................18091
Windsor...................................17366
Winfield...................................17889
Wingate, R. Br. Bellefonte....16880
Wireton, R. Br. Glenwillard..15092
Wissinoming, Sta.
  Philadelphia.....................19124
Witmer....................................17585
Womelsdorf.............................19567
  Stouchsburg, R. Br..........19558
Wood.......................................16694
Woodbury................................16695
Woodland.................................16881
Woodlyn (1st)..........................19094
Woodward................................16882
Woolrich..................................17779
Worcester................................19490
Wormleysburg, Br. Lemoyne..17043
Worthington.............................16262
Worthville................................15784
Woxall.....................................18979
Wrights, R. Br. Port
  Allegany..........................16752
Wrightstown, Br. Newtown....18940
Wrightsville (1st).....................17368
Wyalusing...............................18853
Wyano.....................................15695
Wycombe.................................18980
Wylie, Sta. Pittsburgh...........15219
Wyncote (1st)..........................19095
Wynnewood (1st).....................19096
Wyoming, Br. Pittston...........18644
Wyomissing, Br. Reading......19610
Wysox.....................................18854
Yardley, Br. Morrisville.........19067
Yatesboro................................16263
Yeadon, Br. Lansdowne.........19050
Yeagertown.............................17099
Yellow House...........................19568
Yerkes.....................................19491
Yoe, Br. Dallastown..............17313

YORK (1st) (see appendix)	Youngsville	16371	Zieglerville	19492
York Haven	17370	Youngwood (1st)	15697	Zion Grove	17985
York New Salem	17371	Yukon	15698	Zionhill	18981
York Springs	17372	Zelienople (1st)	16063	Zionsville	18092
Youngstown	15696	Zerbe, R. Br. Tremont	17981	Zullinger	17272

ALLENTOWN　181

POST OFFICE BOXES

Box Nos.
A-M	Main Office	05
1-1910	Main Office	05
3000-3999	Wescosville Branch	06

RURAL ROUTES

1	04
2	03
3	04
4	03

STATIONS, BRANCHES AND UNITS

Wescosville Br	06
General Delivery	05
Postmaster	01

APARTMENTS, HOTELS, MOTELS

Allen Gardens, 800 So 12th	03
Allen-Towne House Motel 647 Union Blvd	03
Americus Hotel 541 Hamilton	05
Colonial & Colonial Arms, 218 S 15th	02
Devonshire Apartments, 31st & Devonshire	03
Episcopal House, 1440 Walnut	02
Executive 901 So Jefferson	03
Hamilton Crest, 2122 Walnut	04
Hamilton Hotel 627 Hamilton	01
Hamilton Square 117 S 4th 350 Hickory Ln	02
Hampshire House, 15th 1/2 Hamilton	02
Highland Dwellings 2145 Livingston, 2144 Highland	04
Holiday Inn Of Allentown, Route 3	04
John Cross Towers, 1339 Allen	02
Livingston, 1411 Hamilton	02
Majestic, 127 N 8th	01
Regent, 923 Hamilton	01
Tourinns Motel Route 3	04
Traylor Hotel 1436 Hamilton	05
Tremont Apartments	04
Trexler Park 3616 Tilghman	04
Trout Hall Gardens	02
Valley View, S 15th & Elm	02

BUILDINGS

Administration, 31 S Penn	05
Allen Law, 133 N 5th	02
B & B, 546 Hamilton	01
Center Square, 11 N 7th	01
Colonial Theatre, 517 Hamilton	01
Commerce, 12 N 7th	01
Commonwealth, 514 Hamilton	01
Farr, 739 Hamilton	01
Federal, 442 Hamilton	01

Hamilton Law, 527 Hamilton	01
Hunsicker, 17 N 7th	01
Liberty Square Medical Center, 501 N 17th	04
Medical Arts, 941 Hamilton	01
Odd Fellows, 118 N 9th	02
Penn Trust, 801 Hamilton	01
Pennsylvania Power & Light Company, 901 Hamilton	01
Somach, 1132 Hamilton	01
Wetherhold & Metzger 719 Hamilton	01
Y M C A & W Y C A, 425 S 15th	02
Young, 714 Hamilton	05

GOVERNMENT OFFICES

City Hall, 435 Hamilton	01
Federal, 442 Hamilton	01
Lehigh County Court House, 455 Hamilton	05

HOSPITALS

Allentown Hospital, 1627 Chew	02
Allentown Osteopathic Hospital, 1736 Hamilton	04
Allentown State Hospital, 1700 Hanover Ave	03
Sacred Heart Hospital, 421 Chew W	02

UNIVERSITIES AND COLLEGES

Cedar Crest College, 30th & Walnut	04
Muhlenberg College, 2301 Chew	04
Penn Wesleyan College 1414 E Cedar St	03

ALTOONA　166

POST OFFICE BOXES

Box Nos.
1-2032	Main Office	03

RURAL ROUTES

1,2,3,4	01

STATIONS, BRANCHES AND UNITS

Juniata Sta	01
Lakemont Br	02
Veterans Administration HospSta	03
General Delivery	03
Postmaster	03

BETHLEHEM　180

POST OFFICE BOXES

Box Nos.
1-800	Main Office	16
1001-1484	Moravian Sta	18

2001-2872	Lehigh Valley Br	01
3001-3178	Butztown Br	17
4001-4094	Tenth Ave Station Sta	18

RURAL ROUTES

1,2	17
3,4,5	15
6	17

STATIONS, BRANCHES AND UNITS

Butztown Br	17
Freemansburg Br	17
Kaywin Br	18
Lehigh University Sta	15
Lehigh Valley Br	01
Moravian Sta	18
Tenth Avenue Sta	18
General Delivery	15
Postmaster	16

CHESTER　190

POST OFFICE BOXES

Box Nos.
1-86	Aston	14
1-846	Main Office	16
1001-1159	Brookhaven	15

STATIONS, BRANCHES AND UNITS

Aston Br	14
Brookhaven Br	15
Eddystone Br	13
Widener College Sta	13
General Delivery	13
Postmaster	13

HOSPITALS

Crozer-Chester Medical Center, 15th & Upland Ave	13
Sacred Heart Hospital, 9th & Wilson St	13

UNIVERSITIES AND COLLEGES

Widener College 14th & Chestnut St	13

ERIE　165

POST OFFICE BOXES

Box Nos.
1-1440	Main Office	12
1501-1925	Perry Square Sta	07
2000-2999	Main Office	12
3001-3368	South Erie Sta	08
4000-6300	Main Office	12
7001-7999	Wesleyville Br	10
8000-8999	Presque Isle Br	05
9000-9500	Pine Avenue Sta	04

RURAL ROUTES

3,4,5	09
6,7	10
9,10	09

STATIONS, BRANCHES AND UNITS

Nagle Road Br.	10
Perry Square Sta.	07
Pine Avenue Sta.	04
West Plaza Br.	05
West Ridge Br.	06
General Delivery	01
Postmaster	01

APARTMENTS, HOTELS, MOTELS

Audrey, 518 Holland	07
Boston, 516 E 6	07
Brownstone, 26 North Park Row	01
Center City 814 Sassafras	01
Downtowner, 205 W 10	01
El Patio, 2950 W Lake Rd	05
Fleming, 210 W 8	01
Glenwood Towers, 4601 Glenwood Park Ave	09
Hamel, 446-58 W 9	02
Harborview House, 210 W 6	07
Holiday Inn South, Rts 90 & 97	12
Holiday Inn, 18 W 18	01
Howard Johnson, 7575 Waterford Pike Rd.	09
Kenilworth, 351-53 W 6	07
Keystone, 1206 E Lake Rd.	07
Lininger, 425-31 Peach	07
Parade 701-03 Parade	03
Peach Hill, 2631 Peach	08
Pittsburgh, 2182 W 8	05
Plymouth, 604-08 Chestnut	02
Princeton, 238 W 8	07
Richford, 515 State	01
Schaaf, 10 E 34	04
Schaaf, 3004-16 State	08
Schaaf, 3309 State	08
Schaaf, 9 E 33	04
Scotts, 2930 W 6	05
Sharp, 727 French	01
Thirty-Five Thirty-Five, 3535 State	08
Town House 925 French	01

BUILDINGS

Baldwin, 1001 State	01
Commerce, 10 E 12	01
Marine Bank, 901-05 State	01
Masonic Temple, 24 W 8	01
Palace, 913 State	01
Professional, 1611 Peach	01
Rothrock, 121 W 11	01
Sumner Nichols 155 West 8th	01

HOSPITALS

Doctors 252 W 11	01
Erie Osteopathic, 5515 Peach	09
Grandview, 4728 Lake Pleasant Rd.	04

Hamot, 4 E 2	12
Saint Vincents, 232 W 25	12
Veterans, 135 E 38	01
Zem Zem, 1645 W 8	05

UNIVERSITIES AND COLLEGES

Behrend Campus (Penn State U, Station Rd	10
Gannon, 10 9 W 6	01
Mercyhurst, 501 E 38	01
Villa Maria, 2551 W Lake Rd	05

HARRISBURG   171

POST OFFICE BOXES

Box Nos.		
A-W	Federal Square Sta.	08
1-1299	Federal Square Sta.	08
1301-3999	Main Office	05
4000-4999	Paxtang Br.	11
5000-5999	Camp Curtin Sta.	10
6000-6999	Linglestown Br.	12
7000-7999	Steelton Br.	13

RURAL ROUTES

1	11
2	10
3,4	12

STATIONS, BRANCHES AND UNITS

Camp Curtin Sta.	10
Chambers Hill Br.	11
Colonial Park Br.	09
Federal Square Sta.	08
Hill Sta.	04
Linglestown Br.	12
Lower Paxton Br.	09
Paxtang Br.	11
Penbrook Br.	03
Rutherford Heights Br.	11
Steelton Br.	13
West End Sta.	02
General Delivery	05
Postmaster	05

APARTMENTS, HOTELS, MOTELS

Allen Hall	04
Beaufort Manor, 4100 Beechwood Ln	12
Bistline House 1291 S 28th	11
Blue Mountain, Rd 4	12
Brookridge Terrace	09
Brookwood Gardens, 2500 Brookwood	04
Capitol Hill 327 Market	01
Colonial Crest	09
Colonial, 420 Market	01
Donaldson, 204 N 2nd	01
East Park Garden, 200 N 40th	11
English Village, 3300 Paxton	11
Executive House, 101 S 2nd	05
Governor, Box 2101	01
Grayco, 115 North	01
Greene Hall	04
Harrisburg Park, 1400 S	

15th	04
Holiday East, Box 1855	05
Holiday Inn Town, Box 1855	05
Holiday West, Box 1855	05
Hoy Towers, 300 Mohn	13
Jackson Lick, 1300 N 6th	02
Locust Grove, Locust Grove Ct	09
Mitchell, 105 North	01
Mitchell, 611 N Front	01
Nationwide Inn, 500 Race	04
Packer House, 1700 State	03
Parkview, 2400 Market	03
Parkway, 925 N Front	02
Paxton Park, 600 Santanna Dr	09
Penn Harris Motor Inn, Box 2653	05
Penn Harris, Box 2651	05
Plaza, 423 Market	01
Presbyterian, 322 N 2nd	01
R D 4	12
Revere Hall	04
River House, 2311 N Front	10
Riverview Manor, 1519 N Front	02
Royal, 422 Market	01
Saint James, 405-A Market	01
Schuyler Hall	04
Scottsdale, 1021 S Progress Ave	11
Thornwood, 220 Thornwood Rd	04
Towne House, 660 Boas	02
Twin Lakes Manor 4401 Union Deposit Road	11
Warner, 17 N 2nd	01
Wayne Hall	04
Y M C A, 701 N Front	01
Y W C A, 4th & Walnut	01

BUILDINGS

Barto, 231 State	01
Bergner, 6 N 3rd	01
Blackstone, 112 Market	01
Brotherhood, 2107 N 6th	10
Calder, 16 N 2nd	01
Colonial Park Medical 4900 Constitution Avenue	09
Columbus, 229 Walnut	01
Commerce, 300 N 2nd	01
Dauphin, 203 Market	01
Farm Show, 1030 Maclay	20
Federal Office, 228 Walnut	08
Feller, 301 Market	01
Hall, 112 N 2nd	01
Kel-Front, 1801 N Front	02
Keystone, 20 S 3rd	01
Kline, 210 Walnut	01
Market Square, 2 N 2nd	01
Payne-Shoemaker, 240 N 3rd	01
Riverside Medical, 1919 N Front	02
Riverside Office Center, 2101 N Front	10
Scottish Rite Cathedral 2701 N 3rd	10
Shore Drive Office Center, 2001 N Front	02
State Street, 500 N 3rd	01
State Theatre, 212 Locust	01

Zembo Temple, 3rd &
 Division 10

GOVERNMENT OFFICES

All Other State Departments.... 20
Bureau Of Motor Vehicles,
 Transp And Safety Bldg 22
City Hall, 423 Walnut 01
Department Of Revenue,
 Finance Building.................. 27
Employment Security, Labor
 & Industry Bldg 21
Liquor Control, N W Office
 Bldg 24
Municipal, 423 Walnut............. 01
Personal Income Tax, Finance
 Bldg 29
Property & Supply, Main
 Capital 25
Public Instruction, Education
 Bldg 26
Taxes For Education, 1846
 Brookwood 28
Traffic Safety, Transp And
 Safety Bldg 23
United States Court House,
 Federal Office Bldg.............. 08
United States Post Office,
 811 Market 05

HOSPITALS

Community General
 Osteopathic, 4300
 Londonderry Rd 09
Dauphin County, 1205 S
 28th 11
Harrisburg Polyclinic, Box
 3410 Gpo 05
Harrisburg, Front & Mulberry.. 01
Mental 05
Pennsylvania State (Pouch
 A) 05

JOHNSTOWN   159

POST OFFICE BOXES

Box Nos.
1-184   Conemaugh Br..... 09
1-1017   Main Office 07

RURAL ROUTES

1 06
2,3 04
4,5 05
6 09

STATIONS, BRANCHES AND UNITS

Conemaugh Br 09
East Hills Br............................. 04
Geistown Br.............................. 04
Westwood Br............................ 05
General Delivery 01
Postmaster 01

APARTMENTS, HOTELS, MOTELS

Belmont Homes 04
Carriage Hill Apts 05
Center Town Apts 01
College Park Apts 04
Coopersdale Homes 06
Edwards Hill Apts 05
Norwood Gardens Apts............ 06
Oakhurst Homes 06
Soloman St Homes 02
Vine St Towers Apts 01

BUILDINGS

Carnegie 01
City Hall 01
Federal Bldg-U S Post Office.. 01
First National Bank.................. 01
Fisher.. 01
Johnstown Bank & Trust......... 01
Park 01
Savings Bank Plz 01
Swank.. 01
U S Bank................................... 01

LANCASTER   176

POST OFFICE BOXES

Box Nos.
1-1799   Lancaster........ 04
5000-5500   Neffsville Br..... 01

RURAL ROUTES

2 03
4 02
6 02
7 03

STATIONS, BRANCHES AND UNITS

Neffsville Br 01
General Delivery 04
Postmaster 04

APARTMENTS, HOTELS, MOTELS

Barrcrest Manor, 1705
 Marietta Ave 03
Buchanan, 206 N Queen.......... 04
Cedar Acres, Old
 Philadelphia Pk.................... 02
Conestoga West, 200 Stone
 Mill Rd 03
Congress Inn, Lincoln Hwy E.. 04
Devon House, 1527 Fruitville
 Pk.. 01
Essex House, 145 Maple
 Lane 01
Garden Spot Motel, Lincoln
 Hwy E.................................. 02
George Ross House, 114 E
 Lemon 02
Grand View Apts, Mcgrann
 Blvd..................................... 01
Hamilton Apts, Duke &
 Walnut................................. 02

Hilton Inn N. Queen And
 Chestnut Sts...................... 04
Holiday Inn East 1800
 Hempstead Rd 01
Holiday Inn, 1492 Lititz Pike .. 01
Host Corral 2250 Lincoln
 Highway E............................ 04
Host Farms, 2300 Lincoln
 Highway E............................ 04
Host Motel, 30 Keller Ave 01
Howard Johnson'S Motor
 Lodge, 2100 Lincoln Hwy
 E 04
King Douglas, 105 E King 02
La Chateau De Eden Butter
 Rd 01
Lancaster Court, 1100
 Wabank Rd 03
Landis Vally Motor Inn, 2363
 Oregon Pike......................... 01
Long Home Apts, Race &
 Marietta Aves...................... 03
Manor House, 1400
 Millersville Pk 03
Mayfair, 800 Pleasure Rd....... 01
Oxford House, 146 Maple
 Lane 01
President Buchanan, 1400
 Passey Ln............................ 03
Quality Court 500 Centerville
 Rd 01
River Park Gardens, 1125-
 1255 E Orange 02
Roseville House, 401 Eden
 Rd 01
Saint Charles Apartment,
 400 Euclid Ave 03
Spring Manor, 700
 Millersville Rd...................... 03
Stevens House, Prince &
 King 03
Sweet Briar, Oregon Pike....... 01
Towne House, 742 N Duke...... 02
Travel Lodge, 2101 Columbia
 Ave 03
Treadway Inn 222 Eden Rd 03
Twin Towers, 403 W James..... 01
Wabank Country Club
 Estates, Michelle Dr........... 03
Wheatland Arms, 1115
 Marietta Ave 03
Willows The, Lincoln Hwy E ... 02
1722 Motor Lodge 1722 Old
 Philadelphia Pike................. 02

BUILDINGS

Agriculture, 45-47 N Duke...... 02
Appel, 33 N Duke..................... 02
Coho, 53 N Duke...................... 02
Conestoga Bank Bldg, 28
 Penn Square......................... 03
Fulton Bank Bldg, 8 Penn
 Square.................................. 02
Greist Bldg, 2-8 N Queen........ 03
West End Medical Center,
 822 Marietta Ave................. 03
Y M C A, 572 N Queen............. 03
Y W C A, 149 E Orange............ 02

GOVERNMENT OFFICES

Federal Bldg, 48-50 W Chestnut	04
Lancaster County Court House, 51 E King	02
Lancaster County Health & Welfare, 630 Janet Ave	01
Lancaster School District Bldg, 225 W Orange	04
Lancaster Township Adm Bldg, 1240 Maple Ave	03
Manheim Township Muni Bldg, 1500 Lititz Pike	01
Manor Township Office, 1695 Temple Ave	03
Municipal Bldg, 120 N Duke	04
Public Safety Bldg, 208 N Duke	02

HOSPITALS

Conestoga View, 900 E King	02
Lancaster County Hospital, 900 E King	02
Lancaster General Hospital, 525 N Duke	04
Lancaster Osteopathic Hospital, 1100 E Orange	04
St Joseph Hospital, 250 College Ave	04

UNIVERSITIES AND COLLEGES

Franklin & Marshall, College Ave	04
Lancaster Country Day School, 725 Hamilton Rd	03
Lancaster Theological Seminary, James & College Ave	03
Stevens Trade School, 750 E King	02

LEVITTOWN 190

POST OFFICE BOXES

Box Nos.		
1-269	A Sta	59
301-778	Main Office	58

STATIONS, BRANCHES AND UNITS

Fallsington Br	54
Newportville Br	56
General Delivery	58
Postmaster	58

APARTMENTS, HOTELS, MOTELS

Brittany Springs, Oxford Valley Rd	57
Camelot, Marion & Edgley Ave	55
Country Club Park, 1228 New Rodgers Rd	56
Country Manor, Lincoln Hwy	56
Fallsington Manor, 8590 Newportville-Fallsington Rd	54

Falls Creek 9101 Newportville Rd	54
Hamilton, 2130 New Rodgers Rd	56
Hidden Manor, 201 Woodburne Rd	56
Kenwood Court, Haines Rd	55
Madrid, 1338 New Rodgers Rd	56
Mill Creek Manor, 130 Tullytown-Fallsington Rd	54
Mill Creek, 7030 Mill Creek Rd	57
Orangewood, Orangewood Dr	57
Parkview, 2000 New Rodgers Rd	56
Queen Anne Court, 1550 Woodburne Rd	57
Racquet Club East, 1970 New Rodgers Rd	56
Valley Green, 3501 Oxford Valley Rd	57
Village Of Penbrook Apts 9071 Mill Creek Rd	54
Violetwood Garden Apts., 6750 Mill Creek Rd	57
Woodbourne Apts. 1350 Woodbourne Rd	57

MC KEESPORT 151

POST OFFICE BOXES

Box Nos.		
1-96	Boston Br	35
1-805	Main Office	34

STATIONS, BRANCHES AND UNITS

Boston Br	35
Central Br	32
Port Vue Br	33
Versailles Br	32
White Oak Br	31
General Delivery	34
Postmaster	34

APARTMENTS, HOTELS, MOTELS

Penn Mckee Hotel 130 5th Ave	32
Penn Sheratan Hotel 624 Lysle Blvd	32

HOSPITALS

Mckeesport Hospital 1500 5th Ave	32

MEDIA 190

POST OFFICE BOXES

Box Nos.		
1-114	Elwyn Br	63
1-267	Springfield Br	64
1-319	Moylan Br	65
1-572	Main Office	63
37-389	Wallingford Br	86

STATIONS, BRANCHES AND UNITS

Darling Rural Br	63
Elwyn Br	63
Franklin Center Rural Br	63
Moylan Br	65
Springfield Br	64
Wallingford Br	86
Wawa Rural Br	63
General Delivery	63
Postmaster	63

NEW CASTLE 161

POST OFFICE BOXES

Box Nos.		
1-1020	Main Office	03
1401-1552	Main Office	03
2201-2346	Mahoningtown Sta	02
4000-4999	South Side Office	01
5001-5999	Neshannock Br	05

RURAL ROUTES

2	01
3	05
4	01
5	05
6	01
7	02

STATIONS, BRANCHES AND UNITS

Cascade Br	01
Mahoningtown Sta	02
Neshannock Br	05
South New Castle Sta	01
General Delivery	01
Postmaster	01

APARTMENTS, HOTELS, MOTELS

Castle Arms, N. Mercer : Falls	01
Lawrence Manor 211 W Moody Ave	01
Mc Grath Manor 814 W Washington	01
New Penn Hotel 20 S Mercer	01
Skyview Towers 219 N Beaver	01

BUILDINGS

Centennial 7 S Mill	01
Central 101 S Mercer	01
First Federal Plaza 25 N Mill	01
First National Bank 101 E Washington	01
Lawrence Savings : Trust 223 E Washington	01

HOSPITALS

Jameson Memorial 222 W Leasure Ave	05

St Francis S Mercer At
Phillips 01

UNIVERSITIES AND COLLEGES

New Castle Business College
316 Rhodes Pl 01

NORRISTOWN　194

POST OFFICE BOXES

Box Nos.
1-226	Eagleville Br.....	08
1-261	Bridgeport Br ...	05
1-292	Audubon Br	07
1-294	Fairview Village Br	09
1-389	King Of Prussia Br	06
1-999	Main Office	04

RURAL ROUTES

1,3 01

STATIONS, BRANCHES AND UNITS

Audubon Br	07
Bridgeport Br	05
Eagleville Br	08
Fairview Village Br	09
Hospital Sta	01
King Of Prussia Br	06
Park Ridge Br	01
General Delivery	01
Postmaster	01

PHILADELPHIA　191

POST OFFICE BOXES

Box Nos.
A-H	William Penn Annex Sta	05
1-1999	William Penn Annex Sta	05
2000-2399	Middle City Sta	03
2400-2599	Southwark Sta..	47
2600-2699	Fairmount Sta ..	21
2700-2799	Olney Sta	20
2800-2899	Spring Garden Sta	22
2900-2999	Oak Lane Sta ...	26
3000-3199	Wadsworth Sta..	50
3200-3399	Fairmount Sta ..	21
3400-3599	Spring Garden Sta	22
3600-3799	Kensington Sta	25
3800-3999	Schuylkill Sta ..	46
4000-4099	Chestnut Hill Sta	18
4100-4299	Germantown Sta	44
4300-4399	Chestnut Hill Sta	18
4400-4499	Nicetown Sta ...	40
4500-4599	West Park Sta ..	31

4600-4699	Manayunk Sta...	27
4700-4799	Richmond Sta ...	34
4800-4899	Frankford Sta ...	24
4900-4999	Mount Airy Sta .	19
5000-5099	Fox Chase Sta..	11
5100-5199	Logan Sta.........	41
5200-5299	Oak Lane Sta ...	26
5300-5399	Paschall Sta.....	42
5400-5599	Kingsessing Sta	43
5600-5699	East Falls Sta ..	29
5700-5799	Olney Sta	20
5800-5899	Roxborough Sta	28
5900-5999	Bridesburg Sta..	37
6000-6099	Torresdale Sta ..	14
6100-6199	Bustleton Sta ...	15
6200-6299	Holmesburg Sta	36
6300-6399	West Market Sta	39
6400-6499	Point Breeze Sta	45
6500-6599	East Germantown Sta	38
6600-6699	Boulevard Sta ..	49
6700-6999	North Philadelphia Sta	32
7000-7099	Boulevard Sta ..	49
7100-7199	Elkins Park Br..	17
7200-8799	General Post Office	01
8800-8899	Elkins Park Br..	17
8900-8999	Tacony Sta	35
9001-9299	Lester Br	13
9300-9499	West Market Sta	39
9500-9599	Frankford Sta ...	24
9600-9699	West Park Sta ..	31
9700-9899	Nicetown Sta ...	40
9900-9999	Chestnut Hill Sta	18
11000-11099	Logan Sta.........	41
11100-11199	Holmesburg Sta	36
11200-11299	Elkins Park Br..	17
11300-11399	Bridesburg Sta..	37
11400-11499	Fox Chase Sta..	11
11500-11699	Somerton Sta ...	16
11700-11799	General Post Office	01
11800-11899	Roxborough Sta	28
11900-11999	Point Breeze Sta	45
12000-12199	William Penn Annex Sta	05
12200-12299	Germantown Sta	44
12300-12399	Mount Airy Sta .	19
12400-12599	Overbrook Sta...	51
12600-12699	East Falls Sta ..	29
12700-12799	Richmond	34
12800-12999	Commerce Sta...	08
13000-13999	General Post Office	01
14000-14099	Spring Garden Sta	22
14100-14299	East Germantown ..	38
14300-14599	Bustleton..........	15

14600-14999	Richmond	34
15000-15199	Fairmount Sta ..	21
15200-15299	Kensington	25
15300-15399	Fox Chase Sta..	11
15400-15499	Boulevard	49
15500-15699	West Park	31
15700-15999	Middle City.......	03
16000-16399	Torresdale........	14
16400-16499	Spring Garden..	22
16600-16799	West Market	39
16800-16999	Paschall	42
17000-17599	Wm Penn Annex..........	05
17600-17999	Tacony.............	35
18000-18099	Southwark	47
18100-18299	Somerton	16
18300-18499	Olney	20
18500-18599	East Falls	29
18600-18799	North Philadelphia ...	32
18800-18999	Mount Airy.......	19
19500-19699	Frankford.........	24
19700-19899	Kingsessing......	43
20000-20199	Pt Breeze.........	45
20200-20499	Wadsworth........	50
20500-20799	East Germantown ...	38
20800-20999	Logan	41
21000-21299	Torresdale........	14
21300-21499	Oak Lane	26
21500-21699	West Park	31
21700-21899	Schuylkill	46
22000-22999	Wm Penn Annex..........	05
24000-24299	West Market	39
24300-24599	Olney	20
24600-24799	Fox Chase........	11
24800-24999	Fairmount	21
25000-25199	Southwark	47

STATIONS, BRANCHES AND UNITS

Boulevard Sta...........................	49
Bridesburg Sta..........................	37
Bustleton Sta............................	15
Castor Sta.................................	49
Chestnut Hill Sta.......................	18
Commerce Sta............................	08
Continental Sta..........................	06
East Falls Sta...........................	29
East Germantown Sta.................	38
Elkins Park Br...........................	17
Fairhill Sta................................	33
Fairmont Sta..............................	21
Federal Reserve Sta...................	07
Fidelity Sta................................	09
Forteith Street Sta.....................	04
Fox Chase Sta...........................	11
Frankford Sta.............................	24
Germantown Sta.........................	44
Girard Avenue Sta......................	22
Holmesburg Sta..........................	36
Hunting Park Sta........................	40
John Wanamaker Sta..................	07
Kensington Sta...........................	25
Lester Br...................................	13
Logan Sta..................................	41
Lynnewood Br............................	50
Manayunk Sta............................	27
Mayfair Sta................................	36
Middle City Sta..........................	02
Mount Airy Sta...........................	19
Naval Hospital Sta.....................	45

ZIP CODES
PHILADELPHIA, Pennsylvania

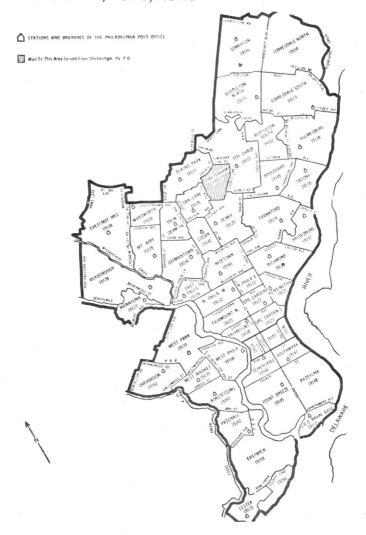

STATIONS AND BRANCHES OF THE PHILADELPHIA POST OFFICE

Mail To This Area Served From Cheltenham, Pa P O

Nicetown Sta. ... 40
North Philadelphia Sta. ... 33
Number Fifty Six Sta. ... 07
Oak Lane Sta. ... 26
Olney Sta. ... 20
Overbrook Sta. ... 51
Paschall Sta. ... 42
Penn Center Sta. ... 03
Point Breeze Sta. ... 45
Richmond Sta. ... 34
Rockledge Br. ... 11
Rosehill Sta. ... 40
Roxborough Sta. ... 28
Schuykill Sta. ... 46
Sixtieth Street Sta. ... 39
Somerton Sta. ... 16
Southwark Sta. ... 47
Spring Garden Sta. ... 22
Tacony Sta. ... 35
Torresdale Sta. ... 14
U.S. Naval Base Sta. ... 12
Vernon Park Sta. ... 44
Wadsworth Sta. ... 50
West Market Street Sta. ... 39
West Park Sta. ... 31
William Penn Annex Sta. ... 05
Wissinoming Sta. ... 24
General Delivery. ... 04
Postmaster. ... 04

APARTMENTS, HOTELS, MOTELS

Adams House, City Line &
    Monument Ave. ... 31
Adelphia, NE 13th &
    Chestnut ... 07
Alden Park, Wissahickon &
    School House ... 44
Ambassador Towne House,
    21st & Chestnut ... 03
Ashbourne Manor, 155 E
    Godfrey Ave. ... 20
Astoria, 2 No 12th ... 07
Atrium, 2555 Welsh Rd. ... 14
Barclay, 18th & Rittenhouse
    Sq. ... 03
Beekman Place 2746
    Belmont Ave. ... 31
Bellevue-Stratford, SW Broad
    & Walnut. ... 02
Benjamin Franklin, SE 9th &
    Chestnut ... 05
Birchwood Hill, 5115
    Wissakickon Ave ... 44
Brierhurst, 4527 Walnut ... 39
Cambridge, Wissahickon &
    School House ... 44
Carl Mackley, M & Bristol. ... 24
Casa Fermi 13th & Lombard. ... 47
Chatham, NE Cor 20th &
    Walnut. ... 03
Chestnut Hill Village, 7900-B
    Stenton Ave ... 18
Divine Tracy, 20 S 36th. ... 04
Dorchester, 226 W
    Rittenhouse Sq ... 03
Drake, 1512 Spruce ... 02
Duffield House, 3701
    Conshohocken Ave ... 31
Duval Manor, Johnson &
    Greene. ... 44
Elkins Park House 7900 Old
    York Rd ... 17

Evergreen Park Manor,
    Woodward & Roosevelt
    Blvd. ... 15
Evergreen Towers, 8900
    Roosevelt Blvd ... 15
Greene Manor 259 W
    Johnson ... 44
Hamilton Court, 39th &
    Chestnut ... 04
Holiday Park 2804 Welsh Rd. ... 52
Holly Court, 9115 Academy
    Rd ... 36
Hopkinson House,
    Washington Sq South ... 06
Independence Plaza 3120 W
    School House Lane ... 44
Iroquois, City Ave & 47th ... 31
Jefferson House, City Line &
    Monument Ave ... 31
John F. Kennedy House, 1901
    J F Kennedy Blvd ... 03
Kenilworth, Wissahickon &
    School House ... 44
Kevon Arms, 52nd &
    Montgomery Ave. ... 31
Krewstown Park, 8875
    Krewstown Rd ... 15
Latham 135 So 17th. ... 03
Lebanon Arms, Bryn Mawr &
    Lebanon Av ... 31
Lynnewood Gardens, Mather
    Way ... 17
Manheim Gardens, Manheim
    & Schuyler ... 44
Manor, Wissahickon & School
    House ... 44
Mayfair House, Lincoln Dr &
    Johnson ... 44
Morgan House, Stenton Ave
    & Mermaid Ln. ... 18
Park City West 3900 Ford Rd. ... 31
Park Drive Manor, Lincoln Dr
    & Harvey. ... 44
Park Terrace, Rowland Ave &
    Rhawn ... 36
Park Towne Place, 2200
    Benjamin Franklin
    Parkway ... 30
Parkway House, 2201
    Benjamin Franklin
    Parkway. ... 30
Penn Center House, 1900
    John F Kennedy Blvd ... 03
Penn Towers, 1801 John F
    Kennedy Blvd ... 03
Penn Wynn House, 2201 Bryn
    Mawr Ave ... 31
Penn-Center Inn, NE 20th &
    Market ... 03
Philadelphian, 2401
    Pennsylvania Ave ... 30
Plaza, 18th & Parkway ... 03
Presidential, City Line Av &
    Monument ... 31
Ridge Carlton 7373 Ridge
    Ave ... 28
Rittenhouse Claridge, 18th &
    Walnut. ... 03
Rittenhouse Plaza, 1901
    Walnut. ... 03
Rittenhouse Savoy, 1810
    Rittenhouse Sq ... 03

Rittenhouse Square, 1830
    Rittenhouse Sq ... 03
Rittenhouse Towers 222 W
    Rittenhouse Sq ... 03
River Park House, 3600
    Conshohocken Ave. ... 31
Robert Morris, NW 17th &
    Arch. ... 03
Roosevelt, SE 23rd & Walnut. ... 03
Saint Regis, 2200 Tremont. ... 15
School Lane House, 5450
    Wissahickon Ave ... 44
Sheraton, 1725 John F
    Kennedy Blvd ... 03
Society Hill Towers, 2nd &
    Locust ... 06
Stevenson Terrace, 10th &
    Godfrey Ave. ... 41
Summit Park West 8200
    Henry Ave. ... 28
Sylvania, SW Juniper &
    Locust ... 07
Touraine, 1520 Spruce. ... 02
Twenty-Six-O-One Parkway,
    2601 Pennsylvania Ave ... 30
Upsal Gardens, 246 W Upsal. ... 19
Warwick, NW 17th & Locust. ... 03
Washington House, City Line
    Av & Monument. ... 31
Watergate Apts, 3601
    Conshohocken Ave. ... 31
Welshwood 2661 Willits Rd ... 14
West Village, 3901
    Conshohocken Ave. ... 31
William Penn House, 1919
    Chestnut ... 03
Windsor, 17th & Parkway ... 03
Wissahickon Gardens,
    Manheim At Schuyler. ... 44

BUILDINGS

American Patriot 112 So
    16th ... 02
Architects, 117 S 17th. ... 03
Atlantic Richfield 260 S
    Broad ... 02
Ayer, 210 W Washington Sq. ... 06
Bankers Securities, NW Cor
    Juniper & Walnut ... 07
Beury, 3701 N Broad ... 40
Boulevard, 18:9 John F
    Kennedy Blvd. ... 03
Bourse, 5th Above Chestnut. ... 06
Broad-Locust, 1405 Locust ... 02
Brown Brothers, 1531
    Walnut. ... 02
Bulletin, 30th & Market. ... 04
Central Medical, 1737
    Chestnut ... 03
Chamber Of Commerce, 121
    S Broad ... 07
Chestnut East, 841 Chestnut. ... 07
City Center, SE Cor Broad &
    Cherry. ... 07
Civic Center Museum Civic
    Center Blvd And 34th. ... 04
Commerce, 401 N Broad. ... 08
Federal Reserve Bank Of
    Philadelphia, 925
    Chestnut ... 01
Fidelity 123 S Broad. ... 09
Fox, 1612 Market St. ... 03

Fruit Produce, 3301 S Galloway............ 48
Girard Stephen, 21 S 12th..... 07
Girard Trust. S Penn Sq & Broad.......... 02
Guarantee Trust, 1420 Walnut........... 02
I B, 1700 Market........... 03
In ependence, SE Cor 5th & Walnut........... 06
Inquirer 400 No Broad........... 30
Insurance Company Of North America, 16th & Arch..... 03
Jefferson, 1015-Chestnut....... 07
Jewelry Trade, 740 Sansom ... 06
Keystone Auto Club, 2040 Market........... 03
Lafayette 437 Chestnut......... 06
Land Title, SW Cor Broad & Chestnut........... 10
Lankenau Medical, Lancaster Ave & City Line............ 51
Lewis Tower, 15th & Locust ... 02
Liberty Trust, NE Cor Broad & Arch............ 07
Mall, NE Cor 4th & Chestnut . 06
Medical Tower, 255 S 17th.... 03
One East Penn Square, Market & Juniper............ 07
Packard, SE Cor 15th & Chestnut 02
Penn Square, NE Cor Juniper & Filbert............ 07
Pennsylvania Lumbermens, SE Cor Broad & Walnut..... 07
Pennsylvania State Office, 1400 Spring Garden 30
Pennsylvania 1500 Chestnut .. 02
Pennwalt 3 Benj Franklin Parkway........... 02
Phila Civic Center 34th And Civic Center Blvdh........... 04
Philadelphia National Bank, NE Cor Broad & Chestnut.. 07
Philadelphia Saving Fund Society, 12th & Market....... 07
Professional, 1831 Chestnut... 03
Provident Trust, SE Cor 17th & Chestnut 03
Public Ledger, 6th & Chestnut 06
Reading Terminal, 12th & Market........... 07
Robinson 42 So 15th............ 02
Rohm & Haas, 28 So 6th....... 06
Schaff, 15th & Race............ 02
Shubert, 250 S Broad........... 02
Stock Exchange, 120 S 17th... 03
Suburban Station, 1617 John F Kennedy Blvd.......... 03
Sun Oil, 1608 Walnut........... 03
Terminal Commerce, 400 N 13th........... 08
Terminal Commerce, 401 N Broad........... 08
U G I, NW Cor Broad & Arch.. 02
Western Saving SE Cor Broad & Chestnut 07
Widener, Chestnut & Juniper.. 07
Wilford, 33rd & Arch............ 04
Witherspoon, 1321 Walnut...... 07

2 Penn Center Plaza, SW Cor 15th & John F Kennedy Blvd............ 02
3 Penn Center Plaza, NW Cor 15th & Market............ 02
4 Penn Center Plaza, SW 16th & John F Kennedy..... 03
5 Penn Center Plaza 16th Market........... 03
6 Penn Center Plaza, 16 N 17th........... 03
7 Penn Center Plaza, SE Cor 17th & John F Kennedy..... 03

GOVERNMENT OFFICES

City Hall Annex Filbert & Juniper........... 07
City Hall Broad & Market 07
Internal Revenue Service Center, 11601 Roosevelt Blvd............ 55
Municipal Services NE Cor 15th & J F Kennedy Blvd ... 07
Naval Pub & Forms Ctr, 5801 Tabor Rd............ 11
State Office 1400 Spring Garden 30
United States Courthouse, 9th & Chestnut............ 07
United States Custom House, 2nd & Chestnut............ 06
United States Mint Independence Mall............ 06

HOSPITALS

Albert Einstein Med Ctr, Nthn Div, Old York & Tabor Rds............ 41
Albert Einstein Medical Ctr Daroff Div 1425 S 5th........ 47
All Saints 8601 Stenton Ave... 18
American Oncologic, Central & Shelmire Aves............ 11
Chestnut Hill, 8815 Germantown Ave............ 18
Childrens Heart Hospital Of Philadelphia, Conshohocken Av 31
Childrens, 18th & Bainbridge............ 46
Doctors 1700 Vine............ 03
Eastern Penna Psychiatric Institute........... 29
Episcopal, Front & Lehigh Ave............ 25
Frankford, Frankford Ave & Wakeling............ 24
Friends Hospital For Mental & Nervous Disorders........ 24
Germantown, Penn & Chew..... 24
Graduate Hospital University Of Pennsylvania 46
Hahnemann Medical, 230 N Broad............ 02
Institute, 111 N 49th St........ 39
Jeanes, Hasbrook Ave & Hartel............ 11
Jefferson, 11th & Walnut........ 07
John F. Kennedy, Langdon & Cheltenham Ave............ 24
Juniata Park Medical Center,

Castor & Wyoming Ave...... 24
Kensington, 136 W Diamond .. 22
Lankenau, Lancaster W Of City Line............ 51
Memorial, 5800 Ridge Ave..... 28
Mercy Douglass, 50th & Woodland Ave 43
Methodist Episcopal, Broad & Wolf............ 48
Metropolitan 201 No 8th........ 06
Misericordia, 54th & Cedar Ave 43
Moss Rehabilitation, 12th & Tabor Rd............ 41
Naval, 17th & Pattison Ave.... 45
Nazareth, 2601 Holme Ave 52
Northeastern, Allegheny Ave & Tulip............ 34
Olney, Palmetto & Devereaux.. 11
Oncologic, Central & Shelmire Aves............ 11
Osteopathic Hospital Of Philadelphia, 48th & Spruce............ 39
Parkview Castor And Wyoming Aves............ 24
Pennsylvania, 8th & Spruce... 07
Philadelphia General, 34th & Civic Center Blvd............ 04
Philadelphia State, Southampton Rd & Roosevelt Blvd............ 54
Presbyterian, 51 N 39th........ 04
Rolling Hill, 60 E Township Line Rd............ 17
Roxborough Memorial Ridge Ave & Rector............ 28
Sacred Heart Home For Incurables, 1315 W Hunting Park Ave 40
Saint Agnes, 1900 S Broad..... 45
Saint Christophers, 2600 No Lawrence............ 33
Saint Josephs, 16th & Girard Ave............ 30
Saint Lukes & Childrens Medical, Franklin & Thompson............ 22
Saint Marys, Frankford Ave & Palmer............ 25
Saint Vincents, 70th & Woodland Ave 42
Shriners, 8400 Roosevelt Blvd............ 52
Skin & Cancer, 3322 N Broad 40
Stetson, 1745 N 4th............ 22
Temple University (Samaritan, 3401 N Broad 40
University, 34th & Spruce...... 04
Veterans Administration, University & Woodland Ave............ 04
West Park, 3905 Ford Rd....... 31
Wills, 16th & Spring Garden ... 30
Womans Medical, 3300 Henry Ave 29

UNIVERSITIES AND COLLEGES

Chestnut Hill College, Germantown & Northwestern Aves	18
Community College Of Philadelphia, 34 S 11th	07
Drexel Univ NE Corner 32nd & Chestnut	04
Dropsie, Broad Below York	32
Eastern Baptist Theological Seminary	51
Girard, Girard & Corinthian Av	21
Hahnemann Medical, 230 No Broad	02
Holy Family, NE Frankford & Grant Av	14
Jefferson Medical 11th & Walnut	07
La Salle, 20th & Olney Ave	41
Moore College Of Art 20th And Race St	03
Penna State College Of Optometry, 6100 N 12th	41
Philadelphia College Of Arts, NW Cor Broad & Pine	02
Philadelphia College Of Osteopathy, City Line & Monument	31
Philadelphia College Of Textiles & Science	44
Philadelphia College Pharmacy & Science, 43rd & Kingsessing	04
Saint Charles Seminary, City Line & Wynnewd Rd	51
Saint Josephs, 54th & City Line	31
Temple University, Broad & Montgomery Ave	22
University Of Pennsylvania, 34th & Spruce	04
Womans Medical Of Pennsylvania, 3300 Henry Ave	29

PITTSBURGH   152

POST OFFICE BOXES

Box Nos.

1-3999	General Post Office	30
4000-4099	Arsenal Sta	01
4100-4224	Bellevue Br	02
4225-4299	Carson Sta	03
4300-4399	Corliss Sta	04
4400-4599	Crafton Br	05
4600-5574	East Liberty Sta	06
5575-5674	Hazelwood Sta	07
5675-5799	Homewood Sta	08
5800-5899	Millvale Br	09
5900-5999	Mount Oliver Sta	10
6000-6099	Mount Washington Sta	11
6100-7099	Allegheny Sta	12

7100-7599	Oakland Sta	13
7600-7699	Observatory Sta	14
7700-7899	Sharpsburg Br	15
7900-8099	South Hills Br	16
8100-8249	Squirrel Hill Sta	17
8250-8374	Swissvale Br	18
8451-8599	Wabash Br	20
8600-8999	Wilkinsburg Br	21
9000-9299	Bloomfield Sta	24
9300-9399	Neville Island Br	25
9500-9599	Etna Br	23
9600-9699	Brookline Sta	26
9700-9799	West View Br	29
9800-9899	Brentwood Br	27
9900-10099	Kilbuck Sta	33
10100-10299	Shadyside Sta	32
10300-10499	Castle Shannon Br	34
10500-10699	Penn Hills Br	35
10700-10799	Carson Sta	03
10800-10999	Pleasant Hills Br	36
11000-11199	Mcknight Br	37
11200-11599	Blawnox Br	38
11600-11900	Mount Lebanon Br	28
12000-12199	Veterans Hospital Sta	40
12300-12499	Greater Pittsburgh Airport	31
12500-12999	Upper St Clair Br	41
13000-13499	Cedarhurst Br	43
14000-14499	Plum Br	39
15000-15499	Mcknight Br	37
15500-15999	Montour Br	44
18000-18499	Pleasant Hills Br	36
34000-39999	General Post Office	30
40000-40999	Arsenal Sta	01
41000-41499	Bellevue Br	02
56751-56899	Homewood Sta	08
59000-59499	Mt Oliver Sta	10
71000-71499	Oakland Sta	13
86000-86499	Wilkinsburg Br	21
95000-95499	Etna Br	23
96000-96499	Brookline Sta	26
98000-98999	Brentwood Br	27

RURAL ROUTES

5	05

STATIONS, BRANCHES AND UNITS

Allegheny Sta	12
Arsenal Sta	01
Aspinwall Br	15
Avalon Br	02
Bellevue Br	02
Berkeley Hills Br	37
Blawnox Br	38
Bloomfield Sta	24
Brentwood Br	27
Brookline Sta	26
Broughton Br	36
Carson Sta	03

Castle Village Br	36
Castle Shannon Br	34
Cedarhurst Br	43
Corliss Sta	04
Crafton Br	05
Dormont Br	16
East Liberty Sta	06
Emsworth Br	02
Etna Br	23
Ewalt Sta	12
Federal Reserve Sta	30
Forest Hills Br	21
Fourth Avenue Sta	22
Fox Chapel Br	38
Gateway Center Sta	22
Greater Pittsburgh Airport Br	31
Hazelwood Sta	07
Holiday Park Br	39
Homewood Sta	08
Ingram Br	05
Kilbuck Sta	33
Laurel Gardens Br	29
Lebanon Church Sta	15122
Lincoln Place Sta	07
Manor Oak Br	20
Mc Knight Br	37
Millvale Br	09
Montour Br	44
Mount Lebanon Br	28
Mount Oliver Sta	10
Mount Washington Sta	11
Neville Island Br	25
North Bessemer Br	35
Oakland Sta	13
Observatory Sta	14
Parcei Post Sta	33
Parkway Center Br	20
Penn Hills Br	35
Perrysville Br	39
Pleasant Hills Br	36
Plum Br	39
Renton Br	39
Shadyside Sta	32
Sharpsburg Br	15
South Hills Br	16
Squirrel Hill Sta	17
Swissvale Br	18
Union Trust Br	19
Universal Br	35
Upper Saint Clair Br	41
Uptown Sta	19
Veterans Hospital Sta	40
Village Br	41
Wabash Br	20
West View Br	29
Wilkinsburg Br	21
Wylie Sta	19
General Delivery	30
Postmaster	19

APARTMENTS, HOTELS, MOTELS

Abbeyville, 115 Abbeyville Rd	28
Abigail, 2307 Brownsville Rd	10
Academy Mansion, 50 Academy Ave	28
Addison Hall, 131 Edgewood Ave	18
Admiral, 5615 Ellsworth	32
Admiral, 590 S Negley Av	32
Akron 4514 Centre Ave	13
Akron, 275 N Craig	13
Alder Court, 6104 Alder	06

Alder Village, 5944 Alder....... 32
Alderdice, 640 Washington
   Rd.. 28
Alderson, 5835 Alderson........ 17
Alexandria, 131 S Negley
   Ave....................................... 06
Alhambra, 209 S Mathilda.... 24
Alta Vista, 139 Lincoln Ave.... 02
Alvern Gardens, Vermont Av
   & Greenridge........................ 34
Alvin Court,1 Windsor Road.... 39
Ambassador East, 1601 Penn
   Ave....................................... 21
Ambassador West 1601 Penn
   Ave....................................... 21
Ambassador, 4733 Center
   Ave....................................... 13
Amberson Gardens, 1 Bayard
   Rd.. 13
Amberson Towers 5 Bayard
   Road..................................... 13
Andrea 201 E Swissvale......... 18
Ansonia, 5742 Holden............ 32
Ansonia, 652 Maryland Ave.... 32
Ardmore Gardens, 1635-1645
   Ardmore Blvd........................ 21
Arlington, 515 South Aiken
   Ave....................................... 32
Armada, 5620 Hobart............. 17
Atwood 1, 3609 Dawson......... 13
Atwood 2, 3609 Dawson......... 13
Atwood 3, 3609 Dawson......... 13
Auburn Towers 6290 Auburn
   St... 06
Aurora, 137 Bausman.............. 10
Avalon Arms, 841 California
   Ave....................................... 02
Avon Court, 15 Bower Hill
   Rd.. 28
Avon, 3436 Ward..................... 13
Balbach 305 E Swissvale
   Ave....................................... 18
Baldwin Court Knoedler-
   Wolfe, Keeport & Macassar
   Dr.. 36
Bard, 3444 Ward...................... 13
Baum Grove, 5762 Baum
   Blvd....................................... 06
Bayard Manor, 4600 Bayard... 13
Bayard, 218 N Craig................ 13
Baywood Arms, 119 Baywood
   Ave....................................... 28
Baywood Manor, 125
   Baywood Ave......................... 28
Beacon, 5600 Munhall Rd....... 17
Bedford Dwelling, Bedford
   Ave....................................... 19
Beechview, 1500 Fallowfield
   Ave....................................... 16
Belcrest, 811 South Negley
   Ave....................................... 32
Bellcrest Mansionettes,
   Bellcrest Ave.......................... 27
Bellefield Dwellings, 4400
   Center Ave............................. 13
Bellefonte, 5500 Elmer........... 32
Bellevue Courts, 50 Summer
   Ave....................................... 02
Bellevue Gables, 25 Hawley
   Ave....................................... 02
Bellevue Gables, 30 Sprague
   Ave....................................... 02

Bellevue-Stratford, 215 South
   Millvale Ave........................... 24
Belmar Towers, 245 Lincoln
   Ave....................................... 02
Belmont, 259 Beverly Rd........ 16
Belvedere Arms, 5914
   Walnut................................... 32
Belvedere, 5523 Ellsworth
   Ave....................................... 32
Berkeley, 405 Franklin Ave...... 21
Berkshire, 26 Academy Ave.... 28
Beverly Court, 221 Beverly
   Rd.. 16
Beverly, 222 North Craig......... 13
Bigelow, Bigelow Sq............... 19
Blenheim, 4952 Friendship
   Ave....................................... 24
Bradberry, 1112 Reddour........ 13
Braeside Manor, 2135
   Wightman.............................. 17
Breezwood, 560 Allenby Ave... 18
Brentmor Junior, 3902
   Brownsville Rd....................... 27
Brentmor, 3840 Brownsville
   Rd.. 27
Brentshire Terrace, 2531
   Brownsville Rd....................... 10
Brentshire Village, Pyramid
   Dr.. 27
Brentwood Arms, 3820
   Brownsville Rd....................... 27
Brittany,3500 Brownsville Rd . 27
Bryn Mawr, Bryn Mawr Ct...... 21
Bryn Mawr, 3301 Iowa........... 19
Buchanan, 211 Buchanan Pl... 28
Burkey, 37 Washington Ave.... 02
Burlington, 324 Mckee Pl....... 13
California, 5735 Ellsworth
   Ave....................................... 32
California, 909 California
   Ave....................................... 02
Cambridge Hall, 4630 5th
   Ave....................................... 13
Cambridge House, 1112 Mt
   Royal Blvd............................. 23
Capon, 600 Rebecca Ave........ 21
Carlton House, 550 Grant....... 30
Carol 4909 Centre Ave........... 13
Carol, 72-76 S Freemont......... 13
Carriage House, 1515 Penn
   Ave....................................... 21
Carvel Hall, 436 Franklin
   Ave....................................... 21
Cary Hall, 305 East
   Swissvale Ave........................ 18
Casablanca, 5731 Ellsworth
   Ave....................................... 32
Castle Stanton, 5652 Stanton
   Ave....................................... 06
Castleton, 5612 Hempstead
   Rd.. 17
Castletone Shady Dr : Castle
   Shannon Blvd......................... 28
Cathedral Mansions, 4716
   Ellsworth Ave......................... 13
Cecil, 525 Brushton Ave.......... 08
Center Court, 4716 Center
   Ave....................................... 13
Center-Negley, 5551 Center
   Ave....................................... 32
Central Arms, 101 Central
   Sq... 28

Central Square (A B C), 721
   Roselawn Ave......................... 28
Central Square (E F G), 722
   Wisteria Ave.......................... 28
Centre Avenue 4750 Centre
   Ave....................................... 13
Centre Villa Court 5527
   Centre Ave............................. 32
Charlemagne, 420 N
   Chestnut................................ 02
Chateaugay, 500 Hoodridge
   Dr.. 34
Chatham Center Apt Towers... 19
Chatham S, Chatham Park
   Dr.. 20
Chatham Village........................ 11
Chatham W, Oakville Dr......... 20
Chaucer Hall, 131 Edgewood
   Ave....................................... 18
Chestnut Manor, 415
   Chestnut St............................ 02
Chestnut Manor, 731
   California Ave......................... 02
Cliffside Manor........................... 02
Clover Leaf Towers, 10 Clover
   Dr.. 36
Clover Leaf Village, 1
   Marhoefer Dr........................ 36
College Gardens, 5820
   Elwood.................................. 32
Colonial Arms, 253 Beverly
   Rd.. 16
Colonial Terrace, 5440 5th
   Ave....................................... 32
Colonial, 717 Buchanan Pl..... 28
Columbian, 855 Rebecca
   Ave....................................... 21
Concord Plaza, 5532 Covode.. 17
Coronado 5260 Centre Ave..... 32
Craft, 3225 Joe Hammer Sq.... 13
Crafton Acres A, 102 W
   Steuben Ave.......................... 05
Crafton Acres B, 102 W
   Steuben Ave.......................... 05
Crafton Acres C, 102 W
   Steuben Ave.......................... 05
Craig-Manor, 317 North
   Craig..................................... 13
Craigwood Manor, 225 E
   Swissvale Ave........................ 18
Cricklewood Hill 700 Forbes
   Ave....................................... 19
D'Arlington, 504 N Neville....... 13
Dagmar, 271 North Craig........ 13
Dana, 510 S Highland Ave..... 06
Delaware, 1139 N Highland
   Ave....................................... 06
Denholm, 202 Lincoln Ave...... 06
Denny, 1 St Johns Pl.............. 01
Denny, 3417 Liberty Ave........ 01
Denny, 3422 Denny................. 01
Denny, 3500 Howley............... 01
Denslow, 3622 California........ 12
Devon Towers, 4920 Centre
   Ave....................................... 13
Devonshire, 331 Devonshire.... 13
Devonshire, 4910 Center Ave.. 13
Devonshire, 5871 Ellsworth
   Ave....................................... 32
Dietrich, 3301 Brighton Rd..... 12
Dimling, 403 Oakland Ave...... 13
Dithridge, 144 North

Dithridge 13
Dover Gables, 555 S Negley
  Ave 32
Burban Hall, 4630 5th Ave 13
East Liberty Gardens 06
East Mall, 5805 Penn Mall,
  W 06
Edgemere Courts, 130 La
  Crosse 18
Edgewater, 322 Mckee Pl 13
Edgewood Courts, 233-
  Edgewood Ave 18
Edgewood, 100 West
  Hutchinson Av 18
Elean Hall, 208 Darragh 13
Ellison, 634 Washington Rd ... 28
Ellsworth, 5806 Ellsworth
  Ave 32
Elm, 100 Elm 18
Elmer, 5501 Elmer 32
Elsinore, 294 Craft Ave 13
Elwood Gardens, 5819
  Elwood 32
Embassy, 230 Beverly Rd 06
Emerson, 270 Emerson 06
Emerson, 6111 Alder 06
Englewood 5712 Forbes Ave ... 17
English Terrace Homes, 3200
  5th Ave 13
English Terrace, 2720 Shady
  Ave 17
English Terrace, 5851
  Morrowfield Ave 17
Etewanda, 224 East End Ave ... 21
Euclid, 16 South Euclid Ave 02
Fairfax The, 4614 Fifth Ave 13
Fairview, 630 Maryland Ave 32
Fairway, 6703 Saltsburg Rd 35
Federal Dwellings, 11
  Federal 12
Fifth-Aiken, 5401 5th Ave 32
Fifth-Maryland, 5800 5th Ave .. 32
Fifth-Morewood, 825
  Morewood Ave 13
Fifth-Negley, 5700 5th Ave 32
Fifth-Neville, 4705 5th Ave 13
Fifty-One Hundred, 5100 5th
  Ave 32
Forbes Craig, 4531 Forbes
  Ave 13
Forbes Manor, 5624 Forbes
  Ave 17
Forest Arms, 588 Forest Ave ... 02
Forty-Seven-Fifty Centre
  Avenue 4750 Centre
  Avenue 13
Franklin, 200 Franklin Ave 21
Franklin, 305 Atwood 13
Friendship, 4901 Friendship
  Ave 24
Front Royal, 6005 5th Ave 32
Frontenac, 490 South
  Highland Ave 06
Frontenac, 5931 Howe 06
Gable, 4800 Ellsworth Ave 13
Gable, 601 Clyde 13
Garden Court, 416 Oakland
  Ave 13
Garden Courts, 2235
  Braddock Ave 18
Garden Villa, 3304
  Brownsville Rd 27
Garfield Heights High Rise,

5330 Fern 24
Gateway Towers, 320 Fort
  Duquesne Blvd 22
Gay Lebanon, 434 Cochran
  Rd 28
General Forbes 5636 Forbes
  Ave 17
General Neville Mansionettes .. 25
General Neville, 1150
  Bowerhill Rd 43
Georgian Junior, 255
  Melwood Ave 13
Georgian, 5437 Ellsworth 32
Gerber, 724 South Negley
  Ave 32
Gilbert, 500 North Negley
  Ave 06
Glen Elm, Glen Elm Dr 36
Gordon Arms 128 Highland
  Mall North 06
Governor, 5935 Kirkwood 06
Graham Hall, 5525 Ellsworth
  Ave 32
Greenlee Village, Victoria Dr .. 27
Greentree Gardens, 833
  Greentree Rd 20
Hack, 116 Central Sq 28
Haddon Hall 124 La Crosse 18
Haddon Hall 4730 Centre
  Ave 13
Hamilton-Larimer, 6290
  Auburn 06
Hampton Hall, 166 North
  Dithridge 13
Heatherstone, 5300 5th Ave ... 32
Heidelburg, 401 S Braddock
  21
Hempstead, 5620 Hempstead
  Rd 17
Herford, 816 Ivy 32
Heritage, 2522 Columbia
  Ave 18
Herr, 1020 Wallace Ave 21
Hiawatha, 3833 Hiawatha 12
Highland Hall, 370 S.
  Highland Ave 06
Highland House, 5700
  Bunkerhill 06
Highland Pines, Highland
  Pines Dr 37
Highland Towers, 340 South
  Highland Ave 06
Highland, 341 South
  Highland Ave 06
Highwood, 372 South
  Highland Ave 06
Hobart Court, 5555 Hobart 17
Hobart, 5703 Hobart 17
Holland, 3420 Louisa 13
Holmes, 704 South Negley
  Ave 32
Homer, 5334 Jackson 06
Howard, 1137 North Highland
  Ave 06
Hunter 1328 Pocono Street 18
Idaho, 5460 Penn Ave 06
Iroquis 3604 Forbes Ave 13
Jacksonia, 110 Jacksonia 12
Jamestown, Jamestown Ct 16
Jeanette, 732 South Millvale ... 13
Jefferson, 3440 Louisa 13
Jefferson, 5660 Forward Ave ... 17

Kamins Cottages, 5552
  Beacon 17
Kenmawr, 401 Shady Ave 06
Kennilworth, 5700 Center
  Ave 06
Key Royale, 646 Grandview
  Ave 02
Keystone, 813 Wood 21
King Edward Annex, 225
  Melwood Ave 13
King Edward, 4609 Bayard 13
Kings Arms, 800 S Negley
  Ave 32
Kingston 301 So. Home
  Avenue 02
Kingston, 5721 Elmer 32
Kirkpatrick, 4122 Butler 01
Kirkwood, 5935 Kirkwood 06
Koch 5115 Centre Ave 32
La Belle, 5672 Hobart 17
Laketon Garden, 3511
  Laketon Rd 35
Lancaster, 314 Mckee Pl 13
Lane, 228 Union 21
Lane, 701 Mifflin Ave 21
Larsen, 42 Academy Ave 28
Laurel Ridge 100 102 104
  106 15th 29
Laurel Village, 700 Penn
  Center Blvd 35
Le Grand, 1411 Grandview
  Av 11
Lebanon Hall, 318
  Washington Rd 16
Lebanon Vue, 400 Cochran
  Rd 28
Leland Park, Keeport Dr 36
Leland Park, Knoedler Dr 36
Leland Park, Youngridge Dr 36
Lennox 1, 223 South
  Mathilda 24
Lennox 2, 223 South
  Mathilda 24
Lennox 3, 223 South
  Mathilda 24
Leonard, 5619 Hobart 17
Lexington House, 401 North
  Lexington Ave 08
Lexington, 7233 Penn Ave 08
Liberty Park 6209 Broad St 06
Lillian 2841 Centre Ave 19
Limbaugh, 1700 Crafton
  Blvd 05
Lincoln, 215 Lincoln Ave 02
Lincoln, 324 South Mathilda ... 24
Linden, 3430 Bates 13
Linwood, 6801 Mcpherson
  Blvd 08
Linwood, 75 North Linwood
  Ave 05
Lockhart 3200 Forbes Ave 13
Lois, 501 North Highland
  Ave 06
London Hall, 3100
  Brownsville Rd 27
London Terrace, 135 North
  13
Lorraine, 422 North Highland
  Ave 06
Louise, 87 Knox Ave 10
Manor House 1726 Aurelius 18
Manor House 425 N Neville 13

Manor, 111 Maple Ave............ 18
Manor, 5231 5th Ave.............. 32
Maple, The Cambridge Ct....... 18
Maplewood 5716 Forbes Ave .. 17
Margaretta 5818 East Liberty
  Blvd............................... 06
Mariana, 6780 Fifth Ave......... 08
Mark Twain, 406 North
  Neville.......................... 13
Markham, 60 Markham Dr....... 28
Marlin Arms, 5245 Center
  Ave............................... 32
Marshall, 807 Wood.............. 21
Martinque, 4746 Baum Blvd .. 13
Maryland Gardens, 5814
  Elmer............................ 32
Maryland, 510 Protectory Pl.... 19
Maxon Towers, 6315 Forbes
  Ave............................... 17
Mayflower, 725 South Negley
  Ave............................... 32
Mc Curdy, 201 California
  Ave............................... 02
Mc Curdy, 223 Park Ave........ 02
Melvin Penn, Beulah Rd........ 35
Melwood, 334 Melwood......... 13
Midtown Towers 643 Liberty
  Ave............................... 22
Milton The, 3526 Forbes Ave.. 13
Model, 556 Dunfermline........ 08
Moderncrest, 147 South
  Negley Av....................... 06
Moderne Terrace 5219 Centre
  Ave............................... 06
Montrose Manor, 5939 5th
  Ave............................... 32
Montvue 5 Grandview Ave...... 11
Morewood Garden, 1060
  Morewood Ave.................. 13
Morewood 4924 Centre Ave.... 13
Morrison Court, 187 Morrison
  Dr............................... 16
Morrow, 510 Mifflin Ave........ 21
Morrowfield, 2715 Murray
  Ave............................... 17
Murray Beacon, 1914 Murray
  Ave............................... 17
Navarre, 618 N Saint Clair...... 06
Negley Court, 5620 5th Ave.... 32
Negley Gardens, 400 N
  Negley Ave..................... 06
Negley Park, 1001 N Negley ... 06
Negley Park, 5545 Wellesley
  Av............................... 06
Negley Park, 5570 Hampton ... 06
Negley, 300 N Negley Ave...... 06
Negley, 5607 Elmer.............. 32
Nelda, 7522 Bennett............. 08
Netherlands The, 5721
  Elwood.......................... 32
Neville A, 554 Neville........... 13
Neville B, 554 Neville........... 13
Neville C, 554 Neville........... 13
Neville Township Apartments.. 25
New Englander, 619 Center
  Ave............................... 29
New President, 720 South
  Negley Ave..................... 32
New Wendover, 5562 Hobart... 17
New Yorker, 819 College Ave.. 32
Noble Manor, Brett St........... 05
Noble Manor, Chessland St ... 05

Noble Manor, Poplar St.......... 05
Norfolk, 1131 North Highland
  Av............................... 06
Normandy, 5520 5th Ave....... 32
North Windsor, 234 Melwood
  Ave............................... 13
Northway, 411-481 Browns
  Lane............................. 37
Oakland 3401 Forbes Ave...... 13
Oakmont The, 152 North
  Balph Ave....................... 02
Ohara, 1 Ohara Pl............... 01
Ohara, 3625 Liberty Ave........ 01
Ohara, 510 37th................. 01
Olympia, 320 Mckee Pl......... 13
Ontario, 631 Maryland Ave..... 32
Overlook 4179 Centre Ave...... 13
Pacific, 329 South Pacific
  Ave............................... 24
Palm Garden Village, 873
  Boggs Ave....................... 11
Panama, 5752 Ellsworth Ave... 32
Park Mansions, 5023 Frew
  Ave............................... 13
Park Place 1, 611 Alger......... 07
Park Place 2, 611 Alger......... 07
Park Plaza, 128 North Craig.... 13
Park View Arms, 336 Perry
  Highway.......................... 29
Park View, 1401 North Saint
  Clair............................ 06
Parkline Court, Parkline Dr..... 27
Parkview, 45 N Balph Ave...... 02
Parkway, 2041 Wightman....... 17
Patterson, 906 Wood............ 21
Peacock Manor, 924
  Farragut......................... 06
Peerless, 624 Whitney Ave..... 21
Pendale Towers 460
  Washington Rd.................. 28
Penn Aiken, 5401 Penn Ave.... 06
Penn Brad 7508 Penn Ave...... 08
Penn Circle Towers, 6231
  Penn Ave........................ 06
Penn Dwellings, 7150 Penn
  Ave............................... 08
Penn Lincoln, 789 Penn Ave... 21
Penn Manor, 113 Enright Pl.... 06
Penn Plaza, 5600 Penn Ave.... 06
Penn Shady, 226 Shady Ave.... 06
Penn Towers 1100 Penn
  Center Blvd..................... 35
Penn Towers, 11979
  Frankstown Rd.................. 35
Pennley Park, Penn Ave &
  North Negley Ave.............. 06
Pennsylvania, 4403 Center
  Ave............................... 13
Pennwood, 5722 Kentucky
  Ave............................... 32
Pennwood, 623 Whitney Ave... 21
Perry Manor, 810 Perry Hwy.... 29
Perrysville, 400 Perrysville
  Ave............................... 29
Pershing, 758 Penn Ave........ 21
Phillips, 312 Mckee Pl.......... 13
Pittsburgh Hilton,
  Commonwealth Pl.............. 30
Plymouth Hall 131 Edgewood
  Ave............................... 18
Point Breeze Manor, 6721
  Thomas Blvd.................... 08

Portland Manor, 5622
  Stanton Ave..................... 06
Potomac, 5722 Baum Blvd..... 06
President The, 306 Craft Ave ... 13
Princess Ann, 321 Beverly
  Rd............................... 16
Princess, 7203 Idlewild.......... 08
Prospect Mansions, 1685
  Parkline Dr..................... 27
Queensbury 220 S Home Ave.. 02
Ralston, 301 Warrington Ave... 10
Rayette, 6712 Thomas Blvd..... 08
Revere, 309 Edgewood Ave..... 18
Ridgeview, Ridgewood Ave...... 29
Ritz, 738 Brookline Blvd........ 26
Roberta, 1713 Termon Ave 12
Rockledge, 3201 Faronia........ 04
Roosevelt, 607 Penn Ave 30
Rosemont, 5504 Penn Ave...... 06
Rosmyl The, 900 Ross Ave...... 21
Royal Manor, 765 College
  Ave............................... 32
Royal Plaza, 5506 5th Ave 32
Royal Windsor 1, 216
  Melwood Ave.................... 13
Royal Windsor 2, 216
  Melwood Ave.................... 13
Royal Windsor 3, 216
  Melwood Ave.................... 13
Royal Windsor 4, 216
  Melwood Ave.................... 13
Royal York, 3955 Bigelow
  Blvd............................. 13
Royal, 500 Todd Ave............ 21
Ruskin Villa Annex 1104
  Mulberry........................ 21
Ruskin Villa, 735 Wallace
  Ave............................... 21
Ruskin, 120 Ruskin Ave......... 13
Ruth Gardens, 5728 Beacon.... 17
Ruth, 2700 Broadway........... 16
Rutledge Hall, 600 South
  Negley Ave..................... 32
Saint James, 5237 5th Ave..... 32
Saint Regis, 5806 Howe 32
Saint Regis, 905 Maryland
  Ave............................... 32
Savoy, 571 Coal................. 21
Sceneridge, 3336 Brownsville
  Rd............................... 27
Schenley Arms, 4041 Bigelow
  Blvd............................. 13
Schenley House, 151 North
  Craig............................ 13
Schenley Park, 4000 5th Ave.. 13
Seneca, 2039 5th Ave.......... 19
Seton Hall, 120 North
  Homewood Ave.................. 08
Seven Hundred Thirty 730 S
  Negley Ave..................... 32
Shady East 607 Shady Ave..... 06
Shady Grove, 6300 Howe 06
Shamrock, 56 South
  Freemont........................ 02
Sherwood Hall 131 Edgewood
  Ave............................... 18
Shirley, 133 North Dithridge... 13
Siebert Point, 3279 Babcock
  Blvd............................. 37
Skyline, 1620 Skyline Dr....... 27
Skyview, 1550 Radford Rd...... 27
Smith, 815 Mill.................. 21

Smith, 822 Ross Ave 21
South Aiken, 545 South Aiken
Ave 32
South Windsor, 216 Melwood
Ave 13
Stanford, 502 Jeanette 21
Stanton Arms, 5701 Stanton
Ave 06
Star, 740 Kelly Ave 21
Stephen Foster, 400 North
Neville 13
Stratford Arms, 5700
Munhall Rd 17
Stratford Hall 139 Edgewood
Ave 18
Summerlea, 5713 Elwood 32
Swissvale Apartments 1,
2103 S Braddock 18
Swissvale Apartments 2,
2103 S Braddock 18
Templeton, 753 Penn Ave 21
Ten Negley, 5700 Ellsworth
Ave 32
Terrace Court, 2123 Shady
Ave 17
Terrace Village 1 19
Terrace Village 2 13
Thames Manor, 585 South
Negley Ave 32
Thirty Five Hundred Fifth
Avenue, 3500 5th Ave 19
Thomas, 6716 Thomas Blvd 08
Tiffany, 925 California Ave 02
Town House, 6218 5th Ave 32
Townley Manor, 101 Lloyd
Ave 18
Triangle Hall, 5701 Munhall
Rd 17
Trinity The, Cambridge Ct 18
Tudor Hall 4825 Centre Ave 13
University Square No 1, 4625
5th Ave 13
University Square 2, 4601
5th Ave 13
Valley Vue, Keeport Dr 36
Valley Vue, Travis Dr 36
Valley Vue, Youngridge Dr 36
Valmar Gardens, 2648
Robinson Blvd 35
Venetian Garden, 100
Newburn Dr 16
Virginia Manor Greentree &
Cochran Rd 20
Virginia Manor, 5680
Munhall Rd 17
Virginia, 320 South Mathilda 24
Wabash, 318 Mckee Pl .... -13
Walden Court, 6349 Walnut 06
Waldorf Towers 100 Mcknight
Cir 37
Waldorf, 732 Roselawn Ave 28
Walker, 800 Ross Ave 21
Wallace, 2018 Noble 18
Wallace, 5013 Lincoln Ave 02
Wallace, 512 Wallace Ave 21
Walnut Court, 5706 Walnut 32
Walnut Manor, 5920 Walnut 32
Walnut Terrace, 275 Walnut 38
Walnut, 5614 Walnut 32
Warwick Plaza, 5048 5th
Ave 32
Washington Arms, 769 Shady

Dr East 28
Washington Plaza, 1420
Centre Ave 19
Washingtonian, 1670
Washington Rd 28
Wayland, 6 South Fremont 02
Webster Hall, 4415 5th Ave 13
Webster Towers, 240
Melwood Ave 13
Wellesley Dwellings, 5517
Wellesley Ave 06
Wellington, 131 Sycamore 11
Wellington, 241 Melwood Ave 13
Welton, 3 Mcdevitt Pl 13
Welton, 335 Melwood Ave 13
Wendover, 5557 Hobart 17
Westminster Manor, 5227 5th
Ave 32
Westminster, 800 South
Aiken Ave 32
White Oaks, 799 Stevens Dr 37
Wightman, 2130 Wightman 17
Wilburton, 235 South Millvale
Ave 24
William Penn, William Penn
Place 30
William Penn, 1805 Penn
Ave 21
William Pitt, 5610 Elmer 32
Williams, 125 Sycamore 11
Willmar 4524 Forbes Ave 13
Wilson Arms, 549 North
Neville 13
Wilson, 741 Rebecca Ave 21
Wiltshire, 225 South Millvale
Ave 24
Windcrest 7801 Lloyd 18
Windsor Hall, 131 Edgewood
Ave 18
Windsor, 221 South Millvale 24
Windsor, 3320 Ward 13
Windsor, 5630 Hobart 17
Winebiddle, 210 South
Winebiddle 24
Winslow, 525 Larimer Ave 06
Wisteria, Wisteria Ave 28
Wood Hill, 1309 Wood 21
Woodland Gardens, 5925 5th
Ave 32
Woodland Manor, 5826 5th
Ave 32
Woodland 735 Presque Isle
Dr 39
Woodland, 5176 Margaret
Morrison 13
Woodland, 5836 5th Ave 32
Woodward Court, 221
Buchanon Pl 28
Yale, 5700 Jackson 06
Yorkshire, 2145 Wightman 17

BUILDINGS

Abbott 100 Smithfield 22
Agricultural, 1730 Smallman 22
Alcoa, 425 6th Ave 19
Allegheny Center, Bldgs 1-10 12
Allegheny County Court
House, 436 Grant 19
Allegheny County, 542 Forbes
Ave 19
Allegheny Towers, 625
Stanwix 22

Allegheny 429 Forbes Ave 19
Ardmore, 2300 Ardmore
Boulevard 21
Arrott, 401 Wood 22
Baum, 818 Liberty Ave 22
Beatty, 5907 Penn Ave 06
Bell Telephone Company 635
Grant 19
Benedum-Trees, 221 4th Ave 22
Berlin, 237 5th Ave 22
Bonn, 713 Penn Ave 22
Buhl, 204 5th Ave 22
Caldwell & Graham, 700
Penn Ave 21
Caldwell, 800 Wood 21
Carlton Center, 923 Penn
Ave 22
Catanzaro, 2018 Smallman 22
Centennial, 241 Fourth Ave 22
Central Warehouse, 222 W
Carson 19
Century, 130 7th 22
Chamber Of Commerce, 411
Seventh Ave 19
Chatham Center, Fifth Ave 19
City County, 414 Grant 19
Civic, 200 Ross 19
Clark, 717 Liberty Ave 22
Colonial, 205 Ross St 19
Commonwealth Annex, 317
3rd Ave 22
Commonwealth, 316 4th Ave 22
Conestoga, 7 Wood 22
Continental Insurance 200 S
Craig 13
Council Of Churches, 220
Grant 19
Duquesne Light Company
435 6th Ave 19
Educational Institute, 212
Ninth St 22
Empire, 501 Liberty Ave 22
Equitable Gas, 420
Boulevard Of The Allies 19
Ewart, 925 Liberty Ave 22
Federal Offices, 1000 Liberty
Ave 22
Federated Investors, 421 7th
Avenue 19
Fidelity, 341 4th Ave 22
Fifth-Grant, 508 Grant 22
Fifth-Wood, 256 5th Ave 22
First Federal, 600 Grant 19
Flannery, 3530 Forbes Ave 13
Forbes And Murray, 5800
Forbes Ave 17
Forbes, 3619 Forbes Ave 13
Fort Pitt Federal, 524 Penn
Ave 22
Freehold, 311 4th Ave 22
Frick, 437 Grant 19
Frick, 450 5th Ave 19
Fruit Exchange, 66 21st 22
Fulton, 101 6th 22
Gateway Polytechnic, 100 7th
St 22
Gateway Towers, 320 Fort
Duquesne Blvd 22
Gateway View Plaza, 1600 W.
Carson 19
Gateway 2, 603 Stanwix 22
Gateway 3, 401 Liberty Ave 22
Gateway 4, 444 Liberty Ave 22*

Gateway 5, 60 Boulevard Of
The Allies 22
Golden Center, 300 Stanwix ... 22
Granite, 313 6th Ave 22
Grant, 310 Grant 19
Graphic Arts, 422 1st Ave 19
Greater Beneficial Union
4254 Clairton Blvd 27
Gulf, 435 7th Ave 19
Heinz Hall Of Performing Arts
600 Penn Ave 22
Highland 117 Highland Mall
S 06
House, 4 Smithfield 22
International Business
Machines, 60 Blvd Of The
Allies 22
Investment, 237 4th Ave 22
Irish, 800 Penn Ave 22
Jenkins Arcade, 509 Liberty
Ave 22
Jenkins, 504 Penn Ave 22
Jones Law Annex 530 Fourth
Ave 19
Jones Law 311 Ross 19
Kern, 1136 Greenfield Ave 17
Keystone, 322 4th Ave 22
Kirkwood On The Mall 121
Highland Mall N 06
Koppers, 436 7th Ave 19
Kossmann, 100 Forbes Ave 22
Lando, 907 Penn Ave 22
Law & Finance, 425 4th Ave 19
Lawyers, 428 Forbes Ave 19
Libbie, 245 4th Ave 22
Liberty 6101 Penn Mall E 06
Live Stock Exchange, Herrs
Island 22
Loeffler, 121 Meyran Ave 13
Magee, 334 4th Ave 22
Maloney, 337 Boulevard Of
The Allies 22
Manor Oak No 1 20
Manor Oak No 2 1910
Cochran Rd 20
Manor, 564 Forbes Ave 19
Martin, 119 Federal 12
Masonic Temple, 4227 Fifth
Ave 13
Masonic, 523 Lincoln Ave 02
May, 119 5th Ave 22
Mc Crady-Nicklos, 304 Ross ... 19
Mc Kay, 1005 Liberty Ave 22
Medical Arts 3700 Fifth Ave ... 13
Medical Center East 211 N
Whitfield 06
Medical, 3401 Fifth Ave ....• 13
Memorial Hall, 5th Ave &
Bigelow Blvd 13
New Bell Telephone, 201
Stanwix 22
Nine-Twenty-Four Penn
Avenue, 924 Penn Ave .... 22 •
North American Rockwell,
301-307 Fifth Ave 22
Oliver Henry W, 535
Smithfield 22
One Hundred Fifth Ave, 100
Fifth Ave .... • 22
One Oliver Plaza, 210 Sixth
Ave 22
Park, 351 5th Ave 22
Parkway Ctr 1 875 Greentree

Rd *20
Parkway Ctr 2, 875 Greentree
Rd 20
Parkway Ctr 3, 875 Greentree
Rd 20
Parkway Ctr 4, 875 Greentree
Rd 20
Parkway Ctr 5, 875 Greentree
Rd 20
Parkway Ctr 6, 875 Greentree
Rd 20
Parkway Ctr 7, 875 Greentree
Rd 20
Parkway Ctr 8 875 Greentree
Rd 20
Penn Central Station 22
Penn Oak Professional, 77
Universal Rd 35
Penn Rose, 1627 Penn Ave 22
Penn Wood, 620 Penn Ave 21
Penn, 721 Penn Ave 21
Penn, 810 Penn Ave 22
Pennsylvania Lines Produce,
90 21st 22
Pennsylvania, 110 19th 22
Peoples Bank, 301 4th Ave 22
Pgh & Lerr, Smithfield And
West Carson 19
Physicians, 121 University
Place 13
Pitt-Penn Terminal, 1320
Penn Ave 22
Pittsburgh Life, 219 6th 22
Pittsburgh National Bank
128 5th Ave 22
Plaza, 535 5th Ave 19
Plumbers, 1901 5th Ave ....•..... 22
Porter H K 601 Grant 19
Ppg Industries, 420 Fort
Duquesne Blvd 22
Press, Boulevard Of The
Allies 22
Professional, 722 Penn Ave 21
Public Safety, 100 Grant 19
Public School Administrative,
341 Bellefield Ave 13
Publication, 209 9th 22
Rea, 704 2nd Ave 19
Remington-Rand, 312
Stanwix 22
Renshaw, 217 9th 22
Ross, 4828 Liberty Ave 24
Rudd, 342 Boulevard Of The
Allies 22
Saint Clair, 1725 Washington
Rd 41
Second Federal, 335 5th Ave .. 22
Seven Eleven Penn Avenue,
711 Penn Ave 22
Shields, 822 Wood .... 21 •
Smithfield Diamond, 415
Smithfield 22
Smithfield Plaza 650
Smithfield 22
Smithfield, 610 Smithfield 22
Standard Life, 345 4th Ave 22
State Office, 300 Liberty Ave .. 22
Stevenson, 666 Washington
Rd 28
Syria Mosque, Bigelow Blvd 13
Templeton, 739 Penn Ave 21
Terminal 307 Carson E 19

Terrace Arcade, 107 Terrace
Ct 27
Thirty Five Hundred Fifth
Avenue, 3500 5th Ave 13
Three Hundred Sixth Ave, 300
Sixth Ave 22
Three Rivers Stadium, 400
Stadium Circle 12
Triangle 305 7th Ave 22
Try Street Terminal, 600 2nd
Ave 19
Union Bank, 306 4th Ave 22
Union Title 210 Grant 19
Union Trust, 435 5th Ave 19
Union Trust, 523 Grant 19
United States Post Office &
Court House, 700 Grant 19
United States Steel 600
Grant 19
Wallace 6005 Penn Circle S ... 06
Westinghouse, 11 Stanwix 22
Whitehall Terrace 4120
Brownsville Rd 27
Wilkinsburg Bank, 901 Wood .. 21
Y M C A (Central), 304 Wood
St 22
Y M C A (E Liberty), 122
South Whitfield 06
Y W C A (Central), 305 Wood
St 22

GOVERNMENT OFFICES

Chamber Of Commerce, 411
7th Ave 19
Federal Offices, 1000 Liberty
Ave 22
United States Courthouse,
700 Grant 19

HOSPITALS

Allegheny General, 320 E
North Ave 12
C. Howard Marcy State
Hospital, Leech Farm Rd 06
Childrens Hospital Of
Pittsburgh, 125 De Sota
St 13
Columbia, 312 Penn Ave 21
De Paul Institute, Dorchester
Ave 26
Divine Providence Of
Pittsburgh, 215 W
Montgomery Ave 12
Doctors, 215 S Negley Ave 06
Eye & Ear, 230 Lothrop 13
Fairview Sanitarium 5601
Forbes Ave 17
John J Kane, 201 Kane Blvd ... 43
Magee Womens Hosp 13
Mercy, 1400 Locust 19
Montefiore, 3459 5th Ave 13
North Hills Passavant, 9100
Babcock Blvd 37
Pittsburgh, 6655 Frankstown
Av 06
Presbyterian, 230 Lothrop 13
Saint Clair Memorial, 1000
Bower Hill Rd 43
Saint Francis, 408 45th 01
Saint Johns General, 3331

Veterans Administration, Leech Farm Rd	06
Veterans Administration, University Dr	40
Veterans, Delafield Rd	40
West Penn, 4800 Friendship Ave	24
Western State Psychiatric, De Sota & Ohara	13
Womens Magee Hosp., Forbes Ave & Halket	13

UNIVERSITIES AND COLLEGES

Allegheny Community, 808 Ridge Ave	17
Carlow College, 3333 5th Ave	13
Carnegie-Mellon University, Frew Ave & Margaret Morrison	13
Chatham College, Woodland Rd	32
Duquesne University, 801 Bluff	19
Point Park, Wood St & Blvd Of Allies	22
Robert Morris, 610 Fifth Ave	19
University Of Pittsburgh, 4200 Fifth Ave	13
Mcclure Ave	12
Saint Josephs 2117 E Carson	03
Saint Margaret Memorial, 265 46th	01
Shady Side, 5230 Center Ave.	32
South Hills Ear Nose & Throat, 315 Mount Lebanon Blvd	34
South Side, 151 South 20th	03
Suburban General, South Jackson Ave	02
Tuberculosis League Of Pittsburgh, 2851 Bedford Ave	19

PITTSTON 186

POST OFFICE BOXES

Box Nos.

1-145	Duryea Br	42
1-177	Avoca Br	41
1-212	West Pittston Br	43
1-318	Wyoming Br	44
251-787	Main Office	40

RURAL ROUTES

1	43
2	41
3	44

STATIONS, BRANCHES AND UNITS

Avoca Br	41
Dupont Br	41
Duryea Br	42
Exeter Br	43
Jenkins Br	40
West Pittston Br	43
West Wyoming Br	44

READING 196

POST OFFICE BOXES

Box Nos.

1-227	Shillington Br	07
1-348	Wyomissing Br	10
1-1702	Main Office	03
2000-2149	Sinking Spring Br	08
2501-2658	West Lawn Br	09
3000-3266	Hampden Sta	04
3500-3799	Laureldale Br	05
4001-4236	Mount Penn Sta	06

RURAL ROUTES

1	07
2	05
3,4	06
5,6	08

STATIONS, BRANCHES AND UNITS

Hampden Sta	04
Laureldale Br	05
Mount Penn Br	06
Parcel Post Sta	03
Shillington Br	07
Sinking Spring Br	08
West Lawn Br	09
West Reading Br	02
Wyomissing Br	10
General Delivery	03
Postmaster	03

APARTMENTS, HOTELS, MOTELS

Abraham Lincoln, 100 N 5th	03
Alden Terrace, 1401 Ridge Ave	07
Antietam Arms, 850 Carsonia Ave	06
Berkshire, 101 N 5th	03
Brighter, 205 Penn St	01
Brookline Manor, 1100 E Wyoming Blvd	02
Carsonia Manor, 810 N 25th	06
Daniel Boone, 1022 Penn	02
Edgemont Terrace, 1515 Hill Rd	02
Hampden House, 2001 Hampden Blvd	04
Hodges, 601 N 5th St	01
Hollywood Court, 2703 Hollywood Ct	06
Metropolitan, 920 N 4th St	01
Mifflin Park, 30 Mifflin Blvd	07
Monahan, 125 S 4th St	02
Mt Penn Manor, 601 S 19th St	06
Oak Forest, Pricetown & Reservoir Rds	04
Pennhurst Mansion, 2252 Fairview Ave	06
Pennside Manor, 707 N 25th	06
Saylor, 1 N 9th St	01
Sherwood Terrace, 1400 Pershing Blvd	07
Springside Manor, 100-200 Springside Dr	07

Washington Towers	01
Woodland Plaza, Bern & Woodland	10
Wynwood At Wyomissing, 855 N Park Rd	10
Wyomissing Park, 215 Alden Ter	07

BUILDINGS

Administration, 8th & Washington	01
Baer, 529 Court	01
Balis, 24 N 6th	01
Berks County Trust, 35 N 6th	01
Berks Title, 607 Washington	01
Caster, 434 Walnut	01
Colonial Trust, 447 Penn	01
Corbit, 147 N 5th	01
Medical Arts, 230 N 5th	01
Staufer, 62 S 6th	02
Y M C A, 631 Washington	01

GOVERNMENT OFFICES

City Hall, 8th & Washington	01
Courthouse, 33 N 6th	01

HOSPITALS

Community General, 135 N 6th	01
Reading, 6th & Spruce	03
Saint Josephs, 12th & Walnut	03

UNIVERSITIES AND COLLEGES

Albright College, 13th & Exeter	04
Mc Canns Business, 134 S 5th	02
Mount Alvernia, 464 St Bernadine	07
Pennsylvania State University, 814 Hill Ave	10
Reading Business Institute, 949 Penn	01

SCRANTON 185

POST OFFICE BOXES

Box Nos.		
1-83	West Scranton Sta	04
1-118	Dickson City Br	19
1-135	Dunmore Br	12
1-238	Taylor-Old Forge Br	17
1-1355	Main Office	01

RURAL ROUTES

1	08

STATIONS, BRANCHES AND UNITS

Dickson City Br	19
Dunmore Br	12
Marywood College Sta	09

Moosic Br	07
North Scranton Sta	08
Old Forge Br	18
South Side Sta	05
Taylor-Old Forge Br	17
Throop Br	12
West Scranton Sta	04
General Delivery	01
Postmaster	03

APARTMENTS, HOTELS, MOTELS

Adams, 408 Adams Ave	10
Bellefonte Donny Dr	05
Carter, 801 Mulberry	10
Casey Inn, Adams & Lackawanna	03
Clay Avenue, 520 Clay Ave	10
Country Day, 1100 Quincy Ave	10
Duckworth, 711 Linden	10
Florence, 643 Adams	10
Greenwood Motel, 3505 Birney Ave	05
Hilton Inn 229 N Washington Ave	03
Holiday Inn Motel, Franklin Ave & Mulberry	03
Jackson Heights 1000 Jackson	04
Jermyn, Wyoming Ave & Spruce	03
Riverside Apartments	05
Rockledge Terrace 607 N Main Tay	17
Scranton, 500 Wyoming Ave	09
Taylor Village 600 Oak St Tay	17
Viewmont Village	08
Washington Ave West 537 N Washington Ave	09
Washington Plaza 600 N Washington Ave	09
Wyoming, 229 Wyoming Ave	03

BUILDINGS

Administration, 425 N Washington Ave	03
Brooks, 436 Spruce	03
Catholic Youth Center, 500 Jefferson Ave	10
Connell, 129 N Washington	03
Davidow, 411 Spruce	03
First Federal, 149 Adams	03
Glen Alden, 310 Jefferson	03
Jewish Community Center, 601 Jefferson Ave	10
Mears, 327 N Washington Ave	03
Medical Arts, 327 N Washington Ave	03
Miller, 422 Spruce	03
North Eastern National Bank, Wyoming Ave & Spruce St	03
Scranton Life, 538 Spruce	03
Scranton National Bank, 108 N Washington Ave	03
Scranton Real-Estate, 314 N Washington Ave	03
Scranton Times, 145 Penn	03

Y M C A, 419 Mulberry St	03
Y W C A, 638 Linden St	03

GOVERNMENT OFFICES

Chamber Of Commerce, 426 Mulberry	03
Court House Annex	03
Court House, 200 N Washington	03
Internal Revenue, Connell Bldg	14
Municipal Bldg, Washington & Mulberry	03

HOSPITALS

Community Medical Center E, 316 Colfax Ave	01
Mercy Heights, 930 Hickory	01
Mercy, 746 Jefferson Ave	01
Moses Taylor, 700 Quincy	10
Saint Josephs Maternity, 2010 Adams	09
State General, Mulberry & Franklin	01
West Mountain Sanitorium, Newton Rd	04

UNIVERSITIES AND COLLEGES

International Correspondence Schools, Keyser Ave & Oak St	15
Johnson School, 3427 N Main Ave	08
Marywood, 2300 Adams Ave	09
Pennsylvania State University, Keystone Industrial Park	12
Scranton Lackawanna Junior, 635 Linden	03
University Of Scranton, 4 Ridge Row	10

UPPER DARBY   190

POST OFFICE BOXES

Box Nos.

1-449	Main Office	84
501-899	Havertown Br	83

STATIONS, BRANCHES AND UNITS

Havertown Br	83
Manoa Br	83
Terminal Sta	82
General Delivery	82
Postmaster	82

GOVERNMENT OFFICES

Social Security Adm, 6801 Ludlow	82

WILKES BARRE   187

POST OFFICE BOXES

Box Nos.

A-H	North End Sta	05
1-117	Ashley Br	06
1-147	Mountaintop	07
1-184	Luzerne Br	09
1-1387	Main Office	03
1001-1508	Kingston Br	04
1601-1700	North End Sta	05
1701-1916	Shavertown Br	08
5006-5119	Sta A	10

RURAL ROUTES

1,2	02
3,4	07
5	08

STATIONS, BRANCHES AND UNITS

Ashley Br	06
Bear Creek Rural Br	18602
Edwardsville Br	04
Forty Fort Br	04
Gateway Br	04
Kingston Br	04
Luzerne Br	09
Mountain Top Br	07
Narrows Br	04
North End Sta	05
Peely Br	06
Plains Br	05
Shavertown Br	08
Sugar Notch Br	06
Swoyerville Br	04
Trucksville Br	08
Veterans Hospital Sta	03
General Delivery	03
Postmaster	01

APARTMENTS, HOTELS, MOTELS

Carousel Motel, 400 Kidder	02
Florence, 95 W Ross	02
Genettis, 77 E Market	01
Grand, 81 E Market	01
Holiday Inn	02
Host Motel, 500 Kidder	03
Irving, 307 S River	02
Ludwig, 273 S River	02
Margarida, 117 N Main	01
Margarida, 7 E Jackson	01
Margarida, 8 Bennett	01
Minrose, 267 S Franklin	02
Riverside, 120-130 W Ross	02
Riverside, 92-96 W River	02
Sandor, 110-116 W Ross	02
Sterling, Market & River	03
Wilkes, 45 N Main	01

BUILDINGS

Bennett, 2 N Main	01
Blue Cross, 15 S Franklin	01
First National Bank, 11 W Market	01
Golde, 2 E Northampton	01
I B E, 69 Public Square	01

Russian, 84 E Market 01
United Penn Bank, 8 W
    Market........................... 01
Veterans Administration, 19
    N Main 01

HOSPITALS

General, North River........... 02
Mercy, 196 Hanover 03
Nesbitt Memorial, 562
    Wyoming Ave.................. 04
Valley Crest, East End Blvd.... 02
Veterans Administration
    Hosp, East End Blvd 03
Wyoming Valley, 149 Dana 02

UNIVERSITIES AND COLLEGES

Kings, 133 N River............... 02
Luzerne County Community
    College, 19 N River........... 02
Penna. State University
    Wilkes Barre Campus,
    Shavertown Br. 08
Wilkes-Barre Business
    College, 69 Public Square.. 01
Wilkes, 184 S River.............. 03

YORK   174

POST OFFICE BOXES

Box Nos.
A-M   Jacobus Br 07
1-300   Jacobus Br 07
1-2356   Main Office 05
3001-3999   East York Br..... 02
6121-6267   Hellam Br 06

RURAL ROUTES

1 04
2 03
3 02
4 04
5 02
6 04
7 02
8 03
9 02
11,12 06

STATIONS, BRANCHES AND UNITS

East York Br........................... 02
Hellam Br............................... 06
Jacobus Br.............................. 07
General Delivery 05
Postmaster.............................. 05

APARTMENTS, HOTELS, MOTELS

Barnharts, 3021 E Market St . 02
Billy Bud Inn 334 Arsenal
    Rd 02
Canterbury Court Apts, 199
    Silver Spur Dr.................... 02
Carroll Apartments, 51 S
    Beaver St........................... 01
Cedar Village Apartments
    404 Cedar Village Rd......... 02

Char-Hill, R D 3 02
Chateau, R D 9........................ 02
Colonial Crest Apartments
    2160 D Maplewood Dr....... 03
Colonial, P O Box 547........... 05
Colony Park Apartments,
    1720 Devers Road 04
Congress Inn 2810 E Market
    Street 02
Country Club Manor
    Apartments, Country Club
    Road................................. 03
Crestwood Arms Apartments,
    Suburban Road 03
Eastern Blvd Apartments,
    Eastern Blvd & Mill Rd....... 02
Elm Terrace Apartments, 450
    Madison Ave 04
Flamingo, 3600 E Market St... 02
Holiday Inn, 2600 E Market
    St 02
Howard Johnson, Arsenall
    Road Interchange 02
Lafayette Plaza Apartments,
    3201 E Market St 02
Leisureville Apts, Lark Cir...... 04
Milner, P O Box 547............... 05
Modernaire, 3311 E Market
    St 02
North Hills Apartments, 1800
    North Hills Rd.................... 02
Penn, 49 N George St............. 01
Playland Pool 2810 E Market
    Street 02
Spheel Grund, 3522 E Market
    St 02
Springetts Manor 16 Jamison
    Drive................................. 02
Suburban Park Apartments
    2685 Carnegie Road........... 02
Travelodge, 132-140 N
    George St 01
Vern-Mar Apartments, 2101 E
    Market St 02
Village East 3400 E Market
    Street 02
York Hills Apartments, 1927
    Queenswood Drive.............. 03
York Valley Inn (Quality
    Courts), 3883 E Market St . 02
Yorkshire Apartments, 3205
    Market St 02
Yorktowne, P O Box 1106 05
Yost Apartments, 958 E
    Market St 03

BUILDINGS

Crispus Attucks, 125 E
    Maple St 03
Y M C A, 90 N Newberry St.... 01
Y W C A, 320 E Market St....... 03

GOVERNMENT OFFICES

City Hall, P O Box 509........... 05
County Home, R D 7 02
County Jail, 319 Chestnut St... 03
Court House, 28 E Market St.. 01
United States Post Office,
    200 S George St 05

HOSPITALS

Memorial Osteopathic, 325 S
    Belmont St........................ 03
York Hospital, 1001 S George
    St 05

UNIVERSITIES AND COLLEGES

Penn State Campus, 1031
    Edgecombe Ave.................. 03
School Administration, P O
    Box 1927............................ 05
Thompson School Of
    Business & Technology,
    1253 W Market................... 04
York College Of Pa, Country
    Club Road.......................... 05

PUERTO RICO

(Abbreviation: PR)

Acueducto, Br. Cayey 00633
Adjuntas 00601
Aguada 00602
Aguadilla (1st) 00603
   Borinquen Road, Sta. 00603
   Coloso, R. Br.....................00641
   Ramey A F B, Br..............00604
   Victoria Street, Sta.........00603
Aguas Buenas 00607
Aguirre 00608
Aibonito 00609
Almirante Norte, Br. Vega
   Baja 00763
Almirante Sur, Br. Vega
   Baja 00763
Altamesa, Sta. San Juan 00921
Alto Del Manzano, Br. Las
   Marias 00670
Anasco 00610
Angeles 00611
Arecibo (1st) 00612
Arroyo 00615
Asomante, Sta. Aibonito........00609
Atalaya, Sta. Aguada 00602
Bajadero 00616
Bajura, Br. Vega Alta 00762
Barceloneta 00617
Barinas, Br. Yauco 00768
Barranquitas 00618
Barriada Blondet, Br.
   Guayama 00654
Barriada Marin, Br.
   Guayama 00654
Barrio Cantito, Br. Manati 00701
Barrio Carmen, Br.
   Guayama 00654
Barrio Cortes, Br. Manati......00701
Barrio Espinar, Sta. Aguada...00602
Barrio Obrero, Sta. San Juan
   (see appendix)
Bartolo, Br. Castaner 00631
Bitumul, Sta. San Juan..........00917
Boca, Br. Guayanilla 00656
Boqueron 00622
Boquillas, Br. Manati 00701
Borinquen Road, Sta.
   Aguadilla...........................00603
Cabezas, Sta. Fajardo 00648
Cabo Rojo (1st) 00623
Caguas (1st) 00625
Camarones, Sta. Guaynabo....00657
Camino Nuevo, Br. Yabucoa..00767
Camuy 00627
Canovanas 00629
Caparra Heights, Br. San
   Juan (see appendix)
Carolina (1st) 00630
Carpenter Road, Sta. San
   Juan 00917
Carrasquillo, Sta. Cayey........00633
Caserio Roig, Sta. Humacao...00661
Casilla Gobernador, Br.
   Cayey ....0065..
Castaner 00631
Cayey (1st) 00633
Ceiba 00635
Central Eureka, Sta.
   Hormigueros 00660
Central Igualdad, Br.

Mayaguez 00708
Central San Vicente, Br.
   Vega Baja 00636
Cerrilios, Br. Cabo Rojo 00623
Cerro Gordo, Br. San
   Lorenzo 00754
Ciales 00638
Cidra 00639
Coamo 00640
Colegio Univ Decayey, Sta.
   Cayey 0065J
College, Sta. Mayaguez.........00708
Collores, Br. Juana Diaz........00665
Coloso, R. Br. Aguadilla 00641
Comerio 00642
Consumo, Br. Mayaguez.......00708
Corazon, Br. Guayama 00654
Corozal 00643
Corozo, Br. Boqueron.............00622
Coto Laurel 00644
Country Club, Sta. San Juan ...00924
Cuatro Calles, Br. Arroyo 00615
Cuatro Esquinas, Br. Cabo
   Rojo 00623
Cuesta Las Piedras, Br.
   Mayaguez 00708
Culebra 00645
Cuyon, Sta. Aibonito 00609
Delicias, Br. Cabo Rojo.........00623
Descalabrado, Br. Santa
   Isabel 00757
Dorado 00646
Dorado Beach, Br. Dorado 00646
Duey, Br. Yauco.....................00768
Duque, Br. Naguabo. 00718
El Albanico, Sta. Aibonito 00609
El Amendro, Br. San Juan......00632
El Bajo, Br. Patillas 00723
El Torito, Br. Cayey 00633
Emajaguas, Br. Maunabo 00707
Ensenada 00647
Esperanza, Sta. Vieques 00765
Fajardo (1st) 00648
Fernandez Juncos, Sta. San
   Juan (see appendix)
Fios, Sta. San Sebastian 00755
Florida 00650
Fort Buchanan, Br. San
   Juan 00934
Fortuna, Br. Juana Diaz 00651
Garrochales 00652
Grand Stand, Br. Guayama.....00654
Guamani, Br. Guayama..........00654
Guanica 00653
Guaniquilla Barrio, Br. Cabo
   Rojo 00623
Guaraquao, Sta. Guaynabo 00657
Guardarraya, Br. Patillas 00723
Guayama (1st) 00654
Guayanes. Br. Yabucoa 00767
Guayanilla 00656
Guaynabo 00657
Gurabo 00658
Hacienda Santa Rita, Br.
   Guanica 00653
Hatillo 00659
Hato Rey, Sta. San Juan
   (see appendix)
Hato Viejo, Br. Arecibo.........00612
Hato Viejo Cumbre, Br.
   Ciales 00638
Hoconuco Alto, Br. San

German 00753
Honduras, Br. Barranquitas....00618
Hormigueros 00660
Hucares, Br. Naguabo............00718
Humacao (1st) 00661
Imbery, Br. Barceloneta 00617
International Airport, Br. San
   Juan 00913
Isabela (1st) 00662
Isla Verde, Br. Carolina 00630
Jagual, Br. San Lorenzo.........00754
Jauca, Sta. Santa Isabel 00757
Jayuya 00664
Joyuda, Br. Cabo Rojo...........00623
Juana Diaz..............................00665
Juana Matos, Br. San Juan.....00632
Juncos 00666
Junquito, Br. Humacao...........00661
Kofresi, Sta. Cabo Rojo.........00623
La Garita, Br. Cabo Rojo 00623
La Placita, Sta. Cayey...........00633
La Plata 00668
La Sierra, Br. Comerio 00642
La Trocha, Sta. Vega Baja 00763
La Tuna, Br. Cabo Rojo 00623
La Vega, Sta. Barranquitas 00618
Laguna, Br. Vega Baja 00763
Lajas 00667
Lajas Arriba, Br. Lajas..........00667
Lares 00669
Las Flores, Br. Coamo...........00640
Las Granjas, Br. Vega Baja 00763
Las Marias 00670
Las Piedras 00671
Las Rocas, Sta. Guaynabo 00657
Lizas, Br. Maunabo 00707
Llanos, Br. Coamo 00640
Lluberas, Br. Yauco................00768
Loiza 00672
Loiza Street, Sta. San Juan
   (see appendix)
Luquillo 00673
Macana, Br. Guayanilla 00656
Magas Arriba, Br.
   Guayanilla.........................00656
Maguayo, Br. Lajas 00667
Magueyes, Br. Barceloneta 00617
Maizales, Br. Naguabo...........00718
Mamey, Sta. Guaynabo..........00657
Manati (1st) 00701
Mareas, Br. Guayama 00654
Maresua, Br. San German 00753
Maricao 00706
Marina, Sta. Mayaguez..........00708
Maton, Br. Cayey....................00633
Maunabo 00707
Mayaguez (1st)........................00708
Mercedita 00715
Moca 00716
Monserrate, Sta. Vega Baja 00763
Monte Bello, Br. Manati 00701
Monte Grande, Br. Cabo
   Rojo 00623
Monte Santo, Sta. Vieques 00765
Montoso, Br. Mayaguez.........00708
Morales Diaz, Br. Cabo Rojo..00623
Morovis 00717
Munoz Rivera, Sta.
   Guaynabo 00657
Naguabo 00718
Naranjito 00719
Naval Station, Sta. San
   Juan 00932

Nazario, Br. San German........00753
Nogueras, Br. Cidra 00639
Old San Juan, Sta. San
    Juan 00902
Olimpo, Br. Guayama.............00654
Orocovis.................................00720
Palmarejo, Br. Lajas 00667
Palmarllano, Sta. Lares 00669
Palmas Altas, Br.
    Barceloneta........................00617
Palmer....................................00721
Palo Hincado, Br.
    Barranquitas........................00618
Palomas, Br. Yauco................00768
Parcelas Coqui, Br. Aguirre ...00608
Parcelas Palmarejo, Br.
    Coamo..................................00640
Pastillo, Br. Juana Diaz 00665
Pasto, Br. Guayanilla..............00656
Pasto Viejo, Br. Cayey............00633
Patillas...................................00723
Penuelas.................................00724
Pesa Cialitos, Br. Ciales........00638
Pitahaya, Br. Arroyo 00615
Playa, Sta. Ponce...................00731
Playa Cortada, Sta. Santa
    Isabel...................................00757
Polvora, Sta. Cayey.................00633
Polvorin Ward, Sta. Cayey......00633
Ponce (1st) 00731
Pozas, Br. Ciales....................00638
Pueblito, Br. Manati................00701
Puente Blanco, Br. Arroyo......00615
Puente De Jobos, Br.
    Guayama...............................00654
Puerta De Tierra, Sta. San
    Juan 00906
Puerto Real.............................00740
Pugnado, Br. Manati...............00701

Pulguillas, Br. Aibonito...........00609
Punta Santiago 00741
Quebrada Hondo, Br. San
    Lorenzo................................00754
Quebrada Vueltas, Sta.
    Fajardo.................................00648
Quebradillas...........................00742
Quemado, Br. Mayaguez 00708
Ramey A F B, Br. Aguadilla....00604
Retiro Tea, Br. San German....00753
Rincon 00743
Rio Arriba, R. Sta. Arecibo.....00612
Rio Blanco..............................00744
Rio Grande 00745
Rio Piedras, Sta. San Juan
    (see appendix)
Rosario 00746
Rosario Alto, Br. San
    German.................................00753
Rubias, R. Br. Yauco 00768
Sabana Abajo, Br. Carolina....00630
Sabana Eneas, Br. San
    German.................................00753
Sabana Grande 00747
Sabana Hoyos.........................00748
Sabana Seca...........................00749
Saint Just 00750
Salinas...................................00751
Salud Ward, Sta. Mayaguez....00708
San Antonio............................00752
San German (1st) 00753
San Ildefonzo, Sta. Coamo....00640
San Jose, Sta. San Juan 00930
SAN JUAN (1st) (see
    appendix)
San Lorenzo............................00754
San Luis, Sta. Aibonito 00609
San Martin, Sta. San Juan 00924

San Sebastian (1st)...............00755
Santa Ana, Br. Mayaguez.......00708
Santa Catalina, Br. Coamo....00640
Santa Isabel...........................00757
Santa Maria, Sta. Vieques.....00765
Santiago, Br. San German......00753
Santurce, Sta. San Juan
    (see appendix)
Seco, Br. Maunabo.................00707
Sierra Baja, Br. Guayanilla.....00656
Sitio Romero, Sta. Villalba....00766
Toa Alta 00758
Toa Baja.................................00759
Toita, Br. Cayey......................00633
Tres Hermanos, Br. Anasco.....00610
Trujillo, Br. San Juan.............00760
Trujillo Alto.............................00760
University, Sta. San Juan........00931
Usabon, Sta. Aibonito 00609
Utuado (1st)............................00761
Vega Alta 00762
Vega Baja (1st).......................00763
Victoria Street, Sta.
    Aguadilla..............................00603
Vieques...................................00765
Villalba...................................00766
Walcott, Br. Arecibo 00612
Yabucoa..................................00767
Yauco (1st)..............................00768
Yaurel, Br. Arroyo...................00615
Yuquiyu...................................00769
Yuquiyu, Br. Luquillo..............00769

SAN JUAN 009
POST OFFICE BOXES

Box Nos.

Box Nos.	Location	
A-Z	Caparra Heights Sta	22
A-Z	Hato Rey Sta......	19
A-Z	Main Office	36
A-Z	Rio Piedras Sta................	28
A-Z	University Of Puerto Rico Sta................	31
1-1392	San Juan Sta. ..	02
1-1924	Hato Rey Sta......	19
1-5092	Main Office	36
AA-AK	Caparra Heights Sta	22
AA-AZ	Main Office	36
AA-AZ	Rio Piedras Sta................	28
AA-AZ	University Of P. R. Sta............	31
AA-XX	Hato Rey Sta......	19
BA-BK	Caparra Heights Sta	22
BA-BN	University Of P. R. Sta. ..	31
BA-BZ	Main Office	36
BA-BZ	Rio Piedras Sta................	28
CA-CK	Caparra Heights Sta	22
CA-CN	Main Office	36
CA-CS	Rio Piedras Sta................	28
DA-DQ	Caparra Heights Sta	22
EA-EK	Caparra Heights Sta	22
GA-GH	Caparra Heights Sta	22
SS-ZZ	Caparra Heights Sta	22
1401-3072	San Juan Sta..	03
3081-3992	San Juan Sta..	04
3751-4049	San Jose Sta.	30
4001-5000	San Juan Sta..	05
5001-5524	Puerta De Tierra Sta	06
5601-5760	San Juan Sta..	05
5701-5917	Puerta De Tierra Sta	06
6001-6899	Loiza Street Sta................	14
7001-7899	Barrio Obrero Sta................	16
8001-8899	Fernandez Juncos Sta......	10
9001-10249	Santurce Sta...	08
10001-10998	Caparra Heights Sta	22
11001-11937	Fernandez Juncos Sta......	10
12001-12386	Loiza Street Sta................	14
13001-13962	Santurce Sta...	08
14001-14594	Barrio Obrero Sta................	16
20001-21337	Rio Piedras Sta................	28
21301-23190	University Of	

	Puerto Rico Sta................	31

RURAL ROUTES

1................		14
2,3................		28

STATIONS, BRANCHES AND UNITS

Altamesa Sta................	21
Barrio Obrero Sta................	16
Bitumul Sta................	17
Caparra Heights Br................	22
Carpenter Road Sta................	17
Country Club Sta................	24
El Amendro Br................	00632
Fernandez Juncos Sta................	10
Fort Buchanan Br................	34
Hato Rey Sta................	17
International Airport Br................	13
Juana Matos Br................	00632
Loiza Street Sta................	11
Naval Station Sta................	32
Old San Juan Sta................	02
Puerta De Tierra Sta................	06
Rio Piedras Sta................	23
San Jose Sta................	30
San Martin Sta................	24
Santurce Sta................	07
Trujillo Br................	00760
University Sta................	31
General Delivery................	36
Postmaster................	36

APARTMENTS, HOTELS, MOTELS

Altamesa Gardens, San Ignacio & San Alfonso.......	21
Americana, Boca De Cangrejos Rd, Isla Verde..	13
Atlantic Beach, 1 Vendig....	07
Borinquen Towers, Roosevelt & Ensenada	20
Capitol, 800 Ponce De Leon Ave	07
Caribbean Towers, 762 Ponce De Leon Ave (Stc)	07
Caribe Hilton, San Geronimo..	01
Central, 202 San Jose (Sj)......	01
Concordia Gardens, 65 Inf Ave	24
Condado Beach, 1071 Ashford Ave......................	07
Condado Del Mar, Ashford Ave......................	07
Condado Plaza, 1351 Magdalena Ave.	07
Condado Towers, 30 Washington	07
Coral Beach, Isla Verde Rd	13
Darlington, Fdez Jcos Ave Stop 10 (Stc)	07
Darlington, Munoz Rivera Ave (Rp)......................	25
Del Mar, Delcasse & Marselle......................	07
El Convento, Cristo (Sj)........	01
El Monte, 165 Hostos (Hr)......	07
El Portal, 76 Condado..........	07
Gallardo, 1102 Magdalena Ave......................	07
Golden Beach, Isla Verde Rd..	13
Iberia, 604 Ponce De Leon	

Ave......................	07
Isla Verde Towers, Isla Verde Rd......................	13
Jardines De Guayama, Guayama St......................	17
La Concha, Ashford Ave..........	07
La Rada, 1020 Ashford Ave......	07
Laguna Gardens, Isla Verde Rd......................	13
Litheda, Cupey Bajo............	26
Los Robles, Las Americas & Nevarez Ave	27
Mirabel, 606 Ponce De Leon Ave......................	07
Miramar Charterhouse, 600 Olimpo......................	07
Normandie, Escambron Ave	01
Olimpo Courts, 603 Miramar Ave......................	07
Palace, 157 Tetuan..............	01
Pierre, 105 De Diego Ave (Stc)......................	11
Pine Grove, Isla Verde Rd......	14
San Cristobal, 450 Norzagaray......................	01
San Geronimo, Ashford Ave	07
San Juan Intercontinental, Isla Verde Rd	13
San Rafael,)miramar(..........	07
Sheraton, Ashford Ave..........	07
Town House, 65 Inf Ave..........	23

BUILDINGS

Alcazar, 562 Trigo................	07
Ashford Medical, Ashford Ave......................	07
Banco De Ponce, Ponce De Leon Ave, Stop 18 1/2	07
Banco De San Juan, Tanca & Tetuan......................	01
Banco Popular Ctr. Ponce De Leon & Munoz Rivera Ave (Hr)......................	18
Banco Popular, 206 Tetuan	01
Capitol, Ponce De Leon Ave (Sj)......................	01
Center, De Diego Ave Stop 22 (Stc)......................	09
Chase Manhattan Bank, Ponce De Leon & Park St (Stc)......................	09
Chase Manhattan Bank, 1058 Munoz Rivera Ave (Rp)......................	27
Cobian Center, Ponce De Leon Ave & Park (Stc)........	09
Eastern Airline, 155 De Diego Ave, Stop 22	11
El Imparcial, 450 Comercio	01
El Koury, Fernandez Juncos Ave & Villamil St............	07
El Mundo, 383 F D Roosevelt Ave......................	18
Empire, De Diego Ave (Stc)	09
First Federal Savings, Munoz Rivera Ave (Rp)............	27
First Federal Savings, Ponce De Leon Ave & Park St (Stc)......................	09
First National City Bank, Munoz Rivera Ave & Margarita	25
First National City Bank,	

Roberto H Todd Ave (Stc)... 07
First National City Bank, 252
  Ponce De Leon Ave (Hr)...... 18
Las Americas Professional,
  Domenech Ave 18
New York Dept Store, Ponce
  De Leon Ave, Stop 16 1/2.. 07
Ochoa, 300 Comercio (Sj)...... 01
Padin, Fortaleza & Cruz.......... 01
Pan Am, Ponce De Leon Ave
  & Bolivia (Hr) 17
Professional, De Diego Ave
  (Stc) 09
Puerto Rico Development,
  Ponce De Leon Ave, Stop
  33 (Hr)................................. 18
San Martin, Ponce De Leon
  Ave & Park St (Stc)............ 09
San Rafael, Ponce De Leon
  Ave & Miramar Ave 07

HOSPITALS

Auxilio Mutuo, Ponce De Leon

Ave Stop 37 (Hr)................. 17
Centro Medico Universitario
  Centro Medico Grounds 35
Doctors Hospital, 1395 San
  Rafael (Stc) 09
Fernandez Garcia, 358 Ponce
  De Leon Ave(Hr)................. 18
Guadalupe, 435 Ponce De
  Leon Ave (Hr)..................... 17
Instituto Oftalmico, 160
  Ponce De Leon Ave (Sj)...... 01
Julia, Ponce De Leon Ave
  Stop 31 (Hr)......................... 17
Los Maestros, Domenech Ave
  (Hr)..................................... 18
Mimiya, 303 De Diego Ave
  (Stc) 09
Pavia, Europa & Asia............. 09
Presbyterian, 1451 Ashford
  Ave 07
Professional, 310 De Diego
  Ave (Stc) 09
San Carlos, 1822 Ponce De
  Leon Ave (Stc) 09

San Jorge, 258 San Jorge
  (Stc).................................... 12
Veterans, Puerto Nuevo........... 20
Woman'S, 450 Saldana (Stc).. 09

MILITARY INSTALLATIONS

U S Naval Base, Fern'Z
  Juncos Ave & Munoz
  Rivera Expy........................ 32
U S Navy Annex, Hwy 2 34

UNIVERSITIES AND COLLEGES

Immaculada, 1709 Ponce De .
  Leon Ave (Stc) 09
Puerto Rico Junior College,
  Cupey Bajo Rd Km 3.0...... 26
Tropical School Of Medicine,
  Ponce De Leon Ave (Sj)...... 01
University Of Puerto Rico,
  Ponce De Leon Ave (Rp)..... 31

RHODE ISLAND
(Abbreviation: RI)

Adamsville.............................02801
Albion...................................02802
Alton....................................02803
Annex, Sta. Providence............02903
Anthony, Sta. Coventry...........02816
Ashaway...............................02804
Ashton, Br. Pawtucket............02864
Barrington (1st)....................02806
Block Island...........................02807
Bradford...............................02808
Bristol (1st)..........................02809
Bristol Ferry, R. Sta.
   Portsmouth.........................02811
Broadway, Sta. Newport..........02840
Brown, Sta. Providence...........02912
Carolina................................02812
Centerdale, Br. Providence......02911
Central Falls, Br. Pawtucket....02863
Charlestown...........................02813
Chepachet.............................02814
Clayville................................02815
Coddington Point, Br.
   Newport.............................02840
Conimicut, Sta. Warwick..........02889
Coventry (1st)........................02816
Coventry Center, Sta.
   Coventry.............................02816
Cranston, Br. Providence
   (see appendix)
Cumberland, Br. Pawtucket....02864
Cumberland Hill, Br.
   Pawtucket...........................02864
Darlington, Sta. Pawtucket...02860
Davisville, Sta. North
   Kingstown............................02854
East Greenwich (1st)............02818
East Providence, Br.
   Providence (see appendix)
East Side, Sta. Providence.....02906
Edgewood, Sta. Providence.....02905
Elmwood, Sta. Providence.....02907
Escoheag..............................02821

Esmond, Br. Providence..........02917
Exeter...................................02822
Fiskeville...............................02823
Fleet, Br. Newport..................02840
Forestdale..............................02824
Foster...................................02825
Friar, Sta. Providence.............02918
Garden City, Br. Providence....02920
Glendale................................02826
Greene..................................02827
Greenville..............................02828
Harmony................................02829
Harrisville..............................02830
Hope....................................02831
Hope Valley............................02832
Hopkinton..............................02833
Howard..................................02834
Hoxsie, Sta. Warwick..............02889
Jamestown.............................02835
Johnston, Br. Providence........02919
Kenyon..................................02836
Kingston, Br. Wakefield..........02881
Lincoln, Br. Pawtucket............02865
Little Compton........................02837
   Acoaxet, R. Br....................02701
Manville.................................02838
Mapleville..............................02839
Middletown, Br. Newport........02840
Misquamicut, Sta. Westerly.....02891
Narragansett, Br. Wakefield....02882
Naval Hospital, MOU.
   Newport.............................02840
Naval Training Station, Br.
   Newport.............................02840
Newport (1st).........................02840
North, Sta. Providence...........02908
North Kingstown (1st)............02852
   Davisville, Sta....................02854
   Quonset Point, Br. 02819
North Scituate........................02857
Oakland.................................02858
Olneyville, Sta. Providence......02909
Parcel Post Annex, Sta.
   Westerly.............................02891
Pascoag.................................02859

PAWTUCKET (1st) (see
   appendix)
Peace Dale, Sta. Wakefield
   (see appendix)
Pilgrim, Sta. Warwick.............02888
Portsmouth (1st)....................02871
   Bristol Ferry, R. Sta..........02811
PROVIDENCE (1st) (see
   appendix)
Prudence Island.....................02872
Quonset Point, Br. North
   Kingstown...........................02819
Riverside, Br. Providence........02915
Rockville................................02873
Rumford, Br. Providence.........02916
Saunderstown........................02874
Scarborough Beach, R. Br.
   Wakefield...........................02882
Shannock...............................02875
Slatersville.............................02876
Slocum..................................02877
Tiverton.................................02878
WAKEFIELD (1st) (see
   appendix)
Wallum Lake...........................02884
Walnut Hill, Sta.
   Woonsocket.........................02895
Warren (1st)..........................02885
WARWICK (1st) (see
   appendix)
Warwick Neck, Sta. Warwick...02889
Watch Hill, Sta. Westerly.......02891
Weekapaug, Sta. Westerly......02891
West Barrington......................02890
West Kingston.........................02892
West Warwick (1st).................02893
Westerly (1st)........................02891
Weybosset Hill, Sta.
   Providence..........................02903
Wildes Corner, Sta. Warwick...02886
Wood River Junction..............02894
Woonsocket (1st)....................02895
Wyoming................................02898

PAWTUCKET 028

POST OFFICE BOXES

Box Nos.
A-D	Darlington Br	61
1-206	Central Falls Br	63
1-237	Cumberland Br	64
1-305	Lincoln Br	65
1-449	Ashton Br	64
1-1640	Main Office	62
2001-3032	Darlington Br	61

RURAL ROUTES

1	65
2,3	64
4	65
5	64

STATIONS, BRANCHES AND UNITS

Ashton Br	64
Central Falls Br	63
Cumberland Br	64
Cumberland Hill Br	64
Darlington Sta	60
Lincoln Br	65
General Delivery	60
Postmaster	60

PROVIDENCE 029

POST OFFICE BOXES

Box Nos.
1-2000	Annex Sta	01
2001-2300	Edgewood Sta	05
2301-2600	East Side Sta	06
2601-2900	Elmwood Sta	07
2901-3200	North Sta	08
3201-3500	Olneyville Sta	09
3501-3800	Cranston Br	10
3801-4100	Centerdale Br	11
4101-4400	East Providence Br	14
4401-4700	Riverside Br	15
4701-5000	Rumford Br	16
5001-5380	Esmond Br	17
6000-7000	Main Office	04
7001-8000	Johnston Br	19
8001-9000	Garden City Br.	20

RURAL ROUTES

1,2	19
3,4	17
5	20

STATIONS, BRANCHES AND UNITS

Annex Sta	03
Brown Sta	12
Centerdale Br	11
Cranston Br	10
East Providence Br	14
East Side Sta	06
Edgewood Sta	05

Elmwood Sta	07
Esmond Br	17
Friar Sta	18
Garden City Br	20
Johnston Br	19
North Sta	08
Olneyville Sta	09
Riverside Br	15
Rumford Br	16
Weybosset Hill Sta	03
General Delivery	04
Postmaster	04

APARTMENTS, HOTELS, MOTELS

Colonial Hilton At Cranston, 1150 Narragansett Blvd	05
Dreyfus, 119 Washington	03
Holiday Inn, 21 Atwells Ave	03
Minden, 123 Waterman	06
Mohican, 344 Washington	03
Sheraton-Biltmore, 11 Dorrance	02
Wayland Manor, 500 Angell	06

BUILDINGS

Amica, 10 Weybosset	03
Blue Cross, 31 Canal	03
Hospital Trust, 15 Westminster	03
Howard, 10 Dorrance	03
Industrial Bank, 111 Westminster	03
Journal, 75 Fountain	02
Packet, 165 South Main	03
Physicians Office, 110 Lockwood	03
State House, 82 Smith	03
State Office, 101 Smith	03
Turks Head, 76 Westminster	03
Union Trust, 170 Westminster	03

GOVERNMENT OFFICES

City Hall, 25 Dorrance	03
Custom House, 24 Weybosset	03

HOSPITALS

Bradley 1011 Veterans Parkway	15
Charles V Chapin, 157 Eaton	08
Cranston General, 1763 Broad	05
Jane Brown, 44 Lockwood	02
Miriam, 14 Summit Ave	06
Our Lady Of Fatima, 200 High Service Ave N Providence	04
Providence Lying-In, 50 Maude	08
Rhode Island, 593 Eddy	02
Roger Williams General, 825 Chalkstone Ave	08
Saint Josephs, 21 Peace	07
Veterans Administration, Davis Park	08

UNIVERSITIES AND COLLEGES

Brown University, Prospect	12
Bryant College, Douglas Pike	17
Johnson & Wales Junior, Abbott Pk Pl	03
Pembroke, 172 Meeting	12
Providence College, River Ave	08
Rhode Island Junior, 199 Promenade	08
Rhode Island School Of Design, 14 College	03
Rhode Island, Mt Pleasant Ave	08
Roger Williams Junior, 160 Broad	03

WAKEFIELD 028

POST OFFICE BOXES

Box Nos.
1-209	Peace Dale	83
1-328	Kingston Br	81
1-552	Main Office	80
1-789	Narragansett Br	82

RURAL ROUTES

1	79
2	82
3	79
4	82
5	79
6,7	82

STATIONS, BRANCHES AND UNITS

Kingston Br	81
Narragansett Br	82
Peace Dale Sta	83
Scarborough Beach Rural Br	82
General Delivery	80
Postmaster	80

APARTMENTS, HOTELS, MOTELS

Faculty Apts	81
University Garden Apts	81

BUILDINGS

Narragansett Research Ctr	82

HOSPITALS

South County Hospital	79

UNIVERSITIES AND COLLEGES

Mount St Joseph College	80
University Of R I	81

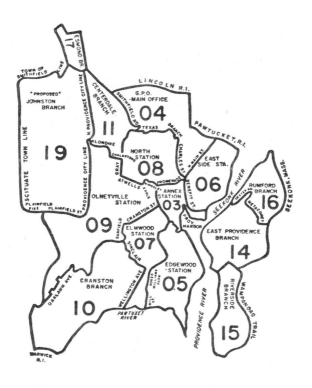

ZIP CODES
PROVIDENCE, Rhode Island
029 + Two Digits shown = Zip Code

WARWICK 028

POST OFFICE BOXES

Box Nos.
1-149	Conimicut Sta ..	89
1-392	Main Office	87
451-507	Conimicut Sta ..	89
701-909	Pilgrim Sta.......	88

RURAL ROUTES

1..	86

STATIONS, BRANCHES AND UNITS

Conimicut Sta	89
Hoxsie Sta	89

Pilgrim Sta...............................	88
Warwick Neck Sta	89
Wildes Corner Sta	86
General Delivery	87
Postmaster	87

APARTMENTS, HOTELS, MOTELS

Airport Motor Lodge 2082	
Post Rd..............................	86
Howard Johnsons Motor	
Lodge 24 Jefferson Blvd.....	88
Redwood Motor Lodge 2282	
Post Rd..............................	86
Rhode Island Yankee Motor	
Lodge 2081 Post Rd...........	86
Youngs Tourist Court 3880	
Post Rd..............................	86

GOVERNMENT OFFICES

Federal Aviation Adm..............	86
Weather Bureau.......................	86

HOSPITALS

Kent County Memorial	
Hospital...............................	86

MILITARY INSTALLATIONS

Air National Guard...................	86
Army Reserve...........................	86

SOUTH CAROLINA
(Abbreviation: SC)

Abbeville (1st)...................29620
Adams Run.........................29426
Adamsburg, R. Br. Union.......29380
Aiken (1st).........................29801
Alcolu...............................29001
Allendale (1st)....................29810
Alvin................................29427
Anderson (1st)...................29621
Andrews............................29510
Arcadia.............................29320
Ariail, R. Br. Easley............29640
Arlington, R. Br. Greer.......29651
Awendaw...........................29429
Aynor...............................29511
Baldwin Mills, R. Br.
  Chester...........................29706
Ballentine..........................29002
Bamberg (1st)....................29003
Baptist College, R. Br.
  Charleston........................29411
Barnwell (1st).....................29812
  Hilda, R. Br......................29813
  Kline, R. Br......................29814
Batesburg...........................29006
Bath..................................29816
Beaufort (1st).....................29902
  Burton, Br........................29902
  Laurel Bay, R. Br..............29902
  Marine Corps Air Station,
    Br.................................29902
  Naval Hospital, Br.............29902
  Parris Island, Br...............29905
Beech Island, R. Br. North
  Augusta...........................29842
Belton (1st).........................29627
Belvedere, Br. North
  Augusta............................29841
Bennettsville (1st)................29512
Berea, Br. Greenville............29601
Bethera.............................29430
Bethune.............................29009
Bishopville (1st)..................29010
Blacksburg.........................29702
Blackstock..........................29014
Blackville...........................29817
Blair..................................29015
Blenheim............................29516
Bluffton.............................29910
Blythewood.........................29016
Bob Jones University, Sta.
  Greenville.........................29614
Boiling Springs, R. Br.
  Spartanburg.......................29303
Bonneau.............................29431
Borden, R. Br. Rembert........29017
Bowling Green.....................29703
Bowman.............................29018
Boykin..............................29019
Bradley.............................29819
Branchville.........................29432
Branwood, Sta. Greenville
  (see appendix)
Broad Street, Sta. Sumter....29150
Brunson............................29911
Bucksport, R. Br. Conway....29527
Buffalo.............................29321
Burgess.............................29517
Burton, Br. Beaufort............29902
Cades...............................29518
Calhoun Falls......................29628

Callison.............................29820
Camden (1st)......................29020
Cameron............................29030
  Lone Star, R. Br................29077
Campobello.........................29322
Canadys.............................29433
Capitol, Sta. Columbia..........29211
Carlisle..............................29031
Carolina Mills, R. Br. Dillon...29537
Cassatt.............................29032
Catawba.............................29704
Cateechee..........................29629
Cayce (1st).........................29033
Cedar Spring, Br.
  Spartanburg.......................29303
Cedar Terrace, Sta.
  Columbia...........................29209
Centenary...........................29519
Central..............................29630
Chapin..............................29036
Chappells...........................29037
CHARLESTON (1st) (see
  appendix)
Charleston A F B, Br.
  Charleston.........................29404
Charleston Heights, Br.
  Charleston.........................29405
Cheraw (1st).......................29520
Cherokee Falls.....................29705
Cherry Grove Beach, Br.
  North Myrtle Beach............29582
Cherry Road, Sta. Rock Hill...29730
Chesnee.............................29323
Chester (1st):......................29706
  Baldwin Mills, R. Br...........29706
  Hemlock, R. Br..................29706
  Lowrys, R. Br....................29725
Chesterfield.........................29709
Citadel, Sta. Charleston.........29409
City View, Br. Greenville.......29611
Clarks Hill.........................29821
Clearwater..........................29822
Clemson (1st)......................29631
Clemson University, Sta.
  Clemson...........................29631
Cleveland...........................29635
Clifton..............................29324
Clinton (1st).......................29325
Clio..................................29525
Clover (1st).......................29710
COLUMBIA (1st) (see
  appendix)
Conestee............................29636
Converse............................29329
Conway (1st).......................29526
  Bucksport, R. Br...............29527
Coosawhatchie, R. Br.
  Ridgeland.........................29912
Cope................................29038
Cordesville.........................29434
Cordova.............................29039
Cottageville........................29435
Coward.............................29530
Cowpens.............................29330
Crescent Beach, Sta. North
  Myrtle Beach.....................29582
Crocketville, R. Br. Hampton...29913
Cross...............................29436
Cross Anchor.......................29331
Cross Hill...........................29332
Dale, R. Br. Seabrook..........29914
Dalzell.............................29040
Darlington (1st)....................29532

Dovesville, R. Br.................29540
Daufuskie Island...................29915
Davis Station........................29041
Denmark.............................29042
Dentsville, Br. Columbia.........29204
Dillon (1st)..........................29536
  Carolina Mills, R. Br..........29537
Donalds.............................29638
Donaldson, Br. Greenville.......29605
Dorchester..........................29437
Dorchester-Waylyn, Br.
  Charleston.........................29405
Dovesville, R. Br. Darlington...29540
Drayton.............................29333
Due West...........................29639
Duncan.............................29334
Dunes, Sta. Myrtle Beach....29577
Dupont, Br. Charleston........29407
Dutch Fork, Br. Columbia....29210
Early Branch.......................29916
Easley (1st).........................29640
Eastover.............................29044
Eau Claire, Sta. Columbia
  (see appendix)
Edgefield...........................29824
Edgemoor...........................29712
Edgewood, Sta. Columbia......29204
Edisto Island.......................29438
Effingham...........................29541
Ehrhardt.............................29081
Elgin.................................29045
Elko..................................29826
Elliott...............................29046
Elloree...............................29047
Enoree...............................29335
Estill.................................29918
  Scotia, R. Br....................29939
Eutawville..........................29048
Fair Play............................29643
Fairfax..............................29827
Fairfield, Br. Hilton Head
  Island..............................29928
Fairforest...........................29336
Farrow Road, Br. Columbia...29203
Federal, Sta. Greenville.........29603
Fingerville..........................29338
Five Points, Sta. Columbia....29205
Florence (1st).......................29501
Floyd Dale..........................29542
Folly Beach.........................29439
Forest Acres, Br. Columbia...29206
Foreston.............................29049
Fork.................................29543
Fort Jackson, Sta. Columbia...29207
Fort Lawn...........................29714
Fort Mill (1st).....................29715
Fort Motte...........................29050
Fountain Inn........................29644
Fripp Island, R. Br.
  Frogmore..........................29920
Frogmore............................29920
Furman.............................29921
Furman University, Br.
  Greenville.........................29613
Gable................................29051
  Sardinia, R. Br..................29143
Gadsden.............................29052
Gaffney (1st).......................29340
Galivants Ferry.....................29544
Garden City Beach, R. Br.
  Murrells Inlet....................29576
Garnett.............................29922
Gaston...............................29053

Georgetown (1st)..............29440
  Maryville, Br.................29440
  Plantersville, R. Br.........29441
Gifford.............................29923
Gilbert.............................29054
Glendale..........................29346
Glenn Springs...................29347
Gloverville.......................29828
Gooches, Br. Lancaster......29720
Goose Creek........).............29445
Gramling..........................29348
Graniteville.......................29829
Gray Court........................29645
  Hickory Tavern, R. Br.....29645
  Owings, R. Br...............29668
Great Falls........................29055
Greeleyville......................29056
Green Pond.......................29446
Green Sea.........................29545
Greenview, Br. Columbia....29203
GREENVILLE (1st) (see
  appendix)
Greenwood (1st)................29646
Greer (1st)........................29651
Gresham...........................29546
Grover..............................29447
Hamer..............................29547
Hampton (1st)...................29924
  Crocketville, R. Br........29913
Hampton Park Terrace, Sta.
  Charleston....................29403
Hanahan, Br. Charleston....29410
Hardeeville........................29927
Harleyville........................29448
Harris, Br. Greenwood.......29646
Hartsville (1st)...................29550
Heath Springs....................29058
Hemingway........................29554
Hemlock, R. Br. Chester......29706
Hickory Grove....................29717
Hickory Tavern, R. Br. Gray
  Court.............................29645
Highway Four Forty One, R.
  Br. Sumter...................29150
Hilda, R. Br. Barnwell.........29813
Hilton Head Island (1st)......29928
Hodges.............................29653
Holly Hill..........................29059
Hollywood.........................29449
Honea Path.......................29654
  Princeton, R. Br...........29674
Hopkins............................29061
Horatio.............................29062
Huger...............................29450
Inman..............................29349
Irmo................................29063
Islandton...........................29929
Isle Of Palms.....................29451
Iva..................................29655
Jackson.............................29831
Jacksonboro.......................29452
James Island, Br.
  Charleston....................29407
Jamestown.........................29453
Jefferson...........................29718
Jenkinsville........................29065
  Monticello, R. Br..........29106
  Parr, R. Br...................29066
Jericho.............................29454
Joanna.............................29351
Johns Island.......................29455
Johnsonville.......................29555
Johnston (1st)....................29832

Jonesville..........................29353
Kathwood, Br. West
  Columbia......................29169
Kennedy Street, Sta.
  Spartanburg..................29302
Kershaw...........................29067
Kinards.............................29355
Kings Creek.......................29719
Kingstree (1st)...................29556
Kline, R. Br. Barnwell.........29814
La France..........................29656
Ladson.............................29456
Lake City (1st)...................29560
Lake View.........................29563
Lamar..............................29069
Lancaster (1st)...................29720
Lando..............................29724
Landrum (1st)....................29356
Lane.................................29564
Langley............................29834
Latta................................29565
Laurel Bay, R. Br. Beaufort....29902
Laurens (1st).....................29360
Leesburg, Br. Columbia......29201
Leesville...........................29070
Lena................................29930
Lesslie, R. Br. Rock Hill......29734
Lexington (1st)...................29072
Liberty.............................29657
Liberty Hill........................29074
Little Mountain...................29075
Little River.........................29566
Little Rock.........................29567
Livingston.........................29076
Lobeco.............................29931
Lockhart...........................29364
Lodge..............................29082
Lone Star, R. Br. Cameron....29077
Longcreek.........................29658
Longs...............................29568
Loris (1st).........................29569
Lowndesville......................29659
Lowrys, R. Br. Chester........29725
Lugoff.............................29078
Luray...............................29932
Lydia...............................29079
Lydia Mills, R. Br. Clinton....29325
Lyman (1st).......................29365
Lynchburg.........................29080
Madison............................29660
Manning (1st)....................29102
Marietta...........................29661
Marine Corps Air Station, Br.
  Beaufort.......................29902
Marion (1st)......................29571
Market Center, Br.
  Columbia......................29205
Martin..............................29836
Maryville, Br. Georgetown....29440
Mauldin (1st).....................29662
Mayesville........................29104
Mayfair, Br. Taylors............29687
Mayo...............................29368
Mc Bee.............................29101
Mc Clellanville....................29458
Mc Coll............................29570
Mc Connells......................29726
Mc Cormick.......................29835
Meggett............................29460
Miley...............................29933
Minturn............................29573
Modoc..............................29838
Moncks Corner (1st)...........29461

Monetta............................29105
Monticello, R. Br.
  Jenkinsville....................29106
Montmorenci......................29839
Moore..............................29369
Mount Carmel.....................29840
Mount Croghan...................29727
Mount Holly.......................29463
Mount Pleasant (1st)...........29464
Mountain Rest....................29664
Mountville.........................29370
Mullins (1st)......................29574
Murrells Inlet.....................29576
Myers, Br. Charleston.........29405
Myrtle Beach (1st)..............29577
Myrtle Beach A F B, Br.
  Myrtle Beach.................29577
Naval Base, Br. Charleston....29408
Naval Hospital, Br. Beaufort....29902
Neeses.............................29107
Nesmith...........................29580
New Easley Highway, Br.
  Greenville.....................29611
New Ellenton......................29809
New Zion...........................29111
Newberry (1st)...................29108
Newry..............................29665
Nichols.............................29581
Ninety Six.........................29666
Norris...............................29667
North...............................29112
  Woodford, R. Br...........29184
North Anderson, Sta.
  Anderson......................29621
North Augusta (1st)............29841
  Beech Island, R. Br........29842
  Belvedere, Br................29841
North Charleston, Br.
  Charleston....................29406
North Myrtle Beach (1st)......29582
Northbridge, Sta. Charleston....29407
Norway.............................29113
Oakley.............................29466
Oakway, R. Br. Westminster....29694
Olanta..............................29114
Olar.................................29843
Ora.................................29371
Orangeburg (1st)...............29115
Osborn, R. Br. Adams Run....29426
Oswego............................29121
Overbrook, Sta. Greenville....29601
Owings, R. Br. Gray Court....29668
Pacolet.............................29372
Pacolet Mills......................29373
Pageland..........................29728
Palmetto Plaza, Sta. Sumter....29150
Pamplico...........................29583
Paris, Br. Taylors................29687
Park Place, Br. Greenville
  (see appendix)
Parksville..........................29844
Parr, R. Br. Jenkinsville.......29066
Parris Island, Br. Beaufort....29905
Patrick.............................29584
Pauline.............................29374
Pawleys Island...................29585
Paxville, R. Br. Manning......29102
Peak................................29122
Peedee.............................29586
Pelham, R. Br. Greer...........29651
Pelion..............................29123
Pelzer..............................29669
Pendleton..........................29670

Perry 29124
Pickens (1st) 29671
Piedmont 29673
Pierpont, R. Br. Charleston 29407
Pineland 29934
Pineville 29468
Pinewood 29125
Pinopolis 29469
Plantersville, R. Br.
  Georgetown 29441
Plum Branch 29845
Pomaria 29126
Port Royal 29935
Poston 29588
Princeton, R. Br. Honea
  Path 29674
Prosperity 29127
Quinby, R. Br. Florence 29501
Rains 29589
Ravenel 29470
Reevesville 29471
Reidville 29375
Rembert 29128
  Borden, R. Br. 29017
Richburg 29729
Richland 29675
Ridge Spring 29129
Ridgeland (1st) 29936
  Coosawhatchie, R. Br. 29912
  Switzerland, R. Br. 29942
Ridgeville 29472
Ridgeway 29130
Rimini 29131
Rion 29132
Riter 29473
Riverland Terrace, R. Br.
  Charleston 29407
Rivers Annex, Br.
  Charleston 29411
Rock Hill (1st) 29730
  Cherry Road, Sta. 29730
  Lesslie, R. Br. 29734
  Winthrop College, Sta. 29730
Rodman 29740
Roebuck 29376
Round O 29474
Rowesville 29133
Ruby 29741
Ruffin 29475
Russellville 29476
Saint Andrews, Br.
  Charleston 29407
Saint Charles 29134
Saint George (1st) 29477
Saint Matthews 29135
Saint Stephen 29479
Salem 29676
Salley 29137
Salters 29590
Saluda 29138
Saluda Gardens, Br. West
  Columbia 29169
Sandy Springs 29677
Sans Souci, Sta. Greenville 29609
Santee 29142
Sardinia, R. Br. Gable 29143
Scotia, R. Br. Estill 29939
Scranton 29591
Seabrook 29940
  Dale, R. Br. 29914
Sellers 29592
Seneca (1st) 29678
Shandon, Sta. Columbia 29205

Sharon 29742
Shaw A F B, Br. Sumter 29152
Sheldon 29941
Shelton 29144
Shoals Junction 29680
Shulerville 29480
Silverstreet 29145
Simpsonville (1st) 29681
Six Mile 29682
Slater 29683
Smoaks 29481
Smyrna 29743
Society Hill 29593
South, Br. Anderson 29621
South Greenwood, Sta.
  Greenwood 29646
South Of The Border, R. Br.
  Hamer 29547
South Windermere, Sta.
  Charleston 29407
Southern Shops, Br.
  Spartanburg 29303
SPARTANBURG (1st) (see
  appendix)
Springdale, Br. West
  Columbia 29169
Springfield 29146
Starr 29684
Startex 29377
State College, Sta.
  Orangeburg 29115
State Park 29147
Stuckey, R. Br. Hemingway 29554
Sullivans Island 29482
Summerton 29148
Summerville (1st) 29483
Sumter (1st) 29150
  Broad Street, Sta. 29150
  Highway Four Forty One,
    R. Br. 29150
  Palmetto Plaza, Sta. 29150
  Shaw A F B, Br. 29152
Sunset 29685
Surfside Beach, Br. Myrtle
  Beach 29577
Swansea 29160
Switzerland, R. Br.
  Ridgeland 29942
Sycamore 29846
Tamassee 29686
Tatum 29594
Taylors (1st) 29687
Tigerville 29688
Tillman 29943
Timmonsville 29161
Townville 29689
Travelers Rest 29690
Trenton 29847
Trio 29595
Troy 29848
Turbeville 29162
Ulmer 29849
Una 29378
Union (1st) 29379
  Adamsburg, R. Br. 29380
University, Sta. Columbia 29208
Valley Falls, R. Br.
  Spartanburg 29303
Van Wyck 29744
Vance 29163
Varnville 29944

Vaucluse 29850
Wade Hampton, Sta.
  Greenville 29607
Wadmalaw Island 29487
Wagener 29164
Walhalla (1st) 29691
Wallace 29596
Walterboro (1st) 29488
Wando 29492
Ward 29166
Ware Shoals (1st) 29692
Warrenville 29851
Waterloo 29384
Wedgefield 29168
Wellford 29385
Wesleyan, R. Br. Central 29630
West Columbia (1st) 29169
West Florence, Sta. Florence 29501
West Pelzer, Sta. Pelzer 29669
West Union 29696
Westminster (1st) 29693
  Oakway, R. Br. 29694
Westville 29175
Whipper Barony, Br.
  Charleston 29405
White Oak 29176
White Pond, R. Br. Williston 29854
White Rock 29177
White Stone 29386
Whitmire 29178
Whitney, Br. Spartanburg 29303
Williams 29493
Williamston 29697
Willington 29852
Williston 29853
  White Pond, R. Br. 29854
Wilson 29179
Windsor 29856
Windy Hill Beach, Sta. North
  Myrtle Beach 29582
Winnsboro (1st) 29180
Winthrop College, Sta. Rock
  Hill 29730
Wisacky 29183
Woodford, R. Br. North 29184
Woodruff (1st) 29388
Yemassee 29945
Yonges Island 29494
York (1st) 29745

CHARLESTON 294

POST OFFICE BOXES

Box Nos.
A-Z	Main Office	02
1-1137	Main Office	02
2000-2999	A Sta	03
3000-3999	St Andrews Br.	07
4000-4999	Charleston Heights Br.	05
5000-5999	North Charleston Br.	06
6000-6999	Myers Br.	05
7000-7999	Charleston Heights Br.	05
9000-9999	Hanahan Br.	10
10000-10999	Rivers Annex Br	11
12000-12999	James Island Br	12

RURAL ROUTES

1	12
2,3	05
4	07
5	12
6	06
7,8,9,10,11	05
12	12
13,14	07
15,16	05
17	12
18	05

STATIONS, BRANCHES AND UNITS

Baptist College Rural Br	11
Charleston A F B Br	04
Charleston Heights Br	05
Citadel Sta	09
Dorchester-Waylyn Br	05
Dupont Br	07
Hampton Park Terrace Sta	03
Hanahan Br	10
James Island Br	07
Myers Br	05
Naval Base Br	08
North Charleston Br	06
Northbridge Sta	07
Pierpont Rural Br	07
Riverland Terrace Rural Br	07
Rivers Annex Br	11
Saint Andrews Br	07
South Windermere Sta	07
Whipper Barony Br	05
General Delivery	01
Postmaster	01

APARTMENTS, HOTELS, MOTELS

Ashley Arms, 1551 Ashley River Rd	07
Ashley House, Lockwood Blvd	01
Ashley Shores, Accabee Rd	05
Ben Tillman Homes, Charleston Hts	05
Berkeley, 63 Rutledge Ave	01
Carlton Arms, 59 Vanderhorst	03
Caroline, 148 Rutledge Ave	03

Charleston Arms, 1551 Hwy 7	07
Chicco Apts, 37 John St, 349 Meeting	03
Courtenay Doughty	03
Daniel Jenkins Homes, Charleston Hts	05
Darlington, 2106 Mount Pleasant	03
Dorchester Gardens, 5600 Dorchester Rd	05
Enston Homes, 900 King	03
Frewil, Vanderhorst & Smith	03
George Legare Homes, Charleston Hts	05
Governor Yeamans, Sedgefield Dr	06
John C Calhoun Homes, North Charleston	06
Kiawah Homes, Rutledge Ave & Mount Pleasant	03
Liberty Homes, North Charleston	06
Marlboro, 140 Queen	01
Murray, 20 Ehrhardt & 112 Doughty	03
Plantation, 1840 Carriage Ln.	07
Riverbend, 864 S Colony Dr	07
Rivercrest, 54 10th Ave	03
Riviera, Old Point Rd	06
Saint Angela, 173 Rutledge Ave	03
Saint Charles, 1085 King	03
Saint James, 193 Congress	03
Saint Regis, 17 8th Ave	03
Sergeant Jasper, West End Broad	01
The Palms, Royal Palm Blvd	07
Tomrad, 24 Thomas	03
Woodmere, 1735 Ashley Hall Rd	07

BUILDINGS

Federal, 334 Meeting	03
Fireproof, Meeting At Chalmers	01
Peoples Office, 18 Broad	01

GOVERNMENT OFFICES

City Hall, 80 Broad	01
Federal Building, 334 Meeting	03
Post Office, 81-83 Broad	01
U S Customs House, 200 E Bay	01

HOSPITALS

Alumni Memorial House, 45 Courtenay Dr	01
Baker Memorial, 55 Ashley Ave	01
Carolina Nursing Center, 341 Calhoun	01
Charles Webb Rehabilitation Center, 325 Calhoun	01
Charleston County Health Dept, 334 Calhoun	01
Easter Seal Orthopedic	

School, 325 Calhoun	01
Mc Clennon Banks, 25 Courtenay Dr	01
Medical Arts, 65 Gadsden	01
Medical College Nurses Home, 75 Doughty	01
Medical College, 55 Doughty	01
Riverside Geriatric & Convalescent Center, 295 Calhoun	01
Roper, 316 Calhoun	01
Saint Francis Nurses, 150 Ashley Ave	01
Saint Francis Xavier 135 Rutledge Ave	01
Veterans Administration, 109 Bee	03

MILITARY INSTALLATIONS

Atlantic Fleet, Naval Base	08
Charleston Air Force Base	04
Charleston Army Depot	06
Charleston Naval Shipyard	08
Commandant Sixth Naval District	08
M E N - R I V Park	08
Marine Barracks	08
Mineforce U S Atlantic Fleet	08
Naval Hospital	08
Naval Housing, Hunley Park	04
Naval Weapons Station	08
Polaris Missile Facilities Atlantic	08
U S Coast Guard Tradd	01
U S Naval Station	08

UNIVERSITIES AND COLLEGES

Ashley Hall School, 172 Rutledge Ave	03
Baptist College At Charleston, U S Hwy 78 At 1-26	11
College Of Charleston, 66 George	01
Medical University Of S C 80 Barre St	01
Palmer College, 125 Bull	01
Porter-Gaud School, Albemarle Rd	07
Technical Education Center, 7000 Rivers Ave	05
The Citadel	09

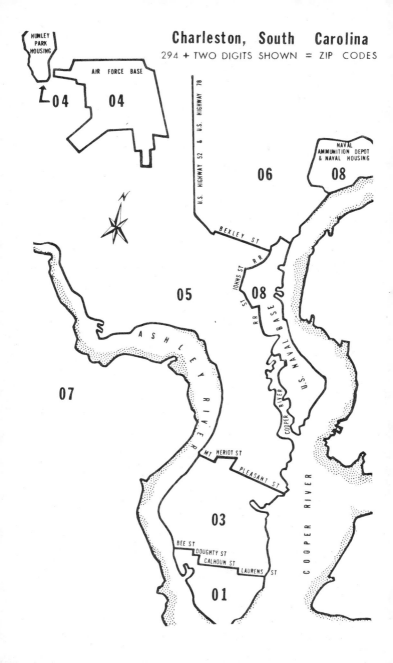

COLUMBIA 292

POST OFFICE BOXES

Box Nos.
1-1999	Columbia	02
3000-3999	Eau Claire Sta.	03
4000-4999	Edgewood Sta	40
5000-5999	Five Points Sta	05
6000-6999	Forest Acres Br	60
9000-9999	Leesburg Br	09
11000-12999	Capitol Sta	11
13000-13999	Market Center Br	01

RURAL ROUTES

1	03
2	10
3	06
4	09
5	03

STATIONS, BRANCHES AND UNITS

Capitol Sta	11
Cedar Terrace Sta	09
Dentsville Br	04
Dutch Fork Br	10
Eau Claire Sta	03
Edgewood Sta	04
Farrow Road Br	03
Five Points Sta	05
Forest Acres Br	06
Fort Jackson Sta	07
Greenview Br	03
Leesburg Br	01
Market Center Br	05
Shandon Sta	05
University Sta	08
General Delivery	01
Postmaster	01

APARTMENTS, HOTELS, MOTELS

Allen-Benedict Court, 1810 Court Plaza	04
Barkoot Apts, 2637 River Drive	01
Barkoot Apts, 3027 Belt Line Blvd	04
Becks Motor Court, 4345 Fort Jackson Blvd	05
Bloomwood Apts, 4426 Blossom Street	05
Camelot-In-The-Hills Apts, 3431 Covenant Rd	04
Capitol Terrace Motor, 1001 Assembly	02
Carnaby Square Apts Garner Ln	10
Carolina Gardens, 101 Pickens	05
Carolina Motel, 2709 Two Notch Rd	04
Carriage Hill Apartments, 5225 Clemson Ave	06
Charles Edwards Apartments, 2 Cibbes Ct	01
Chat N Rest Motel, 1608 Two Notch Rd	04

Chateau Deville Apartments, Chateau Dr	04
Christine Apartments, 927 Daly St	05
Claire Towers Apartments, 1041 Marion	01
Colony Forest Apartments, 3600 W Belt Line Blvd	03
Columbia Gardens, Plowden Road	05
Columbia Motor Court, 3315 Two Notch Rd	04
Cornell Arms Apartments, 1230 Pendleton	01
Coronet Motel, 6320 Main	03
Crescent Manor Apts 1700 Carnegie St	04
Davis & Apartments, 1728 Sumter	01
Davis Apartments, 1728 Sumter	01
Davis Apartments, 1728 Sumter	01
Davis, 1712 Sumter St	02
Downtowner Motor Inn, 1301 Main	02
Durham Apartments, 931 Daly	05
Edisto Apartments, 526 Edisto Ave	05
Edisto Apartments, 611 Waccamaw Ave	05
Elmtree Village, Elmtree Rd & Fairmont Dr	09
Forest Motel, 3111 Two Notch Rd	04
Forest Terrace Apartments, 2000 Belt Line Blvd	04
Glass Manor Motel, 5810 Wilson Blvd	03
Gonzales Gardens, 1505 Garden Plaza	04
Grand Motel, 3003 Two Notch Rd	04
Hall Court Apartments, 2318 Lee	05
Hall Court Apartments, 719 Meadow	05
Hampton Park Apartments, 4427 Blossom	05
Heart Of Columbia Motel, 1011 Assembly	02
Heathwood Court Apts 4100 Stevens Rd	05
Heathwood Court Apts, 4103 Devine	05
Heathwood Court Apts, 700 Pointsettia	05
Hendley Homes, 501 S Bull	05
Highland Park Apartments, 3800 W Ave	03
Hotel Desoto, 1108 Lady St	01
Hunters Motor Court, 2322 Two Notch Rd	04
Jaggers Terrace, 2009 Jaggers Plaza	04
Jamestown Apartments, Bethel Church Road	06
Keenan Apartments, 1208 Elmwood Ave	01
King Cotton Motel, 3211 Two Notch Rd	04

King Court Apartments, 1400 King	05
Lakeshore Apartments, 5625 Percival Road	06
Lamplighter Apartments, 1730 Windover Rd	04
Latimer Manor	03
Matador Motor Inn, 922 Bush River Rd	10
Myron Manor Apartments, 4500 Fort Jackson Blvd	09
New York Avenue Apartments, 2400 Waites Rd	04
Oak-Read, 221 Read	04
Orleans Plaza, 1707 S Belt Line Blvd	05
Orvin Court, 821 Assembly	01
Paddington Apartments, 3700 West Ave	03
Palm Apartments, 5800 Percival Road	06
Palmetto Terrace Apartments, 2000 Sligh Ave	03
Plantation Oaks, 3206 Fernandina Rd	10
Quail Run Apts, 6101 Quail Run Dr	06
Ravenwood Apartments, 4200 Bethel Church Road	06
Regency Square Apartments, 2050 Beltline Blvd	04
Roosevelt Village	03
Rutledge Forest Apts, 3600 Falling Springs Rd	03
Saxon Homes, 2124 Saxon Plaza	04
Senate Plaza, 1520 Senate St	01
Sheraton Inn, 610 Assembly St	01
Singley Apartments, 1616 Green	01
Singley Apartments, 732 Pickens	01
The Hampton House Apartments, 1800 Senate St	01
Thoroughbred Motel, 3411 Two Notch Rd	04
Town House Motel Incorporated, 1619 Gervais	02
Villager Apts, Burnside Drive	09
Wade Hampton, 1201 Main St	02
Washington Carver Village, 3530 Colony Forest Dr	03
Willow Lakes Apts, 5315 Fairfield Rd	03
Wit-Mary Apartments, 1018 Marion	01
Woodland Terrace Apartments, 300 S Belt Line Blvd	05
Woodland Village Apts, 2400 Bush River Rd	10
Woodmere Apartments, 18 Berryhill Rd	10

BUILDINGS

Arcade, 1332 Main............... 01
Baker Bldg, 1616 Hampton
St............................... 01
Barringer, 1338 Main........... 01
City Schools Administration,
1616 Richland............... 01
Columbia, 1203 Gerrais........ 01
County Agricultural, 1508
Washington................. 01
Crawford, 1213 Lady St........ 01
Creason, 1247 Sumter.......... 01
Federal Land Bank, 1401
Hampton..................... 01
Federal Office, 901 Sumter.... 01
First National Bank, 1210
Washington................. 01
Greystone Industrial Park,.... 10
Insurance, 1300 Pickens....... 01
J. Marion Sims Bldg, 2600
Bull St........................ 01
Jefferson Square 1801 Main... 01
John C Calhoun Office, 1228
Senate........................ 01
Klondike, 1813 Main St........ 01
Methodist, 1420 Lady........... 01
Middleburg Office Mall......... 04
Owens, 1321 Lady............... 01
Palmetto State Life, 1310
Lady.......................... 01
Palmetto, 1400 Main........... 01
Richland County Library,
1400 Sumter................ 01
Ritz, 1325 Main................. 01
Rutledge Building.............. 01
Security Federal, 1231
Washington................. 01
Singley, 1215 Lady St.......... 01
South Carolina National Bank
Center 1122 Lady........... 01
South Carolina National
Bank, 1401 Main............ 01
South Carolina National
Bank, 900 Assembly St..... 01
State House...................... 01
Universal, 1725 Sumter........ 01
Varo, 1801 Assembly St........ 01
Wade Hampton Office Bldg.... 01
Y. M. C. A., 1420 Sumter St... 01

GOVERNMENT OFFICES

City Hall, 1737 Main............ 01
Richland County Court
House, 1401 Sumter......... 01
United States Courthouse,
1100 Laurel................. 01

HOSPITALS

Baptist Hospital, 1330 Taylor
St............................. 01
Good Samaritan-Waverly
Hospital, 2202 Hampton
St............................. 04
Providence Hospital, 2435
Forest Dr.................... 04
Richland Memorial Hospital... 03
S. C. State Hospital............ 02
Veterans Hospital.............. 01

Fonta Vis........................ 04
Fontaine Rd..................... 04
Fontana Dr...................... 09
Ford............................. 03
Forest Dr
2400-4199................... 04
4200-5799................... 06
Forest Ridge Ln................. 06
Forestwood Dr.................. 06
Formosa Dr..................... 06
Forsyth.......................... 01
Fort Jackson Blvd
4300-4399................... 05
4400-OUT.................... 09
Foster........................... 03

GREENVILLE   296

POST OFFICE BOXES

Box Nos
A-V   Branwood Sta.. 10
1-3135   Main Office 02
3501-4387   Park Place Br... 08
5001-7015   B Sta............. 06
7051-7999   Branwood Sta.. 10
8001-9044   A Sta............. 04
10001-10396 Federal Sta...... 03

RURAL ROUTES

1................................ 11
2................................ 07
3................................ 09
4................................ 05
5................................ 07
6................................ 07
7................................ 09
8................................ 11
9................................ 09
10............................... 11
11............................... 11

STATIONS, BRANCHES AND UNITS

Berea Br........................ 01
Bob Jones University Sta...... 14
Branwood Sta................... 10
City View Br.................... 11
Donaldson Br................... 05
Federal Sta..................... 03
Furman University Br......... 13
New Easley Highway Br....... 11
Overbrook Sta.................. 01
Park Place Br................... 08
Sans Souci Sta.................. 09
Wade Hampton Sta............. 07
General Delivery............... 02
Postmaster...................... 02

APARTMENTS, HOTELS, MOTELS

Balfer Court Apts, Balfer Dr... 07
Botany Arms, 510 Edwards
Rd........................... 07
Calhoun Towers, 415 N Main.. 01
Carmil Court Apts, 38
Southland Ave.............. 01
Cedar Lane Apts. Columbia
Ave.......................... 11
City Heights Apts. Off
Furman Rd................... 09
Club Key East Apts.
Cleveland Street............ 01

Colony House, Glenwood Rd.... 07
Continental Apts, Glenwood
Rd........................... 07
Court Plaza Apts................ 01
Courtland, 504-92 E Faris
Rd........................... 05
Crestview Apts, Shaw........... 09
Davenport, 400 E
Washington................. 01
East North Court Apts. East
North St. Ext................ 07
Fieldcrest Village, Greenacre
Rd........................... 07
Franklin Court Apts. North
Franklin Rd................. 09
Fredricksburg Apts, Galphin
Dr........................... 09
Glenwood Terrace Apts,
Glenwood Rd................ 07
Hampton Arms Apts, Wade
Hampton Blvd............... 07
Hampton Trace Apts. Wade
Hampton Blvd............... 07
Hillandale Apts................. 09
Kingston Court, Monroe &
Huff......................... 01
Lakeshore Apts. Off Int. 85.... 11
Lane Apts. Lane Ave........... 07
Lavista Villa Apts. Villa View
Dr........................... 09
Lewis Village, Lewis Village... 05
Lullwater Apts. Kadena Pl..... 07
Maryland, 801 E North......... 01
Mc Daniel Heights, Mc Daniel
Heights...................... 01
Mcdaniel Place Apts. 200
Mcdaniel Ave................ 01
Middleton Apts, W Earl........ 09
Mountain View Homes, Perry
Ave.......................... 11
Northway Apts. 3800 East
North St. Ext................ 07
Oak Creek Court Apts.......... 07
Orleans Court Apts, E. North
St............................ 07
Park Heights, 606 University
Ridge........................ 01
Pearce Homes. Hanson Pl...... 07
Pelham East, Pelham Rd....... 07
Piedmont Manor Shemwood
Ln........................... 05
Pinecrest Apts. Eugene St..... 09
Plaza, 100 E Lewis Plaza....... 05
Poinsett, 400 Summit Dr....... 09
River Bend Apts. Cleveland.... 01
Roosevelt Heights, Roosevelt.. 07
Rutherford Court Apts.
Greenbriar St................ 09
Sans Souci Apts. Buncombe
Rd........................... 09
Town Park Apts. E. North St.
Ext.......................... 07
Trianon Village Apts........... 09
University Ridge, University
Ridge........................ 01
Villa Apts. Villa Rd............ 07
Virginia, 10 Manley............ 01
Westgate Manor Lilly........... 11
Wildaire Apts. Rushmore Dr... 07
Williamsburg Manor, Edwards
Rd........................... 07
Windsor, 3701 Buncombe Rd... 09
Woodland Homes, Pearce

Ave 07
Yorktown, Pelham Rd 07

BUILDINGS

Chamber Of Commerce, 19 S
  Irvine 01
County Court House, 309 E
  North 01
County Office, 130 S Main 01
Daniel, 301 N Main 02
Doctor'S, 12 S Calhoun 01
Federal, 300 E Washington 03
Greenville City Hall, 214 S
  Main 02
Greenville Medical Ctr, 24
  Vardry 01
I B M, 200 E Camperdown
  Way 01
Insurance, 135 S Main 01
Lawyers, 301 E North 01
Medical Court, 811
  Pendleton 01
South Carolina National
  Bank, 13 S Main 01
Stokes, 314 E Coffee 01
Stone Avenue, 209 E Stone
  Ave 09
Two Fifty Two, 252 S
  Pleasantburg Dr 07
United, 217 E Stone Ave 09
Vardry Medical Court, 413
  Vardry 01

HOSPITALS

Greenville General, 100
  Mallard 02
Marshall I. Pickens Hospital,
  Grove Rd 05
Roger C Peace Hospital
  Grove Rd 05
Saint Francis, 400 Sumner 02
Shriners, 2100 N
  Pleasantburg Dr 09
Wm G Sirrine Hospital, 1200
  Pendleton 11

UNIVERSITIES AND COLLEGES

Bob Jones University Wade
  Hampton Blvd 14
Furman University Poinsett
  Hwy 13
Greenville Tech Educational
  Center S Pleasantburg Dr .. 06
Holmes Theological Seminary
  115 Briggs Ave 01

SPARTANBURG   293

POST OFFICE BOXES

Box Nos.
1-1999   Main Office 01
2000-3999   Kennedy Street
                Sta 02
4000-4999   B Sta 03
5000-6052   Main Office 01

RURAL ROUTES

1,2 02
3 01
4 02
5 01
6,7,8 03
9 01
11 02
110 03

STATIONS, BRANCHES AND UNITS

Boiling Springs Rural Br 03
Cedar Spring Br 03
Kennedy Street Sta 02
Southern Shops Br 03
Valley Falls Rural Br 03
Whitney Br 03
General Delivery 01
Postmaster 01

APARTMENTS, HOTELS, MOTELS

Abbie, Morningside Dr 01
Archibald Rutledge Apts,
  Centennial St 03
Brockwood Terrace Apts 01
Cabana Inn, 462 E Main 02
Cleveland, 178 W Main 01
Crystal Springs, Woodburn
  Rd 02
Franklin, 186 E Main 01
Georgetown Village Apts,
  1421 Reidville Rd 01
Heart Of Spartanburg, 578 N
  Church 03
Highland Court, 144 W
  Henry 01
Highland Homes, 100
  Highland 01
Holiday Inn, I-85 03
Howard Aden, 630 Howard 03
Howard Johnson, I-85 01
Hub City Courts, Vanderbilt
  Rd 01
Main Street Motel, 700 W
  Main 01
Morgan, 277 Magnolia 01
Northside Apts, Fremont &
  Howard Sts 03
Peach Blossom, I-85 03
Phyllis, Goins Court, Collins
  Ave 01
Pine Street, 150 Pine 02
Ramada Inn 03
Richmond, 225 E Main 01
Schuyler, 269 S Church 01
Travel-Lodge, 416 E Main 02
Woodworth Homes, Baltimore . 01

BUILDINGS

Andrews, 116 Morgan Sq 01
City Hall, 145 W Broad 01
County, 188 Magnolia 01
Federal, 201 Magnolia 01
Medical, 711 N Church 03
Montgomery, 187 N Church ... 01
National Beta, 458 N Church ... 01
News, Herald, 177 W Main 01
Schuyler Office, 296 S

Church 01
U S District Court, 201
  Magnolia 01

HOSPITALS

Mary Black, 1700 Skylyn Dr ... 02
Spartanburg General 101 E
  Wood 03

UNIVERSITIES AND COLLEGES

Converse, 580 E Main 01
Spartanburg Junior, Textile
  Rd 01
Wofford, 429 N Church 01

SOUTH DAKOTA
(Abbreviation: SD)

Aberdeen (1st)	57401
Putney, R. Br.	57402
Academy	57310
Agar	57520
Akaska	57420
Albee	57210
Alcester	57001
Alexandria	57311
Allen	57714
Alpena	57312
Altamont	57211
Amherst	57421
Andover	57422
Ardmore	57715
Arlington	57212
Armour	57313
Artas	57423
Artesian	57314
Ashton	57424
Astoria	57213
Athol	57425
Aurora	57002
Avon	57315
Badger	57214
Baltic	57003
Bancroft	57316
Barnard	57426
Batesland	57716
Bath	57427
Belle Fourche (1st)	57717
Belvidere	57521
Bemis	57215
Beresford	57004
Bethlehem, R. Br. Rapid City	57708
Big Stone City	57216
Bison	57620
Sorum, R. Br.	57654
Black Hawk	57718
Blunt	57522
Bonesteel	57317
Bonilla	57318
Bowdle	57428
Box Elder	57719
Bradley	57217
Brandon	57005
Brandt	57218
Brentford	57429
Bridgewater	57319
Bristol	57219
Britton	57430
Brookings (1st)	57006
Bruce	57220
Bryant	57221
Buffalo	57720
Ladner, R. Br.	57753
Buffalo Gap	57722
Bullhead	57621
Burbank	57010
Burke	57523
Bushnell	57011
Butler	57222
Camp Crook	57724
Canistota	57012
Canning	57524
Canova	57321
Canton	57013
Capa	57525
Caputa	57725
Carpenter	57322

Carter	57526
Carthage	57323
Castle Rock	57726
Castlewood	57223
Cavour	57324
Cedarbutte	57521
Centerville	57014
Central City	57727
Chamberlain (1st)	57325
Chancellor	57015
Chelsea	57431
Cherry Creek, R. Br. Dupree	57622
Chester	57016
Claire City	57224
Claremont	57432
Clark	57225
Clear Lake	57226
Clearfield, R. Br. Winner	57581
Colman	57017
Colome	57528
Colton	57018
Columbia	57433
Commerce, Sta. Sioux Falls	57102
Conde	57434
Corona	57227
Corsica	57328
Corson	57019
Cottonwood	57728
Crandall	57228
Crazy Horse, R. Br. Custer	57730
Creighton	57729
Cresbard	57435
Crocker	57229
Crooks	57020
Custer	57730
Dallas	57529
Dante	57329
Davis	57021
De Smet	57231
Deadwood (1st)	57732
Dell Rapids	57022
Delmont	57330
Dempster	57230
Denby	57733
Dimock	57331
Dixon	57530
Doland	57436
Dolton	57023
Draper	57531
Dupree	57623
Cherry Creek, R. Br.	57622
Eagle Butte	57625
Eden	57232
Edgemont	57735
Egan	57024
Elk Point	57025
Elkton	57026
Ellsworth A F B, Br. Rapid City	57706
Elm Springs	57736
Emery	57332
Enning	57737
Erwin	57233
Esmond	57333
Estelline	57234
Ethan	57334
Eureka	57437
Fairburn	57738
Fairfax	57335
Fairpoint, R. Br. Sturgis	57739
Fairview	57027
Faith	57626
Maurine, R. Br.	57627

Farmer	57336
Farmingdale	57740
Faulkton	57438
Fedora	57337
Ferney	57439
Firesteel	57628
Flandreau	57028
Florence	57235
Forestburg	57338
Fort Meade	57741
Fort Pierre	57532
Fort Thompson	57339
Frankfort	57440
Frederick	57441
Freeman	57029
Fruitdale	57742
Fulton	57340
Gannvalley	57341
Garden City	57236
Garretson	57030
Gary	57237
Gayville	57031
Geddes	57342
Gettysburg	57442
Glad Valley	57629
Glencross	57630
Glenham	57631
Goodwin	57238
Greenway	57444
Gregory	57533
Granville	57239
Groton	57445
Hamill	57534
Hammer	57240
Harrington	57535
Harrisburg	57032
Harrison	57344
Harrold	57536
Hartford	57033
Hayes	57537
Hayti	57241
Hazel	57242
Hecla	57446
Henry	57243
Hereford	57743
Hermosa	57744
Herreid	57632
Herrick	57538
Hetland	57244
Highmore	57345
Stephan, R. Br.	57346
Hill City	57745
Hisle	57539
Hitchcock	57348
Holabird	57540
Hoover	57746
Hosmer	57448
Hot Springs (1st)	57747
Houghton	57449
Hoven	57450
Howard	57349
Howes	57748
Hudson	57034
Humboldt	57035
Hurley	57036
Huron (1st)	57350
Ideal	57541
Interior	57750
Iona	57542
Ipswich	57451
Irene	57037
Iroquois	57353
Isabel	57633

Java 57452
Jefferson 57038
Kadoka 57543
Kaylor 57354
Keldron 57634
Kenel, R. Br. Mc Laughlin 57642
Kennebec 57544
Keyapaha 57545
Keystone 57751
Kidder 57453
Kimball 57355
Kirley 57546
Kranzburg 57245
Kyle 57752
La Bolt 57246
La Plant 57637
Ladner, R. Br. Buffalo 57753
Lake Andes 57356
   Ravinia, R. Br. 57357
Lake City 57247
Lake Norden 57248
Lake Preston 57249
Lane 57358
Langford 57454
Lantry 57636
Lead (1st) 57754
Lebanon 57455
Lemmon 57638
   Shadehill, R. Br. 57653
   Thunder Hawk, R. Br. 57655
Lennox 57039
Leola 57456
Lesterville 57040
Letcher 57359
Lily 57250
Little Eagle 57639
Lodgepole 57640
Longlake 57457
Longvalley 57547
Loomis 57360
Lower Brule 57548
Lowry 57458
Loyalton 57459
Lucas 57549
Ludlow 57755
Lyons 57041
Madison (1st) 57042
Mahto, R. Br. Mc Laughlin 57643
Manderson 57756
Mansfield 57460
Marcus 57757
Marion 57043
   Monroe, R. Br. 57047
Martin 57551
   Vetal, R. Br. 57575
Marty 57361
Marvin 57251
Maurine, R. Br. Faith 57627
Mc Intosh 57641
Mc Laughlin 57642
   Kenel, R. Br. 57642
   Mahto, R. Br. 57643
Meadow 57644
Meckling 57044
Mellette 57461
Menno 57045
Midland 57552
Milbank (1st) 57252
Milesville 57553
Millboro 57554
Miller 57362
Mina 57462
Miranda 57463

Mission 57555
Mission Hill 57046
Mission Ridge 57557
Mitchell (1st) 57301
Mobridge (1st) 57601
Monroe, R. Br. Marion 57047
Montrose 57048
Morristown 57645
Mosher 57558
Mound City 57646
Mount Vernon 57363
Mud Butte 57758
Murdo 57559
Naples 57254
Nemo 57759
New Effington 57255
New Holland 57364
New Underwood 57761
Newell 57760
Nisland 57762
Norbeck 57464
Norris 57560
North Sioux City 57049
Northville 57465
Nunda 57050
Oacoma 57365
Oelrichs 57763
Oglala 57764
Okaton 57562
Okreek 57563
Oldham 57051
Olivet 57052
Onaka 57466
Onida 57564
Opal 57765
Oral 57766
Orient 57467
Ortley 57256
Ottumwa 57563
Owanka 57767
Parade 57647
Parker 57053
Parkston 57366
Parmelee 57566
Peever 57257
Philip 57567
Pickstown 57367
Piedmont 57769
Pierpont 57468
Pierre (1st) 57501
Pine Ridge 57770
Plainview 57771
Plankinton 57368
Platte 57369
Pollock 57648
Porcupine 57772
Prairie City 57649
Presho 57568
Pringle 57773
Provo 57774
Pukwana 57370
Putney, R. Br. Aberdeen 57402
Quinn 57775
Ralph 57650
Ramona 57054
Rapid City (1st) 57701
   Bethlehem, R. Br. 57708
   Ellsworth A F B, Br. 57706
   Rockerville, R. Br. 57701
   Silver City, R. Br. 57781
Ravinia, R. Br. Lake Andes 57357
Raymond 57258
Redfield (1st) 57469

Redig 57776
Redowl 57777
Ree Heights 57371
Reliance 57569
Renner 57055
Reva 57651
Revillo 57259
Ridgeview 57652
Rochford 57778
Rockerville, R. Br. Rapid
   City 57701
Rockham 57470
Roscoe 57471
Rosebud 57570
Rosholt 57260
   White Rock, R. Br. 57277
Roslyn 57261
Roswell 57372
Rowena, R. Br. Sioux Falls 57056
Rutland 57057
Saint Charles 57571
Saint Francis 57572
Saint Lawrence 57373
Saint Onge 57779
Salem 57058
Scenic 57780
Scotland 57059
Selby 57472
Seneca 57473
Shadehill, R. Br. Lemmon 57653
Sherman 57060
Silver City, R. Br. Rapid
   City 57781
Sinai 57061
SIOUX FALLS (1st) (see
   appendix)
Sisseton (1st) 57262
Sky Ranch, R. Br. Camp
   Crook 57724
Smithwick 57782
Sorum, R. Br. Bison 57654
South Shore 57263
Spearfish (1st) 57783
Spencer 57374
Springfield 57062
Stephan, R. Br. Highmore 57346
Stickney 57375
Stockholm 57264
Stoneville, R. Br. Sturgis 57784
Strandburg 57265
Stratford 57474
Sturgis (1st) 57785
   Fairpoint, R. Br. 57739
   Stoneville, R. Br. 57784
Summit 57266
Tabor 57063
Tea 57064
Tekakwitha, R. Br. Sisseton 57262
Terraville 57786
Thunder Hawk, R. Br.
   Lemmon 57655
Timber Lake 57656
Tolstoy 57475
Toronto 57268
Trail City 57657
Trent 57065
Tripp 57376
Tulare 57476
Turton 57477
Tuthill 57574
Twin Brooks 57269
Tyndall 57066
Union Center 57787

University, Sta. Brookings	57006	
Utica	57067	
Vale	57788	
Valley Springs	57068	
Vayland	57377	
Veblen	57270	
Verdon	57478	
Vermillion (1st)	57069	
Vetal, R. Br. Martin	57575	
Viborg	57070	
Vienna	57271	
Virgil	57379	
Vivian	57576	
Volga	57071	
Volin	57072	
Wagner	57380	
Wakonda	57073	
Wakpala	57658	
Walker	57659	
Wall	57790	
Wallace	57272	

Wanblee	57577
Ward	57074
Warner	57479
Wasta	57791
Watauga	57660
Watertown (1st)	57201
Waverly, R. Br.	57202
Waubay	57273
Waverly, R. Br. Watertown	57202
Webster	57274
Wecota	57480
Wentworth	57075
Wessington	57381
Wessington Springs	57382
Westport	57481
Wetonka	57482
Wewela	57578
White	57276
White Lake	57383
White Owl	57792
White River	57579

White Rock, R. Br. Rosholt	57277
Whitehorse	57661
Whitewood	57793
Willow Lake	57278
Wilmot	57279
Winfred	57076
Winner (1st)	57580
Clearfield, R. Br.	57581
Witten	57584
Wolsey	57384
Wood	57585
Woonsocket	57385
Worthing	57077
Wounded Knee	57794
Yale	57386
Yankton (1st)	57078
Zell	57483
Zeona	57795

SIOUX FALLS   571

POST OFFICE BOXES

Box Nos.

	Main Office	01
A-V	Main Office	01
1-1532	Main Office	01

RURAL ROUTES

1,2,3,4,5	01

STATIONS, BRANCHES AND UNITS

Commerce Sta	02
Rowena Rural Br	57056
General Delivery	01
Postmaster	01

APARTMENTS, HOTELS, MOTELS

Ace Motel, 1903 E 10th St	03
Albert, 333 N Phillips Ave	02
Blackstone, 303 W 12th	02
Brown, 401 S Phillips Ave	02
Cambridge, 100 W 17th	04
Carriage Hill Garden, 205 W 18th	05
Colonial, 301 W 21st	05
Costello, 217 S Spring Ave	04
Country Club Estates, 2501 S Kiwanis Ave	05
Delux Motel, 1712 W 12th	04
Edgewood Motel, 4730 N Cliff Ave	04
Edwards, 430 W 10th	04
Harvey Motel, 2400 E 10th	03
Henderson, 115 W 12th	02
Holiday Inn Motel, 1301 W Russell	04
Holiday Inn, Downtown, 100 W 8th	02
Howard Johnson, 3300 W Russell	07

Kenwen, 625 S Phillips Ave	04
Kenwood Manor, 2420 W 18th	04
La Salle, 703 S Summit Ave	04
Laird Hall, 1001 S Phillips Ave	05
Lincoln, 104 N Main Ave	02
Lindendale Motel, 4201 S Minnesota Ave	05
Parkview, 500-600 S Kiwanis Ave	04
Pine Crest Motel, 3601 W 12th	06
Plaza Inn Motel, 2620 E 10th	03
Ramanda Inn Motel, 2400 N Louise Ave	07
Rushmore Motel, 2500 E 10th	03
Rushs Motel, 2401 W Russell	04
Sheraton-Cataract Motor Inn, 106 W 9th	02
Sioux Chief Train Motel, 3627 W 12th	06
Smiths Motel, 1223 W 12th	04
Suburban Motel, 3010 E 10th	03
Sunset Motel, 3921 W 12th	06
Tally Ho, 309 S Conklin Ave	03
Tartan Arms, 620 S 3rd	02
Town House Motel, 415 S Phillips	02
Travelodge Motel, 809 N West Ave	04
Westwick Motel, 5801 W 12th	06
Ymca, 236 S Minnesota Ave	02
Ywca, 300 W 11th	02

BUILDINGS

Boyce Greeley, 231 S Phillips	02
First National Bank, 112 S Phillips	02

Gas Company, 114 S Main	02
Home Federal Savings & Loan, 225 S. Main	02
K Mart, 3000 S Minnesota	05
Kresge, 206 S Phillips	02
National Bank Of South Dakota, 141 N Main	02
National Reserve Bldg, 513 S Main Ave	02
Northwest Bank Bldg, 101 S Main Ave	02
Paulton, 304 S Phillips	02
Sioux Falls Stockyards	02
Western Mall, 2101 W 41st	05

GOVERNMENT OFFICES

City Hall, 230 W 9th	02
Costello Terminal	04
Federal Bldg, 400 S Phillips Ave	02
Joe Foss Field	04
Minnehaha County Courthouse, 415 N Dakota	02

HOSPITALS

Crippled Children, 2501 W 26th	05
Mc Kennan, 800 E 21st	01
Sioux Valley, 1123 S Euclid Ave	05
Veterans, 2501 W 22nd	01

UNIVERSITIES AND COLLEGES

Augustana, 29th & S Summit	02
Nettletons, 100 S. Spring Ave	01
North American Baptist Seminary, 1605 S. Euclid	05
Sioux Falls, 1501 S Prairie Ave	01

TENNESSEE
(Abbreviation: TN)

Acklen, Sta. Nashville............37212
Adams....................................37010
    Sadlersville, R. Br.............37154
Adamsville (1st)....................38310
Afton.....................................37616
Airport, Sta. Nashville...........37217
Airport Mail Facility, Sta.
    Memphis...........................38130
Airport Road, Sta.
    Chattanooga.....................37421
Alamo....................................38001
Alcoa (1st).............................37701
    Mentor, R. Br...................37808
Alexandria.............................37012
Algood, Br. Cookeville...........38501
Allardt...................................38504
Allons....................................38541
Allred....................................38542
Alpine....................................38543
Altamont................................37301
Alton Park, Sta.
    Chattanooga.....................37410
Andersonville.........................37705
Antioch..................................37013
Apison...................................37302
Ardmore................................38449
Arlington................................38002
Armathwaite..........................38506
Arnold A F B, Br. Tullahoma....37389
Arrington...............................37014
Arthur....................................37707
Ashland City (1st)..................37015
Ashport..................................38003
Athens (1st)...........................37303
Atoka.....................................38004
Atwood..................................38220
Auburntown............................37016
Baileyton, R. Br. Greeneville...37743
Bakewell, R. Br. Sale Creek....37304
Banner Springs, R. Br.
    Jamestown........................38557
Baptist, Sta. Nashville...........37203
Bartlett..................................38005
Bath Springs..........................38311
Baxter....................................38544
Bean Station..........................37708
Beech Bluff............................38313
Beechgrove............................37018
Beersheba Springs.................37305
Belfast...................................37019
Bell Buckle............................37020
Belle Meade, Br. Nashville
    (see appendix)
Bellevue.................................37021
Bells......................................38006
Belvidere...............................37306
Bemis....................................38314
Benton...................................37307
Berclair, Sta. Memphis...........38117
Bethel Springs........................38315
Bethpage...............................37022
Big Rock................................37023
Big Sandy..............................38221
Big Spring, R. Br. Decatur.......37323
Binghamton, Sta. Memphis.....38112
Birchwood..............................37308
Blaine....................................37709
Bloomingdale, Br. Kingsport....37660
Bloomington Springs...............38545
Blountville (1st).....................37617

Bluff City...............................37618
Bogota...................................38007
Bold Spring............................37024
Bolivar (1st)...........................38008
Bon Aqua...............................37025
Bone Cave.............................38546
Bordeaux, Br. Nashville..........37218
Braden...................................38010
Bradford.................................38316
Bradyville..............................37026
Brainerd, Sta. Chattanooga
    (see appendix)
Brentwood..............................37027
Briceville...............................37710
Brighton.................................38011
Bristol (1st)............................37620
Brownsville (1st)....................38012
Bruceton (1st)........................38317
Brunswick..............................38014
Brush Creek...........................38547
Buchanan...............................38222
Buena Vista...........................38318
Buffalo Valley.........................38548
Bulls Gap...............................37711
Bumpus Mills.........................38028
Buntyn, Sta. Memphis............38111
Burlington, Sta. Knoxville.......37914
Burlison.................................38015
Burns.....................................37029
Burrville.................................37712
Butler.....................................37640
Bybee....................................37713
Byrdstown..............................38549
Cades....................................38319
Calhoun..................................37309
Camden (1st).........................38320
Campaign...............................38550
Capleville, R. Br. Memphis.....38129
Carroll Reece, Sta. Johnson
    City..................................37601
Carthage (1st)........................37030
Caryville................................37714
Castalian Springs...................37031
Cedar Grove...........................38321
Cedar Hill..............................37032
Celina....................................38551
Centerville.............................37033
Cerro Gordo...........................38322
Chapel Hill............................37034
Chapmansboro........................37035
Charleston.............................37310
Charlotte...............................37036
CHATTANOOGA (1st) (see
    appendix)
Chesterfield...........................38323
Chestnut Mound.....................38552
Chewalla................................38393
Chickamauga, Sta.
    Chattanooga.....................37421
Christiana..............................37037
Chuckey................................37641
Church Hill............................37642
Clairfield...............................37715
Clarkrange.............................38553
Clarksburg.............................38324
Clarksville (1st).....................37040
Cleveland (1st).......................37311
Clifton...................................38425
Clinton (1st)...........................37716
Coalfield................................37719
Coalmont...............................37313
Cokercreek.............................37314
College, Sta. Maryville...........37801

College Grove........................37046
Collegedale (1st)....................37315
Collierville (1st)......................38017
Collinwood.............................38450
Colonial Heights, Br.
    Kingsport..........................37663
Columbia (1st)........................38401
Como.....................................38223
Conasauga..............................37316
Concord..................................37720
Cookeville (1st)......................38501
Copperhill..............................37317
Cordova.................................38018
Cornersville...........................37047
Corryton.................................37721
Cosby....................................37722
Cottage Grove........................38224
Cottontown.............................37048
Counce...................................38326
Covington (1st).......................38019
Cowan....................................37318
Crab Orchard..........................37723
Crawford................................38554
Crockett Mills........................38021
Cross Plains...........................37049
Crosstown, Sta. Memphis.......38104
Crossville (1st).......................38555
Crump....................................38327
Culleoka................................38451
Cumberland City.....................37050
Cumberland Furnace...............37051
Cumberland Gap.....................37724
Cunningham............................37052
Cypress Inn............................38452
Daisy.....................................37319
Dandridge..............................37725
Darden...................................38328
Daus......................................37320
Davis, Sta. Memphis..............38102
Davy Crockett, Sta.
    Greeneville.......................37743
Dayton (1st)...........................37321
De Soto, Sta. Memphis...........38102
Decatur..................................37322
    Big Spring, R. Br..............37323
Decaturville...........................38329
Decherd.................................37324
Deer Lodge............................37726
Del Rio..................................37727
Delano...................................37325
Dellrose.................................38453
Denmark................................38391
Denver...................................37054
Devonia.................................37728
Dickel, R. Br. Tullahoma........37388
Dickson (1st)..........................37055
Dixon Springs.........................37057
Donelson, Br. Nashville..........37214
Dover.....................................37058
Dowelltown............................37059
Downtown, Sta. Maryville.......37801
Doyle.....................................38559
Dresden.................................38225
Drummonds.............................38023
Duck River.............................38454
Ducktown...............................37326
Duff.......................................37729
Dukedom................................38226
Dunlap...................................37327
Dyer......................................38330
Dyersburg (1st).......................38024
Eads......................................38028
Eagan....................................37730

Eagleville..................................37060
East, Sta. Nashville (see appendix)
East Chattanooga, Sta. Chattanooga (see appendix)
East Lake, Sta. Chattanooga..................................37407
East Memphis, Sta. Memphis..................................38111
East Ridge, Br. Chattanooga..................................37412
Eastdale, Sta. Chattanooga....37411
Eastside, Sta. Kingsport........37664
Eaton......................................38331
Eidson....................................37731
Elbridge..................................38227
Elgin.......................................37732
Rugby, R. Br....................37733
Elizabethton (1st)..................37643
Elk Valley...............................37734
Elkton.....................................38455
Ellendale................................38029
Elmwood.................................38560
Elora......................................37328
Emory Gap..............................37735
Englewood...............................37329
English Mountain, R. Br. Sevierville..........................37862
Enville....................................38332
Erie..37736
Erin..37061
Erwin (1st).............................37650
Estes Kefauver, Sta. Johnson City..................................37601
Estill Springs..........................37330
Ethridge..................................38456
Etowah...................................37331
Eva..38333
Evensville...............................37332
Fairfield Glade, Br. Crossville...........................38555
Fairview.................................37062
Fall Branch.............................37656
Farner....................................37333
Farragut, R. Br. Concord........37720
Fayetteville (1st)....................37334
Federal Reserve, Sta. Nashville............................37203
Finger.....................................38334
Finley.....................................38030
Fisk University, Sta. Nashville............................37203
Five Points.............................38457
Flag Pond................................37657
Flat Woods..............................38458
Flintville................................37335
Forbus....................................38561
Forest Hill, R. Br. Germantown.......................38031
Fort Pillow.............................38032
Fosterville..............................37063
Fountain City, Sta. Knoxville....37918
Fowlkes..................................38033
Frankewing.............................38459
Franklin (1st).........................37064
Frayser, Sta. Memphis............38127
Friendship..............................38034
Friendsville.............................37737
Fruitland................................38335
Fruitvale.................................38336
Fulton, R. Br. Henning............38035

Gadsden..................................38337
Gainesboro..............................38562
Gallatin (1st)..........................37066
Gallaway.................................38036
Gassaway................................37070
Gates.....................................38037
Gatlinburg (1st)......................37738
George W Lee, Sta. Memphis............................38126
Georgetown.............................37336
Germantown............................38038
Forest Hill, R. Br............38031
Gibson....................................38338
Gladeville...............................37071
Gleason..................................38229
Glenmary................................37740
Goodlettsville (1st)..................37072
Goodspring..............................38460
Gordonsville............................38563
Grand Junction........................38039
Grandview...............................37337
Granville.................................38564
Graysville...............................37338
Green Brier.............................37073
Green Hills, Sta. Nashville.......37215
Greenback...............................37742
Greeneville (1st).....................37743
Greenfield...............................38230
Grimsley.................................38565
Gruetli...................................37339
Guild.....................................37340
Guys......................................38339
Halls......................................38040
Halls Crossroads, R. Br. Knoxville...........................37918
Hampshire...............................38461
Hampton.................................37658
Harriman (1st)........................37748
Harrison.................................37341
Harrogate...............................37752
Hartford.................................37753
Hartsville...............................37074
Heiskell..................................37754
Helenwood..............................37755
Henderson (1st)......................38340
Hendersonville (1st)................37075
Henning..................................38041
Fulton, R. Br....................38035
Henry.....................................38231
Henry Street, Sta. Morristown.......................37814
Hermitage...............................37076
Hickman.................................38567
Hickory Valley.........................38042
Hickory Withe..........................38043
Highland Heights, Sta. Memphis............................38122
Highland Park, Sta. Chattanooga.....................37404
Highland Plaza, Br. Chattanooga.....................37415
Highway One Hundred, Br. Nashville............................37205
Hilham....................................38568
Hilldale, Sta. Clarksville..........37040
Hillsboro.................................37342
Hiwassee College, R. Br. Madisonville......................37354
Hixson (1st)............................37343
Hohenwald..............................38462
Holiday City, Sta. Memphis.......38118
Holladay.................................38341
Hollow Rock.............................38342

Hollywood, Sta. Memphis........38108
Holtland..................................37077
Hornbeak.................................38232
Hornsby..................................38044
Howell....................................37344
Humboldt (1st)........................38343
Huntingdon (1st).....................38344
Huntland.................................37345
Huntsville...............................37756
Norma, R. Br...................37827
Huron.....................................38345
Hurricane Mills........................37078
Idlewild..................................38346
Indian Mound..........................37079
Iron City.................................38463
Isabella..................................37346
Jacks Creek.............................38347
Jacksboro................................37757
Jackson (1st)..........................38301
Jackson Square, Sta. Oak Ridge..............................37830
Jamestown...............................38556
Banner Springs, R. Br.......38557
Jasper....................................37347
Jefferson City (1st).................37760
Jellico....................................37762
Jere Baxter, Br. Nashville........37216
Joelton...................................37080
Johnson City (1st)...................37601
Jonesboro (1st).......................37659
Karns, R. Br. Knoxville............37921
Kelso......................................37348
Kenton...................................38233
Kepler, R. Br. Rogersville........37857
Kimberlin Heights, R. Br. Knoxville...........................37920
Kimmins..................................37081
KINGSPORT (1st) (see appendix)
Kingston (1st).........................37763
Kingston Springs......................37082
KNOXVILLE (1st) (see appendix)
Kodak.....................................37764
Kyles Ford...............................37765
La Follette (1st)......................37766
La Grange................................38046
La Vergne (1st).......................37086
Laager....................................37349
Laconia..................................38045
Lafayette................................37083
Lake City................................37769
Lamar, Sta. Memphis...............38114
Lancaster................................38569
Lancing..................................37770
Lane.......................................38234
Lascassas...............................37085
Laurel Bloomery......................37680
Lavinia...................................38348
Lawrenceburg (1st).................38464
Leach.....................................38349
Lebanon (1st).........................37087
Lenoir City (1st).....................37771
Lenox.....................................38047
Leoma....................................38468
Lewisburg (1st).......................37091
Lexington (1st)........................38351
Liberty...................................37095
Limestone................................37681
Linden....................................37096
Livingston (1st).......................38570
Lobelville................................37097
Lone Mountain.........................37773

Lonsdale, Sta. Knoxville	37921
Lookout Mountain (1st)	37350
Lookout Valley, Br. Chattanooga	37419
Loretto	38469
Loudon (1st)	37774
Louisville	37777
Lowland	37778
Lupton City	37351
Luray	38352
Luttrell	37779
Lutts	38471
Lyles	37098
Lynchburg	37352
Lynn Garden, Br. Kingsport	37665
Lynnville	38472
Macon	38048
Madison (1st)	37115
Madison College, Br. Madison	37115
Madison Square, Br. Madison	37115
Madisonville	37354
Malesus	38354
Mallory, Sta. Memphis	38109
Manchester (1st)	37355
Mansfield	38236
Martin (1st)	38237
Maryville (1st)	37801
Mascot	37806
Mason	38049
Maury City	38050
Mayland	38572
Maynardville	37807
Mc Donald	37353
Mc Ewen	37101
Mc Kellar, Sta. Memphis	38106
Mc Kenzie (1st)	38201
Mc Lemoresville	38235
Mc Minnville (1st)	37110
Mc Nairy	38353
Medina	38355
Medon	38356
Melrose, Br. Nashville (see appendix)	
MEMPHIS (1st) (see appendix)	
Memphis State University, Sta. Memphis	38111
Mentor, R. Br. Alcoa	37808
Mercer	38392
Michie	38357
Middleton	38052
Midtown, R. Br. Harriman	37748
Midway	37809
Milan (1st)	38358
Milledgeville	38359
Milligan College	37682
Millington (1st)	38053
Naval Air Station Memphis, Sta.	38054
Naval Hospital, Sta.	38054
Rosemark, R. Br.	38053
Milton	37118
Minor Hill	38473
Miston	38056
Mitchellville	37119
Mohawk	37810
Monoville	37121
Monroe	38573
Monteagle	37356
Monterey	38574
Montezuma	38360

Mooresburg	37811
Morley	37812
Morris Chapel	38361
Morrison	37357
Morristown (1st)	37814
Moscow	38057
Mosheim	37818
Moss	38575
Mount Carmel, Br. Church Hill	37642
Mount Juliet	37122
Mount Pleasant	38474
Mount Vernon	37358
Mountain City	37683
Mountain Home	37684
Mulberry	37359
Munford	38058
Murfreesboro (1st)	37130
Murray Lake Hills, Br. Chattanooga	37416
NASHVILLE (1st) (see appendix)	
Naval Air Station Memphis, Sta. Millington	38054
Naval Hospital, Sta. Millington	38054
New Johnsonville	37134
New Market	37820
New Middleton, R. Br. Gordonsville	38563
New Providence, Sta. Clarksville	37040
New River	37824
New Tazewell	37825
Newbern	38059
Newcomb	37819
Newport (1st)	37821
Niota	37826
Nolensville	37135
Norene	37136
Norma, R. Br. Huntsville	37827
Normandy	37360
Norris	37828
North, Sta. Nashville (see appendix)	
North, Sta. Memphis	38107
North Chattanooga, Sta. Chattanooga	37405
North Knoxville, Sta. Knoxville	37917
Northeast, Sta. Nashville	37207
Norwood, Sta. Knoxville	37912
Nunnelly	37137
Oak Ridge (1st)	37830
Oakdale	37829
Oakfield	38362
Oakland	38060
Obion	38240
Ocoee	37361
Old Hickory (1st)	37138
Old Hometown, R. Br. Memphis	38116
Oldfort	37362
Olivehill	38475
Oliver Springs	37840
Oneida (1st)	37841
Only	37140
Ooltewah	37363
Orlinda	37141
Ozone	37842
Pall Mall	38577
Palmer	37365
Palmersville	38241

Palmyra	37142
Paris (1st)	38242
Parkway Village, Br. Memphis	38118
Parrotsville	37843
Parsons	38363
Pegram	37143
Pelham	37366
Persia, R. Br. Rogersville	37844
Petersburg	37144
Petros	37845
Philadelphia	37846
Pickwick Dam	38365
Pigeon Forge, Br. Sevierville	37863
Pikeville	37367
Piney Flats	37686
Pinson	38366
Pioneer	37847
Pleasant Hill	38578
Pleasant Shade	37145
Pleasant View	37146
Pleasantville	37147
Pocahontas	38061
Portland (1st)	37148
Postelle	37368
Powder Springs	37848
Powell	37849
Primm Springs	38476
Prospect	38477
Pruden	37851
Pulaski (1st)	38478
Puryear	38251
Quebeck	38579
Raleigh, Br. Memphis	38128
Ramer	38367
Readyville	37149
Reagan	38368
Red Bank, Br. Chattanooga	37415
Red Boiling Springs	37150
Reliance	37369
Reverie	38062
Riceville	37370
Richard City	37371
Rickman	38580
Riddleton	37151
Ridgely	38080
Ridgetop	37152
Ripley (1st)	38063
Riverside, Sta. Memphis	38113
Rives	38253
Roan Mountain	37687
Robbins	37852
Rock Island	38581
Rockford	37853
Rockvale	37153
Rockwood (1st)	37854
Rogersville (1st)	37857
Kepler, R. Br.	37857
Persia, R. Br.	37844
Rosemark, R. Br. Millington	38053
Rossville	38066
Royal, R. Br. Shelbyville	37160
Rugby, R. Br. Elgin	37733
Russellville	37860
Rutherford	38369
Rutledge	37861
Sadlersville, R. Br. Adams	37154
Saint Andrews	37372
Saint Bethlehem	37155
Saint Elmo, Sta. Chattanooga (see appendix)	

Saint Joseph.................................38481
Sale Creek...................................37373
  Bakewell, R. Br...................37304
Saltillo...38370
Samburg......................................38254
Santa Fe......................................38482
Sardis..38371
Saulsbury.....................................38067
Savannah (1st)............................38372
Scotts Hill...................................38374
Selmer (1st)................................38375
Sequatchie..................................37374
Sevierville (1st)...........................37862
Sewanee (1st).............................37375
Seymour......................................37865
Shady Valley................................37688
Sharon...38255
Sharps Chapel.............................37866
Shawanee....................................37867
Shelby Center, R. Br.
  Memphis...............................38128
Shelbyville (1st)...........................37160
Sherwood.....................................37376
Shiloh..38376
Shop Spring.................................37164
Shouns...37689
Signal Mountain (1st)...................37377
Silerton.......................................38377
Silver Point..................................38582
Slayden..37165
Smartt...37378
Smithville.....................................37166
Smoky Junction............................37868
Smyrna (1st).................................37167
Sneedville....................................37869
Soddy..37379
Somerville (1st)............................38068
South, Sta. Nashville....................37210
South Fulton, Br. Fulton, K
  Y...42041
South Harriman, R. Sta.
  Harriman..............................37748
South Knoxville, Sta.
  Knoxville...............................37920
South Pittsburg (1st)....................37380
Southside.....................................37171
Sparta (1st).................................38583
Speedwell....................................37870
Spencer.......................................38585
Spring City...................................37381
Spring Creek................................38378
Spring Hill...................................37174
Springfield (1st)...........................37172
Springville...................................38256
Stahlman, Sta. Nashville...............37201
Stanton..38069
Stantonville..................................38379
State University, Sta.
  Johnson City.........................37601
Stephen Holston, Sta.
  Bristol...................................37620
Stewart..37175
Strawberry Plains.........................37871
Sugar Tree....................................38380
Summertown.................................38483
Summitville...................................37382
Sunbright.....................................37872
Surgoinsville.................................37873
Sweetwater (1st)..........................37874
Taft...38488
Talbott...37877
Tallassee......................................37878
Tate Springs, R. Br. Bean

Station..37708
Tazewell......................................37879
Teachers College, Sta.
  Nashville...............................37203
Telford..37690
Tellico Plains...............................37385
Ten Mile......................................37880
Tennessee Ridge..........................37118
Tennessee Tech, Sta.
  Cookeville.............................38501
Thompsons Station.......................37179
Thorn Hill....................................37881
Tigrett...38070
Tipton...38071
Tiptonville...................................38079
Tom Murray, Sta. Jackson...........38301
Toone..38381
Townsend.....................................37882
Tracy City....................................37387
Trade..37691
Treadway.....................................37883
Trenton (1st)...............................38382
Trevecca College, Sta.
  Nashville...............................37210
Trezevant.....................................38258
Trimble..38259
Troy..38260
Tuckahoe, R. Br. Strawberry
  Plains....................................37871
Tullahoma (1st)............................37388
  Arnold A F B, Br..................37389
  Dickel, R. Br.........................37388
Turtletown....................................37391
Tusculum College, R. Br.
  Greeneville............................37743
Tyner...37392
Unicoi..37692
Union City (1st)............................38261
Unionville.....................................37180
University, Sta. Knoxville...............37916
University Of Tennessee,
  Sta. Martin............................38237
University Of The South, Br.
  Sewanee................................37375
Uptown, Sta. Knoxville..................37901
Uptown Nashville, Sta.
  Nashville (see appendix)
Vale...38386
Vanleer..37181
Veterans Administration, Br.
  Murfreesboro.........................37130
Victoria..37393
Viola...37394
Vonore...37885
Wales..38484
Walker, Br. Memphis.....................38109
Walland..37886
Walling...38587
Wartburg.....................................37887
Wartrace......................................37183
Washburn.....................................37888
Washington College, R. Br.
  Limestone.............................37681
Watauga......................................37694
Watertown....................................37184
Watts Bar Dam.............................37395
Waverly..37185
Waynesboro..................................38485
West, Sta. Nashville......................37209
West Greene, Sta.
  Greeneville............................37743
West Knoxville, Sta.

Knoxville......................................37919
Westel...37889
Western State Hospital..................38074
Westmoreland...............................37186
Westpoint.....................................38486
Westport......................................38387
Westwood, Br. Memphis................38109
White, Sta. Memphis.....................38117
White Bluff..................................37187
White House.................................37188
White Pine...................................37890
Whitehaven, Sta. Memphis............38116
Whites Creek................................37189
Whitesburg...................................37891
Whiteside.....................................37396
Whiteville.....................................38075
Whitleyville...................................38588
Whitwell.......................................37397
Wilder..38589
Wildersville...................................38388
Williamsport.................................38487
Williston.......................................38076
Winchester (1st)...........................37398
Winfield.......................................37892
Winona..37893
Woodbine, Sta. Nashville..............37211
Woodbury (1st)............................37190
Woodland Mills.............................38271
Woodlawn....................................37191
Wrigley, R. Br. Lyles.....................37098
Wynnburg.....................................38077
Yorkville......................................38389
Yuma..38390

CHATTANOOGA   374

POST OFFICE BOXES

Box Nos.

1-1749	Main Office	01
1801-1999	East Lake Sta	07
2001-2294	St Elmo Sta	09
2501-2799	East Lake Sta	07
3001-3308	Highland Park Sta	04
4001-4299	North Chattanooga Sta	05
4300-4537	Red Bank Br	15
4801-4915	North Chattanooga Sta	05
5001-5395	East Chatt Sta	06
6001-6339	Main Office	01
6501-6598	B Sta	08
7001-7086	Alton Park Sta	10
8001-8568	Brainerd Sta	11
9001-9402	East Ridge Br	12
11001-11273	Main Office	01
15000-15700	Red Bank Br	15
21001-21300	Chickamauga Sta	21

RURAL ROUTES

2	16
3,4	09
5	05
6	21
8	09

STATIONS, BRANCHES AND UNITS

Airport Road Sta	21
Alton Park Sta	10
Brainerd Sta	11
Chickamauga Sta	21
East Chattanooga Sta	06
East Lake Sta	07
East Ridge Br	12
Eastdale Sta	11
Highland Park Sta	04
Highland Plaza Br	15
Lookout Valley Br	19
Murray Lake Hills Br	16
North Chattanooga Sta	05
Red Bank Br	15
Saint Elmo Sta	09
General Delivery	01
Postmaster	01

APARTMENTS, HOTELS, MOTELS

Alamo Plaza, 3000 Broad St S	08
Albemarle, 324 Mc Callie Ave	02
Albert Pick Motel, 3210 Broad S	09
Ayrshire, 418 Mc Callie Ave	02
Aztec, 2833 Dayton Blvd	15
Barbizon Terrace, 3945 Manor Dr	11
Battery Heights, 3401 Campbell St	06
Belmeade, 3725 Fountain Ave	12
Belvoir Hills, Bacon Tr	12

Bimini	12
Bimini, 400 S Seminole	11
Boynton Ter, 953 Boynton Dr	03
Brainerd 3201 Brainerd Rd	11
Brainerd, 30 S Germantown	11
Brookwood, 621 Memorial Dr	15
Cardo, 1001 N Natchez Rd	05
Chateau Royale, 25 Germantown Rd., S	11
Colonial, 100 Joyce Ave	15
Continental, 1414 Continental Dr	05
Dallas Manor, 1103 E Dallas Rd	05
Dayton Manor, 101 Joyce Ave	15
Dellwood 3205 Dellwood Pl	11
Downtowner, 901 Carter	02
El Cortijo, Pine St	16
El Matador, 3204 Redding Rd	15
Elks Golden Gateway, 1221 Grove St	03
Fort Wood, 870 Vine	03
Fountainbleau, 950 Spring Creek Rd	12
Glenwood Gardens, 2612 Gelnwood Pkwy	04
Grey Fox, 4105 Dayton Blvd	15
Hill Crest, Trenton St	15
Hogshead, 600 Georgia Ave	03
Holiday Inn East, 5505 Brainerd Rd	11
Holiday Inn Se, 6700 Ringgold Rd	21
Holiday Inn South, 2100 Market S	08
Holiday Inn, 401 9th W	02
Key, 831 Georgia Ave	01
Knox Manor, 2717 Folts Dr	15
Lakeshore Country Club, Lake Resort Dr	15
Laurel, Dayton Blvd	15
Lomenacque, Ringgold Rd	12
Mary Walker Towers	08
Meadowbrook Manor, Meadowbrook Dr	15
Montview, 30 Tunnel Blvd	11
Mountain Creek, Mountain Creek Rd	05
Normandy, 3501 Dayton Blvd	15
North River, Lyndon Ave	15
Patten, 1 E 11th	01
Read House, 2 W 9th	01
Renner, 656 Houston	03
Ridgeway, 1200 Poplar St Cts	03
Riviera River St	05
Robinson, 622 Georgia Ave	01
Royal Arms, 314 Mcbrien Rd	11
Shepherd Hills, 404 Tunnel Blvd	11
Snooty Fox, Bacon Trl	12
St Barnabas, 6th St W	02
Stuart Manor, 2914 Haywood Ave	15
The Towers, 501 W 9th	02
Three Kings, Peace St	15
Thrippence, 3620 Fountain Ave	12
Twinam, 528 E 4th	03
Versailles, 3001 Dayton Blvd	15
Virginia, 409 E 4th	03
Williamsburg Daytona Blvd	15

BUILDINGS

American National Bank, 736 Market	02
Blue Cross, 801 Pine St	02
Brainerd Professional, 314 Mcbrien Rd	11
Chattanooga Bank, 11 W 8th	02
Chattanooga Federal, 817 Broad	02
Doctors, 744 Mc Callie Ave	02
Dome, 738 Georgia Ave	02
Edney, 1100 Market	02
Emerson, 100 E 10th	02
Gateway Professional, 1001 Carter St	02
Hamilton National Bank, 701 Market	02
Interstate, 540 Mc Callie Ave	02
Jackson, 103 E 7th	02
James, 735 Broad	02
Mac Lellan, 721 Broad	02
Medical Arts, 546 Mc Callie Ave	02
Pioneer, 801 Broad	02
Professional, 301 Mc Callie Ave	02
Provident, Fountain Sq.	02
Sisken Trans, 1478 Market	08
United Bank Bldg, 701 Chestnut St	02
Volunteer, 9th & Georgia Ave.	02
Whitehall, 960 E 3rd St	03
Zayre W 9th	02
5700-6200	11

GOVERNMENT OFFICES

City Hall, 100 E 11th	02
Federal Building, 900 Georgia Ave	02
Hamilton County Court House, E 7th	02

HOSPITALS

Bork Memorial, 2626 Walker Rd	21
Campbell 525 Mccallie	02
Childrens, 1001 Glenwood Dr.	06
Erlanger Hospital, 241 Wiehl	03
Memorial, 2300 Citico Ave	04
Moccasin Bend Psychiatric, Moccasin Bend Rd	05
Parkridge, 2333 Mccallie Ave.	04
Tennessee Chest Disease, 2501 Milne Ave	06
Tepper Pediatrics, 511 Mccallie Ave	02
Womans 863 Mccallie	03

UNIVERSITIES AND COLLEGES

Chattanooga State Tech, Amnicola Hwy	06
Tenn Temple, 1815 Union Ave	04
Univ Of Tenn At Chattanooga, 615 Mccallie Ave	01

KINGSPORT 376

POST OFFICE BOXES

Box Nos.
A-V	Kingsport	62
1-1492	Kingsport	62
3000-3999	Eastside Br	64
4000-4999	Lynn Garden Br	65
5001-5999	Colonial Heights Br	63

RURAL ROUTES

1,2	60
3	64
4,5,6,7 *	60
8	64
9	63
10	64
11,12	63
13	64

STATIONS, BRANCHES AND UNITS

Bloomingdale Br	60
Colonial Heights Br	63
Eastside Sta	64
Lynn Garden Br	65
General Delivery	62
Postmaster	62

KNOXVILLE 379

POST OFFICE BOXES

Box Nos.
1-2612	Main Office	01
3001-3467	North Knoxville Sta	17
4001-4999	Lonsdale Sta	21
5001-5500	Fountain City Sta	18
6001-6237	Burlington Sta	14
8001-8999	University Of Tennessee Sta	16
9001-9999	South Knoxville Sta	20
10001-10999	West Knoxville Sta	19
12000-12999	Norwood Sta	12

RURAL ROUTES

1	12
2	18
3	20
4,5,6	14
7	21
8	14
9,10	20
11,12,13	18
14	19
15	21
16	20
17,18	21
19	20
20	21

21	19
22	21
23	20
24,25	19

STATIONS, BRANCHES AND UNITS

Burlington Sta	14
Fountain City Sta	18
Halls Crossroads Rural Br	18
Karns Rural Br	21
Kimberlin Heights Rural Br	20
Lonsdale Sta	21
North Knoxville Sta	17
Norwood Sta	12
South Knoxville Sta	20
University Sta	16
Uptown Sta	01
West Knoxville Sta	19
General Delivery	01
Postmaster	01'

APARTMENTS, HOTELS, MOTELS

Andrew Johnson, 914 Gay SW	02
Carlton Towers, 414 Forest Park Blvd	19
Dunbar, 105 Gay SW	02
Empire, 319 Depot Ave NW	17
Farragut, 530 Gay SW	02
Fort Sanders Manor, 400 17th SW	16
Hamilton House Apartments, 1400 Kenesaw Ave SW	19
Jackson, 432 Walnut SW	02
Knoxville, 408 Main Ave SW	02
Norris, 309 Depot Ave NW	17
Park, 510 Walnut SW	02
Parkway, 3701 Chapman Highway SW	20
Saint James, 311 Wall Ave SW	02
Shelbourne Towers, 840 20th SW	16
Southland, 409 Wall Ave SW	02
Taliwa Court, 120 Taliwa Ct SE	20
Y M C A, 605 Clinch Ave SW	02
Y W C A, 420 Clinch Ave SW	02

BUILDINGS

Arnstein, 501 Market	02
Bank Of Knoxville, 623 Market SW	02
Blount Professional, Blount Ave SE	20
Burwell, 602 Gay SW	02
Cherokee, 402 Church SW	02
Daylight, 503 Union Ave SW	02
Daylight, 517 Union Ave SW	02
Empire, 624 Market SW	02
Fidelity-Bankers Trust, 502 Gay SW	02
Flat-Iron, 705 Broadway NE	17
Greater Tennessee, Market & Cumberland SW	02
Hamilton National Bank, 531 Gay SW	02

Journal, 618 Gay SW	02
Mercantile, 623 Gay SW	02
Park National Bank, 312 Union SW	02
Seven-O-Six Walnut, 706 Walnut SW	02

GOVERNMENT OFFICES

Knox County Court House, Main Ave & Gay SW	02
Knox County Criminal Court & Jail, 913 Gay SW	02
Knox County Jail, 913 Gay SW	02
Tennessee State Offices, Cumberland & Locust SW	02
Tennessee Supreme Court, Cumberland & Locust SW	02
United States Post Office, Main & Walnut SW	02

HOSPITALS

Beverly Hills Sanitarium, Tazewell Pike NE	18
East Tennessee Baptist, Blount Ave SE	20
East Tennessee Crippled Children, 1912 Laurel Ave SW	16
East Tennessee Tuberculosis, Tazewell Pike NE	18
Eastern State, 5908 Lyons View Park SW	19
Fort Sanders Presbyterian, 1901 Clinch Ave SW	16
Saint Marys, Oak Hill Ave NE	17
University Of Tennessee Clinic Infirmary, 820 Temple SW	16
University Of Tennessee Hospital, Alcoa Highway SW	20

UNIVERSITIES AND COLLEGES

Cooper Institute Of Business, 720 5th SW	17
Draughons Business College, 325 Clinch SW	02
Knoxville Business College, 209 Church SW	02
Knoxville College, 901 College NW	21
National Business College, 302 Gay SW	02
University Of Tennessee W, Cumberland Ave SW	16

MEMPHIS 381

POST OFFICE BOXES

Box Nos.
1-1999	Main Office	01
3000-3999	Front Street Sta	03
4000-4999	Crosstown Sta	04

6000-6999	Mc Kellar Sta...	05
7000-7999	North Sta...	07
8000-8999	Hollywood Sta...	08
9000-9999	Mallory Sta ...	09
11000-11999	East Memphis Sta...	11
12000-12999	Binghamton Sta...	12
13000-13999	Riverside Sta...	13
14000-14999	Lamar Sta...	14
16000-16999	Whitehaven Sta...	16
17000-17999	White Sta...	17
18000-18999	Holiday City Sta...	18
22000-22999	Highland Heights Sta...	22
26000-26999	Lee Sta...	26
27000-27999	Frayser Sta...	27
28000-28999	Raleigh Br...	28
29001-29146	Buntyn Sta...	11
29201-29348	Station 7...	27
30000-30999	Air Mail Facility Sta...	30
38000-38999	Germantown Br...	38
80000-0099999	Memphis State Univ...	52
161000-161220	Whitehaven Sta...	16

RURAL ROUTES

1		28
2		27
3		28
4		09
5,6,7,8		28
9		09
10		28
11		18
12		09
14,15		38

STATIONS, BRANCHES AND UNITS

Airport Mail Facility Sta...	30
Berclair Sta...	17
Binghamton Sta...	12
Buntyn Sta...	11
Capleville Rural Br...	29
Crosstown Sta...	04
Davis Sta...	02
De Soto Sta...	02
East Memphis Sta...	11
Frayser Sta...	27
George W Lee Sta...	26
Highland Heights Sta...	22
Holiday City Sta...	18
Hollywood Sta...	08
Lamar Sta...	14
Mallory Sta...	09
Mc Kellar Sta...	06
Memphis State University Sta...	11
North Sta...	07
Old Hometown Rural Br...	16
Parkway Village Br...	18

Raleigh Br...	28
Riverside Sta...	13
Shelby Center Rural Br...	28
Walker Br...	09
Westwood Br...	09
White Sta...	17
Whitehaven Sta...	16
General Delivery...	01
Postmaster...	01

APARTMENTS, HOTELS, MOTELS

Albert Pick 300 N 2nd St...	05
Ambassador, 347 S Main St...	02
Americana Apartments, 2050 Winchester Rd...	16
Belvedere Apartments, 1733 Union Ave...	04
Cherokee Cabana Apartments, 2856 Kimball Ave...	14
Chisca Plaza, 272 S Main St...	01
Continental Luxury Apartments, 1422 Lamar Ave...	04
Embassy Apartments, 475 S Perkins...	17
Gilmore Apartments, 6 S McLean Blvd...	04
Goodman House, 777 Court Ave...	01
Holiday Tower, 383 Madison Ave...	03
Kimbrough Towers, 172 Kimbrough Pl...	04
Mayfair Apartments, 2277 Union Ave...	04
Oak Acres Apartments, 1128 Craft Rd...	16
Park Terrace Apartments, 2195 Poplar Ave...	04
Park Towers, 57 N Somerville St...	04
Parkview Manor, 1914 Poplar Ave...	04
Parkway House, 1960 N Parkway...	12
Rosecrest Apartments, 45 S Idlewild...	04
Sheraton-Peabody, 149 Union Ave...	01
Tennessee, 80 S 3rd St...	03
The Tower Apartments, 91 N Main St...	03
Town House Apartments, 1437 Central Ave...	04
University Towers Incorporated, 1380 Lamar Ave...	04
Viking 110 Monroe Ave...	01
Woodmont Towers, 1550 N Parkway...	12
Yorktown Apartments, 4010 Jackson Ave...	28

BUILDINGS

Century, 3294 Poplar...	11
Clark Tower 5100 Poplar Ave...	37
Commerce Title, 12 S Main St...	03

Cotten Exchange, 65 Union Ave...	J3
Court Square, 128 S Court...	03
Deluxe Arcade, 12 N 2nd St...	03
Dermon, 46 N 3rd St...	03
Du Pont, 22 S 2nd...	03
Emmons, 4745 Poplar Ave...	17
Exchange Building, 130 Madison Ave...	03
Falls, 22 N Front St...	03
Federal Securities, 81 Monroe Ave...	03
First American Bank, 147 Jefferson Ave...	03
First National Bank, 165 Madison Ave...	03
Goodwyn Institute 127 Madison Ave...	03
Hickman, 248 Madison Ave...	03
Joyner Rembert, 3340 Poplar Ave...	11
Lee, 114 Madison Ave...	03
Lincoln American Tower, 60 N Main St...	03
Mc Call, 79 Mccall Pl...	03
Mid South, 3181 Poplar Ave...	11
Nonconnah Corp. Center-Executive Park Plaza, 3003 Airways...	31
P & S, 899 Madison...	03
Shrine, 66 Monroe Ave...	03
Sterick, 8 N 3rd St...	03
Tenoke 161 Jefferson Ave...	03
Union Planters National Bank, 67 Madison Ave...	03
White Station Tower, 5050 Poplar Ave...	17
100 North Main, 100 North Main St...	03
2600 Poplar, 2600 Poplar Ave...	12
3355 Poplar, 3355 Poplar Ave...	11
3373 Poplar, 3373 Poplar Ave...	11
63 South Main, 63 S Main St...	03
81 Madison, 81 Madison Ave...	03

GOVERNMENT OFFICES

Chief Inspector Southern Region U S Postal Service...	61
City Hall, 125 N Main...	03
Defense Supply Agency 2163-65 Airways Blvd...	14
Federal Office, 167 N Main...	03
Internal Revenue Service Center, 3131 Democrat Rd...	10
State Office, 170 N Main...	03

HOSPITALS

Baptist Memorial 899 Madison...	46
Bowld William F, 951 Court...	03
Campbell Clinic, 869 Madison...	04
Crippled Adults, 1248 La Paloma...	14

E H Crump Memorial, 853
Jefferson.................... 03
Gailor Psychiactric, 42 N
Dunlap....................... 03
Gartly-Ramsay, 696 Jackson... 05
John Gaston, 860 Madison 03
Le Bonheur Childrens, 848
Adams........................ 03
Methodist, 1265 Union........ 04
Oakville Memorial
Sanatorium, Oakville........ 18
Saint Joseph, 220 Overton
Ave.......................... 01
Saint Jude, 332 N
Lauderdale................... 01
Shelby County, Route 8 Box
500.......................... 28
Tennessee Psychiatric
Institute, 865 Poplar........ 04
Terrell Memorial, 698
Williams..................... 26
Veterans Administration,
1030 Jefferson............... 04
West Tennessee Tuberculosis,
842 Jefferson................ 03

UNIVERSITIES AND COLLEGES

Christian Brothers, 650 E
Parkway S.................... 04
Draughon'S Business, 253
Madison...................... 01
Lausanne School For Girls,
1381 Massey Rd............... 17
Le Moyne Owen, 807 Walker
Ave.......................... 26
Memphis Academy Of Arts,
Overton Park................. 12
Memphis College Of Music,
1822 Overton Park............ 12
Memphis Hebrew Academy,
390 S White Station Rd...... 17
Memphis State University,
Southern Ave................. 52
Owen S A Junior College, 370
S Orleans.................... 26
Saint Agnes Academy, 4830
Walnut Grove................. 17
Siena, 4405 Poplar Ave....... 17
Southern College Of
Optometry 1246 Union
Ave.......................... 04
Southwestern, 2000 N
Parkway...................... 12
University Of Tennessee, 847
Union........................ 03

NASHVILLE   372

POST OFFICE BOXES

Box Nos.
A-0   Uptown Sta...... 19
1-1999   Main Office..... 02
2001-2499 Donelson Br..... 14
2501-3299 Uptown Sta...... 19
3500-3999 Airport Sta..... 17
4501-4999 Jere Baxter..... 16
5001-5499 East Sta........ 06
5500-5999 North Sta....... 08
6001-6499 Acklen Sta...... 12

6501-6999 Green Hills
           Sta............. 15
7001-7499 South Sta....... 10
7501-7999 West Sta........ 09
8001-8499 Northeast Sta... 07
8501-8999 Woodbine Sta.... 11
9001-9699 Melrose Br...... 04
11000-11999 Woodbine Sta... 11
12000-12600 Acklen Sta..... 12
15000-15999 Green Hills
           Sta............. 15
40000-40999 Melrose Sta.... 04
50001-50478 Belle Meade
           Sta............. 05
60000-60999 East Sta....... 06

RURAL ROUTES

1............................ 14
2............................ 09
3............................ 18
4............................ 11
5............................ 21

STATIONS, BRANCHES AND UNITS

Acklen Sta................... 12
Airport Sta.................. 17
Baptist Sta.................. 03
Belle Meade Br............... 05
Bordeaux Br.................. 18
Donelson Br.................. 14
East Sta..................... 06
Federal Reserve Sta.......... 03
Fisk University Sta.......... 03
Green Hills Sta.............. 15
Highway One Hundred Br....... 05
Jere Baxter Br............... 16
Melrose Br................... 04
North Sta.................... 08
Northeast Sta................ 07
South Sta.................... 10
Stahlman Sta................. 01
Teachers College Sta......... 03
Trevecca College Sta......... 10
Uptown Nashville Sta......... 19
West Sta..................... 09
Woodbine Sta................. 11
General Delivery............. 02
Postmaster................... 02

APARTMENTS, HOTELS, MOTELS

Academy, Masonwood Dr........ 07
Alexandria, 3901 West End.... 05
Ambassador, 2418 Kirkland
Ave.......................... 12
Arlington, 1711 18th Avenue
S............................ 12
Barbizon, 2006 Broadway...... 03
Belle Meade Terrace, 118
Harding Pl................... 05
Belle Meade Towers, 105
Leake........................ 05
Bellwood Terrace, 500
Bowling...................... 12
Belmont Court, 1915 Belmont
Blvd......................... 12
Blackstone, 3300 West End
Ave.......................... 03
Bow-Mar Apartments, 276
White Bridge Rd.............. 09
Cabana, 2020 Beech Ave....... 04

Caldwell Court, 550 Harding
Pl........................... 11
Capri, 261 White Bridge Rd... 09
Carmichael Towers, 2321
West End Ave................. 03
Catahna, 111 Acklen Park
Dr........................... 03
Clarendon, 130 7th Ave S..... 03
Continental Apartments,
3415 West End Ave............ 03
Corvair, 2611 Belmont Blvd... 12
Courtland, 3401 West End
Ave.......................... 03
Dville, 246 White Bridge Rd.. 09
Elysian Gardens, Harding Pl.. 11
Executive House, 860
Murfreesboro Rd.............. 17
Fairfax, 107 Fairfax......... 03
Fairmount, 107 Acklen Park
Dr........................... 03
Forest Hill, 2600 Hillsboro
Rd........................... 12
Fountains,the, 97 White
Bridge....................... 05
Glencourt, 615 Belle Meade
Blvd......................... 05
Graylyn, 913 20th Ave S...... 12
Green Hills Terrace, 1900
Richard Jones Rd............. 15
Grenada, 200 25th Ave N...... 03
Harding Court, 3101 West
End Ave...................... 03
Harding House, 4200 West
End Ave...................... 05
Heatherwood, 709 N 12th St... 06
Hermitage, 231 6th Ave N..... 19
Hickory Hill, Stewart Ferry
Pike......................... 14
Hillcrest, 236 Stewart Ferry
Pike......................... 14
Hillsboro Court, 1405 21st
Ave S........................ 12
Hillsboro Gardens, 3206
Hillsboro Rd................. 15
Imperial House, Bosley
Springs Rd................... 05
Iroquois, 3301 Long Blvd..... 03
Jacksonian, 3010 West End
Ave.......................... 03
James Robertson, 118 7th
Ave N........................ 03
Jefferson 2115 Portland Av).. 12
Kirkland, 2415 Kirkland Pl... 12
Lindsley, 15 Lindsley Ave.... 10
Marlborough, 200 8th Ave S... 03
Mayflower, 1925 21st Ave S... 12
Metro Manor Apartments,
500 5th Ave N................ 19
Mikado, 3815 West End Ave.... 05
Noel, 200 4th Ave N.......... 19
Oxford House, 1313 21st Ave
S............................ 12
Park Lawn, 2016 Terrace Pl... 03
Park Manor, 115 Woodmont
Blvd......................... 05
Park Road, 3416 West End
Ave.......................... 03
Peabody Courts, 1411 21st
Ave S........................ 12
Raleigh, 200 7th Ave S....... 03
Robert E Lee, 2108 Hayes..... 03
Royal Arms East, 2011
Richard Jones Rd............. 15

581

Royal Oaks, 4505 Harding Rd 05
Statler Hilton Airport Inn, International Plaza 17
Sun Valley, 256 Stewart Ferry Pike 14
Versailles, 3000 Hillsboro Rd. 15
Washington, 2001 21st Ave S 12
Wellington Arms, 4225 Harding Rd 05
Windsor Towers, 4215 Harding Rd 05
Woodmont Terrace, 910 Woodmont Blvd 04

BUILDINGS

Albert, 146 7th Ave N 03
American Trust, 305 Union 01
Andrew Jackson State Office, 500 Deaderick 19
Arcade, 225 4th Ave N 19
Baker 110 21st Ave S 03
Bennie Dillon, 700 Church 03
Broadway National Bank, 300 Broad 01
Capitol Boulevard, 226 Capitol Blvd 19
Capitol Towers 510 Gay 19
Central Services, 503 5th Ave N 19
Commerce Union Bank, 400 Union 19
Cordell Hull, 436 6th Ave N 19
Court Square, 3rd & Jas Robt Pkwy 01
Doctors, 702 Church 03
Exchange, 311 Church 01
Federal Office, 701 Broadway 03
First American National Bank, 326 Union 19
First Federal, 236 4th Ave N 19
Green Hills Shopping Center 15
Greyhound Terminal, 517 Commerce 03

Hayes, 1710 Hayes 03
Highway, 6th & Deaderick 19
International Business Machines, 450 James Robertson Pky 19
J C Bradford, 170 4th Ave N. 19
Life & Casualty Tower, 4th & Church 19
Live Stock Exchange, 901 2nd Ave N 01
Medical Arts, 1211 21st Ave S 12
Mid-State Medical Center 2000 Church 03
Morris Memorial, 4th & Cedar 01
Municipal Safety, 110 Public Square 01
Nashville Trust, 315 Union 01
Parkway Towers, 404 James Robertson Pky 19
Saint Catherine Hall, 2001 Church 03
Stahlman, 3rd & Union 01
State Capitol 15
State Library & Archives, 411 7th Ave N 19
Sudekum, 6th & Church 19
Supreme Court, 401 7th Ave.. 19
Third National Bank, 201 4th Ave N 19
Tuck, 1123 Church 03
War Memorial, 300 Capitol Blvd 19
Westmont, 201 22nd Ave N. 03

GOVERNMENT OFFICES

City Office, 2nd Ave S & Lindsley 10
County Court House, Public Square 01
Federal Office Bldg, 701 Broadway 03
National Guard Center 04
United States Courthouse, 801 Broadway 03

HOSPITALS

Baptist, 2000 Church 36
Bordeaux, County Hospital Rd 18
Central State, Murfeesboro Rd 17
City General, 72 Hermitage Ave 10
Donelson, 3055 Lebanon Rd.. 14
Hubbard, 1005 18th Ave N. 08
Middle Tennessee Tuberculosis, Ben Allen Rd 16
Park View, 230 25th Ave N 03
Riverside Sanitarium & Hospital, 800 Youngs Lane 07
Saint Thomas, 2000 Hayes.... 03
Vanderbilt, 21st Ave S 03
Veterans Administration, 1310 24th Ave S 03

MILITARY INSTALLATIONS

National Guard Center 04

UNIVERSITIES AND COLLEGES

Aquinas Junior 4210 Harding Rd 05
Belmont College, 16th Ave S & Belcourt 03
David Lipscomb, Granny White Pike 03
Fisk University, 17th Ave N 03
Meharry Medical, 1005 18th Ave N 08
Peabody, 21st Ave S 03
Scarritt, 1008 19th Ave S 03
Trevecca Nazarene, 333 Murfreesboro Rd 10
University Of Tennessee, 810 Broadway 03
Vanderbilt University, 21st Ave S 03

TEXAS
(Abbreviation: TX)

Abbott...................................76621
Abernathy.............................79311
ABILENE (1st) (see appendix)
Abilene Christian College, Sta. Abilene...............79601
Ace.......................................77326
Ackerly.................................79713
Adamsville, R. Br. Lampasas.......................76510
Addicks, R. Br. Houston.....77079
Addison................................75001
Adkins..................................78101
Adrian..................................79001
Afton....................................79220
Agua Dulce...........................78330
Aiken....................................79221
Air Terminal, Sta. Midland...79701
Airlawn, Sta. Dallas.............75235
Airport Mail Facility, Sta. Houston.............................77060
Alamo (1st)...........................78516
Alamo Heights, Br. San Antonio (see appendix)
Alanreed..............................79002
Alba.....................................75410
Albany..................................76430
Albert...................................78601
Albert Thomas, Br. Houston...77058
Aledo...................................76008
Algerita, R. Br. San Saba....76877
Alice (1st).............................78332
Alief.....................................77411
Allen....................................75002
Alleyton, R. Br. Columbus....78935
Allison..................................79003
Alma, R. Br. Ennis...............75119
Almeda, Sta. Houston (see appendix)
Alpine (1st)...........................79830
Alta Loma............................77510
Altair...................................77412
Alto......................................75925
Alvarado..............................76009
Alvin (1st)............................77511
Alvord..................................76225
AMARILLO (1st) (see appendix)
Amherst...............................79312
Anahuac...............................77514
Anderson..............................77830
Andice, R. Br. Georgetown...78626
Andrews (1st)........................79714
Florey, R. Br.......................79732
Angelo State University, Sta. San Angelo.....................76901
Angleton (1st).......................77515
Anna....................................75003
Annona.................................75550
Anson...................................79501
Anson Jones, Sta. Houston...77009
Antelope...............................76350
Anthony................................88021
Anton...................................79313
Apple Springs.......................75926
Appleby, R. Br. Nacogdoches..................75961
Aquilla.................................76622
Aransas Pass (1st)...............78336
Arapaho, Sta. Richardson....75080

Arcadia.................................77517
Archer City...........................76351
Argyle..................................76226
ARLINGTON (1st) (see appendix)
Arlington Heights, Sta. Fort Worth..............................76107
Armstrong.............................78338
Arp.......................................75750
Art..76820
Artesia Wells........................78001
Arthur City...........................75411
Asherton..............................78827
Aspermont............................79502
Astrodome, Sta. Houston (see appendix)
Astroworld, Sta. Houston.....77025
Atascosa..............................78002
Athens (1st)..........................75751
Atlanta (1st).........................75551
Aubrey.................................76227
AUSTIN (1st) (see appendix)
Austwell...............................77950
Avalon.................................76623
Avery...................................75554
Avinger................................75630
Avoca..................................79503
Avonbell, Sta. Amarillo........79106
Axtell...................................76624
Azle (1st).............................76020
B U, Sta. Waco.....................76706
Bacliff.................................77518
Bagwell................................75412
Bailey..................................75413
Baird....................................79504
Bakersfield, R. Br. Mc Camey..............................79717
Balch Springs, Br. Mesquite...75149
Ballinger (1st).......................76821
Balmorhea............................79718
Bandera...............................78003
Bangs..................................76823
Banquete..............................78339
Bardwell...............................75101
Barker..................................77413
Barksdale.............................78828
Barnhart...............................76930
Barnum.................................75927
Barrett, R. Br. Crosby..........77532
Barry...................................75102
Barstow...............................79719
Bartlett................................76511
Basin, R. Br. Big Bend National Park...................79834
Bastrop.................................78602
Batesville.............................78829
Batson..................................77519
Bay City (1st).......................77414
Bayside.................................78340
Baytown (1st)........................77520
Beacon Hill, Sta. San Antonio (see appendix)
Beasley.................................77417
BEAUMONT (1st) (see appendix)
Bebe....................................78603
Beckville..............................75631
Bedford.................................76021
Bedias..................................77831
Bee House............................76512
Beeville (1st).........................78102
Bellaire (1st).........................77401
Bellevue...............................76228

Bellmead, Br. Waco (see appendix)
Bells....................................75414
Bellville...............................77418
Belmont................................78604
Belton (1st)...........................76513
Ben Arnold............................76517
Ben Bolt...............................78342
Ben Franklin.........................75415
Ben Wheeler.........................75754
Benavides.............................78341
Benbrook, Br. Fort Worth......76126
Bend.....................................76824
Benjamin...............................79505
Berclair.................................78107
Berea, R. Br. Jefferson.........75657
Bergheim, R. Br. Boerne.......78004
Bergstrom A F B, MOU. Austin..............................78743
Berry Street, Sta. Fort Worth (see appendix)
Bertram................................78605
Best......................................76931
Bettie...................................75632
Beverly, Br. Waco..................76711
Beverly Hills, Sta. Dallas (see appendix)
Big Bend National Park.........79834
Big Lake...............................76932
Big Sandy (1st)......................75755
Big Spring (1st).....................79720
Big Town, Sta. Mesquite.......75149
Big Wells.............................78830
Bigfoot.................................78005
Biggs Afb, Br. El Paso..........79908
Birome.................................76625
Bishop..................................78343
Bivins...................................75555
Black....................................79004
Blackwell.............................79506
Blanco..................................78606
Blanket................................76432
Bledsoe................................79314
Bleiblerville..........................78931
Blessing...............................77419
Bloomburg............................75556
Blooming Grove....................76626
Bloomington.........................77951
Blossom................................75416
Blue Mound, Br. Fort Worth...76131
Blue Ridge............................75004
Bluegrove.............................76352
Bluff Dale.............................76433
Bluffton................................78607
Blum....................................76627
Bob Harris, Sta. Pasadena....77502
Bob Lyons, Sta. Galveston....77550
Boca Chica, R. Br. Brownsville.....................78520
Boerne (1st)..........................78006
Bergheim, R. Br...............78004
Sisterdale, R. Br..............78006
Welfare, R. Br..................78036
Bogata.................................75417
Boling..................................77420
Bomarton.............................76353
Bon Wier..............................75928
Bonham (1st)........................75418
Booker.................................79005
Booth...................................77421
Borger (1st)...........................79007
Phillips, Br......................79071
Philrich, Sta....................79007

Yows Street Annex, Sta.	79007
Boston	75557
Bovina	79009
Bowie (1st)	76230
Boyd	76023
Boys Ranch	79010
Brackettville	78832
Brady (1st)	76825
Brandon	76628
Brashear	75420
Brazoria	77422
Breckenridge (1st)	76024
Bremond	76629
Brenham (1st)	77833
Bridge City (1st)	77611
Bridgeport	76026
Briggs	78608
Briscoe	79011
Bristol, R. Br. Ennis	75119
Broaddus	75929
Broadway, Sta. Mesquite	75149
Bronco, R. Br. Plains	79315
Bronson	75930
Bronte	76933
Brook Hollow, Sta. Dallas	75247
Brookeland	75931
Brookesmith	76827
Brooks A F B, Br. San	
Antonio	78235
Brookshire	77423
Brookside Village, R. Br.	
Pearland	77581
Brookston	75421
Brownfield (1st)	79316
Brownsboro	75756
Brownsville (1st)	78520
Brownwood (1st)	76801
Bruceville	76630
Bruni	78344
Bryan (1st)	77801
Bryson	76027
Buchanan Dam	78609
Buckeye	77424
Buckholts	76518
Buda	78610
Buffalo	75831
Buffalo Gap	79508
Bula	79320
Bullard	75757
Bulverde, R. Br. Wetmore	78163
Buna	77612
Burkburnett (1st)	76354
Burke, R. Br. Diboll	75941
Burkett	76828
Burkeville	75932
Burleson (1st)	76028
Burlington	76519
Burnet (1st)	78611
Burton	77835
Bushland	79012
Byers	76357
Bynum	76631
Cactus	79013
Caddo	76029
Caddo Mills	75005
Caldwell	77836
Call	75933
Calliham	78007
Calvert	77837
Camden	75934
Cameron (1st)	76520
Camp Dale Robertson, R. Br.	
Avinger	75630
Camp San Saba	76829
Camp Verde, R. Br. Center	
Point	78010
Camp Wood	78833
Campbell	75422
Campbellton	78008
Canadian	79014
Canton	75103
Canutillo	79835
Canyon (1st)	79015
Canyon City, R. Br. New	
Braunfels	78130
Capitol, Sta. Austin	78711
Caradan	76830
Carbon	76435
Cardinal, Sta. Athens	75751
Carey	79222
Carl Range, Sta. Irving	75060
Carlsbad	76934
Carlton	76436
Carmine	78932
Carrizo Springs	78834
Carrollton (1st)	75006
Carswell A F B, Sta. Fort	
Worth	76127
Carta Valley	78835
Carthage (1st)	75633
Casa View, Sta. Dallas	75228
Cason	75636
Castell	76831
Castroville	78009
Mico, R. Br.	78056
Cat Spring	78933
Catarina	78836
Cayuga	75832
Cedar Bayou, R. Sta.	
Baytown	77520
Cedar Creek	78612
Cedar Hill	75104
Cedar Lane	77415
Cedar Park	78613
Cedar Valley, R. Br. Austin	78746
Cee Vee	79223
Celeste	75423
Celina	75009
Center (1st)	75935
Center Point	78010
Centerville	75833
Central, Sta. Fort Worth	76102
Central Park, Sta. Houston	77011
Centralia	75834
Chalk	79224
Chandler	75758
Channelview (1st)	77530
Channing	79018
Chapman Ranch	78347
Chappell Hill	77426
Charleston, R. Br. Lake	
Creek	75424
Charlotte	78011
Chatfield	75105
Cheapside	77952
Cherokee	76832
Chester	75936
Chico	76030
Chicota	75425
Childress (1st)	79201
Chillicothe	79225
Chilton	76632
China	77613
China Spring	76633
Chireno	75937
Chriesman	77838
Christine	78012
Christoval	76935
Cibolo	78108
Cisco (1st)	76437
Civic Center, Sta. Houston	77061
Clairemont	79509
Clairette	76441
Clarendon	79226
Clarksville (1st)	75426
Clarkwood, Sta. Corpus	
Christi	78406
Claude	79019
Clay, R. Br. Somerville	77839
Clayton	75637
Cleburne (1st)	76031
Clemville	77427
Cleo	76833
Cleveland (1st)	77327
Clifton (1st)	76634
Clint	79836
Clodine, R. Br. Richmond	77469
Clute (1st)	77531
Clyde	79510
Coahoma	79511
Cocenter, Sta. Pampa	79065
Cockrell Hill, Br. Dallas	75211
Coldspring	77331
Coleman (1st)	76834
College Station (1st)	77840
Redmond Terrace, Sta.	77840
South, R. Br.	77840
Collegeport	77428
Colleyville	76034
Collinsville	76233
Colmesneil	75938
Colonial, Sta. Waco	76707
Colorado City (1st)	79512
Columbus (1st)	78934
Alleyton, R. Br.	78935
Glidden, R. Br.	78943
Comanche (1st)	76442
Combes	78535
Comfort	78013
Commerce (1st)	75428
Como	75431
Comstock	78837
Concan	78838
Concepcion	78349
Concord	77850
Cone	79321
Conroe (1st)	77301
Converse	78109
Conway	79020
Cookville	75558
Coolidge	76635
Cooper	75432
Copeville	75018
Coppell	75019
Copperas Cove (1st)	76522
Coronado, Sta. El Paso	79915
CORPUS CHRISTI (1st) (see appendix)	
Corrigan	75939
Corsicana (1st)	75110
Emhouse, R. Br.	75110
Navarro, R. Br.	75151
Cost	78614
Cotton Center	79021
Cottonwood, R. Br. Baird	79504
Cotulla	78014
Coupland	78615
Courtney	77851
Covington	76636

Coy City................................78110
Coyanosa..............................79730
Crandall................................75114
Crane....................................79731
Cranfills Gap.........................76637
Crawford...............................76638
Creedmoor, R. Br. Austin.......78744
Cresson................................76035
Cresthaven, Sta. San
  Antonio (see appendix)
Crestwood, Sta. Odessa.........79760
Crockett (1st).......................75835
Crosby..................................77532
Crosbyton.............................79322
Cross Plains..........................76443
Crowell.................................79227
Crowley.................................76036
Crystal Beach, R. Br. Port
  Bolivar..............................77650
Crystal City (1st)...................78839
Cuero (1st)............................77954
Cumby...................................75433
Cuney....................................75759
Cunningham...........................75434
Cushing.................................75760
Cut And Shoot, R. Br.
  Conroe...............................77301
Cypress.................................77429
Cypress Mill, R. Br. Marble
  Falls..................................78654
D'Hanis.................................78850
Daingerfield...........................75638
Daisetta................................77533
Dal Rich, Sta. Richardson......75080
Dale......................................78616
Dalhart (1st).........................79022
Dallardsville..........................77332
DALLAS (1st) (see appendix)
Damon...................................77430
Danbury.................................77534
Danciger................................77431
Danevang...............................77432
Darrouzett.............................79024
Davilla..................................76523
Dawn.....................................79025
Dawson..................................76639
Dayton...................................77535
De Berry................................75639
De Kalb.................................75559
De Leon.................................76444
De Soto (1st).........................75115
Deanville...............................77852
Decatur (1st).........................76234
Deer Park (1st)......................77536
Del Rio (1st).........................78840
Del Valle...............................78617
Dell City...............................79837
Delmita.................................78536
Denison (1st).........................75020
Dennis...................................76037
Denton (1st)..........................76201
  North Texas, Sta................76203
  T W U, Sta..........................76204
Denver City (1st)...................79323
Denver Harbor, Sta. Houston...77020
Deport...................................75435
Dermott.................................79515
Desdemona.............................76445
Detroit...................................75436
Devers...................................77538
Devine...................................78016
Dewalt...................................77433
Deweyville.............................77614

Dial.......................................79026
Dialville................................75761
Diana.....................................75640
Diboll....................................75941
Dickens.................................79229
Dickinson (1st)......................77539
Dike......................................75437
Dilley....................................78017
Dime Box...............................77853
Dimmitt (1st).........................79027
Dinero...................................78350
Dobbin...................................77333
Dodd City..............................75438
Dodge....................................77334
Dodson..................................79230
Dogwood, R. Br. Woodville.....75979
Donie....................................75838
Donna (1st)...........................78537
Doole.....................................76836
Dorchester.............................75030
Doss......................................78618
Doucette................................75942
Dougherty..............................79231
Douglass................................75943
Douglassville.........................75560
Downtown, Sta. Corpus
  Christi...............................78403
Downtown, Sta. Bryan.............77801
Downtown, Sta. Amarillo.........79105
Downtown, Sta. Freeport.........77541
Driftwood...............................78619
Dripping Springs.....................78620
Driscoll.................................78351
Dryden...................................78851
  Pumpville, R. Br................78876
Dublin...................................76446
Duffau...................................76447
Dumas (1st)...........................79029
Dumont..................................79232
Duncanville (1st)....................75116
Dundee, R. Br. Holliday..........76358
Dunlay...................................78018
Dunn......................................79516
Dyess A F B, Br. Abilene........79607
Eagle Lake.............................77434
Eagle Pass (1st).....................78852
  Normandy, R. Br.................78875
Earth.....................................79031
East Austin, Sta. Austin (see
  appendix)
East Bernard..........................77435
East Grand, Sta. Dallas..........75223
East Houston, Sta. Houston
  (see appendix)
East Oak Cliff, Sta. Dallas.....75203
East Side, Sta. Lamesa...........79331
East Texas, Sta. Commerce.....75428
Easter, R. Br. Hereford..........79045
Easterly.................................77854
Eastland (1st)........................76448
Easton...................................75641
Eastwood, Sta. Houston..........77023
Ecleto....................................78111
Ector.....................................75439
Edcouch................................78538
Eddy......................................76524
Eden......................................76837
Edgewood..............................75117
Edinburg (1st)........................78539
Edmonson..............................79032
Edna (1st)..............................77957
Edom, R. Br. Brownsboro........75756
Edroy.....................................78352

Egypt.....................................77436
El Campo (1st).......................77437
El Indio.................................78860
EL PASO (1st) (see
  appendix)
El Sauz.................................78544
Elbert....................................76359
Eldorado................................76936
Electra...................................76360
Elgin......................................78621
Eliasville...............................76038
Elkhart..................................75839
Ellinger.................................78938
Ellington A F B, Br. Houston...77030
Ellwood, Sta. Lubbock (see
  appendix)
Elm Mott...............................76640
Elmaton.................................77440
Elmendorf..............................78112
Elmo.....................................75118
Elsa......................................78543
Elysian Fields........................75642
Emhouse, R. Br. Corsicana......75110
Emory....................................75440
Encinal..................................78019
Encino...................................78353
Energy...................................76452
Enloe.....................................75441
Ennis (1st).............................75119
Enochs...................................79324
Eola......................................76937
Era..76238
Escobas.................................78354
Estelline................................79233
Etoile....................................75944
Euless (1st)...........................76039
Eustace.................................75124
Evadale.................................77615
Evant.....................................76525
Everman, Br. Fort Worth........76140
Exchange Park, Sta. Dallas.....75235
Fabens...................................79838
Fair Park, Sta. Dallas (see
  appendix)
Fairbanks, Sta. Houston (see
  appendix)
Fairchilds, R. Br. Richmond....77469
Fairfield................................75840
Fairview, Sta. Houston...........77006
Falcon Heights.......................78545
Falfurrias (1st).......................78355
Falls City..............................78113
Fannin...................................77960
Farmers Branch, Br. Dallas.....75234
Farmersville...........................75031
Farnsworth.............................79033
Farwell..................................79325
Fashing.................................78020
Fate......................................75032
Fayetteville............................78940
Fentress.................................78622
Ferris....................................75125
Field Creek............................76838
Fieldton.................................79326
Fife.......................................76839
Fischer..................................78623
Fisk.......................................76840
Flat.......................................76526
Flatonia.................................78941
Flint......................................75762
Flomot...................................79234
Florence................................76527
Floresville.............................78114

Florey, R. Br. Andrews............79732
Flour Bluff, R. Sta. Corpus
   Christi.................................78418
Floyd, R. Br. Greenville 75401
Floydada (1st) 79235
Fluvanna...............................79517
Flynn....................................77855
Follett...................................79034
Forest...................................75945
Forest Hills, Sta. Tyler..........75701
Forestburg.............................76239
Forney...................................75126
Forreston...............................76041
Forsan...................................79733
Fort Bliss, Br. El Paso (see
   appendix)
Fort Davis..............................79734
Fort Hancock.........................79839
Fort Hood, Br. Killeen 76544
Fort Mc Kavett......................76841
Fort Sam Houston, Sta. San
   Antonio...............................78234
Fort Stockton (1st) 79735
Fort Wolters, Br. Mineral
   Wells...................................76067
FORT WORTH (1st) (see
   appendix)
Foster Place, Sta. Houston
   (see appendix)
Fowlerton..............................78021
Francitas...............................77961
Frankel City...........................79737
Franklin.................................77856
Franklin, Sta. Houston (see
   appendix)
Frankston..............................75763
Fred......................................77616
Fredericksburg (1st) 78624
Fredonia................................76842
Freeport (1st) 77541
Freer....................................78357
Freestone..............................77542
Fresno...................................77545
Friendswood...........................77546
Friona...................................79035
Frisco...................................75034
Fritch...................................79036
Fronton.................................78546
Frost....................................76641
Fruitvale...............................75127
Fulbright, R. Br. Detroit 75436
Fulshear................................77441
Fulton...................................78358
Gail......................................79738
Gainesville (1st)....................76240
Galena Park (1st)..................77547
Gallatin.................................75764
Galveston (1st)......................77550
Ganado.................................77962
Garciasville............................78547
Garden City...........................79739
Garden Oaks, Sta. Houston....77018
GARLAND (1st) (see
   appendix)
Garner, R. Br. Weatherford 76042
Garrett, R. Br. Ennis 75119
Garrison................................75946
Garwood................................77442
Gary.....................................75643
Gatesville (1st)......................76528
   Ireland, R. Br....................76536
   Pearl, R. Br.......................76563
   The Grove, R. Br. 76576

Gause...................................77857
Gay Hill...............................77858
Geneva..................................75947
Genoa, Sta. Houston (see
   appendix)
George West..........................78022
Georgetown (1st)...................78626
Geronimo..............................78115
Giddings (1st)........................78942
Gilchrist................................77617
Gillett...................................78116
Gilliland, R. Br. Truscott 79260
Gilmer (1st)...........................75644
Girard...................................79518
Girvin...................................79740
Gladewater (1st)....................75647
Glazier..................................79037
Glen Cove.............................76843
Glen Flora.............................77443
Glen Rose..............................76043
Glencrest, Sta. Fort Worth.....76119
Glendale................................75843
Glidden, R. Br. Columbus 78943
Gober...................................75443
Godley..................................76044
Golden..................................75444
Golden Acres, Sta.
   Pasadena............................77503
Goldsboro..............................79519
Goldsmith..............................79741
Goldthwaite...........................76844
Goliad...................................77963
Gonzales (1st)........................78629
Goodfellow A F B, Sta. San
   Angelo...............................76901
Goodland................................79327
Goodlett, R. Br. Quanah 79252
Goodrich................................77335
Gordon...................................76453
Gordonville............................76245
Goree....................................76363
Gorman.................................76454
Gouldbusk.............................76845
Graford..................................76045
Graham (1st).........................76046
Granbury (1st).......................76048
Grand Prairie (1st)................75050
Grand Saline..........................75140
Grandfalls.............................79742
Grandview..............................76050
Granger.................................76530
Grangerland, R. Br. Conroe 77301
Grapeland..............................75844
Grapevine (1st)......................76051
Gray A F B, MOU. Killeen 76544
Grayback, R. Br. Electra 76360
Grayburg...............................77618
Great S W Airport, Sta. Fort
   Worth.................................76125
Great Southwest, Sta.
   Arlington............................76011
Green Acres, Sta. Tyler..........75701
Greens Bayou, Sta. Houston...77015
Greenville (1st)......................75401
Greenville Avenue, Sta.
   Dallas (see appendix)
Greenwood.............................76246
Greggton, Sta. Longview........75601
Gregory..................................78359
Grit.......................................76846
Groesbeck..............................76642
Groom...................................79039
Groves (1st)...........................77619

Hitchcock...............................77563
Hobson..................................78117
Hochheim...............................77967
Hockley.................................77447
Holland..................................76534
Holliday.................................76366
   Dundee, R. Br..................76358
Hondo (1st) 78861
Honey Grove..........................75446
Hooks....................................75561
HOUSTON (1st) (see
   appendix)
Houston Heights, Sta.
   Houston.............................77008
Howe.....................................75059
Hubbard.................................76648
Huffman.................................77336
Hufsmith, R. Br. Tomball.......77337
Hughes Springs.......................75656
Hull.......................................77564
Humble (1st) 77338
Hungerford.............................77448
Hunt......................................78024
Huntington.............................75949
Huntsville (1st) 77340
   Sam Houston College,
   Sta....................................77340
Hurlwood...............................79328
Hurst (1st).............................76053
Hutchins...............................75141
Hutto....................................78634
Hye.......................................78635
Idalou...................................79329
Imperial.................................79743
Indian Gap.............................76535
Industrial, Sta. Dallas (see
   appendix)
Industry.................................78944
Inez......................................77963
Ingleside................................78362
Ingram..................................78025
Inwood, Sta. Dallas 75209
Iola.......................................77861
Iowa Park (1st) 76367
Ira..79527
Iraan.....................................79744
Iredell...................................76649
Ireland, R. Br. Gatesville 76536
Irene.....................................76650
Irving (1st)............................75060
Irvington, Sta. Houston (see
   appendix)
Italy......................................76651
Itasca...................................76055
Ivanhoe.................................75447
Izoro, R. Br. Copperas Cove...76522
J Frank Dobie, Sta. San
   Antonio (see appendix)
Jacinto City, Br. Houston 77029
Jacksboro..............................76056
Jacksonville (1st) 75766
James Moody, Sta. Victoria....77901
Jarrell...................................76537
Jasper (1st) 75951
Jayton...................................79528
Jefferson (1st)........................75657
Jensen Drive, Sta. Houston....77026
Jermyn..................................76057
Jewett...................................75846
Joaquin.................................75954
Joe Pool, Sta. Dallas.............75224
John Allen, Sta. Houston.......77007

John Foster, Sta. Pasadena	77502
Johnson City	78636
Johnsville	76459
Joinerville	75658
Jonesboro	76538
Jonestown, R. Br. Leander	78641
Jonesville	75659
Josephine	75064
Joshua	76058
Jourdanton	78026
Judson	75660
Junction	76849
Juno	76938
Justiceburg	79330
Justin	76247
Kamay	76369
Karnack	75661
Karnes City	78118
Katemcy	76850
Katy	77450
Kaufman (1st)	75142
Keene	76059
Keller	76248
Kellerville	79049
Kelly A F B, Br. San Antonio	78241
Keltys, Sta. Lufkin	75901
Kemah	77565
Kemp	75143
Kempner	76539
Kendalia	78027
Kendleton	77451
Kenedy (1st)	78119
Mineral, R. Br.	78125
Kennard	75847
Kennedale	76060
Kenney	77452
Kent, R. Br. Van Horn	79855
Kerens	75144
Kermit (1st)	79745
Kerrick	79051
Kerrville (1st)	78028
Kildare	75562
Kilgore (1st)	75662
Killeen (1st)	76541
Fort Hood, Br.	76544
Gray A F B, MOU.	76544
Harker Heights, Br.	76541
Killeen Army Base, MOU.	76544
Killeen Army Base, MOU.	
Killeen	76544
Kingsbury	78638
Kingsland	78639
Kingsley, Sta. Garland	75041
Kingsville (1st)	78363
Kingsville Naval, Br.	
Kingsville	78363
Kirbyville (1st)	75956
Kirkland	79238
Kirvin	75848
Kleberg	75145
Kleberg, Sta. Corpus Christi	78404
Klondike	75448
Knickerbocker	76939
Knippa	78870
Knott	79748
Knox City	79529
Kopperl	76652
Kosse	76653
Kountze	77625
Kress	79052
Krum	76249
Kurten	77862
Kyle	78640

La Blanca	78558
La Coste	78039
La Feria	78559
La Grange (1st)	78945
La Joya	78560
La Marque (1st)	77568
La Porte (1st)	77571
La Pryor	78872
La Salle	77969
La Vernia	78121
La Villa	78562
La Ward	77970
Lackland A F B, Br. San Antonio (see appendix)	
Ladonia	75449
Lago Vista, R. Br. Leander	78641
Laguna Park, R. Br. Clifton	76634
Laird Hill	75666
Lake Air, Sta. Waco	76710
Lake Brownwood, R. Br. Brownwood	76801
Lake Creek	75450
Charleston, R. Br.	75424
Lake Dallas	75065
Lake Jackson (1st)	77566
Lake Kiowa, R. Br. Gainesville	76240
Lake Worth, Br. Fort Worth	76135
Lakehills, R. Br. Pipe Creek	78063
Lakeview	79239
Lakewood, Sta. Dallas	75214
Lamar Park, Sta. Corpus Christi (see appendix)	
Lamar Tech, Sta. Beaumont	77705
Lamesa (1st)	79331
Lamkin, R. Br. Gustine	76460
Lampasas (1st)	76550
Adamsville, R. Br.	76510
Lancaster (1st)	75146
Lane City	77453
Laneville	75667
Langtry	78871
Lapham, Sta. San Antonio	78216
Laredo (1st)	78040
Laredo A F B, MOU. Laredo	78040
Lariat	79335
Larue	75770
Lasara	78561
Latexo	75849
Laughlin A F B, MOU. Del Rio	78840
Laurel Heights, Sta. San Antonio	78212
Lavon	75066
Lawn	79530
Lazbuddie	79053
Leaday	76851
League City (1st)	77573
Leakey	78873
Leander	78641
Leary, R. Br. Texarkana	75501
Ledbetter	78946
Leesburg	75451
Leesville	78122
Lefors	79054
Leggett	77350
Legion, Br. Kerrville	78028
Lela	79055
Lelia Lake	79240
Leming	78050
Lenorah	79749
Leon Junction	76552
Leona	75850

Leonard	75452
Leroy	76654
Levelland (1st)	79336
Lewisville (1st)	75067
Lexington	78947
Liberty (1st)	77575
Liberty Hill	78642
Lillian	76061
Lincoln	78948
Lindale (1st)	75771
Mount Sylvan, R. Br.	75777
Linden	75563
Lindsay	76250
Lingleville	76461
Linn	78563
Lipan	76462
Lipscomb	79056
Lissie	77454
Little Elm	75068
Little River	76554
Littlefield (1st)	79339
Liverpool	77577
Livingston (1st)	77351
Llano	78643
Lobo, R. Br. Van Horn	79855
Lockhart (1st)	78644
Lockney	79241
Lodi	75564
Lohn	76852
Lolita	77971
Lometa	76853
London	76854
Lone Grove	78646
Lone Oak	75453
Lone Star	75668
Long Branch	75669
Long Mott	77972
Long Point, Sta. Houston	77055
Longview (1st)	75601
Longworth	79531
Loop	79342
Lopeno	78564
Loraine	79532
Lorena	76655
Lorenzo	79343
Los Angeles	78051
Los Ebanos	78565
Los Fresnos	78566
Los Indios	78567
Los Jardines, Sta. San Antonio	78237
Los Saenz, Sta. Roma	78584
Lott	76656
Louise	77455
Love Field Terminal, Sta. Dallas	75235
Lovelady	75851
Loving	76062
Lowake	76855
Lozano	78568
LUBBOCK (1st) (see appendix)	
Luckenbach	78647
Lueders	79533
Lufkin (1st)	75901
Luling (1st)	78648
Lumberton, R. Br. Silsbee	77656
Luther	79751
Lyford	78569
Lyons	77863
Lytle	78052
Mabank (1st)	75147
Macdona	78054

Madisonville (1st)	77864
Magnolia	77355
Magnolia Springs	75957
Main Place, Sta. Dallas	75250
Malakoff	75148
Malone	76660
Manchaca	78652
Manor	78653
Mansfield	76063
Manvel	77578
Maple	79344
Marathon	79842
Marble Falls (1st)	78654
Marfa	79843
Marietta	75566
Marion	78124
Markham	77456
Marlin (1st)	76661
Marquez	77865
Marshall (1st)	75670
Mart	76664
Martindale	78655
Martinsville	75958
Mary Hardin Baylor, Sta. Belton	76513
Maryneal	79535
Mason	76856
Masterson	79058
Matador	79244
Matagorda	77457
Mathis	78368
Maud	75567
Mauriceville	77626
Maverick, R. Br. Ballinger	76821
Maxwell	78656
May	76857
Maydelle	75772
Maypearl	76064
Maysfield	76555
Mc Adoo	79243
Mc Allen (1st)	78501
Mc Camey, Bakersfield, R. Br.	79752
	79717
Mc Caulley	79534
Mc Coy	78053
Mc Dade	78650
Mc Faddin	77973
Mc Gregor (1st)	76657
Mc Kinney (1st)	75069
Mc Lean	79057
Mc Leod	75565
Mc Murry, Sta. Abilene	79605
Mc Nair, R. Br. Baytown	77520
Mc Nary	79841
Mc Neil	78651
Mc Queeney	78123
Meadow	79345
Medical Center, Sta. Dallas	75219
Medina	78055
Medina Base, Br. San Antonio	78236
Megargel	76370
Melissa	75071
Melvin	76858
Memorial Park, Br. Houston (see appendix)	
Memphis	79245
Menard	76859
Mentone	79754
Mercedes (1st)	78570
Merchandise Mart, Sta. Dallas	75201
Mercury	76860

Mereta	76940
Meridian	76665
Merit	75072
Merkel	79536
Mertens	76666
Mertzon	76941
Meskill, Sta. Texas City	77590
Mesquite (1st)	75149
Mexia (1st)	76667
Meyersville	77974
Miami	79059
Mico, R. Br. Castroville	78056
Middle Water	79060
Midfield	77458
Midkiff	79755
Midland (1st)	79701
Midlothian	76065
Midway	75852
Milam	75959
Milano	76556
Miles	76861
Milford	76670
Millersview	76862
Millican	77866
Millsap	76066
Minden	75680
Mineola (1st)	75773
Mineral, R. Br. Kenedy	78125
Mineral Wells (1st)	76067
Minerva, R. Br. Cameron	76520
Mingus	76463
Mirando City	78369
Mission (1st)	78572
Missouri City (1st)	77459
Mitchell Avenue, Sta. Waco (see appendix)	
Mobeetie	79061
Moline	76863
Monahans (1st)	79756
Monroe City	77579
Monroe Street, Sta. Wichita Falls	76309
Mont Belvieu	77580
Montague	76251
Montalba	75853
Monte Alto, Br. Edcouch	78538
Montgomery	77356
Moody	76557
Moore	78057
Moran	76464
Morgan	76671
Morgan Mill	76465
Morse	79062
Morton	79346
Moscow	75960
Mosheim	76672
Moss Hill, R. Br. Liberty	77575
Moulton	77975
Mound	76558
Mount Calm	76673
Mount Enterprise	75681
Mount Pleasant (1st)	75455
Mount Selman	75776
Mount Sylvan, R. Br. Lindale	75777
Mount Vernon	75457
Mountain Home	78058
Muenster	76252
Muldoon	78949
Muleshoe (1st)	79347
Mullin	76864
Mumford	77867
Munday	76371

Murchison	75778
Murryhill, Sta. Lubbock	79413
Myra	76253
Nacogdoches (1st)	75961
Nada	77460
Naples	75568
Nash	75569
Natalia	78059
Natural Bridge Caverns, R. Br. San Antonio	78218
Naval Air, Sta. Corpus Christi (see appendix)	
Navarro, R. Br. Corsicana	75151
Navasota (1st)	77868
Nazareth	79063
Neches	75779
Nederland (1st)	77627
Needville	77461
Nemo	76070
Nevada	75073
New Baden	77870
New Boston	75570
New Braunfels (1st)	78130
New Caney	77357
New Deal	79350
New Home, R. Br. Wilson	79383
New London	75682
New Summerfield	75780
New Ulm	78950
New Waverly	77358
Newark	76071
Newcastle	76372
Newgulf	77462
Newport	76254
Newsome	75459
Newton	75966
Nimitz, Sta. San Antonio	78216
Nixon	78140
Nocona (1st)	76255
Nolan	79537
Nolanville	76559
Nome	77629
Nordheim	78141
Normandy, R. Br. Eagle Pass	78875
Normangee	77871
Normanna	78142
North Amarillo, Sta. Amarillo (see appendix)	
North Austin, Sta. Austin (see appendix)	
North College, Sta. Lubbock (see appendix)	
North Lake, Sta. Dallas	75238
North Port Arthur, Sta. Port Arthur	77640
North Texas, Sta. Denton	76203
North Uvalde, Sta. Uvalde	78801
North Zulch	77872
Northfield	79246
Northgate, Sta. El Paso	79924
Northpark, Sta. Dallas	75225
Northwest, Sta. Austin (see appendix)	
Norton	76865
Notrees	79759
Novice	79538
Number Fourteen, Sta. Lubbock	79412
Number Two, Sta. Paris	75460
Nursery	77976
O'Brien	79539
O'Donnell	79351

Oak Forest, Sta. Houston
(see appendix)
Oak Hill, R. Br. Austin.............78746
Oak Island, R. Br. Anahuac....77514
Cahalla.......................................76560
Oakhurst....................................77359
Oakland......................................78951
Oaks, Br. Fort Worth (see
appendix)
Oakville, R. Br. Three Rivers...78060
Oakwood....................................75855
Odell...79247
Odem..78370
Odessa (1st)..............................79760
Oglesby......................................76561
Oilton..78371
Oklaunion..................................76373
Old Glory....................................79540
Old Ocean..................................77463
Olden..76466
Olmito..78575
Otmos Park, Br. San
Antonio..................................78212
Olney (1st).................................76374
Olton..79064
Omaha..75571
Onalaska....................................77360
Orange (1st)...............................77630
Orange Grove.............................78372
Orangefield................................77639
Orchard......................................77464
Ore City.....................................75683
Orient, R. Br. San Angelo.....76942
Orla..79770
Osceola......................................76674
Otey, R. Br. Rosharon.............77583
Ottine..78658
Otto..76675
Ovalo..79541
Overton......................................75684
Ozona...76943
Paducah.....................................79248
Paige..78659
Paint Rock.................................76866
Paisano Annex, Sta. El Paso
(see appendix)
Palacios......................................77465
Palestine (1st)...........................75801
Palm Village, Sta.
Brownsville............................78520
Palmer..75152
Palo Pinto..................................76072
Paluxy..76467
Pampa (1st)...............................79065
Pandale......................................76944
Pandora......................................78143
Panhandle..................................79068
Panna Maria..............................78144
Panola..75685
Pantex, R. Br. Amarillo.......79069
Paradise.....................................76073
Paris (1st)..................................75460
Park Cities, Br. Dallas..........75205
Park Place, Sta. Houston.....77017
PASADENA (1st) (see
appendix)
Patricia......................................79352
Patroon......................................75967
Pattison.....................................77466
Pattonville.................................75468
Pawnee......................................78145
Peacock.....................................79542
Pear Ridge, Br. Port Arthur...77640

Pear Valley................................76867
Pearl, R. Br. Gatesville........76563
Pearland (1st)............................77581
Pearsall......................................78061
Peaster.......................................76074
Pecan Gap.................................75469
Pecos (1st).................................79772
Peggy...78062
Pendleton..................................76564
Penelope....................................76676
Penitas.......................................78576
Pennington................................75856
Penwell......................................79776
Pep..79353
Perrin...76075
Perry...76677
Perryton (1st)............................79070
Petersburg.................................79250
Petrolia......................................76377
Pettit..79354
Pettus..78146
Petty...75470
Pflugerville................................78660
Pharr (1st).................................78577
Phillips, Br. Borger................79071
Philrich, Sta. Borger.............79007
Pickton......................................75471
Pierce...77467
Pilot Point.................................76258
Pinehurst...................................77362
Pineland.....................................75968
Pioneer Town, R. Br.
Wimberley..............................78676
Pipe Creek................................78063
Pittsburg (1st)...........................75686
Placedo......................................77977
Placid, R. Br. Rochelle.........76868
Plains...79355
Bronco, R. Br................79315
Plainview (1st)...........................79072
Plano (1st).................................75074
Plantation, Sta. Lake
Jackson..................................77566
Plantersville..............................77363
Pleasant Grove, Sta. Dallas
(see appendix)
Pleasanton (1st).........................78064
Pledger......................................77468
Plum...78952
Point...75472
Point Comfort............................77978
Pointblank..................................77364
Pollok...75969
Polytechnic, Sta. Fort Worth
(see appendix)
Ponder.......................................76259
Ponta..75781
Pontotoc....................................76869
Poolville.....................................76076
Port Acres, R. Br. Port
Arthur.....................................77640
Port Aransas..............................78373
Port Arthur (1st)........................77640
Port Bolivar...............................77650
Port Isabel.................................78578
Port Lavaca (1st).......................77979
Port Mansfield, R. Br.
Raymondville.........................78580
Port Neches (1st).......................77651
Port O'Connor...........................77982
Portairs, Sta. Corpus Christi
(see appendix)
Porter...77365

Portland.....................................78374
Post..79356
Postoak......................................76260
Poteet..78065
Poth...78147
Pottsboro...................................75076
Pottsville....................................76565
Powderly....................................75473
Powell..75153
Poynor.......................................75782
Prairie Hill.................................76678
Prairie Lea.................................78661
Prairie View, Br. Hempstead...77445
Premont.....................................78375
Presidio......................................79845
Preston, Sta. Dallas...............75225
Price...75687
Priddy..76870
Primera, R. Br. Harlingen.....78550
Princeton....................................75077
Proctor.......................................76468
Progreso.....................................78579
Prosper......................................75078
Pumpville, R. Br. Dryden.......78876
Purdon.......................................76679
Purmela.....................................76566
Putnam......................................76469
Pyote..79777
Quail..79251
Quanah (1st)..............................79252
Queen City.................................75572
Quemado...................................78877
Quinlan......................................75474
Quitaque....................................79255
Quitman.....................................75783
Rainbow.....................................76077
Ralls...79357
Ranchland, Sta. El Paso.......79915
Randolph...................................75475
Randolph A F B, Br.
Universal City.........................78148
Ranger.......................................76470
Rankin..79778
Ratcliff.......................................75858
Ravenna.....................................75476
Raymond A Stewart Jr, Sta.
Galveston................................77550
Raymondville (1st).....................78580
Raywood....................................77582
Reagan.......................................76680
Highbank, R. Br...............76644
Realitos......................................78376
Red Oak.....................................75154
Red Rock...................................78662
Red Springs...............................76378
Redford......................................79846
Redmond Terrace, Sta.
College Station.......................77840
Redwater...................................75573
Reese A F B, R. Br.
Lubbock..................................79401
Refugio (1st)..............................78377
Reklaw.......................................75784
Renner..75079
Rhome..76078
Rice..75155
Richards.....................................77873
Richardson (1st).........................75080
Richland.....................................76681
Richland Hills, Br. Fort
Worth......................................76118
Richland Springs.......................76871
Richmond (1st)..........................77469

589

Ridge.....................................77874
Ridglea, Sta. Fort Worth (see appendix)
Riesel....................................76682
Ringgold................................76261
Rio Frio.................................78879
Rio Grande City.....................78582
Rio Hondo..............................78583
Rio Vista................................76683
Riomedina..............................78066
Rising Star.............................76471
River Oaks, Sta. Houston.......77019
Riverside, Sta. Fort Worth.....76111
Riverside................................77367
Riviera...................................78379
Roanoke.................................76262
Roans Prairie..........................77875
Roaring Springs.....................79256
Robert Lee.............................76945
Robinson, Br. Waco...............76706
Robstown (1st).......................78380
Roby......................................79543
Rochelle.................................76872
     Placid, R. Br..................76868
Rochester..............................79544
Rock Island...........................77470
Rockdale (1st)........................76567
Rockland................................75970
Rockport (1st)........................78382
Rocksprings............................78880
Rockwall................................75087
Rockwood...............................76873
Roganville..............................75971
Rogers....................................76569
Roma......................................78584
Romayor.................................77368
Roosevelt................................76874
Ropesville...............................79358
Rosanky..................................78953
Roscoe...................................79545
Rosebud..................................76570
Rosenberg (1st)......................77471
Rosharon.................................77583
Ross..76684
Rosser....................................75157
Rosston...................................76263
Rotan.....................................79546
Round Mountain.....................78663
Round Rock............................78664
Round Top...............................78954
Rowena...................................76875
Rowlett...................................75088
Roxton....................................75477
Roy Miller, Sta. Corpus Christi (see appendix)
Roy Royall, Sta. Houston (see appendix)
Royal Lane, Sta. Dallas (see appendix)
Royalty...................................79779
Royse City..............................75089
Rule..79547
Runge.....................................78151
Rusk (1st)...............................75785
Rye...77369
S F A, Sta Nacogdoches........75961
S W B T S, Sta. Fort Worth....76122
Sabinal...................................78881
Sabine Pass............................77655
Sachse, R. Br. Garland...........75040
Sacul......................................75788
Sadler....................................76264
Sagerton.................................79548

Saginaw, Br. Fort Worth........76179
Saint Hedwig..........................78152
Saint Jo..................................76265
Salado....................................76571
Salineno.................................78585
Salt Flat.................................79847
Salt Gap.................................76876
Saltillo...................................75478
Sam Houston, Sta. Houston....77052
Sam Houston College, Sta.
     Huntsville.........................77340
Sam Rayburn, R. Br. Jasper...75951
Samnorwood...........................79077
San Angelo (1st).....................76901
     Angelo State University, Sta.........................76901
     Goodfellow A F B, Sta.......76901
     Herring, Sta.....................76901
     Orient, R. Br....................76942
SAN ANTONIO (1st) (see appendix)
San Augustine (1st)................75972
San Benito (1st)......................78586
San Carlos, R. Br. Edinburg...78539
San Diego...............................78384
San Elizario............................79849
San Felipe..............................77473
San Isidro...............................78588
San Jacinto, Sta. Amarillo.....79106
San Juan.................................78589
San Leon, R. Br. Dickinson....77539
San Marcos (1st).....................78666
San Perlita.............................78590
San Saba................................76877
San Ygnacio............................78067
Sand, R. Br. Lamesa...............79331
Sanderson...............................79848
Sandia....................................78383
Sandy.....................................78665
Sanford...................................79078
Sanger....................................76266
Santa Anna.............................76878
Santa Elena.............................78591
Santa Maria.............................78592
Santa Rosa..............................78593
Santo......................................76472
Saragosa.................................79780
Saratoga..................................77585
Sargent, Br. Bay City.............77414
Sarita.....................................78385
Saspamco................................78153
Satin.......................................76685
Savoy......................................75479
Schertz...................................78154
Schulenburg (1st)....................78956
Schwertner.............................76573
Scotland.................................76379
Scottsville..............................75688
Scroggins................................75480
Scurry....................................75158
Seabrook (1st).........................77586
Seadrift..................................77983
Seagoville (1st).......................75159
Seagraves...............................79359
Sealy......................................77474
Sebastian................................78594
Segno......................................77370
Seguin (1st)............................78155
Selman City............................75689
Seminary Hill, Sta. Fort Worth (see appendix)
Seminole (1st).........................79360
Serna, Sta. San Antonio (see

appendix)
Seymour (1st).........................76380
Shady Oaks, Sta. Hurst...........76053
Shafter...................................79850
Shallowater.............................79363
Shamrock................................79079
Sharpstown, Sta. Houston (see appendix)
Sheffield.................................79781
Shelbyville.............................75973
Shepherd................................77371
Sheppard A F B, Br. Wichita
     Falls.................................76311
Sheridan.................................77475
Sherman (1st).........................75090
Sherwood...............................76948
Sherwood Shores, R. Br.
     Marble Falls.....................78654
Shiner.....................................77984
Shiro......................................77876
Sidney.....................................76474
Sierra Blanca..........................79851
Silsbee (1st)............................77656
Silver......................................76949
Silverton.................................79257
Simms....................................75574
Simonton................................77476
Singleton................................77877
Sinton (1st).............................78387
Sisterdale, R. Br. Boerne.......78006
Sivells Bend, R. Br.
     Gainesville.......................76240
Six Flags Over Texas, Sta.
     Arlington..........................76010
Skellytown..............................79080
Skidmore................................78389
Slaton (1st).............................79364
     Southland, R. Br...............79368
Slidell.....................................76267
Slocum, R. Br. Elkhart...........75839
Smiley.....................................78159
Smithfield...............................76080
Smithland................................75690
Smithville...............................78957
Smyer.....................................79367
Snook.....................................77878
Snyder (1st)............................79549
Somerset.................................78069
Somerville..............................77879
     Clay, R. Br........................77839
Sonora....................................76950
Sourlake.................................77659
South, Sta. College Station....77840
South Amarillo, Sta. Amarillo (see appendix)
South Austin, Sta. Austin (see appendix)
South Bend.............................76081
South Dallas, Sta. Dallas.......75215
South End, Sta. Beaumont.....77705
South Fort Worth, Sta. Fort Worth...........................76128
South Houston (1st)................77587
South Oak Cliff, Sta. Dallas (see appendix)
South Padre Island, R. Br.
     Port Isabel.......................78578
South Park, Sta. Houston (see appendix)
South Plains............................79258
South Post Oak, Sta.
     Houston (see appendix)
South San Antonio, Sta. San

Antonio (see appendix)
South Temple, Sta. Temple....76501
Southlake, R. Br. Grapevine....76051
Southland, R. Br. Slaton.......79368
Southmayd..........................76268
Southmore, Sta. Houston......77004
Spade................................79369
Speaks...............................77985
Spearman (1st)....................79081
Spicewood..........................78669
Splendora...........................77372
Spofford..............................78882
Spring................................77373
Spring Branch......................78070
Spring Hill, Br. Longview.......75601
Springlake...........................79082
Springtown..........................76082
Spur..................................79370
Spurger...............................77660
Stacy.................................76879
Stafford (1st).......................77477
Stamford (1st)......................79553
Stanton..............................79782
Staples...............................78670
Star..................................76880
Startzville, R. Br. New
  Braunfels..........................78130
Stephenville (1st).................76401
Sterling City........................76951
Stinnett..............................79083
Stock Yard, Sta. Fort Worth
  (see appendix)
Stockdale............................78160
Stonewall............................78671
Stonewall Mall, Sta. Corpus
  Christi..............................78410
Stowell...............................77661
Stratford.............................79084
Strawn...............................76475
Streetman............................75859
Sublime..............................77986
Sudan................................79371
Sugar Land (1st)...................77478
Sul Ross, Sta. Alpine.............79830
Sullivan City........................78595
Sulphur Bluff.......................75481
Sulphur Springs (1st).............75482
Summerfield.........................79085
Summit Heights, Sta. El
  Paso................................79930
Sumner...............................75486
Sundown.............................79372
Sunnyvale, R. Br. Mesquite....75149
Sunray...............................79086
Sunset, Sta. Lubbock.............79407
Sunset................................76270
Sutherland Springs................78161
Sweeny..............................77480
Sweet Home.........................77987
Sweetwater (1st)...................79556
Sylvester.............................79560
T C U, Sta. Fort Worth...........76129
T W U, Sta. Denton...............76204
Taft..................................78390
Tahoka...............................79373
Talco................................75487
Talpa................................76882
Tanglewood.........................78958
Tarleton, Sta. Stephenville.....76401
Tarpley..............................78883
Tarzan...............................79783
Tatum................................75691
Taylor (1st)..........................76574

Teague...............................75860
Tech, Sta. Lubbock................79409
Tehuacana...........................76686
Telegraph............................76883
Telephone............................75488
Telferner.............................77988
Telico, R. Br. Ennis...............75119
Tell..................................79259
Temple (1st).........................76501
Tenaha...............................75974
Tennessee Colony..................75861
Tennyson.............................76953
Terlingua............................79852
Terminal Annex, Sta. Dallas
  (see appendix)
Terrell (1st).........................75160
Terrell Wells, Sta. San
  Antonio (see appendix)
Texarkana (1st).....................75501
Texas City (1st)....................77590
Texhoma..............................73949
Texline...............................79087
Texon................................76954
Thalia, R. Br. Crowell............79227
The Grove, R. Br. Gatesville....76576
Thicket...............................77374
Thomaston...........................77989
Thompsons...........................77481
Thorndale............................76577
Thorntoff.............................76687
Thrall................................76578
Three Rivers.........................78071
  Oakville, R. Br.....................78060
Throckmorton........................76083
Tigua, Sta. El Paso...............79915
Tilden...............................78072
Timpson..............................75975
Tioga................................76271
Tivoli................................77990
Tobe Hahn, Sta. Beaumont......77706
Tokio................................79376
Tolar................................76476
Tom Bean............................75489
Tomball (1st)........................77375
  Hufsmith, R. Br....................77337
Tornillo..............................79853
Tow..................................78672
Town Hall, R. Br. Mesquite.....75149
Toyah................................79785
Toyahvale............................79786
Trent.................................79561
Trenton..............................75490
Trickham, R. Br. Santa
  Anna...............................76878
Trinidad.............................75163
Trinity...............................75862
Troup................................75789
Troy..................................76579
Truscott..............................79260
Tuleta...............................78162
Tulia (1st)...........................79088
Turkey...............................79261
Turnersville.........................76580
Tuscola..............................79562
Twitty...............................79090
Tye..................................79563
Tyler (1st)...........................75701
Tynan...............................78391
Uhland, R. Br. Kyle...............78640
Umbarger............................79091
Universal City (1st)................78148
University, Sta. Austin...........78712

University Of Dallas, Sta.
  Irving..............................75060
University Park, Sta. Wichita
  Falls (see appendix)
University Park, Sta. San
  Antonio (see appendix)
Utopia...............................78884
Uvalde (1st).........................78801
Valentine............................79854
Valera................................76884
Valley Hi, Br. San Antonio.....78227
Valley Mills.........................76689
Valley Spring........................76885
Valley View..........................76272
Van..................................75790
Van Alstyne.........................75095
Van Horn.............................79855
Van Vleck............................77482
Vancourt.............................76955
Vanderbilt...........................77991
Vanderpool...........................78885
Vealmoor, R. Br. Big Spring....79720
Vega.................................79092
Venus...............................76084
Vera.................................76383
Verhalen, R. Br. Pecos...........79772
Veribest.............................76886
Vernon (1st).........................76384
Veterans Administration,
  Sta. Temple.......................76501
Veterans Administration, Br.
  Waco...............................76711

Viboras..............................78392
Vickery, Sta. Dallas..............75231
Victoria (1st).......................77901
Vidauri..............................77992
Vidor (1st)..........................77662
View.................................79564
Vigo Park, R. Br. Tulia..........79088
Village, Sta. Midland.............79701
Village, Br. Dallas.................75205
Village Mills........................77663
Vincent, R. Br. Coahoma........79511
Vineyard.............................76085
Voca.................................76887
Von Ormy............................78073
Voss.................................76888
Votaw...............................77376
Voth, R. Sta. Beaumont.........77709
WACO (1st) (see appendix)
Wadsworth...........................77483
Waelder..............................78959
Wainwright, Sta. San
  Antonio............................78208
Waka................................79093
Wake Village, Br. Texarkana....75501
Walburg.............................78673
Wall.................................76957
Waller...............................77484
Wallis...............................77485
Wallisville..........................77597
Walnut Hill, Sta. Dallas (see
  appendix)
Walnut Springs......................76690
Warda...............................78960
Waring...............................78074
Warren...............................77664
Warrenton............................78961
Washburn, R. Br. Claude........79019
Washington...........................77880
Waskom..............................75692

Watauga, R. Br. Keller 76248
Water Valley 76958
Waxahachie (1st) 75165
Wayside 79094
Weatherford (1st) 76086
  Garner, R. Br. 76042
Webb A F B, Br. Big Spring ... 79720
Webster (1st) 77598
Wedgwood, Sta. Fort Worth
  (see appendix)
Weesatche 77993
Weimar 78962
Weinert 76388
Weir 78674
Welch 79377
Weldon 75863
Welfare, R. Br. Boerne 78036
Wellborn 77881
Wellington 79095
Wellman 79378
Wells 75976
Weslaco (1st) 78596
West 76691
West Austin, Sta. Austin 78703
West Columbia 77486
West Galveston, R. Br.
  Galveston 77550
West Odessa, R. Br. Odessa ... 79760
West Orange, Br. Orange 77630
West Point 78963
West Port Arthur, Sta. Port
  Arthur 77640
West Side, Sta. Beaumont
  (see appendix)
West Texas, Sta. Canyon 79015
Westbrook 79565
Westfield, Br. Houston 77090
Westhoff 77994
Westminster 75096
Weston 75697

Westview, Sta. Waco (see
  appendix)
Wetmore 78163
Wharton (1st) 77488
Wheeler 79096
Wheelock 77882
White Deer 79097
White Oak 75693
White Rock, Sta. Dallas 75218
White Settlement, Br. Fort
  Worth 76108
Whiteface 79379
Whitehouse 75791
Whitesboro 76273
Whitewright 75491
Whitharral 79380
Whitney 76692
Whitsett 78075
Whitt 76090
Whon 76889
WICHITA FALLS (1st) (see
  appendix)
Wickett 79788
Wiergate 75977
Wildorado 79098
Wildwood, R. Br. Village
  Mills 77663
Wilford Hall U S A F Hosp,
  Br. San Antonio 78236
William Beaumont Hospital,
  Br. El Paso 79920
William Rice, Sta. Houston 77005
Willis 77378
Willow City 78675
Wills Point (1st) 75169
Wilmer 75172
Wilson 79381
  New Home, R. Br. 79383
Wimberley 78676

Winchester 78964
Windom 75492
Windthorst 76389
Winfield 75493
Wingate 79566
Wink 79789
Winkler 75864
Winnie 77665
Winnsboro (1st) 75494
Winona 75792
Winters 79567
Woden 75978
Wolfe City 75496
Wolfforth 79382
Woodlake 75865
Woodlawn 75694
Woodsboro 78393
Woodson 76091
Woodville (1st) 75979
Wortham 76693
Wrightsboro 78677
Wylie (1st) 75098
Yancey 78886
Yantis 75497
Yoakum (1st) 77995
Yorktown 78164
Yows Street Annex, Sta.
  Borger 79007
Ysleta, Sta. El Paso (see
  appendix)
Zapata 78076
Zavalla 75980
Zephyr 76890

ABILENE 796

POST OFFICE BOXES

Box Nos.
1-3282	Main Office	04
511-656	Dyess Afb Br	07
5001-5694	A Sta	05

RURAL ROUTES

1 2	01
3	05
4	01
5	05
6	01

STATIONS, BRANCHES AND UNITS

Abilene Christian College Sta	01
Dyess A F B Br	07
Hardin Simmons Sta	01
Mc Murry Sta	05
General Delivery	04
Postmaster	04

APARTMENTS, HOTELS, MOTELS

Abilene Manor, 609 Leggett Dr	05
Abilene Towers, 1102 N 3rd	01
Bowyer, 1705 S 3rd	02
Camelot, 5241 Alamo	05
Elmwood W Manor, 4025 S 7th	05
Fontaine, 2433 N 3rd	03
Le Martinique, 302 N Mockingbird	03
Maison Blanche, 2800 Sayles Blvd	05
Radford Hills, 765 E N 10th	01
Rio Vista, 4028 S 7th	05
Shoji House, 3201 N 3rd	03
Spanish Arms, 1717 N 6th	03
Twenty-One Twenty-One, 2121 N 6th	03
Villa Chateau, 2102 Beechwood	03
West Woods Terrace, 600 Westwood	03

BUILDINGS

Abilene Savings, 402 Cedar	01
Alexander, 102 Pine	01
C & T, 1333 N 2nd	01
Citizens National Bank, 402 Cypress	01
City Hall, 555 Walnut	01
Clinic, 598 Westwood	03
County Courthouse, S 3rd & Oak	02
Crescendo, 1052 N 5th	01
Duffy, 471 Cypress	01
Federal, 300 Pine	01
First National Bank, 401 Cypress	01
First State Bank, S 4th & Oak	02
Meadows Medical Center, 1325 Hickory	01

Mims, 1049 N 3rd	01
Oil & Gas, 1209 N 4th	01
Permian, 317 N Willis	03
Petroleum, 451 Pine	01
Professional, 1101 N 19th	01
Southwest Savings & Loan, 340 Hickory	01
West Texas Utilities, 1062 N 3rd	01

HOSPITALS

Cox Memorial, 618 Cedar	01
Hendrick Memorial, N 19th & Hickory	01
West Texas Medical Center, 650 E Hwy 80	01

MILITARY INSTALLATIONS

Dyess A F B	07

UNIVERSITIES AND COLLEGES

Abilene Christian College	01
Hardin Simmons University	01
Mc Murry College	05

AMARILLO 791

POST OFFICE BOXES

Box Nos.
1-2974	Downtown Sta	05
3000-3999	San Jacinto Sta	06
4000-4999	Main Office	05
5000-5999	North Amarillo Sta	07
6000-8999	South Amarillo Sta	09
9001-9278	Downtown Sta	05
10000-10999	Avonbell Sta	06
11000-11000	Main Office	05

RURAL ROUTES

1	06
2	01
3	07

STATIONS, BRANCHES AND UNITS

Avonbell Sta	06
Downtown Sta	05
North Amarillo Sta	07
Pantex Rural Br	79069
San Jacinto Sta	06
South Amarillo Sta	09
General Delivery	05
Postmaster	05

APARTMENTS, HOTELS, MOTELS

Amarillo, 2217 Polk	09
Ashby, 821 Evergreen	07
Astoria Park, 3116 W 15th	02
Badger, 1115 Jackson	01
Beverly Towers, 2706 Arcadia	09
Bon Vie 2815 W 27th	09
Carrolton, 1700 Jackson	02

Casa De Warren 4215 Western	09
Clifton, 920 Bryan	02
Continental, 1300 Jackson	01
Eden Roc, 2700 Westhaven Cir	09
El Dorado 4300 Prairie	09
Fairfax, 1218 W 10th	01
Fleetwood 3506 Janet	09
Green Acres, 3105 Plains Blvd	02
Greenhaven, 300 N Jefferson	07
Heritage 3320 Western	09
Imperial, 1501 W 9th	01
La Tour, 2028 Austin	09
Lantern Square 7208 W 34th	09
Lucerne, 1109 Polk	01
Mandalay, 3005 W 27th	09
Mark Twain, 500 W 10th	01
Medallion, 3001 W 27th	09
Modern Manor, 3404 Janet	09
Otis, 2306 W 6th	06
Palo Duro, 1601 Jackson	02
Paramount Terrance, 3809 Virginia	09
Parkview Manor, 121 Goliad	06
Resident, 1417 Harrison	01
Royal Palace, 1124 N Mirror	07
Talmage, 1401 Van Buren	01
Toscosa, 2118 Taylor	09
Villa, 2005 Austin	05
Vineyard Manor, 1205 Polk	01
West Hills Arms, 4218 W 2nd	06
Western Sky, 3007 W 27th	09
Westwood, 2008 Austin	09
Wolflin Village, 2301 Austin	09

BUILDINGS

Alta, 1500 Taylor	01
Amarillo National Bank	01
Amarillo Petroleum, 211 W 8th	01
Amarillo, 301 Polk	01
American National Bank, 116 W 7th	01
Bank Of The Southwest, 2201 Civic Cir	09
Barfield, 600 Polk	01
Bivins, 420 Polk	01
Brayboy, 2710 Civic Cir	09
Colonial Plaza, 1310 W 9th	01
Doctors, 1422 Tyler	01
First National Bank, 112 W 8th	01
Fisk, 724 Polk	01
Herring Plaza	01
Insurance, 212 East 6th	01
Mays, 908 Polk	01
Paramount, 811 Polk	01
Phoenix, 804 Rusk	06
Plaza One	01
Professional, 600 W 8th	01
Rule, 217 Polk	01
Santa Fe, 900 Polk	01
Springer, 1217 W 10th	01
Urban, 800 Bryan	06
Vaughn, 320 Polk	01
Western, 112 E 5th	01

GOVERNMENT OFFICES

County Court House Annex, 600 Taylor	
County Court House, 511 Taylor	0
Old Post Office, 620 Taylor	0i
United States Post Office, 207 East 5th	0i

HOSPITALS

Amarillo Hospital District, 2208 West 6th	06
Amarillo Osteopathic, 2828 W 27th	09
High Plains Baptist, 1600 Wallace	06
Hillhaven Convalescent, 2423 Line	06
Northwest Texas, 2103 W 6th	06
Saint Anthony, 735 N Polk	07
Veterans Administration, W 66th & Bell Ave	06

ARLINGTON 760

POST OFFICE BOXES

Box Nos.		
1-1652	Main Office	10
3451-3629	Sta A	10
5001-6279	Great Southwest Sta	11

RURAL ROUTES

2,3,4,5	10

STATIONS, BRANCHES AND UNITS

Great Southwest Sta	11
Six Flags Over Texas Sta	10
General Delivery	10
Postmaster	10

APARTMENTS, HOTELS, MOTELS

Arlington Villa, 2601 W Randol Mill Rd	12
Cibola Inn, 1601 E Division	11
Six Flags Inn, Ave H & 107th	11

BUILDINGS

Forum 303 3000 E Pioneer Pkwy	10
Great Southwest Corp, 520 Ave H East	11
Six Flags Mall, 2801 E. Division	11
Six Flags Over Texas, 2201 Road To Six Flags	11

HOSPITALS

Arlington Community Hospital, 711 W Randol Mill Rd	12
Arlington Memorial Hospital, 800 W Randol Mill Rd	12

UNIVERSITIES AND COLLEGES

University Of Texas At Arlington	10

AUSTIN 787

POST OFFICE BOXES

Box Nos.		
A-Z	University Of Texas Sta	12
1-2999	Main Office	67
3000-3999	South Austin Sta	04
4000-4999	North Austin Sta	51
5000-5999	West Austin Sta	03
6000-6999	East Austin Sta	02
7000-8999	University Of Texas Sta	12
9000-9999	Northwest Sta	57
12000-13999	Capitol Sta	11
20001-23199	Bergstrom A F B	43

RURAL ROUTES

1	02
2	04
3	51
4	57
5	04
6	46
7,8,9	03
10	46

STATIONS, BRANCHES AND UNITS

Bergstrom AFB MOU	43
Capitol Sta	11
Cedar Valley Rural Br	46
Creedmoor Rural Br	44
East Austin Sta	02
North Austin Sta	23
Northwest Sta	56
South Austin Sta	04
University Sta	12
West Austin Sta	03
General Delivery	67
Postmaster	10
Star Route A	46

APARTMENTS, HOTELS, MOTELS

Alamo, 400 W 6th	01
Austin, 701 Congress Ave	01
Cambridge Tower, 1801 Lavaca	01
Castilian, 2323 San Antonio	05
Commodore Perry, 800 Brazos	01
Downtowner Motor Inn, 300 E 11th	01
Driskill, 117 E 7th	01
Gondolier-Ramada Motor,	

1001 S Interregional	41
Hardin House North, 801 W 24th	05
Holiday Inn Motor, 20 N Interregional	02
Holiday Inn Motor, 6901 Interregional Hwy	52
Jester Center Hall, 101 E 21st	05
Ramada Inn, 5650 Interregional Hwy	51
Sheraton-Crest Inn, 101-105 E 1st	01
Terrace Motor, 1201 S Congress Ave	04
Villa Capri Motor, 2360 Interregional Hwy	05
Westgate, 1122 Colorado	01

BUILDINGS

American National Bank Building, 111 W 6th	01
Austin National Bank, 501 Congress Ave	01
Austin Savings & Loan	01
Bolm	01
Brown	01
Bryan-Day	01
Capital National Bank	01
City National Building, 221 E 9th	01
Commodore Perry Hotel, 108 E 8th	01
Ernest O Thompson, 910 Colorado	01
Federal	01
First Austin	01
First Federal Savings & Loan Association	01
First National Life	01
Internal Revenue Service Center	40
International Life Insurance	01
John H Reagan State Office	01
Littlefield	01
Lowich	01
Medical Arts Sq.	05
Medical Park Tower	05
Nash	01
Page	01
Perry-Brooks	01
Richmond Bldg 1411 West Ave	01
Sam Houston State Office	01
Scarbrough	01
State Capitol	11
State Dept Of Public Safety	51
State Finance	01
State Health	56
State Highway	01
State Insurance	01
State Library	01
Texas Employment Commission	01
Texas State Bank	01
Travis	01
Tribune	01
U S Treasury	01
V A Data Processing Center	41
V F W, 1011 San Jacinto	01
Vaughn	01
Westgate	01

GOVERNMENT OFFICES

County Court House	67
Supreme Court	11

HOSPITALS

Brackenridge, 1400 East Ave.	01
Holy Cross, 2600 E 19th	02
Medical Arts Square	05
Medical Park Tower, 1301 W 38th	05
Saint Davids, 919 E 32nd	05
Seton, 600 W 26th	05
Shoalcreek Hospital, 3501 Mills Ave	31

UNIVERSITIES AND COLLEGES

Austin Presbyterian Theological Seminary, 100 W 27th	05
Episcopal Theological Seminary, 606 Rathervue Pl.	05
Huston-Tillotson, 1820 E 8th	02
Lutheran Concordia, 3400 East Ave.	05
Maryhill 3101 S Congress	04
Saint Edwards University, 3101 S Congress Ave	04
The University Of Texas, 200 W 21st	12

BEAUMONT   777

POST OFFICE BOXES

Box Nos.

1-4314	Main Office	04
5001-5599	West Side Sta	02
6001-6399	South End Sta	05
7001-7999	Tobe Hahn Sta	06
10001-13999	Lamar Tech	10

RURAL ROUTES

1	06
2,4	05
5	06

STATIONS, BRANCHES AND UNITS

Lamar Tech Sta	05
South End Sta	05
Tobe Hahn Sta	06
Voth Rural Sta	09
General Delivery	04
Postmaster	04

BUILDINGS

American Center	01
Beaumont Savings & Loans	01
Biscamp	02
Doctors	01
F & M	01
First Federal Savings & Loan	01
General Finance	01
Gilbert	01

Goodhue	01
Kaufman	01
Mc Faddin	02
North	02
Perlstein	01
Petroleum	01
Ridgewood Center	03
San Jacinto	01

GOVERNMENT OFFICES

City Hall	04
Court House	01

HOSPITALS

Baptist	04
Saint Elizabeth	02

UNIVERSITIES AND COLLEGES

Lamar Tech	10

CORPUS CHRISTI   784

POST OFFICE BOXES

Box Nos.

1-2831	Downtown Sta	03
3000-3999	Kleberg Sta	04
4000-4999	Main Office	08
5000-5999	Roy Miller Sta	05
6000-6999	Lamar Park Sta	11
7000-7999	Portairs Sta	15
8001-8669	Gulfway Sta	12
9000-9999	Main Office	08
10001-10260	Stonewall Mall	10
60001-60296	Clarkwood	06

RURAL ROUTES

1	15
2	08
3	15

STATIONS, BRANCHES AND UNITS

Clarkwood Sta	06
Downtown Sta	03
Flour Bluff Rural Sta	18
Gulfway Sta	12
Kleberg Sta	04
Lamar Park Sta	11
Naval Air Sta	18
Portairs Sta	15
Roy Miller Sta	05
Stonewall Mall Sta	10
General Delivery	08
Postmaster	08

BUILDINGS

Atlantic-Mobil, 602 Winnebago	01
Bevly, 1220 S Staples	04
Center, 416 N Chaparral	01
Citizens Standard Insurance, 1305 N Shoreline	01
Corpus Christi State National Bank, 502 N Water	01
Cullen Mall 4800 S Alameda	12

Doctors, 3154 Reid Dr	04
Driscoll, 609 N Broadway	01
Federal, 521 Starr	01
Guaranty National Tower, 711 N Carancahua	01
Gulf Security, 1806 S Alameda	04
Hawn, 817 N Carancahua	01
International Business Machines, 520 S Chaparral	01
Jones, 317 Peoples	01
Kaffie, 205 N Chaparral	01
Klee Square, 505 S Water	01
La Ratama Library, 505 Mesquite	01
Lozano, 403 S Staples	01
Medical Arts, 1001 Louisiana	04
Medical Center, 2482 Morgan Ave	05
Medical Dental, 1807 S Alameda	04
Medical Plaza, 1411-15 3rd St	04
Oil Industries, 723 N Broadway	01
Padre Staples Mall 53-5400 Padre Island	11
Palm Plaza, 1800 S Staples	04
Park Tower, 901 N Carancahua	01
Parkdale Plaza	11
Petroleum Tower, 811 N Carancahua	01
Smith, 425 Schatzel	01
Southern Bankers, 1630 S Brownlee	04
Stonewall Mall 10500 Leopard	10
Sullivan, 3105 Leopard	08
Sun Texaco, 922 N Carancahua	01
Swantner & Gordon	01
Tejas, 719 N Broadway	01
Town And Country, 4100 S Alameda	11
United Savings, 3765 S Alameda	11
Vaughn Plaza, 711 N Carancahua	01
Weber 319 Mesquite	01
Wilson Tower, 606 N Carancahua	01
Wilson, 545 N Broadway	01
Woodlawn Center	08
1800 S Staples Bldg, 1800 S Staples	04
600 Broadway, 601 N Broadway	01

GOVERNMENT OFFICES

City Hall, 302 S. Shoreline	01
County Court House, 1111 N Mesquite	01

HOSPITALS

Corpus Christi Osteopathic, 1502 Tarlton	15
Doctors Hospital, 3160 Reid	04

Driscoll Foundation, 3533 S
Alameda.................................. 11
Memorial Hospital, 2606
Hospital.................................. 05
Physicians & Surgeons
General, 4626 Weber....... 11
Spohn Hospital, 1436 3rd.... 04
Thoma-Spann, 1546 S
Brownlee............................... 04
U S Naval Hospital, Naval Air
Station................................... 19

MILITARY INSTALLATIONS

Army Aero Depot
Maintenance Center............ 19
Naval Air Station, Naval
Base...................................... 19

UNIVERSITIES AND COLLEGES

Del Mar College...................... 04
University Of Corpus Christi... 11

DALLAS   752

POST OFFICE BOXES

Box Nos.
1-3699   Main Office 21
3701-4599   A Sta................. 08
5001-6499   Terminal Annex
Sta......... 22
7001-7999   Inwood Sta...... 09
8001-8499   Park Cities Br .. 05
8501-8999   South Oak Cliff
Sta............ 16
9501-9999   Lakewood Sta.. 14
10001-10999 Industrial Sta...... 07
11001-11499 East Grand
Sta............ 23
12001-12999 Preston Sta 25
15001-15399 Merchandise
Mart Sta 01
15401-15999 South Dallas
Sta............ 15
17001-17999 Pleasant Grove
Sta............ 17
18001-18999 White Rock
Sta............ 18
19001-19999 Medical Center
Sta............ 19
20001-20999 Walnut Hill
Sta............ 20
21001-21999 Beverly Hills
Sta............ 11
22001-22299 Terminal Annex
Sta............ 22
23001-23999 East Oak Cliff
Sta............ 03
24001-24999 Joe Pool Sta 24
26001-26999 Fair Park Sta...... 26
28001-28999 Casa View Sta .. 28
29001-29999 Walnut Hill
Sta............ 29
30001-30999 Royal Lane
Sta............ 30
31001-31999 Vickery.............. 31
34001-34999 Farmers
Branch....... 34
35001-36259 Airlawn Sta 35
38001-38999 Northlake.......... 38

45001-45999 Exchange Park.. 35
47001-47999 Brook Hollow
Sta. 47
50001-50999 Main Place
Sta.............. 50
57001-57999 Industrial.......... 07
61001-61999 Dallas-Fort
Worth Airport,
Tx.............. 61
64001-64999 Greenville
Avenue............ 06

RURAL ROUTES

1... 24
2... 16
8... 11

STATIONS, BRANCHES AND UNITS

Airlawn Sta............................... 35
Beverly Hills Sta...................... 11
Brook Hollow Sta..................... 47
Casa View Sta.......................... 28
Cockrell Hill Br........................ 11
East Grand Sta.......................... 23
East Oak Cliff Sta..................... 03
Exchange Park Sta.................... 35
Fair Park Sta............................ 10
Farmers Branch Br................... 34
Greenville Avenue Sta.............. 06
Industrial Sta............................ 12
Inwood Sta............................... 09
Joe Pool Sta............................. 24
Lakewood Sta........................... 14
Love Field Terminal Sta........... 35
Main Place Sta.......................... 50
Medical Center Sta................... 19
Merchandise Mart Sta.............. 01
North Lake Sta.......................... 38
Northpark Sta............................ 25
Park Cities Br........................... 05
Pleasant Grove Sta................... 17
Preston Sta............................... 25
Royal Lane Sta.......................... 30
South Dallas Sta....................... 15
South Oak Cliff Sta................... 39
Terminal Annex Sta.................. 02
Vickery Sta............................... 31
Village Br................................. 05
White Rock Sta......................... 18
General Delivery....................... 21
Postmaster................................ 21

APARTMENTS, HOTELS, MOTELS

Adolphus, 1321 Commerce 21
Argyle, 3721 Hall 19
Athena, 6335 W Northwest
Hwy 25
Baker, 1400 Commerce............ 21
Crest Park, 4242 Lomo Alto.... 19
Dallas, 312 S Houston............. 22
Fairmont, 1717 N Akard 01
Gold Crest, 3601 Turtle
Creek....................................... 19
Highlander, 4217 Lomo Alto... 19
Hockaday Village, 5615
Belmont................................... 06
Manor House, 1222
Commerce............................... 02

Park Towers, 3310
Fairmount................................ 01
Preston Tower, 6211 W
Northwest Hwy........................ 25
Sheraton-Dallas, Southland
Center...................................... 21
Statler-Hilton, 1914
Commerce................................ 21
Towers, 3883 Turtle Creek...... 19
Turtle Creek North, 3701
Turtle Creek............................ 19
Turtle Creek, 3525 Turtle
Creek....................................... 19
Wedgewood, 2511 Wedglea..... 11
White Plaza, 1933 Main........... 21
Whitmore, 1019 Commerce..... 02

BUILDINGS

Adolphus Tower, 1412 Main ... 02
Alford, 318 Cadiz..................... 07
Apparel Mart, 2300 N
Stemmons Fwy......................... 07
Atlantic, 408 Bullington........... 01
Baptist, 703 N Ervay............... 01
Blanton Towers, 3300 W
Mockingbird............................ 35
Blue Cross, 100 N Central
Expressway.............................. 01
Braniff, 400 N Exchange
Park... 35
Carter Towers, 351 W
Jefferson................................. 08
City Hall 2014 Main................. 01
Coke, 710 N St Paul................. 01
Collum, 318 N St Paul.............. 01
Continental, 1500 Jackson....... 01
Corrigan Tower, 212 N St
Paul... 01
Cotton Exchange, 608 N St
Paul... 01
Dallas Athletic Club, 1805
Elm.. 01
Dallas Federal Savings &
Loan, 1505 Elm....................... 01
Dallas Trade Mart, 2100 N
Stemmons Fwy......................... 07
Davis, 1309 Main...................... 02
Day, 425 S Field 02
Doctors, 3707 Gaston.............. 46
Elm Place, 1015 Elm................ 02
Empire Bank, 1806 Main.......... 01
Empire Central, 7701 N
Stemmons Fwy......................... 47
Empire Life, 1712 Commerce... 01
Employers Insurance, 423 S
Akard....................................... 02
Exchange Bank, 100 N
Exchange Park.......................... 35
Expressway Tower, 6116 N
Central Expwy.......................... 06
Fidelity Union Life, 1511
Bryan....................................... 01
Fidelity Union Tower, 1507
Pacific..................................... 01
First National Bank, 1401
Elm.. 02
Five Eleven North Akard.......... 01
Five Hundred South Ervay....... 01
Fourteen Sixteen Commerce.... 01
Frito-Lay, 300 N Exchange
Park... 35

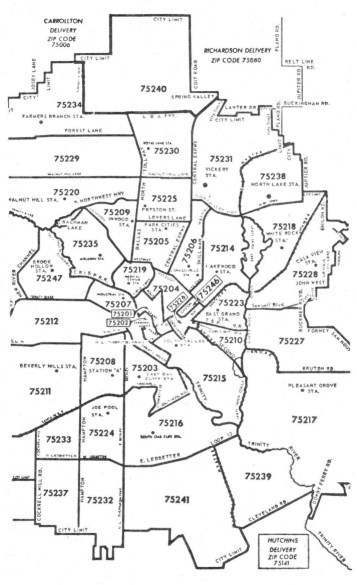

ZIP CODES
Dallas TX

Gaston Medical, 3607 Gaston ... 46
Gibraltar Life, 2006 Bryan ... 01
Great American Of Dallas, 2020 Live Oak ... 01
Great National Life, 1604 Main ... 01
Guardian Savings & Loan, 1215 Main ... 02
Hartford, 408 N St Paul ... 01
Home Furnishing Mart, 2000 N Stemmons Fwy ... 07
Hudson & Hudson, 109 N Akard ... 01
Insurance Plz., 411 N. Akard ...
International Business Machines, 2911 Cedar Springs ... 19
Kirby, 1509 Main ... 01
L T V Tower, 1525 Elm ... 01
Lacy, 1521 Commerce ... 01
Life, 311 S Akard ... 02
Locke Medical, 6011 Harry Hines ... 35
Love Field Terminal, 8008 Cedar Springs ... 35
Main Bank, 810 Main ... 02
Majestic, 1921 Elm ... 01
Market Hall, 2200 N Stemmons Fwy ... 07
Mayflower, 411 N Akard ... 01
Meadows, 5636 Milton ... 06
Medical Arts, 1717 Pacific ... 01
Melba, 1913 Elm ... 01
Mercantile Bank, 1700 Main .. 01
Mercantile Continental, 1810 Commerce ... 01
Mercantile Dallas, 1807 Commerce ... 01
Mercantile Securities, 1802 Main ... 01
Merchandise Mart, 500 S. Ervay ... 01
Metropolitan Federal, 1401 Main ... 02
Mobil, 108 S Akard ... 02
National Bankers Life, 202 S Ervay ... 01
Noel Page, 6440 N Central Expwy ... 06
Oak Cliff Bank And Trust, 400 S Zang ... 08
Oakwood Tower, 3626 Hall ... 19
One Lee Park West, 3303 Lee Pky ... 19
One Main Place ... 50
Praetorian, 1607 Main ... 01
Preston Forest Tower, 5925 Forest Ln ... 30
Records, 509 Main ... 02
Reliance Life, 505 N Ervay ... 01
Republic Bank Tower, 325 N St Paul ... 01
Republic Bank, 300 N Ervay .. 01
Reserve Life, 403 S Akard ... 02
Santa Fe 2, 1118 Jackson ... 02
Santa Fe 3, 1104 Wood ... 02
Santa Fe 4, 1033 Young ... 02
Simons, 1528 Main ... 01
Southland Center, 400 Olive... 01
Southwest, 701 Elm ... 02
Southwestern Life, 1807

Ross ... 01
States General Life, 708 Jackson ... 02
Stemmons Empire, 8435 N. Stemmons Fwy ... 47
Stemmons Tower East 2700 N Stemmons Fwy ... 07
Stemmons Tower North, 2710 N Stemmons Fwy ... 07
Stemmons Tower South, 2726 N Stemmons Fwy ... 07
Stemmons Tower West, 2730 N Stemmons Fwy ... 07
Thomas, 1314 Wood ... 02
Tower, 1907 Elm ... 01
Trinity Universal, 820 N Harwood ... 01
Two Eleven North Ervay ... 01
Two-O-Nine Browder ... 01
United Fidelity, 1025 Elm ... 02
Universal, 903 Ross ... 01
University Computing, 1949 N Stemmons Fwy ... 07
Wholesale Merchants, 912 Commerce ... 02
Wilson, 1621 Main ... 01
1516 Commerce ... 01
1716 Commerce ... 01
2001 Bryan Tower ... 01

GOVERNMENT OFFICES

Dallas County Court House, 600 Commerce ... 02
Dallas Water Utility ... 77
Federal U S Court House 1100 Commerce ... 02
Federal, Bryan & Ervay ... 01
Old County Court House, 100 S. Houston ... 02
Postal Data Center ... 99

HOSPITALS

Baylor, 3500 Gaston ... 46
Beverly Hills, 1353 N Westmoreland ... 11
Chester, 3330 S Lancaster ... 16
Dallas Osteopathic, 5003 Ross ... 06
East Dallas, 6003 Victor ... 14
Gaston, 3525 Gaston ... 46
Granville C. Morton, 9000 Harry Hines ... 35
Medical Arts, Medical Arts Building ... 01
Methodist, 301 W Colorado ... 22
Parkland Memorial, 5201 Harry Hines ... 35
Presbyterian, 8200 Walnut Hill ... 31
Saint Paul, 5909 Harry Hines ... 35
Stevens Park, 2100 W. Colorado ... 11
Timberlawn, 4600 Samuell ... 21
Veterans, 4500 S Lancaster .. 16
Woodlawn, 3819 Maple ... 19

UNIVERSITIES AND COLLEGES

Bishop, 3837 Simpson-Stuart Rd ... 41

Dallas Baptist, 7501 W Kiest. 11
Dallas Theological Seminary, 3901 Swiss ... 04
Dallas, 500 N Akard ... 01
El Centro, 801 Main ... 02
Southern Methodist University, Hillcrest & University ... 22

EL PASO   799

POST OFFICE BOXES

Box Nos.
A-N — Main Office ... 51
O-BB — Main Office ... 52
1-70 — Main Office ... 40
71-140 — Main Office ... 41
141-240 — Main Office ... 42
241-512 — Main Office ... 43
521-740 — Main Office ... 44
741-920 — Main Office ... 45
921-1112 — Main Office ... 46
1121-1340 — Main Office ... 47
1341-1612 — Main Office ... 48
1621-1830 — Main Office ... 49
1831-2040 — Main Office ... 50
2041-2250 — Main Office ... 51
2251-2460 — Main Office ... 52
3001-3914 — Station A ... 23
4001-4999 — Northgate Sta... 14
6001-6636 — Fort Bliss Br... 06
8001-8099 — Biggs A F B Br ... 08
9000-9145 — Paisano Annex Sta ... 82
9151-9295 — Paisano Annex Sta ... 83
9301-9445 — Paisano Annex Sta ... 84
9451-9566 — Paisano Annex Sta ... 85
9571-9685 — Paisano Annex Sta ... 86
9691-9764 — Paisano Annex Sta ... 87
9771-9844 — Paisano Annex Sta ... 88
9851-9924 — Paisano Annex Sta ... 89
9931-10004 — Paisano Annex Sta ... 90
10011-10102 — Paisano Annex Sta ... 91
10111-10188 — Paisano Annex Sta ... 92
10191-10268 — Paisano Annex Sta ... 93
10271-10385 — Paisano Annex Sta ... 94
10391-10545 — Paisano Annex Sta ... 95
10551-10690 — Paisano Annex.. 96
10691-10762 — Paisano Annex.. 97
12000-12867 — Coronado Sta ... 12
17001-17971 — Ysleta Sta ... 17
20000-20999 — Paisano Annex Sta ... 98
26001-26999 — Ranchland Sta. 26

31001-31578 Summit Heights Station............ 31

RURAL ROUTES

1,2	27
3	35
4	34

STATIONS, BRANCHES AND UNITS

Biggs AFB Br.	08
Coronado Sta.	15
Fort Bliss Br.	06
Northgate Sta.	24
Paisano Annex Sta.	05
Ranchland Sta	15
Summit Heights Sta.	30
Tigua Sta.	15
William Beaumont Hospital Br.	20
General Delivery	40
Postmaster	10
Principal Firms	99
Ysleta Sta.	07

APARTMENTS, HOTELS, MOTELS

Barbara Bassett, 6401 Gateway Blvd West	25
Caballero Motor, 6416 Montana Ave.	42
Chateau, 4510 Arlen Ave.	04
Chelsea Plaza Apartments 600 Chelsea.	03
Cielo Vista, 6812 Cielo Vista Dr.	25
Colonial Motor, 8601 Dyer	04
Colonial Terrace Residential, 1413 Montana Ave	02
Corinthian Plaza, 4155 Krupp Dr.	02
Del Camino Motor, 4910 Alameda Ave.	93
Desert Hills Motor, 4501 N Mesa.	49
Desert Villa, 1630 Mescalero Dr.	25
Downtowner Motor Inn, 325 N Kansas.	47
El Dorado, 303 Mesita Dr.	02
El Nido, 202 Alicia Dr.	05
Fairmount, 1800 N Stanton	02
Fountain Plaza, 4141 Westcity Ct.	02
Gardner, 311 E Franklin Ave.	40
Gateway, 104 S Stanton.	49
Hallmark, 1620 Mescalero Dr.	25
Hillmark, 5000 Alabama.	30
Hilton Inn, International Airport.	49
Holiday Inn - Downtown, 113 W. Missouri Ave.	01
Holiday Inn-Midtown, 4800 Gateway Blvd East	05
Holiday Inn, 6655 Gateway Blvd West	90
Howard Johnson Motor Lodge, 8887 Gateway Blvd West	25
Iberville, 5216 Carousel Dr.	12
Imperial 400, 6363 Montana Ave.	25

La Posta Motor Lodge, 4111 N Mesa	02
La Quenta Motel, 6140 Gateway Blvd E	05
Lakeside Village, 112 Little Flower Rd.	15
Mc Coy, Pioneer Plaza.	41
Mountain Shadows, 2400 Morehead Ave.	30
Northgate, 5249 Wren Ave.	24
Paisano Annex Sta.	05
Paso Del Norte, 115 S El Paso.	47
Plaza Motor, Corner Mills & Oregon.	49
Ramada Inn, 6099 Montana Ave.	84
Rodeway Inn, 6201 Gateway Blvd West.	25
Royal Lodge Motel, 1401 N Mesa.	02
Sagewood, 10000 Rushing Blvd.	24
Saint Regis, 323 N Oregon.	40
Sands Motel, 6941 Alameda Ave.	15
Starlite, 4651 Titanic Ave.	04
Sun Plaza, 1221 E San Antonio Ave.	01
Sunrise Arms, 4554 Hercules Ave.	04
Sunset Inn 4532 N Mesa.	12
Surrey Park, 351 Thunderbird Dr.	12
Sutton Place, 350 Thunderbird Dr.	12
The Diplomat, 601 W Yandell Dr.	02
The Executive House, 4501 Krupp Dr.	02
The Hawthorne House, 1700 Hawthorne.	02
The T W C Apts, 100 W Robinson Ave.	02
The Williamsburg, 300 W Schuster Ave.	02
Thunderbird Motor, 6405 N Mesa.	12
Travelodge Downtown, 1301 N Mesa.	02
Travelodge East, 6308 Montana Ave.	25
Travelodge El Paso Center 600 N Kansas.	01
Van Horne Park, Airport Rd.	06
Villa Del Norte, C301 Delta Dr.	05
Villa Holiday, 9400 Montrose Ct.	25
Villa Riviera, 4165 Krupp Dr.	02
Villa Sierra, 2425 Mckinley Ave.	30

BUILDINGS

Abdou, 111 N Mesa.	01
American Bank Of Commerce, 416 N Stanton.	01
Banner, 215 N Mesa.	01
Bassett Tower, 301 Texas Ave.	01
Blumenthal, 102 S El Paso.	01
Caples, 300 E San Antonio Ave.	01
Coles, 202 1/2 E. San Antonio Ave.	01
Cotton Exchange, 104 1/2 N Stanton.	01
El Paso International, 119 N Stanton.	01
El Paso National Bank, 201 E Main Dr.	01
El Paso Natural Gas Company, 304 Texas Ave.	01
El Paso Professional Center, 1812 N Oregon.	02
Electric, 215 N Stanton.	01
First National, 109 N Oregon.	01
Fortune Coronado Tower, 6004 N Mesa.	12
International Airport.	25
Luther, 218 N Campbell.	01
Medical Arts, 415 E Yandell Dr.	02
Medical Center Of El Paso, 1501 Arizona Ave.	02
Mills, 303 N Oregon.	01
Southwest National Bank, 300 E Main Dr.	01
State National Bank Plaza 221 N Kansas.	01
Sun Dancer, 6130 Montana Ave.	25
Surety Towers, 6001 Gila Rd.	05
University Towers, 1900 N Oregon.	02

GOVERNMENT OFFICES

El Paso Chamber Of Commerce, 820 N. Mesa St.	02
El Paso City-County, 500 E San Antonio Ave.	01
United States Courthouse, 511 E San Antonio Ave.	01

HOSPITALS

Campbell & 5th St Hospital Inc.	01
Delgado Green Cross, 118 N Harris.	07
El Paso Doctors Hospital 300 Waymore.	02
Four Seasons Nursing, 1600 Murchison Dr.	02
General R E Thomason, 4815 Alameda Ave.	05
Hotel Dieu, 1014 N Stanton.	02
Medi-Center Of America 2301 N Oregon.	02
Newark, 1109 E 5th Ave.	01
Providence Memorial, 2001 N Oregon.	02
Southwestern General 2001 Murchison Dr.	02
St Joseph Hospital The 1155 Idaho.	02
Suntowers, 1801 N Oregon.	02
Tigua General, 7722 North Loop Dr.	15
Valley Community, 7365	

Alameda Ave...................... 15
William Beaumont General
(Military Addresses Only).... 20

MILITARY INSTALLATIONS

Biggs A F B (Military
Addresses Only)................. 18
Fort Bliss Air Defense Center
(Military Addresses Only).... 16

UNIVERSITIES AND COLLEGES

Administrative Mail U Of
Texas At El Paso................. 99
Hotel Dieu School Of Nursing,
Arizona & Campbell........... 02
Jesus & Mary Academy, 1501
Sun Bowl Dr..................... 02
Loretto Academy, 4600 Hueco
Ave................................ 03
Lydia Patterson Institute, 517
S Florence....................... 01
Radford School For Girls,
2001 Radford.................... 03
Roger Bacon, 2400 Marr..... 0°
Saint Anthonys Seminary,
4601 Hastings Dr............... 03
University Of Texas At El Pa,
College Campus................. 0?

FORT WORTH 761

POST OFFICE BOXES

Box Nos.
1-2499	Main Office	01
2500-2599	Great Southwestern Airport Sta.	25
3000-3999	Polytechnic Sta.	05
4000-4999	Stock Yard Sta.	06
5000-5999	White Settlement Br.	08
6000-6999	Seminary Hill Sta.	15
7000-7999	Riverside Sta.	11
8000-8999	Handley Sta.	12
9000-9999	Arlington Heights Sta	07
10000-10999	Oaks Br	14
11000-11999	Berry Street Sta.	09
12000-12999	Ridglea Sta	16
13000-13999	Richland Hills Br	18
14000-14999	Haltom City Br.	17
15000-15999	Glencrest Sta.	19
16000-16999	Wedgwood Sta.	33
17000-17999	Central Sta.	02
21000-21999	Benbrook Br	26
22000-22999	S W Baptist Seminary	22
26000-26999	Ridglea Sta	16
27000-27999	Carswell Air Force Sta	27
28000-28999	South Fort Worth Sta	28
29000-30999	T C U Sta	29
40000-40999	Everman Br	40
48000-48999	Watagua Br	48
79000-79999	Saginaw Br	79

RURAL ROUTES

1	79
2	35
3	34
4	12
5	16
7	19
8	08
9	79
10	35
12	35
13	19

STATIONS, BRANCHES AND UNITS

Arlington Heights Sta.	07
Benbrook Br.	26
Berry Street Sta.	09
Blue Mound Br.	31
Carswell AFB Sta.	27
Central Sta.	02
Everman Br.	40
Glencrest Sta.	19
Great S W Airport Sta.	25
Haltom City Br.	17
Handley Sta.	12
Lake Worth Br.	35
Oaks Br.	14
Polytechnic Sta.	03
Richland Hills Br.	18
Ridglea Sta.	16
Riverside Sta.	11
Saginaw Br.	79
Seminary Hill Sta.	15
South Fort Worth Sta.	28
Stock Yard Sta.	06
SWBTS Sta.	22
TCU Sta.	29
Wedgewood Sta.	32
White Settlement Br.	08
General Delivery	01
Postmaster	01

APARTMENTS, HOTELS, MOTELS

Commercial, 505 Main.	02
Crestwood Place, 3900 White Settlement Rd.	07
Downtowner, 1016 Houston	02
Highland Park, 5302 Byers	07
Loring, 3101 Camp Bowie Blvd.	07
Plaza, 303 Main.	02
Ridgeway Manor, 3901 Westridge	16
Sheraton 815 Main	02
Town House, 600 W 3rd.	02
Worth, 310 W 7th.	02

BUILDINGS

Bailey, 600 Bailey	07
Baker, 110 W 7th.	02
Bewley, 212 W 7th.	02
Burk Burnett, 504 Main.	02
Century, 108 W 8th.	02
City Hall, 1000 Throckmorten.	02
Civil Courts, 100 N Houston.	02
Commerce, 307 W. 7th.	02
Continental Life, 714 Main.	02
Continental National Bank,	

200 W 7th	02
County Court House, 100 W Weatherford.	02
County Jail, 300 W. Belknap.	02
Criminal Courts, 300 W Belknap.	02
Dan Waggoner, 206 W 6th.	02
Doctor'S, 800 5th Ave.	04
Electric, 408 W 7th.	02
Ellison, 103 Main.	02
Equitable Savings, 811 Lamar.	02
Federal Courts, 501 W 10th.	02
First Life Insurance, 301 E 5th.	02
First National Bank, No. 1 Burnett Plaza.	02
Flat Iron, 1004 Houston.	02
Fort Worth Club - N, 307 W 6th.	02
Fort Worth Club - S, 306 W 7th.	02
Fort Worth Club-S, 304 W 7th.	02
Fort Worth National Bank, 115 W 7th.	02
Fort Worth Public Library, 210 W 9th.	02
Fritz G Lanahhafederal, 811 Taylor.	02
Fruit And Produce Terminal, 11101 11115 Jones.	02
Hughes, 411 W 7th.	02
James, 1/2 Houston.	02
Kirk-Mac, 600 Texas.	02
Lawyers, 503 1/2 Main.	02
Live Stock Exchange, 131 E. Exchange.	02
Lumbermens, 711 W. 7th.	02
Mallick Tower, 1 Summit Ave.	02
Mckeever, 2509 W. Berry.	09
Meacham, 110 W. 5th.	02
Medical Arts, 600 W 10th.	02
Medical Plaza & Office.	04
Mid-Continent, 106 W. 6th.	02
Mutual Savings, 815 Throckmorton.	02
Neil P Anderson, 411 W 7th.	02
Nine Ten Houston, 910 Houston.	02
Oil Gas Bldg, 309 W 7th.	02
Petroleum, 109 E. 9th.	02
Professional, 1216 Pennsylvania.	04
Rowan, 6000 Camp Bowie Blvd.	16
Schick, 208 W 6th.	02
Seminary South Office, Seminary South Shopping Center.	15
Service Life Center, 307 W 7th.	02
Shick, 208 W 6th.	02
Sinclair, 106 W 5th.	02
Stuart, 617 Texas.	02
Summit Center, 1330 Summit.	02
Summit, 1500 W 5th.	02
T & P Freight, 70 Jennings.	02
T & P Passenger, 221 W Lancaster.	02
Tarrant Savings, 600 Taylor.	02
Terminal, Meacham Field.	06

Trans-America Life, 103 E 7th	02
U. S. Courts, 501 W 10th	02
Union Bank, 100 Main	02
University Plaza, 100 N. University Dr.	07
W. T. Waggoner, 810 Houston	02
Western, 2525 Ridgmar Blvd.	16
Ymca, 512 Lamar	02
Ywca, 512 W 4th	02

HOSPITALS

All Saints Episcopal, 1400 Enderly Pl.	01
Boulevard, 3705 Camp Bowie Blvd.	07
Coffey Clinic, 306 W Broadway	04
Convalescent Center, 1000 6th Ave	04
Cook, 1212 W. Lancaster	02
Dorsey, 401 E 6th	02
Duncan Memorial, 2306 Hemphill	10
Elmwood Sanatorium, 2805 Kimbo Rd	11
Fifth Ave Clinic, 650 5th Ave.	04
Fort Worth Childrens, 1400 Cooper	04
Fort Worth Osteopathic, 1000 Montgomery	07
Glenview, 7501 Glenview	18
Harris Hospital, 1300 W Cannon	04
Howard Sanitorium, 921 W Cannon	04
John Peter Smith, 1500 S Main	04
Lake Worth Osteopathic, 6613 Jacksboro Highway	35
Medicenter, 815 8th Ave	04
Methodist, 1300 W Cannon	04
National Institute Of Mental Health, 3150 Horton	19
Northwest Hospital & Clinic, 2100 Highway 183	06
Saint Joseph, 1401 S Main	04
T And R Clinic, 2919 Markum Dr	17
Usaf Regional	27
Usphs, 3150 Horton	19
White Settlement Hospital, 701 S Cherry Ln	08

UNIVERSITIES AND COLLEGES

Brantley-Craughon, 1401 Henderson	02
Fort Worth Christian College, 7517 Bogart	18
South Campus	19
Southwestern Baptist Theological Seminary	15
Texas Christian University, Tcu Campus	29
Texas Wesleyan College, Twc Campus	05

GARLAND 750

POST OFFICE BOXES

Box Nos.

1-1568	Main Office	40
2001-2795	Kingsley Sta	41

RURAL ROUTES

1,2,3	40

STATIONS, BRANCHES AND UNITS

Kingsley Sta	41
Sachse Rural Br.	40
General Delivery	40
Postmaster	40

HOUSTON 770

POST OFFICE BOXES

Box Nos.

1-3399	Main Office	01
4001-4240	Franklin Sta	14
5001-5544	Harrisburg Sta	12
6501-6988	William Rice Sta	05
7001-7497	Houston Heights Sta	08
7501-7994	John Allen Sta	07
8001-8494	Southmore Sta	04
8501-8960	Anson Jones Sta	09
9001-9592	Central Park Sta	11
9601-9999	Greens Bayou Sta	15
10001-10379	Garden Oaks Sta	10
10501-10948	Oak Forest Sta	18
11001-11447	Roy Royall Sta	16
12001-12599	Park Place Sta	17
12601-12897	Park Place Hobby	17
13001-13592	River Oaks Sta	19
14001-14716	Foster Place Sta	21
15001-15669	Denver Harbor Sta	20
16001-16380	Irvington Sta	22
17001-17239	Veterans Hospital Sta	31
18001-18755	Eastwood Sta	23
19001-19554	Memorial Park Br	24
20001-20629	Astrodome Sta	25
21001-21482	Jensen Drive Sta	26
22001-22822	Highland Village Sta	27
23001-23297	East Houston Br	28
24001-24444	Jacinto City Br	29
25001-25194	William Rice Sta	05
26001-26944	Gulfgate Sta	32
27001-27635	Julius Melcher Sta	27
33001-33630	South Park Sta	33
34001-34627	Genoa Br	34
35001-35999	South Post Oak Sta	35
36001-36880	Sharpstown Sta	36
39001-39262	Kinwood Br	39
40001-40552	Fairbanks Sta	40
45290-45924	Almeda Br	45
52001-53617	Sam Houston Sta	52
55001-55657	Long Point Sta	55
58001-58868	Albert Thomas	58
60151-60774	Airport Mail Facility Sta	60
61001-61679	Civic Center Sta	61
66001-66916	Fairview Sta	06
70001-70358	John Allen Sta	07
88001-88094	Southmore Sta	04
90001-90665	Westfield	90
94001-94198	Oak Forest Sta	18
99001-99119	Central Park Sta	11

RURAL ROUTES

2	18
3	45
4	36
5	28
6	90
7	16
8	24
9,10	40
11	16
12,14	40
15	28
16	90
17	40
18	36
19,22,23	40
24	28
30	88
31	40

STATIONS, BRANCHES AND UNITS

Addicks Rural Br.	79
Airport Mail Facility Sta	60
Albert Thomas Br.	58
Almeda Sta.	45
Anson Jones Sta.	09
Astrodome Sta.	25
Astroworld Sta.	25
Central Park Sta.	11
Civic Center Sta.	61
Denver Harbor Sta.	20
East Houston Sta.	28
Eastwood Sta.	23
Ellington AFB Br.	30
Fairbanks Sta.	40
Fairview Sta.	06
Foster Place Sta.	21
Franklin Sta.	02
Garden Oaks Sta.	18
Genoa Sta.	34
Greens Bayou Sta.	15
Gulfgate Sta.	32
Harrisburg Sta.	12
Highland Village Sta.	27
Houston Heights Sta.	08
Irvington Sta.	22
Jacinto City Br.	29

Jensen Drive Sta................... 26
John Allen Sta..................... 07
Long Point Sta.................... 55
Memorial Park Br................ 24
Oak Forest Sta.................... 08
Park Place Sta.................... 17
River Oaks Sta.................... 19
Sam Houston Sta................. 52
Sharpstown Sta................... 36
Southmore Sta.................... 04
South Park Sta.................... 33
South Post Oak Sta............. 35
Westfield Br...................... 90
William Rice Sta................. 05
General Delivery................. 52
Postmaster........................ 13

APARTMENTS, HOTELS, MOTELS

Ardmore, 5900 Ardmore......... 21
Auditorium, 705 Texas.......... 52
Bayou De Ville, 2500 Mac
   Gregor Way...................... 04
Bayou Oaks, 8100 River Dr.... 17
Bellefontaine, 3203
   Bellefontaine.................. 25
Ben Milam, 1521 Texas.......... 52
Bissonett Plaza, 5202
   Buffalo Speedway.............. 05
Braes-Field, 3822 Braeswood
   N.............................. 25
Bryan, 1500 Capitol............. 02
Carrousel, 3499 Evergreen...... 17
Century National Bank
   Building, 2100 Travis........ 02
Continental Houston, 101
   Main.......................... 02
Crosstimber Oaks, 2612
   Crosstimbers E................ 16
Dallas Avenue, 507 Dallas..... 02
De George, 1418 Preston....... 52
Downtowner Motel,1015
   Texas.......................... 02
Earle, 600 Preston.............. 02
El Tropical, 3501 Mac Gregor
   Way........................... 04
Fleetwood, 2102 Telephone
   Rd............................. 23
Fourteen Hundred Hermann
   Drive, 1400 Hermann Dr.... 04
Garden Oaks Village, 3403 N
   Shepherd Dr................... 18
Gilbert, 7925 Gulf Freeway..... 17
Glen Echo, 7939 Sarita......... 12
Griggs Field, 3600 Griggs
   Rd............................. 21
Hermann, 1400 Hermann Dr.... 04
Hillcroft, 6203 Jessamine...... 36
Hillside, 5200 Memorial Dr.... 07
Judson, 711 La Branch.......... 02
Kipling Plaza,2203 Kipling..... 06
La Fonda West, 2827 Sage
   Rd............................. 27
La Fonda, 2227 Norfolk......... 06
Lamar, Main & Lamar............ 52
Las Palmas, 3211 Las
   Palmas........................ 27
Lawndale Village, 1500
   Lawndale Plaza................ 23
Lazy Oaks, 1415 Wirt Rd....... 24
Lee, 1114 Polk.................. 02
Mayfair, 1600 Holcombe Blvd
   25

Mc Kinney, 916 Mc Kinney..... 52
Milby, 906 Texas................ 02
Montagu, 804 Fannin............ 52
Montclair, 5220 Weslayan...... 05
Montrose Boulevard, 1002
   Bissonnet..................... 05
Oak Lane, 2720 Revere......... 04
Park Lane....................... 02
Park Towers, 1700 Holcombe
   Blvd E........................ 25
Parkwood, 7331
   Staffordshire................. 25
Patricia Manor, 2522 Patricia
   Manor Pl...................... 12
Pickwick, 3102 Holcombe
   Blvd E........................ 21
Plaza, 5020 Montrose Blvd..... 01
Plum Creek Village, 314
   Winkler Dr.................... 17
Post-Field, 1315 S Post Oak
   Ln............................ 27
Preston Villa, 2200 W
   Alabama....................... 06
Rice, Texas & Main............. 52
River Oaks Gardens, 1601 S
   Shepherd Dr................... 19
Royal Windsor, 5100
   Richmond Ave.................. 27
Sam Houston, 1115 Prairie..... 52
Scarsdale, 1400 S Post Oak.... 27
Shamrock Hilton, South Main.. 01
Shamrock Plaza, 7006 Scott.... 52
Sheraton-Lincoln, 777 Polk.... 52
Sonesta 500 Jefferson......... 02
Stratford, 414 Fannin.......... 52
Tall Timbers, 4040 San
   Felipe Rd..................... 27
Texas State, 720 Fannin........ 52
Town & Country, 2504 Mac
   Gregor Way S................. 21
Tudor City, 611 La Branch..... 04
Waldorf Arms, 5602 San
   Jacinto....................... 04
Warwick, 5701 Main 01
William Penn, 1421 Texas...... 52
Wilshire Village, 1701 W
   Alabama....................... 06

BUILDINGS

Abstract & Title, 617
   Caroline...................... 02
Adams Petroleum Center,
   6910 Fannin................... 25
American General Life, 2727
   Allen Pky..................... 19
Bank Of Commerce, 709
   Travis........................ 02
Bank Of The Southwest, 900
   Travis........................ 02
Bankers Mortgage, 708 Main.. 02
Bettes, 201 Main............... 02
C & I Life, 1006 Main.......... 02
Capitol National Bank, 1300
   Main.......................... 02
Century National Bank, 2120
   Travis........................ 02
Citizens State Bank, 400
   Main.......................... 02
Columbia Life, 1007 Preston.. 02
Continental Bank, 220 Main.... 02
Cotton Exchange, 1300
   Prairie....................... 02
Cotton, 502 Caroline........... 02

County Civil Courts, 301
   Fannin........................ 02
De George, 3520 Montrose..... 06
Eastern Airlines 3700
   Greenway Plz.................. 46
Electric, 611 Walker........... 02
Family Law Center, 1115
   Congress...................... 02
Fannin Bank, 1020 Holcombe
   Blvd E........................ 25
Federal Land Bank, 430
   Lamar......................... 02
Federal Office, 515 Rusk....... 02
Federal, 701 San Jacinto....... 02
First City National Bank,
   1021 Main..................... 02
Gibralter, 2302 Fannin......... 02
Gid Neal, 5510 Greenbriar...... 05
Guaranty, 1302 Main........... 02
Gulf Annex, 717 Travis......... 02
Gulf, 712 Main................. 02
Hermann Professional, 6410
   Fannin........................ 25
Houston Bank & Trust, 1801
   Main.......................... 02
Houston Bar Center, 723
   Main.......................... 02
Houston Natural Gas, 1200
   Travis........................ 01
Houston Office Center, 6001
   Gulf Freeway.................. 23
Houston Title, 1212 Dallas..... 02
Humble, 800 Bell............... 02
Jesse H. Jones Hall, 615
   Louisiana..................... 02
Kirby, 3801 Kirby Dr........... 06
Kress, 707 Main................ 02
Kurth, 5013 Fannin............. 04
Legal Arts, 312 Fannin......... 02
Lincoln Liberty Life, 711 Polk. 02
Live Stock Exchange, 4904
   Calhoun Rd.................... 04
M W Kellogg 3800 Greenway
   Plz........................... 46
Main, 1216 Main................ 02
Mc Donald, 618 Prairie......... 02
Medical Arts, 1215 Walker..... 02
Mellie Esperson, 815 Walker... 02
Melrose, 1121 Walker........... 02
Memorial Professional, 1010
   Louisiana..................... 02
Merchants Exchange, 202
   Travis........................ 02
Niels Esperson, 804 Travis..... 02
Oil & Gas, 706 Lamar.......... 02
Old National Life, 5619
   Fannin........................ 04
One Main Plaza 1 Main.......... 02
One Shell Plz, 910 Louisiana.. 02
Petroleum, 1314 Texas......... 02
Post Oak Towers, 5045
   Westheimer Rd................. 27
Prudential, 1100 Holcombe
   Blvd E........................ 25
Republic, 1016 Preston......... 02
Robert Neal, 1220 Polk......... 02
Salvation Army, 204 Travis..... 02
San Jacinto Saving, 905 Or
   907 Main...................... 02
San Jacinto, 911 Walker........ 02
Scanlan, 405 Main.............. 02
South Coast Life, 800 Main.... 02
Southern States Life, 3317

Montrose Blvd	06
Southwest Towers, 707 Mc Kinney	02
State National Bank, 412 Main	02
Stewart, 403 Fannin	02
Tenneco, 1010 Milam	02
Texaco, 1111 Rusk	02
Texas Gas, 2472 Bolsover	05
Texas National Bank, 1300 Main	02
Two Shell Piz, 701 Walker	02
U. S. Custom House, 701 San Jacinto Or 702 Caroline	02
Union Carbide 3600 Greenway Plz Dr	46
United Gas, 1116 Texas	02
West, 817 Main	02
Western Union, 914 Franklin	02
Wilson, 2601 Main	02
Womens Professional, 6436 Fannin	25
World Trade Center, 1520 Texas	02
Zindler, 218 Fannin	02
1114 Texas Avenue, 1114 Texas	02
500 Jefferson, 500 Jefferson	02
711 Main, 711 Main	02

GOVERNMENT OFFICES

Chamber Of Commerce, 914 Main	02
City Hall, 900 Brazos	02
County Court House, 301 San Jacinto	02

HOSPITALS

Arabia Temple Crippled Children Clinic, 1402 Outer Belt	25
Autrey Memorial, 3602 West Dallas	19
Community, 1405 Holland	29
Doctors, 5815 Airline	22
General Ben Taub, 1502 Outer Belt Dr	25
Hedgecroft Hospital & Clinic, 5120 Montrose Blvd	06
Heights, 1917 Ashland	08
Hermann, 1203 Ross Sterling	25
Homestead Road, 8214 Homestead Road	28
Houston Eye Ear & Throat Hospital, 1010 Louisiana	02
Houston General, 2715 Jensen Dr	26
Jefferson Davis, 1801 Allen Pkwy	19
Little York, 2807 Little York Rd	16
Lockwood, 5001 Lockwood	26
M D Anderson, 6723 Bertner	25
Medical-Arts 1215 Walker	02
Memorial Baptist Central 1100 Louisiana	02
Memorial Baptist Northwest 1635 North Loop W	08
Memorial Baptist Southeast	

7655 Bellfort	17
Memorial Baptist Southwest 6440 High Star	36
Memorial Baptist, 602 Lamar	02
Memorial City General 920 Frostwood	24
Methodist, 6516 Bertner	25
North Houston, 8800 Arkansas	16
Northshore, 1000 Federal Rd	15
Northwest General, 1615 Hillendahl	24
Parkview, 7440 Harrisburg Blvd	11
Riverside General, 2900 Elgin	04
Rockglen, 13131 Rockglen	15
Saint Elizabeths, 4500 Lyons Ave	20
Saint Josephs, 1910 Crawford	02
Saint Lukes Episcopal, 6621 Fannin	25
Sam Houston Memorial, 1615 Hillendahl	55
Spring Branch, 8846 Long Point	55
Texas Childrens, 6621 Fannin	25
Veterans Administration, 2002 Holcombe Blvd	31
Wright Clinic & Hospital, 2407 Main N	09
Yale, 510 W Tidwell	18

MILITARY INSTALLATIONS

Ellington A F B	30

UNIVERSITIES AND COLLEGES

Baylor University College Of Medicine, 1200 M D Anderson	25
Houston Baptist College, 7502 Fondren Rd	36
Sacred Heart Dominican, 6501 Almeda Rd	21
South Texas One Main Plz	02
Texas Southern University, 3201 Wheeler	04
University Of Houston, 3801 Cullen	04
University Of Saint Thomas, 3812 Montrose	06
University Of Texas Post Graduate School, 1400 Outer Belt	25
University Of Texas School Of Dentistry, 6515 Freeman	25
William Marsh Rice University, 6100 Main	01

IRVING 750

POST OFFICE BOXES

Box Nos.		
1-1658	Main Office	60
55000-5699	Carl Range Station	62

RURAL ROUTES

1,2	62
3	60

STATIONS, BRANCHES AND UNITS

Carl Range Sta	60
University Of Dallas Sta	60
General Delivery	60
Postmaster	60

APARTMENTS, HOTELS, MOTELS

Holiday Inn-1930 East Carpenter Fwy	61
Lexington Apartments 909 W. Carpenter Fwy. W	62
Ramada Hacienda Motor Inn - 120 W. Carpenter Fwy. W	62
Villa Inn West 215 E Carpenter Fwy W	62

BUILDINGS

Irving Bank Trust Tower 110 N. Main	60
Professional Tower Bldg. 1711 W. Irving Blvd	61
Southwest Bank Bldg. - 2520 W. Irving Blvd	61

HOSPITALS

Gilbert Medical Surgical 101 S. O Connor Rd	60
Irving Community Hospital-1901 Macarthur Blvd	61
Medical Surgical Clinic 2120 Macarthur Blvd	61
Physicians Surgeons Hospital 1735 W. Irving Blvd	61

UNIVERSITIES AND COLLEGES

University Of Dallas Station	60

LUBBOCK 794

POST OFFICE BOXES

Box Nos.		
1-2999	Main Office	08
3001-3357	Ellwood Sta	10
4001-4720	Tech Sta	09
5000-5834	North College Sta	17
6000-6999	Murryhill Sta	13
7000-7999	Lubbock Christian College	07
8000-9999	Reese Air Force Base R. Sta	01
10001-10436	Main Office	08
16000-16999	Sunset Sta	90

RURAL ROUTES

1	01
2	15
3	01

4	13
5	10
6,7	01
8	07

STATIONS, BRANCHES AND UNITS

Elwood Sta	10
Murryhill Sta	13
North College Sta	10
Number Fourteen Sta	12
Reese A F B Rural Br	01
Sunset Sta	07
Tech Sta	09
General Delivery	08
Postmaster	08

APARTMENTS, HOTELS, MOTELS

Altura Towers, 1617 27th	05
Barcelona, 5416 50th	14
Bel-Aire, 1903 14th	01
Bosque, 1710 Main	01
Browns, 907 Idalou Highway	03
Camelot Mobile Homes, 6001 34th	07
Century House, 1625 16th	01
Circle V, 2103 33rd	11
Clark, 1701 Avenue L	01
Conquistadors, 5300 11th	16
Country Inn, 4021 21st	10
Cresthaven, 1700 E 22nd	04
Cresthaven, 1703 E 23rd	04
De Busk, 226 North Sherman	15
Desert Inn, 2800 43rd	13
Ebony Arms, 2800 Juniper	04
Ficas, 1602 Avenue K	01
Georgian Arms, 2405 8th	01
Greenbriar, 4303 19th	07
Hartford Park, 223 Indiana Ave	15
Heritage Arms, 5540 19th	07
Hub Homes, 4th & Avenue F	01
Indiana Terrace, 221 Indiana	15
Jackson, 1604 45th	12
K-C, 2422 15th	01
Kentwood, 1702 26th	11
Kobs, 1306 Avenue N	01
Lakeland Park, 2411 45th	12
Lakeview, 2102 38th	12
Lawdas Villa, 102 Avenue T	15
Lexington, 4521 Brownfield Hwy	07
Lindsey, 1604 Avenue W	01
Lindsey, 2302 17th	01
Lubbock, 2010 5th	01
Matador, 2301 7th	01
Midway, 1809 Broadway	01
Mimosa, 2410 14th	01
Montclair, 709 Avenue R	01
Nancy, 1621 16th	01
Olney, 116 Avenue X	15
Park Terrace, 2401 45th	12
Parr Place, 1202 23rd	05
Patio, 3300 Toledo	10
Plantation House, 2400 44th	11
Plaza, 2101-2102 34th	11
Plaza, 2102 & 2105 33rd	11
Raider Villa, 1612 Ave Y	01
Redwood, 2419 13th	01
Slater, 1922 5th	01
Stardust, 2301 50th	12
Stoneleigh, 2415 33rd	11

Studio, 1617 Avenue N	01
Summit, 1610 45th	12
Sycamore Park, 4300 E 4th	03
Tally Ho, 5105 Avenue W	12
Tech Arms, 1626 Avenue Y	01
Townhouse, 1801 Main	01
University Village, 3102 4th	15
Varsity Village, 3002 4th	15
Vickery, 2904 Texas	05
Villa West, 5401 4th	15
Villa, 2301 51st	12
Western Air, 2404 10th	01
Westwood Village, 2700 Fordham	15
Wilshire, 1922 5th	01
Wilshire, 722 Avenue T	01
Woody, 1608 Broadway	01

BUILDINGS

All American Security, 1401 19th	01
Briercroft Office Park	12
Carlock & Doughty, 1005 13th	01
Central American Life, 1202 Texas	01
Citizens Tower, 1210 14th	01
Commerce, 1603 Broadway	01
Cotton Exchange, 1320 Texas	01
Court Place Inc 916 Main	01
Federal 1205 Texas	01
Ferguson, 1412 Texas	01
Fields, 1946 Avenue Q	05
First National-Pioneer, 1500 Broadway	01
Gibson, 1414 Avenue J	01
Great Plains Life, 1107 Avenue L	01
Insurance, 2109 Avenue Q	05
Jones-Malone, 1203 University	01
Kerr-Easter, 1002 14th	01
Lubbock National, 916 Main	01
Medical Arts, 1318 Broadway	01
Medical Professional, 3801 19th	10
Myrick, 1215 Ave J	01
Owens, 1114 10th	01
Park Place, 1401 19th	01
Petroleum, 1802 Avenue Q	01
Rogers, 1515 Texas	01
Sanford, 1009 Texas	01
South Plains Mall 6000 Slide Rd	14
Sweetbriar, 1206 Avenue J	01
Wall, 1312 Texas	01
Watson, 1503 Avenue J	01
Weaver, 1106 Broadway	01
Whiteside, 1717 Avenue K	01

HOSPITALS

Highland, 2412 50th	12
Lubbock Osteopathic, 5301 University Ave	13
Methodist, 3615 19th	10
Porter, 2401 19th	01
St MaryOs Of The Plains, 4000 24th	10
University 6610 Quaker	13

West Texas, 1312 Main	01

UNIVERSITIES AND COLLEGES

Lubbock Christian, 5601 19th	07
Texas Technological College Dormitories, University Ave	06
Texas Technological, University Ave	09

PASADENA 775

POST OFFICE BOXES

Box Nos.		
1-3488	Main Office	01
4001-4499	John Foster Sta	02
5001-5499	Golden Acres Sta	03
6001-7232	Bob Harris	02

STATIONS, BRANCHES AND UNITS

Bob Harris Sta	02
Golden Acres Sta	03
John Foster Sta	02
General Delivery	01
Postmaster	01

SAN ANTONIO 782

POST OFFICE BOXES

Box Nos.		
1-300	Main Office	91
601-900	Main Office	93
901-1231	Main Office	94
1241-1540	Main Office	95
1541-1840	Main Office	96
1841-2171	Main Office	97
2181-2480	Main Office	98
2481-2780	Main Office	99
3001-3639	South San Antonio Sta	11
5001-5528	Beacon Hill Sta	01
6001-6999	Alamo Heights Br	09
7001-7779	A Sta	07
8001-8695	Wainwright Sta	08
9001-9394	Guilbeau Sta	04
10001-10357	Hackberry Sta	10
12001-12678	Laurel Heights Sta	12
13001-13440	Cresthaven Sta	13
14001-14535	Harlandale Sta	14
16001-16299	Lapham Sta	46
18001-18428	Serna	18
20001-20399	J Frank Dobie	20
21001-21597	Terrell Wells Sta	21
23001-23355	Highland Hills Sta	23
27001-27394	Valley Hi Sta	27
28001-28529	University Park	

Sta.....	28
30001-30199 Colonies North Contract Sta.....	85
32001-32638 Nimitz Sta.....	16
37001-37392 Los Jardines	37

RURAL ROUTES

1.....	23
2.....	28
3.....	18
4.....	28
5.....	11
6.....	20
7.....	21
8.....	28
9.....	27
10.....	16
11.....	13
12.....	21
13.....	18
14.....	21
15.....	28
16.....	16
17.....	28

STATIONS, BRANCHES AND UNITS

Alamo Heights Br.....	09
Beacon Hill Sta.....	01
Brooks AFB Br.....	35
Cresthaven Sta.....	13
Fort Sam Houston Sta.....	34
Guilbeau Sta.....	04
Hackberry Sta.....	10
Harlandale Sta.....	14
Highland Hills Sta.....	23
J Frank Dobie Sta.....	20
Kelly AFB Br.....	41
Lackland AFB Br.....	36
Lapham Sta.....	16
Laurel Heights Sta.....	12
Los Jardines Sta.....	37
Medina Base Br.....	36
Natural Bridge Caverns Rural Br.....	18
Nimitz Sta.....	16
Olmos Park Br.....	12
Sema Sta.....	18
South San Antonio Sta.....	11
Terrell Wells Sta.....	21
University Park Sta.....	27
Valley Hi Br.....	27
Wainwright Sta.....	08
Wilford Hall USAF Hosp Br.....	36
General Delivery.....	05
Postmaster.....	84

APARTMENTS, HOTELS, MOTELS

Aurora Apartment, 509 Howard.....	12
Bali Hai, 1234 E Mulberry.....	09
Bel-Air Motel, 511 S St Marys.....	05
Belmeade, 119 W Hathaway.....	09
Blue Bonnet, 426 N St Marys.....	05
Calvert, 136 Main Plaza.....	05
Capri, 211 Natalen.....	09
Casa Manana Motor, Highway 90 W.....	27
Crockett, 301 E Crockett.....	05

El Tropicano Motor, 110 Lexington.....	05
Flamingo, 1131 Austin Hwy....	09
Granada Inn, 402 S St Marys.....	05
Grayson House, 819 E Grayson.....	08
Gunter, 205 E Houston.....	05
Highland Hills, 231 Burkedale.....	23
Hillcrest, 1243 Babcock.....	05
Hilton'S Palacio Del Rio, 203 S Alamo.....	05
Holiday, 3535 Broadway.....	09
La Mansion Motor Hotel 112 College.....	05
Le Chalet, 832 E Grayson.....	08
Menger, 204 Alamo Plaza.....	05
Morris, 128 Main Plaza.....	05
Navarro, 116 Navarro.....	05
Nueces, 513 N St Marys.....	05
Pan American, 5433 Broadway.....	09
Park Motel, 3617 Braodway....	09
Park Plaza Motel, 2908 Broadway.....	09
Park Terrace, 201 Humphrey..	09
Ramada Inn, 333 Military Dr NW.....	16
Rio Lado Metel, 1100 N St Marys.....	15
Robert E Lee, 111 W Travis....	05
Saint Anthony, 300 E Travis...	05
Sheraton San Antonio Motor Inn, 1400 Austin Hwy.....	09
South Saint Marys, 610 S St Marys.....	05
Sunset Ridge, 116 Vanderheck.....	09
Thunderbird, 211 W French ...	12
Travelers, 220 Broadway.....	05
Wayfarer Motor Hotel, 601 E Elmira.....	12
Westerner, 1116 Austin Hwy...	09

BUILDINGS

Adams, 8622 Crownhill.....	09
Alamo National, 105 S St Marys.....	05
American Hospital & Life, 106 E Pecan.....	05
Architects & Engineers, 342 W Woodlawn.....	12
Aztec, 211 E Commerce.....	05
Brady, 202 E Houstcn.....	05
Calcasieu, 214 Broadway.....	05
Calvert, 535 S Main.....	04
Eighteen Hundred 1800 Loop 410 NW.....	17
Executive K, 1017 N Main ...	12
Farm & Home, 403 E Travis...	05
Federal, 615 E Houston.....	05
Frost National Bank, Main Plaza W.....	05
Gibbs, 105 N Alamo.....	05
Glass, 4600 Broadway.....	09
Government Personnel Mutual, 800 N W Loop 410.....	16
Gpm 800 Loop 410 NW.....	16
Gunter, 159 E Houston.....	05
Hedrick, 603 N St Marys.....	05
International, 318 W	

Houston.....	05
James K, 419 S Main.....	04
Kallison Professional, 111 W Laurel.....	12
Kallison Tower, 1222 N Main..	12
Kallison, 434 S Main.....	04
Lexington, 109 Lexington.....	05
M-S Tower, 730 N Main	05
Majestic, 212 E Houston.....	05
Maverick, 606 N Presa.....	05
Medical Professional, 1303 Mc Cullough.....	12
Mexican Consulate, 127 Navarro	05
Milam, 115 E Travis.....	05
Moore, 106 Broadway.....	05
Morris K, 214 Dwyer.....	04
National Bank Of Commerce, 430 Soledad.....	05
Nix Professional, 414 Navarro	05
Oppenheimer, 212 E Commerce.....	05
Petroleum Center, 900 N E Loop 410.....	09
Petroleum Commerce, 201 N St Marys.....	05
Plaza Professional, 6936 San Pedro.....	16
R L White, 116 E Travis	05
San Antonio Produce Terminal Market, 1500 S Zarzamora.....	07
San Antonio Savings, 111 Soledad.....	05
South Texas, 603 Navarro.....	05
Texas Continental, 406 W Market.....	05
Texas Theatre, 151 E Houston.....	05
Three A Life, 118 Broadway....	05
Three O One, 301 Broadway...	05
Tower Life, 310 S St Marys	05
Travis Park West 711 Navarro	05
Travis, 405 N St Marys.....	05
U S A A, 4119 Broadway.....	88
Western Union, 319 E Commerce.....	05
Y M C A 903 N St Marys........	05

GOVERNMENT OFFICES

City Hall, Military Plaza	05
Court House, Main Plaza S.....	04
Federal, 615 E Houston.....	05

HOSPITALS

Baptist Memorial, 111 Dallas.....	05
Cypress Sanitorium, 300 W Cypress.....	12
Laurelwood Sanatorium, 2717 N Flores.....	12
Luthern General Hospital, 701 S Zarzamora.....	07
Medical & Convalescent, 323 W Cypress.....	12
Medical Arts, Medical Arts Bldg.....	05
Nix Memorial, 414 Navarro	05
Osteopathic Hospital, 210 W	

Ashby	12
Robert B Green, 515 Morales	07
Saints, 501 S Hackberry	03
Salvation Army, 4019 Broadway	09
San Antonio State Tuberculosis, Military Dr SE	23
San Antonio State, 5800 Presa	23
Santa Rosa Medical Center, 519 W Houston	07
Southwest Texas Methodist, Louis Pasteur & Wm Mayo Dr	29

MILITARY INSTALLATIONS

Brooks A F B	35
Ft Sam Houston	34
Kelly AFB	41
Lackland A F B	36
U S A F Security Service	43

UNIVERSITIES AND COLLEGES

Assumption Seminary, 3016 W French	28
Draughons Business, 411 E Martin	05
Durhams Business, 105 San Pedro	05
Incarnate Word, 4301 Broadway	09
International Bible, 2369 Benrus	28
Nazarene Bible Institute, 700 Lombrano	07
Oblate College Of The Southwest, 285 Oblate	16
Our Lady Of The Lake, 411 SW 24th	07
Saint Johns Seminary, 222 E Mitchell	10
Saint Marys University, 2700 Cincinnati	28
Saint Philips, 2111 Nevada	03
San Antonio, 1300 San Pedro	12
Trinity University, 715 Stadium Dr	12
University Of Texas Medical School, 7703 Floyd Curl	29

WACO 767

POST OFFICE BOXES

Box Nos.

1-2451	Main Office	03
3001-3497	Colonial Sta	07
4001-4564	Bellmead Br	05
5001-5444	Mitchell Avenue Sta	08
6001-6445	B U Station	06
7000-8389	Westview Sta	10

RURAL ROUTES

1,2	10
3	08
4,5	05
6	06

7,9	05
10	08

STATIONS, BRANCHES AND UNITS

B U Sta	06
Bellmead Br	04
Beverly Br	11
Colonial Sta	03
Lake Air Sta	10
Mitchell Ave Sta	08
Robinson Br	06
Veterans Administration Br	11
Westview Sta	10
General Delivery	03
Postmaster	01

BUILDINGS

Amicable, 425 Austin	01
Citizens Tower 501 Franklin	01
Federal, 800 Franklin	01
First National Bank, 811 Washington	01
Lake Air National Bank Bldg, 4901 Bosque	10
Liberty, 104 N 6th	01
Medical Arts, 900 Austin	01
Texas Center 900 Washington	01

GOVERNMENT OFFICES

City Hall	01
County Jail, 219 N 6th	01
Court House Annex, 219 N 6th	01
Court House, 501 Washington	01
Vet Admin Regional Office, 1400 N Valley Mills Dr	10

HOSPITALS

Hillcrest Memorial Hospital, 3000 Herring	08
Providence Hospital, 1725 Colcord	07
Veterans	11

UNIVERSITIES AND COLLEGES

Baylor University, 5th & Speight	06
Mclennan Community College, 1400 College	08
Paul Quinn College, 1020 Elm	04
Texas State Technical Inst	05

WICHITA FALLS 763

POST OFFICE BOXES

Box Nos.

1-2611	Main Office	07
3000-3399	Monroe Street Sta	09
4000-4399	University Park Sta	08
5000-5399	Main Office	07
6000-6200	Sheppard A F B Br	11

RURAL ROUTES

1,2	01
3	08
4	01

STATIONS, BRANCHES AND UNITS

Monroe Street Sta	09
Sheppard A F B Br	11
University Park Sta	08
General Delivery	07
Postmaster	07

APARTMENTS, HOTELS, MOTELS

Bel-Air, 918 E Scott	07
Brigadoon, 3220 Seymour Rd.	09
Camelot, 2202 Harrison	08
Catalina, Henrietta Rd	07
Chesterfield, 906 Grant	01
Flamingo, 3136 Seymour Hwy	01
Highlander, 2020 Santa Fe	09
Holiday Inn, 8th & Scott	07
Imperial 400, 306 Scott	01
Islands, 4709 Taft	08
Marchman, 10th & Lamar	07
Ramada Inn, 1211 Red River Expy	07
River Oaks, 1020 Red River Expy	07
Sands, 3153 Seymour Hwy	07
Sherwood Forest, 1717 Hampstead	02
Southmoor, 3709 Southmoor	02
Spanish Trace, 4602 Spanish Trace	10
Timbers, 500 Fillmore	01
Town House, 1112 Sheppard Access Rd	07
Trade Winds, 1212 Broad	07
Triple D, Henrietta Rd	07
Villa, 4027 Eastside Dr	08
Wayfarer, Hwy 287	07
Wichita Manor, 2102-A Virginia Dr	09
William-Mary, 1000 - 10th	01

BUILDINGS

Brook Medical Center, 710 Brook	01
Central Plaza, 211 Oil Center	02
City National Bank, 800 Scott	01
County Court House, 6th & Lamar	01
Featherston, 922 - 8th	01
Federal, 1000 Lamar	01
First National, 708 - 8th	01
First-Wichita Nat'l, 719 Scott	01
Hamilton, 900 - 8th	01
Medical & Surgical, 1518 - 10th	01
Medical Arts, 500 Broad	01
Memorial Auditorium, 1300 - 7th	01
Oil &gas, 813 - 8th	01
Parker Square Bank, Parker Square	08

Petroleum, 726 Scott 01
Radio, 903 Indiana 01
Robertson, 909 - 8th.............. 01

Staley, 705 - 8th.................... 01
Wichita Falls Savings, 800

Lamar............................ 01
Wichita Title, 700 Scott.......... 01

UTAH
(Abbreviation: UT)

Alta, R. Br. Sandy 84070
Altamont 84001
Alton 84710
Altonah 84002
American Fork (1st) 84003
Aneth, R. Br. Montezuma
   Creek 84510
Annabella 84711
Antimony, R. Br. Junction 84712
Arcadia 84605
Aurora 84620
Axtell 84621
Bear River City 84301
Beaver 84713
Ben Lomond, Sta. Ogden 84404
Beryl 84714
Bicknell 84715
   Torrey, R. Br. 84775
Bingham Canyon 84006
Blanding 84511
Bluebell 84007
Bluff 84512
Bonanza 84008
Boulder 84716
Bountiful (1st) 84010
Bridgeland 84012
Brigham City (1st) 84302
   Collinston, R. Br. 84306
Bryce Canyon, R. Br.
   Panguitch 84717
Cache Junction 84304
Cannonville, R. Br. Tropic 84718
Castle Dale 84513
Castle Gate 84514
Cedar City (1st) 84720
   Kanarraville, R. Br. 84742
Cedar Valley 84013
Centerfield 84622
Centerville 84014
Central 84722
Chester, R. Br. Moroni 84623
Circleville 84723
Cisco, R. Br. Green River 84515
Clarkston 84305
Clawson 84516
Clearfield (1st) 84015
   Freeport Center, Sta. 84016
Cleveland 84518
Coalville 84017
Collinston, R. Br. Brigham
   City 84306
Columbia 84519
Corinne 84307
Cornish, R. Br. Lewiston 84308
Cottonwood, Br. Salt Lake
   City 84121
Croydon 84018
Delta 84624
Deseret 84625
Deweyville 84309
Dragerton 84520
Draper 84020
Duchesne 84021
   Fruitland, R. Br. 84027
Dugway 84022
Dutch John 84023
Echo 84024
Eden 84310
Elberta 84626

Elmo 84521
Elsinore 84724
Emery 84522
Enterprise 84725
Ephraim 84627
Escalante 84726
Eureka 84628
Fairgrounds, Sta. Salt Lake
   City 84116
Fairview 84629
Farmington 84025
Fayette, R. Br. Gunnison 84630
Ferron 84523
Fielding 84311
Fillmore 84631
   Scipio, R. Br. 84656
Foothill, Sta. Salt Lake City 84108
Fort Duchesne 84026
   Gusher, R. Br. 84030
   Ouray, R. Br. 84059
   Tridell, R. Br. 84076
Fountain Green 84632
Freeport Center, Sta.
   Clearfield 84016
Fremont 84727
Fruitland, R. Br. Duchesne 84027
Fry Canyon 84524
Garden City 84028
Garland 84312
Garrison 84728
Glen Canyon, R. Br. Kanab 84741
Glendale 84729
Glenwood 84730
Gorder, Sta. Ogden 84403
Goshen 84633
Granger-Hunter, Br. Salt
   Lake City (see appendix)
Grantsville 84029
Green River 84525
   Cisco, R. Br. 84515
Greenville 84731
Greenwich 84732
Grouse Creek 84313
Gunlock 84733
Gunnison 84634
   Fayette, R. Br. 84630
Gusher, R. Br. Fort
   Duchesne 84030
Hanksville 84734
Hanna 84031
Hatch 84735
Heber City 84032
Helper 84526
Henefer 84033
Henrieville 84736
Hiawatha 84527
Hill A F B, Br. Ogden 84406
Hinckley 84635
Holden 84636
Holladay, Br. Salt Lake City 84117
Honeyville 84314
Hooper 84315
Howell 84316
Huntington 84528
Huntsville 84317
Hurricane 84737
Hyde Park 84318
Hyrum 84319
Ibapah 84034
Ivins 84738
Jensen 84035
Joseph 84739
Junction 84740

Antimony, R. Br. 84712
Kamas 84036
Kanab 84741
Kanarraville, R. Br. Cedar
   City 84742
Kanosh 84637
Kaysville (1st) 84037
Kearns, Br. Salt Lake City 84118
Kenilworth 84529
Kingston 84743
Koosharem 84744
La Sal 84530
La Verkin 84745
Laketown 84038
Lapoint 84039
Lark 84040
Layton (1st) 84041
Leamington 84638
Leeds, R. Br. Saint George 84746
Lehi 84043
Levan 84639
Lewiston 84320
   Cornish, R. Br. 84308
Loa 84747
Logan (1st) 84321
Lyman 84749
Lynndyl 84640
Magna (1st) 84044
Mammoth 84641
Manila 84046
Manti 84642
Marysvale 84750
Mayfield 84643
Meadow 84644
Mendon 84325
Mexican Hat 84531
   Monument Valley, R. Br. 84536
Midvale (1st) 84047
Midway 84049
Milford 84751
Millcreek, Br. Salt Lake City 84109
Millville 84326
Minersville 84752
Moab (1st) 84532
Modena 84753
Mona 84645
Monroe 84754
Montezuma Creek 84534
   Aneth, R. Br. 84510
Monticello 84535
Monument Valley, R. Br.
   Mexican Hat 84536
Morgan (1st) 84050
Moroni 84646
   Chester, R. Br. 84623
Mount Carmel 84755
Mount Pleasant 84647
Mountain Home 84051
Murray, Br. Salt Lake City 84107
Myton 84052
Neola 84053
Nephi 84648
New Harmony 84757
Newcastle 84756
Newton 84327
North Ogden, Br. Ogden (see
   appendix)
North Salt Lake (1st) 84054
Oak City 84649
Oakley 84055
Oasis 84650
OGDEN (1st) (see appendix)

Orangeville 84537
Orderville 84758
Orem (1st) 84057
Ouray, R. Br. Fort Duchesne...84059
Panguitch 84759
  Bryce Canyon, R. Br. 84717
Paradise 84328
Paragonah, R. Br. Parowan 84760
Park City 84060
Park Valley 84329
Parowan 84761
  Paragonah, R. Br..............84760
  Summit, R. Br..............84772
Payson 84651
Peoa 84061
Pintura 84762
Pioneer, Sta. Salt Lake City....84111
Pleasant Grove (1st) 84062
Plymouth 84330
Portage 84331
Price (1st) 84501
Providence 84332
Provo (1st) 84601
Randlett 84063
Randolph 84064
Redmond 84652
Richfield (1st) 84701
Richmond 84333
Riverside 84334
Riverton 84065
Rockville, R. Br. Springdale....84763
Roosevelt 84066
Roy (1st) 84067
Rubys Inn 84764
Saint George (1st).................84770
  Leeds, R. Br. 84746

Saint John 84069
Salem 84653
Salina 84654
SALT LAKE CITY (1st) (see
  appendix)
Saltair, R. Br. Salt Lake
  City 84101
Sandy (1st).............................84070
Santa Clara 84765
Santaquin 84655
Scipio, R. Br. Fillmore.............84656
Scofield 84538
Sevier 84766
Sigurd 84657
Smithfield 84335
Snowville 84336
South Ogden, Br. Ogden
  (see appendix)
South Salt Lake, Br. Salt
  Lake City 84115
Spanish Fork (1st) 84660
Spring City 84662
Springdale 84767
  Rockville, R. Br. 84763
  Zion National Park, R.
  Br..............................84767
Springville (1st) 84663
Sterling 84665
Stockton 84071
Sugar House, Sta. Salt Lake
  City (see appendix)
Summit, R. Br. Parowan........84772
Sunnyside 84539
Tabiona 84072
Talmage 84073
Teasdale 84773

Thistle 84666
Thompson 84540
Tooele (1st) 84074
Toquerville 84774
Torrey, R. Br. Bicknell.............84775
Tremonton 84337
Trenton 84338
Tridell, R. Br. Fort Duchesne ..84076
Tropic 84776
  Cannonville, R. Br. 84718
Trout Creek.............................84077
University, Sta. Provo.............84601
Utah State University, Sta.
  Logan.............................84321
Venice 84777
Vernal (1st).............................84078
Vernon 84080
Virgin 84779
Wales 84667
Wallsburg 84082
Washington 84780
Washington Terrace, Br.
  Ogden (see appendix)
Wellington.............................84542
Wellsville.............................84339
Wendover 84083
West Jordan.............................84084
Whiterocks.............................84085
Willard 84340
Woodruff 84086
Woods Cross.............................84087
Zion National Park, R. Br.
  Springdale.....................84767

OGDEN   844

POST OFFICE BOXES

Box Nos.

1-1640	Main Office	02
2001-2999	Ben Lomond Sta	04
3001-3999	Gorder Sta	03

RURAL ROUTES

1	01
2,3	04
4,5,6	03
7	04

STATIONS, BRANCHES AND UNITS

Ben Lomond Sta	04
Gorder Sta	03
Hill A F B Br	06
North Ogden Br	04
South Ogden Br	03
Washington Terrace Br	03
General Delivery	01
Postmaster	01

APARTMENTS, HOTELS, MOTELS

Ben Lomond, 411 25th	01
Bigler Desert Inn, 1825 Washington Blvd	01
Harrisville Heights, 301 Goodyear	04
Holiday Inn, 3306 Washington Blvd	01
Imperial 400, 1956 Washington Blvd	01
Ramada Inn, 2433 Adams Ave	01
Resthaven, 1910 Washington Blvd	01
Travelode Inn, 2110 Washington Blvd	01
Western, 449 27th	01

BUILDINGS

Bank Of Utah Plaza, 2651 Washington Blvd	01
Bank Of Utah, 2641 Washington Blvd	01
Beatrice, 2954 Washington Blvd	01
Citizens National Bank, 2168 Washington Blvd	01
Commercial Security Bank, 2491 Washington Blvd	01
Eccles, 385 24th	01
Exchange, 600 Exchange Rd	01
Federal Employees Credit Union, 365 Wall Ave	03
Federal, 340 25th	01
First Security Bank, 2404 Washington Blvd	01
Forest Service, 505 25th	01
Kiesel, 2411 Kiesel Ave	01
Medical Dental Center 950 - 25th	01
Municipal, 2549 Washington Blvd	01
North Ogden Municipal, 400 E 2600 N	04
Ogden Clinic 2955 Harrison	

Blvd	03
Virginia Professional, 441 24th	01

GOVERNMENT OFFICES

United States Post Office, 278 24th	01
Western Internal Revenue Service Center, 1160 W 12th	05

HOSPITALS

Mckay-Dee Hospital Center 3939 Harrison Blvd	03
Saint Benedict, 3000 Polk Ave	03

MILITARY INSTALLATIONS

Defense Depot Ogden	01
Hill Air Force Base	06

UNIVERSITIES AND COLLEGES

Stevens Henager, 2644 Washington Blvd	01
Weber State 3750 Harrison Blvd	03

SALT LAKE CITY   841

POST OFFICE BOXES

Box Nos.

1-2610	Main Office	10
6001-6148	Sugar House Sta	06
7001-7416	Murray Br	07
8001-8447	Foothill Sta	08
11001-11999	Pioneer Sta	11
15001-15490	South Salt Lake Br	15
16001-16194	Fairgrounds Sta	16
17001-17497	Holladay Br	17
18451-18578	Kearns Br	18
19001-19316	Granger Hunter Br	19
21101-21446	Cottonwood Br	21

STATIONS, BRANCHES AND UNITS

Cottonwood Br	21
Fairgrounds Sta	16
Foothill Sta	08
Granger-Hunter Br	19
Holladay Br	17
Kearns Br	18
Millcreek Br	09
Murray Br	07
Pioneer Sta	11
Saltair Rural Br	01
South Salt Lake Br	15
Sugar House Sta	06
General Delivery	01
Postmaster	01

APARTMENTS, HOTELS, MOTELS

Alben, 1810 S Main	15

Ambassador, 149 South 5th East	02
Annie Laurie, 326 East 1st South	11
Barbara Worth, 326 East South Temple	11
Bel-Aire, 750 East 2nd South	02
Ben Albert, 130 South 5th East	02
Castle Heights, 141 1st Ave	03
Charleston, 470 South 13th East	02
Clarendon, 53 South 3rd East	11
Congress, 167 South State	11
Covey, 239 East South Temple	11
Crestholme, 336 East South Temple	11
Del Roya, 335 East 3rd South	11
Douglas Arms, 920 East 5th South	02
Eagle Gate, 105 East South Temple	11
Eastcliff, 425 East 2nd South	11
Fairmont, 50 East 5th South	11
Gray Stone, 1170 East 27th South	06
Graylyn, 205 2nd Ave	03
Hillcrest, 155 1st Ave	03
Karen Lee, 4122 South 4000 West	20
Kensington, 174 North Main	03
Kimball, 150 North Main	03
Lafayette, 56 South 3rd East	11
Lorna Doone, 320 East 1st South	11
Los Gables, 131 South 3rd East	11
Miles, 110 West 3rd South	01
Newhouse, 402 South Main	01
Oxford, 119 West North Temple	03
Panorama, 8 Hillside Ave	03
Ritz, 435 East South Temple	11
Roosevelt, 256 East 3rd South	11
Royal Arms, 70 West North Temple	03
Stratton, 49 South 4th East	11
Temple Square, 75 West South Temple	01
University Heights, 130 South 13th East	02
University Village, 2200 Sunnyside Ave	08
Waldorf, 553 East 1st South	02
Wells, 125 1st Ave	03
Woodruff, 235 South 2nd East	11

BUILDINGS

American Oil, 10 West 3rd South	01
Atlas, 36 1/2 West 2nd South	01
Beneficial Life, 57 West South Temple	01
Boston, 1 Exchange Pl	11

Continental Bank, 200 South
  Main.................................... 01
Crandall, 10 West 1st South.. 01
Deseret, 79 South Main......... 01
El Paso Natural Gas, 315
  East 2nd South.................. 11
Executive, 455 East 4th
  South................................ 11
Federal, 125 South State....... 11
First Security Bank, 405
  South Main...................... 11
Judge, 8 East Broadway........ 11
Kearns, 136 South Main........ 01
Kennecott, 5 South Main....... 11
Ness, 28 West 2nd South...... 01
Newhouse, 10 Exchange Pl..... 11
Phillips Petroleum, 68 South
  Main................................ 01
Salt Palace Complex, 100
  South West Temple............ 01
Surety Life, 1935 South
  Main................................ 15

Tribune, 143 South Main........ 11
Union Pacific Depot 3rd West
  And So Temple................... 01
University Club, 136 E S
  Temple............................. 11
Walker Bank, 175 South
  Main................................ 11

HOSPITALS

Cottonwood, 5770 South 3rd
  East................................. 07
Fort Douglas Veterans, 500
  Foothill Blvd...................... 13
Holy Cross, 1045 East 1st
  South............................... 02
Latter-Day Saints, 325 8th
  Ave.................................. 03
Primary Childrens, 320 12th
  Ave.................................. 03
Saint Marks, 803 North 2nd
  West................................ 03

Shriners Childrens, 1275
  Fairfax Ave....................... 03
University, 50 N Medical Dr.... 12
Valley West, 4160 West 3400
  South............................... 20

UNIVERSITIES AND COLLEGES

B Y U Adult Education
  Center, 200 North Main...... 03
L D S Business, 411 E S
  Temple............................. 11
Rowland Hall, 205 1st Ave..... 03
Saint Mary-Of-The-Wasatch,
  3000 East 13th South........ 08
Stevens-Henager, 350 South
  7th East........................... 02
University Of Utah, 1400
  East 2nd South.................. 12
Westminister, 1800 South
  13th East.......................... 05

VERMONT
(Abbreviation: VT)

Adamant 05640
Albany 05820
Alburg 05440
Arlington 05250
Ascutney 05030
Averill, R. Br. Canaan 05901
Bakersfield 05441
Barnard 05031
Barnet 05821
Barre (1st) 05641
Barton 05822
   Glover, R. Br. 05839
Bartonsville 05140
Beebe Plain 05823
Beecher Falls 05902
Bellows Falls (1st) 05101
Belmont 05730
Belvidere Center 05442
Bennington (1st) 05201
Bennington College, Sta.
   Bennington 05201
Benson, R. Br. Fair Haven 05731
Bethel 05032
Bolton Valley, R. Br.
   Richmond 05477
Bomoseen 05732
Bondville 05340
Bradford 05033
Brandon 05733
Brattleboro (1st) 05301
   South Newfane, R. Br. 05351
   West Brattleboro, Sta. 05301
Bread Loaf, R. Br.
   Middlebury 05753
Bridgewater 05034
Bridgewater Corners 05035
Bridport 05734
Bristol 05443
Brookfield 05036
Brownsville 05037
Burlington (1st) 05401
   North Burlington, Sta. 05401
   South Burlington, Br. 05401
   Winooski, Br. 05404
Cabot 05647
Calais 05648
Cambridge 05444
Cambridgeport 05141
Canaan 05903
   Averill, R. Br. 05901
Castleton 05735
Cavendish 05142
Center Rutland 05736
Charlotte 05445
Chelsea 05038
Chester 05143
Chester Depot 05144
Chittenden 05737
Colchester 05446
Concord 05824
   East Concord, R. Sta. 05834
Corinth 05039
Coventry 05825
Craftsbury 05826
Craftsbury Common 05827
Cuttingsville 05738
Danby 05739
Danville 05828
Derby 05829

Derby Line 05830
Dorset 05251
East Arlington 05252
East Barre 05649
East Berkshire 05447
East Burke 05832
East Calais 05650
East Charleston 05833
East Concord, R. Sta.
   Concord 05834
East Corinth 05040
East Dorset 05253
East Dover 05341
East Fairfield 05448
East Hardwick 05836
East Haven 05837
East Highgate, R. Sta.
   Highgate Center 05449
East Middlebury 05740
East Montpelier 05651
   North Montpelier, R. Br. 05666
East Poultney 05741
East Randolph 05041
East Ryegate 05042
East Saint Johnsbury 05838
East Thetford 05043
East Wallingford 05742
Eden 05652
   Eden Mills, R. Sta. 05653
Eden Mills, R. Sta. Eden 05653
Ely 05044
Enosburg Falls 05450
Essex 05451
Essex Junction (1st) 05452
Fair Haven 05743
   Benson, R. Br. 05731
Fairfax 05454
Fairfield 05455
Fairlee 05045
Ferrisburg 05456
Florence 05744
Forest Dale 05745
Franklin 05457
Gassetts 05145
Gaysville 05746
Gilman 05904
Glover, R. Br. Barton 05839
Grafton 05146
Granby 05840
Grand Isle 05458
Graniteville 05654
Granville 05747
Greensboro 05841
Greensboro Bend 05842
Groton 05046
Guildhall 05905
Hancock 05748
Hardwick 05843
Hartford 05047
Hartland 05048
Hartland Four Corners 05049
Healdville 05147
Highgate Center 05459
   East Highgate, R. Sta. 05449
Highgate Springs 05460
Hinesburg 05461
Hubbardton 05749
Huntington 05462
Huntington Center, R. Br.
   Huntington 05462
Hyde Park 05655
Hydeville 05750

Irasburg 05845
Island Pond 05846
Isle La Motte 05463
Jacksonville 05342
Jamaica 05343
Jay Peak, R. Br. North Troy 05859
Jeffersonville 05464
Jericho 05465
Jericho Center, R. Sta.
   Jericho 05465
Johnson 05656
Jonesville 05466
Killington 05751
Lake Elmore 05657
Leicester Junction 05752
Londonderry 05148
Lowell 05847
Lower Waterford 05848
Ludlow 05149
Lunenburg 05906
Lyman, Sta. White River
   Junction 05001
Lyndon 05849
Lyndon Center 05850
Lyndonville (1st) 05851
Mad River Glen, R. Br.
   Waitsfield 05673
Madonna, R. Br.
   Jeffersonville 05464
Manchester (1st) 05254
Manchester Center 05255
Manchester Depot, Sta.
   Manchester Center 05255
Marlboro 05344
Marshfield 05658
Mary Meyer, Sta. Townshend 05353
Mc Indoe Falls 05050
Middlebury (1st) 05753
Middletown Springs 05757
Milton 05468
Monkton 05469
Montgomery 05470
Montgomery Center 05471
Montpelier (1st) 05602
Moretown 05660
Morgan 05853
Morgan Center 05854
Morrisville 05661
Moscow 05662
Mount Holly 05758
Mount Snow, R. Br. West
   Dover 05356
New Haven 05472
Newbury 05051
Newfane 05345
Newport (1st) 05855
Newport Center 05857
North Bennington (1st) 05257
North Burlington, Sta.
   Burlington 05401
North Clarendon 05759
North Concord 05858
North Ferrisburg 05473
North Hartland 05052
North Hero 05474
North Hyde Park 05665
North Montpelier, R. Br. East
   Montpelier 05666
North Pomfret 05053
North Pownal 05260
North Springfield 05150
North Thetford 05054

North Troy.....................................05859
Northfield (1st).............................05663
Northfield Falls.............................05664
Norton..05907
Norwich (1st)...............................05055
Orleans...05860
Orwell..05760
Passumpsic...................................05861
Pawlet..05761
Peacham.......................................05862
Perkinsville...................................05151
Peru...05152
Pittsfield......................................05762
Pittsford.......................................05763
Plainfield......................................05667
Plymouth......................................05056
Plymouth, Union...........................05057
Post Mills.....................................05058
Poultney.......................................05764
Pownal...05261
Proctor...05765
Proctorsville.................................05153
Putney (1st).................................05346
Quechee..05059
Randolph (1st)..............................05060
Randolph Center...........................05061
Reading..05062
Readsboro.....................................05350
Richford..05476
Richmond......................................05477
Ripton..05766
Riverton..05668
Rochester......................................05767
Roxbury..05669
Royalton.......................................05063
Rupert..05768
Rutland (1st).................................05701
Ryegate, R. Br. East
    Ryegate...................................05042
Saint Albans (1st).........................05478
Saint Albans Bay...........................05481
Saint Johnsbury (1st).....................05819
Saint Johnsbury Center..................05863
Salisbury.......................................05769
Saxtons River...............................05154
Shaftsbury.....................................05262
Sharon..05065
Sheffield.......................................05866
Shelburne (1st).............................05482

Shelden...05483
Sheldon Springs............................05485
Shoreham......................................05770
South Barre...................................05670
South Burlington, Br.
    Burlington................................05401
South Dorset.................................05263
South Hero....................................05486
South Londonderry........................05155
South Lunenburg...........................05908
South Newbury..............................05066
South Newfane, R. Br.
    Brattleboro..............................05351
South Pomfret...............................05067
South Royalton.............................05068
South Ryegate...............................05069
South Strafford.............................05070
South Wallingford.........................05771
South Woodbury............................05671
South Woodstock...........................05071
Springfield (1st)............................05156
Starksboro.....................................05487
Stockbridge...................................05772
Stowe (1st)...................................05672
Strafford.......................................05072
Stratton Mountain, R. Br.
    South Londonderry...................05155
Sutton...05867
Swanton..05488
Taftsville......................................05073
Thetford..05074
Thetford Center............................05075
Topsham.......................................05076
Townshend....................................05353
    Mary Meyer, Sta......................05353
    West Townshend, R. Br...........05359
Troy..05868
Tunbridge......................................05077
Underhill.......................................05489
Underhill Center............................05490
Union Village.................................05078
Vergennes (1st).............................05491
Vernon..05354
Vershire..05079
Waitsfield......................................05673
Wallingford...................................05773
Wardsboro.....................................05355
Warren..05674
Washington....................................05675

Waterbury.....................................05676
Waterbury Center...........................05677
Waterville......................................05492
Websterville...................................05678
Wells...05774
Wells River....................................05081
West Barnet...................................05870
West Berkshire..............................05493
West Brattleboro, Sta.
    Brattleboro..............................05301
West Burke....................................05871
West Charleston.............................05872
West Danville.................................05873
West Dover....................................05356
West Dummerston...........................05357
West Fairlee...................................05083
West Glover...................................05875
West Halifax..................................05358
West Hartford................................05084
West Newbury................................05085
West Pawlet...................................05775
West Rupert...................................05776
West Rutland..................................05777
West Topsham...............................05086
West Townshend, R. Br.
    Townshend...............................05359
West Wardsboro.............................05360
Westfield.......................................05874
Westford..05494
Westminster...................................05158
Westminster Station.......................05159
Weston..05161
White River Junction (1st).............05001
Whiting...05778
Whitingham...................................05361
Wilder...05088
Williamstown.................................05679
Williamsville..................................05362
Williston..05495
Wilmington....................................05363
Windsor (1st).................................05089
Winooski, Br. Burlington.................05404
Wolcott..05680
Woodbury......................................05681
Woodstock (1st)............................05091
Worcester......................................05682

VIRGINIA
(Abbreviation: VA)

Abingdon (1st) 24210
Accomac 23301
Achilles 23001
Achsah, R. Br. Madison 22708
Afton 22920
Airlie, Br. Warrenton 22186
Alberta 23821
Aldie 22001
ALEXANDRIA (1st) (see appendix)
Alfonso 22421
Allisonia 24310
Alps 22422
Altavista (1st) 24517
Alton 24520
Alum Ridge 24051
Amburg, R. Br. Deltaville 23044
Amelia Court House 23002
Amherst 24521
Amissville 22002
Ammon, R. Br. Ford 23822
Amonate 24601
Ampthill, Br. Richmond 23234
Andersonville 23911
Andover 24215
Annandale (1st) 22003
Appalachia 24216
Appomattox (1st) 24522
Ararat 24053
Arcola 22010
Ark 23003
ARLINGTON (1st) (see appendix)
Arlington Hall, Sta. Arlington 22212
Aroda 22709
Arrington 22922
Arvonia 23004
Ashburn 22011
Ashland (1st) 23005
Assawoman 23302
Atkins 24311
Atlantic 23303
Augusta Springs 24411
Austinville 24312
Axton 24054
Aylett 23009
Aylor 22710
Azalea, Br. Richmond 23227
Backbay, Sta. Virginia Beach 23457
Bacova 24412
Baileys Crossroads, Br. Falls Church 22041
Ballsville 23010
Banco 22711
Bandy 24602
Banner, R. Br. Coeburn 24231
Barboursville 22923
Barhamsville 23011
Barracks Road, Sta. Charlottesville 22903
Barren Springs 24313
Baskerville 23915
Bassett (1st) 24055
Bastian 24314
Basye 22810
Batesville 22924
Battery Park 23304
Bavon 23013

Bay, Sta. Hampton 23363
Bayford 23305
Bayside, Sta. Virginia Beach ...23455
Bealeton 22712
Beaumont 23014
Beaverdam 23015
Beaverlett 23016
Bedford (1st) 24523
Bee 24217
Bellamy 23017
Belle Haven 23306
Belle View, Br. Alexandria 22307
Bellevue, Sta. Richmond 23227
Belmont, R. Br. Spotsylvania 22553
Belspring 24058
Belt Boulevard, Br. Richmond 23224
Ben Hur 24218
Bena 23018
Bennetts Creek, Br. Suffolk 23434
Bent Mountain 24059
Bentonville 22610
Bergton 22811
Berkley, Sta. Norfolk 23523
Berryville (1st) 22611
Beverlyville 22425
Big Island 24526
Big Rock 24603
Big Stone Gap 24219
Birchleaf 24220
Birdsnest 23307
Bishop 24604
Blackridge 23916
Blacksburg (1st) 24060
Blackstone (1st) 23824
Blackwater 24221
Blackwater Bridge, R. Sta. Virginia Beach 23457
Blairs 24527
Blakes 23020
Bland 24315
Bloxom 23308
Blue Grass 24413
Blue Ridge 24064
Bluefield (1st) 24605
Bluemont 22012
Bohannon 23021
Boissevain 24606
Bolar 24414
Bon Air, Br. Richmond 23235
Bondtown, Sta. Coeburn 24230
Boones Mill 24065
Boonesville 22925
Boston 22713
Bowers Hill, R. Sta. Chesapeake 23321
Bowlers Wharf, R. Br. Tappahannock 22560
Bowling Green 22427
Boyce 22620
Boyd Tavern, R. Br. Keswick 22947
Boydton 23917
Boykins 23827
Bracey 23919
Branchville 23828
Brandy Station 22714
Breaks 24607
Bremo Bluff 23022
Briarfield, Sta. Hampton 23369
Bridgewater 22812
Brightwood 22715

Bristol (1st) 24201
Bristow 22013
Broad Rock, Br. Richmond 23224
Broad Run 22014
Broadford 24316
Broadway 22815
Brodnax 23920
Brooke 22430
Brookneal 24528
Browns Store 22431
Brownsburg 24415
Browntown, R. Br. Bentonville 22610
Brucetown 22622
Bruington 23023
Buchanan 24066
Buckingham 23921
Buckroe Beach, Sta. Hampton 23364
Buena Vista (1st) 24416
Buffalo Junction 24529
Buford, Br. Richmond 23235
Bumpass 23024
Burgess 22432
Burke, Br. Springfield 22015
Burkes Garden, Br. Tazewell ...24608
Burkeville 23922
Burnsville 24420
Burr Hill 22433
Butylo 22434
Bybee 22926
Callands 24530
Callao 22435
Callaway 24067
Calverton 22016
Cambria, Sta. Christiansburg 24073
Camden Mills, R. Sta. Chesapeake 23320
Cana 24317
Cape Charles 23310
Cape Charles Air Force Sta, Br. Cape Charles 23310
Capeville 23313
Capron 23829
Cardinal 23025
Caret 22436
Carousel, Br. Richmond 23225
Carrollton 23314
Carrsville 23315
Carson 23830
Cartersville 23027
Carterton, R. Br. Lebanon 24266
Carysbrook 22927
Casanova 22017
Cascade 24069
Cash 23028
Castleton 22716
Castlewood 24224
Catawba 24070
Catawba Sanatorium, R. Br. 24071
Catawba Sanatorium, R. Br. Catawba 24071
Catharpin 22018
Catlett 22019
Cauthornville 23029
Cedar Bluff 24609
Center Cross 22437
Central, Sta. Arlington 22203
Central, Sta. Richmond 23219
Central Martinsville, Sta. Martinsville 24112

Centreville 22020
Ceres 24318
Champlain 22438
Chance 22439
Chancellor, R. Br.
  Fredericksburg 22440
Chantilly 22021
Charles City 23030
Charlotte Court House 23923
CHARLOTTESVILLE (1st) (see
  appendix)
Chase City (1st) 23924
Chatham (1st) 24531
Check 24072
Cheriton 23316
CHESAPEAKE (1st) (see
  appendix)
Chester (1st) 23831
Chester Gap 22623
Chesterfield 23832
Chilhowie 24319
Chincoteague 23336
  Wallops Island, Br. 23337
Christchurch 23031
Christiansburg (1st) 24073
Chuckatuck 23339
Chula, R. Br. Amelia Court
  House 23002
Church Road 23833
Church View 23032
Churchland, Br. Portsmouth 23703
Churchville 24421
Cismont 22928
Civic Center, Sta. Richmond 23240
Claremont 23899
Clarksville (1st) 23927
Claudville 24076
Clayville 23034
Clear Brook 22624
Cleveland 24225
Clifford 24533
Clifton 22024
Clifton Forge (1st) 24422
Clinchburg, R. Br.
  Meadowview 24321
Clinchco 24226
Clinchport 24227
Clintwood 24228
Clover 24534
Cloverdale 24077
Cluster Springs 24535
Cobbs Creek 23035
Cobham, R. Br. Keswick 22929
Coeburn 24230
  Banner, R. Br. 24231
  Bondtown, Sta. 24230
  Tacoma, R. Br. 24232
Coleman Falls 24536
Coles Point 22442
College, Sta. Fredericksburg 22401
Collinsville (1st) 24078
Cologne, R. Br. West Point 23037
Colonial Beach 22443
Colonial Heights (1st) 23834
Columbia 23038
Community, Br. Alexandria 22306
Conaway 24611
Concord 24538
Conicville 22819
Copper Hill 24079
Copper Valley 24080
Corbin 22446
Council, R. Br. Honaker 24260

Court House, Sta. Arlington
  (see appendix)
Courtland 23837
Covesville 22931
Covington (1st) 24426
Craddockville 23341
Cradock, Sta. Portsmouth
  (see appendix)
Craigsville 24430
Creeds, R. Sta. Virginia
  Beach 23457
Crewe (1st) 23930
Criders 22820
Criglersville, R. Br. Madison 22727
Crimora 24431
Cripple Creek 24322
Crittenden 23342
Critz 24082
Crockett 24323
Cross Junction 22625
Crossroads, Br. Roanoke 24012
Crouch 22447
Crozet (1st) 22932
Crozier 23039
Crystal Hill 24539
Cullen 23934
Culpeper (1st) 22701
Cumberland 23040
Cumnor 23041
Customhouse, Sta. Norfolk 23514
Dabneys 23042
Dahlgren 22448
Daleville 24083
Dam Neck, Sta. Virginia
  Beach 23461
Damascus 24236
Dante 24237
Danville (1st) 24541
Darlington Heights 23935
Davenport 24239
Davis Wharf 23345
Dayton 22821
De Bree, Sta. Norfolk 23517
Deep Creek, Sta.
  Chesapeake 23323
Deerfield 24432
Defense General Supply Ctr,
  Br. Richmond 23219
Delaplane 22025
Deltaville 23043
  Amburg, R. Br. 23044
Denbigh, Sta. Newport News 23602
Dendron 23839
Denniston 24548
Dewitt 23840
Diggs 23045
Dillwyn 23936
Dinwiddie 23841
Disputanta 23842
Doe Hill 24433
Dogue 22451
Dolphin 23843
Doran 24612
Doswell 23047
Downings 22452
Downtown, Sta. Leesburg 22075
Dragonville 23048
Drakes Branch 23937
Draper 24324
Drewryville 23844
Driver 23346
Dry Fork 24549
Dryden 24243

Dublin 24084
Duffield 24244
Dugspur 24325
Dulles International Airport,
  Br. Washington, D C 20041
Dumfries 22026
Dundalow, Sta. Suffolk 23434
Dundas 23938
Dungannon 24245
Dunn Loring 22027
Dunnsville 22454
Dutton 23050
Dyke 22935
Eads, Sta. Arlington 22202
Eagle Rock 24085
Earlysville 22936
East End, Sta. Richmond 23223
East Stone Gap 24246
Eastville 23347
Ebony 23845
Eclipse 23349
Edinburg 22824
Edwardsville 22456
Eggleston 24086
Elberon 23846
Elk Creek 24326
Elkton (1st) 22827
Elkwood 22718
Elliston 24087
Emory 24327
Emporia (1st) 23847
Engleside, Br. Alexandria 22309
Epworth 23052
Esmont 22937
Esserville, R. Br. Norton 24274
Etlan, R. Br. Madison 22719
Ettrick, Br. Petersburg 23803
Evergreen 23939
Evington 24550
Ewing 24248
Exeter 24249
Exmore 23350
Faber 22938
Fairfax (1st) 22030
Fairfax Station, Br. Fairfax 22039
Fairfield 24435
Fairlawn, Br. Radford 24141
Falling Creek, Br. Richmond 23234
FALLS CHURCH (1st) (see
  appendix)
Falls Mills 24613
Falmouth, Br.
  Fredericksburg 22401
Fancy Gap 24328
Farmville (1st) 23901
Farnham 22460
Federal Reserve, Sta.
  Richmond 23213
Fentress, R. Sta.
  Chesapeake 23322
Ferncliff 23053
Ferrum 24088
Fieldale 24089
Fife 23054
Fincastle 24090
First Street, Sta. Radford 24141
Fishers Hill 22626
Fishersville 22939
Fleet, Br. Norfolk 23511
Flint Hill 22627
Floyd 24091
Foneswood 22461
Ford 23850

Forest....................................24551
Forest Hill, Sta. Richmond....23225
Fork Union............................23055
Forksville..............................23940
Fort Belvoir (1st)..................22060
Fort Blackmore......................24250
Fort Defiance........................24437
Fort Eustis, Sta. Newport
     News................................23604
Fort Hill, Sta. Lynchburg......24502
Fort Lee, Br. Petersburg........23801
Fort Mitchell........................23941
Fort Monroe, R. Br.
     Hampton..........................23351
Fort Myer, Sta. Arlington......22211
Fort Story, Sta. Virginia
     Beach...............................23459
Foster....................................23056
Fosters Falls..........................24329
Foxwells, R. Br. White Stone..22578
Franconia, Br. Alexandria......22310
Franklin (1st).........................23851
Franktown.............................23354
Fredericks Hall, R. Br.
     Mineral............................23057
Fredericksburg (1st)..............22401
     Chancellor, R. Br...............22440
     College, Sta......................22401
     Falmouth, Br.....................22401
Free Union............................22940
Freeman................................23856
Fries......................................24330
Front Royal (1st)....................22630
Fulks Run..............................22830
Gainesboro, R. Br.
     Winchester........................22636
Gainesville............................22065
Galax (1st).............................24333
Garrisonville.........................22463
Gasburg................................23857
Gate City (1st).......................24251
Geer......................................22941
George Washington, Sta.
     Alexandria........................22305
Gether..................................22464
Glade Spring..........................24340
Gladehill..............................24092
Gladstone.............................24553
Gladys..................................24554
Glasgow................................24555
Glass, R. Br. Hayes................23072
Glen Allen.............................23060
Glen Lea, Br. Richmond........23223
Glen Lyn..............................24093
Glen Wilton..........................24438
Glenns, R. Br. Saluda.............23149
Gloucester.............................23061
Gloucester Point....................23062
Goldbond..............................24094
Goldvein...............................22720
Gonyon..................................22467
Goochland.............................23063
Goode...................................24556
Goodview..............................24095
Gordonsville..........................22942
Gore......................................22637
Goshen..................................24439
Grafton, Br. Yorktown...........23490
Grandin Road, Sta. Roanoke
     (see appendix)
Graves Mill............................22721
Gray......................................23858
Great Bridge, Sta.

Chesapeake............................23320
Great Falls............................22066
Green Bay..............................23942
Greenbackville.......................23356
Greenbush.............................23357
Greenville..............................24440
Greenway, R. Br. Mc Lean.....22067
Greenwood............................22943
Gretna...................................24557
Grimstead.............................23064
Grottoes................................24441
Grundy (1st)..........................24614
     Roseann, R. Br.................24465
     Royal City, Sta................24614
     Stacy, R. Br.....................24616
Gum Spring...........................23065
Gwynn..................................23066
Hacksneck............................23358
Hadensville..........................23067
Hague...................................22469
Halifax..................................24558
Hallieford..............................23068
Hallwood..............................23359
Hamilton...............................22068
Hampden Sydney...................23943
HAMPTON (1st) (see
     appendix)
Hampton Institute, Sta.
     Hampton..........................23368
Hampton Roads, Br. Norfolk..23511
Handsom...............................23859
Hanover................................23069
Harborton.............................23389
Hardy....................................24101
Hardyville.............................23070
Harman.................................24618
Harrisonburg (1st).................22801
Hartfield...............................23071
Hartwood..............................22471
Hatton..................................24560
Hayes....................................23072
     Glass, R. Br....................23072
Hayfield, R. Br. Winchester....22638
Haymarket.............................22069
Haynesville............................22472
Haysi....................................24256
Haywood...............................22722
Head Waters..........................24442
Healing Springs.....................24443
Healys...................................23073
Heathsville.............................22473
Helmet..................................23074
Henry....................................24102
Herndon (1st)........................22070
Hickory, R. Sta. Chesapeake..23322
Hidenwood, Sta. Newport
     News................................23606
Highland Springs....................23075
Hightown..............................24444
Hillsboro, R. Br. Purcellville...22132
Hillsville (1st)........................24343
Hiltons..................................24258
Hinton..................................22831
Hiwassee...............................24347
Hobson..................................23390
Holland.................................23391
Hollins, Br. Roanoke.............24019
Hollins College, Br. Roanoke..24020
Honaker................................24260
     Council, R. Br..................24260
     Venia, R. Br....................24260
Hood.....................................22723
Hopeton, R. Br. Parksley.......23392

Hopewell (1st)........................23860
Horntown..............................23395
Horsepen..............................24619
Horsey..................................23396
Hot Springs...........................24445
Howardsville, R. Br.
     Scottsville........................24562
Howertons.............................22475
Huddleston............................24104
Hudgins................................23076
Hume.....................................22639
Huntly..................................22640
Hurley..................................24620
Hurt......................................24563
Hustle...................................22476
Hyacinth...............................22477
Independence.........................24348
Indian Neck...........................23077
Indian River, Sta.
     Chesapeake.......................23325
Indian Valley.........................24105
Ingram..................................24564
Inman...................................24262
Iron Gate..............................24448
Ironto, R. Br. Elliston.............24087
Irvington...............................22480
Irwin....................................23078
Isle of Wight.........................23397
Ivanhoe................................24350
Ivor......................................23866
Ivy.......................................22945
Jamaica................................23079
James Store...........................23080
Jamestown.............................23081
Jamesville.............................23398
Jarratt..................................23867
Java......................................24565
Jefferson Manor, Br.
     Alexandria........................22303
Jeffersonton..........................22724
Jenkins Bridge.......................23399
Jersey...................................22481
Jetersville.............................23083
Jewell Ridge..........................24622
Jewell Valley.........................24623
Jonesville..............................24263
Jordan Mines.........................24449
Kable, Sta. Staunton..............24401
Kathmoor, R. Br. Alexandria..22310
Kecoughtan, Sta. Hampton....23367
Keeling..................................24566
Keen Mountain......................24624
Keene....................................22946
Keezletown............................22832
Keller....................................23401
Kenbridge.............................23944
Kents Store............................23084
Keokee..................................24265
Keswick.................................22947
     Boyd Tavern, R. Br...........22947
     Cobham, R. Br.................22929
Keysville................................23947
Kilmarnock...........................22482
Kimballton............................24107
King And Queen Court
     House..............................23085
King George..........................22485
     Owens, R. Br...................22532
King William.........................23086
Kinsale..................................22488
L C Page, Sta. Norfolk...........23518
La Crosse..............................23950
Laban...................................23087

Laburnum Manor, Br. Richmond	23222	
Lacey Spring	22833	
Lackey	23402	
Ladysmith	22501	
Lafayette	24108	
Lafayette Boulevard, Sta. Norfolk	23509	
Lahore	22502	
Lakeside, Br. Richmond	23228	
Lambsburg	24351	
Lancaster	22503	
Lanesville	23088	
Laneview	22504	
Lanexa	23089	
Langley A F B, Sta. Hampton	23365	
Laurel, R. Br. Glen Allen	23060	
Laurel Fork	24352	
Lawrenceville (1st)	23868	
Lebanon (1st)	24266	
Lebanon Church	22641	
Lee Hall, Sta. Newport News	23603	
Lee Mont	23403	
Leesburg (1st)	22075	
Lennig	24568	
Leon	22725	
Lewisetta	22505	
Lexington (1st)	24450	
Lightfoot	23090	
Lignum	22726	
Lilian, R. Br. Reedville	22506	
Lincoln, Br. Purcellville	22078	
Lincolnia, Br. Alexandria	22312	
Linden	22642	
Linville	22834	
Lithia	24110	
Little Plymouth, R. Br. West Point	23091	
Lively	22507	
Locust Dale	22948	
Locust Grove	22508	
Locust Hill	23092	
Locustville	23404	
London Bridge, Sta. Virginia Beach	23454	
Long Island	24569	
Loretto	22509	
Lorne	22510	
Lorton	22079	
Lottsburg	22511	
Louisa (1st)	23093	
Trevilians, R. Br.	23170	
Lovettsville	22080	
Lovingston	22949	
Lowesville	22951	
Lowmoor	24457	
Lowry	24570	
Lunenburg	23952	
Luray (1st)	22835	
Lynch Station	24571	
LYNCHBURG (1st) (see appendix)		
Lyndhurst	22952	
Lynnhaven, Sta. Virginia Beach	23452	
Machipongo	23405	
Macon	23101	
Madison	22727	
Achsah, R. Br.	22708	
Criglersville, R. Br.	22727	
Etlan, R. Br.	22719	
Madison Heights	24572	

Madison Mills	22953	
Madisonville, R. Br. Pamplin	23958	
Maidens	23102	
Manakin Sabot	23103	
Manassas (1st)	22110	
Manassas Park, Br. Manassas	22110	
Mangohick	23104	
Mannboro	23105	
Manquin	23106	
Mappsville	23407	
Marine Corps Base, Br. Quantico	22134	
Marion (1st)	24354	
Marionville	23408	
Markham	22643	
Marshall	22115	
Martinsville (1st)	24112	
Maryus	23107	
Mascot	23108	
Massanetta Springs, Br. Harrisonburg	22801	
Massies Mill	22954	
Mathews	23109	
Matoaca, R. Br. Petersburg	23803	
Mattaponi	23110	
Maurertown	22644	
Mavisdale	24627	
Max Meadows	24360	
Maxie	24628	
Mayo	24573	
Mc Clure	24269	
Mc Coy	24111	
Mc Dowell	24458	
Mc Gaheysville	22840	
Mc Kenney	23872	
Mc Lean (1st)	22101	
Greenway, R. Br.	22067	
Meadows of Dan	24120	
Meadowview	24361	
Clinchburg, R. Br.	24321	
Mears	23409	
Mechanicsville (1st)	23111	
Medical College, Sta. Richmond	23219	
Meherrin	23954	
Melfa	23410	
Melrose, Sta. Roanoke	24017	
Mendota	24270	
Meredithville	23871	
Merrifield, Br. Fairfax	22030	
Merry Point	22513	
Messick, Br. Hampton	23362	
Metro, Br. Richmond	23231	
Mid Town, Sta. Portsmouth	23707	
Middlebrook	24459	
Middleburg	22117	
Middletown	22645	
Midland	22728	
Midlothian	23113	
Milan, Sta. Norfolk	23508	
Miles	23114	
Milford	22514	
Mill Gap, R. Br. Monterey	24462	
Millboro	24460	
Millboro Springs, R. Br. Millboro	24460	
Miller Park, Sta. Lynchburg	24501	
Miller School, R. Br. Charlottesville	22901	
Millers Tavern	23115	

Millwood	22646	
Mine Run, R. Br. Unionville	22568	
Mineral	23117	
Fredericks Hall, R. Br.	23057	
Orchid, R. Br.	23117	
Pendletons, R. Br.	23117	
Mint Spring	24463	
Miskimon	22516	
Mission Home	22956	
Mitchells	22729	
Mobjack	23118	
Modern, Sta. Hampton	23366	
Modest Town	23412	
Mollusk	22517	
Moneta	24121	
Monroe	24574	
Montebello	24464	
Monterey	24465	
Mill Gap, R. Br.	24462	
Monticello, R. Br. Charlottesville	22901	
Montpelier	23192	
Montpelier Station	22957	
Montrose Heights, Sta. Richmond	23231	
Montross	22520	
Templeman, R. Br.	22563	
Montvale	24122	
Moon	23119	
Morattico	22523	
Morrisville, R. Br. Remington	22734	
Mosby, Br. Falls Church	22042	
Moseley	23120	
Mount Crawford	22841	
Mount Hermon, Br. Danville	24541	
Mount Holly	22524	
Mount Jackson	22842	
Mount Landing, R. Br. Tappahannock	22560	
Mount Sidney	24467	
Mount Solon	22843	
Mount Vernon	22121	
Mountain Lake, R. Br. Pembroke	24136	
Mouth of Wilson	24363	
Mustoe	24468	
Narrows	24124	
Naruna	24576	
Nassawadox	23413	
Nathalie	24577	
Natural Bridge	24578	
Natural Bridge Station	24579	
Naval Air Station, Br. Norfolk	23511	
Naval Amphibious Base, Br. Norfolk	23521	
Naval Hospital, Sta. Portsmouth	23708	
Naval Weapons Station, Br. Yorktown	23491	
Navy Annex, Br. Washington, D C	20370	
Navy Yard, Sta. Portsmouth	23709	
Naxera	23122	
Nellysford	22958	
Nelson	24580	
Nelsonia	23414	
New Canton	23123	
New Castle	24127	
New Church	23415	
New Hope	24469	

New Kent 23124
New Market 22844
New Point 23125
New River 24129
Newbern 24126
Newcomb Hall, Sta.
  Charlottesville................22901
Newington 22122
Newport 24128
NEWPORT NEWS (1st) (see
  appendix)
Newsoms 23874
Newtown 23126
Nickelsville 24271
Nimrod Hall 24470
Ninde 22526
Nokesville 22123
Nomini Grove 22527
Nora 24272
NORFOLK (1st) (see
  appendix)
Norge 23127
North 23128
North, Sta. Arlington 22207
North Garden 22959
North Springfield, Br.
  Springfield 22151
North Tazewell 24630
Northside, Sta. Richmond ...23222
Northwest, R. Sta.
  Chesapeake 23322
Norton (1st) 24273
  Esserville, R. Br. 24274
Norview, Sta. Norfolk 23513
Norwood 24581
Nottoway 23955
Nuttsville 22528
Oak Grove, R. Br. Colonial
  Beach 22443
Oak Hall 23416
Oakpark 22730
Oakton 22124
Oakwood 24631
Occoquan 22125
Ocean View, Sta. Norfolk ...23503
Oceana, Sta. Virginia Beach ...23453
Oceana N A S, Sta. Virginia
  Beach 23460
Oilville 23129
Oldhams 22529
Olive, Sta. Portsmouth (see
  appendix)
Onancock 23417
Onemo 23130
Onley 23418
Ophelia 22530
Orange (1st) 22960
Orchid, R. Br. Mineral 23117
Ordinary 23131
Oriskany 24130
Orkney Springs 22845
Orlean 22128
Ottoman, R. Br. Lancaster ...22503
Overall 22648
Owens, R. Br. King George ...22532
Oyster 23419
Paces, R. Br. South Boston ...24592
Paeonian Springs 22129
Paint Bank 24131
Painter 23420
Palmer Springs 23957
Palmyra 22963

Pamplin 23958
Parcel Post Annex, Sta.
  Norfolk 23516
Paris ..,..............................22130
Park, Sta. Waynesboro 22980
Parkfairfax, Sta. Alexandria ...22302
Parksley 23421
  Hopeton, R. Br. 23392
Parkview, Sta. Newport
  News 23605
Parrott 24132-
Partlow 22534
Patrick Springs 24133
Patterson 24633
Pearisburg 24134
Peary 23133
Pemberton 23134
Pembroke 24136
Pendletons, R. Br. Mineral ...23117
Penhook 24137
Penn Laird 22846
Pennington Gap 24277
  Woodway, R. Br. 24295
Pentagon, Br. Washington, D
  C 20301
Petersburg (1st) 23803
  Ettrick, Br. 23803
  Fort Lee, Br. 23801
  Matoaca, R. Br. 23803
  Walnut Hill, Sta. 23803
  Western, Sta. 23803
Pettis, R. Br. Staunton 24401
Phenix 23959
Philomont 22131
Phoebus, Sta. Hampton 23363
Pilgrims Knob 24634
Pilot 24138
Pimmit, Br. Falls Church 22043
Pine Dell, Br. Richmond 23229
Pinero 23136
Piney River 22964
Pittsville 24139
Plain View 23137
Pleasant Valley 22848
Pocahontas 24635
Pocoshock, Br. Richmond ...23235
Poquoson, Br. Hampton 23362
Port Haywood 23138
Port Republic 24471
Port Royal 22535
Portlock, Sta. Chesapeake ...23324
PORTSMOUTH (1st) (see
  appendix)
Potomac, Sta. Alexandria ...22301
Pound 24279
Pounding Mill 24637
Powhatan 23139
Prater, R. Br. Vansant 24638
Pratts 22731
Preston King, Sta. Arlington ...22205
Prince George 23875
Princess Anne, Sta. Virginia
  Beach 23456
Prospect 23960
Providence Forge 23140
Pulaski (1st) 24301
Pungo, R. Sta. Virginia
  Beach 23456
Pungoteague 23422
Purcellville 22132
Purdy, R. Br. Emporia 23847
Quantico (1st) 22134

Quicksburg 22847
Quinby 23423
Quinque 22965
Quinton 23141
Radford (1st) 24141
Radford College, Sta.
  Radford 24141
Radiant 22732
Randolph 23962
Raphine 24472
Rapidan 22733
Rappahannock Academy 22538
Raven 24639
Rawlings 23876
Rectortown 22140
Red Ash 24640
  Shortt Gap, R. Br. 24647
Red House 23963
Red Oak 23964
Redart 23142
Redwood 24146
Reedville 22539
  Lilian, R. Br. 22506
Regina 22540
Rehoboth 23965
Reliance 22649
Remington 22734
Remlik, R. Br. Urbanna 23175
Republican Grove 24585
Rescue 23424
Reston, R. Br. Herndon 22070
Reva 22735
Rhoadesville 22542
Rice 23966
Rich Creek 24147
Richardsville 22736
Richlands (1st) 24641
RICHMOND (1st) (see
  appendix)
Ridge, Br. Richmond 23229
Ridgeway 24148
Rileyville 22650
Riner 24149
Ringgold 24586
Ripplemead 24150
Riverdale, Sta. Hampton 23366
Rivermont, Sta. Lynchburg ...24503
Riverton 22651
Rixeyville 22737
ROANOKE (1st) (see
  appendix)
Robley 22543
Rochelle 22738
Rockbridge Baths 24473
Rockfish 22966
Rockville 23146
Rocky Gap 24366
Rocky Mount (1st) 24151
Roda, R. Br. Appalachia 24216
Rollins Fork 22544
Rose Hill 24281
Roseann, R. Br. Grundy 24645
Rosedale 24280
Roseland 22967
Rosslyn, Sta. Arlington 22209
Round Hill 22141
Rowe 24646
Royal City, Sta. Grundy 24614
Ruby 22545
Ruckersville 22968
Rural Retreat 24368
Rushmere 23425

Rustburg.................................24588
Ruther Glen 22546
Ruthville.................................23147
Saint Brides, R. Sta.
  Chesapeake........................23322
Saint Charles 24282
Saint Davids Church............22652
Saint Paul 24283
Saint Stephens Church 23148
Salem (1st) 24153
Saltville.................................24370
Saluda...................................23149
Samos, R. Br. Urbanna.........23175
Sanatorium, R. Br.
  Charlottesville....................22901
Sandston (1st) 23150
Sandy Hook............................23153
Sandy Level 24161
Sanford..................................23426
Saunders, Sta. Richmond 23220
Saxe.......................................23967
Saxis......................................23427
Schley.....................................23154
Schoolfield, Sta. Danville.......24541
Schuyler.................................22969
Scottsburg 24589
Scottsville 24590
  Howardsville, R. Br............24562
Seaford..................................23428
Sealston................................22547
Seapines, Sta. Virginia
  Beach.................................23451
Seaview 23429
Sedley....................................23878
Selma.....................................24474
Seven Corners, Br. Falls
  Church...............................22044
Seven Fountains....................22653
Seven Mile Ford.....................24373
Severn....................................23155
Shacklefords..........................23156
Shadow..................................23157
Shanghai................................23158
Sharps....................................22548
Shawsville 24162
Shenandoah..........................22849
Shenandoah Caverns, R. Br.
  Quicksburg.........................22847
Shiloh 22549
Shipman.................................22971
Shirley Duke, Sta.
  Alexandria..........................22304
Shirlington, Sta. Arlington 22206
Shortt Gap, R. Br. Red Ash 24647
Shumansville.........................22550
Simonsdale, Sta.
  Portsmouth........................23701
Simpsons................................24163
Singers Glen 22850
Skippers.................................23879
Skipwith.................................23968
Smithfield (1st)......................23430
Snell, R. Br. Spotsylvania 22553
Snowden.................................24591
Snowflake, R. Br. Gate City....24251
Somerset................................22972
Somerville..............................22739
South, Sta. Arlington.............22204
South Boston (1st)................24592
South Covington, Sta.
  Covington...........................24426
South Hill (1st)......................23970

South Martinsville, Sta.
  Martinsville........................24112
South Norfolk, Sta.
  Chesapeake........................23324
South Roanoke, Sta.
  Roanoke.............................24014
Southampton, Sta. Hampton..23369
Southside, Sta. Richmond......23224
Sparta....................................22552
Speedwell...............................24374
Spencer..................................24165
Sperryville.............................22740
  Woodville, R. Br................22749
Spotsylvania 22553
Spottswood 24475
Spout Spring 24593
Spring Grove...........................23881
SPRINGFIELD (1st) (see
  appendix)
Springwood, R. Br.
  Buchanan...........................24066.
Sprouses Corner, R. Br.
  Dillwyn..............................23936
Stacy, R. Br. Grundy 24616
Stafford..................................22554
Staffordsville..........................24167
Stage Junction.......................23159
Stanardsville 22973
Stanley...................................22851
Stanleytown (1st)..................24168
Star Tannery..........................22654
State Farm 23160
Staunton (1st).......................24401
Steeles Tavern.......................24476
Stephens City.........................22655
Stephenson............................22656
Sterling..................................22170
Stevensburg...........................22741
Stevensville 23161
Stewart, Sta. Richmond 23221
Stewartsville, R. Br. Vinton....24179
Stonega.................................24285
Stony Creek 23882
Stormont, R. Br. Saluda.........23149
Strasburg (1st).......................22657
Stratford................................22558
Stratford Hills, Br.
  Richmond...........................23225
Stuart.....................................24171
Stuarts Draft..........................24477
Studley...................................23162
Suffolk (1st) 23434
Sugar Grove...........................24375
Sugar Loaf, Br. Roanoke........24018
Sumerduck.............................22742
Sunnyside, R. Br.
  Winchester.........................22601
Sunset Hills, R. Br. Herndon...22070
Supply....................................22559
Surry......................................23883
Susan.....................................23163
Sussex....................................23884
Sutherland.............................23885
Sutherlin................................24594
Sweet Briar............................24595
Swoope..................................24479
Swords Creek.........................24649
Syria.......................................22743
Syringa...................................23165
Tabb, R. Br. Newport News....23602
Tacoma, R. Br. Coeburn.........24232
Tamworth...............................23166
Tangier 23440

Tannersville 24377
Tappahannock (1st) 22560
Tasley....................................23441
Tazewell (1st)........................24651
Temperanceville.....................23442
Temple Trailer, Sta.
  Alexandria..........................22314
Templeman, R. Br. Montross..22563
Tetotum 22564
Thaxton..................................24174
The Plains 22171
Theological Seminary, Sta.
  Alexandria..........................22304
Thomas Corner, Sta. Norfolk...23502
Thornburg..............................22565
Timberlake, Br. Lynchburg 24502
Timberville.............................22853
Tiptop....................................24655
Toano.....................................23168
Toms Brook 22660
Topping..................................23169
Townsend...............................23443
Trammel.................................24289
Trevilians, R. Br. Louisa 23170
Triangle 22172
Triplet....................................23886
Trout Dale..............................24378
Troutville................................24175
Troy..22974
Tuckahoe, Br. Richmond........23229
Tucker Hill, R. Br. Kinsale 22488
Tunstall 23172
Turbeville...............................24596
Twymans Mill 22744
Tye River................................22975
Tyro.......................................22976
Union Hall 24176
Union Level............................23973
Unionville...............................22567
  Mine Run, R. Br................22568
University, Sta.
  Charlottesville....................22903
University of Richmond...........23173
Upperville 22176
Upright...................................22569
Urbanna.................................23175
Valentines..............................23887
Vansant..................................24656
  Prater, R. Br......................24638
Venia, R. Br. Honaker............24260
Vernon Hill.............................24597
Verona (1st) 24482
Vesta.....................................24177
Vesuvius.................................24483
Veterans Administration
  Hosp, Br. Richmond...........23219
Victoria...................................23974
Vienna (1st) 22180
Viewtown...............................22746
Village....................................22570
Villamont...............................24178
Vint Hill Farms, Br.
  Warrenton..........................22186
Vinton (1st) 24179
Virgilina.................................24598
VIRGINIA BEACH (1st) (see
  appendix)
Virginia Union University,
  Sta. Richmond...................23220
Volney....................................24379
Wachapreague........................23480
Wake......................................23176
Wakefield...............................23888

Walkerton................................23177
Wallops Island, Br.
  Chincoteague.....................23337
Walmsley 22571
Walnut Hill, Sta. Petersburg...23803
Walters, R. Br. Windsor..........23481
Wardtown................................23482
Ware Neck..............................23178
Warfield..................................23889
Warm Springs........................24484
Warner...................................23179
Warrenton (1st).....................22186
Warsaw (1st)..........................22572
Warwick, Sta. Newport News..23601
Washington.............................22747
Washingtons Birthplace.........22575
Water View............................23180
Waterford...............................22190
Waterlick...............................22661
Wattsville...............................23483
Waverly..................................23890
Waynesboro (1st)...................22980
Weber City, R. Br. Gate City..24251
Weems...................................22576
Weirwood...............................23484
Wellington, Br. Alexandria......22308
West Annex, MOU. Norfolk......23520
West Augusta..........................24485
West End, Br. Richmond.........23230
West Norfolk, Br.
  Portsmouth.....................23703
West Point (1st) 23181
  Cologne, R. Br................23037
  Little Plymouth, R. Br........23091
West Springfield, Br.
  Springfield 22152

Western, Sta. Petersburg 23803
Westhampton, Sta.
  Richmond.......................23226
Westmoreland........................22577
Westwood, Br. Richmond 23230
Weyers Cave...........................24486
Whaleyville.............................23485
Whitacre.................................22662
White Hall...............................22987
White Marsh............................23183
White Plains............................23893
White Post..............................22663
White Stone 22578
Whitethorne............................24183
Whitetop................................24292
Whitewood..............................24657
Wicomico................................23184
Wicomico Church.....................22579
Williamsburg (1st)...................23185
Williamson Road, Sta.
  Roanoke.........................24012
Williamsville...........................24487
Willis......................................24380
Willis Wharf............................23486
Wilmington 22988
Wilsons...................................23894
Winchester (1st)......................22601
  Gainesboro, R. Br. 22636
  Hayfield, R. Br.................22638
  Sunnyside, R. Br..............22601
Windmill Point, R. Br. White
  Stone.............................22578
Windsor...................................23487
  Walters, R. Br 23481
Wingina 24599
Winterpock, R. Br.

Chesterfield............................23832
Wirtz 24184
Wise..24293
Witch Duck, Sta. Virginia
  Beach.............................23462
Withams 23488
Wolford...................................24658
Wolftown.................................22748
Woodberry Forest....................22989
Woodbridge (1st).....................22191
Woodford.................................22580
Woodlawn................................24381
Woodrow Wilson, R. Br.
  Fishersville......................22939
Woodrum, Sta. Staunton.........24401
Woods Cross Roads..................23190
Woodstock (1st).......................22664
Woodville, R. Br. Sperryville....22749
Woodway, R. Br. Pennington
  Gap 24295
Woolwine................................24185
Wright, Sta. Norfolk.................23505
Wylliesburg.............................23976
Wythe, Sta. Hampton...............23361
Wytheville (1st) 24382
Yale..23897
Yards......................................24659
Yorkshire, Br. Manassas..........22110
Yorktown (1st)..........................23490
  Grafton, Br......................23490
  Naval Weapons Station,
  Br...................................23491
Zacata....................................22581
Zanoni 23191
Zuni..23898

ALEXANDRIA 223

POST OFFICE BOXES

Box Nos.
1-1359	Main Office	13
2001-2297	Potomac Sta.....	01
3001-3348	Parkfairfax Sta.	02
4001-4148	Jefferson Manor Br	03
5001-5127	George Washington Sta	05
6001-6358	Community Br..	06
7001-7900	Belle View	07
9001-9645	Shirley Duke Sta	04
10001-10424	Franconia	10
15001-15160	Engleside Br.....	09

RURAL ROUTES

5		10

STATIONS, BRANCHES AND UNITS

Belle View Br	07
Community Br	06
Engleside Br	09
Franconia Br	10
George Washington Sta	05
Jefferson Manor Br	03
Kathmoor Rural Br	10
Lincolnia Br	12
Parkfairfax Sta	02
Potomac Sta	01
Shirley Duke Sta	04
Temple Trailer Sta	14
Theological Seminary Sta	04
Wellington Br	08
General Delivery	13
Postmaster	13

APARTMENTS, HOTELS, MOTELS

Americana Landmark Apartments, 16 Van Dorn S	04
Auburn Gardens, 101 Glebe Rd E	05
Belle Haven Towers, 6038 Richmond Hwy	03
Beverly Park Gardens, 527 Four Mile Rd	05
Bradlee Apartments, 3810 King	02
Calvert Apartments, 3110 Mt Vernon Ave	05
Chadwick Towers Apartments, 100 Reynolds S	04
Charter House Motel, Edsall Rd & Shirley Hwy	12
Dominion Gardens, 3800 Milan Dr	05
Duchess Gardens, 4309 Duke	04
George Mason Hotel, Prince & Washington	13
Glebe House, 25 Glebe Rd W	05
Goldengate Apartments, 3529 Leesburg Pike	02

Holiday Inn, 6100 Richmond Hwy	03
Holmes Run Apartments, 5465 Morgan N	12
Hunting Terrace Apartments, 1205 Washington S	14
Hunting Towers Apartments, 1200 Washington S	14
Jamestown Village, 1523 Van Dorn N	04
Kent Towers, 5851 Quantrell Ave	12
Landmark Towers, 101 Whiting S	04
Landover House, 3201 Landover	05
Mayfair Mall Apartments, 5335-5405 Duke	04
Mayfair Towers Apartments, 5340 Duke	04
Monticello, 805 King	14
Mount Vernon Apartments, 8259 Russell Rd	09
Mount Vernon Motor Lodge, 7226 Richmond Hwy	06
Normandy Hills, 145 Normandy Hill Dr	04
Olde Colony Motor Lodge, N Washington & 1st	13
Park Alexandria Apartments, 5340 Holmes Run Pky	04
Parkwood Terrace Apartments, 107 Ripley N..	04
Port Royal Apartments, 801 Pitt N	14
Presidential Garden Apartments, Mt Vernon Ave & Russel	05
Presidential Gardens Motor, Mt Vernon & Russell Rd	05
River Towers, 6631 River Towers Dr	07
Riverview Apartments, 1116 Pitt N	14
Seminary Hill Apartments, 4700 Kenmore Ave	04
Seminary Towers East, 4701 Kenmore Ave	04
Seminary Towers West, 4801 Kenmore Ave	04
Shirley Duke Apartments, 4447 Duke	04
Southern Towers Apartments, 4901-5055 Seminary Rd	11
Stones Motel, 4256 King	02
Towne Motel, 808 Washington N	14
Travelers Motel, 5916 Richmond Hwy	03
Van Duke Apartments, 420 Van Dorn N	04
Virginia Lodge, 6027 Richmond Hwy	03
Virginia Motel, 700 Washington N	14
Wagon Wheel Motel, 7212 Richmond Hwy	06
Wapleton Mansion Apartments, 5250 Valley Forge Dr	04
Warwick Village, 1 Kennedy	05

BUILDINGS

Alexandria Medical, 312 Washington S	14
American Red Cross, 615 St Asaph N	14
Bradlee Medical, 3541 King	02
Doniphan, 101 Columbus N	14
Fruit Growers Express, 16 Roth	14
George Washington Masonic Temple	01
Hoffman, 2461 Eisenhower Ave	14

HOSPITALS

Alexandria Hospital, 4320 Seminary Rd	14
Circle Terrace Hospital, 904 Circle Terrace Dr	02
Jefferson Memorial Hospital, 4600 King	02

MILITARY INSTALLATIONS

Cameron Station, 5010 Duke..	14
Defense Documentation Center, 5010 Duke	14
Defense Supply Agency, 5010 Duke	14

ARLINGTON 222

POST OFFICE BOXES

Box Nos.
1-499	Main Office	10
501-999	Courthouse Sta	16
1100-1199	Fort Myer Sta	11
2000-2999	Eads Sta	02
3000-3999	Central Sta	03
4000-4999	South Sta	04
5000-5999	Preston King Sta	05
6000-6999	Shirlington Sta.	06
7000-7999	North Sta	07
9000-9999	Rosslyn Sta	09

STATIONS, BRANCHES AND UNITS

Arlington Hall Sta	12
Central Sta	03
Court House Sta	01
Eads Sta	02
Fort Myer Sta	11
North Sta	07
Preston King Sta	05
Rosslyn Sta	09
Shirlington Sta	06
South Sta	04
General Delivery	10
Postmaster	10

APARTMENTS, HOTELS, MOTELS

Arva Motor Hotel, 2201 Arlington Blvd	01
Cardinal House, 3000 Spout Run Parkway	01

Cherry Blossom Motor Inn,
  3030 Columbia Pike 04
Clarendon Hotel Court, 3824
  Wilson Blvd. 03
Crystal House, 1900 S Eads... 02
Diplomat, 5565 Columbia
  Pike 04
Dominion Arms, 333 S Glebe
  Rd 04
Dominion Plaza, 1200 S
  Court House Rd 04
Dominion Towers, 1201 S
  Court House Rd 04
Dorchester Towers, 2001
  Columbia Pike 04
Executive Central, 1201
  South Scott 04
Executive North, 1850
  Columbia Pike 04
Executive South, 1301 South
  Scott 04
Holiday Inn, Shirley Hwy & S
  Glebe Rd 06
Holiday Inn, 1499 Jefferson
  Davis Highway 02
Holiday Inn, 1850 N Fort
  Myer Dr 09
Hospitality House Motor Inn
  2000 Jefferson Davis Hwy.. 02
Iwo Jima Motor Hotel, 1501
  Arlington Blvd 09
Marriott Motor Hotel, Crystal
  City 02
Marriott Motor Hotel, Key
  Bridge 09
Marriott Motor Hotel, Twin
  Bridges 02
Motel Fifty, 1601 Arlington
  Blvd 09
Park Adams, 2000 North
  Adams 01
Park Arlington, Arlington Blvd
  & N Court House 01
Pentagon Motel, 901 S Clark.. 02
Potomac Towers, 2001 N
  Adams 01
River House South, 1600
  South Joyce 02
River House West, 1400
  South Joyce 02
River House, 1111 S Army
  Navy Dr 02
Shirlington House, 4201
  South 31st 06
South Gate Motor Hotel,
  Shirley Hwy & S Glebe Rd.. 06
Virginian, 1500 Arlington
  Blvd 09
Wildwood Park, 5555
  Columbia Pike 04
Windsor Towers, 5535
  Columbia Pike 04

BUILDINGS

Jefferson, 1021 Arlington
  Blvd 09
Madison, 1111 Arlington
  Blvd 09
Tyler, 1121 Arlington Blvd 09
Washington, 1011 Arlington
  Blvd 09

GOVERNMENT OFFICES

Office Of Naval Research 17

MILITARY INSTALLATIONS

Arlington Hall 12
Fort Myer 11
Henderson Hall 14
Office Of Naval Research 17

CHARLOTTESViLLE   229

POST OFFICE BOXES

Box Nos.
1-1608   Main Office 02
1841-4008   University Sta.... 03
5001-5738   Barracks Road
           Sta. 03

RURAL ROUTES

1,2,3,4,5,6,7,8. 01

STATIONS, BRANCHES AND UNITS

Barracks Road Sta. 03
Miller School Rural Br. 01
Monticello Rural Br. 01
Newcomb Hall Sta. 01
Sanatorium Rural Br. 01
University Sta. 03
General Delivery 01
Postmaster .... ? 02

UNIVERSITIES AND COLLEGES

University Of Virgina 04

CHESAPEAKE   233

POST OFFICE BOXES

Box Nos.
1-299   Bowers Hill
           Rural Sta. 21
301-499   Northwest
           Rural Sta. 22
501-599   Fentress Rural
           Sta. 22
601-999,   Money Order
           Unit 01 22
1001-2099   Main Office 20
5001-5299   So Norfork Sta.. 24
6001-6999   Deep Creek
           Sta. 23
7501-7999   Portlock Sta. 24
13001-13999 Indian River
           Sta. 25
15001-15299 Great Bridge
           Sta. 20

STATIONS, BRANCHES AND UNITS

Bowers Hill Rural Sta. 21
Camden Mills Rural Sta 20
Deep Creek Sta 23
Fentress Rural Sta. 22
Great Bridge Sta. 20
Hickory Rural Sta. 22
Indian River Sta. 25
Northwest Rural Sta. 22
Portlock Sta. 24
Saint Brides Rural Sta. 22
South Norfolk Sta. 24
General Delivery 20
Postmaster 20

APARTMENTS, HOTELS, MOTELS

Cavalier, 1125 S Military
  Hwy 20
Colonial Motor Court, 5109
  Geo Washington Hwy 23
Ellis, Military Hwy 23
Greenbriar, 2412 S Military
  Hwy 20
Holiday Inn, Military Hwy 23
Howard Johnson Motor Lodge,
  Military Hwy 23
Portsmouth, Military Hwy 23
Scotties, 4330 Bainbridge
  Blvd 24
Sunset Manor, Military Hwy.. 23
Travelers, 2109 Bainbridge
  Blvd 24
Virginia Reel, Military Hwy 20

FALLS CHURCH   220

POST OFFICE BOXES

Box Nos.
1-699   Main Office 46
1000-1299   Bailey
           Crossroads
           Br 41
2001-2372   Mosby 42
3001-3099   Pimmit 43
4001-5066   Seven Corners
           Br 44

STATIONS, BRANCHES AND UNITS

Baileys Crossroads Br. 41
Mosby Br. 42
Pimmit Br. 43
Seven Corners Br 44
General Delivery 46
Postmaster 46

BUILDINGS

Anderson, 450 W Broad St 46
City Hall, 300 Park Ave 46
Dominian, 311 Park Ave 46
Donovan, 106 Little Falls........ 46
Falls Church Medical Center,
  6060 Arlington Blvd 44
Fink Professional, 200 Little
  Falls 46
Luria, 6269 Leesburg Pike...... 44
Medical Arts, 2946 Sleepy
  Hollow Rd. 44
Melpar Inc, 7700 Arlington
  Blvd. 46

Nasiff, 5E11 Columbia Pike... 41
Nationwide Insurance, 6506
  Arlington Blvd.................... 42
Park Ave Professional, 313
  Park Ave........................... 46
Professional Bldg, 5600
  Columbia Pike.................. 41
Providence, 6521 Arlington
  Blvd................................. 42
Robertson, 100 N
  Washington....................... 46
Seven Corners Medical, 6305
  Castle Place...................... 44
Seven Corners Professional,
  6319 Castle Place.............. 44
The Lee, 5881 Leesburg Pike.. 41
The Williamsburg, 108 N
  Virginia Ave..................... 46
Virginia, 210 Little Falls........ 46

HOSPITALS

Fairfax Hospital, 3300
  Gallows Rd........................ 46
Northern Va Mental Health,
  3302 Gallows Rd................ 42
Powhatan Nursing Home,
  2100 Powhatan.................. 43
Whitehall Sanitarium, 335
  Little Falls........................ 46

UNIVERSITIES AND COLLEGES

Northern Virginia Community,
  3443 S Carlyn Spring Rd... 41

HAMPTON . 233

POST OFFICE BOXES

Box Nos.
1-657   Main Office 69
600-899   Langley Air
           Force Base
           Sta.............. 65
1200-1999 Wythe Sta........ 62
2000-2999 Poquoson Br..... 62
3000-3999 Phoebus Sta..... 63
4000-4999 Buckroe Beach
           Sta.............. 64
5100-5999 Kecoughtan
           Sta.............. 67
6000-6999 Hampton
           Institute Sta.. 68
7000-7999 Riverdale 66
9000-9999 Briarfield........ 69

STATIONS, BRANCHES AND UNITS

Bay Sta.............................. 63
Briarfield Sta..................... 69
Buckroe Beach Sta.............. 64
Fort Monroe Rural Br.......... 51
Hampton Institute Sta.......... 68
Kecoughtan Sta................... 67
Langley A F B Sta............... 65
Messick Br......................... 62
Modern Sta......................... 66
Phoebus Sta........................ 63
Poquoson Br....................... 62

Riverdale Sta...................... 66
Southampton Sta................. 69
Wythe Sta........................... 61
General Delivery................. 69
Postmaster......................... 69

HOSPITALS

Bayberry............................ 69
Dixie.................................. 69

LYNCHBURG 245

POST OFFICE BOXES

Box Nos.
1-1540   Main Office 05
2001-2999 Miller Park Sta. 01
3001-3999 Rivermont Sta .. 03
4001-4999 Fort Hill Sta 02

RURAL ROUTES

1 02
2...................................... 01
3...................................... 04
4...................................... 03

STATIONS, BRANCHES AND UNITS

Fort Hill Sta....................... 02
Miller Park Sta................... 01
Rivermont Sta 03
Timberlake Br..................... 02
General Delivery................. 05
Postmaster......................... 05

HOSPITALS

Guggenheimer Memorial
  Hospital 1902 Grace
  Street............................... 04
Lynchburg General, 1901
  Tate Springs Rd................ 04
Lynchburg Training School &
  Hospital, Lynchburg, Va 05
Virginia Baptist, 3300
  Rivermont Ave.................. 04

UNIVERSITIES AND COLLEGES

Lynchburg College, 500
  Vernon............................. 04
Randolph Macon Woman'S
  College, 2500 Rivermont
  Ave................................. 04
Virginia Community College.... 02
Virginia Seminary & College,
  2058 Garfield Ave............. 01

NEWPORT NEWS 236

POST OFFICE BOXES

Box Nos.
1-980   Main Office 07
621-1378   Fort Eustis Sta. 04
1001-1899 Warwick Sta 01
2001-2447 Denbigh Sta 02
3001-3368 Lee Hall........... 03

5001-5798 Parkview Sta 05
6001-6500 Hidenwood Sta.. 06

STATIONS, BRANCHES AND UNITS

Denbigh Sta........................ 02
Fort Eustis Sta.................... 04
Hidenwood Sta.................... 06 .
Lee Hall Sta........................ 03
Parkview Sta....................... 05
Tabb Rural Br...................... 02
Warwick Sta........................ 01
General Delivery.................. 07
Postmaster......................... 07

APARTMENTS, HOTELS, MOTELS

Beechmont, 204 Beechmont
  Dr.................................... 02
Beechmont, 335-391
  Beechmont Drive............... 02
Boulevard, 100 Impala Drive.. 06
Cambridge, 5100 - 5134
  Goldsboro Dr..................... 05
Carriage Park, 11100
  Jefferson Ave.................... 01
Chantilly, 5500 Marshall Ave . 05
Christopher Newport, 409
  Logan Pl........................... 01
Clover Leaf Village, 1 - 99
  Traverse Rd....................... 06
College Court, 12373
  Warwick Blvd.................... 06
Colony Hilton, 500 Bulkely Pl . 01
Colony, 13441 Warwick Blvd.. 02
Criston, 2100 2138 Criston
  Dr.................................... 02
Deer Park East, 11430
  Jefferson Ave.................... 01
Deer Park, 11425 Jefferson
  Ave.................................. 01
Denbigh 14262 - 14272 Old
  Courthouse Way................ 02
Dresden Arms, 624 Dresden
  Dr.................................... 01
Dresden Drive, 684 Dresden
  Dr.................................... 01
Dutch Village, 500 Logan Pl... 01
Eastwood, 5 Eastwood Dr,
  420 Shawn Cir................... 02
Glen Garden, 1300 79th St 05
Ivy The, 501 Adams Dr.......... 01
Jamestown, 100 Yeardley Dr... 01
Jefferson East, 711 J Clyde
  Morris Blvd....................... 01
Mariners Park, 410 Logan Pl... 01
Newsome Townhouses,4100-
  4351 Newsome Dr,4100-
  4547 Orcutt Av.................. 07
Orlean Court, 817 Woods Rd.. 06
Pavilion, 11700 Jefferson
  Ave.................................. 06
Presidential, 731 Adams Dr.... 01
Randolph Court, 500
  Bellwood Rd..................... 01
Saint James Terrace, 80
  30th................................. 07
Saint James Terrace, 80
  31st.................................. 07
Saint James Terrace, 85
  29th................................. 07
Sherwood, 3752 - 3778
  Sherwood Pl...................... 02

Tabb Lane, 25 Tabbs Lane..... 02
Tarrytown, 11112 Jefferson
Ave..... 01
Winston Townhouse, 11310-
11411 Winston Pl............. 01

UNIVERSITIES AND COLLEGES

Christopher Newport, Shoe
Lane..... 06

NORFOLK   235

POST OFFICE BOXES

Box Nos.
1-2999	Main Office	01
3000-3999	Customhouse Sta.....	14
4001-4999	Berkley Sta.....	23
5501-5999	Parcel Post Annex Sta.....	16
6001-6999	Milan Sta.....	08
7001-7499	Lafayette Boulevard Sta.....	09
8601-8999	Ocean View Sta.....	03
9501-9999	Wright Sta.....	05
10001-10999	Norview Sta.....	13
11001-11999	Debree Sta.....	17
12001-12999	Thomas Corner Sta.....	02
14001-14999	L C Page Sta	18

STATIONS, BRANCHES AND UNITS

Berkley Sta 23
Customhouse Sta 14
De Bree Sta 17
Fleet Br..... 11
Hampton Roads Br..... 11
L C Page Sta..... 18
Lafayette Boulevard Sta..... 09
Milan Sta..... 08
Naval Air Station Br..... 11
Naval Amphibious Base Br..... 21
Norview Sta..... 13
Ocean View Sta..... 03
Parcel Post Annex Sta..... 16
Thomas Corner Sta..... 02
West Annex Mou..... 20
Wright Sta..... 05
General Delivery 01
Postmaster 01

APARTMENTS, HOTELS, MOTELS

Admiralty, 1170 N Military
Hwy..... 02
Airport, Municipal Airport..... 18
Algonquin House, 7320
Glenroie Ave..... 05
Atlantic, 111 Granby..... 01
Bel-Aire, 1001 N Military
Hwy..... 02
Commodore Maury, 345
Granby..... 10
Del Mar, 5578 Virginia Beach
Blvd..... 02

Fairfax, 117 W City Hall Ave . 01
Gilbert, 225 Granby..... 10
Golden Triangle, 201 E Olney
Rd..... 01
Hague Park, 408 Dundaff..... 07
Hague Towers East, 330 W.
Brambleton Ave..... 10
Holiday Towers, 1850 E Little
Creek Rd..... 18
Interstate, 525 N Military
Hwy..... 02
Jefferson, 232 W Bute..... 10
Lafayette Motor Hotel, 4233
Granby..... 04
Lafayette Tower, 4601
Mayflower Rd..... 08
Monticello, 108 E City Hall
Ave..... 01
Nansemond, 236 W Ocean
View Ave..... 03
New Virginia, 108 E Plume..... 10
Pembroke Towers, 601
Pembroke Ave..... 07
Pine Crest, 9650 Norfolk Ave.. 03
Plaza, 1787 Church St..... 04
Sea Isle, 315 E Ocean View
Ave..... 03
Sheraton Hotel : Motor Inn..... 02
Surf, 2918 E Ocean View
Ave..... 18
Thomas Nelson, 245 Granby
St..... 01
Vanns, 3022 E Ocean View
Ave..... 18
Voyager, 719 E Ocean View
Ave..... 03
Warm Sands, 9635 Shore Dr.. 18

BUILDINGS

Allard, 106 W Olney Rd..... 10
Atlantic National Bank 415
St Paul's Blvd..... 10
Attucks, 1008 Church St..... 10
Bank Of Virginia 500 E
Plume..... 10
Bankers Trust, 109 W City
Hall Ave..... 10
Batleman, 300 Boush..... 10
Bel-Aire, 1600 E Little Creek
Rd..... 18
Board Of Trade, 304 E
Plume..... 10
Citizens Bank, 109 E Main..... 10
City Hall, 810 Union 10
Civic Center, 100 Saint
Paul's Blvd..... 10
Customhouse, 101 E Main
St..... 10
Dean, 201 E Plume St..... 10
Depaul Medical, 110 Kingsley
Lane..... 05
Downtown Plaza Shopping
Center X 200-500 St.
Paul's Blvd..... 10
Driver, 339 Boush..... 10
Duke-Grace, 740 Duke St..... 10
Elray, 7460 Tidewater Dr..... 05
Essex, 315 E Plume..... 10
Executive Medical, 463 N
Military Hwy..... 02
Executive Office, 2 Janaf
Shopping Center..... 02

Federal, 600 Granby..... 10
First & Merchants National
Bank 300 E Main..... 10
First National Bank, 200
Monticello..... 10
Flatiron, 110 W Charlotte 10
Franklin, 700 Duke..... 10
Golden Triangle, 201 E Olney
Road..... 10
Granby Professional, 7314
Granby..... 05
Helena, 101 W Plume..... 10
I B M, 225 W Virginia Beach
Blvd..... 10
Janaf, 112 Janaf Shopping
Center..... 02
Juvenile Court 800 E City
Hall Ave 10
Kresge, 232 Granby..... 10
Larrymore Lawns Medical
Center, 7709 Wildwood
Drive..... 18
Law, 147 Granby..... 10
Lonsdale, 207 Granby..... 10
Maritime Tower, 234
Monticello Ave..... 10
Medical Tower, 400 Gresham
Drive..... 07
Metropolitan Bank & Trust,
700 Church..... 10
Midtown, 112 E Little Creek
Rd..... 05
Monticello Arcade, 208 E
Plume..... 10
Municipal Air Terminal,
Municipal Airport..... 18
Municipal Auditorium, 900
Granby..... 10
National Maritime Union Hall,
523 E Bute 10
Navy Y M C A 500 Dunmore
St..... 10
New Monroe, 254 Granby..... 10
Norfolk Medical Center, 401
Colley Ave..... 07
Pinewood Professional, 1516
Harmon..... 18
Plaza 1 1 Main Plaza E..... 10
Professional Arts, 142 W
York..... 10
Professional Associates, 549
E Brambleton Ave..... 10
Public Safety, 811 E City
Hall Ave..... 10
Rotunda, 415 Saint Paul'S
Blvd..... 10
Royster, 203 Granby..... 10
Scope, 201 E. Brambleton
Avenue..... 10
Selden Arcade, 205 E Plume.. 10
Social Service Bureau, 235 E
Plume..... 10
Southern Bank, 101 Granby.. 10
Southern Office, 1 Southern
Shopping Center..... 05
Southgate Terminal, Foot Of
W Tazewell..... 10
Suburban Professional, 119 E
Little Creek Rd..... 05
Telephone, 120 W Bute..... 10
Tidewater Executive Center,
Center Drive..... 02

Time, 1701 Colley Ave 17
Town Point, 111 W Main........ 10
Twin Towers, 900 Park Ave ... 04
United Va Bank, 5 Main
   Plaza E............................ 10
Virginia National Bank, 1
   Commercial Place 10
Wainwright, 229 W Bute........ 10
Wheat J C 3 Main Plaza E..... 10
Y M C A Central Branch, 312
   W Bute............................ 10
Y M C A Hunton Branch, 812
   Wood............................... 04
Y W C A Phyllis Wheatly
   Branch, 927 Park Ave 04
Y W C A, 249 W Freemason ... 10
Youth Center, 1300
   Kempsville Rd.................... 02
4100, 4101 Granby............... 04
64-West, 586 Virginian Dr 05

HOSPITALS

Depaul, 120 Kingsley Lane 05
Kings Daughters (Childrens),
   609 Colley Ave 07
Lake Taylor City, 1300
   Kempsville Rd.................... 02
Leigh Memorial, 358
   Mowbray Arch 07
Mc Coy-Stokes, 1400 Colonial
   Ave 17
Norfolk Community, 2539
   Corprew Ave..................... 04
Norfolk General, 600
   Gresham Dr....................... 07
Rhodes Dental, 501 E
   Brambleton Ave 10
U S Public Health Service,
   6500 Hampton Blvd 08

MILITARY INSTALLATIONS

Armed Forces Staff College 11
Naval Air Station.................. 11
Naval Amphibious Base......... 21
Naval Supply Center 12
United States Naval Station ... 11

UNIVERSITIES AND COLLEGES

Norfolk State, 2401 Corprew
   Ave 04
Old Dominion, 5201 Hampton
   Blvd................................. 08
Virginia Wesleyan, 1584
   Wesleyan Drive.................. 02

PORTSMOUTH   237

POST OFFICE BOXES

Box Nos.
A-K   Main Office 05
1-1426   Main Office 05
2000-2599   Cradock Sta 02
3000-3317   Olive Sta 01
6000-6647   Churchland....... 03
7000-7250   Mid-Town Sta ... 07

RURAL ROUTES

1.. 03

STATIONS, BRANCHES AND UNITS

Churchland Br..................... 03
Mid Town Sta 07
Naval Hospital Sta............... 08
Navy Yard Sta 09
Simonsdale Sta 01
West Norfolk Br 03
General Delivery 05
Postmaster 05

APARTMENTS, HOTELS, MOTELS

Carver Home, 2500 Queen..... 07
Cherokee Park, 700 Cherokee
   Rd 01
Colonial Manor, 3622
   Princeton Pl...................... 07
Crawford House, 1 Crawford
   Parkway........................... 04
Dale Homes, 240 Dale
   Homes.............................. 04
Edinburg, 344 Court 04
Ft Nelson Towers 333 Green... 04
Fulton, 340 Hatton............... 04
Gates, 200 Effingham............ 04
Glenshellah, 3610 Hartford.... 07
Gloucester, 359 Middle.......... 04
Governor Dinwiddie, 506
   Dinwiddie......................... 05
Hampton Crest, 320
   Dinwiddie......................... 04
Hampton, 528 Hampton Pl..... 04
Harbor Court, 310 Court........ 04
Harbor View, 230 Swimming
   Point................................ 04
Holiday Inn, 10 Crawford
   Parkway........................... 04
Howard Homes, 102 Howard... 07
Ida B Barbour, 1104 Barbour
   Dr 04
Imperial 400, 333 Effingham.. 04
Kellys, 817 County................ 04
Lee Hall, 900 Suburban
   Parkway........................... 02
Lincoln Park, 4 Lexington Dr .. 04
Malvern Hill, 426 King........... 04
Malvern Hill, 511 Dinwiddie... 04
Midtown, 700 Frederick Blvd... 07
Moore, 501 Hampton Pl......... 04
Patio Plaza, 700 Crawford
   Parkway........................... 04
Philgrador, 1015 Blair 04
Portsmouth Gardens, 1
   Lawrence Cir..................... 07
Sussex, 422 King 04
Town & Country, 300 Ansell
   Ave 02
Waterview, 3650 Western Br
   Blvd................................. 07
Westhampton, 538 Hampton
   Pl................................... 04
Westhaven, 4708 County........ 07
Williams Court, 98 Jameson.... 02
Wilson Jeffery Homes............. 07
Wilson Manor, 3501

Commerce............................ 07

BUILDINGS

American Bank, 234 High...... 04
Building & Loan Bldg, 435
   Court St 04
Citizens Trust Bldg, 355
   Crawford Parkway............. 04
Civic Center......................... 04
Federal, 431 Crawford 04
Kirn (New), 339 High 04
Medic-Home Health Center,
   320 Effingham.................. 04
Merchants & Farmers Bank
   Bldg., 430 Crawford St. 04
Municipal, 1 High 04
Portsmouth Medical, 1100
   Hamilton 07
Professional, 505
   Washington 04
Star, 101 High 04

HOSPITALS

Maryview, 3636 High 07
Portsmouth General, 900
   Leckie.............................. 04

MILITARY INSTALLATIONS

Base Coast Guard District,
   Wythe 04
Coast Guard Commander 5th
   Coast Guard District........... 05
Naval Ammunition Depot 02
Naval Hospital..................... 08
Naval Shipyard..................... 09

UNIVERSITIES AND COLLEGES

Frederick Academy, 1801
   Portsmouth Blvd................ 04
Frederick Community College.. 03

RICHMOND   232

POST OFFICE BOXES

Box Nos.
1-180   Capitol.............. 01
1A-1M   Capitol.............. 01
1N-1Y   Capitol.............. 02
2A-2K   Capitol.............. 03
2L-2U   Capitol.............. 04
2V-2Z   Capitol.............. 05
3A-3M   Capitol.............. 06
3N-3Y   Capitol.............. 07
5A-5Z   Capitol.............. 13
6B-6G   Capitol.............. 14
6H-6N   Capitol.............. 15
6O-6Q   Capitol.............. 16
6R-6T   Capitol.............. 17
181-360   Capitol.............. 02
2AB-2AF   Capitol.............. 05
3AB-3AJ   Capitol.............. 08
361-468   Capitol.............. 03
471-568   Capitol.............. 04
571-668   Capitol.............. 05
671-800   Capitol.............. 06

801-980	Capitol	07
981-1140	Capitol	08
1141-1240	Capitol	09
1241-1340	Capitol	10
1341-1440	Capitol	11
1441-1560	Capitol	12
1561-1690	Capitol	13
1651-1818	Capitol	14
1831-1969	Capitol	15
1971-2149	Capitol	16
2151-2309	Capitol	17
2331-2450	Capitol	18
2881-3387	Bon Air Br	35
3401-3998	Ampthill Br	34
4001-4434	Southside Sta	24
4501-4997	Ridge Br	29
5001-5897	Saunders Sta	20
6001-6199	Northside Sta	22
6201-6996	West End Br	30
7001-7475	Stewart Sta	21
7501-7744	Montrose Heights Sta	31
7901-8191	East End Sta	23
8201-8767	Westhampton Sta	26
8801-9097	Forest Hill Sta	25
9101-9247	Bellevue Sta	27
9401-9899	Lakeside Br	28
10001-10510	Civic Center Sta	40
11001-11293	West End	30
12000-12999	Central Sta	41
16000-16999	Northside	22
25001-26432	Richmond	60
26441-27632	Richmond	61

RURAL ROUTES

2		29
5,6,14		31
15		34

STATIONS, BRANCHES AND UNITS

Ampthill Br	34
Azalea Br	27
Bellevue Sta	27
Belt Boulevard Br	24
Bon Air Br	35
Broad Rock Br	24
Buford Br	35
Carousel Br	25
Central Sta	19
Civic Center Sta	40
Defense General Supply Ctr Br	19
East End Sta	23
Falling Creek Br	34
Federal Reserve Sta	13
Forest Hill Sta	25
Glen Lea Br	23
Laburnum Manor Br	22
Lakeside Br	28
Medical College Sta	19
Metro Br	31
Montrose Heights Sta	31
Northside Sta	22
Pine Dell Br	29
Pocoshock Br	35
Ridge Br	29
Saunders Sta	20
Southside Sta	24
Stewart Sta	21

Stratford Hills Br	25
Tuckahoe Br	29
Veterans Administration HospBr	19
Virginia Union University Sta	20
West End Br	30
Westhampton Sta	26
Westwood Br	30
General Delivery	32
Postmaster	32

APARTMENTS, HOTELS, MOTELS

Berkshire Apartments, 300 W Franklin	20
Bon Haven, 2506 Atwell Dr	34
Capitol, 8th & Grace	19
Chesterfield, 900 W Franklin	20
Gresham Court, 1030 W Franklin	20
Imperial Plaza, 1717 Bellevue	27
Jefferson, Franklin & Jefferson	11
John Marshall, 5th & Franklin	13
Keswick Gardens, 5200 Wythe Ave	26
Lexington Tower Apartments, 104 W Franklin	20
Lock Lane, 35 Lock Lane	26
Prestwould, 612 W Franklin	20
Raleigh, 9th & Bank	03
Richmond West, 801 E Broad	19
Sevilla Apartments, 115 N Jefferson	11
Stuart Courts, 1600 Monument Ave	20
The 5100, 5100 Monument Ave	30
Tuckahoe, 5621 Cary St Rd	26
William Byrd, 2501 W Broad	20

BUILDINGS

Blanton, 1220 Bank	19
Broad Grace Arcade, 215 E Broad	19
Broad Grace Arcade, 216 E Grace	19
Builders Exchange, 3701 W Broad	30
Central National Bank, 217 E Broad	19
Consolidated Bank & Trust Company, 328 N 1st	40
Electric, 700 E Franklin	19
Eskimo, 530 E Main	19
Federal, 400 N 8th	40
Fidelity, 9th & Main	19
First & Merchants National Bank, 827 E Main	19
Hermitage	19
James Madison, 109 Governor	19
Life Insurance Company Of Virginia, 914 Capitol	19
Mosque, Laurel & Main	20
Presbyterian, 6 N 6th	19
Professional, 501 E Franklin	19
Richmond Federal, 728 E	

Main	19
Ross, 801 E Main	19
Safety & Welfare, 501 N 9th	19
Sauer, 1900 W Broad	20
Seaboard, 3600 W Broad	30
Southern Bank & Trust Company, 1442 E Main	19
Southern States, 627 E Main	19
State Capitol, Capitol Square	19
State Finance, Capitol Square	19
State Library, 1101 Capitol	19
State Office Building, 9th 1/2 grace	19
State Office, Capitol Square	19
State Planters, 904 E Main	19
Travelers, 1108 E Main	19
Virginia, 500 E Main	19
W R N L Radio Center, 111 N 4th	19
700, 7th & Main	19

GOVERNMENT OFFICES

City Hall 900 E Broad	19
Henrico County Court House, 21st & Main	07

HOSPITALS

Grace, 401 W Grace	20
Johnston-Willis, 2908 Kensington Ave	21
Mcguires 1201 Broad Rock Rd	24
Medical College Of Virginia, 1200 E Broad	19
Retreat For The Sick, 2621 Grove Ave	20
Richmond Community, 1210 Overbrook Rd	20
Richmond Eye Ear Nose & Throat, 408 N 12th	19
Richmond Memorial, 1300 Westwood Ave	27
Saint Elizabeths, 617 W Grace	20
Saint Lukes, 1000 W Grace	20
Saint Mary, 5801 Bremo	26
Sheltering Arms, 1311 Palmyra Ave	27
Stuart Circle, 413 Stuart Cir	20
Tuckers, 212 W Franklin	20
Vet Admin 1201 Broad Rock Rd	24
Westbrook Sanatorium, 1500 Westbrook Av	27

UNIVERSITIES AND COLLEGES

Medical College Of Virginia, 1200 E Broad	19
Presbyterian School Of Christian Education, 1205 Palmyra	27
Smithdeal-Massey Business College, 300 W Grace	01
Union Theological Seminary, 3401 Brook Rd	27
University Of Richmond	

School Of Business
Administration 20
Virginia Commonwealth Univ
(M C V), 1200 E Broad 11
Virginia Commonwealth Univ.
(R p.i.), 901 W. Franklin..... 20
Virginia Union University,
1500 N Lombardy 20

ROANOKE 240

POST OFFICE BOXES

Box Nos.
1-40	Main Office	01
41-301	Main Office	02
311-571	Main Office	03
581-841	Main Office	04
851-1111	Main Office	05
1121-1300	Main Office	06
1301-1600	Main Office	07
1601-1951	Main Office	08
1961-2281	Main Office	09
2291-2611	Main Office	10
2701-2912	Main Office	01
4000-4999	Grandin Road Sta................	15
5000-5999	Williamson Road Sta	12
6000-6999	Melrose Sta	17
7000-7999	Hollins Br	19
8000-8999	South Roanoke .	14
9000-10999	Hollinscollege Br	20

RURAL ROUTES

1	......	12
2	......	19
5,6	......	14
7	......	18

8	......	14
11	......	19

STATIONS, BRANCHES AND UNITS

Crossroads Br.........................	12
Grandin Road Sta...................	15
Hollins Br	19
Hollins College Br	20
Melrose Sta	17
South Roanoke Sta................	14
Sugar Loaf Br.........................	18
Williamson Road Sta.............	12
General Delivery	01
Postmaster	01

SPRINGFIELD 221

POST OFFICE BOXES

Box Nos.
1-999	Main Office	50
1000-1999	N Springfield Br	51

RURAL ROUTES

27	50

STATIONS, BRANCHES AND UNITS

Burke Br 22015
North Springfield Br..............	51
West Springfield Br................	52
General Delivery	50
Postmaster	50

BUILDINGS

Executive Building 6901 Old
Keene Mill Rd 51

VIRGINIA BEACH 234

POST OFFICE BOXES

Box Nos.
1-340	Main Office	58
501-1099	Seapines Sta	51
2001-2999	Lynn Haven Sta..............	52
3001-3999	Oceana Sta	53
4001-4999	London Bridge Sta............	54
5001-5999	Bayside Sta	55
6001-6999	Princess Anne Sta.............	56
7001-7199	Back Bay Sta ...	57
62001-62999	Witch Duck.......	62

RURAL ROUTES

1,2	56
3,4,SR5	57

STATIONS, BRANCHES AND UNITS

Backbay Sta	57
Bayside Sta	55
Blackwater Bridge Rural Sta..	57
Creeds Rural Sta.....................	57
Dam Neck Sta.........................	61
Fort Story Sta	59
London Bridge Sta	54
Lynnhaven Sta.........................	52
Oceana Sta..............................	53
Oceana N A S Sta	60
Princess Anne Sta...................	56
Pungo Rural Sta......................	56
Seapines Sta	51
Witch Duck Sta	62
General Delivery	58
Postmaster	58

WASHINGTON
(Abbreviation: WA)

Aberdeen (1st) 98520
Acme 98220
Addy 99101
Adna 98522
Aeneas 98810
Airway Heights 99001
Albion 99102
Alder 98301
Alderwood Manor, Sta.
　Lynnwood 98036
Algona, Br. Auburn 98002
Allen, R. Br. Bow 98232
Allyn 98524
Almira 99103
Aloha 98525
Amanda Park 98526
Amber 99002
Amboy 98601
American Lake, Br. Tacoma ..98493
Anacortes (1st) 98221
Anatone 99401
Appleton 98602
Ardenvoir 98811
Ariel 98603
Arlington (1st) 98223
Arnada Park Annex, Sta.
　Vancouver (see appendix)
Ashford 98304
Asotin 99402
Auburn (1st) 98002
　Algona, Br. 98002
　Federal Way, Br. 98002
　Pacific, R. Br. 98047
　Redondo, R. Br. 98054
　Westfair, Br. 98002
Azwell, R. Br. Chelan 98816
B And G, Br. Everett 98201
B And M, R. Br. Lake
　Stevens 98258
Bainbridge Island Winslow,
　Br. Seattle 98110
Ballard, Sta. Seattle 98107
Baring 98224
Battle Ground 98604
Bay Center 98527
Beaver 98305
Belfair 98528
BELLEVUE (1st) (see
　appendix)
Bellingham (1st) 98225
Belmont, R. Br. Farmington ..99104
Benge 99105
Benton City 99320
Beverly 99321
Bickleton 99322
Bingen 98605
Bitter Lake, Sta. Seattle (see
　appendix)
Black Diamond 98010
Blaine (1st) 98230
Blakely Island, R. Br. Friday
　Harbor 98222
Blanchard 98231
Bluecreek 99106
Bothell (1st) 98011
Bow ....9823_
Boyds ....9910_
Bremerton (1st) ....9831_
　Gorst, R. Br. ....9833_
　Manette, Sta. ....9831_

Naval Base, Sta. 98314
Sheridan Park, Sta. 98310
Wycoff, Sta. 98310
Brewster 98812
Bridgeport 98813
Brier, Br. Lynnwood 98036
Brinnon 98320
Broadway, Sta. Seattle 98102
Brownstown 98920
Brush Prairie 98606
Buckley 98321
Bucoda 98530
Buena 98921
Burbank 99323
Burien, Br. Seattle (see
　appendix)
Burley 98322
Burlington (1st) 98233
Burton 98013
Camas (1st) 98607
Campus, Sta. Bellingham ..98225
Capitol Hill, Sta. Seattle ..98102
Carbonado 98823
Carlsborg 98324
Carlton 98814
Carnation 98014
Carrolls 98609
Carson 98610
Cascade, Br. Renton 98055
Cashmere (1st) 98815
Castle Rock 98611
Cathlamet 98612
Cedonia 99108
Centerville 98613
Central Park, Br. Aberdeen ..98520
Centralia (1st) 98531
Chattaroy 99003
Chehalis (1st) 98532
Chelan (1st) 98816
Chelan Falls 98817
Cheney (1st) 99004
Chesaw 98818
Chewelah 99109
Chimacum 98325
Chinook 98614
Cinebar 98533
Clallam Bay 98326
Claremont, Sta. Everett 98203
Clarkston (1st) 99403
Clayton 99110
Cle Elum 98922
Clearlake 98235
Clearview, R. Br. Snohomish ..98290
Clearwater, R. Br. Forks 98399
Clinton 98236
Clipper, R. Br. Deming 98244
Colbert 99005
Colfax (1st) 99111
College, Sta. Pullman 99163
College Place (1st) 99324
Colton 99113
Columbia, Sta. Seattle 98118
Colville (1st) 99114
Conconully 98819
Concrete 98237
Connell 99326
Conway 98238
Cook, R. Br. Bingen 98605
Copalis Beach 98535
Copalis Crossing 98536
Cosmopolis 98537
Cougar 98616
Coulee City 99115

Coulee Dam 99116
Country Homes, Br. Spokane ..99218
Coupeville 98239
Cowiche 98923
Creston 99117
Crossroads, Sta. Bellevue ..98008
Crystal Mountain, R. Br.
　Enumclaw 98022
Cumberland, R. Br.
　Enumclaw 98015
Cunningham 99327
Curlew 99118
Curtis 98538
Cusick 99119
Custer 98240
Dallesport 98617
Danville 99121
Darrington 98241
Dash Point, R. Br. Tacoma ..98422
Davenport 99122
Dayton 99328
Deep River 98618
Deer Harbor 98243
Deer Park 99006
Deming 98244
Des Moines, Br. Seattle (see
　appendix)
Dishman, Br. Spokane 99213
Dixie 99329
Dockton 98018
Doty 98539
Dryden 98821
Du Pont 98327
Duvall 98019
East Hill, Br. Kent 98031
East Olympia 98540
East Union, Sta. Seattle 98122
East Wenatchee, Br.
　Wenatchee 98801
Eastgate, Sta. Bellevue 98007
Easton 98925
Eastsound 98245
Eatonville 98328
Edison 98246
Edmonds (1st) 98020
Edwall 99008
Elbe 98330
Electric City 99123
Elk 99009
Ellensburg (1st) 98926
　Vantage, R. Br. 98950
Elma 98541
Elmer City 99124
Eltopia 99330
Endicott 99125
Entiat 98822
Enumclaw (1st) 98022
　Crystal Mountain, R. Br. ..98022
　Cumberland, R. Br. 98015
Ephrata (1st) 98823
Espanola 99010
Ethel 98542
Evans 99126
EVERETT (1st) (see
　appendix)
Everson 98247
Ewan 99127
Fairchild Air Force Base
　(1st) 99011
Fairfield 99012
Fall City 98024
Farmington 99128
Federal, Sta. Seattle 98104

Federal Way, Br. Auburn..........98002
Fern Hill, Sta. Tacoma 98412
Ferndale (1st)......................98248
Fife, R. Br. Tacoma................98424
Finley, R. Br. Kennewick..........99336
Fircrest, Br. Tacoma...............98466
Ford...................................99013
Forest Park, Br. Seattle.......98155
Forks..................................98331
  Clearwater, R. Br.............98399
Fort Lewis, Br. Tacoma...........98433
Fort Steilacoom, Br. Tacoma....98494
Four Lakes...........................99014
Fourth Plain, Sta. Vancouver
  (see appendix)
Fox Island...........................98333
Fpo 98777, Br. Seattle..........98777
Frances...............................98543
Freeland..............................98249
Freeman...............................99015
Friday Harbor........................98250
  Blakely Island, R. Br.........98222
  Roche Harbor, R. Br...........98250
Fruitland, R. Br. Hunters........99129
Galvin.................................98544
Gardiner, R. Br. Sequim..........98334
Garfield..............................99130
Garland, Sta. Spokane............99209
George, R. Br. Quincy.............98824
Georgetown, Sta. Seattle.........98108
Gifford...............................99131
Gig Harbor (1st)....................98335
Glacier, R. Br. Deming............98244
Gleed, R. Br. Yakima..............98904
Glenoma...............................98336
Glenwood..............................98619
Gold Bar.............................98251
Goldendale (1st)....................98620
Gooseprairie, R. Br. Naches......98929
Gorst, R. Br. Bremerton..........98337
Graham................................98338
Grand Coulee.........................99133
Grandview (1st).....................98930
Granger...............................98932
Granite Falls.......................98252
Grapeview............................98546
Grayland..............................98547
Grays River..........................98621
Greenacres...........................99016
Greenbank............................98253
Greenwood, Sta. Seattle..........98103
Grotto................................98254
Hadlock...............................98339
  Port Ludlow, R. Br...........98365
Hamilton..............................98255
Hansville.............................98340
Harper................................98341
Harrah................................98933
Harrington...........................99134
  Mohler, R. Br.................99154
Hartline.............................99135
Hatton................................99332
Hay, R. Br. Lacrosse..............99136
Hayes Park, Sta. Spokane.........99207
Hazel Dell, Br. Vancouver........98660
Heisson...............................98622
Highlands, Sta. Renton............98055
Hillyard, Sta. Spokane...........99207
Hobart................................98025
Holden Village, R. Br.
  Chelan........................98816
Hoodsport............................98548
Hooper................................99333

Hoquiam (1st)........................98550
  Ocean Shores, P. Br..........98551
Humptulips............................98552
Hunters...............................99137
  Fruitland, R. Br.............53129
Husum.................................98623
Hyak..................................98026
Ilwaco................................98624
Inchelium............................99138
Index.................................98256
Indianola............................98342
Inglewood, Br. Bothell...........98011
International, Sta. Seattle
  (see appendix)
Ione..................................99139
Irby, R. Br. Odessa...............99159
Issaquah (1st).......................98027
Joyce.................................98343
Juanita, Br. Kirkland.............98033
K Street, Sta. Tacoma............98405
Kahlotus..............................99335
Kalama................................98625
Kapowsin..............................98344
Keller................................99140
Kelso (1st)...........................98626
Kenmore (1st).........................98028
Kennewick (1st)......................99336
Kent (1st)............................98031
Kettle Falls.........................99141
  Orient, R. Br................99160
Kewa..................................99142
Keyport...............................98345
Kingston..............................98346
Kiona.................................99340
Kirkland (1st)........................98033
Kittitas..............................98934
Klickitat.............................98628
La Center.............................98629
La Conner.............................98257
La Grande.............................98348
La Push...............................98350
Lacey, Br. Olympia..................98503
Lacrosse..............................99143
  Hay, R. Br...................99136
Lake City, Sta. Seattle (see
  appendix)
Lake Hill, Br. Everett............98203
Lake Hills, Sta. Bellevue........98007
Lake Stevens.........................98258
Lakebay...............................98349
  Longbranch, R. Br............98351
Lakeview, Br. Tacoma...............98491
Lakewood..............................98259
Lakewood Center, Br.
  Tacoma (see appendix)
Lamona................................99144
Lamont................................99017
Langley...............................98260
Latah.................................99018
Laurel................................98630
Laurier...............................99146
Leavenworth..........................98826
Lebam.................................98554
Lester, R. Br. Seattle............98035
Liberty Lake.........................99019
Lilliwaup............................98555
Lincoln...............................99147
Lind..................................99341
Littlerock...........................98556
Long Beach............................98631
  Nahcotta, R. Br..............98637
Longbranch, R. Br. Lakebay.......98351
Longmire, R. Br. Tacoma...........98397

Longview (1st).......................98632
Loomis................................98827
Loon Lake.............................99148
Lopez.................................98261
Lowden................................99342
Lowell, Sta. Everett..............98203
Lummi Island.........................98262
Lyle..................................98635
Lyman.................................98263
Lynden (1st)..........................98264
Lynnwood (1st).......................98036
Mabton................................98935
Magnolia, Sta. Seattle...........98199
Malaga................................98828
Malden................................99149
Malo..................................99150
Malone................................98559
Malott................................98829
Manchester...........................98353
Manette, Sta. Bremerton..........98310
Manhattan, Br. Seattle............98148
Manito, Sta. Spokane..............99203
Mansfield.............................98830
Manson................................98831
Maple Falls..........................98266
Maple Valley.........................98038
Marblemount..........................98267
Marcus................................99151
Marietta..............................98268
Marlin................................98832
Marshall..............................99020
Marysville (1st).....................98270
Matlock...............................98560
Mattawa, R. Br. Othello..........99344
Mazama................................98833
Mc Chord A F B, Br.
  Tacoma........................98438
Mc Cleary............................98557
Mc Kenna.............................98558
Mc Micken Heights, Br.
  Seattle.......................98188
Mc Millin............................98352
Mead..................................99021
Medical Lake.........................99022
Medina................................98039
Menlo.................................98561
Mercer Island (1st)..................98040
Mesa..................................99343
Metaline.............................99152
Metaline Falls.......................99153
Methow................................98834
Mica..................................99023
Midway, Sta. Kent..................98031
Milan.................................99024
Millwood, Br. Spokane.............99212
Milton................................98354
Mineral...............................98355
Minnehaha, Br. Vancouver..........98661
Moclips...............................98562
Mohler, R. Br. Harrington........99154
Monitor...............................98836
Monroe (1st)..........................98272
Monta Vista, Br. Tacoma...........98499
Montesano (1st)......................98563
Morton................................98356
Moses Lake (1st).....................98837
Mossyrock.............................98564
Mount Vernon (1st)...................98273
Mountlake Terrace (1st)............98043
Moxee City............................99936
Mukilteo..............................98275
Naches................................98937
  Gooseprairie, R. Br..........98929

White Pass, R. Br. 98937
Nahcotta, R. Br. Long
    Beach 98637
Napavine 98565
Naselle 98638
Naval Air Station, Sta.
    Seattle..........................98115
Naval Base, Sta. Bremerton ..98314
Neah Bay 98357
Neilton 98566
Nespelem 99155
Newman Lake 99025
Newport 99156
Newport Hills, Br. Bellevue ...98006
Nine Mile Falls 99026
    Tumtum, R. Br. 99034
Nooksack 98276
Nordland 98358
North Bend 98045
North Bonneville 98639
North Central, Sta. Spokane ...99205
North City, Br. Seattle 98155
North Fort Lewis, Br.
    Tacoma.........................98433
North Lynnwood, Br.
    Lynnwood 98036
Northgate, Sta. Seattle 98125
Northport 99157
Oak Harbor (1st) 98277
Oakesdale 98158
Oakville 98568
Ocean City 98569
Ocean Park 98640
Ocean Shores, R. Br.
    Hoquiam, ...98551
Odessa 99159
Okanogan (1st) 98840
Olalla 98359
Olga 98279
OLYMPIA (1st) (see
    appendix)
Omak (1st) 98841
Onalaska 98570
Opportunity, Br. Spokane 99214
Orcas 98280
Orchards, Br. Vancouver 98662
Orient, R. Br. Kettle Falls 99160
Orondo 98843
Oroville 98844
Orting 98360
Oso, R. Br. Arlington 98223
Othello (1st) 99344
Otis Orchards 99027
Outlook 98938
Oysterville 98641
Pacific, R. Br. Auburn 98047
Pacific Beach 98571
Packwood 98361
Palisades 98845
Palmer 99048
Palouse 99161
Paradise Inn, R. Br. Tacoma ..98398
Parker 98939
Parkland, Br. Tacoma (see
    appendix)
Parkwater, Sta. Spokane 99211
Pasco (1st) 99301
    Tri Cities, Sta. 99302
Pateros 98846
Paterson 99345
Pe Ell 98572
Peshastin 98847
Pinehurst, Sta. Everett 98203

Plaza 99028
Plymouth 99346
Point Roberts 98281
Pomeroy 99347
Port Angeles (1st) 98362
Port Blakely, Br. Seattle 98110
Port Gamble 98364
Port Ludlow, R. Br. Hadlock ...98365
Port Orchard (1st) 98366
    Retsil, R. Br. 98378
    South Park Village, Br. ...9x366
Port Townsend (1st) 98368
Potlatch 98574
Poulsbo (1st) 98370
Prescott 99348
Preston 98050
Proctor, Sta. Tacoma (see
    appendix)
Prosser (1st) 99350
Pullman (1st) 99163
Puyallup (1st) 98371
Queen Anne, Sta. Seattle
    (see appendix)
Quilcene 98376
Quinault 98575
Quincy (1st) 98848
    George, R. Br. 98824
Rainier 98576
Ralston 99165
Randle 98377
Ravensdale 98051
Raymond (1st) 98577
Reardan 99029
Redmond (1st) 98052
Redondo, R. Br. Auburn 98054
Renton (1st) 98055
Republic 99166
Retsil, R. Br. Port Orchard 98378
Rice 99167
Richland (1st) 99352
Richmond Beach, Br.
    Seattle..........................98160
Ridgefield 98642
Ritzville 99169
Riverside 98849
Riverton Heights, Br. Seattle
    (see appendix)
Roche Harbor, R. Br. Friday
    Harbor 98250
Rochester 98579
Rock Island 98850
Rockford 99030
Rockport 98283
Rollingbay 98061
Ronald 98940
Roosevelt 99356
Rosalia 99170
Rosburg 98643
Rose Hill, Br. Kirkland 98033
Rosewood, Br. Spokane (see
    appendix)
Roslyn 98941
Roy 98580
Royal City 99357
Ryderwood 98581
Saint John 99171
Salkum 98582
Sappho 98379
Satsop 98583
Schwarder, R. Br. Yakima......98905
Sea First, Sta. Seattle 98104
Seabeck 98380

Seahurst 98062
SEATTLE (1st) (see
    appendix)
Seattle Heights (1st) 98063
Seaview 98644
Sedro Woolley (1st) 98284
    Wickersham, R. Br. 98285
Sekiu 98381
Selah 98942
Selleck 98064
Sequim (1st) 98382
    Gardiner, R. Br. 98334
Shaw Island 98286
Shelton (1st) 98584
Sheridan Park, Sta.
    Bremerton 98310
Silvana 98287
Silver Creek 98585
Silverdale 98383
Silverlake 98645
Sixth Avenue, Sta. Tacoma 98406
Skamania 98646
Skamokawa 98647
Skykomish 98288
Skyway, Br. Seattle 98178
Snohomish (1st) 98290
Snoqualmie 98065
Snoqualmie Falls.................98066
Snoqualmie Pass, R. Br.
    Seattle..........................98068
Soap Lake 98851
South Bellingham, Sta.
    Bellingham 98225
South Bend 98586
South Cle Elum 98943
South Colby 98384
South Park Village, Br. Port
    Orchard..........................98366
South Prairie 98385
South Tacoma, Sta. Tacoma ...98409
Southgate, Br. Olympia 98501
Southworth 98386
Spanaway 98387
Spangle 99031
SPOKANE (1st) (see
    appendix)
Spokane International Airprt,
    Br. Spokane 99219
Sprague 99032
Springdale 99173
Stanwood (1st) 98292
Starbuck 99359
Startup 98293
Stehekin 98852
Steilacoom, Br. Tacoma 98388
Steptoe 99174
Stevenson 98648
Stratford 98853
Sultan 98294
Sumas 98295
Sumner (1st) 98390
Sunnyside (1st) 98944
Suquamish 98392
TACOMA (1st) (see
    appendix)
Taholah 98587
Tahuya 98588
Tanglewild, Br. Olympia.........98501
Tekoa 99033
Tenino.............................. °C.89
Terminal, Sta. Tacoma (see
    appendix)

Terminal Annex, Sta. Seattle
(see appendix)
Terminal Annex, Sta.
Spokane 99220
Terrace Heights, Br. Yakima...98901
Thornton 99176
Thorp 98946
Tieton.....................................98947
Tiger.......................................99177
Tillicum, Br. Tacoma..............98492
Times Square, Sta. Seattle.....98101
Tokeland.................................98590
Toledo....................................98591
Tonasket.................................98855
Toppenish (1st).......................98948
Touchet...................................99360
Toutle.....................................98649
Tracyton.................................98393
Trentwood, Br. Spokane 99215
Tri Cities, Sta. Pasco..............99302
Trout Lake..............................98650
Tukwila, Br. Seattle................98188
Tumtum, R. Br. Nine Mile
Falls..................................99034
Tumwater, Br. Olympia 98502
Twisp......................................98856
Tyler.......................................99035
Underwood..............................98651
Union 98592
Union Gap, Br. Yakima..........98903
Uniontown...............................99179
University, Sta. Seattle 98105
Usk 99180

Vader......................................98593
Valley.....................................99181
Valleyford...............................99036
VANCOUVER (1st) (see
appendix)
Vantage, R. Br. Ellensburg....98950
Vashon (1st)...........................98070
Vaughn...................................98394
Veradale 99037
Veterans Administration
Hosp., Sta. Vancouver.........98661
Wahkiacus...............................98670
Waitsburg................................99361
Waldron..................................98297
Walla Walla (1st) 99362
Wallingford, Sta. Seattle.........98103
Wallula...................................99363
Wapato (1st) 98951
Warden....................................98857
Washougal...............................98671
Washtucna...............................99371
Waterville................................98858
Withrow, R. Br. 98863
Wauconda...............................98859
Waukon...................................99038
Wauna....................................98395
Waverly...................................99039
Wedgwood, Sta. Seattle 98115
Weir Park, Br. Camas.............98607
Wellpinit.................................99040
Wenatchee (1st)......................98801
West Richland, R. Br.
Richland............................99352

West Seattle, Sta. Seattle
(see appendix)
West Side, Sta. Yakima 98902
Westfair, Br. Auburn 98002
Westport..................................98595
Whidbey Island Naval Air
Sta, Br. Oak Harbor..........98277
White Center, Br. Seattle
(see appendix)
White Pass, R. Br. Naches......98937
White Salmon..........................98672
White Swan 98952
Wickersham, R. Br. Sedro
Woolley..............................98285
Wilbur.....................................99185
Wiley, R. Br. Yakima..............98906
Wilkeson.................................98396
Wilson Creek...........................98860
Winlock...................................98596
Winona....................................99186
Winthrop..................................98862
Wishram..................................98673
Withrow, R. Br. Waterville......98863
Woodinville..............................98072
Woodland.................................98674
Wycoff, Sta. Bremerton 98310
Yacolt.....................................98675
YAKIMA (1st) (see appendix)
Yelm.......................................98597
Zenith, Br. Seattle..................98188
Zillah......................................98953

631

BELLEVUE   980

POST OFFICE BOXES

Box Nos.		
A-H	Main Office Sta	09
1-2034	Main Office Sta	09

STATIONS, BRANCHES AND UNITS

Crossroads Sta	08
Eastgate Sta	07
Lake Hills Sta	07
Newport Hills Br	06
General Delivery	09
Postmaster	09

APARTMENTS, HOTELS, MOTELS

Bellevue Motel, 1647-104 Ave. NE	04
Eastgate Motel, 14632 Sunset Hwy	07
Fortnighter, 475-100 Ave NE	04
Holiday Inn, 11211 Main	04
Newporter Apts, 5900-119 Ave SE	06
Thunderbird Inn, 818-112 Ave NE	04
Travelodge, 11011 NE 8	04
Villa La Paz, 15200-20 NE 16 Pl	07

BUILDINGS

Bellevue Business Center, 777-106 Ave NE	04
Bellevue Square	04
Benaroya Business Park, 300 120 Ave N)	05
Carlson, 808-106 Ave NE	04
Cascade, 855-106 Ave NE	04
City Hall, 111-116 Ave SE	04
Commons, 1200-112 Ave NE	04
Crossroads Shopping Center, NE 8 & 156 Ave NE	08
Ditty, 612-104 Ave NE	04
Dravo, 225-108 Ave NE	04
Four Hundred, 400-108 Ave NE	04
K-Mart Plaza, 15015 Main	07
Northwest, 700-112 Ave NE	04
Prudential, 700-108 Ave NE	04
Redwood, 845-106 Ave NE	04
Sunset Village, 3080-148 Ave SE	07
Surrey, 10777 Main	04
Tally, 200-112 Ave NE	04

HOSPITALS

Overlake Memorial, 1035-116 Ave NE	04

UNIVERSITIES AND COLLEGES

Bellevue Community College, 3000-145 Pl 9E	07

EVERETT   982

POST OFFICE BOXES

Box Nos.		
1-1999	Main Office Boxes	06
2000-2999	Claremont Station Boxes	03
3000-3999	Lowell Station Boxes	03
4000-4999	Pinehurst Station Boxes	03

RURAL ROUTES

1,2	05
4	04
6,7	05

STATIONS, BRANCHES AND UNITS

B And G Br	01
Claremont Sta	03
Lake Hill Br	03
Lowell Sta	03
Pinehurst Sta	03
General Delivery	01
Postmaster	01

GOVERNMENT OFFICES

City Hall	01
Federal Bldg	01
Snohomish County Court House	01

HOSPITALS

General Hospital (P.O Box 1147)	06
Providence Hospital	01

UNIVERSITIES AND COLLEGES

Everett Community College (P.O. Box 478	06

OLYMPIA   985

POST OFFICE BOXES

Box Nos.		
A-D	Lacey Branch	03
1-2999	Main Office	07
3001-3999	Lacey Branch	03
4001-4999	Tumwater Branch	02

RURAL ROUTES

1	02
2	03
3	06
4,5	01
6	02
7	06
8	02
9	06
10	03

11	02
12	03
13,14,15	02
16	06
17	03
18	01

STATIONS, BRANCHES AND UNITS

Lacey Br	03
Southgate Br	01
Tanglewild Br	01
Tumwater Br	02
General Delivery	01
Postmaster	07

APARTMENTS, HOTELS, MOTELS

Angelus Apt Hotel 204 W 4th	01
Aquarian Trace 301 W. T	02
Capitol Club Apt 3800 Elizabeth	03
Diamond Head Apt 1510 SE 46th	03
El Rio Vista Apt 1275 S 2nd	02
Fir Grove Motel 2307 Pacific	01
Firs Apt 100 NE 68th	06
Fourth Ave Apt 5061/2 E 4th	01
Franklin Hotel Apt 2181/2 E 4th	01
Maple Vista Apt 1517 S Cap W	01
Martin Apt 5th : Wash	01
Olympian Hotel Apt Leg : Wash	01
Tourovilla Apt 7304 M.w	06
Trails End Motel 5300 Cap Blvd	01
Turf Apt Rt 2	03
Villa Capri Apt 600 Black Lake Blvd	02

BUILDINGS

Capitol Theatre Bldg 416 S Wash	01
Employment Security Bldg Cap Campus	04
Federal Bldg 800 S Cap W	01
Gen Admin Bldg Cap Campus	04
Health Bldg Cap Campus	04
Highway Admin Bldg Cap Campus	04
Institutions Bldg Cap Campus	04
Insurance Bldg Cap Campus	04
Legislative Bldv Cap Campus	04
License Bldg Cap Campus	04
Natnumhank Of Commerce Bldg 402 S Cap W	01
Old Capital Bldg Cap Campus	04
Professional Arts Bldg 208 E 11 Th	01
Security Bldg 203 E 4th	01
Union Ave Bldg	04
Union Ave Bldg 120 Union Ave	01

GOVERNMENT OFFICES

City Hall 8th : Plum..............	01
County Court House 1100 S Cap Way................	04
Employment Security Employment Security Bldg..	04
Governor Legislative Bldg......	04
Highway Highway Admin Bldg...................	04
Internal Revenue 1007 S Wash..................	04
Labor And Industry Cap Campus..................	04
Motor Vehicles License Bldg...	04
Public Assistance Cap Campus..................	04
Revenue Cap Campus............	04
Selective Service 800 S Cap Way....................	01
Supreme Court Temple Of Justice....................	04
U.S. Post Office 900 S Jefferson.................	01
Washington State Agencies	04

HOSPITALS

St Peters Hosp 413 N Lilly Rd...................	06

MILITARY INSTALLATIONS

National Guard 515 S Eastside.................	01

UNIVERSITIES AND COLLEGES

Evergreen State College R-15.	05
St Martins College 700 College Way..............	03

SEATTLE   981

POST OFFICE BOXES

Box Nos.

A-D	Columbia Sta...	18
A-H	Queen Anne Sta............	09
A-J	Burien Br.........	66
1-267	University Sta....	05
1-298	Richmond Beach Br......	60
1-299	Port Blakely Br.	10
1-747	Bainbridge Island - Winslow Br......	10
1-1316	Main Office......	11
1301-1399	Capitol Hill Sta............	12
1401	Greenwood Sta.	03
1501	Wallingford Sta............	03
1700-2156	Main Office......	11
3001	International Sta...........	14
3501-3999	Terminal Sta ...	24
5001-5499	Ballard Sta.......	07
6001-6288	Riverton	

	Heights Br......	88
6501-6914	West Seattle Sta............	16
7001	Richmond Highlands Contract Br...	33
7301-7599	Bitter Lake Sta............	33
8801-8999	Skyway Br.........	78
9000	Queen Anne Sta............	09
12301-12939	Main Office	11
15001-15480	Wedgwood Sta..	15
18001-18214	Columbia Sta....	18
22001-22156	East Union Sta............	22
24001-24672	Terminal Station...........	24
25001	Northgate Sta...	25
25501-25746	Lake City Sta ...	25
46001	White Center Br	46
55001-55199	North City Br...	55
66001-66597	Burien Br.........	66
70101-70672	Ballard Sta.......	07
80001-80816	Georgetown Sta............	08
88501-88952	Tukwila Br.......	88
89001-89548	Zenith Br.........	88
98001-98872	Des Moines Br..	88
99001-99274	Magnolia Sta....	99

RURAL ROUTES

4,5,6,7,8..................	10

STATIONS, BRANCHES AND UNITS

Bainbridge Island Winslow Br.................	10
Ballard Sta.................	07
Bitter Lake Sta............	33
Broadway Sta.............	02
Burien Br...................	48
Capitol Hill Sta...........	02
Columbia Sta.............	18
Des Moines Br............	88
East Union Sta...........	22
Federal Sta................	04
Forest Park Br............	55
Gerogetown Sta..........	08
Greenwood Sta...........	03
Internat nal Sta..........	04
Lake City Sta..............	25
Lester Rural Br...........	98035
Magnolia Sta..............	99
Manhattan Br.............	48
McMicken Heights Br..............	88
Naval Air Station Sta..............	15
North City Br..............	55
Northgate Sta.............	25
Port Blakely Br...........	10
Queen Anne Sta..........	09
Richmond Beach Br......	60
Rivertown Heights Br..............	88
Sea First Sta..............	04
Skyway Br.................	78
Snoqualmie Pass Rural Br.......98068
Terminal Annex Sta..............	34
Times Square Sta........	01
Tukwila Br.................	88
University Sta.............	05

Wallingford Sta............	03
Wedgwood Sta............	15
West Seattle Sta..........	16
White Center Br..........	46
Zenith Br...................	88
General Delivery..........	01
Postmaster.................	09

APARTMENTS, HOTELS, MOTELS

Camlin, 1619 9th Ave............	01
Edgewater Inn, 2500 Alaskan Way..................	21
Frye Drive-In, 223 Yesler Way.	04
Heart Of Seattle, 315 Seneca.................	01
Hilton Inn, 17620 Pacific Hwy S................	88
Hungerford, 1100 4th Ave	01
Mayflower, 405 Olive Way......	01
Moore, 1926 2nd Ave...........	01
Olympic, 416 Seneca	11
Seattle Hilton, 1301 6th Ave...	11
Sherwood Motor Inn, 400 N E 45th..................	05
Sorrento, 1001 Terry Ave.......	04
Stratford, 1121 3rd Ave.........	01
Swept Wing Inn Motor, 18601 Pacific Hwy S................	88
Vance, 620 Stewart............	01
Washington Park Towers, 1620 43rd Ave E	02
Washington Plaza, 1900 5th Ave..................	01
Windsor, 1405 6th Ave	01

BUILDINGS

Alaska, 618 2nd Ave............	04
Arcade Plaza, 1321 2nd Ave..	01
Arcade, 1319 2nd Ave..........	01
Arctic, 704 3rd Ave.............	04
Areis, 2366 Eastlake Ave E	02
Central, 810 3rd Ave	04
Chamber Of Commerce, 215 Columbia.................	04
Cobb Medical Center, 1305 4th Ave..................	01
Colman, 811 1st Ave...........	04
County Administration, 500 4th Ave..................	04
Denny, 2200 6th Ave...........	21
Dexter Horton, 710 2nd Ave....	04
Exchange, 821 2nd Ave........	04
Federal Office, 909 1st Ave....	04
Fischer Studio, 1519 3rd Ave.	01
General Insurance, 4347 Brooklyn Ave NE............	05
Green.joshua, 1425 4th Ave ...	01
Hoge, 701 2nd Ave	04
I B M, 1200 5th Ave............	01
Jones. 1331 3rd Ave............	01
King County Court House, 516 3rd Ave................	04
Labor Temple, 2800 1st Ave....	21
Lander St Annex, 2460 4th Ave S..................	34
Lloyd, 603 Stewart............	01
Logan, 500 Union..............	01
Lowman, 107 Cherry...........	04
Lyon, 607 3rd Ave.............	04
Maritime, 911 Western Ave.....	04
Medical Dental, 509 Olive Way.................	01

Metropole, 423 2nd Ave............ 04
Northern Life, 1100 3rd Ave.... 01
Northwestern Life, 120 6th
  Ave N 09
Norton, 801 2nd Ave............... 04
Olympic National Life, 920
  2nd Ave................................ 04
Pacific, 720 3rd Ave............... 04
Park Place, 1200 6th Ave....... 01
Plaza 600, 600 Stewart 01
Polson, 71 Columbia............... 04
Public Safety, 610 3rd Ave..... 04
Republic, 1511 3rd Ave.......... 01
Sage; 1305 3rd Ave................ 01
Seaboard, 1506 Westlake
  Ave 01
Seattle District Office, 415
  1st Ave N.............................. 09
Seattle Municipal, 600 4th
  Ave 04
Seattle Public Library, 1000
  4th Ave................................ 04
Seattle Tower, 1218 3rd Ave... 01
Seattle-First National Bank,
  1001 4th Ave........................ 54
Securities, 1904 3rd Ave........ 01
Sixth & Pine, 523 Pine 01
Skinner, 1326 5th Ave............ 01
Smith Tower, 506 2nd Ave 04
Teamsters Hall, 552 Denny
  Way 09
Terminal Annex, 2445 3rd
  Ave S.................................... 34
Terminal Sales, 1932 1st
  Ave....................................... 01
Times Square, 414 Olive
  Way 01
Tower, 1807 7th Ave............... 01
U S Court House, 1010 5th
  Ave 04
Union Federal Savings, 1505
  4th Ave................................ 01
United Pacific, 1000 2nd
  Ave....................................... 04
University District, 1107 NE
  45th 05
Vance, Joseph, 1402 3rd Ave . 01
Washington, 1325 4th Ave...... 01
White Henry Stuart, 1318 4th
  Ave......̥............................... 01

HOSPITALS

Ballard General, 5409 Barnes
  Ave NW................................ 07
Burien General, 16200 8th
  Ave SW................................. 66
Children'S Orthopedic, 4800
  Sand Point Way N E 05
Doctors, 909 University........... 01
Firland Sanatorium, 1704 NE
  150th..................................... 55
Group Health, 201 16th Ave
  E... 12
Harborview, 325 9th Ave 04
King County Central Blood
  Bank, 921 Terry Ave............. 04
King County 1, 325 9th Ave.... 04
King County 2, 100 Crockett .. 09
King County 3, 1704 NE
  150th..................................... 55
Northgate General, 120
  Northgate Plaza.................... 25
Northwest, 1551 N 120th 33

Providence, 530 17th Ave...... 22
Riverton General, 12844
  Military Rd S........................ 68
Saint Frances Cabrini, 918
  Terry Ave.............................. 04
Seattle General, 1309
  Summit Ave........................... 01
Seneca Summit Surgery,
  1305 Seneca.......................... 01
Standring Memorial, 12845
  12th Ave SW......................... 46
Swedish, 1212 Columbia......... 04
U S Public Health Service,
  1131 14th Ave S 14
United States Veterans
  Administration, 4435
  Beacon Ave S....................... 08
University Of Washington,
  1959 NE Pacific.................... 95
Virginia Mason, 1111 Terry
  Ave....................................... 01
West Seattle General, 2601
  SW Webster........................... 26

UNIVERSITIES AND COLLEGES

Seattle Community College,
  Central Campus Admin
  1718 Bdwy............................. 22
Seattle Community College,
  Dist 5, 401 Queen Anne
  Ave N 09
Seattle Pacific, 3307 3rd Ave
  W.. 19
Seattle University, 900
  Broadway............................... 22
Univ Of Washington, Adm
  Bldg, 4000 15th Ave N E... 05

SPOKANE   992

POST OFFICE BOXES

Box Nos.
1-999	Millwood Br......	12
1-999	Parkwater Sta ..	11
1-999	Trentwood Br...	15
1-2299	Main Office	10
2500-3999	Terminal Annex Sta.,.........	20
4000-4999	B Sta..................	02
5000-5999	North Central Sta.................	05
6000-6999*	Hillyard Sta.......	07
7200-7499	Hays Park Sta..	07
7500-7999	Rosewood Br	08
8000-8999	Manito Sta	03
9000-9999	Garland Sta........	09
13000-13999	Dishman Br.......	13
14000-14999	Opportunity Br..	14
19000-19999	Spokane Intl Airport Br	19

RURAL ROUTES

1..	04
2..	07
3..	03
4..	04
5..	08
6..	07
7..	06
10..	04

11 08

STATIONS, BRANCHES AND UNITS

Country Homes Br.................. 18
Dishman Br............................. 13
Garland Sta............................. 09
Hayes Park Sta....................... 07
Hillyard Sta............................ 07
Manito Sta.............................. 03
Millwood Br............................ 12
North Central Sta.................... 05
Opportunity Br........................ 14
Parkwater Sta......................... 11
Rosewood Br........................... 08
Spokane International
  AirprtBr................................ 19
Terminal Annex Sta................. 20
Trentwood Br.......................... 15
General Delivery..................... 10
Postmaster.............................. 10

APARTMENTS, HOTELS, MOTELS

Adlon, 526 1/2 W Main Ave ... 01
Alberta, 172 1/2 S Madison.... 04
Alberts, 152 S Pine................. 02
Alexander, 423 1/2 W Main
  Ave....................................... 01
Alexandria, 623 S Howard 04
Altadena, 608 Stevens S.......... 04
Argonne, 101 N Argonne......... 06
Arlington, 302 W Sprague
  Ave....................................... 04
Avalon, 507 W 5th Ave............ 04
Avenida, 2009 W Pacific Ave.. 04
Blackstone, 803 W 3rd Ave..... 04
Breslin, 729 S Bernard........... 04
Briggs, 225 S Wall.................. 04
Brownstone, 223 S Browne..... 04
Brunot Hall, 2209 W Pacific
  Ave....................................... 04
Cambridge Court, 206 W 8th
  Ave....................................... 04
Carlyle, 206 S Post................. 04
Coeur D Alene, 228 N
  Howard................................. 10
Colonial, 124 1/2 N Post........ 01
Como, 403 W 1st Ave.............. 04
Cooper-George, 707 W 5th
  Ave....................................... 04
Culmstock Arms, 328 W 8th
  Ave....................................... 04
Daniel, 525 W Sinto Ave......... 01
Davenport, 807 W Sprague
  Ave....................................... 10
Del Cardo, 726 W 1st Ave...... 04
Dresden, 707 N Monroe.......... 01
Dunsmuir, 21 E 2nd Ave 02
Earl, 224 S Lincoln................. 04
Elizabethan, 1429 W 9th Ave. 04
Espanola, 155 S Oak............... 04
Fairmont, 315 W Riverside
  Ave....................................... 01
Felix, 1108 W 1st Ave............. 04
Franklin Hall, 704 W 6th Ave. 04
Granby Court, 28 N Madison.. 01
Grand Coulee, 1401 W 1st
  Ave....................................... 04
Hosea, 1821 E Sprague Ave.... 02
Jefferson, 618 S Jefferson...... 04
Kempis, 523 S Washington...... 04
Knickerbocker, 507 S Howard. 04
Kozy, 303 S Adams................. 04

Lloyd, 1006 W Mansfield Ave . 05
Marlboro, 180 S Cannon........ 04
Monrovia, 508 S Monroe....... 04
Montvale, 108 S Monroe........ 04
Mount Vernon, 1303 W 10th
  Ave 04
New Madison, 1029 W 1st
  Ave 04
Norland, 235 W Trent Ave..... 01
Otis, 110 S Madison 04
Oxford, 319 1/2 W Sprague
  Ave 04
Oxford, 702 S Bernard 04
Parkwater, 1916 N Airport..... 06
Parsons, 108 S Jefferson 04
Pedicord, 213 W Riverside
  Ave 01
Pine Court, 27 E 8th Ave....... 02
Ridpath, 515 W Sprague....... 10
Roosevelt, 524 W 7th Ave...... 04
Saint Regis, 109 N Bernard ... 01
San Marco, 1230 W Sprague
  Ave 04
Seymour, 125 W 6th Ave....... 04
Sunshine, 5 S Cedar.............. 04
Victoria, 618 W 1st Ave......... 04
Villa Nova, 1418 W Riverside
  Ave 01
Vista Court, 627 S Bernard.... 04
Washington, 1417 N
  Washington.............................. 01
Washington, 327 1/2 W 2nd
  Ave 04
Wellington, 605 S Stevens...... 04
Westminster, 2301 W Pacific
  Ave 04

BUILDINGS

Bank Of Washington, 9 N
  Post.. 01
Bon Marche, 214 N Wall........ 01
Chancery, 1023 W Riverside
  Ave 10
Chronicle, 926 W Sprague
  Ave 04
Civic, 1020 W Riverside Ave... 01
Columbia, 107 S Howard........ 04
Fidelity Plaza......................... 01
Fidelity, 522 W Riverside Ave. 01
First National, 502 W
  Riverside Ave........................... 01
Great Western, 905 W
  Riverside................................... 01
Hillyard Branch, Spokane &
  Eastern Bank, 3009 E
  Olympic Ave............................. 07
Hutton, 9 S Washington......... 04
Hyde, 611 1/2 W Riverside
  Av 01
Lincoln, 818 W Riverside Ave. 01
Masonic Temple, 1108 W
  Riverside Ave........................... 01
Medical Center, 820 S Mc
  Clellan...................................... 04
Mohawk, 515 W Riverside
  Ave 01
Monroe, 1821 N Monroe......... 05
North Spokane Professional,
  5901 N Lidgerwood.............. 07
Northtown Office, 4407 N
  Division.. 07

Old National, 422 W
  Riverside Ave........................... 01
Parkade Plaza........................ 01
Paulsen Medical & Dental,
  407 W Riverside Ave............. 01
Paulsen, 421 W Riverside
  Ave 01
Peyton, 10 N Post................... 01
Review, 927 W Riverside Ave . 01
Rookery, 14 N Howard............ 01
Sherwood, 510 W Riverside
  Ave 01
Sixth Avenue Medical, 508 W
  6th Ave..................................... 04
Spokane & Eastern, 601 W
  Riverside Ave........................... 01
Spokane Coliseum, 1101 N
  Howard...................................... 01
State Theatre, 903 W
  Sprague Ave............................ 04
Symons, 7 S Howard.............. 04
Telephone, 501 W 2nd Ave.... 04
Washington Trust, 713 W
  Sprague Ave............................ 04
Zukor, 705 W Riverside Ave.... 01

GOVERNMENT OFFICES

Chamber Of Commerce, 1020
  W Riverside Ave....................... 01
City Hall, 221 N Wall............. 01
County-City Public Safety
  Bldg, 1100 W Mallon Ave.... 01
Farm Credit Banks Of
  Spokane Bldg, 705 W 1st
  Ave 04
Spokane County Court House,
  1116 W Broadway Ave........... 01
U S Court House, 920 W
  Riverside Ave........................... 01
U S Federal Bldg & Post
  Office, 904 W Riverside
  Ave 01
United States Post Office
  Terminal Annex, 703 E
  Trent Ave.................................. 02

HOSPITALS

Deaconess, 800 W 5th Ave..... 10
Holy Family, 5633 N
  Lidgerwood.............................. 20
Sacred Heart, 101 W 8th
  Ave 04
Saint Luke'S Memorial, 711 S
  Cowley...................................... 10
Shriners Hospital For
  Crippled Children, 820 N
  Summit Blvd............................ 01
Valley General Hospital
  12606 E Mission Ave........... 20
Veterans Administration
  Hospital, 4815 N
  Assembly.................................. 08

UNIVERSITIES AND COLLEGES

Fort Wright College Of Holy
  Names, W 4000 Randolph
  Rd 04
Gonzaga University, 502 E
  Boone Ave................................ 02

Spokane Community (East
  Miss Campus) 3403 E
  Mission Ave.............................. 02
Spokane Falls Community, Ft
  Wright Campus, W 3410
  Ft Wright.................................. 04
Whitworth College, Country
  Homes Estate........................... 18

TACOMA   984

POST OFFICE BOXES

Box Nos.
1-350   Fern Hill Sta..... 12
1-447   Lakeview Br...... 91
1-570   Tillicum Br...... 92
1-2277   Main Office..... 01
1-448S   South Tacoma
             Sta..................... 09
3001-3470   Lakewood
             Center Br....... 99
4000-4299   Mc Chord Air
             Force Base
             Br 38
5001-5294   Kay Street Sta.. 05
7001-7358   Proctor........... 07
9001-9480   South Tacoma
             Sta..................... 09
11001-11397 Terminal Annex
             Sta..................... 11
33001-33208 Fort Lewis....... 33
44001-44669 Parkland Br...... 44
94001-94999 Fort
             Steilacoom...... 94

RURAL ROUTES

2.. 24
6.. 22
12.. 24

STATIONS, BRANCHES AND UNITS

American Lake Br.................. 93
Dash Point Rural Br.............. 22
Fern Hill Sta......................... 12
Fife Br.................................... 24
Fircrest Br............................. 66
Fort Lewis Br......................... 33
Fort Steilacoom Br................ 94
K Street Sta........................... 05
Lakeview Br........................... 91
Lakewood Center Br.............. 99
Longmire Rural Br..............98397
McChord AFB Br.................... 38
Monta Vista Br....................... 99
North Fort Lewis Br............... 33
Paradise Inn Rural Br........... 98398
Parkland Br............................ 44
Proctor Sta............................ 07
Sixth Avenue Sta................... 06
South Tacoma Sta................. 09
Steilacoom Br......................98388
Terminal Sta.......................... 04
Tillicum Br............................. 92
General Delivery.................... 02
Postmaster............................ 02

APARTMENTS, HOTELS, MOTELS

Ambassador House, 3502
  92nd S..................................... 09

Americana, 242 St Helens S.... 02
Ansonia, 219 Tacoma Ave N... 03
Broadmoor, 431 Broadway S.. 02
Buckingham, 1001 Yakima
　N.. 03
Cambridge, 415 6th Ave......... 02
Capri, 4910 108th St SW........ 99
Carlton, 1552 Jefferson Ave
　S.. 02
Finnisterre, 601 Jackson Ave
　N.. 06
Holiday Inn, 3518 Pacific
　Hwy E................................... 01
Ingleside, 205 Tacoma Ave
　N.. 03
Manor House, 5800 100th
　SW.. 99
Miramar, 7320 6th Ave........... 06
Olympic Manor, 7301 6th
　Ave....................................... 06
Olympic, 304 Tacoma Ave S... 02
Olympus, 815 Pacific Ave S... 02
Park Towers 220 Tacoma Ave
　S.. 02
Rainier Village, 9206 Pacific
　Ave S.................................... 44
Saint James, 821 Yakima
　Ave S.................................... 05
Sky Terrace, 235 Broadway
　S.. 02
Thunderbird, 8210
　Steilacoom Blvd SW............. 98
Town House, 117 Tacoma
　Ave N. 03
Vista Manor, 319 Tacoma
　Ave N. 03
Walker, 405 6th Ave............... 02
Washington, 518 7th S............ 02
Winthrop, 773 Broadway S. 02

BUILDINGS

County-City, 930 Tacoma Ave
　S.. 02
Federal, 1102 A...................... 02
Labor Temple, 950 Fawcett
　Ave S.................................... 02
Medical Arts, 740 St. Helens
　Ave S.................................... 02
Perkins, 1103 A...................... 02
Public Service, 1301 Tacoma
　Ave S.................................... 02
Puget Sound Bank, 1117
　Pacific Ave S........................ 02
Rust, 950 Pacific Ave S.......... 02
Tacoma, 1015 A...................... 02
Washington Plaza, 1201
　Pacific Ave S........................ 02
Washington, 1019 Pacific
　Ave S.................................... 02

HOSPITALS

Allenmore, 1901 Union Ave
　S.. 05
Doctors, 737 Fawcett S........... 02
Lakewood General, 5702
　100th SW............................. 99
Madigan General, Fort Lewis.. 31
Mary Bridge Childrens, 311 L
　S.. 05
Puget Sound General, 215 36
　S.. 08

Saint Josephs, 1812 Eye S...... 01
Tacoma General, 315 K S........ 05
United States Veterans,
　American Lake....................... 93
Western State, Fort
　Steilacoom............................ 94

UNIVERSITIES AND COLLEGES

Pacific Lutheran University,
　Parkland................................ 47
Tacoma Community College,
　5900 12th S.......................... 65
University Of Puget Sound,
　1500 Warner N. 16

VANCOUVER　　986

POST OFFICE BOXES

Box Nos.
1-1500　　　　Main Office 60
1501-2000　　Arnada Park
　　　　　　　Annex Sta........ 63
2001-2500　　Fourth Plain
　　　　　　　Sta.................... 61
2501-3000　　Orchards Br...... 62

RURAL ROUTES

1,2,5..................................... 62
6,7.. 65

STATIONS, BRANCHES AND UNITS

Arnada Park Annex Sta............ 63
Fourth Plain Sta...................... 61
Hazel Dell Br.......................... 60
Minnehaha Br.......................... 61
Orchards Br............................ 62
Veterans Administration
　HospSta................................ 61
General Delivery...................... 60
Postmaster.............................. 60

APARTMENTS, HOTELS, MOTELS

Aloha, 708 NE 78.................... 65
Fort Motel, 500 E 13th............ 60
Franklin Court, 1013
　Franklin................................ 60
Mid Columbia Manor, 515
　Washington........................... 60
Normandy, 316 E 7th............... 60
Riviera, 105 E 5th.................... 60
Travelodge, 601 Broadway....... 60
Valley, 1800 Simpson Ave 60
Van Vista Plaza 410 W 13th
　St.. 60

BUILDINGS

Adams, 1105 Broadway............ 60
American Legion, 301 E 7th..... 60
Carpenters Union Hall, 612 E
　Mc Laughlin Blvd.................. 63
Central, 1206 1/2 Main............ 60
Clark County Court House,
　1200 Franklin........................ 60
Clark County P U D, 1200
　Fort Vancouver Way............. 63
Elks Club, 105 W Evergreen

Blvd...................................... 60
Federal, 500 W 12th................ 60
Ford, 601 Main....................... 60
Fort Vancouver Regional Libr,
　1007 E Mill Plain Blvd.......... 63
Freeway, 1401 C..................... 63
Labor Temple, 205 11th.......... 60
Masonic Temple, 2500 NE
　78.. 65
Medical Arts, 1104 Main 60
Municipal, 210 E 13th............. 60
Pacific Tel N W, 112 11th........ 60
Patio, 108 W Evergreen Blvd.. 60
State-Federal Office, 1408
　Franklin................................ 60
Vancouver School Dist 37,
　605 N Devine Rd.................. 61

HOSPITALS

U S Veterans, 1603 Fourth
　Plain Blvd............................ 61
Vancouver Memorial, 3400
　Main..................................... 63
600 NE 92 Ave P O Box
　1687..................................... 61

UNIVERSITIES AND COLLEGES

Clark, 1925 Ft Vancouver
　Way..................................... 63

YAKIMA　　989

POST OFFICE BOXES

Box Nos.
1-1999　　　　Main Office 01
2000-2999　　West Side Sta .. 02
3000-3999　　Union Gap Br... 03

RURAL ROUTES

1.. 01
2.. 02
3.. 01
4.. 02
5.. 03
6.. 02
7.. 03
8.. 02

STATIONS, BRANCHES AND UNITS

Gleed Rural Br........................ 04
Schwarder Rural Br................. 05
Terrace Heights Br.................. 01
Union Gap Br.......................... 03
West Side Sta.......................... 02
Wiley Rural Br......................... 06
General Delivery...................... 01
Postmaster.............................. 01

APARTMENTS, HOTELS, MOTELS

Chieftain, 17 S 2nd................. 01
Chinook, Box 821.................... 01
Yakima, P O Box 22................. 01

BUILDINGS

City Hall, 129 N 2nd.............. 01
Federal, 25 S 3rd.................. 01
Larson, 6 S 2nd.................... 01
Miller, 205 E Yakima Ave....... 01
Yakima County Courthouse, N
  2nd & E B 01

HOSPITALS

Saint Elizabeth, 110 So 9th
  Ave.................................... 02
Vally Osteopathic, 3003
  Tieton Dr............................ 02
Yakima Valley Memorial,
  2811 Tieton Dr................... 02

MILITARY INSTALLATIONS

Yakima Firing Center............. 01

UNIVERSITIES AND COLLEGES

Yakima Valley College, 16th
  Ave & W Nob Hill............... 02

WEST VIRGINIA
(Abbreviation: WV)

Abraham 25955
Accoville 25606
Adolph 26247
Adrian 25231
Advent 26210
Albright 26519
Alderson 24910
Alexander 26211
Algoma 24807
Alkol 25501
Allen Junction 25810
Alloy 25002
Alma 26320
Alpoca 24710
Alta 26655
Alton 26212
Alum Bridge 26321
Alum Creek 25003
Alvy 26322
Amboy 26701
Ameagle 25004
Amherstdale 25607
Amigo 25811
Amma 25005
Anawalt 24808
Anmoore 26323
Annamoriah 26130
Ansted 25812
Anthony 24914
Antioch 26702
Apple Grove 25502
Arbovale 24915
Arbuckle 25006
Arden, R. Br. Moatsville 26324
Arnett 25007
Arnoldsburg 25234
Arthur 26816
Arthurdale 26520
Artie 25008
Asbury 24916
Asco 24809
Ashford 25009
Ashland 24810
Ashton 25503
Athens 24712
Auburn 26325
Augusta 26704
Aurora 26705
　Horse Shoe Run, R. Br. 26769
Auto 24917
Avondale 24811
Baileysville 24812
Baisden 25608
Baker 26801
Bakerton, R. Br. Harpers
　Ferry 25410
Bald Knob 25010
Baldwin 26326
Ballard 24918
Ballengee 24919
Bancroft 25011
Bandytown 25012
Barboursville (1st) 25504
Barnabus 25609
Barnum 26706
Barrackville 26559
Barrett 25013
Bartley 24813
Bartow 24920
Basin, R. Br. Herndon 24727

Baxter, R. Br. Rivesville 26560
Bayard 26707
Beard 24921
Beards Fork 25014
Beartown, R. Br. Bradshaw 24814
Beaver 25813
Beckley (1st) 25801
Beckwith 25814
Beech Bottom 26030
Beeson 24714
Belington 26250
Belle 25015
　Diamond, R. Br. 25015
　Quincy, R. Br. 25016
　Shrewsbury, R. Br. 25184
Bellepoint, Sta. Hinton 25951
Belleville 26133
Bellview, Sta. Fairmont 26554
Belmont 26134
Belva 26656
Bens Run 26135
Bentree 25018
Benwood 26031
Berea 26327
Bergoo 26298
Berkeley Springs 25411
Berwind 24815
Besoco, R. Br. Rhodell 25815
Bethany 26032
Beverly 26253
Beverly Hills, Sta.
　Huntington 25705
Bickmore 25019
Big Chimney, R. Br.
　Charleston 25302
Big Creek 25505
Big Otter 25020
Big Run 26561
Big Sandy 24816
Big Springs 26137
Bigbend 26136
Bim 25021
Birch River 26610
Blackberry City 25664
Blacksville 26521
Blair 25022
Blandville 26328
Bloomery 26817
Bloomingrose 25024
Blount 25025
Blue Creek 25026
Blue Jay 25816
Bluefield (1st) 24701
Bluewell, R. Br. Bluefield 24701
Bob White 25028
Boggs 26299
Bolair, R. Br. Webster
　Springs 26288
Bolivar, R. Br. Harpers Ferry ...25426
Bolt 25817
Bomont 25030
Boomer 25031
Booth 26522
Borderland 25665
Bowden 26254
Bozoo 24923
Bradley 25818
Bradshaw 24817
　Beartown, R. Br. 24814
Braeholm 25610
Bramwell 24715
Branchland 25506
Brandonville 26523

Brandywine 26802
Breeden 25666
Brenton 24818
Bretz 26524
Bridgeport (1st) 26330
Bristol 26332
Broaddus, Br. Philippi 26416
Brohard 26138
Brooks 25957
Brownton 26334
Bruceton Mills 26525
Bruno 25611
Buckeye 24924
Buckhannon (1st) 26201
　Queens, R. Br. 26231
Bud 24716
Buffalo 25033
Bunker Hill 25413
Burlington 26710
Burning Springs 26139
Burnsville 26335
　Copen, R. Br. 26615
Burnt House 26336
Burnwell 25034
Burton 26562
Cabin Creek 25035
　Chelyan, R. Br. 25041
Cabins 26855
Cairo 26337
Caldwell 24925
Calvin 26660
Camden 26338
Camden On Gauley 26208
Cameron 26033
Camp Creek 25820
Canebrake 24819
Cannelton 25036
Canvas 26662
Capels 24820
Capitol, Sta. Charleston 25311
Capon Bridge 26711
Capon Springs 26823
Carbon 25037
Caretta 24821
Carlisie 25821
Carolina 26563
Cascade 26526
Cashmere 24926
Cass 24927
Cassville 26527
Catawba, R. Br. Fairmont 26564
Cedar Grove 25039
Cedarville 26611
Center Point 26339
Central Station 26340
Centralia 26612
Century 26214
Ceredo 25507
Chapmanville (1st) 25508
Charles Town (1st) 25414
CHARLESTON (1st) (see
　appendix)
Charlton Heights 25040
Charmco 25958
Chattaroy 25667
Chauncey 25612
Chelyan, R. Br. Cabin Creek 25041
Cherry Grove 26803
Cherry Run 25418
Chesapeake, Br. Charleston 25315
Chester (1st) 26034
Chloe 25235
Cinco, R. Br. Charleston 25306

Circleville.............................26804
Clarksburg (1st)..................26301
  Nutter Fort Stonewood,
    Br.................................26301
  Wilsonburg, R. Br.,..........26461
Clay...................................25043
Clear Creek........................25044
Clear Fork...........................24822
Clem..................................26614
Clendenin...........................25045
Cleveland............................26215
Clifftop...............................25822
Clifton................................25237
Clintonville.........................24923
Clio....................................25046
Clothier..............................25047
Clover................................25238
Clover Lick.........................24929
Coal City............................25823
Coal Fork, R. Br. Charleston...25306
Coal Mountain.....................24823
Coaldale............................24717
Coalton..............................26257
Coalwood............................24824
Coburn...............................26565
Coketon.............................26258
Colcord..............................25048
Colfax................................26566
Colliers...............................26035
Comfort..............................25049
Cool Ridge..........................25825
Coopers..............................24713
Copen, R. Br. Burnsville......26615
Cora...................................25634
Core...................................26522
Corinne...............................25846
Corinth...............................26713
Corley................................26615
Cornstalk............................24931
Corton................................25055
Costa..................................25063
Cottageville.........................25233
Cottle.................................26201
Cove, Sta. Weirton...............26056
Cove Gap............................25500
Covel..................................24716
Cowen................................26629
Coxs Mills...........................26347
Crab Orchard.......................25827
Craigsville...........................26205
Cranberry............................25828
Crawford.............................26343
Crawley...............................24931
Creston...............................26141
Crichton..............................25961
Crites.................................25615
Cross Lanes, Br. Nitro.........25143
Crown.................................25616
Crown Hill...........................25052
Crum..................................25669
Crumpler.............................24825
Cucumber............................24826
Culloden.............................25510
Cunard...............................25830
Curtin................................26204
Cuzzart...............................26536
Cyclone..............................24827
Dailey................................26259
Dallas.................................26036
Danese...............................25831
Daniels...............................25832
Danville..............................25053

Davin..................................25617
Davis..................................26260
Davisville............................26142
Davy...................................24828
Dawes................................25054
Dawmont.............................26344
Dawson...............................24952
Decota................................25055
Deep Water..........................25057
Dehue................................25618
Delbarton............................25670
Dellslow..............................26531
Delray................................26714
Diamond, R. Br. Belle........25015
Diana..................................26217
Dille...................................26617
Dingess...............................25671
Dink...................................25058
Dixie..................................25059
Dorcas................................26835
Dorothy...............................25060
Dothan................................25833
Dott...................................24721
Downtown, Sta. Wheeling....26003
Drennen..............................26667
Droop.................................24933
Dry Creek............................25062
Drybranch............................25061
Dryfork...............................26263
Duck...................................25063
Duhring...............................24722
Dunbar (1st)........................25064
Duncan...............................25240
Dunlow...............................25511
Dunmore.............................24934
Durbin................................26264
Earling................................25619
East Bank............................25067
East Beckley, Sta. Beckley....25801
East Lynn............................25512
Eastgulf...............................25835
Eastside, Sta. Fairmont.......26554
Eccles................................25836
Eckman...............................24829
Edgarton.............................25672
Edmond...............................25837
Eglon.................................26716
Elbert.................................24830
Eleanor...............................25070
Elgood................................24723
Elizabeth.............................26143
Elk Garden...........................26717
Elkhorn...............................24831
Elkins (1st)..........................26241
Elkview...............................25071
Ellamore.............................26267
Ellenboro.............................26346
Elm Grove, Sta. Wheeling....26003
Elmira.................................26618
Elton..................................25965
Emmett...............................25620
Emoryville, R. Br. Elk
  Garden................................26717
English................................24832
Enterprise............................26568
Erbacon..............................26203
Eskdale...............................25075
Ethel..................................25076
Eureka................................26144
Evans.................................25241
Everettville...........................26533
Excelsior, R. Sta. War.........24833

Exchange.............................26619
Fairdale..............................25839
Fairlea, R. Br. Lewisburg......24902
Fairmont (1st).......................26554
  Bellview, Sta.......................26554
  Catawba, R. Br....................26554
  Eastside, Sta.......................26554
  Monongah, Br.......................26554
  Watson, Sta.........................26554
Fairview..............................26570
Falling Rock..........................25079
Falling Waters.......................25419
Falls Mill.............................26620
Fanrock...............................24834
Farmington...........................26571
Fayetteville...........................25840
Federal, Sta. Bluefield.........24701
Fenwick...............................26202
Ferrellsburg..........................25513
Filbert................................24835
Fireco, R. Br. Coal City........25823
Fisher................................26818
Five Forks............................26145
Flat Top...............................25841
Flatwoods............................26621
Flemington...........................26347
Floe...................................25242
Flower................................26622
Fola...................................25080
Follansbee...........................26037
Folsom................................26348
Forest Hill...........................24935
Fort Ashby...........................26719
Fort Gay.............................25514
Fort Neal, Sta. Parkersburg..26101
Fort Seybert.........................26806
Fort Spring...........................24936
Foster................................25081
Four States..........................26572
Frame, R. Br. Elkview.........25071
Frametown...........................26623
  Servia, R. Br........................26637
Frank.................................24937
Frankford.............................24938
Franklin...............................26807
Fraziers Bottom.....................25082
Freeman..............................24724
French Creek........................26218
  Frenchton, R. Br..................26219
Frenchton, R. Br. French
  Creek................................26219
Friars Hill............................24939
Friendly...............................26146
Gaines................................26220
Gallagher.............................25083
Gallipolis Ferry......................25515
Galloway.............................26349
Gandeeville..........................25243
Gap Mills.............................24941
Garrison..............................25084
Garten................................25842
Gary...................................24836
Gassaway.............................26624
Gauley Bridge.......................25085
Gauley Mills.........................26240
Gay...................................25244
Gem...................................26625
Genoa................................25517
Gerrardstown........................25420
Ghent.................................25843
Gilbert................................25621
Gilboa................................26671

Gilliam ... 24837
Gilmer ... 26350
Given ... 25245
Glace ... 24942
Glady ... 26268
Glasgow ... 25086
Glen ... 25088
Glen Dale ... 26038
Glen Daniel ... 25844
Glen Easton ... 26039
Glen Ferris ... 25090
Glen Fork ... 25845
Glen Jean ... 25846
Glen Morgan ... 25847
Glen Rogers ... 25848
Glen White ... 25849
Glendon ... 26626
Glengary ... 25421
Glenhayes ... 25519
Glenville ... 26351
Glenwood ... 25520
Goffs ... 26353
Gordon ... 25093
Gormania ... 26720
Grafton (1st) ... 26354
Grant Town ... 26574
Grantsville ... 26147
Granville ... 26534
Grassy Meadows ... 24943
Great Cacapon ... 25422
Green Bank ... 24944
Green Spring ... 26722
Green Sulphur Springs ... 25966
Greenville ... 24945
Greenwood ... 26360
Griffithsville ... 25521
Grimms Landing ... 25095
Guardian ... 26221
Guyandotte, Sta. Huntington ... 25702
Gypsy ... 26361
Hacker Valley ... 26222
Hager ... 25522
Hallburg ... 25101
Halltown ... 25423
Hambleton ... 26269
Hamlin ... 25523
Hampden ... 25623
Hancock ... 25424
Handley ... 25102
Hanover ... 24839
Hansford ... 25103
Harman ... 26270
Harmony ... 25246
Harper ... 25851
Harpers Ferry ... 25425
   Bakerton, R. Br. ... 25410
   Bolivar, R. Br. ... 25426
Harrison ... 25105
Harrisville ... 26362
Hartford ... 25247
Harts ... 25524
Harvey ... 25852
Hastings ... 26365
Havaco ... 24841
Haywood ... 26366
Hazelgreen ... 26367
Hazelton ... 26535
Heaters ... 26627
Hebron ... 26368
Hedgesville ... 25427
Helen ... 25853
Helvetia ... 26224
Hemphill ... 24842

Henderson ... 25106
Hendricks ... 26271
Henlawson ... 25624
Hensley ... 24843
Hepzibah ... 26369
Herndon ... 24726
   Basin, R. Br. ... 24727
Hernshaw ... 25107
Herold ... 26628
Hewett ... 25108
Hiawatha ... 24729
Hico ... 25854
High View ... 26808
Highland ... 26371
Hillsboro ... 24946
Hilltop ... 25855
Hines ... 25967
Hinton (1st) ... 25591
Hix ... 25968
Holcomb, R. Br. Richwood ... 26262
Holden ... 25625
Hollywood ... 24947
Hometown ... 25109
Hominy Falls, R. Br.
   Summersville ... 26673
Hopemont ... 26723
Horner ... 26372
Horse Shoe Run, R. Br.
   Aurora ... 26769
Hugheston ... 25110
Hundred ... 26575
Hunt, R. Br. Man ... 25635
HUNTINGTON (1st) (see
   appendix)
Hurricane (1st) ... 25526
Hurst ... 26373
Hutchinson ... 25627
Huttonsville ... 26273
Iaeger ... 24844
Idamay ... 26576
Ikes Fork ... 24845
Independence ... 26374
Indian Mills ... 24949
Indore ... 25111
Industrial ... 26375
Institute ... 25112
Inwood ... 25428
Ireland ... 26376
Isaban ... 24846
Itmann ... 24847
Ivanhoe ... 26227
Ivydale ... 25113
Jacksonburg ... 26377
Jane Lew ... 26378
Jeffrey ... 25114
Jenkinjones ... 24848
Jere ... 26536
Jesse ... 24849
Job ... 26274
Jodie ... 26674
Jolo ... 24850
Jonben ... 25856
Jones Springs ... 25429
Jordan ... 26577
Josephine ... 25857
Josephs Mills ... 26379
Julian ... 25529
Jumping Branch ... 25969
Junction ... 26824
Junior ... 26275
Justice ... 24851
Kanawha City, Sta.
   Charleston ... 25304

Kanawha Falls ... 25115
Kanawha Head ... 26228
Kasson ... 26380
Kayford ... 25116
Kearneysville ... 25430
Kegley ... 24731
Kellysville ... 24732
Kenna ... 25248
Kenova ... 25530
Kentuck ... 25249
Kerens ... 26276
Kermit ... 25674
Keslers Cross Lanes ... 26675
Kessler ... 25970
Keyser (1st) ... 26726
Keystone ... 24852
Kiahsville ... 25534
Kieffer ... 24950
Kilsyth ... 25859
Kimball ... 24853
Kimberly ... 25118
Kincaid ... 25119
Kingmont ... 26578
Kingston ... 25120
Kingwood (1st) ... 26537
Kirby ... 26729
Kistler ... 25628
Knob Fork ... 26579
Kopperston ... 24854
Kyle ... 24855
Lahmansville ... 26731
Lake ... 25121
Lakin ... 25250
Lanark ... 25860
Landes, R. Br. Petersburg ... 26832
Landville ... 25629
Lanham, R. Br. Poca ... 25159
Lansing ... 25862
Lashmeet ... 24733
Lavalette ... 25535
Lawton ... 25863
Layland ... 25864
Le Roy ... 25252
Leckie ... 24856
Leet ... 25536
Leewood ... 25122
Left Hand ... 25251
Lehew ... 26843
Leivasy ... 26676
Lenore ... 25676
Leon ... 25123
Leopold ... 26382
Lerona ... 25971
Lesage ... 25537
Leslie ... 25972
Lester ... 25865
Letart ... 25253
Letter Gap ... 25255
Levels ... 25431
Lewisburg (1st) ... 24901
   Fairlea, R. Br. ... 24902
Liberty ... 25124
Lima ... 26383
Linden ... 25256
Lindside ... 24951
   Rock Camp, R. Br. ... 24967
Linn ... 26384
Little Birch ... 26629
Little Falls ... 26540
Littleton ... 26581
Liverpool ... 25257
Lizemores ... 25125
Lobata ... 25677

Lochgelly.....................25866
Lockbridge..................25973
Lockney......................25258
Lockwood, R. Br.
   Summersville........26677
Logan (1st)..................25601
London.......................25126
Long Branch................25867
Longacre.....................25127
Lookout......................25868
Looneyville.................25259
Lorado.......................25630
Lorentz......................26229
Lost City....................26810
Lost Creek..................26385
Lost River...................26811
Lumberport.................26386
Lundale......................25631
Lyburn.......................25632
Lynco........................24857
Maben........................25870
Mabie........................26278
Mabscott....................25871
Mac Arthur.................25873
Mace.........................26279
Macfarlan...................26148
Madison......................25130
Mahan........................25131
Mahone......................26402
Maidsville...................26541
Malden, R. Br. Charleston....25306
Mallory......................25634
Mammoth....................25132
Man..........................25635
Manheim.....................26403
Mannington.................26582
Maplewood..................25874
Marfrance....................25975
Marianna, R. Br. Pineville....24859
Marlinton....................24954
Marmet, Br. Charleston....25315
Marshall University, Sta.
   Huntington............25703
Martinsburg (1st)...........25401
Mason........................25260
Masontown..................26542
Matewan.....................25678
Matheny......................24860
Mathias......................26812
Matoaka.....................24736
Maxwelton..................24957
Maybeury...................24861
Maysel.......................25133
Maysville....................26833
Mc Alpin....................25869
Mc Comas...................24735
Mc Connell.................25633
Mc Dowell...................24858
Mc Graws....................25875
   Saulsville, R. Br......25876
Mc Mechen.................26040
Mc Whorter.................26401
Mead.........................25877
Meador......................25682
Meadow Bluff...............24958
Meadow Bridge............25976
Meadow Creek.............25977
Meadowbrook..............26404
Medley......................26734
Merrimac, R. Br. Williamson....25661
Metz.........................26685
Miami........................25134
Middlebourne..............26149

Midkiff......................25540
Midway......................25878
Milam........................26838
Mill Creek...................26280
Mill Point...................24959
Millstone....................25261
Millville.....................25432
Millwood....................25262
Milton.......................25541
Minden......................25879
Mineralwells...............26150
Mingo........................26281
Minnehaha Springs........24960
Minnora.....................25263
Moatsville...................26405
   Arden, R. Br..........26324
Mohawk.....................24862
Monaville...................25636
Monongah, Br. Fairmont....26554
Montana Mines............26586
Montcalm...................24737
Montcoal....................25135
Monterville..................26282
Montgomery (1st).........25136
Montrose....................26283
Moorefield..................26836
Morgantown (1st).........26505
   Sabraton, Sta.........26505
   Star City, Br..........26505
   Westover, Br..........26505
Morrisvale...................25542
Moundsville (1st)..........26041
Mount Alto..................25264
Mount Carbon..............25139
Mount Clare................26408
Mount Gay..................25637
Mount Hope................25880
Mount Lookout............26678
Mount Nebo................26679
Mount Storm...............26739
Mount Zion.................26151
Mountain....................26407
Mouth of Seneca..........26884
Moyers......................26813
Mud..........................25543
Mullens......................25882
Munday......................26152
Murraysville................26153
Myra.........................25544
Myrtle.......................25684
Nallen.......................26680
Naoma.......................25140
Napier.......................26631
Naugatuck..................25685
Nebo.........................25141
Nellis........................25142
Nemours....................24738
Neola, R. Br. White Sulphur
   Springs................24961
Nettie.......................26681
Neville, Sta. Beckley.......25801
New Creek..................26743
New Cumberland..........26047
New England...............26154
New Haven..................25265
New Manchester...........26056
New Martinsville (1st).....26155
New Milton..................26411
New Richmond.............24867
Newberne...................26409
Newburg....................26410
Newell.......................26050
Newhall.....................24866

Newton......................25266
Newton D Baker V A Center,
   Br. Martinsburg......25401
Newtown....................25686
Newville.....................26632
Nicut........................26633
Nimitz.......................25978
Nitro (1st)..................25143
Nobe.........................26158
Nolan........................25687
Normantown...............25267
North Matewan............25688
North Parkersburg, Sta.
   Parkersburg..........26101
North Spring................24869
Northfork....................24868
Northriver Mills............26744
Norton.......................26285
Nutter Fort Stonewood, Br.
   Clarksburg...........26301
Oak Hill (1st)...............25901
Oakvale, R. Br. Princeton....24739
Oceana......................24870
Odd..........................25902
Ohley........................25147
Old Fields...................26845
Omar.........................25638
Omps........................25433
Ona..........................25545
Onego.......................26886
Orgas........................25148
Orient Hill, R. Br. Charmco....25958
Orlando......................26412
Orma.........................25268
Osage........................26543
Ottawa......................25149
Ovapa.......................25150
Owings......................26413
Oxford, R. Br. West Union....26414
Packsville, R. Br.
   Whitesville...........25151
Paden City..................26159
Page.........................25152
Pageton.....................24871
Palermo.....................25546
Palestine....................26160
Panther......................24872
Parcoal......................26265
Parkersburg (1st)..........26105
Parsons......................26287
Patterson Creek............26746
Paw Paw....................25434
Pax..........................25904
Paynesville..................24873
Peach Creek................25639
Pecks Mill...................25547
Pemberton..................25905
Pence Springs..............24962
Pennsboro..................26415
Pentress.....................26544
Perkins......................26634
Perry.........................26844
Petersburg..................26847
   Landes, R. Br........26832
Peterstown..................24963
Petroleum...................26161
Pettus, R. Br. Whitesville....25153
Peytona.....................25154
Philippi (1st)...............26416
Pickaway....................24964
Pickens......................26230
Pie...........................25689
Piedmont....................26750

Pigeon	25155
Pinch	25156
Pine Grove	26419
Pineville	24874
Marianna, R. Br.	24859
Piney View	25906
Pipestem	25979
Pisgah	26545
Pliny	25158
Poca	25159
Poe	26683
Point Pleasant (1st)	25550
Points	25437
Pond Gap	25160
Pool	26684
Port Amherst, R. Br. Charleston	25306
Porters Falls	26162
Powellton	25161
Power	26054
Powhatan	24877
Pratt	25162
Premier	24878
Prenter	25163
Prichard	25555
Prince	25907
Princeton (1st)	24740
Oakvale, R. Br.	24739
Princewick	25908
Procious	25164
Proctor	26055
Prosperity	25909
Pullman	26421
Purgitsville	26852
Pursglove	26546
Queens, R. Br. Buckhannon	26231
Quick, R. Br. Clendenin	25045
Quincy, R. Br. Belle	25016
Quinnimont	25910
Quinwood	25981
Rachel	26587
Racine	25165
Radnor	25556
Ragland	25690
Rainelle	25962
Raleigh	25911
Ramage	25166
Ramsey	25912
Rand, Br. Charleston	25306
Ranger	25557
Rangoon	26232
Ranson	25438
Ravencliff	25913
Ravenswood (1st)	26164
Rawl	25691
Raysal	24875
Reader	26167
Red Creek	26289
Red House	25168
Red Jacket	25692
Redstar	25914
Reedsville	26547
Reedy	25270
Renick	24966
Replete	26233
Reynoldsville	26422
Rhodell	25915
Besoco, R. Br.	25815
Richwood	26261
Holcomb, R. Br.	26262
Ridgeley	26753
Ridgeview	25169
Ridgeway	25440

Riffle	26635
Rig	26854
Rio	26755
Ripley	25271
Rippon	25441
Riverton	26814
Rivesville	26588
Baxter, R. Br.	26560
Roanoke	26423
Robertsburg	25172
Robinette	25642
Robson	25173
Rock	24747
Rock Camp, R. Br. Lindside	24967
Rock Castle	25272
Rock Cave	26234
Rock Creek	25174
Rock View	24880
Rockport	26169
Roderfield	24881
Romance	25175
Romney	26757
Ronceverte	24970
Rosedale	26636
Rosemont	26424
Rossmore	25643
Rowgh Run	26860
Rowlesburg	26425
Runa	26688
Rupert	25984
Russellville	26689
Sabine	25916
Sabraton, Sta. Morgantown	26505
Saint Albans (1st)	25177
Saint George	26290
Saint Marys	26170
Salem	26426
Salt Rock	25559
Saltpetre	25558
Sand Fork	26430
Sand Ridge	25274
Sandstone	25985
Sandyville	25275
Sarah Ann	25644
Sarton	24973
Saulsville, R. Br. Mc Graws	25876
Saxon	25180
Scarbro	25917
Scherr, R. Br. Keyser	26726
Scott Depot	25560
Secondcreek	24974
Seebert	24975
Selbyville	26236
Servia, R. Br. Frametown	26637
Seth	25181
Shady Spring	25918
Shanks	26761
Sharon	25182
Sharples	25183
Shaw	26762
Shenandoah Junction	25442
Shepherdstown	25443
Sherman	26173
Sherrard	26057
Shinnston	26431
Shirley	26434
Shively	25561
Shoals	25562
Shock	26638
Short Creek	26058
Shrewsbury, R. Br. Belle	25184
Sias	25563
Simon	24882

Simpson	26435
Sinks Grove	24976
Sissonville, Br. Charleston	25320
Sistersville	26175
Skelton	25919
Skygusty	24883
Slab Fork	25920
Slanesville	25444
Slatyfork	26291
Sleepy Creek	25445
Smithburg	26436
Smithers	25186
Smithfield	26437
Smithville	26178
Smoot	24977
Sod	25564
Sophia	25921
Stotesbury, R. Br.	25929
South Charleston, Br. Charleston	25303
South Williamson Ky, Br. Williamson	25661
Southside	25187
Spanishburg	25922
Spelter	26438
Spencer (1st)	25276
Sprague	25926
Sprigg	25693
Spring Dale	25986
Spring Hill, Br. Charleston	25309
Springfield	26763
Springton	24748
Spurlockville	25565
Squire	24884
Stanaford	25927
Star City, Br. Morgantown	26505
Statts Mills	25279
Steeles, R. Br. Iaeger	24844
Stephenson	25928
Stickney	25188
Stirrat	25645
Stollings	25646
Stonewall, Sta. Charleston	25302
Stony Bottom	24979
Stotesbury, R. Br. Sophia	25929
Stouts Mills	26439
Strange Creek	26639
Streeter	25987
Stumptown	25280
Sugar Grove	26815
Sullivan	25930
Sumerco	25567
Summerlee	25931
Summersville (1st)	26651
Hominy Falls, R. Br.	26673
Lockwood, R. Br.	26677
Summit Point	25446
Sundial	25189
Superior	24886
Surveyor	25932
Sutton	26601
Sweet Springs	24980
Sweetland	25568
Swiss	26690
Switchback	24887
Switzer	25647
Sylvester	25193
Tad	25201
Talcott	24981
Tallmansville	26237
Tams	25933
Tanner	26179
Taplin	25648

Tariff	25281
Teays	25569
Terra Alta	26764
Terry	25934
Tesla	26640
Thacker	25694
Thomas	26292
Thornton	26440
Thorpe	24888
Three Churches	26765
Thurmond	25936
Tioga	26691
Toll Gate	26442
Tornado	25202
Triadelphia	26059
Trout	24982
Troy	26443
True	25988
Tunnelton	26444
Turtle Creek	25203
Twilight	25204
Twin Branch	24889
Tyler Heights, Br. Charleston	25312
Uler	25282
Uneeda	25205
Unger	25447
Union	24983
Upper Tract	26866
Upperglade	26266
Vadis	26445
Valley Bend	26293
Valley Chapel	26446
Valley Fork	25283
Valley Grove	26060
Valley Head	26294
Vallscreek	24890
Van	25206
Varney	25696
Verdunville	25649
Verner	25650
Vicars	25284
Victor	25938
Vienna, Br. Parkersburg	26101
Virginville	26061
Vivian	24891

Volga	26238
Vulcan	25697
Wadestown	26589
Waiteville	24984
Walker	26180
Walkersville	26447
Wallace	26448
Wallback	25285
Walton	25286
Wana	26590
Waneta	26295
War	24892
Excelsior, R. Sta.	24833
Wardensville	26851
Warriormine	24894
Warwood, Sta. Wheeling	26003
Washington (1st)	26181
Watson, Sta. Fairmont	26551
Waverly	26184
Wayne (1st)	25570
Wayside	24985
Webster Springs	26288
Weirton (1st)	26062
Welch (1st)	24801
Wellsburg (1st)	26070
Wendel	26450
West Columbia	26287
West Hamlin	25571
West Huntington, Sta. Huntington	25704
West Liberty	26074
West Logan, R. Br. Logan	25601
West Milford	26451
West Union	26456
Oxford, R. Br.	26414
Weston (1st)	26452
Westover, Br. Morgantown	26505
Wharncliffe	25651
Wharton	25208
Wheeling (1st)	26003
Whitby	25939
White Oak	25989
White Sulphur Springs (1st)	24986
Neola, R. Br.	24961
Whitesville	25209
Packsville, R. Br.	25151

Pettus, R. Br.	25153
Whitman	25652
Whitmer	26296
Whittaker	25210
Wick	26185
Widen	25211
Wikel	24990
Wilbur	26459
Wilcoe	24895
Wildcat	26460
Wiley Ford	26767
Wileyville	26186
Wilkinson	25653
Williams Mountain	25212
Williamsburg	24991
Williamson (1st)	25661
Williamstown	26187
Willis Branch, R. Br. Mount Hope	25880
Willow Bend	24992
Willow Island	26190
Wilsie	26641
Wilson	26768
Wilsonburg, R. Br. Clarksburg	26461
Wilsondale	25699
Winding Gulf	25941
Windsor Heights	26075
Winfield	25213
Winifrede	25214
Winona	25942
Wolf Pen	24896
Wolf Summit	26462
Wolfcreek	24993
Wolfe	24751
Woodville	25572
Worth	24897
Worthington	26591
Wyatt	26463
Wyco	25943
Wymer	26297
Wyoming	24898
Yawkey	25573
Yellow Spring	26865
Yolyn	25654
Yukon	24899

CHARLESTON 253

POST OFFICE BOXES

Box Nos.

1-54	Malden R Br....	06
1-210	Sissonville Br...	20
1-307	Port Amherst R. Sta....	06
1-313	Main Office	21
20-77	Coal Fork R. Sta....	06
42-1045	Rand Br....	06
131-274	Tyler Heights Br	12
181-324	Chesapeake R Br	15
321-633	Main Office	22
401-888	Big Chimney R. Sta....	02
621-953	Main Office	23
961-1233	Main Office	24
1241-1513	Main Office	25
1521-1793	Main Office	26
1801-2073	Main Office	27
2081-2393	Main Office	28
2401-2633	Main Office	29
2641-2993	Main Office	30
3001-3112	Main Office	31
3121-3232	Main Office	32
4001-4444	Kanawha City Sta....	04
5001-5356	Capitol Sta	11
6001-6812	Stonewall Sta....	02
8001-8767	South Charleston Br.	03
9001-9457	Spring Hill Br...	09
10001-10194	C Sta....	12
15001-15216	Marmet Br....	15

RURAL ROUTES

1	....	12
2	....	14
4,5	....	12
6	....	11
7	....	09

STATIONS, BRANCHES AND UNITS

Big Chimney Rural Br.....	02
Capitol Sta	11
Chesapeake Br	15
Cinco Rural Br	06
Coal Fork Rural Br....	06
Kanawha City Sta....	04
Malden Rural Br....	06
Marmet Br....	15
Port Amherst Rural Br	06
Rand Br....	06
Sissonville Br	20
South Charleston Br....	03
Spring Hill Br....	09
Stonewall Sta	02
Tyler Heights Br	12
General Delivery	01
Postmaster....	01

APARTMENTS, HOTELS, MOTELS

Ambassador, 19 Bradford St..	01
Argonne, 27 Ruffner Ave....	11
Broadmoor, 1545 Lewis....	11
Cavalier, 1316 Virginia St E...	01
Charleston & Holiday Inn 02, 600 Kanawha Blvd E....	01
Chateau, 24 Bradford	01
Daniel Boone, Capitol At Washington....	28
Dupont, 170 Summers....	01
Edgewater, 1330 Kanawha Blvd E	01
Fairfax Hall, 1317 Lee	01
Grant, 1012 Quarrier....	01
Greenbrier Garden, 714 Canterbury Dr....	14
Harding, 1201 Lee	01
Heart O'Town, Broad & Washington Sts....	24
Holiday Inn 01, 2 Kanawha Blvd E....	01
Holley, 1006 Quarrier....	30
Imperial Towers, Round Hill Road....	14
Kanawha Village, 3900 Mccorkle Ave....	04
Lee Terrace, 1319 Lee St E....	01
Madison Hall, 1317 Lee....	01
Midtown Motel, 1316 Kanawha Blvd E	01
One Morris, 1 Morris....	01
Regal, 1424 Kanawha Blvd E....	01
Richmond, 105 Bradford....	01
Riverview Terrace, 1108 Kanawha Blvd E	01
Sherwood, 1134 Lee....	01
Town House, 1202 Kan Blvd 'E	01
Washington, 129 Summers....	22
Worthy, 1018 Quarrier....	01

BUILDINGS

Arcade, 710 Virginia St E....	01
Atlas, 1031 Quarrier....	01
Berman, 612 Virginia St E....	01
Capitol City, 807 Quarrier....	01
Charleston National Plaza	01
City Of Charleston, 501 Virginia St E....	01
Commerce Square....	01
Courthouse, 407-09 Virginia St E....	01
Davidson, 910 Quarrier....	01
Day & Night, 710 Lee....	01
Dominion, 804 Quarrier....	01
Embleton, 922 Quarrier....	01
Federal, 500 Quarrier....	01
Kanawha Banking & Trust, 111 Capitol....	01
Kanawha County Library, 123 Capitol....	01
Kanawha Valley, 300 Capitol..	01
Knight, 901 Quarrier....	01
L & S, 812 Quarrier....	01
Masonic Temple, 820 Virginia E....	01
May, 818 1/2 Quarrier....	01
Medical Arts, 1021-25 Quarrier....	01
Morrison, 815 Quarrier....	01
National Bank Commerce Bldg	01
Nelson, 1018 Kanawha Blvd	
E....	01
Noyes, 200 Broad....	01
Odd Fellows, 717 Lee....	01
Ott, Corner Dunbar & Quarr	01
Payne, 811 Lee....	01
Peoples, 179 Summers....	01
Professional, 1036 Quarrier....	01
Security, 100 Capitol....	01
Smallridge, 1013 Quarrier	01
State Capitol, 1800 Kanawha Blvd E....	05
Terminal, 20 Capitol	01
Union, 723 Kanawha Blvd E...	01
Y M C A, 311 Capitol	01
Y W C A, 1114 Quarrier....	01

HOSPITALS

Charleston General, 1201 Elmwood Ave....	25
Charleston Memorial, 3300 Noyes Ave SE....	04
Ear & Eye Clinic, 1306 Kanawha Blvd....	01
Herbert J Thomas Memorial, 4605 Mccorkle Ave SW....	09
Highland, 56th & Noyes Ave SE....	04
Kanawha Valley, 1014 Virginia St E	01
Mc Millan, Morris At Lee....	32
Mountain State, 1301 Virginia St E....	27
Saint Francis, 333 Laidley....	01
Southern Hills, 30 Mc Corkle SW....	03
Staats, 123 Washington St W....	02

UNIVERSITIES AND COLLEGES

Morris Harvey College, 2300 Mccorkle Avenue, S.e....	04

HUNTINGTON 257

POST OFFICE BOXES

Box Nos.

1-147	Huntington	06
151-300	Huntington	07
301-410	Huntington	08
411-510	Huntington	09
511-610	Huntington	10
611-760	Huntington	11
761-940	Huntington	12
941-1090	Huntington	13
1091-1270	Huntington	14
1271-1420	Huntington	15
1421-1600	Huntington	16
1601-1700	Huntington	17
1701-1800	Huntington	18
1801-1897	Huntington	19
1901-2078	Huntington	20
2081-2127	Huntington	21
2131-2187	Huntington	22
2201-2236	Huntington	23
2261-2396	Huntington	24
2401-2536	Huntington	25
3001-3199	Guyandotte Sta....	02

5401-5587	Marshall University Sta.................	03
8001-8158	Beverly Hills Sta.................	05
9001-9519	West Huntington Sta.................	04

RURAL ROUTES

1.......................................	01
2.......................................	02
3.......................................	01
4,5....................................	04

STATIONS, BRANCHES AND UNITS

Beverly Hills Sta......................	05
Guyandotte Sta........................	02
Marshall University Sta.............	03
West Huntington Sta...............	04
General Delivery	01
Postmaster	01

APARTMENTS, HOTELS, MOTELS

Appollo, 749 3rd.....................	01
Arlington, 639 9th...................	01
Ashworth, 1801 3rd Ave	03
Belford Village, 612 11th Ave...............................	01
Bertram, 612 9th Ave.	01
Biggs, 1030 9th......................	01
Biggs, 902 11th Ave................	01
Biltmore, 936 7th Ave.............	07
Burgess, 1143 9th Ave............	01
Bush, 1011 6th Ave.................	01
Cabell, 333 14th......................	01
Clark, 912 6th........................	01
College, 329 15th....................	01
Conley, 1026 12th Ave............	01
Del-Mar, 1018 12th Ave..........	01
Denning, 819 10th Ave...........	01
Emmons Junior, 1209 3rd Ave......................................	01
Emmons Senior, 1201 3rd Ave......................................	01
Executive, 1020 9th Ave.........	01
Fifth Ave, 901 5th Ave............	08
Frederick, 940 4th Ave:..........	16
Golden, 1300 Kanawha Ter.....	01
Grace, 1029 10th....................	01
Grace, 940 11th Ave...............	01
Guthrie, 541 6th Ave	01
Hamil, 815 10th Ave...............	01
Harlan, 1134 9th Ave.............	01
Holiday Inn, 3325 Route 60....	24
Holiday, 419 6th.....................	01
Huff, 535 4th Ave...................	01
Huntington, 901 6th Ave	01
Keister, 603 Trenton Pl..........	01
Kenmore, 410 12th.................	01
La Salle, 1024 8th..................	01
Malone, 625 6th Ave...............	01
Marcum Terrace Housing Development, Olive St & St Louis.............................	05
Milner, 4th Ave & 7th.............	01
Morgan, 640 9th Ave	01
Mossman,. 1239 Charleston Ave......................................	01
Northcott Court Housing Development, Doulton Ave & 16th...............................	01
Pack, 932 9th Ave..................	01
Park Lane, 1028 8th...............	01
Park Terrace, 1320 12th........	01
Parkview, 726 13th Ave..........	01
Patrician, 839 9th Ave...........	01
Powell, 930 11th Ave.............	01
Price, 2823 Collis Ave............	02
Prichard, 9th St & 6th Ave.....	22
Ritter Park, 938 13th Ave......	01
Roxen, 1001 11th Ave............	01
Southworth, 928 9th Ave.......	01
Stone Lodge, 5600 Route 60..	13
Summers, 1112 9th................	01
Summers, 901 11th Ave.........	01
Tomkies, 1231 10th Ave.........	01
Tourist, 343 Washington Ave..	01
Traymore, 339 6th Ave...........	01
Traymore, 612 Trenton Pl......	01
University, 329 16th..............	01
Uptowner Arms, 1342-44 4th Ave...................................	01
Uptowner Motel, 1415 4th Ave...................................	22
Virginia, 427 7th....................	01
Vison, 1122 13th....................	01
Washington Arms, 963 Washington Ave...................	04
Washington Square Housing Development, 8th Ave & 16th...................................	03
Wheeler, 1145 9th Ave...........	01

BUILDINGS

C & O, 407 11th.....................	01
Chafin, 517 9th	01
Federal, 502 8th	01
Fifth Ave, 824 5th Ave...........	01
First Huntington National Bank, 10th St & 4th Ave ...	01
Guaranty National Bank, 919 5th Ave................................	10
Huntington State Hospital, 1530 Norway Ave...............	09
Huntington Trust & Savings Bank, 1050 4th Ave...........	21
Twentieth Street Bank, 1956 3rd Ave............................	03
West Virginia, 912 4th Ave.....	01

GOVERNMENT OFFICES

Cabell County Court House, 5th Ave & 8th...................	01
City Hall, 802 5th Ave............	17
United States Courthouse, 5th Ave & 9th...................	01
United States Post Office, 5th Ave & 9th...................	01

HOSPITALS

Cabell-Huntington, 1340 16th...................................	01
Guthrie, 6th Ave & 6th..........	01
Huntington Hospital Inc, 1230 6th Ave.....................	19

Saint Marys, 2900 1st Ave.....	01
Veterans Administration, 1540 Spring Vally Dr.........	01

UNIVERSITIES AND COLLEGES

Marshall University, 4th Ave & 16th	01

WISCONSIN
(Abbreviation: WI)

Abbotsford 54405
Abrams 54101
Adams 53910
Adell 53001
Afton 53501
Albany 53502
Algoma (1st) 54201
Allenton 53002
Alma 54610
Alma Center 54611
Almena 54805
Almond 54909
Altoona 54720
Alvin, R. Br. Iron River, M I ...49936
Amberg 54102
Amery (1st) 54001
Amherst 54406
Amherst Junction 54407
Aniwa 54408
Antigo (1st) 54409
   Phlox, R. Br. 54464
Appleton (1st) 54911
Arbor Vitae 54510
Arcadia 54612
Arena 53503
Argonne 54511
   Hiles, R. Br. 54533
Argyle 53504
Arkansaw 54721
Arkdale 54613
Arlington 53911
Armstrong Creek 54103
Arpin 54410
Ashippun 53003
Ashland (1st) 54806
Ashwaubenon, Br. Green
   Bay 54304
Astico 53912
Athelstane 54104
Athens 54411
Auburndale 54412
Augusta 54722
Auroraville 54920
Avalon 53505
Avoca 53506
Babcock 54413
Bagley 53801
Baileys Harbor 54202
Baldwin 54002
Balsam Lake 54810
Bancroft 54921
Bangor 54614
Baraboo (1st) 53913
Barneveld 53507
Barron (1st) 54812
Barronett 54813
Barton, Sta. West Bend 53095
Bassett 53101
Bay City 54723
Bay View, Sta. Milwaukee 53207
Bayfield 54814
Bear Creek 54922
Beaver 54105
Beaver Dam (1st) 53916
Beetown 53802
Beldenville 54003
Belgium (1st) 53004
Belleville 53508
Belmont 53510
Beloit (1st) 53511

Benet Lake, R. Br. Trevor 53102
Bennett 54815
Benoit 54816
Benton 53803
Berlin (1st) 54923
Big Bend 53103
Big Falls 54926
Billings Park, Sta. Superior 54880
Birchwood 54817
Birnamwood 54414
Black Creek 54106
Black Earth 53515
Black River Falls (1st) 54615
Blair 54616
Blanchardville 53516
Blenker 54415
Bloom City 54617
Bloomer 54724
Bloomington 53804
Blue Mounds 53517
Blue River 53518
Bonduel 54107
   Navarino, R. Br. 54108
Boscobel 53805
Boulder Junction 54512
Bowler 54416
Boyceville 54725
Boyd 54726
Bradley, Sta. Milwaukee (see
   appendix)
Branch 54203
Brandon 53919
Brantwood 54513
Briggsville 53920
Brill 54818
Brillion (1st) 54110
Bristol 53104
Brodhead (1st) 53520
Brokaw 54417
Brookfield (1st) 53005
Brooklyn 53521
Brooks 53921
Brookwood, Sta. Madison
   (see appendix)
Brown Deer, Br. Milwaukee
   (see appendix)
Brownsville 53006
Browntown 53522
Bruce 54819
Brule 54820
Brussels 54204
Bryant 54418
Burkhardt, R. Br. Hudson 54016
Burlington (1st) 53105
Burnett 53922
Butler (1st) 53007
Butte Des Morts 54927
Butternut 54514
Byron 53009
Cable 54821
Cadott 54727
Caledonia 53108
Cambria 53923
Cambridge 53523
Cameron 54822
Camp Douglas 54618
Camp Lake 53109
Campbellsport 53010
Canton 54823
Caroline 54928
Carrollville, Sta. Oak Creek 53154
Cascade 53011
Casco 54205

Cashton 54619
Cassville 53806
Cataract 54620
Catawba 54515
Cato 54206
Cavour 54516
Cazenovia 53924
Cecil 54111
Cedar Grove 53013
Cedarburg (1st) 53012
Center Valley, R. Br. Black
   Creek 54106
Centuria 54824
Chaseburg 54621
Chelsea 54419
Chetek 54728
Chili 54420
Chilton (1st) 53014
Chippewa Falls (1st) 54729
City Point, R. Br. Pittsville 54466
Clam Falls, R. Br. Frederic 54825
Clam Lake 54517
Clayton 54004
Clear Lake 54005
Clearwater Lake 54518
Cleveland 53015
Clinton 53525
Clintonville (1st) 54929
Clyman 53016
Cobb 53526
Cochrane 54622
Colby 54421
Coleman 54112
Colfax 54730
Colgate 53017
Collins 54207
Coloma 54930
Columbus (1st) 53925
Combined Locks 54113
Comstock 54826
Conover 54519
Conrath 54731
Coon Valley 54623
Cornell 54732
Cornucopia 54827
Cottage Grove 53527
Couderay 54828
Crandon 54520
Crivitz 54114
Cross Plains 53528
Cuba City 53807
Cudahy (1st) 53110
Cumberland 54829
Curtiss 54422
Cushing 54006
Custer 54423
Dairyland, R. Br. Danbury 54830
Dale 54931
Dallas 54733
Dalton 53926
Danbury 54830
   Dairyland, R. Br. 54830
   Webb Lake, R. Br. 54892
Dane 53529
Darien 53114
Darlington 53530
De Forest (1st) 53532
De Pere (1st) 54115
De Soto 54624
Deer Park 54007
Deerbrook 54424
Deerfield 53531
Delafield 53018

Delavan (1st) 53115
Dellwood, R. Br. Friendship 53927
Denmark 54208
Deronda 54008
Dickeyville 53808
Dodge 54625
Dodgeville (1st) 53533
Dorchester 54425
Dousman 53118
Downing 54734
Downsville 54735
Doylestown 53928
Dresser 54009
Drummond 54832
Dunbar 54119
Durand 54736
Eagle 53119
Eagle River (1st) 54521
Earl 54833
East Ellsworth, Br.
  Ellsworth 54011
East End, Sta. Superior 54880
East Side, Sta. Madison (see
  appendix)
East Troy (1st) 53120
Eastman 54626
Eau Claire (1st) 54701
Eau Galle 54737
Eden 53019
Edgar 54426
Edgerton (1st) 53534
Edgewater 54834
Edmund 53535
Egg Harbor 54209
Eland 54427
Elcho 54428
Elderon 54429
Eldorado 54932
Eleva 54738
Elk Mound 54739
Elkhart Lake 53020
Elkhorn (1st) 53121
Ellison Bay 54210
Ellsworth 54011
Elm Grove (1st) 53122
Elmwood 54740
Elroy 53929
Elton 54430
Embarrass 54933
Emerald 54012
Endeavor 53930
Ephraim 54211
Ettrick 54627
Eureka 54934
Evansville (1st) 53536
Exeland 54835
Fair Water 53931
Fairchild 54741
Fairview, Br. Milwaukee (see
  appendix)
Fall Creek 54742
Fall River 53932
Federal, Sta. Milwaukee 53202
Fence 54120
Fennimore 53809
Fenwood 54431
Ferryville 54628
Fifield 54524
Fish Creek 54212
Florence 54121
Fond du Lac (1st) 54935
Fontana 53125
Footville 53537

Forest Junction 54123
Forestville 54213
Fort Atkinson (1st) 53538
Fountain City 54629
Fox Lake 53933
Fox Point, Br. Milwaukee 53217
Foxboro 54836
Francis Creek 54214
Franklin, R. Br. Hales
  Corners 53132
Franksville 53126
Fred John, Sta. Milwaukee
  (see appendix)
Frederic 54837
  Clam Falls, R. Br. 54825
Fredonia 53021
Freedom, R. Br. Kaukauna 54131
Fremont 54940
French Island, Br. La
  Crosse 54601
Friendship 53934
  Dellwood, R. Br. 53927
Friesland 53935
Galesville 54630
Galloway 54432
Gays Mills 54631
Genesee Depot 53127
Genoa 54632
Genoa City 53128
Germantown 53022
Gile 54525
Gillett 54124
Gillingham 54633
Gilman 54433
  Jump River, R. Br. 54434
Gilmanton 54743
Gleason 54435
Glen Flora 54526
Glen Haven 53810
Glenbeulah 53023
Glenwood City 54013
Glidden 54527
Goodman 54125
Gordon 54838
Gotham 53540
Grafton (1st) 53024
Grand Marsh 53936
Grand View 54839
Granton 54436
Grantsburg 54840
Gratiot 53541
GREEN BAY (1st) (see
  appendix)
Green Lake (1st) 54941
Green Valley 54127
Greenbush 53026
Greendale (1st) 53129
Greenfield, Br. Milwaukee
  (see appendix)
Greenleaf 54126
Greenville 54942
Greenwood 54437
Gresham 54128
Gurney 54528
Hager City 54014
Hales Corners (1st) 53130
  Franklin, R. Br. 53132
Hamburg 54438
Hammond 54015
Hampton, Sta. Milwaukee
  (see appendix)
Hancock 54943
Hannibal 54439

Hanover 53542
Harbor, Sta. Milwaukee 53204
Harshaw 54529
Hartford (1st) 53027
Hartland (1st) 53029
Hatley 54440
Haugen 54841
Haven 53030
Hawkins 54530
Hawthorne 54842
Hayward (1st) 54843
Hazel Green 53811
Hazelhurst 54531
Heafford Junction 54532
Helenville 53137
Herbster 54844
Hertel 54845
Hewitt 54441
High Bridge 54846
Highland 53543
Hilbert 54129
Hiles, R. Br. Argonne 54533
Hilldale, Sta. Madison (see
  appendix)
Hillpoint 53937
Hillsboro 54634
Hillsdale 54744
Hilltop, Sta. Milwaukee (see
  appendix)
Hingham 53031
Hixton 54635
Holcombe 54745
Hollandale 53544
Holmen 54636
Honey Creek 53138
Horicon (1st) 53032
Hortonville 54944
Howard, Br. Green Bay 54303
Howards Grove - Millersville,
  R. Br. Sheboygan 53081
Hubertus 53033
Hudson (1st) 54016
Humbird 54746
Hurley 54534
Hustisford 53034
Hustler 54637
Independence 54747
Ingram 54535
Iola 54945
Irma 54442
Iron Belt 54536
Iron Ridge 53035
Iron River 54847
Ironton 53938
Itasca, Sta. Superior 54880
Ixonia 53036
Jackson 53037
Janesville (1st) 53545
Jefferson (1st) 53549
Jim Falls 54748
Johnson Creek 53038
Juda 53550
Jump River, R. Br. Gilman 54434
Junction City 54443
Juneau 53039
Kansasville 53139
Kaukauna (1st) 54130
  Freedom, R. Br. 54131
Kellnersville 54215
Kempster 54444
Kendall 54638
Kennan 54537
Kenosha (1st) 53140

Keshena...............................54135
Kewaskum (1st)....................53040
Kewaunee (1st)....................54216
Kiel (1st)............................53042
Kieler.................................53812
Kimberly.............................54136
King...................................54946
Kingston.............................53939
Knapp................................54749
Knowles.............................53043
Kohler (1st)........................53044
Krakow..............................54137
La Crosse (1st)....................54601
La Farge............................54639
La Pointe...........................54850
La Valle.............................53941
La Verne Dilweg, Sta. Green
  Bay.................................54303
Lac Du Flambeau.................54538
Ladysmith (1st)...................54848
Lake Delton........................53940
Lake Geneva (1st)...............53147
Lake Mills (1st)...................53551
Lake Nebagamon..................54849
Lake Tomahawk.....................54539
Lakewood...........................54138
Lancaster (1st)....................53813
Land O Lakes.......................54540
Lannon...............................53046
Laona................................54541
Larsen...............................54947
Layton Park, Sta. Milwaukee
  (see appendix)
Lebanon..............................53047
Lena..................................54139
Leopolis.............................54948
Lewis.................................54851
Lily...................................54445
Limeridge...........................53942
Linden...............................53553
Little Chute........................54140
Little Suamico......................54141
Livingston...........................53554
Lodi...................................53555
Loganville...........................53943
Lomira...............................53048
Lone Rock..........................53556
Long Lake...........................54542
Loomis, R. Br. Peshtigo.........54158
Loretta...............................54852
Lowell...............................53557
Loyal.................................54446
Lublin................................54447
Luck..................................54853
Luxemburg..........................54217
Lyndon Station.....................53944
Lynxville............................54640
Lyons................................53148
MADISON (1st) (see
  appendix)
Maiden Rock........................54750
Malone...............................53049
Manawa.............................54949
Manchester.........................53945
Manitowish Waters
  Winchester, R. Br................54567
Manitowoc (1st)....................54220
Maple................................54854
Maplewood..........................54226
Marathon............................54448
Marengo.............................54855
Maribel..............................54227
Marinette (1st)....................54143

Marion...............................54950
Markesan............................53946
Marquette............................53947
Marshall.............................53559
Marshfield (1st)...................54449
Mason................................54856
Mather...............................54641
Mattoon.............................54450
Mauston (1st)......................53948
Mayfair, Br. Milwaukee...........53226
Mayville (1st)......................53050
Mazomanie..........................53560
Mc Farland..........................53558
Mc Naughton.......................54543
Medford (1st)......................54451
Mellen...............................54546
Melrose..............................54642
Melvina, R. Br. Cashton.........54619
Menasha (1st)......................54952
Menekaunee, Sta. Marinette....54143
Menomonee Falls (1st)..........53051
Menomonie (1st)..................54751
Mequon, Br. Thiensville..........53092
Mercer...............................54547
Merrill (1st)........................54452
Merrillan............................54754
Merrimac............................53561
Merton...............................53056
Mid City, Sta. Milwaukee........53208
Middle Inlet........................54148
Middleton, Br. Madison..........53562
Midway, Br. Green Bay..........54301
Mikana..............................54857
Milan................................54453
Milladore............................54454
Millston.............................54643
Milltown.............................54858
Milton...............................53563
Milton Junction....................53564
MILWAUKEE (1st) (see
  appendix)
Mindoro.............................54644
Mineral Point.......................53565
Minocqua (1st)....................54548
Minong..............................54859
Mishicot.............................54228
Mondovi.............................54755
Monico..............................54549
Monona, Br. Madison............53716
Monroe (1st).......................53566
Montello.............................53949
Montfort.............................53569
Monticello..........................53570
Montreal.............................54550
Morrisonville.......................53571
Mosinee.............................54455
Mount Calvary.....................53057
Mount Hope........................53816
Mount Horeb.......................53572
Mount Sterling.....................54645
Mountain............................54149
Mukwonago.........................53149
Muscoda.............................53573
Muskego.............................53150
Nashotah............................53058
Navarino, R. Br. Bonduel........54108
Necedah.............................54646
Neenah (1st).......................54956
Neillsville (1st)....................54456
Nekoosa.............................54457
Nelson...............................54756
Nelsonville..........................54458
Neopit...............................54150

Neosho..............................53059
Neshkoro............................54960
New Auburn.........................54757
New Franken........................54229
New Glarus..........................53574
New Holstein (1st)................53061
New Lisbon..........................53950
New London (1st)..................54961
New Munster........................53152
New Richmond (1st)..............54017
Newald...............................54551
Newburg.............................53060
Newton...............................53063
Niagara..............................54151
Nichols...............................54152
North Fond Du Lac, Br. Fond
  du Lac..............................54935
North Freedom.....................53951
North Lake...........................53064
North Prairie.......................53153
Northfield, R. Br. Hixton.........54635
Northside, Sta. La Crosse.......54601
Norwalk.............................54648
Oak Creek (1st)...................53154
Oakdale.............................54649
Oakfield.............................53065
Oconomowoc (1st)................53066
Oconto (1st)........................54153
Oconto Falls........................54154
Odanah..............................54861
Ogdensburg.........................54962
Ogema...............................54459
Ojibwa...............................54862
Okauchee............................53069
Omro.................................54963
Onalaska (1st).....................54650
Oneida...............................54155
Ontario..............................54651
Oostburg.............................53070
Oregon...............................53575
Orfordville..........................53576
Osceola..............................54020
Oshkosh (1st)......................54901
Osseo................................54758
Owen.................................54460
Oxford...............................53952
Packwaukee........................53953
Palmyra.............................53156
Pardeeville..........................53954
Park Falls (1st)....................54552
Parklawn, Sta. Milwaukee.......53216
Patch Grove........................53817
Pearson.............................54462
Peebles..............................53071
Pelican Lake........................54463
Pell Lake............................53157
Pembine.............................54156
Pence................................54553
Pepin................................54759
Peshtigo,
  Loomis, R. Br....................54158
Pewaukee (1st)....................53072
Phelps...............................54554
Phillips...............................54555
Phlox, R. Br. Antigo..............54464
Pickerel..............................54465
Pickett...............................54464
Pigeon Falls........................54760
Pine River...........................54965
Pittsville............................54466
Plain.................................53577
Plainfield............................54966
Platteville (1st)....................53818

Pleasant Prairie.............53158
Plover.............54467
Plum City.............54761
Plymouth (1st).............53073
Polar, R. Br. Bryant.............54418
Poplar.............54864
Port Edwards (1st).............54469
Port Washington (1st).............53074
Port Wing.............54865
Portage (1st).............53901
Porterfield.............54159
Poskin.............54866
Potosi.............53820
Potter.............54160
Pound.............54161
Powers Lake.............53159
Poy Sippi.............54967
Poynette.............53955
Prairie Du Chien (1st).............53821
Prairie Du Sac.............53578
Prairie Farm.............54762
Preble, Sta. Green Bay.............54302
Prentice.............54556
Prescott.............54021
Presque Isle.............54557
Princeton.............54968
Pulaski (1st).............54162
Pulcifer.............54164

RACINE (1st) (see appendix)
Radisson.............54867
Randolph (1st).............53956
Random Lake.............53075
Readfield.............54969
Readstown.............54652
Redgranite.............54970
Reedsburg (1st).............53959
Reedsville.............54230
Reeseville.............53579
Rewey.............53580
Rhinelander (1st).............54501
Rib Lake.............54470
Rice Lake (1st).............54868
Richfield.............53076
Richland Center (1st).............53581
Ridgeland.............54763
Ridgeway.............53582
Ringle.............54471
Rio.............53960
Rio Creek.............54231
Riplinger, R. Br. Spencer.............54472
Ripon (1st).............54971
River Falls (1st).............54022
Roberts.............54023
Rochester.............53167
Rock Falls.............54764
Rock Springs.............53961
Rockfield.............53077
Rockland.............54653
Rosendale.............54974
Rosholt.............54473
Rothschild.............54474
Royalton.............54975
Rubicon.............53078
Rudolph.............54475
Saint Cloud.............53079
Saint Croix Falls.............54024
Saint Germain.............54558
Saint Nazianz.............54232
Salem.............53168
Salvatorian Center, Sta. New
  Holstein.............53061
Sand Creek.............54765
Sarona.............54870

Sauk City.............53583
Saukville.............53080
Saxeville.............54976
Saxon.............54559
Sayner.............54560
Scandinavia.............54977
Schofield (1st).............54476
Seneca.............54654
Sextonville.............53584
Seymour.............54165
Sharon.............53855
Shawano (1st).............54166
Sheboygan (1st).............53081
Sheboygan Falls (1st).............53085
Sheldon.............54766
Shell Lake.............54871
Sheridan.............54477
Sherwood.............54169
Shiocton.............54170
Shorewood, Br. Milwaukee.............53211
Shullsburg.............53586
Silver Lake.............53170
Sinsinawa.............53824
Siren.............54872
Sister Bay.............54234
Slinger.............53086
Sobieski.............54171
Soldiers Grove.............54655
Solon Springs.............54873
Somers.............53171
Somerset.............54025
South Byron.............53087
South Milwaukee (1st).............53172
South Range.............54874
South Wayne.............53587
Sparta (1st).............54656
Spencer.............54479
  Riplinger, R. Br.............54472
Spooner (1st).............54801
Spring Green.............53588
Spring Valley.............54767
Springbrook.............54875
Springfield.............53176
Stanley.............54768
Star Prairie.............54026
Starlake.............54561
State Street, Sta. Racine.............53404
Stetsonville.............54480
Steuben.............54657
Stevens Point (1st).............54481
Stiles.............54172
Stitzer.............53825
Stockbridge.............53088
Stockholm.............54769
Stoddard.............54658
Stone Lake.............54876
Stoughton (1st).............53589
Stratford.............54484
Strum.............54770
Sturgeon Bay (1st).............54235
Sturtevant.............53177
Suamico.............54173
Sullivan.............53178
Summit Lake.............54485
Sun Prairie (1st).............53590
Superior (1st).............54880
Suring.............54174
Sussex.............53089
Taycheedah.............53090
Taylor.............54659
Teutonia, Sta. Milwaukee.............53206
Theresa.............53091
Thiensville (1st).............53092

Thorp (1st).............54771
Three Lakes.............54562
Tiffany.............53592
Tigerton.............54486
Tilleda.............54978
Tisch Mills.............54240
Tomah (1st).............54660
Tomahawk (1st).............54487
Tony.............54563
Townsend.............54175
Trego.............54888
Trempealeau.............54661
Trevor.............53179
  Benet Lake, R. Br.............53102
Tri City, Sta. Oak Creek.............53154
Tripoli.............54564
Troy Center.............53180
Tunnel City.............54662
Turtle Lake.............54889
Twin Lakes.............53181
Two Rivers (1st).............54241
Underhill.............54176
Union Center.............54962
Union Grove (1st).............53182
Unity.............54488
University, Sta. Madison.............53715
Upper Third Street, Sta.
  Milwaukee.............53212
Upson.............54565
Uptown, Sta. Racine.............53403
Valders.............54245
Valley Fair, Br. Appleton.............54911
Vandyne.............54979
Verona, Br. Madison.............53593
Vesper.............54489
Veterans Administration
  Hosp, Sta. Madison.............53705
Victory, R. Br. De Soto.............54663
Villard, Sta. Milwaukee.............53209
Viola.............54664
Viroqua (1st).............54665
Wabeno.............54566
Waldo.............53093
Wales.............53183
Walworth (1st).............53184
Warrens.............54666
Wascott.............54890
Washburn.............54891
Washington Island.............54246
Waterford.............53185
Waterloo (1st).............53594
Watertown (1st).............53094
Waubeka, R. Br. Fredonia.............53021
Waukau.............54980
Waukesha (1st).............53186
Waumandee, R. Br.
  Cochrane.............54622
Waunakee.............53597
Waupaca (1st).............54981
Waupun (1st).............53963
Wausau (1st).............54401
Wausaukee.............54177
Wautoma.............54982
Wauwatosa, Br. Milwaukee
  (see appendix)
Wauzeka.............53826
Wayside, R. Br. Greenleaf.............54126
Webb Lake, R. Br. Danbury.............54892
Webster.............54893
Wentworth.............54894
West Allis, Br. Milwaukee.............53214
West Bend (1st).............53095
West De Pere, Sta. De Pere.............54115

West Lima	54668
West Racine, Sta. Racine (see appendix)	
West Salem	54669
Westboro	54490
Westby	54667
Western, Sta. Milwaukee	53210
Westfield	53964
Weyauwega	54983
Weyerhauser	54895
Wheeler	54772
White Lake	54491
Whitefish Bay, Br. Milwaukee	53217
Whitehall	54773
Whitelaw	54247
Whitewater (1st)	53190
Whittlesey	54492
Wild Rose	54984
Willard	54493
Williams Bay	53191
Wilmot (1st)	53192
Wilson	54027
Wilton	54670
Winchester, R. Br. Manitowish Waters	54567
Wind Lake, Br. Waterford	53185
Windsor	53598
Winnebago	54985
Winneconne	54986
Winter	54896
Wisconsin Dells (1st)	53965
Wisconsin Rapids (1st)	54494
Withee	54498
Wittenberg	54499
Wonewoc	53968
Wood	53193
Woodford	53599
Woodland	53099
Woodman	53827
Woodruff	54568
Woodville	54028
Woodworth	53194
Wrightstown	54180
Wyeville	54671
Wyocena	53969
Yuba	54672
Zachow	54182
Zenda	53195

GREEN BAY   543

POST OFFICE BOXES

Box Nos.
1-1572	Main Office	05
2001-2524	A Sta	06
3001-3999	Dilweg	03

RURAL ROUTES

1,2,3	01
4,5	03
6	01
7	03
8	01
9,10	03

STATIONS, BRANCHES AND UNITS

Ashwaubenon Br	04
Howard Br	03
La Verne Dilweg Sta	03
Midway Br	01
Preble Sta	02
General Delivery	05
Postmaster	05

APARTMENTS, HOTELS, MOTELS

Arena Motel, 871 Highland Ave	04
Bay Motel, Military Ave	04
Beaumont Inn, 406 N Washington	05
Downtowner Motel, 321 S Washington	01
Gladstone, 1529 W Mason	03
Hi-Way 141 Motel, 217 N Main Blvd	02
Holiday Inn Of Green Bay, Route 7	05
Imperial 400, 119 N Monroe	01
Midway Motor Lodge, 780 Packer Dr	04
North Star Motel, 1111 N Military	03
Northland, 304 N Adams	05
Packer City Motel, R 3	01
Skylit Motel, 565 W Morris	04
Valley Motel, 116 N Military	03

BUILDINGS

Bellin, 130 E Walnut	01
Columbus, 414 E Walnut	01
Federal, 325 E Walnut	01
Minahan, 205 E Walnut	01
Nicolet, 225 N Adams	01
Northern, 305 E Walnut	01
Sheridan, 226 N Washington	01

GOVERNMENT OFFICES

Brown County Courthouse Annex, 306 E Walnut	01
Brown County Courthouse, 100 S Jefferson	01

HOSPITALS

Bellin Hospital, 744 S Webster Ave	01
Brown County Hospital, Route 6	01
Saint Marys Hospital, 1726 Shawano Ave	03
Saint Vincents Hospital, 835 S Van Buren	05

MADISON   537

POST OFFICE BOXES

Box Nos.
1-2999	Main Office	01
3000-3999	East Side Sta	04
4000-4999	Brookwood Sta	11
5000-5999	Hilldale Sta	05
6000-6999	Monona Br	16

RURAL ROUTES

1	04
2,3,4	11
5	04

STATIONS, BRANCHES AND UNITS

Brookwood Sta	11
East Side Sta	04
Hilldale Sta	05
Monona Br	16
Middleton Br	53562
University Sta	15
Verona Br	53593
Veterans Administration Hosp Sta	05
General Delivery	03
Postmaster	01

APARTMENTS, HOTELS, MOTELS

Aloha Inn, 3177 E Washington Ave	04
Ambassador, 522 N Pinckney	03
Bel Aire, 3351 W Beltine Hwy	13
Bellevue, 29 E Wilson	03
Capitol, 208 King St	01
Cardinal, 416 E Wilson	03
Carpenter, 222 S Carroll	03
Clarendon, 1620 Monroe	11
Claridge, 333 W Washington Ave	03
Eagle Heights	05
Edgewater, 666 Wisconsin Ave	01
Fess, 123 E Doty	01
Hamacher, 5101 University Ave	05
Holiday Inn No 1, 4402 E Washington Ave	04
Holiday Inn No 2, 6301 E Broadway	04
Howard Johnsons, 4838 E Washington Ave	04
Ivy Inn, 2355 University Ave	05
Kennedy Manor, 1 Langdon	03
Lake Shore, 122 E Gilman	03
Loraine, 123 W Washington Ave	01
Madison Inn, 601 Langdon	03
Madison Traveledge, 909 W Beltine Hwy	13
Madison, 4402 E Broadway	16
Mayflower, 2500 Perry St	13
Motel Royal, 705 Redland Dr	14
Park Tower, 4801 Sheboygan Ave	05
Park, 22 S Carroll	03
Quisling Towers, 1 E Gilman	03
Sands Motel, 2800 W Broadway	13
Sherman Terrace, 1601 Sherman Ave	04
Spences, 3575 E Washington Ave	04
Sterling, 901 W Beltine Hwy	13
Town Campus, 441 N Frances	03
Trails End, 99 W Beltine Hwy	13
Vikingtown, 4353 W Beltine Hwy	11
Washington, 636 W Washington Ave	03
Wilson, 522 E Wilson	03

BUILDINGS

Anchor, 25 W Main	03
Bank Of Madison, 1 W Main	03
City-County, 210 Monona Ave	09
Commercial State Bank, 102 State	03
First National Bank, 1 S Pinckney	03
Gay, 16 N Carroll	03
Hilldale State Bank, 401 N Segoe Rd	05
Insurance, 119 Monona Ave	03
Lake City Bank, 1202 N Sherman Ave	04
Memorial Union, 770 Langdon	06
Park Bank, 2401 S Park	13
State Capitol, Capitol Square	02
State Office, 1 W Wilson	02
State Office, 4802 Sheboygan Ave	02
Tenney, 110 E Main	03
United Bank & Trust	03
Westgate Bank, 670 S Whitney Way	11

HOSPITALS

Central Colony & Training School, 317 Knutson Dr	04
Madison General, 202 S Park	15
Mendota State Hospital, 301 Troy Dr	04
Methodist, 309 W Washington Ave	03
Morningside Sanatorium, 300 Femrite Dr	16
Saint Marys Hospital, 720 South Brooks	15
University Hospitals, 1300 University Ave	06
Veterans Administration Hospital, 2500 Overlook Ter	05
Wisconsin Neurological Foundation, 1954 E Washington Ave	04

UNIVERSITIES AND COLLEGES

Edgewood, 855 Woodrow	11
Madison Area Technical College, 211 N Carroll	03
Madison Business, 215 W Washington Ave	03
University Of Wisconsin	06

MILWAUKEE 532

POST OFFICE BOXES

Box Nos.

1-2199	Main Office	01
2200-2399	Upper Third Street Sta	12
2400-2699	West Allis Br	14
2700-2899	Fairview Br	19
2900-3199	Hampton Sta	18
3200-3399	Mid-City Sta	08
3400-3599	Teutonia Sta	06
3600-3799	Whitefish Bay Br	17
3800-4099	Hilltop Sta	05
4100-4399	Western Sta	10
4400-4599	Bay View Sta	07
4600-4999	Layton Park Sta	15
5000-5399	Harbor Sta	04
5400-5699	Shorewood Br	11
5700-5999	Greenfield Br	20
6000-6499	Villard Sta	09
6500-6799	Parklawn Sta	16
6800-6999	Tuckaway Sta	21
7000-7499	Wauwatosa Br	13
7500-7699	Swan Sta	22
8000-8199	Bradley Sta	23
8200-8399	Fred John	25
8400-8599	Wauwatosa Br	26
8600-8799	Root River Br	27
23000-23999	Bradley Sta	23
90000-92199	Federal	02

RURAL ROUTES

1	23

STATIONS, BRANCHES AND UNITS

Bay View Sta	07
Bradley Sta	23
Brown Deer Br	09
Fairview Br	19
Federal Sta	02
Fox Point Br	17
Fred John Sta	25
Greenfield Br	20
Hampton Sta	18
Harbor Sta	04
Hilltop Sta	05
Layton Park Sta	15
Mayfair Br	26
Mid City Sta	08
Parklawn Sta	16
Shorewood Br	11
Teutonia Sta	06
Upper Third Street Sta	12
Villard Sta	09
Wauwatosa Br	13
West Allis Br	14
Western Sta	10

Whitefish Bay Br	17
General Delivery	01
Postmaster	03

APARTMENTS, HOTELS, MOTELS

Abbot Crest, 1226 W Wisconsin Ave	33
Ambassador, 2308 W Wisconsin Ave	33
Antlers, 616 N 2nd	03
Astor, 924 E Juneau Ave	02
Belmont, 751 N 4th	03
Biltmore Grand, 1343 W Wisconsin Ave	33
Continental Motel, 3001 W Wisconsin Ave	08
Cudahy Tower, 925 E Wells	02
Holiday Inn Of America Central, 1926 W. Wisconsin Ave	33
Holiday Inn Of America-Midtown, 2611 W. Wisconsin Ave	33
Milwaukee Inn, 916 E State	02
Pan American Motel, 3808 W Wisconsin Ave	08
Pfister, 424 E Wisconsin Ave	02
Plankinton, 609 N Plankinton Ave	03
Plaza, 1007 N Cass	02
Ramada Inn,633 W. Michigan St	03
Red Carpet Inn, 4747 S Howell Ave	07
Sheraton Schroeder, 509 W Wisconsin Ave	03
Shorecrest, 1962 N Prospect Ave	02
Stratford, 1404 W Wisconsin Ave	33
Towne, 723 N 3rd	03
Tyrolean Town House, 1673 S 108th	14
Wisconsin, 720 N 3rd	03
1028 Juneau	02

BUILDINGS

Badger Bus Depot, 635 N 7th	33
Greyhound Bus Depot, 606 N 7th	33
Marine Plaza, 111 E Wisconsin Ave	02
Union Depot, 433 W Saint Paul Ave	03
War Memorial, 730 N Lincoln Memorial Dr	02
1st Wisconsin National Bank, 735 N Water	02

GOVERNMENT OFFICES

City Hall, 200 E Wells	02
County Court House, 901 N 9th	33
Milwaukee County Airport, 5300 S Howell	07
Milwaukee Municipal, 841 N Broadway	02
Milwaukee Safety, 822 W Kilbourn Ave	33

Post Office, 345 W. St. Paul Ave	03
Public Library, 814 W Wisconsin Ave	33

HOSPITALS

Columbia, 3321 N Maryland Ave	11
Deaconess, 620 N 19th	33
Doctors, 2711 W Wells	08
Emergency City, 1230 W Grant	15
Johnston Municipal, 1230 W Grant	15
Lakeview, 10010 W Blue Mound Rd	26
Lutheran Hospital Milwaukee, 2200 N Kilbourn Ave	33
Milwaukee Childrens, 1700 W Wisconsin Ave	33
Milwaukee County General, 8700 W Wisconsin Ave	26
Milwaukee Sanitarium, 1220 Dewey Ave	13
Mount Sinai, 948 N 12th	33
Nicolet, 1971 W. Capitol Dr	06
Northwest General, 5310 W Capitol Dr	16
Sacred Heart Rehabilitation, 1545 S Layton Blvd	15
Saint Anthonys, 1004 N 10th	33
Saint Camillus, 10100 W Bluemound Rd	26
Saint Francis, 3237 S 16th	15
Saint Josephs, 5000 W Chambers	10
Saint Lukes, 2900 W Oklahoma Ave	15
Saint Mary's Hill, 1445 S 32nd	15
Saint Marys, 2320 N Lake Dr	11
Saint Michaels, 2400 W Villard Ave	09
West Allis Memorial, 8901 W Lincoln Ave	27

UNIVERSITIES AND COLLEGES

Alverno, 3401 S 39th	15
Cardinal Stritch, 6801 N Yates Rd	17
Concordia, 3126 W Kilbourn Ave	08
Layton Art School, 1362 N Prospect Ave	02
Marquette University, 615 N 11th	33
Milwaukee School Of Engineering, 1025 N. Milwaukee	01
Mount Mary, 2900 N Menomonee River Pkwy	22
Saint Francis Seminary, 3257 S Lake Dr	07
University Of Wisconsin In Milwaukee, 3203 N Downer	01

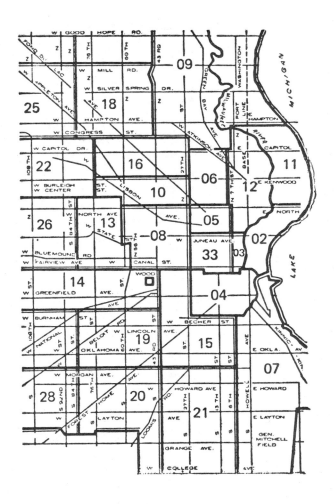

ZIP CODES
MILWAUKEE, Wisconsin
532 + two digits shown = zip code

RACINE   534

POST OFFICE BOXES

Box Nos.

1-799	Main Office	01
1-799	Racine	01
801-899	Uptown Sta	03
901-1199	West Racine Sta	05

RURAL ROUTES

1	02
2	03

STATIONS, BRANCHES AND UNITS

State Street Sta	04
Uptown Sta	03
West Racine Sta	05
General Delivery	01
Postmaster	01

APARTMENTS, HOTELS, MOTELS

Clayton House, 5005 Washington	06
Holiday Inn, 3700 Northwestern Ave	05
Racine Motor Inn, 535 Main	03

BUILDINGS

American Bank, 441 Main St.	03
Badger, 610 Main St	03
Baker, 523 Main St	03
First National Bank, 500 Wisconsin Ave	03
Main 1/2 Lake, 423 Main	03

GOVERNMENT OFFICES

City Hall, 730 Washington Ave	03

Court House, 730 Wisconsin Ave

Court House, 730 Wisconsin Ave	03
Safety Bldg, 730 Center	03

HOSPITALS

Racine County Home, 2433 S Green Bay	06
Saint Lukes, 1320 Wisconsin Ave	03
Saint Marys, 1526 Grand Ave	03

UNIVERSITIES AND COLLEGES

Dominican College, 5915 Erie	02
Vocational & Adult School, 800 Center	03

WYOMING

(Abbreviation: WY)

Acme	82830
Afton	83110
Airport, Sta. Cheyenne	82001
Aladdin, R. Br. Sundance	82710
Albin	82050
Alcova	82620
Alpine, R. Br. Thayne	83127
Alva	82711
Arapahoe, R. Br. Riverton	82510
Arminto, R. Br. Casper	82630
Arvada	82831
Auburn	83111
Baggs	82321
Bairoil	82322
Banner	82832
Basin	82410
Bear Lodge, R. Br. Dayton	82836
Bedford, R. Br. Thayne	83112
Beulah	82712
Big Horn	82833
Big Piney	83113
Bill	82631
Bondurant	82922
Bosler	82051
Boulder	82923
Buffalo (1st)	82834
Saddlestring, R. Br.	82840
Buford	82052
Burlington	82411
Burns	82053
Burris	82511
Byron	82412
Canyon, Sta. Yellowstone	
National Park	82190
Carlile, R. Br. Moorcroft	82713
Carpenter	82054
Casper (1st)	82601
Arminto, R. Br.	82630
Hilltop, Sta.	82601
Shirley Basin, R. Br.	82601
Sunside, Sta.	82601
Centennial	82055
Cheyenne (1st)	82001
Chugwater	82210
Clearmont	82835
Cody (1st)	82414
Cokeville	83114
Colter Bay, R. Br. Jackson	83001
Cora	82925
Cowley	82420
Crowheart	82512
Daniel	83115
Dayton	82836
Deaver	82421
Devils Tower	82714
Diamondville	83116
Dixon	82323
Douglas	82633
Orin, R. Br.	82652
Dubois	82513
Dwyer	82211
Eden, R. Br. Rock Springs	82926
Edgerton	82635
Elk Mountain	82324
Emblem	82422
Encampment	82325
Ethete, R. Br. Lander	82520
Etna, R. Br. Thayne	83118
Evanston (1st)	82930

Evansville	82636
Fairview	83119
Farson	82932
Fishing Bridge, Sta.	
Yellowstone National	
Park	82190
Fort Bridger	82933
Fort Laramie	82212
Fort Washakie	82514
Four Corners, R. Br.	
Newcastle	82715
Foxpark, R. Br. Laramie	82057
Francis E Warren A F B, Br.	
Cheyenne	82001
Frannie	82423
Freedom	83120
Frontier	83121
Garland	82424
Garrett	82058
Gas Hills, R. Br. Riverton	82501
Gillette (1st)	82716
Glendo	82213
Glenrock	82637
Granger	82934
Granite Canon	82059
Grass Creek	82425
Green River (1st)	82935
Greybull	82426
Grover	83122
Guernsey	82214
Hamilton Dome	82427
Hanna	82327
Hartville	82215
Hawk Springs	82217
Hiland	82638
Hillsdale	82060
Hilltop, Sta. Casper	82601
Horse Creek	82061
Hudson	82515
Hulett	82720
Huntley	82218
Hyattville	82428
Iron Mountain	82062
Jackson (1st)	83001
Colter Bay, R. Br.	83001
Teton Village, R. Br.	83025
Jay Em	82219
Jeffrey City, R. Br. Rawlins	82310
Jelm, R. Br. Laramie	82063
Kaycee	82639
Keeline	82220
Kelly	83011
Kemmerer	83101
Kinnear	82516
Kirby, R. Br. Worland	82430
La Barge	83123
Lagrange	82221
Lamont	82328
Lance Creek	82222
Lander (1st)	82520
Laramie (1st)	82070
Foxpark, R. Br.	82057
Jelm, R. Br.	82063
University, Sta.	82071
Leiter	82837
Linch	82640
Lingle	82223
Little America	82929
Lonetree	82936
Lost Springs	82224
Lovell	82431

Lusk	82225
Lyman	82937
Lysite	82642
Manderson	82432
Manville	82227
Mc Fadden	82080
Mc Kinnon	82938
Medicine Bow	82329
Meeteetse	82433
Meriden	82081
Midwest	82643
Mills (1st)	82644
Moneta	82645
Moorcroft	82721
Carlile, R. Br.	82713
Moose	83012
Moran	83013
Morton	82522
Mountain View	82939
Natrona	82662
New Haven	82722
Newcastle (1st)	82701
Four Corners, R. Br.	82715
Node	82228
Number One, Sta. Cheyenne	82001
Old Faithful, Sta.	
Yellowstone National	
Park	82190
Opal	83124
Orin, R. Br. Douglas	82652
Osage	82723
Oshoto	82724
Otto	82434
Pahaska, R. Br. Cody	82414
Parkman	82838
Pavillion	82523
Pine Bluffs	82082
Pinedale	82941
Point of Rocks, R. Br. Rock	
Springs	82942
Powder River	82648
Powell (1st)	82435
Ralston	82440
Ranchester	82839
Rawlins (1st)	82301
Jeffrey City, R. Br.	82310
Recluse	82725
Reliance	82943
Riverton (1st)	82501
Arapahoe, R. Br.	82510
Gas Hills, R. Br.	82501
Sand Draw, R. Br.	82501
Robertson	82944
Rock River	82083
Rock Springs (1st)	82901
Eden, R. Br.	82926
Point of Rocks, R. Br.	82942
Rockypoint	82726
Rozet	82727
Ryan Park	82330
Saddlestring, R. Br. Buffalo	82840
Sage	83125
Saint Stephens	82524
Sand Draw, R. Br. Riverton	82501
Saratoga	82331
Savery	82332
Seminoe Dam	82333
Shawnee	82229
Shell	82441
Sheridan (1st)	82801
Shirley Basin, R. Br. Casper	82601
Shoshoni	82649

CAROLINE ISLANDS

Post Office ZIP Code

Kanifay, R. Br. Yap, Caroline
Islands 96943
Koror, Caroline Islands............96940
Kusaie, Caroline Islands 96944
Map, R. Br. Yap, Caroline
Islands 96943
Metelanim, R. Br. Ponape,
Caroline Islands...............96941
Ponape, Caroline Islands 96941
Rumung, R. Br. Yap,
Caroline Islands...............96943
Truk, Caroline Islands............96942
Uh, R. Br. Ponape, Caroline
Islands 96941
Yap, Caroline Islands............96943

GUAM

Post Office ZIP Code

Agana, Guam (1st) 96910
Agat, Sta. Agana, Guam.......96910
Anderson A F B, Br. Agana,
Guam 96910
Barrigada, Sta. Agana,
Guam 96910
Inarjan, R. Sta. Agana,
Guam 96910
Merizo, R. Sta. Agana,
Guam 96910
Naval Air Station, Br.
Agana, Guam................96910

Naval Station, Br. Agana,
Guam 96910
Santa Rita, Sta. Agana,
Guam 96910
Sinajana, Sta. Agana,
Guam 96910
Talofofo, R. Sta. Agana,
Guam 96910
Tamuning, Sta. Agana,
Guam 96910
Umatac, R. Sta. Agana,
Guam 96910
Yona, R. Sta. Agana. Guam ...96910

MARIANA ISLANDS

Post Office ZIP Code

Capitol Hill, R. Br. Saipan,
Mariana Islands.................96950
Rota, Mariana Islands 96951
Saipan, Mariana Islands
(1st) 96950
San Jose Village, R. Br.
Saipan, Mariana Islands....96950

MARSHALL ISLANDS

Eyebe, Marshall Islands..........96970
Majuro, Marshall Islands 96960

SAMOA

Post Office ZIP Code

Eastern District Samoa, Br.
Pago Pago Samoa 96920
Fitiuta, Br. Pago Pago
Samoa 96799
Ofu-Manua Samoa, Br. Pago
Pago Samoa......................96920
Olosega Maua Samoa, Br.
Pago Pago Samoa 96920
Pago Pago Samoa (1st).........96799
Ta'U Manu'A, Br. Pago Pago
Samoa 96799

VIRGIN ISLANDS

Post Office ZIP Code

Charlotte Amalie (1st)............00801
Christiansted (1st)..................00820
Cruz Bay...............................00830
Downtown, Sta.
Christiansted......................00820
Frederiksted (1st)....................00840
Kingshill...............................00850
Kronprindsens Gade, Sta.
Kingshill...............................00850
Kronprindsens Gade, Sta.
Charlotte Amalie.................00801

WAKE

Wake, Wake Island.................96798

Zip Codes Frequently Used

ADDRESS	ZIP CODE